Prentice Hall Geometry: Tools for a Changing World

Differentiated Scope of C

B = Basic Course C = Core Course E = Enriched Cc

A Hands-On Approach to Geometry

If you prefer a more hands-on approach to Geometry, consider the following suggestions:

- Use the Work Together activities within the lessons. These activities emphasize the discovery of concepts through use of concrete materials.
- Provide opportunities for your students to work with dynamic geometry software, such as Prentice Hall's *Secondary Math Lab Toolkit.* Software activities appear in the Technology Toolbox features in the Student Text.

A Formal Approach to Geometry

If you prefer a more formal, proof-centered approach to Geometry, consider the following suggestions:

- Re-order the chapters as follows: 1, 2, 4, 5, 7, 8, 9, 6, 10, 12. Cover Chapters 3 and 11 as time permits. Note that if you decide to cover the chapters in a different order, you may not be able to assign all problems from Mixed Reviews and Cumulative Reviews.
- Make a point of assigning the problems that involve deductive reasoning and proof.

Chapter 1: Tools of Geometry	B	C	E
1-1: Using Patterns and Inductive Reasoning	✔	✔	✔
Math Toolbox: Probability	✔	✔	✔
1-2: Points, Lines, and Planes	✔	✔	✔
1-3: Segments, Rays, Parallel Lines and Planes	✔	✔	✔
Math Toolbox: Solving Linear Equations	✔	✔	✔
1-4: Measuring Angles and Segments	✔	✔	✔
1-5: Good Definitions	✔	✔	✔
1-6: Basic Constructions	✔	✔	✔
Math Toolbox: Exploring Constructions		✔	✔
1-7: Using Deductive Reasoning	✔	✔	✔
1-8: The Coordinate Plane	✔	✔	✔
Chapter 2: Investigating Geometric Figures			
2-1: Triangles	✔	✔	✔
Math Toolbox: Exploring the Exterior Angles of a Polygon		✔	✔
2-2: Polygons	✔	✔	✔
Math Toolbox: Exploring Equations of Lines	✔	✔	✔
2-3: Parallel and Perpendicular Lines in the Coordinate Plane	✔	✔	✔
Math Toolbox: Writing Linear Equations		✔	✔
2-4: Classifying Quadrilaterals	✔	✔	✔
2-5: Circles	✔	✔	✔
2-6: Congruent and Similar Figures	✔	✔	✔
2-7: Isometric and Orthographic Drawings		✔	✔
Chapter 3: Transformations: Shapes in Motion			
3-1: Reflections	✔	✔	✔
Math Toolbox: Matrices			✔
3-2: Translations	✔	✔	✔
3-3: Rotations	✔	✔	✔
3-4: Compositions of Reflections			✔

Chapter 3: Transformations: Shapes in Motion, *(cont'd.)*	B	C	E
Math Toolbox: Kaleidoscopes		✔	✔
3-5: Symmetry	✔	✔	✔
3-6: Tessellations		✔	✔
3-7: Dilations	✔	✔	✔
Chapter 4: Triangle Relationships			
4-1: Using Logical Reasoning	✔	✔	✔
4-2: Isosceles Triangles	✔	✔	✔
4-3: Preparing for Proof	✔	✔	✔
Math Toolbox: Investigating Midsegments		✔	✔
4-4: Midsegments of Triangles	✔	✔	✔
4-5: Using Indirect Reasoning	✔	✔	✔
Math Toolbox: Solving Inequalities	✔	✔	✔
4-6: Triangle Inequalities	✔	✔	✔
4-7: Bisectors and Locus	✔	✔	✔
Math Toolbox: Exploring Special Segments in Triangles		✔	✔
4-8 Concurrent Lines		✔	✔
Chapter 5: Measuring in the Plane			
5-1: Understanding Perimeter and Area	✔	✔	✔
5-2: Areas of Parallelograms and Triangles	✔	✔	✔
Math Toolbox: Simplifying Radicals	✔	✔	✔
5-3: The Pythagorean Theorem and Its Converse	✔	✔	✔
5-4: Special Right Triangles	✔	✔	✔
5-5: Areas of Trapezoids	✔	✔	✔
5-6: Areas of Regular Polygons		✔	✔
5-7: Circles: Circumference and Arc Length	✔	✔	✔
5-8: Areas of Circles, Sectors, and Segments of Circles	✔	✔	✔
Math Toolbox: Exploring Area and Circumference		✔	✔

Prentice Hall Geometry: Tools for a Changing World

Differentiated Scope of Course

B = Basic Course   C = Core Course   E = Enriched Course

Chapter 6: Measuring in Space	B	C	E
6-1: Space Figures and Nets	✔	✔	✔
Math Toolbox: Dimensional Analysis	✔	✔	✔
6-2: Surface Areas of Prisms and Cylinders	✔	✔	✔
6-3: Surface Areas of Pyramids and Cones	✔	✔	✔
6-4: Volumes of Prisms and Cylinders	✔	✔	✔
6-5: Volumes of Pyramids and Cones	✔	✔	✔
6-6: Surface Areas and Volumes of Spheres		✔	✔
6-7: Composite Space Figures			✔
6-8: Geometric Probability	✔	✔	✔
Chapter 7: Reasoning and Parallel Lines			
Math Toolbox: Exploring Parallel Lines and Related Angles	✔	✔	✔
7-1: Parallel Lines and Related Angles	✔	✔	✔
Math Toolbox: Systems of Linear Equations			✔
7-2: Proving Lines Parallel	✔	✔	✔
7-3: Constructing Parallel and Perpendicular Lines		✔	✔
Math Toolbox: Perspective Drawing		✔	✔
7-4: Parallel Lines and Perspective Drawing			✔
7-5: Exploring Spherical Geometry		✔	✔
Chapter 8: Proving Triangles Congruent			
8-1: Proving Triangles Congruent: SSS and SAS	✔	✔	✔
Math Toolbox: Exploring SSA and AAA		✔	✔
8-2: Proving Triangles Congruent: ASA and AAS	✔	✔	✔
8-3: Congruent Right Triangles	✔	✔	✔
8-4: Using Congruent Triangles in Proofs	✔	✔	✔
8-5: Using More than One Pair of Congruent Triangles		✔	✔
Math Toolbox: Solving Quadratic Equations		✔	✔
Chapter 9: Quadrilaterals			
9-1: Properties of Parallelograms	✔	✔	✔
9-2: Proving That a Quadrilateral Is a Parallelogram	✔	✔	✔
Math Toolbox: Exploring the Diagonals of Parallelograms		✔	✔
9-3: Properties of Special Parallelograms	✔	✔	✔

Chapter 9: Quadrilaterals *(cont'd.)*	B	C	E
Math Toolbox: Exploring Quadrilaterals within Quadrilaterals			✔
9-4: Trapezoids and Kites	✔	✔	✔
Math Toolbox: Rational Expressions			✔
9-5: Organizing Coordinate Proofs		✔	✔
9-6: Using Coordinate Geometry in Proofs		✔	✔
Chapter 10: Similarity			
10-1: Ratio, Proportion, and Similarity	✔	✔	✔
Math Toolbox: Direct Variation		✔	✔
10-2: Proving Triangles Similar: AA, SAS, and SSS	✔	✔	✔
10-3: Similarity in Right Triangles	✔	✔	✔
10-4: Proportions and Similar Triangles	✔	✔	✔
10-5: Perimeters and Areas of Similar Figures	✔	✔	✔
Math Toolbox: Exploring Similar Solids			✔
10-6: Areas and Volumes of Similar Solids	✔	✔	✔
Chapter 11: Right Triangle Trigonometry			
11-1: The Tangent Ratio	✔	✔	✔
Math Toolbox: Exploring Trigonometric Ratios			✔
11-2: The Sine and Cosine Ratios	✔	✔	✔
11-3: Angles of Elevation and Depression		✔	✔
Math Toolbox: Literal Equations	✔	✔	✔
11-4: Vectors and Trigonometry			✔
11-5: Adding Vectors			✔
11-6: Trigonometry and Area			✔
Chapter 12: Chords, Secants, and Tangents			
12-1: Circles in the Coordinate Plane	✔	✔	✔
Math Toolbox: Polar Coordinates			✔
12-2: Properties of Tangents	✔	✔	✔
12-3: Properties of Chords and Arcs	✔	✔	✔
12-4: Inscribed Angles	✔	✔	✔
12-5: Angles Formed by Chords, Secants, and Tangents		✔	✔
Math Toolbox: Exploring Chords and Secants			✔
12-6: Circles and Lengths of Segments			✔

PRENTICE HALL MATHEMATICS

A wider variety of tools to help students achieve greater math success.

Reaching Today's Students

All the motivation & management tools you need for today's classroom

KEY FEATURES:

- **Comprehensive coverage** of core concepts with an abundance of practice
- **Integrated approach to content**—easily incorporate algebra, geometry, probability, and data analysis topics into your instruction
- **Hundreds of real-world and problem-solving applications**
- **Ongoing assessment questions** within the lesson that prepare students for the types of questions found on today's standardized tests
- **Lesson parts** that allow you to vary pacing and meet the needs of all students

PRINT COMPONENTS:

- Student Edition
- Teacher's Edition
- Teaching Resources
- Practice Workbook
- Practice Workbook Answer Book
- Spanish Practice Workbook
- Spanish Resources
- Teaching Transparencies
- Student Edition Answers on Transparencies
- Test-Taking Tips on Transparencies
- Daily Skills Warm-Up Transparencies
- Daily Cumulative Review Masters
- Solution Key
- Lesson Planners Plus
- Assessment Success Kit
- Mathematics Standardized Test Prep, Student Edition
- Mathematics Standardized Test Prep, Teacher's Edition
- Student Manipulatives Kit
- Overhead Manipulatives Kit

GEOMETRY: Tools for a Changing World

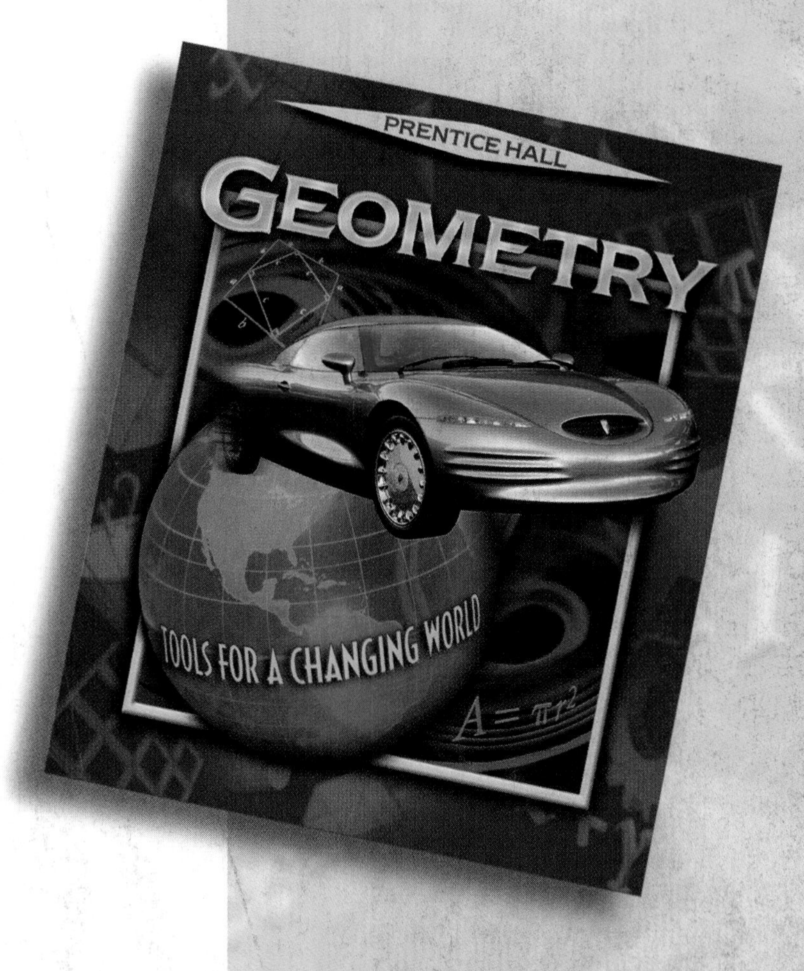

SOLID COVERAGE OF FORMAL GEOMETRY CONCEPTS

Prentice Hall Geometry provides students with a complete formal Geometry course—covering all the topics required to meet local and national testing and curriculum guidelines. The text builds and connects synthetic, coordinate, and transformational approaches, as well as three-dimensional geometry.

REVIEW AND INTEGRATION OF ALGEBRA TOPICS

Algebra 1 skills are reviewed at point-of-use, ensuring that students maintain these skills. Algebra integration within coordinate geometry topics, plus probability and statistics connections, are found throughout.

REASONING & PROOF INTEGRATED THROUGHOUT

Prentice Hall Geometry gives students the skills they need to better understand and master a wide range of proof—by emphasizing reasoning, logic, writing arguments, and analyzing arguments. Proofs are developed gradually, beginning with reasoning skills in Chapter 1.

HANDS-ON APPROACH ENHANCES VISUALIZATION

To help students more effectively visualize concepts, the text integrates optional paper-folding, computer, manipulative, and construction-based activities.

TECHNOLOGY COMPONENTS:

- Video Field Trips, Vol. II: Geometry Applications
- Graphing Calculator Handbook
- Calculator-Based Laboratory (CBL) Activities
- Scientific Calculator TI-34 10 Pack
- Graphing Calculator TI-83 10 Pack
- Graphing Calculator TI-92+ 10 Pack
- Computer Item Generator with Standardized Test Practice on CD-ROM (MAC/WIN)
- Secondary Math Lab Toolkit™ CD-ROM (MAC/WIN)
- Multimedia Geometry CD-ROM (MAC/WIN)
- Resource Pro® with Planning Express® CD-ROM (MAC/WIN)
- Interactive Math: Lessons & Tools CD-ROM
- Interactive Student Tutorial CD-ROM (MAC/WIN)
- Internet site: www.phschool.com

PRENTICE HALL: Tools for a Changing World

PRE-ALGEBRA

1. Algebraic Expressions and Integers
2. Solving One-Step Equations and Inequalities
3. Decimals and Equations
4. Factors, Fractions, and Exponents
5. Operations with Fractions
6. Ratios, Proportions, and Percents
7. Solving Equations and Inequalities
8. Linear Functions and Graphing
9. Spatial Thinking
10. Area and Volume
11. Right Triangles in Algebra
12. Data Analysis and Probability
13. Nonlinear Functions and Polynomials

GEOMETRY

1. Tools of Geometry
2. Investigating Geometric Figures
3. Transformations: Shapes in Motion
4. Triangle Relationships
5. Measuring in the Plane
6. Measuring in Space
7. Reasoning and Parallel Lines
8. Proving Triangles Congruent
9. Quadrilaterals
10. Similarity
11. Right Triangle Trigonometry
12. Chords, Secants, and Tangents

ALGEBRA

1. Tools of Algebra
2. Functions and Their Graphs
3. Algebraic Concepts and Simple Equations
4. Equations and Inequalities
5. Graphing and Writing Linear Equations
6. Systems of Equations and Inequalities
7. Quadratic Equations and Functions
8. Exponents and Exponential Functions
9. Right Triangles and Radical Expressions
10. Polynomials
11. Rational Expressions and Functions

ADVANCED ALGEBRA

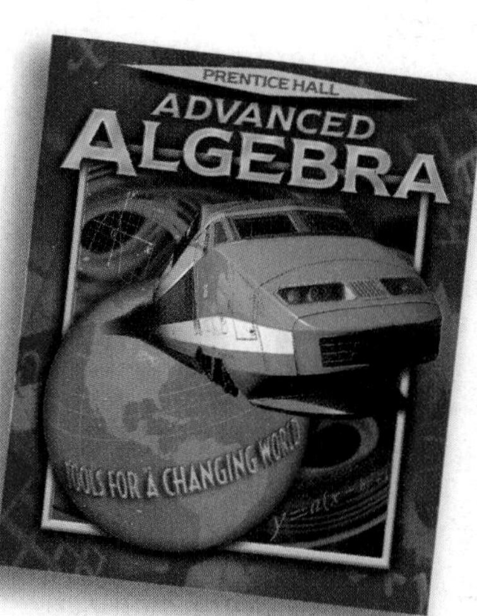

1. Models, Functions, and Permutations
2. Linear Relationships and Functions
3. Matrices
4. Linear Systems
5. Quadratic Equations and Functions
6. Polynomials and Polynomial Functions
7. Exponential and Logarithmic Functions
8. Rational Functions
9. Periodic Functions and Trigonometry
10. Quadratic Relations
11. More Probability and Statistics
12. Sequences and Series

TEACHER'S EDITION

PRENTICE HALL

GEOMETRY

AUTHORS

Laurie E. Bass

Art Johnson

Basia Rinesmith Hall

Dorothy F. Wood

Contributing Author

Simone W. Bess

Algebra Authors

Allan Bellman

Theodore J. Gardella

Sadie Chavis Bragg

Bettye C. Hall

Suzanne H. Chapin

William G. Handlin, Sr.

Edward Manfre

TOOLS FOR A CHANGING WORLD

PRENTICE HALL

Needham, Massachusetts

Upper Saddle River, New Jersey

Glenview, Illinois

REVIEWERS

Series Reviewers

James Gates, Ed.D.
Executive Director Emeritus, National Council of Teachers of Mathematics
Reston, Virginia

Vinetta Jones, Ph.D.
National Director, Equity 2000, The College Board, New York, New York

Geometry

Sandra Argüelles Daire
Miami Senior High School
Miami, Florida

Priscilla P. Donkle
South Central High School
Union Mills, Indiana

Tom Muchlinski, Ph.D.
Wayzata High School
Plymouth, Minnesota

Bonnie Walker
Texas ASCD
Houston, Texas

Karen Doyle Walton, Ed.D.
Allentown College of Saint Francis de Sales
Center Valley, Pennsylvania

Algebra

John J. Brady III
Hume-Fogg High School
Nashville, Tennessee

Elias P. Rodriguez
Leander Junior High School
Leander, Texas

Dorothy S. Strong, Ed.D.
Chicago Public Schools
Chicago, Illinois

Art W. Wilson, Ed.D.
Abraham Lincoln High School
Denver, Colorado

Advanced Algebra

Eleanor Boehner
Methacton High School
Norristown, Pennsylvania

Laura Price Cobb
Dallas Public Schools
Dallas, Texas

William Earl, Ed.D.
Formerly Mathematics Education Specialist
Utah State Office of Education
Salt Lake City, Utah

Staff Credits

The people who made up the Geometry *team—representing editorial, design, marketing, page production, manufacturing, technology, electronic publishing, and advertising and promotion—and their managers are listed below. Bold type denotes core team members.*

Alison Anholt-White, Jackie Zidek Bedoya, Barbara A. Bertell, Bruce Bond, Ellen Brown, Judith D. Buice, Kathy Carter, Kerri Caruso, **Linda M. Coffey**, **Noralie V. Cox**, Sheila DeFazio, Edward de Leon, Christine Deliee, Gabriella Della Corte, Robert G. Dunn, Barbara Flockhart, Audra Floyd, David Graham, Maria Green, Bridget A. Hadley, Joanne Hudson, Vanessa Hunnibell, Mimi Jigarjian, **Linda D. Johnson**, Elizabeth A. Jordan, Russell Lappa, **Catherine Martin-Hetmansky**, Eve Melnechuk, Cindy A. Noftle, Caroline M. Power, Roger E. Powers, Martha G. Smith, Kira Thaler, Robin Tiano, Christina Trinchero, Stuart Wallace, Cynthia A. Weedel, **Jeff Weidenaar**, **Pearl B. Weinstein**, Mary Jane Wolfe, Stewart Wood, David Zarowin

We would like to give special thanks to our National Math Consultants, Ann F. Bell, Liz Cunningham, Shawyn Jackson, Sandra Mosteller, and Loretta Rector, for all their help in developing this program.

Printed in the United States of America.

ISBN: 0-13-050186-7

3 4 5 6 7 8 9 10 04 03 02 01 00

Geometry Authors

Laurie E. Bass is a classroom teacher at the Fieldston School in Riverdale, New York. Ms. Bass has a wide base of teaching experience, ranging from grades 6 and 7 through Advanced Placement Calculus. She also has been a contributing writer of a number of publications, including software-based activities for the Algebra 1 classroom. One of her areas of special interest is geometric exploration on the computer. Chapters 2, 7, 9

Basia Rinesmith Hall, Mathematics Instructional Supervisor, East District, Houston Independent School District, Houston, Texas, is a 1992 winner of the Presidential Award for Excellence in Mathematics Teaching. Ms. Hall was a member of the NCTM Professional Teaching Standards Review Committee, served on the writing committee of the Texas Essential Knowledge Skills (TEKS), and is President of the Texas Council of Teachers of Mathematics (1996–1998). Chapters 3, 8, 11

Art Johnson, Ed.D., is a classroom teacher in Nashua High School, Nashua, New Hampshire. Dr. Johnson is a frequent speaker and workshop leader and the recipient of a number of awards, including the Tandy Prize for Teaching Excellence in 1995 and a 1992 Presidential Award for Excellence in Mathematics Teaching. He was profiled by the Disney Corporation in the American Teacher of the Year Program. Chapters 1, 6, 10

Dorothy F. Wood, formerly with the Kern High School District in Bakersfield, California, is an active member of the California Mathematics Council and a frequent presenter at their conferences. She is also a leader of middle and high school staff-development workshops sponsored by schools, districts, and county offices. As Teacher Leader and Evaluator, she serves numerous schools in the California Department of Education Mathematics Demonstration Program. Chapters 4, 5, 12

Contributing Author

Simone W. Bess, Ed.D., Adjunct Mathematics Instructor at the University of Cincinnati and Cincinnati State Technical and Community College, came to mathematics education through a career in engineering at General Electric Aircraft Engines. She is a frequent speaker at professional meetings around the country, and has special interests in integrating diversity in the classroom and supporting girls and women in mathematics careers. Dr. Bess has also been active in coordinating a number of NSF-funded programs for minority students, K–12.

Algebra & Advanced Algebra Authors

Allan Bellman
Blake High School
Silver Spring, Maryland

Sadie Chavis Bragg, Ed.D.
The City University of New York
New York, New York

Suzanne H. Chapin, Ed.D.
Boston University
Boston, Massachusetts

Theodore Gardella
Formerly, Bloomfield Public Schools
Bloomfield Hills, Michigan

Bettye C. Hall
Formerly, Unified School District
Houston, Texas

William G. Handlin, Sr.
Spring Woods High School
Houston, Texas

Edward Manfre
Albuquerque, New Mexico

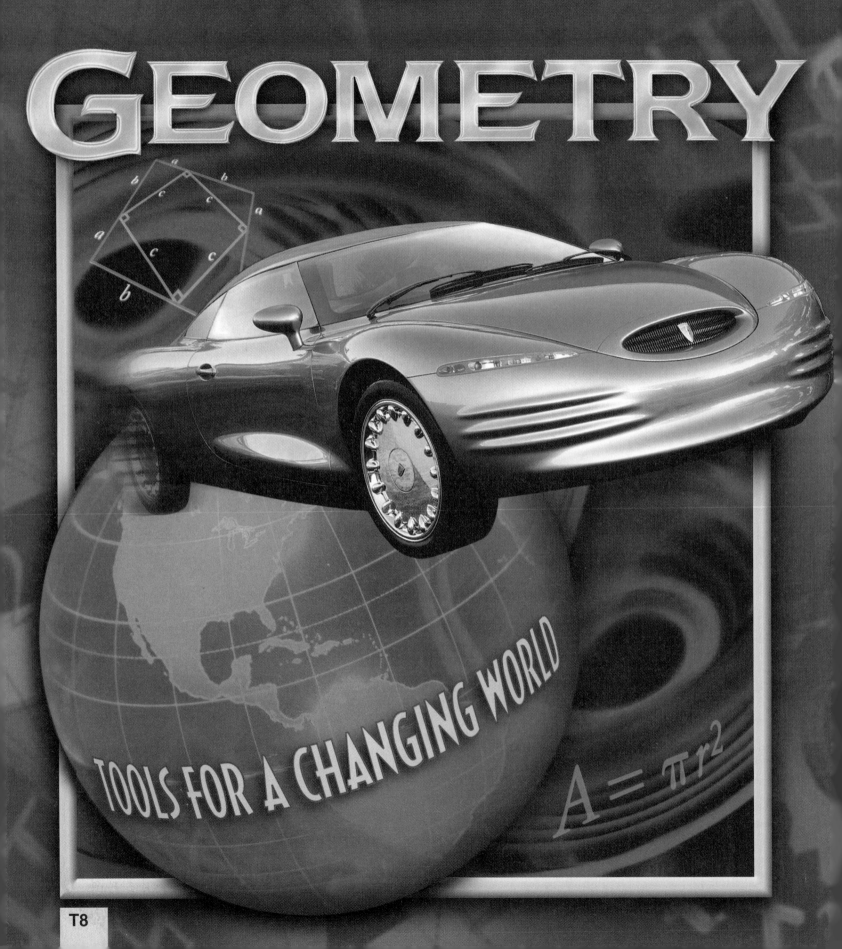

PRENTICE HALL

GEOMETRY

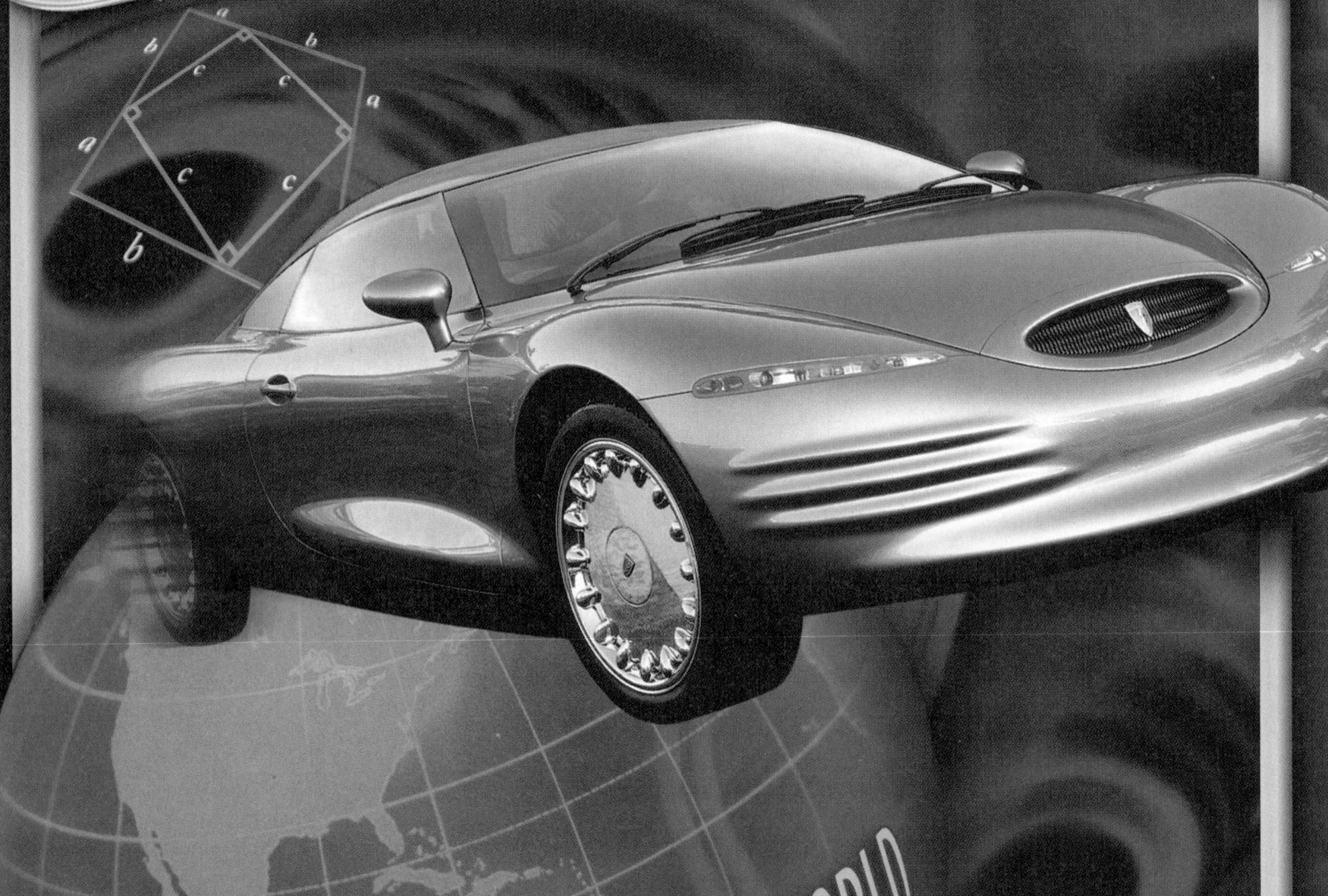

TOOLS FOR A CHANGING WORLD

$A = \pi r^2$

PRENTICE HALL MATH

GEOMETRY

TOOLS FOR A CHANGING WORLD

CONTENTS

Geometry Contents

The "To the Student" pages help students understand how they learn and how the textbook relates to their daily lives. The Skills Handbook provides an in-text tutorial of skills that students may need to review. Extra Practice pages for each chapter contain additional exercises correlated to each lesson. The Glossary/Study Guide provides not only a definition and a page reference but also an example of each vocabulary term.

CHAPTER

1 Tools of Geometry

Connections and Applications

Students develop inductive and deductive reasoning skills as they learn the basics of geometry. They make and test conjectures about mathematical and real-world patterns. They draw and measure two- and three-dimensional figures. As they build their geometric vocabulary, they write and test their own definitions. Chapter 1 also introduces coordinate geometry, which is stranded throughout the text.

CHAPTER 2

Investigating Geometric Figures

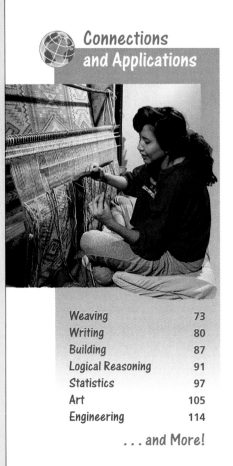

Connections and Applications

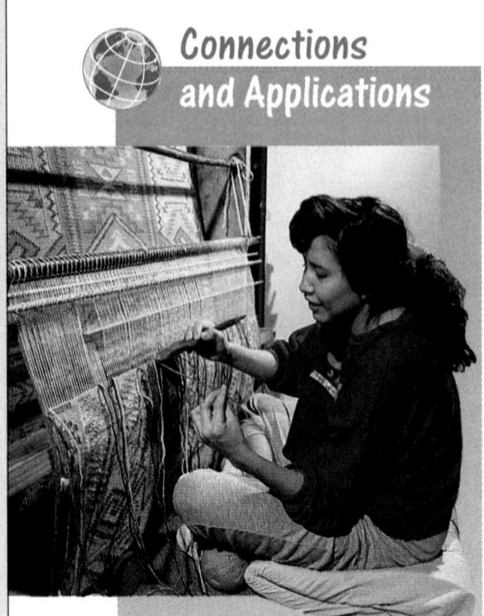

Through hands-on activities, students investigate properties of the basic figures of geometry — triangles, quadrilaterals and other polygons, as well as circles. They use hands-on materials to explore congruency and similarity, concepts that are revisited throughout the text. Students apply their algebra skills as they study parallel and perpendicular lines in the coordinate plane.

CHAPTER 3

Transformations: Shapes in Motion

Connections and Applications

Students expand their hands-on study of congruence and similarity by discovering the properties of reflections, translations, rotations, glide reflections, and dilations. The relevance of transformations is emphasized through real-world applications and works of art. In the rest of the course, students revisit transformations in a variety of contexts.

CHAPTER

4 Triangle Relationships

Connections and Applications

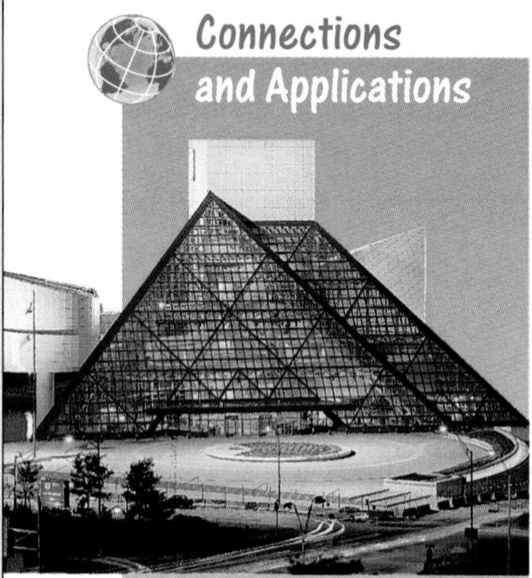

Students are exposed to deductive argument in informal, real-life situations and in mathematical settings related to properties of triangles. As students improve their reasoning skills, the groundwork is laid for later, more in-depth work with proof.

CHAPTER

5 Measuring in the Plane

Connections and Applications

Using a variety of investigative tools, students discover formulas for the areas of polygons and circles, and apply them to solve real-world problems. Students study area-based proofs of the Pythagorean Theorem – which are more visual and convincing than the traditional proofs. Finally, they use algebra to deduce the properties of 30°-60°-90° and 45°-45°-90° triangles.

CHAPTER 6

Measuring in Space

Connections and Applications

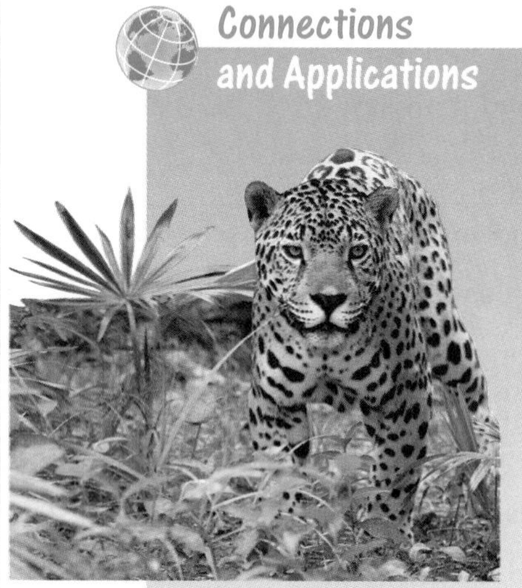

Students develop and improve their spatial visualization and reasoning skills with three-dimensional figures. They begin by drawing nets of solids. Using area formulas of plane figures as a starting point, students develop the formulas for surface area and volume of prisms, cylinders, pyramids, cones, and spheres. The last lesson provides an opportunity for students to review concepts from Chapters 5 and 6 in the context of geometric probability.

Reasoning and Parallel Lines

Connections and Applications

Network News
Analyzing and Designing Networks

Students investigate properties of parallel lines and write deductive arguments to justify their conclusions. They apply properties of parallel lines to real-world situations, constructions, and drawing in one- and two-point perspective. Finally, they explore spherical geometry (in which no parallel lines exist!) and contrast it with Euclidean geometry.

CHAPTER

8 Proving Triangles Congruent

ASSESSMENT

Chapter Project

Tri Tri Again

Using Triangles to Build Bridges

Building on the strong foundation of congruency established in earlier chapters, students use manipulatives and technology to discover conditions that ensure congruent triangles. A gradual introduction to proof provides students with the confidence and the solid conceptual understanding they need to write well-reasoned deductive arguments.

CHAPTER 9

Quadrilaterals

Connections and Applications

Students apply what they have learned about triangles to develop properties of parallelograms, trapezoids, and kites. They continue to develop their mathematical reasoning abilities and their algebraic skills by learning to write coordinate proofs.

CHAPTER

10 Similarity

Connections and Applications

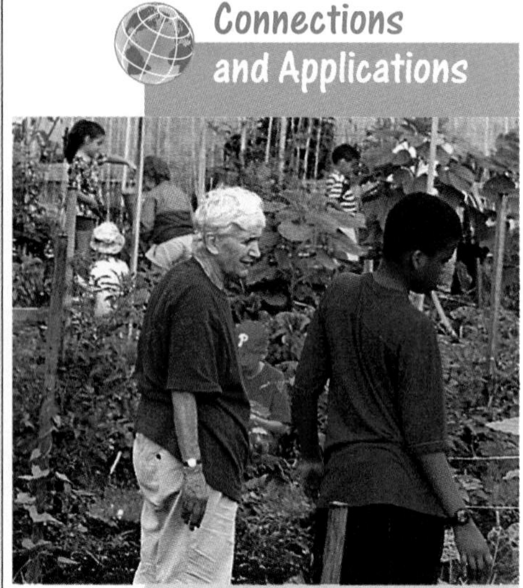

Similarity is an important strand throughout the text. In Chapter 2, students learned that two figures are similar if they have the same shape but not necessarily the same size. In Chapter 3, they studied similarity from another perspective, dilations. Now, in addition to learning how to prove triangles similar, students apply similarity to study fractals, scale drawings, and the connections between areas and volumes of similar figures.

CHAPTER 11

Right Triangle Trigonometry

Connections and Applications

ASSESSMENT

Chapter Project

Measure for Measure
Measuring Distance Indirectly

Right-triangle trigonometry comes alive with a variety of connections to the real world. Lessons on vectors provide an interesting and relevant context for application of trigonometric ratios. Connections to area involve more applications of trigonometry and simultaneously review significant concepts.

CHAPTER 12

Chords, Secants, and Tangents

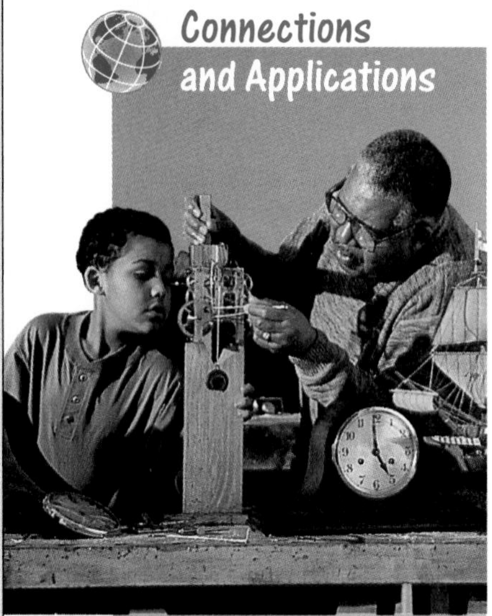

Connections and Applications

ASSESSMENT

Chapter Project

Go For a Spin
Using Circles in Art

Students study circles from an algebraic point of view by writing equations of circles in the coordinate plane. They use compasses, protractors, MIRAs™, and software to make conjectures about circles, chords, tangents, and secants, and then write well-constructed justifications in a variety of formats — two-column proofs, paragraph proofs, flow proofs, and coordinate proofs.

PRENTICE HALL MATH

"After reviewing all of the chapters, I believe I can say that you have done an excellent job interpreting the NCTM Standards, both the process standards as well as the content standards."

James Gates, Ed.D.
Executive Director Emeritus
National Council of Teachers of Mathematics

"I am glad to see that the Prentice Hall textbook will contain information that will answer the most popular questions asked by students: When and where are we going to use this? and Do I really have to know this?"

Elias P. Rodriguez
Mathematics Teacher
Leander, Texas

"The Prentice Hall book was fun, and I learned a lot! I had trouble reading our old book's examples. The examples in the Prentice Hall book were much easier to understand. I learn more by using the examples, and this helped a lot! My grades went up this quarter."

Heidi S.
Field-test student

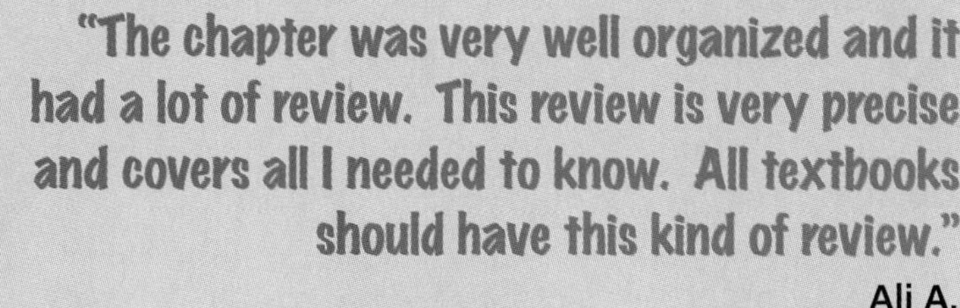

"The chapter was very well organized and it had a lot of review. This review is very precise and covers all I needed to know. All textbooks should have this kind of review."

Ali A.
Field-test student

Teachers and students across the country helped Prentice Hall develop this program. They identified the teaching tools that you can use to motivate students and manage instruction. We would like to hear from you. Write us at Prentice Hall Math, 160 Gould Street, Needham, MA 02494, or visit us on the Internet at http://www.phschool.com.

Tools to Help You Succeed

Why did we name our program "Tools for a Changing World"?

Because you've said

...not all **STUDENTS** have the same learning style;

...not all **TEACHERS** have the same teaching style;

...and no two **CLASSROOM** environments are the same.

It is for these reasons that we offer you a wide variety of teaching tools to help you MOTIVATE your students and MANAGE instruction.

PRENTICE HALL MATH

TOOLS FOR A CHANGING WORLD

brings together the widest variety of Teaching Tools.

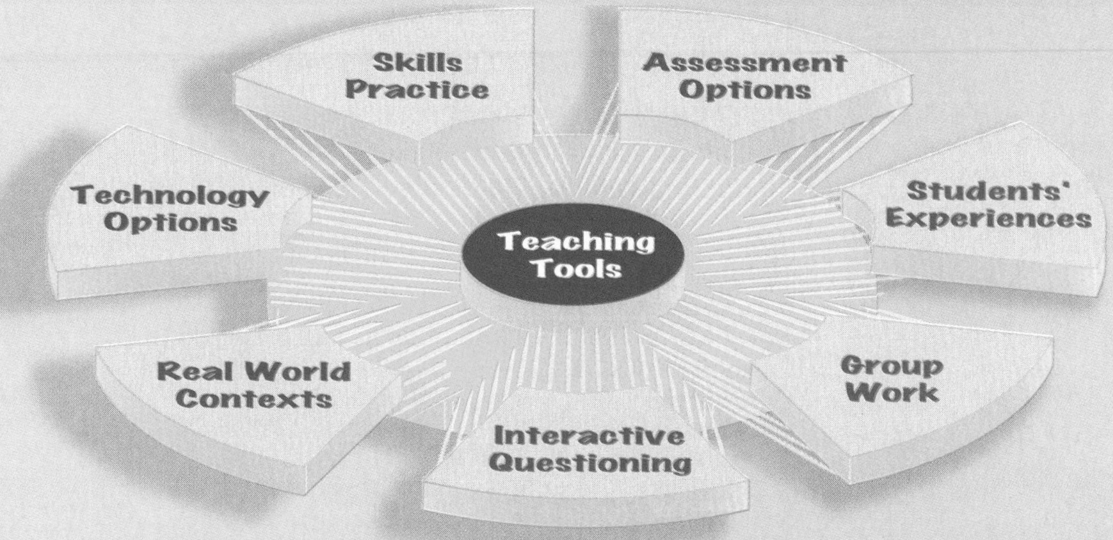

Using these tools, Prentice Hall Math helps you address the *motivation* and *management* issues you've told us are foremost on your mind.

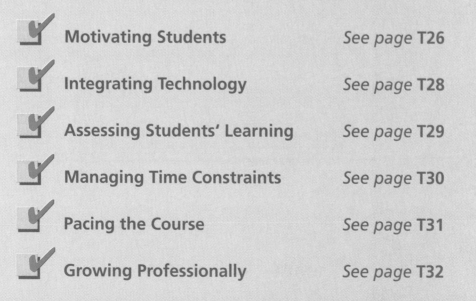

- Motivating Students — *See page* T26
- Integrating Technology — *See page* T28
- Assessing Students' Learning — *See page* T29
- Managing Time Constraints — *See page* T30
- Pacing the Course — *See page* T31
- Growing Professionally — *See page* T32

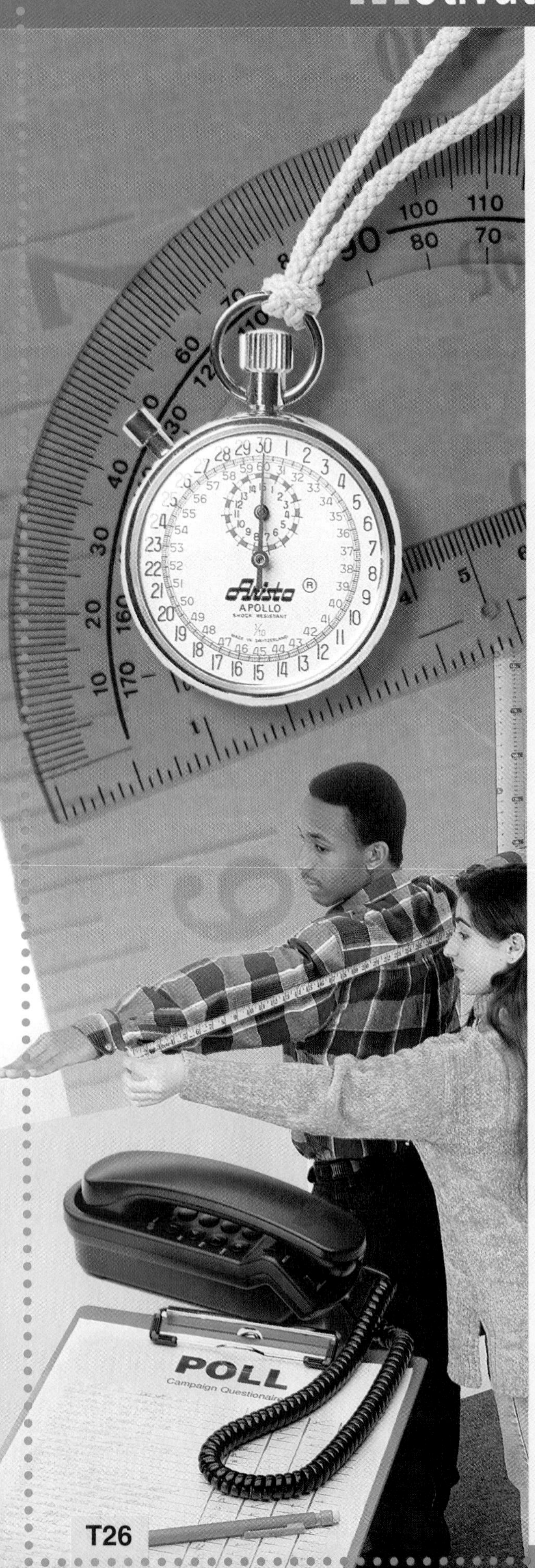

How can I motivate students to *want* to learn math?

BY USING ANY OR ALL OF THESE RESOURCES.	*Where do I look?*
The Relating to the Real World completely worked-out Examples and practice exercises show students just how often math is used in their lives today and in the future.	Student Edition
Chapter Projects are long-term projects that provide a real-world connection to the math content of the chapter.	Student Edition
Video Field Trips support the chapter projects or other real-world connections for each chapter in the Student Edition.	Video Field Trips
Suggestions for Connecting to the Students' World provide opportunities for discussing how students apply math in their lives.	Teacher's Edition
Connecting to Prior Knowledge sections show students how new math concepts are related to material previously learned.	Teacher's Edition
The Student Manipulatives Kit engages students in a hands-on experience when discovering and connecting math concepts.	Student Manipulatives Kit
Multimedia Math Labs combine animation, graphics, video, and Math Tools in chapter-long Math Labs to spark the students' interest in the mathematics of each chapter.	Multimedia Math Labs
Secondary Math Lab Toolkit™ gives you and students software-based Integrated Math Labs with Math Tools for exploration.	Secondary Math Lab Toolkit™
Prentice Hall's Internet Home Page offers a special section on Math, including projects of the month, exciting links, and a calendar of events.	Internet http://www.phschool.com

How can I help *all* students become lifelong learners?

BY USING ANY OR ALL OF THESE RESOURCES.	*Where do I look?*
In Work Together explorations students use a variety of tools, including algebra, technology, and manipulatives, to discover geometric concepts. In these activities students learn to work cooperatively, just as they will in the workplace.	Student Edition
Think and Discuss interactive questions offer students opportunities to communicate with their peers by practicing their listening, thinking, talking, and writing skills.	Student Edition
ESL and Diversity suggestions help reach students of various backgrounds to make their math experience fulfilling.	Teacher's Edition
Learning Styles sections provide suggestions for teaching concepts to students of different learning styles (tactile, auditory, kinesthetic, visual).	Teacher's Edition
Alternative Activities offer students of varying learning styles another way of understanding the lesson concepts.	Teaching Resources
Spanish Resources help students whose first language is Spanish to understand and apply concepts.	Teaching Resources
Study Skills Handbook offers students tips for successful studying that can be applied to other subject areas.	Teaching Resources
Secondary Math Lab Toolkit™ gives students the opportunity to integrate software into their learning, just as they will be using technology in most jobs.	Secondary Math Lab Toolkit™

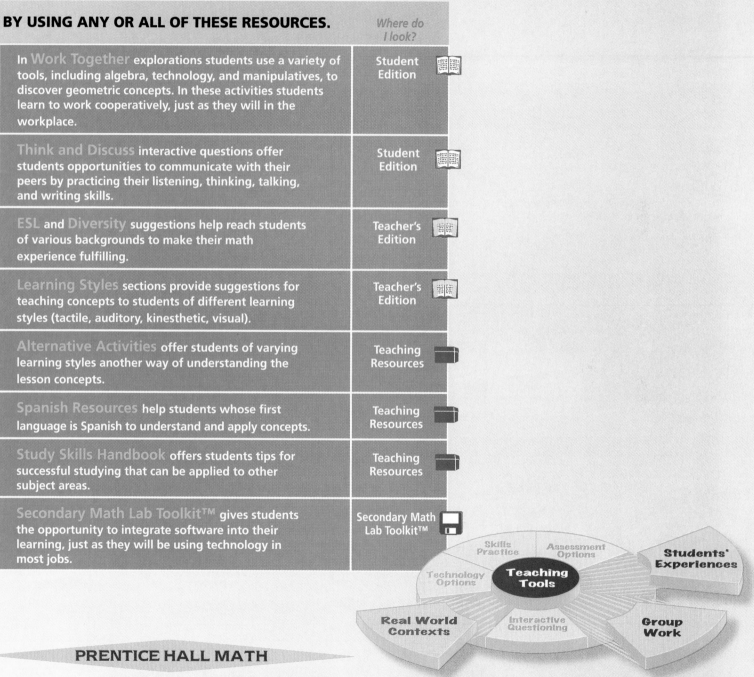

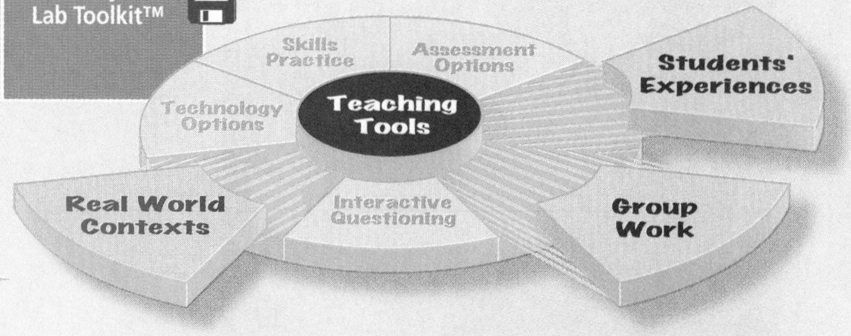

PRENTICE HALL MATH

Helping you manage
the widest variety of motivational tools to

Reach All Students

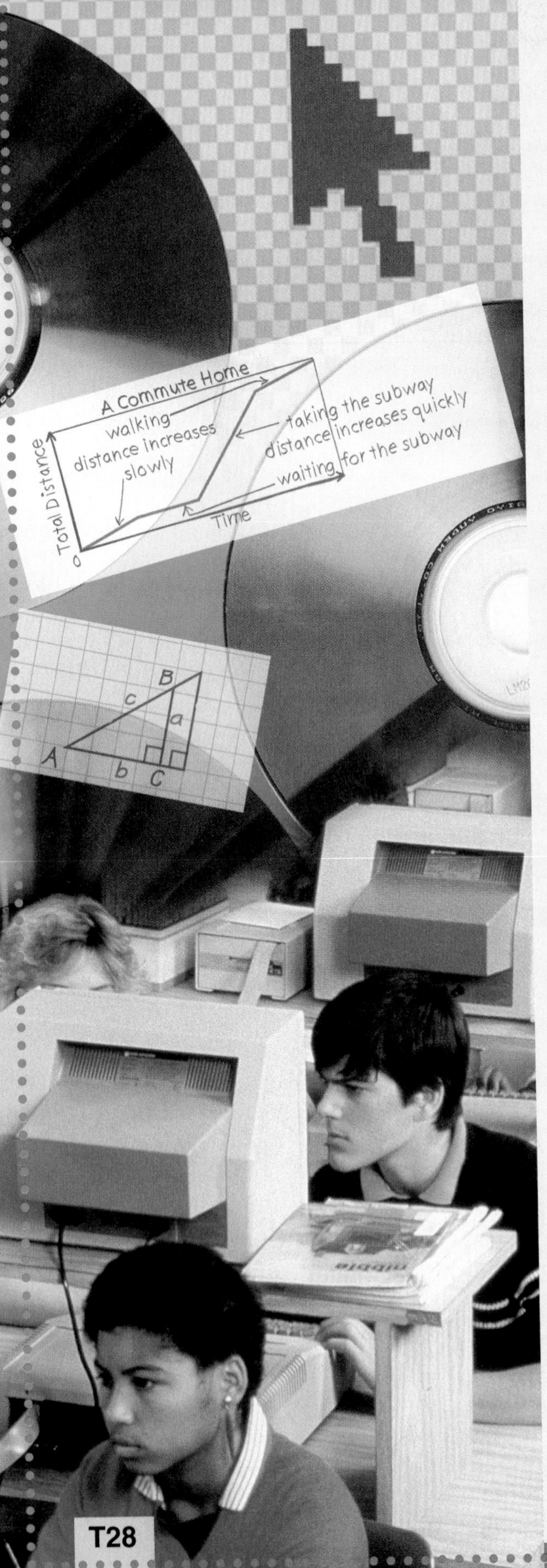

What technology tools are available for me to use?

USE ANY OR ALL OF THESE RESOURCES.	Where do I look?
The Student Edition assumes the use of scientific calculators and incorporates investigations that use geometry software to explore and develop geometric concepts.	Student Edition
A Technology Options side column correlates all the technology components available in the program to each lesson.	Teacher's Edition
Graphing Calculator Handbook provides step-by-step instructions to guide students using a variety of calculators as they work on topics in some Student Edition lessons.	Graphing Calculator Handbook
Calculator-Based Laboratory™ Activities takes advantage of powerful CBL™ equipment and provides activities that relate to the math concepts in the Student Edition.	CBL Activities
Multimedia Math Labs feature CD-ROM–based Labs with QuickTime™ movies, animations, and the Secondary Math Lab Toolkit™ — all keyed to the program objectives.	Multimedia Math Labs
Secondary Math Lab Toolkit™ gives you and students software-based Integrated Math Labs with Math Tools for exploration.	Secondary Math Lab Toolkit™
Prentice Hall's Internet Home Page offers a special section on Math, including projects of the month, exciting links, and a calendar of events.	Internet http://www.phschool.com
The Resource Pro™ CD-ROM package helps you to plan by including many of the supplemental materials in an easy-to-access format.	Resource Pro™

Technology Options
Skills Practice
Assessment Options
Teaching Tools
Students' Experiences
Group Work
Interactive Questioning
Real World Contexts

PRENTICE HALL MATH

Helping you manage the many and varied options for

Using Technology

Where do I look for options to evaluate students' success?

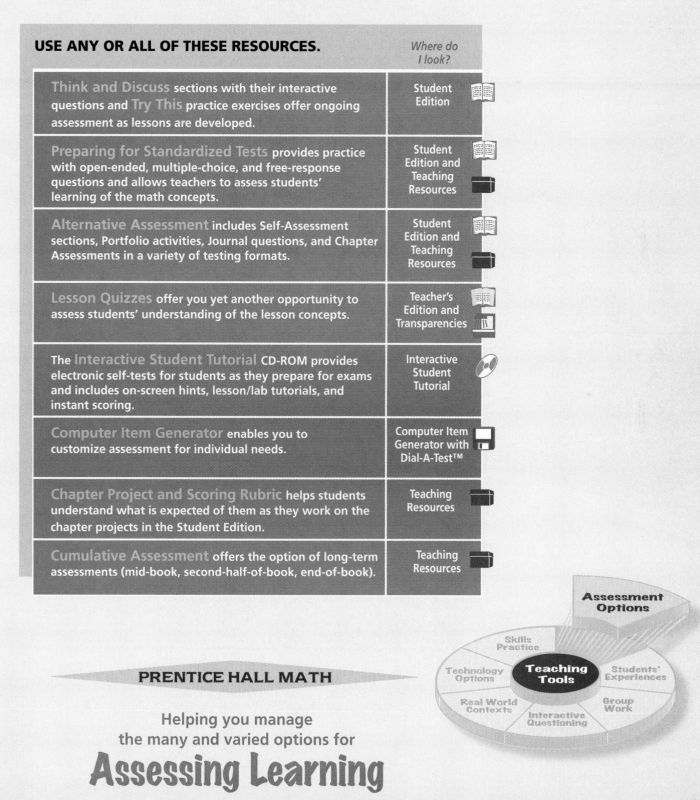

USE ANY OR ALL OF THESE RESOURCES.

	Where do I look?
Think and Discuss sections with their interactive questions and **Try This** practice exercises offer ongoing assessment as lessons are developed.	Student Edition
Preparing for Standardized Tests provides practice with open-ended, multiple-choice, and free-response questions and allows teachers to assess students' learning of the math concepts.	Student Edition and Teaching Resources
Alternative Assessment includes Self-Assessment sections, Portfolio activities, Journal questions, and Chapter Assessments in a variety of testing formats.	Student Edition and Teaching Resources
Lesson Quizzes offer you yet another opportunity to assess students' understanding of the lesson concepts.	Teacher's Edition and Transparencies
The **Interactive Student Tutorial** CD-ROM provides electronic self-tests for students as they prepare for exams and includes on-screen hints, lesson/lab tutorials, and instant scoring.	Interactive Student Tutorial
Computer Item Generator enables you to customize assessment for individual needs.	Computer Item Generator with Dial-A-Test™
Chapter Project and Scoring Rubric helps students understand what is expected of them as they work on the chapter projects in the Student Edition.	Teaching Resources
Cumulative Assessment offers the option of long-term assessments (mid-book, second-half-of-book, end-of-book).	Teaching Resources

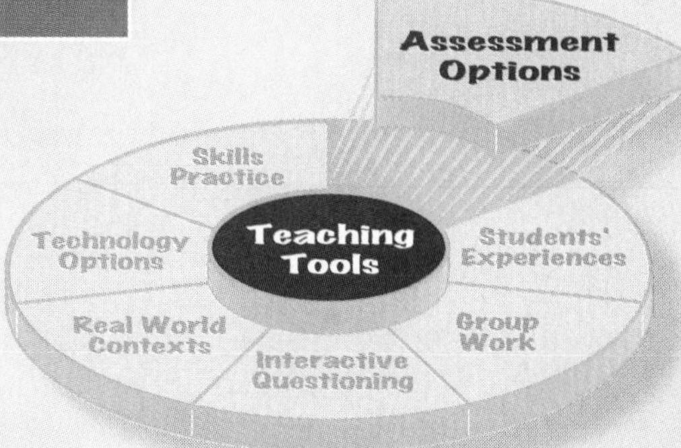

PRENTICE HALL MATH

Helping you manage the many and varied options for

Assessing Learning

Managing Time Constraints

How can I free up my time for teaching?

BY USING ANY OR ALL OF THESE RESOURCES.	Where do I look?
Work Together activities in the lesson itself provide cooperative group work without having to supplement the textbook.	Student Edition
Lessons divided into Parts, with titles announcing each new math concept, break the lesson into manageable sections.	Student Edition
Assignment Options that correlate to the lesson parts in the Student Edition offer you a quick and handy assignment, no matter how much of the lesson you cover during a class period.	Teacher's Edition
Chapter Support Files are organized chapter-by-chapter to keep the shuffling of booklets to a minimum and to help you easily find the resources you need.	Teacher's Edition
Classroom Manager pulls together Lesson Planners and Chapter Organizers that streamline your planning time.	Classroom Manager
Transparencies provide clear visual support to facilitate instruction and learning.	Transparencies
Computer Item Generator is a data bank of test items that allows you to quickly customize practice and assessment.	Computer Item Generator with Dial-A-Test™
Resource Pro™ is a CD-ROM–based package, containing supplemental materials and planning tools, that enables you to customize each lesson quickly and easily.	Resource Pro™

PRENTICE HALL MATH

Helping you manage your time!

How can I cover my objectives while accommodating different schedules?

BY USING THE FOLLOWING COURSE PACING GUIDE.

This chart is provided merely as a guide to help you customize your course. To accommodate flexible scheduling, many lessons are subdivided into parts. In your Teacher's Edition, these parts are indicated in red by the symbol Part ▼. The Assignment Options in each lesson indicate the practice exercises in the Student Edition that correspond to the parts of each lesson.

	Chapter 1 (8 lessons)	Chapter 2 (7 lessons)	Chapter 3 (7 lessons)	Chapter 4 (8 lessons)	Chapter 5 (8 lessons)	Chapter 6 (8 lessons)
Traditional Class Periods (40–45 minutes)	18	17	14	15	16	17
Two-Year Geometry Class Periods (40–45 minutes)	28	27	24	28	25	28
Block Scheduling Class Periods (90 minutes)	9	7	7	8	9	8

		Chapter 7 (5 lessons)	Chapter 8 (5 lessons)	Chapter 9 (6 lessons)	Chapter 10 (6 lessons)	Chapter 11 (6 lessons)	Chapter 12 (6 lessons)	TOTALS
Traditional Class Periods (40–45 minutes)		8	12	10	12	9	12	**160**
Two-Year Geometry Class Periods (40–45 minutes)	Review* 20	21	24	23	25	22	25	**320**
Block Scheduling Class Periods (90 minutes)		4	6	5	6	5	6	**80**

*Suggested review: Wrap Ups for Chapters 1–6 and Lessons 4-3, 4-4, 4-5, and 4-6

AND BY USING THIS PACING RESOURCE.

	Where do I look?
Detailed Chapter Pacing Options precede each chapter and give you lesson-by-lesson pacing suggestions for that specific chapter.	Teacher's Edition 

How can I find ideas and materials that will help me grow professionally?

BY TAKING ADVANTAGE OF SOME OR ALL OF THESE ACTIVITIES.

	Where do I look?
Lesson-specific or chapter-specific Teaching Notes at point of use offer you professional support.	Teacher's Edition
Professional Development Package offers you all the training tools necessary for customized professional development.	Professional Development Package
The Prentice Hall Internet Home Page provides, among other things, a calendar of professional events and a variety of links to other sites on the Web that offer content ideas as well as growth opportunities.	Internet http://www.phschool.com
Prentice Hall Summer Seminars, focusing on math issues and technology, bring together math educators and experts for a variety of interactive and hands-on sessions.	Watch your mail for special flyers.
Prentice Hall Consultant Workshops offer you experiences during in-service training to learn about specific math issues.	Contact your local Prentice Hall sales representative.

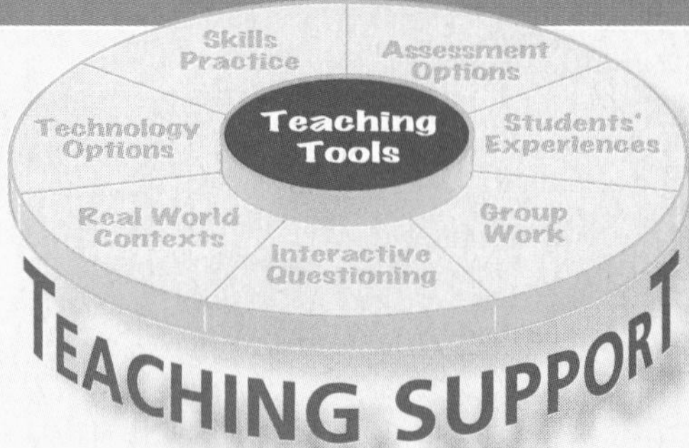

PRENTICE HALL MATH

Helping you manage the many and varied options for effective

Professional Development

PRENTICE HALL

GEOMETRY

Prentice Hall dedicates
this mathematics program
to all mathematics educators
and their students.

PRENTICE HALL
Needham, Massachusetts
Upper Saddle River, New Jersey
Glenview, Illinois

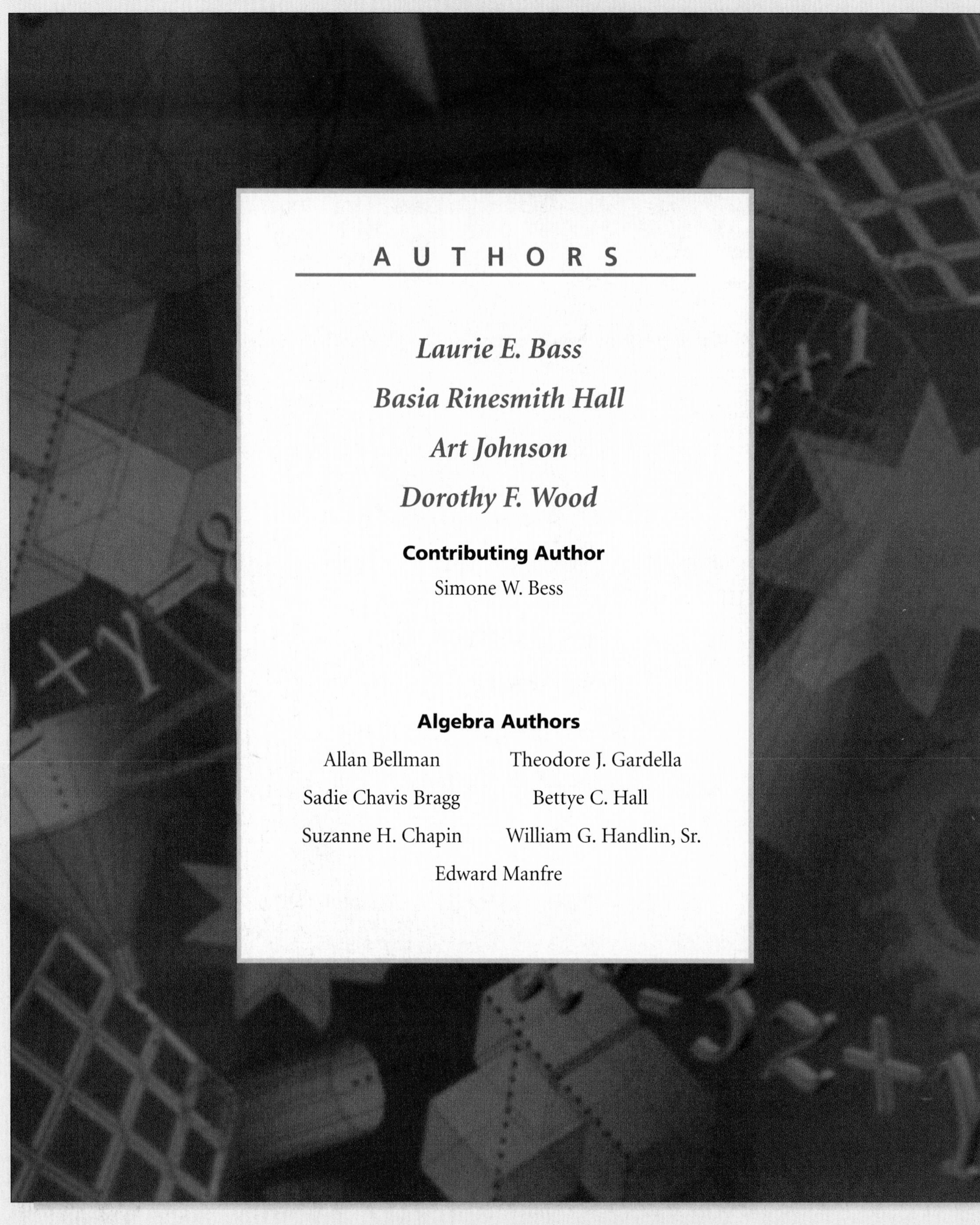

AUTHORS

Laurie E. Bass

Basia Rinesmith Hall

Art Johnson

Dorothy F. Wood

Contributing Author

Simone W. Bess

Algebra Authors

Allan Bellman
Theodore J. Gardella
Sadie Chavis Bragg
Bettye C. Hall
Suzanne H. Chapin
William G. Handlin, Sr.
Edward Manfre

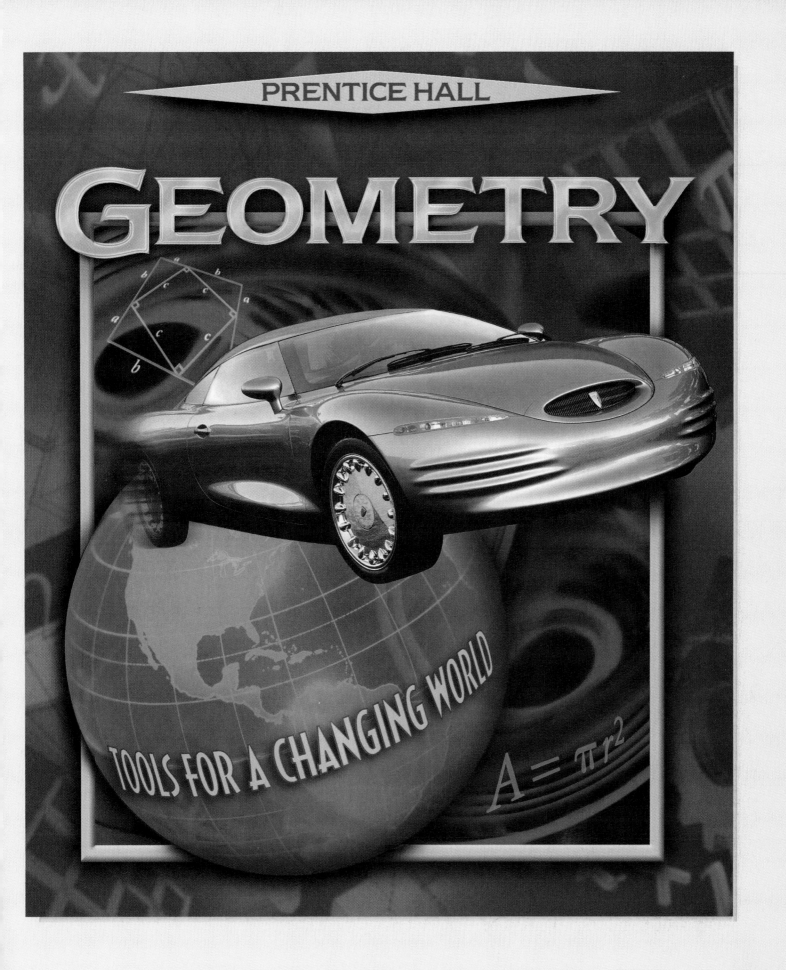

PRENTICE HALL

GEOMETRY

TOOLS FOR A CHANGING WORLD

$A = \pi r^2$

Authors, Geometry

Laurie E. Bass
The Fieldston School
Riverdale, New York

Basia Rinesmith Hall
East District
Houston Independent School District
Houston, Texas

Art Johnson, Ed.D.
Nashua High School
Nashua, New Hampshire

Dorothy F. Wood
Formerly, Kern High School District
Bakersfield, California

Contributing Author
Simone W. Bess, Ed.D.
University of Cincinnati
College of Education
Cincinnati, Ohio

Authors, Algebra & Advanced Algebra

Allan Bellman
Blake High School
Silver Spring, Maryland

Sadie Chavis Bragg, Ed.D.
Borough of Manhattan
Community College
The City University of New York
New York, New York

Suzanne H. Chapin, Ed.D.
Boston University
Boston, Massachusetts

Theodore J. Gardella
Formerly, Bloomfield Hills Public Schools
Bloomfield Hills, Michigan

Bettye C. Hall
Mathematics Consultant
Houston, Texas

William G. Handlin, Sr.
Spring Woods High School
Houston, Texas

Edward Manfre
Mathematics Consultant
Albuquerque, New Mexico

Printed in the United States of America.

ISBN: 0-13-050185-9

2 3 4 5 6 7 8 9 10 04 03 02 01 00

REVIEWERS

Series Reviewers

James Gates, Ed.D.
Executive Director Emeritus, National Council of Teachers of Mathematics, Reston, Virginia

Vinetta Jones, Ph.D.
National Director, EQUITY 2000, The College Board, New York, New York

Geometry

Sandra Argüelles Daire
Miami Senior High School
Miami, Florida

Priscilla P. Donkle
South Central High School
Union Mills, Indiana

Tom Muchlinski, Ph.D.
Wayzata High School
Plymouth, Minnesota

Bonnie Walker
Texas ASCD
Houston, Texas

Karen Doyle Walton, Ed.D.
Allentown College of
Saint Francis de Sales
Center Valley, Pennsylvania

Algebra

John J. Brady III
Hume-Fogg High School
Nashville, Tennessee

Elias P. Rodriguez
Leander Junior High School
Leander, Texas

Dorothy S. Strong, Ed.D.
Chicago Public Schools
Chicago, Illinois

Art W. Wilson, Ed.D.
Abraham Lincoln High School
Denver, Colorado

Advanced Algebra

Eleanor Boehner
Methacton High School
Norristown, Pennsylvania

Laura Price Cobb
Dallas Public Schools
Dallas, Texas

William Earl, Ed.D.
Formerly Mathematics
Education Specialist
Utah State Office of Education
Salt Lake City, Utah

Staff Credits

The people who made up the *Geometry* team — representing editorial, design, marketing, page production, editorial services, production, manufacturing, technology, electronic publishing, and advertising and promotion — and their managers are listed below. Bold type denotes core team members.

Alison Anholt-White, Jackie Zidek Bedoya, Barbara A. Bertell, Bruce Bond, Ellen Brown, Judith D. Buice, Kathy Carter, Kerri Caruso, **Linda M. Coffey, Noralie V. Cox,** Sheila DeFazio, Edward de Leon, Christine Deliee, Gabriella Della Corte, Robert G. Dunn, Barbara Flockhart, Audra Floyd, David Graham, Maria Green, Bridget A. Hadley, Joanne Hudson, Vanessa Hunnibell, Mimi Jigarjian, **Linda D. Johnson,** Elizabeth A. Jordan, Russell Lappa, **Catherine Martin-Hetmansky,** Eve Melnechuk, Cindy A. Noftle, Caroline M. Power, Roger E. Powers, Martha G. Smith, Kira Thaler, Robin Tiano, Christina Trinchero, Stuart Wallace, Cynthia A. Weedel, **Jeff Weidenaar, Pearl B. Weinstein,** Mary Jane Wolfe, Stewart Wood, David Zarowin

We would like to give special thanks to our National Math Consultants, Ann F. Bell, Liz Cunningham, Shawyn Jackson, Sandra Mosteller, and Loretta Rector, for all their help in developing this program.

To the Student

Students like you helped Prentice Hall develop this program. They identified tools you can use to help you learn now in this course and beyond. In this special "To the Student" section and throughout this program, you will find the **tools you need to help you succeed.** We'd like to hear how these tools work for you. Write us at Prentice Hall Mathematics, 160 Gould Street, Needham, MA 02494 or visit us at http://www.phschool.com.

"... Instead of problem after problem of pointless numbers, we should have a chance to think and to truly understand what we are doing. I personally think that we all should be taught this way."
Chris, Grade 9
Carson City, NV

"... I learn mathematics best when I draw a diagram or make a graph that helps show what the problem is that I will solve."
Amy, Grade 11
Columbia, SC

"... I like to review what I learn as I go, rather than cramming the night before a test."
Ali, Grade 10
St. Paul, MN

Use this "To the Student" section to help students understand how they learn. It also shows how this textbook relates what they experience daily to the math they're learning and will need in the workplace of the future.

LEARN About Learning!

What comes to your mind when you hear the word **style**? Maybe it's hair style, or style of dress, or walking style. Have you ever thought about your learning style? Just like your hair or your clothes or your walk, everybody has a learning style that they like best because it works best for them. Look around you now. What do you see? Different styles … some like yours, some different from yours. That's the way it is with learning styles, too.

What's Your Best Learning Style?

I understand math concepts best when I...

- ❑ A. Read about them.
- ❑ B. Look at and make illustrations, graphs, and charts that show them.
- ❑ C. Draw sketches or handle manipulatives to explore them.
- ❑ D. Listen to someone explain them.

When I study, I learn more when I...

- ❑ A. Review my notes and the textbook.
- ❑ B. Study any graphs, charts, diagrams, or other illustrations.
- ❑ C. Write ideas on note cards; then study the ideas.
- ❑ D. Explain what I know to another person.

When I collaborate with a group, I am most comfortable when I...

- ❑ A. Take notes.
- ❑ B. Make visuals for display.
- ❑ C. Demonstrate what I know to others.
- ❑ D. Give presentations to other groups or the whole class.

Look for a pattern in your responses.
"A" responses suggest that you learn best by reading;
"B" responses indicate a visual learning style;
"C" responses suggest a tactile, or hands-on, learning style;
"D" responses signal that you probably learn best by listening and talking about what you are learning.

Students determine their dominant learning style by taking this quick and easy survey.

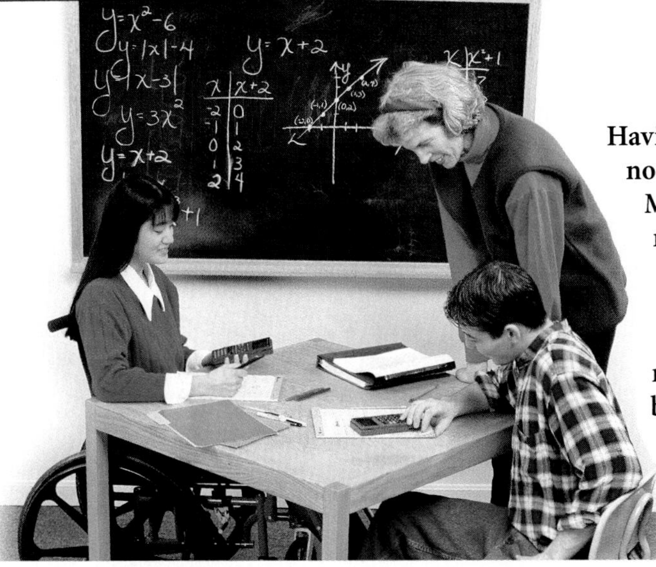

Having a preferred learning style does not limit you to using just that one. Most people learn by using a combination of learning styles. You'll be amazed by the ways that knowing more about yourself and how you learn will help you be successful — not only successful in mathematics, but successful in all your subject areas. When you know how you learn best, you will be well equipped to enter the work place.

Use this chart to help you strengthen your different learning styles.

Learning Style	Learning Tips
Learning by ***reading***	* Schedule time to read each day. * Carry a book or magazine to read during wait time. * Read what you like to read—it's OK not to finish a book.
Learning by using ***visual*** cues	* Visualize a problem situation. * Graph solutions to problems. * Let technology, such as computers and calculators, help you.
Learning by using ***hands-on*** exploration	* Make sketches when solving a problem. * Use objects to help you solve problems. * Rely on technology as a tool for exploration and discovery.
Learning by ***listening and talking***	* Volunteer to give presentations. * Explain your ideas to a friend. * Listen intently to what others are saying.

Most important, believe in yourself and your ability to learn!

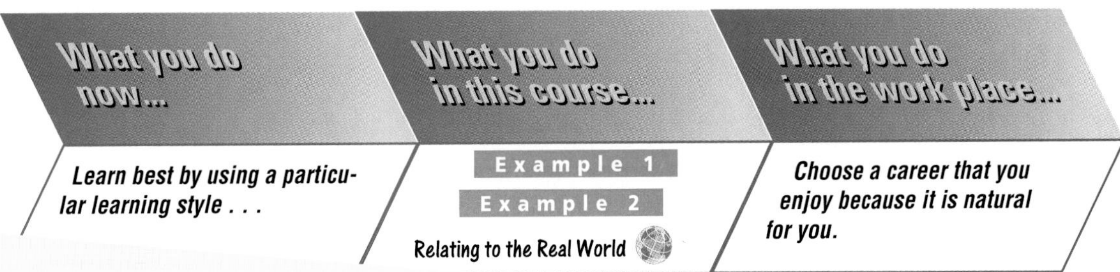

What you do now...
What you do in this course...
What you do in the work place...
Learn best by using a particular learning style . . .
Example 1
Example 2
Relating to the Real World
Choose a career that you enjoy because it is natural for you.

Note the diagram at the bottom of the page that connects instructional methods utilized throughout the program with what students experience today and in their future.

Help Teamwork Work for YOU!

Each of us works with other people on teams throughout our lives. What's your job? Your job on a team, that is. Maybe you play center on your basketball team, maybe you count votes for your school elections, perhaps you help decorate the gym for a school function, or maybe you help make scenery for a community play. From relay races to doing your part of the job in the work place, teamwork is required for success.

TEAMWORK CHECKLIST

- ✔ **Break apart the large task into smaller tasks, which become the responsibility of individual group members.**
- ✔ **Treat the differences in group members as a benefit.**
- ✔ **Try to listen attentively when others speak.**
- ✔ **Stay focused on the task at hand and the goal to be accomplished.**
- ✔ **Vary the tasks you do in each group and participate.**
- ✔ **Recognize your own and others' learning styles.**
- ✔ **Offer your ideas and suggestions.**
- ✔ **Be socially responsible and act in a respectful way.**

What you do now...	What you do in this course...	What you do in the work place...
Play on a team, decorate the gym,or perform in the band...	WORK TOGETHER	*Collaborate with coworkers on projects.*

Both teachers and students can reference this handy Teamwork Checklist while students are working in pairs or in small groups.

Reading + Writing + Talking + Listening:

It's All COMMUNICATION

We communicate in songs. We communicate in letters. We communicate with our body movements. We communicate on the phone. We communicate in cyberspace. It's all talking about ideas and sharing what you know. It's the same in mathematics — we communicate by reading, writing, talking, and listening. Whether we are working together on a project or studying with a friend for a test, we are communicating.

Ways to Communicate What You Know and Are Able to Do

- ✔ Explain to others how you solve a problem.
- ✔ Listen carefully to others.
- ✔ Use mathematical language in your writing in other subjects.
- ✔ Pay attention to the headings in textbooks — they are signposts that help you.
- ✔ Think about videos and audiotapes as ways to communicate mathematical ideas.
- ✔ Be on the lookout for mathematics when you read, watch television, or see a movie.
- ✔ Communicate with others by using bulletin boards and chat rooms found on the Internet.

What you do now...	What you do in this course...	What you do in the work place...
Teach a young relative a sport...	THINK AND DISCUSS	*Written and verbal communication at work.*

Build communication skills with these hints on how students can communicate more effectively with their teachers and their classmates.

Solving PROBLEMS – *a* SKILL You USE Every DAY

Problem solving is a skill — a skill that you probably use without even knowing it. When you think critically in social studies to draw conclusions about pollution and its stress on the environment, or when a mechanic listens to symptoms of trouble and logically determines the cause, you are both using a mathematical problem-solving skill. Problem solving also involves logical reasoning, wise decision making, and reflecting on our solutions.

Tips for Problem Solving

Tips for Problem Solving
Recognize that there is more than one way to solve most problems.
When solving a word problem, read it, decide what to do, make a plan, look back at the problem, and revise your answer.
Experiment with various solution methods.
Understand that it is just as important to know how to solve a problem as it is to actually solve it.
Be aware of times you are using mathematics to solve problems that do not involve computation, such as when you reason to make a wise decision.

What you do now...	What you do in this course...	What you do in the work place...
Make decisions based on changing conditions, such as weather...	PROBLEM SOLVING	*Synchronize the timing of traffic lights to enhance traffic flow.*

Establish problem solving success by helping students understand that there isn't always one answer to or one way of solving a problem.

Studying for the

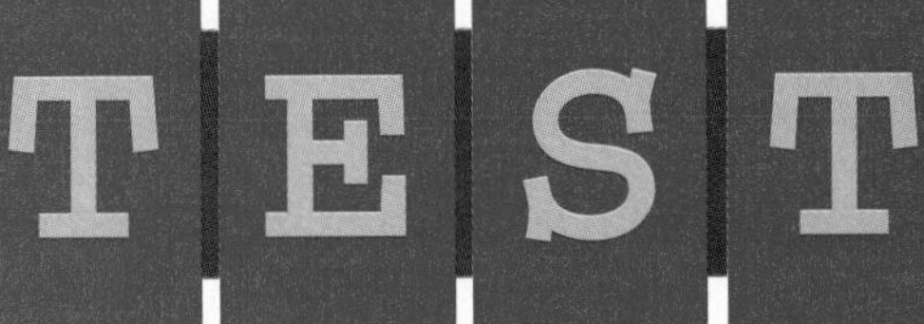

Whatever It May Be

SATs, ACTs, chapter tests, and weekly quizzes — they all test what you know and are able to do. Have you ever thought about **how** you can take these tests to your advantage? You are evaluated now in your classes and you will be evaluated when you hold a job.

Pointers for Gaining Points

- Study as you progress through a chapter, instead of cramming for a test.
- Recognize when you are lost and seek help before a test.
- Review important graphs and other visuals when studying for a test, then picture them in your mind.
- Study for a test with a friend or study group.
- Take a practice test.
- Think of mnemonic devices to help you, such as **P**lease **E**xcuse **M**y **D**ear **A**unt **S**ally, which is one way to remember order of operations (**p**arentheses, **e**xponents, **m**ultiply, **d**ivide, **a**dd, **s**ubtract).
- Reread test questions before answering them.
- Check to see if your answer is reasonable.
- Think positively and visualize yourself doing well on the test.
- Relax during the test... there is nothing there that you have not seen before.

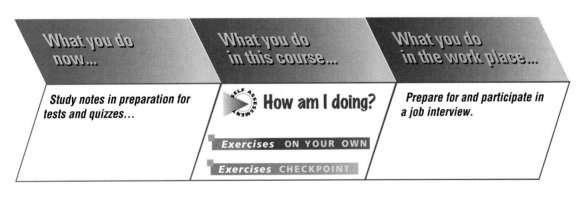

What you do now...	What you do in this course...	What you do in the work place...
Study notes in preparation for tests and quizzes...	SELF ASSESSMENT How am I doing? Exercises ON YOUR OWN Exercises CHECKPOINT	*Prepare for and participate in a job interview.*

These test-taking strategies highlight techniques that students can use to prepare for various assessments leading to success.

PTER 1

Tools of Geometry

To accommodate flexible scheduling, some lessons are divided into parts. Assignment Options are given in the Lesson Planning Options for each lesson.

1-1 Using Patterns and Inductive Reasoning (pp. 4–10)

Key Terms: conjecture, inductive reasoning

1-2 Points, Lines, and Planes (pp. 12–17)

Part 1 Basic Terms

Part 2 Basic Postulates

Key Terms: collinear, coplanar, line, plane, point, postulate, space

1-3 Segments, Rays, Parallel Lines, and Planes (pp. 18–22)

Key Terms: opposite rays, parallel lines, parallel planes, ray, segment, skew lines

1-4 Measuring Angles and Segments (pp. 24–31)

Part 1 Measuring Segments

Part 2 Measuring Angles

Key Terms: acute angle, angle, congruent angles, congruent segments, coordinate, measure of an angle, obtuse angle, right angle, straight angle

1-5 Good Definitions (pp. 32–38)

Part 1 Properties of Good Definitions

Part 2 Bisectors

Key Terms: angle bisector, midpoint, perpendicular lines, segment bisector

1-6 Basic Constructions (pp. 39–44)

Part 1 Constructing Congruent Segments and Congruent Angles

Part 2 Constructing Perpendicular Bisectors and Angle Bisectors

Key terms: compass, construction, straightedge

1-7 Using Deductive Reasoning (pp. 46–52)

Part 1 Connecting Algebra and Geometry

Part 2 Angle Pairs

Key Terms: adjacent angles, complementary angles, deductive reasoning, supplementary angles, theorem, vertical angles

1-8 The Coordinate Plane (pp. 53–57)

Key Term: quadrant

PACING OPTIONS

This chart suggests pacing only for the core lessons and their parts, and it is provided merely as a possible guide. It will help you determine how much time you have in your schedule to cover other features, such as the Chapter Project, Math Toolboxes, Wrap Up, and Assessment.

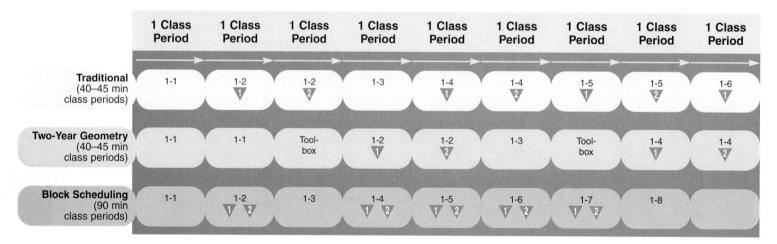

	1 Class Period	1 Class Period	1 Class Period	1 Class Period	1 Class Period	1 Class Period	1 Class Period	1 Class Period	1 Class Period
Traditional (40–45 min class periods)	1-1	1-2 Part 1	1-2 Part 2	1-3	1-4 Part 1	1-4 Part 2	1-5 Part 1	1-5 Part 2	1-6 Part 1
Two-Year Geometry (40–45 min class periods)	1-1	1-1	Tool-box	1-2 Part 1	1-2 Part 2	1-3	Tool-box	1-4 Part 1	1-4 Part 2
Block Scheduling (90 min class periods)	1-1	1-2 Parts 1, 2	1-3	1-4 Parts 1, 2	1-5 Parts 1, 2	1-6 Parts 1, 2	1-7 Parts 1, 2	1-8	

What Students Will Learn and Why

In this chapter, students learn some of the basic terms and postulates of geometry and become familiar with the tools they will use as they study this subject. They use patterns and inductive reasoning to make conjectures. They learn the meaning of point, line, and plane; how segments and rays are related to lines; how to recognize parallel lines and parallel planes; and how to find the length of a segment and the measure of an angle. Students learn what makes a good definition in geometry and how to use a compass and straightedge to perform some basic constructions. They use deductive reasoning to solve problems and test conjectures. Finally, students learn to find distance and midpoints of segments in the coordinate plane.

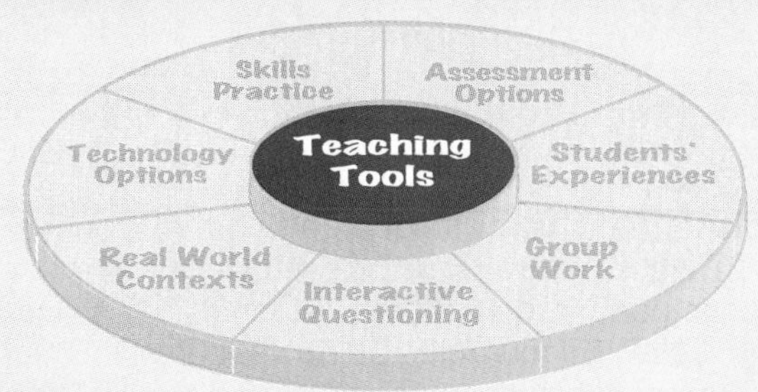

Discussing the Chapter/Building on Experience

The concept map below relates chapter topics to real-world applications. You and your class may wish to add to the map or develop maps of your own. The center oval describes the topic of the chapter. The next level displays topics within the lessons. The outer ovals reflect applications of the content. As you and your class build a concept map, invite students to discuss applications with which they are familiar.

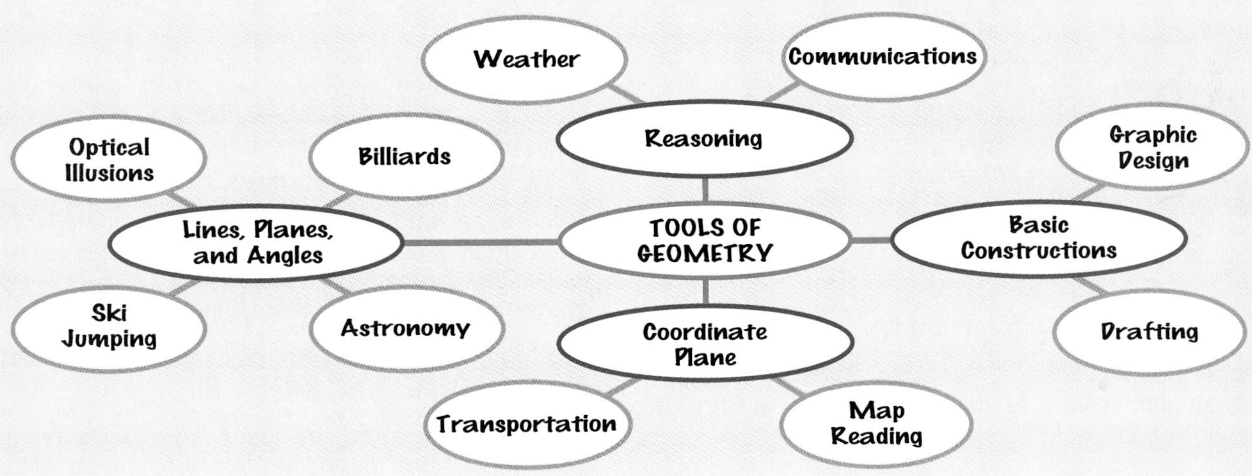

1 Class Period	1 Class Period	1 Class Period	1 Class Period	1 Class Period	1 Class Period	1 Class Period	1 Class Period	1 Class Period	1 Class Period	1 Class Period
1-6 ▽2	1-7 ▽1	1-7 ▽2	1-8							
1-4 ▽2	1-5 ▽1	1-5 ▽2	1-6 ▽1	1-6 ▽2	Tool-box	1-7 ▽1	1-7 ▽2	1-7 ▽2	1-8	1-8

Interactive Questioning Tips

A question is interactive when there is "give and take" between the questioner (teacher or student) and the respondent. In Think and Discuss or when a critical thinking question is asked, it is important to encourage students to explain their answers in detail. Encouraging students to explain their answers promotes active participation and stimulates higher levels of thought. These two elements are essential in developing high-level thinking skills. For example, in Lesson 1-4, Question 5, students are asked to explain why they think absolute value is used to express the distance between two points. Allow students time to compose their answer mentally.

Skills Practice

Every lesson provides skill practice with Try This exercises, Exercises On Your Own, and Exercises Mixed Review. The Student Edition includes Checkpoints (pp. 31, 52) and Preparing for Standardized Tests (p. 65). In the Teacher's Edition, the Lesson Planning Options section for each lesson lists Prerequisite Skills students should know for that lesson. At the back of the Student Edition is the Skills Handbook—mini-lessons on math your students may need to review. The Chapter Support File for Chapter 1 in the Teaching Resources box includes two Practice worksheets per lesson, a worksheet for two Checkpoints, and worksheets for Cumulative Review and Standardized Test Preparation.

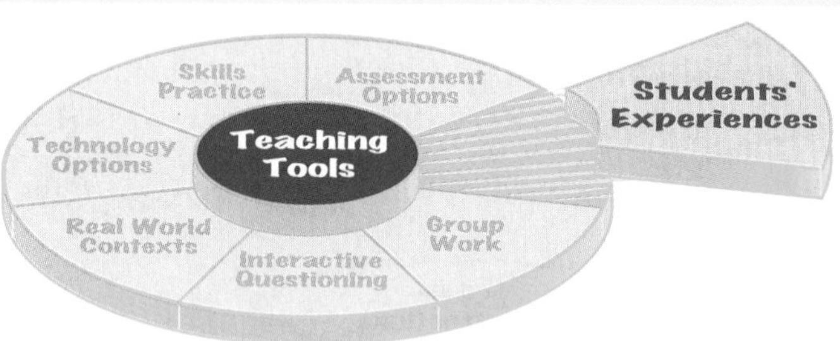

Diverse Learning and Teaching Styles

In your Teacher's Edition, you will find suggestions as to how you can help students complete mathematical tasks in Chapter 1 by reinforcing various learning styles. Here are some examples.

- **Visual learning** use inductive reasoning relying on visual cues (p.7), remember abbreviations by observing the visual representations of a segment, ray, and line (p. 18), benefit from drawings (p. 51)
- **Tactile learning** use index cards to illustrate two planes that intersect on horizontal and vertical lines (p. 14), investigate properties of a Mobius band (p. 36), discuss and perform each step of Construction 1 (p. 40)
- **Auditory learning** take turns explaining the Protractor Postulate to partners (p. 27)
- **Kinesthetic learning** move outdoors to observe and record real-world examples of ways two lines can be related (p. 21)

Alternative Activity for Lesson 1-4

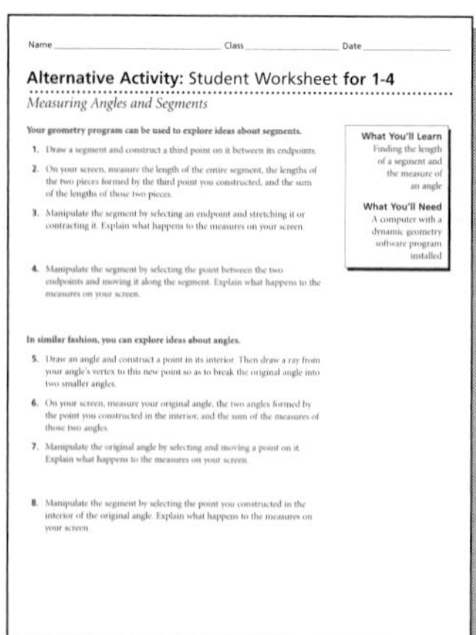

Name ______ Class ______ Date ______

Alternative Activity: Student Worksheet **for 1-4**

Measuring Angles and Segments

Your geometry program can be used to explore ideas about segments.

1. Draw a segment and construct a third point on it between its endpoints.
2. On your screen, measure the length of the entire segment, the lengths of the two pieces formed by the third point you constructed, and the sum of the lengths of those two pieces.
3. Manipulate the segment by selecting an endpoint and stretching it or contracting it. Explain what happens to the measures on your screen.
4. Manipulate the segment by selecting the point between the two endpoints and moving it along the segment. Explain what happens to the measures on your screen.

In similar fashion, you can explore ideas about angles.

5. Draw an angle and construct a point in its interior. Then draw a ray from your angle's vertex to this new point so as to break the original angle into two smaller angles.
6. On your screen, measure your original angle, the two angles formed by the point you constructed in the interior, and the sum of the measures of those two angles.
7. Manipulate the original angle by selecting and moving a point on it. Explain what happens to the measures on your screen.
8. Manipulate the segment by selecting the point you constructed in the interior of the original angle. Explain what happens to the measures on your screen.

What You'll Learn Finding the length of a segment and the measure of an angle

What You'll Need A computer with a dynamic geometry software program installed

for use with Segment Additions and Angle Addition Postulates, uses geometry software to find the lengths of segments and the measures of angles.

Alternative Activity for Lesson 1-5

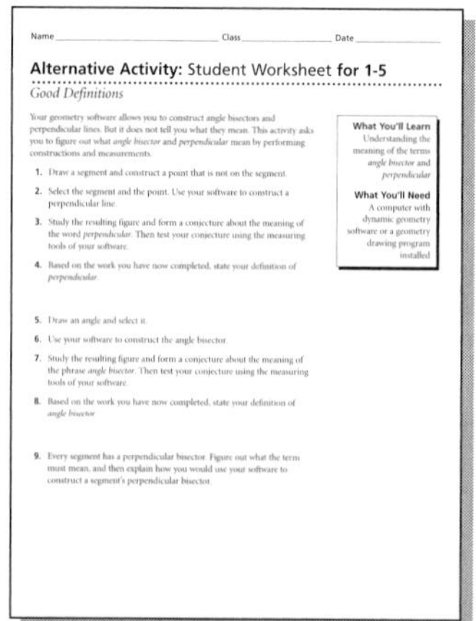

Name ______ Class ______ Date ______

Alternative Activity: Student Worksheet **for 1-5**

Good Definitions

Your geometry software allows you to construct angle bisectors and perpendicular lines. But it does not tell you what they mean. This activity asks you to figure out what *angle bisector* and *perpendicular* mean by performing constructions and measurements.

1. Draw a segment and construct a point that is not on the segment.
2. Select the segment and the point. Use your software to construct a perpendicular line.
3. Study the resulting figure and form a conjecture about the meaning of the word *perpendicular*. Then test your conjecture using the measuring tools of your software.
4. Based on the work you have now completed, state your definition of *perpendicular*.
5. Draw an angle and select it.
6. Use your software to construct the angle bisector.
7. Study the resulting figure and form a conjecture about the meaning of the phrase *angle bisector*. Then test your conjecture using the measuring tools of your software.
8. Based on the work you have now completed, state your definition of *angle bisector*.
9. Every segment has a perpendicular bisector. Figure out what the term must mean, and then explain how you would use your software to construct a segment's perpendicular bisector.

What You'll Learn Understanding the meaning of the terms *angle bisector* and *perpendicular*

What You'll Need A computer with dynamic geometry software or a geometry drawing program installed

for use with definitions presented in the student text, uses geometry software to explore the meaning of the terms *angle bisector* and *perpendicular.*

Alternative Activity for Lesson 1-7

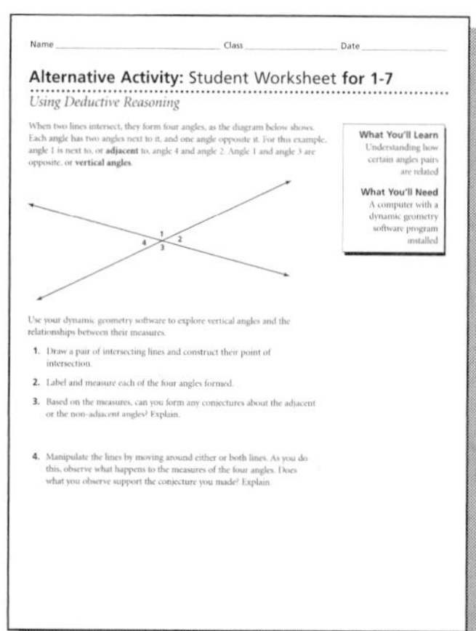

Name ______ Class ______ Date ______

Alternative Activity: Student Worksheet **for 1-7**

Using Deductive Reasoning

When two lines intersect, they form four angles, as the diagram below shows. Each angle has two angles next to it, and one angle opposite it. For this example, angle 1 is next to, or **adjacent** to, angle 4 and angle 2. Angle 1 and angle 3 are opposite, or **vertical angles**.

Use your dynamic geometry software to explore vertical angles and the relationships between their measures.

1. Draw a pair of intersecting lines and construct their point of intersection.
2. Label and measure each of the four angles formed.
3. Based on the measures, can you form any conjectures about the adjacent or the non-adjacent angles? Explain.
4. Manipulate the lines by moving around either or both lines. As you do this, observe what happens to the measures of the four angles. Does what you observe support the conjecture you made? Explain.

What You'll Learn Understanding how certain angles pairs are related

What You'll Need A computer with a dynamic geometry software program installed

for use with the Work Together, uses dynamic geometry software to explore angles formed by intersecting lines.

Skills Practice
Assessment Options
Technology Options
Teaching Tools
Students' Experiences
Real World Contexts
Interactive Questioning
Group Work

Cooperative Learning Tips

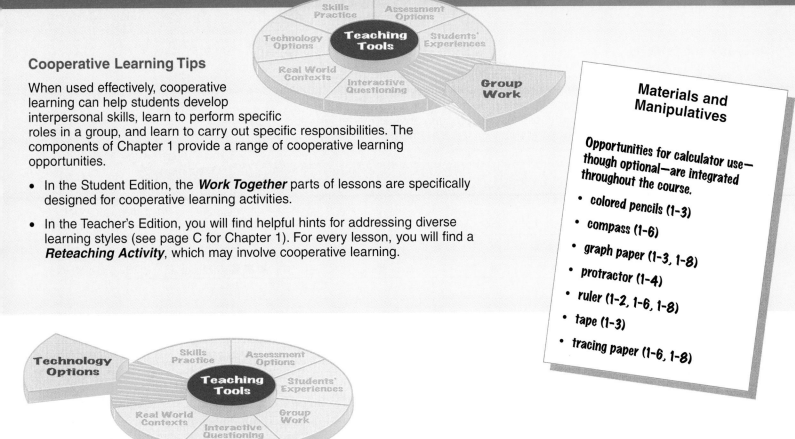

When used effectively, cooperative learning can help students develop interpersonal skills, learn to perform specific roles in a group, and learn to carry out specific responsibilities. The components of Chapter 1 provide a range of cooperative learning opportunities.

- In the Student Edition, the ***Work Together*** parts of lessons are specifically designed for cooperative learning activities.
- In the Teacher's Edition, you will find helpful hints for addressing diverse learning styles (see page C for Chapter 1). For every lesson, you will find a ***Reteaching Activity***, which may involve cooperative learning.

Materials and Manipulatives

Opportunities for calculator use—though optional—are integrated throughout the course.

- colored pencils (1-3)
- compass (1-6)
- graph paper (1-3, 1-8)
- protractor (1-4)
- ruler (1-2, 1-6, 1-8)
- tape (1-3)
- tracing paper (1-6, 1-8)

Technology Options
Skills Practice
Assessment Options
Teaching Tools
Students' Experiences
Real World Contexts
Group Work
Interactive Questioning

TECHNOLOGY OPTIONS

Technology Tools		Chapter Project	1-1	1-2	1-3	1-4	1-5	1-6	1-7	1-8
Calculator		Numerous opportunities throughout for students to use scientific calculators.								
Software	Secondary Math Lab Toolkit™		✔	✔	✔	✔	✔	✔	✔	✔
	Integrated Math Lab					✔				✔
	Computer Item Generator		✔	✔	✔	✔	✔	✔	✔	✔
	Student Edition					✔		✔T		
Video	Video Field Trip	✔								
CD-ROM	Multimedia Geometry Lab			✔	✔	✔		✔		
Internet		See the Prentice Hall site. (http://www.phschool.com)								

✔T indicates Math Toolbox.

The Prentice Hall Geometry program offers you a rich variety of technology options. Be assured that all these options are provided as a means of enriching the program and are not essential for the successful completion of the course.

Assessment Options

The Prentice Hall Geometry Program provides you with many options. From these options, you may choose instructional materials and techniques appropriate for your students, or those necessary to meet your district's curriculum requirements. As the chart indicates, the program also supports your teaching efforts by offering you many choices for assessment.

ASSESSMENT OPTIONS

Assessment Support Materials	Chapter Project	1-1	1-2	1-3	1-4	1-5	1-6	1-7	1-8	Chapter End
Chapter Project	▲■	▲■		▲■	▲■		▲■			▲■
Checkpoints			■		▲■●			▲■●		
Self-Assessment										
Writing Assignment		▲	▲■	▲■	▲■●	▲■	▲	▲●	▲	●▲
Chapter Assessment										▲●
Alternative Assessment		■	■	■	■	■	■	■	■	●■
Cumulative Review										●
Standardized Test Prep		▲■	▲■	▲		▲■		▲■		▲●
Computer Item Generator	Can be used to create custom-made practice or assessment at any time.									

▲ = Student Edition ■ = Teacher's Edition ● = Teaching Resources

Checkpoints

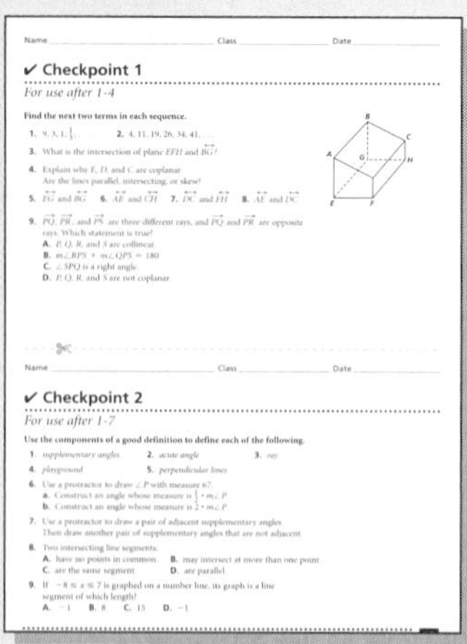

Alternative Assessment

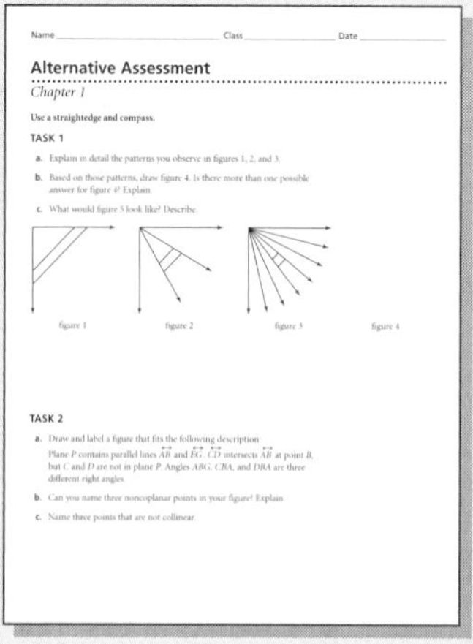

Chapter Assessment

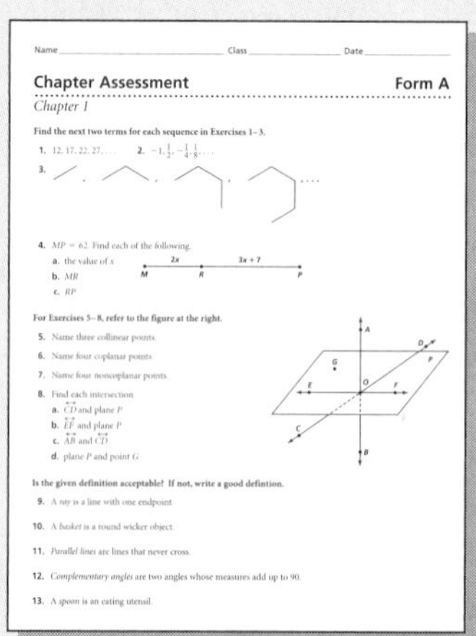

Available in both Form A and Form B

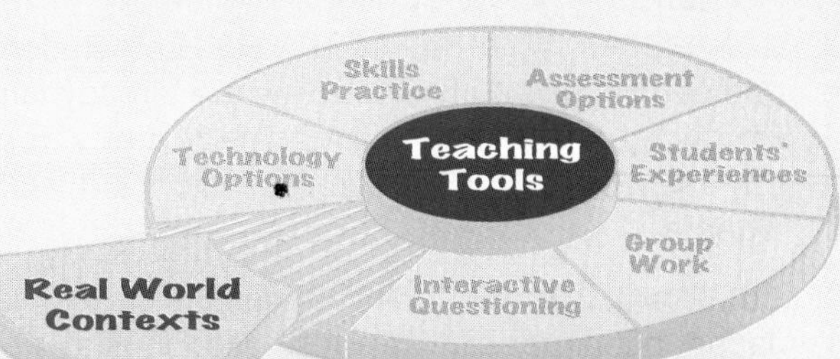

Making the Right Connections

Mathematics is imbedded in nearly every walk of life. The National Council of Teachers of Mathematics (NCTM) encourages educators to recognize these connections and to emphasize them for the purpose of better educating students for success in life and in a global economy. The ***Connections*** chart below highlights these connections for Chapter 1.

CONNECTIONS

Lesson	Interdisciplinary Connections	Career Prep	Other Real World Connections	Math Integration	NCTM Standards
Chapter Project	Art	Graphic Design			Problem Solving Connections
1-1	History	Manufacturing Communications	Marathon Running Fitness Transportation	Algebra	Reasoning Communication Problem Solving
1-2	Astronomy		Navigation Magic	Probability Coordinate Geometry	Communication Problem Solving
1-3	Chemistry Language Arts	Engineering	Navigation	Coordinate Geometry	Communications Problem Solving
1-4	Art	Cartography	Flower Arranging Ski Jumping Travel Mile Markers Billiards	Coordinate Geometry Algebra	Algebra Communication Problem Solving
1-5	Language Arts	Cabinet making		Algebra Coordinate Geometry Geometry in 3 Dimensions	Connections Algebra Communication Problem Solving
1-6	Art	Engineering			Communication Problem Solving
1-7		Medicine Carpentry Auto Repair	Parking Restrictions	Algebra Coordinate Geometry	Reasoning Communication Algebra Problem Solving Structure
1-8	Astronomy		Transportation Communications	Algebra Geometry in 3 Dimensions	Coordinate Geometry Algebra Communication Problem Solving

CHAPTER 1 Tools of Geometry

CONNECTING TO PRIOR LEARNING Have students brainstorm geometric topics with which they are already familiar. Encourage them to think of geometry topics or properties they have studied in courses such as history, art, science, or algebra.

CULTURAL CONNECTIONS Origami is closely associated with Japan, but paper folding is also used in other countries, such as Germany, Spain, South America, England, and the United States. Paper foldings are used for decorations, ceremonial purposes, and to teach math and function design. Ask students to describe objects they have constructed by folding paper.

INTERDISCIPLINARY CONNECTIONS Origami originated in the Orient and may have been derived from an older tradition of cloth folding. Ask students to describe other ancient art forms and their origins, such as sand painting.

ABOUT THE PROJECT Using paper-folding techniques throughout the chapter helps students explore geometric patterns in a fun way. The Find Out questions in this chapter will give students practice making models and using the language of geometry to describe them.

Technology Options

Prentice Hall Technology 

 **Video**

• Video Field Trip 1, "Rising Sun," a look at Japanese culture

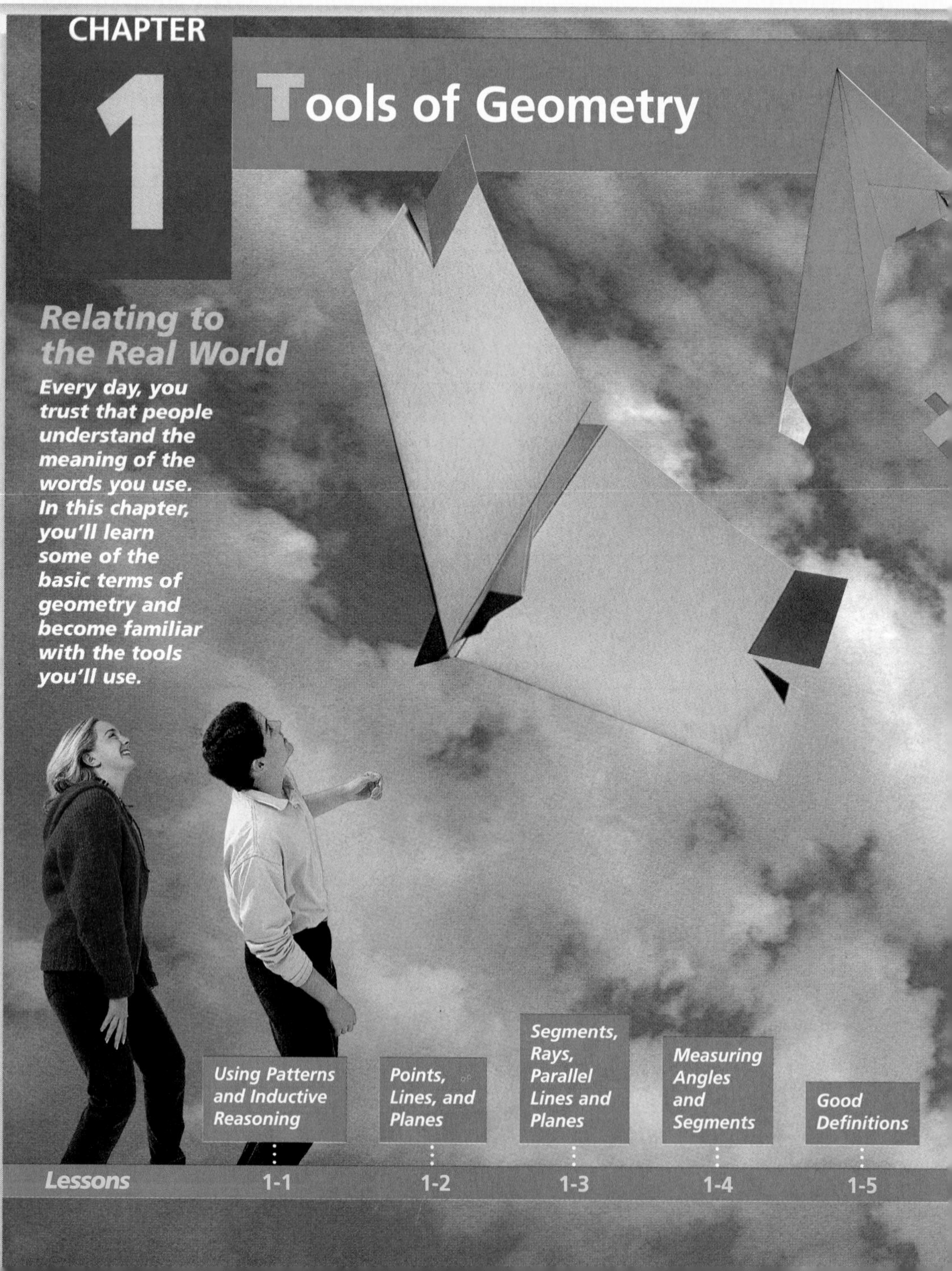

CHAPTER 1 Tools of Geometry

Relating to the Real World

Every day, you trust that people understand the meaning of the words you use. In this chapter, you'll learn some of the basic terms of geometry and become familiar with the tools you'll use.

Launching the Project

PROJECT NOTEBOOK Encourage students to keep all project-related materials in a separate folder or notebook. See Chapter Project and Scoring Rubric in Chapter Support File.

- Assign students to work with a partner or a small group. Have them make paper airplanes using sheets of paper.
- Ask each team to explain to the class how they made their airplane. Make a list of any math-related terms students use in their descriptions.

TRACKING THE PROJECT You may wish to have students read Finishing the Chapter Project on page 58 to help them get an overview of the project. Set benchmark deadlines for students to show their work in progress.

CHAPTER PROJECT

On Folded Wings

Some people look at a plain sheet of paper and see the hidden form of a swan or a seashell waiting to be revealed. Almost magically, with a few meticulous folds, an origami artist can produce startling replicas of animals, flowers, buildings, vehicles, and even people. The ancient art of paper folding has come to us from Japan, where it has thrived since at least the twelfth century. As a child, every time you made a paper airplane or a paper hat, you were practicing the art of origami.

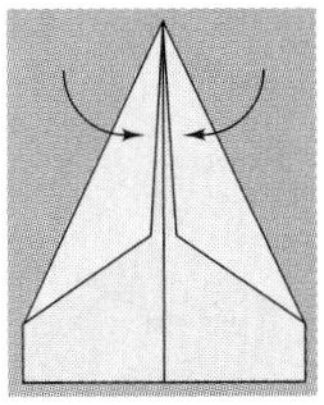

In this chapter project, you will use paper folding to explore geometric patterns. You will make origami models, and then use the language of geometry to tell others how to make them.

To help you complete the project:

- p. 10 *Find Out by Doing*
- p. 22 *Find Out by Creating*
- p. 31 *Find Out by Researching*
- p. 44 *Find Out by Writing*
- p. 58 *Finishing the Project*

Basic Constructions 1-6

Using Deductive Reasoning 1-7

The Coordinate Plane 1-8

Project Resources

Teaching Resources
Chapter Support File, Ch. 1
- Chapter Project Manager and Scoring Rubric

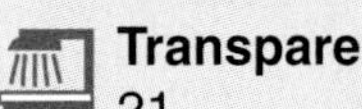

Transparencies
21

Using the Rubric

Sharing the scoring rubric for the project with your students will alert them to your expectations before they begin work on the project.

As students complete each Find Out question in the chapter, you may wish to have them evaluate their own work or a partner's work, based on the scoring rubric. Students should have the opportunity to revise their work after it has been reviewed.

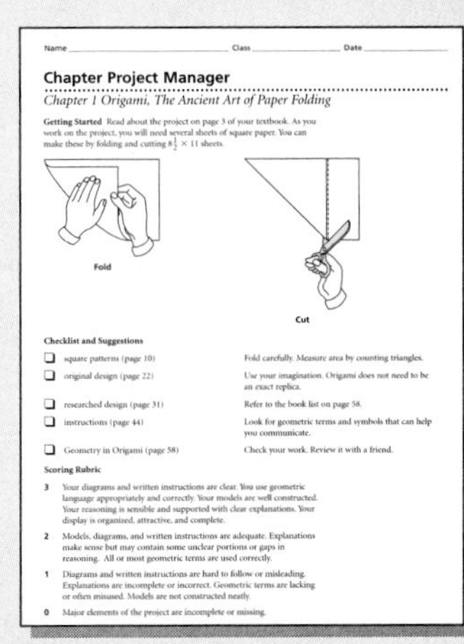

Name ______ Class ______ Date ______

Chapter Project Manager

Chapter 1 Origami, The Ancient Art of Paper Folding

Getting Started Read about the project on page 3 of your textbook. As you work on the project, you will need several sheets of square paper. You can make these by folding and cutting $8\frac{1}{2} \times 11$ sheets.

Checklist and Suggestions

❑ square patterns (page 10)	Fold carefully. Measure area by counting triangles.
❑ original design (page 22)	Use your imagination. Origami does not need to be an exact replica.
❑ researched design (page 31)	Refer to the book list on page 58.
❑ instructions (page 44)	Look for geometric terms and symbols that can help you communicate.
❑ Geometry in Origami (page 58)	Check your work. Review it with a friend.

Scoring Rubric

3 Your diagrams and written instructions are clear. You use geometric language appropriately and correctly. Your models are well constructed. Your reasoning is sensible and supported with clear explanations. Your display is organized, attractive, and complete.

2 Models, diagrams, and written instructions are adequate. Explanations make sense but may contain some unclear portions or gaps in reasoning. All or most geometric terms are used correctly.

1 Diagrams and written instructions are hard to follow or misleading. Explanations are incomplete or incorrect. Geometric terms are lacking or often misused. Models are not constructed neatly.

0 Major elements of the project are incomplete or missing.

1-1 Teaching Notes

PROBLEM OF THE DAY

If you add 5 rows to the bottom of this picture, how many small triangles would you have altogether? 81

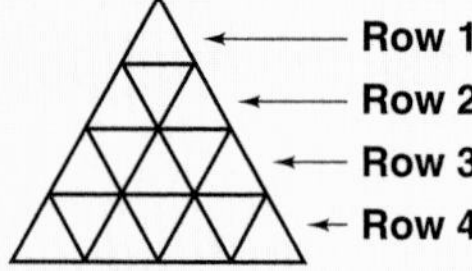

Problem of the Day is also available in Transparencies.

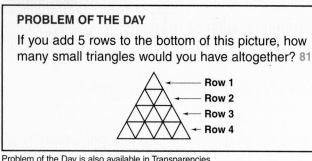

CONNECTING TO PRIOR KNOWLEDGE Ask students about price trends over the past five years in items such as sneakers or movie tickets. Ask them if they can predict the price a year from now and five years from now based on what prices have done in the past. Have them discuss their reasoning.

WORK TOGETHER

ERROR ALERT! Students counting the number of paths to each intersection on Longwood Avenue may count paths that are not the shortest paths. **Remediation:** Emphasize that students should count only the shortest paths to each intersection. Illustrate a type of path that should not be counted as shown here.

Lesson Planning Options

Prerequisite Skills

- Performing operations with real numbers
- Recognizing basic geometric figures

Assignment Options for Exercises On Your Own

Core 1–34, 36
✪**Extension** 35, 37–40

Use Mixed Review to maintain skills.

Resources

 **Student Edition**

Skills Handbook, pp. 662, 663
Extra Practice, p. 648
Glossary/Study Guide

 **Teacher's Edition**

Chapter Support File, Ch. 1
- Practice 1-1 (two worksheets)
- Reteaching 1-1

Classroom Manager 1-1
Glossary, Spanish Resources

 **Transparencies**

3, 14, 20, 22, 26, 27

Connections Manufacturing . . . and more

1-1 Using Patterns and Inductive Reasoning

What You'll Learn

- Using inductive reasoning to make conjectures

...And Why

To sharpen your ability to reason inductively, a powerful tool used in mathematics and in making everyday decisions

WORK TOGETHER

The shortest path from the school to Longwood Avenue is six blocks long. One path is shown below in red.

PROBLEM SOLVING HINT

Copy the diagram. Find the number of ways to reach each intersection. Look for a number pattern.

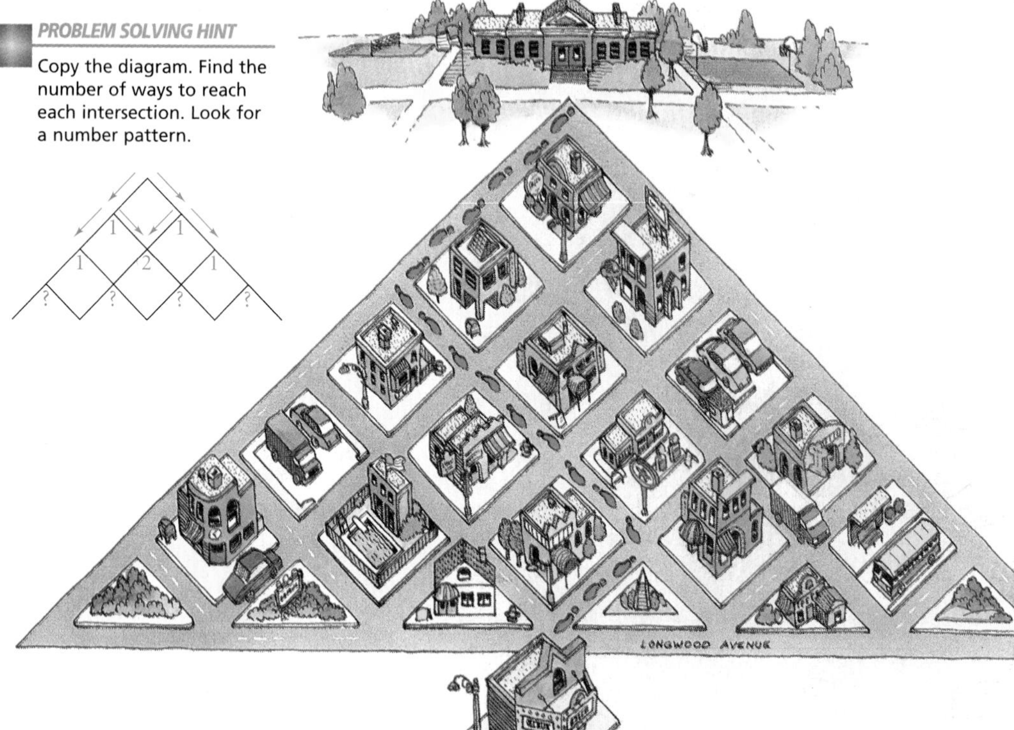

The pattern of numbers you discovered in the Work Together is known as Pascal's Triangle, after the French mathematician Blaise Pascal (1623–1662).

Work with a group to answer the following questions.

1. How many different six-block paths can you take from the school to Longwood Avenue? 64
2. How many of these paths will end at the corner directly across from the movie theater? 20

Have students counting the number of paths to each intersection look at each row of numbers in the Problem Solving Hint. Ask them what patterns they observe and how each row relates to the previous row.

THINK AND DISCUSS

ALGEBRA Questions 3 and 4 You may want to have students write algebraic expressions to represent the patterns. (The pattern in Question 3 can be represented by $2n$ for $n = 1, 2, 3, \ldots$, and the pattern in Question 4 can be represented by $3(2^n)$ for $n = 0, 1, 2, 3, \ldots$).

Example 1 Relating to the Real World 

ALTERNATIVE METHOD Another way to see that the number of small-wheeled skateboards is decreasing by about 3 each month is to find the difference between the number of small-wheeled skateboards in consecutive months. The differences are 3, 4, 3, 3. These differences are all 3 or close to 3, so it is reasonable to predict 3 fewer skateboards in June.

CRITICAL THINKING Discuss with students whether they think this pattern will continue and, if so, for how long. Ask them if it is reasonable to assume that in 15 months from May the company will produce no small-wheeled skateboards.

THINK AND DISCUSS

To answer the questions in the Work Together, you used inductive reasoning. **Inductive reasoning** is a type of reasoning that allows you to reach conclusions based on a pattern of specific examples or past events. Mathematicians have made many discoveries using inductive reasoning.

3. a. Find the next two terms in this sequence: 2, 4, 6, 8, . . . **10, 12**
   b. Describe the pattern you observed.
   Add 2 to each term to get the next term.
4. a. Find the next two terms in this sequence: 3, 6, 12, 24, . . . **48, 96**
   b. Describe the pattern you observed.
   Multiply each term by 2 to get the next term.
5. a. Find the next two terms in this sequence: 1, 2, 4, 5, 10, 11, 22, . . . **23, 46**
   b. Describe the pattern you observed.
   Add 1, then double; add 1, then double; and so on.

A conclusion reached by using inductive reasoning is sometimes called a **conjecture.** For each sequence above, you found the next term by first finding a pattern, and then using the pattern to make a conjecture about the next term. Inductive reasoning from patterns is a powerful thinking process you will use throughout the year in geometry.

6. **Try This** Describe the next term in this sequence.

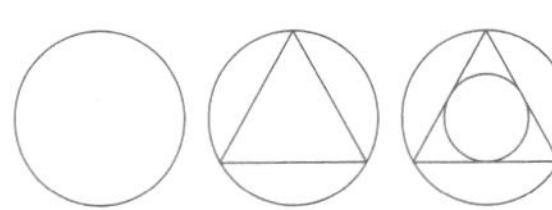

a circle around a triangle around a circle around a triangle

Example 1 Relating to the Real World 

Manufacturing A skateboard shop finds that for five consecutive months sales of skateboards with small wheels (39 mm to 48 mm in diameter) decreased.

January: 58 February: 55 March: 51 April: 48 May: 45

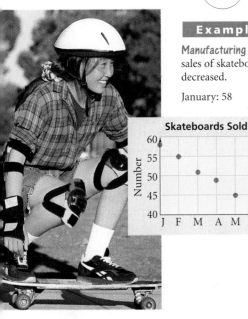

Skateboards Sold

Use inductive reasoning to make a conjecture about the number of small-wheeled skateboards the shop will sell in June.

As the graph at the left shows, the number of small-wheeled skateboards is decreasing by about 3 skateboards each month. The skateboard shop can predict about 42 small-wheeled skateboards will be sold in June.

Not every conjecture or conclusion found by inductive reasoning is correct. The next problem illustrates the limitations of inductive reasoning.

Additional Examples

FOR EXAMPLE 1

Refer to Example 1. If the numbers of small-wheeled skateboards per month from January to May were 34, 38, 43, 47, 51, make a conjecture about the number of small-wheeled skateboards produced in June.
About 55

Discussion: *Do you think the number of small-wheeled skateboards will keep increasing?*

FOR EXAMPLE 2

Explain why the following conjecture is or is not true. "The number of units in the perimeter of a rectangle is greater than the number of square units in its area." **No; for example, a square with a 7-in. side has a perimeter of 28 in. and an area of 49 in.^{2}**

FOR EXAMPLE 3

Use inductive reasoning to find the sum of the first 20 positive even numbers starting with 2. **420**

Discussion: *What pattern did you observe?*

Example 2

Have students note that the points on the circle are not equally spaced. You may want to have students investigate what happens when the six points are equally spaced. (The center region "disappears" because its vertices form a straight angle leaving only 30 regions.)

EXTENSION Goldbach's Conjecture states that if n is an even number greater than 2, then there are always two prime numbers whose sum is n. For example, when $n = 4$, $2 + 2 = 4$ and when $n = 10$, $7 + 3 = 10$. If you have block scheduling or an extended period, you may wish to have students test Goldbach's conjecture for the first 20 even numbers greater than 2. Ask them if each sum is unique.

Example 3

Question 8 Before answering this question, have students use a calculator to confirm that the sum of the first 20 odd numbers is 400.

MAKING CONNECTIONS An elementary school teacher in Germany in the late eighteenth century assigned students the task of adding the numbers 1 through 100. One of her students, Karl Friedrich Gauss, later to become a famous mathematician, used a pattern to find the sum almost immediately. He noticed that there are 50 pairs of numbers who sums are each 101: $50(101) = 5050$.

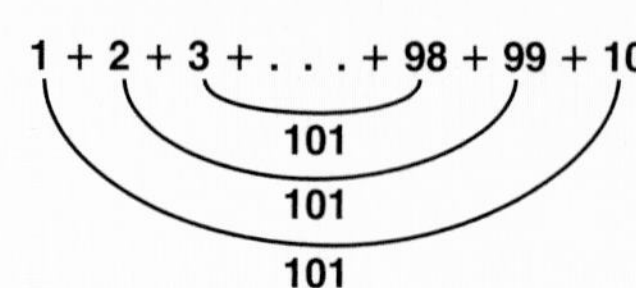

Technology Options

For Exercises 23–24, students may use drawing software. For Exercise 38, students may graph the points using a graphing calculator or graphing software.

Prentice Hall Technology

Software
- Secondary Math Lab Toolkit™
- Computer Item Generator 1-1

Internet
- See the Prentice Hall site. (http://www.phschool.com)

6

Example 2

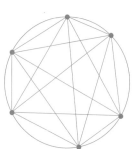

If six points on a circle are joined by as many segments as possible, how many nonoverlapping regions will the segments determine?

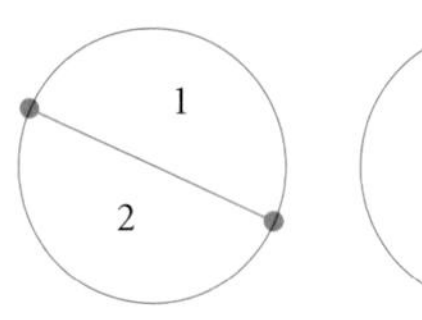

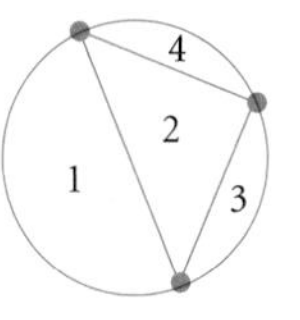

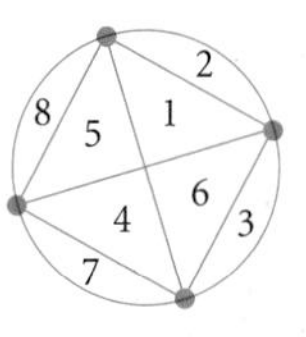

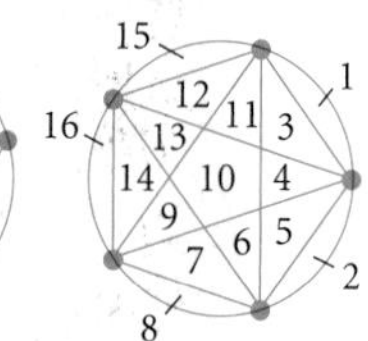

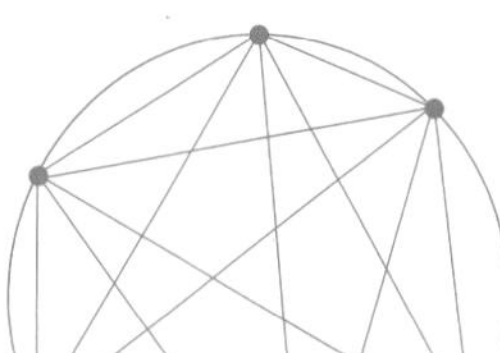

The table at the right shows the data for 2, 3, 4, and 5 points. The number of regions appears to double at each stage. Inductive reasoning would predict that there are 32 regions for 6 points on the circle. And yet, as the diagram at the left shows, there are only 31 regions formed. In this case, the conjecture is incorrect.

Points	Regions
2	2
3	4
4	8
5	16

Because the conjectures arrived at by inductive reasoning are not always true, you should verify them if possible.

7. **Try This** Candace examined five different examples and came up with this **conjecture:** "If any two positive numbers are multiplied, their product is always greater than either of the two numbers." Is her **conjecture** correct? Explain why or why not.
   No; for example, $\frac{1}{2} \times \frac{1}{2} = \frac{1}{4}$.

Sometimes you can use inductive reasoning to solve a problem that at first does not seem to have any pattern.

Example 3

Use inductive reasoning to find the sum of the first 20 odd numbers.

Find the first few sums. Notice that each sum is a perfect square.

$$\begin{aligned} 1 &= 1 = 1^2 \\ 1 + 3 &= 4 = 2^2 \\ 1 + 3 + 5 &= 9 = 3^2 \\ 1 + 3 + 5 + 7 &= 16 = 4^2 \end{aligned}$$

Reasoning inductively, you would expect that the sum of the first 20 odd numbers would be 20^2, or 400.

8. **Try This** What is your **conjecture** for the sum of the first 30 odd numbers? Use your calculator to verify your **conjecture.** 30^2, or 900

Exercises ON YOUR OWN

CRITICAL THINKING Exercises 1–12 Ask students whether any of the sequences end.

Exercises 7 and 8 You may want to provide a hint that the letters may be abbreviations for words.

WRITING Exercise 13 Discuss students' responses. Students may describe the same pattern in more than one way.

ESL VISUAL LEARNING Exercises 17–22 These problems rely on visual cues and require a minimum of verbal cues. They may prove helpful in assessing ESL students' ability to use inductive reasoning to continue patterns.

Exercises 23–24 Students may think in terms of line segments instead of lines, which is acceptable at this point in the text. The distinction will be clarified in Lesson 1-3. You may need to define the word *parallel*. Use objects in the classroom as illustrations, such as the opposite edges of a book, the top and bottom of a bulletin board, or the rows of ceiling tiles.

Exercises ON YOUR OWN

Find the next two terms in each sequence.

1. 5, 10, 20, 40, . . . 80, 160
2. 3, 33, 333, 3333, . . . 33333, 333333
3. 1, −1, 2, −2, 3, . . . −3, 4
4. $1, \frac{1}{2}, \frac{1}{4}, \frac{1}{8}, \ldots$ $\frac{1}{16}, \frac{1}{32}$
5. 15, 12, 9, 6, . . . 3, 0
6. 81, 27, 9, 3, . . . $1, \frac{1}{3}$
7. O, T, T, F, F, S, S, E, . . . N, T
8. J, F, M, A, M, . . . J, J
9. 1, 2, 6, 24, 120, . . . 720, 5040
10. 1, 2, 4, 7, 11, 16, 22, . . . 29, 37
11. $1, \frac{1}{4}, \frac{1}{9}, \frac{1}{16}, \frac{1}{25}, \ldots$ $\frac{1}{36}, \frac{1}{49}$
12. $1, \frac{1}{2}, \frac{1}{3}, \frac{1}{4}, \ldots$ $\frac{1}{5}, \frac{1}{6}$

13. *Writing* Choose two of the sequences in Exercises 9–12 and describe the pattern. See margin.
14. Deano has started working out regularly. When he first started exercising he could do 10 push-ups. After the first month he could do 14 push-ups. After the second month he could do 19, and after the third month he could do 25. How many push-ups would you **predict** he will be able to do after the fifth month of working out? Are you absolutely sure about your prediction? Why or why not? 40; no; he may not be able to continue the pattern indefinitely.
15. Alexa rides a bus to school. On the first day the trip to school took 25 minutes. On the second day the trip took 24 minutes. On the third day the trip took 26 minutes. On the fourth day the trip took 25 minutes. What **conjecture** would you make? The trip takes about 25 min.
16. *History* Leonardo of Pisa (c. 1175–c. 1258) was born in Italy and educated in North Africa. He was one of the the first Europeans to use modern numerals instead of Roman numerals. He is also known for the Fibonacci Sequence: 1, 1, 2, 3, 5, 8, 13, ... Find the next three terms. 21, 34, 55

Draw the next figure in each sequence. 17–22. See margin.

17. 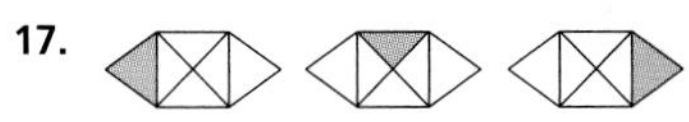 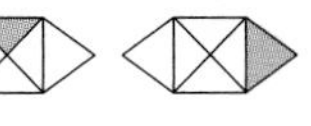
18. 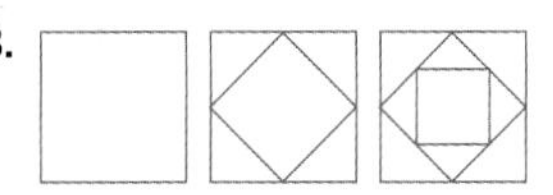 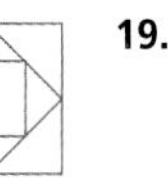
19.
20.
21. 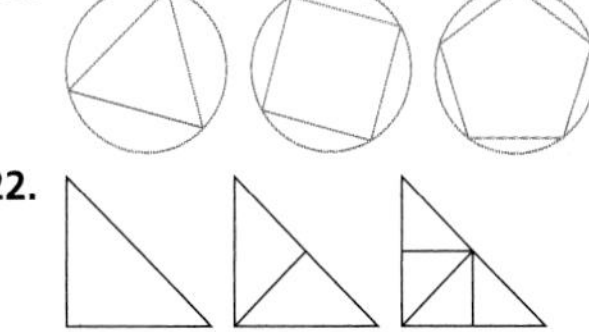
22.

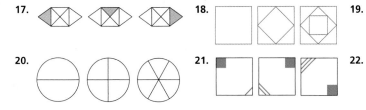

23. Draw two parallel lines on your paper. Locate four points on the paper an equal distance from both lines. Describe the figure you would get if you continued to locate points an equal distance from both lines. a line parallel to the first two and midway between them
24. Draw a line on your paper. Locate four points on the paper that are each 1 in. from the line. Describe the figure you would get if you continued to locate points that are 1 in. from the line. two lines on either side of the original line and 1 in. away from it

TECHNOLOGY HINT
Exercises 23 and 24 could be done using geometry software.

pages 7–10 On Your Own

13. Answers may vary. Sample: (9) Start with 1. Multiply by 2. Multiply the result by 3. Multiply the result by 4, and so on. (10) Start with 1. Add 1. Add 2 to the result. Add 3 to the result. Add 4 to the result, and so on. (11) The value of each term is $\frac{1}{n^2}$, where n is the term number. (12) The value of each term is $\frac{1}{n}$, where n is the term number.

17. 
18. 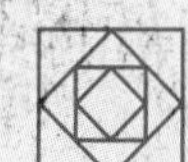
19.
20. 
21. 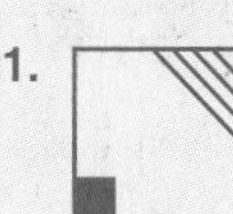
22. 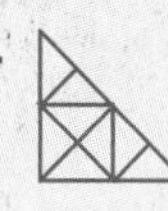

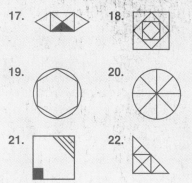

CRITICAL THINKING Exercise 26 Ask students how Jean's statement could be revised so that it is true.

OPEN-ENDED Exercise 30 Ask students to study the pattern for 1, 2, 4, ... and find the next three terms. Answers will include 7, 11, 16 (adding 1, then 2, then 3, then 4, ...) and 8, 16, 32 (doubling each time). Have students discuss the importance of listing enough terms to make a pattern clear.

Exercise 32 Encourage students to predict the next triangular number using a number pattern. Then have them confirm their prediction by drawing the diagram.

EXTENSION Exercise 34 Students may want to create number patterns from dot diagrams that they create. Have them write the corresponding sequence of numbers and describe any patterns they observe.

26. It's correct for numbers greater than 1, and for negative numbers. But $0^2 = 0$, $1^2 = 1$, and $\left(\frac{1}{2}\right)^2 = \frac{1}{4}$.

27a.

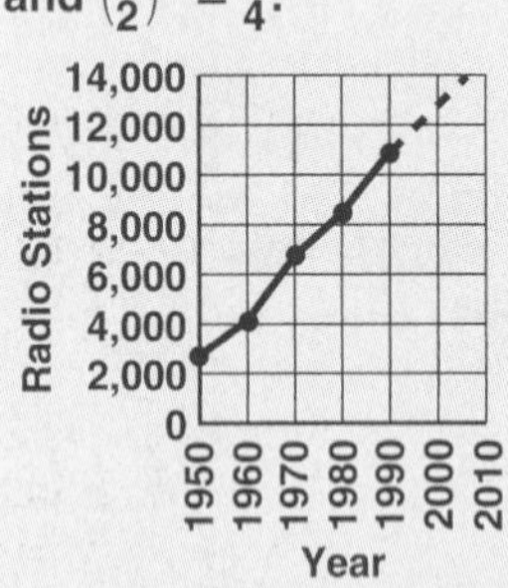

There will be about 15,000 radio stations.

b. Answers may vary. Sample: Very confident; the number of radio stations seems to have increased at a steady rate for 40 years.

25. For the past four years Paulo has grown 2 in. every year. He is now 16 years old and is 5 ft 10 in. tall. He figures that when he is 22 years old he will be 6 ft 10 in. tall. What would you tell Paulo about his **conjecture**? **It's possible but not likely. As he grows older, his rate of growth will slow down and eventually stop.**

26. After testing her idea with eight different numbers, Jean stated the following **conjecture**: "The square of a number is always greater than the number you started with." What would you tell Jean about her **conjecture**? **See margin.**

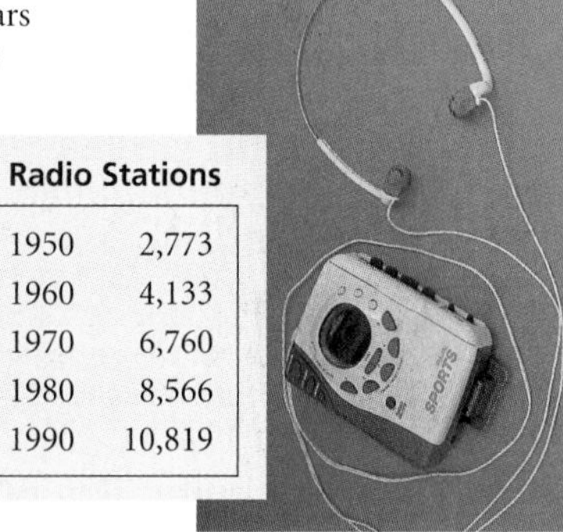

Radio Stations

1950	2,773
1960	4,133
1970	6,760
1980	8,566
1990	10,819

27. a. ***Communications*** The number of radio stations in the United States is increasing. The table shows the number of radio stations for a 40-year period. Make a line graph of the data. Use the graph and inductive reasoning to make a **conjecture** about the number of radio stations in the United States by the year 2010.

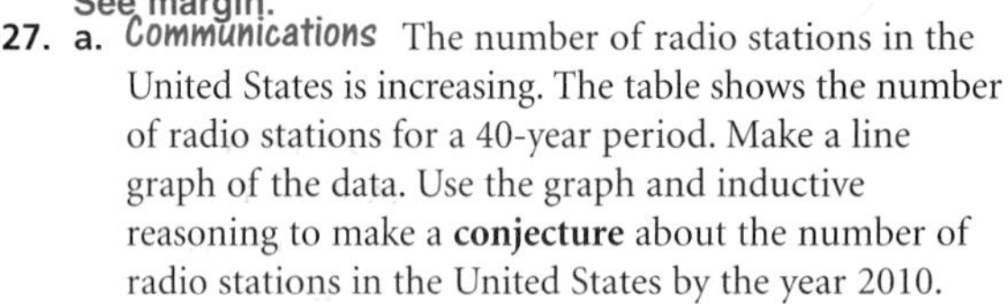

b. How confident are you about your conjecture? Explain. **a–b. See margin.**

Find the next term in each sequence. Check your answer with a calculator.

28.
$12345679 \times 9 = 111111111$
$12345679 \times 18 = 222222222$
$12345679 \times 27 = 333333333$
$12345679 \times 36 = 444444444$
$12345679 \times 45 = ?$ **555555555**

29.
$1 \times 1 = 1$
$11 \times 11 = 121$
$111 \times 111 = 12321$
$1111 \times 1111 = 1234321$
$11111 \times 11111 = ?$ **123454321**

30. ***Open-ended*** Write two different sequences that begin with the same two numbers. **Answers may vary. Sample: 1, 2, 4, 8, 16, . . . and 1, 2, 3, 4, 5, . . .**

31. ***Weather*** The temperature in degrees Fahrenheit determines how fast a cricket chirps. If you heard 20 cricket chirps in 14 seconds, what do you think the temperature would be? **75°**

Chirps per 14 s

5 chirps	45°
10 chirps	55°
15 chirps	65°

32. a. A *triangular number* can be represented by a triangular arrangement of dots. The first two triangular numbers are 1 and 3. What are the next three triangular numbers? **6, 10, 15**

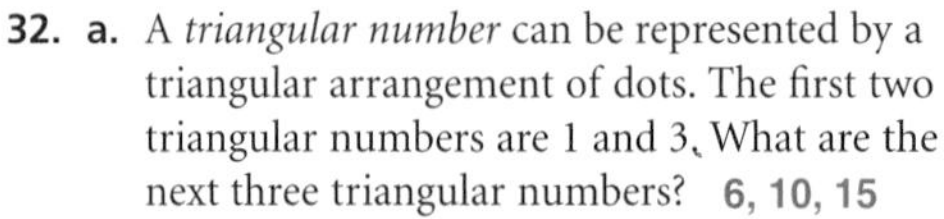

b. What is the tenth triangular number? **55**

c. ***Algebra*** Which of the following expressions represents the nth triangular number? **C**

A. $n(n + 1)$ **B.** $n(n - 2)$ **C.** $\frac{n(n + 1)}{2}$ **D.** $\frac{n(n - 1)}{2}$

33. a. The first two *square numbers* are 1 and 4. Draw diagrams to represent the next two square numbers. **See right.**

b. What is the twentieth square number? Describe the pattern.

c. ***Algebra*** Write an algebraic expression in terms of n for the nth square number. n^2

b. 20^2, or 400; the sequence is the squares of successive counting numbers.

ALTERNATIVE ASSESSMENT Exercise 35 This exercise will help you assess students' ability to judge the reasonableness of conjectures. Have students discuss their answers in small groups.

STANDARDIZED TEST TIP Exercise 36 Remind students to read the question critically. The phrase " a term" should be a clue that the answer may not be the next term in the sequence.

RESEARCH Exercise 37c Students will need a dictionary, encyclopedia, or an almanac to research how leap years are determined. Most on-line services provide these types of sources.

COORDINATE GEOMETRY Exercise 38 Students should use graph paper to plot the ordered pairs.

34. *History* Nicomachus of Gerasa first described *pentagonal numbers* in *Introductio arithmetica* about A.D. 100. The first three pentagonal numbers are shown. Draw a diagram to represent the next pentagonal number. See margin.

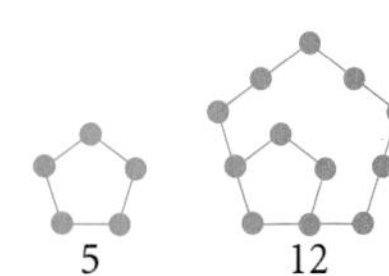

The Race to the Finish Line

Top female runners have been improving about twice as quickly as the fastest men, a new study says. If this pattern continues, women may soon outrun men in competition!

The study is based on world records collected at 10-year intervals, starting in 1905 for men. Reliable women's records were not kept until the 1920s. Women's marathon records date only from 1955.

If the trend continues, the top female and male runners in races ranging from 200 m to 1500 m might attain the same speeds sometime between 2015 and 2055. The rapid improvement in women's marathon records suggests that the marathon record for women will equal that of men even more quickly—perhaps by 2005.

Women's speeds may have improved so quickly because many more women started running competitively in recent decades, according to a professor of anatomy who studies locomotion and gait. This increase in the talent pool of female runners has improved the chance of finding better runners.

35. a. What conclusions were reached in the study mentioned in the newspaper clipping? a–c. See margin.

b. How was inductive reasoning used to reach the conclusions?

c. Explain why the conclusion that women may soon be outrunning men may be incorrect. For which race is the conclusion most suspect? For what reason?

36. *Standardized Test Prep* Which of the following can be a term in the sequence 1, 3, 7, 15, 31, . . . ? D

A. 32 **B.** 47 **C.** 55 **D.** 127 **E.** 128

37. a. *Leap years* have 366 days. 1984, 1988, 1992, 1996, and 2000 are consecutive leap years. Make a **conjecture** about leap years.

b. Which of the following years do you think will be leap years? a–c. See margin.
2010, 2020, 2100, 2400

c. *Research* Find out if your **conjecture** for part (a) and your answer for part (b) are correct. How are leap years determined?

38. a. *Coordinate Geometry* Graph the following points:

$A(1, 5)$ $B(2, 2)$ $C(2, 8)$ $D(3, 1)$
$E(3, 9)$ $F(6, 0)$ $G(6, 10)$ $H(7, -1)$
$I(7, 11)$ $J(9, 1)$ $K(9, 9)$ $L(10, 2)$
$M(10, 8)$ $N(11, 5)$ See margin.

b. Which of the points do not fit the same pattern as the others? *H* and *I*

c. Describe the figure you would get if you continued graphing points that fit the pattern. a circle

QUICK REVIEW

The first coordinate is the *x*-coordinate. The second coordinate is the *y*-coordinate.

34.

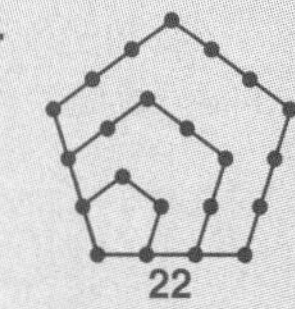

35a. Women may soon outrun men in running competitions.

b. The conclusion was based on continuing the trend shown in past records.

c. The conclusions are based on fairly recent records for women, and those rates of improvement may not continue. The conclusion about the marathon is most suspect because records date only from 1955.

37a. Answers may vary. Sample: Leap years are divisible by 4.

b. Answers may vary. Sample: 2020, 2100, 2400

c. Leap years are divisible by 4 except years ending in 00, which are leap years only if they are divisble by 400.

38a.

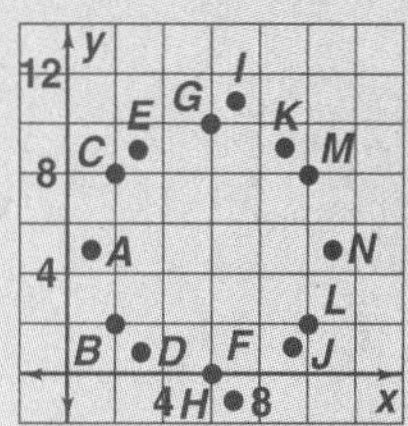

ESL Exercise 39 Review the meaning of *power, base,* and *exponent.*

Chapter Project FIND OUT BY DOING Each student should have a paper square that is at least 6 in. by 6 in. Make sure students read an entire set of directions before beginning the activity. Suggest that they use a ruler to crease their folds so that when they unfold the paper, they can see the creases. Remind students to keep their Find Out exercise work in one place, so they can complete the chapter project at the end of the chapter.

Exercises MIXED REVIEW

Exercises 41–52 Students review graphing ordered pairs in the coordinate plane.

GETTING READY FOR LESSON 1-2 This exercise prepares students for Lesson 1-2 in which they study points and lines.

Wrap Up

THE BIG IDEA Ask students: *Describe how patterns are used to make conjectures. List some of the limitations of making conjectures using patterns.*

RETEACHING ACTIVITY Students use coins to investigate three-dimensional patterns. (Reteaching worksheet 1-1)

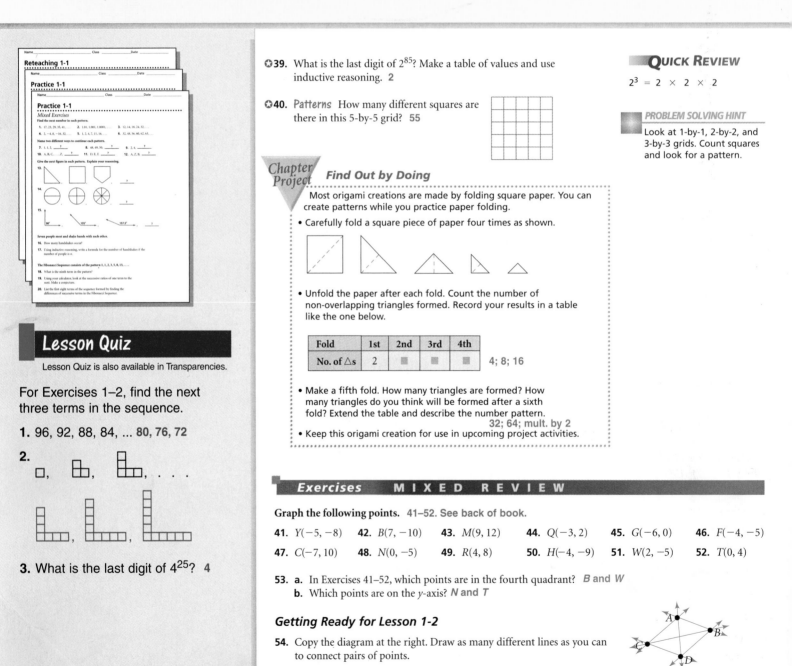

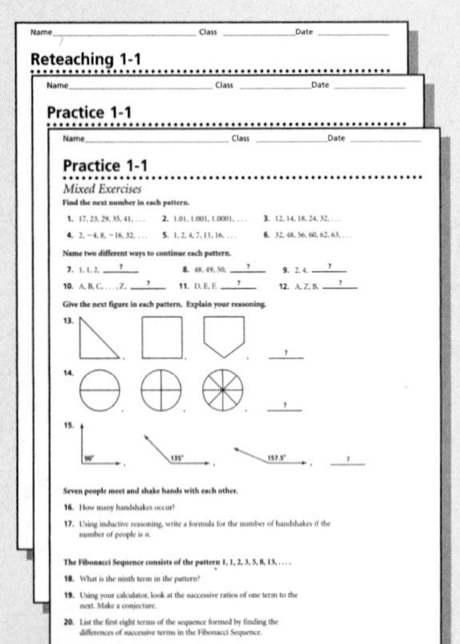

Lesson Quiz

Lesson Quiz is also available in Transparencies.

For Exercises 1–2, find the next three terms in the sequence.

1. 96, 92, 88, 84, ... 80, 76, 72

2.

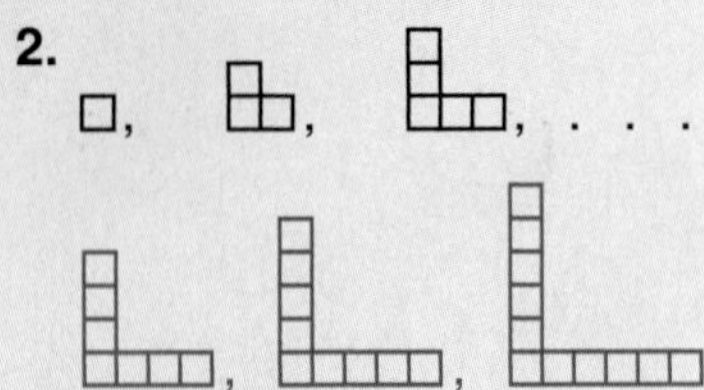

3. What is the last digit of 4^{25}? 4

✪39. What is the last digit of 2^{85}? Make a table of values and use inductive reasoning. 2

✪40. *Patterns* How many different squares are there in this 5-by-5 grid? 55

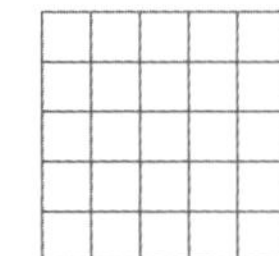

QUICK REVIEW

$2^3 = 2 \times 2 \times 2$

PROBLEM SOLVING HINT

Look at 1-by-1, 2-by-2, and 3-by-3 grids. Count squares and look for a pattern.

Chapter Project ***Find Out by Doing***

Most origami creations are made by folding square paper. You can create patterns while you practice paper folding.

- Carefully fold a square piece of paper four times as shown.

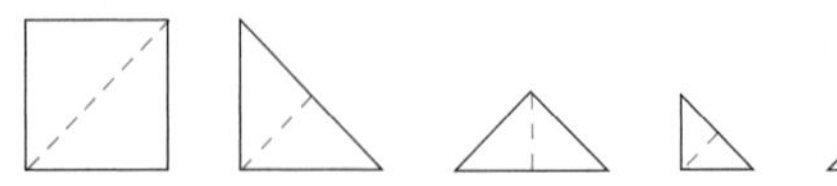

- Unfold the paper after each fold. Count the number of non-overlapping triangles formed. Record your results in a table like the one below.

Fold	1st	2nd	3rd	4th
No. of △s	2	■	■	■

4; 8; 16

- Make a fifth fold. How many triangles are formed? How many triangles do you think will be formed after a sixth fold? Extend the table and describe the number pattern. 32; 64; mult. by 2
- Keep this origami creation for use in upcoming project activities.

Exercises MIXED REVIEW

Graph the following points. 41–52. See back of book.

41. $Y(-5, -8)$ 42. $B(7, -10)$ 43. $M(9, 12)$ 44. $Q(-3, 2)$ 45. $G(-6, 0)$ 46. $F(-4, -5)$
47. $C(-7, 10)$ 48. $N(0, -5)$ 49. $R(4, 8)$ 50. $H(-4, -9)$ 51. $W(2, -5)$ 52. $T(0, 4)$

53. a. In Exercises 41–52, which points are in the fourth quadrant? *B* and *W*
    b. Which points are on the *y*-axis? *N* and *T*

Getting Ready for Lesson 1-2

54. Copy the diagram at the right. Draw as many different lines as you can to connect pairs of points.

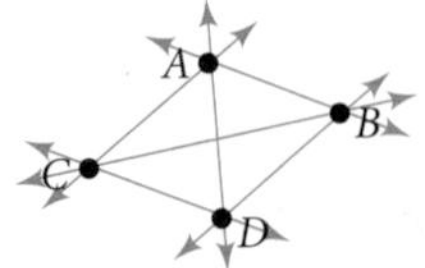

Math ToolboX

In this toolbox, students review finding the probability of an event. Starting in Lesson 1-2, questions about probability may appear in the Exercise sets.

ERROR ALERT! Students sometimes confuse probability with odds and will calculate the ratio of the number of favorable outcomes to the number of unfavorable outcomes. **Remediation:** Reinforce the formula given in the first paragraph. Emphasize that the "number of possible outcomes" includes both favorable and unfavorable outcomes. It may be helpful for students to think of probability of $\frac{1}{5}$, for example, as a "1 out of 5 chance" compared to odds which are "4 to 1."

Exercises 1–12 You may need to review with students the vocabulary associated with the coordinate plane such as *quadrant, origin, ordered pair, coordinate,* and *axis.*

Exercise 17 You may want to point out the relationship among Exercises 13, 14, and 17. That is, since spinning blue and spinning red are mutually exclusive events, $P(\text{blue or red}) = P(\text{blue}) + P(\text{red})$.

ADDITIONAL PROBLEM Two six-sided cubes are tossed. Find each of the following probabilities.

P(two 6's) $\frac{1}{36}$ P(sum is 10) $\frac{1}{12}$

P(both even) $\frac{1}{4}$ P(one odd and one even) $\frac{1}{2}$

Transparencies
5

Math ToolboX — Algebra Review

Probability

Before Lesson 1-2

Probability ranges from 0, an impossible event, to 1, a certain event. You can find the probability of an event using this formula.

$$P(\text{event}) = \frac{\text{number of favorable outcomes}}{\text{number of possible outcomes}}$$

Example 1

What is the probability of answering correctly a four-option multiple choice question if you pick an answer at random?

There are 4 possible outcomes. One of them is correct. The probability of getting the correct answer is $\frac{1}{4}$.

Example 2

Find the probability that a point picked at random from the graph at the right is in the first quadrant.

List the possible outcomes: *A, B, C, D, E, F, G, H, I, J.*
There are 10 outcomes.

List the favorable outcomes: *C* and *D*.
There are 2 favorable outcomes.

The probability of a point picked at random being in the first quadrant is $\frac{2}{10} = \frac{1}{5}$.

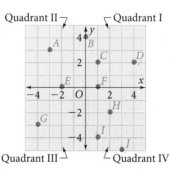

Quadrant II, Quadrant I, Quadrant III, Quadrant IV; points A, B, C, D, E, F, G, H, I, J; axes x, y; −4, −2, O, 2, 4

Use the graph from Example 2 to find each probability. Assume points are picked at random.

1. P(the point is in the fourth quadrant) $\frac{3}{10}$
2. P(the point is on an axis) $\frac{3}{10}$
3. P(the point is at the origin) 0
4. P(the point has a y-coordinate of 2) $\frac{1}{5}$
5. P(the point has an x-coordinate less than 4) $\frac{9}{10}$
6. P(the point is on the x-axis) $\frac{1}{5}$
7. P(the point is to the right of the y-axis) $\frac{3}{5}$
8. P(the point has an x-coordinate of 1) $\frac{3}{10}$
9. P(the point is on the y-axis) $\frac{1}{10}$
10. P(the point is below the x-axis) $\frac{2}{5}$
11. P(the point has a y-coordinate greater than 1) $\frac{2}{5}$
12. P(the point is in the third quadrant) $\frac{1}{10}$

Use the spinner at the right. Find each probability.

13. P(blue) $\frac{1}{3}$
14. P(red) $\frac{1}{3}$
15. P(yellow or red) $\frac{2}{3}$
16. P(purple) 0
17. P(blue or red) $\frac{2}{3}$
18. P(yellow or red or blue) 1

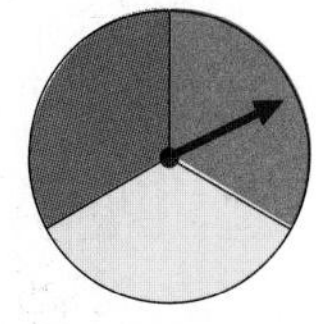

1-2 Teaching Notes

PROBLEM OF THE DAY

How many numbers in the set 100, 101, 102, 103, ..., 999 do not contain the digits 2, 5, 7, or 8? 180

Problem of the Day is also available in Transparencies.

CONNECTING TO PRIOR KNOWLEDGE Ask students if they have ever viewed a constellation. Most will be familiar with the Big Dipper. See if students can sketch the Big Dipper. Ask: "How many stars are in the Big Dipper? How many lines are used to connect the stars to form the Big Dipper?"

WORK TOGETHER

Have each student complete Question 1. Then have a different person in each group draw the diagrams with four points, five points, and six points. Have groups discuss whether or not the number of lines depends on where the dots are placed on the circle.

MAKING CONNECTIONS The same constellation can have different names depending on how the points are connected. For example, in Scotland the stars in the Big Dipper are connected to form the Plow.

Lesson Planning Options

Prerequisite Skills

- Graphing points in the coordinate plane
- Finding the probability that an event will occur

Assignment Options for Exercises On Your Own

To provide flexible scheduling, this lesson can be subdivided into parts.

1 **Core** 1–26, 43–46
✪**Extension** 48

2 **Core** 27, 29–39, 47
✪**Extension** 28, 40–42

Use Mixed Review to maintain skills.

Resources

Student Edition

Skills Handbook, pp. 673, 679, 681
Extra Practice, p. 648
Glossary/Study Guide

Teaching Resources

Chapter Support File, Ch. 1
- Practice 1-2 (two worksheets)
- Reteaching 1-2

Classroom Manager 1-2
Glossary, Spanish Resources

Transparencies
20, 22

Connections  Astronomy . . . and more

1-2 Points, Lines, and Planes

What You'll Learn

- Understanding basic terms of geometry
- Understanding basic postulates of geometry

...And Why

To lay the foundation for your study of geometry

What You'll Need

- ruler

WORK TOGETHER

Many constellations are named after animals and mythological figures. It takes some imagination to connect the points representing the stars so that the result is a recognizable figure such as Leo the Lion. There are many different ways to connect the points. How many different lines could be used to connect all ten points?

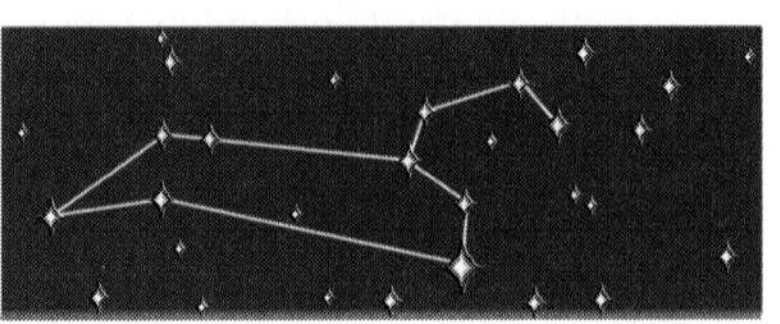

Ten major stars make up the constellation called Leo the Lion.

Work in groups of three. Make a table and look for a pattern to answer the following questions.

1. Put three points on a circle. Now connect the three points with as many lines as possible. How many lines do you need? 3
2. Put four points on another circle. How many lines can you draw connecting four points? 6
3. Repeat for five points on a circle and then for six points. How many lines can you draw to connect the points? five points:10; six points:15
4. Use inductive reasoning to tell how many lines you could draw to connect the ten points of the constellation Leo the Lion. 45

THINK AND DISCUSS

Part  1

Basic Terms

P•
point P

Since stars are so far away, they appear quite small to us. We think of them as points even though they are actually quite large. In geometry a **point** has no size. You can think of it as a location. A point is represented by a small dot and is named by a capital letter. All geometric figures are made up of points. **Space** is the set of all points.

5. *Open-ended* Name something in your classroom that is a physical representation of a point. Answers may vary. Sample: the corner of the room where the walls meet the ceiling.

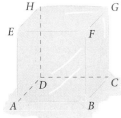

ERROR ALERT! Questions 1–4 Some students may count the lines in both "directions." **Remediation:** Draw a circle with chord $\overline{AB}$. Point out that the line from *A* to *B* is the same line as the one from *B* to *A*.

THINK AND DISCUSS

DIVERSITY Ask students to research and sketch different types of dwellings such as teepees, tents, and igloos. Then ask them to point out and name the geometric shapes in each. Challenge students to name and locate the places in the world where the various dwellings are used.

OPEN-ENDED Question 6 Students' answers may vary from examples of decimal points, periods, or dots on i's, to tips of sharp objects such as sharp pencils, toothpicks, or compasses. Other examples can be found where two lines meet, such as the edges of two scissor blades.

Question 7 Help students come to the understanding that a line is dense with points, meaning that between any two points, no matter how close together, you can always find other points.

CRITICAL THINKING Ask students why you need at least three noncollinear points to determine a plane.

$\overleftrightarrow{AB}$ (or $\overleftrightarrow{BA}$)

You can think of a **line** as a series of points that extends in two opposite directions without end. You can name a line by two points on the line, such as $\overleftrightarrow{AB}$ (read "line *AB*"). Another way to name a line is with a single lowercase letter, such as line *t*.

Answers may vary. Samples: edge of a table, clothesline, grout between square tiles

6. **Open-ended** Describe some physical representations of lines in the real world.
7. **Critical Thinking** Why do you think arrowheads are used when drawing a line or naming a line such as $\overleftrightarrow{AB}$? to show the line continues in both directions without end
8. **Try This** Name the line at the left in as many ways as possible. $\overleftrightarrow{RS}$, $\overleftrightarrow{RW}$, $\overleftrightarrow{SW}$, $\overleftrightarrow{SR}$, $\overleftrightarrow{WR}$, $\overleftrightarrow{WS}$

Pensacola, St. Petersburg, Ft. Lauderdale

The points representing the three towns on this map are collinear.

Points that lie on the same line are **collinear.**

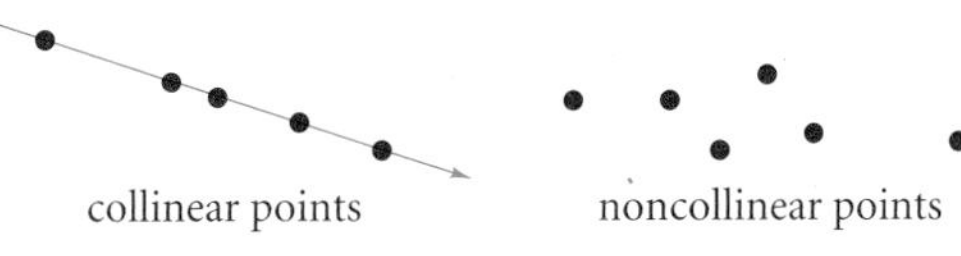

A **plane** is a flat surface that extends in all directions without end. It has no thickness.

9. **Open-ended** Name three objects in your classroom that represent planes. Answers may vary. Samples: walls, floors, desktops

You can name a plane either by a single capital letter or by naming at least three noncollinear points in the plane.

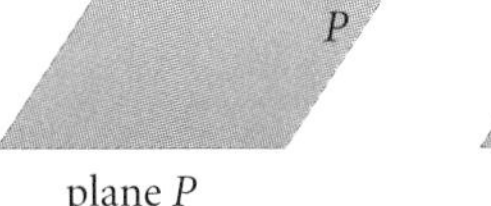

plane *P* plane *ABC*

In the diagram, each surface of the ice cube is part of a plane.

10. How many planes are suggested by the surfaces of the ice cube? 6
11. **Try This** Name the plane represented by the front of the ice cube in several different ways. Answers may vary. Samples: plane *AEF*, plane *AEB*, plane *ABFE*

Points and lines in the same plane are **coplanar.**

12. **Try This** Name a point that is coplanar with the given points.
    a. *E, F, G* *H*
    b. *B, C, G* *F*
    c. *A, D, E* *H*
    d. *D, C, G* *H*
13. **Try This** Name two lines that are coplanar with $\overleftrightarrow{AB}$ and $\overleftrightarrow{DC}$. $\overleftrightarrow{AC}$, $\overleftrightarrow{BD}$, $\overleftrightarrow{AD}$, $\overleftrightarrow{BC}$

Additional Examples

FOR EXAMPLE

Refer to the figure in the example. Are the points *F, H, D,* and *B* coplanar? Yes

Are the points *A, D, C,* and *G* coplanar? No

Discussion: *How do you check whether four points are coplanar?*

TACTILE LEARNING Postulate 1-3 Have students illustrate this postulate by using two index cards or two pieces of stiff paper each cut halfway across. Have them manipulate the cards to illustrate two planes that intersect in a horizontal line and two planes that intersect in a vertical line.

Postulate 1-4 Have students illustrate this postulate using three pencil tips to balance a piece of cardboard. They should discover that the cardboard is balanced as long as the pencils are not in a straight line.

CRITICAL THINKING Ask students to explain why a kitchen stool with three legs does not wobble even if the legs are different lengths. Ask them how the seat might appear if the legs are different lengths. Have them support their explanations with diagrams.

Technology Options

For Exercises 43–46, students may graph the points using a graphing calculator or other graphing software.

Prentice Hall Technology

Software
- Secondary Math Lab Toolkit™
- Computer Item Generator 1-2

CD-ROM
- Multimedia Geometry Lab 1

Internet
- See the Prentice Hall site. (http://www.phschool.com)

Part 2

Basic Postulates

A **postulate** is an accepted statement of fact. You used some of the following geometry postulates in algebra. For example, when you graphed an equation such as $y = -2x + 8$, you began by plotting two points and then you drew the line through those two points.

Postulate 1-1 Through any two points there is exactly one line.

Line t is the only line that passes through points A and B.

In algebra, one way to solve the following system of equations is to graph the two equations.

$$y = -2x + 8$$
$$y = 3x - 7$$

As the graph shows, the two lines intersect at a single point, (3, 2). The solution to the system of equations is $x = 3, y = 2$. This illustrates the following postulate.

Postulate 1-2 If two lines intersect, then they intersect in exactly one point.

14. *Open-ended* Describe two planes in your classroom that intersect. Also describe the intersection of the planes. **Answers may vary. Sample: Two adjacent walls intersect in a line.**

Postulate 1-3 If two planes intersect, then they intersect in a line.

Plane RST and plane STW intersect in $\overleftrightarrow{ST}$.

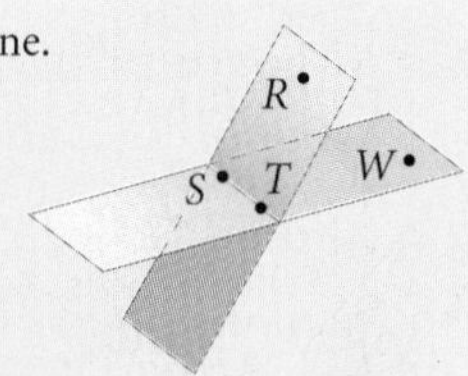

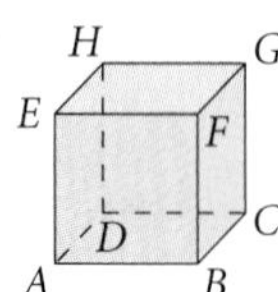

15. a. **Try This** What is the intersection of plane $HGFE$ and plane $BCGF$? $\overleftrightarrow{FG}$
    b. What is the intersection of plane AEF and plane BCG? $\overleftrightarrow{BF}$

A three-legged stool will always be stable, as long as the feet of the stool don't lie on a line. This illustrates the following postulate.

Postulate 1-4 Through any three noncollinear points there is exactly one plane.

Example

Some students may have trouble visualizing planes other than those formed by the sides of the box. If possible, use a clear box such as a plastic food storage container and a piece of stiff paper to show plane *EBCH*.

Exercises ON YOUR OWN

Exercises 1–12 Students may want to construct the diagram using a piece of cardboard as plane *M* and a pencil as $\overleftrightarrow{AC}$.

Exercise 11 Ask students to describe the ways in which a line and a plane can intersect.

Exercises 13–26 Have physical models available. Kleenex® Brand Boutique® tissue boxes work well, but students can use about any box-shaped object.

Who? Euclid is known for compiling all the geometry of his time into postulates and theorems. His masterwork *The Elements* (about 300 B.C.) is the basis for geometry books today.

Example

Are points *E, H, B,* and *C* coplanar?
Are points *E, H, F,* and *B* coplanar?

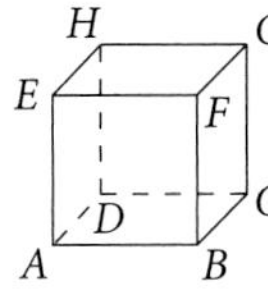

Yes, the plane that contains the three noncollinear points *E, H,* and *B* also contains *C.*

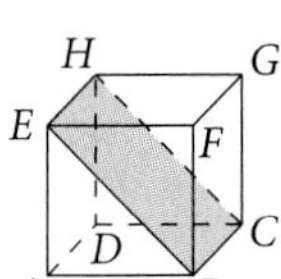

No, points *E, H,* and *F* lie in exactly one plane, which doesn't contain *B.*

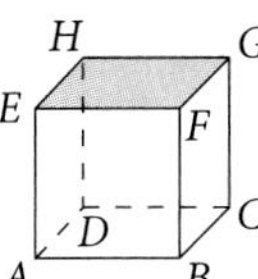

Exercises ON YOUR OWN

Are the points collinear?

1. *A, D, E* no **2.** *B, C, D* yes **3.** *B, C, F* no **4.** *A, E, C* yes **5.** *F, B, D* no

Are the points coplanar?

6. *B, C, D, F* yes **7.** *A, C, D, F* no **8.** *B, D, E, F* no **9.** *A, C, E, F* yes

10. Name plane *M* in another way. Answers may vary. Sample: plane *BCF*

11. What is the intersection of plane *M* and $\overleftrightarrow{AE}$? *C*

12. What is the intersection of $\overleftrightarrow{AE}$ and $\overleftrightarrow{BD}$? *C*

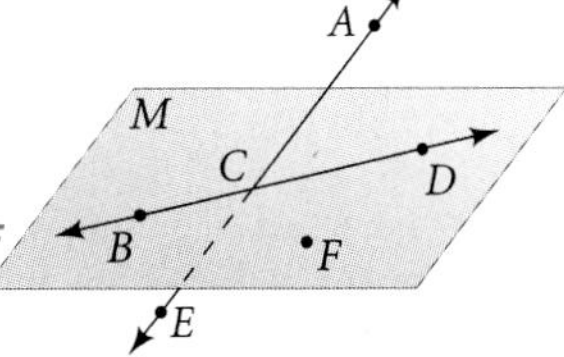

Exs. 1 – 12

Are the following coplanar?

13. *Q, V, R* yes **14.** *X, V, R* yes **15.** *U, V, W, S* no

16. *W, V, Q, T* yes **17.** point *X*, $\overleftrightarrow{QT}$ yes **18.** $\overleftrightarrow{RS}$, point *X* yes

19. $\overleftrightarrow{XW}$, $\overleftrightarrow{UV}$ yes **20.** $\overleftrightarrow{UX}$, $\overleftrightarrow{WS}$ no **21.** $\overleftrightarrow{UV}$, $\overleftrightarrow{WS}$ no

22. What is the intersection of plane *QRST* and plane *RSWV*? $\overleftrightarrow{RS}$

23. What is the intersection of $\overleftrightarrow{UV}$ and plane *QTXU*? *U*

24. Name three lines that intersect at point *S*. Answers may vary. Sample: $\overleftrightarrow{RS}$, $\overleftrightarrow{WS}$, $\overleftrightarrow{TS}$

25. Name two planes that intersect at $\overleftrightarrow{TS}$. Answers may vary. Sample: plane *XWST* and plane *UVST*

26. Name another point that is in the same plane as points *Q, T,* and *W*. *V*

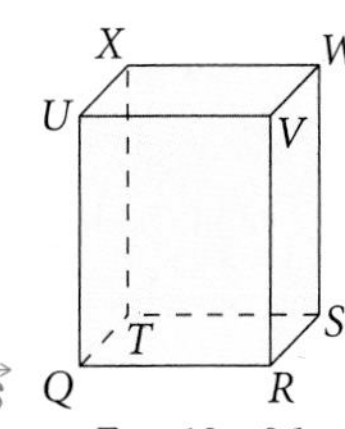

Exs. 13 – 26

RESEARCH Exercise 28 Numerous translations of Euclid's *The Elements* exist. However, they may be too sophisticated for some students. Have students read about Euclid in an encyclopedia and look for material on the Internet.

STANDARDIZED TEST TIP **Exercise 31** The key word in this question is "not." A common error is to choose the first acceptable name without observing that four of the five names are acceptable.

ALTERNATIVE ASSESSMENT **Exercise 32** This exercise can be used to assess students' understanding of Postulate 1-4. Students observe that given a line and a point not on the line, they can find three noncollinear points by choosing any two points on the line and the point not on the line. These three points determine exactly one plane.

ESL **Exercises 34–39** These exercises reinforce the vocabulary in this lesson. Have students work with partners to discuss any unclear terms. Clarify the meanings of the terms "all," "some," and "none."

PROBABILITY Exercise 41a Suggest that students list the possible ways to choose three points from four given (*ABC*, *ABD*, *ACD*, *BCD*), then check to see which of the ways lie in a line.

CONNECTING TO STUDENTS' WORLD Football quarterbacks also use Postulates 1-1 and 1-2 to determine where to throw a pass to a receiver. If you have block scheduling or an extended period, you may wish to take students outside to investigate this application.

pages 15–17 On Your Own

27. The ends of the 3 legs define points that will determine a plane that provides a stable base for the instruments regardless of the unevenness of the terrain.
28. Answers may vary. Sample: Euclid of Alexandria wrote *The Elements* about 300 B.C., and it has gone through about 1000 editions.
29. An infinite number; infinitely many planes can intersect in one line.
30. Postulate 1-1: Through any 2 points there is exactly 1 line.
47. Answers may vary. Sample: a flat roof, an inclined roof and the standing wall that bears their weight

27. Writing Surveyors and photographers use a *tripod*, or three-legged stand, for their instruments. Use one of the postulates to explain why. See margin.

28. Research Find out more about Euclid's book *The Elements*. What made it such a significant book? Where did Euclid get his information? See margin.

29. How many planes contain three collinear points? Explain. See margin.

30. Which postulate is sometimes stated as "Two points determine a line"? See margin.

31. Standardized Test Prep Which of the following is *not* an acceptable name for the plane shown? C
    A. plane *RSZ*
    B. plane *RSWZ*
    C. plane *WSZ*
    D. plane *RSTW*
    E. plane *STZ*

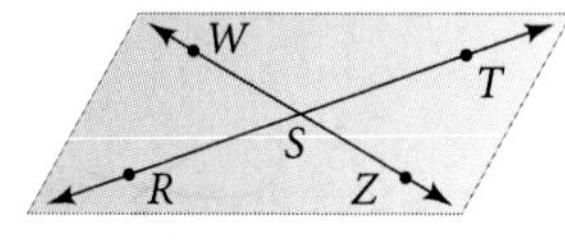

32. How many planes contain each line and point?
    a. $\overleftrightarrow{EF}$ and point *Q* 1
    b. $\overleftrightarrow{PH}$ and point *E* 1
    c. $\overleftrightarrow{FG}$ and point *P* 1
    d. $\overleftrightarrow{EP}$ and point *G* 1
    e. Use inductive reasoning. What do you think is true of a line and a point not on the line? Through a line and a point not on that line there is exactly 1 plane.

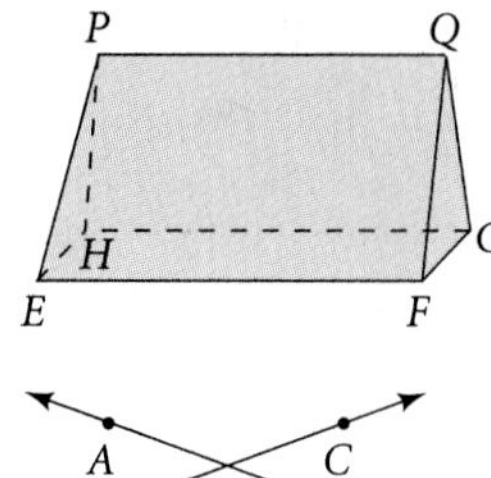

33. Logical Reasoning Suppose two lines intersect. How many planes do you think contain both lines? Use the diagram at the right to explain your answer. 1; points *A*, *B*, and *C* are points on the 2 lines and these 3 points are noncollinear, so exactly 1 plane contains them.

A C B

Complete with *always, sometimes,* or *never* to make a true statement.

34. Intersecting lines are __?__ coplanar. always
35. Two planes __?__ intersect in exactly one point. never
36. Three points are __?__ coplanar. always
37. A line and a point not on the line are __?__ coplanar. always
38. Four points are __?__ coplanar. sometimes
39. Two lines __?__ meet in more than one point. never

Probability **Given points *A, B, C,* and *D* as shown, solve each problem.**

•D

A B C

40. Two points are picked at random. Find *P*(they are collinear). 1
41. Three points are picked at random.
    a. Find *P*(they are collinear). $\frac{1}{4}$
    b. Find *P*(they are coplanar). 1

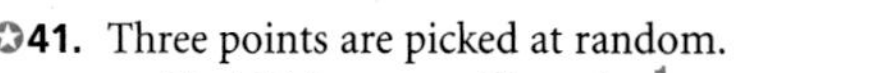

OPEN-ENDED Exercise 47 Emphasize that the three planes need to intersect in a line and not just a point. For example, two walls that meet at a corner and the ceiling are contained in planes that intersect at a point. Three pages of a book (that is fanned out) are contained in planes that intersect in a line.

MAKING CONNECTIONS Exercise 48 When you are crossing a street in a crosswalk, the letters in the word STOP painted on the street for automobiles appear long and narrow. A driver from an approaching car views the letters at an angle so they appear normal.

Exercises MIXED REVIEW

Exercises 49–52 Students review evaluating variable expressions for given values.

GETTING READY FOR LESSON 1-3 These exercises prepare students for the definition of *skew lines*.

Wrap Up

THE BIG IDEA Ask students: *Describe the similarities, differences, and connections between lines and planes.*

RETEACHING ACTIVITY Students use the basic definitions and postulates to identify points, lines, and planes on figures. (Reteaching worksheet 1-2)

✪**42.** Navigation Rescue teams use the principles in Postulates 1-1 and 1-2 to determine the location of a distress signal. In the diagram, a ship at point A receives a signal from the northeast. A ship at point B receives the same signal from due west. Trace the diagram and find the location of the distress signal. Explain how the two postulates help to find the location of the distress signal. See below.

Coordinate Geometry **Are the points collinear? Graph them to find out.**

43. (1, 1), (4, 4), (−3, −3) collinear

44. (2, 4), (4, 6), (0, 2) collinear

45. (0, 0), (8, 10), (4, 6) noncollinear

46. (0, 0), (0, 3), (0, −10) collinear

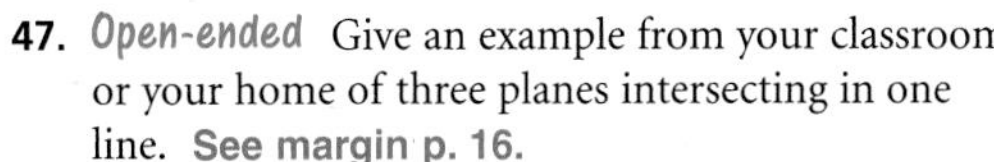

47. Open-ended Give an example from your classroom or your home of three planes intersecting in one line. See margin p. 16.

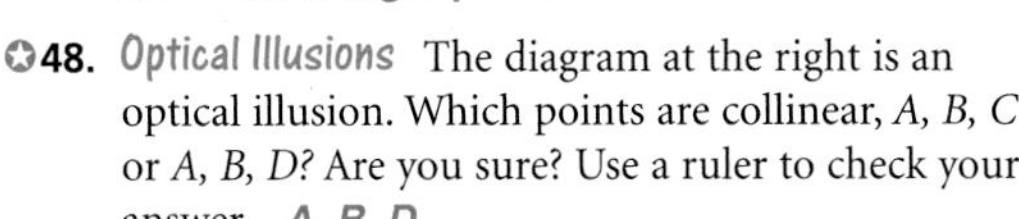

✪**48.** Optical Illusions The diagram at the right is an optical illusion. Which points are collinear, A, B, C or A, B, D? Are you sure? Use a ruler to check your answer. *A, B, D*

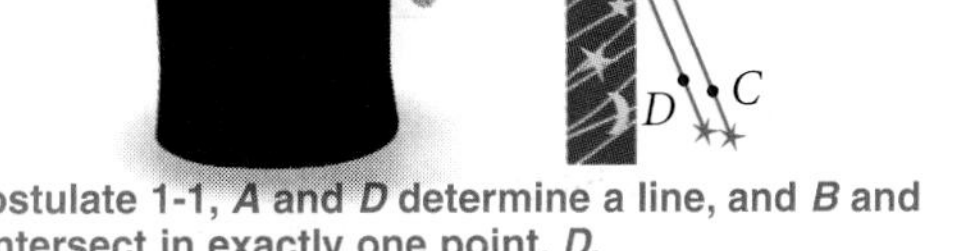

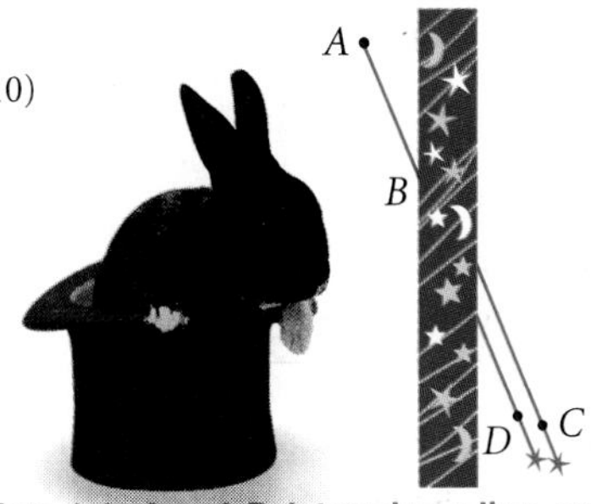

42. Let D be the location of the distress signal. By Postulate 1-1, A and D determine a line, and B and D determine another. By Postulate 1-2, the two lines intersect in exactly one point, D.

Exercises MIXED REVIEW

Algebra **Evaluate each expression for the given values.**

49. $a^2 + b^2$ for $a = 3$ and $b = -5$ 34

50. $\frac{1}{2}bh$ for $b = 8$ and $h = 11$ 44

51. $2\ell + 2w$ for $\ell = 3$ and $w = 7$ 20

52. $b^2 - 4ac$ for $a = 2$, $b = 5$, and $c = 1$ 17

53. Patterns What is the last digit of 3^{45}? Make a table and use inductive reasoning. Explain the pattern. 3

For more practice with evaluating expressions, see Skills Handbook page 673.

Getting Ready for Lesson 1-3

Will the lines intersect or not?

54. no

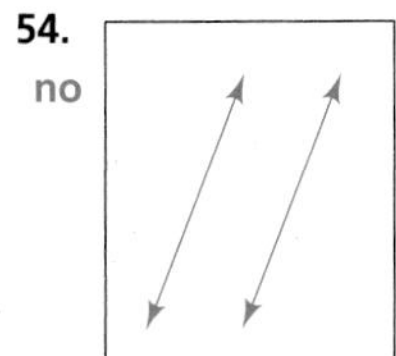

55. yes

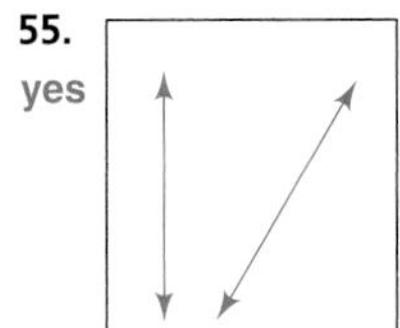

56. no

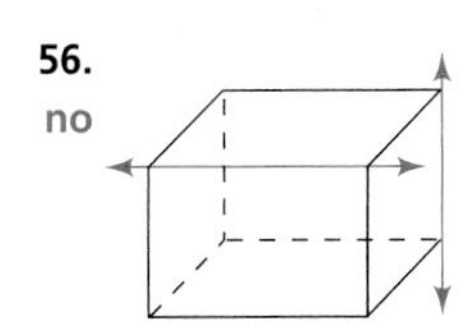

57. no

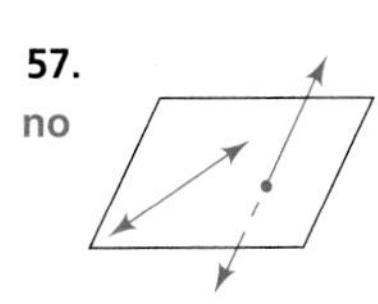

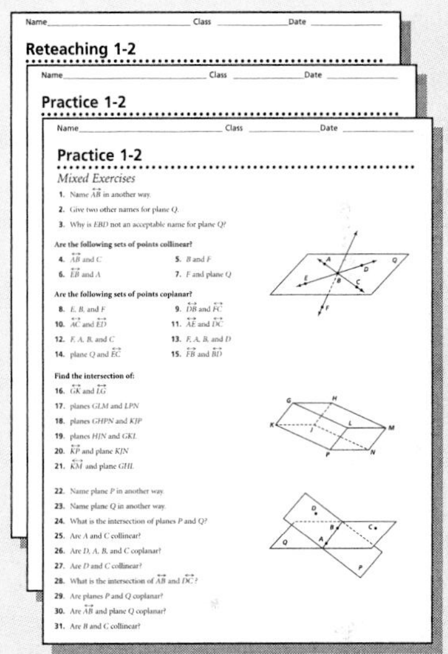

Name______ Class______ Date______

Reteaching 1-2

Name______ Class______ Date______

Practice 1-2

Name______ Class______ Date______

Practice 1-2

Mixed Exercises

1. Name $\overleftrightarrow{AB}$ in another way.
2. Give two other names for plane Q.
3. Why is EBD not an acceptable name for plane Q?

Are the following sets of points collinear?

4. $\overleftrightarrow{AB}$ and C
5. B and F
6. $\overleftrightarrow{EB}$ and A
7. F and plane Q

Are the following sets of points coplanar?

8. E, B, and F
9. $\overleftrightarrow{DB}$ and $\overleftrightarrow{FC}$
10. $\overleftrightarrow{AC}$ and $\overleftrightarrow{ED}$
11. $\overleftrightarrow{AE}$ and $\overleftrightarrow{DC}$
12. F, A, B, and C
13. F, A, B, and D
14. plane Q and $\overleftrightarrow{EC}$
15. $\overleftrightarrow{FB}$ and $\overleftrightarrow{BD}$

Find the intersection of:

16. $\overleftrightarrow{GK}$ and $\overleftrightarrow{LG}$
17. planes GLM and LPN
18. planes $GHPN$ and KJP
19. planes HJN and GKL
20. $\overleftrightarrow{KP}$ and plane KJN
21. $\overleftrightarrow{KM}$ and plane GHL

22. Name plane P in another way.
23. Name plane Q in another way.
24. What is the intersection of planes P and Q?
25. Are A and C collinear?
26. Are D, A, B, and C coplanar?
27. Are D and C collinear?
28. What is the intersection of $\overleftrightarrow{AB}$ and $\overleftrightarrow{DC}$?
29. Are planes P and Q coplanar?
30. Are $\overleftrightarrow{AB}$ and plane Q coplanar?
31. Are B and C collinear?

Lesson Quiz

Lesson Quiz is also available in Transparencies.

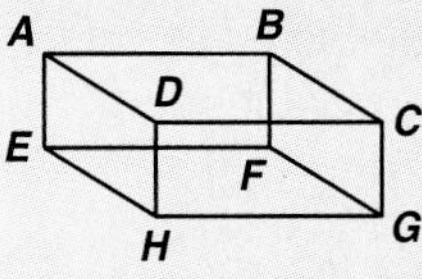

1. Are the points A, D, and C collinear? **No**
2. Are the points A, B, C, and E coplanar? **No**
3. Are $\overleftrightarrow{DH}$ and E coplanar? **Yes**
4. Are $\overleftrightarrow{AB}$ and $\overleftrightarrow{CG}$ coplanar? **No**

1-3 Teaching Notes

PROBLEM OF THE DAY

Find the letter that is the 276th entry in the following sequence: G, L, G, L, L, G, L, L, L, G, L, L, L, L, G, L, L, ... G

Problem of the Day is also available in Transparencies.

CONNECTING TO PRIOR KNOWLEDGE Ask students to describe real-world examples of parallel lines. Examples may include lane dividers, rows of crops, streets on a map, railroad tracks, and so on. Ask them to describe the characteristics of these lines.

THINK AND DISCUSS

In geometry, betweenness implies collinearity. For example, $\overline{AB}$ contains all the points between A and B that lie on the same line as A and B.

VISUAL LEARNING Students can remember the meaning of the abbreviations $\overline{AB}$, $\overrightarrow{AB}$, and $\overleftrightarrow{AB}$ by observing that visual representations of a segment, ray, and line, respectively, are —, →, ↔.

Lesson Planning Options

Prerequisite Skills

- Understanding of points, lines, and planes

Assignment Options for Exercises On Your Own

Core 1–34, 37, 39
Extension 35–36, 38

Use Mixed Review to maintain skills.

Resources

Student Edition

Extra Practice, p. 648
Glossary/Study Guide

Teaching Resources

Chapter Support File, Ch. 1
- Practice 1-3 (two worksheets)
- Reteaching 1-3

Classroom Manager 1-3
Glossary, Spanish Resources

Transparencies
23, 28

1-3 Segments, Rays, Parallel Lines and Planes

What You'll Learn

- Relating segments and rays to lines
- Recognizing parallel lines and parallel planes

...And Why

To provide a vocabulary of terms needed for communicating in geometry

What You'll Need

graph paper, colored pencils, tape

THINK AND DISCUSS

Many geometric figures, such as squares and angles, use only the parts of lines called segments and rays.

A **segment** is the part of a line consisting of two *endpoints* and all points between them.

A **ray** is the part of a line consisting of one *endpoint* and all the points of the line on one side of the endpoint.

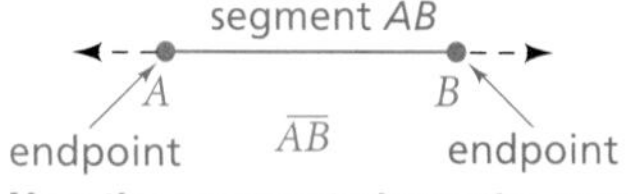

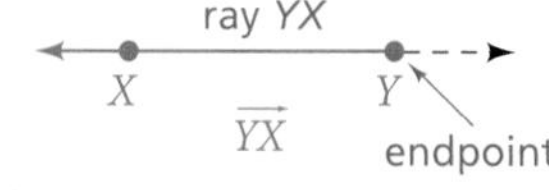

1. Is $\overline{AB}$ the same as $\overline{BA}$? Explain. Yes; the segments have the same endpoints and contain the same points between them.
2. Is $\overrightarrow{YX}$ the same as $\overrightarrow{XY}$? Explain. No, they have different endpoints and continue in opposite directions.
3. How is a ray like a line? How is a ray different from a line? A ray extends forever in one direction, while a line extends forever in both directions.

A ray in geometry is named after the rays of the sun.

Opposite rays are two collinear rays with the same endpoint. Opposite rays always form a line.

4. a. Name four different rays in the figure below. Answers may vary. Sample: $\overrightarrow{LP}$, $\overrightarrow{PQ}$, $\overrightarrow{PL}$, $\overrightarrow{QL}$
   b. Name two opposite rays. $\overrightarrow{PL}$ and $\overrightarrow{PQ}$

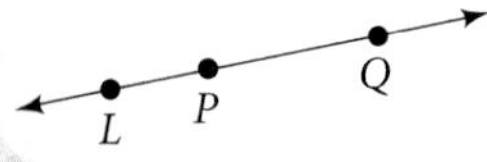

Lines that do not intersect may or may not be coplanar. **Parallel lines** are coplanar lines that do not intersect. Segments and rays are parallel if they lie in parallel lines.

You can use arrowheads to show parallel lines.

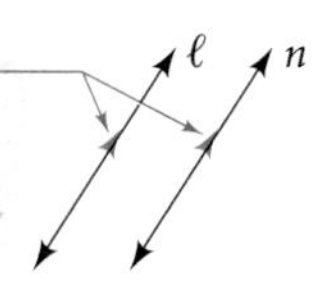

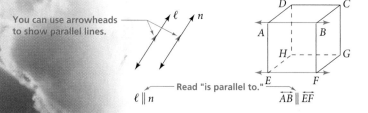

Read "is parallel to."

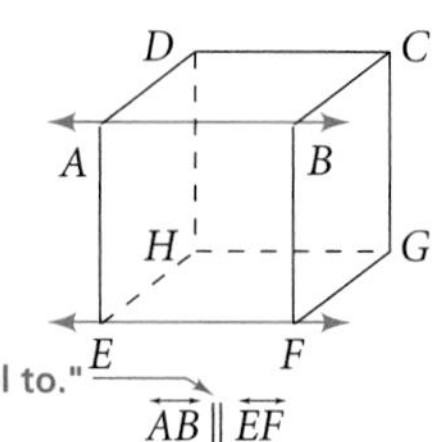

ERROR ALERT! Questions 4b Some students may claim that $\overrightarrow{PQ}$ and $\overrightarrow{QP}$ are opposite rays sharing the endpoint P and Q. **Remediation:** Reinforce that opposite rays have only one point in common, namely their endpoint. On the diagram or on the board, show that $\overrightarrow{PQ}$ and $\overrightarrow{QP}$ have many points in common.

MAKING CONNECTIONS Air traffic controllers keep eastbound and westbound airplanes from colliding by having them cruise at different altitudes. The airplanes thus pass each other in parallel planes.

Example

Drawing representations of planes may be difficult for some students. Suggest students use colored pencils to differentiate the different planes.

5. Name all the segments shown at the left that are parallel to:
   a. $\overline{DC}$ $\overline{AB}$, $\overline{GH}$, $\overline{JI}$
   b. $\overline{GJ}$ $\overline{AD}$, $\overline{EF}$, $\overline{BC}$, $\overline{HI}$
   c. $\overline{AE}$ $\overline{DF}$

Skew lines do not lie in the same plane. They are neither parallel nor intersecting.

$\overleftrightarrow{AB}$ and $\overleftrightarrow{HI}$ are skew.

Parallel planes are planes that do not intersect.

plane $ABCD \parallel$ plane $GHIJ$

6. Name some other pairs of skew lines in the diagram at the left. Answers may vary. Sample: $\overleftrightarrow{AB}$ and $\overleftrightarrow{GJ}$, $\overleftrightarrow{AB}$ and $\overleftrightarrow{DJ}$
7. Name two more pairs of parallel planes. plane $ABHG \parallel$ plane $DCIJ$, plane $ADJG \parallel BCIH$

A box diagram is a good way to represent parallel lines and segments, skew lines, and parallel planes. Some other ways to draw planes are shown below.

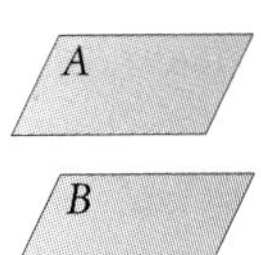

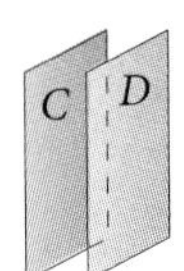

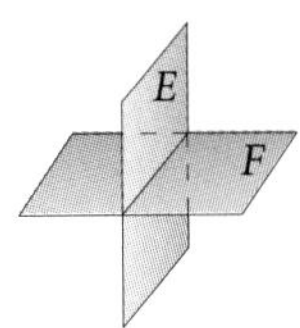

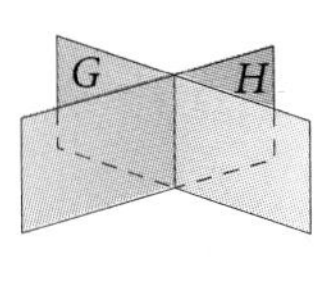

8. Which pairs of planes shown above are parallel? Which are intersecting? *A and B, C and D; E and F, G and H*

Example

Draw planes A and B intersecting in $\overleftrightarrow{FG}$.

Using graph paper will help you draw parallel lines and representations of planes.

Step 1

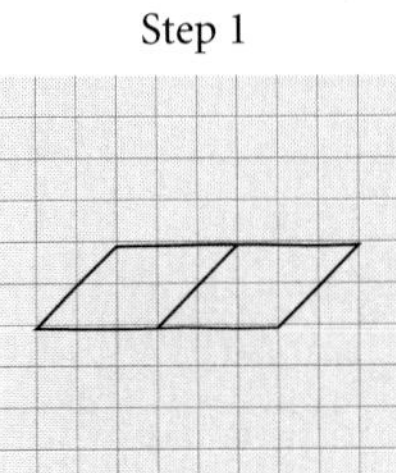

Step 2

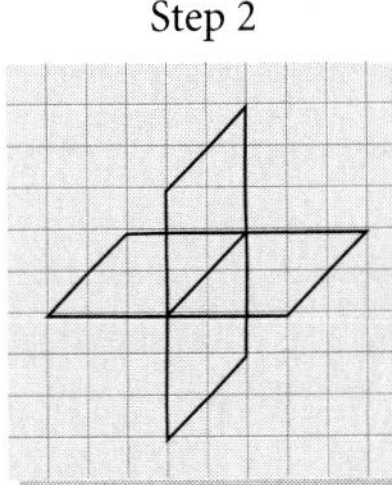

Step 3

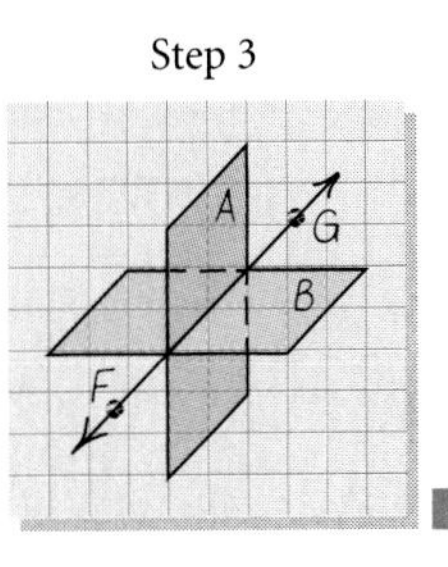

9. **Try This** Use graph paper and colored pencils to draw pairs of parallel and intersecting planes like those above Question 8. Check students' work.

Additional Examples

FOR EXAMPLE

Draw plane C and D intersecting in $\overleftrightarrow{XY}$.

Discussion: *Describe the steps you used to draw the planes.*

Answers may vary. Sample:

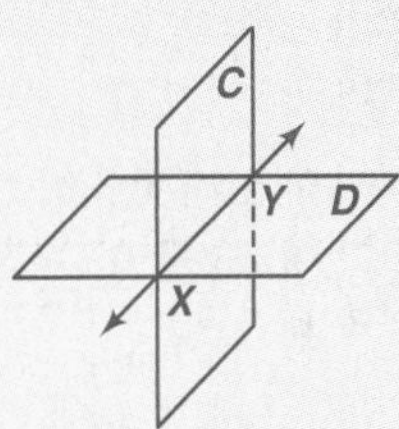

Draw planes F and G intersecting in a vertical line $\overleftrightarrow{RS}$.

Discussion: *Describe the steps you used to draw the planes.*

Answers may vary. Sample:

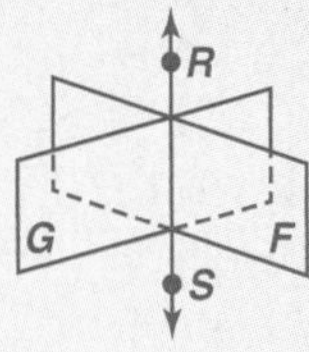

WORK TOGETHER

ALTERNATIVE ASSESSMENT This activity can help you assess students' understanding of parallel lines, skew lines, and parallel planes. It may help students to tape a piece of paper with the appropriate vertex labeled on it to each corner of the stack of books. Have students take turns recording answers to Questions 10–12.

Exercises ON YOUR OWN

Exercises 9–12 Students may need a ruler or straightedge. Some may prefer to use graph paper, although this is not necessary.

ESL **Exercises 21-30** These exercises reinforce the meanings of the new vocabulary taught in this lesson as well as "always," "sometimes," and "never." You may want to have students work with partners to discuss unfamiliar terms.

Technology Options

Exercises 9–12 can be sketched using drawing software. For Exercises 21–30, students may investigate the different cases using geometry software.

Prentice Hall Technology

Software

- Secondary Math Lab Toolkit™
- Computer Item Generator 1-3

CD-ROM

- Multimedia Geometry Lab 1

Internet

- See the Prentice Hall site. (http://www.phschool.com)

WORK TOGETHER

Work in pairs to answer these questions about the lines and planes determined by the surfaces of a rectangular solid.

Stack your geometry books to form a rectangular solid. Label the vertices *P*, *Q*, *R*, *S*, *T*, *U*, *V*, and *W*. Identify each of the following.

10. three pairs of parallel planes **See below.**
11. all lines that are parallel to $\overleftrightarrow{PQ}$ $\overleftrightarrow{TU}$, $\overleftrightarrow{SR}$, $\overleftrightarrow{VW}$
12. all lines that are skew to $\overleftrightarrow{PQ}$ $\overleftrightarrow{TW}$, $\overleftrightarrow{UV}$, $\overleftrightarrow{SW}$, $\overleftrightarrow{RV}$

10. plane *PQR* and plane *TUV*, plane *PQU* and plane *SRV*, plane *PST* and plane *QRV*

Exercises ON YOUR OWN

Name all the segments that are parallel to the given segment.

1. $\overline{AC}$ $\overline{DF}$
2. $\overline{EF}$ $\overline{BC}$
3. $\overline{AD}$ $\overline{CF}$, $\overline{BE}$

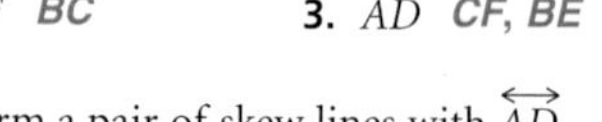

4. Name all the lines that form a pair of skew lines with $\overleftrightarrow{AD}$. $\overleftrightarrow{BC}$, $\overleftrightarrow{EF}$
5. Name a pair of parallel planes. plane *ABC* and plane *DEF*

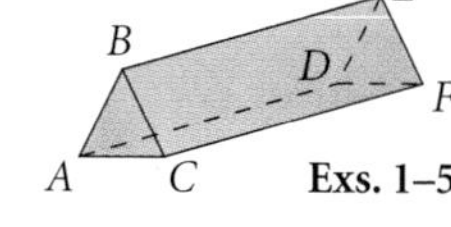

Exs. 1–5

Use the line at the right for Exercises 6–8. 6a. $\overrightarrow{TW}$ and $\overrightarrow{TS}$ or $\overrightarrow{TW}$ and $\overrightarrow{TR}$

6. a. Name a pair of opposite rays with point *T* as endpoint.
   b. Name another pair of opposite rays. $\overrightarrow{SR}$ and $\overrightarrow{ST}$ or $\overrightarrow{SR}$ and $\overrightarrow{SW}$
7. Name all the segments shown. $\overline{RS}$, $\overline{RT}$, $\overline{RW}$, $\overline{ST}$, $\overline{SW}$, $\overline{TW}$
8. Name $\overrightarrow{RT}$ two other ways. $\overrightarrow{RS}$, $\overrightarrow{RW}$

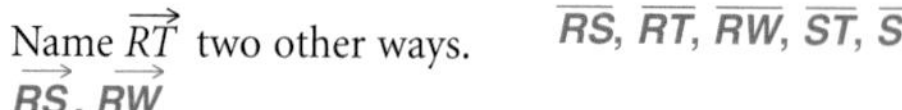

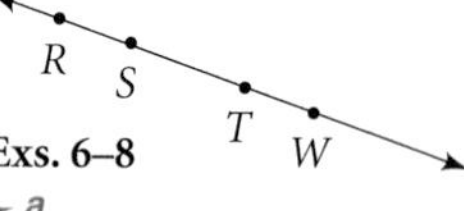

Exs. 6–8

Make a separate sketch for each of the following.

9. Draw three parallel lines *a*, *t*, and *q*.
10. Draw parallel planes *A* and *B*.
11. Draw $\overleftrightarrow{AB}$, $\overleftrightarrow{CD}$, and $\overleftrightarrow{EF}$ so that $\overleftrightarrow{AB} \parallel \overleftrightarrow{CD}$, $\overleftrightarrow{AB}$ and $\overleftrightarrow{EF}$ are skew, and $\overleftrightarrow{CD}$ and $\overleftrightarrow{EF}$ are skew. See margin p. 21.
12. Draw planes *C* and *D*, intersecting in $\overleftrightarrow{XY}$. See margin p. 21.

9. a, t, q

10.

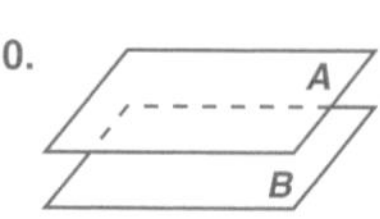

Write *true* or *false*.

13. $\overleftrightarrow{CB} \parallel \overleftrightarrow{GF}$ false
14. $\overleftrightarrow{ED} \parallel \overleftrightarrow{HG}$ false
15. plane *AED* $\parallel$ plane *FGH* true
16. plane *ABH* $\parallel$ plane *CDF* false
17. $\overleftrightarrow{AB}$ and $\overleftrightarrow{HG}$ are skew lines. true
18. $\overleftrightarrow{AE}$ and $\overleftrightarrow{BC}$ are skew lines. false
19. $\overleftrightarrow{CF}$ and $\overleftrightarrow{AI}$ are skew lines. true
20. $\overleftrightarrow{CF}$ and $\overleftrightarrow{AJ}$ are skew lines. false

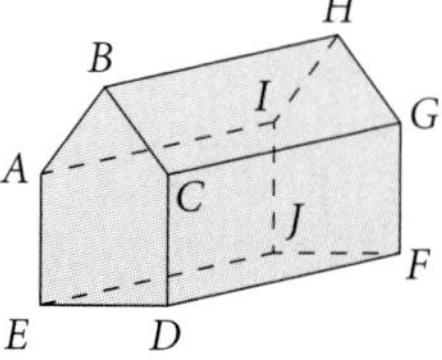

KINESTHETIC LEARNING Exercise 31 If you have block scheduling or an extended period, take students outside and ask them to find and record examples for each of the different ways that two lines can be related.

MAKING CONNECTIONS Exercise 32 Because Earth's axis is at a 23.4° tilt, any plane that cuts through the center of the earth and its two poles is at a 23.4° angle to Earth's horizontal orbital plane. The tilt in the earth alternately tips the North and South poles toward the Sun, which causes the seasons.

CRITICAL THINKING Exercise 35 Students may want to construct the described situation using index cards or other sturdy paper.

RESEARCH Exercise 36 Students should be able to find this information in a chemistry book or encyclopedia. You may wish to ask the science department in your school for three-dimensional models of atoms for students to examine.

Complete with *always, sometimes,* or *never* to make a true statement.

21. $\overrightarrow{AB}$ and $\overrightarrow{BA}$ are __?__ the same ray. never
22. $\overrightarrow{AB}$ and $\overrightarrow{AC}$ are __?__ the same ray. sometimes
23. $\overline{AX}$ and $\overline{XA}$ are __?__ the same segment. always
24. $\overleftrightarrow{TQ}$ and $\overleftrightarrow{QT}$ are __?__ the same line. always
25. Two parallel lines are __?__ coplanar. always
26. Skew lines are __?__ coplanar. never
27. Opposite rays __?__ form a line. always
28. Two lines in the same plane are __?__ parallel. sometimes
29. Two planes that do not intersect are __?__ parallel. always
30. Two lines that lie in parallel planes are __?__ parallel. sometimes

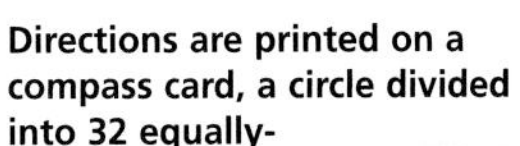
Directions are printed on a compass card, a circle divided into 32 equally-spaced compass points.

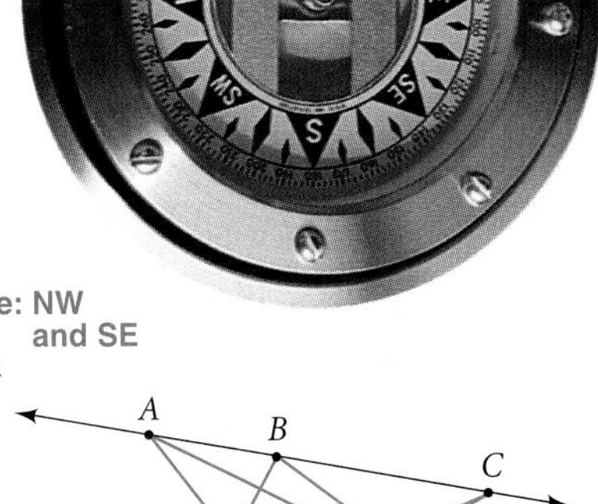

31. **Writing** **Summarize** the different ways that two lines may be related. Give examples from the real world that illustrate the relationships. See margin.
32. **Navigation** North and south are directions on a compass that are on opposite rays. Name two other pairs of compass directions that are on opposite rays. Answers may vary. Sample: NW and SE
33. **Coordinate Geometry** $\overrightarrow{AB}$ has endpoint $A(2, 3)$ and goes through $B(4, 6)$. Give some possible coordinates for point C so that $\overrightarrow{AB}$ and $\overrightarrow{AC}$ will be opposite rays. Graph your answer. See margin.

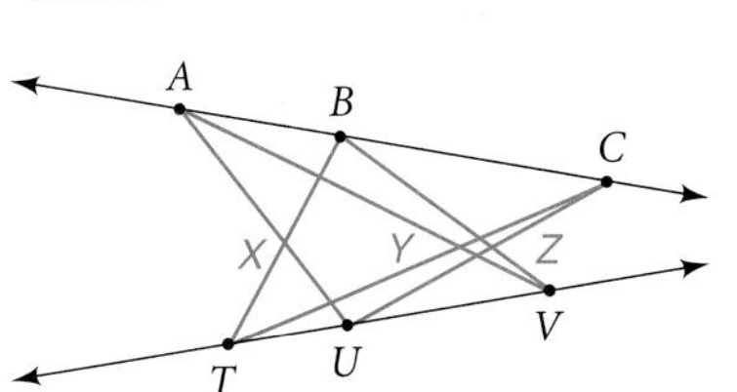

34. **Inductive Reasoning** Draw a diagram similar to the one shown.
   Step 1: Draw $\overline{AU}$ and $\overline{BT}$. Label their intersection point as X.
   Step 2: Draw $\overline{AV}$ and $\overline{CT}$. Label their intersection point as Y.
   Step 3: Draw $\overline{BV}$ and $\overline{CU}$. Label their intersection point as Z.
   Make a **conjecture** about points X, Y, and Z. They are collinear.
35. **Critical Thinking** Suppose two parallel planes A and B are each intersected by a third plane C. What do you think will be true of the intersection of planes A and C and the intersection of planes B and C? Give an example in your classroom. See margin.
36. **Research** In diamond, each carbon atom bonds to four other carbon atoms in a three-dimensional network. In graphite, each carbon atom bonds to three other carbon atoms in the same plane. The "sheets" or planes of graphite are parallel. Find out how these structures affect the properties of diamond and graphite.
   Answers may vary. Sample: The diamond structure makes it tough, strong, hard and durable. The graphite structure makes it soft and slippery.

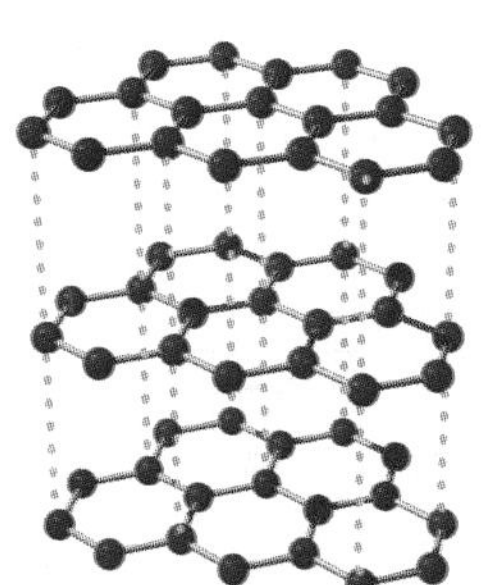

pages 20–22 On Your Own

11. 12.

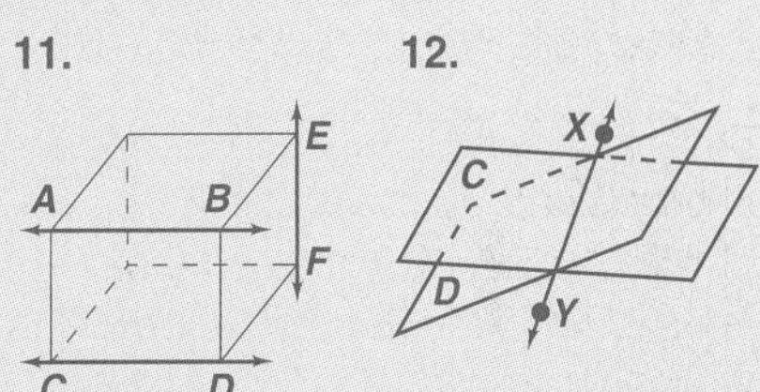

31. Lines can be coplanar or skew. If they are coplanar, they can be parallel or intersecting.
   Answers may vary. Sample: Skew lines—vapor trails of a north-bound jet and a west-bound jet at different altitudes, Parallel lines—train tracks, Intersecting lines—two edges of a roof that meet at the peak

33.

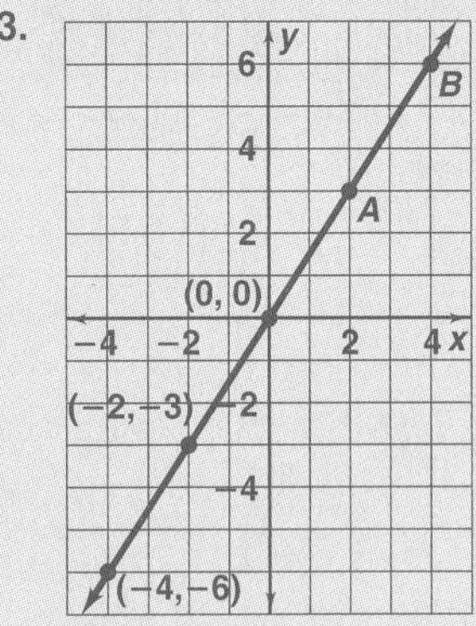

Answers may vary. Samples: (0, 0), (−2, −3), and (−4, −6).

35. The lines of intersection are parallel. Answers will vary. Sample: the ceiling and floor intersect a wall in two parallel lines.

WRITING Exercise 38 Have students give examples of how *skew* can be used in nonmathematical sentences.

Chapter Project **FIND OUT BY CREATING** Have students work in groups. Provide each student with several paper squares and a paper lunch bag in which they can store their origami figures. Allow time for students to share their figures with other groups.

Exercises MIXED REVIEW

Exercises 40–42 Students use inductive reasoning to determine terms in a pattern.

Exercises 43–45 Students review the symbols for geometric figures.

GETTING READY FOR LESSON 1-4 By reviewing absolute value and inequalities, these exercises prepare students to find the lengths of line segments.

JOURNAL Suggest that students sketch their examples and label the geometric terms they illustrate.

Wrap Up

THE BIG IDEA Ask students: *Explain how two planes can be related and how two lines in those planes can be related.*

RETEACHING ACTIVITY Students identify different pairs of skew, parallel, and intersecting lines. (Reteaching worksheet 1-4)

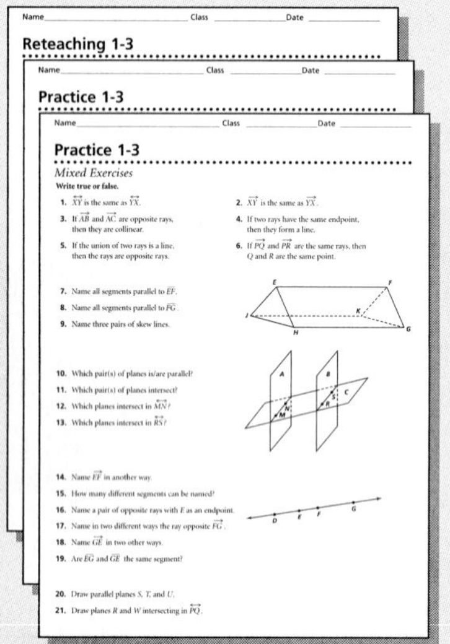

Name ______ Class ______ Date ______

Reteaching 1-3

Name ______ Class ______ Date ______

Practice 1-3

Name ______ Class ______ Date ______

Practice 1-3

Mixed Exercises

Write true or false.

1. $\overleftrightarrow{XY}$ is the same as $\overleftrightarrow{YX}$.
2. $\overrightarrow{XY}$ is the same as $\overrightarrow{YX}$.
3. If $\overrightarrow{AB}$ and $\overrightarrow{AC}$ are opposite rays, then they are collinear.
4. If two rays have the same endpoint, then they form a line.
5. If the union of two rays is a line, then the rays are opposite rays.
6. If $\overrightarrow{PQ}$ and $\overrightarrow{PR}$ are the same rays, then Q and R are the same point.
7. Name all segments parallel to $\overline{EF}$.
8. Name all segments parallel to $\overline{FG}$.
9. Name three pairs of skew lines.
10. Which pair(s) of planes is/are parallel?
11. Which pair(s) of planes intersect?
12. Which planes intersect in $\overleftrightarrow{MN}$?
13. Which planes intersect in $\overleftrightarrow{RS}$?
14. Name $\overrightarrow{EF}$ in another way.
15. How many different segments can be named?
16. Name a pair of opposite rays with E as an endpoint.
17. Name in two different ways the ray opposite $\overrightarrow{FG}$.
18. Name $\overrightarrow{GE}$ in two other ways.
19. Are $\overline{EG}$ and $\overline{GE}$ the same segment?
20. Draw parallel planes S, T, and U.
21. Draw planes R and W intersecting in $\overleftrightarrow{PQ}$.

Lesson Quiz

Lesson Quiz is also available in Transparencies.

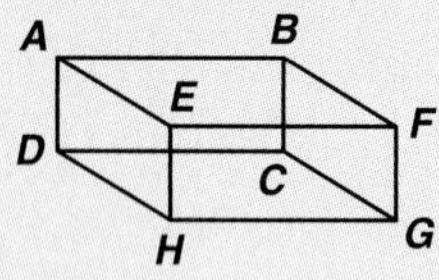

1. Name a line that forms a pair of skew lines with $\overleftrightarrow{EH}$.
   Sample: $\overleftrightarrow{AB}$, $\overleftrightarrow{DC}$, $\overleftrightarrow{CG}$, $\overleftrightarrow{BF}$

2. Name a pair of parallel planes.
   Answers may vary. Sample: Planes AEF and DHG, ADH and BCG, EFG and ABC

3. Name a line that forms a pair of parallel lines with $\overleftrightarrow{CG}$.
   $\overleftrightarrow{BF}$, $\overleftrightarrow{DH}$, or $\overleftrightarrow{AE}$

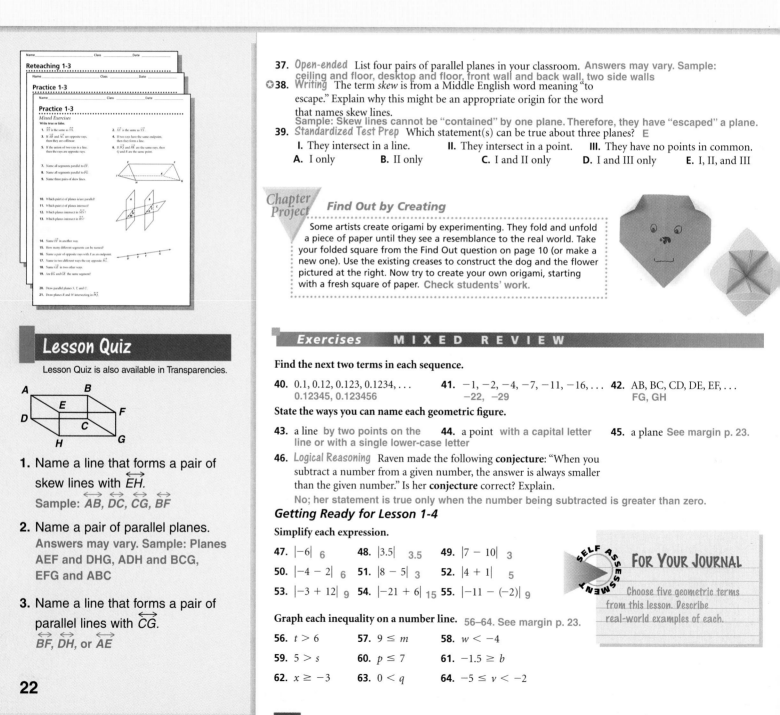

37. *Open-ended* List four pairs of parallel planes in your classroom. Answers may vary. Sample: ceiling and floor, desktop and floor, front wall and back wall, two side walls

38. *Writing* The term *skew* is from a Middle English word meaning "to escape." Explain why this might be an appropriate origin for the word that names skew lines.
    Sample: Skew lines cannot be "contained" by one plane. Therefore, they have "escaped" a plane.

39. *Standardized Test Prep* Which statement(s) can be true about three planes? E
    I. They intersect in a line. **II.** They intersect in a point. **III.** They have no points in common.
    A. I only **B.** II only **C.** I and II only **D.** I and III only **E.** I, II, and III

Chapter Project

Find Out by Creating

Some artists create origami by experimenting. They fold and unfold a piece of paper until they see a resemblance to the real world. Take your folded square from the Find Out question on page 10 (or make a new one). Use the existing creases to construct the dog and the flower pictured at the right. Now try to create your own origami, starting with a fresh square of paper. Check students' work.

Exercises MIXED REVIEW

Find the next two terms in each sequence.

40. 0.1, 0.12, 0.123, 0.1234, ... 0.12345, 0.123456

41. −1, −2, −4, −7, −11, −16, ... −22, −29

42. AB, BC, CD, DE, EF, ... FG, GH

State the ways you can name each geometric figure.

43. a line by two points on the line or with a single lower-case letter

44. a point with a capital letter

45. a plane See margin p. 23.

46. *Logical Reasoning* Raven made the following **conjecture**: "When you subtract a number from a given number, the answer is always smaller than the given number." Is her **conjecture** correct? Explain.
    No; her statement is true only when the number being subtracted is greater than zero.

Getting Ready for Lesson 1-4

Simplify each expression.

47. $|-6|$ 6
48. $|3.5|$ 3.5
49. $|7 - 10|$ 3
50. $|-4 - 2|$ 6
51. $|8 - 5|$ 3
52. $|4 + 1|$ 5
53. $|-3 + 12|$ 9
54. $|-21 + 6|$ 15
55. $|-11 - (-2)|$ 9

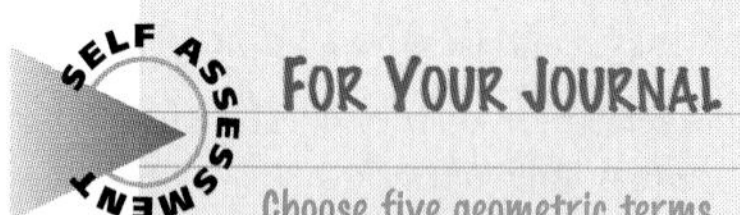

SELF ASSESSMENT
FOR YOUR JOURNAL
Choose five geometric terms from this lesson. Describe real-world examples of each.

Graph each inequality on a number line. 56–64. See margin p. 23.

56. $t > 6$
57. $9 \le m$
58. $w < -4$
59. $5 > s$
60. $p \le 7$
61. $-1.5 \ge b$
62. $x \ge -3$
63. $0 < q$
64. $-5 \le v < -2$

Math ToolboX

In this chapter, students solve linear equations to find the lengths of segments, the measures of angles, and the coordinates of points. This toolbox reviews the basic skills for solving linear equations including combining like terms and isolating all the variables on one side of the equation.

Example 1

Make sure students understand why $a - b = a + (-b)$ and how the Distributive Property is applied.

Example 2

ERROR ALERT! Students may lose track of signs when moving variables and constants to opposite sides of the equals sign. **Remediation:** Encourage students to perform one step at a time, first moving the variables to one side, then moving the constants to the other side. It may be helpful for some students to write out each step instead of performing some only mentally. Also, remind students to check their answer in the original equation.

ALTERNATE ASSESSMENT You can use Exercises 2–3 to evaluate students' understanding of combining like terms and Exercises 1 and 4 to evaluate students' understanding of isolating the variable on one side.

Math ToolboX Algebra Review

Solving Linear Equations

Before Lesson 1-4

Sometimes you need to combine like terms when you are solving linear equations.

Example 1

Solve $(5x + 8) - (2x - 9) = 38$.

$(5x + 8) + (-1)(2x - 9) = 38$	$-(2x - 9) = (-1)(2x - 9)$
$5x + 8 - 2x + 9 = 38$	Use the Distributive Property.
$3x + 17 = 38$	Simplify.
$3x = 21$	Subtract 17 from each side.
$x = 7$	Divide each side by 3.

When you are solving equations with variables on both sides, first get all the variables on the same side of the equation.

Example 2

Solve $4x - 9 = 7x - 15$.

$4x - 9 = 7x - 15$	
$-9 = 3x - 15$	Subtract $4x$ from each side.
$6 = 3x$	Add 15 to each side.
$2 = x$	Divide each side by 3.

Solve.

1. $5x + 10 - 6x + 3 = 6 - 2x - 2$ −9
2. $(6a - 54) - (5a + 27) = 23$ 104
3. $(2 + 4y) - (y + 9) = 26$ 11
4. $7t - 8t + 4 = 5t - 2$ 1
5. $(9k + 30) - (4k + 10) = 100$ 16
6. $6x + 17 = 9x + 2$ 5
7. $(3x + 10) - 5x = 6x - 50$ $\frac{15}{2}$
8. $(3y - 5) + (5y + 20) = 135$ 15
9. $10n + 12 = 14n - 12$ 6
10. $13c + 40 = 9c - 20 + c$ −20
11. $(4w - 28) + (11w + 13) = 180$ 13
12. $7f + 16 = 3f + 48$ 8
13. $(7a + 3) + (-a - 5) = -16$ $-\frac{7}{3}$
14. $3x - 35 = 9x - 59$ 4
15. $7y + 44 = 12y + 11$ $\frac{33}{5}$
16. $(11x - 37) + (5x + 59) = 54$ 2
17. $(7t - 21) + (t + 4) = 15$ 4
18. $(5w + 24) + (2w + 13) = 156$ 17

page 22 Mixed Review

45. with the word *plane* followed either by a single capital letter or the names of at least 3 noncollinear points in the plane

56. 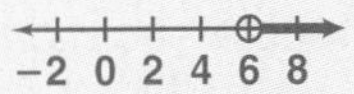 −2 0 2 4 6 8

57. 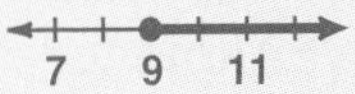 7 9 11

58. 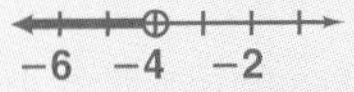 −6 −4 −2

59. 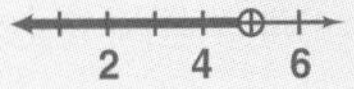 2 4 6

60. 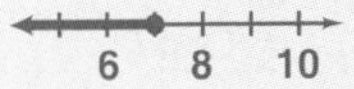 6 8 10

61. 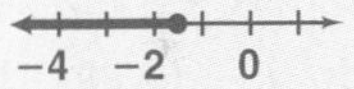 −4 −2 0

62. 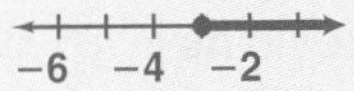 −6 −4 −2

63. 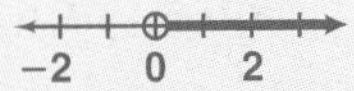 −2 0 2

64.  −6 −4 −2

1-4 Teaching Notes

PROBLEM OF THE DAY

What is the least number of line segments you can draw end to end to connect the nine dots on the grid? 4

Problem of the Day is also available in Transparencies.

CONNECTING TO PRIOR KNOWLEDGE Ask students if they have ever seen "mile" markers on the side of a highway. Ask them if the numbers on the "mile" markers increased or decreased as they went along. Discuss what the markers mean.

WORK TOGETHER

Students may need help reading the map. Help them identify mileage markers and different routes. Discuss the map symbols and what they represent.

MAKING CONNECTIONS The task of a cartographer or map maker has been simplified by the development of modern technological devices. Satellites can now take pictures of the earth which computers can project onto flat surfaces. Cartographers have easy access to biological, geological, and atmospheric tables which have been gathered and stored in computer data banks.

Lesson Planning Options

Prerequisite Skills

- Finding absolute value
- Solving one-variable equations

Assignment Options for Exercises On Your Own

To provide flexible scheduling, this lesson can be subdivided into parts.

1 **Core** 1–14, 24
Extension 27–28

2 **Core** 15–23, 32–36
Extension 25–26, 29–31

Use Mixed Review to maintain skills.

Resources

Student Edition
Skills Handbook, pp. 666, 673, 677
Extra Practice, p. 648
Glossary/Study Guide

Teaching Resources
Chapter Support File, Ch. 1
- Practice 1-4 (two worksheets)
- Reteaching 1-4
- Alternative Activity 1-4

Classroom Manager 1-4
Glossary, Spanish Resources

Transparencies
4, 12, 23

Connections Travel . . . and more

1-4 Measuring Angles and Segments

What You'll Learn

- Finding the length of a segment and the measure of an angle

...And Why

To understand the building blocks of many geometric figures

What You'll Need

protractor

WORK TOGETHER

Your family is traveling on Interstate 80 through Nebraska. You entered the highway at mileage marker 126. You decided to drive as far as you could before stopping for breakfast within $1\frac{1}{2}$ hours. Assume that on the highway you drive at an average speed of 60 mi/h. Work with a partner to answer these questions.

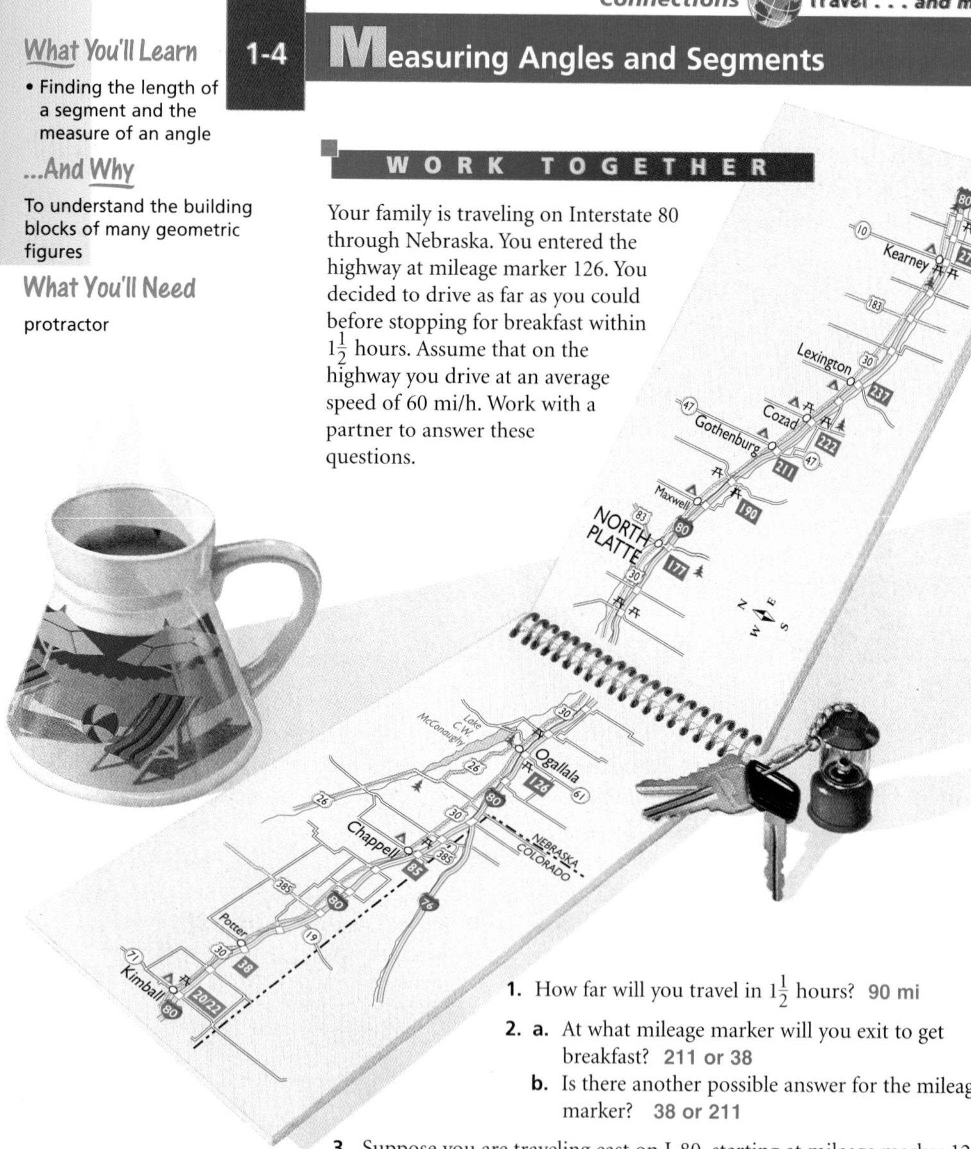

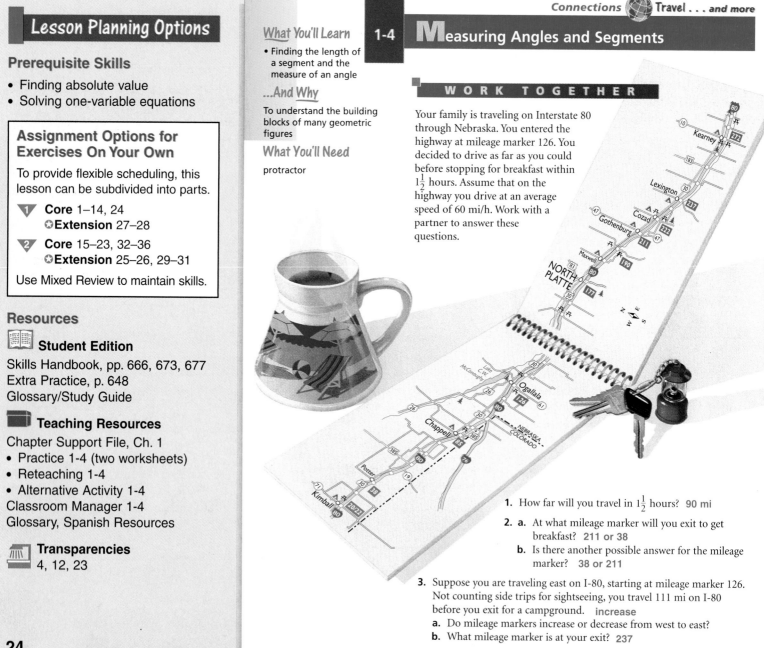

1. How far will you travel in $1\frac{1}{2}$ hours? 90 mi
2. a. At what mileage marker will you exit to get breakfast? 211 or 38
   b. Is there another possible answer for the mileage marker? 38 or 211
3. Suppose you are traveling east on I-80, starting at mileage marker 126. Not counting side trips for sightseeing, you travel 111 mi on I-80 before you exit for a campground. increase
   a. Do mileage markers increase or decrease from west to east?
   b. What mileage marker is at your exit? 237
4. Does the *direction* you travel affect the *distance* you travel? No

THINK AND DISCUSS

Ruler Postulate Point out that the length of a segment is denoted by writing the endpoints without a bar over them. Remind students that the vertical bars around *a* – *b* indicate absolute value.

Example 1

You may need to review the definition of absolute value. Have students check the solution using a number line.

Point out, on diagrams, how tick marks are used to show congruent segments.

CRITICAL THINKING Ask students why $\overline{AB} = \overline{CD}$ would not be correct.

THINK AND DISCUSS

Part 1

Measuring Segments

If you picture straightening out the map of Interstate 80, you will have a model for a number line. The mileage markers represent *coordinates*.

Postulate 1-5
Ruler Postulate

The points of a line can be put into a one-to-one correspondence with the real numbers so that the distance between any two points is the absolute value of the difference of the corresponding numbers.

the length of AB → $AB = |a - b|$ ← **coordinate of *A***, **coordinate of *B***

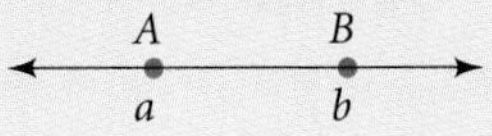

5. *Critical Thinking* Why do you think that absolute value is used to express the distance between two points?
Distance is a positive number.

Example 1

PROBLEM SOLVING HINT
Draw a diagram.

Find QS if the coordinate of Q is -3 and the coordinate of S is 21.

$QS = |-3 - 21| = |-24| = 24$

6. Suppose you subtracted -3 from 21 in Example 1. Would you get the same result? Why or why not? **Yes; $|-3 - 21| = 24 = |21 - (-3)|$**
7. **Try This** Find AB if the coordinate of point A is -8, and the coordinate of point B is 11. **19**

Two segments with the same length are **congruent** ($\cong$). In other words, if $AB = CD$, then $\overline{AB} \cong \overline{CD}$. You can use these statements interchangeably. Segments can be marked alike to show that they are congruent.

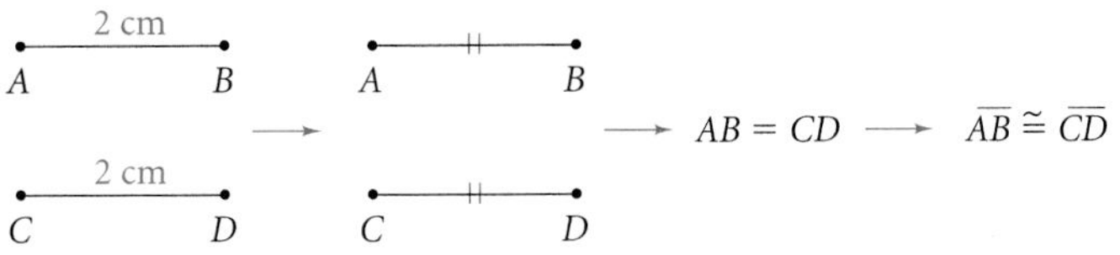

8. a. **Try This** Name two segments that are congruent. **$\overline{AB}$, $\overline{BC}$**
   b. Name a second pair of congruent segments. **$\overline{CD}$, $\overline{DE}$**

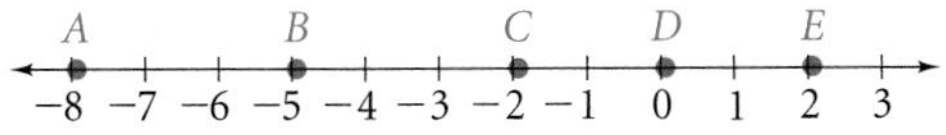

Additional Examples

FOR EXAMPLE 1

Find BC if the coordinate of B is -12 and the coordinate of C is -5. **7**

Discussion: *How can you check your answer?*

FOR EXAMPLE 2

Refer to the diagram in Example 2. If $DT = 85$, find the value of x. Then find DS and ST. **$x = 21$, $DS = 34$, $ST = 51$**

Discussion: *What postulate do you use to solve this problem?*

Example 2

This problem is solved in two steps: finding the value of x and then evaluating the expressions for DS and ST.

Question 11 When naming angles with three letters, the vertex should be the middle letter. For example $\angle COD$ and $\angle DOC$ describe the same angle but $\angle DCO$ does not.

ERROR ALERT! Students whose experiences with measurement have been primarily measuring distances might assume that the measure of an angle is related to the "lengths" of the rays drawn. **Remediation:** Reinforce that the measure of an angle measures the opening of the angle. Also remind students that the rays drawn are just representations and that rays extend infinitely in one direction.

Technology Options

For Exercise 21, students may draw and measure angles using geometry software. For Exercise 30, students may replicate the activity using geometry software.

Prentice Hall Technology 

Software
- Secondary Math Lab Toolkit™
- Integrated Math Lab 23
- Computer Item Generator 1-4

CD-ROM
- Multimedia Geometry Lab 1

Internet
- See the Prentice Hall site. (http://www.phschool.com)

Postulate 1-6
Segment Addition Postulate

If three points A, B, and C are collinear and B is between A and C, then $AB + BC = AC$.

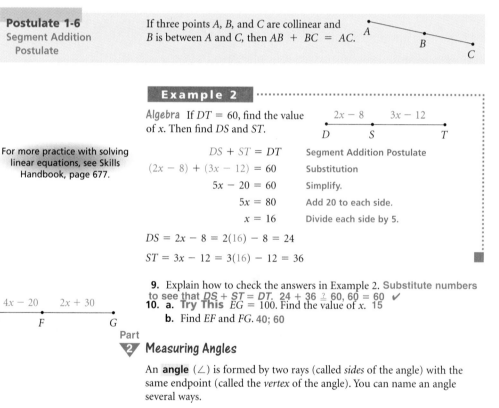

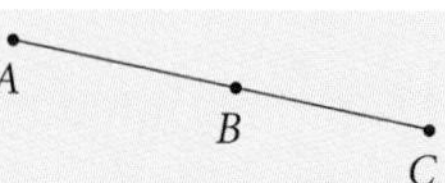

Example 2

Algebra If $DT = 60$, find the value of x. Then find DS and ST.

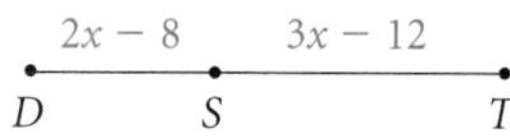

For more practice with solving linear equations, see Skills Handbook, page 677.

$DS + ST = DT$	Segment Addition Postulate
$(2x - 8) + (3x - 12) = 60$	Substitution
$5x - 20 = 60$	Simplify.
$5x = 80$	Add 20 to each side.
$x = 16$	Divide each side by 5.

$DS = 2x - 8 = 2(16) - 8 = 24$

$ST = 3x - 12 = 3(16) - 12 = 36$

9. Explain how to check the answers in Example 2. **Substitute numbers to see that $DS + ST = DT$. $24 + 36 \stackrel{?}{=} 60$, $60 = 60$ ✓**

10. a. **Try This** $EG = 100$. Find the value of x. **15**
    b. Find EF and FG. **40; 60**

Part 2

Measuring Angles

An **angle** ($\angle$) is formed by two rays (called *sides* of the angle) with the same endpoint (called the *vertex* of the angle). You can name an angle several ways.

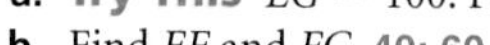

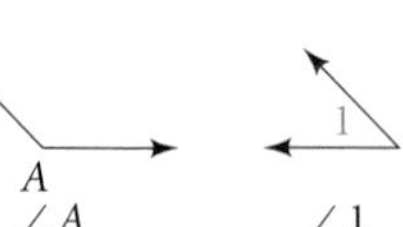

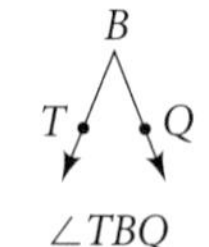

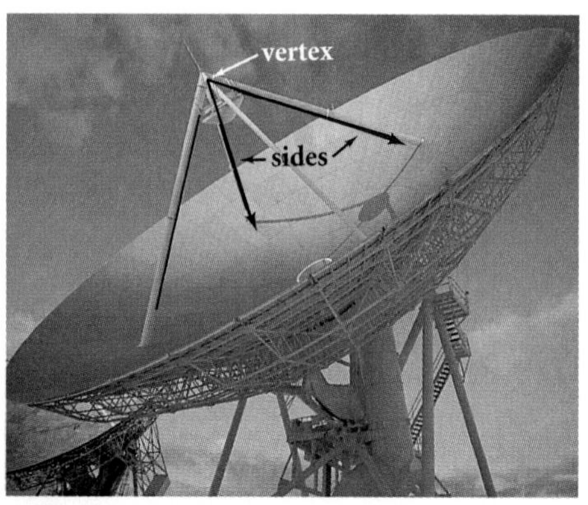

11. a. Name $\angle 1$ two other ways. **$\angle AEC$, $\angle CEA$**
    b. Name $\angle CED$ two other ways.
    c. Would it be correct to refer to any of the angles at the right as $\angle E$? Why or why not?

    A, C, 1, 2, E, D

    b. $\angle 2$, $\angle DEC$
    c. No; there are 3 angles shown with E as their vertex.

Angles are measured in *degrees*. The *measure* of $\angle A$ is written as $m\angle A$.

$m\angle A = 80$

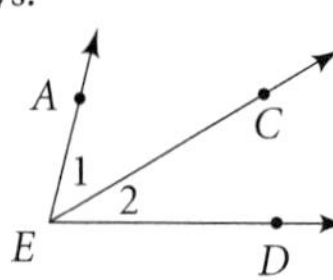

AUDITORY LEARNING Protractor Postulate Have students take turns with a partner explaining the postulate in their own words.

DIVERSITY Students with fine motor difficulties may have problems using a protractor. You may want to have students work in pairs so they can assist each other as needed.

Question 12 Some students may lack experience with protractors. Demonstrate how to line up a protractor with a ray and how to choose the appropriate scale. One tip to give students is to choose the scale for which one of the sides passes through zero. Another is to visually estimate whether the angle is acute or obtuse and use the corresponding scale.

When you use a *protractor* to measure angles you are applying the following postulate.

Postulate 1-7
Protractor Postulate

Let $\overrightarrow{OA}$ and $\overrightarrow{OB}$ be opposite rays in a plane. $\overrightarrow{OA}$, $\overrightarrow{OB}$ and all the rays with endpoint O that can be drawn on one side of $\overleftrightarrow{AB}$ can be paired with the real numbers from 0 to 180 in such a way that:

a. $\overrightarrow{OA}$ is paired with 0 and $\overrightarrow{OB}$ is paired with 180.

b. If $\overrightarrow{OC}$ is paired with x and $\overrightarrow{OD}$ is paired with y, then $m\angle COD = |x - y|$.

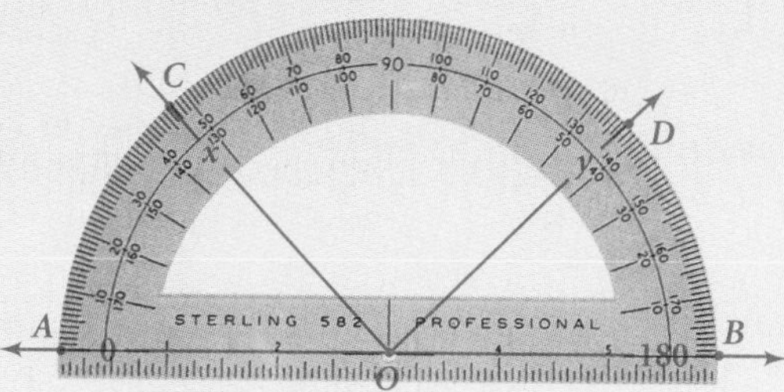

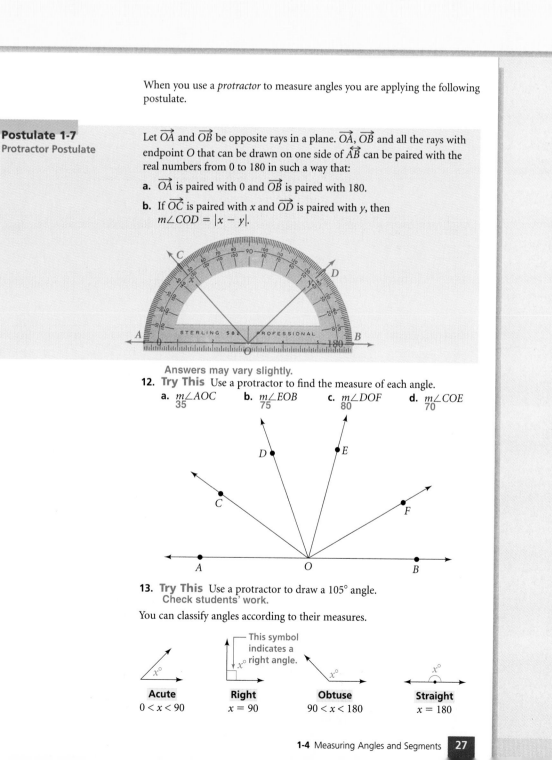

Answers may vary slightly.

12. Try This Use a protractor to find the measure of each angle.

a. $m\angle AOC$ 35 **b.** $m\angle EOB$ 75 **c.** $m\angle DOF$ 80 **d.** $m\angle COE$ 70

13. Try This Use a protractor to draw a 105° angle.
Check students' work.

You can classify angles according to their measures.

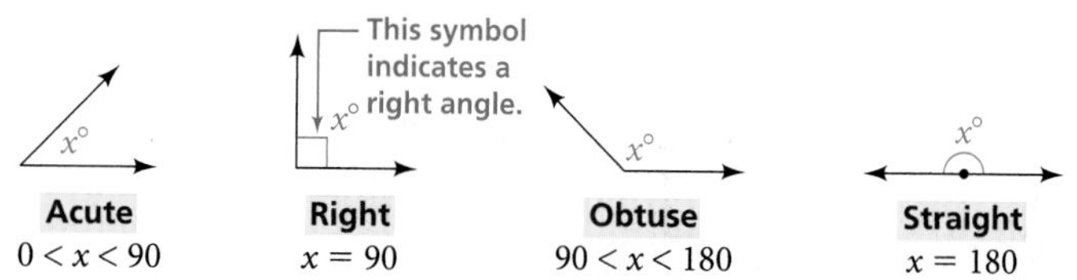

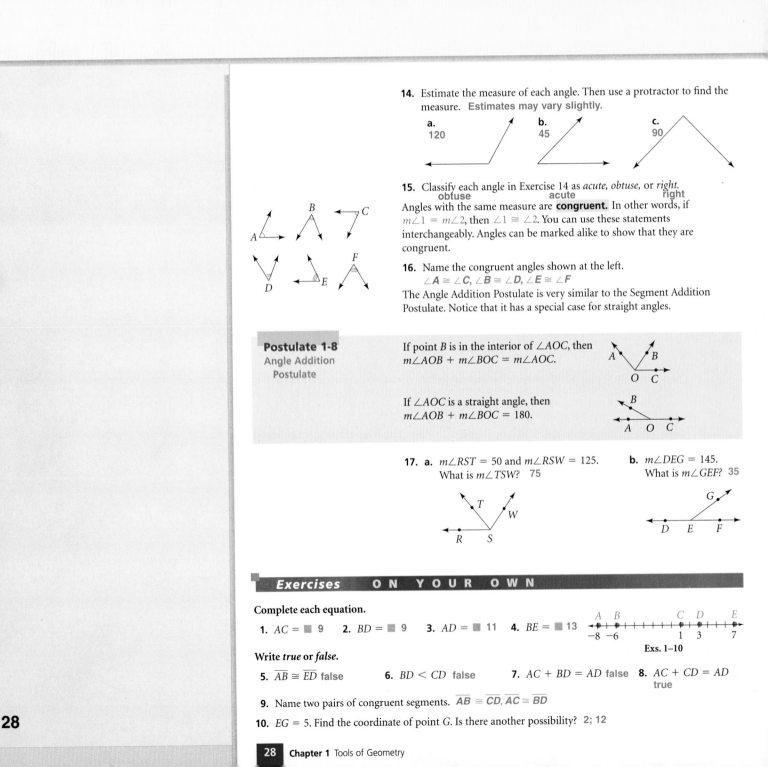

ESTIMATION Question 14 Students can use a corner of a piece of paper (90° angle) to help them estimate the measure of an angle. When students measure the angles with a protractor, allow up to about 2° of variation.

Angle Addition Postulate A point is in the interior of an angle if it does not lie on the sides of the angle and lies on a segment whose endpoints are on the sides of the angle. Since a straight angle has no interior, the angle addition postulate for straight angles is stated separately.

Exercises ON YOUR OWN

Exercises 1–4 Students may want to copy the number line and fill in the other coordinates along the scale. These problems can be completed by counting the units between the numbers on the number line or by taking the absolute value of the difference between the coordinates of the endpoints.

14. Estimate the measure of each angle. Then use a protractor to find the measure. Estimates may vary slightly.

a. 120 b. 45 c. 90

15. Classify each angle in Exercise 14 as *acute, obtuse,* or *right.* obtuse acute right

Angles with the same measure are **congruent.** In other words, if $m\angle 1 = m\angle 2$, then $\angle 1 \cong \angle 2$. You can use these statements interchangeably. Angles can be marked alike to show that they are congruent.

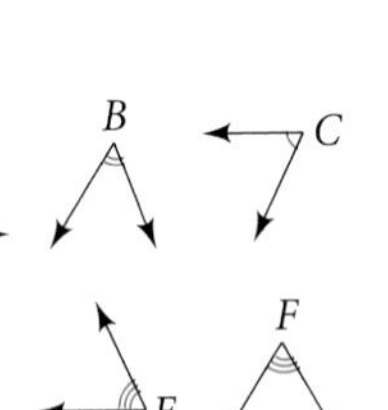

16. Name the congruent angles shown at the left.
$\angle A \cong \angle C$, $\angle B \cong \angle D$, $\angle E \cong \angle F$

The Angle Addition Postulate is very similar to the Segment Addition Postulate. Notice that it has a special case for straight angles.

Postulate 1-8
Angle Addition Postulate

If point B is in the interior of $\angle AOC$, then $m\angle AOB + m\angle BOC = m\angle AOC$.

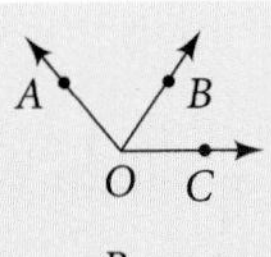

If $\angle AOC$ is a straight angle, then $m\angle AOB + m\angle BOC = 180$.

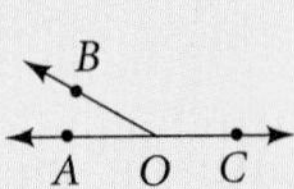

17. a. $m\angle RST = 50$ and $m\angle RSW = 125$. What is $m\angle TSW$? 75

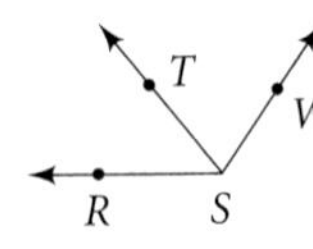

b. $m\angle DEG = 145$. What is $m\angle GEF$? 35

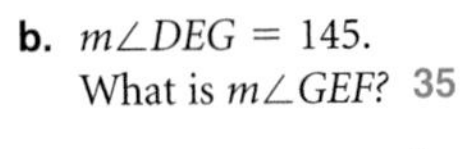

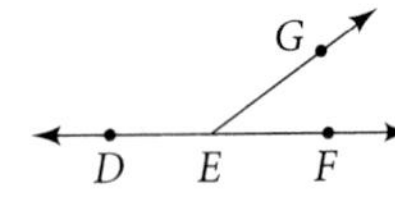

Exercises ON YOUR OWN

Complete each equation.

1. $AC =$ ■ 9 **2.** $BD =$ ■ 9 **3.** $AD =$ ■ 11 **4.** $BE =$ ■ 13

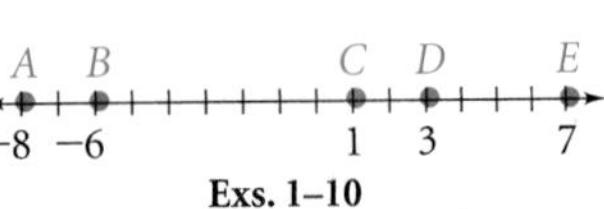

Exs. 1–10

Write *true* or *false*.

5. $\overline{AB} \cong \overline{ED}$ false **6.** $BD < CD$ false **7.** $AC + BD = AD$ false **8.** $AC + CD = AD$ true

9. Name two pairs of congruent segments. $\overline{AB} \cong \overline{CD}$, $\overline{AC} \cong \overline{BD}$

10. $EG = 5$. Find the coordinate of point G. Is there another possibility? 2; 12

ALTERNATIVE ASSESSMENT **Exercises 11–12, 15–16** These exercises help you assess students' understanding of the Segment Addition Postulate and both cases of the Angle Addition Postulate. Have students compare answers with partners.

ALGEBRA Exercises 13–14 Some students will stop after they find the value of *x*. Remind them to find the values of *RS* and *ST*.

CONNECTING TO STUDENTS' WORLD Exercise 17 Have students write their first names using block letters. Then have them count the number of acute, right, and obtuse angles suggested by the letters.

ESL Exercises 20 and 26 Reinforce the meanings of the new vocabulary taught in this lesson as well as the English words that may be unfamiliar such as *ski-jumping*, *billiards*, and *shot*. You may want to have students work with partners to discuss unfamiliar terms.

EXTENSION Exercise 24 Have students graph all possible locations of point *B*.

Use the figure at the right for Exercises 11–14.

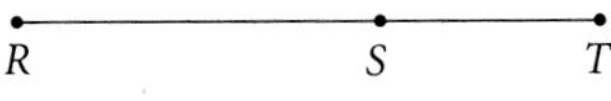

11. If $RS = 15$ and $ST = 9$, then $RT = \blacksquare$. 24
12. If $ST = 15$ and $RT = 40$, then $RS = \blacksquare$. 25
13. Algebra If $RS = 3x + 1$, $ST = 2x - 2$, and $RT = 64$, find the value of x. Then find RS and ST. 13; 40; 24
14. Algebra If $RS = 8y + 4$, $ST = 4y + 8$, and $RT = 15y - 9$, find the value of y. Then find RS and ST. 7; 60; 36

Use the figure at the right for Exercises 15–17.

Q P V M N

15. If $m\angle MQV = 90$ and $m\angle VQP = 35$, what is $m\angle MQP$? 125
16. If $m\angle MVQ = 55$, what is $m\angle QVP$? 125
17. Judging by appearance, name each of the following. Answers may vary. Samples:
    a. two acute angles $\angle QVM$, $\angle PVN$
    b. two obtuse angles $\angle QVP$, $\angle MVN$
    c. two right angles $\angle MQV$, $\angle QNP$
18. Without using your protractor, sketch angles with the following measures. Then use your protractor to see how close you are.
    a. 30 b. 60 c. 120
    Check students' work.
19. Open-ended The mileage markers on highways are an example of a numbering system that resembles a number line. Give another example. Answers may vary. Sample: tape measure

20. Ski Jumping This ski jumper is using a new style of jumping. The skis are at an angle rather than parallel. Measure the angle formed by the two skis. about 43°

Estimation **Estimate the measure of each angle. Then use a protractor to measure it. Classify each angle.** 21–23. Estimates may vary slightly.

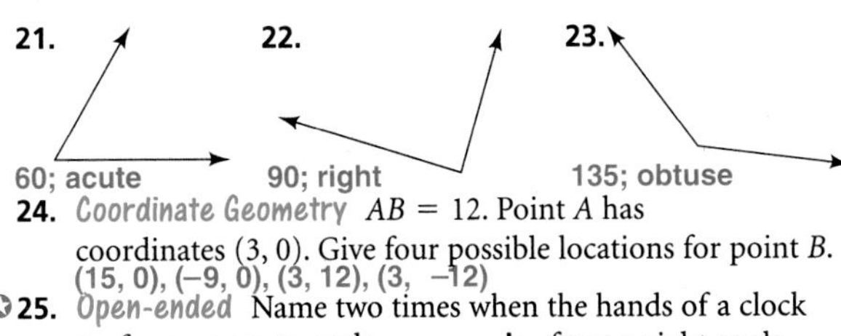

21. 60; acute 22. 90; right 23. 135; obtuse

24. Coordinate Geometry $AB = 12$. Point A has coordinates (3, 0). Give four possible locations for point B. (15, 0), (−9, 0), (3, 12), (3, −12)
25. Open-ended Name two times when the hands of a clock
    a. form an acute angle. b. form a right angle.
    c. form an obtuse angle. d. form a straight angle.
    Answers may vary. Sample: a. 1:00, 2:00 b. 3:00, 9:00
26. Billiards In billiards, the cue ball may bounce off a cushion on any shot. If there is no spin on the shot, $\angle 1$ and $\angle 2$ will be congruent. Find the measures of $\angle 1$ and $\angle 2$. 30; 30

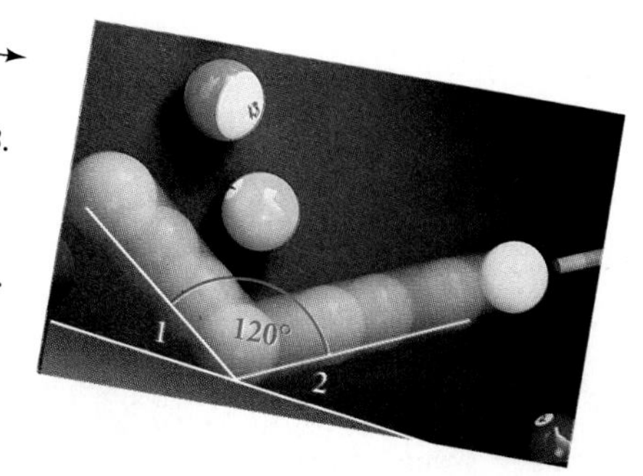

25c. 4:00, 5:00 d. 6:00, about 9:16

WRITING Exercise 29 Have students give examples of how the word *acute* is used in nonmathematical sentences.

DIVERSITY Exercise 36 You may want to allow discussion of popular art forms in different cultures. Invite students to bring in samples of such art and create a display in the classroom.

Chapter Project **FIND OUT BY RESEARCHING** Refer students to Finishing the Chapter Project on page 58 for a list of possible sources.

Exercises MIXED REVIEW

Exercises 37–39 Students use inductive reasoning to determine terms in patterns.

Exercises 40–43 Students review the meanings of the terms *point, line,* and *plane.*

GETTING READY FOR LESSON 1-5 These exercises prepare students for drawing perpendicular lines and angle bisectors.

Checkpoint page 31

4. (1) Each term is 2.5 greater than the preceding term.
(2) Each term is the same as the preceding term with the next consecutive digit added at the end.
(3) Each term is −3 times the preceding term.

27. Algebra If $AD = 12$ and $AC = 4y - 36$, find the value of y. 15

28. Algebra If $ED = x + 4$ and $DB = 3x - 8$, find EB. 20

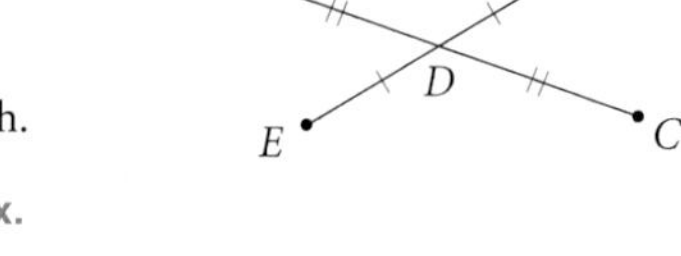

29. Writing The word "acute" can mean *sharp* in conversational English. Explain why this meaning describes an acute angle.
The two rays come together to form a sharp point at the vertex.

30. Technology Leon constructed an angle. Then he constructed a ray from the vertex of the angle to a point in the interior of the angle. He measured all the angles formed. Then he moved the interior ray.

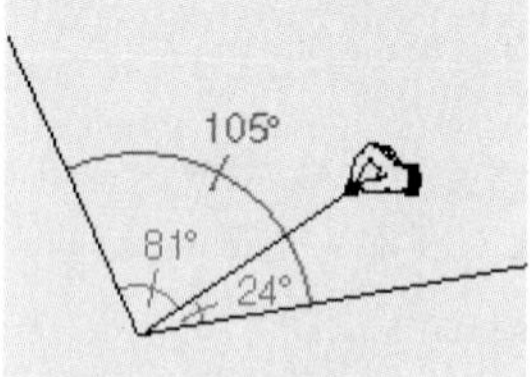

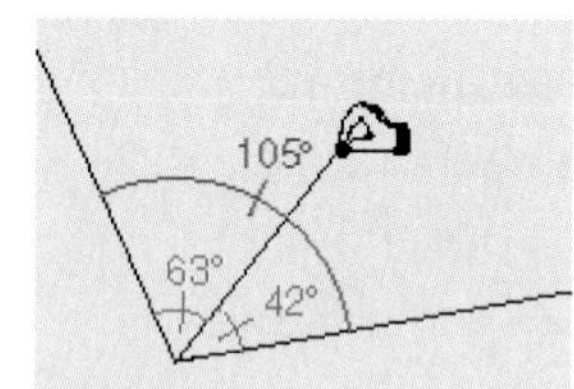

a. The sum of the measures of the 2 smaller angles remains 105.

a. Patterns What patterns do you observe? See above right.
b. What postulate does this support? Angle Addition Postulate

31. Golf Fun Copy the diagram. (1) Estimate the distance in centimeters from the tee to the hole. Estimate the angle in degrees from the tee to the hole. (2) Use a ruler and protractor to plot your estimate. This is stroke 1. Add a penalty stroke if you land in the sand or the water. (3) Continue until you are at most 0.5 cm from the hole marked by the flag. What was your score? Check students' work.

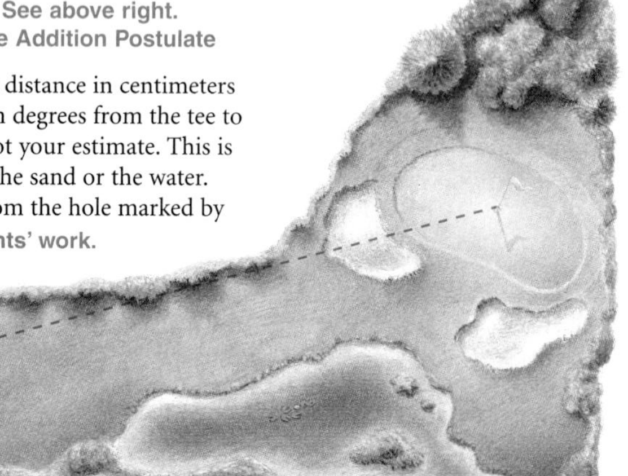

Algebra **Solve for *x*.**

32. $m\angle AOC = 7x - 2$, $m\angle AOB = 2x + 8$, $m\angle BOC = 3x + 14$ 12

33. $m\angle AOB = 4x - 2$, $m\angle BOC = 5x + 10$, $m\angle COD = 2x + 14$ 8

34. $m\angle AOB = 28$, $m\angle BOC = 3x - 2$, $m\angle AOD = 6x$ 18

35. $m\angle AOB = 4x + 3$, $m\angle BOC = 7x$, $m\angle AOD = 16x - 1$ 7

36. Decorating Japanese flower arranging makes precise use of angles to create a mood. A vertical stem is matched with 0. Other stems are matched with numbers from 0 to 90 in both directions from the vertical. What numbers would the flowers shown be paired with on a standard protractor?
45 or 135; 75 or 105; 15 or 165

Wrap Up

THE BIG IDEA Ask students: *Summarize the Ruler Postulate and the Protractor Postulate in your own words.*

RETEACHING ACTIVITY Students measure and classify angles found on a five-pointed star. (Reteaching worksheet 1-4)

Exercises CHECKPOINT

In this Checkpoint, your students will assess their own progress on Lessons 1-1 to 1-4.

Exercise 14 Make sure students use three letters to name the angles.

Chapter Project **Find Out by Researching**

Choose one of the origami creations pictured on pages 2 and 3. Find a book that contains directions for making the figure, and follow the directions to make your favorite origami creation.

Exercises MIXED REVIEW

Find the next term in each sequence.

37. 5, 10, 15, 20, ... 25 **38.** 5, 25, 125, 625, ... 3,125 **39.** 14, 18, 22, 26, ... 30

Complete each statement.

40. Three points are always __?__. coplanar

41. Intersecting lines are always __?__. coplanar

42. Two intersecting planes intersect in a __?__. line

43. Two points are always __?__. collinear

44. A 24-cm segment is divided into two segments. One segment is three times as long as the other. Find the lengths of both segments. 6 cm and 18 cm

Getting Ready for Lesson 1-5

Sketch each figure.

45. $\overline{CD}$ **46.** $\overrightarrow{GH}$ **47.** $\overleftrightarrow{AB}$ **48.** line m

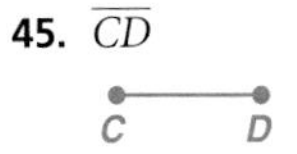

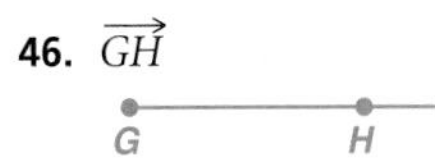

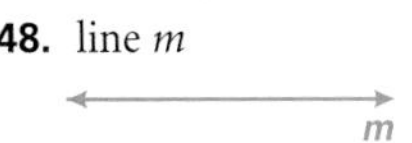

Exercises CHECKPOINT

Find the next two terms in each sequence.

1. 19, 21.5, 24, 26.5, ... 29, 31.5 **2.** 3.4, 3.45, 3.456, 3.4567, ... 3.45678, 3.456789 **3.** −2, 6, −18, 54, ... −162, 486

4. **Writing** Describe the pattern of the sequences in Exercises 1–3. See margin p. 30.

Are the following coplanar?

5. *A, E, F, B* yes **6.** *F, C, B, H* no **7.** $\overleftrightarrow{DC}$, point *E* yes **8.** *D, G, B* yes **9.** $\overleftrightarrow{GC}$, $\overleftrightarrow{BC}$ yes

10. What is the intersection of plane *EFGH* and $\overleftrightarrow{DH}$? *H*

11. Name all the segments parallel to $\overline{HG}$. $\overline{DC}$, $\overline{EF}$, $\overline{AB}$

12. Name two skew lines. Sample: $\overleftrightarrow{AB}$ and $\overleftrightarrow{EH}$

13. Name two parallel planes. Sample: plane *ABFE* ∥ plane *DCGH* or plane *HEFG* ∥ plane *ABCD*

14. Name an acute, an obtuse, and a right angle. Sample: ∠*EAB*; ∠*AEF*; ∠*EHG*

15. **Algebra** If $AB = 4x + 5$ and $DC = 3x + 8$, find AB. 17

Exs. 5–15

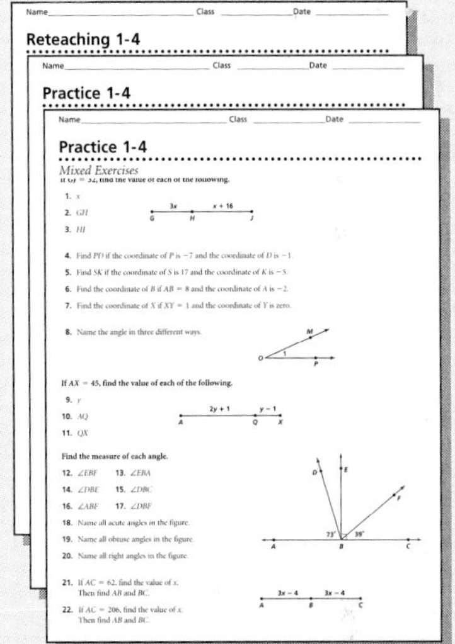
Reteaching 1-4

Practice 1-4

Practice 1-4
Mixed Exercises

Lesson Quiz

Lesson Quiz is also available in Transparencies.

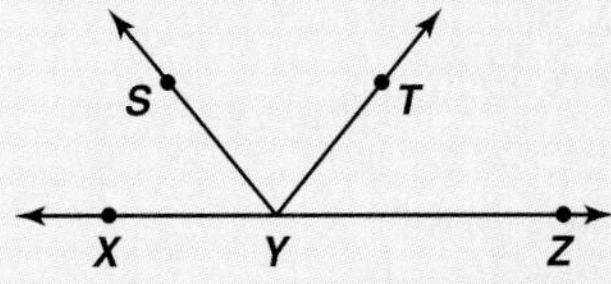

1. If $XY = 7$ and $XZ = 19$, then find YZ. 12

2. If $m\angle XYS = 50$ and $m\angle XYT = 130$, find $m\angle SYT$. 80

3. Name an acute angle. ∠*XYS*, ∠*SYT*, or ∠*TYZ*

4. Use a protractor to draw an obtuse angle. Label its measure. Answers will vary. Sample:

1-5 Teaching Notes

PROBLEM OF THE DAY

How many times do the hands of a clock cross in 12 hours? 12

Problem of the Day is also available in Transparencies.

CONNECTING TO PRIOR KNOWLEDGE Ask students to share experiences about using directions to assemble something or following instructions for a recipe. Ask them what was most important about how the directions were written.

WORK TOGETHER

Question 2 Students should describe what a polyglob *is* and not what it *is not.*

EXTENSION Questions 1–2 Have students think of an object and a name for the object, and then draw pictures of what the object is and what it is not. The pictures should be almost alike. State the name and have other students come up with the definition.

Lesson Planning Options

Prerequisite Skills

- Solving one-variable equations
- Graphing on number lines and coordinate planes

Assignment Options for Exercises On Your Own

To provide flexible scheduling, this lesson can be subdivided into parts.

Core 1–8, 29–40
Extension 44

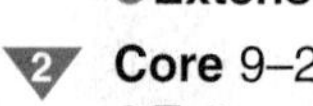
Core 9–28, 45–54
Extension 41–43, 55

Use Mixed Review to maintain skills.

Resources

Student Edition

Skills Handbook, pp. 677, 679
Extra Practice, p. 648
Glossary/Study Guide

Teaching Resources

Chapter Support File, Ch. 1
- Practice 1-5 (two worksheets)
- Reteaching 1-5
- Alternative Activity 1-5

Classroom Manager 1-5
Glossary, Spanish Resources

Transparencies
24, 29

Connections  Language Arts . . . and more

1-5 Good Definitions

What You'll Learn
- Identifying a good definition
- Understanding the meaning of terms like *bisector* and *perpendicular*

...And Why

To sharpen a skill that is a key to communicating

WORK TOGETHER

Work with a partner to identify what makes a figure a *polyglob.*

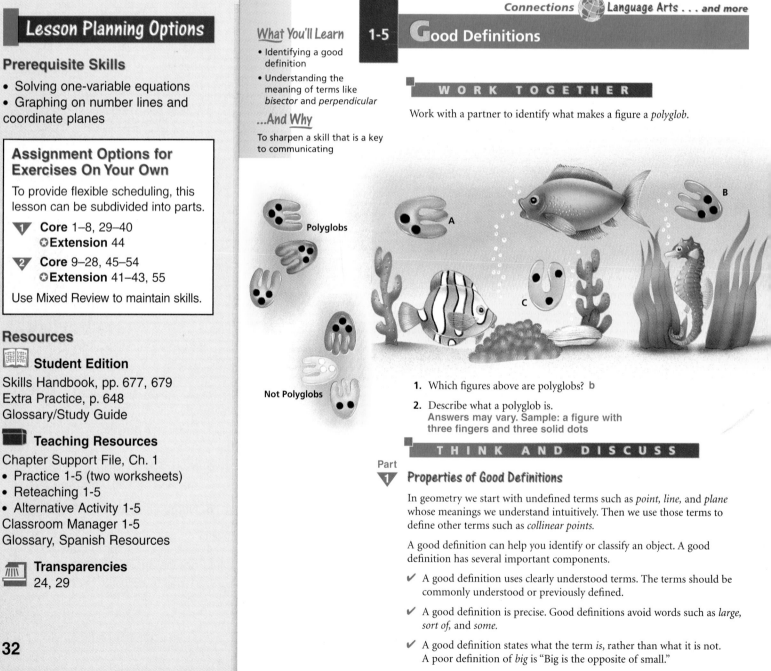

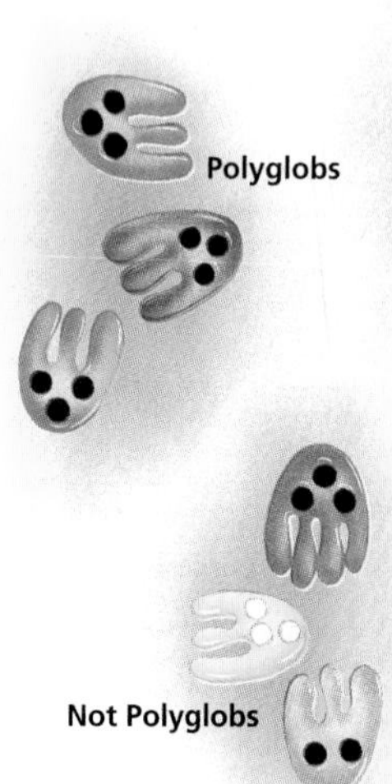

1. Which figures above are polyglobs? b
2. Describe what a polyglob is.
   Answers may vary. Sample: a figure with three fingers and three solid dots

THINK AND DISCUSS

Part 1

Properties of Good Definitions

In geometry we start with undefined terms such as *point, line,* and *plane* whose meanings we understand intuitively. Then we use those terms to define other terms such as *collinear points.*

A good definition can help you identify or classify an object. A good definition has several important components.

✔ A good definition uses clearly understood terms. The terms should be commonly understood or previously defined.

✔ A good definition is precise. Good definitions avoid words such as *large, sort of,* and *some.*

✔ A good definition states what the term *is,* rather than what it is not. A poor definition of *big* is "Big is the opposite of small."

THINK AND DISCUSS

The geometry we are studying is called Euclidean geometry. There are other types of geometry that establish relationships among points, lines, and planes differently. For example, in spherical geometry, a "point" is a point on a sphere while a "line" is a great circle (the circle formed when a plane intersects a sphere through its center).

MAKING CONNECTIONS The earliest examples of dictionaries are from classical Greece, many being glossaries of difficult terms in Homer's poems. The first general dictionary was compiled by Marcus Verrius Flaccus about 20 B.C.

Example 1 Relating to the Real World 

Point out to students that while a counterexample can show a definition is wrong, an example cannot show that a definition is acceptable.

Question 6 Check that students recognize that a segment bisector can be a ray, line, or line segment of any length that intersects the given segment at its midpoint.

A **midpoint** of a segment is a point that divides a segment into two congruent segments.

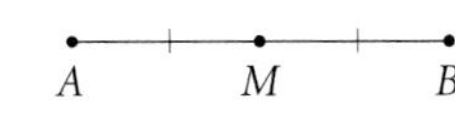

3. What previously defined terms are used in the definition of *midpoint?* segment, congruent

A good definition is *reversible.*

If $\overline{AM} \cong \overline{MB}$, then M is the midpoint of $\overline{AB}$.

If N is the midpoint of $\overline{CD}$, then $\overline{CN} \cong \overline{ND}$.

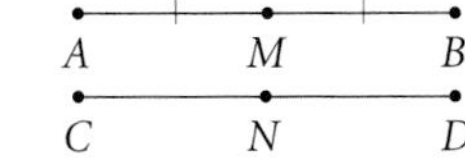

QUICK REVIEW

A right angle is an angle whose measure is 90.

4. a. If $\angle A$ is a right angle, what is the measure of $\angle A$? 90
   b. If $m\angle B = 90$, classify $\angle B$. $\angle B$ is a right angle.

Notice that you can use the definition of a right angle to justify your answer to each part of question 4.

One way to test a definition is to look for a *counterexample* that shows that the definition is wrong.

Example 1 Relating to the Real World 

Language Arts Is the following an acceptable definition? Explain.

An airplane is a vehicle that flies.

The definition is not acceptable because a helicopter is also a vehicle that flies, and a helicopter is not an airplane.

5. **Try This** Is the following an acceptable definition? Explain.

   A square is a figure with four right angles.
   No; a figure with four right angles may be a rectangle that is not a square.

Part 2 Bisectors

6. Answers may vary. Sample a segment bisector is a line, segment, or ray that intersects the midpoint of a given segment.

6. Study the diagrams below and write a definition of a *segment bisector.*

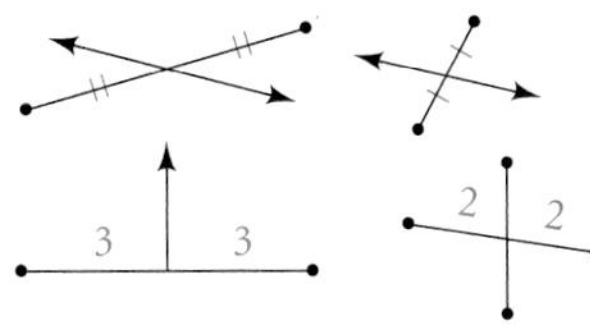

Segment bisectors

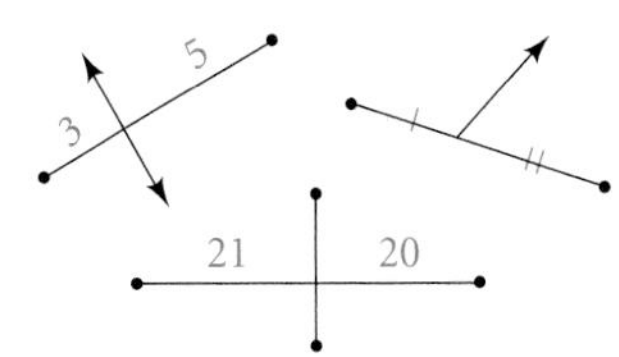

Not segment bisectors

Perpendicular lines are two lines that intersect to form right angles. The symbol $\perp$ is read as "is perpendicular to." In the diagram at the right, $\overleftrightarrow{AB} \perp \overleftrightarrow{CD}$.

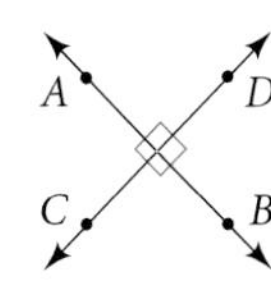

Additional Examples

FOR EXAMPLE 1

Explain why the following statement is or is not acceptable as a definition. Soccer is a game played with a ball.
No; there are many games played with a ball.

Discussion: *How can you make this definition acceptable?*

FOR EXAMPLE 2

Refer to the diagram in Example 2.
$\overrightarrow{KN}$ bisects $\angle JKL$. $m\angle JKN = 4x + 7$ and $m\angle NKL = 5x - 5$.
Solve for x and find $m\angle JKN$.
$x = 12$, $m\angle JKN = 55$

Discussion: *What definition are you using to solve this problem?*

ERROR ALERT! Question 7b Because $\overleftrightarrow{EA}$ appears horizontal and $\overleftrightarrow{CG}$ appears vertical, students may quickly respond that $\overleftrightarrow{CG}$ is perpendicular to $\overleftrightarrow{EA}$. **Remediation:** Have students find the measures of the angles formed by these intersecting lines.

Example 2

Help students recognize that they can find without evaluating $3x + 5$. Since $\overrightarrow{KN}$ bisects $\angle JKL$, $m\angle NKL = m\angle JKN = 50$. However, finding $m\angle NKL$ will serve as a check of their work.

Question 10 You may want to have students model the solution from Example 2 and justify each step. Check that when students write the equation, they do not use the degree symbol shown in the diagram.

Exercises ON YOUR OWN

Exercise 1 Have students use the illustrations to define *monopar*. Then have them compare their definitions.

Exercises 8 and 13 Check that students use the correct symbols for segments and angles and not the symbols for length and angle measure.

Technology Options

For Exercises 23–28, students may draw the figures using geometry software.

Prentice Hall Technology 

Software
- Secondary Math Lab Toolkit™
- Computer Item Generator 1-5

Internet
- See the Prentice Hall site. (http://www.phschool.com)

A $5 bill was folded in half. *How does the fold line meet the top step of the Lincoln Memorial?*

It is the ⊥ bisector of the step.

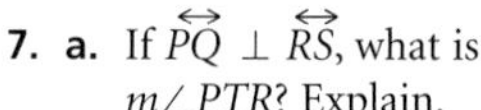

7. a. If $\overleftrightarrow{PQ} \perp \overleftrightarrow{RS}$, what is $m\angle PTR$? Explain.

   b. Which lines, if any, are perpendicular? Explain.

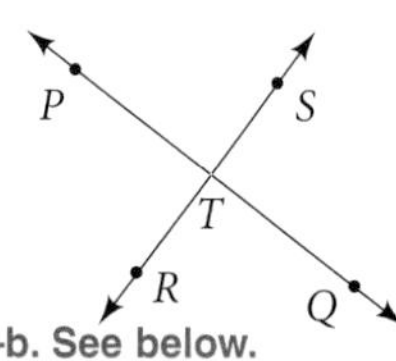

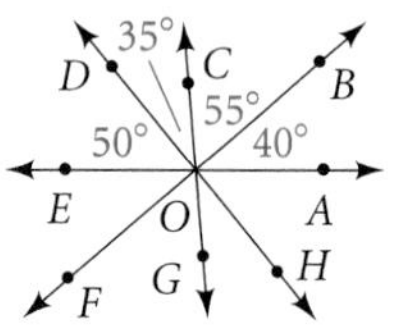

a–b. See below.

A **perpendicular bisector** of a segment is a line, segment, or ray that is perpendicular to a segment at its midpoint.

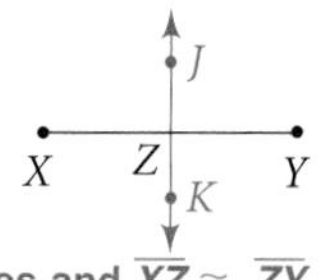

8. If you know that $\overleftrightarrow{JK}$ is the perpendicular bisector of $\overline{XY}$, what can you conclude about angles and segments in the diagram? **$\angle XZJ$, $\angle KZY$, $\angle YZJ$, and $\angle XZK$ are right angles and $\overline{XZ} \cong \overline{ZY}$.**

An **angle bisector** is a ray that divides an angle into two congruent angles.

9. a. **Given:** $\overrightarrow{CD}$ bisects $\angle ACB$. Name the congruent angles.

   b. **Given:** $\angle RSW \cong \angle WST$ What can you conclude?

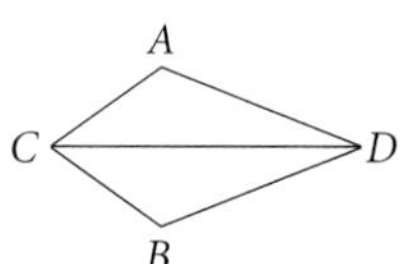

$\angle ACD \cong \angle DCB$

$\overrightarrow{SW}$ bisects $\angle RST$.

Example 2

$\overrightarrow{KN}$ bisects $\angle JKL$.
$m\angle JKN = 5x - 25$
$m\angle NKL = 3x + 5$
Solve for x and find $m\angle JKN$.

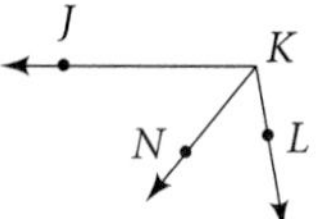

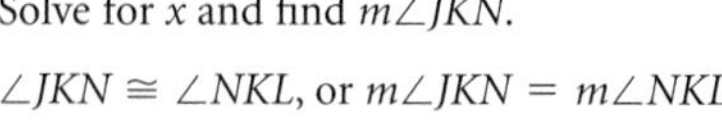

$\angle JKN \cong \angle NKL$, or $m\angle JKN = m\angle NKL$	Def. of $\angle$ bisector
$5x - 25 = 3x + 5$	Substitution
$5x - 25 + 25 = 3x + 5 + 25$	Add 25 to each side.
$5x = 3x + 30$	Simplify.
$5x - 3x = 3x - 3x + 30$	Subtract $3x$ from each side.
$2x = 30$	Simplify.
$x = 15$	Divide each side by 2.
$m\angle JKN = 5(15) - 25 = 50$	Substitute 15 for x.

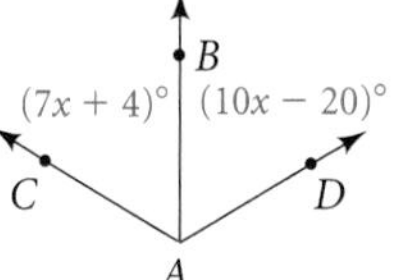

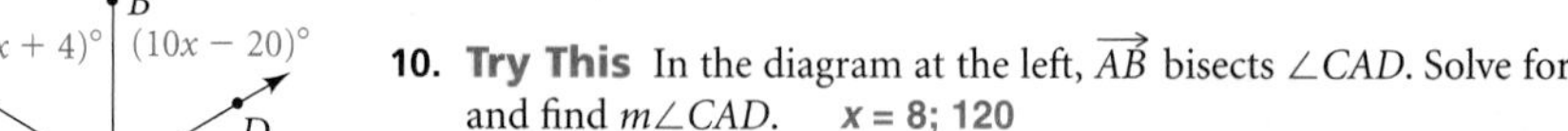

10. **Try This** In the diagram at the left, $\overrightarrow{AB}$ bisects $\angle CAD$. Solve for x and find $m\angle CAD$. **x = 8; 120**

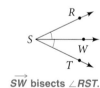

7 a. 90. Perpendicular lines form right angles, which measure 90.
b. $\overleftrightarrow{DH} \perp \overleftrightarrow{FB}$. By the Angle Addition Postulate, $m\angle DOB = 90$; then by definition, $\overleftrightarrow{DH} \perp \overleftrightarrow{FB}$.

ALTERNATIVE ASSESSMENT **Exercises 15–22** Selections of these exercises can be used to assess students' understanding of bisectors and perpendicular lines. Ask students to justify their answers by using definitions.

Exercises 23–28 Students should fold paper or use a protractor and ruler to draw each figure accurately.

Exercises 29–33 Students may want to copy the number line onto graph paper to more easily "see" the distance between the points.

Exercise 34 Have students define *vertical angles* from the illustrations. Then have them check their definitions with the one given in the Glossary.

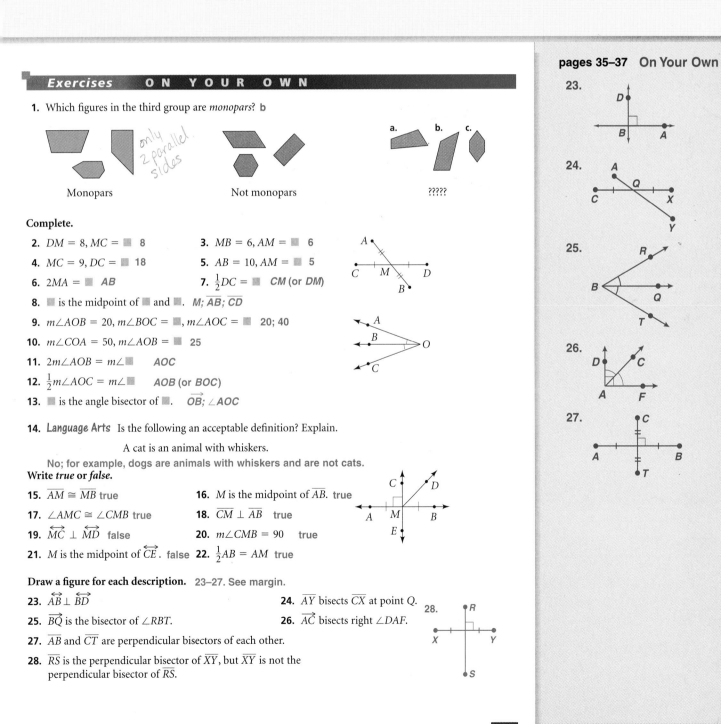

Exercises ON YOUR OWN

1. Which figures in the third group are *monopars*? b

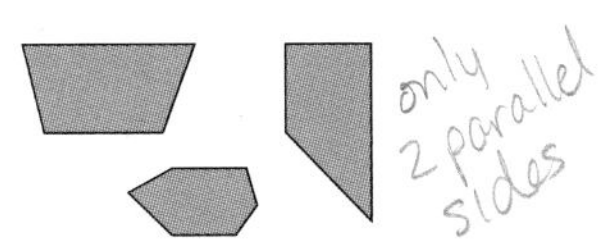

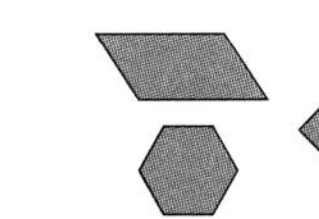

Monopars

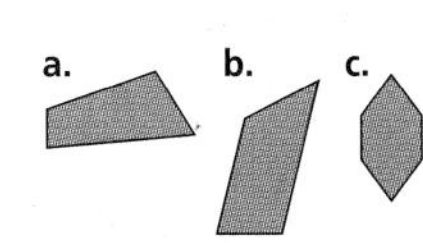

Not monopars

a. b. c.

?????

Complete.

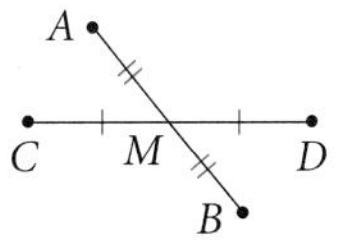

2. $DM = 8, MC =$ ■ 8
3. $MB = 6, AM =$ ■ 6
4. $MC = 9, DC =$ ■ 18
5. $AB = 10, AM =$ ■ 5
6. $2MA =$ ■ *AB*
7. $\frac{1}{2}DC =$ ■ *CM* (or *DM*)

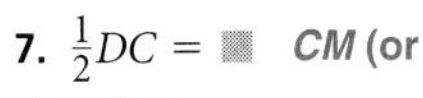

8. ■ is the midpoint of ■ and ■. *M*; $\overline{AB}$; $\overline{CD}$

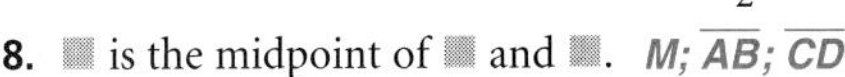

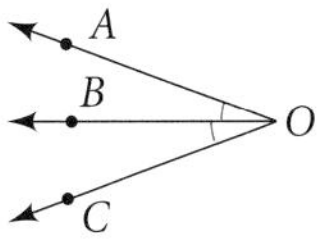

9. $m\angle AOB = 20, m\angle BOC =$ ■, $m\angle AOC =$ ■ 20; 40
10. $m\angle COA = 50, m\angle AOB =$ ■ 25
11. $2m\angle AOB = m\angle$■ *AOC*
12. $\frac{1}{2}m\angle AOC = m\angle$■ *AOB* (or *BOC*)
13. ■ is the angle bisector of ■. $\overrightarrow{OB}$; $\angle AOC$

14. **Language Arts** Is the following an acceptable definition? Explain.

A cat is an animal with whiskers.

No; for example, dogs are animals with whiskers and are not cats.

Write *true* or *false*.

15. $\overline{AM} \cong \overline{MB}$ true
16. *M* is the midpoint of $\overline{AB}$. true
17. $\angle AMC \cong \angle CMB$ true
18. $\overline{CM} \perp \overline{AB}$ true

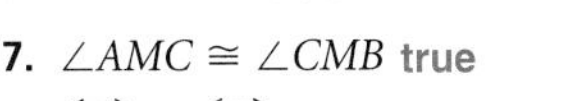

19. $\overleftrightarrow{MC} \perp \overleftrightarrow{MD}$ false
20. $m\angle CMB = 90$ true

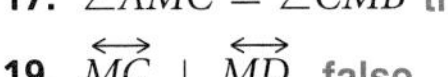

21. *M* is the midpoint of $\overleftrightarrow{CE}$. false
22. $\frac{1}{2}AB = AM$ true

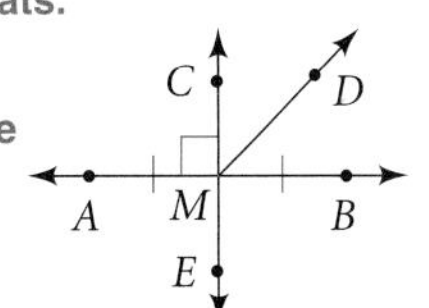

Draw a figure for each description. 23–27. See margin.

23. $\overleftrightarrow{AB} \perp \overleftrightarrow{BD}$
24. $\overline{AY}$ bisects $\overline{CX}$ at point *Q*.
25. $\overrightarrow{BQ}$ is the bisector of $\angle RBT$.
26. $\overrightarrow{AC}$ bisects right $\angle DAF$.

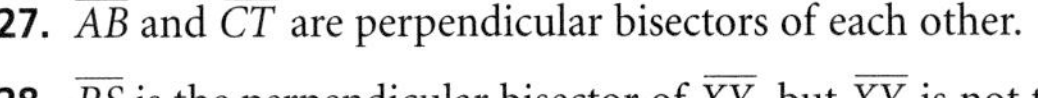

27. $\overline{AB}$ and $\overline{CT}$ are perpendicular bisectors of each other.
28. $\overline{RS}$ is the perpendicular bisector of $\overline{XY}$, but $\overline{XY}$ is not the perpendicular bisector of $\overline{RS}$.

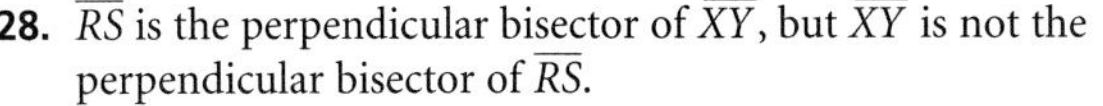

28.

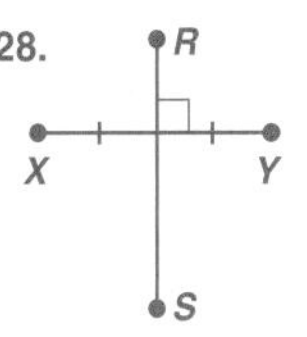

pages 35–37 On Your Own

23.

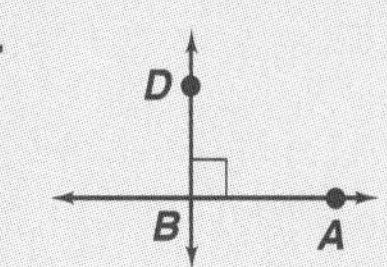

24.

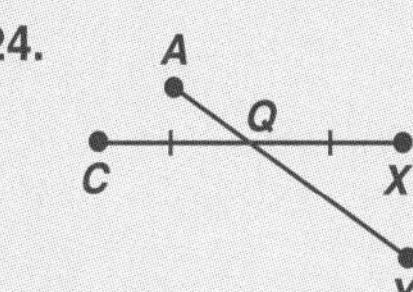

25.

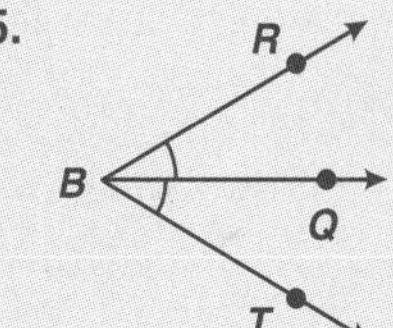

26.

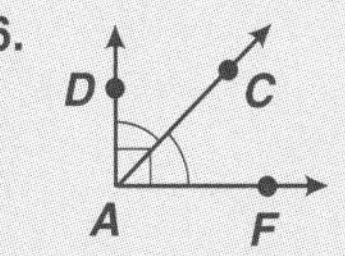

27.

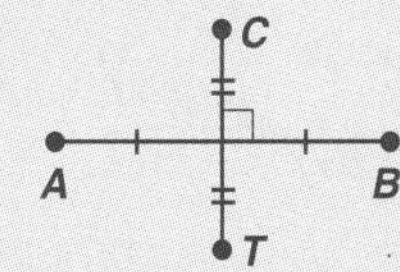

EXTENSION Exercise 41c Have students create three-dimensional models to illustrate their answers.

TACTILE LEARNING Exercise 43 If you have block scheduling or an extended period, have students investigate other properties of a Mobius band. They can show that it has only one side and one edge, observe what happens when they cut the band from 43b along its center again, or observe what happens when they cut the original band along a path that is one-third of the way in from the edges. Students can also investigate what happens when a strip of paper is twisted twice, taped together, and then cut along its center.

43b. Answers may vary. Sample: No; cutting the Möbius band does not produce 2 ≅ figures.

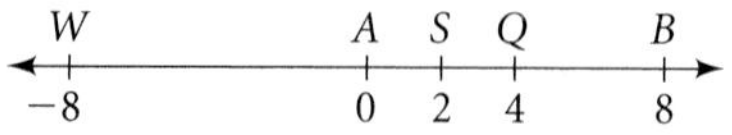

W at −8; A at 0; S at 2; Q at 4; B at 8

29. What is the midpoint of $\overline{AB}$? **Q**

30. What is the coordinate of the midpoint of $\overline{QB}$? **6**

31. What is the coordinate of the midpoint of $\overline{WA}$? **−4**

32. The coordinate of the midpoint of $\overline{AR}$ is -5. What is the coordinate of point R? **−10**

33. The coordinate of the midpoint of $\overline{ST}$ is 7. What is the coordinate of point T? **12**

34. Which figures in the third group are *vertical angles?* **c**

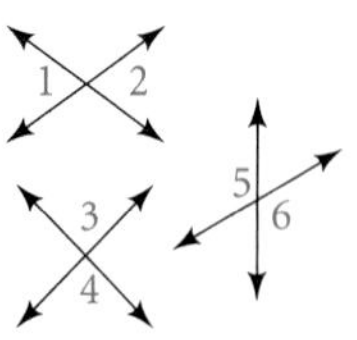

Vertical angles

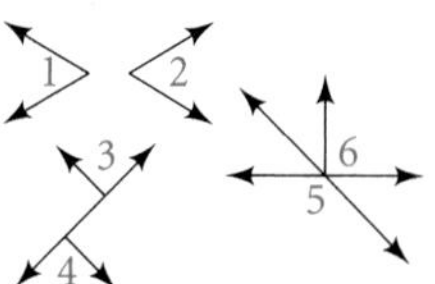

Not vertical angles

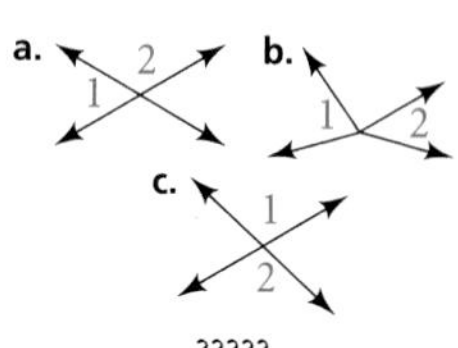

?????

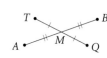

Algebra Solve for *x*.

35. $AB = 24, MB = 2x + 4$ **4**

36. $TM = 3x + 5, MQ = x + 17$ **6**

37. $TQ = 4x + 16, TM = 20$ **6**

38. $MB = 8x + 7, AB = 126$ **7**

39. $TM = \frac{1}{2}x - 4, TQ = 12$ **20**

40. $AM = 5x - 1, AB = 38$ **4**

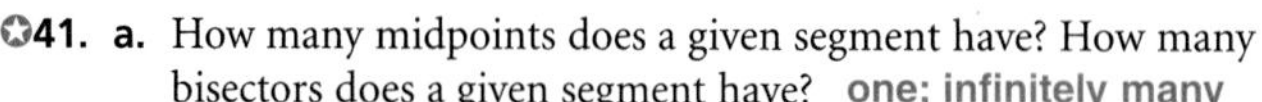

41. a. How many midpoints does a given segment have? How many bisectors does a given segment have? **one; infinitely many**

b. Given a segment, consider any one plane that contains the segment. How many lines in that plane are perpendicular bisectors of the given segment? **one**

c. *Geometry in 3 Dimensions* Given a segment, how many lines are there in space that are perpendicular bisectors of the given segment? **infinitely many**

42. *Coordinate Geometry* Find the coordinates of the midpoint of $\overline{AB}$ with endpoints $A(0, 5)$ and $B(0, 13)$. **(0, 9)**

43. a. *Manipulatives* Cut out a strip of paper about 11 in. long and 1 in. wide. Twist it once and tape the ends together. You now have a *Möbius band.*

b. Cut the Möbius band along its center. Does cutting the band bisect it? Explain your answer. **See margin.**

43a. Check students' work.

44. *Writing* If point M is the midpoint of $\overline{AB}$, you know that $\overline{AM} \cong \overline{MB}$. How is AM related to AB? Write an equation about AM and AB and explain why your equation is correct.
$AM = \frac{1}{2}AB$. Since $AM = MB$ and $AM + MB = AB$, $2AM = AB$, or $AM = \frac{1}{2}AB$.

Exercise 47 Have students define linear pair from the illustrations. Then have them check their definitions with the one given in the Glossary.

STANDARDIZED TEST TIP **Exercise 53** Drawing a diagram is an effective strategy for answering the question.

45. *Open-ended* Describe some perpendicular lines in your home or classroom. **Answers may vary. Sample: the side and top of a door, the grout lines on square tiles**

46. *Language Arts* Is the following an acceptable definition? Explain.
An obtuse angle is an angle whose measure is greater than 90.
No; the measure of an obtuse angle must also be less than 180.

47. Which angles in the third group form a *linear pair?* **b**

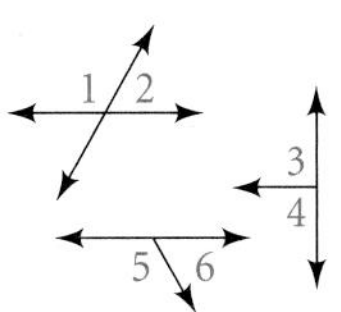
Linear pairs

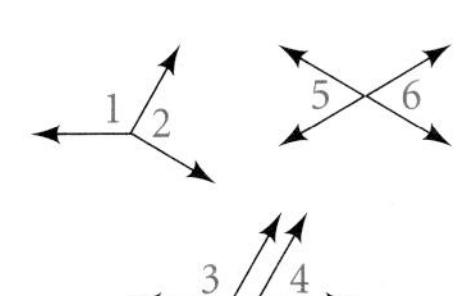
Not linear pairs

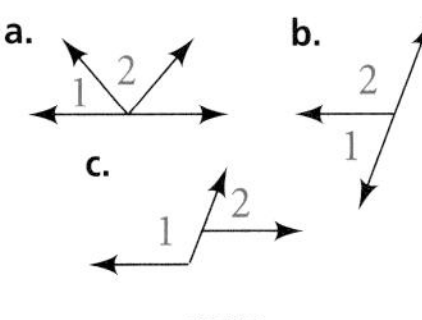
?????

Algebra $\overrightarrow{BX}$ **is the bisector of $\angle ABC$. Complete each equation.**

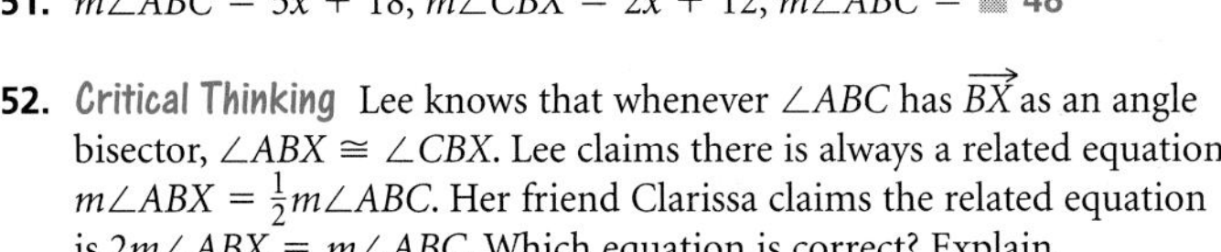

48. $m\angle ABX = 5x$, $m\angle XBC = 3x + 10$, $m\angle ABC =$ ■ **50**

49. $m\angle ABC = 4x - 12$, $m\angle ABX = 24$, $x =$ ■ **15**

50. $m\angle ABX = 4x - 16$, $m\angle CBX = 2x + 6$, $x =$ ■ **11**

51. $m\angle ABC = 5x + 18$, $m\angle CBX = 2x + 12$, $m\angle ABC =$ ■ **48**

52. *Critical Thinking* Lee knows that whenever $\angle ABC$ has $\overrightarrow{BX}$ as an angle bisector, $\angle ABX \cong \angle CBX$. Lee claims there is always a related equation, $m\angle ABX = \frac{1}{2}m\angle ABC$. Her friend Clarissa claims the related equation is $2m\angle ABX = m\angle ABC$. Which equation is correct? Explain. A diagram may be helpful. **Both; they are equivalent. Multiply both sides of Lee's equation by 2 to produce Clarissa's equation.**

53. *Standardized Test Prep* Point M is the midpoint of $\overline{PQ}$. Which of these is *not* true? **D**
A. $\overline{PM} \cong \overline{MQ}$
B. $PM + MQ = PQ$
C. $MQ = \frac{1}{2}PQ$
D. $\overrightarrow{PM}$ and $\overrightarrow{PQ}$ are opposite rays.
E. $PQ = 2PM$

54. *Writing* Write a definition of a line parallel to a plane. **Answers may vary. Sample: A line parallel to a given plane is one that does not intersect the plane.**

55. Study the figures below. Complete the definition of a line perpendicular to a plane. A line is perpendicular to a plane if it is __?__ to every line in the plane that __?__. **perpendicular; it intersects**

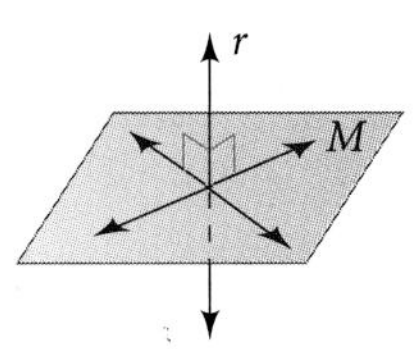
Line $r \perp$ plane M.

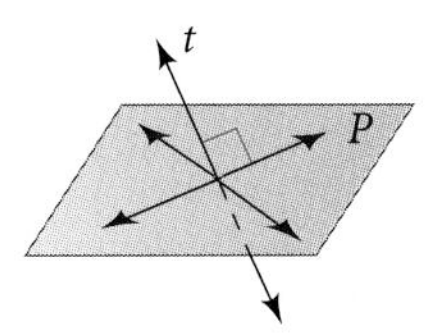
Line t is not $\perp$ plane P.

Geometry at Work page 38

Position the square to find X so that $AX = BX$. Then repeat the procedure to locate point Y on the other side of $\overline{AB}$ from X. $\overleftrightarrow{XY}$ is the $\perp$ bisector of $\overline{AB}$.

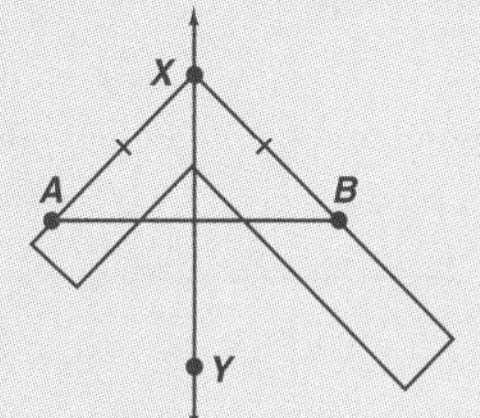

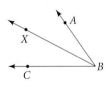

Exercises MIXED REVIEW

Exercises 56–61 Students review properties of rays and angles.

GETTING READY FOR LESSON 1-6 These exercises prepare students to construct bisectors of segments and angles.

Wrap Up

THE BIG IDEA Ask students: *Describe the three types of bisectors discussed in this lesson.*

RETEACHING ACTIVITY Students investigate line segments and angles by folding paper. (Reteaching worksheet 1-5)

Geometry at Work

For further information about the training and skills necessary for woodworking, contact your local artisan guild, technical schools, or community colleges.

Encourage students to investigate these topics:

- the training necessary to become a skilled woodworker
- the math and computer skills used by woodworkers
- the type of businesses or contractors that hire woodworkers

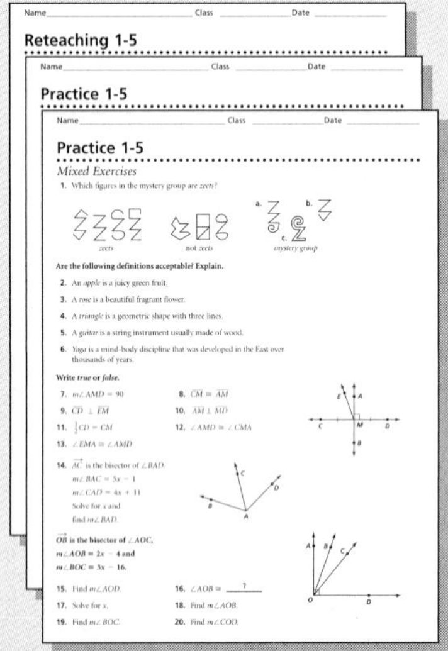
Name ______ Class ______ Date ______

Reteaching 1-5

Name ______ Class ______ Date ______

Practice 1-5

Name ______ Class ______ Date ______

Practice 1-5

Mixed Exercises

1. Which figures in the mystery group are *zeets*?

zeets *not zeets* *mystery group* a. b. c.

Are the following definitions acceptable? Explain.

2. An *apple* is a juicy green fruit.
3. A *rose* is a beautiful fragrant flower.
4. A *triangle* is a geometric shape with three lines.
5. A *guitar* is a string instrument usually made of wood.
6. *Yoga* is a mind-body discipline that was developed in the East over thousands of years.

Write *true* or *false*.

7. $m\angle AMD = 90$
8. $\overline{CM} \cong \overline{AM}$
9. $\overline{CD} \perp \overline{EM}$
10. $\overline{AM} \perp \overline{MD}$
11. $\frac{1}{2}CD = CM$
12. $\angle AMD \cong \angle CMA$
13. $\angle EMA \cong \angle AMD$
14. $\overrightarrow{AC}$ is the bisector of $\angle BAD$. $m\angle BAC = 5x - 1$, $m\angle CAD = 4x + 11$. Solve for x and find $m\angle BAD$.

$\overrightarrow{OB}$ **is the bisector of** $\angle AOC$, $m\angle AOB = 2x - 4$ **and** $m\angle BOC = 3x - 16$.

15. Find $m\angle AOD$.
16. $\angle AOB \cong$ __?__
17. Solve for x.
18. Find $m\angle AOB$.
19. Find $m\angle BOC$.
20. Find $m\angle COD$.

Lesson Quiz

Lesson Quiz is also available in Transparencies.

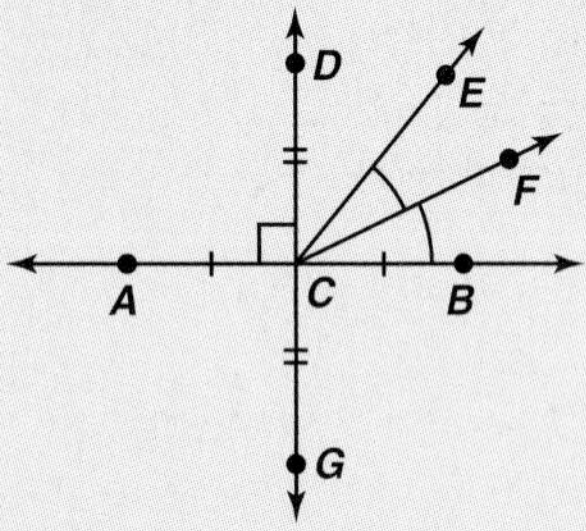

1. If $AC = 7$, then find AB. 14
2. __?__ is the angle bisector of __?__. $\overleftrightarrow{CF}$, $\angle BCE$
3. $m\angle ACG =$ __?__ 90
4. $CG = 2x + 2$, $DC = 5x - 1$. Find x and CG. $x = 1$, $CG = 4$

Exercises MIXED REVIEW

Use the diagram at the right for Exercises 56–60.

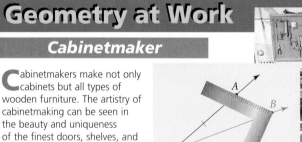

56. Find each measure.

a. $m\angle AOC$ 80 b. $m\angle AOD$ 125

c. $m\angle DOB$ 65 d. $m\angle BOE$ 90

57. Name an obtuse angle. Sample: $\angle AOD$
58. Name an acute angle. Sample: $\angle AOB$
59. Name a right angle. $\angle BOE$
60. Name all the rays. $\overrightarrow{OA}$, $\overrightarrow{OB}$, $\overrightarrow{OC}$, $\overrightarrow{OD}$, $\overrightarrow{OE}$
61. Draw opposite rays $\overrightarrow{RS}$ and $\overrightarrow{RW}$. Find RS if $SW = 8$ and $RW = 5$. 3

Getting Ready For Lesson 1-6

62. $\overleftrightarrow{AX}$ is the perpendicular bisector of $\overline{QS}$ at point M. Name two congruent segments. $\overline{QM} \cong \overline{MS}$
63. $\overrightarrow{PT}$ is the bisector of $\angle APR$. Name two congruent angles. $\angle APT \cong \angle TPR$
64. $\overrightarrow{OR}$ is the bisector of right $\angle TOS$. Find $m\angle TOR$. 45

Geometry at Work

Cabinetmaker

Cabinetmakers make not only cabinets but all types of wooden furniture. The artistry of cabinetmaking can be seen in the beauty and uniqueness of the finest doors, shelves, and tables. The craft of the profession is in knowing which types of wood and tools to use, and how to use them.

The carpenter's square is one of the most useful of the cabinetmaker's tools. It can be applied to a variety of measuring tasks. The figure shows how to use a carpenter's square to bisect $\angle O$.

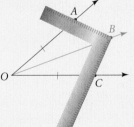

First, mark equal lengths OA and OC on the sides of the angle. Then position the square so that $AB = BC$ to locate point B. Finally, draw $\overrightarrow{OB}$. $\overrightarrow{OB}$ bisects $\angle O$.

Mini Project: Make a carpenter's square out of cardboard. Mark the edges in equal intervals as shown in the figure. Draw a line segment. Then demonstrate how you can use the square to draw the perpendicular bisector of the segment. See margin p. 37.

1-6 Teaching Notes

PROBLEM OF THE DAY

Start with the letter C on top and move down the diagram. You can only move to one of the letters below, directly to the right or left. How many different paths spell COMPASS? 20

```
      C
    O   O
  M   M   M
P   P   P   P
  A   A   A
    S   S
      S
```

Problem of the Day is also available in Transparencies.

CONNECTING TO PRIOR KNOWLEDGE Ask students to use a ruler and a protractor to draw a segment 5 cm long and a 50° angle. Then have them use the ruler and protractor to draw bisectors of the segment and the angle.

WORK TOGETHER

Have students work in pairs to draw segments of different lengths and angles of different measures. Suggest one student draw an acute angle and the other an obtuse angle.

THINK AND DISCUSS

Students may not understand the difference between *drawing* and *constructing.* Emphasize that when drawing, a ruler and protractor can be used. In constructions, only a compass and straightedge can be used.

What You'll Learn

- Using a compass and straightedge to construct congruent angles and congruent segments
- Using a compass and straightedge to bisect segments and angles

...And Why

To lay the foundation for more complex constructions you will use in later chapters

What You'll Need

ruler, compass, tracing paper

Connections Art . . . and more

1-6 Basic Constructions

WORK TOGETHER

Use a ruler to draw a segment on tracing paper. Fold the paper so that one endpoint lies on the other endpoint. Unfold the paper and compare your result with a partner's.

1. What kinds of angles are formed by the segment and the fold line? right angles
2. What is the relationship between the original segment and the segments determined by the fold line? The original segment is twice as long.
3. What geometric term best describes the fold line? perpendicular bisector

Draw an angle on tracing paper. Fold the paper so that one side of the angle lies on the other side and the fold line goes through the vertex of the angle.

4. What geometric term best describes the fold line? angle bisector

THINK AND DISCUSS

Part 1

Constructing Congruent Segments and Angles

Another method for creating the bisectors you made in the Work Together is by construction. A **construction** uses a straightedge and a compass to make geometric figures. A **straightedge** is a ruler with no markings on it. (You may use a ruler as a straightedge, but you have to ignore the markings.) A **compass** is a geometric tool used to draw circles and parts of circles called arcs.

The four basic constructions involve constructing congruent segments and angles as well as constructing bisectors of segments and angles.

Lesson Planning Options

Prerequisite Skills

- Using a compass
- Recognizing congruence

Assignment Options for Exercises On Your Own

To provide flexible scheduling, this lesson can be subdivided into parts.

1 **Core** 1, 4–11
Extension 18

2 **Core** 2, 3, 12–17
Extension 19

Use Mixed Review to maintain skills.

Resources

Student Edition

Extra Practice, p. 648
Glossary/Study Guide

Teaching Resources

Chapter Support File, Ch. 1
- Practice 1-6 (two worksheets)
- Reteaching 1-6

Classroom Manager 1-6
Glossary, Spanish Resources

Transparencies

24

MAKING CONNECTIONS Napoleon Bonaparte (1769–1821), a famous emperor of France, is also credited with the following theorem: If three triangles with equal side lengths are constructed off the sides of *any* triangle, then the centers of the circles which circumscribe each triangle are vertices of another triangle with equal side lengths.

TACTILE LEARNING Construction 1 Illustrate each step of the construction on the board or using an overhead projector. Have students work in pairs to discuss and perform each step.

DIVERSITY Some students may not be physically able to use a compass and straightedge. Have students work in pairs and share the responsibilities for reading and following the instructions.

ERROR ALERT! Some students may squeeze the compass too hard and change its setting; some compasses may "slip" by themselves. **Remediation:** Have students check the compass opening after using it to draw an arc. If their "squeeze" is too strong, suggest a better way to hold the compass. If it slips, try to fix it yourself or give the student a different compass.

Additional Examples

FOR EXAMPLE

Use the segments given in the example. Construct a triangle whose sides have lengths *a, a,* and *b.*

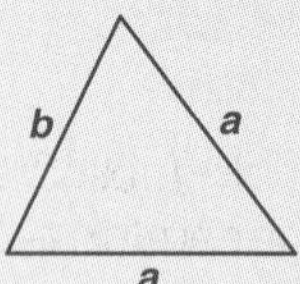

Discussion: *One student constructs a segment with length* a *first and another student constructs a segment with length* b *first. Will their resulting triangles be different?*

Construction 1
Congruent Segments

Construct a segment congruent to a given segment.

Given: $\overline{AB}$

Step 1
Draw a ray with endpoint C.

Step 2
Open the compass to the length of $\overline{AB}$.

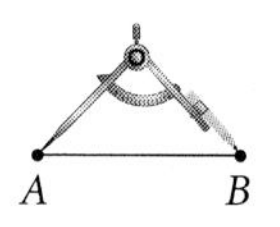

Step 3
With the same compass setting, put the compass point on C. Draw an arc that intersects the ray. Label the point of intersection D.

$\overline{CD} \cong \overline{AB}$

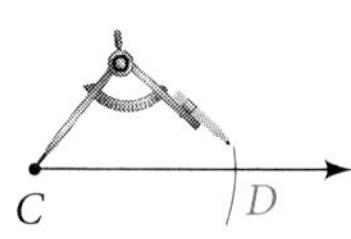

Construction 2
Congruent Angles

Construct an angle congruent to a given angle.

Given: $\angle A$

Step 1
Draw a ray with endpoint S.

Step 2
With the compass point on point A, draw an arc that intersects the sides of $\angle A$. Label the points of intersection B and C.

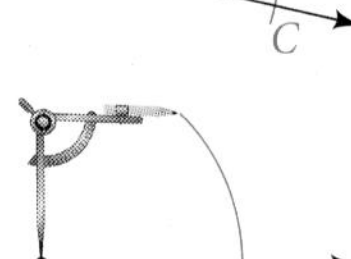

Step 3
With the same compass setting, put the compass point on point S. Draw an arc that intersects the ray at point R.

Step 4
Open the compass to the length of $\overline{BC}$. Keeping the same compass setting, put the compass point on R. Draw an arc to determine point T.

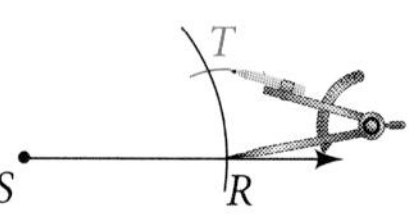

Step 5
Draw $\overrightarrow{ST}$.

$\angle S \cong \angle A$

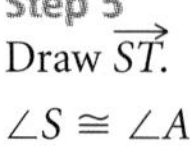

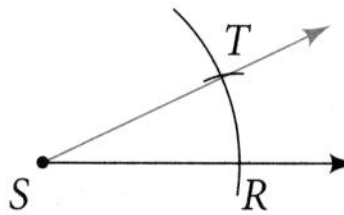

Example

Carefully review Steps 2 and 3 with students. Help them to understand that a segment from R to any point on the arc drawn in Step 2 will have length b and a segment from S to any point on the arc drawn in Step 3 will have length c. By choosing the point where the arcs intersect, a triangle is formed with sides of lengths a, b, and c.

Allow time for students to experiment using a SAFE-T Compass.® Have them make different-sized circles and arcs. Using a SAFE-T Compass® allows students to use wooden, mechanical, or colored pencils and simplifies constructions because no setting adjustments are necessary.

Question 7 Have students work in pairs or small groups first to discuss what steps they will take, then to construct the triangle.

6. Construct an angle ≅ to $\angle X$. Construct an angle ≅ to $\angle Y$ inside $\angle X$ and sharing a side and vertex with $\angle X$.

You can use these constructions to construct different geometric figures.

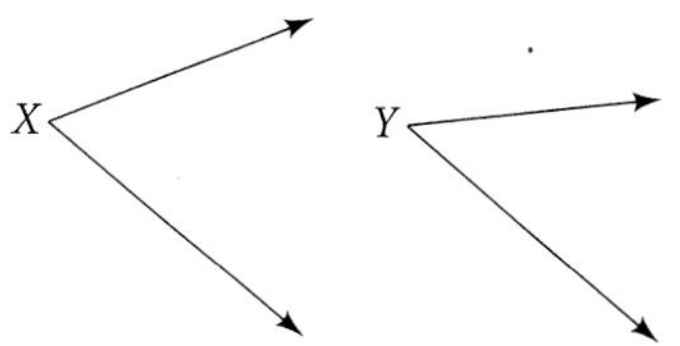

5. **Try This** Draw angles like $\angle X$ and $\angle Y$. Then construct $\angle Z$ so that $m\angle Z = m\angle X + m\angle Y$. See margin p. 42.
6. Describe how you would construct an angle, $\angle D$, so that $m\angle D = m\angle X - m\angle Y$.

To draw a circle or an arc with a SAFE-T-COMPASS®, use the center hole of the white dial as the center.

You can use a compass and straightedge to construct triangles with sides of specific lengths.

Example

Construct a triangle whose sides have the given lengths.

Step 1
Use Construction 1 to construct $\overline{RS}$ with length a.

Step 2
Open the compass to the length b. Put the compass point on R and draw an arc.

Step 3
Open the compass to the length c. Put the compass point on S and draw an arc. Be sure the two arcs intersect. Label the intersection of the arcs as point T.

Step 4
Draw segments from point T to both R and S.

7. **Try This** Draw $\overline{XY}$. Then construct a triangle with three sides the length of $\overline{XY}$. See below.

Part 2

Constructing Perpendicular Bisectors and Angle Bisectors

The next two constructions will show you how to bisect segments and bisect angles. These constructions and Construction 2 are based on *congruent triangles*. You will see *why* the constructions work in future chapters.

7.

Technology Options

Exercises 1–12 may be completed using the *construct* and *draw* tools in geometry software.

Prentice Hall Technology

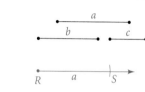

Software
- Secondary Math Lab Toolkit™
- Computer Item Generator 1-6

CD-ROM
- Multimedia Geometry Lab 1

Internet
- See the Prentice Hall site. (http://www.phschool.com)

Construction 3 As students read Step 1, emphasize that the opening of the compass needs to be greater than half the length of the segment. Have students tell why. Then make sure students draw their arcs large enough so that they intersect.

Question 8 This construction requires that students use both Construction 3 and Construction 4. Have students work in small groups or with a partner first to plan their steps , then to construct the angle.

Exercises ON YOUR OWN

ALTERNATIVE ASSESSMENT **Exercises 1–9** A selection of these exercises can be used to assess students' ability to construct segments and angles. Emphasize that students carefully follow each step of the construction as described in the lesson and ask them to leave all construction marks on their figures.

CRITICAL THINKING Exercise 12 Students must recognize that $45 = \frac{1}{2}(90)$ and $135 = 45 + 90$, then construct a 90° angle by constructing a perpendicular bisector of a segment. Realizing that they must construct a segment in order to begin will be a difficult first step for some.

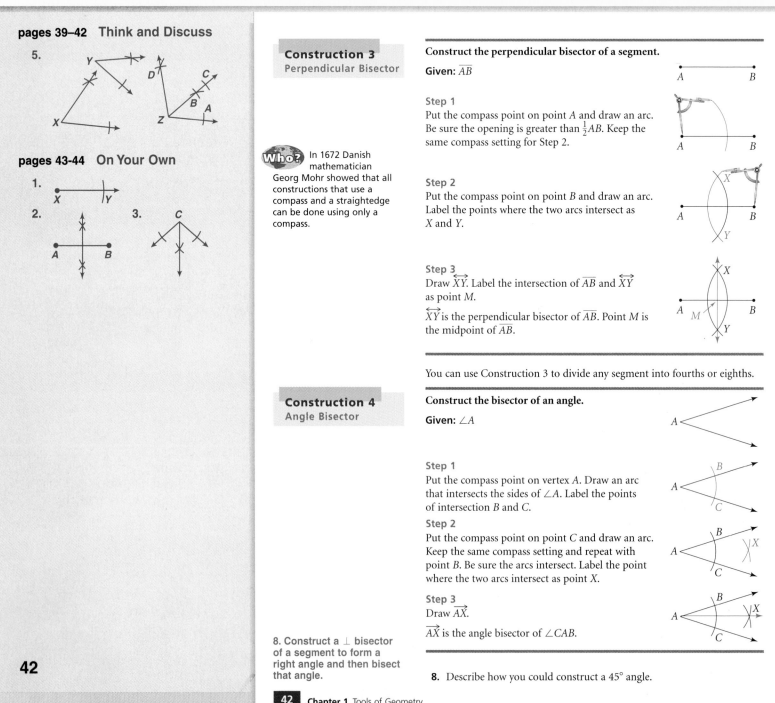

pages 39–42 Think and Discuss

5.

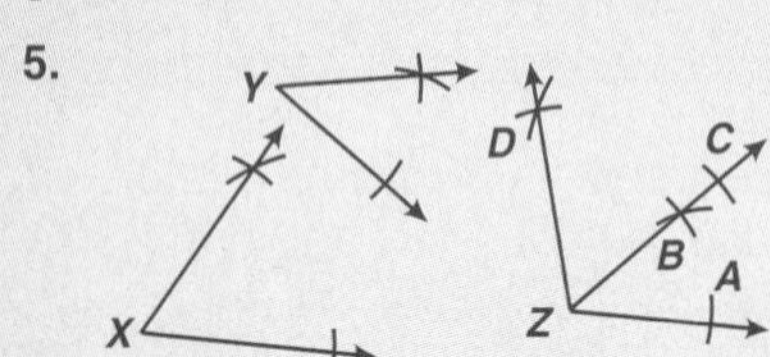

pages 43-44 On Your Own

1.

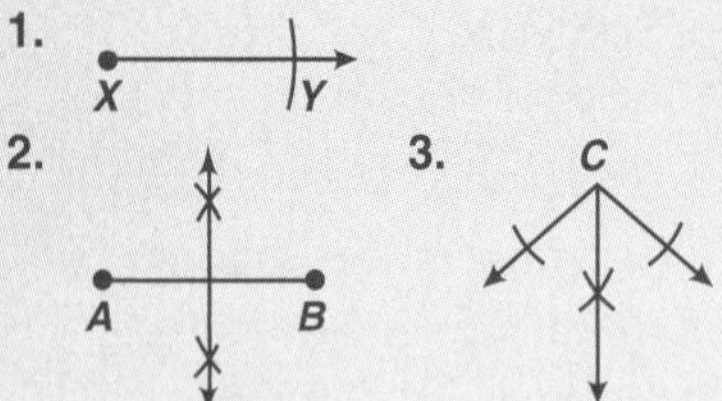

2. 3.

Construction 3
Perpendicular Bisector

Construct the perpendicular bisector of a segment.

Given: $\overline{AB}$

Step 1
Put the compass point on point A and draw an arc. Be sure the opening is greater than $\frac{1}{2}AB$. Keep the same compass setting for Step 2.

Who? In 1672 Danish mathematician Georg Mohr showed that all constructions that use a compass and a straightedge can be done using only a compass.

Step 2
Put the compass point on point B and draw an arc. Label the points where the two arcs intersect as X and Y.

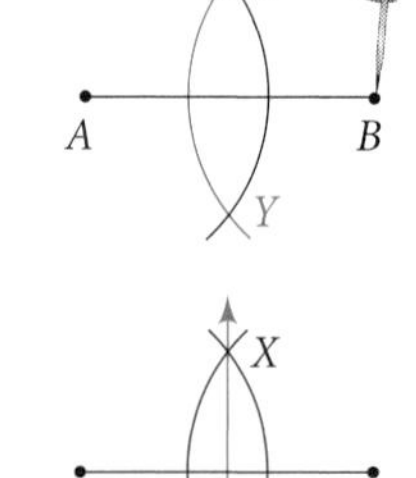

Step 3
Draw $\overleftrightarrow{XY}$. Label the intersection of $\overline{AB}$ and $\overleftrightarrow{XY}$ as point M.

$\overleftrightarrow{XY}$ is the perpendicular bisector of $\overline{AB}$. Point M is the midpoint of $\overline{AB}$.

You can use Construction 3 to divide any segment into fourths or eighths.

Construction 4
Angle Bisector

Construct the bisector of an angle.

Given: $\angle A$

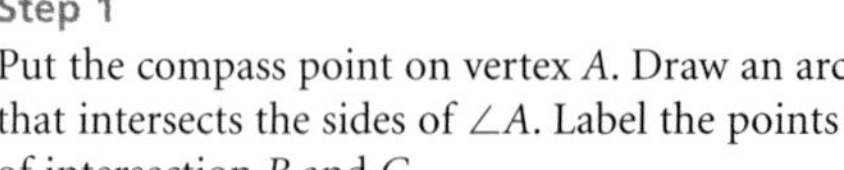

Step 1
Put the compass point on vertex A. Draw an arc that intersects the sides of $\angle A$. Label the points of intersection B and C.

Step 2
Put the compass point on point C and draw an arc. Keep the same compass setting and repeat with point B. Be sure the arcs intersect. Label the point where the two arcs intersect as point X.

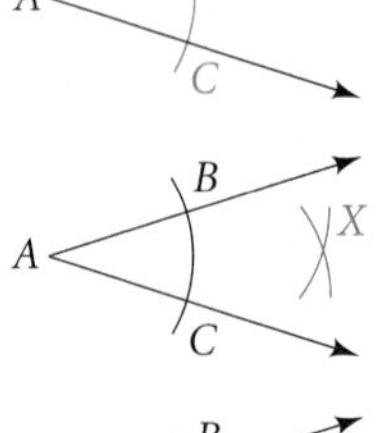

Step 3
Draw $\overrightarrow{AX}$.

$\overrightarrow{AX}$ is the angle bisector of $\angle CAB$.

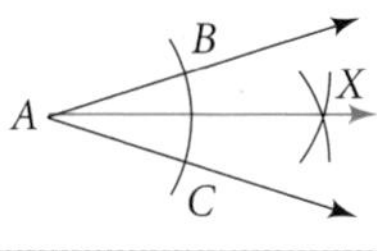

8. Construct a ⊥ bisector of a segment to form a right angle and then bisect that angle.

8. Describe how you could construct a 45° angle.

WRITING Exercise 13 Encourage students to include diagrams along with their explanations.

Exercises 15–16 Have students compare their results with those drawn by others in the class. Ask them what reasoning they used to make their conjectures.

ERROR ALERT! Exercise 17b Due to inaccurate constructions or measurements, students may not conclude that each angle is 60° and thus may not be able to answer Exercise 17c. **Remediation:** Have students work in groups and compare their results. Have them check the accuracy of their constructions and measurements until they can all agree on an answer.

Exercises ON YOUR OWN

Draw a diagram similar to the given one. Then do the construction. **1–3. See margin p. 42.**

1. Construct $\overline{XY}$ congruent to $\overline{AB}$. Check your work with a ruler.
2. Construct the perpendicular bisector of $\overline{AB}$. Check your work with a ruler and a protractor.
3. Construct the angle bisector of $\angle C$. Check your work with a protractor. **4–11. See margin.**

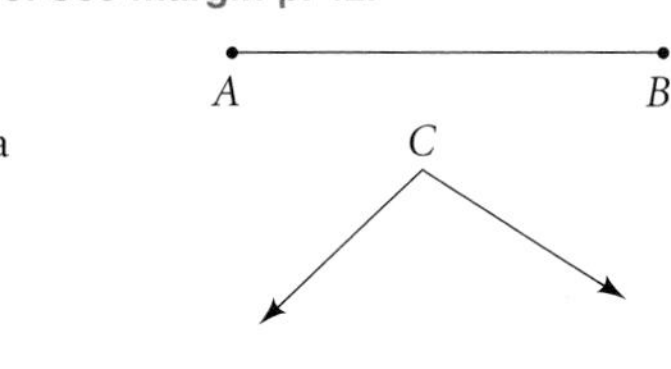

4. Construct $\overline{DE}$ so that $DE = TR + PB$.
5. Construct $\overline{QS}$ so that $QS = TR - PB$.
6. Construct $\overline{XY}$ so that $XY = 2TR$.
7. Construct $\angle B$ so that $m\angle B = m\angle 1 + m\angle 2$.
8. Construct $\angle C$ so that $m\angle C = m\angle 1 - m\angle 2$.
9. Construct $\angle D$ so that $m\angle D = 2m\angle 2$.

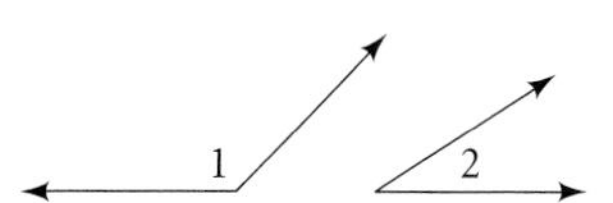

10. Draw an angle that is about 120°. Then construct a congruent angle.
11. Use a ruler to draw two segments that are 4 cm and 5 cm long. Then construct a triangle with sides 4 cm, 4 cm, and 5 cm long.
12. a. Construct a 45° angle. **See right.**
    b. Construct a 135° angle. **See part (a). 180° − 45° = 135°**

12a.

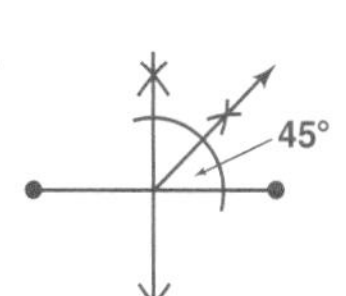
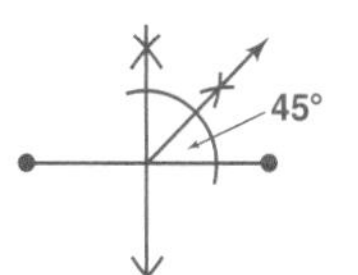
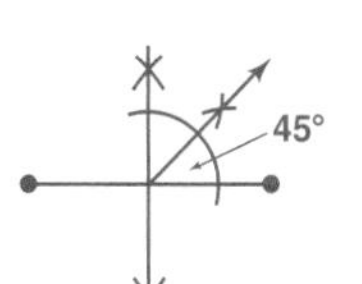
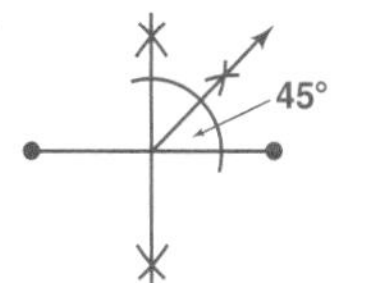
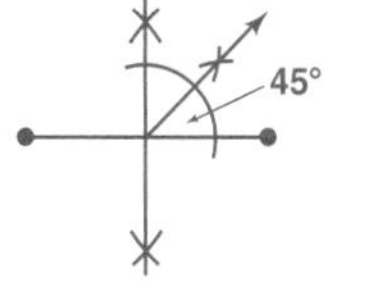

13. **Writing** Describe how to construct the midpoint of a segment. **Construct a ⊥ bisector. Its intersection with the segment is the midpoint of the segment.**
14. **Open-ended** Which method do you prefer for bisecting an angle—paper folding or construction with compass and straightedge? Why? **Answers may vary. Sample: compass and straightedge; it is more precise.**
15. **Patterns** Draw a large triangle with three acute angles. Construct the angle bisectors of all three angles of the triangle. What is true about the intersection of the three angle bisectors? Repeat for another triangle that has an obtuse angle. Make a **conjecture** about the three angle bisectors of any triangle. **The angle bisectors of the 3 angles of any triangle intersect in a single point.**
16. **Patterns** Draw a large triangle with three acute angles. Construct the perpendicular bisectors of all three sides. What is true about the intersection of the three perpendicular bisectors? Repeat for another triangle that has an obtuse angle. Make a **conjecture** about the three perpendicular bisectors of the sides of any triangle. **The ⊥ bisectors of the 3 sides of any triangle intersect in a single point.**
17. a. Draw a segment, $\overline{AB}$. Construct a triangle whose sides are all congruent to $\overline{AB}$. **sample:**
    b. Measure the angles of the triangle. **60**
    c. **Writing** Describe how to construct a 60° angle and a 30° angle. **Construct a 60° angle by constructing an equilateral triangle. Bisect one of the angles to construct a 30° angle.**

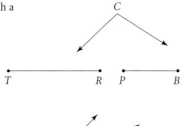

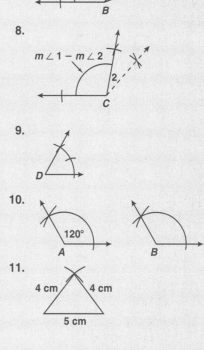

4. TR PB D E
5. TR Q S PB
6. TR TR X Y
7. $m\angle 1 + m\angle 2$ 1 2 B
8. $m\angle 1 - m\angle 2$ 2 C

9. D

10.

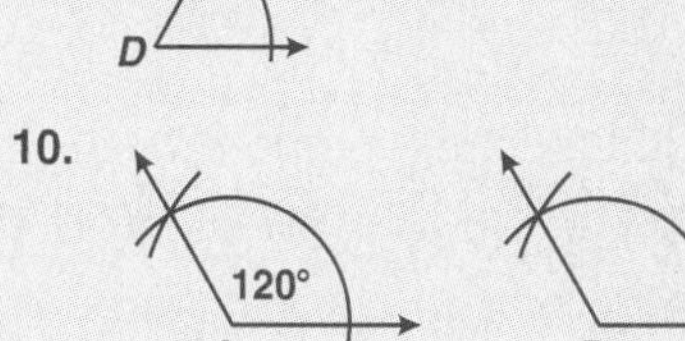

11.

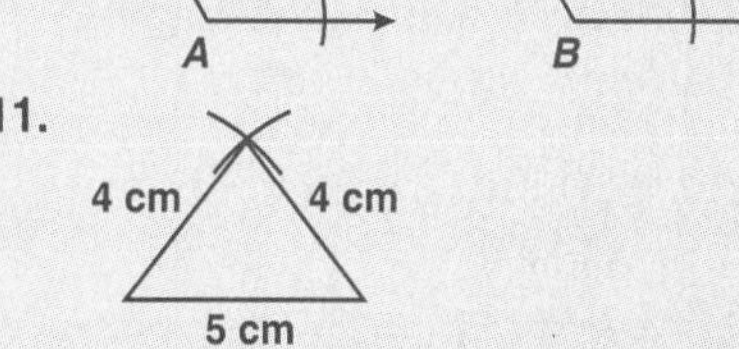

CONNECTING TO STUDENTS' WORLD Exercise 18 Ask students to describe some company logos that have geometric designs (e.g., the CBS or Chrysler logos). Have students create a logo using a compass and straightedge.

Chapter Project **FIND OUT BY WRITING** The class may decide to share their origami figures and instructions with other classes. If possible, send the instructions to middle school math classes and ask the students to create the figures.

Exercises MIXED REVIEW

Exercise 24 Students may want to use a real-life example as a model for their sketch. One possible example is a corner of a room where two walls meet with the ceiling.

GETTING READY FOR LESSON 1-7 These exercises prepare students to find the measures of supplements and complements of angles.

Wrap Up

THE BIG IDEA Ask students: *Describe how to construct a triangle with a 90° angle and two congruent sides.*

RETEACHING ACTIVITY Students construct angles that are congruent to sums and differences of given angles. (Reteaching worksheet 1-6)

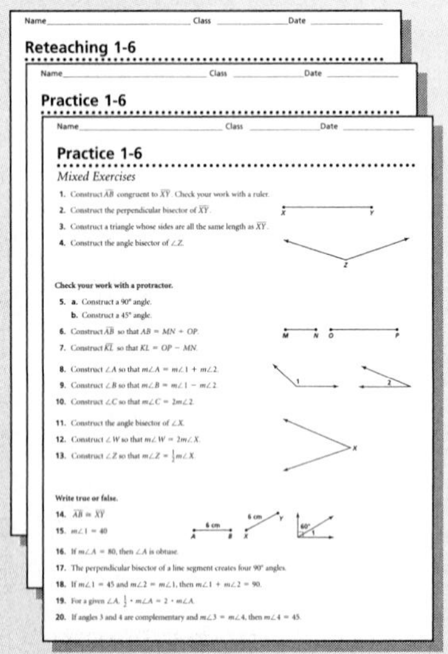

Name______ Class______ Date______

Reteaching 1-6

Name______ Class______ Date______

Practice 1-6

Name______ Class______ Date______

Practice 1-6

Mixed Exercises

1. Construct $\overline{AB}$ congruent to $\overline{XY}$. Check your work with a ruler.
2. Construct the perpendicular bisector of $\overline{XY}$.
3. Construct a triangle whose sides are all the same length as $\overline{XY}$.
4. Construct the angle bisector of $\angle Z$.

Check your work with a protractor.

5. a. Construct a 90° angle.
   b. Construct a 45° angle.
6. Construct $\overline{AB}$ so that $AB = MN + OP$.
7. Construct $\overline{KL}$ so that $KL = OP - MN$.
8. Construct $\angle A$ so that $m\angle A = m\angle 1 + m\angle 2$.
9. Construct $\angle B$ so that $m\angle B = m\angle 1 - m\angle 2$.
10. Construct $\angle C$ so that $m\angle C = 2m\angle 2$.
11. Construct the angle bisector of $\angle X$.
12. Construct $\angle W$ so that $m\angle W = 2m\angle X$.
13. Construct $\angle Z$ so that $m\angle Z = \frac{1}{2}m\angle X$.

Write true or false.

14. $\overline{AB} \cong \overline{XY}$
15. $m\angle 1 = 40$
16. If $m\angle A = 80$, then $\angle A$ is obtuse.
17. The perpendicular bisector of a line segment creates four 90° angles.
18. If $m\angle 1 = 45$ and $m\angle 2 = m\angle 1$, then $m\angle 1 + m\angle 2 = 90$.
19. For a given $\angle A$, $\frac{1}{2} \cdot m\angle A = 2 \cdot m\angle A$.
20. If angles 3 and 4 are complementary and $m\angle 3 = m\angle 4$, then $m\angle 4 = 45$.

Lesson Quiz

Lesson Quiz is also available in Transparencies.

1. Draw a line segment. Call it $\overline{AB}$.
   a. Construct a segment congruent to $\overline{AB}$. Call it $\overline{XY}$.
   b. Construct the perpendicular bisector of $\overline{AB}$. Call it $\overleftrightarrow{GH}$.
2. Draw an angle with measure about 60. Label it $\angle C$.
   a. Then construct an angle congruent to $\angle C$. Label it $\angle D$.
   b. Construct the angle bisector of $\angle C$. Label it $\overrightarrow{CE}$.

Exercises 1–2. Answers may vary. Sample: See back of book.

18. **Art** You can create intricate designs using your compass. Follow these directions to design a *daisy wheel.* **a–d. Check students' work.**
    a. Construct a circle. Keeping the same compass setting, put the compass point on the circle and construct an arc. The endpoints of the arc should be on the circle.
    b. Keeping the same compass setting, put the compass point on each endpoint of the first arc and draw two new arcs.
    c. Continue to make arcs around the circle from the new endpoints of arcs until you get a six-petal daisy wheel.
    d. Personalize your daisy wheel by decorating it.

19. a. Use your compass to draw a circle. Locate three points *A*, *B*, and *C* on the circle. **a–b. Answers may vary. See margin p. 45 for samples.**
    b. Construct the perpendicular bisectors of $\overline{AB}$ and $\overline{BC}$.
    c. **Critical Thinking** Label the intersection of the two perpendicular bisectors as point *O*. Describe point *O*. **Point *O* is the center of the circle.**

Chapter Project

Find Out by Writing

Origami artists use a special notation to communicate how to construct their creations. To communicate your design, you can use the language of geometry instead. Use geometric terms and symbols along with sketches to write directions for the origami you created in the Find Out question on page 22. Test your directions by having a classmate construct your model following your directions.

Exercises MIXED REVIEW

Use the number line at the right to find the length of each segment.

A B C D
−4 0 8 12

20. $\overline{AC}$ **12** 21. $\overline{AD}$ **16** 22. $\overline{CD}$ **4** 23. $\overline{BC}$ **8**

24. Make a sketch of three planes intersecting at one point. **Answers may vary. Sample:**

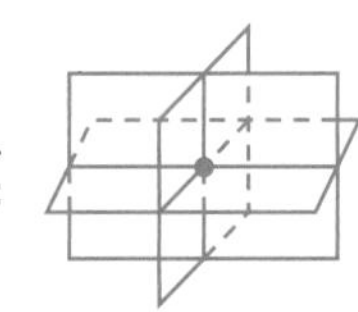

Getting Ready For Lesson 1-7

25. Find the value of *x*. **50**

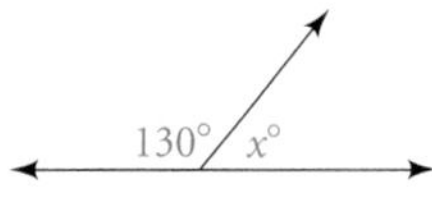

26. Find the value of *y*. **35**

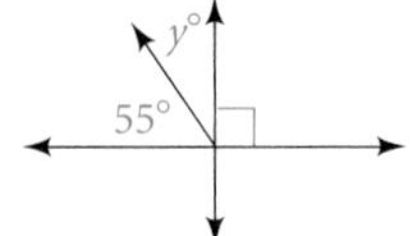

27. Find the value of *z*. **45**

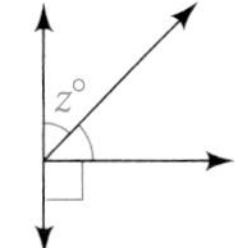

Math ToolboX

In this toolbox, students extend their understanding of constructions by using geometry software to investigate the difference between *draw* and *construct* tools. The software enables students to see that constructions are dependent upon the initial figure (segment, angle, triangle, etc.).

Investigate

Students will see that, using the *construction* tool, a perpendicular bisector to a segment will remain a perpendicular bisector to that segment no matter how that segment is changed. However, when a line is drawn perpendicular to a segment using the *draw* tool, as the segment is changed, the relationship between the line and the segment also changes.

ERROR ALERT! Some students may not be familiar with how to draw or construct using geometry software. **Remediation:** Allow students time to explore the tools before beginning this activity. Pair students more familiar with the software with students who are less familiar.

ADDITIONAL PROBLEM Draw a segment with endpoints *A* and *B*. Construct $\triangle ABC$ with three sides of length *AB*. Then draw $\triangle XYZ$. Drag the vertices until $XY = YZ = ZX$. Manipulate both triangles and observe the side lengths. Are the sides always congruent in $\triangle ABC$? yes in $\triangle XYZ$? no

Math ToolboX Technology

Exploring Constructions

After Lesson 1-6

Points, lines, and figures are created in geometry software using *draw* or *construct* tools. A figure created by *draw* has no constraints. When the figure is manipulated it moves or changes size freely. A figure created by *construct* is dependent upon an existing object. When you manipulate the existing object, the *construct* object moves or resizes similarly.

In this activity you will explore the difference between *draw* and *construct*. Before you begin, familiarize yourself with your software's tools.

Construct

Check students' work.

- Draw $\overline{AB}$ and construct perpendicular bisector $\overleftrightarrow{DC}$.
- Draw $\overline{EF}$ and construct *G*, any point on $\overline{EF}$. Draw $\overleftrightarrow{HG}$. Find *EG*, *GF*, and $m\angle HGF$. Attempt to drag *G* so that $EG = GF$. Attempt to drag *H* so that $m\angle HGF = 90$. Were you able to draw the perpendicular bisector of $\overline{EF}$? Explain.

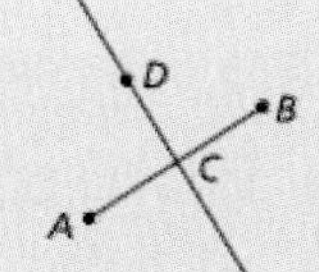

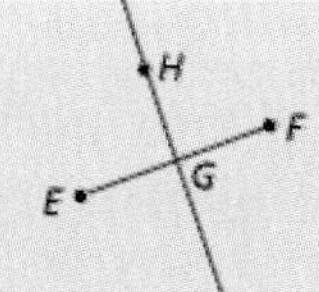

Investigate

- Drag *A* and *B*. Observe *AC*, *CB*, and $m\angle DCB$. Is $\overleftrightarrow{DC}$ always the perpendicular bisector of $\overline{AB}$ no matter how you manipulate the figure? yes
- Drag *E* and *F*. Observe *EG*, *GF*, and $m\angle HGF$. How is the relationship between $\overline{EF}$ and $\overleftrightarrow{HG}$ different from the relationship between $\overline{AB}$ and $\overleftrightarrow{DC}$? $\overleftrightarrow{HG}$ intersects $\overline{EF}$, but it is not the perpendicular bisector of $\overline{EF}$.

Summarize

Write a description of the general difference between *draw* and *construct*. Use your description to explain why the relationship between $\overline{EF}$ and $\overleftrightarrow{HG}$ differs from the relationship between $\overline{AB}$ and $\overleftrightarrow{DC}$. See margin.

Extend

Draw $\angle JKL$ and construct its angle bisector, $\overrightarrow{KM}$. Draw $\angle NOP$. Draw $\overrightarrow{OQ}$ in the interior of $\angle NOP$. Drag *Q* until $m\angle NOQ = m\angle QOP$. Manipulate both figures and observe the different angle measures. Is $\overrightarrow{KM}$ always the angle bisector of $\angle JKL$? Is $\overrightarrow{OQ}$ always the angle bisector of $\angle NOP$?

$\overrightarrow{KM}$ is always the angle bisector of $\angle JKL$.

$\overrightarrow{OQ}$ is not always the bisector of $\angle NOP$.

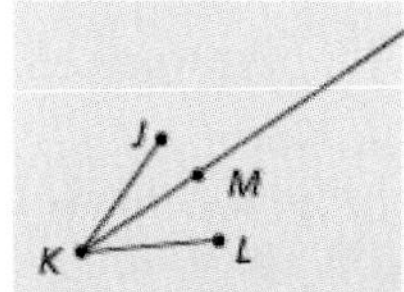

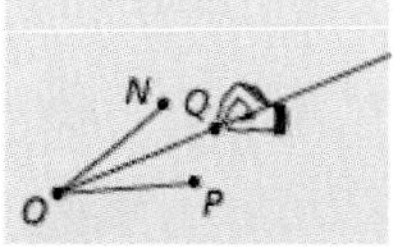

Materials and Manipulatives

- Geometry software

pages 43–44 On Your Own

19a–b. Answers may vary. Sample:

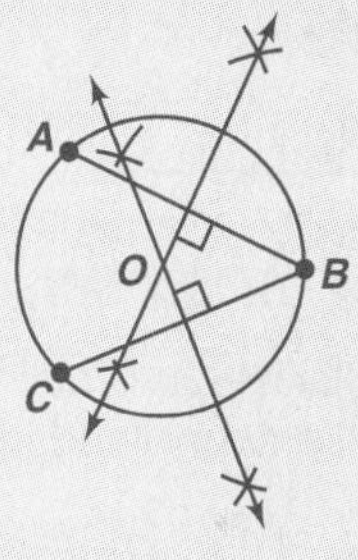

Math Toolbox page 45

SUMMARIZE

A figure created by *draw* has no constraints. A figure created by *construct* is dependent upon an existing object. Since $\overleftrightarrow{DC}$ was constructed as the $\perp$ bisector of $\overline{AB}$, it remains the $\perp$ bisector through any manipulation. Since point *G* was constructed on $\overline{EF}$, the only restriction on $\overleftrightarrow{HG}$ during any manipulation is that it must contain point *G* which has to be on $\overline{EF}$.

1-7 Teaching Notes

PROBLEM OF THE DAY

If $a * b = ab - 1$ and $a \wedge b = \frac{(a + b)}{2}$, then find $2 * [(5 \wedge 3) \wedge (8 * 1)]$. 10

Problem of the Day is also available in Transparencies.

CONNECTING TO PRIOR KNOWLEDGE Have students recall any properties of equality from algebra they can remember. Display the equations $y + 4 = 20$ and $\frac{x}{2} = 20$. Ask students what conclusions they can make about x and y and the reasons for their conclusions.

THINK AND DISCUSS p. 46

DIVERSITY Discuss with students jobs that require people to use deductive reasoning. Try to include a variety of occupations that use different skills and require different educational backgrounds.

AUDITORY LEARNING Have students take turns explaining the properties of equality to a partner. With each explanation, have the student give an example of the property using real numbers.

Lesson Planning Options

Prerequisite Skills

- Understanding the properties of equality from algebra
- Solving one-variable equations

Assignment Options for Exercises On Your Own

To provide flexible scheduling, this lesson can be subdivided into parts.

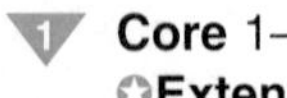
Core 1–10, 29–31
Extension 34–38

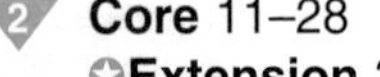
Core 11–28
Extension 32–33

Use Mixed Review to maintain skills.

Resources

Student Edition

Skills Handbook, p. 664
Extra Practice, p. 648
Glossary/Study Guide

Teaching Resources

Chapter Support File, Ch. 1
- Practice 1-7 (two worksheets)
- Reteaching 1-7
- Alternative Activity 1-7

Classroom Manager 1-7
Glossary, Spanish Resources

Transparencies

20, 25

Connections: Auto Repair . . . and more

1-7 Using Deductive Reasoning

What You'll Learn

- Using deductive reasoning to solve problems and verify conjectures
- Understanding how certain angle pairs are related

...And Why

To reach valid conclusions in geometry and in life

What You'll Need

- tracing paper

THINK AND DISCUSS

Part 1

Connecting Algebra and Geometry

Deductive reasoning is a process of reasoning logically from given facts to a conclusion. If the given facts are true, deductive reasoning always produces a valid conclusion. In geometry, we accept postulates and properties as true and use deductive reasoning to prove other statements.

1. **Try This** Maria's parents tell her she can go to the mall with her friends if she finishes her homework. Maria shows her parents her completed homework. What conclusion can you make?
She can go to the mall.

Many people use deductive reasoning in their jobs. A physician diagnosing a patient's illness uses deductive reasoning. A mechanic trying to determine what is wrong with a car uses deductive reasoning. A carpenter uses deductive reasoning to determine what materials are needed at a work site.

Do you remember these Properties of Equality and Real Numbers from algebra?

Properties of Equality and Real Numbers

Addition Property	If $a = b$, then $a + c = b + c$.
Subtraction Property	If $a = b$, then $a - c = b - c$.
Multiplication Property	If $a = b$, then $a \cdot c = b \cdot c$.
Division Property	If $a = b$, then $\frac{a}{c} = \frac{b}{c}$ $(c \neq 0)$.
Substitution Property	If $a = b$, then b can replace a in any expression.
Distributive Property	$a(b + c) = ab + ac$

Example 1

Point out that the justification for the first step comes from geometry. Once variables are substituted, each justification comes from algebra.

Question 2 The reflexive, symmetric, and transitive properties can also be used to describe verbal relationships. For example, "is a cousin of" is symmetric (only), "is shorter than" is transitive (only), and "has the same first name as" is reflexive, symmetric, and transitive. Students may enjoy stating and classifying other verbal relationships.

WORK TOGETHER

ALTERNATIVE METHOD Have students place a piece of tracing paper over the intersecting angles and shade ∠1. Then with their pencil point on the point of intersection of the lines, have them rotate the tracing paper slowly about the point of intersection until the shaded area is over ∠2. Students can repeat this activity with ∠3 and ∠4.

You may not realize it, but you use deductive reasoning every time you solve an equation.

Example 1

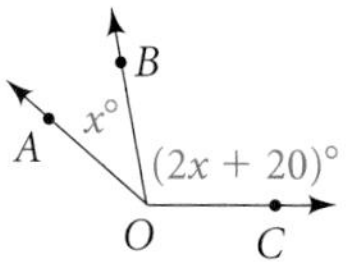

Algebra $m\angle AOC = 140$. Solve for x and justify each step.

$m\angle AOB + m\angle BOC = m\angle AOC$	Angle Addition Postulate
$x + (2x + 20) = 140$	Substitution
$3x = 120$	Subtraction Property of Equality
$x = 40$	Division Property of Equality

These properties of congruence follow from the properties of equality.

QUICK REVIEW

Properties of Equality

Reflexive Property
$a = a$

Symmetric Property
If $a = b$, then $b = a$.

Transitive Property
If $a = b$ and $b = c$, then $a = c$.

Properties of Congruence

Reflexive Property	$\overline{AB} \cong \overline{AB}$
	$\angle A \cong \angle A$
Symmetric Property	If $\overline{AB} \cong \overline{CD}$, then $\overline{CD} \cong \overline{AB}$.
	If $\angle A \cong \angle B$, then $\angle B \cong \angle A$.
Transitive Property	If $\overline{AB} \cong \overline{CD}$ and $\overline{CD} \cong \overline{EF}$, then $\overline{AB} \cong \overline{EF}$.
	If $\angle A \cong \angle B$ and $\angle B \cong \angle C$, then $\angle A \cong \angle C$.

2. **Try This** Name the property of equality or congruence illustrated.
   a. $\angle K \cong \angle K$
   b. If $2x - 8 = 10$, then $2x = 18$.
   c. If $\overline{RS} \cong \overline{TW}$ and $\overline{TW} \cong \overline{PQ}$, then $\overline{RS} \cong \overline{PQ}$.
   d. If $m\angle A = m\angle B$, then $m\angle B = m\angle A$.

a. Reflexive Property of ≅
b. Addition Property of =
c. Transitive Property of ≅
d. Symmetric Property of =

Part 2

WORK TOGETHER

Draw two intersecting lines. Number the angles as shown.

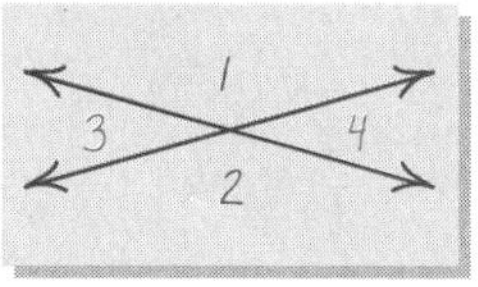

3. Fold the sides of ∠1 onto ∠2. What do you notice? ∠1 ≅ ∠2
4. Fold the sides of ∠3 onto ∠4. What do you notice? ∠3 ≅ ∠4
5. Compare your results with those of others in your group. Make a **conjecture** about the angles formed by two intersecting lines.
   When 2 lines intersect, the angles across from each other are ≅.

Additional Examples

FOR EXAMPLE 1

Refer to the diagram in Example 1. $m\angle AOB = 40$, $m\angle BOC = 3x + 15$, and $m\angle AOC = 4x - 15$. Solve for x and justify each step.

$m\angle AOB + m\angle BOC = m\angle AOC$
(Angle Addition Postulate)

$40 + 3x + 15 = 4x - 15$
(Substitution)

$3x + 70 = 4x$
(Addition Property of Equality)

$70 = x$
(Subtraction Property of Equality)

FOR EXAMPLE 2

Refer to the diagram in Example 2. If $m\angle 1 = 150$, find the measures of ∠2 and ∠3. 150; 30

THINK AND DISCUSS p. 48

Students may remember vertical angles from Exercise 34 in Lesson 1-5. You might want to suggest that the term "vertical" is used because the angles share the same vertex, although not all angles that share the same vertex are vertical angles.

The illustrations show that complementary and supplementary angles can be adjacent or nonadjacent. You may want to use a triangle with angle measures 90, 60 and 30 and a quadrilateral with angle measures 70, 70, 110, and 110 to show that complementary and supplementary angles can share a side.

ERROR ALERT! Students may mistakenly think that three angles whose measures have a sum of 90 or 180 are complementary or supplementary, respectively. **Remediation:** Reinforce that the terms *complementary* and *supplementary* are used to describe relationships between two angles.

ESL Students may want to create flash cards writing the terms *vertical angles, adjacent angles, complementary angles,* and *supplementary angles* on one side and the definitions along with diagrams on the other.

Technology Options

For Exercise 19, students may use geometry software to plot points *A*, *O*, and *X*, then pick point *B* and measure $\angle BOA$ and $\angle AOX$.

Prentice Hall Technology

Software
- Secondary Math Lab Toolkit™
- Computer Item Generator 1-7

Internet
- See the Prentice Hall site. (http://www.phschool.com)

THINK AND DISCUSS

Angle Pairs

In the Work Together you made a conjecture about a pair of angles that has a special name, *vertical angles*. You will learn about several important angle pairs in this lesson.

vertical angles

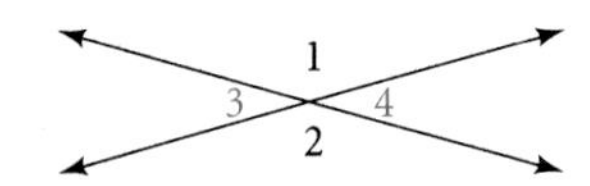

two angles whose sides are opposite rays

adjacent angles

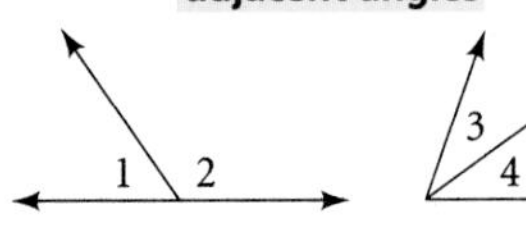

two coplanar angles with a common side, a common vertex, no common interior points

complementary angles

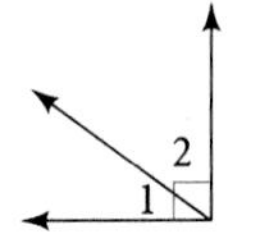

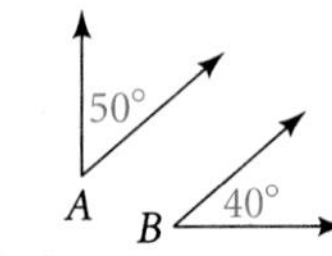

two angles, the sum of whose measures is 90

supplementary angles

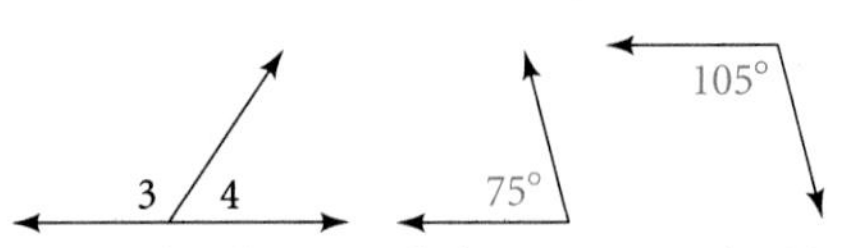

two angles, the sum of whose measures is 180

6. a. Name two pairs of adjacent angles in the photo at the left. See below left.
   b. Name two pairs of supplementary angles. Answers may vary. Samples: $\angle AFB$ and $\angle BFE$, $\angle EFD$ and $\angle DFA$

6a. Answers may vary. Samples: $\angle CFD$ and $\angle CFB$, $\angle BFC$ and $\angle BFA$

In the Work Together you used inductive reasoning to make a conjecture. Now, based on what you know, you can use deductive reasoning to show that your conjecture is always true.

Theorem 1-1
Vertical Angles Theorem

Vertical angles are congruent.

Example 2

Write a convincing argument that the Vertical Angles Theorem is true.

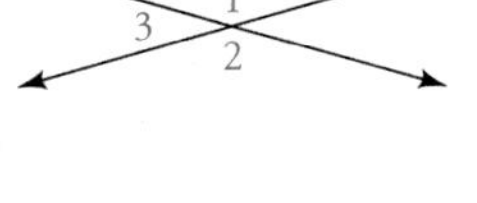

You are given that $\angle 1$ and $\angle 2$ are vertical angles. You must show that $\angle 1 \cong \angle 2$.

By the Angle Addition Postulate,
$m\angle 1 + m\angle 3 = 180$ and $m\angle 2 + m\angle 3 = 180$.
By substitution, $m\angle 1 + m\angle 3 = m\angle 2 + m\angle 3$. Subtract $m\angle 3$ from each side, and you get $m\angle 1 = m\angle 2$, or $\angle 1 \cong \angle 2$.

Example 2

ALGEBRA Help students understand that the process of writing a convincing argument is similar to the process students use for problem solving. They should first read the question, then consider what information they are given, what they are trying to prove, and what relationships they can use to prove it.

Example 3

CRITICAL THINKING Have students explain why it can be concluded that $m\angle 1 + m\angle 2 = m\angle 3 + m\angle 2$.

You may want to review the marks used to indicate congruent segments and angles, right angles, perpendicular lines, and parallel lines.

A convincing argument that uses deductive reasoning is also called a *proof.* A conjecture that is proven is a **theorem.** The Vertical Angles Theorem is actually a special case of the following theorem.

Theorem 1-2 Congruent Supplements Theorem

If two angles are supplements of congruent angles (or of the same angle), then the two angles are congruent.

Example 3

Write a convincing argument that supplements of the same angle are congruent.

Given: $\angle 1$ and $\angle 2$ are supplementary.
$\angle 3$ and $\angle 2$ are supplementary.

Prove: $\angle 1 \cong \angle 3$

Because $\angle 1$ and $\angle 2$ are supplementary, $m\angle 1 + m\angle 2 = 180$.
Because $\angle 3$ and $\angle 2$ are supplementary, $m\angle 3 + m\angle 2 = 180$.
So $m\angle 1 + m\angle 2 = m\angle 3 + m\angle 2$.
Therefore, $m\angle 1 = m\angle 3$, and $\angle 1 \cong \angle 3$.

7. **Try This** An argument is convincing only if any reasons that are not stated are clearly understood. What is the reason that $m\angle 1 = m\angle 3$? **Subtraction Prop. of =**

The next theorem is much like the Congruent Supplements Theorem.

Theorem 1-3 Congruent Complements Theorem

If two angles are complements of congruent angles (or of the same angle), then the two angles are congruent.

As you will see in Chapter 4, a proof may take many different forms. The format of a proof is not important. Logical use of deductive reasoning is.

You can draw certain conclusions directly from diagrams. You can conclude that angles are
- vertical angles
- adjacent angles
- adjacent supplementary angles.

Unless there are marks that give this information, you cannot assume that
- angles or segments are congruent
- an angle is a right angle
- lines are perpendicular or parallel.

8. What can you conclude? Explain. **a–c. See margin.**

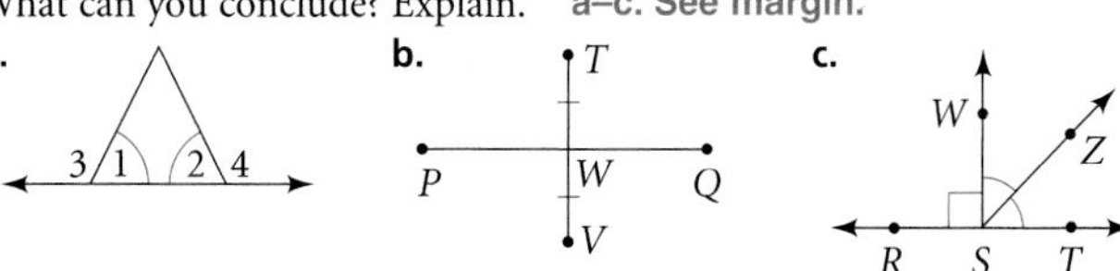

pages 48–49 Think and Discuss

8a. $\angle 1 \cong \angle 2$ as they are marked. From the Angle Add. Post., $\angle 3$ and $\angle 1$ as well as $\angle 4$ and $\angle 2$ are supplements. $\angle 3 \cong \angle 4$ by the Congruent Supplements Thm.

b. $\overline{TW} \cong \overline{WV}$ as they are marked congruent. $\overline{PQ}$ bisects $\overline{TV}$ by definition of segment bisector.

c. $\angle RSW$ is a right angle and $\angle WSZ \cong \angle ZST$ because of markings. $\angle WST$ is a right angle by def. of $\perp$ lines. $m\angle RSW = 90$ by def. of right angle. $m\angle WSZ = m\angle ZST = 45$ because they are $\cong$ and the sum of their measures is 90.

Exercises ON YOUR OWN

ALTERNATIVE ASSESSMENT **Exercises 1–10** These exercises can be used to assess students' understanding of the properties of equality and congruence. Check that students understand that Exercises 6–8 are examples of properties of equality because lengths and measures are real numbers.

ALGEBRA **Exercise 14** Ask students to share their methods for finding the solution with the class. Some may solve for x or y independently ($3x = 75$, $y + 75 = 180$) while others may solve a system of equations $\begin{cases} 3x + y = 180 \\ y + 75 = 180 \end{cases}$.

COORDINATE GEOMETRY **Exercise 19b** Most students will find the coordinates visually. Others who are familiar with coordinate geometry may use the fact that the product of the slopes of two perpendicular lines is -1.

ALGEBRA **Exercise 21** Students can solve this problem similarly to how they solved Exercise 14.

pages 50–52 On Your Own

26. $m\angle DOA = 55$ as vert. angles are $\cong$. $m\angle DOB = m\angle AOC = 125$ as these are supplements of $\angle BOC$.
27. $\angle EIG$ and $\angle FIH$ are right angles by the markings. $\angle EIF \cong \angle GIH$ because they are complements of the same angle.
28. $\angle JPK \cong \angle JPM$ by the markings. Also by the Angle Add. Post., $\angle JPK$ and $\angle KPL$ are supplements and $\angle JPM$ and $\angle MPL$ are supplements. $\angle KPL \cong \angle MPL$ as supplements of $\cong$ angles are $\cong$.
32. Because $\angle 1$ and $\angle 2$ are complementary, $m\angle 1 + m\angle 2 = 90$. Because $\angle 3$ and $\angle 2$ are complementary, $m\angle 3 + m\angle 2 = 90$. So $m\angle 1 + m\angle 2 = m\angle 3 + m\angle 2$ by Substitution. Therefore, $m\angle 1 = m\angle 3$, and $\angle 1 \cong \angle 3$.
33. Because $\angle 1$ and $\angle 2$ are supplementary, $m\angle 1 + m\angle 2 = 180$. Because $\angle 3$ and $\angle 4$ are supplementary, $m\angle 3 + m\angle 4 = 180$. So, $m\angle 1 + m\angle 2 = m\angle 3 + m\angle 4$. Because $\angle 2 \cong \angle 4$, $m\angle 2 = m\angle 4$. Thus, by Subtraction Prop. of =, $m\angle 1 = m\angle 3$ and $\angle 1 \cong \angle 3$.

Exercises ON YOUR OWN

Name the property that justifies each statement.

1. $\angle Z \cong \angle Z$ Reflexive Prop. of $\cong$
2. If $12x = 84$, then $x = 7$. Division Prop. of =
3. If $\overline{ST} \cong \overline{QR}$, then $\overline{QR} \cong \overline{ST}$. Symmetric Prop. of $\cong$
4. If $3x + 14 = 80$, then $3x = 66$. Subtraction Prop. of =
5. If $2x + y = 5$ and $x = y$, then $2x + x = 5$. Substitution Prop.
6. If $AB - BC = 12$, then $AB = 12 + BC$. Add. Prop. of =
7. If $m\angle A = 15$, then $3m\angle A = 45$. Mult. Prop. of =
8. $QR = QR$ Reflexive Prop. of =
9. If $\angle 1 \cong \angle 2$ and $\angle 2 \cong \angle 3$, then $\angle 1 \cong \angle 3$. Trans. Prop. of $\cong$
10. $2(3x + 5) = 6x + 10$ Dist. Prop.
11. **Writing** How is a theorem different from a postulate? A theorem can be proven; a postulate is assumed to be true.
12. **Open-ended** Give an example of vertical angles in your home. Answers may vary. Sample: scissors or salad tongs

Algebra **Find the values of the variables.**

13. 9

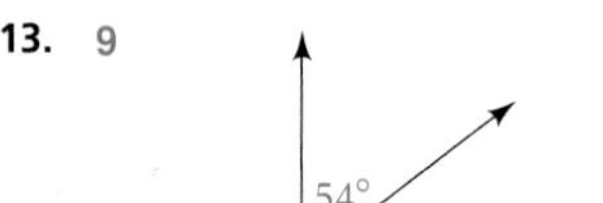

14. x = 25; y = 105

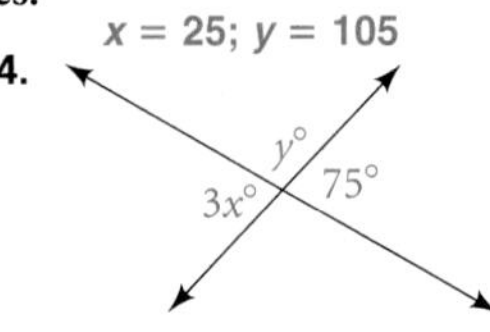

15. 18

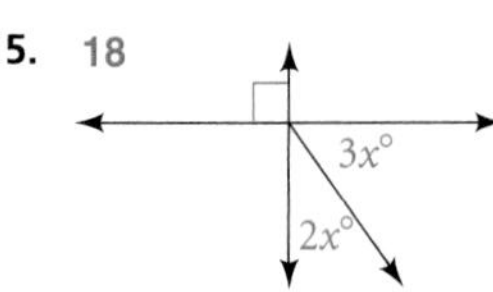

16. 15

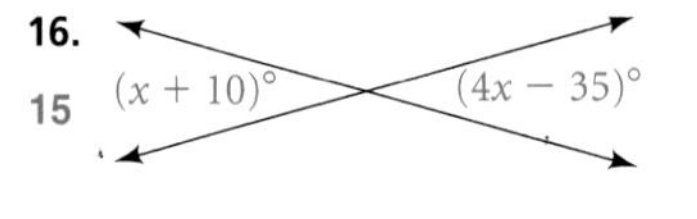

17. 10

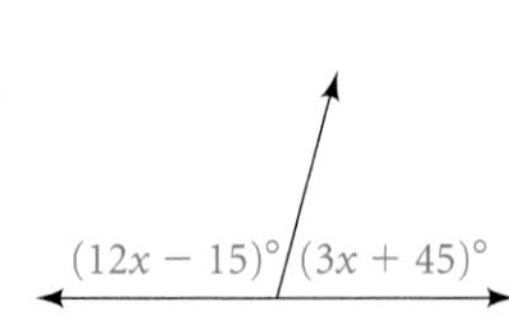

18. 11

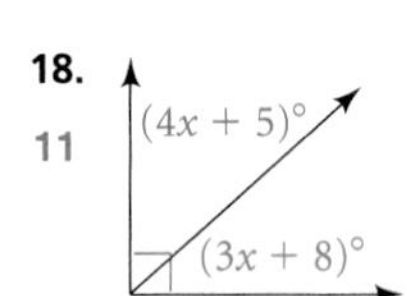

19. a. **Coordinate Geometry** $\angle AOX$ contains points $A(1, 3)$, $O(0, 0)$, and $X(4, 0)$. Find the coordinates of a point B so that $\angle BOA$ and $\angle AOX$ are adjacent complementary angles. B can be any point on the positive y-axis, for example, (0, 5).
    b. Find the coordinates of a point C so that $\overrightarrow{OC}$ is a side of a different angle that is adjacent to and complementary to $\angle AOX$. Answers may vary. Sample: (3, –1)
    c. $\angle DOE$ contains points $D(2, 3)$, $O(0, 0)$, and $E(5, 1)$. Find the coordinates of a point F so that $\overrightarrow{OF}$ is a side of an angle that is adjacent to and supplementary to $\angle DOE$. Answers may vary. Sample: (–5, –1)
20. **Algebra** $\angle A$ and $\angle B$ are supplementary angles. $m\angle A = 3x + 12$ and $m\angle B = 2x - 22$. Find the measures of both angles. $m\angle A = 126$; $m\angle B = 54$
21. **Algebra** Solve for x and y. $x = 14$; $y = 15$

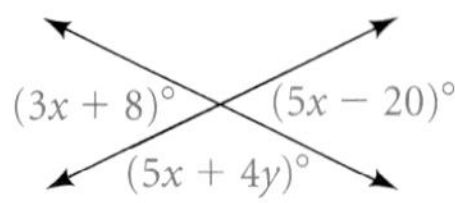

STANDARDIZED TEST TIP Exercise 22 Remind students that figures are not always drawn to scale, so they cannot assume that one angle is larger than another by how they appear.

VISUAL LEARNING Exercises 23–24 Students may benefit from the following drawings.

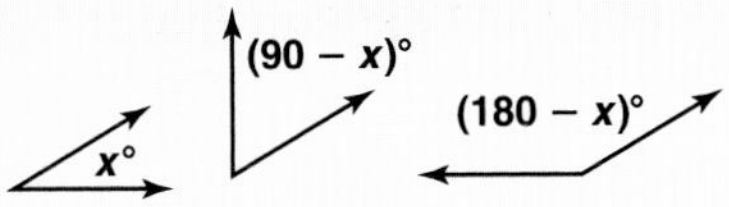

$x°$ $(90 - x)°$ $(180 - x)°$

Exercises 26–28 Have students work in groups to find as many relationships among the angles as possible.

Exercises 32–33 Have students copy the "Given" and "Prove" onto their homework papers before they begin writing their arguments. Remind them to justify each of the statements in their arguments.

22. *Standardized Test Prep* In the diagrams at the right, which is greater, x or y? y

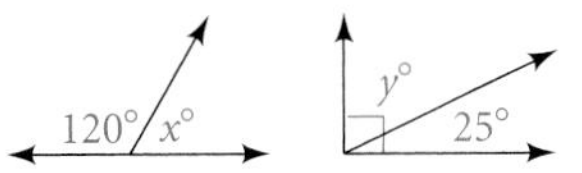

23. *Critical Thinking* If possible, find the measures of the angles described. If it is not possible, explain why.
    a. congruent adjacent supplementary angles 90
    b. congruent adjacent complementary angles 45
    c. congruent vertical angles Not possible; all vertical angles are ≅.

24. *Algebra* The measure of a supplement of ∠1 is six times the measure of a complement of ∠1. Find the measures of ∠1, its supplement, and its complement. $m\angle 1 = 72$; supplement, 108; complement, 18

25. One angle is twice as large as its complement. Find the measures of both angles. 30 and 60

PROBLEM SOLVING HINT

Let $x = m\angle 1$. Then $180 - x$ = measure of its supplement, and $90 - x$ = measure of its complement.

What can you conclude about the angles in each diagram? Justify your answers. 26–28. See margin p. 50.

26.

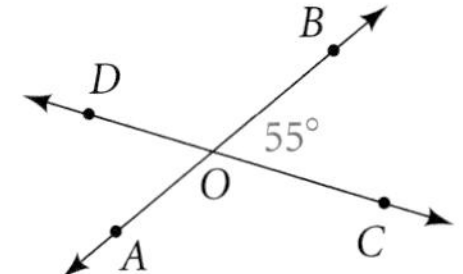

27.

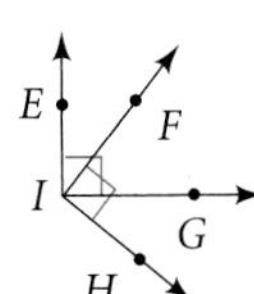

28.

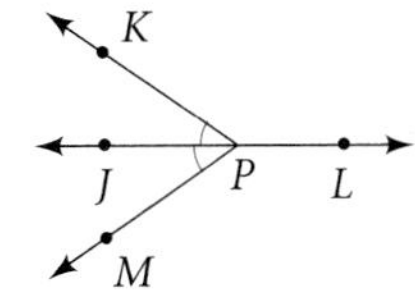

Give a reason for each step.

29. $3x - 15 = 105$
    $3x = 120$
    $x = 40$
    Add. Prop. of =; Div. Prop. of =;

30. $12y + 24 = 96$
    $12y = 72$
    $y = 6$
    Subtr. Prop. of =; Div. Prop. of =

31. $\frac{1}{2}x - 5 = 10$
    $2(\frac{1}{2}x - 5) = 20$
    $x - 10 = 20$
    $x = 30$
    Mult. Prop. of =; Distr. Prop.; Add. Prop. of =

✪32. *Preparing for Proof* Write a convincing argument that complements of the same angle are congruent.

Given: ∠1 and ∠2 are complementary.
∠3 and ∠2 are complementary.
Prove: ∠1 ≅ ∠3 See margin p. 50.

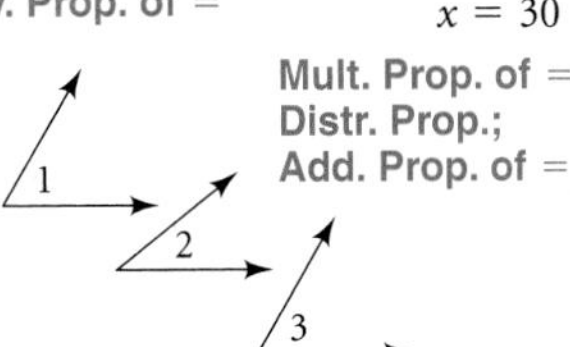

✪33. *Preparing for Proof* Write a convincing argument that supplements of congruent angles are congruent.

Given: ∠1 and ∠2 are supplementary.
∠3 and ∠4 are supplementary.
∠2 ≅ ∠4
Prove: ∠1 ≅ ∠3 See margin p. 50.

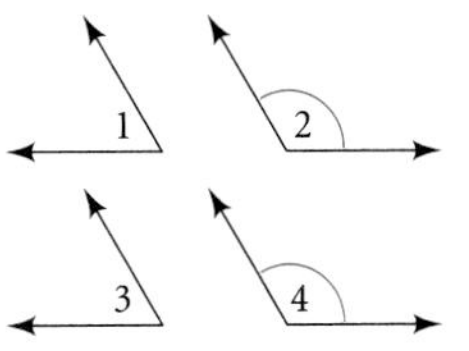

page 52 Mixed Review

39.

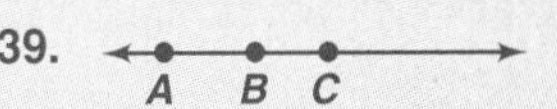

40.

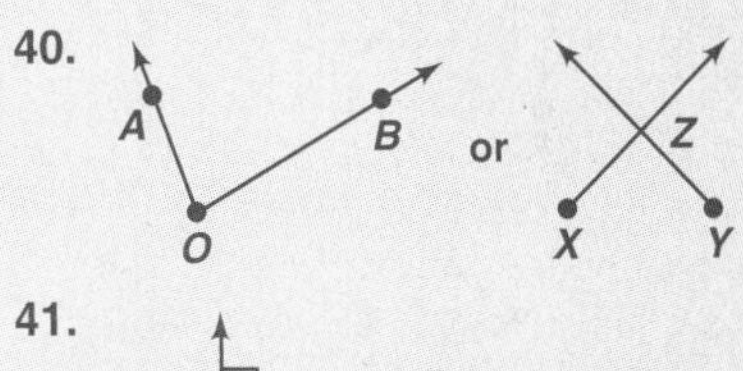

41. m ℓ

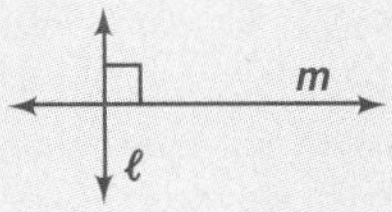

Checkpoint page 52

2a.

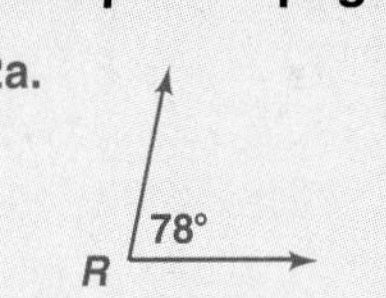

b.

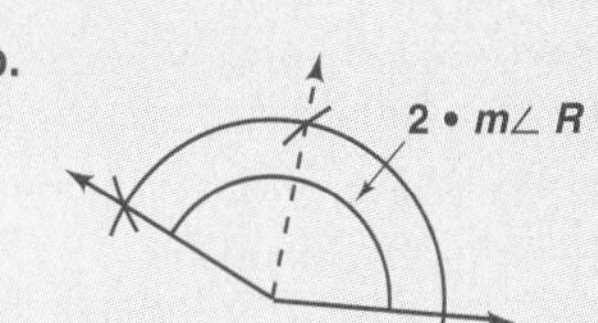

c.

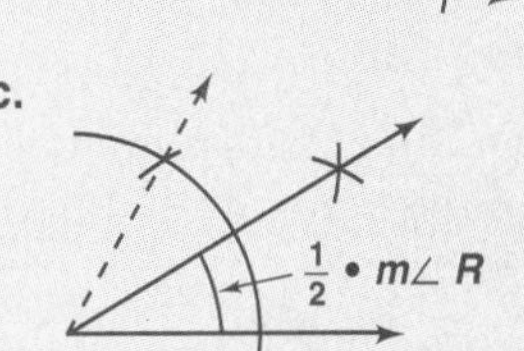

3. $m\angle 1 + m\angle 2 = 90$

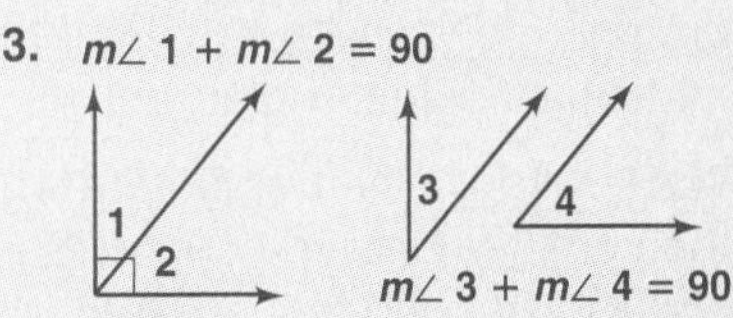

Exercises MIXED REVIEW

Exercises 39–41 Have students label and name the points, rays, and lines.

GETTING READY FOR LESSON 1-8 These exercises prepare students for using the distance formula in Lesson 1-8.

Wrap Up

THE BIG IDEA Ask students: *Describe the difference between inductive and deductive reasoning. Give examples to support your answer.*

RETEACHING ACTIVITY Students are given the statements of an argument out of order. They must rearrange the statements in the correct order. (Reteaching worksheet 1-7)

Exercises CHECKPOINT

In this Checkpoint, your students will assess their own progress on Lessons 1-5 to 1-7.

Exercise 2 Students will need a protractor and a compass.

Exercise 3 Students will need a protractor.

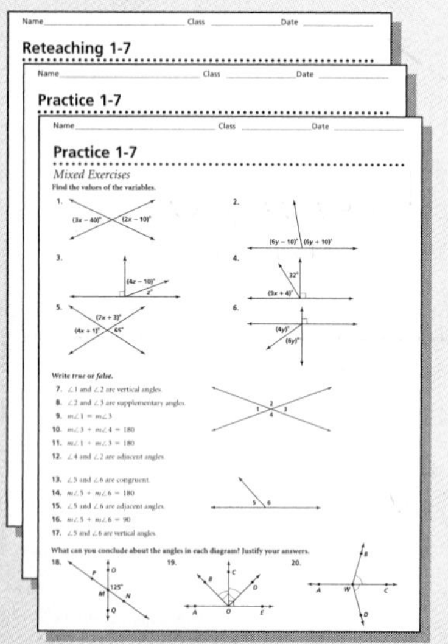

Lesson Quiz

Lesson Quiz is also available in Transparencies.

1. Name the property of congruence that justifies the following statement. If $\overline{QR} \cong \overline{OP}$, then $\overline{OP} \cong \overline{QR}$. **Symmetric Property**
2. The measures of two complementary angles are $3x + 4$ and $5x + 6$. Find x. $x = 10$
3. The measures of two vertical angles are $4x - 10$ and $2x + 8$. Find the measures of the angles. **26**
4. Write a convincing argument why the complements of congruent angles are congruent. Given: $\angle 1$ and $\angle 2$ are complements, $\angle 3$ and $\angle 4$ are complements, $\angle 2 \cong \angle 4$ Prove: $\angle 1 \cong \angle 3$. **See back of book.**

Use the cartoon and deductive reasoning to answer *yes* or *no*. Explain any *no*.

34. Could a person with a red car park here on Tuesday at 10:00 A.M? No; red cars may not park.
35. Could a man with a beard park here on Monday at 10:30 A.M.? No; guys with beards may not park on Mon.
36. Could a woman with a wig park here on Saturday at 10:00 A.M.? yes
37. Could a person with a blue car park here on Tuesday at 9:05 A.M.? No; parking is not allowed from 6:49 A.M. to 9:11 A.M. on Tues.
38. Could a person with a convertible with leather seats park here on Sunday at 6:00 P.M.? yes

NO PARKING THIS SIDE
M-W-F 4:00AM-5:30AM
7:37AM-10:12 AM
12:31 PM-4:19 PM
7:06PM-10:13PM
T-TH-S-SU 2:30AM-2:37AM
6:49AM-9:11AM
11:42AM-5:07 PM
• NO RED CARS
• NO CARS WITH VINYL SEATS
• NO GUYS WITH BEARDS ON MONDAYS

Exercises MIXED REVIEW

Sketch each of the following. 39–41. See margin p. 51.

39. three collinear points
40. two intersecting rays
41. two perpendicular lines
42. Find the next three terms in the sequence: $1, 1, \frac{1}{2}, \frac{1}{3}, \frac{1}{5}, \frac{1}{8}, \ldots$ $\frac{1}{13}, \frac{1}{21}, \frac{1}{34}$

Getting Ready for Lesson 1-8

Calculator **Find the square root of each number to the nearest tenth.**

43. 25 5
44. 17 4.1
45. 123 11.1
46. 48 6.9
47. 96 9.8
48. 1023 32.0

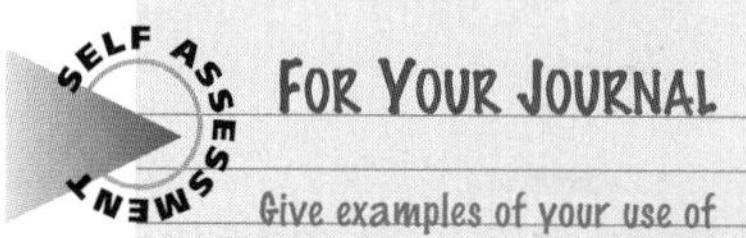

Give examples of your use of deductive and inductive reasoning in the last month.

Exercises CHECKPOINT

1. Writing What are the components of a good definition? A good definition states precisely what a term is, using commonly understood or previously defined terms.
2. a. Use a protractor to draw $\angle R$ with measure 78.
   b. Construct an angle whose measure is $2 \cdot m\angle R$.
   c. Construct an angle whose measure is $\frac{1}{2} \cdot m\angle R$.
   a–c. See margin p. 51.
3. Open-ended Use a protractor to draw a pair of adjacent complementary angles. Then draw another pair of complementary angles that are *not* adjacent. See margin p. 51.
4. Standardized Test Prep If $-6 \leq x \leq 1$ is graphed on a number line, its graph is which of the following? C
   A. 7 points B. 8 points C. a segment D. a line E. a ray

1-8 Teaching Notes

PROBLEM OF THE DAY

A rectangle measures 10 units by 15 units and is tiled with unit-square tiles. How many tiles are crossed by one diagonal of the rectangle? 20

Problem of the Day is also available in Transparencies.

CONNECTING TO PRIOR KNOWLEDGE Discuss with students types of maps they have seen such as world maps, globes, state maps, local maps, subway maps, bike and hiking paths, and elevation maps.

WORK TOGETHER

You may need to review with students how to use a scale to find distances on a map.

CONNECTING TO STUDENTS' WORLD Have students bring in local maps and develop a coordinate system and scale. Then have them find the coordinates of two locations on a diagonal street and find the distance between the two locations using the distance formula.

Connections Transportation . . . *and more*

1-8 The Coordinate Plane

What You'll Learn

- Finding the distance between two points in a coordinate plane
- Finding the coordinates of the midpoint of a segment in a coordinate plane

...And Why

To improve skills such as map reading

What You'll Need

tracing paper, ruler, graph paper

WORK TOGETHER

Much of New York City is laid out in a rectangular grid, as shown in this map. Most of the streets in the grid are either parallel or perpendicular.

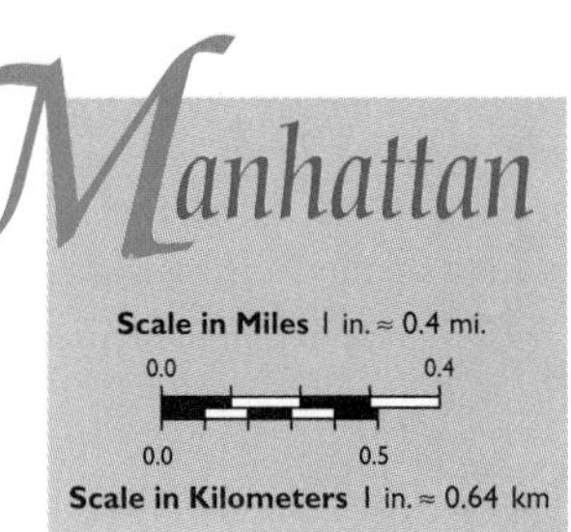

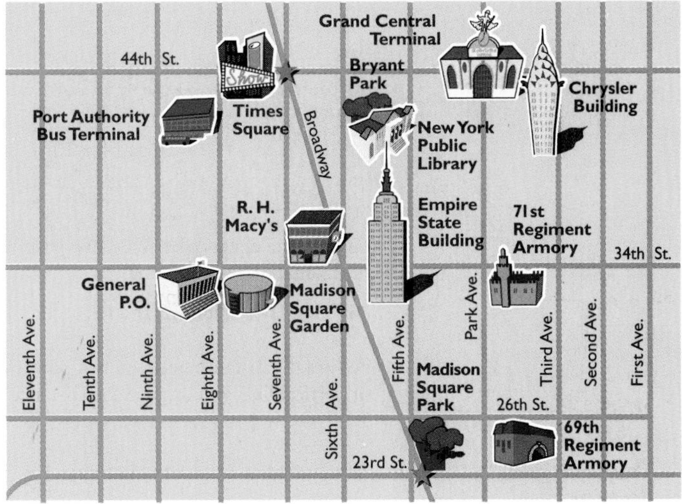

Yvonne's family is on the corner of 44th Street and 7th Avenue. They plan to walk to Madison Square Park at 23rd Street and 5th Avenue. There are several possible routes they can take.

Work with your group. Trace the routes on the map and answer the following questions.

1. Yvonne's father wants to walk east on 44th Street until they reach 5th Avenue. He then plans to walk south on 5th Avenue to Madison Square Park. About how long is his route? 1.4 mi
2. Yvonne's mother wants to walk south on 7th Avenue until they reach 23rd Street. She then plans to walk east on 23rd Street to Madison Square Park. About how long is her route? 1.4 mi
3. Yvonne notices on the map that Broadway cuts across the grid of streets and leads to Madison Square Park. She suggests walking all the way on Broadway. About how long is her route? 1.1 mi
4. Whose route is the shortest? Why? 4. Yvonne's; the shortest distance between two points is a straight line.
5. Whose route is the longest? Why?

5. Yvonne's mother's and father's routes are the same length; both paths have a turn in them.

Lesson Planning Options

Prerequisite Skills

- Finding distance on a number line
- Using a calculator to find square roots

Assignment Options for Exercises On Your Own

Core 1–25, 27–31

✪**Extension** 26, 32–33

Use Mixed Review to maintain skills.

Resources

Student Edition

Skills Handbook, p. 673
Extra Practice, p. 648
Glossary/Study Guide

Teaching Resources

Chapter Support File, Ch. 1
- Practice 1-8 (two worksheets)
- Reteaching 1-8

Classroom Manager 1-8
Glossary, Spanish Resources

Transparencies
5, 25

THINK AND DISCUSS

Students were shown distance on a number line in Lesson 1-4. Show how vertical and horizontal segments not on the axes can be thought of as part of a number line.

Some students may be familiar with the distance formula from algebra. Some may also be familiar with the Pythagorean Theorem from which the distance formula is derived. The Pythagorean Theorem is presented in Lesson 5-3.

Example 1 Relating to the Real World

CRITICAL THINKING As students read the problem, discuss how the directions can be used to plot points on a coordinate grid. Help students understand that the distance formula is used to find the solution because the two locations do not lie on the same vertical or horizontal line.

Additional Examples

FOR EXAMPLE 1

Refer to the diagram for Example 1. Symphony Station is 1 mi east and 2 mi north of City Plaza and Elm Station is 3 mi west and 6 mi south of City Plaza. How far is Symphony Station from Elm Station?

Let $(x_1, y_1) = (1, 2)$ and $(x_2, y_2) = (-3, -6)$.

$d = \sqrt{(1-(-3))^2 + (2-(-6))^2}$
$= \sqrt{16 + 64} = \sqrt{80} \approx 8.9$

about 8.9 mi

FOR EXAMPLE 2

Find the coordinates of the midpoint of $\overline{AB}$ with endpoints $A(2, 3)$ and $B(-5, 7)$. $(-1.5, 5)$

Discussion: *Does it matter which point is chosen as (x_1, y_1)?*

THINK AND DISCUSS

You can think of a point as a dot, and a line as a series of points. In coordinate geometry you can describe a point with an ordered pair (x, y) and a line with an equation $y = mx + b$.

QUICK REVIEW

The x- and y-axes divide the coordinate plane into four quadrants.

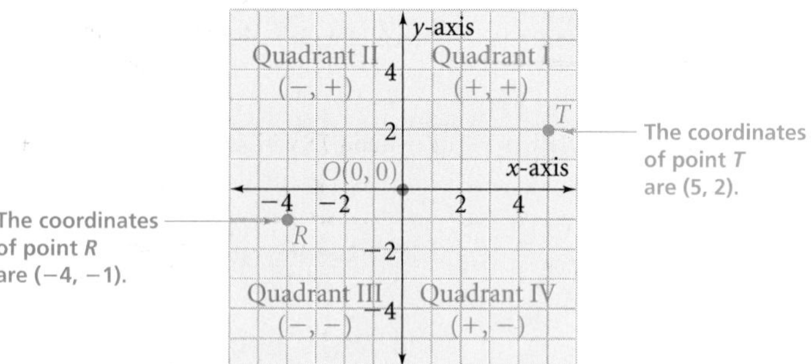

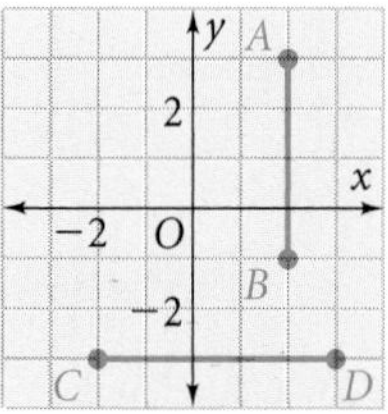

Finding the distance between two points is easy if the points lie on a horizontal or a vertical line.

6. **Try This** Find AB and CD in the graph at the left. 4; 5

To find the distance between two points that are not on the same horizontal or vertical line, you can use the Distance Formula.

The Distance Formula

The distance d between two points $A(x_1, y_1)$ and $B(x_2, y_2)$ is

$$d = \sqrt{(x_2 - x_1)^2 + (y_2 - y_1)^2}.$$

Example 1 Relating to the Real World

Transportation Luisa takes the subway from Oak Station to Jackson Station each morning. Oak Station is 1 mi west and 2 mi south of City Plaza. Jackson Station is 2 mi east and 4 mi north of City Plaza. How far does she travel by subway?

Let (x_1, y_1) and (x_2, y_2) represent Oak and Jackson, respectively. Then, $x_1 = -1, x_2 = 2, y_1 = -2,$ and $y_2 = 4$.

$d = \sqrt{(x_2 - x_1)^2 + (y_2 - y_1)^2}$ Use the Distance Formula.

$d = \sqrt{(2-(-1))^2 + (4-(-2))^2}$ Substitute.

$d = \sqrt{3^2 + 6^2}$ Simplify.

$d = \sqrt{9 + 36} = \sqrt{45}$

45  6.7082039 Use your calculator.

Luisa travels about 6.7 mi by subway.

ERROR ALERT! **Question 8** Students using calculators must make sure that the correct order of operations is used. **Remediation:** Give students enough time to practice using the distance formula. They will need to use memory or parentheses keys. By working in groups, students can check each other's work.

EXTENSION Question 11 Have students work in groups to generalize the diagram by finding coordinates for R, M_1, and M_2 when S has coordinates (x_1, y_1) and T has coordinates (x_2, y_2).

Example 2

VISUAL LEARNING Have students check the results by graphing the segment and midpoint on a coordinate plane.

The system of longitude and latitude lines on Earth is a type of coordinate system.

7. In Example 1 suppose you let (x_1, y_1) be $(2, 4)$ and (x_2, y_2) be $(-1, -2)$. Would you get the same result? Why or why not? See below.

8. *Calculator* Find the length of $\overline{AB}$ with endpoints $A(1, -3)$ and $B(-4, 4)$ to the nearest tenth. 8.6

You know how to find the midpoint of a segment on a number line. Now you will use a similar process to find the midpoint of a segment in the coordinate plane.

Graph $\overline{TS}$ with endpoints $T(4, 3)$ and $S(8, 5)$. Let $\overline{TR}$ be a horizontal segment and $\overline{SR}$ be a vertical segment. Add the coordinates to your drawing as you answer these questions.

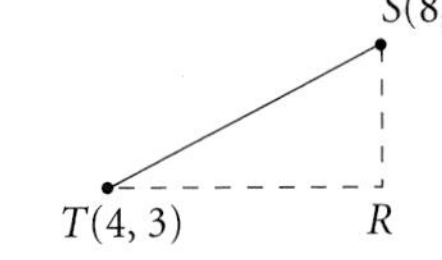

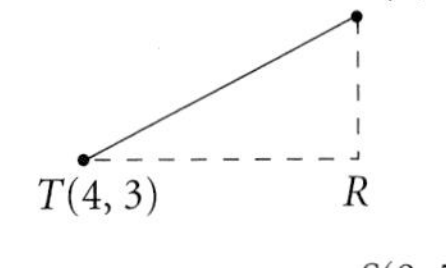

9. What are the coordinates of point R? (8, 3)

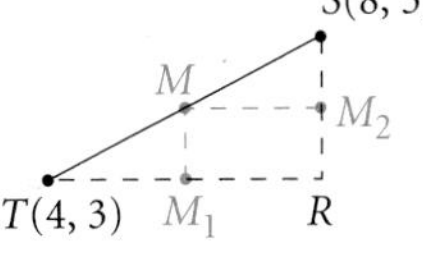

10. a. What are the coordinates of M_1, the midpoint of $\overline{TR}$? (6, 3)
    b. What are the coordinates of M_2, the midpoint of $\overline{SR}$? (8, 4)

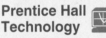

11. What are the coordinates of M, the midpoint of $\overline{TS}$? (6, 4)

This specific case shows you how the Midpoint Formula was developed.

The Midpoint Formula

The coordinates of the midpoint M of $\overline{AB}$ with endpoints $A(x_1, y_1)$ and $B(x_2, y_2)$ are the following:

$$M = \left(\frac{x_1 + x_2}{2}, \frac{y_1 + y_2}{2}\right)$$

Example 2

QUICK REVIEW

$\frac{x_1 + x_2}{2}$ is the *arithmetic mean* of x_1 and x_2. Another word for arithmetic mean is *average*.

Find the coordinates of the midpoint M of $\overline{QS}$ with endpoints $Q(3, 5)$ and $S(7, -9)$.

Let $x_1 = 3, x_2 = 7, y_1 = 5$, and $y_2 = -9$.

$$x\text{-coordinate of } M = \frac{x_1 + x_2}{2} = \frac{3 + 7}{2} = \frac{10}{2} = 5$$

$$y\text{-coordinate of } M = \frac{y_1 + y_2}{2} = \frac{5 + (-9)}{2} = \frac{-4}{2} = -2$$

The coordinates of point M are $(5, -2)$.

12. **Try This** Find the coordinates of the midpoint of $\overline{AB}$ with endpoints $A(2, -5)$ and $B(6, 13)$. (4, 4)

7. Yes; the differences between coordinates have opposite signs from those in Example 1, but when you square them, the result is the same.

Technology Options

In Exercises 7–15, students may write a program on a computer or graphing calculator that will calculate the distance between two points when their coordinates are entered.

Prentice Hall Technology

Software
- Secondary Math Lab Toolkit™
- Integrated Math Lab 24
- Computer Item Generator 1-8

Internet
- See the Prentice Hall site. (http://www.phschool.com)

Exercises ON YOUR OWN

Exercises 16–21 Encourage students to graph the segment and midpoint to check that each answer is reasonable.

Exercise 23 Have students discuss their methods for finding the solution. Possible methods include: using the formula to write and solve two equations, or reading the results from a graph, checking, and revising if necessary.

ALTERNATIVE ASSESSMENT **Exercises 29–31** These exercises can help you assess students' ability to use the midpoint and distance formulas. Students should carefully determine the coordinates of each endpoint. They can use the graphs to estimate the midpoints and distances to check that their answers are reasonable.

ESL VISUAL LEARNING **Exercise 33** Before students begin this problem, you may want to display a model of a three-dimensional coordinate system and discuss which directions are *positive* and *negative* on each axis.

pages 56–57 On Your Own

1–6.

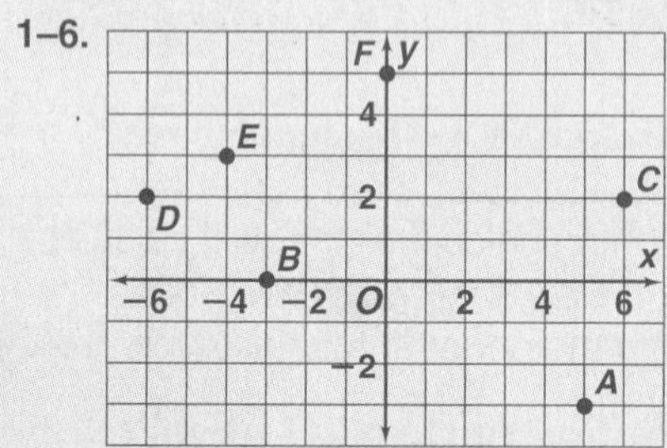

26a. $D(3, 6)$ or $D(-5, 2)$

b. exactly one point $E(-5, 2)$

c. $G(1, 0)$ or $G(-1, 4)$

d. $H(3, 4)$ or $H(2, 6)$

33b.

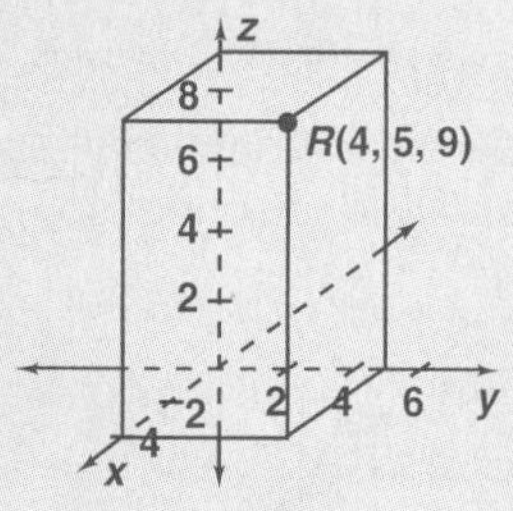

Exercises ON YOUR OWN

Graph each point in the same coordinate plane. 1–6. See margin.

1. $A(5, -3)$ **2.** $B(-3, 0)$ **3.** $C(6, 2)$ **4.** $D(-6, 2)$ **5.** $E(-4, 3)$ **6.** $F(0, 5)$

Choose **Use mental math, pencil and paper, or a calculator to find the distance between the points to the nearest tenth.**

7. $J(2, -1), K(2, 5)$ 6 **8.** $L(10, 14), M(-8, 14)$ 18 **9.** $N(-11, -11), P(-11, -3)$ 8

10. $A(0, 3), B(0, 12)$ 9 **11.** $C(12, 6), D(-8, 18)$ 23.3 **12.** $E(6, -2), F(-2, 4)$ 10

13. $Q(12, -12), T(5, 12)$ 25 **14.** $R(0, 5), S(12, 3)$ 12.2 **15.** $X(-3, -4), Y(5, 5)$ 12.0

Find the coordinates of the midpoint of $\overline{HX}$.

16. $H(0, 0), X(8, 4)$ (4, 2) **17.** $H(-1, 3), X(7, -1)$ (3, 1) **18.** $H(13, 8), X(-6, -6)$ $\left(\frac{7}{2}, 1\right)$

19. $H(7, 10), X(5, -8)$ (6, 1) **20.** $H(-6.3, 5.2), X(1.8, -1)$ (−2.25, 2.1) **21.** $H\left(5\frac{1}{2}, -4\frac{3}{4}\right), X\left(2\frac{1}{4}, -1\frac{1}{4}\right)$ $\left(3\frac{7}{8}, -3\right)$

22. The midpoint of $\overline{QS}$ is the origin. Point Q is located in Quadrant II. What quadrant contains point S? IV

23. $M(5, 12)$ is the midpoint of $\overline{AB}$. The coordinates of point A are (2, 6). What are the coordinates of point B? (8, 18)

24. The midpoint of $\overline{QT}$ has coordinates $(3, -4)$. The coordinates of point Q are (2, 3). What are the coordinates of point T? (4, −11)

25. The coordinates of A, B, C, and D are given at the right. Graph the points and draw the segments connecting them in order. Are the lengths of the sides of $ABCD$ the same? Explain.
No; $AD = AB \approx 4.2$, $DC = CB \approx 3.2$.

$A(-6, 2)$ $B(-3, 5)$
$C(-6, 6)$ $D(-9, 5)$

26. *Open-ended* Graph $A(-2, 1)$ and $B(2, 3)$. Draw $\overleftrightarrow{AB}$. For each point described, give two sets of possible coordinates if they exist. Otherwise write "exactly one point" and give the coordinates.

a. point D so that $\overleftrightarrow{CD}$ contains $C(-1, 4)$ and is parallel to $\overleftrightarrow{AB}$

b. point E so that $\overleftrightarrow{AE}$ is parallel to $\overleftrightarrow{BC}$, $\overleftrightarrow{BC}$ contains $C(-1, 4)$, and $\overleftrightarrow{EC}$ is parallel to $\overleftrightarrow{AB}$

c. point G so that $\overleftrightarrow{FG}$ contains $F(0, 2)$ and is perpendicular to $\overleftrightarrow{AB}$

d. point H so that $\overleftrightarrow{HJ}$ contains $J(4, 2)$ and is perpendicular to $\overleftrightarrow{AB}$

26a–d. Answers may vary. See margin for samples.

27. *Writing* Why do you think that some cities are designed with a rectangular grid instead of a triangular grid or some other shape? See above right.

27. Answers may vary. Sample: for convenience in specifying and locating addresses

28. Graph the points $A(2, 1)$, $B(6, -1)$, $C(8, 7)$, and $D(4, 9)$. Draw quadrilateral $ABCD$. Use the Midpoint Formula to determine the midpoints of $\overline{AC}$ and $\overline{BD}$. What do you notice?
Midpoint of AC, (5, 4); midpoint of BD, (5, 4); they are the same.

Exercises MIXED REVIEW

Exercises 34–39 Have students draw complementary and supplementary angles. If such an angle cannot be drawn, have students explain why.

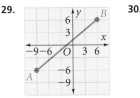

SELF ASSESSMENT PORTFOLIO Share with students the criteria you will use to assess their work in portfolios, as well as how you plan to use the results. Students should understand how the rubrics assess their work, how each piece in the portfolio counts, and how the scores they get in their portfolios will affect their overall evaluation.

Wrap Up

THE BIG IDEA Ask students: *Draw a triangle on the coordinate plane and find the length and midpoint of each side.*

RETEACHING ACTIVITY Students find the lengths of sides of a triangle in the coordinate plane by using the distance formula. (Reteaching worksheet 1-8)

For each graph, find (a) the length of $\overline{AB}$ to the nearest tenth and (b) the coordinates of the midpoint of $\overline{AB}$. 29–31. See below.

29. 30. 31.

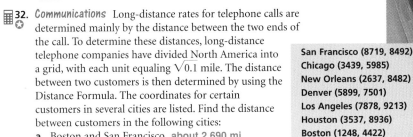

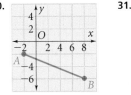

32. **Communications** Long-distance rates for telephone calls are determined mainly by the distance between the two ends of the call. To determine these distances, long-distance telephone companies have divided North America into a grid, with each unit equaling $\sqrt{0.1}$ mile. The distance between two customers is then determined by using the Distance Formula. The coordinates for certain customers in several cities are listed. Find the distance between customers in the following cities:
   a. Boston and San Francisco about 2,690 mi
   b. Houston and Chicago about 934 mi
   c. Denver and New Orleans about 1,077 mi

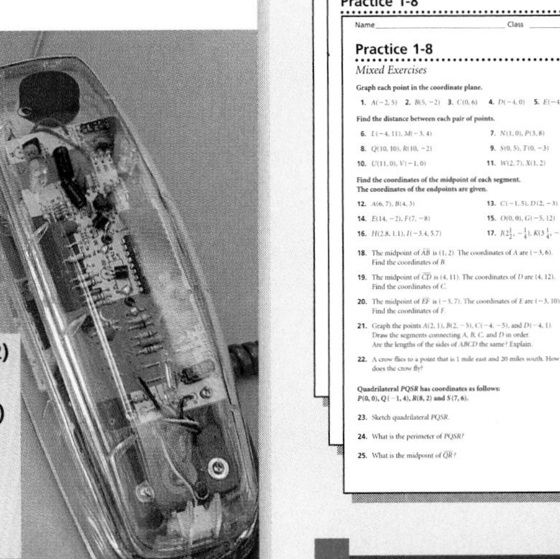

San Francisco (8719, 8492)
Chicago (3439, 5985)
New Orleans (2637, 8482)
Denver (5899, 7501)
Los Angeles (7878, 9213)
Houston (3537, 8936)
Boston (1248, 4422)

33. **Geometry in 3 Dimensions** You can use three coordinates (x, y, z) to locate points in three dimensions. Point P has coordinates $(3, -3, 5)$.
   a. Give the coordinates of points A, B, C, D, E, F, and G. See below.
   b. Draw three axes like those shown. Then graph $R(4, 5, 9)$. See margin p. 56.

33a. $A(0, 0, 0)$, $B(3, 0, 0)$, $C(3, -3, 0)$, $D(0, -3, 0)$ $E(0, 0,5)$, $F(3, 0, 5)$, $G(0, -3, 5)$

Exercises MIXED REVIEW

Find the measure of the complement and supplement of each angle, if possible.

34. $m\angle B = 56$ 34; 124
35. $m\angle R = 18$ 72; 162
36. $m\angle D = 179$
37. $m\angle P = 23.5$ 66.5; 156.5
38. $m\angle T = 108$ not possible; 72
39. $m\angle E = 78$ 12; 102
40. The length of $\overline{AC}$ is 45. If $AB = x + 8$ and $BC = 3x - 3$, find the value of x. 10

36. not possible; 1

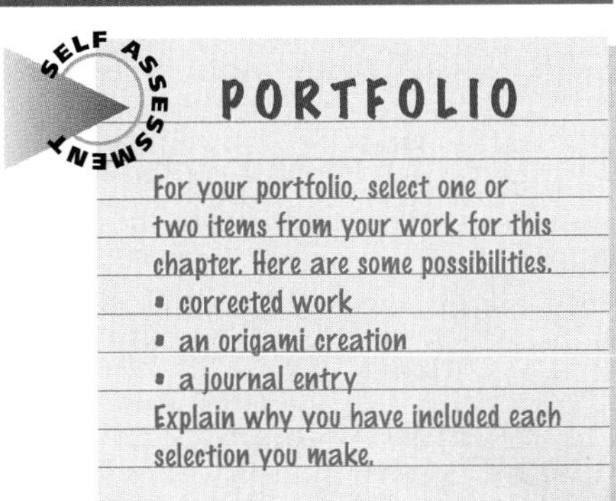

SELF ASSESSMENT
PORTFOLIO
For your portfolio, select one or two items from your work for this chapter. Here are some possibilities.
• corrected work
• an origami creation
• a journal entry
Explain why you have included each selection you make.

29a. 19.2
b. (–1.5, 0)

30a. 10.8
b. (3, –4)

31a. 5.4
b. (–1, 0.5)

Lesson Quiz

Lesson Quiz is also available in Transparencies.

1. Find the distance between $K(5, -6)$ and $L(3, 4)$ to the nearest tenth. 10.2
2. Find the coordinates of the midpoint of the segment with endpoints $E(3, 7)$ and $F(-2, -1)$. (0.5, 3)
3. The midpoint of $\overline{AB}$ has coordinates (3, 4). Point A has coordinates $(-3, -2)$. Find the coordinates of point B. (9, 10)

Finishing the Chapter Project

PROJECT DAY You may wish to plan a project day on which students share their completed projects. Encourage groups to explain their processes as well as their products.

PROJECT NOTEBOOK Have students review their project work and bring their notebooks up to date.

- Have students review their figures, the methods for creating them, and the vocabulary used in writing their instructions.
- Ask groups to share the origami figure that is their favorite. Also ask them what they found most difficult about creating origami figures and what they found most difficult about writing the directions.

SCORING RUBRIC

3 Student's origami figures are created correctly. Instructions are neat and well-organized. Geometry vocabulary is used accurately and appropriately.

2 Student's origami figures are created correctly with few minor flaws. Directions are neat and organized. Geometry vocabulary is used fairly accurately and appropriately and with few inaccuracies.

1 Student's origami figures contain several flaws. Directions are not well organized. Geometry vocabulary is used infrequently.

0 Major elements are incomplete or missing.

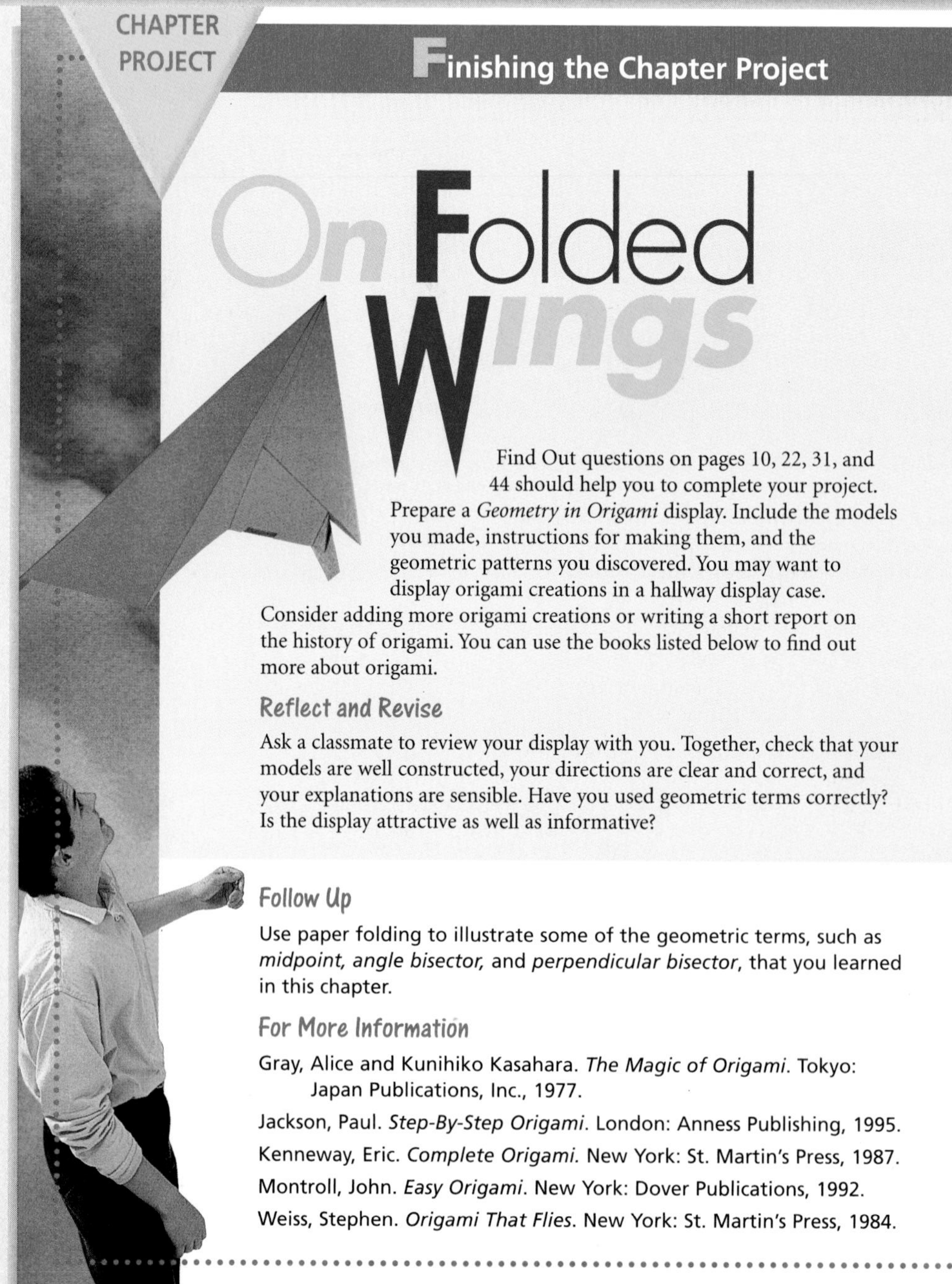

CHAPTER PROJECT

Finishing the Chapter Project

On Folded Wings

Find Out questions on pages 10, 22, 31, and 44 should help you to complete your project. Prepare a *Geometry in Origami* display. Include the models you made, instructions for making them, and the geometric patterns you discovered. You may want to display origami creations in a hallway display case. Consider adding more origami creations or writing a short report on the history of origami. You can use the books listed below to find out more about origami.

Reflect and Revise

Ask a classmate to review your display with you. Together, check that your models are well constructed, your directions are clear and correct, and your explanations are sensible. Have you used geometric terms correctly? Is the display attractive as well as informative?

Follow Up

Use paper folding to illustrate some of the geometric terms, such as *midpoint, angle bisector,* and *perpendicular bisector,* that you learned in this chapter.

For More Information

Gray, Alice and Kunihiko Kasahara. *The Magic of Origami.* Tokyo: Japan Publications, Inc., 1977.

Jackson, Paul. *Step-By-Step Origami.* London: Anness Publishing, 1995.

Kenneway, Eric. *Complete Origami.* New York: St. Martin's Press, 1987.

Montroll, John. *Easy Origami.* New York: Dover Publications, 1992.

Weiss, Stephen. *Origami That Flies.* New York: St. Martin's Press, 1984.

Wrap Up

HOW AM I DOING? Have students work in small groups. Ask each group to make a short presentation of a key idea from this chapter. Each presentation must include a visual aid and a sample problem.

KEY TERMS The numbers in parentheses direct students to the pages where the terms are used or defined. Students should be able to (1) write a simple explanation of each term, (2) illustrate the term with a diagram, or (3) show an example that uses the term.

Exercise 1 Students may describe the pattern in more than one way. For example, each term in the pattern is four more than the previous term. Also the pattern is every other odd number.

1 Wrap Up

Key Terms

acute angle (p. 27)
adjacent angles (p. 48)
angle (p. 26)
angle bisector (p. 34)
collinear (p. 13)
compass (p. 39)
complementary angles (p. 48)
congruent angles (p. 28)
congruent segments (p. 25)
conjecture (p. 5)
construction (p. 39)
coordinate (p. 25)
coplanar (p. 13)
deductive reasoning (p. 46)
inductive reasoning (p. 5)
line (p. 13)
measure of an angle (p. 26)
midpoint (p. 33)
obtuse angle (p. 27)
opposite rays (p. 18)
parallel lines (p. 18)
parallel planes (p. 19)
perpendicular bisector (p. 34)
perpendicular lines (p. 33)
plane (p. 13)
point (p. 12)
postulate (p. 14)
proof (p. 49)
quadrant (p. 54)
ray (p. 18)
right angle (p. 27)
segment (p. 18)
segment bisector (p. 33)
skew lines (p. 19)
space (p. 12)
straight angle (p. 27)
straightedge (p. 39)
supplementary angles (p. 48)
theorem (p. 49)
vertical angles (p. 48)

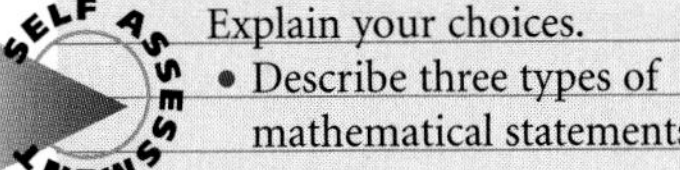

How am I doing?

- State three ideas from this chapter that you think are important. Explain your choices.
- Describe three types of mathematical statements.

Using Patterns and Inductive Reasoning 1-1

You use **inductive reasoning** when you make conclusions from specific examples or patterns. You can use inductive reasoning to make conjectures. A **conjecture** describes a conclusion reached from observations or inductive reasoning. Because conjectures are not always valid, you should verify them if possible.

Find the next two terms of each sequence and describe the pattern.

1. 1, 5, 9, 13, . . . 17, 21
2. 1, 3, 7, 15, 31, . . . 63, 127
3. $\frac{1}{2}, \frac{2}{3}, \frac{3}{4}, \frac{4}{5}, \ldots$ $\frac{5}{6}, \frac{6}{7}$
4. 0, 1, −2, 3, −4, . . . 5, −6
5. Draw the next figure in the sequence.

   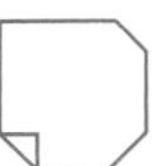

6. a. *Calculator* Find the last two digits of 76^2, 76^4, 276^2, and 376^3. 76
   b. Make a **conjecture** about powers of numbers whose last two digits are 76. The last two digits will always be 76.

1. Add 4 to the previous term to get the next term.
2. Add consecutively increasing powers of 2 to the previous term to get the next term.
3. Add 1 to numerator and denominator of the preceding term to get the next term.
4. Write the sequence of whole numbers and then change the signs of the even whole numbers.

Resources

 **Student Edition**

Extra Practice, p. 634
Glossary/Study Guide

 **Teaching Resources**

Student Skills Handbook
Glossary, Spanish Resources

Exercises 8–13 There is more than one correct answer for each exercise. If students are working in groups, you may want to have each group member give a different answer, if possible.

OPEN-ENDED Exercise 20 Make sure students describe the situation *and* how deductive reasoning is used.

Basic Concepts 1-2, 1-3

Points that lie on a line are **collinear**. Points and lines in the same plane are **coplanar**.

Two coplanar lines that do not intersect are **parallel**. Two lines in space that are not parallel and do not intersect are **skew**. Two planes that do not intersect are **parallel**.

Segments and **rays** are parts of lines.

7. *Critical Thinking* Explain why the postulate "Through any three noncollinear points there is exactly one plane" applies only to noncollinear points. If the points were collinear, an infinite number of planes would pass through them.

Use the figure to answer Exercises 8–13. 8–13. Answers may vary. Samples are given.

8. Name two intersecting lines. $\overleftrightarrow{QR}$ and $\overleftrightarrow{RS}$
9. Name a pair of skew lines. $\overleftrightarrow{QR}$ and $\overleftrightarrow{SC}$
10. Name three noncollinear points. *Q*, *R*, and *S*
11. Name four noncoplanar points. *Q*, *R*, *S*, *C*
12. Name a pair of parallel planes. plane *QRST* and plane *ABCD*
13. Name three lines that intersect at *D*. $\overleftrightarrow{AD}$, $\overleftrightarrow{CD}$, $\overleftrightarrow{TD}$

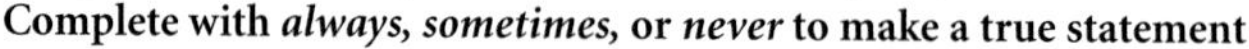

Complete with *always, sometimes,* or *never* to make a true statement

14. A line and a point are __?__ coplanar. always
15. Two segments are __?__ coplanar. sometimes
16. Skew lines are __?__ coplanar. never
17. Opposite rays __?__ have the same endpoint. always
18. Two points are __?__ collinear. always
19. Parallel lines are __?__ skew. never

Angles, Segments, and Deductive Reasoning 1-4, 1-7

Segments with the same length are **congruent.** An **angle** is formed by two rays with the same endpoint. Angles are measured in degrees. Angles with the same measure are **congruent.**

Deductive reasoning is the process of reasoning logically from given facts to a conclusion. If the given facts are true, deductive reasoning always produces a valid conclusion.

Special relationships exist between certain angle pairs. For example, vertical angles are congruent. The sum of the measures of a pair of **complementary angles** is 90. The sum of the measures of a pair of **supplementary angles** is 180.

20. *Open-ended* Describe a real-world situation where you use deductive reasoning. 20. Answers may vary. Sample: You want to use your own money to buy a bicycle that costs \$320. You have \$275. You cannot buy the bike.

21. Find possible coordinates of point *Q* on the number line so that $PQ = 5$. 3 or −7

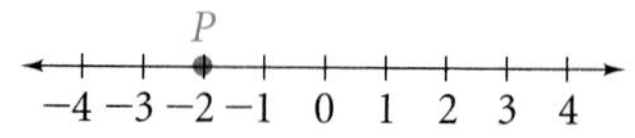

Exercises 22–24 You may want to have students describe what definitions and postulates they used in solving each problem.

Exercises 25–27 Students' conclusions should be about properties of the figure. Students do not need to find angle measures or segment lengths.

ALGEBRA Exercise 30 Students can check their answers by evaluating the variable expressions for BE and EK to see whether they are equal.

Algebra **Find the value of each variable in the diagrams below.**

22. 18

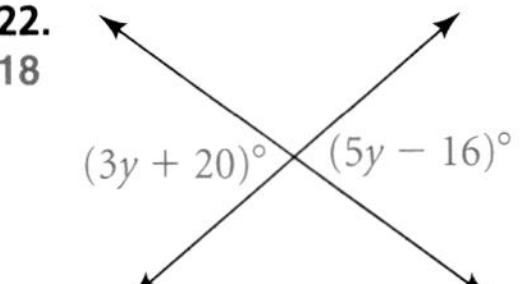

23. 31

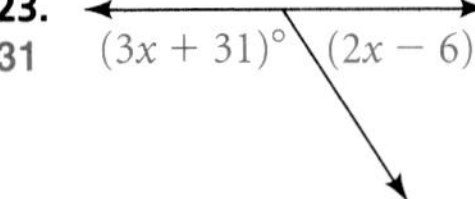

24. 20

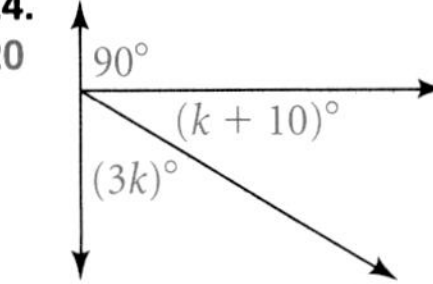

What can you conclude from each diagram? Justify your answers. 25–27. See margin.

25.

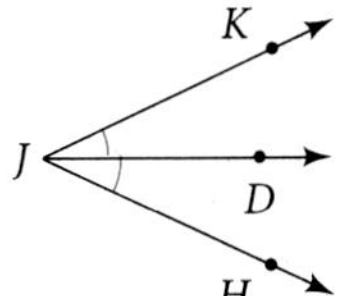

26.

27.

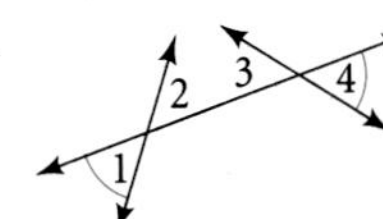

Good Definitions 1-5

A good definition is precise. A good definition uses terms that have been previously defined or are commonly accepted.

The **midpoint** of a segment divides a segment into two congruent segments. **Perpendicular lines** intersect at right angles. A **perpendicular bisector** of a segment is perpendicular to a segment at its midpoint. An **angle bisector** divides an angle into two congruent angles.

28. **Writing** Rico defines a book as something you read. Explain what's wrong with this definition. Write a good definition for the word *book*. See below.

29. **Critical Thinking** In the diagram at the right, $\overleftrightarrow{LJ}$ is the perpendicular bisector of $\overline{BK}$. Is $\overleftrightarrow{BK}$ necessarily the perpendicular bisector of $\overline{LJ}$? Explain. See below.

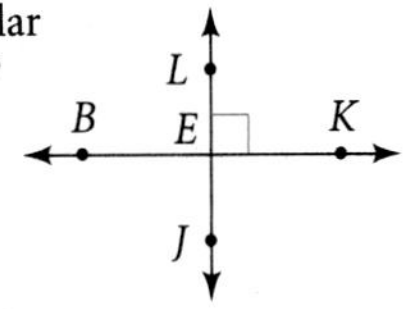

30. **Algebra** In the diagram at right, point E is the midpoint of $\overline{BK}$, $BE = 3y - 2$, and $EK = 2y + 1$. Find the value of y. 3

L
B E K
J

31. Find the coordinate of the midpoint of $\overline{GH}$. 1

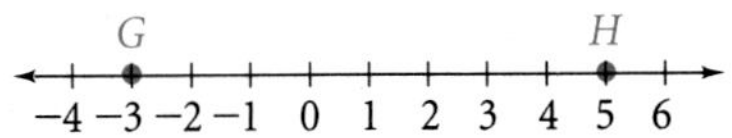

32. **Standardized Test Prep** In which figure is the $m\angle 1$ *not* equal to 60? D

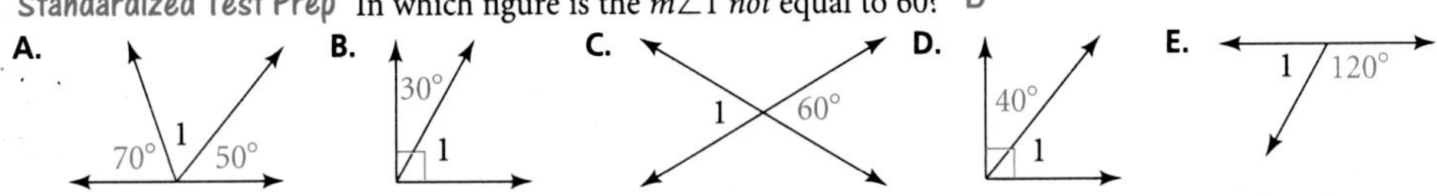

28. Something you read could be a newspaper or traffic sign. A book is a collection of printed pages permanently bound together along one edge. It is usually longer than a magazine.

29. No; $\overleftrightarrow{BK}$ may not bisect $\overline{LJ}$.

Wrap Up pages 59–62

25. $m\angle KJD + m\angle DJH = m\angle KJH$ by the Angle Add. Post.; $m\angle KJD = m\angle DJH$ by the markings; $\overrightarrow{JD}$ bisects $\angle KJH$ by the definition of angle bisector.

26. $AB = CD$ by the markings; $AC = BD$ by the Seg. Add. Post.

27. $\angle 1 \cong \angle 4$ by the markings; $\angle 1 \cong \angle 2$ and $\angle 3 \cong \angle 4$ because vert. angles are $\cong$; $\angle 2 \cong \angle 3$ by the Trans. Prop. of $\cong$.

WRITING Exercise 35 Encourage students to check their descriptions by performing the construction.

ALTERNATIVE ASSESSMENT **Exercises 36–41** Have students connect the points in these exercises to form a plane figure Then have them find the length and midpoint of each segment they draw.

Remind students that the new mathematical terms in this chapter are defined in the Glossary/Study Guide in the back of the book.

Getting Ready For Chapter 2

Students may work these exercises independently or in small groups. The skills previewed will help prepare students to investigate polygons.

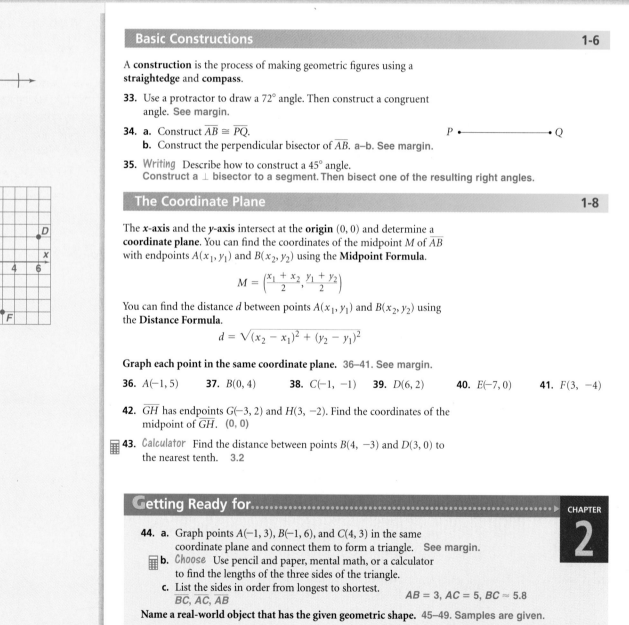

33.

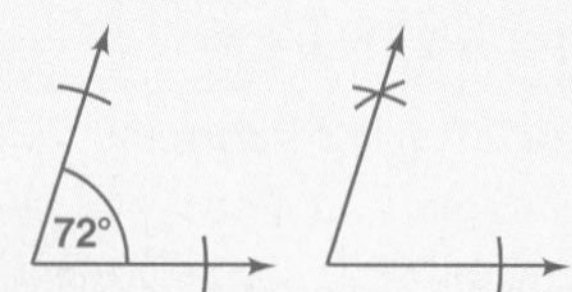

34a–b.

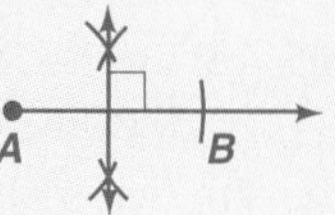

36–41.

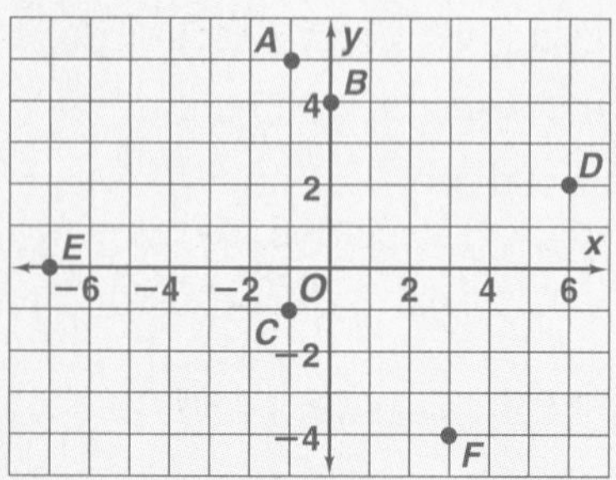

44a.

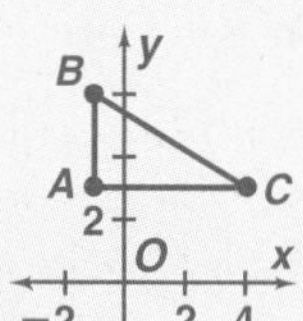

62

Basic Constructions 1-6

A **construction** is the process of making geometric figures using a **straightedge** and **compass**.

33. Use a protractor to draw a 72° angle. Then construct a congruent angle. **See margin.**

34. a. Construct $\overline{AB} \cong \overline{PQ}$. P • ——— • Q
b. Construct the perpendicular bisector of $\overline{AB}$. **a–b. See margin.**

35. *Writing* Describe how to construct a 45° angle.
Construct a ⊥ bisector to a segment. Then bisect one of the resulting right angles.

The Coordinate Plane 1-8

The ***x*-axis** and the ***y*-axis** intersect at the **origin** (0, 0) and determine a **coordinate plane.** You can find the coordinates of the midpoint M of $\overline{AB}$ with endpoints $A(x_1, y_1)$ and $B(x_2, y_2)$ using the **Midpoint Formula.**

$$M = \left(\frac{x_1 + x_2}{2}, \frac{y_1 + y_2}{2}\right)$$

You can find the distance d between points $A(x_1, y_1)$ and $B(x_2, y_2)$ using the **Distance Formula.**

$$d = \sqrt{(x_2 - x_1)^2 + (y_2 - y_1)^2}$$

Graph each point in the same coordinate plane. **36–41. See margin.**

36. $A(-1, 5)$ **37.** $B(0, 4)$ **38.** $C(-1, -1)$ **39.** $D(6, 2)$ **40.** $E(-7, 0)$ **41.** $F(3, -4)$

42. $\overline{GH}$ has endpoints $G(-3, 2)$ and $H(3, -2)$. Find the coordinates of the midpoint of $\overline{GH}$. **(0, 0)**

43. *Calculator* Find the distance between points $B(4, -3)$ and $D(3, 0)$ to the nearest tenth. **3.2**

Getting Ready for CHAPTER 2

44. a. Graph points $A(-1, 3)$, $B(-1, 6)$, and $C(4, 3)$ in the same coordinate plane and connect them to form a triangle. **See margin.**
b. *Choose* Use pencil and paper, mental math, or a calculator to find the lengths of the three sides of the triangle. **AB = 3, AC = 5, BC ≈ 5.8**
c. List the sides in order from longest to shorter. **$\overline{BC}$, $\overline{AC}$, $\overline{AB}$**

Name a real-world object that has the given geometric shape. **45–49. Samples are given.**

45. triangle **yield sign** **46.** circle **clock** **47.** rhombus **quadrilaterals in a chain link fence** **48.** cylinder **soup can** **49.** cube **child's building block**

Assessment

ENHANCED MULTIPLE CHOICE QUESTIONS are more complex than traditional multiple choice questions, which assess only one skill. Enhanced multiple choice questions assess the processes that students use, as well as the end results. The questions are written so that students use more than one strategy to solve the problem. Using multiple strategies is encouraged by the National Council of Teachers of Mathematics (NCTM). **Exercise 36** is an enhanced multiple choice question.

FREE RESPONSE QUESTIONS do not give answer choices. Some exercises have more than one possible answer. Students need to give only one correct response. **Exercises 1–4, 6–21, 23–35, and 37–45** are free response questions.

WRITING EXERCISES allow students to describe how they think about and understand the concepts they have learned. **Exercise 22** is a writing exercise.

OPEN-ENDED PROBLEMS allow for more than one solution. Students must construct their own responses instead of choosing from possible answers. The student responses will help you determine the depth of their understanding and any possible areas of difficulty. **Exercise 5** is an open-ended problem.

1 Assessment

Find the next two terms in each sequence.

1. 8, −4, 2, −1, . . . $\frac{1}{2}, -\frac{1}{4}$
2. 0, 2, 4, 6, 8, . . . 10, 12
3. 

4. 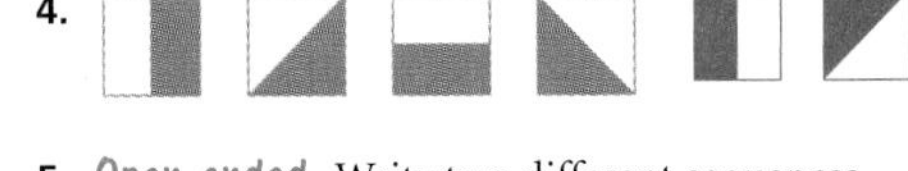
5. *Open-ended* Write two different sequences whose first three terms are 1, 2, 4. Describe each pattern. See margin.

Use the figure to answer Exercises 6–10.

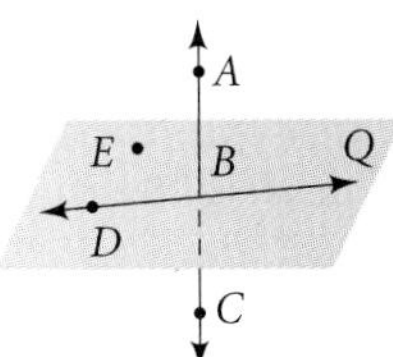

6. Name three collinear points. *A, B, C*
7. Name four coplanar points. *A, B, C, D* (or *A, B, C, E*)
8. Name four noncoplanar points. See margin.
9. What is the intersection of $\overleftrightarrow{AC}$ and plane *Q*? *B*
10. How many planes contain each line and point?
    a. $\overleftrightarrow{BD}$ and point *A* 1 b. $\overleftrightarrow{AB}$ and point *C*
    c. $\overleftrightarrow{BE}$ and point *C* 1 d. $\overleftrightarrow{BD}$ and point *E* 1
    10b. infinitely many

Is the definition of the term in red acceptable? If not, write a good definition. 11–12. See margin.

11. A pencil is a writing instrument.
12. Vertical angles are angles that are congruent.
13. Complementary angles are angles that form a right angle. No; complementary angles are two angles the sum of whose measures is 90.

Complete with *always, sometimes,* or *never* to make each statement true.

14. $\overrightarrow{LJ}$ and $\overrightarrow{TJ}$ are _?_ opposite rays. never
15. Four points are _?_ coplanar. sometimes
16. Skew lines are _?_ noncoplanar. always
17. Two lines that lie in parallel planes are _?_ parallel. sometimes
18. The intersection of two planes is _?_ a point. never
19. *Algebra* $JK = 48$. Find the value of x. 10

J —— H —— K, $4x - 15$, $2x + 3$

Algebra **Use the figure to find the values of the variables in Exercises 20 and 21.**

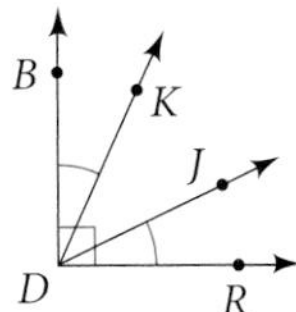

20. $m\angle BDK = 3x + 4$, $m\angle JDR = 5x - 10$ 7
21. $m\angle BDJ = 7y + 2$, $m\angle JDR = 2y + 7$ 9
22. *Writing* Why is it useful to have more than one way of naming an angle? See margin.

Name the property of equality or congruence that justifies each statement.

23. If $UV = KL$ and $KL = 6$, then $UV = 6$. Transitive Prop. of =
24. If $m\angle 1 + m\angle 2 = m\angle 4 + m\angle 2$, then $m\angle 1 = m\angle 4$. Subtr. Prop. of =
25. $\angle ABC \cong \angle ABC$ Refl. Prop. of ≅
26. If $\frac{1}{2}m\angle D = 45$, then $m\angle D = 90$. Mult. Prop. of =
27. If $\angle DEF \cong \angle HJK$, then $\angle HJK \cong \angle DEF$. Symm. Prop. of ≅

Resources

Teaching Resources

Chapter Support File, Ch. 1
- Chapter Assessment, Forms A and B
- Alternative Assessment

Chapter Assessment, Spanish Resources

Teacher's Edition

See also p. 2E for assessment options

Software
Computer Item Generator

Assessment pages 63–64

5. 1, 2, 4, 8, 16, 32, . . . and 1, 2, 4, 7, 11, 16, ... In the 1st sequence, each term is twice the preceding term. In the 2nd sequence, consecutive counting numbers are added to get from one term to the next.
8. *A, B, D, E* (or *A, C, D, E* or *B, C, D, E*)
11. No; a pencil is a writing instrument with a graphite center.
12. No; vert. angles are 2 angles whose sides are opposite rays.
22. Answers may vary. Sample: Some ways of naming an angle can help emphasize a side or vertex.

33. 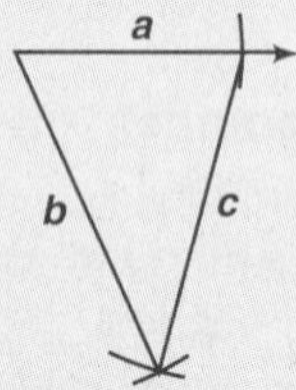

42. $m\angle VNM = 62$ because vert. angles are ≅. $m\angle LNV = m\angle PNM = 118$ because both angles are supplementary to $\angle LNP$.

45. 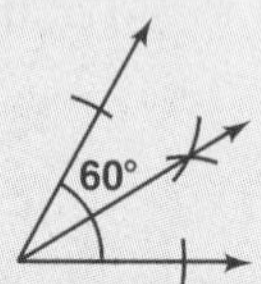

Preparing for Standardized Tests page 65

14. Inductive reasoning uses observations to make reasonable conjectures. Deductive reasoning is the process of reasoning logically from given facts to a conclusion.

Use the figure to complete Exercises 28–32.

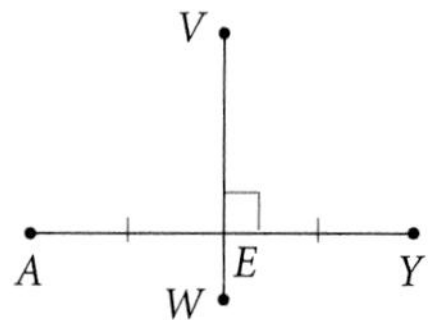

28. $\overline{VW}$ is the __?__ of $\overline{AY}$. perp. bisector

29. $EW + EV =$ ■ VW

30. If $EY = 3.5$, then $AY =$ ■. 7

31. $\frac{1}{2}$■ $= AE$ AY

32. ■ is the midpoint of ■. E; $\overline{AY}$

33. Construct a triangle whose sides have the given lengths. See margin.

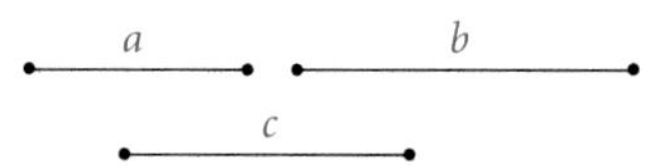

Algebra **Use the figure to complete Exercises 34 and 35. $\overrightarrow{AE}$ bisects $\angle DAC$. Find the values of the variables.**

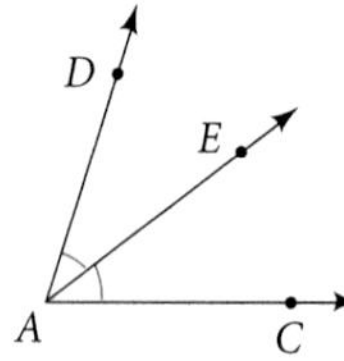

34. $m\angle DAE = 4y + 4$, $m\angle CAE = 6y - 12$ 8

35. $m\angle CAE = 6c - 12$, $m\angle DAC = 72$ 8

36. *Standardized Test Prep* The measure of an angle is $2z$. What is the measure of its supplement? E
 A. $90 - 2z$
 B. 180
 C. $2z$
 D. $2z - 180$
 E. $180 - 2z$

37. Find the measure of each angle.

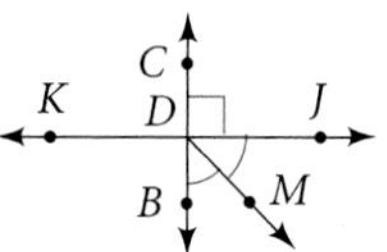

a. $\angle CDM$ 135 b. $\angle KDM$ 135
c. $\angle JDK$ 180 d. $\angle JDM$ 45
e. $\angle CDB$ 180 f. $\angle CDK$ 90

Use the graph to complete Exercises 38–41.

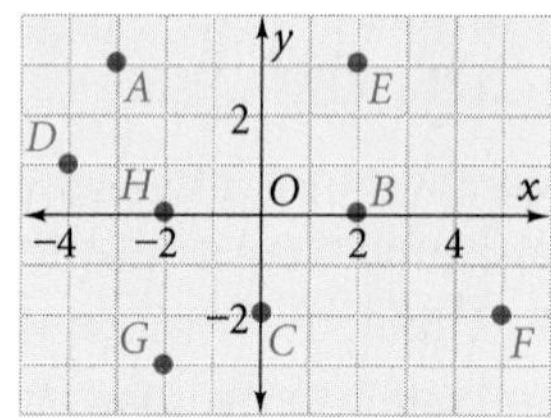

38–40. See below.

38. Find the coordinates of each labeled point.

39. Find the coordinates of the midpoint of $\overline{EH}$.

40. Find the coordinates of the midpoint of $\overline{AF}$.

41. Find the length of each segment to the nearest tenth.
 a. $\overline{AC}$ 5.8 b. $\overline{BH}$ 4.0
 c. $\overline{GB}$ 5.0 d. $\overline{AF}$ 9.4

What can you conclude from each diagram? Justify your answers. 42. See margin.

42. 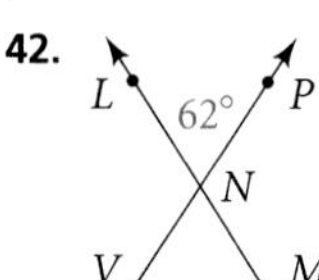

43. 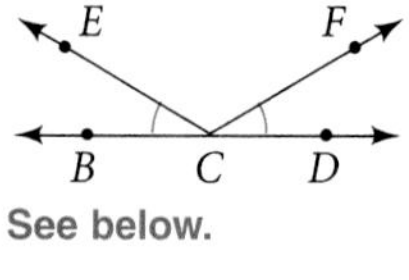

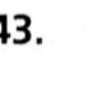

See below.

44. The coordinates of the midpoint of $\overline{RS}$ are $(-1, 1)$. The coordinates of R are $(3, 3)$. What are the coordinates of S? $(-5, -1)$

45. Use a protractor to draw a 60° angle. Then construct its bisector. See margin.

38. $A(-3, 3)$, $B(2, 0)$, $C(0, -2)$, $D(-4, 1)$, $E(2, 3)$, $F(5, -2)$, $G(-2, -3)$, $H(-2, 0)$

39. $\left(0, \frac{3}{2}\right)$ 40. $\left(1, \frac{1}{2}\right)$

43. $\angle BCE \cong \angle DCF$ by the markings and thus $\angle BCF \cong \angle ECD$ by the Angle Add. Post.

Preparing for Standardized Tests

Standardized tests, such as those administered for state assessment, the SAT, or the ACT, include regular math questions, quantitative comparison questions, open-ended problems, and free response questions (which the SAT calls *grid-ins*).

MULTIPLE CHOICE QUESTIONS are followed by five answer choices, one of which is correct. **Exercises 1–7** are multiple choice questions.

QUANTITATIVE COMPARISON QUESTIONS ask students to compare two quantities. **Exercises 8–11** are quantitative comparison questions.

FREE RESPONSE QUESTIONS do not give answer choices. Students must provide one correct answer on their own. **Exercise 13 and 14** are free response questions.

OPEN-ENDED PROBLEMS allow for more than one solution. Students must construct their own responses instead of choosing a single answer. The responses students give will help you determine the depth of their understanding and what difficulties, if any, they are experiencing. **Exercise 12** is an open-ended problem.

STANDARDIZED TEST TIP **Exercise 6** Students often make subtraction errors with the distance formula. The answer choices include answers that are results of common errors. Students should check their work carefully and not assume their answers are correct just because they appear as possible choices.

1 Preparing for Standardized Tests

For Exercises 1–7, choose the correct letter.

1. The intersection of two planes is
   A. a point. B. a ray. C. a segment.
   D. a line. E. none of the above D

2. Estimate $m\angle BCD$. B

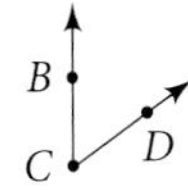

   A. 25 B. 55 C. 85
   D. 105 E. 125

3. Which is the next figure in the sequence? E

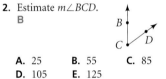

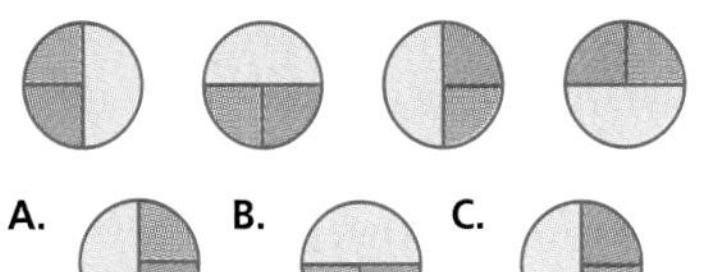

   A. B. C.
   D. E. none of the above

4. Find the values of x and y. C

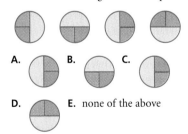

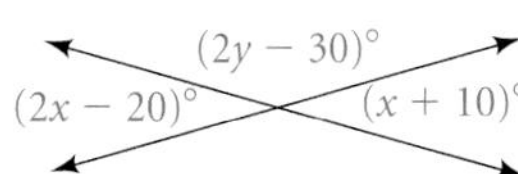

   A. $x = 40, y = 140$ B. $x = 10, y = 170$
   C. $x = 30, y = 85$ D. $x = 30, y = 90$
   E. none of the above

5. Two right angles can be E
   I. vertical. II. adjacent.
   III. complementary. IV. supplementary.

   A. I and II B. II and III C. III and IV
   D. I and IV E. I, II, and IV

6. Find the distance between $A(4, -5)$ and $B(-2, 1)$ to the nearest tenth. A
   A. 8.5 B. 7.2 C. 6.7 D. 6.3 E. 4.5

12. Answers may vary. Sample: angle measure 10 — comp. 80, supp. 170; angle measure 25 — comp. 65, supp. 155; angle measure 63 — comp. 27, supp. 117

7. Which point lies the farthest from the origin?
   A. $(0, -7)$ B. $(-3, 8)$ C. $(-4, -3)$
   D. $(5, 1)$ E. $(-6, 0)$ B

For Exercises 8–11, compare the boxed quantity in Column A with the boxed quantity in Column B. Choose the best answer.

A. The quantity in Column A is greater.
B. The quantity in Column B is greater.
C. The two quantities are equal.
D. The relationship cannot be determined on the basis of the information supplied.

$\overline{MV}$ bisects $\overline{NW}$.

M, W, E, N, V

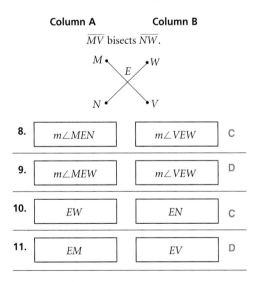

	Column A	Column B	
8.	$m\angle MEN$	$m\angle VEW$	C
9.	$m\angle MEW$	$m\angle VEW$	D
10.	EW	EN	C
11.	EM	EV	D

12. **Open-ended** Write the measures of three noncongruent acute angles. Find the complement and supplement of each. See below left.

13. Find the coordinates of the midpoint of $\overline{CD}$ with endpoints $C(5, 7)$ and $D(10, -3)$. $\left(\frac{15}{2}, 2\right)$

14. **Writing** Explain the difference between inductive and deductive reasoning. See margin p. 64.

Resources

Teaching Resources

Chapter Support File, Ch. 1
- Standardized Test Practice
- Cumulative Review

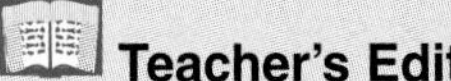

Teacher's Edition

See also p. 2E for assessment options.

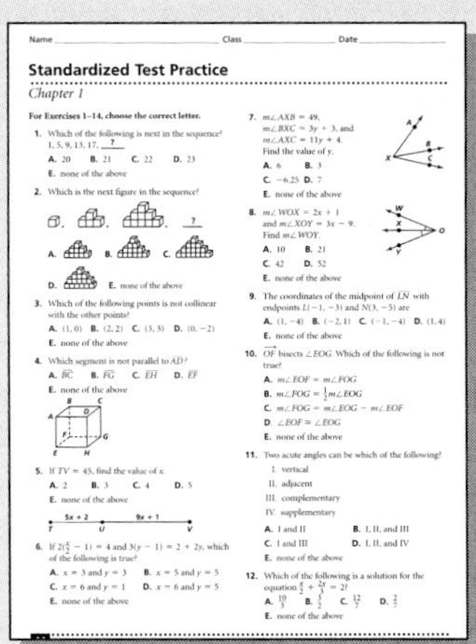
Standardized Test Practice
Chapter 1
For Exercises 1–14, choose the correct letter.

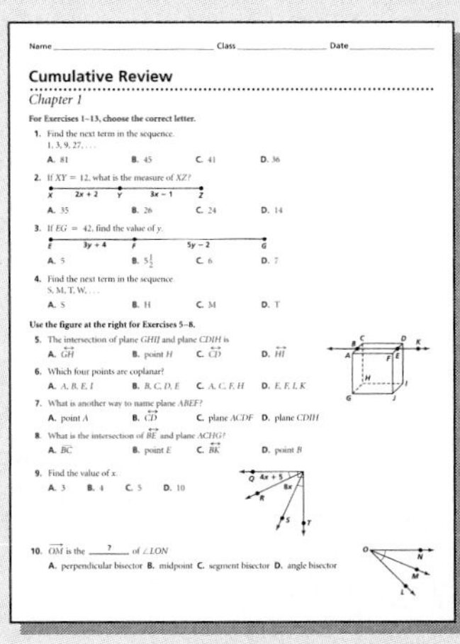
Cumulative Review
Chapter 1
For Exercises 1–13, choose the correct letter.

CHAPTER 2 Investigating Geometric Figures

To accommodate flexible scheduling, some lessons are divided into parts. Assignment Options are given in the Lesson Planning Options for each lesson.

2-1 Triangles (pp. 68–74)

Part 1 The Triangle Angle-Sum Theorem

Part 2 Exterior Angles of a Triangle

Key Terms: acute, corollary, equiangular, equilateral, exterior angle, isosceles, obtuse, remote interior angles, right, scalene

2-2 Polygons (pp. 76–81)

Part 1 Polygons and Interior Angles

Part 2 Exterior Angles

Key Terms: concave, convex, equiangular polygon, equilateral polygon, polygon, regular polygon

2-3 Parallel and Perpendicular Lines in the Coordinate Plane (pp. 83–88)

Part 1 Slope and Graphing Lines

Part 2 Parallel and Perpendicular Lines

2-4 Classifying Quadrilaterals (pp. 90–95)

Key Terms: isosceles trapezoid, kite, parallelogram, rectangle, rhombus, square, trapezoid

2-5 Circles (pp. 96–101)

Part 1 Parts of a Circle

Part 2 Central Angles and Arcs

Key Terms: adjacent arcs, circle, central angle, diameter, major arc, minor arc, radius, semicircle

2-6 Congruent and Similar Figures (pp. 102–108)

Part 1 Congruent Figures

Part 2 Similar Polygons

Key Terms: congruent circles, congruent polygons, similarity ratio, similar

2-7 Isometric and Orthographic Drawings (pp. 109–115)

Part 1 Isometric Drawings

Part 2 Orthographic Drawings

Key Terms: foundation drawing, isometric drawing, orthographic drawing

PACING OPTIONS

This chart suggests pacing only for the core lessons and their parts, and it is provided merely as a possible guide. It will help you determine how much time you have in your schedule to cover other features, such as the Chapter Project, Math Toolboxes, Wrap Up, and Assessment.

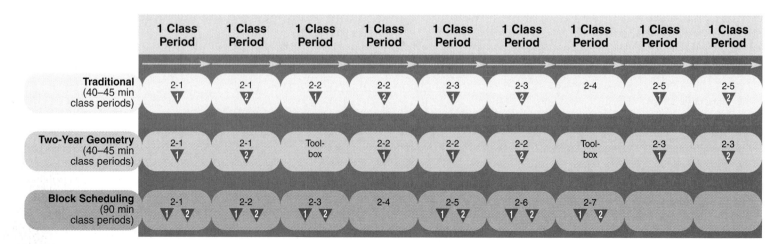

	1 Class Period	1 Class Period	1 Class Period	1 Class Period	1 Class Period	1 Class Period	1 Class Period	1 Class Period	1 Class Period
Traditional (40–45 min class periods)	2-1 Part 1	2-1 Part 2	2-2 Part 1	2-2 Part 2	2-3 Part 1	2-3 Part 2	2-4	2-5 Part 1	2-5 Part 2
Two-Year Geometry (40–45 min class periods)	2-1 Part 1	2-1 Part 2	Tool-box	2-2 Part 1	2-2 Part 1	2-2 Part 2	Tool-box	2-3 Part 1	2-3 Part 2
Block Scheduling (90 min class periods)	2-1 Parts 1, 2	2-2 Parts 1, 2	2-3 Parts 1, 2	2-4	2-5 Parts 1, 2	2-6 Parts 1, 2	2-7 Parts 1, 2		

What Students Will Learn and Why

In this chapter, students expand on their understanding of basic geometric concepts by investigating shapes that occur often in everyday life: polygons, lines, and circles. Students classify triangles and other polygons, and they connect geometry to algebra by relating *parallel* and *perpendicular* to the concept of *slope*. They explore angles and arcs of a circle and apply those ideas to circle graphs. They learn about congruence and similarity, and they draw three-dimensional figures using isometric and orthographic drawings, which are important in design and engineering.

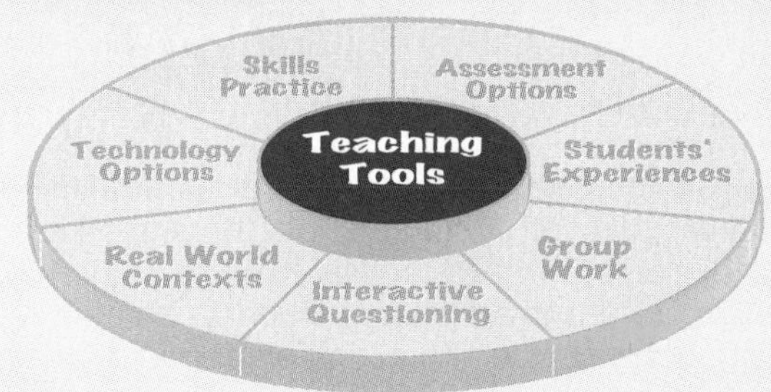

Discussing the Chapter/Building on Experience

The concept map below relates chapter topics to real-world applications. You and your class may wish to add to the map or develop maps of your own. The center oval describes the topic of the chapter. The next level displays topics within the lessons. The outer ovals reflect applications of the content. As you and your class build a concept map, invite students to discuss applications with which they are familiar.

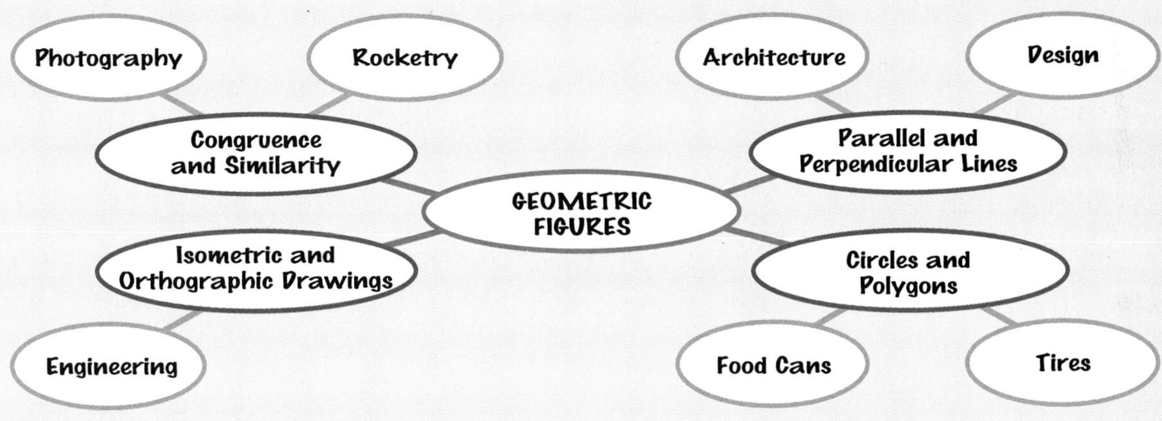

1 Class Period	1 Class Period	1 Class Period	1 Class Period	1 Class Period	1 Class Period	1 Class Period	1 Class Period	1 Class Period	1 Class Period	1 Class Period
2-6 ▼1	2-6 ▼2	2-7 ▼1	2-7 ▼2							
2-3 ▼2	Tool-box	2-4	2-4	2-5 ▼1	2-5 ▼2	2-6 ▼1	2-6 ▼2	2-6 ▼2	2-7 ▼1	2-7 ▼2

Interactive Questioning Tips

A question is interactive when there is "give and take" between the questioner (teacher or student) and the respondent. In Think and Discuss or when a critical thinking question is asked, it is important to encourage students to analyze the question throughly before attempting an answer. For example, in Lesson 2-4, Example 2, stúdents are asked to explain how they know that a certain quadrilateral is not a square. Students must analyze the parts of the question—what are the characteristics of a quadrilateral; what are the characteristics of a square; how do these characteristics compare or contrast.

Skills Practice

Every lesson provides skill practice with Try This exercises, Exercises On Your Own, and Exercises Mixed Review. The Student Edition includes Checkpoints (pp. 88,108) and Cumulative Review (p. 121). In the Teacher's Edition, the Lesson Planning Options section for each lesson lists Prerequisite Skills students should know for that lesson. At the back of the Student Edition is the Skills Handbook—mini-lessons on math your students may need to review. The Chapter Support File for Chapter 2 in the Teaching Resources box includes two Practice worksheets per lesson, a worksheet for two Checkpoints, and worksheets for Cumulative Review and Standardized Test Preparation.

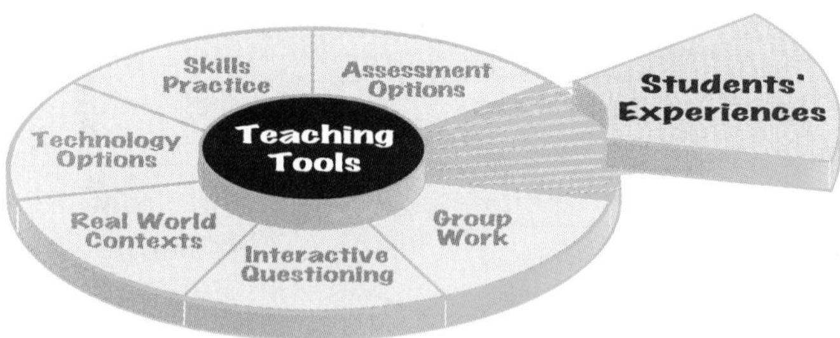

Diverse Learning and Teaching Styles

In your Teacher's Edition, you will find suggestions as to how you can help students complete mathematical tasks in Chapter 2 by reinforcing various learning styles. Here are some examples.

- **Visual learning** trace triangles and cut out interior angles (p. 69), describe the appearance of lines in graphs (p. 83), copy and color circles to illustrate answers to exercises (p. 99)
- **Tactile learning** model quadrilaterals using geoboards (p. 91), draw answers to exercises (p. 95), use a compass and straightedge to draw and label a circle (p. 97)
- **Auditory learning** describe a triangle using new vocabulary (p. 71), practice naming polygons, sides, and vertices (p. 77)
- **Kinesthetic learning** demonstrate that the sum of the exterior angles of a polygon is 360° (p.78), demonstrate why a circle is 360° (p. 98), draw different views of real-world objects (p. 113)

Alternative Activity for Lesson 2-1

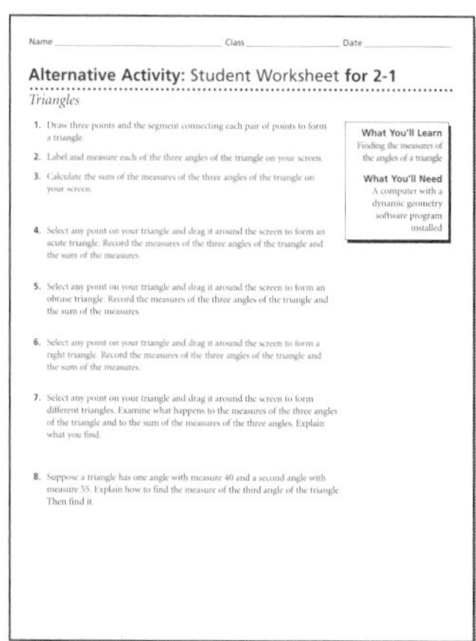

Name ______ Class ______ Date ______

Alternative Activity: Student Worksheet **for 2-1**

Triangles

1. Draw three points and the segment connecting each pair of points to form a triangle.
2. Label and measure each of the three angles of the triangle on your screen.
3. Calculate the sum of the measures of the three angles of the triangle on your screen.
4. Select any point on your triangle and drag it around the screen to form an acute triangle. Record the measures of the three angles of the triangle and the sum of the measures.
5. Select any point on your triangle and drag it around the screen to form an obtuse triangle. Record the measures of the three angles of the triangle and the sum of the measures.
6. Select any point on your triangle and drag it around the screen to form a right triangle. Record the measures of the three angles of the triangle and the sum of the measures.
7. Select any point on your triangle and drag it around the screen to form different triangles. Examine what happens to the measures of the three angles of the triangle and to the sum of the measures of the three angles. Explain what you find.
8. Suppose a triangle has one angle with measure 40 and a second angle with measure 55. Explain how to find the measure of the third angle of the triangle. Then find it.

What You'll Learn Finding the measures of the angles of a triangle

What You'll Need A computer with a dynamic geometry software program installed

for use with the Work Together and Example 1, uses geometry software to draw triangles and measure angles.

Alternative Activity for Lesson 2-2

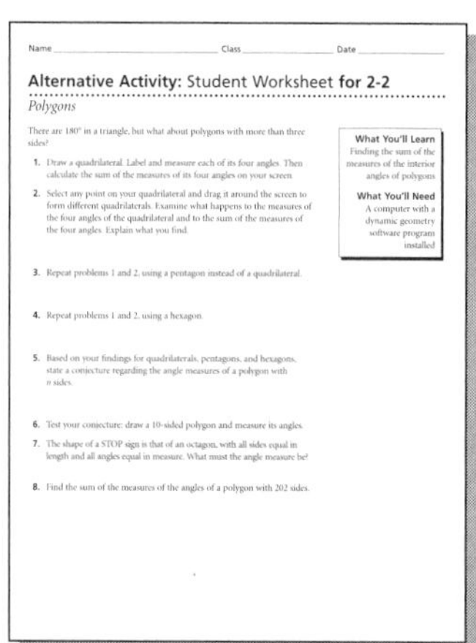

Name ______ Class ______ Date ______

Alternative Activity: Student Worksheet **for 2-2**

Polygons

There are 180° in a triangle, but what about polygons with more than three sides?

1. Draw a quadrilateral. Label and measure each of its four angles. Then calculate the sum of the measures of its four angles on your screen.
2. Select any point on your quadrilateral and drag it around the screen to form different quadrilaterals. Examine what happens to the measures of the four angles of the quadrilateral and to the sum of the measures of the four angles. Explain what you find.
3. Repeat problems 1 and 2, using a pentagon instead of a quadrilateral.
4. Repeat problems 1 and 2, using a hexagon.
5. Based on your findings for quadrilaterals, pentagons, and hexagons, state a conjecture regarding the angle measures of a polygon with n sides.
6. Test your conjecture: draw a 10-sided polygon and measure its angles.
7. The shape of a STOP sign is that of an octagon, with all sides equal in length and all angles equal in measure. What must the angle measure be?
8. Find the sum of the measures of the angles of a polygon with 202 sides.

What You'll Learn Finding the sum of the measures of the interior angles of polygons

What You'll Need A computer with a dynamic geometry software program installed

for use with the Work Together and Example 3, uses geometry software to draw polygons, change the shapes, and find the sum of the angle measures.

Alternative Activity for Lesson 2-5

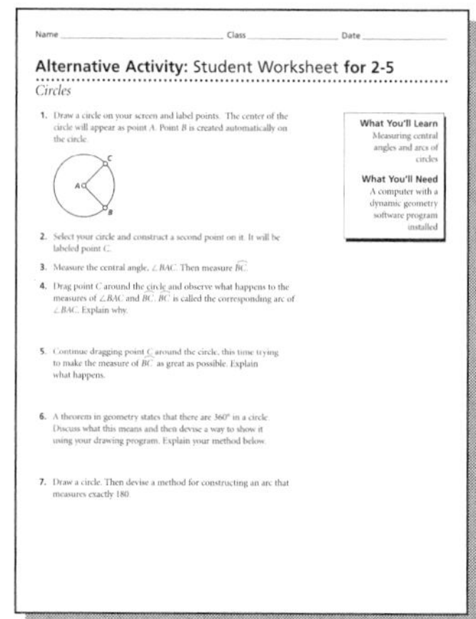

Name ______ Class ______ Date ______

Alternative Activity: Student Worksheet **for 2-5**

Circles

1. Draw a circle on your screen and label points. The center of the circle will appear as point A. Point B is created automatically on the circle.
2. Select your circle and construct a second point on it. It will be labeled point C.
3. Measure the central angle, $\angle BAC$. Then measure $\overset{\frown}{BC}$.
4. Drag point C around the circle and observe what happens to the measures of $\angle BAC$ and $\overset{\frown}{BC}$. $\overset{\frown}{BC}$ is called the corresponding arc of $\angle BAC$. Explain why.
5. Continue dragging point C around the circle, this time trying to make the measure of $\overset{\frown}{BC}$ as great as possible. Explain what happens.
6. A theorem in geometry states that there are 360° in a circle. Discuss what this means and then devise a way to show it using your drawing program. Explain your method below.
7. Draw a circle. Then devise a method for constructing an arc that measures exactly 180.

What You'll Learn Measuring central angles and arcs of circles

What You'll Need A computer with a dynamic geometry software program installed

for use with Part 2, uses geometry software to draw circles and angles and arcs.

Cooperative Learning Tips

When used effectively, cooperative learning can help students develop interpersonal skills, learn to perform specific roles in a group, and learn to carry out specific responsibilities. The components of Chapter 2 provide a range of cooperative learning opportunities.

- In the Student Edition, the ***Work Together*** parts of lessons are specifically designed for cooperative learning activities.
- In the Teacher's Edition, you will find helpful hints for addressing diverse learning styles (see page C for Chapter 2). For every lesson, you will find a ***Reteaching Activity***, which may involve cooperative learning.

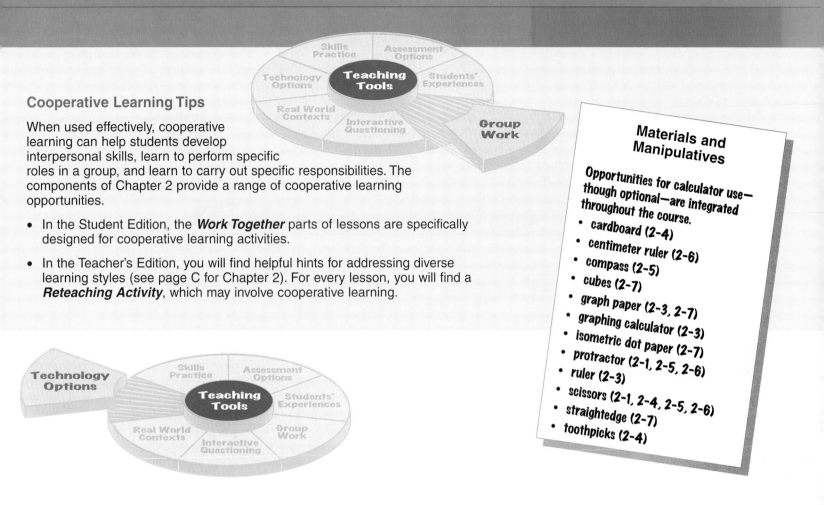

Materials and Manipulatives

Opportunities for calculator use—though optional—are integrated throughout the course.

- cardboard (2-4)
- centimeter ruler (2-6)
- compass (2-5)
- cubes (2-7)
- graph paper (2-3, 2-7)
- graphing calculator (2-3)
- isometric dot paper (2-7)
- protractor (2-1, 2-5, 2-6)
- ruler (2-3)
- scissors (2-1, 2-4, 2-5, 2-6)
- straightedge (2-7)
- toothpicks (2-4)

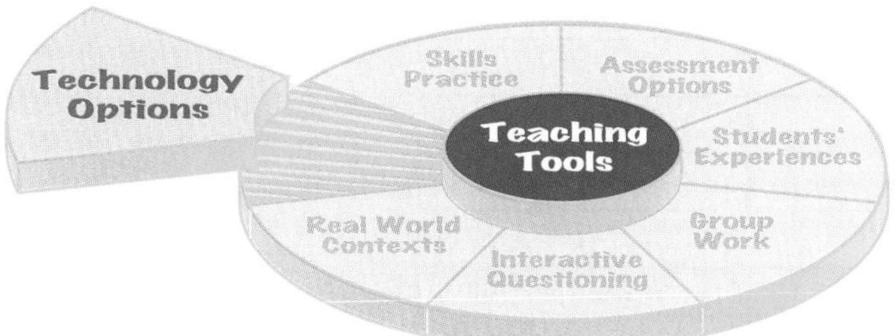

TECHNOLOGY OPTIONS

Technology Tools		Chapter Project	2-1	2-2	2-3	2-4	2-5	2-6	2-7
Calculator		Numerous opportunities throughout for students to use scientific calculators.							
Software	Secondary Math Lab Toolkit™		✔	✔	✔	✔	✔	✔	✔
	Integrated Math Lab				✔			✔	
	Computer Item Generator		✔	✔	✔	✔	✔	✔	✔
	Student Edition			✔T	✔T				
Video	Video Field Trip	✔							
CD-ROM	Multimedia Geometry Lab		✔	✔		✔	✔		
Internet		See the Prentice Hall site. (http://www.phschool.com)							

✔T indicates Math Toolbox.

The Prentice Hall Geometry program offers you a rich variety of technology options. Be assured that all these options are provided as a means of enriching the program and are not essential for the successful completion of the course.

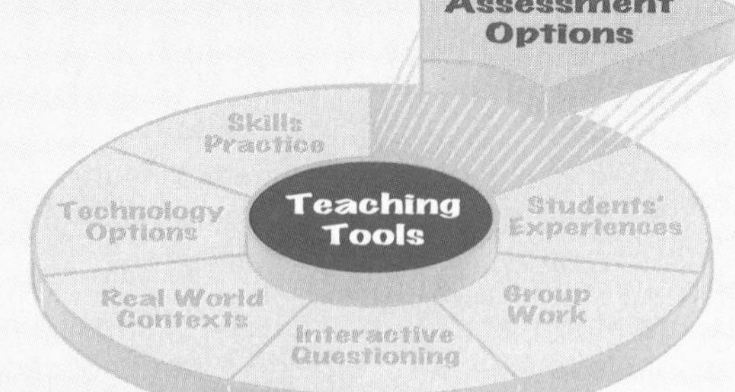

Assessment Options

The Prentice Hall Geometry Program provides you with many options. From these options, you may choose instructional materials and techniques appropriate for your students, or those necessary to meet your district's curriculum requirements. As the chart indicates, the program also supports your teaching efforts by offering you many choices for assessment.

ASSESSMENT OPTIONS

Assessment Support Materials	Chapter Project	2-1	2-2	2-3	2-4	2-5	2-6	2-7	Chapter End
Chapter Project	▲■●	▲■	▲■		▲■		▲■	▲■	▲■
Checkpoints				▲■●			▲■●		
Self-Assessment				▲■		▲■		▲■	▲■
Writing Assignment		▲	▲■	▲■	▲■●	▲■	▲	▲■	●
Chapter Assessment									▲●
Alternative Assessment		■	■	■	■	■	■	■	●■
Cumulative Review									●▲■
Standardized Test Prep		▲■		▲■			▲■		▲■●
Computer Item Generator	Can be used to create custom-made practice or assessment at any time.								

▲ = Student Edition ■ = Teacher's Edition ● = Teaching Resources

Checkpoints

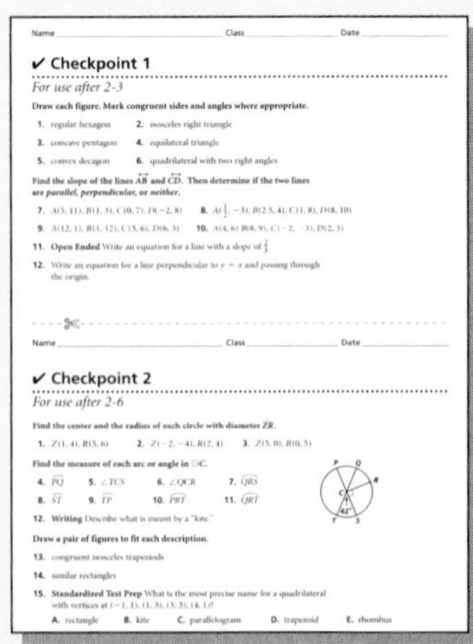

Checkpoint 1

For use after 2-3

Checkpoint 2

For use after 2-6

Alternative Assessment

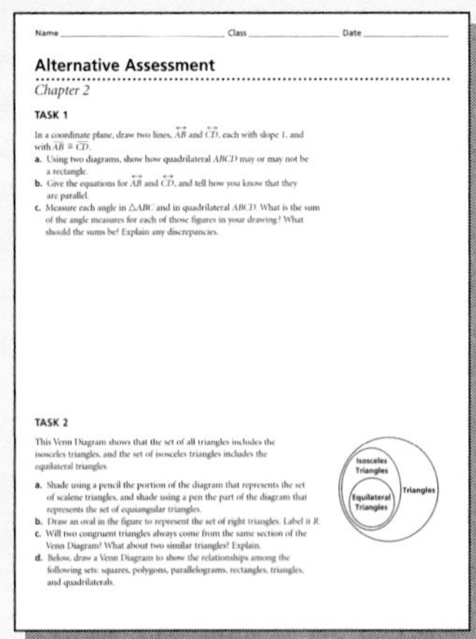

Alternative Assessment

Chapter 2

Chapter Assessment

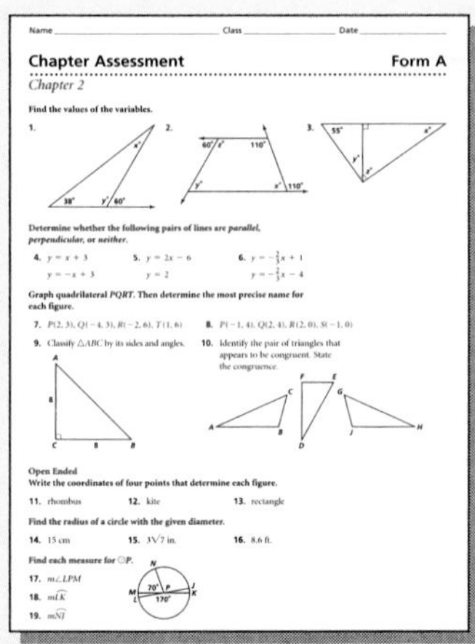

Chapter Assessment Form A

Chapter 2

Available in both Form A and Form B

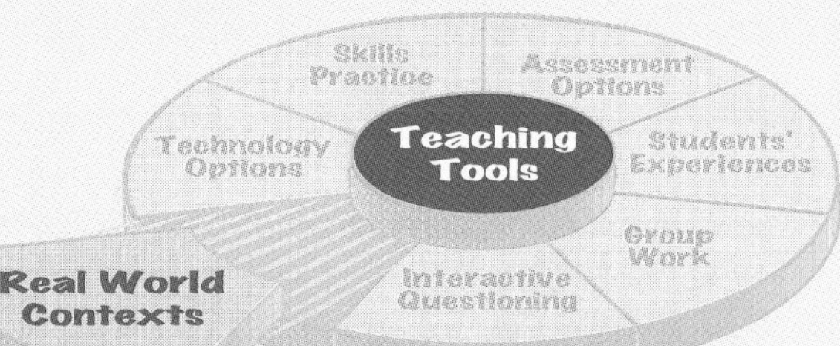

Making the Right Connections

Mathematics is imbedded in nearly every walk of life. The National Council of Teachers of Mathematics (NCTM) encourages educators to recognize these connections and to emphasize them for the purpose of better educating students for success in life and in a global economy. The ***Connections*** chart below highlights these connections for Chapter 2.

CONNECTIONS

Lesson	Interdisciplinary Connections	Career Prep	Other Real World Connections	Math Integration	NCTM Standards
Chapter Project	History				Problem Solving Communication Algebra Logical Reasoning
2-1	Music	Construction Design	Furniture Design Grand Piano Weaving	Algebra Spherical Geometry Probability	Problem Solving Communication Algebra Logical Reasoning
2-2	Drama	Industry Marketing	Manufacturing Design Theater-in-the-Round	Probability Data Analysis	Problem Solving Communication Algebra Logical Reasoning
2-3	Writing	Architecture	Building Cycling Lines of Longitude	Data Analysis Algebra Mental Math	Problem Solving Communication Algebra Logical Reasoning
2-4	Art History Science	Industry	Cubism	Algebra	Problem Solving Communication Algebra Logical Reasoning
2-5	Economics Computer Science	Marketing Research	Printing Travel Amusement Parks Satellites	Algebra Statistics	Problem Solving Communication Algebra Logical Reasoning
2-6	Art	Science	Photography Rocketry	Fractals	Problem Solving Communication Algebra Logical Reasoning
2-7	Writing Design	Industrial Design Engineering	Movies Building	Probability	Problem Solving Communication Algebra Logical Reasoning

CHAPTER 2 Investigating Geometric Figures

CONNECTING TO PRIOR LEARNING Ask students for examples of geometric shapes they can see in the classroom or outside the window. Discuss why certain objects may be the shape they are. For example, ask: *Why is a cup or glass round? Why does cereal come in rectangular boxes? Why are roofs triangular-shaped?*

CULTURAL CONNECTIONS The ancient Chinese game of tangrams is classified as a "packing problem." The object of such puzzles is to "pack" a number of pieces into a specified shape or container. Ask students if they have ever played the "15-puzzle," the goal of which is to arrange square tiles numbered 1–15 in increasing order in a 4-by-4 square tray.

INTERDISCIPLINARY CONNECTIONS Computers can be programmed "to play" games such as nim and tic-tac-toe. Because no perfect strategy is known for chess, a computer can be programmed to play skillfully but, as of yet, has not been able to win consistently against chess champions. Students may want to research the success of chess-playing computers.

Technology Options

Prentice Hall Technology

Video
Video Field Trip 2, "Mazed and Confused," a visit to a topiary maze

CHAPTER 2 Investigating Geometric Figures

Relating to the Real World

Take a look around you. Chances are that the objects you see are made of simple geometric figures. The door is rectangular; the light fixture is circular; the windowpanes are square. In order to make sense of the world, you need to start with these basic figures. And that's what you'll learn in this chapter—the basic characteristics of the geometric figures that you see every day.

Lessons	2-1	2-2	2-3	2-4	2-5
	Triangles	Polygons	Parallel and Perpendicular Lines in the Coordinate Plane	Classifying Quadrilaterals	Circles

ABOUT THE PROJECT The Chapter Project gives students an opportunity to manipulate geometric figures by creating and solving shape puzzles in order to see how the figures relate to each other. In the Find Out questions found throughout the chapter, students create tangram pieces and use them to form triangles, quadrilaterals, pentagons, and hexagons. Students then create pentominoes and use them to make rectangles. Students also create Soma pieces, three-dimensional figures made out of cubes.

Launching the Project

PROJECT NOTEBOOK Encourage students to keep all project-related materials in a separate folder or notebook. See Chapter Project and Scoring Rubric in Chapter Support File.

- Ask students to give examples of games they have played that involve geometric shapes (e.g., checkers, Chinese checkers, Jenga®).
- Have students create magic squares by placing the numbers 1–9 in the squares of a 3-by-3 grid so that all the rows, columns, and diagonals have the same sum.
- Have students cut a paper square along its two diagonals. Then have them describe shapes they can make with two, three, and four pieces.

TRACKING THE PROJECT You may wish to have students read Finishing the Project on page 116 to help them get an overview of the project. Set benchmark deadlines for students to show their work in progress.

CHAPTER PROJECT

AMAZING SPACE

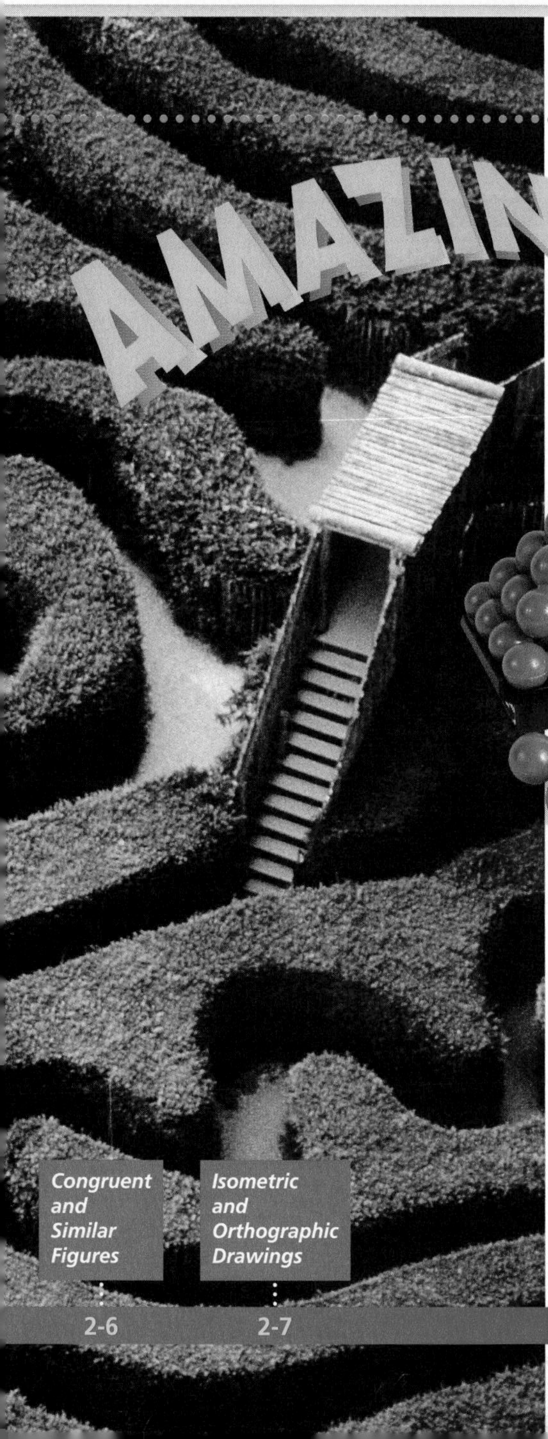

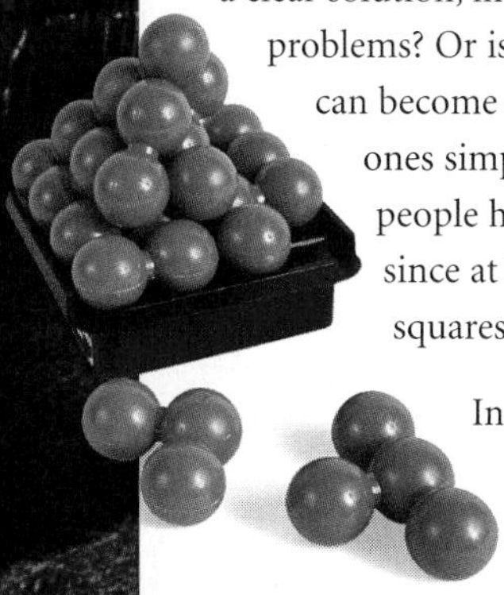

What is it about puzzles that makes them so popular? Is it that they always have a clear solution, in contrast to real-life problems? Or is it the way simple tasks can become complex and complex ones simple? Whatever the reasons, people have been solving puzzles since at least 2400 B.C. when magic squares were popular in China.

In this chapter project, you will explore shape puzzles, such as tangrams, which also originated in China. As you solve puzzles and create your own, you will see how simple shapes can mystify and enlighten—revealing secrets of how our world fits together.

To help you complete the project:

- p. 74 *Find Out by Doing*
- p. 81 *Find Out by Exploring*
- p. 95 *Find Out by Analyzing*
- p. 107 *Find Out by Investigating*
- p. 115 *Find Out by Modeling*
- p. 116 *Finishing the Project*

Project Resources

Teaching Resources

Chapter Support File, Ch. 2
- Chapter Project Manager and Scoring Rubric

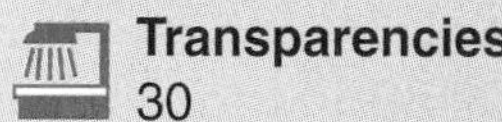

Transparencies
30

Using the Rubric

Sharing the scoring rubric for the project with your students will alert them to your expectations before they begin work on the project.

As students complete each Find Out question in the chapter, you may wish to have them evaluate their own work or a partner's work based on the scoring rubric. Students should have the opportunity to revise their work after it has been reviewed.

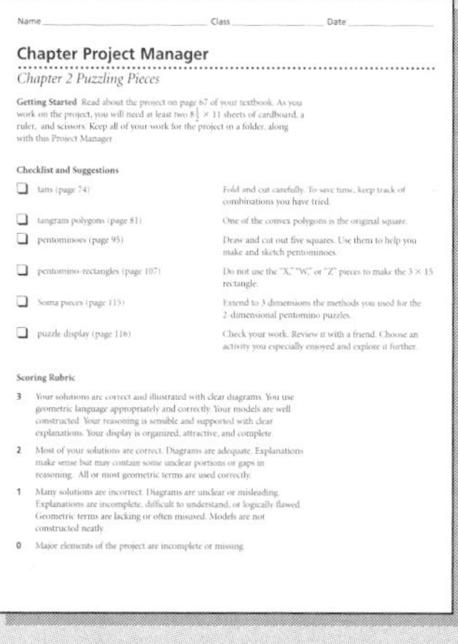
Chapter Project Manager
Chapter 2 Puzzling Pieces

2-1 Teaching Notes

PROBLEM OF THE DAY

The area of one tangram piece is given. Find the total area of all seven pieces.

16 square units

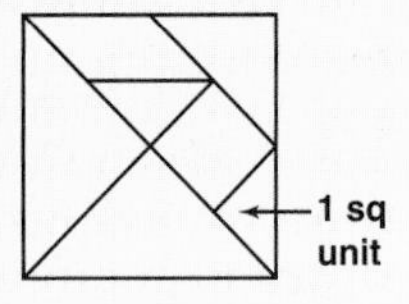

Problem of the Day is also available in Transparencies.

CONNECTING TO PRIOR KNOWLEDGE Ask students to draw one triangle with three sides of equal length, one with two sides of equal length, and one with no sides of equal length. Then have them classify each angle of the triangles.

WORK TOGETHER

ALTERNATIVE METHOD Use geometry software to construct a triangle and measure its angles. Use the calculator function of the software to find the sum of the measures of the angles. The sum will be about 180. Have students drag any vertex of the triangle and observe the change in angle measures as well as the constancy of their sum.

Have students draw triangles beginning with any size angle so they can see that the sum is independent of the different types of angles used.

Lesson Planning Options

Prerequisite Skills

- Solving one-variable equations
- Recognizing supplementary and vertical angles

Assignment Options for Exercises On Your Own

To provide flexible scheduling, this lesson can be subdivided into parts.

 **Core** 10–17, 21–22, 25–26
Extension 29

 **Core** 1–9, 18–20, 23, 27–28
Extension 24, 30–34

Use Mixed Review to maintain skills.

Resources

 **Student Edition**

Skills Handbook, p. 666
Extra Practice, p. 649
Glossary/Study Guide

 **Teaching Resources**

Chapter Support File, Ch. 2
- Practice 2-1 (two worksheets)
- Reteaching 2-1
- Alternative Activity 2-1

Classroom Manager 2-1
Glossary, Spanish Resources

 **Transparencies**
31, 35, 36

2-1 Triangles

What You'll Learn
- Finding the measures of angles of a triangle
- Classifying triangles

...And Why

To increase your knowledge of triangles, the simplest polygons used in the design of furniture, buildings, and bridges

What You'll Need
- scissors
- protractor

WORK TOGETHER

Work in a group to explore the angle measures of triangles.

- Have each member of your group draw and cut out a large triangle.
- Number the angles and tear them off.
- Place the three angles adjacent to each other to form one angle.

1. Compare your results with group members. Describe your observations. See left.
2. Make a **conjecture** about the sum of the measures of the angles of a triangle. See left.

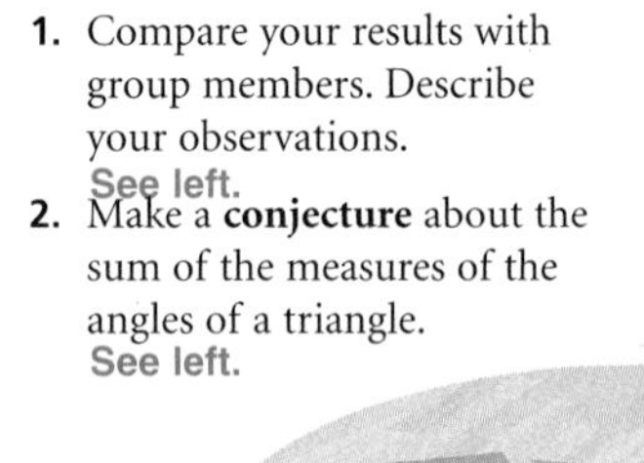

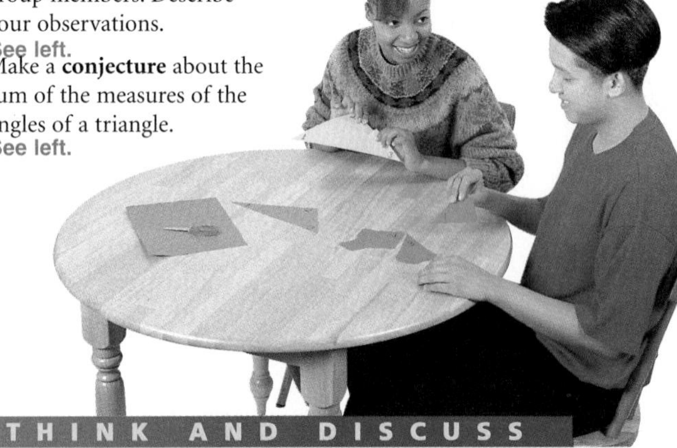

TECHNOLOGY HINT

The Work Together could be done using geometry software.

1. The three angles form a straight angle.
2. The sum of measures of angles of a triangle is 180.

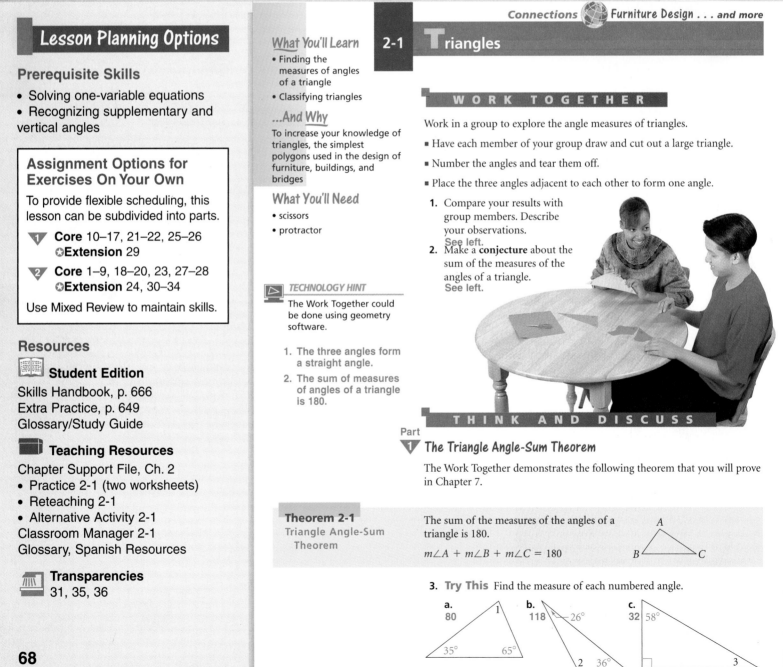

THINK AND DISCUSS

Part 1 **The Triangle Angle-Sum Theorem**

The Work Together demonstrates the following theorem that you will prove in Chapter 7.

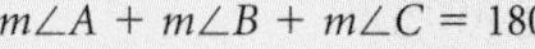

Theorem 2-1
Triangle Angle-Sum Theorem

The sum of the measures of the angles of a triangle is 180.

$m\angle A + m\angle B + m\angle C = 180$

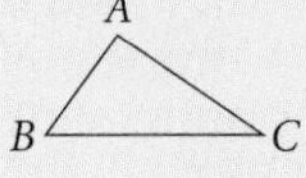

3. **Try This** Find the measure of each numbered angle.

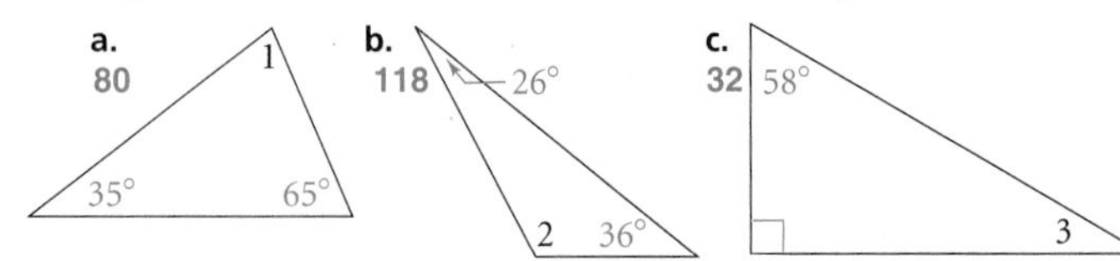

THINK AND DISCUSS

ERROR ALERT! Question 3 Some students may be confused by the three numbers in the triangle thinking that they are all angle measures. **Remediation:** Point out that the numbers 1, 2, and 3 are used to name the angles and are not measures.

Example 1

Discuss with students other ways to find the values of *y* and *z*. For example, *z* can be found by setting the sum of the angle measures of $\triangle FGH$ equal to 180 and solving for *z*. Once *z* is found, set the sum of the angle measures of $\triangle JGH$ equal to 180 and solve for *y*.

Question 5b Some students may recognize that $x = y$ because the angles are vertical angles and thus congruent. Others may use the Congruent Supplements Theorem to explain why $x = y$.

ESL To help students remember the meaning of *remote interior angle,* use the word remote in other contexts, such as a remote island or a television remote control.

VISUAL LEARNING Question 6 You may want to have students trace their triangles first, then cut out two remote interior angles. Arranging the cut-outs on their original drawings may help students see more clearly the relationship between the exterior angle and the remote interior angles.

Example 1

G, 21°, 39°, 65°, $x°$, $y°$, $z°$, F, J, H

Find the values of *x*, *y*, and *z*.

To find the value of *x*, use $\triangle FJG$.

$65 + 39 + x = 180$ Triangle Angle-Sum Theorem
$104 + x = 180$ Simplify.
$x = 76$ Subtract 104 from each side.

To find the value of *y*, look at $\angle FJH$. It is a straight angle.

$m\angle GJF + m\angle GJH = 180$ Angle Addition Postulate
$76 + y = 180$ Substitution
$y = 104$ Subtract 76 from each side.

To find the value of *z*, use $\triangle GJH$.

$104 + 21 + z = 180$ Triangle Angle-Sum Theorem
$125 + z = 180$ Simplify the left side.
$z = 55$ Subtract 125 from each side.

PROBLEM SOLVING
Look Back Check your answers by finding the sum of the measures of the angles in each triangle.

4. $m\angle F + m\angle FGH + m\angle H = 180$; $65 + (39 + 21) + z = 180$; $z = 55$

4. **Critical Thinking** Describe how you could use $\triangle FGH$ instead of $\triangle GJH$ to find the value of *z*. **See left.**

5. **Try This** Find the values of *x* and *y*.

a.  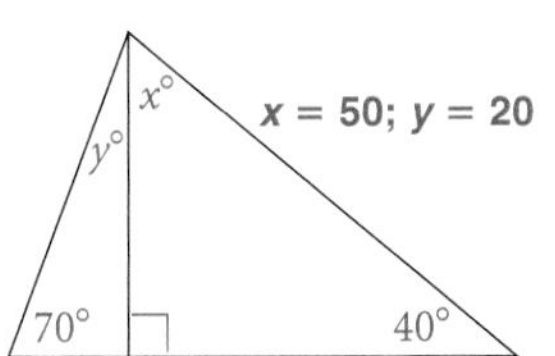

$x = 50$; $y = 20$

b. 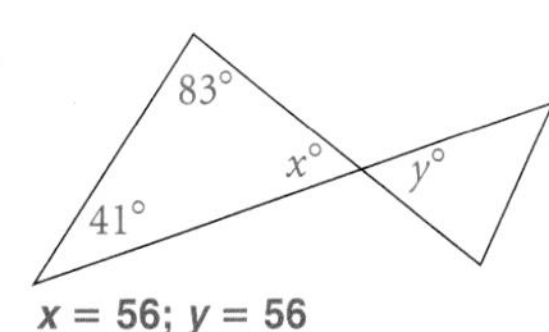

$x = 56$; $y = 56$

Part 2

Exterior Angles of a Triangle

1 ← exterior angle
3, 2
remote interior angles

An **exterior angle** of a polygon is an angle formed by a side and an extension of a side. For each exterior angle of a triangle, the two nonadjacent interior angles are called its **remote interior angles.**

6. a. **Manipulatives** Draw and label a large triangle like the one shown at the left. Cut out the two remote interior angles and place them on the exterior angle as shown. What do you observe? **$\angle 2$ and $\angle 3$ cover $\angle 1$ without overlapping.**

   b. Make a **conjecture** about the measure of an exterior angle of a triangle. **The measure of an exterior angle of a triangle = the sum of the measures of its 2 remote interior angles.**

Your **conjecture** in Question 6 is the basis of the following theorem, which you will justify in Exercise 32.

Additional Examples

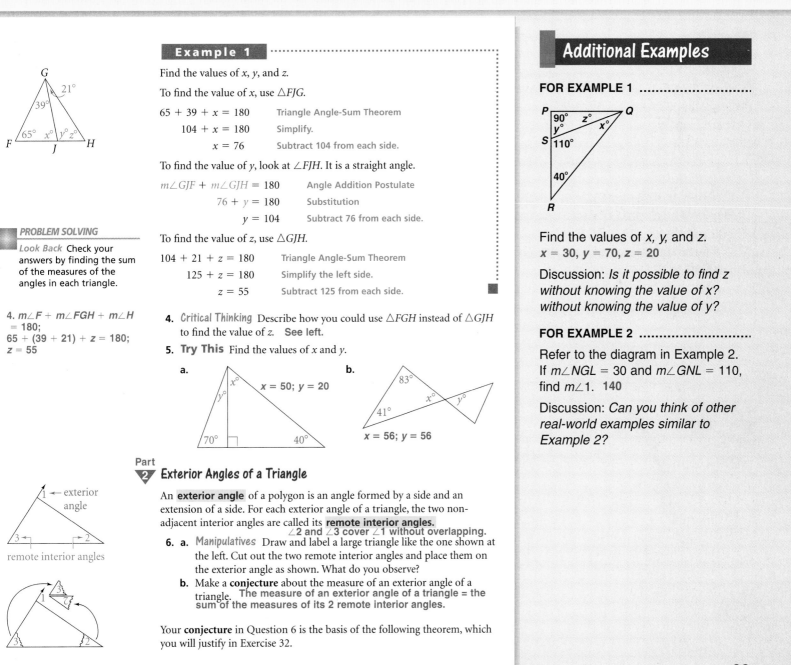

FOR EXAMPLE 1

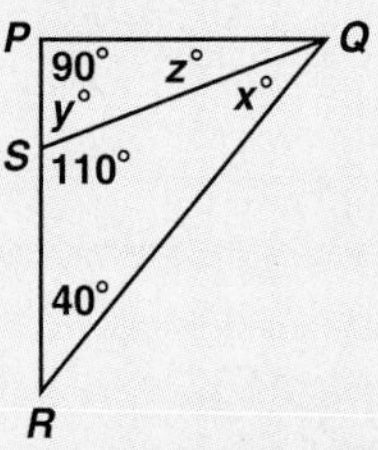

Find the values of *x*, *y*, and *z*.
$x = 30$, $y = 70$, $z = 20$

Discussion: *Is it possible to find z without knowing the value of x? without knowing the value of y?*

FOR EXAMPLE 2

Refer to the diagram in Example 2. If $m\angle NGL = 30$ and $m\angle GNL = 110$, find $m\angle 1$. **140**

Discussion: *Can you think of other real-world examples similar to Example 2?*

Exterior Angle Theorem Exercise 32 provides an opportunity for students to complete a proof of this theorem.

Question 7 You may want to have students find the measures of all six exterior angles of each triangle. Point out that the angle formed by the extensions of two sides is not an exterior angle.

Example 2 Relating to the Real World

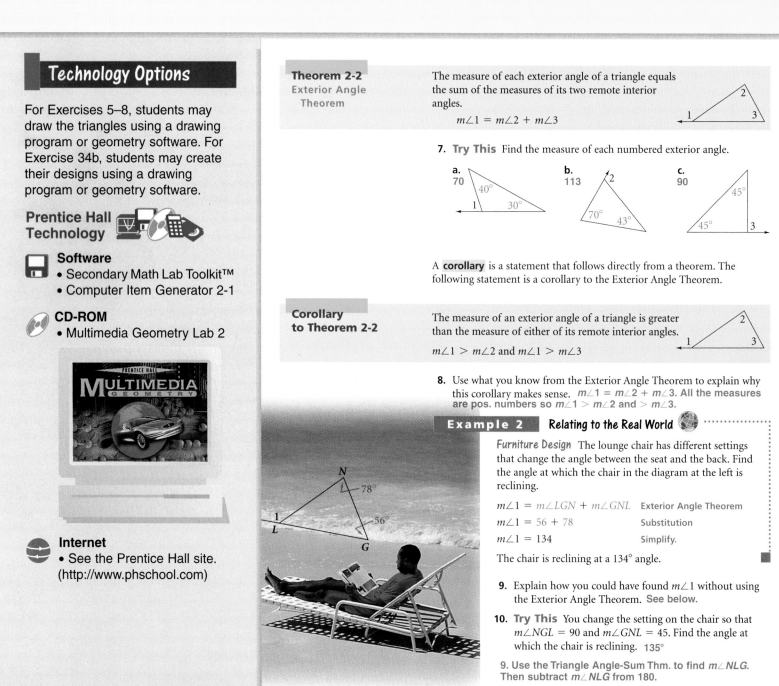

Discuss with students the greatest and least possible measures of ∠1 and what the chair would look like when ∠1 has these measures.

Technology Options

For Exercises 5–8, students may draw the triangles using a drawing program or geometry software. For Exercise 34b, students may create their designs using a drawing program or geometry software.

Prentice Hall Technology

Software
- Secondary Math Lab Toolkit™
- Computer Item Generator 2-1

CD-ROM
- Multimedia Geometry Lab 2

Internet
- See the Prentice Hall site. (http://www.phschool.com)

Theorem 2-2 Exterior Angle Theorem

The measure of each exterior angle of a triangle equals the sum of the measures of its two remote interior angles.

$m\angle 1 = m\angle 2 + m\angle 3$

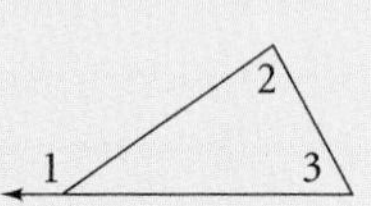

7. **Try This** Find the measure of each numbered exterior angle.

a. 70

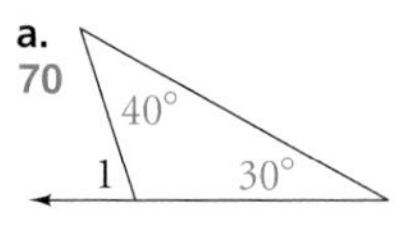

b. 113

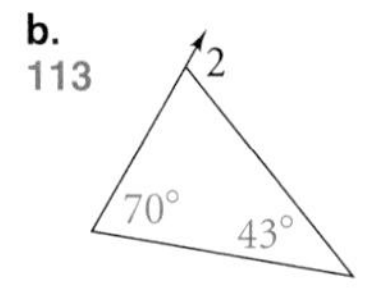

c. 90

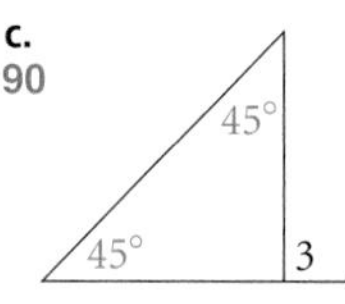

A **corollary** is a statement that follows directly from a theorem. The following statement is a corollary to the Exterior Angle Theorem.

Corollary to Theorem 2-2

The measure of an exterior angle of a triangle is greater than the measure of either of its remote interior angles.

$m\angle 1 > m\angle 2$ and $m\angle 1 > m\angle 3$

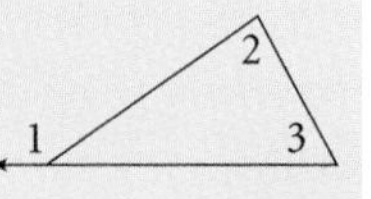

8. Use what you know from the Exterior Angle Theorem to explain why this corollary makes sense. $m\angle 1 = m\angle 2 + m\angle 3$. All the measures are pos. numbers so $m\angle 1 > m\angle 2$ and $> m\angle 3$.

Example 2 Relating to the Real World

Furniture Design The lounge chair has different settings that change the angle between the seat and the back. Find the angle at which the chair in the diagram at the left is reclining.

N 78° 1 L 56° G

$m\angle 1 = m\angle LGN + m\angle GNL$	Exterior Angle Theorem
$m\angle 1 = 56 + 78$	Substitution
$m\angle 1 = 134$	Simplify.

The chair is reclining at a 134° angle.

9. Explain how you could have found $m\angle 1$ without using the Exterior Angle Theorem. See below.

10. **Try This** You change the setting on the chair so that $m\angle NGL = 90$ and $m\angle GNL = 45$. Find the angle at which the chair is reclining. 135°

9. Use the Triangle Angle-Sum Thm. to find $m\angle NLG$. Then subtract $m\angle NLG$ from 180.

AUDITORY LEARNING Working with a partner, have one student describe a triangle using the vocabulary presented on page 71. The other student should sketch the triangle. Then have students switch roles and repeat the activity.

Question 11c At this point in the text, students do not know that equilateral implies equiangular. However, students will easily discover through drawing that an obtuse equilateral triangle is impossible.

Exercises ON YOUR OWN

Exercises 1–4 Students should measure the sides and angles carefully. They can check for angle-measurement error by finding the sum of the three angle measures.

Exercises 5–8 You may want students to label angle measures and side lengths in their triangles.

LOGICAL REASONING Exercise 9 Students can use a sketch to illustrate their answers but justifications should be based on definitions, postulates, theorems, and corollaries.

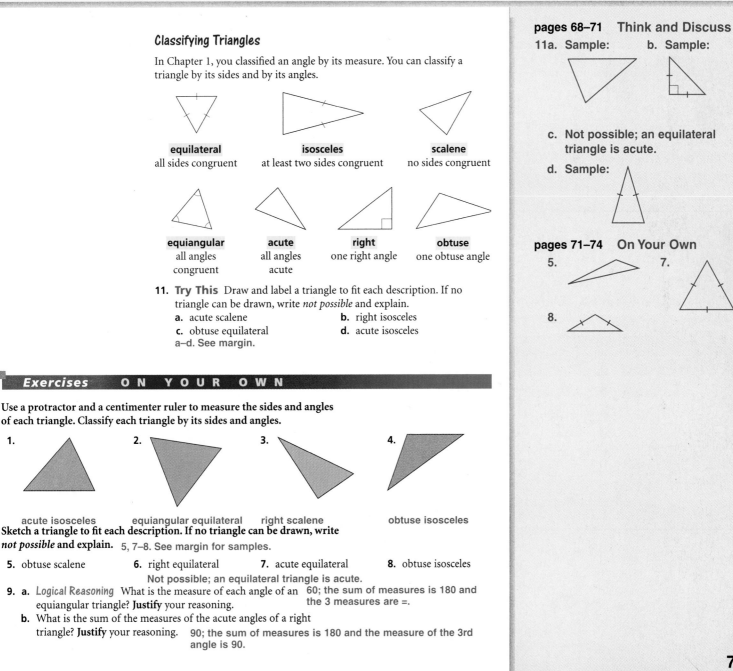

Classifying Triangles

In Chapter 1, you classified an angle by its measure. You can classify a triangle by its sides and by its angles.

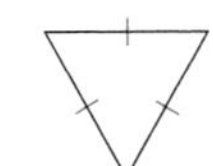

equilateral
all sides congruent

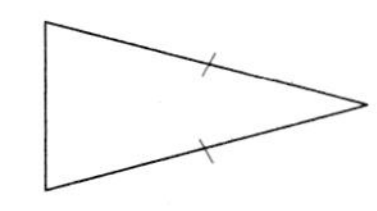

isosceles
at least two sides congruent

scalene
no sides congruent

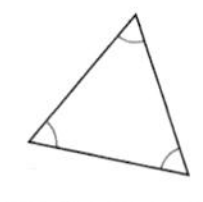
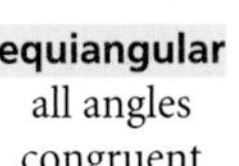

equiangular
all angles congruent

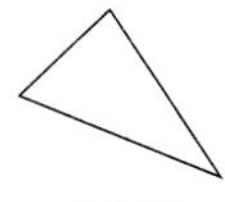

acute
all angles acute

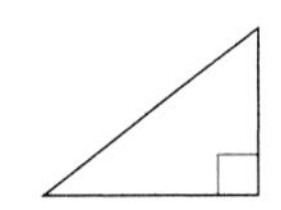

right
one right angle

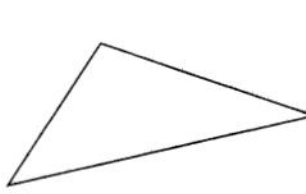

obtuse
one obtuse angle

11. **Try This** Draw and label a triangle to fit each description. If no triangle can be drawn, write *not possible* and explain.
    a. acute scalene **b.** right isosceles
    c. obtuse equilateral **d.** acute isosceles
    a–d. See margin.

Exercises ON YOUR OWN

Use a protractor and a centimeter ruler to measure the sides and angles of each triangle. Classify each triangle by its sides and angles.

1. 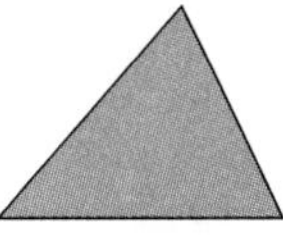
acute isosceles

2. 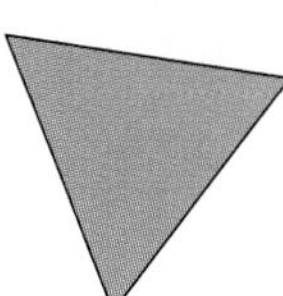
equiangular equilateral

3. 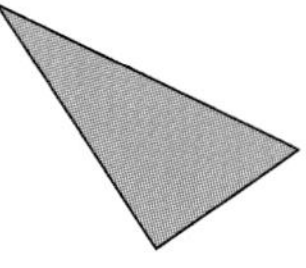
right scalene

4. 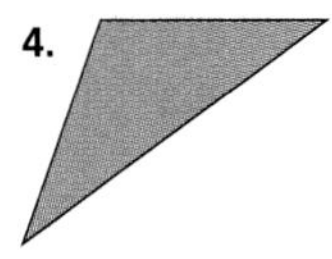
obtuse isosceles

Sketch a triangle to fit each description. If no triangle can be drawn, write *not possible* and explain. 5, 7–8. See margin for samples.

5. obtuse scalene **6.** right equilateral **7.** acute equilateral **8.** obtuse isosceles

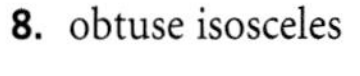
Not possible; an equilateral triangle is acute.

9. a. Logical Reasoning What is the measure of each angle of an equiangular triangle? **Justify** your reasoning. 60; the sum of measures is 180 and the 3 measures are =.

b. What is the sum of the measures of the acute angles of a right triangle? **Justify** your reasoning.

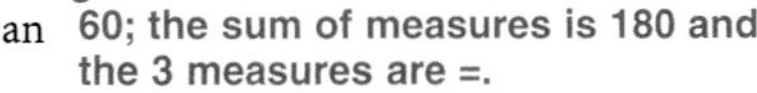
90; the sum of measures is 180 and the measure of the 3rd angle is 90.

pages 68–71 Think and Discuss

11a. Sample:

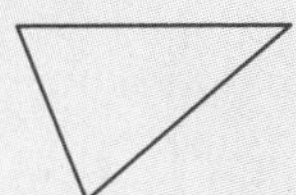

b. Sample:

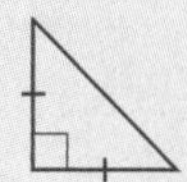

c. Not possible; an equilateral triangle is acute.

d. Sample:

pages 71–74 On Your Own

5. 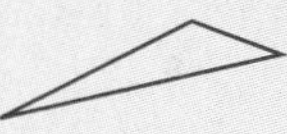

7. 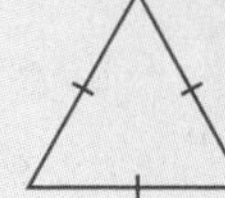

8.

ALTERNATIVE ASSESSMENT **Exercises 18–20** These exercises will help you assess students' understanding of the Triangle Angle-Sum Theorem and the Exterior Angle Theorem by observing their ability to apply the correct theorems to find each missing value.

STANDARDIZED TEST TIP **Exercise 21** Help students see that they do not need to solve for x in each answer choice. They can find the sum of the variables and check if the coefficient of the sum is a factor of 180.

ALGEBRA Exercise 24 Students may prefer to use Guess, Check, and Revise to solve this problem.

CRITICAL THINKING Exercise 26 If students have trouble getting started, suggest they experiment with triangles to test Rosa's claim.

23. Yes; no; every equilateral △ has three ≅ sides, so at least 2 sides are always ≅; in an isosceles △ 2 sides are ≅ but they need not be ≅ to the 3rd side.

26. Answers may vary. Sample: The ratio of the angle measures of an isosceles right triangle is 1:1:2. The ratio of the length of the sides is not 1:1:2.

72

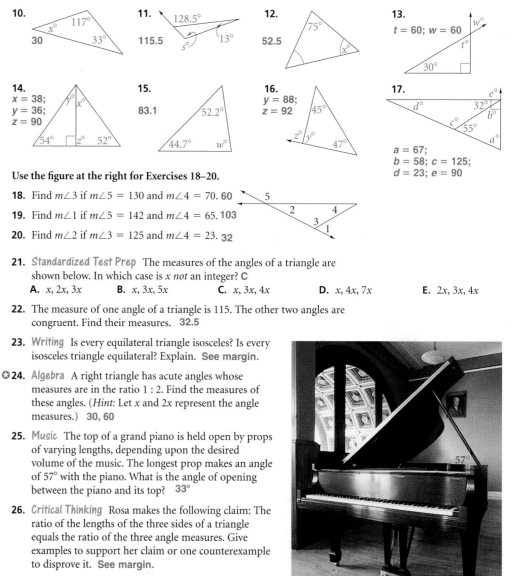

Choose **Use paper and pencil, mental math, or a calculator to find the values of the variables.**

10. **30**

11. 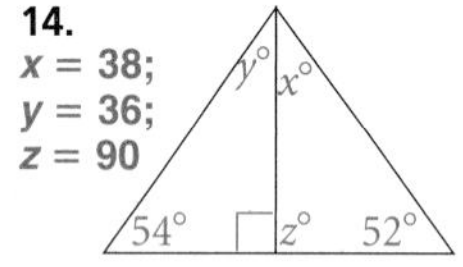 **115.5**

12. 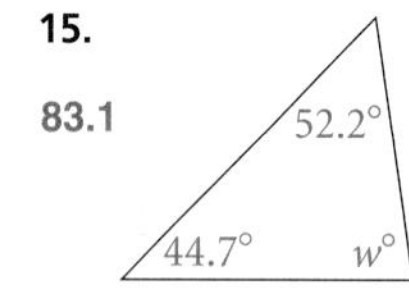 **52.5**

13. 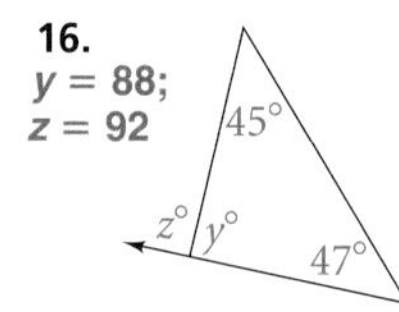 **$t = 60$; $w = 60$**

14. **$x = 38$; $y = 36$; $z = 90$**

15. **83.1**

16. **$y = 88$; $z = 92$**

17. 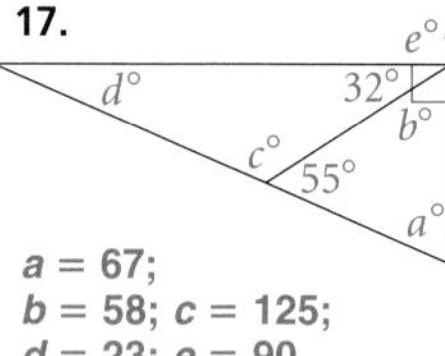 **$a = 67$; $b = 58$; $c = 125$; $d = 23$; $e = 90$**

Use the figure at the right for Exercises 18–20.

18. Find $m\angle 3$ if $m\angle 5 = 130$ and $m\angle 4 = 70$. **60**

19. Find $m\angle 1$ if $m\angle 5 = 142$ and $m\angle 4 = 65$. **103**

20. Find $m\angle 2$ if $m\angle 3 = 125$ and $m\angle 4 = 23$. **32**

21. *Standardized Test Prep* The measures of the angles of a triangle are shown below. In which case is x *not* an integer? **C**

A. $x, 2x, 3x$ **B.** $x, 3x, 5x$ **C.** $x, 3x, 4x$ **D.** $x, 4x, 7x$ **E.** $2x, 3x, 4x$

22. The measure of one angle of a triangle is 115. The other two angles are congruent. Find their measures. **32.5**

23. *Writing* Is every equilateral triangle isosceles? Is every isosceles triangle equilateral? Explain. **See margin.**

24. *Algebra* A right triangle has acute angles whose measures are in the ratio 1 : 2. Find the measures of these angles. (*Hint:* Let x and $2x$ represent the angle measures.) **30, 60**

25. *Music* The top of a grand piano is held open by props of varying lengths, depending upon the desired volume of the music. The longest prop makes an angle of 57° with the piano. What is the angle of opening between the piano and its top? **33°**

26. *Critical Thinking* Rosa makes the following claim: The ratio of the lengths of the three sides of a triangle equals the ratio of the three angle measures. Give examples to support her claim or one counterexample to disprove it. **See margin.**

ALGEBRA Exercise 30 You may want to remind students to look at the hint for Exercise 24.

PROBABILITY Exercise 31 Students will need to have answered Exercise 9a correctly to solve this problem.

LOGICAL REASONING Exercise 32 You may want students to rewrite the Exterior Angle Theorem followed by the completed statements a–d.

Exercise 33 You may need to review with students how to solve equations of the form $\sqrt{x} = a$.

OPEN-ENDED Exercise 34b Students may want to color their designs and display them in the classroom.

Algebra **Find the measures of the angles of each triangle. Classify each triangle by its angles.**

27. 37, 78, 65; acute

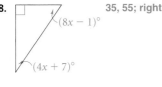

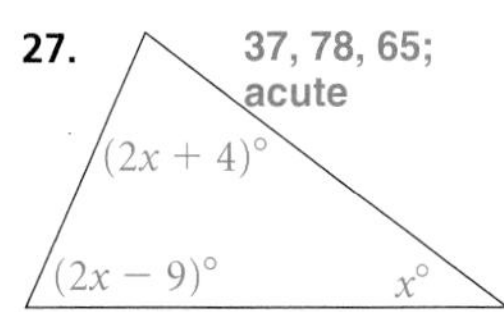

28. 35, 55; right

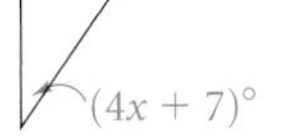

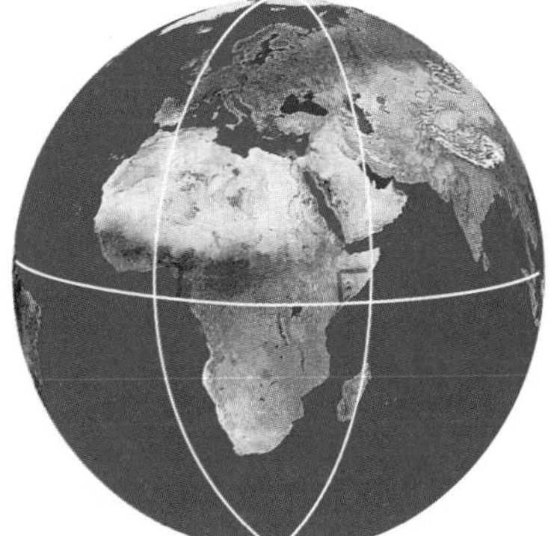

29. Geometry on a Sphere Suppose you were measuring the angles of a triangle on a globe. The meridians of longitude pass through both poles and are perpendicular to the equator. Will the sum of the measures of the angles of this triangle be equal to, greater than, or less than 180? Explain. > 180; measures of both angles at the equator = 90 and the angle at the pole has pos. measure.

30. a. Algebra The ratio of the angle measures in $\triangle BCR$ is 2 : 3 : 4. Find the angle measures. 40, 60, 80

b. What type of triangle is $\triangle BCR$? acute

31. a. Probability Find the probability that a triangle is equiangular if the measure of each of its angles is a multiple of 30. $\frac{1}{3}$

b. Find the probability that a triangle is equiangular if the measure of each of its angles is a multiple of 20. $\frac{1}{7}$

PROBLEM SOLVING HINT

Make a table showing all possibilities.

32. Logical Reasoning Complete the following statements to **justify** the Exterior Angle Theorem.

a. By the Angle Addition Postulate, $m\angle 1 + m\angle 4 =$ ■. 180

b. By the Triangle Angle-Sum Theorem, $m\angle 2 + m\angle 3 + m\angle 4 =$ ■. 180

c. By the _?_ Property, $m\angle 1 + m\angle 4 = m\angle 2 + m\angle 3 + m\angle 4$. Substitution

d. By the _?_ Property of Equality, $m\angle 1 = m\angle 2 + m\angle 3$. Subtraction

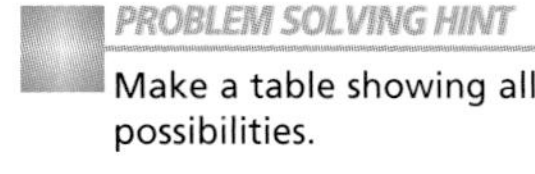

33. The measures of the angles of $\triangle RST$ are $\sqrt{x}$, $2\sqrt{x}$, and $3\sqrt{x}$.

a. Find the value of x and the measures of the angles. 900; 30, 60, 90

b. What type of triangle is $\triangle RST$? right

34. Weaving Patricia Tsinnie, a Navajo weaver, often uses isosceles triangles in her designs. 34a–b. Check students' work.

a. Trace the design shown below. Then use a colored pencil to outline isosceles triangles used in the design.

b. Open-ended Make a repeated design of your own that uses isosceles triangles.

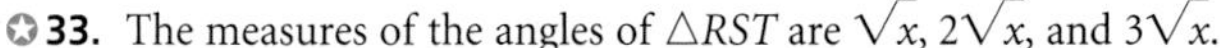

Chapter Project **FIND OUT BY DOING** After students make a set of tans, they may want to trace the pieces onto poster board and store them in a plastic bag for future use. Remind students to keep their Find Out exercise work in one place so they can complete the Chapter Project.

Exercises MIXED REVIEW

Exercise 39 Make sure students read the problem carefully and do not assume that $\angle AOC$ is a right angle.

GETTING READY FOR LESSON 2-2 These exercises prepare students to find the sum of the measures of the angles of a polygon.

Wrap Up

THE BIG IDEA Ask students: *Describe how triangles are classified.*

RETEACHING ACTIVITY Students use theorems to find missing angle measures in a rectangle, then classify the triangles they find. (Reteaching worksheet 2-1)

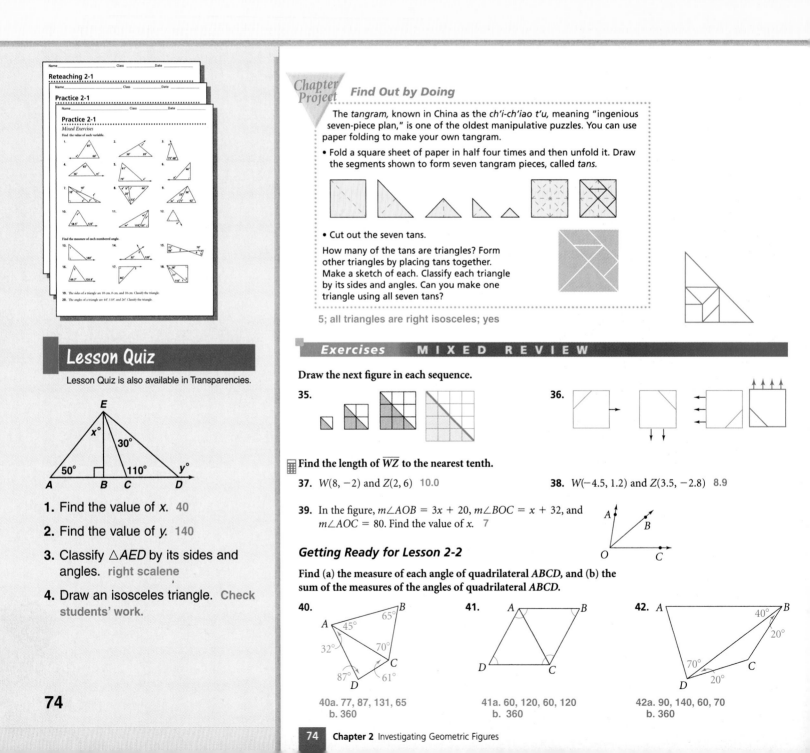

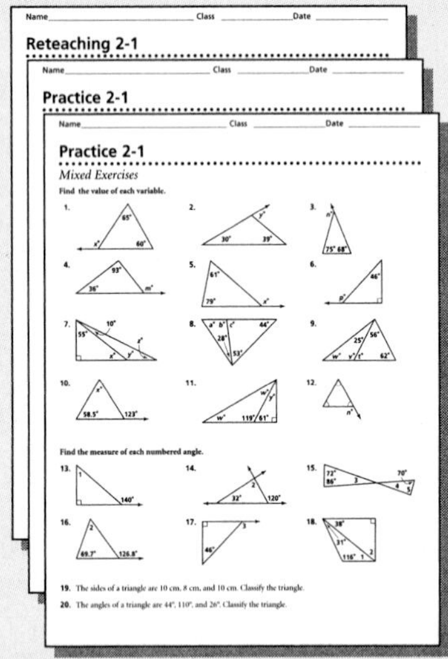

Reteaching 2-1

Practice 2-1

Practice 2-1
Mixed Exercises
Find the value of each variable.

Find the measure of each numbered angle.

Lesson Quiz

Lesson Quiz is also available in Transparencies.

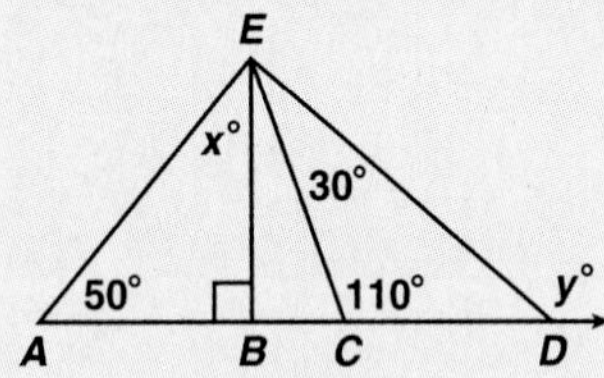

1. Find the value of x. 40
2. Find the value of y. 140
3. Classify $\triangle AED$ by its sides and angles. right scalene
4. Draw an isosceles triangle. Check students' work.

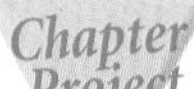

Find Out by Doing

The *tangram,* known in China as the *ch'i-ch'iao t'u,* meaning "ingenious seven-piece plan," is one of the oldest manipulative puzzles. You can use paper folding to make your own tangram.

- Fold a square sheet of paper in half four times and then unfold it. Draw the segments shown to form seven tangram pieces, called *tans.*

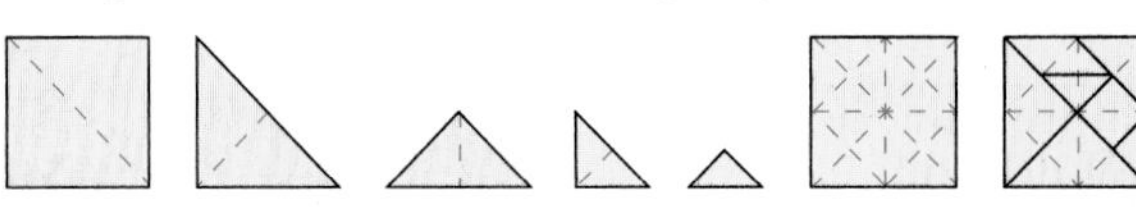

- Cut out the seven tans.

How many of the tans are triangles? Form other triangles by placing tans together. Make a sketch of each. Classify each triangle by its sides and angles. Can you make one triangle using all seven tans?

5; all triangles are right isosceles; yes

Exercises MIXED REVIEW

Draw the next figure in each sequence.

35.

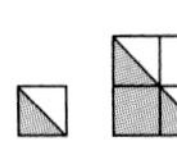

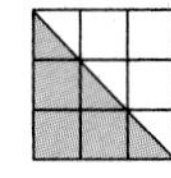

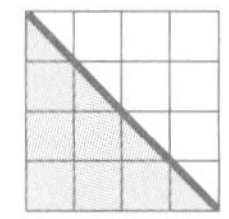

36.

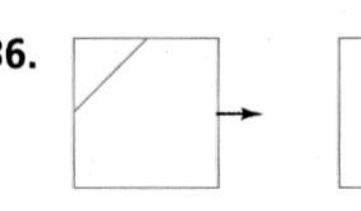

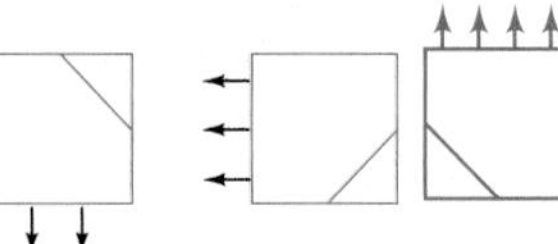

Find the length of $\overline{WZ}$ to the nearest tenth.

37. $W(8, -2)$ and $Z(2, 6)$ 10.0

38. $W(-4.5, 1.2)$ and $Z(3.5, -2.8)$ 8.9

39. In the figure, $m\angle AOB = 3x + 20$, $m\angle BOC = x + 32$, and $m\angle AOC = 80$. Find the value of x. 7

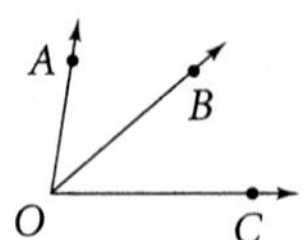

Getting Ready for Lesson 2-2

Find (a) the measure of each angle of quadrilateral *ABCD,* and (b) the sum of the measures of the angles of quadrilateral *ABCD.*

40.

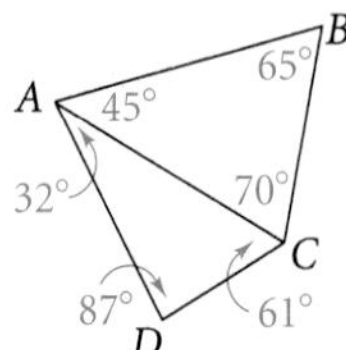

40a. 77, 87, 131, 65
b. 360

41.

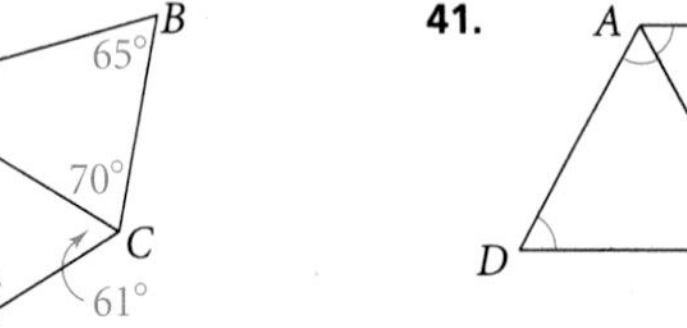

41a. 60, 120, 60, 120
b. 360

42.

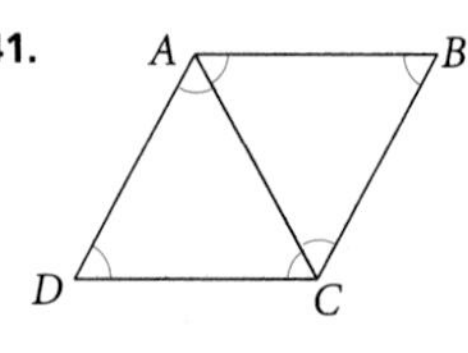

42a. 90, 140, 60, 70
b. 360

Math ToolboX

Students use geometry software to explore the exterior angles of a polygon. The software enables students to manipulate the polygon while observing that the sum of the exterior angles remains the same. The Polygon Exterior Angle-Sum Theorem is formally presented in Lesson 2-2.

Construct

ERROR ALERT! Students may extend each side of the polygon in more than one direction. **Remediation:** Make sure students extend each side in only one direction so that there is only one exterior angle at each vertex.

Investigate

Remind students what it means for a polygon to be convex.

Conjecture

Students may want to compare their results with others, before making their conjectures.

Extend

If possible, have students use software to decrease the size of the polygon as shown in the diagrams.

ADDITIONAL PROBLEM Have students repeat the *Construct* and *Investigate* activities with other polygons to verify their conjectures.

Math ToolboX Technology

Exploring the Exterior Angles of a Polygon

With Lesson 2-2

Work in pairs or small groups.

Construct

Use geometry software. Construct a convex polygon. Extend each side as shown. To measure the exterior angles you will need to mark a point on each ray.

Check students' work.

Investigate

- Measure each exterior angle.
- Calculate the sum of the measures of the exterior angles. 360
- Manipulate the polygon, making sure it remains convex. Observe the sum of the measures of the exterior angles.

Conjecture

- Write a conjecture about the sum of the measures of the exterior angles (one at each vertex) of a convex polygon.
  The sum of measures of the exterior angles of a polygon is always 360.
- Test your conjecture with another polygon.

Extend

The figures below show a polygon that is decreasing in size until finally it "disappears." Describe how these figures could be used as a justification for your conjecture.

When the polygon "disappears," the angles become adjacent. The sum of their measures is 360.

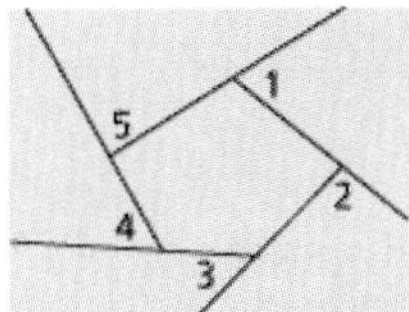

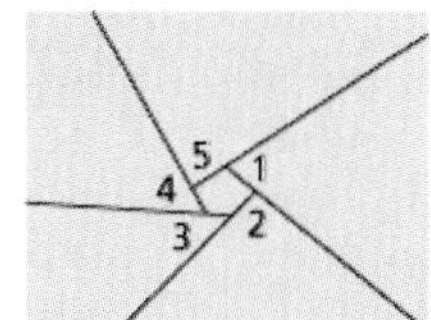

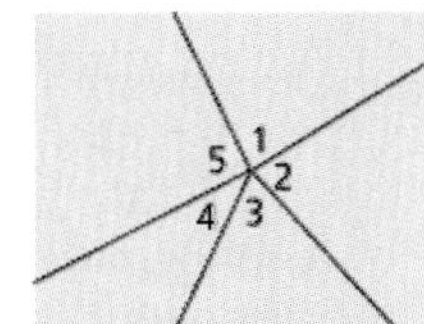

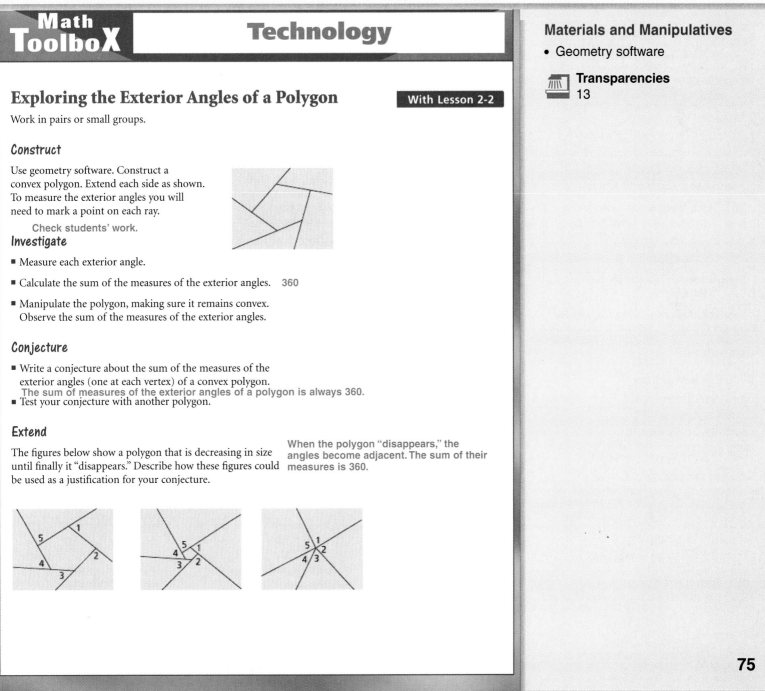

Materials and Manipulatives

- Geometry software

Transparencies
13

2-2 Teaching Notes

PROBLEM OF THE DAY

How many isosceles triangles are in the diagram? 60

Problem of the Day is also available in Transparencies.

CONNECTING TO PRIOR KNOWLEDGE Ask students to list words beginning with the prefixes *tri-*, *quad-*, *pent-*, and *oct-*. Examples include triathlon, quadriplegic, pentameter, and octopus. Discuss the meanings of the words and prefixes.

THINK AND DISCUSS p. 76

ESL Begin by drawing some familiar examples of polygons such as triangles, squares, and regular pentagons. Then sketch figures that are not polygons and discuss why they are not polygons.

Students may wonder why the 11-gon is not in the list of polygons. An 11-gon, also called an undecagon, is not very common. Also point out that *n*-gon is the term used when the number of sides is not known.

Lesson Planning Options

Prerequisite Skills

- Applying the Triangle Angle-Sum Theorem
- Solving one-variable equations

Assignment Options for Exercises On Your Own

To provide flexible scheduling, this lesson can be subdivided into parts.

1 **Core** 1–9, 28–29
Extension 27, 30

2 **Core** 10–17, 19–26
Extension 18

Use Mixed Review to maintain skills.

Resources

Student Edition

Skills Handbook, p. 670
Extra Practice, p. 649
Glossary/Study Guide

Teaching Resources

Chapter Support File, Ch. 2
- Practice 2-2 (two worksheets)
- Reteaching 2-2
- Alternative Activity 2-2

Classroom Manager 2-2
Glossary, Spanish Resources

Transparencies
13, 31

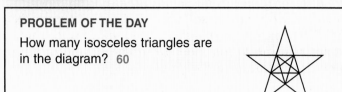

Connections Manufacturing . . . and more

2-2 Polygons

What You'll Learn

- Classifying polygons
- Finding the sum of the measures of the interior and exterior angles of polygons

...And Why

To increase your understanding of polygons, which are found in art and nature as well as in manufactured products

THINK AND DISCUSS

Part 1

Polygons and Interior Angles

Walking around a city, you can see polygons in buildings, windows, and traffic signs. The grillwork in the photo is a combination of different polygons that form a pleasing pattern.

A **polygon** is a closed plane figure with at least three sides. The sides intersect only at their endpoints and no adjacent sides are collinear. To identify a polygon, start at any vertex and list the other vertices consecutively.

Polygon	Number of Sides
triangle	3
quadrilateral	4
pentagon	5
hexagon	6
heptagon	7
octagon	8
nonagon	9
decagon	10
dodecagon	12
n-gon	*n*

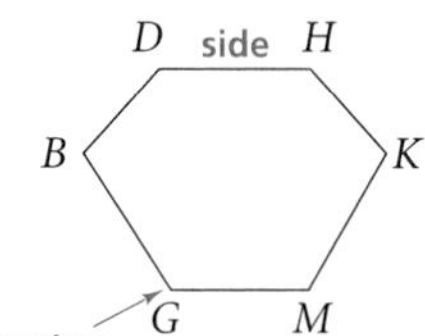

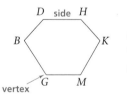

polygon *DHKMGB*

sides: $\overline{DH}, \overline{HK}, \overline{KM}, \overline{MG}, \overline{GB}, \overline{BD}$
vertices: *D, H, K, M, G, B*
angles: $\angle D, \angle H, \angle K, \angle M, \angle G, \angle B$

You can classify polygons by the number of sides. The most common polygons are listed at the left.

A polygon is **convex** if no diagonal contains points outside the polygon.

A polygon is **concave** if a diagonal contains points outside the polygon.

QUICK REVIEW

A diagonal of a polygon is a segment that connects two nonconsecutive vertices.

In this textbook, the term *polygon* refers to a convex polygon unless otherwise stated.

1. ***Open-ended*** Draw a convex and a concave octagon. Draw diagonals and explain why one octagon is convex and the other is concave. See back of book.

AUDITORY LEARNING Using the polygons on page 76, have students practice naming polygons, sides, and vertices. You may want to point out that the vertex they start with does not matter but that naming the vertices consecutively does.

WORK TOGETHER

VISUAL LEARNING After students have sketched the polygons, have them use shading to indicate the interior angles. After dividing the polygons into triangles, have them use a different color shading for all the angles in each triangle. This will help convince students that the sum of the measures of the angles of the triangles equals the sum of the measures of the interior angles of the polygon.

THINK AND DISCUSS p. 77

Polygon Interior Angle-Sum Theorem Remind students that if they ever forget the formula given in this theorem, they can always use the method from the Work Together to find the sum of the measures of the angles.

Question 3 Point out to students that using the Polygon Interior Angle-Sum Theorem takes less than drawing the polygons and their diagonals.

Example 1

ESTIMATION To check that the answer is reasonable, have students estimate that the sum of $m\angle T$, $m\angle R$, $m\angle V$, and $m\angle M$ which is about 400, so $m\angle Y$ should be about 140.

WORK TOGETHER

You can use triangles and the Triangle Angle-Sum Theorem to find the measures of the interior angles of a polygon. Work with a partner. Record your data in a table like the one shown below.

- Sketch polygons with 4, 5, 6, 7, and 8 sides.
- Divide each polygon into triangles by drawing all the diagonals from one vertex.
- Multiply the number of triangles by 180 to find the sum of the measures of the interior angles of each polygon.

2. **Inductive Reasoning** Look for a pattern in the table. Write a rule for finding the sum of the measures of the interior angles of a polygon with n sides. See margin p. 79.

Polygon	Number of Sides	Number of Triangles Formed	Sum of the Interior Angle Measures
(quadrilateral sketch)	4	■	■ • 180 = ■

THINK AND DISCUSS

The results of the Work Together suggest the following theorem.

Theorem 2-3
Polygon Interior Angle-Sum Theorem

The sum of the measures of the interior angles of an n-gon is $(n - 2)180$.

3. **Try This** Find the sum of the measures of the interior angles of each polygon.
   a. 15-gon 2340
   b. 20-gon 3240
   c. decagon 1440
   d. dodecagon 1800

Example 1

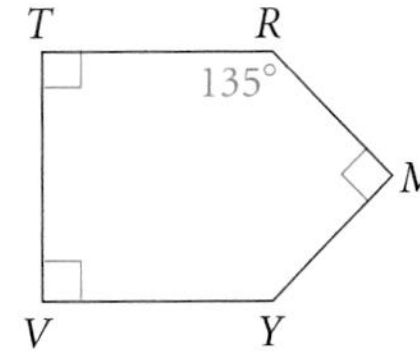

Find $m\angle Y$ in $TVYMR$.

Use the Polygon Interior Angle-Sum Theorem for $n = 5$.

$$m\angle T + m\angle V + m\angle Y + m\angle M + m\angle R = (5 - 2)180$$
$$90 + 90 + m\angle Y + 90 + 135 = 540$$
$$m\angle Y + 405 = 540$$
$$m\angle Y = 135$$

Additional Examples

FOR EXAMPLE 1

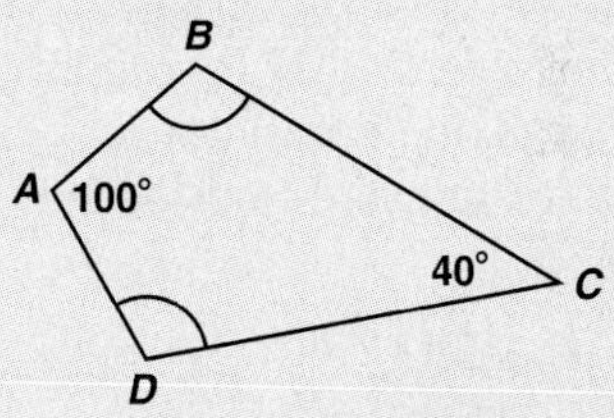

If $m\angle B = m\angle D$, find $m\angle B$ in $ABCD$.

$m\angle A + m\angle B + m\angle C + m\angle D =$
$(4 - 2)180$

$100 + m\angle B + 40 + m\angle D = 360$
$m\angle B + m\angle D + 140 = 360$
$m\angle B + m\angle D = 220$
$2m\angle B = 220$
$m\angle B = 110$

Discussion: *What theorem did you apply to find $m\angle B$?*

FOR EXAMPLE 2

Find the measures of an interior and an exterior angle of a regular hexagon. **Measure of one exterior angle = 60; measure of one interior angle = 120.**

Discussion: *Which method did you use? Why?*

Question 4 The Toolbox on page 75 provides a direct way for students to investigate the sum of the exterior angles of a polygon using geometry software.

ALTERNATIVE METHOD Have students draw a polygon with one exterior angle at each vertex. Then have them cut out the exterior angles and tape the vertices together. Ask students to make a conjecture about the sum of the exterior angles of a polygon based on their taped figures.

KINESTHETIC LEARNING Use masking tape to make a large polygon on the floor showing one exterior angle at each vertex. Have students start at one vertex and walk around the polygon in the direction of the exterior angles. When the students return to the starting point, they have made five turns totaling 360°.

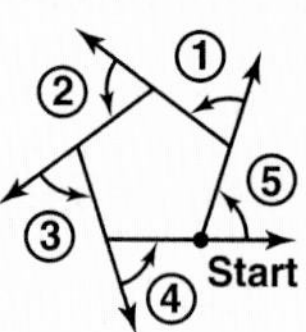

Technology Options

For Exercises 5–8, students may use geometry software to draw the polygons. For Exercise 27, students may use a graphing calculator or other graphing software to draw the scatter plot.

Prentice Hall Technology

Software

- Secondary Math Lab Toolkit™
- Computer Item Generator 2-2

CD-ROM

- Multimedia Geometry Lab 2

Internet

- See the Prentice Hall site. (http://www.phschool.com)

78

Part 2

Exterior Angles

Technology The figures below show one exterior angle drawn at each vertex of each polygon.

4. a. Find the sum of the measures of the exterior angles (one at each vertex) of each polygon. 360; 360; 360

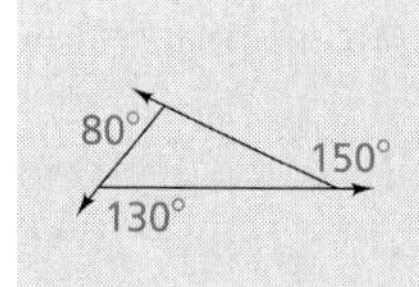

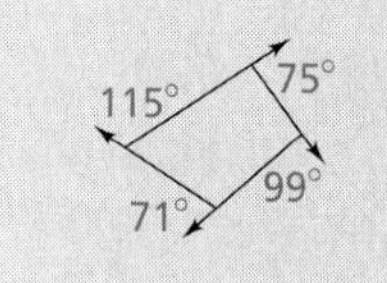

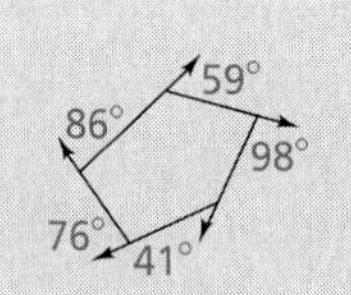

b. Make a conjecture about the sum of the measures of the exterior angles (one at each vertex) of a polygon.
The sum of measures of exterior angles of a polygon is 360.

This inductive reasoning leads to the following theorem.

Theorem 2-4
Polygon Exterior Angle-Sum Theorem

The sum of the measures of the exterior angles of a polygon, one at each vertex, is 360.

An **equilateral polygon** has all sides congruent. An **equiangular polygon** has all angles congruent. A **regular polygon** is equilateral and equiangular.

Regular Octagon

Example 2

Find the measure of an interior angle and an exterior angle of a regular octagon.

Method 1: Find the measure of an interior angle first.

Sum of the measures of the interior angles = $(8 - 2)180 = 1080$

- Measure of one interior angle $= \frac{1080}{8} = 135$
- Measure of its adjacent exterior angle $= 180 - 135 = 45$

Method 2: Find the measure of an exterior angle first.

Sum of the measures of the exterior angles = 360

- Measure of one exterior angle $= \frac{360}{8} = 45$
- Measure of its adjacent interior angle = $180 - 45 = 135$

5. Try This Find the measure of an interior angle and an exterior angle of a regular dodecagon. 150; 30

Example 2

Two methods are presented for finding the solution. Take time to discuss both methods and why each works.

Question 5 You may want to provide students with a visual model of a regular dodecagon. Use the method described in Exercises 5–8 to prepare one in advance on a transparency.

Example 3 *Relating to the Real World* 

Help students see that the four right triangles are congruent. Also emphasize that ∠1 is an exterior angle but ∠2 is not, and check that they understand why.

Exercises ON YOUR OWN

MAKING CONNECTIONS Exercises 1–4 A diamond cutter uses diamonds to cut another diamond so that the flat surfaces of the diamond are polygons. Some of the more popular cuts are the "brilliant cut," "oval cut," "marquise cut," and "pear cut."

Exercises 5–8 These exercises provide a good opportunity for students to work in groups. Students should draw a point on a piece of paper, then use two protractors to form a circle.

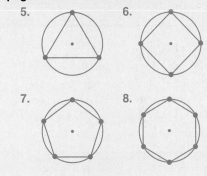

Example 3 *Relating to the Real World* 

Manufacturing Mindco, a toy manufacturer, is packaging a Chinese checkers game. The game consists of colored pegs and a regular hexagonal wooden board. Mindco is packaging the game in a rectangular box using four right triangles made of foam. Find the measures of the acute angles of each foam triangle.

∠1 is an exterior angle of a regular hexagon.

Find $m\angle 1$ and then use the Triangle Angle-Sum Theorem to find $m\angle 2$.

$6 \cdot m\angle 1 = 360$	Sum of the measures of the exterior ∆s of a polygon = 360.
$m\angle 1 = 60$	Divide each side by 6.
$m\angle 1 + m\angle 2 + 90 = 180$	Triangle Angle-Sum Thm.
$60 + m\angle 2 + 90 = 180$	Substitution
$m\angle 2 + 150 = 180$	Simplify.
$m\angle 2 = 30$	Subtract 150 from each side.

The measures of the acute angles of each foam triangle are 60 and 30.

page 77 Work Together

2.

4	2	2 • 180 = 360
5	3	3 • 180 = 540
6	4	4 • 180 = 720
7	5	5 • 180 = 900
8	6	6 • 180 = 1080

The sum of measures of interior angles of an n-gon is $(n - 2) \cdot 180$.

pages 79–81 On Your Own

5. 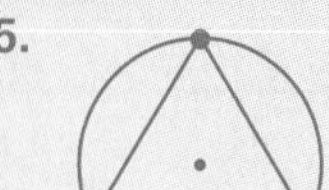
6. 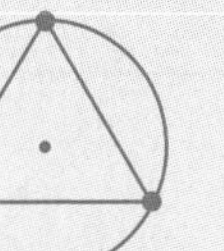 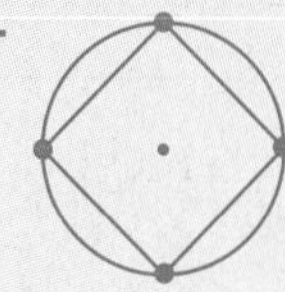
7.  
8. 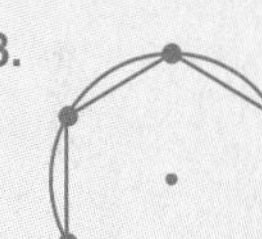

Exercises ON YOUR OWN 

Classify each polygon by its number of sides. Identify which polygons are convex and which are concave.

1. 
convex dodecagon

2. 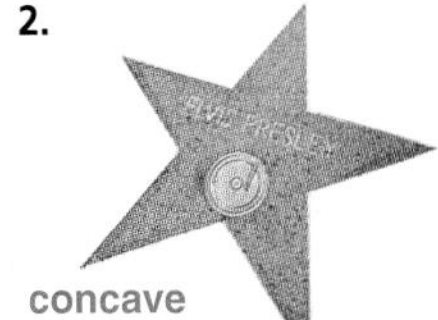
concave decagon

3. 
convex octagon

4. 
concave pentagon

Draw each regular polygon.

Sample: dodecagon 5–8. See margin.

Draw a circle. Use a protractor to locate 12 points equidistant around a circle. (These points will be located every 30 degrees around a circle, since 360° ÷ 12 = 30°.) Connect these points to form a regular dodecagon.

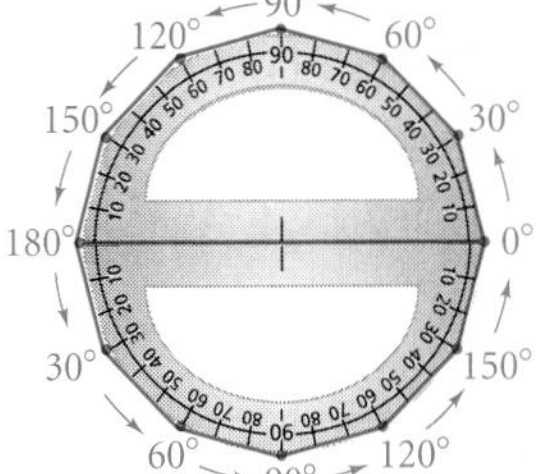

5. triangle
6. quadrilateral
7. pentagon
8. hexagon

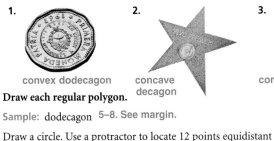

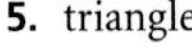

CONNECTING TO STUDENTS' WORLD Exercise 9 Have students investigate the shapes of sports stadiums and identify whether the stadiums themselves or any sections of the stadiums form polygonal shapes.

Exercise 13 Students may have some trouble substituting y for n in the formulas.

ALTERNATIVE ASSESSMENT Exercises 14–17 These exercises can help you assess students' understanding of the Polygon Exterior Angle-Sum Theorem. Students are given the measure of one exterior angle of a polygon and are asked to find the number of sides.

WRITING Exercise 18 You may want to suggest that students use a technique similar to that which they used to solve Exercises 14–17 to find the number of sides such a polygon would have.

ERROR ALERT! Exercise 28 Students may not include the measure of an interior angle of a triangle or a dodecagon in the sample space. **Remediation:** Review the meaning of the symbols $\leq$ and $\geq$.

CRITICAL THINKING Exercise 30 Have students explain why 360 is subtracted.

27a. (20, 162), (40, 171), (60, 174), (80, 175.5), (100, 176.4), (120, 177), (140, 177.4), (160, 177.8), (180, 178), (200, 178.2)

b.

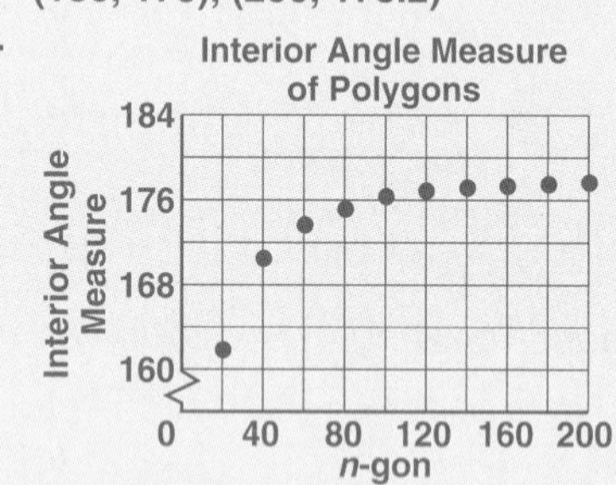

c. very close to 180

d. No; a regular polygon with all straight angles would have all its vertices on a straight line.

29a.

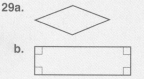

b.

9. *Design* A theater-in-the-round is constructed so that the audience surrounds the stage. Such theaters are not always circular in shape, however. Classify the theater-in-the-round shown in the diagram below the photo, by the number of sides. Find the measure of each numbered angle.
octagon; $m\angle 1 = 135$; $m\angle 2 = 45$

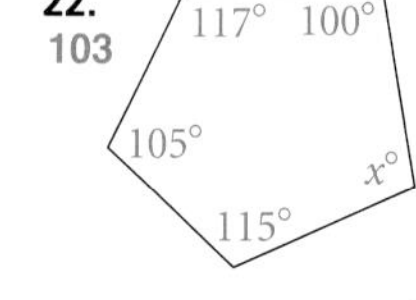

Find the measure of an interior angle and an exterior angle for each regular polygon. $\frac{180y - 360}{y}; \frac{360}{y}$

10. pentagon 108; 72
11. nonagon 140; 40
12. 18-gon 160; 20
13. y-gon

The measure of an exterior angle of a regular polygon is given. Find the number of sides.

14. 72 5
15. 36 10
16. 18 20
17. x $\frac{360}{x}$

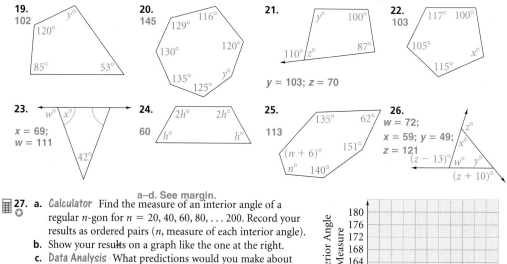

18. *Writing* Keach said that he drew a regular polygon and measured one of its interior angles. He got 130°. Explain to him why this is impossible. Answers may vary. Sample: The measure of the exterior angle is 50. Then the polygon must have $\frac{360}{50}$ sides. But this number is not an integer.

Choose **Use pencil and paper, mental math, or a calculator to find the values of the variables.**

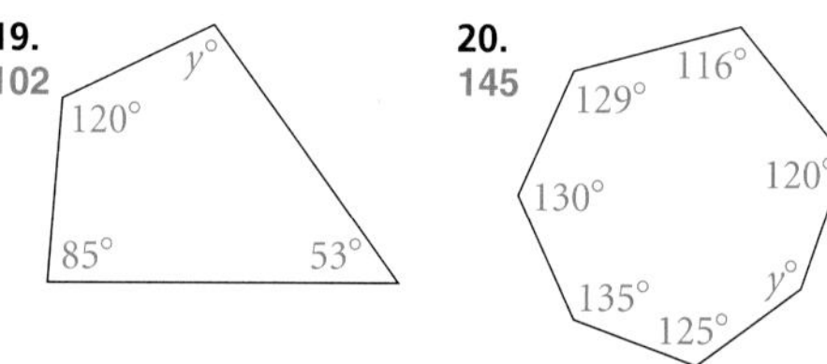

21. y = 103; z = 70

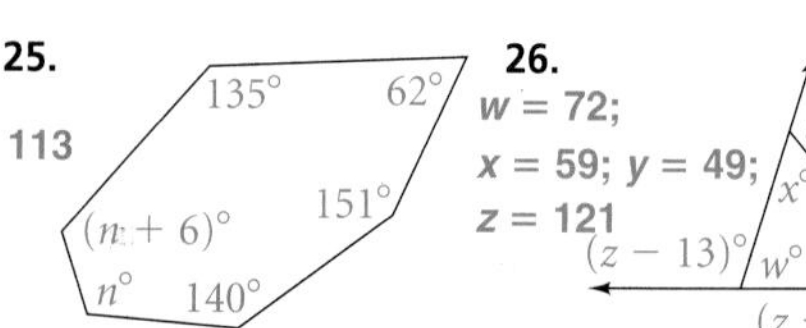

23. $x = 69$; $w = 111$

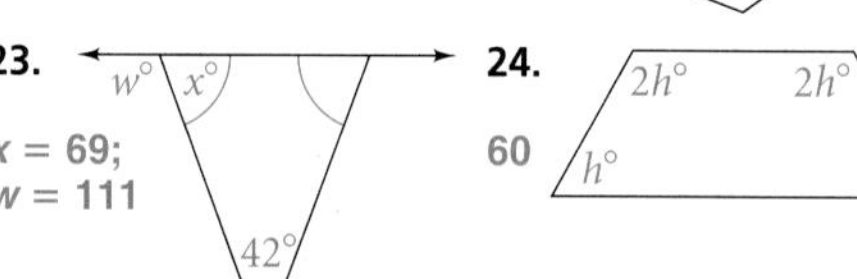

25. 113

26. $w = 72$; $x = 59$; $y = 49$; $z = 121$

27. a–d. See margin.
a. *Calculator* Find the measure of an interior angle of a regular n-gon for $n = 20, 40, 60, 80, \ldots 200$. Record your results as ordered pairs (n, measure of each interior angle).
b. Show your results on a graph like the one at the right.
c. *Data Analysis* What predictions would you make about the measure of an interior angle of a regular 1000-gon?
d. Is there a regular n-gon with an interior angle of 180°? Explain.

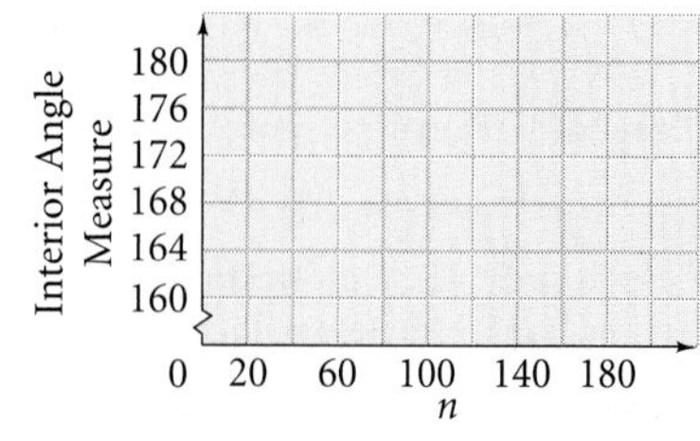

28. *Probability* Find the probability that the measure of an interior angle of a regular n-gon is a positive integer if n is an integer and $3 \leq n \leq 12$. $\frac{4}{5}$

Chapter Project **FIND OUT BY EXPLORING** Students should use the tans they created in Lesson 2-1. Remind students to check very carefully whether two shapes they find are truly different shapes. Have them continue to work on this problem throughout Chapter 2, as time allows.

Exercises MIXED REVIEW

Exercises 35–37 You may also want students to classify each triangle according to its angle measures.

Exercise 37 Students should first solve for x using the Angle Addition Postulate. Then have them share their methods for finding y.

GETTING READY FOR LESSON 2-3 These exercises provide practice evaluating the slope formula, which prepares students to work with slopes of parallel and perpendicular lines.

Wrap Up

THE BIG IDEA Ask students: *Restate the Polygon Interior Angle-Sum Theorem and the Polygon Exterior Angle-Sum Theorem and give an example illustrating each.*

RETEACHING ACTIVITY Students apply the Polygon Interior Angle-Sum and Polygon Exterior Angle-Sum Theorems to find the measures of interior and exterior angles of polygons. (Reteaching worksheet 2-2)

29. a. *Open-ended* Sketch a quadrilateral that is not equiangular. a–b. See margin p. 80.
    b. Sketch an equiangular quadrilateral that is not regular.

30. *Critical Thinking* Laura suggests another way to find the sum of the measures of the interior angles of an n-gon. She picks an interior point of the figure, draws segments to each vertex, counts the number of triangles, multiplies by 180, then subtracts 360. Does her method work? Explain. Yes; the sum of measures of angles at the interior point is 360. The sum of angle measures of all the triangles is $180n$. $180n - 360 = (n - 2) \cdot 180$

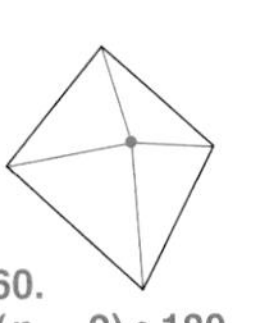

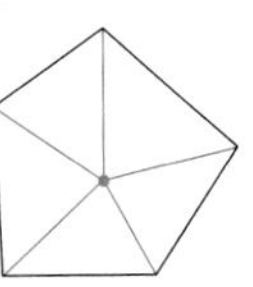

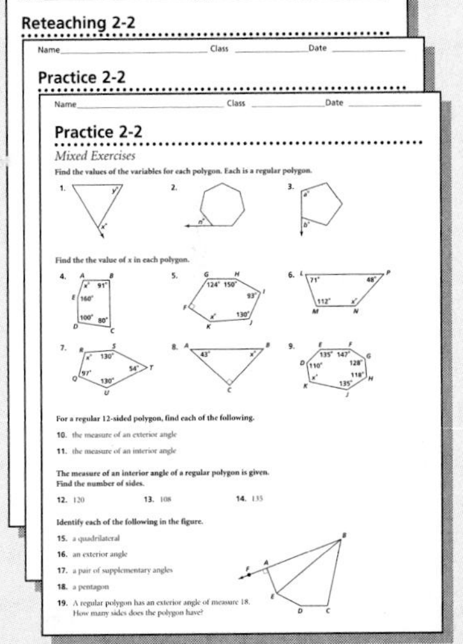

Name ___ Class ___ Date ___

Reteaching 2-2

Name ___ Class ___ Date ___

Practice 2-2

Name ___ Class ___ Date ___

Practice 2-2

Mixed Exercises

Find the values of the variables for each polygon. Each is a regular polygon.

1. 2. 3.

Find the the value of x in each polygon.

4. 5. 6.

7. 8. 9.

For a regular 12-sided polygon, find each of the following.

10. the measure of an exterior angle
11. the measure of an interior angle

The measure of an interior angle of a regular polygon is given. Find the number of sides.

12. 120 13. 108 14. 135

Identify each of the following in the figure.

15. a quadrilateral
16. an exterior angle
17. a pair of supplementary angles
18. a pentagon
19. A regular polygon has an exterior angle of measure 18. How many sides does the polygon have?

Chapter Project

Find Out by Exploring

In 1942, two mathematicians at the University of Chekiang in China proved that only 13 convex polygons could be formed by using all 7 tans. They were able to form 1 triangle, 6 quadrilaterals, 2 pentagons, and 4 hexagons. Try to make these using your set of tans. Make a sketch of each figure. See back of book.

Exercises MIXED REVIEW

Identify the following.

31. a pair of opposite rays $\overrightarrow{RT}$ and $\overrightarrow{RK}$
32. two right angles $\angle BRT$ and $\angle BRK$
33. a pair of supplementary angles
34. a pair of complementary angles

Answers may vary. Sample: $\angle BRT$ and $\angle BRK$ 34. $\angle BRM$ and $\angle MRK$

Choose **Use paper and pencil, mental math, or a calculator to find the values of the variables.**

35. 40.25

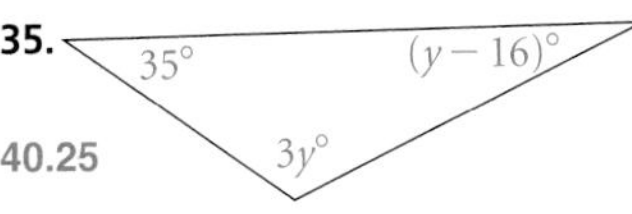

36. 27.5

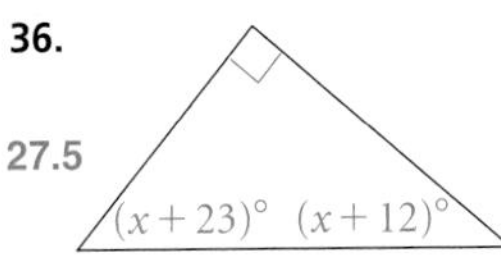

37. $x = 104$; $y = 35$

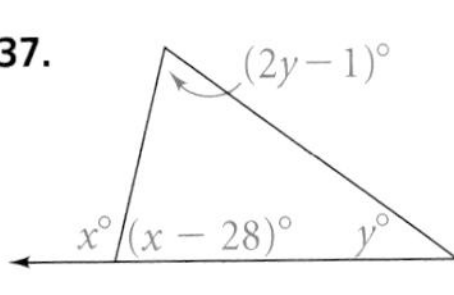

38. The measure of an angle is one-third the measure of its supplement. Find the measures of the angles. 45 and 135

39. The measure of an angle is four times the measure of its complement. Find the measures of the angles. 72 and 18

Getting Ready for Lesson 2-3

Find $\frac{y_2 - y_1}{x_2 - x_1}$.

40. $(x_1, y_1) = (3, 5)$ and $(x_2, y_2) = (1, 4)$ $\frac{1}{2}$
41. $(x_1, y_1) = (-2, 6)$ and $(x_2, y_2) = (3, 1)$ -1
42. $(x_1, y_1) = (1, -8)$ and $(x_2, y_2) = (1, 2)$ undefined
43. $(x_1, y_1) = (-5, 3)$ and $(x_2, y_2) = (1, 3)$ 0

Lesson Quiz

Lesson Quiz is also available in Transparencies.

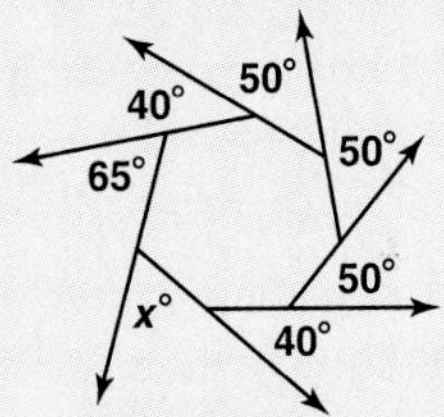

1. Classify the polygon. heptagon
2. Find the sum of the measures of the interior angles. 900
3. Find x. 65

Math ToolboX

Students use graphing calculators to explore equations of lines and make conjectures about how the values of m and b in $y = mx + b$ affect the graph of the line. In the Extend, students explore the slopes of parallel and perpendicular lines. These topics will be addressed formally in Lesson 2-3.

The graphing calculator enables students to graph many lines quickly so they can easily view how lines vary as the values of m and b vary.

ERROR ALERT! Students' graphing calculators may not have a zoom feature to use to create a square window.
Remediation: Have students consult the owner's manual to set the origin in the center of the viewing window.

Investigate

Students may wonder about equations of the form $y = x - b$. Help them see that every equation of that form can be rewritten as $y = x + (-b)$.

Conjecture

Students can test their conjectures by graphing equations of the form $y = mx + b$.

ADDITIONAL PROBLEM Ask students to find a pair of equations whose graphs are parallel and cross the y-axis two units apart. Then ask students to find a pair of equations whose graphs are perpendicular and intersect at (0, 2).

Materials and Manipulatives

- Graphing calculator

Transparencies
5, 8, 9, 10

Investigate

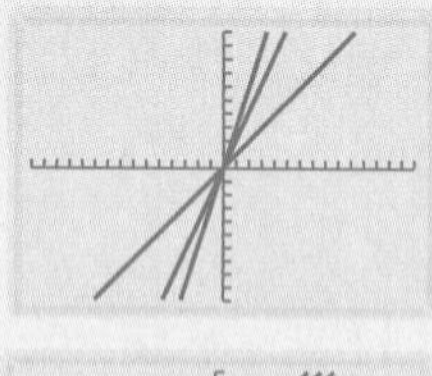

The value of m affects the steepness of the line.

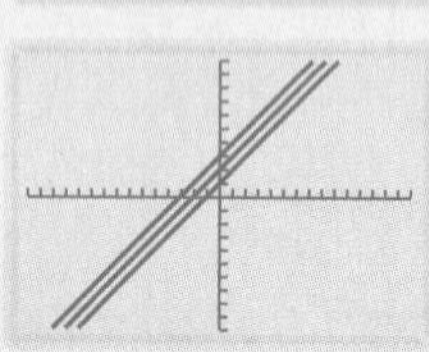

Changing the value of b shifts the line vertically.

Conjecture

Answers may vary. Samples: A line with pos. value of m goes from the lower left to the upper right. The greater the abs. value of m the steeper the line. For neg. values of b, the line shifts down by the number of units = to the abs. value of b. The line passes through the origin if $b = 0$.

Extend

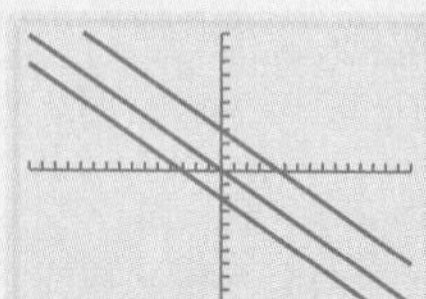

The lines are ∥; the values of m are =; lines with equations that have = values of m are ∥.

Math ToolboX — Technology

Exploring Equations of Lines

With Lesson 2-3

Work in pairs or small groups. To make sure that the viewing grid on your graphing calculator screen is square, press ZOOM 5.

Investigate See margin.

- Use your graphing calculator to graph the lines $y = x$, $y = 2x$, and $y = 3x$. Experiment with other equations of lines in the form $y = mx$. Substitute fractions and negative numbers for m. How does the value of m affect the graph of a line?
- Graph the lines $y = x + 1$, $y = x + 2$, and $y = x + 3$. Experiment with other equations of lines in the form $y = x + b$. Substitute fractions and negative numbers for b. How does the value of b affect the graph of a line?

Conjecture See margin.

When you graph an equation in the form $y = mx + b$, how do the values of m and b affect the graph of the line? List all your **conjectures.**

Extend

- Graph the lines $y = -\frac{2}{3}x$, $y = -\frac{2}{3}x + 3$, and $y = -\frac{2}{3}x - 2$. What appears to be true of these lines? How are the values of m related? Make a **conjecture** about the graphs of equations of lines where the values of m are the same. Test your **conjecture** by graphing several equations of lines where the values of m are the same. See margin.
- Graph each pair of lines:

a. $y = \frac{1}{2}x$, $y = -2x$ a–c. See back of book.

b. $y = \frac{3}{4}x$, $y = -\frac{4}{3}x$

c. $y = 5x$, $y = -\frac{1}{5}x$

What appears to be true of these lines? For each pair, how are the values of m related? Make a **conjecture** about the graphs of equations of lines where the product of the values of m is -1. Test your **conjecture** by graphing several pairs of equations of lines where the product of the values of m is -1.

2-3 Teaching Notes

PROBLEM OF THE DAY

Find the sum of the measures of the angles shown. 2880

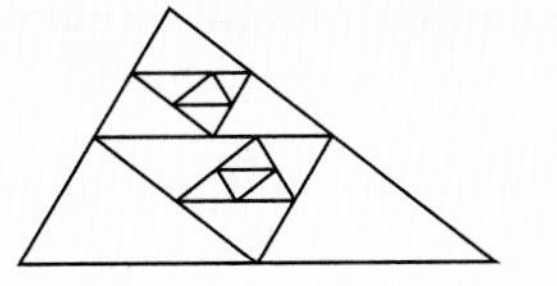

Problem of the Day is also available in Transparencies.

CONNECTING TO PRIOR KNOWLEDGE Have students make a table of values to graph $y = -\frac{1}{2}x + 5$ and $y = 2x - 1$. Ask them how the lines appear to be related.

THINK AND DISCUSS p. 83

VISUAL LEARNING Have students describe the appearance of the lines in each of the four graphs. Emphasize that a line with a positive slope rises *from left to right* and a line with a negative slope falls from *left to right.*

Question 1 Students will often confuse the slope of a vertical line with the slope of a horizontal line. You may need to review that $\frac{0}{1} = 0$ and $\frac{1}{0}$ is undefined. Then, for the horizontal and vertical lines shown in the diagram, have students choose two pairs of points on each and try to apply the slope formula.

MENTAL MATH Question 2b Students should be able to answer this question based on the graphs from part a.

Connections Architecture . . . and more

2-3 Parallel and Perpendicular Lines in the Coordinate Plane

What You'll Learn

- Graphing lines in the coordinate plane
- Recognizing parallel and perpendicular lines by their slopes

...And Why

To familiarize yourself with parallel and perpendicular lines, which are essential to the construction of houses, furniture, and machinery

What You'll Need

graph paper, ruler

THINK AND DISCUSS

Part 1

Slope and Graphing Lines

In everyday life the word *slope* refers to the steepness of a mountain, the grade of a road, or the pitch of a roof. In algebra, the *slope* of a line is the ratio of the vertical change to the horizontal change between any two points on a line.

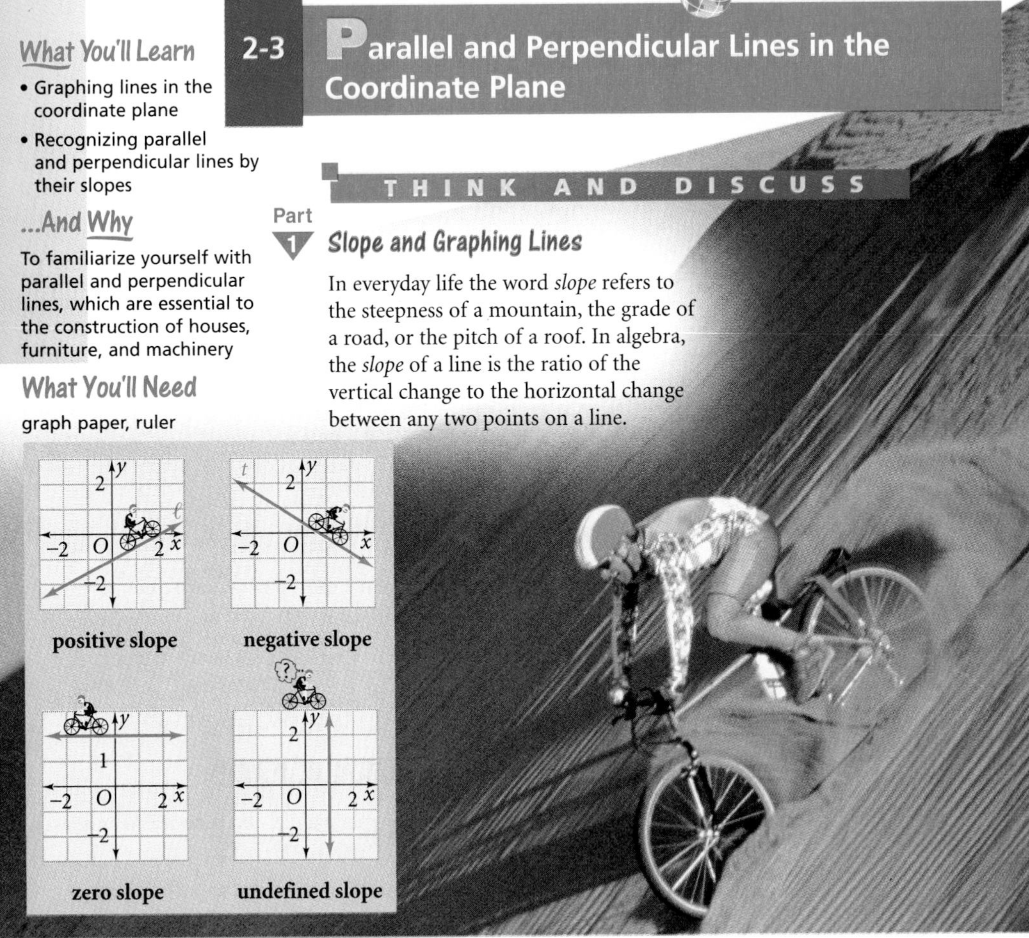

QUICK REVIEW

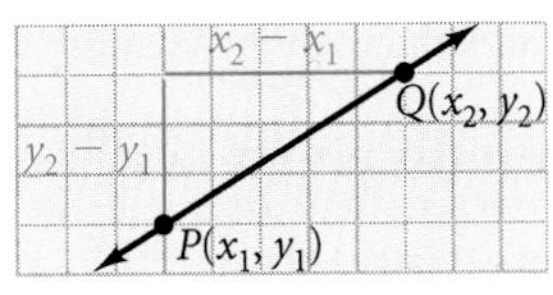

$$\text{Slope} = \frac{\text{vertical change (rise)}}{\text{horizontal change (run)}}$$

$$m = \frac{y_2 - y_1}{x_2 - x_1}$$

1. a. Use $\frac{\text{vertical change}}{\text{horizontal change}}$ to find the slopes of line ℓ and line t shown above. $\frac{1}{2}; -\frac{2}{3}$
   b. Explain why the slope of a horizontal line is zero. b. The vertical change is 0.
   c. Explain why the slope of a vertical line is undefined. The horizontal change is 0. Division by 0 is undefined.
2. **Try This** Use these pairs of points to answer parts (a)–(c).
   $R(-3, -4), S(5, -4)$ $C(-2, 2), D(4, -2)$
   $K(-3, 3), T(-3, 1)$ $P(3, 0), Y(0, -5)$
   a. See back of book.
   a. Graph and label a line that contains each pair of points.
   b. **Mental Math** Decide whether the slope of each line is positive, negative, zero, or undefined. 0; neg.; undef.; pos.
   c. Find the slope of each line. 0; $-\frac{2}{3}$; undefined; $\frac{5}{3}$

Lesson Planning Options

Prerequisite Skills

- Recognizing that division by zero is undefined
- Recognizing equations of vertical and horizontal lines

Assignment Options for Exercises On Your Own

To provide flexible scheduling, this lesson can be subdivided into parts.

1 **Core** 1–3, 23
✪**Extension** 26, 29

2 **Core** 4–22, 24–25
✪**Extension** 27–28

Use Mixed Review to maintain skills.

Resources

Student Edition

Skills Handbook, pp. 670, 678, 679
Extra Practice, p. 649
Glossary/Study Guide

Teaching Resources

Chapter Support File, Ch. 2
- Practice 2-3 (two worksheets)
- Reteaching 2-3

Classroom Manager 2-3
Glossary, Spanish Resources

Transparencies

5, 8, 9, 10, 32

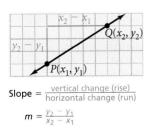

Example 1

Help students see that another point on the line can be found by moving three units up and four units right from (4, 5) or by moving three units down and four units left from (0, 2).

ERROR ALERT! **Question 3** Students sometimes plot the y-intercept on the x-axis. **Remediation:** Explain that the y-intercept is the y-coordinate where the line crosses the y-axis. The coordinates of this point are $(0, b)$.

Question 4 Point out that the slope of $-\frac{1}{2}$ is equivalent to $\frac{-1}{2}$ or $\frac{1}{-2}$ but not $\frac{-1}{-2}$. Have students use a graph to show why this is true.

WORK TOGETHER

The Math Toolbox on page 82 provides an alternative activity for exploring the slopes of parallel and perpendicular lines using a graphing calculator.

Question 5a Students may be unsure as to which points on a line to use when finding the slope. Help them see that the slope of a line does not depend on which points on the line they choose to use.

Question 6 Students may have difficulty seeing pairs of perpendicular lines other than vertical and horizontal lines. Students may want to use a protractor to confirm that the perpendicular lines shown in the graph intersect at a 90° angle.

Additional Examples

FOR EXAMPLE 1

Graph the line $y = -x + 3$.

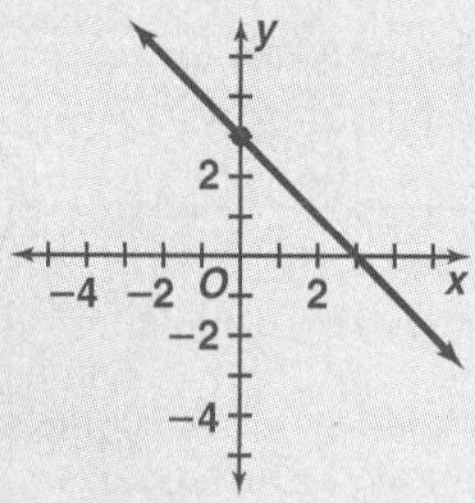

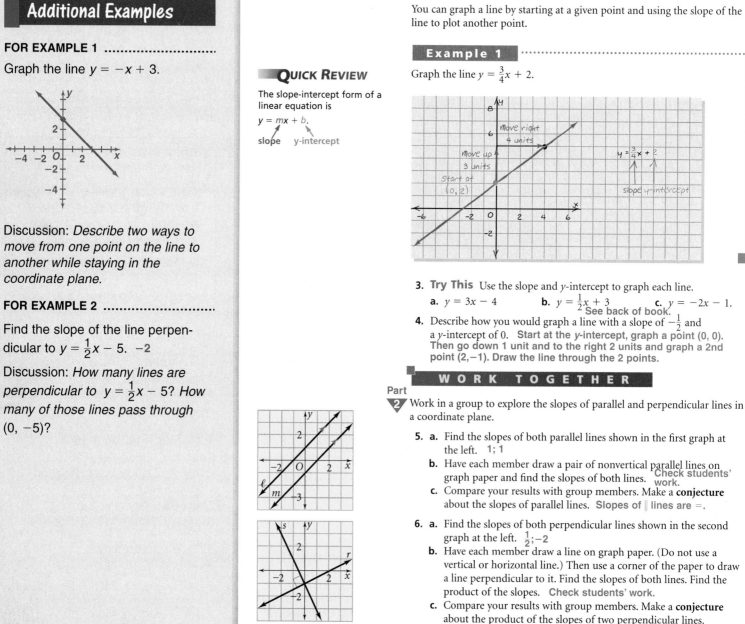

Discussion: *Describe two ways to move from one point on the line to another while staying in the coordinate plane.*

FOR EXAMPLE 2

Find the slope of the line perpendicular to $y = \frac{1}{2}x - 5$. -2

Discussion: *How many lines are perpendicular to $y = \frac{1}{2}x - 5$? How many of those lines pass through $(0, -5)$?*

84

QUICK REVIEW

The slope-intercept form of a linear equation is

$y = mx + b$.

slope y-intercept

You can graph a line by starting at a given point and using the slope of the line to plot another point.

Example 1

Graph the line $y = \frac{3}{4}x + 2$.

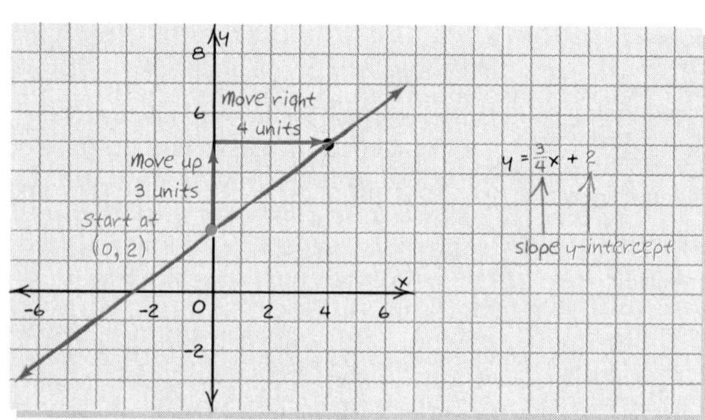

3. **Try This** Use the slope and y-intercept to graph each line.
   a. $y = 3x - 4$ b. $y = \frac{1}{2}x + 3$ c. $y = -2x - 1$. See back of book.
4. Describe how you would graph a line with a slope of $-\frac{1}{2}$ and a y-intercept of 0. Start at the y-intercept, graph a point (0, 0). Then go down 1 unit and to the right 2 units and graph a 2nd point (2, −1). Draw the line through the 2 points.

WORK TOGETHER

Part 2 Work in a group to explore the slopes of parallel and perpendicular lines in a coordinate plane.

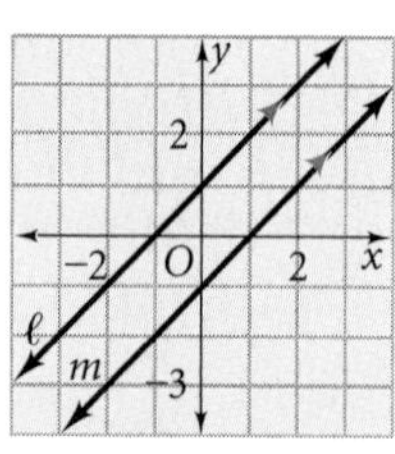

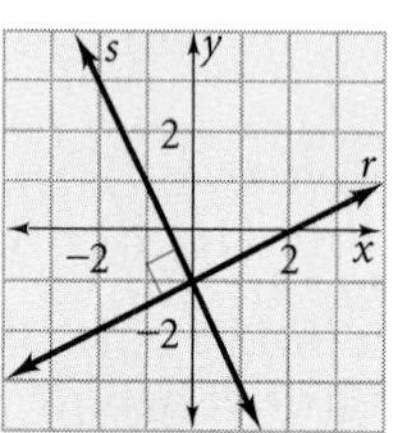

5. a. Find the slopes of both parallel lines shown in the first graph at the left. 1; 1
   b. Have each member draw a pair of nonvertical parallel lines on graph paper and find the slopes of both lines. Check students' work.
   c. Compare your results with group members. Make a **conjecture** about the slopes of parallel lines. Slopes of ∥ lines are =.
6. a. Find the slopes of both perpendicular lines shown in the second graph at the left. $\frac{1}{2}; -2$
   b. Have each member draw a line on graph paper. (Do not use a vertical or horizontal line.) Then use a corner of the paper to draw a line perpendicular to it. Find the slopes of both lines. Find the product of the slopes. Check students' work.
   c. Compare your results with group members. Make a **conjecture** about the product of the slopes of two perpendicular lines. The product of slopes of ⊥ lines is −1.

THINK AND DISCUSS p. 85

Discuss with students how the algebraic properties of parallel and perpendicular lines connect algebra and geometry. While the relationship between the lines does not depend on coordinates (i.e., take away the coordinates and the lines would still be parallel or perpendicular), the coordinates give mathematicians a numerical way to describe the relationship.

EXTENSION You may want students to research René Descartes, the first mathematician to introduce coordinates into the study of geometry.

Questions 7 and 8 You may want to review equations of vertical lines ($x = a$) and equations of horizontal lines ($y = c$).

Example 2

One method for finding the slope of a line perpendicular to $y = -3x + 4$ is to solve the equation $-3 \cdot m = -1$ as presented in the text. Another method is to take the negative reciprocal of -3, $-\left(\frac{1}{-3}\right) = \frac{1}{3}$. If students use this second method, caution them to find the *negative* reciprocal and not just the reciprocal of the given slope.

Question 11 This question demonstrates that perpendicularity in a plane is not a transitive relationship. In other words, $t \perp k$ and $k \perp s$ implies $t \parallel s$, *not* $t \perp s$.

THINK AND DISCUSS

Parallel and Perpendicular Lines

Your observations in the Work Together are summarized below.

Slopes of Parallel and Perpendicular Lines

The slopes of nonvertical parallel lines are equal. Two lines with the same slope are parallel. Vertical lines are parallel.

The product of the slopes of two perpendicular lines, neither of which is vertical, is -1. If the product of the slopes of the two lines is -1, then the lines are perpendicular. A horizontal and a vertical line are perpendicular.

7. No 2 lines are $\parallel$; (b) and (c) are $\perp$.

8a. (graph: y, 4, 2, x, −2, O)

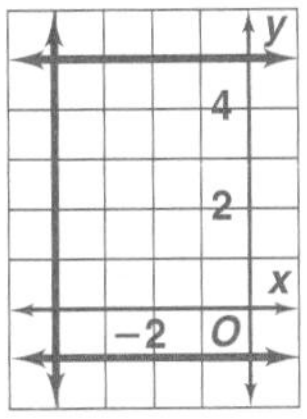

7. **Try This** Which of these lines are parallel? Which are perpendicular?
   a. $y = 2x + 1$ b. $y = -x$ c. $y = x - 4$
   d. $y = \frac{1}{2}$ e. $y = -2x + 3$ See above left.
8. a. Graph $y = 5$, $y = -1$, and $x = -4$. See above left.
   b. Which lines are parallel? Which are perpendicular?
   $y = 5$ and $y = -1$ are $\parallel$; $x = -4$ is $\perp$ to the other 2.

Example 2

Find the slope of a line perpendicular to $y = -3x + 4$.

The slope of line $y = -3x + 4$ is -3.
Let m be the slope of the perpendicular line.

$-3 \cdot m = -1$ The product of the slopes is -1.

$m = \frac{1}{3}$ Divide each side by -3.

Sample: $y = -3x - 12$

9. **Open-ended** Give an equation of a line parallel to $y = -3x + 4$.

Architecture There are parallel and perpendicular lines in the photo at the left.

10. If line $k \parallel$ line ℓ and line $r \parallel$ line ℓ, what is the relationship between lines k and r? $k \parallel r$
11. If line $t \perp$ line k and line $s \perp$ line k, what is the relationship between lines t and s? $t \parallel s$

Questions 10 and 11 demonstrate the following theorems.

Theorem 2-5 Two lines parallel to a third line are parallel to each other.

Theorem 2-6 In a plane, two lines perpendicular to a third line are parallel to each other.

Technology Options

For Exercises 12–19, students may use a graphing software to draw each pair of lines. For Exercise 29, students may use a graphing software to draw the scatter plot.

Prentice Hall Technology

Software
- Secondary Math Lab Toolkit™
- Integrated Math Lab 25
- Computer Item Generator 2-3

Internet
- See the Prentice Hall site. (http://www.phschool.com)

Exercises ON YOUR OWN

MENTAL MATH Exercise 1 Students should be able to answer this question visually, without finding the slopes.

WRITING Exercise 3 Students may want to support their explanations with real-world examples of zero slope and no slope.

ALTERNATIVE ASSESSMENT Exercises 4–9 These exercises can help you assess students' understanding of the relationship between slopes of parallel and perpendicular lines.

STANDARDIZED TEST TIP Exercise 20 Suggest that it might be helpful to rewrite the equations in the slope-intercept form $y = mx + b$ by solving for y.

pages 86–87 On Your Own

21a, c.

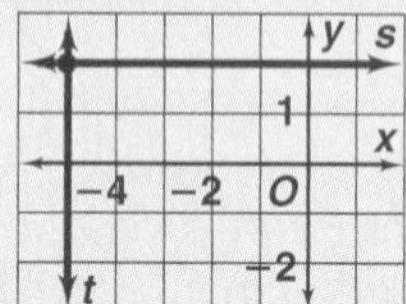

22a, c.

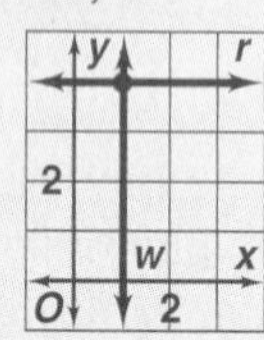

23. Answers may vary. Sample: Yes; the ramp cannot be straight, but it can have 3 turns between 4 straight parts so the total length is at least 36 ft.

25.

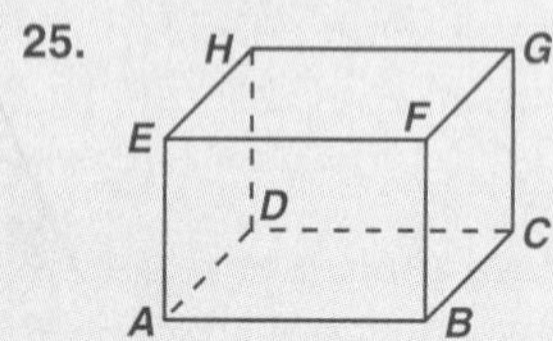

a. $\overleftrightarrow{AB} \perp \overleftrightarrow{FB}$, $\overleftrightarrow{BC} \perp \overleftrightarrow{FB}$, $\overleftrightarrow{AB} \perp \overleftrightarrow{BC}$

b. $\overleftrightarrow{AB} \perp \overleftrightarrow{BC}$, $\overleftrightarrow{BC} \perp \overleftrightarrow{CG}$, $\overleftrightarrow{AB}$ and $\overleftrightarrow{CG}$ are skew lines.

Exercises ON YOUR OWN

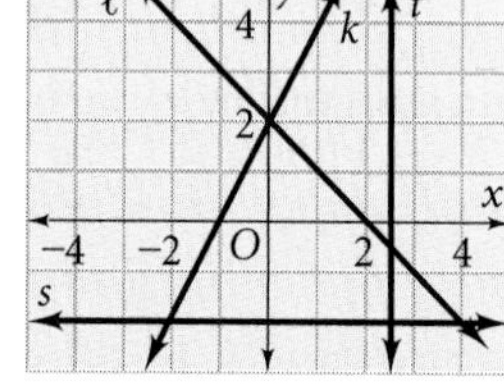

1. Identify the slope of each line in the graph as positive, negative, zero, or undefined. *k*: pos.; ℓ: neg.; *s*: 0; *t*: undef.
2. a. What is the slope of the *x*-axis? Explain. 0
   b. What is the slope of the *y*-axis? Explain. Undefined
3. *Writing* A classmate claims that having no slope and having a slope of 0 are the same. Is your classmate right? Explain. No; lines with no slope are vert. Lines with slope 0 are horizontal.

11. No; the slopes of the sides are $\frac{3}{5}$, $-\frac{5}{8}$, and $-\frac{8}{3}$. No 2 sides are ⊥.

Choose **Use pencil and paper, mental math, or a calculator to find the slopes of $\overleftrightarrow{AB}$ and $\overleftrightarrow{CD}$. Then determine if the lines are parallel, perpendicular, or neither.**

4. $A(-1, \frac{1}{2})$, $B(-1, 2)$, $C(3, 7)$, $D(3, -1)$ undef.; undef.; ∥
5. $A(-2, 3)$, $B(-2, 5)$, $C(1, 4)$, $D(2, 4)$ undef.; 0; ⊥
6. $A(2, 4)$, $B(5, 4)$, $C(3, 2)$, $D(0, 8)$ 0; −2; neither
7. $A(-3, 2)$, $B(5, 1)$, $C(2, 7)$, $D(1, -1)$ $-\frac{1}{8}$; 8; ⊥
8. $A(1, -3)$, $B(3, 2)$, $C(4, 5)$, $D(2, 0)$ $\frac{5}{2}$; $\frac{5}{2}$ parallel
9. $A(4.5, 5)$, $B(2, 5)$, $C(1.5, -2)$, $D(3, -2)$ 0; 0; parallel
10. Use slope to show that the opposite sides of hexagon *RSTUVW* are parallel. See right.
11. Use slope to determine whether a triangle with vertices (3, 2), (8, 5), and (0, 10) is a right triangle. Explain. See above right.

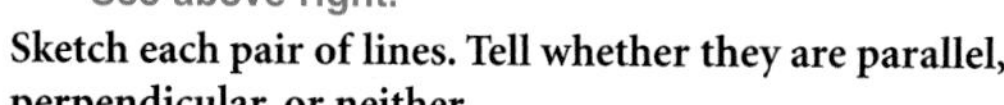

10. Slope of $\overline{WR}$ and $\overline{TU}$ is 1; slope of $\overline{RS}$ and $\overline{UV}$ is 0; slope of $\overline{ST}$ and $\overline{VW}$ is −1. Lines with = slope are ∥.

Sketch each pair of lines. Tell whether they are parallel, perpendicular, or neither.

12. $y = 5x - 4$; $x = 2$ neither
13. $y = \frac{1}{3}x - 1$; $y = -3x + 5$ perpendicular
14. $x = -2$; $x = 0$ parallel
15. $y = -4$; $y = \frac{1}{4}$ parallel
16. $y = 2.5x + 1$; $y = 2.5$ neither
17. $y = x - \frac{1}{2}$; $y = x + 1$ parallel
18. $y = \frac{3}{4}x - 2$; $y = -2$ neither
19. $y = -7$; $x = -5$ perpendicular
20. *Standardized Test Prep* Which of the lines is *not* parallel to the line $y = -\frac{2}{3}x + 8$? D

    A. $2x + 3y = 1$ B. $4x = 3 - 6y$ C. $x = -1.5y$ D. $24 = 2x - 3y$ E. $9y = -6x - 2$

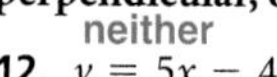

21. a. Sketch vertical line *t* containing (−5, 2). See margin.
    b. Write an equation for line *t*. $x = -5$
    c. On the same graph, sketch horizontal line *s* containing (−5, 2). See margin.
    d. Write an equation for line *s*. $y = 2$
    e. What is the relationship between line *t* and line *s*? Explain. The lines are ⊥; a horizontal line is always ⊥ to a vertical line.
22. a. Sketch line *w* perpendicular to $y = 5$, and containing (1, 4). See margin.
    b. Write an equation for line *w*. $x = 1$
    c. On the same graph, sketch line *r* parallel to $y = 5$, and containing (1, 4). See margin.
    d. Write an equation for line *r*. $y = 4$
    e. What is the relationship between line *r* and line *w*? Explain. The lines are ⊥; a line with slope 0 is ⊥ to a line with undefined slope.

DIVERSITY Exercise 23 Students may have seen ramps that "zig-zag" toward an entrance rather than approach it directly. Discuss why the ramp was made that way. Help students see that a slope of $\frac{1}{12}$ means that the ramp rises one foot for every twelve feet measured horizontally.

OPEN-ENDED Exercise 24 It may help students to begin with a diagram.

GEOMETRY ON A SPHERE Exercise 27 This exercise demonstrates how relationships between lines in Euclidean geometry can be different from those in non-Euclidean geometries.

23. *Building* A law concerning wheelchair accessibility states that the slope of a ramp must be no greater than $\frac{1}{12}$. A local civic center plans to install a ramp. The height from the pavement to the main entrance is 3 ft and the distance from the sidewalk to the building is 10 ft. Is it possible for the center to design a ramp that complies with this law? Explain. See margin p. 86.

24. a. *Open-ended* Find the equations of two lines perpendicular to line $y = 3x - 2$. Sample: $y = -\frac{1}{3}x + 1$, $y = -\frac{1}{3}x - 3$
    b. Find the equations of two lines parallel to line $y = 3x - 2$. Sample: $y = 3x + 1$, $y = 3x$

25. *Manipulatives* Use straws, toothpicks, or pencils.
    a. *Geometry in 3 Dimensions* Show how two lines that are each perpendicular to a third line can be perpendicular to each other. a–b. See margin p. 86.
    b. Show how two lines that are each perpendicular to a third line can be skew to each other.

26a,d. See margin.

26. a. Graph the points $A(1, 7)$, $B(2, 5)$, and $C(5, -1)$.
    b. What appears to be the relationship between these three points? They are collinear.
    c. Find the slopes of $\overleftrightarrow{AB}$, $\overleftrightarrow{BC}$, and $\overleftrightarrow{AC}$. -2; -2; -2
    d. *Logical Reasoning* Use part (c) to **justify** your answer to part (b).

27. *Geometry on a Sphere* Suppose you are investigating "lines" on a globe. The lines pass through both poles and are perpendicular to the equator. Are the lines of longitude "parallel" to each other? Explain. Answers may vary. Sample: No; the "lines" intersect twice.

28. a. Sketch line c with a slope -5 and line f with slope $\frac{1}{5}$. 28a–b. See margin.
    b. On the same graph, sketch line w perpendicular to line f.
    c. What is the relationship between line c and line w? Explain. $c \parallel w$; in a plane, 2 lines $\perp$ to a 3rd are $\parallel$.

29. a. *Calculator* Find the slopes of each line containing the origin and $(\frac{1}{n}, 10)$ for $n = 1, 2, 3, \ldots 10$. Record your results as ordered pairs (n, slope).
    b. Show your results on a graph like the one shown.
    c. *Data Analysis* What predictions can you make about the slope of the line when $n = 100$?
    d. *Critical Thinking* Do you think that the slope will get infinitely large? Explain your reasoning.

29a–d. See margin.

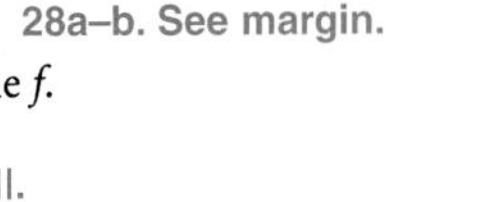

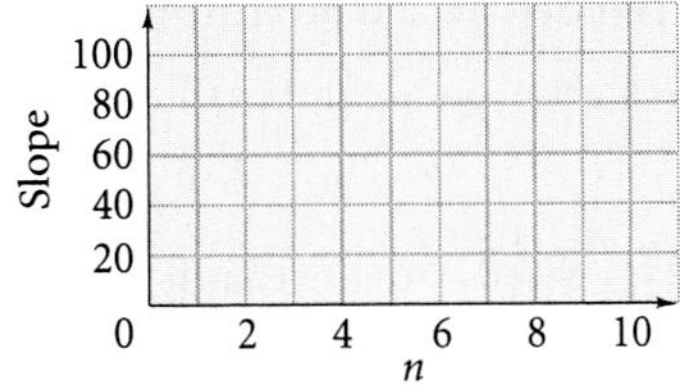

26a.

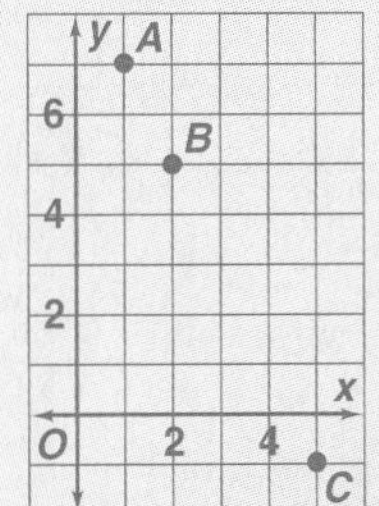

d. Since $\overleftrightarrow{AB}$ and $\overleftrightarrow{BC}$ have the same slope and are not $\parallel$, they must be the same line. Therefore *A*, *B*, and *C* must be collinear.

28a–b.

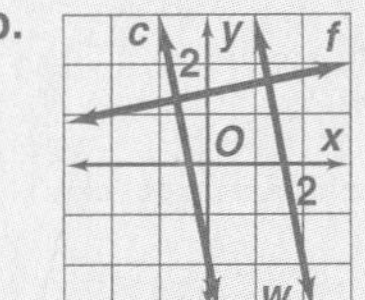

29a. (1, 10), (2, 20), (3, 30), (4, 40), (5, 50), (6, 60), (7, 70), (8, 80), (9, 90), (10, 100)

b.

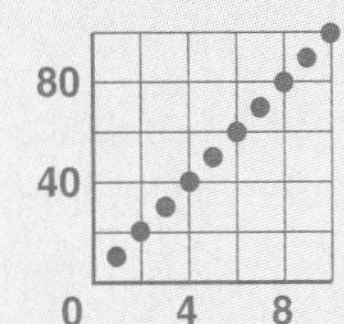

c. The slope is 1000.

d. Sample: Yes; you can make the slope as steep as you want, but it will never be vertical.

Exercises MIXED REVIEW

Exercises 31–32 Students review the meanings of complementary and supplementary angles.

Exercise 33 You may want to suggest students let x and $3x$ represent the measures of acute angles.

GETTING READY FOR LESSON 2-4 These exercises prepare students for classifying quadrilaterals.

Wrap Up

THE BIG IDEA Ask students: *Given the line $y = -4x + 5$, write an equation of a line parallel to it and an equation of a line perpendicular to it. Explain your methods. How are the lines you found related?*

RETEACHING ACTIVITY Students find the slopes of lines parallel and perpendicular to a given line. (Reteaching worksheet 2-3)

Exercises CHECKPOINT

In this Checkpoint, your students will assess their own progress on Lessons 2-1 to 2-3.

Exercises 10–13 Students can graph the lines to check their answers.

OPEN-ENDED Exercise 14 Students may want to start with a graph and then write the equation.

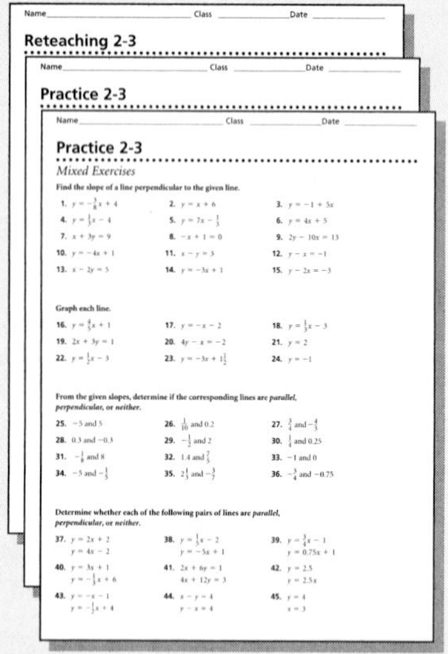
Reteaching 2-3

Practice 2-3

Practice 2-3

Mixed Exercises

Lesson Quiz

Lesson Quiz is also available in Transparencies.

1. Graph the line $y = -\frac{2}{3}x + 2$. See back of book.

Determine whether the lines are parallel, perpendicular, or neither.

2. $y = -\frac{1}{2}x + 5 \quad y = 2x - 3$ perpendicular

3. $y = -5 \quad y = 3$ parallel

4. $\overleftrightarrow{AC}$ and $\overleftrightarrow{EG}$, given $A(3, 2)$, $C(5, 6)$, $E(-1, 4)$, and $G(-2, 2)$ parallel

88

Exercises MIXED REVIEW

Use the diagram for the Exercises 30–32.

30. Name an acute angle, an obtuse angle, a right angle, and a straight angle. $\angle RTD$ or $\angle CTD$; $\angle DTY$; $\angle RTY$ or $\angle RTC$; $\angle CTY$

31. Find $m\angle DTR$ when $m\angle CTD = 64.5$. 25.5

32. Find the value of x when $m\angle CTD = x + 32$ and $m\angle DTY = 3x + 20$. Then find the measures of both angles. 32; 64 and 116

33. The measure of one acute angle of a right triangle is three times the measure of the other acute angle. Find the measures of the angles. 22.5 and 67.5

Getting Ready for Lesson 2-4

In each quadrilateral below, name any sides that appear to be parallel.

34. 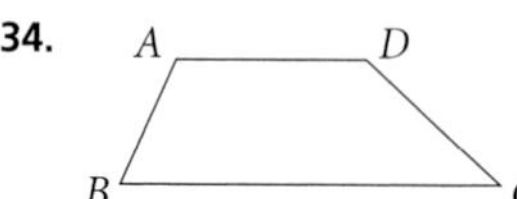

$\overline{AD}$ and $\overline{BC}$

35. 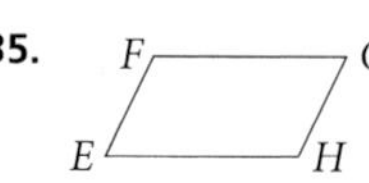

$\overline{FG}$ and $\overline{EH}$, $\overline{EF}$ and $\overline{GH}$

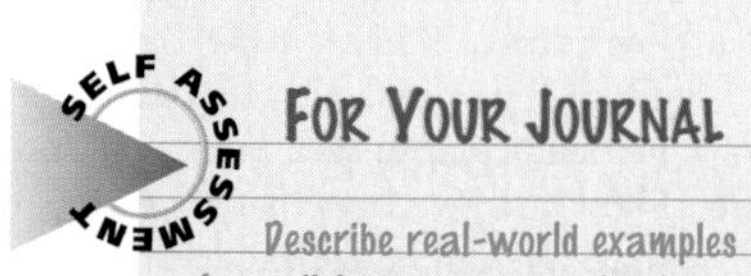

SELF ASSESSMENT
FOR YOUR JOURNAL
Describe real-world examples of parallel and perpendicular lines that you see on the way to school.

Exercises CHECKPOINT

Draw each figure. Mark congruent sides and angles. 1–8. See margin p. 89.

1. equilateral triangle **2.** isosceles triangle **3.** right triangle **4.** acute triangle

5. obtuse triangle **6.** regular octagon **7.** concave decagon **8.** convex nonagon

9. *Writing* Describe two methods you can use to find the measure of each interior angle of a regular polygon. (1) Divide 360 by n to find the exterior angle measure. Subtract the result from 180. (2) Multiply 180 by $n - 2$ and divide the result by n.

Find the slope of lines $\overleftrightarrow{RS}$ and $\overleftrightarrow{TV}$. Then determine if $\overleftrightarrow{RS}$ and $\overleftrightarrow{TV}$ are *parallel, perpendicular,* or *neither.* 10. $-\frac{2}{5}$; $\frac{5}{2}$; perpendicular 11. 1; −1; perpendicular

10. $R(-2, 6)$, $S(3, 4)$, $T(2, 5)$, $V(0, 0)$

11. $R(6, -1)$, $S(7, 0)$, $T(3, -4)$, $V(0, -1)$

12. $R(9, 1)$, $S(5, 6)$, $T(3, 8)$, $V(-2, 4)$ $-\frac{5}{4}$; $\frac{4}{5}$; perpendicular

13. $R(5, -7)$, $S(-4, -9)$, $T(6, 2)$, $V(-3, 0)$ $\frac{2}{9}$; $\frac{2}{9}$ parallel

14. a. *Open-ended* Write an equation of a nonvertical line with a y-intercept of 2. Sample: $y = 3x + 2$

b. Write an equation of a line perpendicular to this line having the same y-intercept. For sample in part (a): $y = -\frac{1}{3}x + 2$

Math ToolboX

Students are given the slope and a point on a line or two points on a line to write linear equations using the slope-intercept form presented in Lesson 2-3.

Example 1

Have students check that (8, −3) lies on the line by substituting (8, −3) for (*x, y*) in the equation of the line and by graphing the line.

Example 2

Help students see that once they use the two points to find the slope, the problem is similar to Example 1.

ERROR ALERT! Students may think that the equation of the line depends on which of the two points are substituted. **Remediation:** Have students verify that if (9, −2) is substituted to find *b* instead of (3, 4), the resulting equation of the line will be the same.

ALTERNATIVE ASSESSMENT Have students draw a quadrilateral in the coordinate plane. Have them label the vertices with their coordinates, then find the equation of the line containing each side.

Math ToolboX Algebra Review

Writing Linear Equations

After Lesson 2-3

When you know the slope of a line and a point on it, you can use the slope-intercept form of a line to write a linear equation.

Example 1

Write an equation of a line that has a slope of $\frac{1}{4}$ and contains the point $R(8, -3)$.

$y = mx + b$	Use the slope-intercept form.
$-3 = \frac{1}{4}(8) + b$	Substitute the slope and the *x*- and *y*-coordinates of the point.
$-3 = 2 + b$	Simplify.
$-5 = b$	Solve for *b*.

The equation of the line is $y = \frac{1}{4}x - 5$.

You can also use the slope-intercept form of a linear equation when you know the coordinates of two points on the line.

Example 2

Write an equation of a line containing $A(9, -2)$ and $B(3, 4)$.

$m = \frac{y_2 - y_1}{x_2 - x_1}$	Use the formula to find the slope.
$m = \frac{4 - (-2)}{3 - 9} = -1$	Substitute the coordinates of both points.
$y = -1x + b$	Substitute −1 for *m* in $y = mx + b$.
$4 = -1(3) + b$	Substitute the coordinates of one of the points and solve for *b*.
$7 = b$	

The equation of the line is $y = -1x + 7$ or $y = -x + 7$.

Write an equation of the line with the given slope, and containing point *T*.

1. $m = 3, T(0, 5)$ **2.** $m = \frac{2}{3}, T(-6, -1)$ **3.** $m = -\frac{1}{2}, T(4, -8)$ **4.** $m = 1, T(-1, 3)$

5. $m = -\frac{5}{4}, T(4, 3)$ **6.** $m = -1, T(-1, -8)$ **7.** $m = \frac{3}{2}, T(4, 4)$ **8.** $m = \frac{3}{4}, T(-12, -9)$

Write an equation of the line containing points *C* and *D*.

9. $C(9, -2), D(3, 4)$ **10.** $C(2, 1), D(-2, 3)$ **11.** $C(0, 3), D(-5, 0)$ **12.** $C(-5, 0), D(-2, 1)$

13. $C(2, 0), D(3, 5)$ **14.** $C(3, -1), D(2, -3)$ **15.** $C(0, 0), D(8, -2)$ **16.** $C(-8, 3), D(4, -6)$

1. $y = 3x + 5$
2. $y = \frac{2}{3}x + 3$
3. $y = -\frac{1}{2}x - 6$
4. $y = x + 4$
5. $y = -\frac{5}{4}x + 8$
6. $y = -x - 9$
7. $y = \frac{3}{2}x - 2$
8. $y = \frac{3}{4}x$
9. $y = -x + 7$
10. $y = -\frac{1}{2}x + 2$
11. $y = \frac{3}{5}x + 3$
12. $y = \frac{1}{3}x + \frac{5}{3}$
13. $y = 5x - 10$
14. $y = 2x - 7$
15. $y = -\frac{1}{4}x$
16. $y = -\frac{3}{4}x - 3$

Transparencies 5, 8, 9

Checkpoint page 88

1. 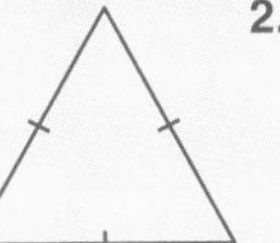
2. 
3. 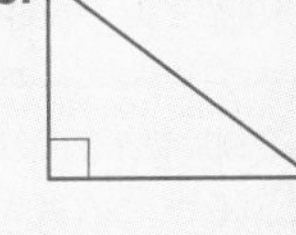
4. 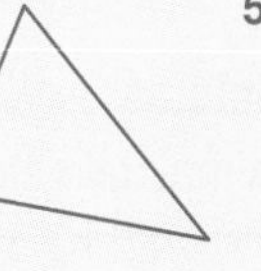
5. 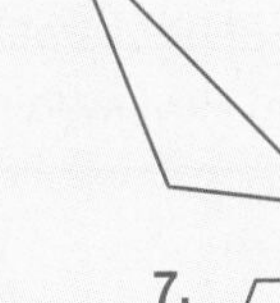
6. 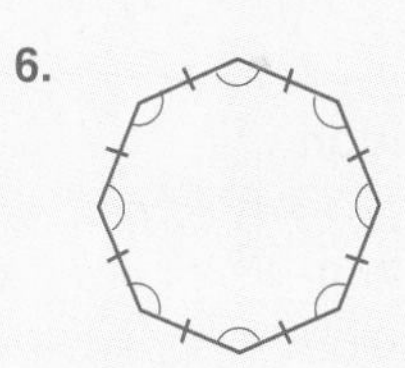
7. 
8. 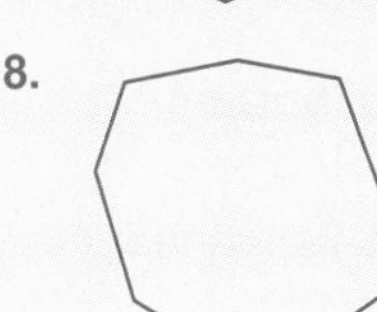

2-4 Teaching Notes

PROBLEM OF THE DAY

Each angle has a measure of 60. Find the number of equilateral triangles in this picture. 48

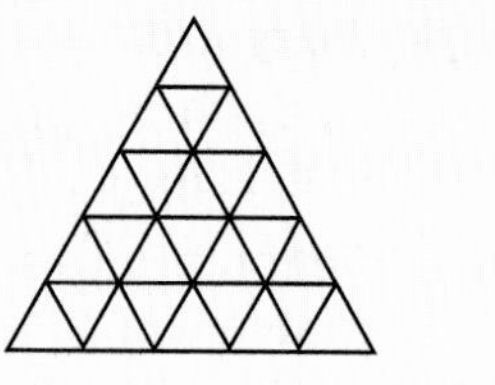

Problem of the Day is also available in Transparencies.

CONNECTING TO PRIOR KNOWLEDGE Have students review the sum of the measures of the interior angles of a quadrilateral. Have them find the measure of one interior angle of a *regular* quadrilateral.

WORK TOGETHER

In this activity, students explore the properties of quadrilaterals before formal definitions are presented. Students should use graph paper for their sketches.

ERROR ALERT! Students may assume that all the quadrilaterals they draw can be classified by one of the special names given at the top of the page. **Remediation:** Draw examples of quadrilaterals that cannot be classified with the special names given. Explain that the best name for such a figure is quadrilateral.

Lesson Planning Options

Prerequisite Skills

- Using the distance formula
- Finding slope

Assignment Options for Exercises On Your Own

Core 1–27

✪**Extension** 28–31

Use Mixed Review to maintain skills.

Resources

Student Edition

Skills Handbook, pp. 678, 679
Extra Practice, p. 649
Glossary/Study Guide

Teaching Resources

Chapter Support File, Ch. 2
- Practice 2-4 (two worksheets)
- Reteaching 2-4

Classroom Manager 2-4
Glossary, Spanish Resources

Transparencies

32, 37, 38

What You'll Learn
- Defining and classifying special types of quadrilaterals

...And Why

To learn about the most commonly used polygons in buildings, architecture, and design

What You'll Need
- toothpicks

Connections  Kites . . . and more

2-4 Classifying Quadrilaterals

WORK TOGETHER

Some quadrilaterals have special names.

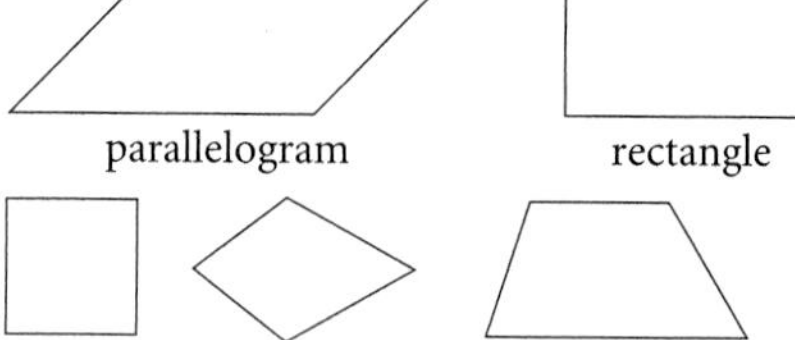

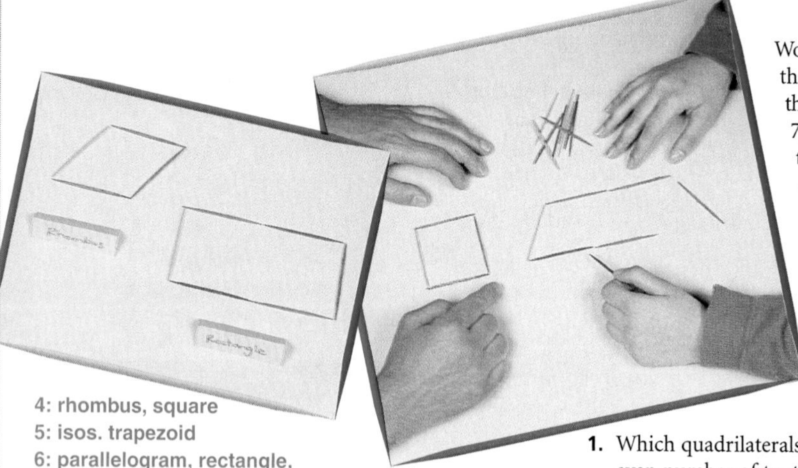

Work in a group to build all the different quadrilaterals that you can using 4, 5, 6, 7, and 8 toothpicks. Each toothpick represents a side or a part of a side. Sketch and name each quadrilateral you form. Two examples are shown at the left.

4: rhombus, square
5: isos. trapezoid
6: parallelogram, rectangle, kite
7: isos. trapezoid, trapezoid
8: square, rectangle, rhombus, kite, parallelogram, isos. trapezoid

1. Which quadrilaterals can you build with an even number of toothpicks? with an odd number of toothpicks? Explain.
even: parallelogram, rectangle, rhombus, square, kite, isos. trapezoid
odd: trapezoid, isos. trapezoid

THINK AND DISCUSS

As you made quadrilaterals out of toothpicks, you probably noticed some of the properties of special quadrilaterals. 2–3. Answers may vary. Samples are given.

2. What appears to be true about the sides of the following quadrilaterals?
   a. rhombus **b.** trapezoid **c.** parallelogram **d.** kite
   a. All sides are ≅. Opposite sides are parallel.
   2b. 2 opposite sides are ∥ and the other 2 are not.
   c. Opposite sides are ∥. Opposite sides are ≅.
   2d. 2 adj. sides are ≅ and the other 2 adj. sides are ≅.
3. What appears to be true about the angles of a rectangle and a square?
   All the angles are rt. angles.

THINK AND DISCUSS

As you discuss the definitions of special quadrilaterals with students, you may want to review how to mark figures to indicate parallel lines, congruent sides, and right angles.

ESL **TACTILE LEARNING** Have students model the quadrilaterals using geoboards. As they create a figure have them pronounce its name aloud. Check students' pronunciation of *isosceles*, *trapezoid,* and *rhombus.*

Example 1

LOGICAL REASONING **Question 5** Before students answer this question, display a Venn diagram showing the relationships between triangles, isosceles triangles, and equilateral triangles. Review how the diagram illustrates the relationships among these triangles.

You can use characteristics of special quadrilaterals to define them.

Special Quadrilaterals

A **parallelogram** is a quadrilateral with both pairs of opposite sides parallel. In Chapter 9, you will prove that both pairs of opposite sides are also congruent. The symbol for a parallelogram is ▱.

A **rhombus** is a parallelogram with four congruent sides.

A **rectangle** is a parallelogram with four right angles.

A **square** is a parallelogram with four congruent sides and four right angles.

A **kite** is a quadrilateral with two pairs of adjacent sides congruent and no opposite sides congruent.

A **trapezoid** is a quadrilateral with exactly one pair of parallel sides.

An **isosceles trapezoid** is a trapezoid whose nonparallel sides are congruent.

Example 1

Judging by appearance, name *DEFG* in as many ways as possible.

It is a quadrilateral because it has four sides.

It is a parallelogram because both pairs of opposite sides are parallel.

It is a rectangle because it has four right angles.

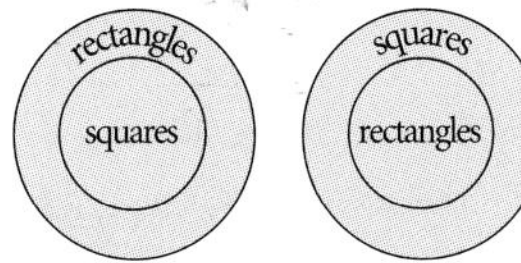

4. Which name do you think gives the most information about *DEFG*? Explain. **Sample: Rectangle; a rectangle is a parallelogram and a quadrilateral.**
5. *Logical Reasoning* Which Venn diagram at the left shows the relationship between rectangles and squares? Explain. **Sample: 1st diagram; all squares are rectangles, but not all rectangles are squares.**

Additional Examples

FOR EXAMPLE 1

Judging by appearance, name the quadrilateral in as many ways as possible. **quadrilateral, parallelogram, rhombus**

Discussion: *Can you draw a different quadrilateral that has the same relationships among its sides and angles?*

FOR EXAMPLE 2

Given $C(1, 2)$, $D(5, 2)$, $E(7, -2)$, and $F(-1, -2)$, determine the most precise name for quadrilateral *CDEF*. **isosceles trapezoid**

Discussion: *Explain why CDEF is not a parallelogram.*

FOR EXAMPLE 3

Refer to the diagram in Example 3. If $KT = x + 4$, $KB = 2x + 4$, $JB = y - 4$, and $JT = 2x$, find the values of x and y. $x = 4$, $y = 16$

EXTENSION If you have block scheduling or an extended class period, have students use magazines and newspapers to find real-world examples of each type of special quadrilateral. Then have them use these examples to create a poster or mobile of the diagram on page 92.

ALTERNATIVE METHOD Have pairs of students draw ten different special quadrilaterals on index cards, one per card, labeling each quadrilateral with its most precise name. One student should sort the ten cards into two piles according to a certain characteristic. For example, the two piles might be quadrilaterals that have right angles and quadrilaterals that do not. The partner then tries to determine what property the student used to make the two piles.

Technology Options

For Exercises 16–19, students may use a graphing calculator to graph the points.

Prentice Hall Technology

Software
- Secondary Math Lab Toolkit™
- Computer Item Generator 2-4

CD-ROM
- Multimedia Geometry Lab 2

Internet
- See the Prentice Hall site. (http://www.phschool.com)

The diagram below shows the relationships among special quadrilaterals.

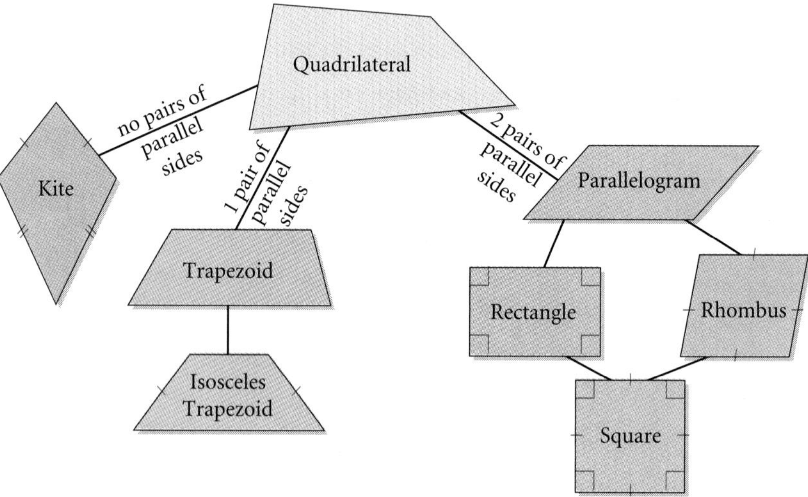

You can use the definitions of special quadrilaterals and what you know about slope and distance to classify a quadrilateral.

Example 2

Determine the most precise name for quadrilateral *LMNP*.

Find the slope of each side.

slope of $\overline{LM} = \frac{3-2}{3-1} = \frac{1}{2}$ slope of $\overline{NP} = \frac{2-1}{5-3} = \frac{1}{2}$

slope of $\overline{MN} = \frac{3-2}{3-5} = -\frac{1}{2}$ slope of $\overline{LP} = \frac{2-1}{1-3} = -\frac{1}{2}$

Both pairs of opposite sides are parallel, so *LMNP* is a parallelogram.

Now use the Distance Formula to see if any of the sides are congruent.

$LM = \sqrt{(3-1)^2 + (3-2)^2} = \sqrt{5}$

$MN = \sqrt{(3-5)^2 + (3-2)^2} = \sqrt{5}$

$NP = \sqrt{(5-3)^2 + (2-1)^2} = \sqrt{5}$

$LP = \sqrt{(1-3)^2 + (2-1)^2} = \sqrt{5}$

All sides are congruent, so *LMNP* is a rhombus.

For practice with radicals, see Skills Handbook, page 674.

6. Explain how you know that *LMNP* is *not* a square. **The product of slopes of adjacent sides is not −1, so the sides are not ⊥.**

7. Try This Determine the most precise name for quadrilateral *ABCD* with vertices $A(0, 4)$, $B(3, 0)$, $C(0, -4)$, $D(-3, 0)$. **rhombus**

Example 2

Help students understand that both pairs of opposite sides are parallel because the lines containing the sides have the same slope.

ERROR ALERT! **Question 6** Students may erroneously say $\frac{-1}{2} \times \frac{1}{2} = -1$ and mistakenly claim that *LMNP is* a square.
Remediation: Review how to multiply fractions.

Question 7 Make sure students can distinguish between a kite and a parallelogram.

Example 3

Have students discuss a plan for solving this problem. Use the fact that $KB = JB$ to find x. Substitute the value of x to find KT, then use the fact that $KT = JT$ to find y.

Exercises ON YOUR OWN

MAKING CONNECTIONS Exercises 1–4 A pantograph is made of four rods held together by pins to form a loose-jointed parallelogram. This mechanical instrument is used by drafters to enlarge or reduce a drawing.

You can use the definitions of special quadrilaterals to find lengths of sides of objects like kites.

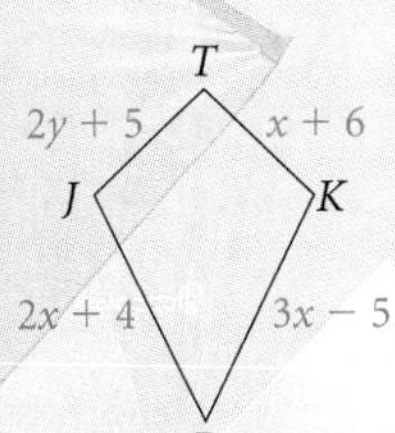

Example 3

Find the values of the variables in the kite at the left.

$KB = JB$	Definition of kite
$3x - 5 = 2x + 4$	Substitution
$x - 5 = 4$	Subtract $2x$ from each side.
$x = 9$	Add 5 to each side.
$KT = x + 6, KT = 15$	Substitute 9 for x.
$KT = JT$	Definition of kite
$15 = 2y + 5$	Substitution
$10 = 2y$	Subtract 5 from each side.
$5 = y$	Divide each side by 2.

8. What are the lengths of the longer sides of the kite? 22
9. What types of triangles are formed when you draw diagonal $\overline{KJ}$? isosceles
10. What types of triangles are formed when you draw diagonal $\overline{BT}$? scalene

Exercises ON YOUR OWN

Judging by appearance, name each quadrilateral in as many ways as possible.

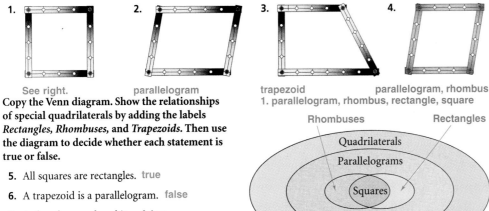

1. 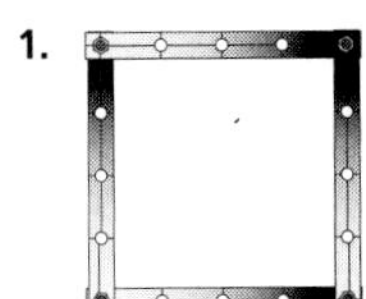
See right.

2. 
parallelogram

3. 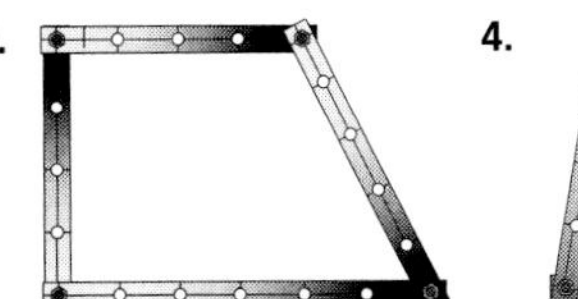
trapezoid

4. 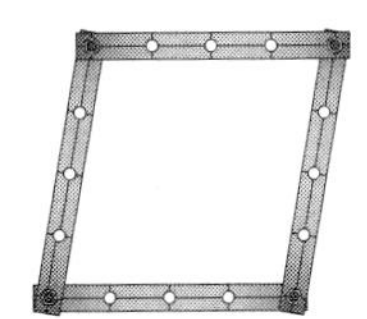
parallelogram, rhombus

1. parallelogram, rhombus, rectangle, square

Copy the Venn diagram. Show the relationships of special quadrilaterals by adding the labels *Rectangles, Rhombuses,* and *Trapezoids.* Then use the diagram to decide whether each statement is true or false.

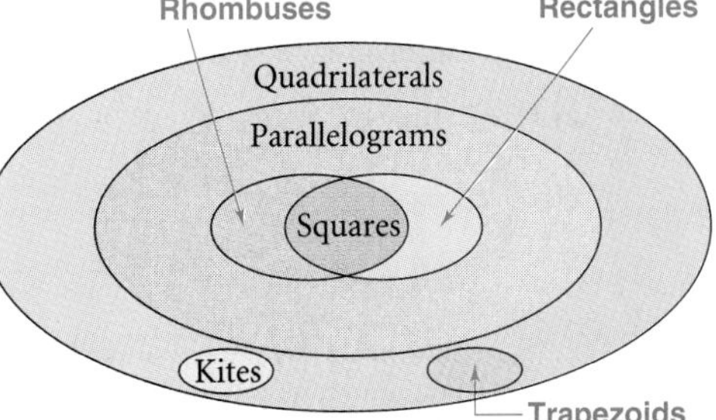

5. All squares are rectangles. true
6. A trapezoid is a parallelogram. false
7. A rhombus can be a kite. false
8. Some parallelograms are squares. true
9. A quadrilateral is a parallelogram. false

93

CONNECTING TO STUDENTS' WORLD Exercise 10 Students may want to create their own artwork. Suggest that students draw everyday objects such as flowers, animals, or people using geometric shapes.

ALTERNATIVE ASSESSMENT Exercises 11–13 These exercises can help you assess students' understanding of the properties of the special quadrilaterals.

Exercise 20 Lead students to observe the fold lines on the unfolded parallelogram and conjecture that the diagonals of a parallelogram bisect each other. Students will study this and other properties of parallelograms in Chapter 9.

pages 93–95 On Your Own

11. 12.

13.

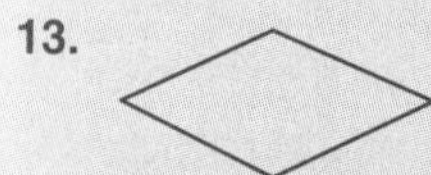

14. Sample: A rhombus has 4 ≅ sides. A kite has 2 pairs of ≅ sides. Opp. sides of a rhombus are ∥. Opp. sides of a kite are not ∥.

15a. Sample:

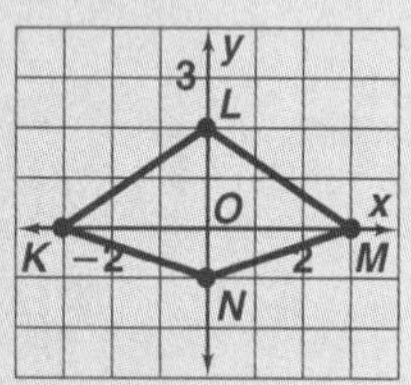

Find Out By Analyzing

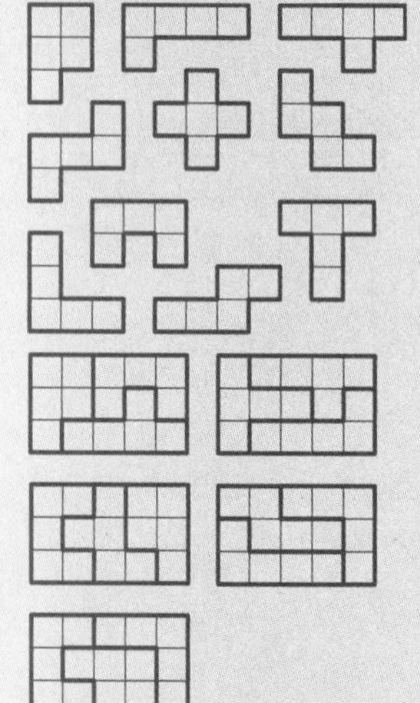

94

10. *Art* Inspired by Cubists like Pablo Picasso, American artist Charles Demuth created *My Egypt*. Identify the geometric figures in this oil painting. List all the special quadrilaterals you see.
rectangle, square, trapezoid

Draw each figure on graph paper. 11–14. See margin.

11. parallelogram that is neither a rectangle nor a rhombus
12. trapezoid with a right angle
13. rhombus that is not a square
14. *Writing* Describe the difference between a rhombus and a kite.
15. a. *Open-ended* Graph and label points $K(-3, 0)$, $L(0, 2)$, and $M(3, 0)$. Find possible coordinates for point N so that $KLMN$ is a kite. See margin.
    b. Explain why there is more than one possible fourth vertex. All points on the negative y-axis are equidistant from K and M.

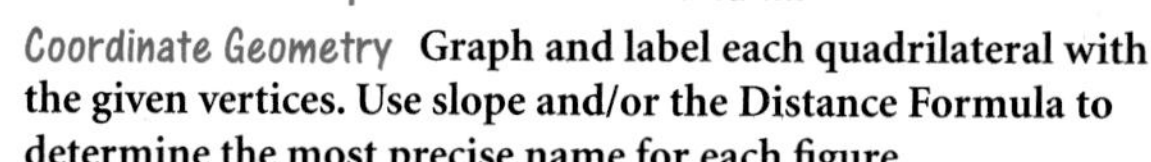

Coordinate Geometry **Graph and label each quadrilateral with the given vertices. Use slope and/or the Distance Formula to determine the most precise name for each figure.**

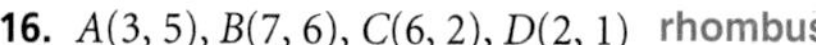

16. $A(3, 5)$, $B(7, 6)$, $C(6, 2)$, $D(2, 1)$ rhombus
17. $W(-1, 1)$, $X(0, 2)$, $Y(1, 1)$, $Z(0, -2)$ kite
18. $J(2, 1)$, $K(5, 4)$, $L(7, 2)$, $M(2, -3)$ trapezoid
19. $R(-2, -3)$, $S(4, 0)$, $T(3, 2)$, $V(-3, -1)$ rectangle
20. *Paper Folding* Fold a rectangular piece of paper in half horizontally and then vertically. Draw and then cut along the line connecting the two corners containing a fold. What quadrilateral do you find when you unfold the paper? Explain. Rhombus; the sides of the quadrilateral are ≅ because they come from the same cut.

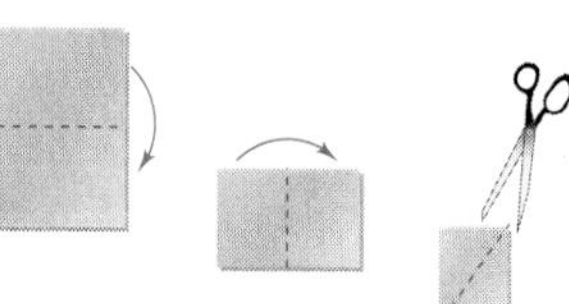

Name all special quadrilaterals that satisfy the given conditions. Make a sketch to support your answer.

21. exactly one pair of congruent sides
some isos. trapezoids, some trapezoids
22. two pairs of parallel sides
parallelogram, rhombus, rectangle, square
23. four right angles
rectangle, square
24. adjacent sides that are congruent
kite, some trapezoids, rhombus, square

Algebra **Find the values of the variables and the lengths of the sides.**

25. kite $ABCD$

B, $x + 2$, C, 13, $x + 4$, A, $y - 6$, D

$x = 11$; $y = 21$; 13, 13, 15, 15

26. isosceles trapezoid $DEFG$

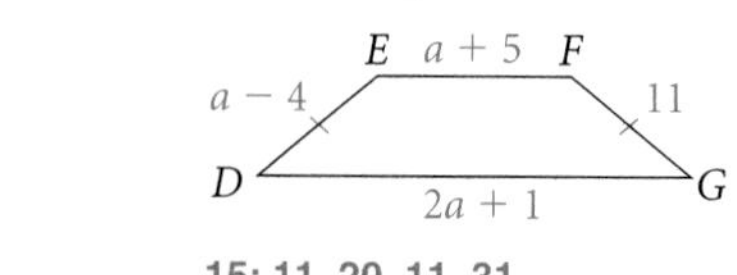

15; 11, 20, 11, 31

27. rhombus $HIJK$

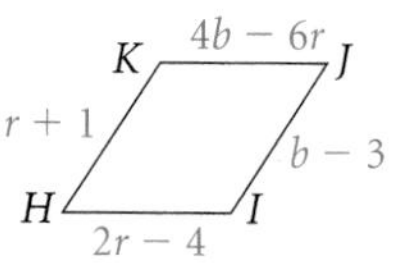

$b = 9$; $r = 5$; 6, 6, 6, 6

TACTILE LEARNING Exercises 28–31 Students may want to draw their answers and cover them with a piece of paper to check that the part remaining uncovered matches the sketch in the text.

Chapter Project **FIND OUT BY ANALYZING** Have students draw their pentominoes on grid paper and then glue them to poster board and keep the set for the Find Out investigation in Lesson 2-6. Emphasize that students check carefully that the pentominoes they make are all different.

Exercises MIXED REVIEW

Exercise 34 Students apply what they know about angles of a triangle to find measures of angles formed by three intersecting lines.

GETTING READY FOR LESSON 2-5 These exercises prepare students for measuring central angles and arcs.

Wrap Up

THE BIG IDEA Ask students: *Define each type of special quadrilateral and give a real-world example for each.*

RETEACHING ACTIVITY Students draw quadrilaterals with certain characteristics, then name them in as many ways as possible. (Reteaching worksheet 2-4)

Part of each quadrilateral is covered. Name all special quadrilaterals that each could be. Explain each choice.

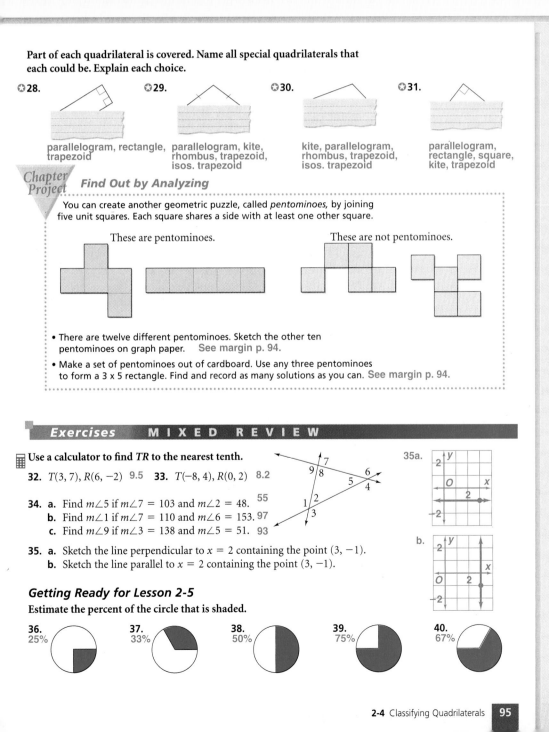

28. 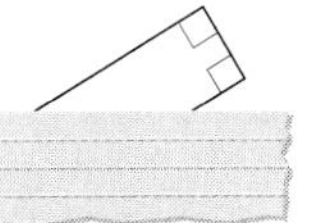
parallelogram, rectangle, trapezoid

29. 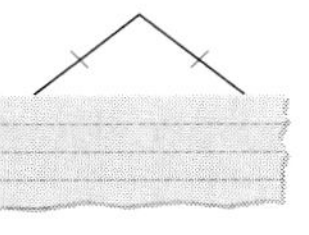
parallelogram, kite, rhombus, trapezoid, isos. trapezoid

30. 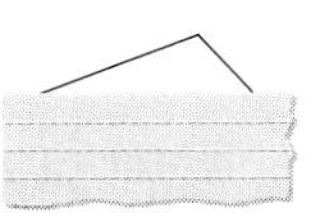
kite, parallelogram, rhombus, trapezoid, isos. trapezoid

31. 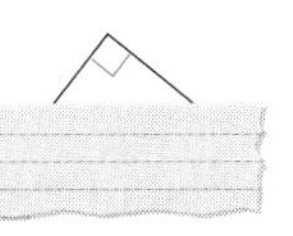
parallelogram, rectangle, square, kite, trapezoid

Chapter Project ***Find Out by Analyzing***

You can create another geometric puzzle, called *pentominoes,* by joining five unit squares. Each square shares a side with at least one other square.

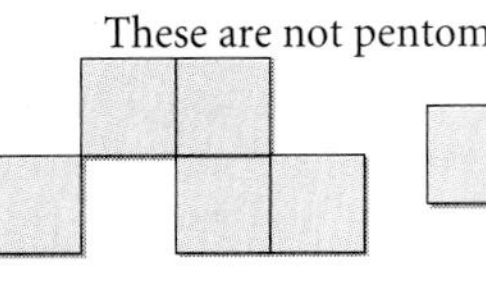
These are pentominoes.

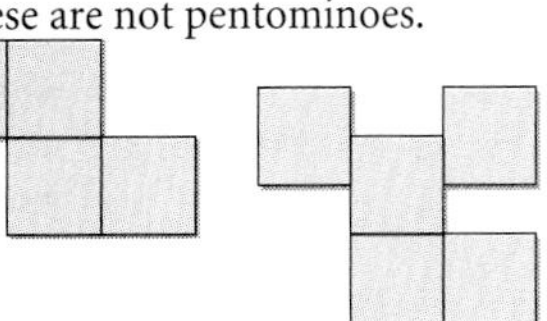
These are not pentominoes.

- There are twelve different pentominoes. Sketch the other ten pentominoes on graph paper. See margin p. 94.
- Make a set of pentominoes out of cardboard. Use any three pentominoes to form a 3 x 5 rectangle. Find and record as many solutions as you can. See margin p. 94.

Exercises MIXED REVIEW

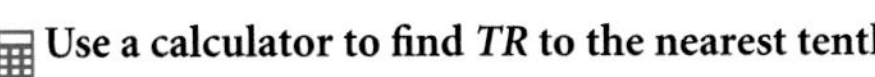
Use a calculator to find TR to the nearest tenth.

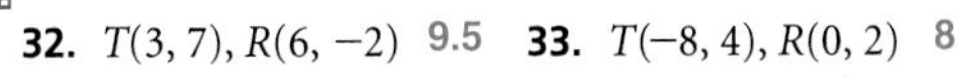
32. $T(3, 7), R(6, -2)$ 9.5 33. $T(-8, 4), R(0, 2)$ 8.2

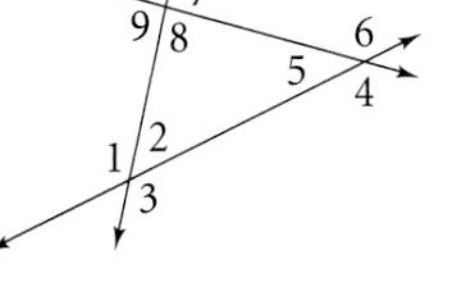

34. a. Find $m\angle 5$ if $m\angle 7 = 103$ and $m\angle 2 = 48$. 55
b. Find $m\angle 1$ if $m\angle 7 = 110$ and $m\angle 6 = 153$. 97
c. Find $m\angle 9$ if $m\angle 3 = 138$ and $m\angle 5 = 51$. 93

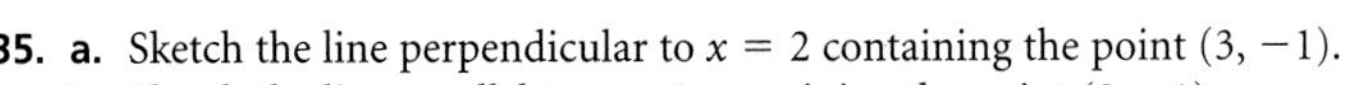
35. a. Sketch the line perpendicular to $x = 2$ containing the point $(3, -1)$.
b. Sketch the line parallel to $x = 2$ containing the point $(3, -1)$.

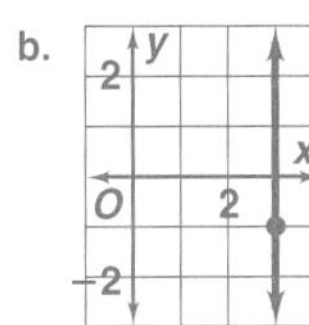

Getting Ready for Lesson 2-5

Estimate the percent of the circle that is shaded.

36. 25% 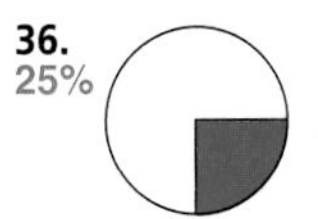

37. 33% 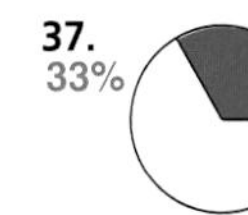

38. 50% 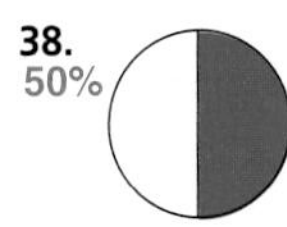

39. 75% 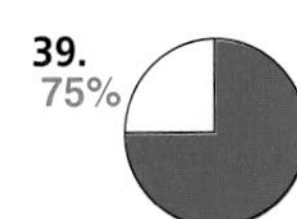

40. 67% 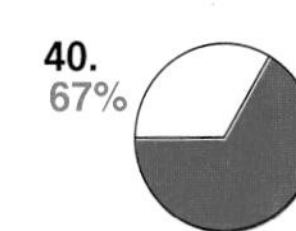

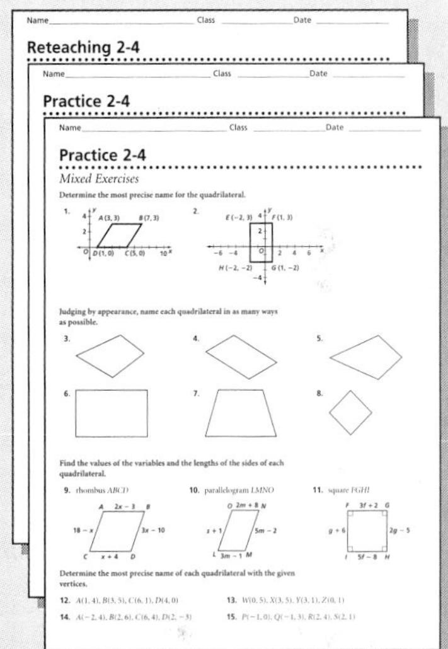
Reteaching 2-4
Practice 2-4
Practice 2-4
Mixed Exercises

Lesson Quiz

Lesson Quiz is also available in Transparencies.

1. Given $G(2, 4)$, $H(6, 4)$, $I(0, -2)$, and $J(4, -2)$, determine the most precise name for quadrilateral $GHIJ$. parallelogram
2. Find the lengths of the sides of the isosceles trapezoid. 11, 8, 11, and 12

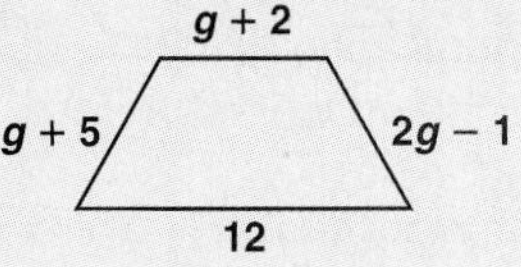

3. Draw a parallelogram that has right angles but is not a square. Students should draw a rectangle so that the length does not equal the width.

2-5 Teaching Notes

PROBLEM OF THE DAY

How many squares are in the figure? 7

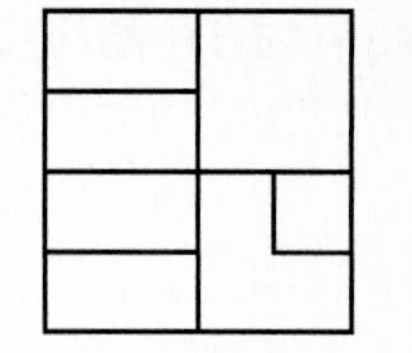

Problem of the Day is also available in Transparencies.

CONNECTING TO PRIOR KNOWLEDGE Discuss with students what the measurements mean in the following phrases: 10-in. pizza, 14-in. tire, and 6-ft round table.

WORK TOGETHER

To prevent students from reading the definition of circle given in the textbook, have students cover the page under the Work Together activity with their notebooks.

ERROR ALERT! Students often think that a circle includes its interior. **Remediation:** Make sure students' definitions clearly define only those points equidistant from the center of the circle.

Lesson Planning Options

Prerequisite Skills

- Using the midpoint and distance formulas
- Finding percents

Assignment Options for Exercises On Your Own

To provide flexible scheduling, this lesson can be subdivided into parts.

1. **Core** 10–20, 22–27
   Extension 48
2. **Core** 1–9, 21, 28–38, 40–47
   Extension 39, 49–50

Use Mixed Review to maintain skills.

Resources

Student Edition

Skills Handbook, p. 671
Extra Practice, p. 649
Glossary/Study Guide

Teaching Resources

Chapter Support File, Ch. 2
- Practice 2-5 (two worksheets)
- Reteaching 2-5
- Alternative Activity 2-5

Classroom Manager 2-5
Glossary, Spanish Resources

Transparencies
4, 12, 33

Connections Amusement Parks . . . and more

2-5 Circles

What You'll Learn

- Measuring central angles and arcs of circles.
- Displaying data in a circle graph.

...And Why

To learn about a geometric figure at the heart of the design of many things, including amusement park rides, satellite orbits, and circle graphs

What You'll Need

- compass
- protractor

WORK TOGETHER

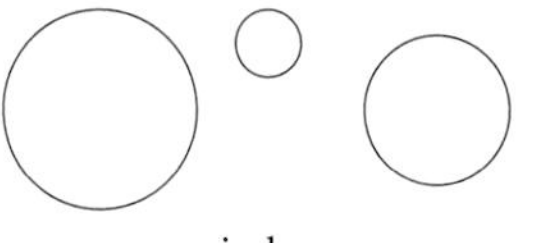

circles

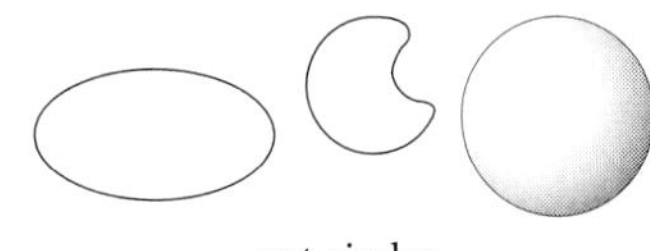

not circles

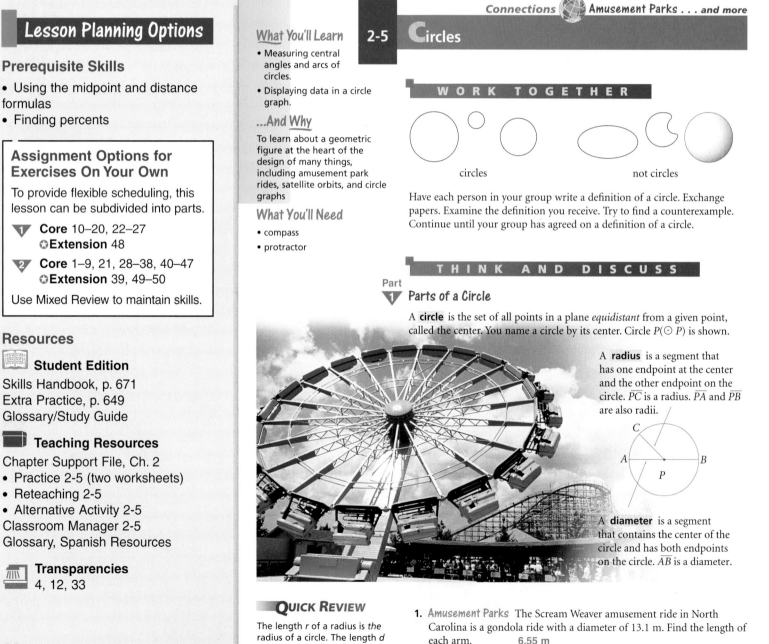

Have each person in your group write a definition of a circle. Exchange papers. Examine the definition you receive. Try to find a counterexample. Continue until your group has agreed on a definition of a circle.

THINK AND DISCUSS

Part 1 **Parts of a Circle**

A **circle** is the set of all points in a plane *equidistant* from a given point, called the center. You name a circle by its center. Circle $P (\odot P)$ is shown.

A **radius** is a segment that has one endpoint at the center and the other endpoint on the circle. $\overline{PC}$ is a radius. $\overline{PA}$ and $\overline{PB}$ are also radii.

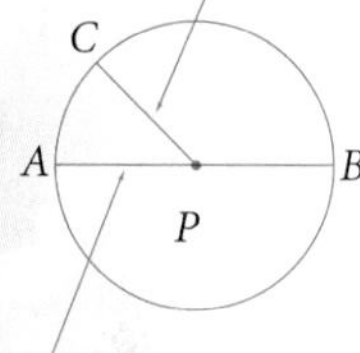

A **diameter** is a segment that contains the center of the circle and has both endpoints on the circle. $\overline{AB}$ is a diameter.

QUICK REVIEW

The length *r* of a radius is *the* radius of a circle. The length *d* of a diameter is *the* diameter of a circle. $d = 2r$

1. Amusement Parks The Scream Weaver amusement ride in North Carolina is a gondola ride with a diameter of 13.1 m. Find the length of each arm. 6.55 m
2. Complete: The center of a circle is the _?_ of a diameter. midpoint

THINK AND DISCUSS

ESL TACTILE LEARNING Have students use a compass and straightedge to draw and label a circle with its center, diameter, and radius. Make sure students understand that *radii* is the plural of *radius.*

Question 1 Refer students to the Quick Review which explains the relationship between the point-set and measurement concepts of diameter and radius.

Example 1

Students may be accustomed to seeing a diameter of a circle drawn horizontally. Students can convince themselves that $\overline{AB}$ is the diameter by tracing the circle and $\overline{AB}$, then folding the paper along $\overline{AB}$. They should see that the two halves of the circle are the same so $\overline{AB}$ must go through the center.

Question 3 When students find the radius, make sure that they find the distance between the center and one of the endpoints and not between the two endpoints.

Example 2 Relating to the Real World 

You may need to review how to find percents. Make sure students understand how to use the percent key on their calculators or how to change percents to decimals or fractions. Also remind them that "of" implies multiplication.

Students may want to add the angle measures to see that they total 360.

Example 1

Coordinate Geometry $\overline{AB}$ is a diameter of the circle. Find the coordinates of the center and the radius of the circle.

The center P of the circle is the midpoint of the diameter.

$P = \left(\frac{-3+5}{2}, \frac{2+4}{2}\right)$ Use the Midpoint Formula.

$P = (1, 3)$ Simplify.

The radius is the distance from the center to any point on the circle.

$PB = \sqrt{(1-5)^2 + (3-4)^2}$ Use the Distance Formula.

$PB = \sqrt{(-4)^2 + (-1)^2}$ Simplify.

$PB = \sqrt{16+1} = \sqrt{17}$

The center of the circle is (1, 3). The radius is $\sqrt{17}$.

For practice with radicals, see Skills Handbook, page 674.

3. **Try This** Find the coordinates of the center and the radius of a circle with diameter $\overline{AB}$ whose endpoints are $A(1, 3)$ and $B(7, -5)$. (4, −1); 5

Part 

Central Angles and Arcs

You often see circle graphs in newspapers and magazines. When you make a circle graph you have to find the measure of each wedge, or central angle. A **central angle** is an angle whose vertex is the center of the circle.

Example 2 Relating to the Real World

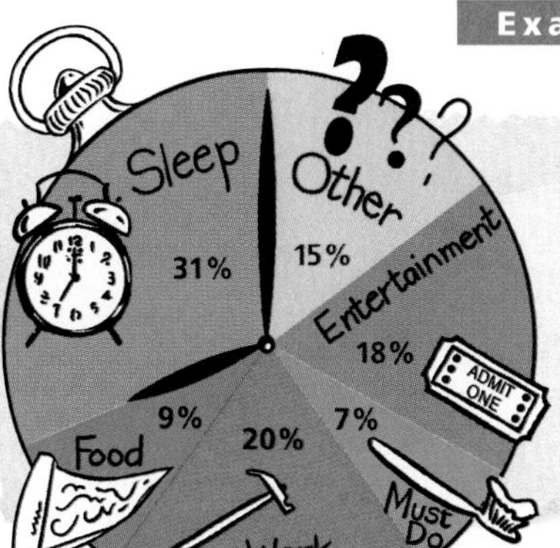

Source: *The New York Times*

How Do You Spend Your Day?

To learn how people really spend their time, a market research firm studied the hour-by-hour activities of more than 3,000 people. The participants were between 18 and 90 years old. Each participant was sent a 24-h recording sheet every March for 3 years from 1992 to 1994. The study found that people spend most of their time sleeping, working, and watching television.

Statistics Find the measure of each central angle in the circle graph.

Since there are 360 degrees in a circle, multiply each percent by 360 to find the measure of each central angle in the circle graph.

Sleep: 31% of 360 = 111.6
Food: 9% of 360 = 32.4
Work: 20% of 360 = 72
Must Do: 7% of 360 = 25.2
Entertainment: 18% of 360 = 64.8
Other: 15% of 360 = 54

Additional Examples

FOR EXAMPLE 1

A diameter of a circle has endpoints $A(-3, -2)$ and $B(1, 4)$. Find the coordinates of the center and the radius. (−1, 1), $\sqrt{13}$

Discussion: *Describe two ways to find the length of the radius?*

FOR EXAMPLE 3

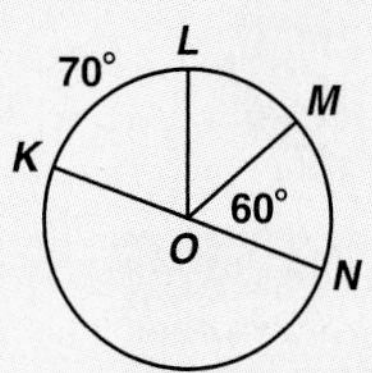

Find the measure of each arc.

a. $\widehat{MN}$ 60 b. $\widehat{LM}$ 50
c. $\widehat{KLM}$ 120 d. $\widehat{LKN}$ 250

Discussion: *Name two other major arcs.*

KINESTHETIC LEARNING If you have block scheduling or an extended class period, take students outside to demonstrate why a circle is 360°. Have students draw coordinate axes in the dirt. Standing at the "origin," a student can act as a human compass by using a meter stick extended at arm's length and touching the ground. Without changing the angle between the arm and the body, have the student slowly rotate around the origin tracing a circle in the dirt. They should see that they moved through four 90° quadrants or 360°. Students can use a similar method to draw arcs of different measures.

Have students practice naming the three types of arcs — semicircles, minor arcs, and major arcs — using the appropriate number of points and the appropriate symbols.

Example 3

Point out that the number written inside of the circle indicates the angle measure and the number written outside the circle indicates the arc measure.

Question 6 Make sure students can locate the center of their circle. Suggest that they mark it in order to know where to center the protractor.

Technology Options

For Exercises 49–50, students may use geometry software to make the circle graphs.

Prentice Hall Technology 

 **Software**
- Secondary Math Lab Toolkit™
- Computer Item Generator 2-5

 **CD-ROM**
- Multimedia Geometry Lab 2

 **Internet**
- See the Prentice Hall site. (http://www.phschool.com)

98

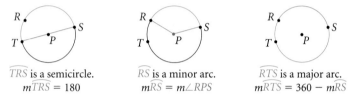

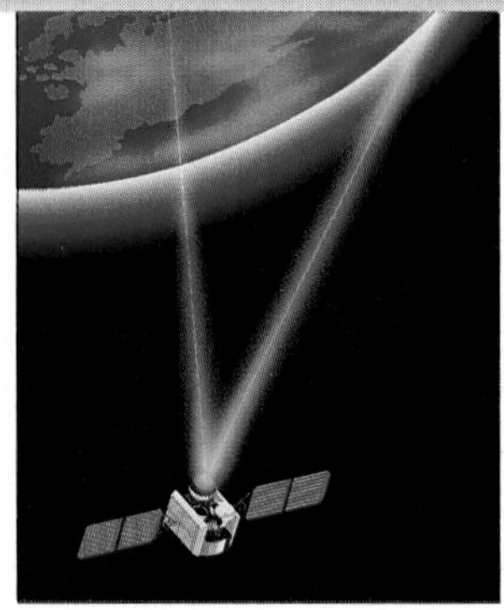

 Geosynchronous satellites stay above the same point on Earth's equator. They orbit Earth in a near-circular path every 24 hours at a distance 42,000 km from the Earth's center. The radius of Earth is about 6000 km. How far above Earth's surface are these satellites? 36,000 km

An *arc* is a part of a circle. There are three types of arcs: a *semicircle*, a *minor arc*, and a *major arc*.

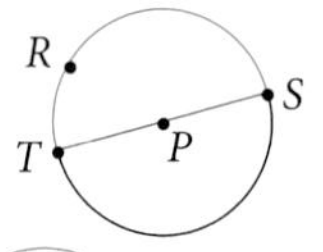

$\overset{\frown}{TRS}$ is a semicircle.
$m\overset{\frown}{TRS} = 180$

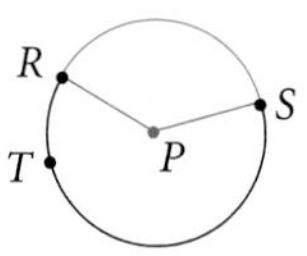

$\overset{\frown}{RS}$ is a minor arc.
$m\overset{\frown}{RS} = m\angle RPS$

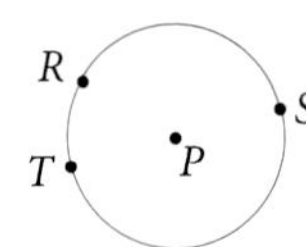

$\overset{\frown}{RTS}$ is a major arc.
$m\overset{\frown}{RTS} = 360 - m\overset{\frown}{RS}$

A **semicircle** is half a circle. The measure of a semicircle is 180. A **minor arc** is shorter than a semicircle. The measure of a minor arc is the measure of its corresponding central angle. A **major arc** is longer than a semicircle. The measure of a major arc is 360 minus the measure of its related minor arc.

4. **Critical Thinking** What kind of arcs can you name with only two points? What kind of arcs must you name with three points? Why? See margin p. 99.

Adjacent arcs are two arcs in the same circle that have exactly one point in common. You can add the measures of adjacent arcs just as you can add the measures of adjacent angles.

Arc Addition Postulate

The measure of the arc formed by two adjacent arcs is the sum of the measures of the two arcs.

$m\overset{\frown}{ABC} = m\overset{\frown}{AB} + m\overset{\frown}{BC}$

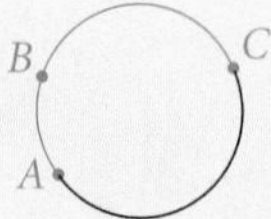

Example 3

Find the measure of each arc.

a. $\overset{\frown}{BC}$ **b.** $\overset{\frown}{BD}$ **c.** $\overset{\frown}{ABC}$ **d.** $\overset{\frown}{AB}$ **e.** $\overset{\frown}{BAD}$

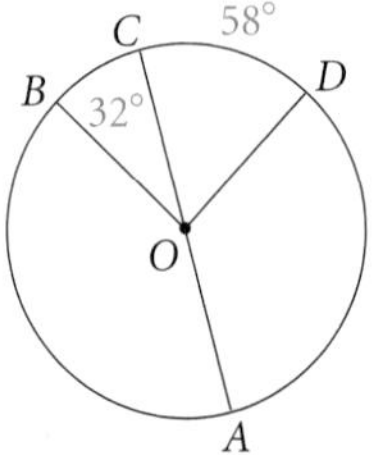

a. $m\overset{\frown}{BC} = m\angle BOC = 32$
b. $m\overset{\frown}{BD} = 32 + 58 = 90$ — $m\overset{\frown}{BD} = m\overset{\frown}{BC} + m\overset{\frown}{CD}$
c. $m\overset{\frown}{ABC} = 180$ — $\overset{\frown}{ABC}$ is a semicircle.
d. $m\overset{\frown}{AB} = 180 - 32 = 148$
e. $m\overset{\frown}{BAD} = 360 - m\overset{\frown}{BD}$
$= 360 - 90 = 270$

5. **Try This** Find $m\angle COD$, $m\overset{\frown}{CDA}$, and $m\overset{\frown}{AD}$. 58; 180; 122
6. **a.** Use a compass to draw a circle. Then use a protractor to draw $\overset{\frown}{JK}$ with measure 75. Check students' work.
   b. Explain how to draw a longer arc that has a measure of 75. See left.

6b. Draw a circle with the same center and a greater radius. The arc on that circle with the same central angle is a longer arc with measure 75.

Exercises ON YOUR OWN

VISUAL LEARNING Exercises 1–9 Students may want to copy the circle and use different colors on their copies to illustrate their answers.

ERROR ALERT! **Exercise 13** Students may multiply $2 \times 6\sqrt{2}$ and get $12\sqrt{4}$. Students may make a similar mistake in Exercise 17. **Remediation:** Review performing operations with radicals.

MAKING CONNECTIONS Exercise 20 The most massive single issue of a newspaper was the *Sunday New York Times* on September 14, 1987, which contained 1612 pages and weighed 12 pounds.

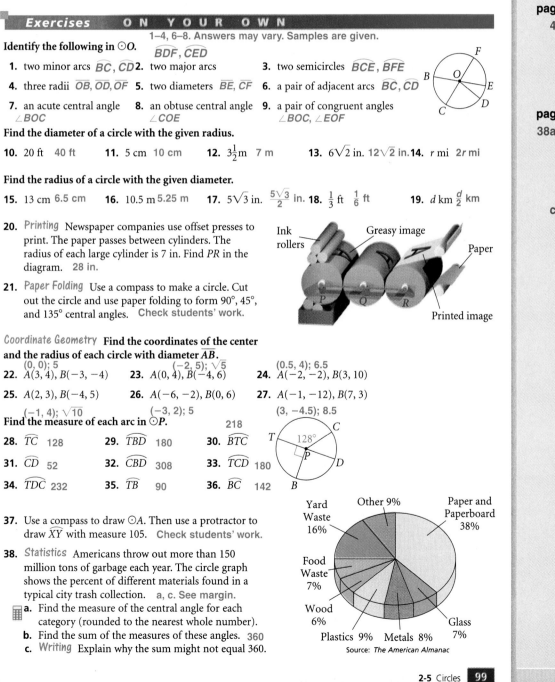

Exercises 22–27 Students can check their answers by sketching each circle in the coordinate plane.

ALTERNATIVE ASSESSMENT **Exercise 37** This exercise will help you assess students' understanding of arc measure by observing their ability to draw a circle and a central angle to create a 105° arc.

CONNECTING TO STUDENTS' WORLD Exercise 38 Have students contact their local government to find information on the volume of trash the community disposes of through recycling and by other means.

Exercises ON YOUR OWN

1–4, 6–8. Answers may vary. Samples are given.

Identify the following in ⊙O.

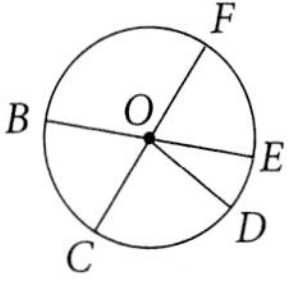

1. two minor arcs $\overset{\frown}{BC}, \overset{\frown}{CD}$
2. two major arcs $\overset{\frown}{BDF}, \overset{\frown}{CED}$
3. two semicircles $\overset{\frown}{BCE}, \overset{\frown}{BFE}$
4. three radii $\overline{OB}, \overline{OD}, \overline{OF}$
5. two diameters $\overline{BE}, \overline{CF}$
6. a pair of adjacent arcs $\overset{\frown}{BC}, \overset{\frown}{CD}$
7. an acute central angle $\angle BOC$
8. an obtuse central angle $\angle COE$
9. a pair of congruent angles $\angle BOC, \angle EOF$

Find the diameter of a circle with the given radius.

10. 20 ft 40 ft
11. 5 cm 10 cm
12. $3\frac{1}{2}$m 7 m
13. $6\sqrt{2}$ in. $12\sqrt{2}$ in.
14. r mi $2r$ mi

Find the radius of a circle with the given diameter.

15. 13 cm 6.5 cm
16. 10.5 m 5.25 m
17. $5\sqrt{3}$ in. $\frac{5\sqrt{3}}{2}$ in.
18. $\frac{1}{3}$ ft $\frac{1}{6}$ ft
19. d km $\frac{d}{2}$ km

20. *Printing* Newspaper companies use offset presses to print. The paper passes between cylinders. The radius of each large cylinder is 7 in. Find PR in the diagram. 28 in.

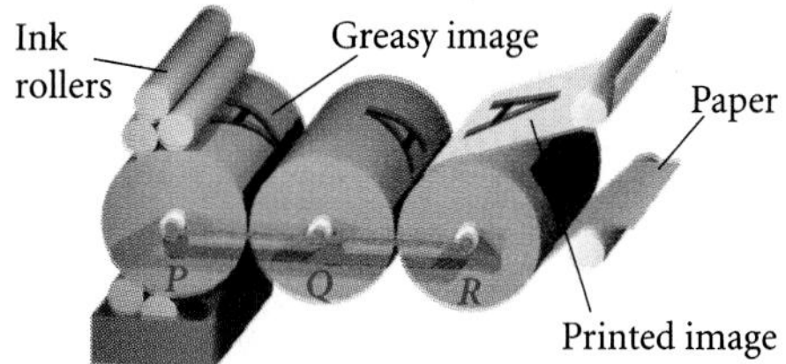

21. *Paper Folding* Use a compass to make a circle. Cut out the circle and use paper folding to form 90°, 45°, and 135° central angles. Check students' work.

Coordinate Geometry **Find the coordinates of the center and the radius of each circle with diameter $\overline{AB}$.**

22. $A(3, 4), B(-3, -4)$ (0, 0); 5
23. $A(0, 4), B(-4, 6)$ $(-2, 5)$; $\sqrt{5}$
24. $A(-2, -2), B(3, 10)$ (0.5, 4); 6.5
25. $A(2, 3), B(-4, 5)$ $(-1, 4)$; $\sqrt{10}$
26. $A(-6, -2), B(0, 6)$ $(-3, 2)$; 5
27. $A(-1, -12), B(7, 3)$ $(3, -4.5)$; 8.5

Find the measure of each arc in ⊙P.

T C 128° P D B

28. $\overset{\frown}{TC}$ 128
29. $\overset{\frown}{TBD}$ 180
30. $\overset{\frown}{BTC}$ 218
31. $\overset{\frown}{CD}$ 52
32. $\overset{\frown}{CBD}$ 308
33. $\overset{\frown}{TCD}$ 180
34. $\overset{\frown}{TDC}$ 232
35. $\overset{\frown}{TB}$ 90
36. $\overset{\frown}{BC}$ 142

37. Use a compass to draw ⊙A. Then use a protractor to draw $\overset{\frown}{XY}$ with measure 105. Check students' work.

38. *Statistics* Americans throw out more than 150 million tons of garbage each year. The circle graph shows the percent of different materials found in a typical city trash collection. a, c. See margin.
    a. Find the measure of the central angle for each category (rounded to the nearest whole number).
    b. Find the sum of the measures of these angles. 360
    c. *Writing* Explain why the sum might not equal 360.

Yard Waste 16% | Other 9% | Paper and Paperboard 38% | Food Waste 7% | Wood 6% | Plastics 9% | Metals 8% | Glass 7%

Source: *The American Almanac*

pages 96–98 Think and Discuss

4. Minor arcs; major arcs and semicircles; for each major arc, there is a minor arc with the same endpoints; 2 semicircles have the same endpoints.

pages 99–101 On Your Own

38a. Paper and Paperboard: 137, Glass: 25, Metals: 29, Plastics: 32, Wood: 22, Food Waste: 25, Yard Waste: 58, Other: 32

c. If all the measures are rounded up, the sum will be greater than 360.

ALGEBRA Exercise 45 Help students understand why $m\widehat{PQ} = m\widehat{SR}$.

RESEARCH Exercise 48 Students can use an encyclopedia. Have them look up both "Zulu" and "Africa."

DIVERSITY Exercise 49 This problem provides a good opportunity to discuss customs and traditions of different nationalities and how they affect what a person does in a 24-h period.

CONNECTING TO STUDENTS' WORLD Exercise 50 Have students conduct a survey in school of who uses the Internet and display the data in a circle graph.

Exercises MIXED REVIEW

JOURNAL To get students started, ask them what circular objects they used at breakfast or to get to school.

50. Who Is Using the Internet?

Age	Percent
18-24	20%
25-29	20%
30-34	15%
35-44	25%
44-54	15%
55+	3%
refused to answer	2%

page 101 Mixed Review

56.

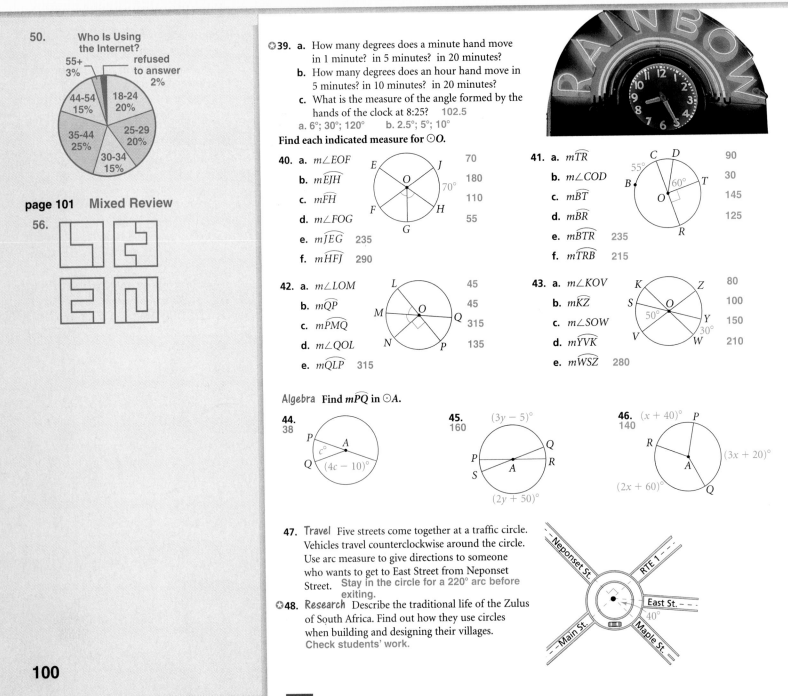

39. a. How many degrees does a minute hand move in 1 minute? in 5 minutes? in 20 minutes?
b. How many degrees does an hour hand move in 5 minutes? in 10 minutes? in 20 minutes?
c. What is the measure of the angle formed by the hands of the clock at 8:25? 102.5
a. 6°; 30°; 120° b. 2.5°; 5°; 10°

Find each indicated measure for ⊙O.

40. a. $m\angle EOF$ 70
b. $m\widehat{EJH}$ 180
c. $m\widehat{FH}$ 110
d. $m\angle FOG$ 55
e. $m\widehat{JEG}$ 235
f. $m\widehat{HFJ}$ 290

41. a. $m\widehat{TR}$ 90
b. $m\angle COD$ 30
c. $m\widehat{BT}$ 145
d. $m\widehat{BR}$ 125
e. $m\widehat{BTR}$ 235
f. $m\widehat{TRB}$ 215

42. a. $m\angle LOM$ 45
b. $m\widehat{QP}$ 45
c. $m\widehat{PMQ}$ 315
d. $m\angle QOL$ 135
e. $m\widehat{QLP}$ 315

43. a. $m\angle KOV$ 80
b. $m\widehat{KZ}$ 100
c. $m\angle SOW$ 150
d. $m\widehat{YVK}$ 210
e. $m\widehat{WSZ}$ 280

Algebra Find $m\widehat{PQ}$ in ⊙A.

44. 38 $c°$, $(4c - 10)°$

45. 160 $(3y - 5)°$, $(2y + 50)°$

46. 140

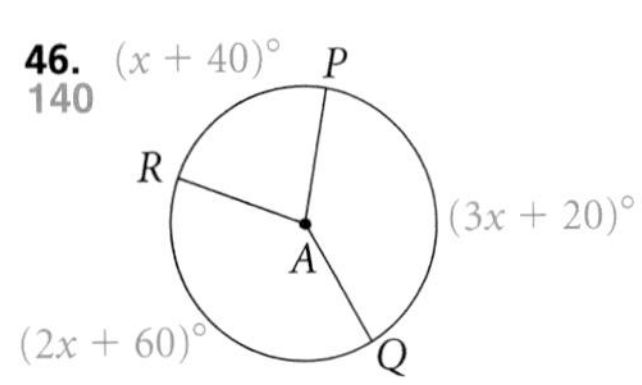

47. **Travel** Five streets come together at a traffic circle. Vehicles travel counterclockwise around the circle. Use arc measure to give directions to someone who wants to get to East Street from Neponset Street. Stay in the circle for a 220° arc before exiting.

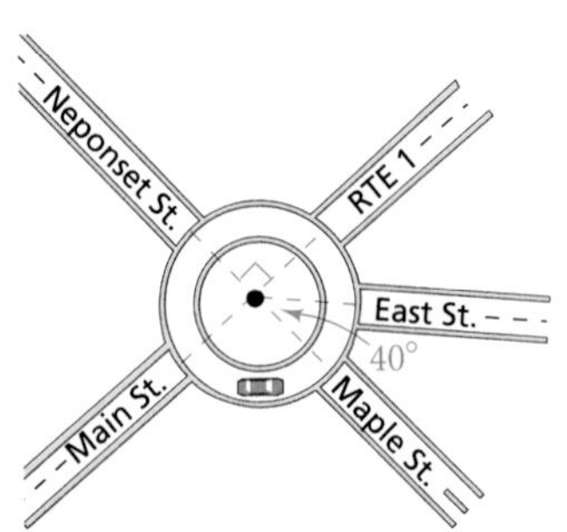

48. **Research** Describe the traditional life of the Zulus of South Africa. Find out how they use circles when building and designing their villages. Check students' work.

Exercises 51–54 Students review finding measures of interior and exterior angles.

GETTING READY FOR LESSON 2-6 These exercises prepare students for identifying congruent figures. Explain that by dividing the grid using either a vertical or horizontal line, *all* the resulting pieces are congruent, so this describes only one division. Suggest that students cut out a 4 by 4 grid so that they can cut it in half and test congruence by placing one half on top of the other.

Wrap Up

THE BIG IDEA Ask students: *Describe a circle, the three types of arcs of a circle, how the arcs are named, and how their measures are found.*

RETEACHING ACTIVITY Students make circle graphs using data they collect in class, finding the percents needed to calculate the central angle. (Reteaching worksheet 2-5)

49. *Open-ended* Make a circle graph showing how you spend a 24-hour weekday.
Check students' work.

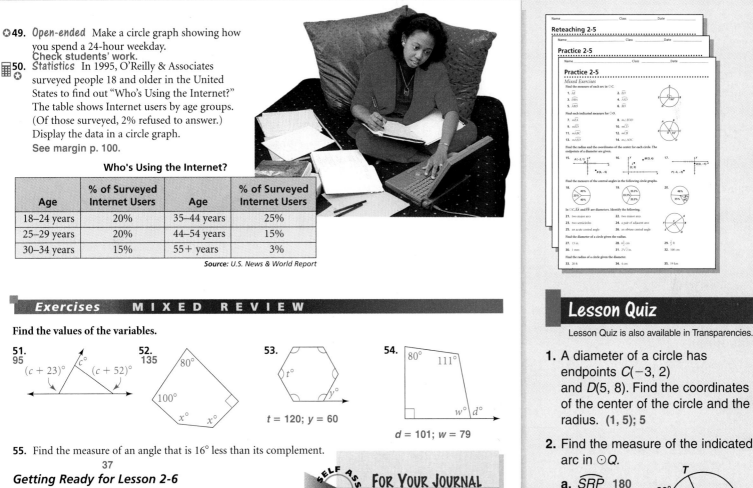

50. *Statistics* In 1995, O'Reilly & Associates surveyed people 18 and older in the United States to find out "Who's Using the Internet?" The table shows Internet users by age groups. (Of those surveyed, 2% refused to answer.) Display the data in a circle graph.
See margin p. 100.

Who's Using the Internet?

Age	% of Surveyed Internet Users	Age	% of Surveyed Internet Users
18–24 years	20%	35–44 years	25%
25–29 years	20%	44–54 years	15%
30–34 years	15%	55+ years	3%

Source: *U.S. News & World Report*

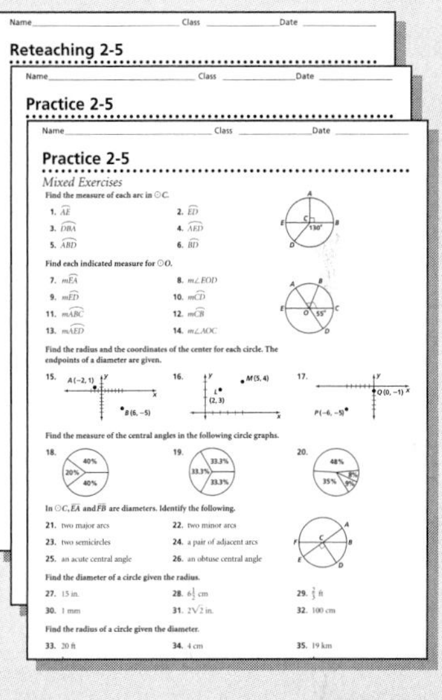
Name Class Date
Reteaching 2-5
Name Class Date
Practice 2-5
Name Class Date
Practice 2-5
Mixed Exercises

Exercises MIXED REVIEW

Find the values of the variables.

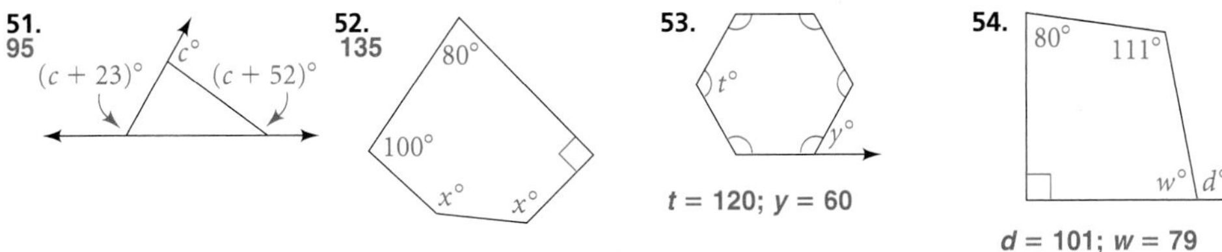

51. 95
52. 135
53. $t = 120$; $y = 60$
54. $d = 101$; $w = 79$

55. Find the measure of an angle that is 16° less than its complement. 37

Getting Ready for Lesson 2-6

56. The diagram below at the left shows a 4-by-4 square on graph paper. You can divide the square into two identical pieces by cutting along grid lines. One way to do this is to make a vertical or a horizontal line. Another way is shown below at the right. Find the four other ways of doing this. **See margin p. 100.**

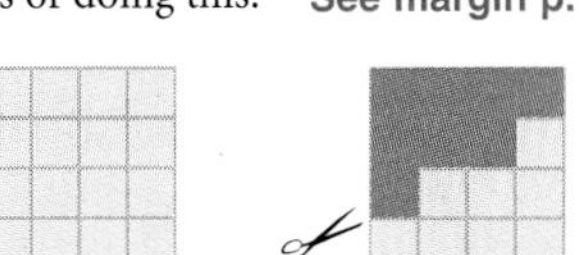

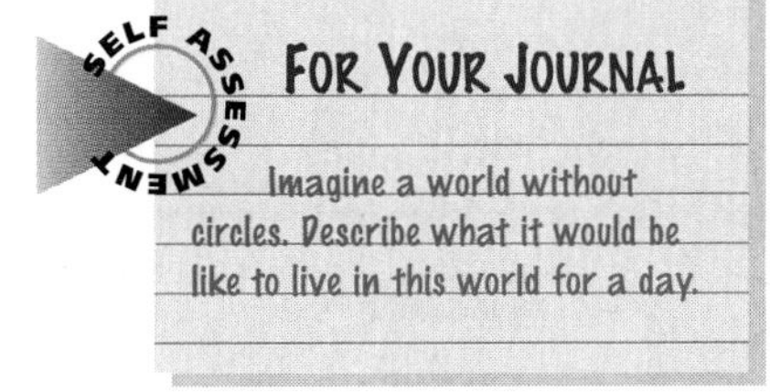

SELF ASSESSMENT
FOR YOUR JOURNAL
Imagine a world without circles. Describe what it would be like to live in this world for a day.

Lesson Quiz

Lesson Quiz is also available in Transparencies.

1. A diameter of a circle has endpoints $C(-3, 2)$ and $D(5, 8)$. Find the coordinates of the center of the circle and the radius. **(1, 5); 5**

2. Find the measure of the indicated arc in ⊙*Q*.
   a. $\widehat{SRP}$ **180**
   b. $\widehat{RST}$ **230**
   c. $\widehat{PT}$ **100**

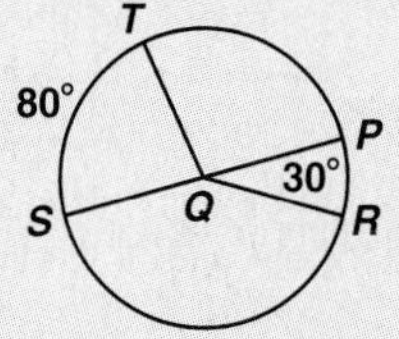

2-6 Teaching Notes

PROBLEM OF THE DAY

Suppose a copy machine can reduce a picture to 70% of its original size. What is the result of two consecutive reductions? 49% of its original size

Problem of the Day is also available in Transparencies.

CONNECTING TO PRIOR KNOWLEDGE Discuss with students examples of scale models with which they are familiar, such as doll houses, matchbox cars, and model airplanes. Also compare objects such as utensils for infants and adults and chairs and desks in elementary and high schools.

THINK AND DISCUSS

ERROR ALERT! Students may think that ∠X corresponds to ∠Q, ∠B to ∠Y, etc. because they are in the same relative positions on the two figures. **Remediation:** Make sure students can identify corresponding parts. Students can trace and cut out one of the figures and place it on top of the other figure so that corresponding parts "match."

Example 1 Relating to the Real World 

Point out that there is more than one way to show a congruence correspondence. For example, the congruence of the fins can be expressed as *SPACE* ≅ *DTRWB* or *SECAP* ≅ *DBWRT*.

Lesson Planning Options

Prerequisite Skills

- Writing and solving proportions
- Finding perimeter

Assignment Options for Exercises On Your Own

To provide flexible scheduling, this lesson can be subdivided into parts.

1. **Core** 1–10, 25–27, 38
   Extension 32–34
2. **Core** 11–24, 28–31, 35–37, 40–44
   Extension 39, 45

Use Mixed Review to maintain skills.

Resources

Student Edition

Skills Handbook, pp. 675, 676
Extra Practice, p. 649
Glossary/Study Guide

Teaching Resources

Chapter Support File, Ch. 2
- Practice 2-6 (two worksheets)
- Reteaching 2-6

Classroom Manager 2-6
Glossary, Spanish Resources

Transparencies

4, 33

Connections Rocketry . . . and more

2-6 Congruent and Similar Figures

What You'll Learn

- Measuring congruent and similar figures
- Using properties of congruence and similarity

...And Why

To model real-world situations, such as mass production and photography

What You'll Need

- scissors
- protractor
- centimeter ruler

THINK AND DISCUSS

Part 1

Congruent Figures

Congruent figures have exactly the same size and shape. When two figures are congruent you can slide, flip, or turn one so that it fits exactly on the other one.

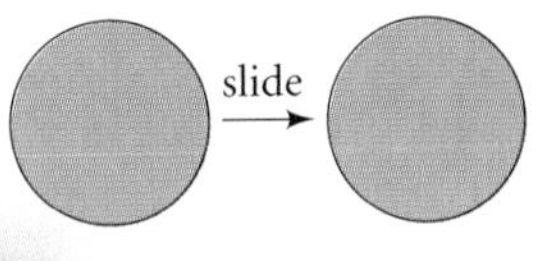

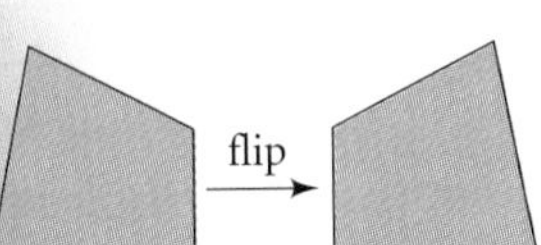

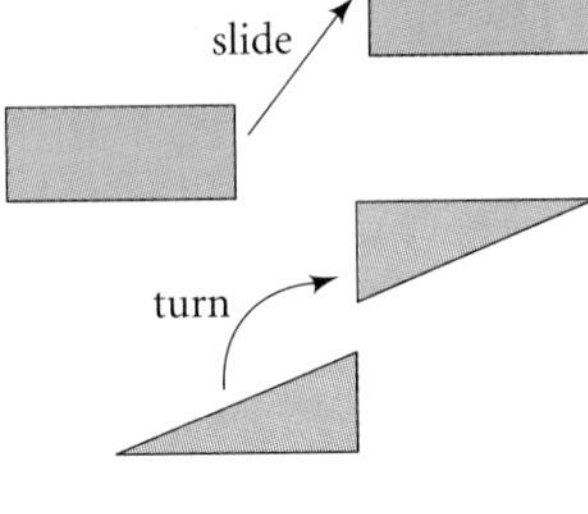

Congruent circles have congruent radii. **Congruent polygons** have congruent corresponding parts. The matching angles and sides of congruent polygons are called *corresponding parts.* Matching vertices are *corresponding vertices.* When you name congruent polygons, always list corresponding vertices in the same order.

X A B C Q R Y P

C corresponds to *R*.
∠*B* corresponds to ∠*Q*.
$\overline{AX}$ corresponds to $\overline{PY}$.
ACBX ≅ *PRQY*

Example 1 Relating to the Real World 

Rocketry The fins of the rocket are congruent pentagons. Find $m\angle B$.

Because the fins are congruent, $\angle B \cong \angle E$. So you can find $m\angle B$ by first finding $m\angle E$.

132° C A R W E B S 88° P T D

By the Polygon Interior Angle-Sum Theorem, you know that the sum of the measures of the interior angles of pentagon *SPACE* is (5 − 2)180, or 540.

$$m\angle S + m\angle P + m\angle A + m\angle C + m\angle E = 540$$
$$88 + 90 + 90 + 132 + m\angle E = 540$$
$$400 + m\angle E = 540$$
$$m\angle E = 140$$

So $m\angle E = m\angle B = 140$.

Example 2

Question 1 Students may want to sketch the triangles to find the corresponding segments. Also, help students identify the corresponding segments from the letters.

ESL Suggest that students think of congruent figures as "clones" and similar figures as "enlargements" or "reductions."

Example 3

ERROR ALERT! If students use the proportion $\frac{DA}{FR} = \frac{AY}{RI}$, they will get a similarity ratio of $\frac{3}{2}$. **Remediation:** Help students understand that they found the ratio of the lengths of the sides of $\triangle DAY$ to $\triangle FRI$.

ALTERNATE METHOD The Look Back demonstrates that RI can be found by solving $\frac{RI}{AY} = \frac{2}{3}$ or $RI = \frac{2}{3}AY$.

Question 3 Review the meaning of perimeter. Have students compare their results with what they know about the perimeters of congruent figures.

CRITICAL THINKING Question 4 This question demonstrates that congruent figures are also similar figures.

Example 2

$\triangle TJD \cong \triangle RCF$. List congruent corresponding parts.

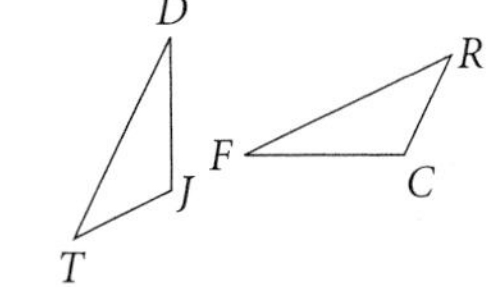

$\overline{TJ} \cong \overline{RC}$ $\quad \overline{JD} \cong \overline{CF}$ $\quad \overline{DT} \cong \overline{FR}$

$\angle T \cong \angle R$ $\quad \angle J \cong \angle C$ $\quad \angle D \cong \angle F$

1. **Try This** $\triangle WYS \cong \triangle MKV$. List congruent corresponding parts. $\overline{WY} \cong \overline{MK}$; $\overline{YS} \cong \overline{KV}$; $\overline{SW} \cong \overline{VM}$; $\angle W \cong \angle M$; $\angle Y \cong \angle K$; $\angle S \cong \angle V$

Part 2

Similar Polygons

QUICK REVIEW

Corresponding sides are *proportional* if the ratios of their lengths are equal.

Two figures that have the same shape but not necessarily the same size are similar ($\sim$). Two polygons are **similar** if (1) corresponding angles are congruent and (2) corresponding sides are proportional. The ratio of the lengths of corresponding sides is the **similarity ratio.**

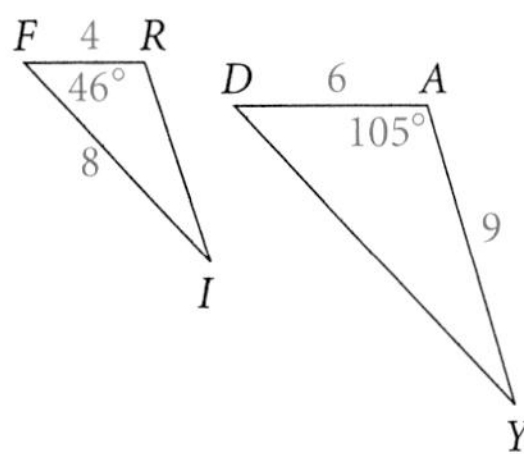

Example 3

$\triangle FRI \sim \triangle DAY$. Find:

a. the similarity ratio **b.** $m\angle R$ **c.** RI

a. Since $\overline{FR}$ and $\overline{DA}$ are corresponding sides, the similarity ratio is $\frac{FR}{DA} = \frac{4}{6} = \frac{2}{3}$.

b. $\angle R$ corresponds to $\angle A$, so $m\angle R = m\angle A$.
$m\angle A = 105$, so $m\angle R = 105$.

c. Write a proportion to solve for RI.

$\frac{FR}{DA} = \frac{RI}{AY}$

$\frac{4}{6} = \frac{RI}{9}$ Substitution

$36 = 6 \cdot RI$ Use cross-products.

$6 = RI$ Divide each side by 6.

PROBLEM SOLVING

Look Back Describe how you could use the similarity ratio to solve for *RI*.

Multiply *AY* by the similarity ratio.

2. **Try This** Find DY and $m\angle D$. 12; 46

3. **a.** Find the perimeter of $\triangle FRI$. 18
   b. Find the perimeter of $\triangle DAY$. 27
   c. What is the ratio of the perimeter of $\triangle FRI$ to the perimeter of $\triangle DAY$? $\frac{2}{3}$
   d. Compare your answer to part (c) to the similarity ratio. Make a **conjecture** about the ratio of the perimeters of similar figures.
   e. Test your **conjecture** by drawing and measuring other pairs of similar polygons. Check students' work.

d. The ratio of perimeters of similar figures = the similarity ratio.

4. **Critical Thinking** What type of similar figures have a similarity ratio of 1? congruent figures

Additional Examples

FOR EXAMPLE 1

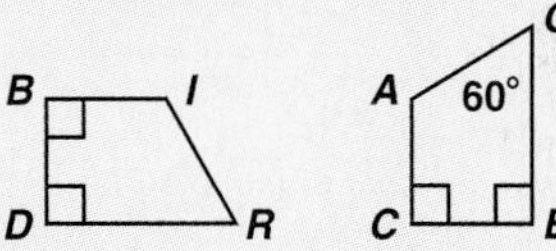

BIRD $\cong$ *CAGE*. Find $m\angle I$. 120

Discussion: *Is the following statement true:* RIBD $\cong$ GACE*? Explain.*

FOR EXAMPLE 2

List the congruent corresponding parts of *ACBX* and *PRQY* on page 102.

$\overline{AC} \cong \overline{PR}$, $\overline{CB} \cong \overline{RQ}$, $\overline{BX} \cong \overline{QY}$, $\overline{XA} \cong \overline{YP}$, $\angle A \cong \angle P$, $\angle C \cong \angle R$, $\angle B \cong \angle Q$, $\angle X \cong \angle Y$

Discussion: *What can you say about the number of vertices of congruent polygons?*

FOR EXAMPLE 3

$\triangle ABC \sim \triangle XYZ$, $AB = 2$, $BC = 5$, and $XY = 6$. Find the similarity ratio. $\frac{1}{3}$

Discussion: *What can you say about sides $\overline{AB}$ and $\overline{ZX}$?*

Example 4 Relating to the Real World 

It may help students to write the proportions in words first.

$$\frac{\text{width of photo}}{\text{width of poster}} = \frac{\text{length of photo}}{\text{length of poster}}$$

CRITICAL THINKING Question 6 Review with students the methods for checking whether a proportion is true, such as checking for equal cross products and simplifying both sides to the same fraction.

WORK TOGETHER

Have students use the tans they created in Lesson 2-1, or provide a tangram handout for the students to cut. Students should keep track of their responses by sketching the figures and labeling the sketches with the pieces used.

Technology Options

For Exercise 29, students may use geometry software to create fractal designs.

Prentice Hall Technology 

Software
- Secondary Math Lab Toolkit™
- Integrated Math Lab 26
- Computer Item Generator 2-6

Internet
- See the Prentice Hall site. (http://www.phschool.com)

Example 4 Relating to the Real World 

24 in.
x
4 in.
6 in.

Photography You want to enlarge a photo that is 4 in. tall and 6 in. wide into a poster. The poster will be 24 in. wide. How tall will it be?

$\frac{6}{24} = \frac{4}{x}$ Write a proportion.

$6 \cdot x = 24 \cdot 4$ Use cross-products.

$x = 16$ Divide each side by 6.

The poster will be 16 in. tall.

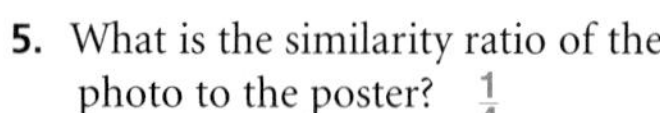

5. What is the similarity ratio of the photo to the poster? $\frac{1}{4}$

6. **Critical Thinking** A school photo package comes with an 8 in.-by-10 in. photo and a 5 in.-by-7 in. photo. Are the photos similar? Explain.

   No, $\frac{8}{5} \neq \frac{10}{7}$.

WORK TOGETHER

Trace the diagram and cut out the seven pieces. (Or use the tans you made in Lesson 2-1.)

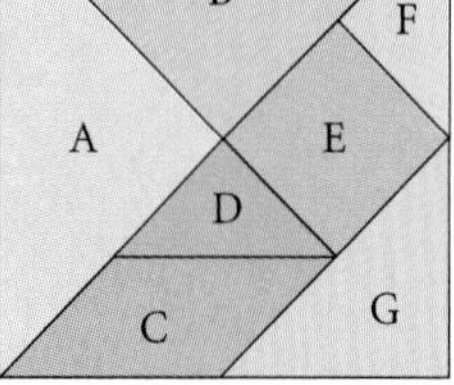

7. Which pieces are congruent? A and B, D and F
8. Which pieces are similar? (Check that all pairs of corresponding angles are congruent and that corresponding sides are proportional.) A, B, D, F, G
9. Find other congruent and similar pairs by placing pieces together. Record your answers. See margin p. 105.

   Here are some examples:

congruent

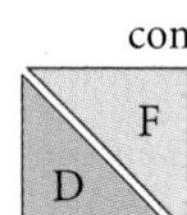

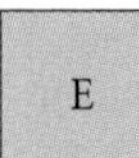

similar

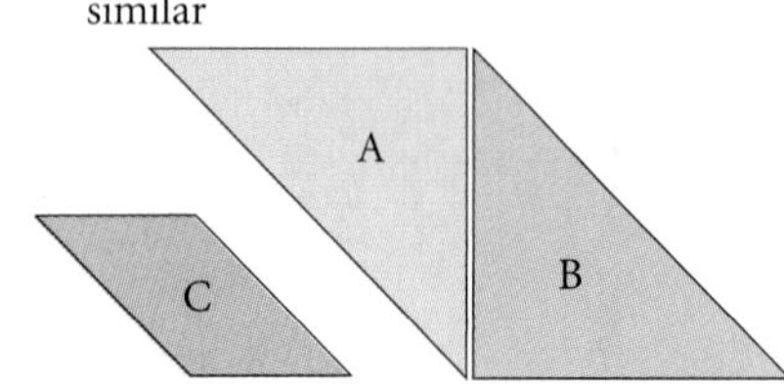

Exercises ON YOUR OWN

Exercise 1 Students may want to trace and cut out the figures to manipulate them.

Exercises 2–10 Students can identify the corresponding parts using the name of the figures or using the sketches. Encourage students to use the method they prefer.

Exercises 25–26 Some students may want to sketch congruent quadrilaterals and label the vertices.

Exercises ON YOUR OWN

1. Identify the pairs of triangles that appear to be congruent. A and H, B and G, C and E, F and D

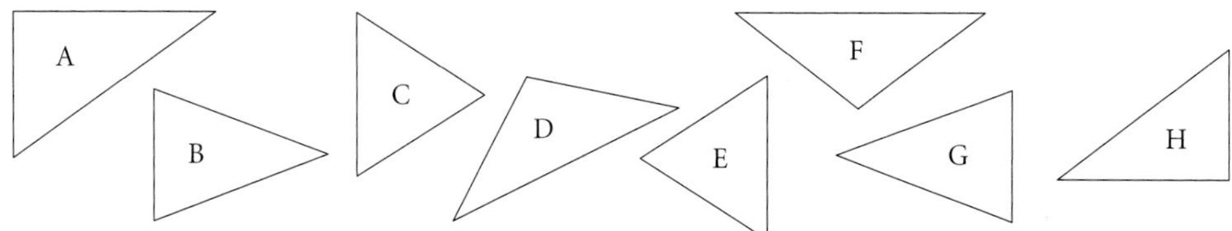

△LMC ≅ △BJK. Complete the congruence statements.

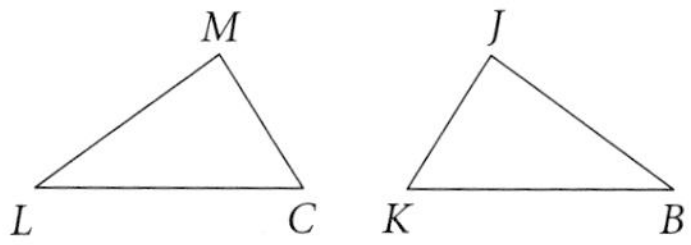

2. $\overline{LC} \cong$ ■ $\overline{BK}$
3. $\overline{KJ} \cong$ ■ $\overline{CM}$
4. $\overline{JB} \cong$ ■ $\overline{ML}$
5. $\angle L \cong$ ■ $\angle B$
6. $\angle K \cong$ ■ $\angle C$
7. $\angle M \cong$ ■ $\angle J$
8. $\triangle CML \cong$ ■ $\triangle KJB$
9. $\triangle KBJ \cong$ ■ $\triangle CLM$
10. $\triangle MLC \cong$ ■ $\triangle JBK$

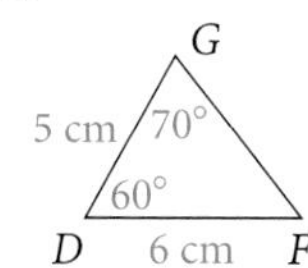

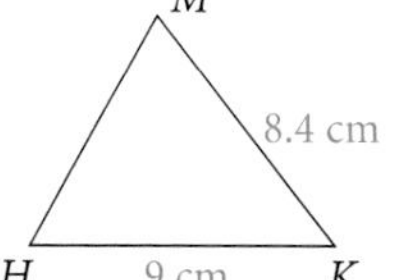

JDRT ~ JHYX. Complete the proportions and congruence statements.

D R H Y J X T

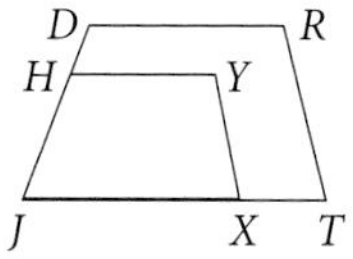

11. $\frac{JD}{JH} = \frac{DR}{■}$ HY
12. $\frac{RT}{YX} = \frac{■}{JX}$ JT
13. $\frac{■}{DR} = \frac{YX}{RT}$ HY
14. $\angle D \cong$ ■ $\angle JHY$
15. $\angle Y \cong$ ■ $\angle R$
16. $\angle T \cong$ ■ $\angle YXJ$

△DFG ~ △HKM. Use the diagram to find the following.

G 5 cm 70° 60° D 6 cm F

M 8.4 cm H 9 cm K

17. the similarity ratio of △DFG to △HKM $\frac{2}{3}$
18. the similarity ratio of △HKM to △DFG $\frac{3}{2}$
19. $m\angle F$ 50
20. $m\angle K$ 50
21. $m\angle M$ 70
22. $\frac{DF}{HK}$ $\frac{2}{3}$
23. HM 7.5 cm
24. GF 5.6 cm

In Exercises 25–27, POLY ≅ SIDE.
25–26. See below.

25. List four pairs of congruent angles.
26. List four pairs of congruent sides.
27. Complete the congruence statements.
    a. $OLYP \cong$ ■ IDES
    b. $DESI \cong$ ■ LYPO
28. **Art** An art class is painting a mural for a spring festival. The students are working from a diagram that is 48 in. long and 36 in. high. Find the length of the mural if its height is to be 12 ft. 16 ft

25. $\angle P \cong \angle S$; $\angle O \cong \angle I$; $\angle L \cong \angle D$; $\angle Y \cong \angle E$
26. $\overline{PO} \cong \overline{SI}$; $\overline{OL} \cong \overline{ID}$; $\overline{LY} \cong \overline{DE}$; $\overline{YP} \cong \overline{ES}$

page 104 Work Together

9. Samples:

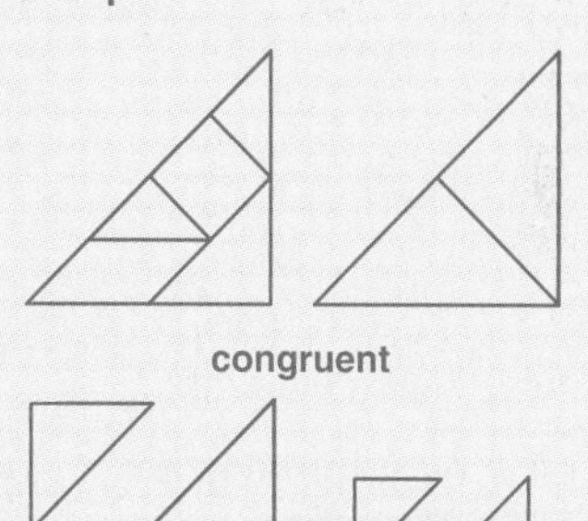

congruent

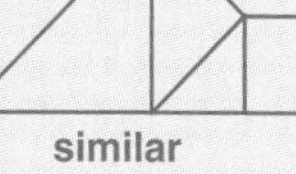

similar

RESEARCH Exercise 29 Students can find information on fractals in an encyclopedia. They may also want to research Georg Cantor and Benoit Mandelbrot. Numerous books are also available at the library that describe fractals in nature.

ALTERNATIVE ASSESSMENT Exercises 32–34 These exercises can help you to assess students' ability to identify congruent figures by how they list corresponding vertices.

STANDARDIZED TEST TIP Exercise 38 Once students see that H corresponds with C, have them visualize possible locations for H.

pages 105–107 On Your Own

30a. Sample:

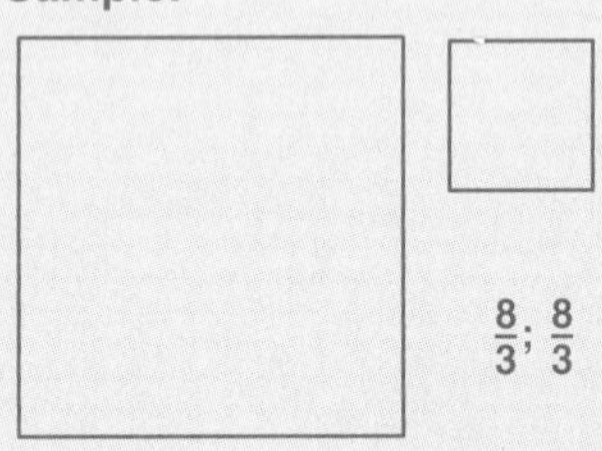

$\frac{8}{3}, \frac{8}{3}$

b. Yes; all the angles are ≅ and the lengths of the corresp. sides have = ratios.

c. Sample:

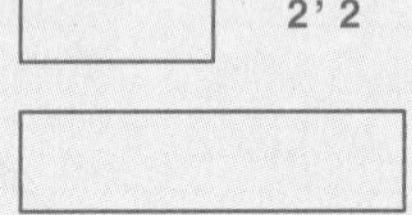

$\frac{3}{2}, \frac{1}{2}$

d. Answers may vary. Sample: No; all the angles are ≅, but the ratios of the lengths of the corresp. sides need not be =.

e. All squares are similar; not all rectangles are similar; the lengths of corresp. sides of any 2 squares have = ratios and the corresp. angles are ≅; the lengths of corresp. sides of 2 rectangles need not have = ratios. Use diagrams for parts (a) and (c).

29. *Research* A *fractal* is a self-similar geometric pattern. It is made up of parts that are similar to the object itself. A good example of this is a fern frond. Break off any leaflet and the leaflet looks like a small fern frond. Investigate fractals and **summarize** your findings. Check students' work.

30. **a.** Draw two different-sized squares on graph paper. Find the ratio of each pair of corresponding sides.
b. Are these squares similar? Explain.
c. Draw two different-sized rectangles on graph paper. Find the ratio of each pair of corresponding sides.
d. Are these rectangles similar? Explain.
e. *Writing* Are all squares similar? Are all rectangles similar? Explain. Sketch pictures to support your conclusion.
a–e. See margin.

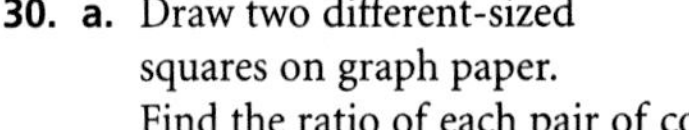

31. *Critical Thinking* Kimi claims that all circles are similar. Is she right? Explain. Yes; the ratios of radii, diameters, and circumferences of 2 circles are =.

Write a congruence statement for each pair of triangles.

32.

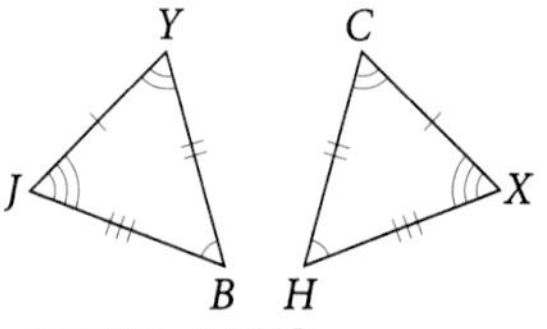

△BJY ≅ △HXC

33.

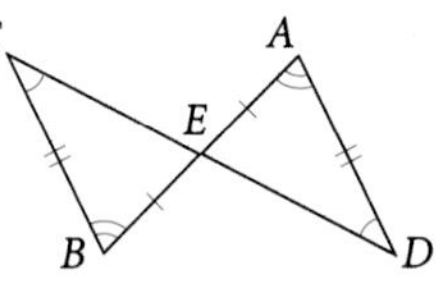

E is the midpoint of $\overline{CD}$.
△BEC ≅ △AED

34.

$\overrightarrow{TK}$ bisects ∠PTR.
△KPT ≅ △KRT

Choose **Use pencil and paper, mental math, or a calculator to find the values of the variables.**

35.

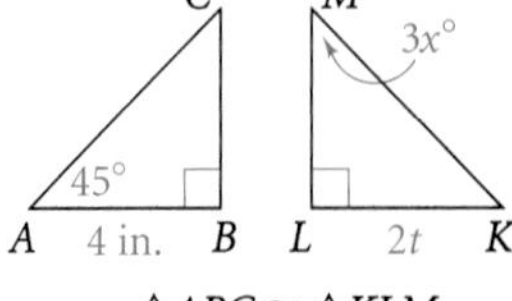

△ABC ≅ △KLM
$t = 2$ in.; $x = 15$

36.

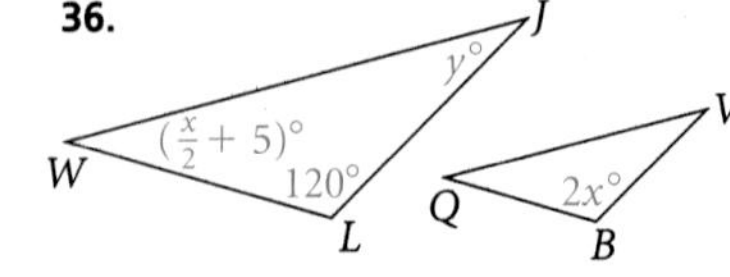

△WLJ ~ △QBV
$x = 60$; $y = 25$

37.

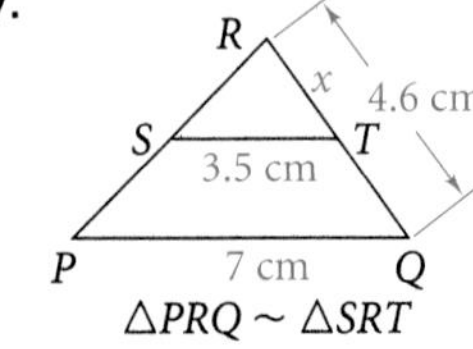

△PRQ ~ △SRT
2.3 cm

38. *Standardized Test Prep* △KJH is congruent to the triangle shown. Which of these *cannot* be the coordinates of point H? E

A. (5, 0) **B.** (5, 4) **C.** (6, 4)
D. (6, 0) **E.** (7, 0)

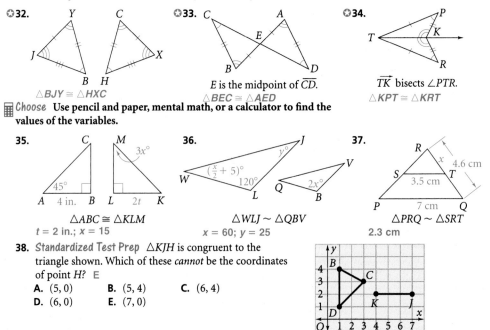

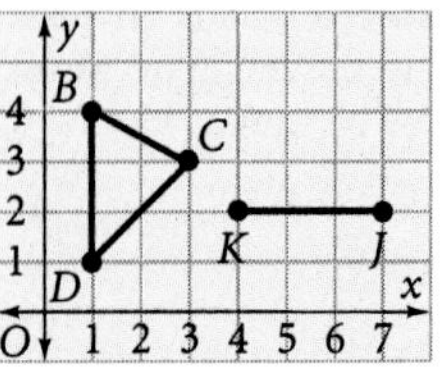

KINESTHETIC LEARNING Exercise 39 If students have access to a copy machine, have them compare the side lengths and angle measures of the original and enlarged triangles.

STANDARDIZED TEST TIP Exercise 44 Remind students that circles are congruent if their radii are congruent.

OPEN-ENDED Exercise 45 To help students get started, discuss the two properties of similar figures.

Chapter Project **FIND OUT BY INVESTIGATING** Students should use the pentominoes that they created in Lesson 2-4. Extend this activity by asking whether they can use the pentominoes to make other enlargements of any of the other pentominoes.

39. When you make an enlargement on a copy machine, the enlargement is similar to the original. You are making an enlargement of $\triangle ABC$. Suppose you choose the 120% enlargement setting. This means that the similarity ratio of the enlargement to the original is $\frac{120}{100}$, or $\frac{6}{5}$.

A 10 cm C; 53°; 37°; 6 cm; 8 cm; 90°; B

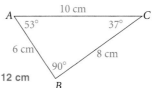

a. Find the lengths of the sides of the enlargement. **7.2 cm; 9.6 cm; 12 cm**

b. Find the measures of the angles of the enlargement. **53; 90; 37**

c. Suppose you use the 150% setting. Find the lengths of the sides of the triangle. **9 cm; 12 cm; 15 cm**

The triangles are similar. Find the similarity ratio of the first to the second.

40. $\frac{2}{1}$

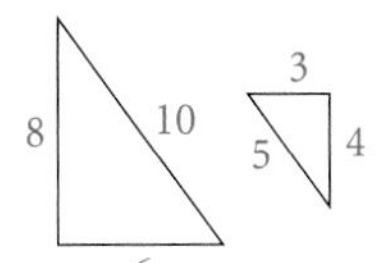

41. $\frac{3}{4}$

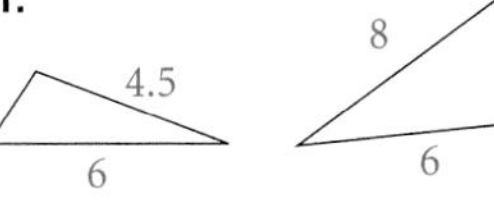

42. $\frac{3}{1}$

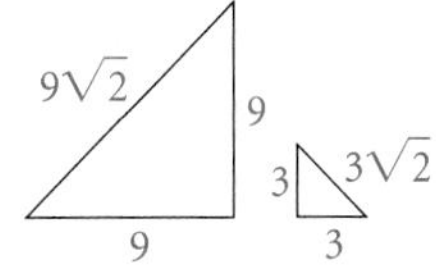

43. a. *Photography* Is an 8 in.-by-10 in. photograph similar to a 16 in.-by 20 in. photograph? Explain. **yes; $\frac{8}{16} = \frac{10}{20}$**

b. Is a 4 in.-by-5 in. photograph similar to a 5 in.-by-7 in. photograph? Explain. **no; $\frac{4}{5} \neq \frac{5}{7}$**

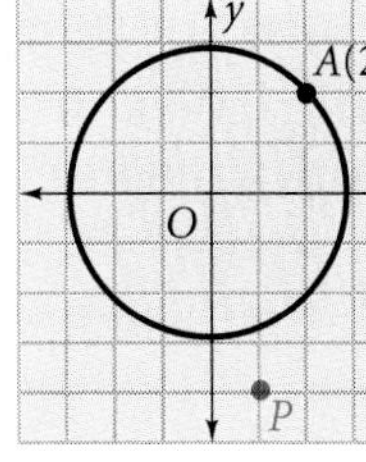

44. *Standardized Test Prep* The circle shown is congruent to a circle with center $P(1, -4)$. Which of these *cannot* be the coordinates of a point on $\odot P$? **D**

A. $(-1, -2)$ B. $(-1, -6)$ C. $(3, -2)$ D. $(3, -4)$ E. $(3, -6)$

45. *Open-ended* Draw two quadrilaterals that have sides in the ratio 2 : 1 and yet are not similar. **See sample at right.**

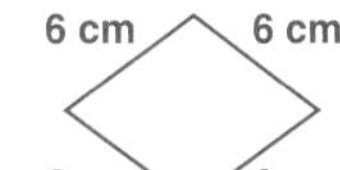

rhombus

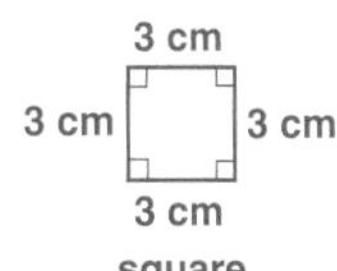

square

Chapter Project ***Find Out by Investigating***

Use the pentominoes you made in the Find Out exercise on page 95 to investigate similarity.

- How many more pentominoes will it take to complete the 3-by-15 rectangle below? How do you know? Complete the rectangle and record your solution on graph paper. **6; there are 30 1-by-1 squares to be covered.**

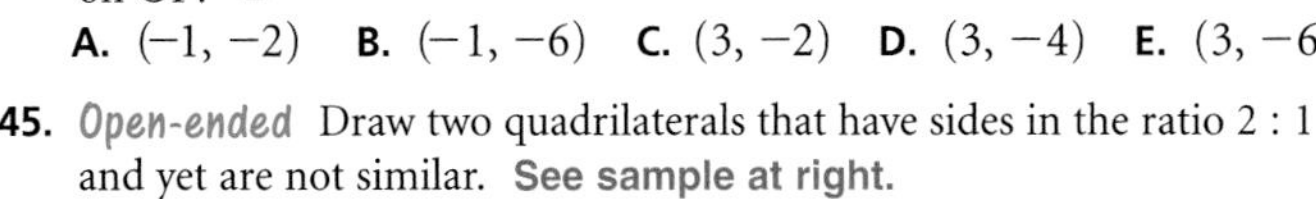

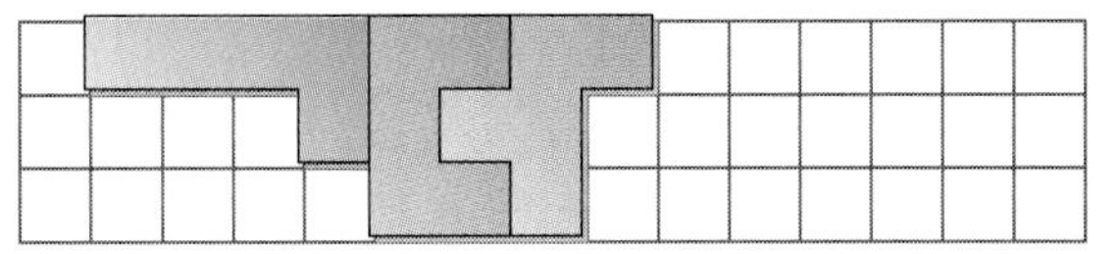

- Is this 3-by-15 rectangle *similar* to the rectangular pentomino piece? Explain. If it is, what is the similarity ratio? **yes; $\frac{3}{1} = \frac{15}{5}$; 3**

page 108 Mixed Review

46.

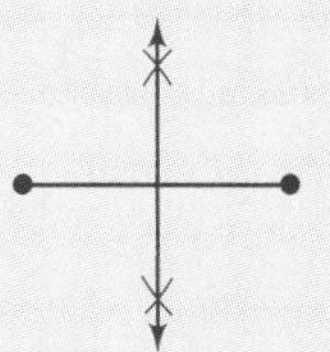

47.

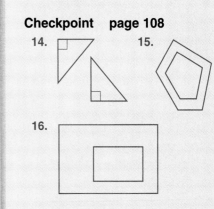

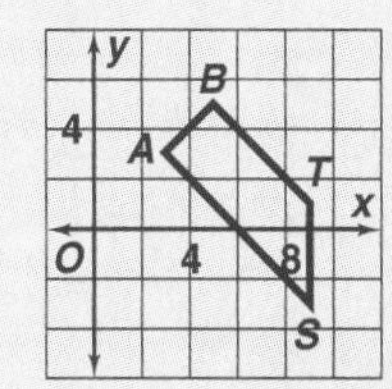

Trapezoid; slope of $\overline{BT}$ = slope of $\overline{AS}$.

Trapezoid; slope of $\overline{AB} \neq$ slope of $\overline{ST}$.

Checkpoint page 108

14. **15.**

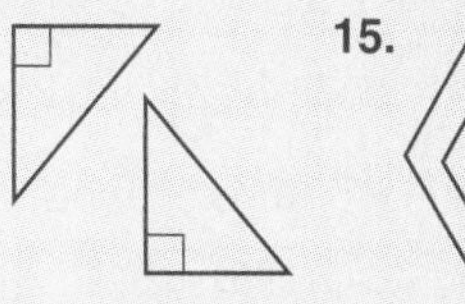

16.

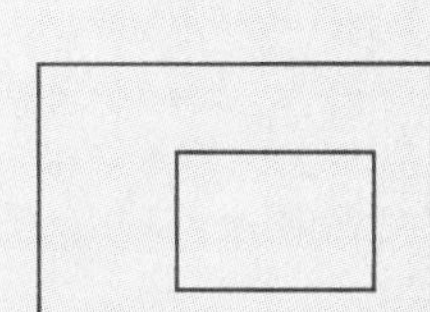

Exercises MIXED REVIEW

JOURNAL Have students review what it means for a polygon to be regular.

Exercise 46 Students will need a compass and straightedge to construct a perpendicular bisector of a segment.

GETTING READY FOR LESSON 2-7 These exercises prepare students for drawing orthographic views of objects.

Wrap Up

THE BIG IDEA Ask students: *What is the difference between congruence and similarity?*

RETEACHING ACTIVITY Students compare and classify polygons as congruent, similar, or neither, giving the similarity ratio if similar. (Reteaching worksheet 2-6)

Exercises CHECKPOINT

In this Checkpoint, your students will assess their own progress on Lessons 2-4 to 2-6.

Exercises 1–4 Make sure students find the radius and not the diameter.

MENTAL MATH Exercise 17 Students can eliminate some of the answer choices by sketching the quadrilateral.

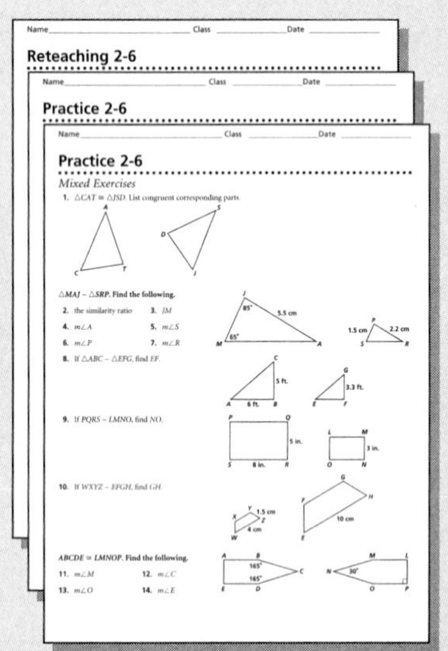

Name____ Class ____ Date ____

Reteaching 2-6

Name____ Class ____ Date ____

Practice 2-6

Name____ Class ____ Date ____

Practice 2-6

Mixed Exercises

1. $\triangle CAT \cong \triangle JSD$. List congruent corresponding parts.

$\triangle MAJ \sim \triangle SRP$. Find the following.

2. the similarity ratio
3. JM
4. $m\angle A$
5. $m\angle S$
6. $m\angle P$
7. $m\angle R$
8. If $\triangle ABC \sim \triangle EFG$, find EF.
9. If $PQRS \sim LMNO$, find NO.
10. If $WXYZ \sim EFGH$, find GH.

$ABCDE \cong LMNOP$. Find the following.

11. $m\angle M$
12. $m\angle C$
13. $m\angle O$
14. $m\angle E$

Lesson Quiz

Lesson Quiz is also available in Transparencies.

For Exercises 1–2, $\triangle CAT \cong \triangle DOG$.

1. List the congruent corresponding parts. $\overline{CA} \cong \overline{DO}$, $\overline{AT} \cong \overline{OG}$, $\overline{TC} \cong \overline{GD}$, $\angle C \cong \angle D$, $\angle A \cong \angle O$, $\angle T \cong \angle G$

2. If $m\angle C = 90$, and $m\angle A = 40$, find $m\angle G$. 50

For Questions 3–4, $AEGH \sim XZLM$, $EG = 3$, $GH = 6$, $ZL = 1$.

3. Find the similarity ratio. 3

4. Find LM. 2

Exercises MIXED REVIEW

46. **Constructions** Draw a 3-in. segment. Construct the perpendicular bisector of that segment. Check your work with a ruler and a protractor. See margin p. 107.

47. **Coordinate Geometry** Connect $A(3, 3)$, $B(5, 5)$, $T(9, 1)$, and $S(9, -3)$ in order. What type of quadrilateral is $ABTS$? Explain. See margin p. 107.

48. $M(-1, 0)$ is the midpoint of $\overline{AB}$. The coordinates of A are $(5, 1)$. Find the coordinates of B. $(-7, -1)$

49. What is the measure of each interior angle of a regular 18-gon? 160

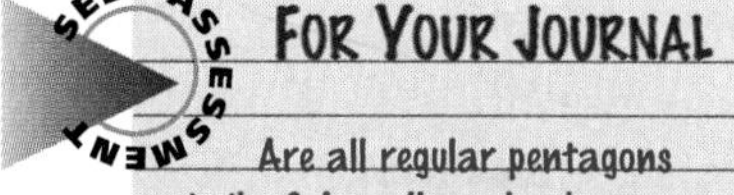

FOR YOUR JOURNAL

Are all regular pentagons similar? Are all regular hexagons similar? Make a conjecture about regular polygons and similarity. Justify your reasoning.

Getting Ready for Lesson 2-7

Imagine you are looking down at each of these figures from above. Describe the geometric figure you see.

50. 
a circle

51. 
a rectangle

52. 
a rectangle

Exercises CHECKPOINT

Find the center and radius of each circle with diameter $\overline{AB}$.

1. $A(4, 1)$, $B(7, 5)$ (5.5, 3); 2.5
2. $A(0, 8)$, $B(3, 6)$ (1.5, 7); $\frac{\sqrt{13}}{2}$
3. $A(-3, 9)$, $B(4, -2)$ (0.5, 3.5); $\frac{\sqrt{170}}{2}$
4. $A(-2, -5)$, $B(-8, 4)$ (−5, −0.5); $\frac{\sqrt{117}}{2}$

Find the measure of each arc or angle in $\odot A$.

5. $\angle WAX$ 65
6. $\widehat{RX}$ 90
7. $\angle SAR$ 25
8. $\widehat{TRW}$ 245
9. $\angle TAW$ 115
10. $\widehat{RT}$ 90
11. $\widehat{SR}$ 25
12. $\widehat{XST}$ 180
13. $\widehat{STW}$ 180

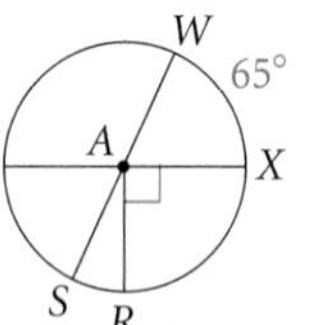

Draw a pair of figures to fit each description. 14–16. See margin p. 107.

14. congruent right triangles
15. similar pentagons
16. similar rectangles

17. What is the most precise name for a quadrilateral with vertices at (3, 5), (−1, 4), (7, 4), and (3, −5)? A
A. kite **B.** rectangle **C.** parallelogram **D.** rhombus **E.** trapezoid

2-7 Teaching Notes

PROBLEM OF THE DAY

How can eight congruent line segments be used to make a square and four equilateral triangles? **Make a pyramid with a square base.**

Problem of the Day is also available in Transparencies.

CONNECTING TO PRIOR KNOWLEDGE Have students create a scale drawing of the classroom or a room in their home. Have them include objects like furniture, appliances, and fixtures. Discuss how they represented three-dimensional objects. Did they draw the objects from a front view, side view, or top view?

THINK AND DISCUSS

ESL **VISUAL LEARNING** Give real-world examples of one-dimensional (i.e., a decimal point, a dot on an i or j, a period), two dimensional (i.e., images in a photograph or painting, your signature), and three-dimensional objects.

Make sure students have plenty of isometric dot paper and graph paper to use throughout this lesson.

DIVERSITY Because of poor visualization and drawing skills, some students may have great difficulty with this lesson. Provide many practice examples and opportunities to improve visual and drawing skills to remedy these difficulties.

Connections Animation . . . and more

2-7 Isometric and Orthographic Drawings

What You'll Learn

- Drawing isometric and orthographic views of objects

...And Why

To practice a skill used in industries of all sorts

What You'll Need

- isometric dot paper
- graph paper
- straightedge
- cubes

THINK AND DISCUSS

Part 1

Isometric Drawings

The figures that you've studied so far in this chapter have been two-dimensional. The *faces* of three-dimensional figures are two-dimensional. Many types of industries use two-dimensional drawings of three-dimensional objects. The makers of some animated cartoons for example, use computers to create *wire-frame models* of three-dimensional characters. These wire-frame images—basically complicated stick figures—are made up of polygons.

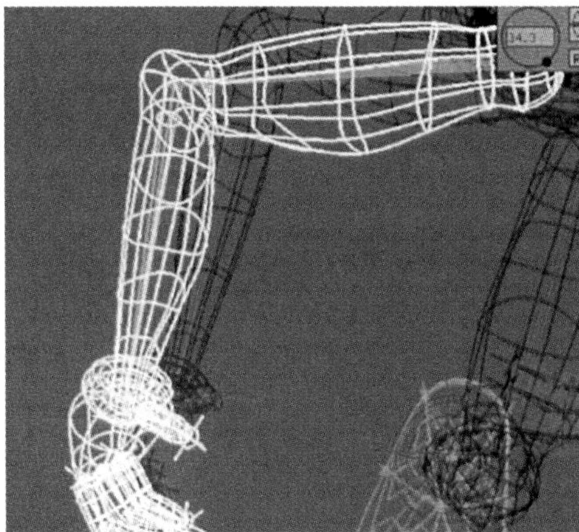

The wire frame model of the insect's leg is made up of polygons. Notice how they are joined to give the illusion of a curved surface.

The computer forms the final image by adding a "skin" to the wire-frame and then lighting the figure.

One way to show a three-dimensional object is with an isometric drawing. An **isometric drawing** shows a corner view. It shows three sides of an object in a single drawing. Here are two examples.

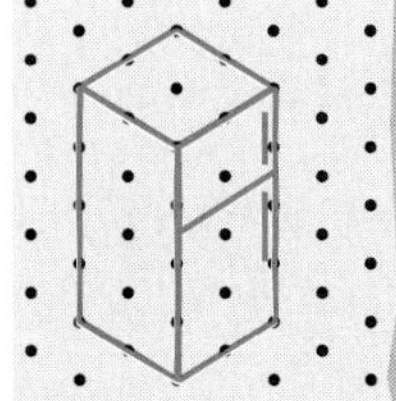

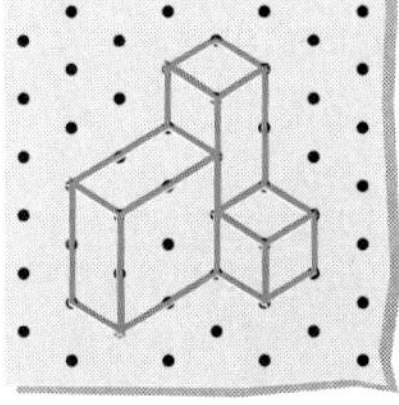

Lesson Planning Options

Prerequisite Skills

- Drawing different views of a cube

Assignment Options for Exercises On Your Own

To provide flexible scheduling, this lesson can be subdivided into parts.

 **Core** 1–8 (a), 16
✪**Extension** 12–15

 **Core** 1–8 (b), 9–11, 17–24
✪**Extension** 25

Use Mixed Review to maintain skills.

Resources

Student Edition

Extra Practice, p. 649
Glossary/Study Guide

Teaching Resources

Chapter Support File, Ch. 2
- Practice 2-7 (two worksheets)
- Reteaching 2-7

Classroom Manager 2-7
Glossary, Spanish Resources
Chapter Support File, Ch. 11

 **Transparencies**
6, 34

Example 1

Students may want to begin by first creating isometric drawings of one cube, then two cubes, then the figure in Example 1. Some may find it easier to draw all the edges of each cube, then erase the edges that are hidden.

Question 1 If wooden or plastic cubes are not available, students may use sugar cubes.

MAKING CONNECTIONS As of 1996, the Sears Tower in Chicago was the tallest office building in the world. The national headquarters for Sears, Roebuck, and Company, it was built between August, 1970, and May, 1973. It contains 110 floors, 104 elevators, and 16,100 windows.

Example 2

Some students may find it easier to create the foundation drawing in the same orientation as the isometric drawing.

Additional Examples

FOR EXAMPLE 1

Use four cubes to make a structure that has three cubes in the bottom layer and one cube in the center of the top layer. Create an isometric drawing of the cube structure.

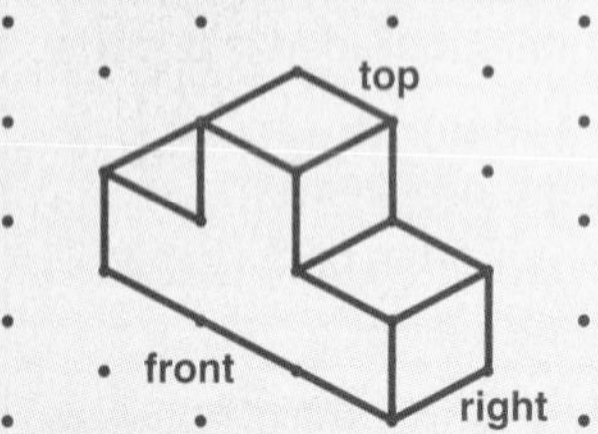

FOR EXAMPLE 2

Create a foundation drawing for the figure in Additional Example 1.

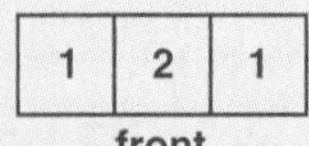

front

FOR EXAMPLE 3

Create an orthographic drawing for the figure in Additional Example 1.

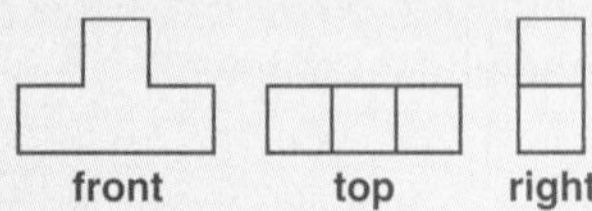

You can use isometric dot paper to draw cube structures.

Example 1

Create an isometric drawing of the cube structure at the left.

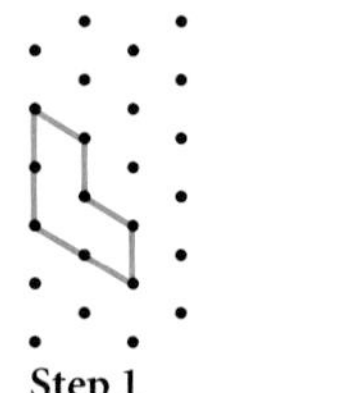
Step 1

Step 2

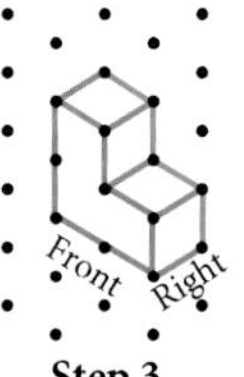

Step 3

1. **Try This** Build a structure using 4 cubes. Create an isometric drawing of your structure. **Check students' work.**

Another way to show some types of three-dimensional objects is with a foundation drawing. A **foundation drawing** shows the base of a structure and the height of each part. The diagram at the right is a foundation drawing of the Sears Tower in Chicago.

54	67	54
67	98	67
41	98	41

The Sears Tower is made up of nine sections. The numbers tell how many stories tall each section is.

Example 2

Create a foundation drawing for the isometric drawing below.

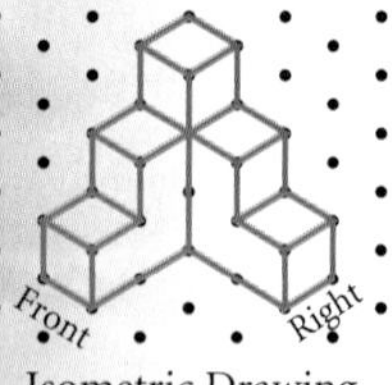

Isometric Drawing

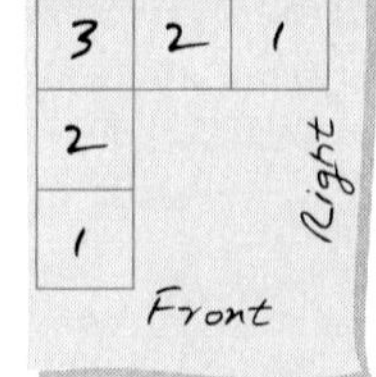

Foundation Drawing

2. a. How many cubes are needed to make the structure in Example 2? **9**
   b. Which drawing did you use to answer part (a), the foundation drawing or the isometric drawing? Why? **Foundation; the total number of cubes is the sum of the numbers in each square.**

Point out that for consistency, an orthographic drawing should show the front, top, and right side views.

MAKING CONNECTIONS It was not until the former Soviet Union sent a space probe around the moon in 1959 that any view of the moon, other than a front view, had been seen.

OPEN-ENDED Question 3 Suggest that students choose objects they can stand over to see the top view and raise to eye level to view the front and right side.

Example 3

ERROR ALERT! Students may think that the right view in the orthographic drawing of the first isometric drawing should show three faces, not two. **Remediation:** Students should draw the view they see when the figure is at eye level. It may help students to build the second figure with cubes and view it from the front, top, and right side.

Part 2

Orthographic Drawings

A third way to show three-dimensional figures is with an orthographic drawing. An **orthographic drawing** shows a top view, front view, and right-side view. Here is an example.

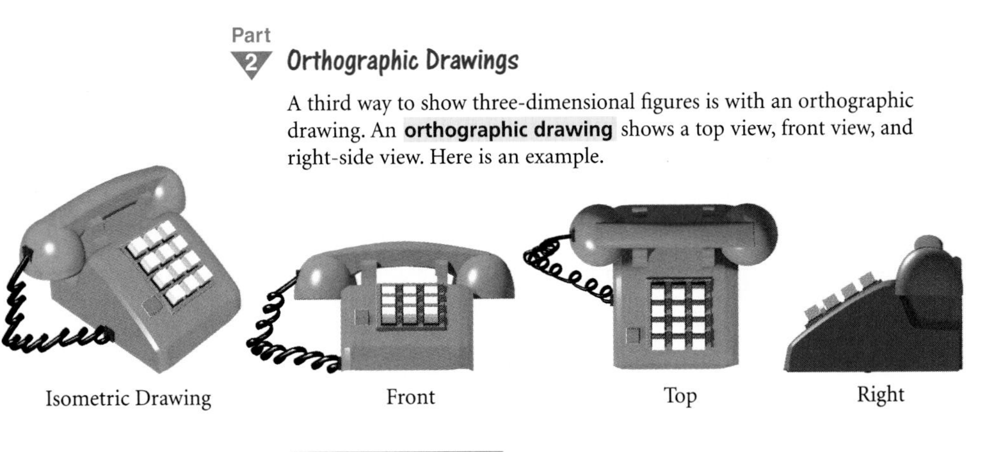

Isometric Drawing | Front | Top | Right

Example 3

Create an orthographic drawing for each isometric drawing at the left.

Isometric Drawing

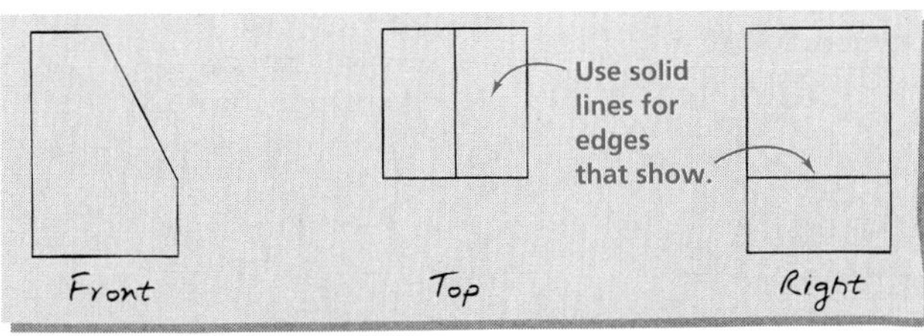

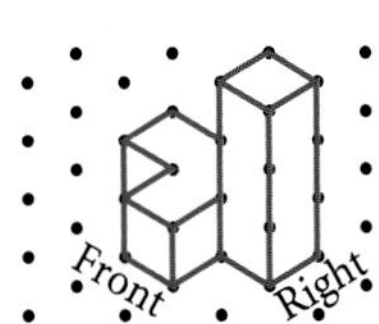

Isometric Drawing

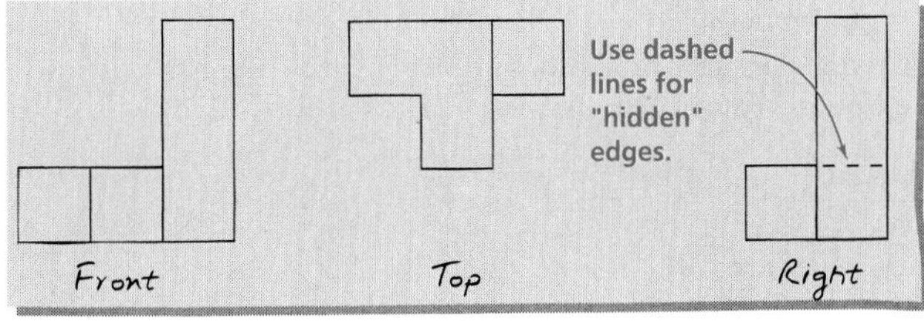

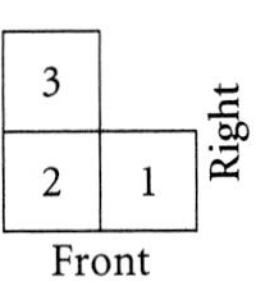

3. *Open-ended* Choose a simple object in your classroom. Make an orthographic drawing showing three views. Check students' work.

4. a. *Manipulatives* Build a cube structure for the foundation drawing at the left. Then create an isometric drawing for the structure.
   b. Create an orthographic drawing showing a top view, front view, and right-side view. a–b. See back of book.

Technology Options

Prentice Hall Technology

Software
- Secondary Math Lab Toolkit™
- Computer Item Generator 2-7

Internet
- See the Prentice Hall site. (http://www.phschool.com)

WORK TOGETHER

Some students may be able to complete these steps more quickly than others. Carefully arrange groups so that students can work at their own pace and so that one students does not do all the work.

Exercises ON YOUR OWN

Exercises 1–8 Students may want to use cubes before drawing the figures.

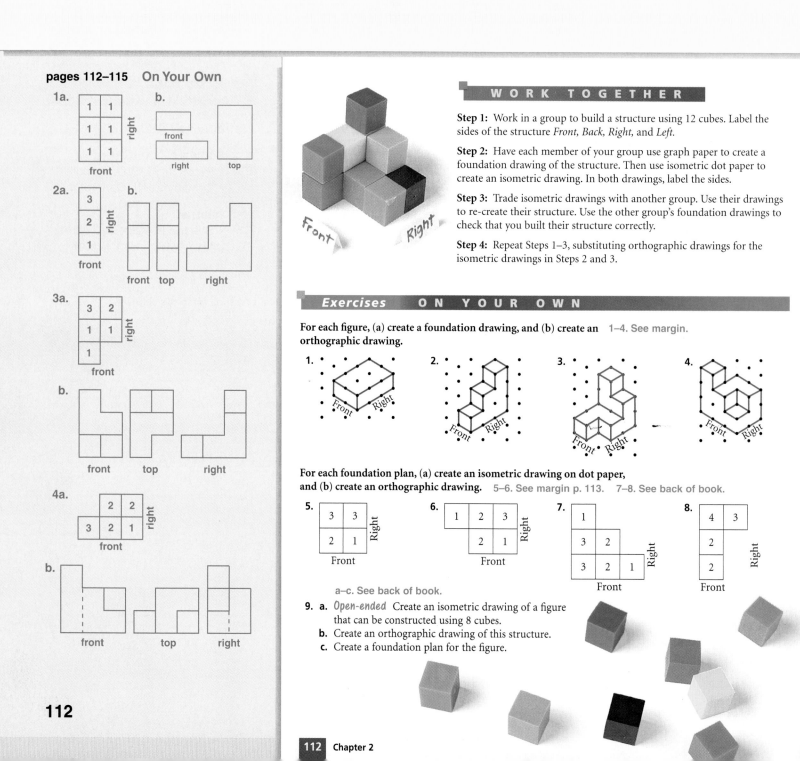

---

pages 112–115 On Your Own

1a.

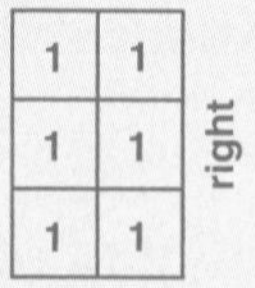

1	1
1	1
1	1

front, right

b. front, right, top

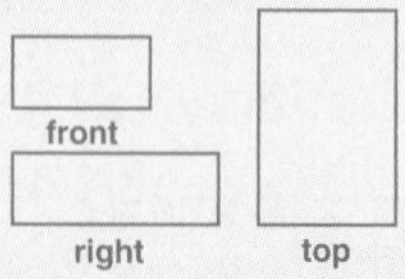

2a.

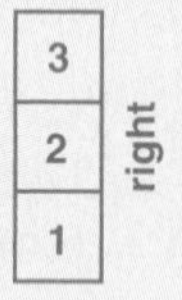

3
2
1

front, right

b. front, top, right

3a.

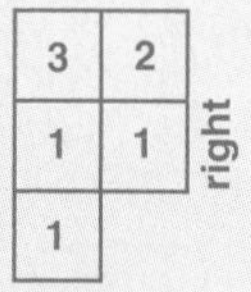

3	2
1	1
1	

front, right

b. front, top, right

4a.

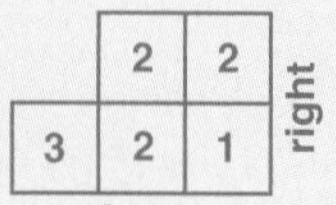

	2	2
3	2	1

front, right

b. front, top, right

112

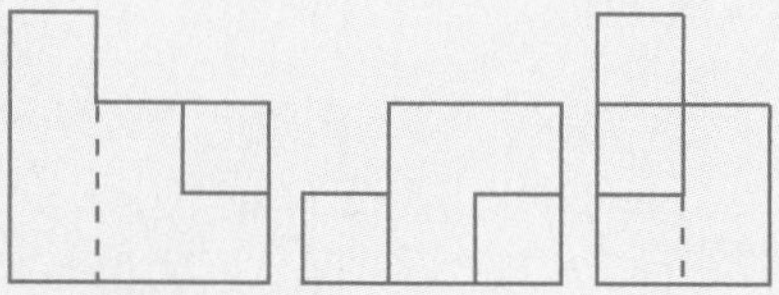

WORK TOGETHER

Step 1: Work in a group to build a structure using 12 cubes. Label the sides of the structure *Front, Back, Right,* and *Left.*

Step 2: Have each member of your group use graph paper to create a foundation drawing of the structure. Then use isometric dot paper to create an isometric drawing. In both drawings, label the sides.

Step 3: Trade isometric drawings with another group. Use their drawings to re-create their structure. Use the other group's foundation drawings to check that you built their structure correctly.

Step 4: Repeat Steps 1–3, substituting orthographic drawings for the isometric drawings in Steps 2 and 3.

Exercises ON YOUR OWN

For each figure, (a) create a foundation drawing, and (b) create an orthographic drawing. 1–4. See margin.

1. 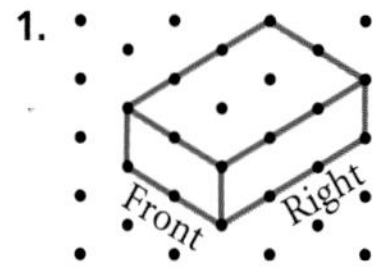

2. 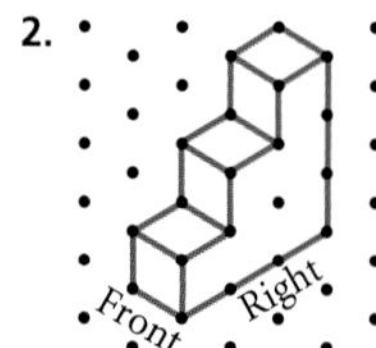

3. 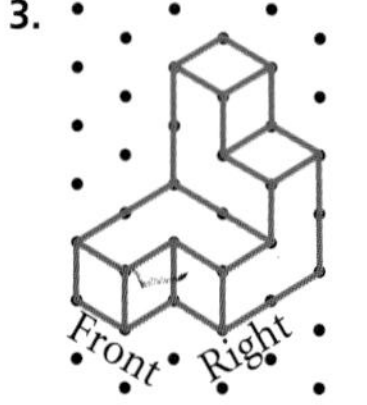

4. 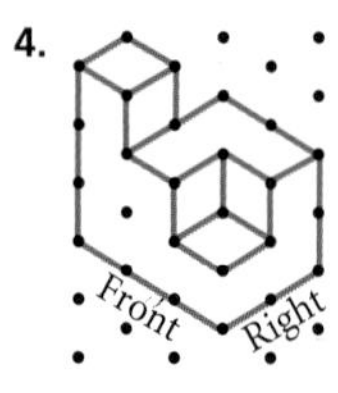

For each foundation plan, (a) create an isometric drawing on dot paper, and (b) create an orthographic drawing. 5–6. See margin p. 113. 7–8. See back of book.

5.

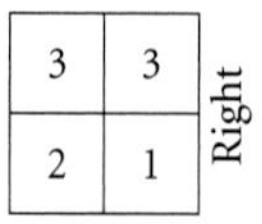

3	3
2	1

Front, Right

6.

1	2	3
	2	1

Front, Right

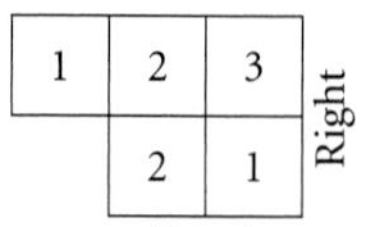

7. 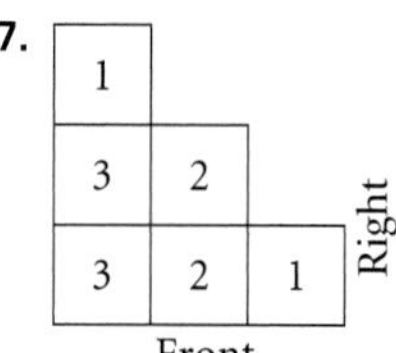

8. 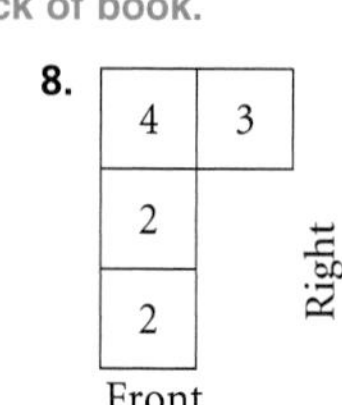

a–c. See back of book.

9. a. *Open-ended* Create an isometric drawing of a figure that can be constructed using 8 cubes.
   b. Create an orthographic drawing of this structure.
   c. Create a foundation plan for the figure.

KINESTHETIC LEARNING Exercise 11 If you have block scheduling or an extended class period, take students outside to draw different views of objects such as cars, buses, buildings, houses, and stadium bleachers.

Exercises 12–15 Use visual models to illustrate cross sections. Cut large potatoes into different prisms, cones, and cylinders. Have students predict cross sections before slicing the potato models.

PROBABILITY Exercise 16 Students may want to recreate Jake's structure with cubes of their own. Students can use markers or masking tape to indicate painted faces.

Read the comic strip and complete Exercises 10 and 11.

SHOE by Jeff MacNelly

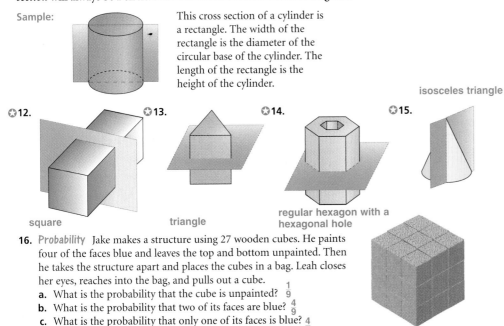

10. What type of drawing that you've studied in this lesson is a "bird's-eye view"? orthographic top view

11. *Writing* Photographs of the Washington Monument are typically not taken from a bird's-eye view. Describe a situation in which you would want a photo showing a bird's-eye view. Sample: You need a photograph to make a topographic map of the area.

Cross Sections **Imagine cutting straight through an orange. The *cross section* will always be a circle. Describe the cross section in each diagram.**

Sample:

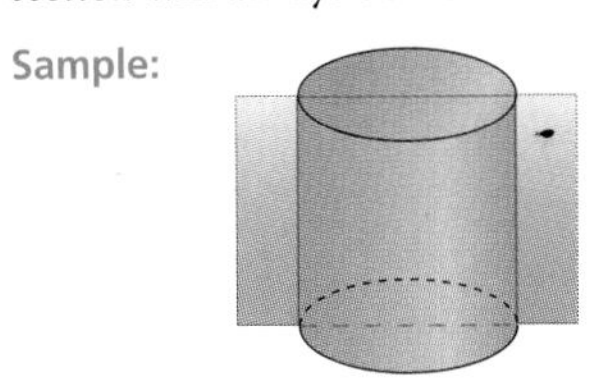

This cross section of a cylinder is a rectangle. The width of the rectangle is the diameter of the circular base of the cylinder. The length of the rectangle is the height of the cylinder.

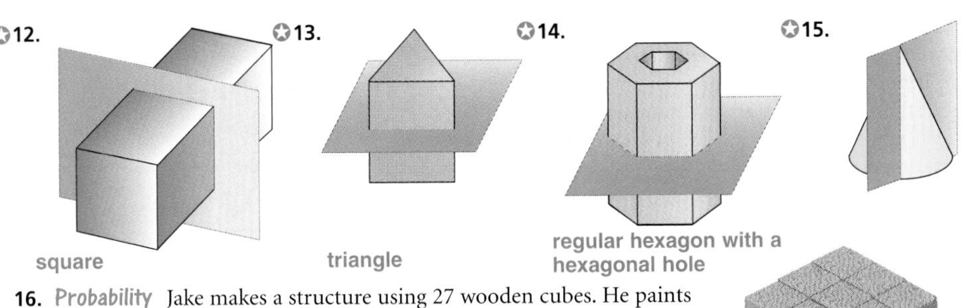

12. square
13. triangle
14. regular hexagon with a hexagonal hole
15. isosceles triangle

16. *Probability* Jake makes a structure using 27 wooden cubes. He paints four of the faces blue and leaves the top and bottom unpainted. Then he takes the structure apart and places the cubes in a bag. Leah closes her eyes, reaches into the bag, and pulls out a cube.

a. What is the probability that the cube is unpainted? $\frac{1}{9}$

b. What is the probability that two of its faces are blue? $\frac{4}{9}$

c. What is the probability that only one of its faces is blue? $\frac{4}{9}$

5a.

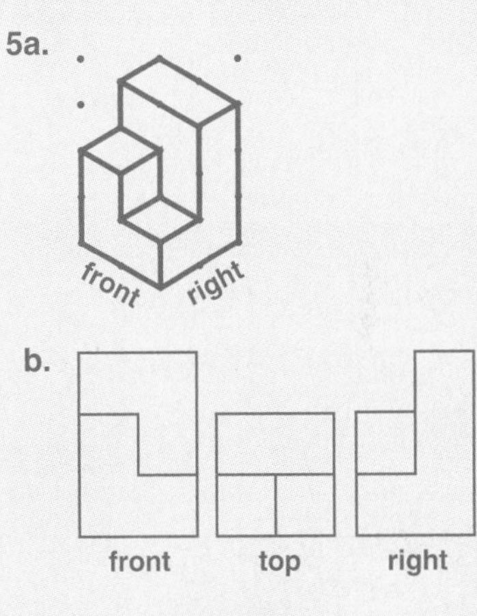

b.

6a.

b.

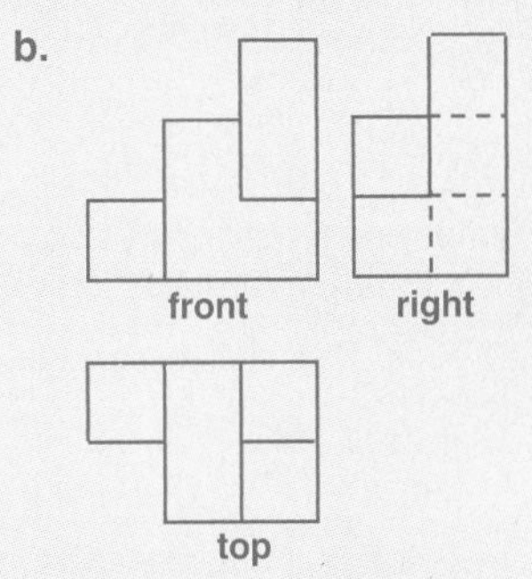

ALTERNATIVE ASSESSMENT Exercises 17–20 These exercises can help you assess students' ability to model figures with orthographic drawings. Some students may want to build each figure shown in the isometric drawings so they can more easily recognize their front, top, and side views.

Chapter Project **FIND OUT BY MODELING** Have students work in small groups to build the Soma pieces. Make sure students check that each piece they build is different. If students use sugar cubes, they may have trouble keeping them glued together.

Exercises MIXED REVIEW

Exercise 28 Students use the fact that, through a point, there is just one line having a given slope to see that if two segments with the same slope have a point in common then they must lie on the same line.

SELF ASSESSMENT **PORTFOLIO** Share with students the criteria you will use to assess their work in portfolios, as well as how you plan to use the results. Students should understand how the rubrics assess their work, how each piece in the portfolio counts, and how the scores they get in their portfolios will affect their overall evaluation.

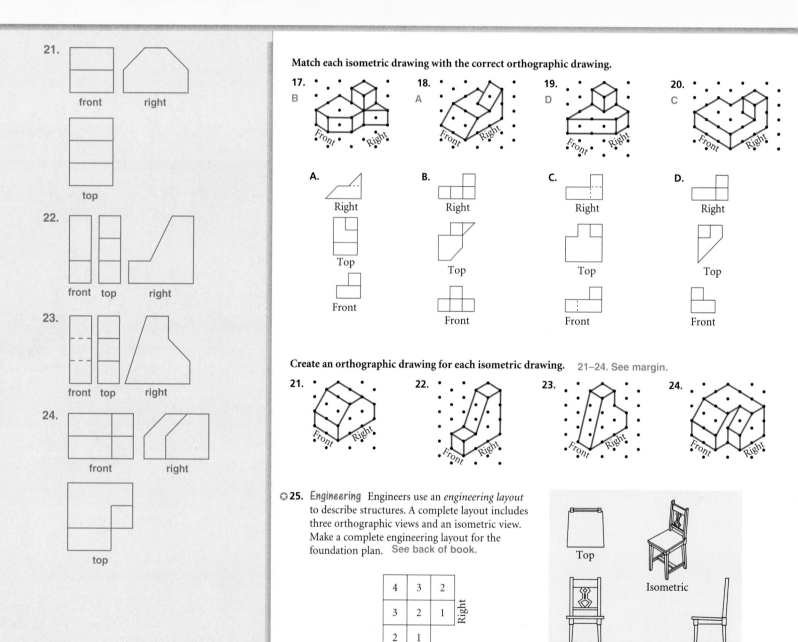

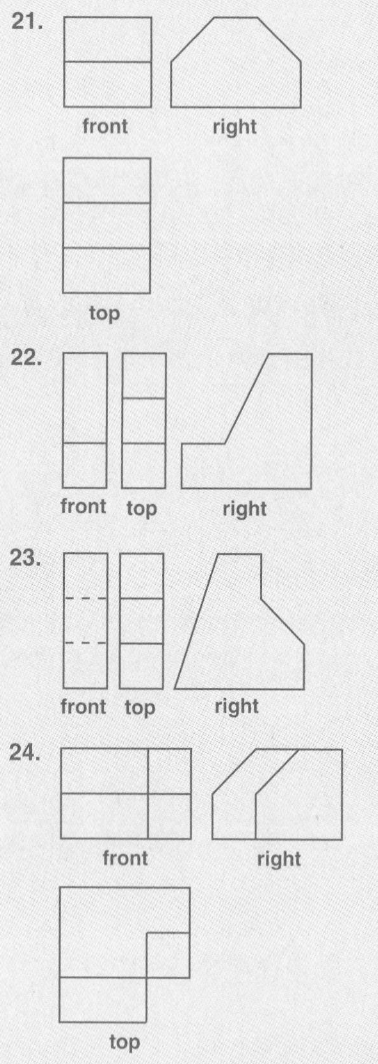

Match each isometric drawing with the correct orthographic drawing.

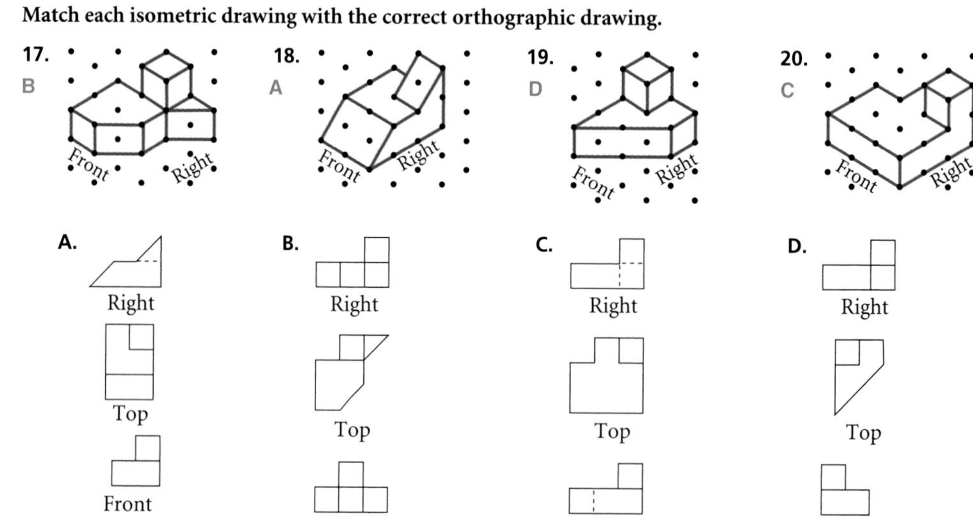

Create an orthographic drawing for each isometric drawing. 21–24. See margin.

21.

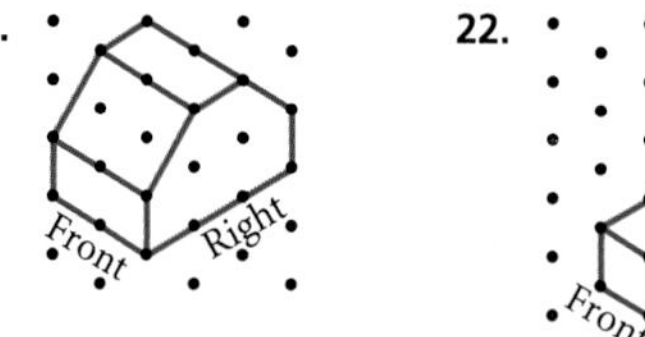

23.

24.

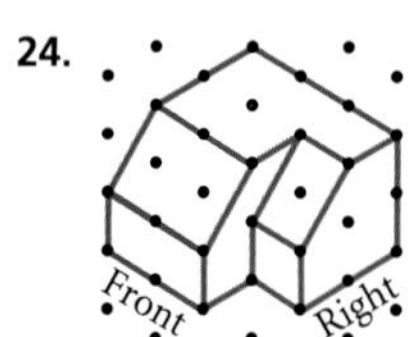

25. **Engineering** Engineers use an *engineering layout* to describe structures. A complete layout includes three orthographic views and an isometric view. Make a complete engineering layout for the foundation plan. See back of book.

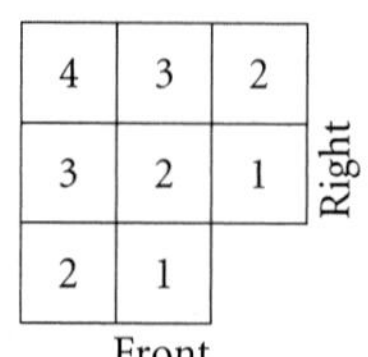

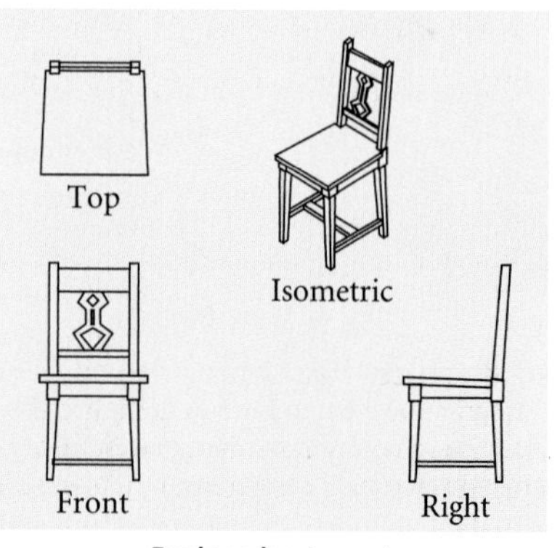

Engineering Layout

Wrap Up

THE BIG IDEA Ask students: *Describe the difference between an isometric and an orthographic drawing. Which type of drawing do you think best describes an object? Explain.*

RETEACHING ACTIVITY Students create isometric and orthographic drawings of objects. (Reteaching worksheet 3-7)

Geometry at Work

For further information about the training and skills necessary to be a industrial designer, contact accredited institutions that offer industrial design degrees such as Arizona State University, or the Massachusetts College of Art.

You can also contact the CORE Industrial Design Network on the Internet at http://www.core77.com.

Encourage students to investigate these topics:

- the training necessary to become an industrial designer
- the math and computer skills used by industrial designers
- the types of industries that hire interior designers

In the Mini Project, student should specify whether their drawing shows the right shoe or the left shoe.

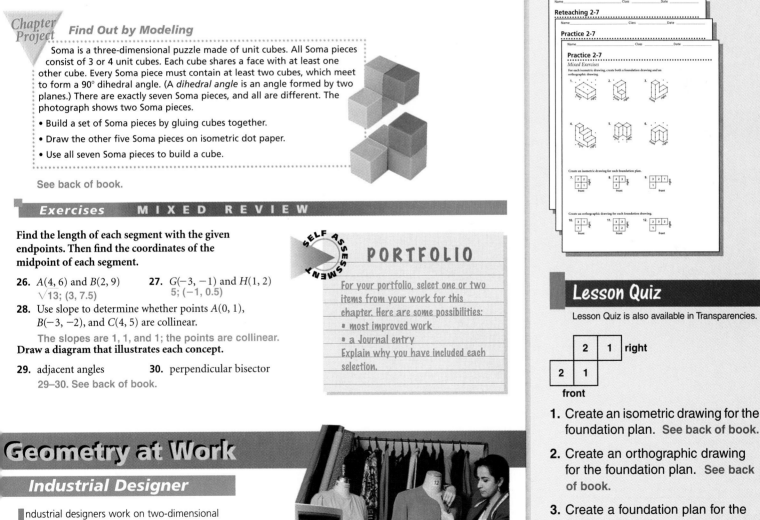

Chapter Project

Find Out by Modeling

Soma is a three-dimensional puzzle made of unit cubes. All Soma pieces consist of 3 or 4 unit cubes. Each cube shares a face with at least one other cube. Every Soma piece must contain at least two cubes, which meet to form a 90° dihedral angle. (A *dihedral angle* is an angle formed by two planes.) There are exactly seven Soma pieces, and all are different. The photograph shows two Soma pieces.

- Build a set of Soma pieces by gluing cubes together.
- Draw the other five Soma pieces on isometric dot paper.
- Use all seven Soma pieces to build a cube.

See back of book.

Exercises MIXED REVIEW

Find the length of each segment with the given endpoints. Then find the coordinates of the midpoint of each segment.

26. $A(4, 6)$ and $B(2, 9)$ $\sqrt{13}$; (3, 7.5)

27. $G(-3, -1)$ and $H(1, 2)$ 5; (−1, 0.5)

28. Use slope to determine whether points $A(0, 1)$, $B(-3, -2)$, and $C(4, 5)$ are collinear.
The slopes are 1, 1, and 1; the points are collinear.

Draw a diagram that illustrates each concept.

29. adjacent angles

30. perpendicular bisector

29–30. See back of book.

SELF ASSESSMENT

PORTFOLIO

For your portfolio, select one or two items from your work for this chapter. Here are some possibilities:

- most improved work
- a Journal entry

Explain why you have included each selection.

Geometry at Work

Industrial Designer

Industrial designers work on two-dimensional surfaces to develop products that have three-dimensional appeal to consumers. They use computer-aided design (CAD) software to create two-dimensional screen images and manipulate them for three-dimensional effects. Fashion designers use CAD to study their creations on electronic human forms from various angles and distances.

Mini Project: Design an athletic shoe. Use an engineering layout to display your design. Include three orthographic views and an isometric view.

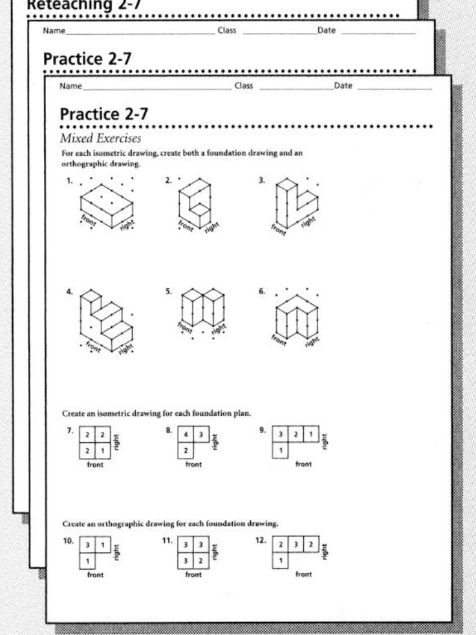

Lesson Quiz

Lesson Quiz is also available in Transparencies.

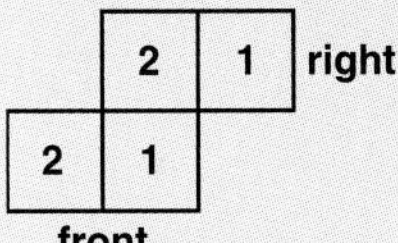

1. Create an isometric drawing for the foundation plan. See back of book.
2. Create an orthographic drawing for the foundation plan. See back of book.
3. Create a foundation plan for the figure given below. See back of book.

Finishing the Chapter Project

PROJECT DAY You may wish to plan a project day on which students share their completed projects. Encourage groups to explain their process as well as their product.

PROJECT NOTEBOOK Have students review their project work and bring their notebooks up to date.

- Have students review the tangram pieces, pentominoes, and Soma pieces they created for the project. Also have them review the figures they created using these objects.
- Ask students to share any insights they found in completing the project, such as patterns they discovered. Also, ask which figures students found easy to make and which were more difficult.

SCORING RUBRIC

3 Student's models are created correctly and the instructions for making them are accurate. The display is clear, organized, and uses geometric terms correctly.

2 Student's models are created correctly and most of the instructions for making them are accurate. The display is clear, organized, and uses geometric terms with only minor errors.

1 Student's models are created with minor errors. The instructions have minor flaws. The display is organized but geometric terms are used improperly or unclearly.

0 Major elements are incomplete or missing.

CHAPTER PROJECT

Finishing the Chapter Project

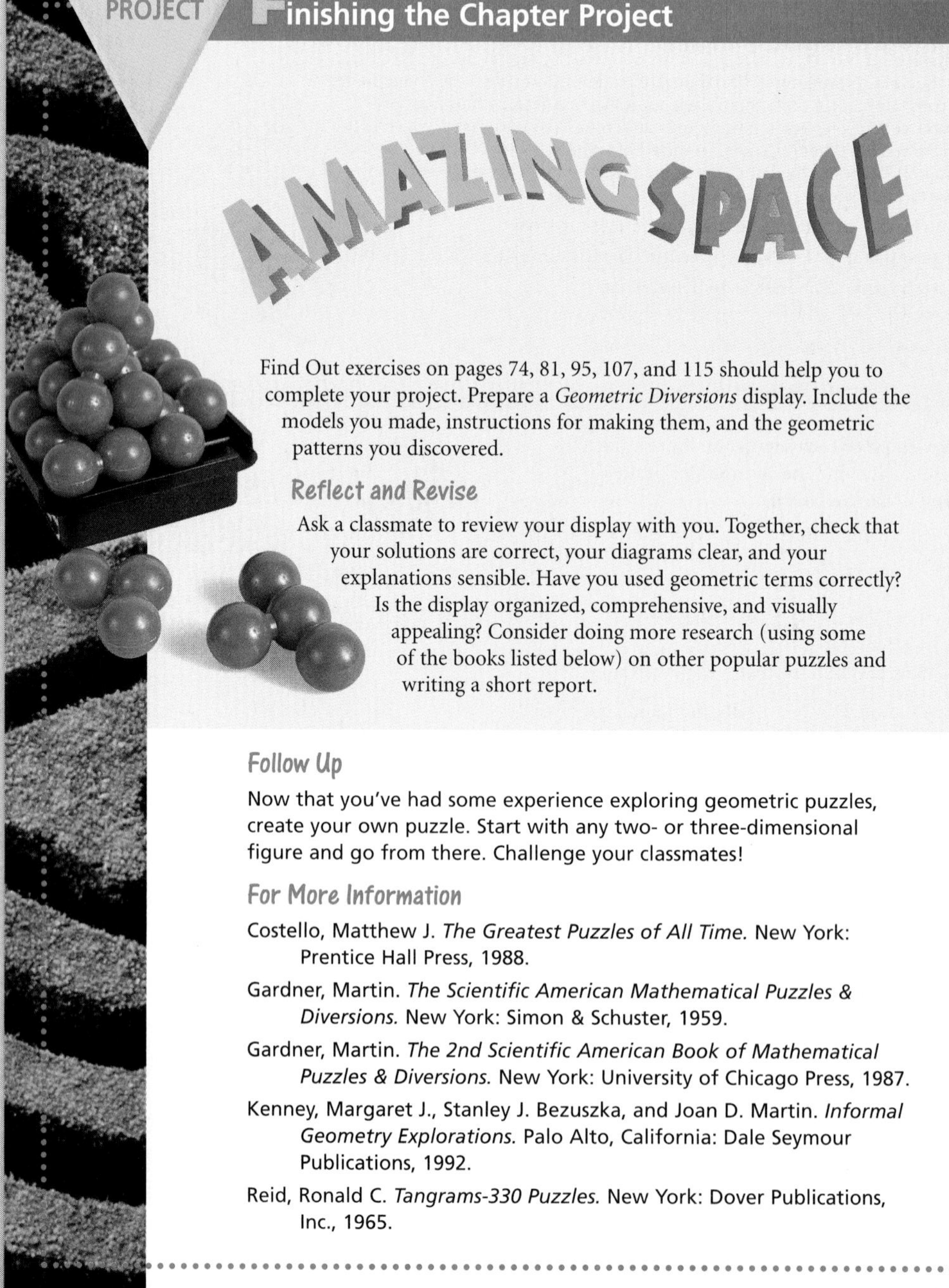

Find Out exercises on pages 74, 81, 95, 107, and 115 should help you to complete your project. Prepare a *Geometric Diversions* display. Include the models you made, instructions for making them, and the geometric patterns you discovered.

Reflect and Revise

Ask a classmate to review your display with you. Together, check that your solutions are correct, your diagrams clear, and your explanations sensible. Have you used geometric terms correctly? Is the display organized, comprehensive, and visually appealing? Consider doing more research (using some of the books listed below) on other popular puzzles and writing a short report.

Follow Up

Now that you've had some experience exploring geometric puzzles, create your own puzzle. Start with any two- or three-dimensional figure and go from there. Challenge your classmates!

For More Information

Costello, Matthew J. *The Greatest Puzzles of All Time.* New York: Prentice Hall Press, 1988.

Gardner, Martin. *The Scientific American Mathematical Puzzles & Diversions.* New York: Simon & Schuster, 1959.

Gardner, Martin. *The 2nd Scientific American Book of Mathematical Puzzles & Diversions.* New York: University of Chicago Press, 1987.

Kenney, Margaret J., Stanley J. Bezuszka, and Joan D. Martin. *Informal Geometry Explorations.* Palo Alto, California: Dale Seymour Publications, 1992.

Reid, Ronald C. *Tangrams-330 Puzzles.* New York: Dover Publications, Inc., 1965.

Wrap Up

HOW AM I DOING? Have students work in small groups. Ask each group to make a short presentation describing the geometric figures presented in the chapter. Each presentation must include a visual aid and a sample problem.

KEY TERMS The numbers in parentheses direct students to the pages where the terms (or symbols) are used or defined. Students should be able to (1) write a simple explanation of each term, (2) illustrate the term with a diagram, or (3) show an example that uses the term.

Exercises 1–4 Make sure students find the values of the variables *and* classify each triangle.

STANDARDIZED TEST TIP **Exercise 5** Make sure that students do not conclude that a triangle is not obtuse if they find $x < 90$.

2 Wrap Up

Key Terms

acute triangle (p. 71)
adjacent arcs (p. 98)
circle (p. 96)
central angle (p. 97)
concave (p. 76)
congruent circles (p. 102)
congruent polygons (p. 102)
convex (p. 76)
corollary (p. 70)
diameter (p. 96)
equiangular polygon (p. 78)
equiangular triangle (p. 71)
equilateral polygon (p. 78)
equilateral triangle (p. 71)
exterior angle (p. 69)
foundation drawing (p. 110)
isometric drawing (p. 109)
isosceles trapezoid (p. 91)
isosceles triangle (p. 71)
kite (p. 91)
major arc (p. 98)
minor arc (p. 98)
obtuse triangle (p. 71)
orthographic drawing (p. 111)
parallelogram (p. 91)
polygon (p. 76)
radius (p. 96)
rectangle (p. 91)
regular polygon (p. 78)
remote interior angle (p. 69)
rhombus (p. 91)
right triangle (p. 71)
scalene triangle (p. 71)
semicircle (p. 98)
similar polygons (p. 103)
similarity ratio (p. 103)
square (p. 91)
trapezoid (p. 91)

How am I doing?

- State three ideas from this chapter that you think are important. Explain your choices.
- Describe different ways of classifying triangles and quadrilaterals.

Resources

Student Edition
Extra Practice, p. 635
Glossary/Study Guide

Teaching Resources
Study Skills Handbook
Glossary, Spanish Resources

Triangles 2-1

The sum of the measures of the angles of a triangle is 180. The measure of each **exterior angle** of a triangle equals the sum of the measures of its two **remote interior angles,** and is therefore greater than the measure of either remote interior angle.

You can classify triangles according to their sides and angles.

Find the values of the variables. Then classify each triangle by its sides and angles.

1. 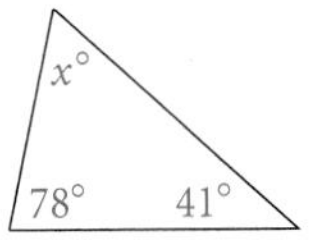

61; scalene acute

2. 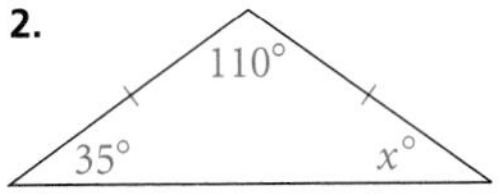

35; isosceles obtuse

3. 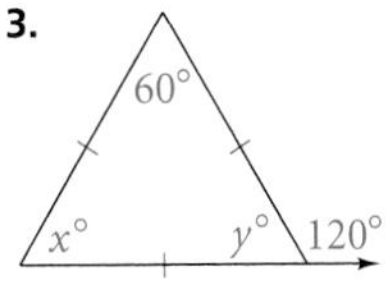

$x = 60$; $y = 60$; equilateral; equiangular

4. 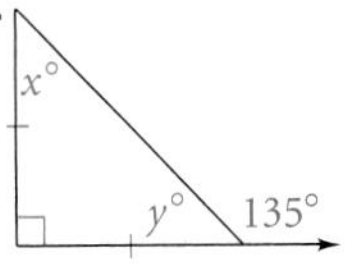

$x = 45$; $y = 45$; isosceles; right

5. ***Standardized Test Prep*** The measures of the angles of different triangles are shown below. Which triangle is obtuse? D
   A. $x + 10, x - 20, x + 25$ B. $x, 2x, 3x$
   C. $20x + 10, 30x - 2, 7x + 1$ D. $10x - 3, 14x - 20, x + 3$
   E. none of the above

Exercises 10–12 Point out to students that there are two parts to these exercises: finding x and finding the lengths of the sides.

Exercises 13–16 Most common errors made by students when finding slope include subtracting incorrectly, subtracting the coordinates in the numerator and the denominator in different orders, subtracting x-coordinates from y-coordinates, and switching the numerator and denominator.

ALTERNATIVE ASSESSMENT **Exercises 13, 14, and 16** To assess students' skills in classifying quadrilaterals, have students draw *ABCD* in Exercises 13, 14, and 16 and determine the most precise name for each quadrilateral.

Wrap Up **pages 117–119**

29.

Polygons and Classifying Quadrilaterals 2-2, 2-4

A **polygon** is a closed plane figure with at least three sides. A polygon is **convex** if no diagonal contains points outside the polygon. Otherwise, it is **concave**. A **regular polygon** is equilateral and equiangular.

The sum of the measures of the interior angles of an n-gon is $(n - 2)180$. The sum of the measures of the exterior angles (one at each vertex) of an n-gon is 360.

Quadrilaterals have four sides. Some quadrilaterals have special names.

Find the measure of each interior angle and exterior angle for each regular polygon.

6. a hexagon 120; 60 **7.** an octagon 135; 45 **8.** a decagon 144; 36 **9.** a 24-gon 165; 15

Algebra **Find the values of the variables and the lengths of the sides.**

10. isosceles trapezoid *ABCD*

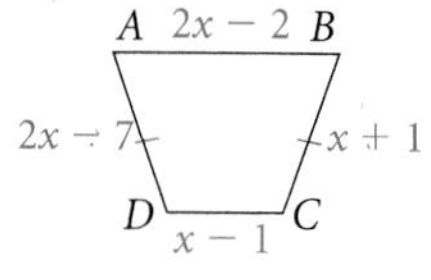

8; 14, 9, 7, 9

11. kite *KLMN*

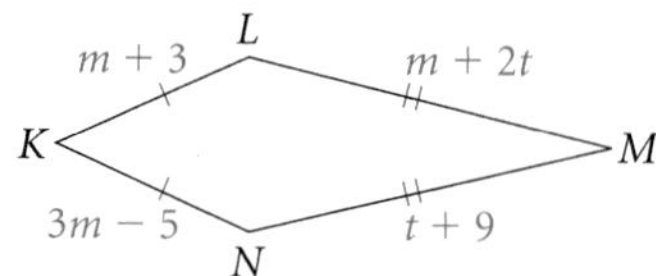

$m = 4$; $t = 5$; 7, 14, 14, 7

12. rhombus *PQRS*

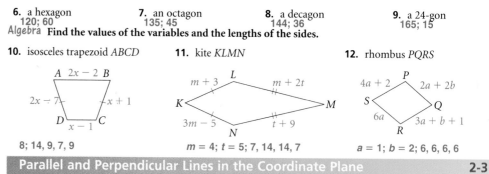

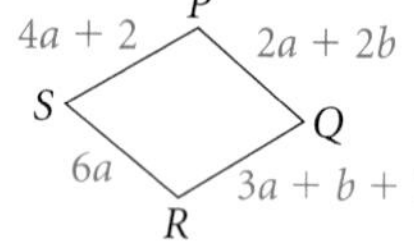

$a = 1$; $b = 2$; 6, 6, 6, 6

Parallel and Perpendicular Lines in the Coordinate Plane 2-3

The slopes of two nonvertical parallel lines are equal. Two lines parallel to a third line are parallel to each other.

The product of the slopes of two nonvertical perpendicular lines is -1. In a plane, two lines perpendicular to a third line are parallel to each other.

Find the slopes of $\overleftrightarrow{AB}$ and $\overleftrightarrow{CD}$. Then determine if the lines are parallel, perpendicular, or neither.

13. $A(-1, -4)$, $B(2, 11)$, $C(1, 1)$, $D(4, 10)$ 5; 3; neither

14. $A(2, 10)$, $B(-1, -2)$, $C(3, 7)$, $D(0, -5)$ 4; 4; parallel

15. $A(-3, 3)$, $B(0, 2)$, $C(1, 3)$, $D(-2, -6)$ $-\frac{1}{3}$; 3; perpendicular

16. $A(-1, 3)$, $B(6, 10)$, $C(-6, 0)$, $D(4, 10)$ 1; 1; parallel

Circles 2-5

A **circle** is the set of all points in a plane equidistant from one point called the center. The measure of a minor arc is the measure of its corresponding central angle. The measure of a major arc is 360 minus the measure of its related minor arc. **Adjacent arcs** have exactly one point in common.

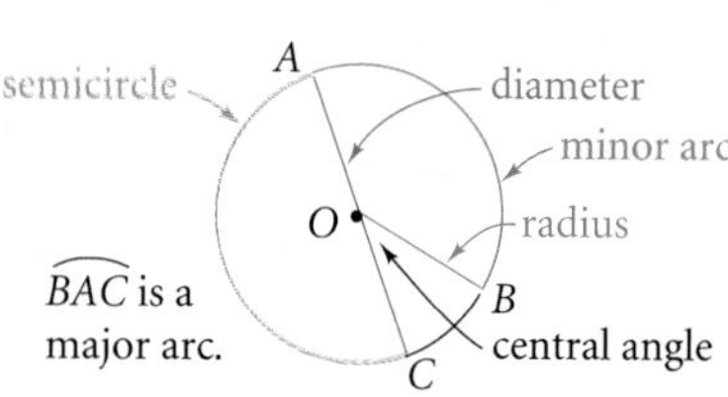

$\widehat{BAC}$ is a major arc.

Wrap Up

HOW AM I DOING? Have students work in small groups. Ask each group to make a short presentation describing the geometric figures presented in the chapter. Each presentation must include a visual aid and a sample problem.

KEY TERMS The numbers in parentheses direct students to the pages where the terms (or symbols) are used or defined. Students should be able to (1) write a simple explanation of each term, (2) illustrate the term with a diagram, or (3) show an example that uses the term.

Exercises 1–4 Make sure students find the values of the variables *and* classify each triangle.

STANDARDIZED TEST TIP **Exercise 5** Make sure that students do not conclude that a triangle is not obtuse if they find $x < 90$.

2 Wrap Up

Key Terms

acute triangle (p. 71)
adjacent arcs (p. 98)
circle (p. 96)
central angle (p. 97)
concave (p. 76)
congruent circles (p. 102)
congruent polygons (p. 102)
convex (p. 76)
corollary (p. 70)
diameter (p. 96)
equiangular polygon (p. 78)
equiangular triangle (p. 71)
equilateral polygon (p. 78)
equilateral triangle (p. 71)
exterior angle (p. 69)
foundation drawing (p. 110)
isometric drawing (p. 109)
isosceles trapezoid (p. 91)
isosceles triangle (p. 71)
kite (p. 91)
major arc (p. 98)
minor arc (p. 98)
obtuse triangle (p. 71)
orthographic drawing (p. 111)
parallelogram (p. 91)
polygon (p. 76)
radius (p. 96)
rectangle (p. 91)
regular polygon (p. 78)
remote interior angle (p. 69)
rhombus (p. 91)
right triangle (p. 71)
scalene triangle (p. 71)
semicircle (p. 98)
similar polygons (p. 103)
similarity ratio (p. 103)
square (p. 91)
trapezoid (p. 91)

How am I doing?

- State three ideas from this chapter that you think are important. Explain your choices.
- Describe different ways of classifying triangles and quadrilaterals.

Resources

Student Edition
Extra Practice, p. 635
Glossary/Study Guide

Teaching Resources
Study Skills Handbook
Glossary, Spanish Resources

Triangles 2-1

The sum of the measures of the angles of a triangle is 180. The measure of each **exterior angle** of a triangle equals the sum of the measures of its two **remote interior angles,** and is therefore greater than the measure of either remote interior angle.

You can classify triangles according to their sides and angles.

Find the values of the variables. Then classify each triangle by its sides and angles.

1.
61; scalene acute

2.
35; isosceles obtuse

3. 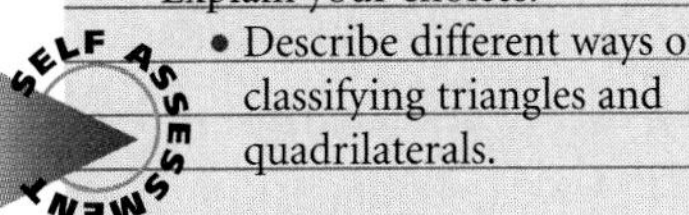

$x = 60$; $y = 60$; equilateral; equiangular

4.
$x = 45$; $y = 45$; isosceles; right

5. ***Standardized Test Prep*** The measures of the angles of different triangles are shown below. Which triangle is obtuse? D
   A. $x + 10, x - 20, x + 25$
   B. $x, 2x, 3x$
   C. $20x + 10, 30x - 2, 7x + 1$
   D. $10x - 3, 14x - 20, x + 3$
   E. none of the above

Exercises 10–12 Point out to students that there are two parts to these exercises: finding x and finding the lengths of the sides.

Exercises 13–16 Most common errors made by students when finding slope include subtracting incorrectly, subtracting the coordinates in the numerator and the denominator in different orders, subtracting x-coordinates from y-coordinates, and switching the numerator and denominator.

ALTERNATIVE ASSESSMENT **Exercises 13, 14, and 16** To assess students' skills in classifying quadrilaterals, have students draw *ABCD* in Exercises 13, 14, and 16 and determine the most precise name for each quadrilateral.

Wrap Up pages 117–119

29.

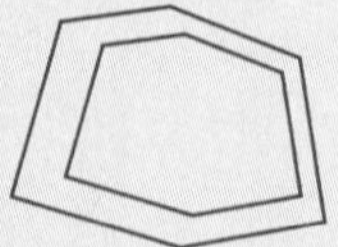

Polygons and Classifying Quadrilaterals 2-2, 2-4

A **polygon** is a closed plane figure with at least three sides. A polygon is **convex** if no diagonal contains points outside the polygon. Otherwise, it is **concave.** A **regular polygon** is equilateral and equiangular.

The sum of the measures of the interior angles of an n-gon is $(n - 2)180$. The sum of the measures of the exterior angles (one at each vertex) of an n-gon is 360.

Quadrilaterals have four sides. Some quadrilaterals have special names.

Find the measure of each interior angle and exterior angle for each regular polygon.

6. a hexagon 120; 60
7. an octagon 135; 45
8. a decagon 144; 36
9. a 24-gon 165; 15

Algebra **Find the values of the variables and the lengths of the sides.**

10. isosceles trapezoid *ABCD*

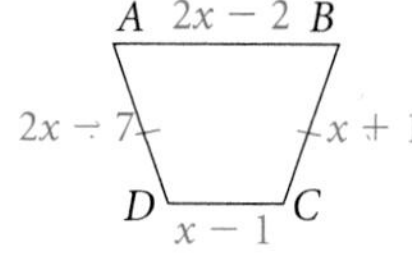

8; 14, 9, 7, 9

11. kite *KLMN*

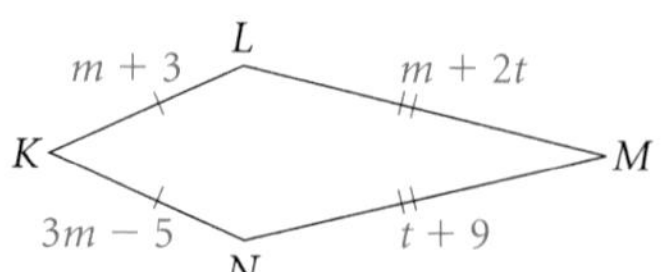

$m = 4$; $t = 5$; 7, 14, 14, 7

12. rhombus *PQRS*

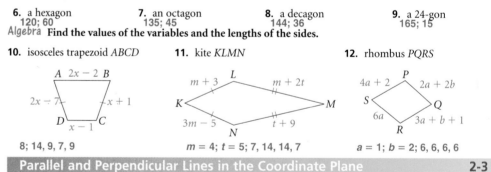

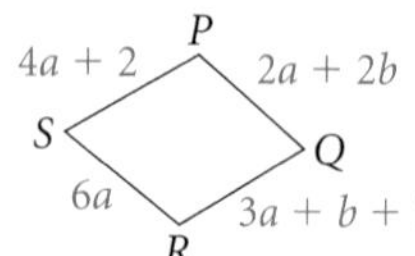

$a = 1$; $b = 2$; 6, 6, 6, 6

Parallel and Perpendicular Lines in the Coordinate Plane 2-3

The slopes of two nonvertical parallel lines are equal. Two lines parallel to a third line are parallel to each other.

The product of the slopes of two nonvertical perpendicular lines is -1. In a plane, two lines perpendicular to a third line are parallel to each other.

Find the slopes of $\overleftrightarrow{AB}$ and $\overleftrightarrow{CD}$. Then determine if the lines are parallel, perpendicular, or neither.

13. $A(-1, -4)$, $B(2, 11)$, $C(1, 1)$, $D(4, 10)$ 5; 3; neither

14. $A(2, 10)$, $B(-1, -2)$, $C(3, 7)$, $D(0, -5)$ 4; 4; parallel

15. $A(-3, 3)$, $B(0, 2)$, $C(1, 3)$, $D(-2, -6)$ $-\frac{1}{3}$; 3; perpendicular

16. $A(-1, 3)$, $B(6, 10)$, $C(-6, 0)$, $D(4, 10)$ 1; 1; parallel

Circles 2-5

A **circle** is the set of all points in a plane equidistant from one point called the center. The measure of a minor arc is the measure of its corresponding central angle. The measure of a major arc is 360 minus the measure of its related minor arc. **Adjacent arcs** have exactly one point in common.

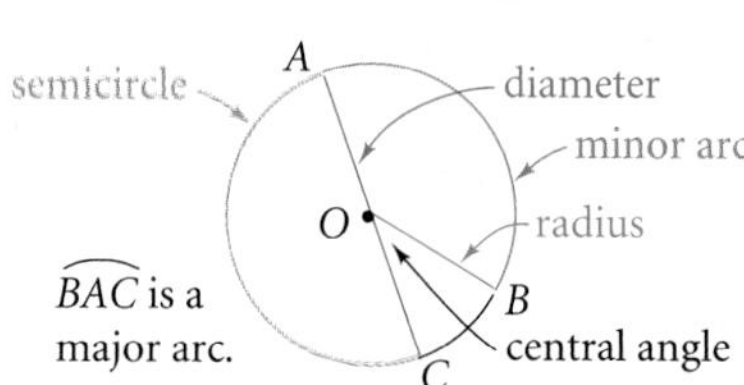

Exercises 17–20 Students can find the radius by finding the length of the segment between the center and one of the points on the circle or by finding the length of the diameter and dividing by 2.

OPEN-ENDED Exercise 29 Students may want to draw two circles of different sizes and use the method given on page 79 to draw two rectangular hexagons.

Remind students that the new mathematical terms in this chapter are defined in the Glossary/Students Guide in the back of the book.

Getting Ready for Chapter 3

Students may work these exercises independently or in small groups. The skills previewed will help prepare students for working with transformations.

Find the coordinates of the center and the radius of each circle with diameter $\overline{AB}$.

17. $A(4, 0), B(4, 6)$ $(4, 3); 3$

18. $A(2, -3), B(0, 1)$ $(1, -1); \sqrt{5}$

19. $A(-4, -5), B(2, -1)$ $(-1, -3); \sqrt{13}$

20. $A(7, 2), B(4, 8)$ $(5.5, 5); \frac{3\sqrt{5}}{2}$

Find each measure.

21. $m\angle APD$ 30

22. $m\widehat{AC}$ 120

23. $m\widehat{ABD}$ 330

24. $m\angle CPA$ 120

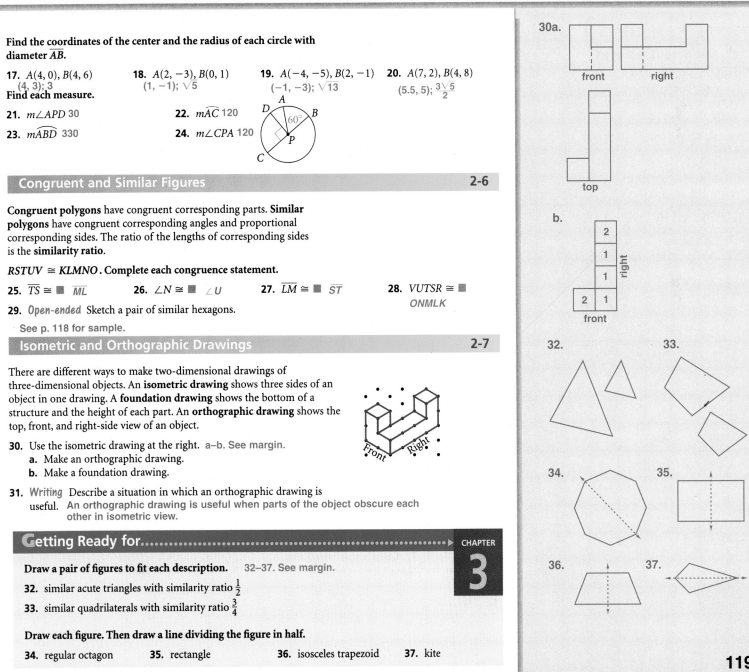

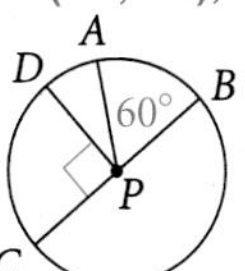

Congruent and Similar Figures 2-6

Congruent polygons have congruent corresponding parts. **Similar polygons** have congruent corresponding angles and proportional corresponding sides. The ratio of the lengths of corresponding sides is the **similarity ratio.**

***RSTUV* ≅ *KLMNO*. Complete each congruence statement.**

25. $\overline{TS} \cong$ ■ $\overline{ML}$

26. $\angle N \cong$ ■ $\angle U$

27. $\overline{LM} \cong$ ■ $\overline{ST}$

28. $VUTSR \cong$ ■ $ONMLK$

29. *Open-ended* Sketch a pair of similar hexagons.
See p. 118 for sample.

Isometric and Orthographic Drawings 2-7

There are different ways to make two-dimensional drawings of three-dimensional objects. An **isometric drawing** shows three sides of an object in one drawing. A **foundation drawing** shows the bottom of a structure and the height of each part. An **orthographic drawing** shows the top, front, and right-side view of an object.

30. Use the isometric drawing at the right. a–b. See margin.
   a. Make an orthographic drawing.
   b. Make a foundation drawing.

31. *Writing* Describe a situation in which an orthographic drawing is useful. An orthographic drawing is useful when parts of the object obscure each other in isometric view.

Getting Ready for... CHAPTER 3

Draw a pair of figures to fit each description. 32–37. See margin.

32. similar acute triangles with similarity ratio $\frac{1}{2}$

33. similar quadrilaterals with similarity ratio $\frac{3}{4}$

Draw each figure. Then draw a line dividing the figure in half.

34. regular octagon **35.** rectangle **36.** isosceles trapezoid **37.** kite

30a.

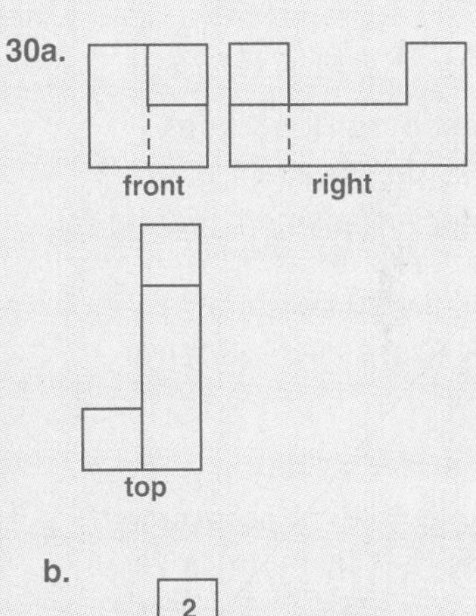

b.

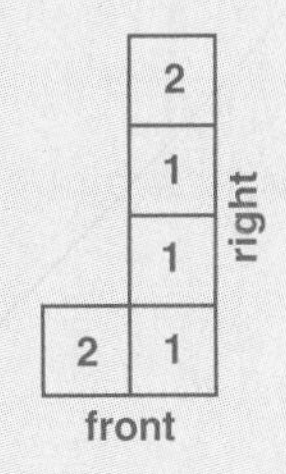

32. 33.

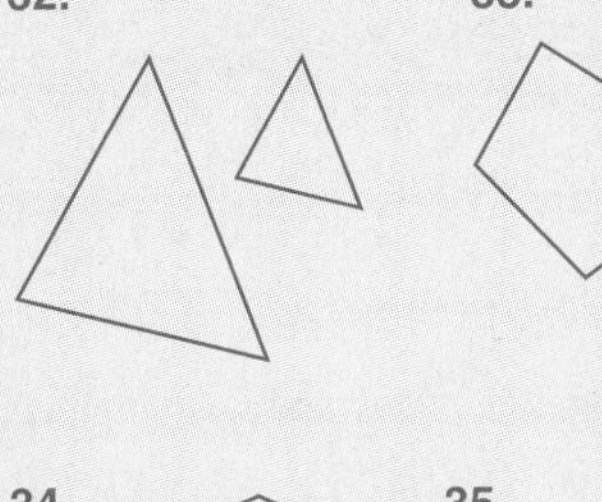

34. 35.

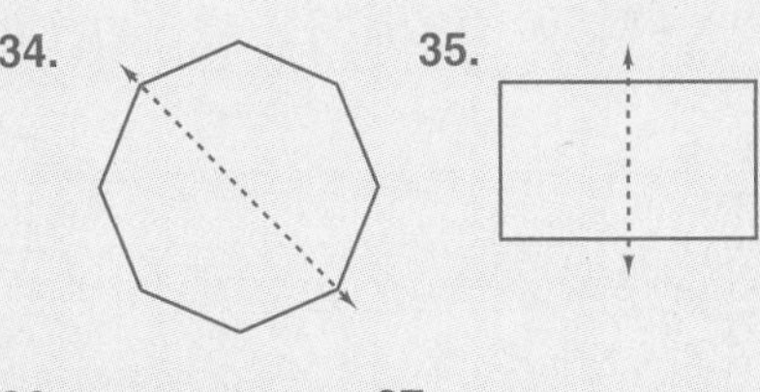

36. 37.

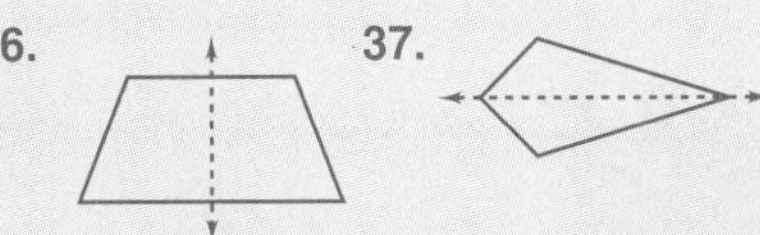

Assessment

ENHANCED MULTIPLE CHOICE QUESTIONS are more complex than traditional multiple choice questions, which assess only one skill. Enhanced multiple choice questions assess the processes that students use, as well as the end results. The questions are written so that students use more than one strategy to solve the problem. Using multiple strategies is encouraged by the National Council of Teachers of Mathematics (NCTM). **Exercise 25** is an enhanced multiple choice question.

FREE RESPONSE QUESTIONS do not give answer choices. Some exercises have more than one possible answer. Students need to give only one correct response. **Exercises 1–6, 8–14, 16–24 and 26–27** are free response questions.

WRITING EXERCISES allow students to describe how they think about and understand the concepts they have learned. **Exercise 7** is a writing exercise.

OPEN-ENDED PROBLEMS allow for more than one solution. Students must construct their own responses instead of choosing from possible answers. The student responses will help you determine the depth of their understanding and any possible areas of difficulty. **Exercise 15** is an open-ended problem.

Resources

Teaching Resources

Chapter Support File, Ch. 2
- Chapter Assessment, Forms A and B
- Alternative Assessment

Chapter Assessment, Spanish Resources

Teacher's Edition

See also p. 66E for assessment options

Software
Computer Item Generator

Assessment page 120

7. If no diagonal contains points outside the polygon, then it is convex. If not, then it is concave.

15a. Sample: (0, 0), (2, 2), (4, 0), (2, −2)
b. Sample: (2, 3), (5, −1), (4, −3), (1, 1)
c. Sample: (1, 2), (4, 8), (5, 0), (8, 6)
d. Sample: (0, 5), (5, 0), (5, 2), (2, 5)

2 Assessment

Use a protractor and a centimeter ruler to classify each triangle by its angles and sides.

1. 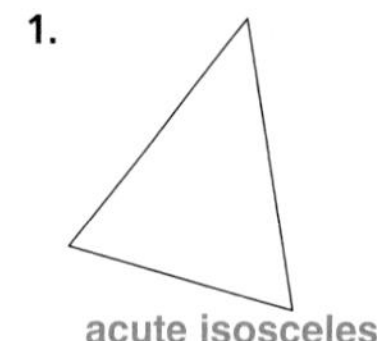
acute isosceles

2. obtuse scalene

Algebra **Find the values of the variables.**

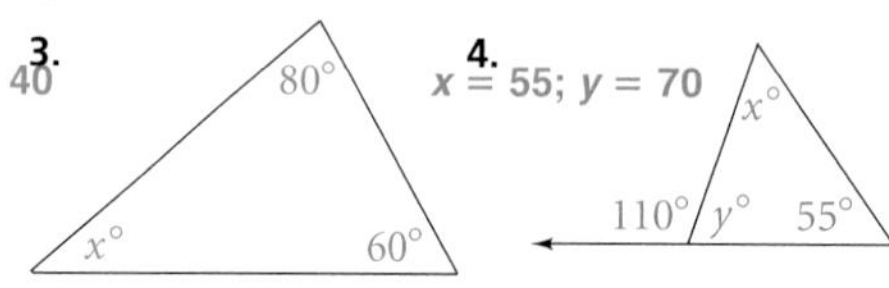

3. 40

4. $x = 55$; $y = 70$

5. 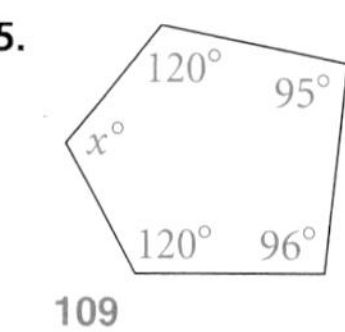

109

6. 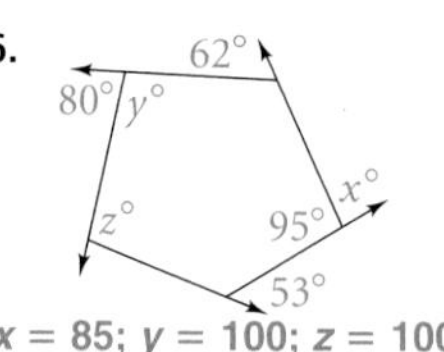

$x = 85$; $y = 100$; $z = 100$

7. *Writing* Explain how you can determine if a polygon is concave or convex.
See margin.

Sketch each pair of lines. Tell whether they are *parallel, perpendicular,* or *neither.*

8. $y = 4x + 7$
$y = -\frac{1}{4}x - 3$
perpendicular

9. $y = 3x - 4$
$y = 3x + 1$
parallel

10. $y = x + 5$
$y = -5x - 1$
neither

11. $y = x - 6$
$y = -x + 2$
perpendicular

Coordinate Geometry **Graph quadrilateral *ABCD*. Then determine the most precise name for each figure.**

12. $A(1, 2)$, $B(11, 2)$, $C(7, 5)$, $D(4, 5)$ trapezoid

13. $A(3, -2)$, $B(5, 4)$, $C(3, 6)$, $D(1, 4)$ kite

14. $A(1, -4)$, $B(1, 1)$, $C(-2, 2)$, $D(-2, -3)$
parallelogram

15. *Open-ended* Write the coordinates of four points that determine each figure.
a. square
b. parallelogram
c. rectangle
d. trapezoid
a–d. See margin.

Find the radius of a circle with the given diameter.

16. 6 ft
3 ft

17. 5.1 m
2.55 m

18. $4\sqrt{5}$ in.
$2\sqrt{5}$ in.

Find each measure for ⊙*P*.

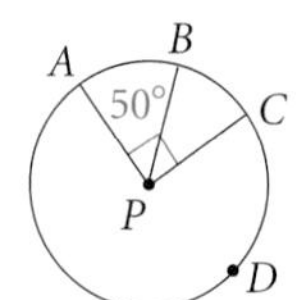

19. $m\angle BPC$ 40

20. $m\widehat{AB}$ 50

21. $m\widehat{ADC}$ 270

22. $m\widehat{ADB}$ 310

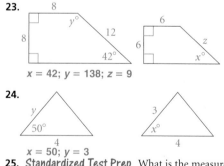

Find the values of the variables for each pair of similar figures.

23. $x = 42$; $y = 138$; $z = 9$

24. 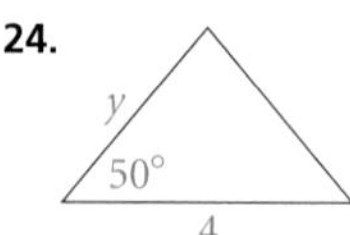

$x = 50$; $y = 3$

25. *Standardized Test Prep* What is the measure of each exterior angle of a regular 12-gon? B

A. 150 B. 30 C. 300 D. 210 E. 36

26–27. See back of book.

Use the figure below for Exercises 26 and 27.

26. Create an isometric drawing.

27. Create an orthographic drawing.

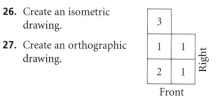

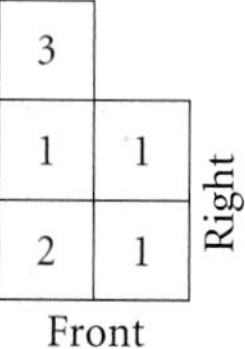

Cumulative Review

Item	Review Topic	Chapter
1	Classifying Quadrilaterals	2
2	Planes	1
3, 12	Parallel and Perpendicular Lines in the Coordinate Plane	2
4	Circles	2
5	Measuring Angles	1
6	Triangles	2

Item	Review Topic	Chapter
7, 11	Coordinate Plane	1
8	Using Patterns	1
9	Deductive Reasoning	1
10	Polygons	2
13	Isometric Drawings	2
14	Basic Constructions	1

2 Cumulative Review

For Exercises 1–10, choose the correct letter.

1. What is a name for the quadrilateral below? D

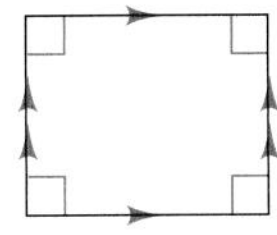

I. square **II.** rectangle **III.** rhombus **IV.** parallelogram
A. I only **B.** IV only **C.** I and II **D.** II and IV **E.** I and III

2. Which can be the intersection of three distinct planes? C
I. a point **II.** a line **III.** a plane **IV.** a ray
A. I only **B.** II only **C.** I and II **D.** II and IV **E.** I, II, and III

3. Which line is parallel to $y = 3x - 2$? E
A. $y = \frac{1}{3}x + 5$ **B.** $y = 3$
C. $y = -3x + 1$ **D.** $y = -\frac{1}{3}x - 4$
E. none of the above

4. Find the diameter of a circle with radius $6\sqrt{5}$. A
A. $12\sqrt{5}$ **B.** $6\sqrt{10}$ **C.** $3\sqrt{5}$
D. $6\sqrt{2.5}$ **E.** none of the above

5. What is $m\angle CDF$? C

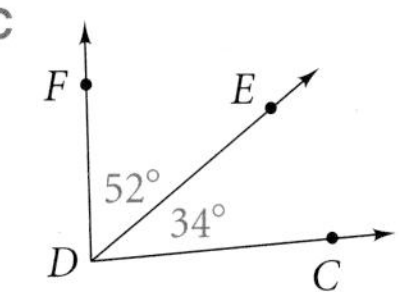

A. 18 **B.** 274 **C.** 86 **D.** 94
E. cannot be determined from the information given

6. $\triangle ABC$ is obtuse. Two vertices of the triangle are $A(3, 4)$ and $B(-1, 1)$. What could be the coordinates of point C? A
A. $(-1, -3)$ **B.** $(3, 1)$ **C.** $(0, 0)$
D. $(-1, 4)$ **E.** none of the above

7. What is the length of the segment with endpoints at $A(1, 7)$ and $B(-3, -1)$? B
A. 8 **B.** $4\sqrt{5}$ **C.** 40 **D.** $2\sqrt{10}$ **E.** $\sqrt{5}$

8. What is the next number in the pattern $1, -4, 9, -16 \ldots$? D
A. -25 **B.** -5 **C.** 5 **D.** 25 **E.** 35

Compare the boxed quantity in Column A with the boxed quantity in Column B. Choose the best answer.

A. The quantity in Column A is greater.
B. The quantity in Column B is greater.
C. The two quantities are equal.
D. The relationship cannot be determined on the basis of the information supplied.

	Column A	Column B	
	$\angle A$ is a supplement of $\angle B$.		
9.	$m\angle A$	$m\angle B$	D
10.	the measure of each interior angle of a regular hexagon	the measure of each exterior angle of a regular octagon	A

Find each answer.

11. What are the coordinates of the midpoint of $\overline{CD}$ with endpoints $C(5, 3)$ and $D(0, -7)$? (2.5, −2)

12. ***Open-ended*** Write an equation of a line perpendicular to the line $y = 6x + 4$. Sample: $y = -\frac{1}{6}x - 2$

13. Create an isometric drawing for this foundation plan. See back of book.

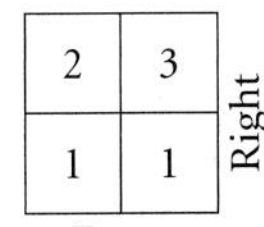

14. Draw an angle. Then construct another angle congruent to the first. Check students' work.

Resources

Teaching Resources
Chapter Support File, Ch. 2
- Cumulative Review
- Standardized Test Practice

Teacher's Edition
See also p. 66E for assessment options.

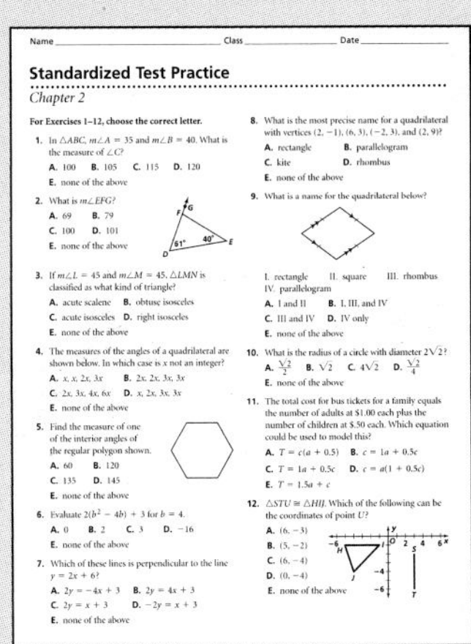

Standardized Test Practice
Chapter 2

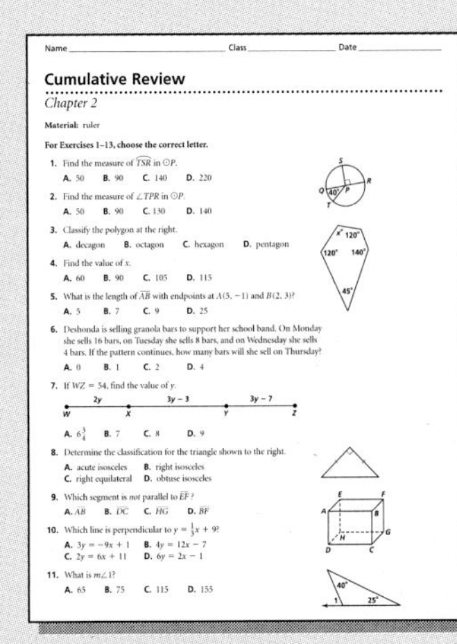

Cumulative Review
Chapter 2

CHAPTER 3 Transformations: Shapes in Motion

To accommodate flexible scheduling, some lessons are divided into parts. Assignment Options are given in the Lesson Planning Options for each lesson.

PACING OPTIONS

This chart suggests pacing only for the core lessons and their parts, and it is provided merely as a possible guide. It will help you determine how much time you have in your schedule to cover other features, such as the Chapter Project, Math Toolboxes, Wrap Up, and Assessment.

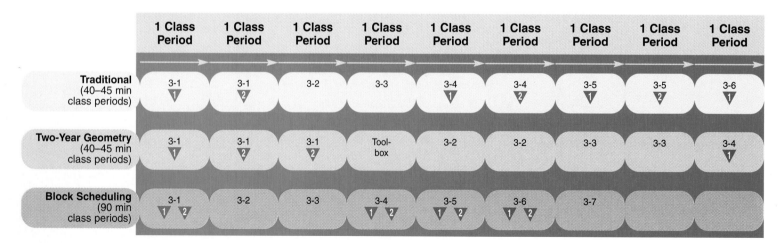

	1 Class Period	1 Class Period	1 Class Period	1 Class Period	1 Class Period	1 Class Period	1 Class Period	1 Class Period	1 Class Period
Traditional (40–45 min class periods)	3-1 Part 1	3-1 Part 2	3-2	3-3	3-4 Part 1	3-4 Part 2	3-5 Part 1	3-5 Part 2	3-6 Part 1
Two-Year Geometry (40–45 min class periods)	3-1 Part 1	3-1 Part 2	3-1 Part 2	Toolbox	3-2	3-2	3-3	3-3	3-4 Part 1
Block Scheduling (90 min class periods)	3-1 Parts 1, 2	3-2	3-3	3-4 Parts 1, 2	3-5 Parts 1, 2	3-6 Parts 1, 2	3-7		

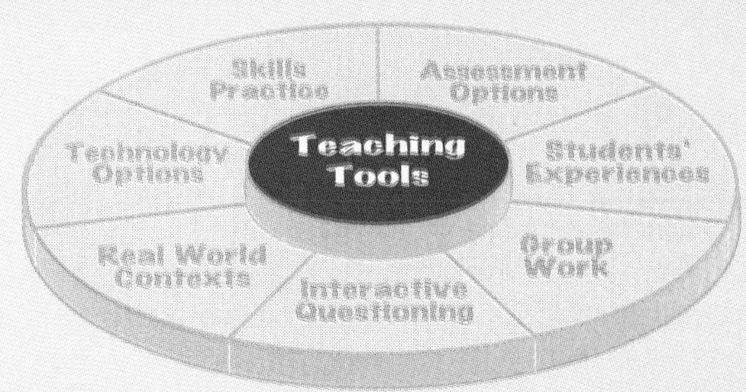

What Students Will Learn and Why

In this chapter, students learn to describe changes in shape and size with transformational geometry and how to recognize isometries. They identify and describe reflections, translations, and rotations. They learn how composition of reflections are related to other isometries. They learn how to identify glide reflections, symmetries, and figures that tessellate. Finally, students learn how to locate dilation images of figures. The principles presented in the chapter have applications in many diverse fields such as science, architecture, music, and history.

Discussing the Chapter/Building on Experience

The concept map below relates chapter topics to real-world applications. You and your class may wish to add to the map or develop maps of your own. The center oval describes the topic of the chapter. The next level displays topics within the lessons. The outer ovals reflect applications of the content. As you and your class build a concept map, invite students to discuss applications with which they are familiar.

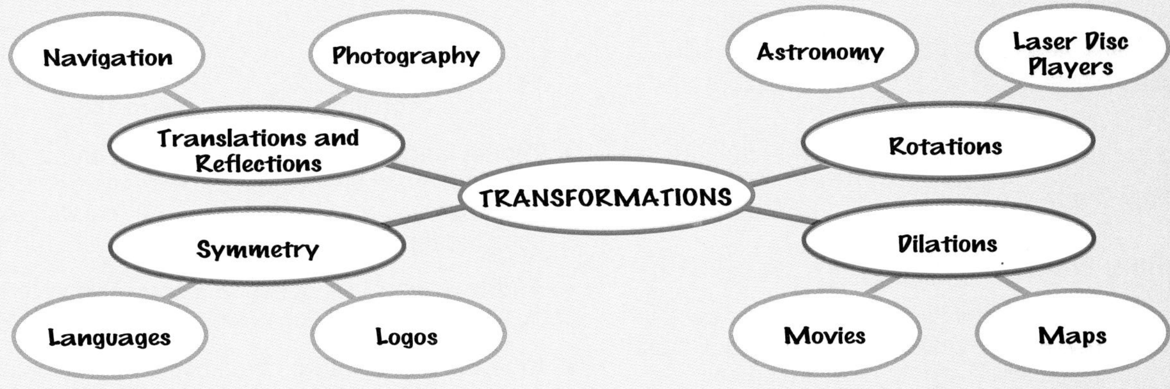

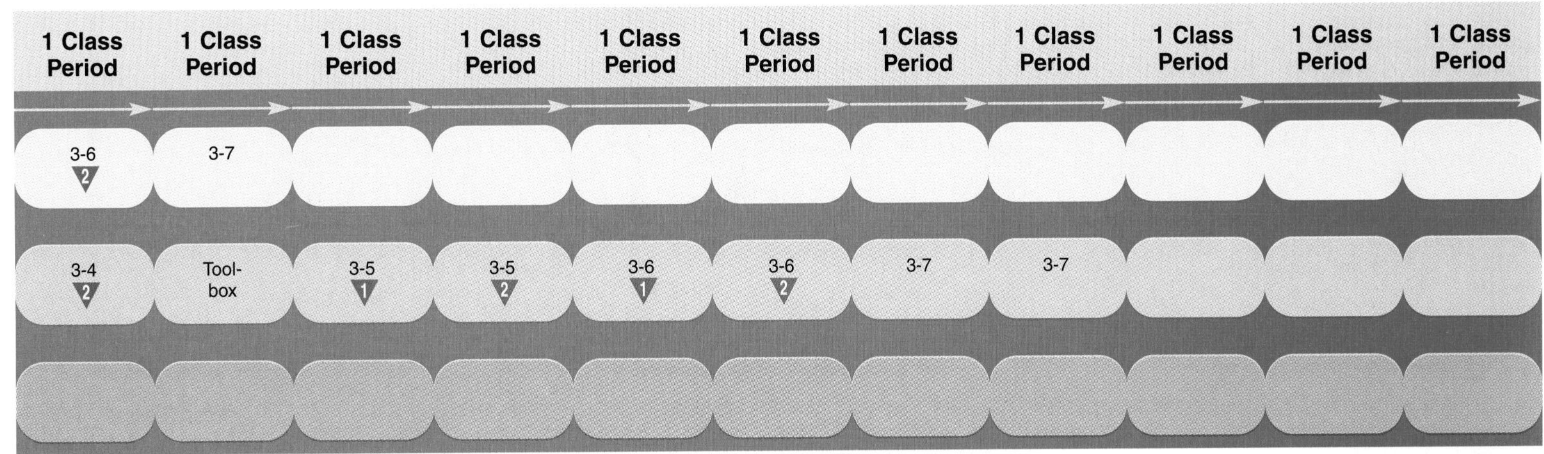

1 Class Period	1 Class Period	1 Class Period	1 Class Period	1 Class Period	1 Class Period	1 Class Period	1 Class Period	1 Class Period	1 Class Period	1 Class Period
3-6 ▽2	3-7									
3-4 ▽2	Tool-box	3-5 ▽1	3-5 ▽2	3-6 ▽1	3-6 ▽2	3-7	3-7			

Interactive Questioning Tips

A question is interactive when there is "give and take" between the questioner (teacher or student) and the respondent. In Think and Discuss or when a critical thinking question is asked, it is important not to accept one-word answers. Coax more information from a student by asking follow-up questions like "How do you know?" or "Why do you think so?" Encouraging students to expand on their answers promotes active participation and stimulates higher levels of thought. These two elements are essential in developing high-level thinking skills. For example, in Lesson 3-4, students are asked to explain why a glide reflection changes orientations.

Skills Practice

Every lesson provides skill practice with Try This exercises, Exercises On Your Own, and Exercises Mixed Review. The Student Edition includes Checkpoints (pp. 143, 158) and Preparing for Standardized Tests (p. 179). In the Teacher's Edition, the Lesson Planning Options section for each lesson lists Prerequisite Skills students should know for that lesson. At the back of the Student Edition is the Skills Handbook—mini-lessons on math your students may need to review. The Chapter Support File for Chapter 3 in the Teaching Resources box includes two Practice worksheets per lesson, a worksheet for two Checkpoints, and worksheets for Cumulative Review and Standardized Test Preparation.

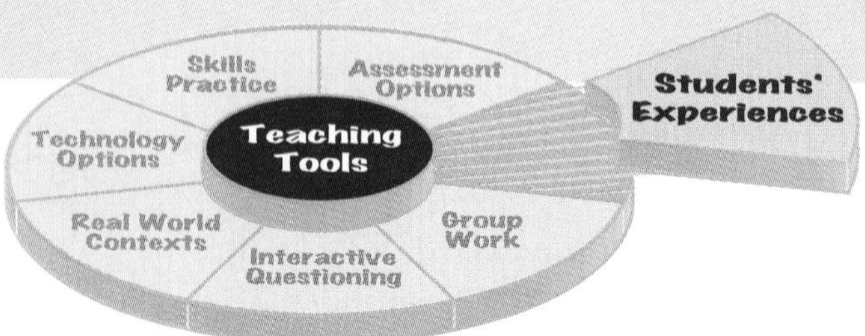

Diverse Learning and Teaching Styles

In your Teacher's Edition, you will find suggestions as to how you can help students complete mathematical tasks in Chapter 3 by reinforcing various learning styles. Here are some examples.

- **Visual learning** use puzzle pieces to model slides, flips, and turns (p.124), use a tracing of a tessellation to find symmetries (p.163), use diagrams to verify that multiplying the coordinates of the point of a diagram by the scale factor gives the coordinates of its image (p.168)
- **Tactile learning** use paper folding to create the reflection image of quadrilaterals (p.125), use mirrors to investigate the properties of reflections (p. 126), create pavement tiling using pattern blocks (p.159)
- **Auditory learning** describe a composition of isometries (p.147)
- **Kinesthetic learning** use a coordinate grid on the floor of the classroom and physically represent points and "act out" translations (p.133), stand at the center of a circle and describe what they see as other students slowly walk around the circle (p.140), analyze and discuss the symmetry of a car hubcap (p.155)

Alternative Activity for Lesson 3-1

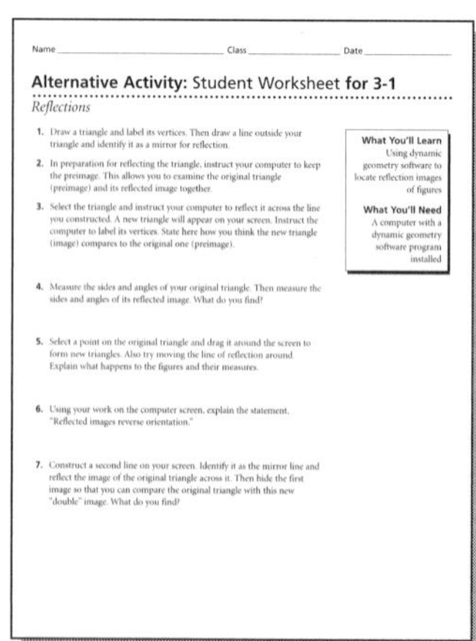

Name ______ Class ______ Date ______

Alternative Activity: Student Worksheet **for 3-1**

Reflections

1. Draw a triangle and label its vertices. Then draw a line outside your triangle and identify it as a mirror for reflection.
2. In preparation for reflecting the triangle, instruct your computer to keep the preimage. This allows you to examine the original triangle (preimage) and its reflected image together.
3. Select the triangle and instruct your computer to reflect it across the line you constructed. A new triangle will appear on your screen. Instruct the computer to label its vertices. State here how you think the new triangle (image) compares to the original one (preimage).
4. Measure the sides and angles of your original triangle. Then measure the sides and angles of its reflected image. What do you find?
5. Select a point on the original triangle and drag it around the screen to form new triangles. Also try moving the line of reflection around. Explain what happens to the figures and their measures.
6. Using your work on the computer screen, explain the statement, "Reflected images reverse orientation."
7. Construct a second line on your screen. Identify it as the mirror line and reflect the image of the original triangle across it. Then hide the first image so that you can compare the original triangle with this new "double" image. What do you find?

What You'll Learn
Using dynamic geometry software to locate reflection images of figures

What You'll Need
A computer with a dynamic geometry software program installed

for use with Example 2, uses geometry software to draw the reflection images of figures and identify isometries through measurement.

Alternative Activity for Lesson 3-3

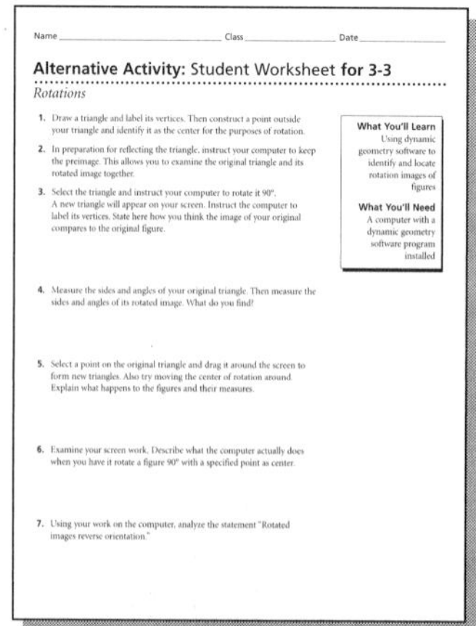

Name ______ Class ______ Date ______

Alternative Activity: Student Worksheet **for 3-3**

Rotations

1. Draw a triangle and label its vertices. Then construct a point outside your triangle and identify it as the center for the purposes of rotation.
2. In preparation for reflecting the triangle, instruct your computer to keep the preimage. This allows you to examine the original triangle and its rotated image together.
3. Select the triangle and instruct your computer to rotate it 90°. A new triangle will appear on your screen. Instruct the computer to label its vertices. State here how you think the image of your original compares to the original figure.
4. Measure the sides and angles of your original triangle. Then measure the sides and angles of its rotated image. What do you find?
5. Select a point on the original triangle and drag it around the screen to form new triangles. Also try moving the center of rotation around. Explain what happens to the figures and their measures.
6. Examine your screen work. Describe what the computer actually does when you have it rotate a figure 90° with a specified point as center.
7. Using your work on the computer, analyze the statement "Rotated images reverse orientation."

What You'll Learn
Using dynamic geometry software to identify and locate rotation images of figures

What You'll Need
A computer with a dynamic geometry software program installed

for use with Example 1, uses geometry software to draw the rotated images of figures and identify isometries through measurement.

Alternative Activity for Lesson 3-7

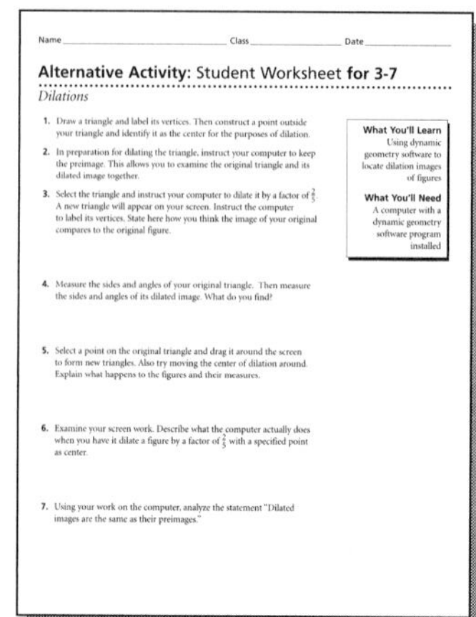

Name ______ Class ______ Date ______

Alternative Activity: Student Worksheet **for 3-7**

Dilations

1. Draw a triangle and label its vertices. Then construct a point outside your triangle and identify it as the center for the purposes of dilation.
2. In preparation for dilating the triangle, instruct your computer to keep the preimage. This allows you to examine the original triangle and its dilated image together.
3. Select the triangle and instruct your computer to dilate it by a factor of $\frac{2}{5}$. A new triangle will appear on your screen. Instruct the computer to label its vertices. State here how you think the image of your original compares to the original figure.
4. Measure the sides and angles of your original triangle. Then measure the sides and angles of its dilated image. What do you find?
5. Select a point on the original triangle and drag it around the screen to form new triangles. Also try moving the center of dilation around. Explain what happens to the figures and their measures.
6. Examine your screen work. Describe what the computer actually does when you have it dilate a figure by a factor of $\frac{2}{5}$ with a specified point as center.
7. Using your work on the computer, analyze the statement "Dilated images are the same as their preimages."

What You'll Learn
Using dynamic geometry software to locate dilation images of figures

What You'll Need
A computer with a dynamic geometry software program installed

for use with the Work Together and Think and Discuss, uses geometry software to draw the dilation images of figures and informally identify similarity of figures.

Cooperative Learning Tips

When used effectively, cooperative learning can help students develop interpersonal skills, learn to perform specific roles in a group, and learn to carry out specific responsibilities. The components of Chapter 3 provide a range of cooperative learning opportunities.

- In the Student Edition, the ***Work Together*** parts of lessons are specifically designed for cooperative learning activities.
- In the Teacher's Edition, you will find helpful hints for addressing diverse learning styles (see page C for Chapter 3). For every lesson, you will find a ***Reteaching Activity***, which may involve cooperative learning.

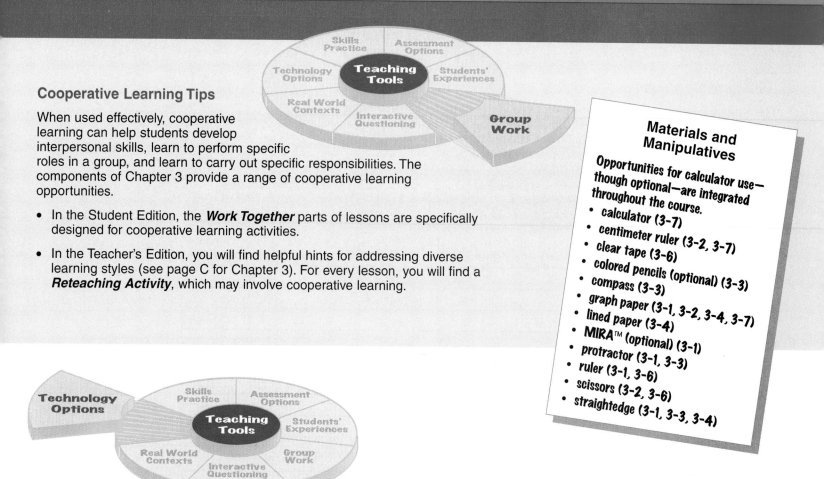

Materials and Manipulatives

Opportunities for calculator use—though optional—are integrated throughout the course.

- calculator (3-7)
- centimeter ruler (3-2, 3-7)
- clear tape (3-6)
- colored pencils (optional) (3-3)
- compass (3-3)
- graph paper (3-1, 3-2, 3-4, 3-7)
- lined paper (3-4)
- MIRA™ (optional) (3-1)
- protractor (3-1, 3-3)
- ruler (3-1, 3-6)
- scissors (3-2, 3-6)
- straightedge (3-1, 3-3, 3-4)

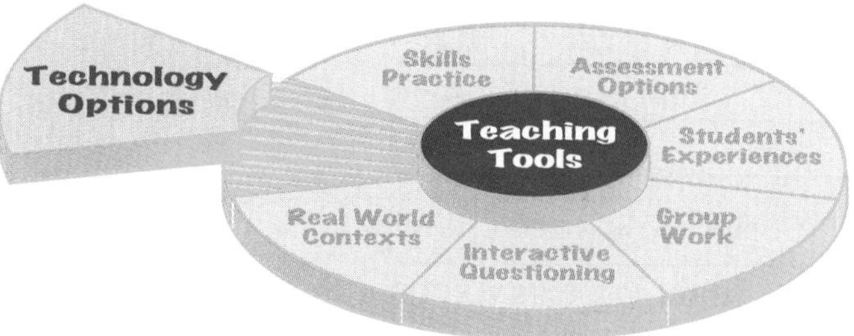

TECHNOLOGY OPTIONS

Technology Tools		Chapter Project	3-1	3-2	3-3	3-4	3-5	3-6	3-7
Calculator		Numerous opportunities throughout for students to use scientific calculators.							
Software	Secondary Math Lab Toolkit™		✔	✔	✔	✔	✔	✔	✔
	Integrated Math Lab			✔				✔	
	Computer Item Generator		✔	✔	✔	✔	✔	✔	✔
	Student Edition						✔T		✔
Video	Video Field Trip	✔							
CD-ROM	Multimedia Geometry Lab		✔	✔	✔	✔			
Internet		See the Prentice Hall site. (http://www.phschool.com)							

✔T indicates Math Toolbox.

The Prentice Hall Geometry program offers you a rich variety of technology options. Be assured that all these options are provided as a means of enriching the program and are not essential for the successful completion of the course.

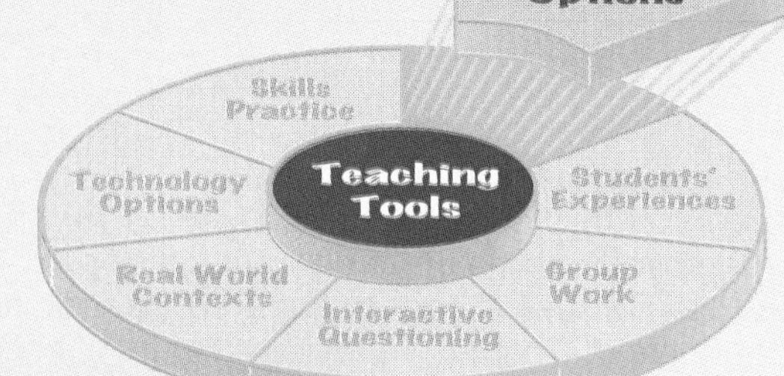

Assessment Options

The Prentice Hall Geometry Program provides you with many options. From these options, you may choose instructional materials and techniques appropriate for your students, or those necessary to meet your district's curriculum requirements. As the chart indicates, the program also supports your teaching efforts by offering you many choices for assessment.

ASSESSMENT OPTIONS

Assessment Support Materials	Chapter Project	3-1	3-2	3-3	3-4	3-5	3-6	3-7	Chapter End
Chapter Project	▲■●		▲■	▲■	▲■	▲■		▲■	▲■
Checkpoints				▲■●		▲■●			
Self-Assessment		▲■					▲■	▲■	▲■
Writing Assignment		▲■	▲	▲■	▲●	▲	▲■	▲■●	●▲
Chapter Assessment									▲■●
Alternative Assessment		■	■	■	■	■	■	■	●■
Cumulative Review									●
Standardized Test Prep		▲■		▲■				▲■	▲■●
Computer Item Generator	Can be used to create custom-made practice or assessment at any time.								

▲ = Student Edition ■ = Teacher's Edition ● = Teaching Resources

Checkpoints

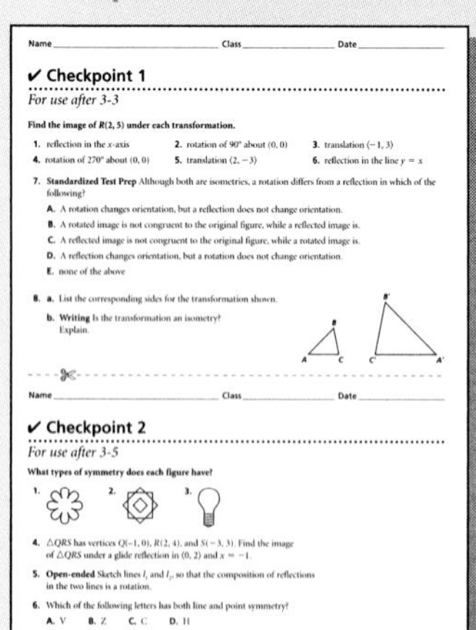
Name ______ Class ______ Date ______

✔ Checkpoint 1

For use after 3-3

Find the image of $R(2, 5)$ under each transformation.

1. reflection in the x-axis
2. rotation of 90° about (0, 0)
3. translation (−1, 3)
4. rotation of 270° about (0, 0)
5. translation (2, −3)
6. reflection in the line $y = x$
7. **Standardized Test Prep** Although both are isometries, a rotation differs from a reflection in which of the following?
   A. A rotation changes orientation, but a reflection does not change orientation.
   B. A rotated image is not congruent to the original figure, while a reflected image is.
   C. A reflected image is not congruent to the original figure, while a rotated image is.
   D. A reflection changes orientation, but a rotation does not change orientation.
   E. none of the above
8. a. List the corresponding sides for the transformation shown.
   b. **Writing** Is the transformation an isometry? Explain.

Name ______ Class ______ Date ______

✔ Checkpoint 2

For use after 3-5

What types of symmetry does each figure have?

1. 2. 3.

4. $\triangle QRS$ has vertices $Q(-1, 0)$, $R(2, 4)$, and $S(-3, 3)$. Find the image of $\triangle QRS$ under a glide reflection in (0, 2) and $x = -1$.
5. **Open-ended** Sketch lines l_1 and l_2 so that the composition of reflections in the two lines is a rotation.
6. Which of the following letters has both line and point symmetry?
   A. V B. Z C. C D. H

Alternative Assessment

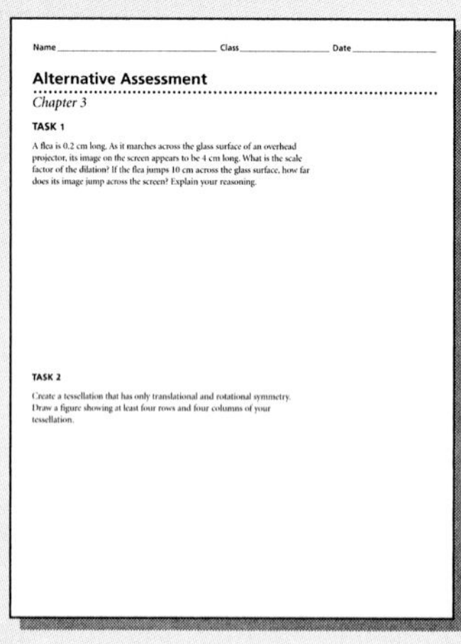
Name ______ Class ______ Date ______

Alternative Assessment

Chapter 3

TASK 1

A flea is 0.2 cm long. As it marches across the glass surface of an overhead projector, its image on the screen appears to be 4 cm long. What is the scale factor of the dilation? If the flea jumps 10 cm across the glass surface, how far does its image jump across the screen? Explain your reasoning.

TASK 2

Create a tessellation that has only translational and rotational symmetry. Draw a figure showing at least four rows and four columns of your tessellation.

Chapter Assessment

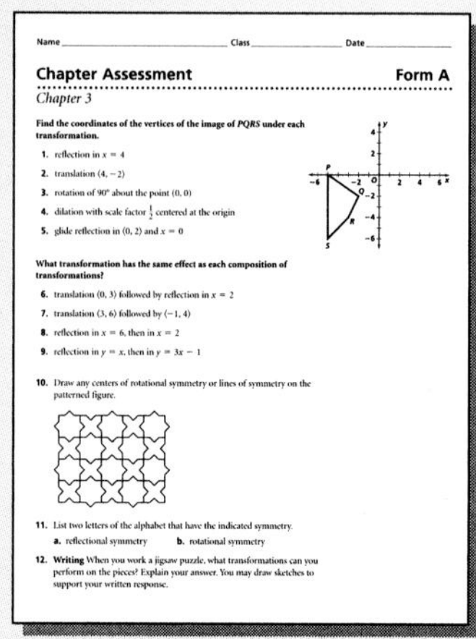
Name ______ Class ______ Date ______

Chapter Assessment **Form A**

Chapter 3

Find the coordinates of the vertices of the image of $PQRS$ under each transformation.

1. reflection in $x = 4$
2. translation (4, −2)
3. rotation of 90° about the point (0, 0)
4. dilation with scale factor $\frac{1}{2}$ centered at the origin
5. glide reflection in (0, 2) and $x = 0$

What transformation has the same effect as each composition of transformations?

6. translation (0, 3) followed by reflection in $x = 2$
7. translation (3, 6) followed by (−1, 4)
8. reflection in $x = 6$, then in $x = 2$
9. reflection in $y = x$, then in $y = 3x - 1$
10. Draw any centers of rotational symmetry or lines of symmetry on the patterned figure.
11. List two letters of the alphabet that have the indicated symmetry.
    a. reflectional symmetry b. rotational symmetry
12. **Writing** When you work a jigsaw puzzle, what transformations can you perform on the pieces? Explain your answer. You may draw sketches to support your written response.

Available in both Form A and Form B

Making the Right Connections

Mathematics is imbedded in nearly every walk of life. The National Council of Teachers of Mathematics (NCTM) encourages educators to recognize these connections and to emphasize them for the purpose of better educating students for success in life and in a global economy. The ***Connections*** chart below highlights these connections for Chapter 3.

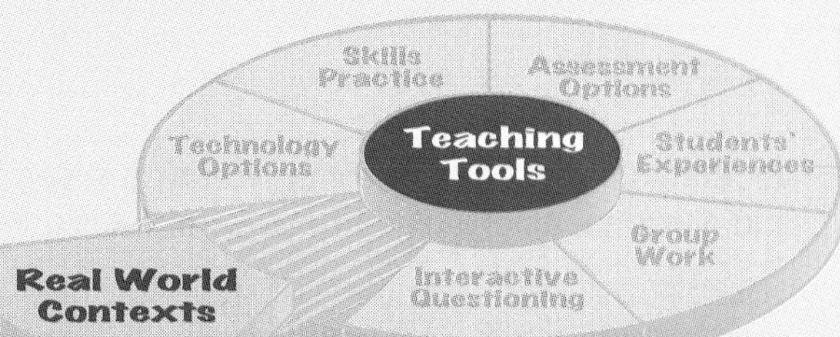

CONNECTIONS

Lesson	Interdisciplinary Connections	Career Prep	Other Real World Connections	Math Integration	NCTM Standards
Chapter Project	Art History	Design	Space Rockets Pottery Currency		Problem Solving Connections
3-1	History Chemistry	Engineering	Emergency Vehicles Surveillance Medicine	Coordinate Geometry	Geometry and Spatial Sense Communication Problem Solving
3-2	Art Music	Photography Graphic Design Manufacturing	Navigation	Coordinate Geometry	Geometry and Spatial Sense Communication Problem Solving
3-3	Art Astronomy Language Arts	Engineering	Native American Art	Coordinate Geometry	Communication Problem Solving Connections Geometry and Spatial Sense
3-4	Art	Architecture	Kaleidoscope Wallpaper Patterns	Coordinate Geometry Probability	Geometry and Spatial Sense Communication Problem Solving
3-5	Art Literature	Design	Languages Logos Rug Designs	Geometry in 3 Dimensions Algebra Coordinate Geometry	Communication Geometry and Spatial Sense Problem Solving
3-6	Art	Architecture	Escher Prints Honeycomb Mosaics		Connections Geometry and Spatial Sense Communication Problem Solving
3-7	Art	Cartography Architecture Graphic Design	Human Development Movies Maps Photographs	Coordinate Geometry	Geometry and Spatial Sense Communication Problem Solving

CHAPTER 3 **Transformation: Shapes in Motion**

CONNECTING TO PRIOR LEARNING Elicit from students examples of geometric patterns they have observed (wallpaper, stencils, floor tiles, tapestries, etc.). Explain that geometric patterns can be created using slides, flips, turns, and dilations, all of which are types of transformations.

CULTURAL CONNECTIONS Ask students if they have ever seen authentic Ukrainian-painted eggs, Native American pottery, Japanese kimonos, or African cloth. Ask knowledgeable students to present a visual display of repeating patterns found in these objects.

INTERDISCIPLINARY CONNECTIONS In ancient Greek and Roman buildings, a sculptured *frieze* often decorated the center section of an *entablature*, found above the *colonnade.* Have interested students give a verbal/visual presentation of popular frieze designs from ancient or contemporary buildings.

ABOUT THE PROJECT Students identify frieze patterns that were created using reflections, translations, rotations, and glide reflections. Students learn how to classify the patterns by their symmetries. They also design their own patterns.

Technology Options

Prentice Hall Technology

Video

• Video Field Trip 3, "Cultural Patterns," a look at African cultural designs

CHAPTER 3

Transformations: Shapes in Motion

Relating to the Real World

Many geometric figures in the real world do not sit still. They move; they change shape; they change size. You can describe these changes with transformational geometry. The principles you will study here have applications in many diverse fields—from science and architecture to music and history.

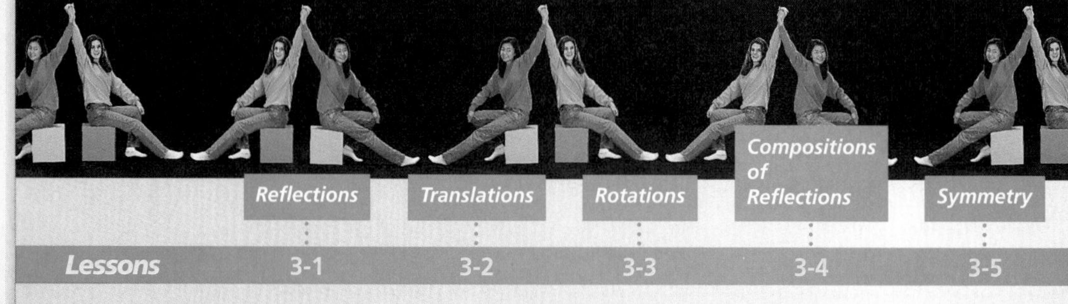

Lessons	3-1	3-2	3-3	3-4	3-5
	Reflections	Translations	Rotations	Compositions of Reflections	Symmetry

Launching the Project

PROJECT NOTEBOOK Encourage students to keep all project-related materials in a separate folder or notebook. See Chapter Project Manager and Scoring Rubric in Chapter Support File.

- Assign students to work with a partner or in small groups. Have students refer to the center row of the photograph on pages 122–123. Ask groups to describe any patterns they see.
- Have teams each draw a nonregular polygon, trace it, and cut it out. Then have them use their cutouts to create patterns similar to the one in the photograph.

TRACKING THE PROJECT You may wish to have students read Finishing the Chapter Project on page 173 to help them get an overview of the project. Set benchmark deadlines for students to show their work in progress.

CHAPTER PROJECT

Ukrainian painted eggs, dollar bills, Native American pottery, Japanese kimonos, automobile tire treads, and African cloth are products of vastly diverse cultures, but these things all have something in common. They contain strips of repeating patterns, called *frieze patterns.*

In this chapter project, you will explore the underlying relationships among frieze patterns from around the world. You will also create your own designs. You will see how distinct civilizations—separated by oceans and centuries—are linked by their use of geometry to express themselves and to beautify their world.

To help you complete the project:

- **p. 137** *Find Out by Investigating*
- **p. 143** *Find Out by Modeling*
- **p. 150** *Find Out by Investigating*
- **p. 158** *Find Out by Classifying*
- **p. 171** *Find Out by Creating*
- **p. 173** *Finishing the Project*

Project Resources

Teaching Resources

Chapter Support File, Ch. 3
- Chapter Project Manager and Scoring Rubric

Transparencies
39

Using the Rubric

Sharing the scoring rubric for the project with your students will alert them to your expectations before they begin work on the project.

As students complete each Find Out question in the chapter, you may wish to have them evaluate their own work or a partner's work based on the scoring rubric. Students should have the opportunity to revise their work after it has been reviewed.

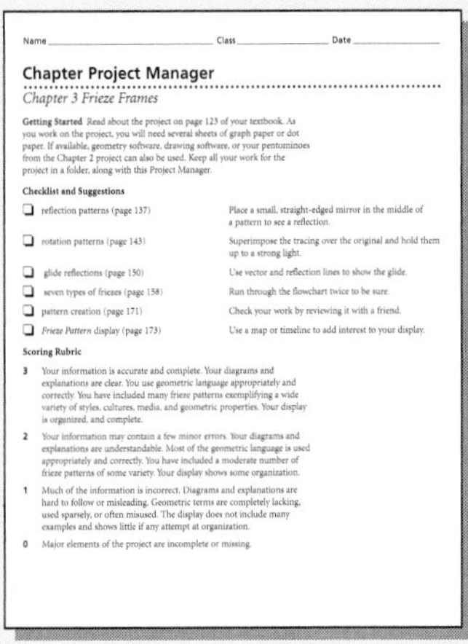

Name ____________ Class ____________ Date ____________

Chapter Project Manager

Chapter 3 Frieze Frames

Getting Started Read about the project on page 123 of your textbook. As you work on the project, you will need several sheets of graph paper or dot paper. If available, geometry software, drawing software, or your pentominoes from the Chapter 2 project can also be used. Keep all your work for the project in a folder, along with this Project Manager.

Checklist and Suggestions

- ❑ reflection patterns (page 137) — Place a small, straight-edged mirror in the middle of a pattern to see a reflection.
- ❑ rotation patterns (page 143) — Superimpose the tracing over the original and hold them up to a strong light.
- ❑ glide reflections (page 150) — Use vector and reflection lines to show the glide.
- ❑ seven types of friezes (page 158) — Run through the flowchart twice to be sure.
- ❑ pattern creation (page 171) — Check your work by reviewing it with a friend.
- ❑ *Frieze Pattern* display (page 173) — Use a map or timeline to add interest to your display.

Scoring Rubric

3 Your information is accurate and complete. Your diagrams and explanations are clear. You use geometric language appropriately and correctly. You have included many frieze patterns exemplifying a wide variety of styles, cultures, media, and geometric properties. Your display is organized, and complete.

2 Your information may contain a few minor errors. Your diagrams and explanations are understandable. Most of the geometric language is used appropriately and correctly. You have included a moderate number of frieze patterns of some variety. Your display shows some organization.

1 Much of the information is incorrect. Diagrams and explanations are hard to follow or misleading. Geometric terms are completely lacking, used sparsely, or often misused. The display does not include many examples and shows little if any attempt at organization.

0 Major elements of the project are incomplete or missing.

3-1 Teaching Notes

PROBLEM OF THE DAY

The diagram below shows nine points and eight lines, each line determined by three points. Rearrange the points so that ten lines can be drawn, each determined by three of the points.

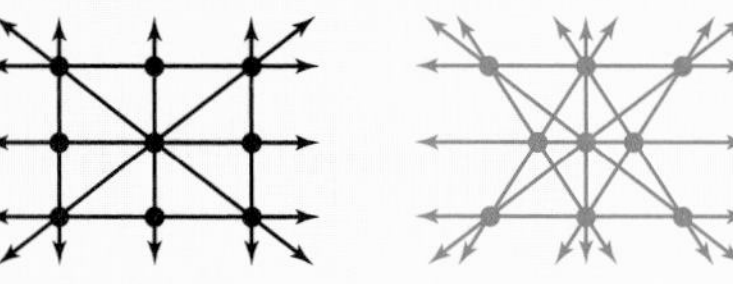

Problem of the Day is also available in Transparencies.

CONNECTING TO PRIOR KNOWLEDGE Ask students: *If △ABC ≅ △EFG, name the corresponding sides and angles.*

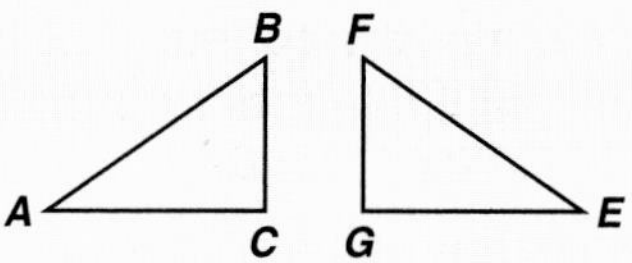

THINK AND DISCUSS p. 124

VISUAL LEARNING Have students use puzzle pieces to model slides, flips, and turns. Their irregular shapes make it easier for students to see how the transformations affect the orientation of the pieces.

Lesson Planning Options

Prerequisite Skills

- Understanding properties of congruent figures
- Graphing in the coordinate plane

Assignment Options for Exercises On Your Own

To provide flexible scheduling, this lesson can be subdivided into parts.

1 **Core** 4–9 (a,b), 18
✪**Extension** 19

2 **Core** 1–3, 4–9 (c), 10–17, 20, 22–28
✪**Extension** 21, 29

Use Mixed Review to maintain skills.

Resources

Student Edition

Extra Practice, p. 650
Glossary/Study Guide

Teaching Resources

Chapter Support File, Ch. 3
- Practice 3-1 (two worksheets)
- Reteaching 3-1
- Alternative Activity 3-1

Classroom Manager 3-1
Glossary, Spanish Resources

Transparencies
5, 40, 44, 45

Connections Engineering . . . and more

3-1 Reflections

What You'll Learn
- Identifying isometries
- Locating reflection images of figures

...And Why

To describe and explain the kinds of motions you encounter every day

What You'll Need
- straightedge
- protractor
- ruler
- graph paper
- MIRA™ (optional)

THINK AND DISCUSS

Part 1

An Introduction to Transformations

Have you ever put together a jigsaw puzzle? Think about opening the box and emptying all of the puzzle pieces onto a table.

1. Describe the kinds of motions you use to put the pieces together. Answers may vary. Sample: flips, slides, turns

You probably didn't realize it, but you use transformations when you assemble a puzzle. A **transformation** is a change in position, shape, or size of a figure. The photos below illustrate four basic transformations that you will study. Each transformed figure is the **image** of the original figure. The original figure is called the **preimage.**

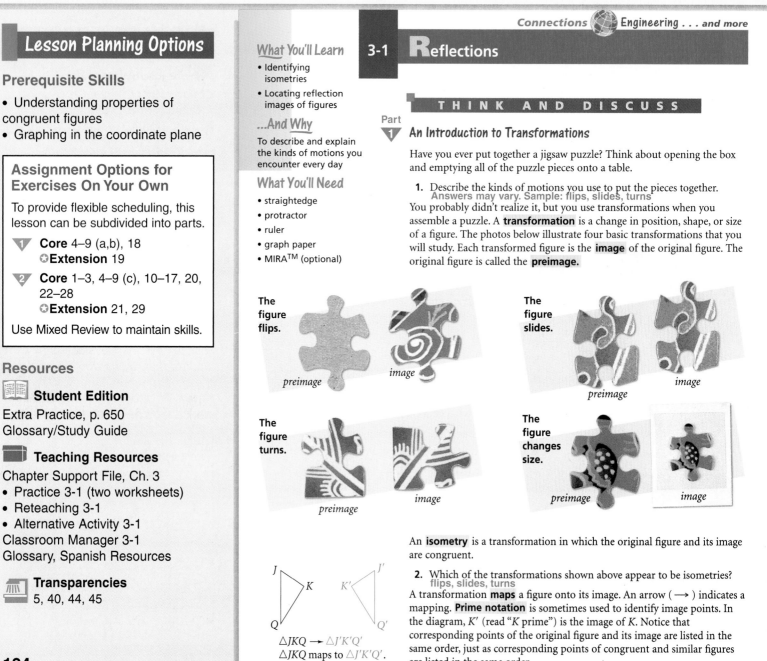

The figure flips.

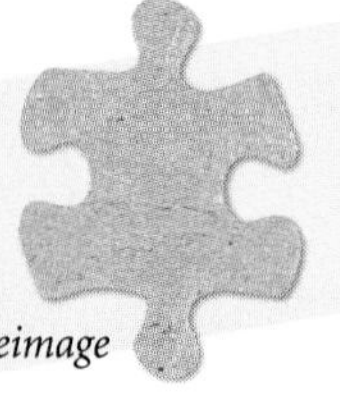
preimage

image

The figure slides.

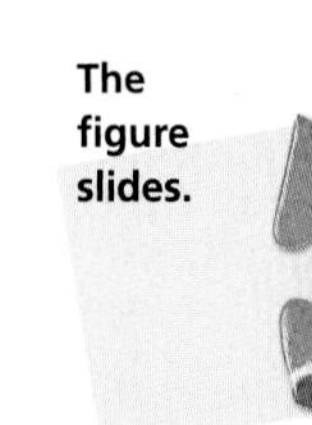
preimage

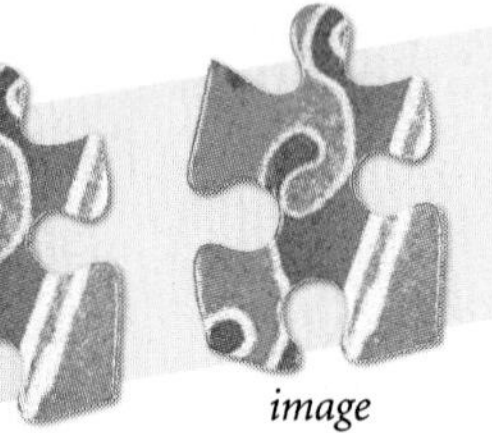
image

The figure turns.

preimage

image

The figure changes size.

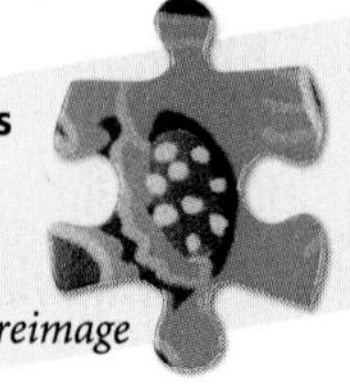
preimage

image

An **isometry** is a transformation in which the original figure and its image are congruent.

2. Which of the transformations shown above appear to be isometries? flips, slides, turns

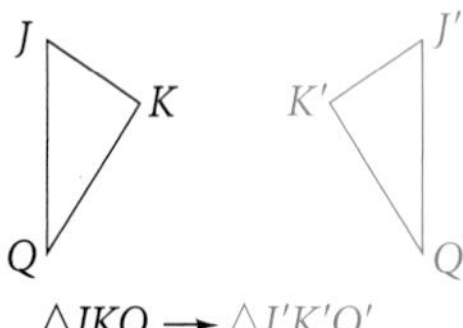

$\triangle JKQ \rightarrow \triangle J'K'Q'$
$\triangle JKQ$ maps to $\triangle J'K'Q'$.

A transformation **maps** a figure onto its image. An arrow (⟶) indicates a mapping. **Prime notation** is sometimes used to identify image points. In the diagram, K' (read "K prime") is the image of K. Notice that corresponding points of the original figure and its image are listed in the same order, just as corresponding points of congruent and similar figures are listed in the same order.

Example 1

Question 4 Students may want to draw quadrilaterals *TORN* and *SAKE* so they can see the corresponding sides and angles. Suggest that students draw irregular quadrilaterals so corresponding parts are more obvious.

WORK TOGETHER

TACTILE LEARNING Students can use either paper folding or MIRA™ to create the reflection image of their quadrilaterals. If students are using paper folding, tracing paper should be used.

Question 5 Students verify that the figures are congruent by using rulers and protractors.

EXTENSION Have students draw line *j* so that it contains a side of quadrilateral *MATH* and then draw the reflection image in line *j*. Have students next draw line *j* so that it intersects quadrilateral *MATH* in two points, then draw the reflection image in line *j*. Ask students if their responses to Questions 5 and 6 are the same for these reflections.

Example 1

In the diagram, $E'F'G'H'$ is the image of $EFGH$.

a. Name the images of $\angle F$ and $\angle H$.

b. List all pairs of corresponding sides.

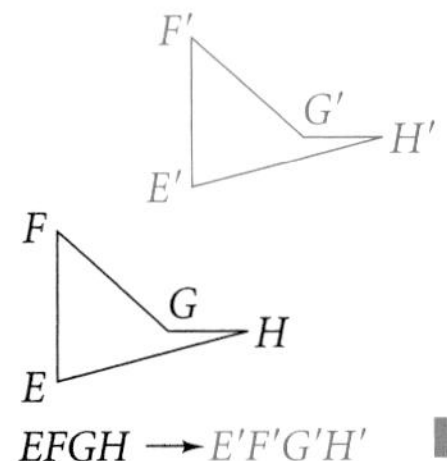

a. $\angle F'$ is the image of $\angle F$.
$\angle H'$ is the image of $\angle H$.

b. $\overline{EF}$ and $\overline{E'F'}$; $\overline{FG}$ and $\overline{F'G'}$;
$\overline{EH}$ and $\overline{E'H'}$; $\overline{GH}$ and $\overline{G'H'}$

3. Which of the four types of transformations shown on the previous page is illustrated in Example 1? slide

4. **Try This** List the corresponding segments and angles for the transformation $TORN \longrightarrow SAKE$. $\angle T$ and $\angle S$, $\angle O$ and $\angle A$, $\angle R$ and $\angle K$, $\angle N$ and $\angle E$; $\overline{TO}$ and $\overline{SA}$, $\overline{OR}$ and $\overline{AK}$, $\overline{RN}$ and $\overline{KE}$, $\overline{NT}$ and $\overline{ES}$

Part 2

Reflections

A flip is also known as a *reflection.* You see reflections almost every day. This morning, for example, you probably looked in the mirror before you headed out the door. In the following activity, you will investigate some properties of reflections.

WORK TOGETHER

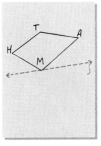

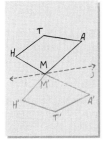

- Have each person in your group use a straightedge to draw a quadrilateral *MATH* on the top half of a sheet of paper. Draw a line *j* that intersects the quadrilateral at *M*.
- Fold the paper along line *j*, then use a straightedge to trace the reflection image of *MATH* onto the bottom portion of your paper. (You could also create the image by using a MIRA™.) Label the corresponding vertices of the image *M'*, *A'*, *T'*, and *H'*.

5. Measure corresponding angles and segments in *MATH* and *M'A'T'H'*. Is a reflection an isometry? Explain. Yes; $MATH \cong M'A'T'H'$

6. Make a **conjecture** about the image of a point that lies on the line of reflection. (*Hint:* Consider point *M* and its image.) The point is its own image.

7. a. In your original figure, did you write the labels *M*, *A*, *T*, and *H* in clockwise or counterclockwise order around the quadrilateral?

b. In the reflection image, do the labels *M'*, *A'*, *T'*, and *H'* appear in clockwise or counterclockwise order around the quadrilateral?

c. What property of reflections do parts (a) and (b) suggest?

a. Answers may vary. Sample: counterclockwise
b. Answers may vary. Sample: clockwise
c. Reflection reverses orientation.

Additional Examples

FOR EXAMPLE 1

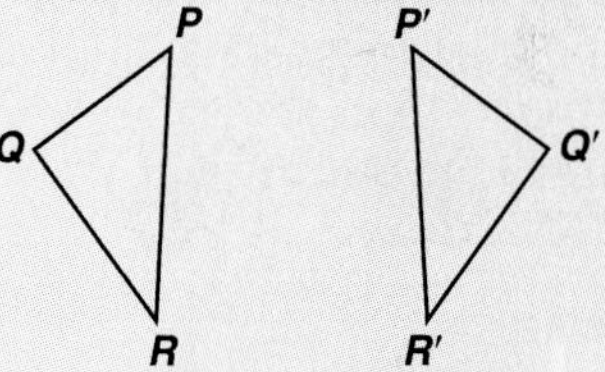

In the diagram, $P'Q'R'$ is the image of PQR.

a. Name the images of $\angle Q$ and $\angle R$. $\angle Q'$, $\angle R'$

b. List all pairs of corresponding sides. $\overline{PQ}$ and $\overline{P'Q'}$, $\overline{QR}$ and $\overline{Q'R'}$, $\overline{RP}$ and $\overline{R'P'}$

Discussion: *What type of transformation is illustrated?*

FOR EXAMPLE 2

Refer to the diagram in Example 2. Copy $\triangle ABC$ and draw its reflection image in $x = 2$.

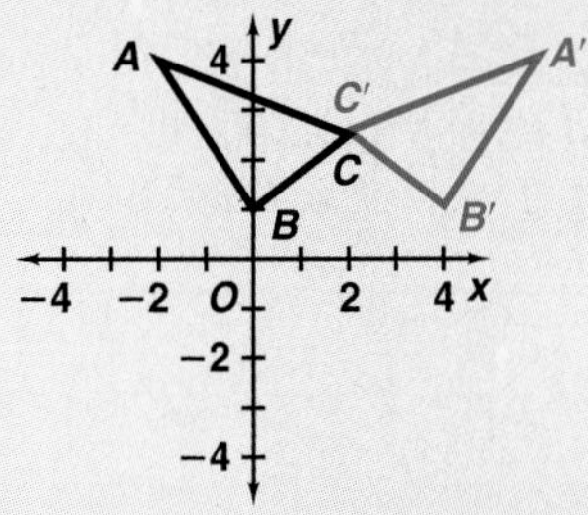

Discussion: *Name the coordinates of the vertices of $\triangle ABC$ and $\triangle A'B'C'$. What do you notice?*

THINK AND DISCUSS p. 126

ESL Discuss with students words that have the root *flex-* such as reflex, reflection, and flexible. Ask them how these words and the geometric meaning of reflection are related.

TACTILE LEARNING Have students use mirrors to investigate the properties of reflections. Have them hold a clock with a moving second hand up to a mirror and observe that the second hand is moving counterclockwise in the reflection. Then have them hold a 12-in. ruler perpendicular to the plane of the mirror and observe that the end of the ruler appears 12 inches away from the mirror in the reflection.

Example 2

Students now have three methods for finding a reflection image of a figure: paper folding, using MIRA™, and finding image points such that the line of reflection is the perpendicular bisector of the segment connecting a point and its image. Discuss with students why these methods produce the same results.

ERROR ALERT! In part b, the line of reflection passes through the figure. Students may be confused by this and reflect the figure about one of its vertices. **Remediation:** It sometimes helps students to reflect the part of the figure on one side of the line first, then to reflect the part of the figure on the other side of the line. Point out that parts "change sides."

Technology Options

For Exercises 10–17, students may use geometry software to draw the triangles and their reflections.

Prentice Hall Technology

Software
- Secondary Math Lab Toolkit™
- Computer Item Generator 3-1

CD-ROM
- Multimedia Geometry Lab 3

Internet
- See the Prentice Hall site. (http://www.phschool.com)

126

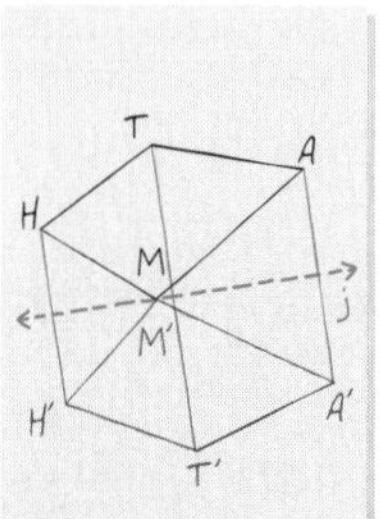

- Use a straightedge to draw segments $\overline{AA'}$, $\overline{TT'}$, and $\overline{HH'}$.

8. a. Line *j* divides each segment you drew into two parts. Compare the lengths of the two parts of each of the segments. They are =.
   b. Line *j* forms four angles with each segment you drew. Use a protractor to find the measures of each of the angles. 90
   c. Use your answers to parts (a) and (b) to complete the statement: Line *j* is the __?__ of the segment that connects a point and its image. ⊥ bisector

THINK AND DISCUSS

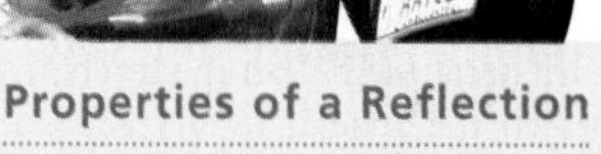

When you look at a word in a mirror, the image appears to be "backwards." The reflected word has the opposite **orientation** of the original word. Notice that the orientation of the word AMBULANCE in the photograph is reversed. The fronts of emergency vehicles often have mirror-image words on them so that drivers looking through rear-view mirrors can easily read them.

You discovered both of the following properties of reflections in the Work Together.

Properties of a Reflection

A reflection reverses orientation.

In the diagram, $\triangle BUG$ has *clockwise* orientation, so its image $\triangle B'U'G'$ has *counterclockwise* orientation.

A reflection is an isometry.

In the diagram, $\triangle BUG \cong \triangle B'U'G'$.

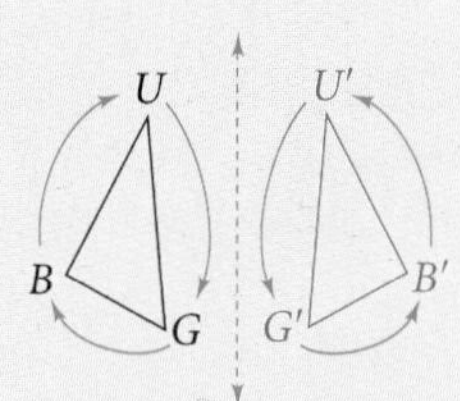

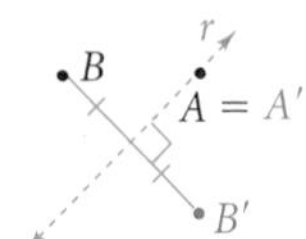

The other properties of reflections that you explored in the Work Together form the basis of the definition of a reflection. A **reflection** in line *r* is a transformation for which the following are true.

- If a point *A* is on line *r*, then the image of *A* is itself (that is, $A = A'$).
- If a point *B* is not on line *r*, then *r* is the perpendicular bisector of $\overline{BB'}$.

Example 3 Relating to the Real World 

Lead students to understand that to minimize the amount of pipe needed to connect the towns, the sum of the distances between the towns and the pumping station should be as small as possible.

MAKING CONNECTIONS You may want to point out to students that in a reflection the angle of incidence equals the angle of reflection. For example, on a miniature golf hole as shown below, *P* indicates the point on the wall, ideally, where the ball should be hit from the tee to get a hole-in-one.

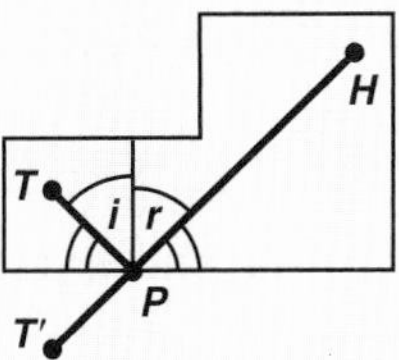

9. **Critical Thinking** Suppose you are given a point R and its reflection image R'. How could you find the line of reflection?
Construct the ⊥ bisector of $\overline{RR'}$.

Example 2

Coordinate Geometry Copy $\triangle ABC$ and draw its reflection image in each line.

a. the x-axis b. the y-axis

You can find A', B', and C' by paper folding or by locating points such that the line of reflection is the perpendicular bisector of $\overline{AA'}$, $\overline{BB'}$, and $\overline{CC'}$.

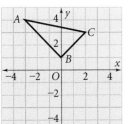

a. 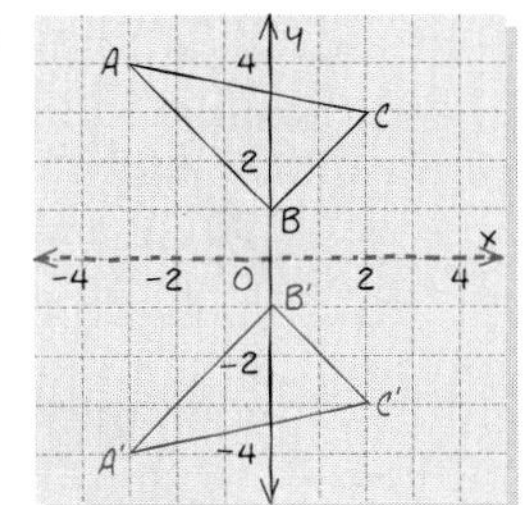

b. 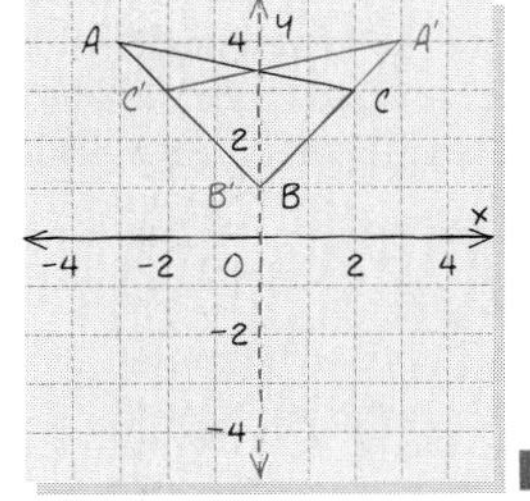

10. **Try This** Copy $\triangle ABC$ and draw its reflection image in $x = 3$.

See margin.

Example 3 Relating to the Real World 

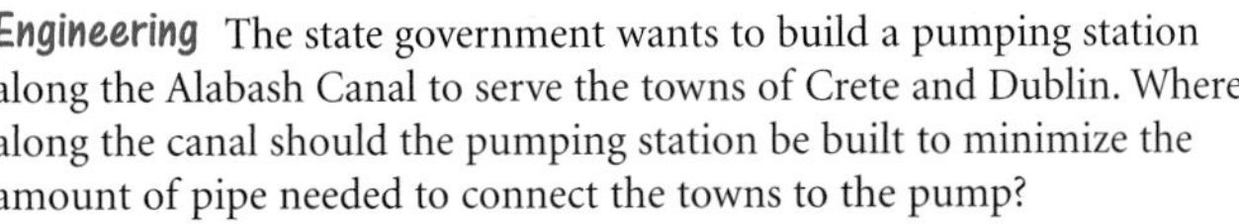

Engineering The state government wants to build a pumping station along the Alabash Canal to serve the towns of Crete and Dublin. Where along the canal should the pumping station be built to minimize the amount of pipe needed to connect the towns to the pump?

You need to find the point P on ℓ such that $DP + PC$ is as small as possible. Locate C', the reflection image of C in ℓ. Because a reflection is an isometry, $PC = PC'$, and $DP + PC = DP + PC'$. The sum $DP + PC'$ is smallest when D, P, and C' are collinear. So the pump should be located at the point P where $\overline{DC'}$ intersects ℓ.

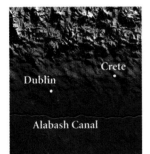

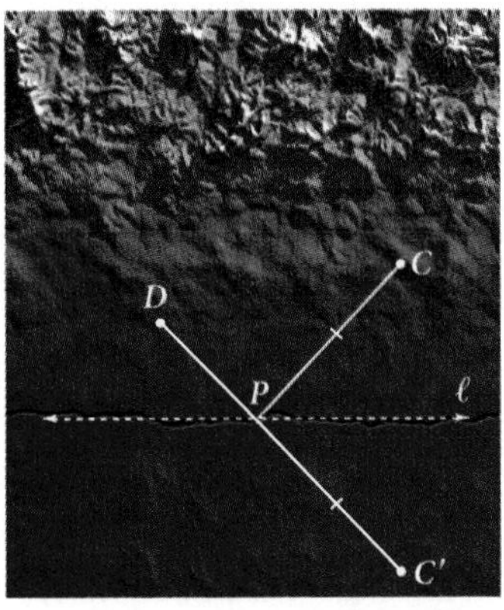

11. **Critical Thinking** Ursula began to solve Example 3 by reflecting point D in line ℓ. Will her method work? Explain. **Yes; the intersection of $\overline{D'C}$ and ℓ is the point P where the pump should be located.**

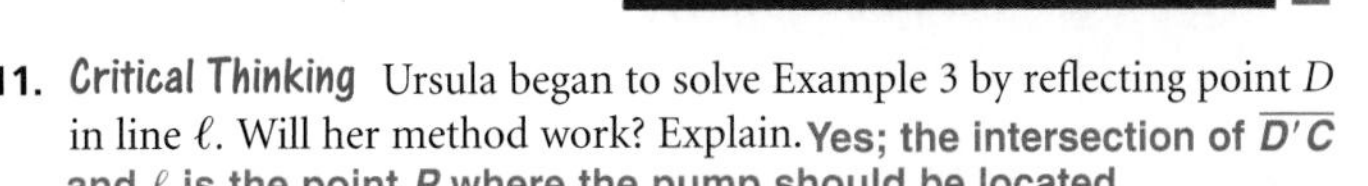

pages 126–127 Think and Discuss

10. 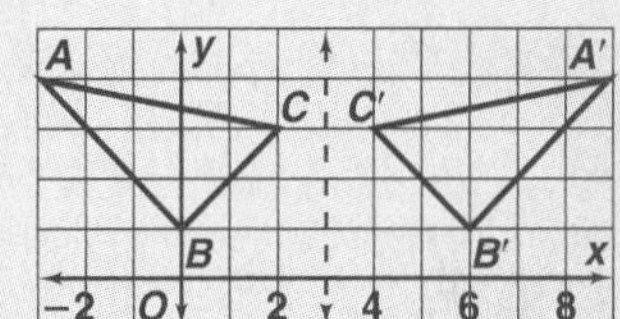

Exercises ON YOUR OWN

Exercise 2 The line of reflection passes through the figure. Refer students to Example 2b for a similar problem.

Exercise 3 Students discover that the letters B, O, and X are symmetric. Students may want to investigate what other letters have this property.

Exercises 4–9 Encourage students to copy the figures and draw arrows from the vertices (as shown on page 126) to indicate orientation.

COORDINATE GEOMETRY Exercises 10–17 Have students label the coordinates of the vertices of the reflection image. Have them compare the coordinates of the figures with those of their reflection images in Exercises 10, 11, and 14. Discuss what patterns they notice. Then have them make the same comparisons in Exercises 12, 13, and 15.

WRITING Exercise 19 Some of the students' examples may be a combination of more than one transformation. For example, using a protractor to measure an angle, you must slide and turn the protractor so that it aligns with one side of the angle.

Exercise 20 Suggest students find the image of C (or D) under a reflection in the mirrored wall. They can then use the second property of reflections to deduce the following: the distance from C (or D) to the mirrored wall is the same as the distance of C' (D') to the mirrored wall.

pages 128–130 On Your Own

4a. $\overline{ID}$ and $\overline{I'D'}$, $\overline{DS}$ and $\overline{D'S'}$, $\overline{SI}$ and $\overline{S'I'}$

5a. $\overline{PQ}$ and $\overline{P'Q'}$, $\overline{QR}$ and $\overline{Q'R'}$, $\overline{RS}$ and $\overline{R'S'}$, $\overline{SP}$ and $\overline{S'P'}$

6a. $\overline{OW}$ and $\overline{O'W'}$, $\overline{WE}$ and $\overline{W'E'}$, $\overline{EZ}$ and $\overline{E'Z'}$, $\overline{ZO}$ and $\overline{Z'O'}$

7a. $\overline{AR}$ and $\overline{A'R'}$, $\overline{RT}$ and $\overline{R'T'}$, $\overline{TA}$ and $\overline{T'A'}$

8a. $\overline{AB}$ and $\overline{A'B'}$, $\overline{BC}$ and $\overline{B'C'}$, $\overline{CA}$ and $\overline{C'A'}$

9a. $\overline{RI}$ and $\overline{R'I'}$, $\overline{IT}$ and $\overline{I'T'}$, $\overline{TR}$ and $\overline{T'R'}$

10.
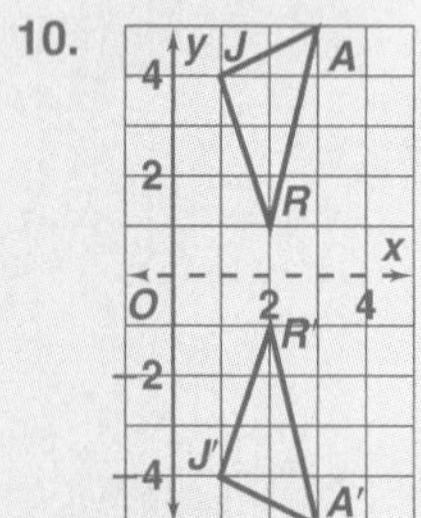

11.
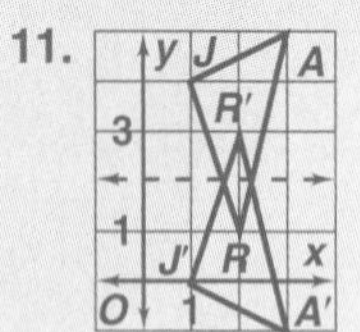

12.
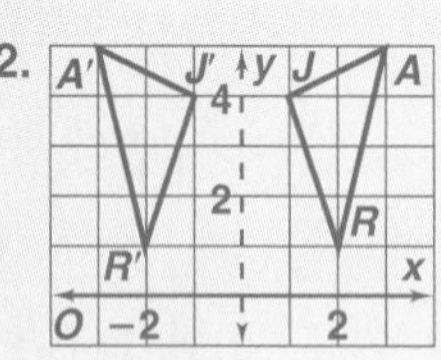

13.
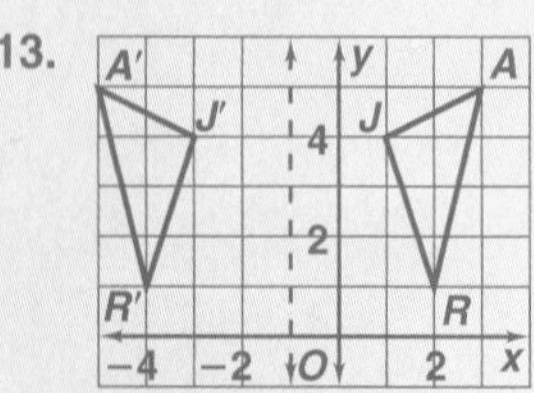

Exercises ON YOUR OWN

Copy each diagram, then find the reflection image of the figure in line ℓ.

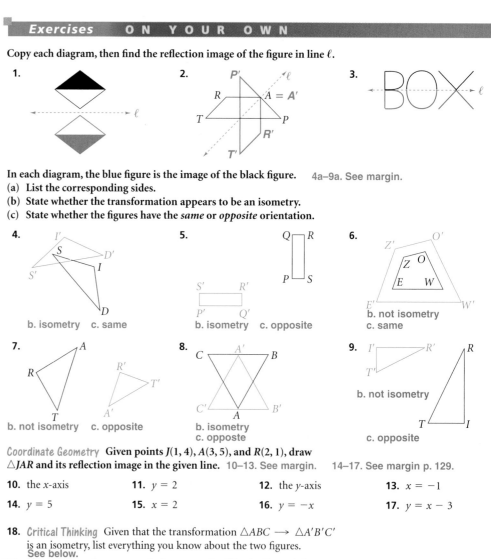

1.

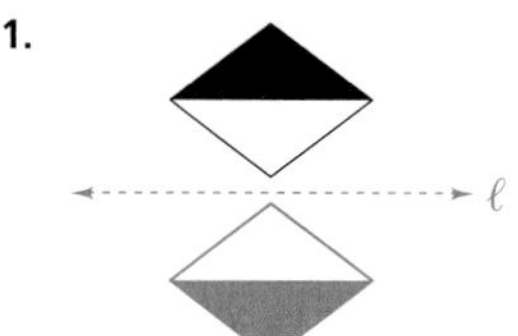

2.

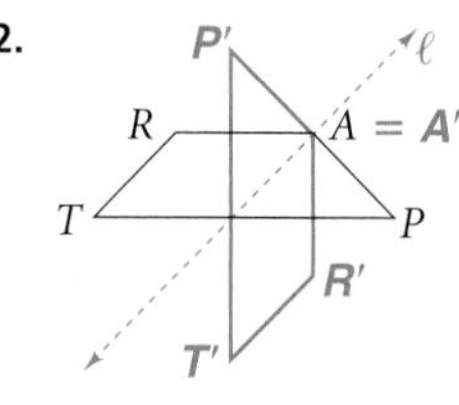

3.

In each diagram, the blue figure is the image of the black figure. 4a–9a. See margin.

(a) List the corresponding sides.

(b) State whether the transformation appears to be an isometry.

(c) State whether the figures have the *same* or *opposite* orientation.

4.

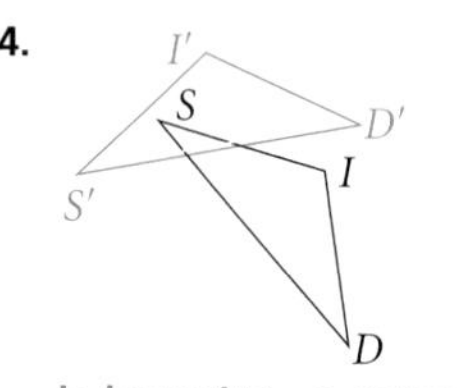
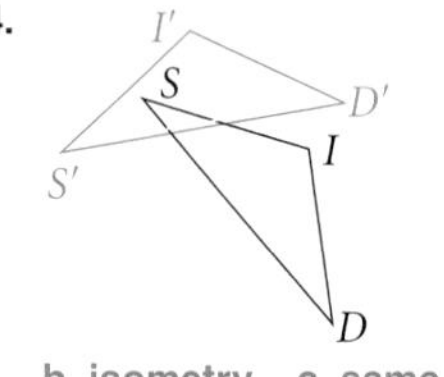

b. isometry c. same

5.

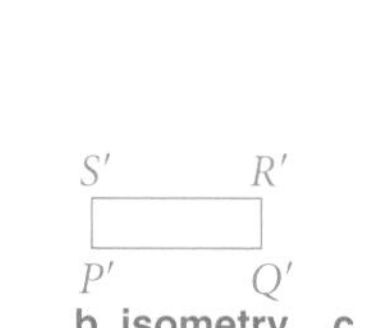

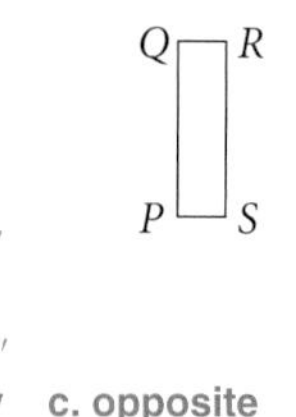

b. isometry c. opposite

6.

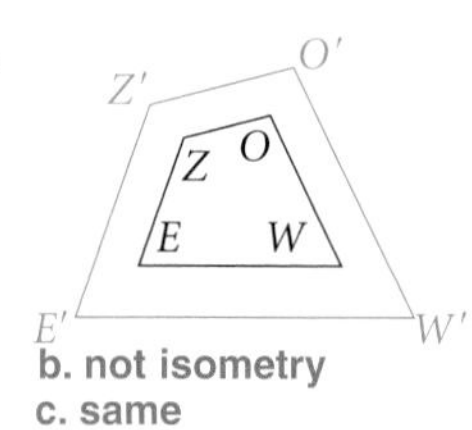

b. not isometry
c. same

7.

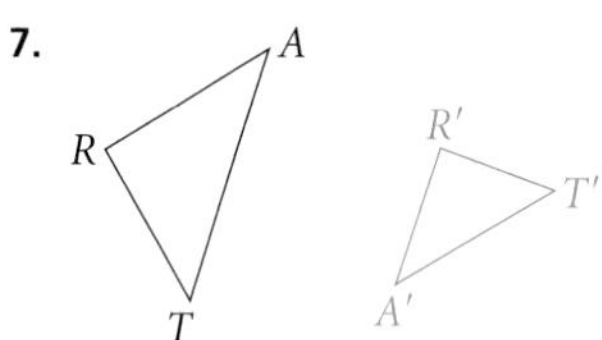

b. not isometry c. opposite

8.

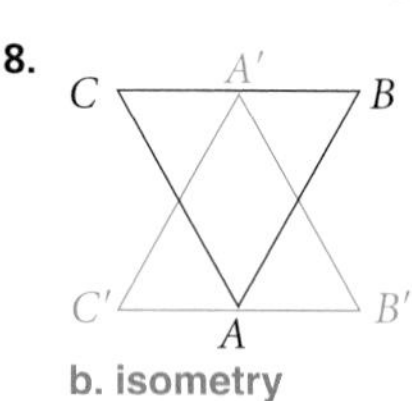

b. isometry
c. opposte

9.

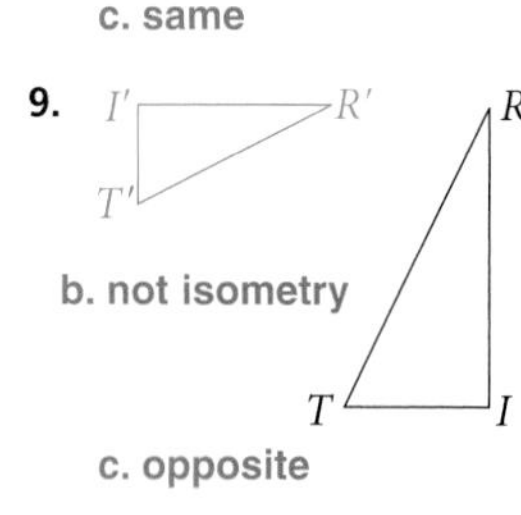

b. not isometry
c. opposite

Coordinate Geometry **Given points $J(1, 4)$, $A(3, 5)$, and $R(2, 1)$, draw $\triangle JAR$ and its reflection image in the given line.** 10–13. See margin. 14–17. See margin p. 129.

10. the x-axis	**11.** $y = 2$	**12.** the y-axis	**13.** $x = -1$
14. $y = 5$	**15.** $x = 2$	**16.** $y = -x$	**17.** $y = x - 3$

18. **Critical Thinking** Given that the transformation $\triangle ABC \longrightarrow \triangle A'B'C'$ is an isometry, list everything you know about the two figures.
See below.

19. **Writing** Describe an example from everyday life of a flip, a slide, a turn, and a size change. See margin p. 129.

20. **Surveillance** SafeCo specializes in installing security cameras in department stores. Copy the diagram onto your paper. At what point on the mirrored wall should camera C be aimed in order to photograph door D?

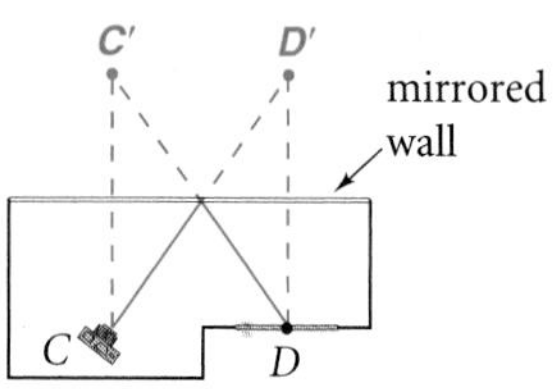

18. $\angle A \cong \angle A'$, $\angle B \cong \angle B'$, $\angle C \cong \angle C'$, $\overline{AB} \cong \overline{A'B'}$, $\overline{BC} \cong \overline{B'C'}$, $\overline{CA} \cong \overline{C'A'}$

ALTERNATIVE ASSESSMENT **Exercises 22–24** You can assess students' understanding of reflections by their ability to draw the line of reflection. Some students may connect corresponding points and draw the perpendicular bisector. Others may use paper folding to find the line.

MAKING CONNECTIONS Exercise 25 Point out to students that the "R" in "R-isomer" stands for *recto* which comes from the Latin word *recto* which means "on the right side." The "S" in "S-isomer" stands for *sinister* which is Latin for "on the left side."

CRITICAL THINKING Exercise 25 Ask students to explain the title of the article.

STANDARDIZED TEST TIP **Exercise 26** By using the strategy of drawing a diagram, choices *B*, *C*, and *E* can immediately be eliminated because the reflection of points in the second quadrant, such as $(-4, 5)$, are points in the fourth quadrant.

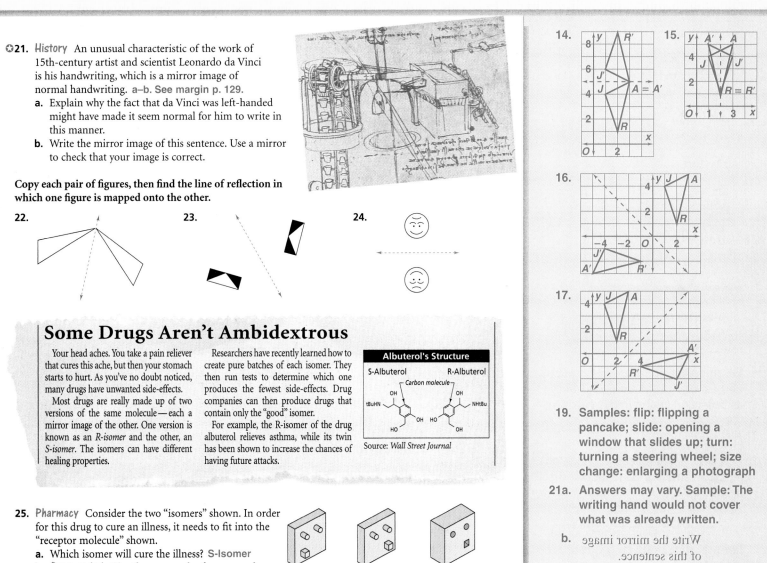

21. *History* An unusual characteristic of the work of 15th-century artist and scientist Leonardo da Vinci is his handwriting, which is a mirror image of normal handwriting. **a–b. See margin p. 129.**

a. Explain why the fact that da Vinci was left-handed might have made it seem normal for him to write in this manner.

b. Write the mirror image of this sentence. Use a mirror to check that your image is correct.

Copy each pair of figures, then find the line of reflection in which one figure is mapped onto the other.

22.

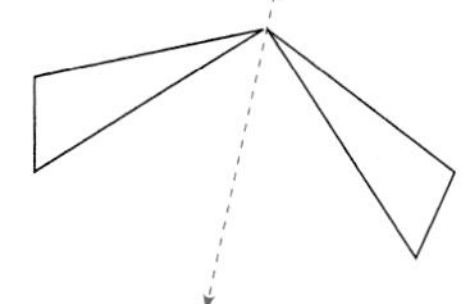

23.

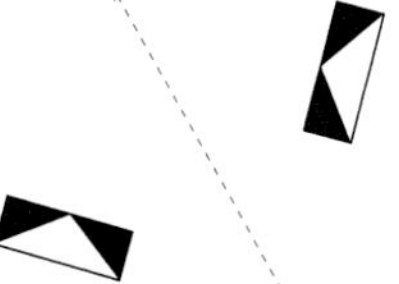

24.

Some Drugs Aren't Ambidextrous

Your head aches. You take a pain reliever that cures this ache, but then your stomach starts to hurt. As you've no doubt noticed, many drugs have unwanted side-effects.

Most drugs are really made up of two versions of the same molecule—each a mirror image of the other. One version is known as an *R-isomer* and the other, an *S-isomer*. The isomers can have different healing properties.

Researchers have recently learned how to create pure batches of each isomer. They then run tests to determine which one produces the fewest side-effects. Drug companies can then produce drugs that contain only the "good" isomer.

For example, the R-isomer of the drug albuterol relieves asthma, while its twin has been shown to increase the chances of having future attacks.

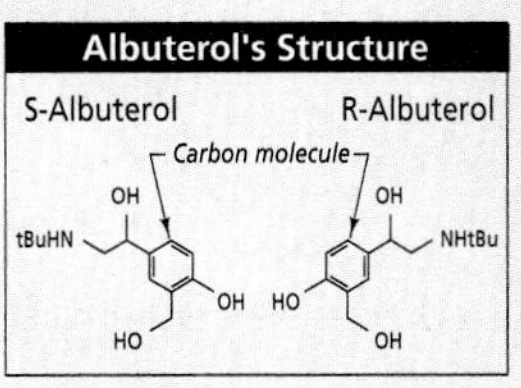

Source: *Wall Street Journal*

25. *Pharmacy* Consider the two "isomers" shown. In order for this drug to cure an illness, it needs to fit into the "receptor molecule" shown.

S-Isomer R-Isomer Receptor Molecule

a. Which isomer will cure the illness? **S-Isomer**

b. *Open-ended* Give three examples from everyday life of objects that come in a left-handed version and a right-handed version.
Samples: gloves, shoes, scissors

26. *Standardized Test Prep* What is the image of $(-4, 5)$ under a reflection in the line $y = x$? **A**

A. $(5, -4)$ **B.** $(4, 5)$ **C.** $(-4, -5)$ **D.** $(4, -5)$ **E.** $(-5, 4)$

14.

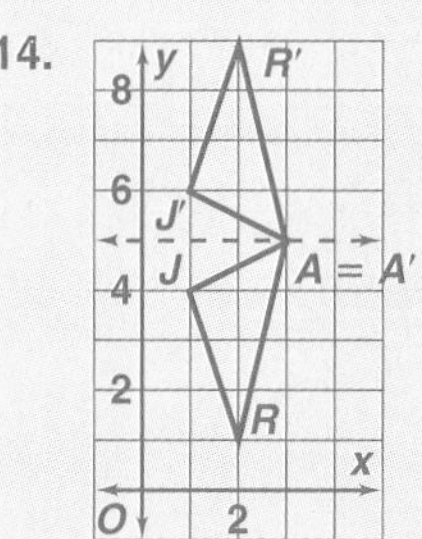

15.

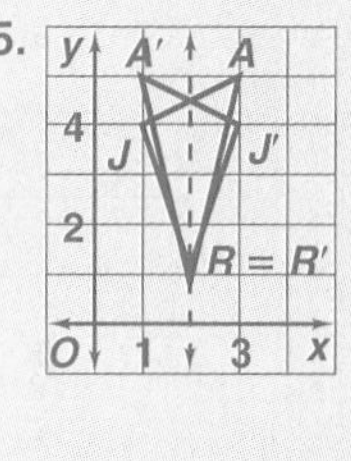

16.

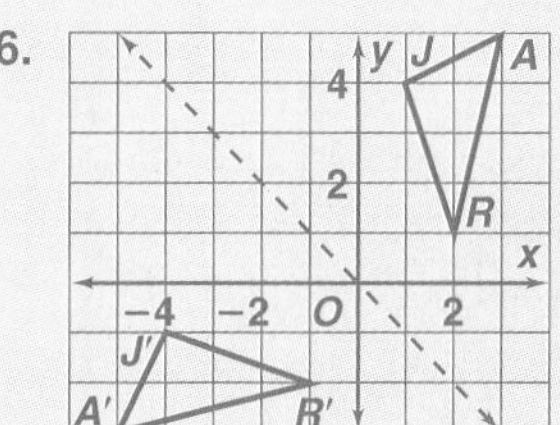

17.

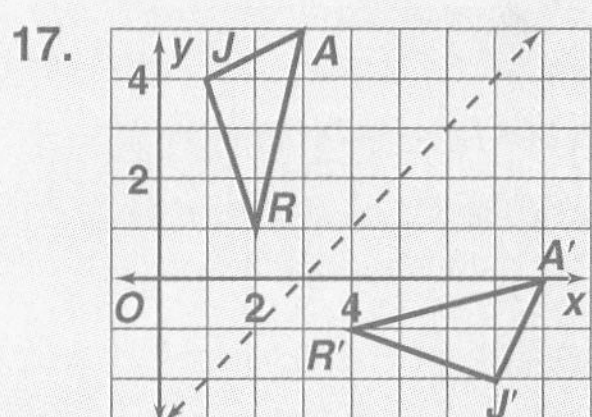

19. **Samples: flip: flipping a pancake; slide: opening a window that slides up; turn: turning a steering wheel; size change: enlarging a photograph**

21a. **Answers may vary. Sample: The writing hand would not cover what was already written.**

b. Write the mirror image of this sentence. (printed in mirror image)

Exercise 27 Have students describe the cartoon by writing captions for each of the four blocks.

Exercises MIXED REVIEW

Exercises 30–32 Students classify quadrilaterals.

Exercise 33 Students review finding midpoints and slopes and writing the equation of a line.

JOURNAL Have students include some real-world examples of reflections in their journal entries.

GETTING READY FOR LESSON 3-2 Students identify a slide and observe that each vertex is moved the same distance and in the same direction.

Wrap Up

THE BIG IDEA Ask students to describe two ways to find the reflection of a figure in a line. Ask them to describe how the preimage and image of a figure are related.

RETEACHING ACTIVITY Students use paper folding and scissors to investigate reflections of cutouts in the *x*-axis and *y*-axis. (Reteaching worksheet 3-1)

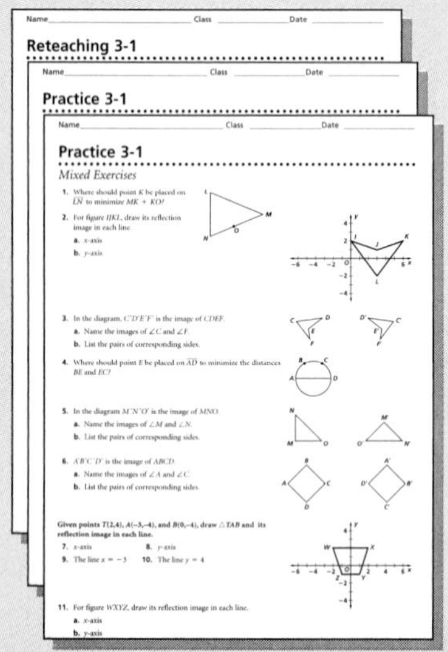

Lesson Quiz

Lesson Quiz is also available in Transparencies.

1. Given points $E(-2, 2)$, $F(-3, -5)$ and $G(-1, -1)$, draw $\triangle EFG$ and its reflection image in the *y*-axis. **$\triangle E'F'G'$ with $E'(2, 2)$, $F'(3, -5)$, and $G'(1, -1)$**
2. $A'B'C'D'$ is the reflection image of $ABCD$. Name the corresponding sides. **$\overline{AB}$ and $\overline{A'B'}$, $\overline{BC}$ and $\overline{B'C'}$, $\overline{CD}$ and $\overline{C'D'}$, $\overline{DA}$ and $\overline{D'A'}$**
3. In the scale drawing, where along the wall should the mirror be placed so someone in the chair can see the door?

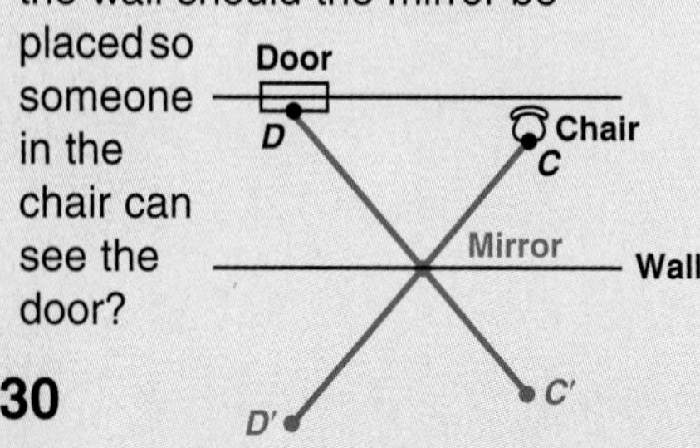

27. Which panels in the comic strip show the kind of reflection you studied in this lesson? Explain your answer. **See margin p. 131.**
28. **28a. See margin p. 131.**
    a. **Paper Folding** Plot the points $Y(-2, 5)$, $A(5, 0)$, and $K(-1, -2)$. Draw $\triangle YAK$, then use paper folding to find its image in $y = x$. Label the image $\triangle Y'A'K'$.
    b. **Patterns** Look for a pattern in the coordinates of $\triangle YAK$ and $\triangle Y'A'K'$. Write a general rule for finding the image of any point under a reflection in $y = x$. **b. Switch the coordinates.**
29. **Critical Thinking** Under a reflection, do all points move the same distance? If not, which points move the farthest? **No; the points farthest from the line of reflection move the farthest.**

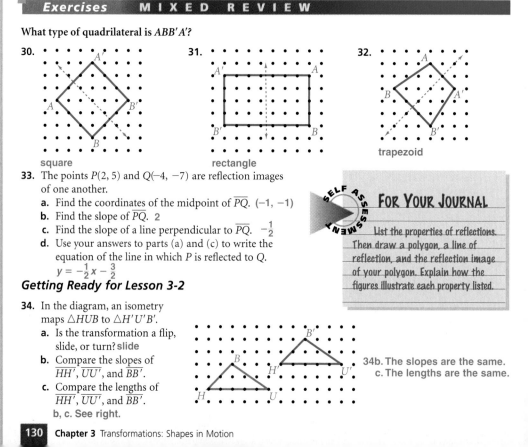

Source: *K-Hito (Ricardo Garcia López). "Macaco."© K-Hito*

Exercises MIXED REVIEW

What type of quadrilateral is $ABB'A'$?

30. 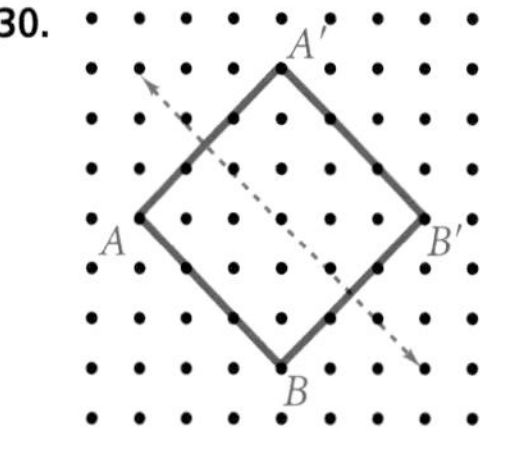

square

31. 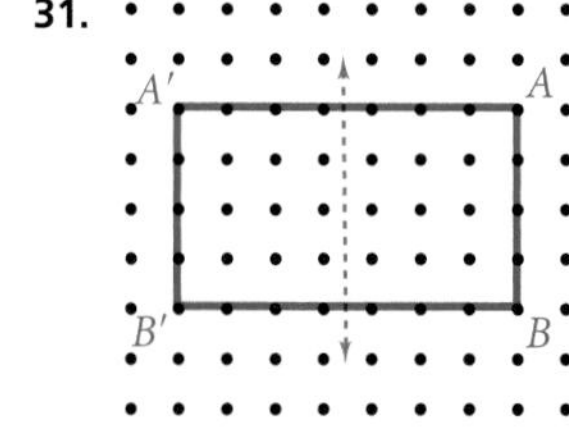

rectangle

32. 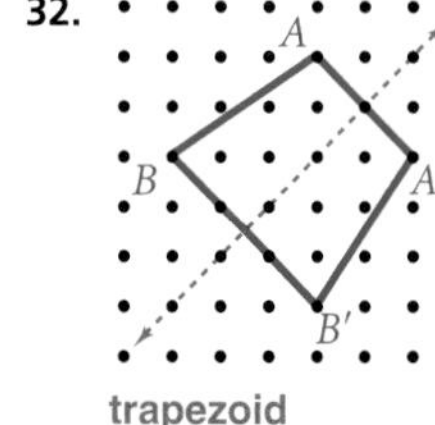

trapezoid

33. The points $P(2, 5)$ and $Q(-4, -7)$ are reflection images of one another.
    a. Find the coordinates of the midpoint of $\overline{PQ}$. **(−1, −1)**
    b. Find the slope of $\overline{PQ}$. **2**
    c. Find the slope of a line perpendicular to $\overline{PQ}$. **$-\frac{1}{2}$**
    d. Use your answers to parts (a) and (c) to write the equation of the line in which P is reflected to Q. **$y = -\frac{1}{2}x - \frac{3}{2}$**

FOR YOUR JOURNAL

List the properties of reflections. Then draw a polygon, a line of reflection, and the reflection image of your polygon. Explain how the figures illustrate each property listed.

Getting Ready for Lesson 3-2

34. In the diagram, an isometry maps $\triangle HUB$ to $\triangle H'U'B'$.
    a. Is the transformation a flip, slide, or turn? **slide**
    b. Compare the slopes of $\overline{HH'}$, $\overline{UU'}$, and $\overline{BB'}$.
    c. Compare the lengths of $\overline{HH'}$, $\overline{UU'}$, and $\overline{BB'}$.
    b, c. See right.

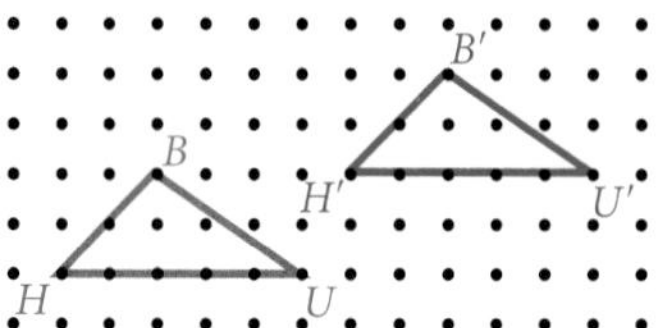

34b. The slopes are the same.
c. The lengths are the same.

Math ToolboX

Students review how to add and subtract matrices. In Lesson 3-2, students will use matrices to represent coordinates of figures and translations. They will also find the coordinates of the images of translations using matrix addition.

Example

Have students notice that the dimensions of the solution are the same as the dimensions of the matrices being added.

ERROR ALERT! **Exercise 2** Some students may have trouble mentally subtracting corresponding entries, especially when the entries are negative numbers. **Remediation:** These students may want to write expressions for each entry, then simplify: $-6 - (-4) = -2$, $3 - (-9) = 12$, $-8 - 3 = -11$, $1 - 5 = -4$.

Exercise 9 Check that students understand what the labels on the matrices represent by asking them to identify different entries, such as the number of tenth graders involved in drama.

ADDITIONAL PROBLEM Have students create and solve a matrix problem like Exercise 9. For example, they could write matrices that represent the number of boys and girls wearing sneakers and other kinds of shoes in two of their classes, then find the sum.

Math ToolboX — Algebra Review

Matrices

Before Lesson 3-2

A **matrix** is a rectangular arrangement of numbers. A matrix is usually written inside brackets. You identify the size of a matrix by the number of rows and columns. This matrix has two rows and three columns, so it is a 2×3 matrix. Each item in a matrix is called an **entry.**

$$\begin{bmatrix} -1 & 4 & 9 \\ -5 & 3 & 7 \end{bmatrix}$$

You can add or subtract matrices if they are the same size. You do this by adding or subtracting corresponding entries.

Example

Add $\begin{bmatrix} 6 & -5 \\ 0 & 3 \end{bmatrix} + \begin{bmatrix} 1 & 8 \\ -2 & 10 \end{bmatrix}$.

$$\begin{bmatrix} 6 & -5 \\ 0 & 3 \end{bmatrix} + \begin{bmatrix} 1 & 8 \\ -2 & 10 \end{bmatrix} = \begin{bmatrix} 6 + 1 & -5 + 8 \\ 0 + (-2) & 3 + 10 \end{bmatrix}$$ Add corresponding entries.

$$= \begin{bmatrix} 7 & 3 \\ -2 & 13 \end{bmatrix}$$

Add or subtract each pair of matrices.

1. $\begin{bmatrix} 3 & 8 \\ 1 & 5 \end{bmatrix} + \begin{bmatrix} 8 & 2 \\ 0 & 7 \end{bmatrix}$ $\begin{bmatrix} 11 & 10 \\ 1 & 12 \end{bmatrix}$

2. $\begin{bmatrix} -6 & 3 \\ -8 & 1 \end{bmatrix} - \begin{bmatrix} -4 & -9 \\ 3 & 5 \end{bmatrix}$ $\begin{bmatrix} -2 & 12 \\ -11 & -4 \end{bmatrix}$

3. $\begin{bmatrix} 1 & -6 \\ 2 & -7 \end{bmatrix} + \begin{bmatrix} \frac{1}{2} & -1 \\ \frac{2}{3} & -2 \end{bmatrix}$ $\begin{bmatrix} \frac{3}{2} & -7 \\ \frac{8}{3} & -9 \end{bmatrix}$

4. $\begin{bmatrix} \frac{1}{3} & \frac{3}{4} \\ \frac{1}{2} & \frac{2}{5} \end{bmatrix} - \begin{bmatrix} -\frac{1}{6} & \frac{1}{4} \\ -\frac{3}{5} & \frac{2}{3} \end{bmatrix}$ $\begin{bmatrix} \frac{1}{2} & \frac{1}{2} \\ \frac{11}{10} & -\frac{4}{15} \end{bmatrix}$

5. $\begin{bmatrix} 2 & 9 \\ 6 & 7 \end{bmatrix} + \begin{bmatrix} 6 & 2.3 \\ 9 & 4.1 \end{bmatrix}$ $\begin{bmatrix} 8 & 11.3 \\ 15 & 11.1 \end{bmatrix}$

6. $\begin{bmatrix} 3 & -7 & 4 \\ 0 & -4 & 9 \end{bmatrix} + \begin{bmatrix} -9 & 4 & 10 \\ 3 & -11 & 2 \end{bmatrix}$

7. $\begin{bmatrix} 5 & -3.5 \\ 10 & 14 \\ -5 & 4.7 \end{bmatrix} + \begin{bmatrix} -6.1 & 0.8 \\ 7 & -5 \\ 8.3 & 9 \end{bmatrix}$ $\begin{bmatrix} -1.1 & -2.7 \\ 17 & 9 \\ 3.3 & 13.7 \end{bmatrix}$

8. $\begin{bmatrix} 4 & 2 & 9 \\ -11 & 20 & 5 \\ -18 & 21 & -2 \end{bmatrix} - \begin{bmatrix} 8 & 17 & 4 \\ -34 & 26 & -9 \\ 3 & 0 & 17 \end{bmatrix}$

6 and 8. See margin.

9. Use the matrices to find the total number of students per grade involved in each activity. See margin.

Greenfield High School North

	Sports	Drama	Debate
9th	146	5	11
10th	201	15	4
11th	205	11	7
12th	176	19	13

Greenfield High School South

	Sports	Drama	Debate
9th	301	13	9
10th	345	8	6
11th	245	11	11
12th	220	11	9

Transparencies
11

pages 128–130 On Your Own

27. First and third panels; the figures in the second panel are not ≅, and the fourth panel shows a slide.

28a.

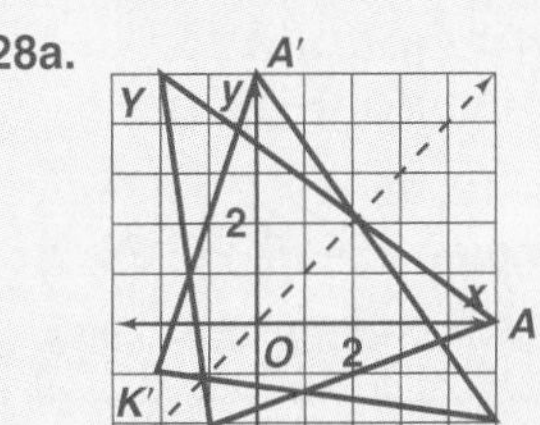

Math Toolbox page 131

6. $\begin{bmatrix} -6 & -3 & 14 \\ 3 & -15 & 11 \end{bmatrix}$

8. $\begin{bmatrix} -4 & -15 & 5 \\ 23 & -6 & 14 \\ -21 & 21 & -19 \end{bmatrix}$

9. $\begin{bmatrix} 447 & 18 & 20 \\ 546 & 23 & 10 \\ 450 & 22 & 18 \\ 396 & 30 & 22 \end{bmatrix}$

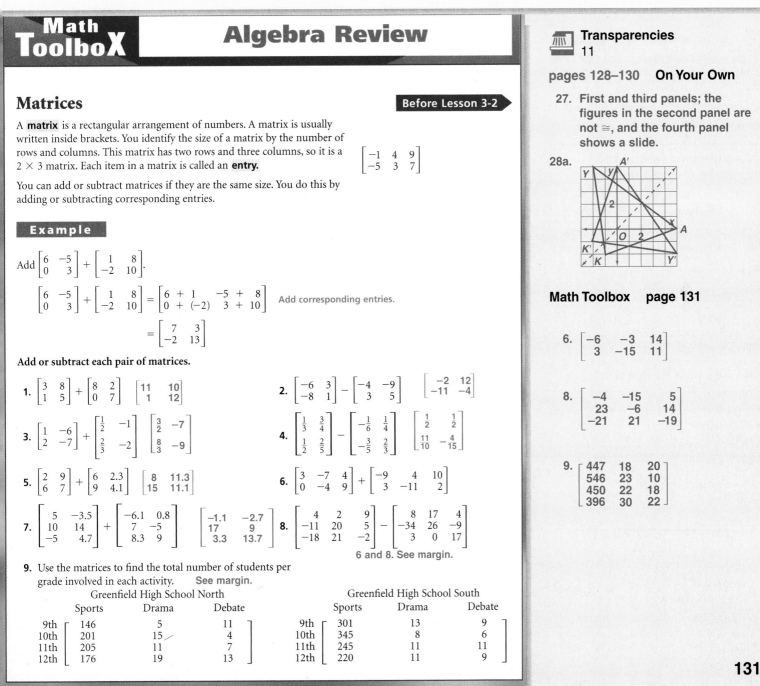

3-2 Teaching Notes

PROBLEM OF THE DAY

Placing no more than one X in each small square, what is the greatest number of X's that can be put in a 3-by-3 square grid without forming a line of three X's in a row horizontally, vertically, or diagonally? 6

Problem of the Day is also available in Transparencies.

CONNECTING TO PRIOR KNOWLEDGE Ask students to make a table of values and sketch the graphs of $y = |x|$, $y = |x| - 5$ and $y = |x| + 3$. Discuss how the graph of $y = |x|$ can be used to draw the other two graphs.

WORK TOGETHER

Have students draw their triangles on lightweight cardboard so they will be easier to trace around. Recommend that they draw triangles having sides of three different lengths. Check that students slide their cutouts without rotating them.

ALTERNATE METHOD If time does not allow for the group activity, use two transparencies with the same triangle drawn on each to illustrate a translation. Start with the two triangles on top of each other. Slide the top triangle to another location and have students discuss Questions 1–4.

Lesson Planning Options

Prerequisite Skills

- Graphing in the coordinate plane
- Adding matrices

Assignment Options for Exercises On Your Own

Core 1–12, 16–19, 21–27
Extension 13–15, 20, 28

Use Mixed Review to maintain skills.

Resources

Student Edition
Skills Handbook, p. 679
Extra Practice, p. 650
Glossary/Study Guide

Teaching Resources
Chapter Support File, Ch. 3
- Practice 3-2(two worksheets)
- Reteaching 3-2

Classroom Manager 3-2
Glossary, Spanish Resources

Transparencies
5, 40, 46

What You'll Learn

- Finding translation images of figures
- Using vectors and matrix addition to represent translations

...And Why

To use translations in the arts, computer graphics, navigation, manufacturing, music, and other fields

What You'll Need

- centimeter ruler
- scissors
- graph paper

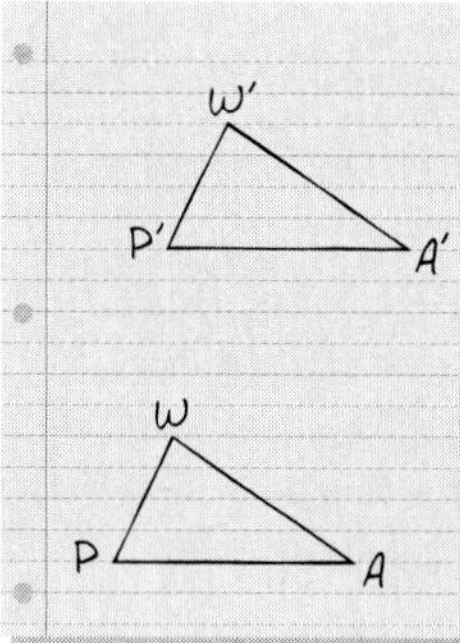

Connections  Photography . . . and more

3-2 Translations

WORK TOGETHER

- Have each member of your group draw a triangle, cut it out, and label it $\triangle PAW$.
- Place your triangle on a sheet of lined paper so that $\overline{PA}$ lies on a horizontal line. Trace the triangle, and label it $\triangle PAW$.
- Slide the cutout to another location on your paper so that $\overline{PA}$ again lies on a horizontal line. Trace the triangle, and label it $\triangle P'A'W'$.

1. Does the transformation $\triangle PAW \longrightarrow \triangle P'A'W'$ appear to be an isometry? Explain. Yes; the triangles are $\cong$.
2. Does the transformation $\triangle PAW \longrightarrow \triangle P'A'W'$ change the orientation of the triangle? Explain. No; the order of vertices in the image is the same as the order of the corresponding vertices in the preimage.

- Use a straightedge to draw $\overline{PP'}$, $\overline{AA'}$, and $\overline{WW'}$. Measure each segment with a ruler.

3. What do you notice about the lengths of the segments? All the lengths are =.
4. Notice the positions of $\overline{PP'}$, $\overline{AA'}$, and $\overline{WW'}$ in relation to one another. What appears to be true about them? Compare your answer with others in your group. The segments are $\parallel$.

THINK AND DISCUSS

The sliding motion that maps $\triangle PAW$ to $\triangle P'A'W'$ in the Work Together is an example of a translation. A **translation** is a transformation that moves points the same distance and in the same direction. In the Work Together, you discovered the following properties of a translation.

Properties of a Translation

A translation is an isometry.

A translation does not change orientation.

5. Elevators, escalators, and people movers all suggest translations. Name some other examples of translations from the real world. Samples: assembly line, positions of a car on a straight road

THINK AND DISCUSS

The concept of vectors may be confusing to some students. Make sure students understand how vectors differ from rays (vectors do not go on forever in one direction) and segments $\overline{AB}$ and $\overline{BA}$ are the same but $\overrightarrow{AB}$ and $\overrightarrow{BA}$ are not). Emphasize that a vector indicates both distance and direction.

Example 1

This translation could also be accomplished by moving each vertex one unit up and three units right. However, naming the horizontal movement first is consistent with ordered pair notation.

ERROR ALERT! **Question 6** Students may confuse ordered pair notation and the slope formula and write the vertical change first. **Remediation:** One way to remember the order of ordered pair notation is to remember that it is similar to an ordered pair (x, y).

Example 2

KINESTHETIC LEARNING Create a coordinate grid on the floor of your classroom using masking tape or meter sticks. (This is easily done if your floor has square tiles.) Have students physically represent the points in Example 2 and "act out" translations that take one point to another.

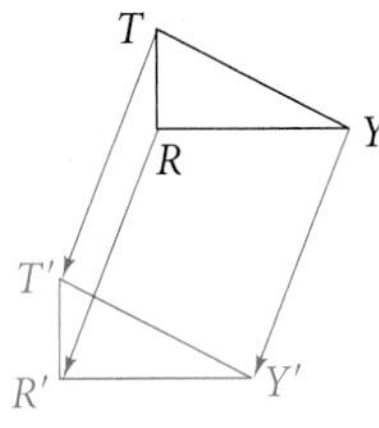

The distance and direction of a translation can be expressed as a *vector*. In the diagram, $\overrightarrow{TT'}$, $\overrightarrow{RR'}$, and $\overrightarrow{YY'}$ are vectors. Vectors have an *initial point* and a *terminal point*. T, R, and Y are initial points, and T', R', and Y' are terminal points. Note that although diagrams of vectors look identical to diagrams of rays, vectors do not go on forever in the indicated direction—they have a fixed length.

Example 1

Use the given vector and rectangle to create a sketch of a box.

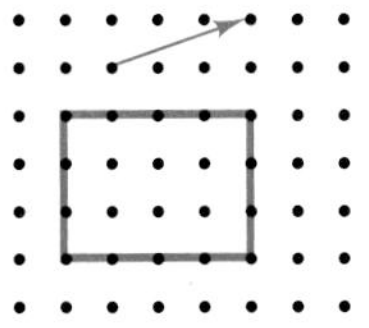

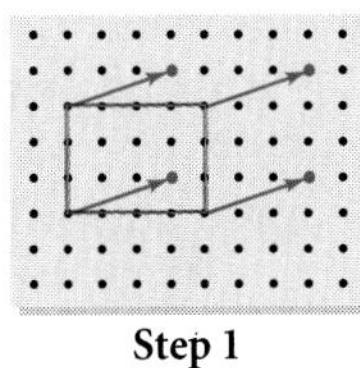

Step 1

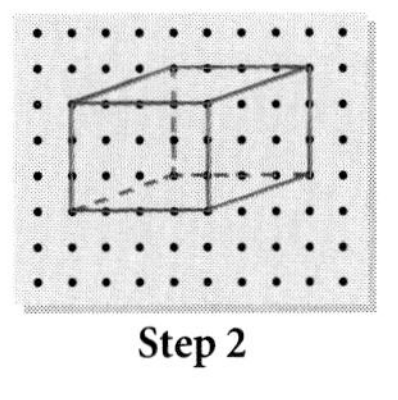

Step 2

Copy the rectangle, then translate each of its vertices 3 units to the right and 1 unit up. Next, connect points to form the box. Use dashed lines for parts of the figure that are hidden from view.

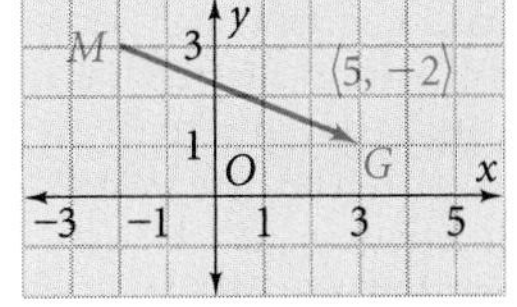

You can use *ordered pair notation*, $\langle x, y\rangle$, to represent a vector on the coordinate plane. In the notation, x represents horizontal change from the initial point to the terminal point and y represents vertical change from the initial point to the terminal point. The notation for vector $\overrightarrow{MG}$ is $\langle 5, -2\rangle$.

6. **Try This** Describe the vector in Example 1 by using ordered pair notation. **$\langle 3, 1\rangle$**
7. Use vector notation to describe the vector with initial point $(1, 3)$ and terminal point $(6, 1)$. **$\langle 5, -2\rangle$**

Example 2

a. What is the image of P under the translation $\langle 0, -4\rangle$?
b. What vector describes the translation $S \longrightarrow U$?

a. The vector $\langle 0, -4\rangle$ represents a translation of 4 units down. The image of P is Q.
b. To get from S to U, you move 3 units left and 6 units down. The vector that describes this translation is $\langle -3, -6\rangle$.

8. **Try This** Refer to the diagram in Example 2.
   a. What is the image of S under the translation $\langle -3, -1\rangle$? ***R***
   b. What vector describes the translation $T \longrightarrow P$? **$\langle 6, 3\rangle$**
9. Describe in words the distance and direction of the translation represented by the vector $\langle 18, 0\rangle$. **18 units to the right**

Additional Examples

FOR EXAMPLE 2

Refer to the diagram in Example 2.

a. What is the image of T under the translation $\langle 3, 4\rangle$? **(0, 3)**

b. What vector describes the translation of R to Q? **$\langle 4, -4\rangle$**

Discussion: *When describing a translation, what direction do you name first?*

FOR EXAMPLE 3

Refer to the diagram in Example 3. Use matrices to find the image of $\triangle SUD$ under the translation $\langle -2, 4\rangle$.

$$\begin{bmatrix} -3 & 0 & 1 \\ 3 & -1 & 6 \end{bmatrix}$$

Discussion: *How do you represent vertices of a preimage using a matrix?*

Example 3

Remind students that to add two matrices, they should add corresponding entries.

Example 4 **Relating to the Real World** 

EXTENSION Vectors are used to describe direction on a map. If you have block scheduling or an extended period, have students use the map to create similar problems where they describe two consecutive paths on the map and then find the resulting distance and direction traveled from the starting point.

ALGEBRA Students may be familiar with the composition of two functions where the second function is performed on the output of the first function. For example, if $f(x) = x^2$ and $g(x) = 3x + 2$, then $g(f(4)) = g(4^2) = 3(4^2) + 2 = 50$.

Exercises ON YOUR OWN

Exercises 1–6 Help students see that because a translation is an isometry, one vector describes the translation no matter how many vertices the figure has.

Technology Options

For Exercises 13–15, students may use geometry software to draw the triangles and their translations.

Prentice Hall Technology 

Software
- Secondary Math Lab Toolkit™
- Integrated Math Lab 27
- Computer Item Generator 3-2

CD-ROM
- Multimedia Geometry Lab 3

Internet
- See the Prentice Hall site. (http://www.phschool.com)

$$\begin{array}{l} \\ x\text{-coordinate} \\ y\text{-coordinate} \end{array} \begin{array}{c} \begin{matrix} S & U & D \end{matrix} \\ \begin{bmatrix} -1 & 2 & 3 \\ -1 & -5 & 2 \end{bmatrix} \end{array}$$

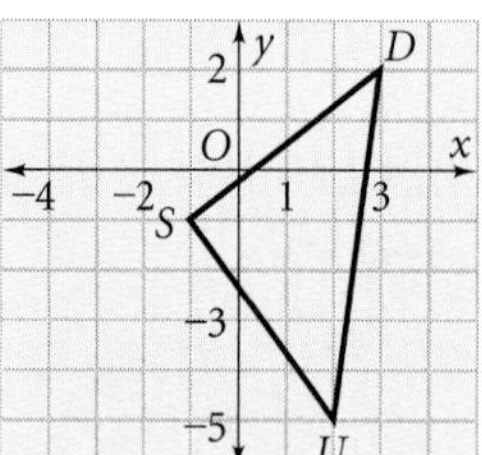

You can use matrices to help you translate figures in the coordinate plane. To do so, start by creating a matrix for the figure, as shown at the left.

Example 3

Use matrices to find the image of $\triangle SUD$ under the translation $\langle 4, -5 \rangle$.

To find the image of $\triangle SUD$, you add 4 to all of the x-coordinates and -5 to all of the y-coordinates.

Vertices of Preimage		Translation Matrix		Vertices of Image
$\begin{matrix} S & U & D \end{matrix}$ $\begin{bmatrix} -1 & 2 & 3 \\ -1 & -5 & 2 \end{bmatrix}$	+	$\begin{bmatrix} 4 & 4 & 4 \\ -5 & -5 & -5 \end{bmatrix}$	=	$\begin{matrix} S' & U' & D' \end{matrix}$ $\begin{bmatrix} 3 & 6 & 7 \\ -6 & -10 & -3 \end{bmatrix}$

10. Check the answer to Example 3 by sketching $\triangle SUD$ and $\triangle S'U'D'$ on the same set of axes. See margin p. 135.

Example 4 **Relating to the Real World** 

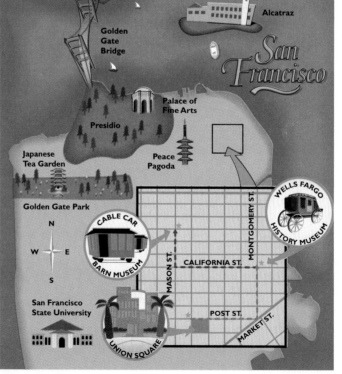

Travel Yolanda Pérez is visiting San Francisco. From her hotel near Union Square, she walked 4 blocks east and 4 blocks north to the Wells Fargo History Museum to see a stagecoach and relics of the gold rush. Then she walked 5 blocks west and 3 blocks north to the Cable Car Barn Museum. How many blocks from her hotel is she now?

As shown in the diagram, she is 1 block west and 7 blocks north of her hotel.

You can also solve this problem by using vectors. The vector $\langle 4, 4 \rangle$ represents a walk of 4 blocks east and 4 blocks north. The vector $\langle -5, 3 \rangle$ represents her second walk. The solution is the sum of the x- and y-coordinates of each vector:
$\langle 4, 4 \rangle + \langle -5, 3 \rangle = \langle -1, 7 \rangle$.

Exercise 5 Students may have difficulty recognizing corresponding points on the two figures. Suggest that they find the coordinates of the vertices.

Exercises 7–12 Students may want to copy the coordinate grid so they can trace the translations.

ERROR ALERT! **Exercise 15** Because the direction vector is pictured above the figure, students may translate the figure up and to the left. **Remediation:** Remind students to find the direction vector from the initial point to the terminal point.

Example 4 shows the composition of two translations. The term **composition** describes any two transformations in which the second transformation is performed on the image of the first transformation. As the solution to Example 4 suggests, a composition of translations can be rewritten as a single translation.

Exercises ON YOUR OWN

In each diagram, the blue figure is the image of the red figure. Use ordered pair notation to represent each translation.

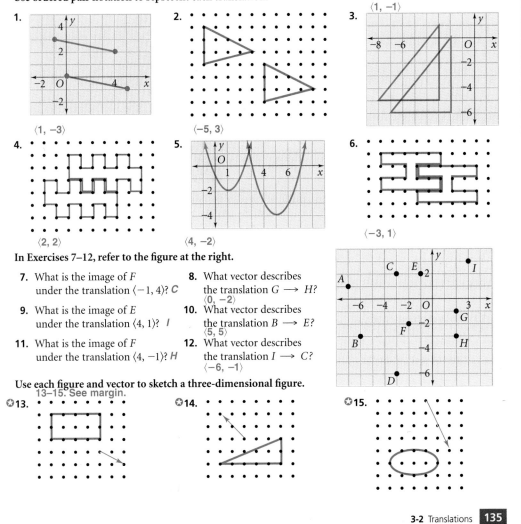

1. 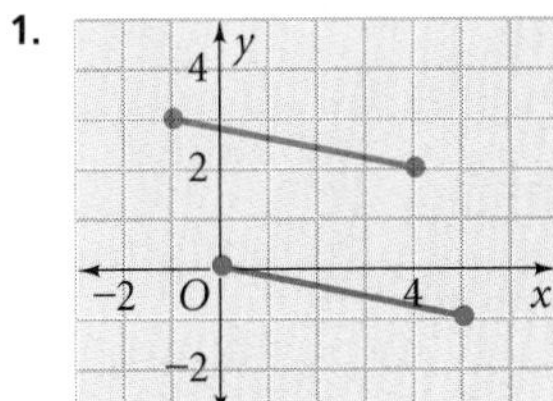
⟨1, −3⟩

2. ⟨−5, 3⟩

3. 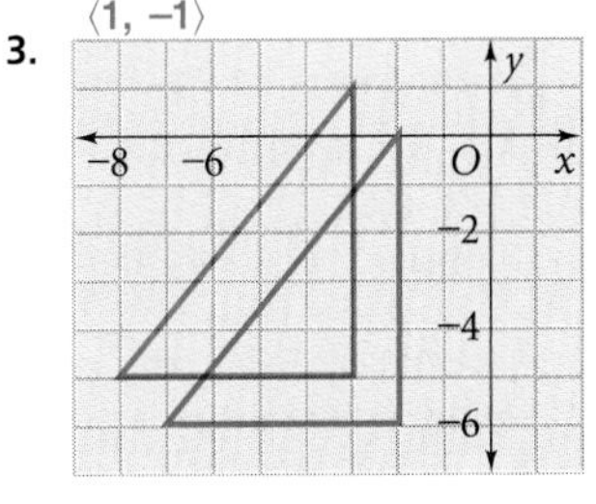
⟨1, −1⟩

4. 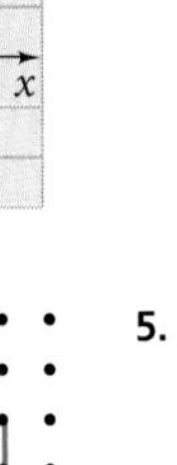
⟨2, 2⟩

5. 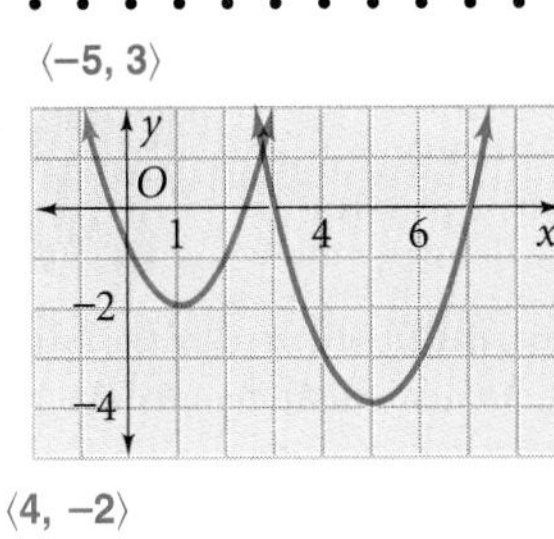
⟨4, −2⟩

6. 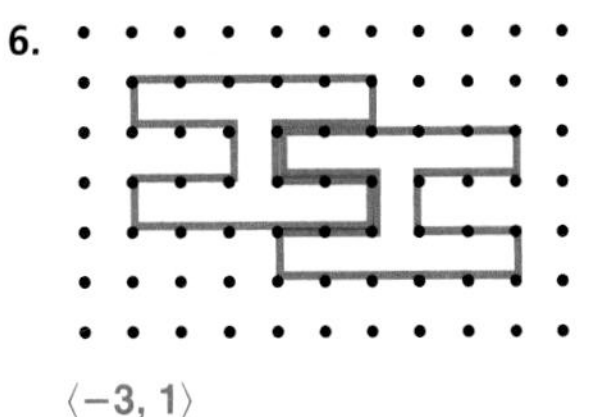
⟨−3, 1⟩

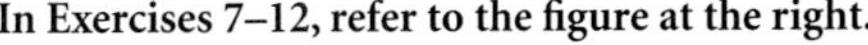

In Exercises 7–12, refer to the figure at the right.

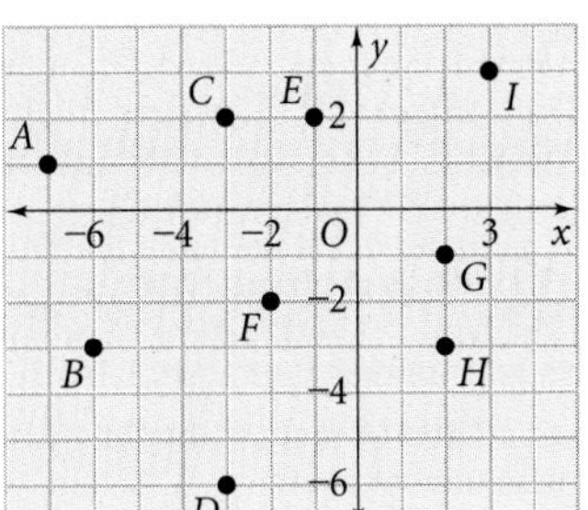

7. What is the image of F under the translation $\langle -1, 4\rangle$? *C*
8. What vector describes the translation $G \longrightarrow H$? ⟨0, −2⟩
9. What is the image of E under the translation $\langle 4, 1\rangle$? *I*
10. What vector describes the translation $B \longrightarrow E$? ⟨5, 5⟩
11. What is the image of F under the translation $\langle 4, -1\rangle$? *H*
12. What vector describes the translation $I \longrightarrow C$? ⟨−6, −1⟩

Use each figure and vector to sketch a three-dimensional figure. 13–15. See margin.

✪13. 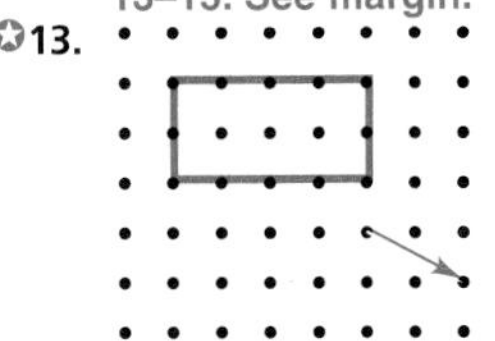

✪14. 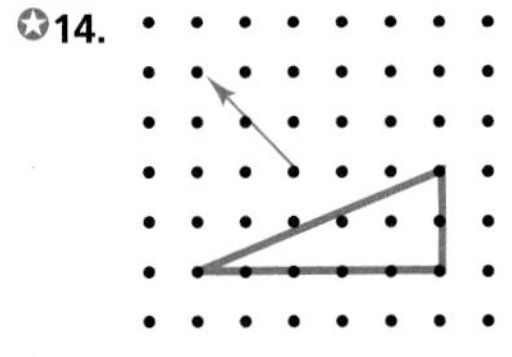

✪15. 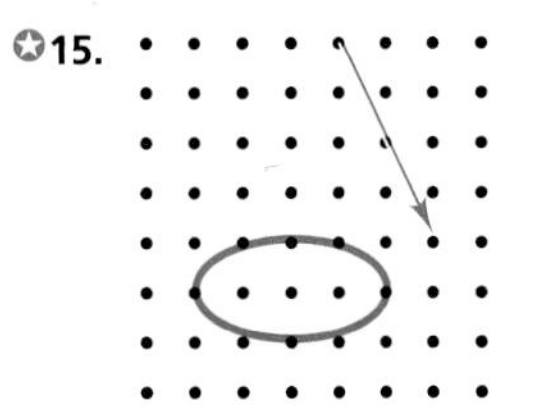

pages 132–135 Think and Discuss

10. 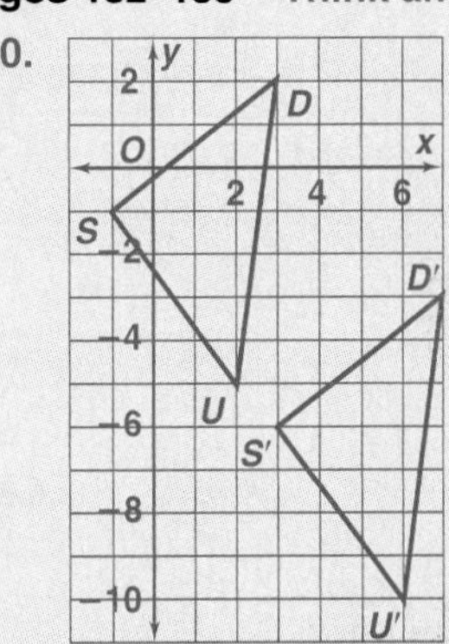

pages 135–137 On Your Own

13. 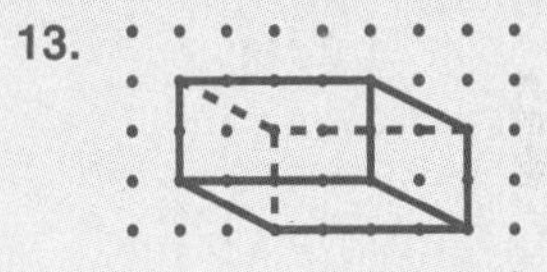

14. 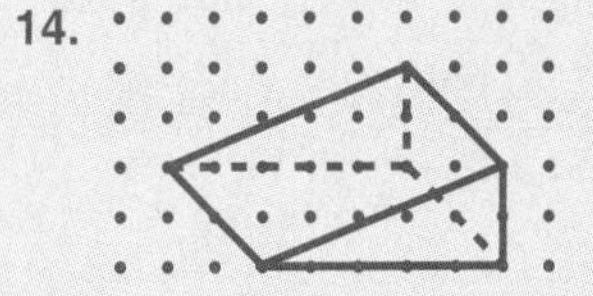

15. 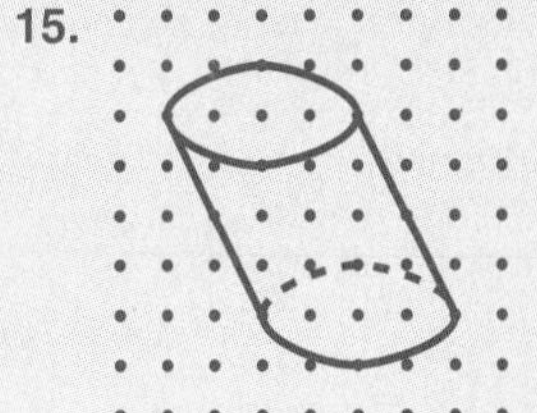

CRITICAL THINKING Exercise 16 Ask students how far Spinnaker Restaurant is from Galveston Bay.

Exercises 17–19 Students can check their results by graphing the preimages and images in the coordinate plane.

CONNECTING TO STUDENTS' WORLD Exercise 20 Have students find examples from cartoons, comic books, or magazines that use translations to suggest motion.

DIVERSITY Exercise 22 You may want to discuss the value of visiting colleges, but be aware of the financial constraints some of your students may have when considering college.

ALTERNATIVE ASSESSMENT Exercise 27 This exercise can help you assess students' understanding of the concepts in this lesson. Compare students' methods. Some students will solve this problem using graphs and others by using matrices.

OPEN-ENDED Exercise 28 Students may want to color or decorate their designs.

16.

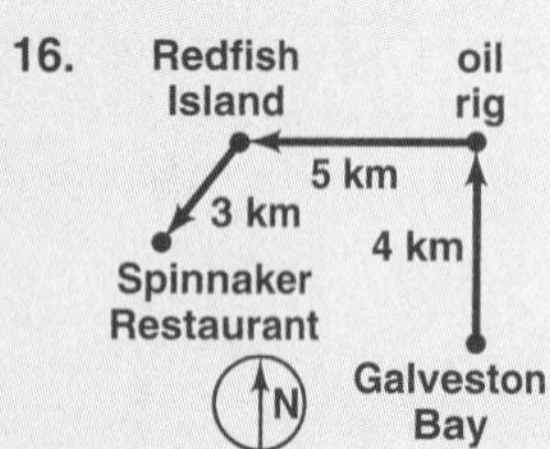

22.

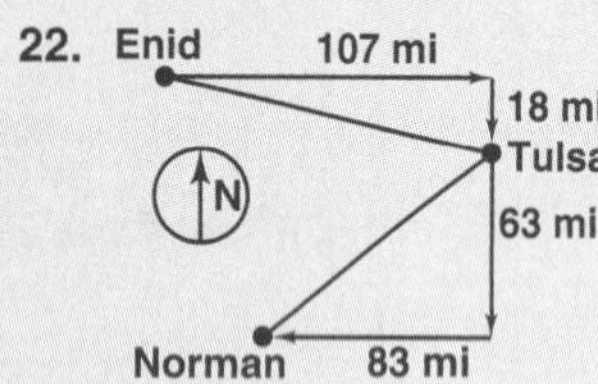

27b.

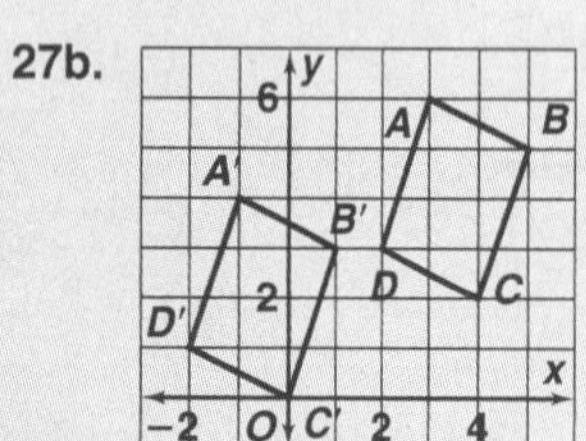

31a.

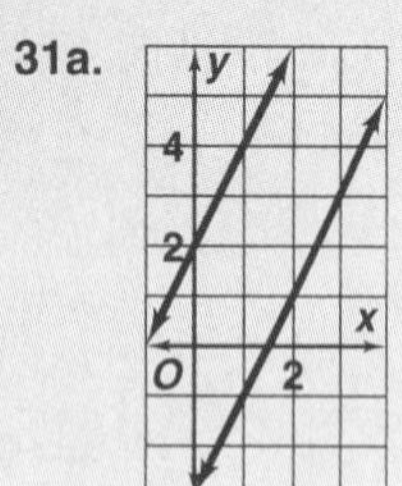

16. *Sailing* Emily left Galveston Bay at the east jetty and sailed 4 km north to an oil rig. She then sailed 5 km west to Redfish Island. Finally, she sailed 3 km southwest to the Spinnaker Restaurant. Draw vectors on graph paper that show her journey. **See margin.**

In Exercises 17–19, use matrix addition to find the image of each figure under the given translation.

17. Figure: $\triangle ACE$ with vertices $A(7, 2)$, $C(-8, 5)$, $E(0, -6)$
Translation: $\langle -9, 4\rangle$ **See below right.**

18. Figure: $\triangle PUN$ with vertices $P(1, 0)$, $U(4, 6)$, $N(-5, 8)$
Translation: $\langle 11, -13\rangle$ **See below right.**

19. Figure: $\square NILE$ with vertices $N(2, -5)$, $I(2, 2)$, $L(-3, 4)$, $E(-3, -3)$
Translation: $\langle -3, -4\rangle$ $\begin{matrix} N' & I' & L' & E' \end{matrix}$ $\begin{bmatrix} -1 & -1 & -6 & -6 \\ -9 & -2 & 0 & -7 \end{bmatrix}$

20. *Photography* When you snap a photograph, a shutter opens to expose the film to light. The amount of time that the shutter remains open is known as the *shutter speed*. The photographer of the train used a long shutter speed to create an image that suggests a translation. Sketch a picture of your own that suggests a translation. **Check students' work.**

21. *Coordinate Geometry* $\triangle MUG$ has coordinates $M(2, -4)$, $U(6, 6)$ and $G(7, 2)$. A translation maps point M to $(-3, 6)$. Find the coordinates of U' and G' under this translation. **$U'(1, 16)$; $G'(2, 12)$**

22. *Visiting Colleges* Nakesha and her parents are visiting colleges. They leave their home in Enid, Oklahoma, and head for Tulsa, which is 107 mi east and 18 mi south of Enid. From Tulsa, they head to Norman, which is 83 mi west and 63 mi south of Tulsa. Where is Norman in relation to Enid? Draw a diagram to show your solution. **See margin for diagram; Norman is 24 mi east and 81 mi south of Enid.**

23. *Writing* Is the transformation $\triangle HYP \longrightarrow \triangle H'Y'P'$ a translation? Explain. **No. Answers may vary. Sample: a translation does not change orientation.**

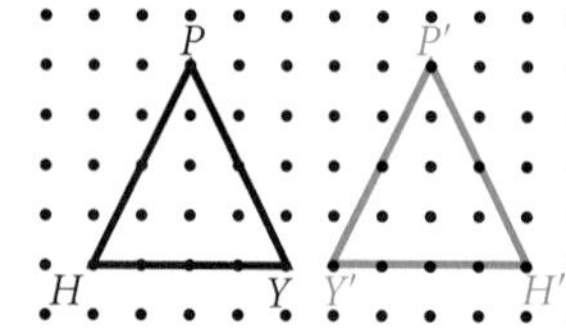

Find a single translation that has the same effect as each composition of translations.

24. $\langle 2, 5\rangle$ followed by $\langle -4, 9\rangle$ **$\langle -2, 14\rangle$**

25. $\langle -3, 7\rangle$ followed by $\langle 3, -7\rangle$ **$\langle 0, 0\rangle$**

26. $\langle 12, 0.5\rangle$ followed by $\langle 1, -3\rangle$ **$\langle 13, -2.5\rangle$**

27. *Coordinate Geometry* $\square ABCD$ has vertices $A(3, 6)$, $B(5, 5)$, $C(4, 2)$, and $D(2, 3)$. The figure is translated so that the image of point C is the origin.
a. Find the vector that describes the translation. **$\langle -4, -2\rangle$**
b. Graph $\square ABCD$ and its image. **See margin.**

17. $\begin{matrix} A' & C' & E' \end{matrix}$ $\begin{bmatrix} -2 & -17 & -9 \\ 6 & 9 & -2 \end{bmatrix}$

18. $\begin{matrix} P' & U' & N' \end{matrix}$ $\begin{bmatrix} 12 & 15 & 6 \\ -13 & -7 & -5 \end{bmatrix}$

Chapter Project **FIND OUT BY INVESTIGATING** Ask students to describe wallpaper borders or stencils they have seen that have frieze patterns. Discuss how the patterns are repeated. You may want to have students look through department store catalogs or home-decorating magazines for examples. Remind students to keep their Find Out exercise work in one place, so they can complete the chapter project at the end of the chapter.

Exercises MIXED REVIEW

GETTING READY FOR LESSON 3-3 These exercises prepare students to describe rotations in Lesson 3-3. Make sure students understand how to find degrees greater than 180°.

Wrap Up

THE BIG IDEA Ask students: *Given a figure and its image under a translation, how do you find the vector that describes the translation? Given the coordinates of a point, how do you find the coordinates of its image under a translation?*

RETEACHING ACTIVITY Students draw a triangle in the first quadrant. They trace the triangle and translate it to each of the other quadrants. Then they name vectors that describe the translations. (Reteaching worksheet 3-2)

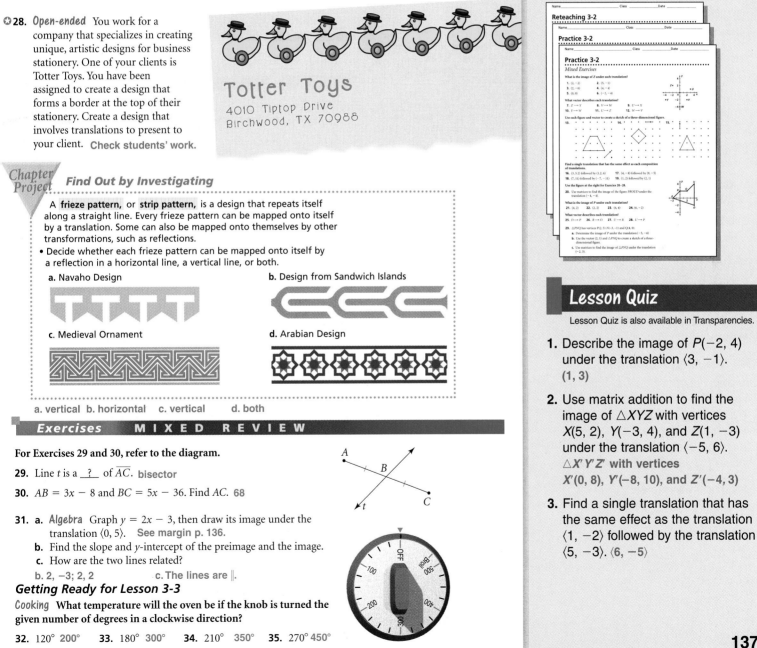

---

28. ***Open-ended*** You work for a company that specializes in creating unique, artistic designs for business stationery. One of your clients is Totter Toys. You have been assigned to create a design that forms a border at the top of their stationery. Create a design that involves translations to present to your client. **Check students' work.**

Find Out by Investigating

A **frieze pattern,** or **strip pattern,** is a design that repeats itself along a straight line. Every frieze pattern can be mapped onto itself by a translation. Some can also be mapped onto themselves by other transformations, such as reflections.

- Decide whether each frieze pattern can be mapped onto itself by a reflection in a horizontal line, a vertical line, or both.

a. Navaho Design

b. Design from Sandwich Islands

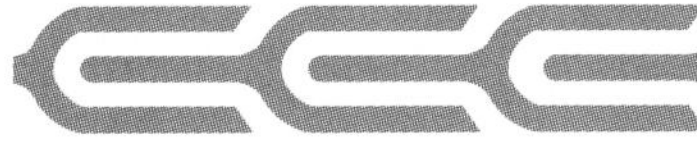

c. Medieval Ornament

d. Arabian Design

a. vertical b. horizontal c. vertical d. both

Exercises MIXED REVIEW

For Exercises 29 and 30, refer to the diagram.

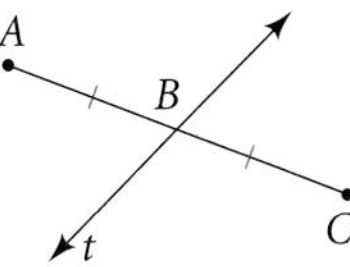

29. Line t is a __?__ of $\overline{AC}$. **bisector**

30. $AB = 3x - 8$ and $BC = 5x - 36$. Find AC. **68**

31. **a.** ***Algebra*** Graph $y = 2x - 3$, then draw its image under the translation $\langle 0, 5\rangle$. **See margin p. 136.**
    b. Find the slope and y-intercept of the preimage and the image.
    c. How are the two lines related?
    b. 2, −3; 2, 2 **c. The lines are ∥.**

Getting Ready for Lesson 3-3

Cooking **What temperature will the oven be if the knob is turned the given number of degrees in a clockwise direction?**

32. 120° **200°** **33.** 180° **300°** **34.** 210° **350°** **35.** 270° **450°**

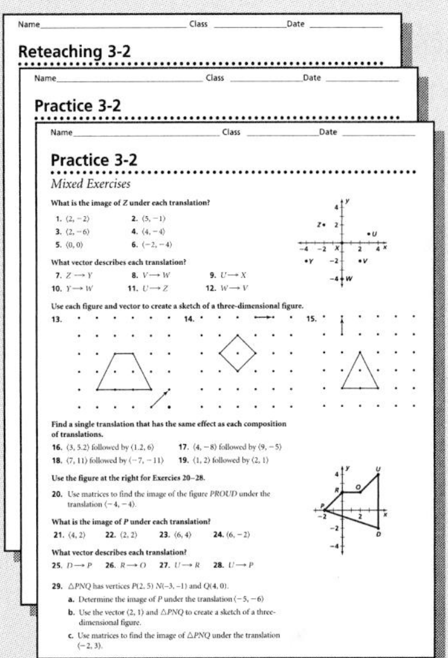
Name Class Date
Reteaching 3-2
Name Class Date
Practice 3-2
Name Class Date
Practice 3-2
Mixed Exercises
What is the image of Z under each translation?
1. $\langle 2, -2\rangle$ 2. $\langle 5, -1\rangle$
3. $\langle 2, -6\rangle$ 4. $\langle 4, -4\rangle$
5. $\langle 0, 0\rangle$ 6. $\langle -2, -4\rangle$
What vector describes each translation?
7. $Z \to Y$ 8. $V \to W$ 9. $U \to X$
10. $Y \to W$ 11. $U \to Z$ 12. $W \to V$
Use each figure and vector to create a sketch of a three-dimensional figure.
13. 14. 15.
Find a single translation that has the same effect as each composition of translations.
16. $\langle 3, 5.2\rangle$ followed by $\langle 1.2, 6\rangle$ 17. $\langle 4, -8\rangle$ followed by $\langle 9, -5\rangle$
18. $\langle 7, 11\rangle$ followed by $\langle -7, -11\rangle$ 19. $\langle 1, 2\rangle$ followed by $\langle 2, 1\rangle$
Use the figure at the right for Exercises 20–28.
20. Use matrices to find the image of the figure $PROUD$ under the translation $\langle -4, -4\rangle$.
What is the image of P under each translation?
21. $\langle 4, 2\rangle$ 22. $\langle 2, 2\rangle$ 23. $\langle 6, 4\rangle$ 24. $\langle 6, -2\rangle$
What vector describes each translation?
25. $D \to P$ 26. $R \to O$ 27. $U \to R$ 28. $U \to P$
29. $\triangle PNQ$ has vertices $P(2, 5)$ $N(-3, -1)$ and $Q(4, 0)$.
a. Determine the image of P under the translation $\langle -5, -6\rangle$
b. Use the vector $\langle 2, 1\rangle$ and $\triangle PNQ$ to create a sketch of a three-dimensional figure.
c. Use matrices to find the image of $\triangle PNQ$ under the translation $\langle -2, 3\rangle$.

Lesson Quiz

Lesson Quiz is also available in Transparencies.

1. Describe the image of $P(-2, 4)$ under the translation $\langle 3, -1\rangle$. **(1, 3)**

2. Use matrix addition to find the image of $\triangle XYZ$ with vertices $X(5, 2)$, $Y(-3, 4)$, and $Z(1, -3)$ under the translation $\langle -5, 6\rangle$. **$\triangle X'Y'Z'$ with vertices $X'(0, 8)$, $Y'(-8, 10)$, and $Z'(-4, 3)$**

3. Find a single translation that has the same effect as the translation $\langle 1, -2\rangle$ followed by the translation $\langle 5, -3\rangle$. **$\langle 6, -5\rangle$**

3-3 Teaching Notes

PROBLEM OF THE DAY

What is the least number of colors necessary to color the figure below if the regions with a common border may not be colored with the same color? 4

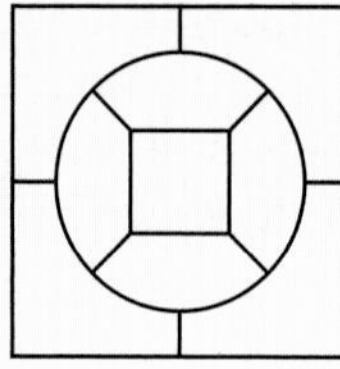

Problem of the Day is also available in Transparencies.

CONNECTING TO PRIOR KNOWLEDGE To prepare students for drawing angles where neither side lies in a horizontal line, have students use a protractor to draw two 60° angles, each in a different position. Then have students draw two 140° angles in different positions.

WORK TOGETHER

Students may benefit from using tracing paper for this activity Have students read through Steps 1–3 before beginning Step 1. As students rotate their papers, make sure that the centers of their circles stay aligned. The results should be kaleidoscopic designs.

Lesson Planning Options

Prerequisite Skills

- Drawing angles
- Constructing congruent line segments

Assignment Options for Exercises On Your Own

Core 1–18, 20–25, 28–30
✪**Extension** 19, 26–27

Use Mixed Review to maintain skills.

Resources

Student Edition

Skills Handbook, p. 665
Extra Practice, p. 650
Glossary/Study Guide

Teaching Resources

Chapter Support File, Ch. 3
- Practice 3-3 (two worksheets)
- Reteaching 3-3
- Alternative Activity 3-3

Classroom Manager 3-3
Glossary, Spanish Resources

Transparencies
5, 12, 41, 47, 48

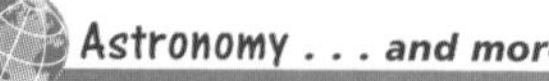

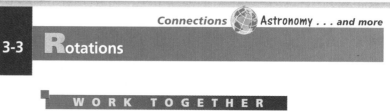

Connections Astronomy . . . and more

3-3 Rotations

What You'll Learn

- Identifying and locating rotation images of figures

...And Why

To understand real-life objects that involve rotation, such as clocks, combination locks, and laser disc players

What You'll Need

- straightedge
- colored pencils (optional)
- protractor
- compass

WORK TOGETHER

Before beginning the activity, have each member of your group fold a piece of paper in half lengthwise and widthwise and then cut it into fourths.

Step 1: Place a piece of the paper over the figure below. Trace the six points on the circle, the center of the circle, and the triangle.

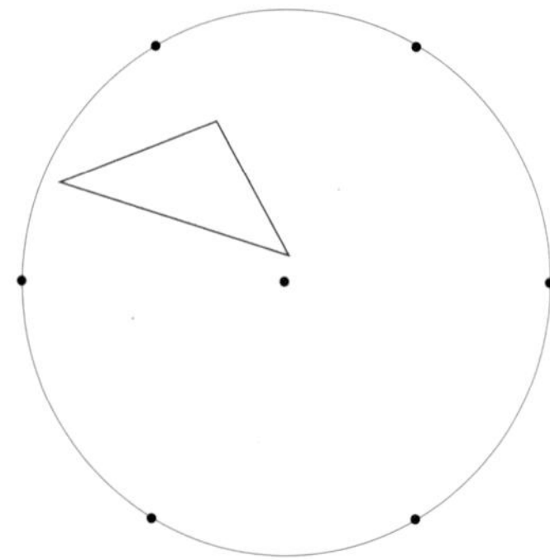

If you start with this in Step 4 . . .

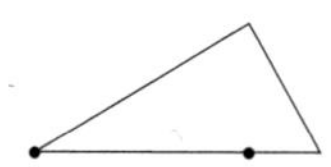

You could end up with this . . .

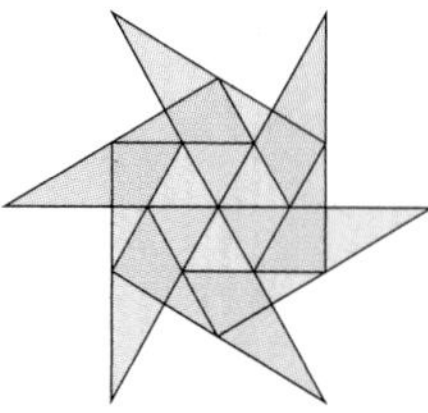

Step 2: Place the point of your pencil on the center of the circle and then rotate the paper until the six points again overlap. Trace the triangle in its new location.

Step 3: Repeat Step 2 until there are six triangles on your paper. Compare drawings within your group to be sure that your results look the same.

Step 4: Now it's your turn to be creative. Place a piece of paper over the figure above, trace the six points on the circle and the center of the circle, and then draw your own triangle on the paper.

Step 5: Place the paper from Step 4 on your desktop, and then use a blank piece of paper to repeat the process in Steps 1–3. Color your design, and then create a display of your group's designs.

THINK AND DISCUSS

In the Work Together, you used rotations to create a design. In order to describe a rotation, you need to know the center of rotation, the angle of rotation, and the direction of the rotation.

THINK AND DISCUSS

Rotations are described in the counterclockwise direction because most students have been taught to measure angles in that direction. You may want to discuss with students rotations described with negative measures indicating clockwise direction. In this book all rotations are described with a positive degree measure.

Question 2 To show how $\overline{TE}$ was rotated about *G*, have students trace the six dots and the center of the circle from the Work Together. Place the center of the circle on *G*. Trace $\overline{TE}$. Rotate the paper through two dots (equivalent to 120°) and draw $\overline{T'E'}$.

Example 1

Have students perform each step in their notebooks. In Step 1, show students how to position their protractors. For Step 2, students may need to review Construction 1 on page 40 of Lesson 1-6.

ERROR ALERT! **Question 4** Some students may think that under a rotation all points move the same distance. **Remediation:** Have students consider a spoke of a spinning bicycle tire. As the tire rotates 360°, the distance the outermost point on the spoke has traveled is greater than the distance the innermost point on the spoke has traveled.

The direction of a rotation can be clockwise or counterclockwise. All rotations in this book will be in a *counterclockwise* direction.

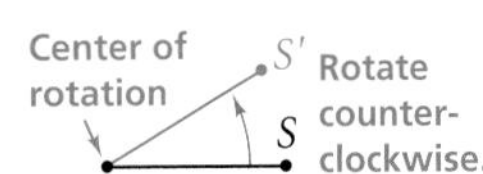

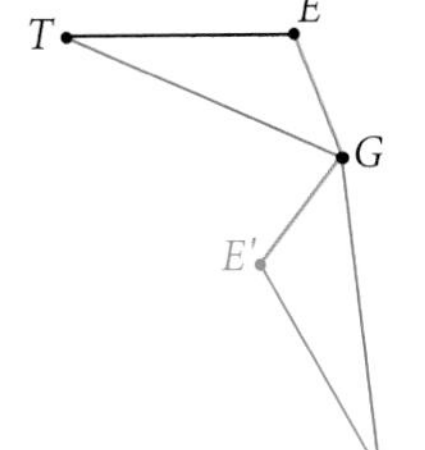

1. What was the angle of each rotation in the Work Together? (*Hint:* Each angle had the same measure.) 60°
2. The diagram at the left shows $\overline{TE}$ rotated 120° about *G*.
   a. What appears to be true of *EG* and *E'G*? Of *TG* and *T'G*?
   b. What appears to be true of $m\angle TGT'$ and $m\angle EGE'$?
   2a. equal; equal b. Both angle measures are 120.

The properties of rotations that you noted in Question 2 form the basis of the definition of a rotation. A **rotation** of $x°$ about a point *R* is a transformation such that:

- For any point *V*, $RV' = RV$ and $m\angle VRV' = x$.
- The image of *R* is itself (that is, $R' = R$).

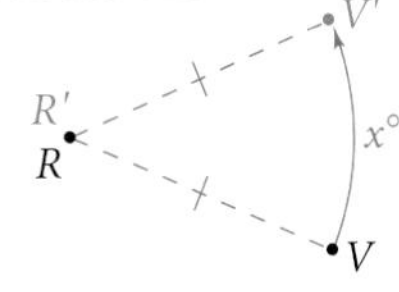

Example 1

Draw the image of $\triangle LOB$ under a 100° rotation about *C*.

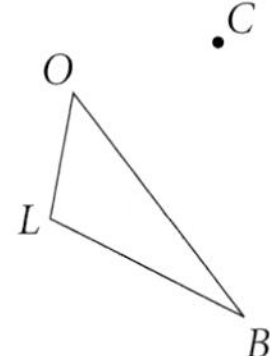

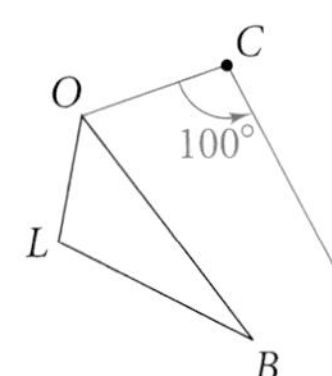

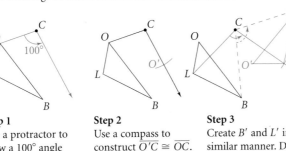

Step 1
Use a protractor to draw a 100° angle with side $\overrightarrow{OC}$.

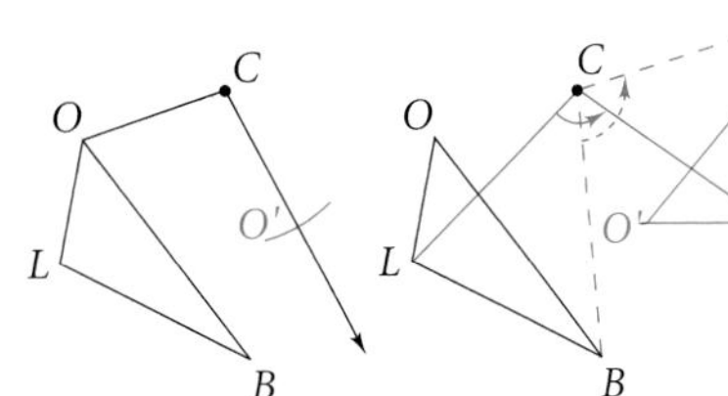

Step 2
Use a compass to construct $\overline{O'C} \cong \overline{OC}$.

Step 3
Create *B'* and *L'* in a similar manner. Draw $\triangle L'O'B'$.

3. **Try This** Draw the image of $\triangle LOB$ under a 90° rotation about *B*. See back of book.
4. **Critical Thinking** Under a rotation, does each point move the same distance? If not, which points move the farthest? No; the points farthest from the center of rotation move the farthest.

A comparison of $\triangle LOB$ and $\triangle L'O'B'$ in Example 1 reveals the following properties of a rotation.

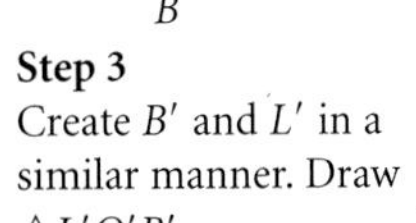

Properties of a Rotation

A rotation is an isometry.

A rotation does not change orientation.

Additional Examples

FOR EXAMPLE 1

Refer to the ΔLOB in Example 1. Copy it and draw its image under a 60° rotation about *C*.

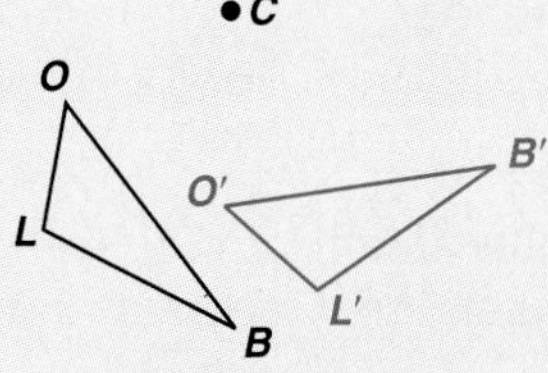

Discussion: *Does the transformation change the orientation? If yes, describe how.*

FOR EXAMPLE 2

Refer to the pentagon in Example 2. Name the image of *A* under a 288° rotation about *X*. *P*

Discussion: *Name another rotation that would map A to P.*

Example 2

Students encountered angles with measures greater than 180 in Exercises 34–35 in Lesson 3-2. Use a circle or a coordinate grid to have students practice drawing angles with measures greater than 180.

Question 7 A 360° rotation is sometimes called a *full turn.*

Example 3 **Relating to the Real World**

KINESTHETIC LEARNING If you have block scheduling or an extended period, take students outside and use chalk to mark a large circle on the pavement. Have a student stand at the center and have another student slowly walking around the circle. Ask the students at the center to remain stationary and to describe what he or she sees. Repeat this activity but have the student at the center rotate more quickly than the students walking around the circle.

Technology Options

For Exercises 1–6, students may want to use geometry software to draw the figures and their images under the rotations.

Prentice Hall Technology

Software
- Secondary Math Lab Toolkit™
- Computer Item Generator 3-3

CD-ROM
- Multimedia Geometry Lab 3

Internet
- See the Prentice Hall site. (http://www.phschool.com)

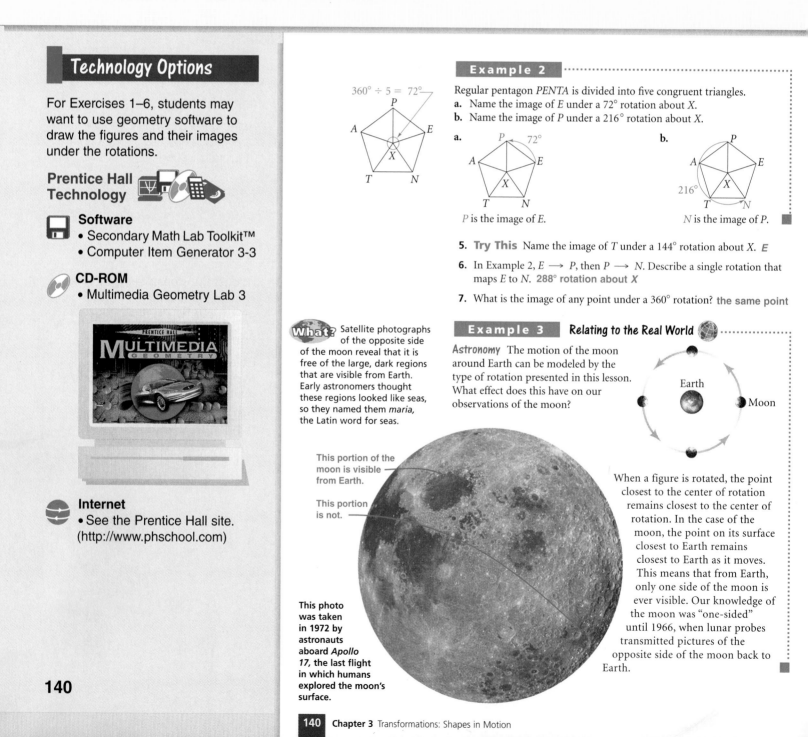

$360° \div 5 = 72°$

P, E, N, T, A, X

Example 2

Regular pentagon *PENTA* is divided into five congruent triangles.

a. Name the image of *E* under a 72° rotation about *X*.

b. Name the image of *P* under a 216° rotation about *X*.

a. (P, 72°, E, A, X, T, N)

P is the image of *E*.

b.

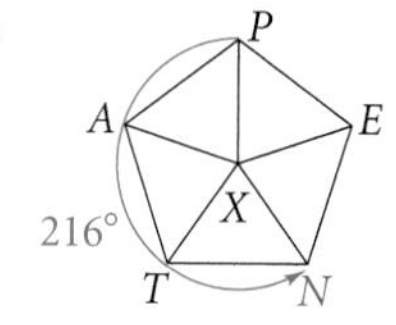

N is the image of *P*.

5. **Try This** Name the image of *T* under a 144° rotation about *X*. **E**
6. In Example 2, $E \longrightarrow P$, then $P \longrightarrow N$. Describe a single rotation that maps *E* to *N*. **288° rotation about *X***
7. What is the image of any point under a 360° rotation? **the same point**

What? Satellite photographs of the opposite side of the moon reveal that it is free of the large, dark regions that are visible from Earth. Early astronomers thought these regions looked like seas, so they named them *maria,* the Latin word for seas.

Example 3 **Relating to the Real World**

Astronomy The motion of the moon around Earth can be modeled by the type of rotation presented in this lesson. What effect does this have on our observations of the moon?

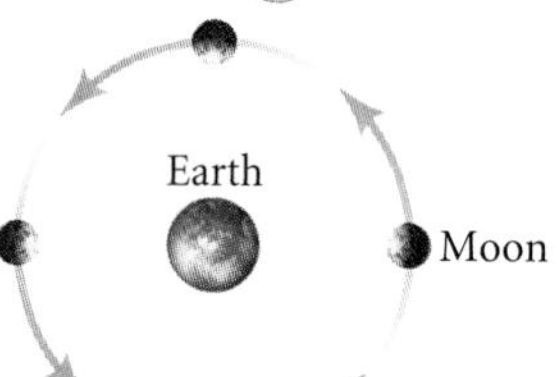

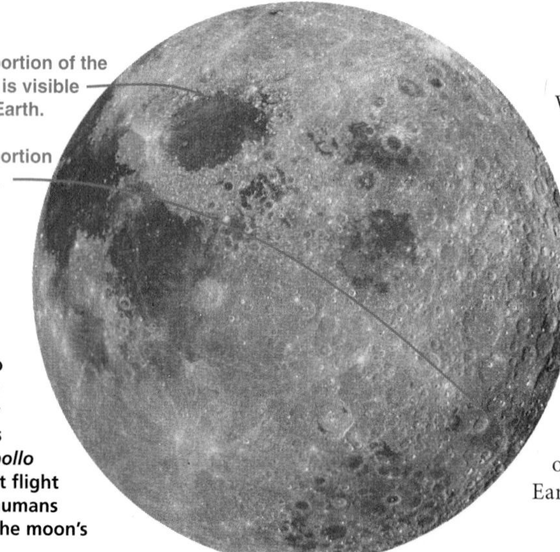

This photo was taken in 1972 by astronauts aboard *Apollo 17,* the last flight in which humans explored the moon's surface.

When a figure is rotated, the point closest to the center of rotation remains closest to the center of rotation. In the case of the moon, the point on its surface closest to Earth remains closest to Earth as it moves. This means that from Earth, only one side of the moon is ever visible. Our knowledge of the moon was "one-sided" until 1966, when lunar probes transmitted pictures of the opposite side of the moon back to Earth.

Exercises ON YOUR OWN

Exercises 1–6 Students draw the images of rotations when the center of rotation is outside the preimage, inside the preimage, and on the preimage.

ALTERNATIVE ASSESSMENT **Exercises 7–9** These exercises can be used to assess students' understanding of the definition of rotation. Have students discuss how they might find the solution. They can trace both figures onto a separate piece of paper and then work with them or use tracing paper on the page to copy one figure and then rotate it onto the other.

Exercises 10–17 Discuss with students the angle measures of the angles of a regular triangle, a regular quadrilateral, and a regular hexagon.

Exercises ON YOUR OWN

Copy each figure and point *P*. Rotate the figure the given number of degrees about *P*. Label the vertices of the image.

1. 60°

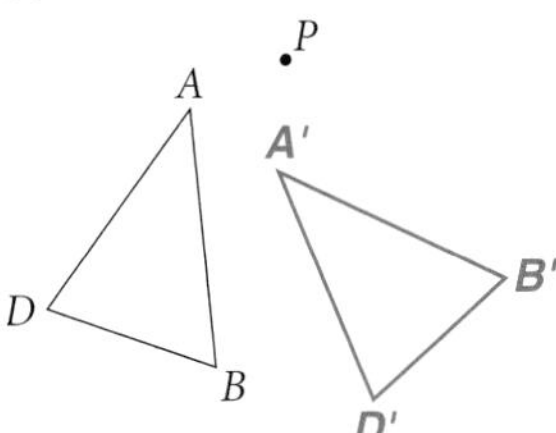

2. 90°

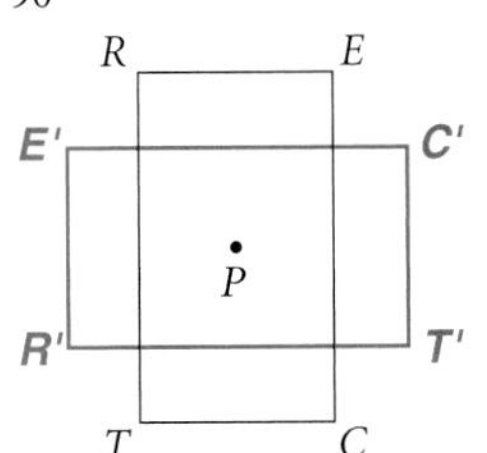

3. 180°

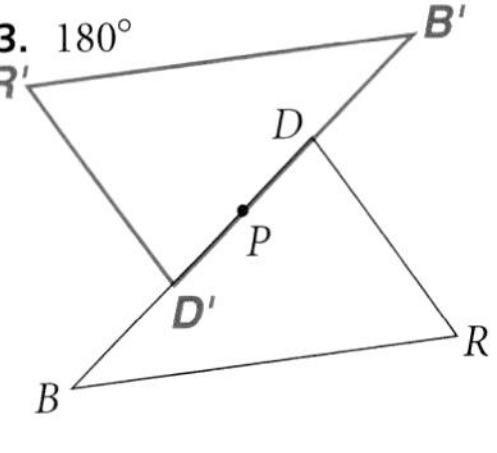

4. 140°

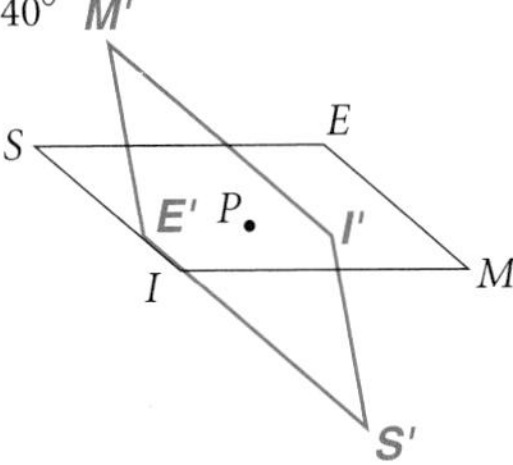

5. 90°

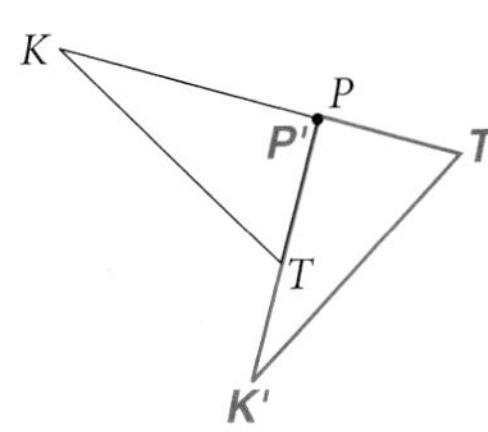

6. 45°

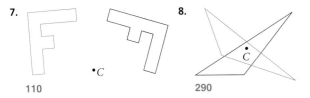

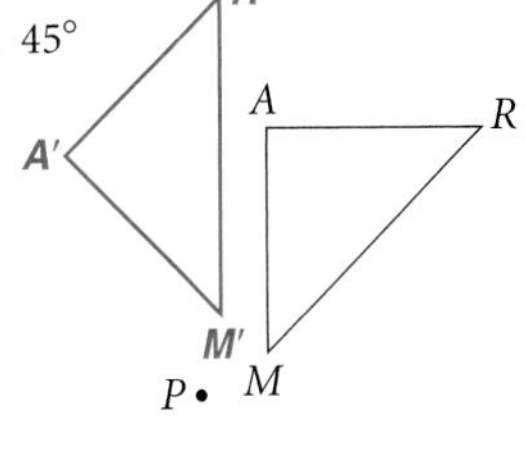

What is the measure of the rotation about *C* that maps the black figure onto the blue figure?

7.

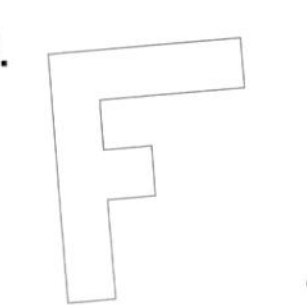

110

8.

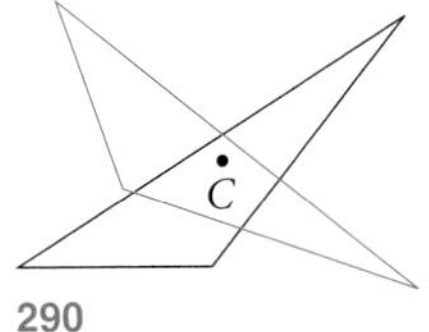

290

9.

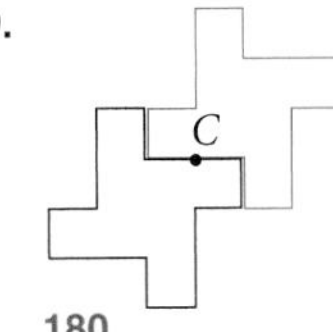

180

The green segments in the figure intersect to form 30° angles. The triangle, quadrilateral, and hexagon are all regular. Find the image of each point or segment.

10. 120° rotation of *B* about *O* H

11. 270° rotation of *L* about *O* M

12. 60° rotation of *E* about *O* C

13. 300° rotation of $\overline{IB}$ about *O* $\overline{BC}$

14. 120° rotation of $\overline{FE}$ about *O* $\overline{CB}$

15. 120° rotation of *F* about *H* I

16. 180° rotation of $\overline{JK}$ about *O* $\overline{LM}$

17. 90° rotation of *L* about *M* J

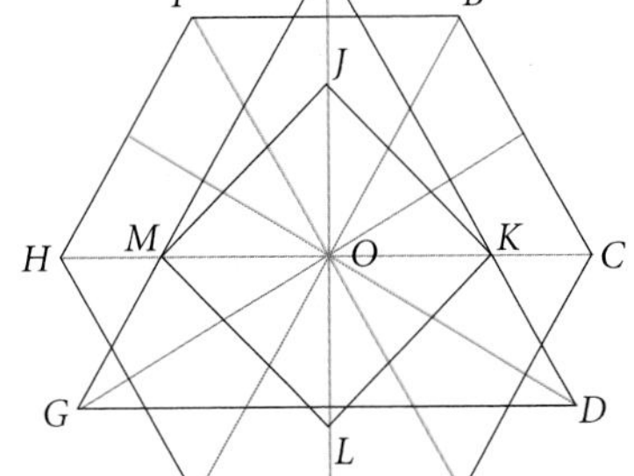

STANDARDIZED TEST TIP Exercise 18 Students can trace the figure and try to rotate, translate, or reflect it to get each of the images.

MAKING CONNECTIONS Exercise 19 If you took a time-lapse photograph of the night sky near the North Star, the arcs showing the movements of stars would be larger for stars farther from the North Star and smaller for those near the North Star. The North Star itself, near the center of rotation, would show little movement.

EXTENSION Exercise 26 Have students find which block letters, for example, H, that also form block letters when they are rotated 180°.

Chapter Project **FIND OUT BY MODELING** Make sure students understand what "onto itself" means. Students will need to experiment to find the center of rotation for each design. Point out that the center of rotation is not always on the figure.

Exercises MIXED REVIEW

WRITING Exercise 37 Have students include a graph of the triangle with their explanations.

pages 141–143 On Your Own

20a–c.

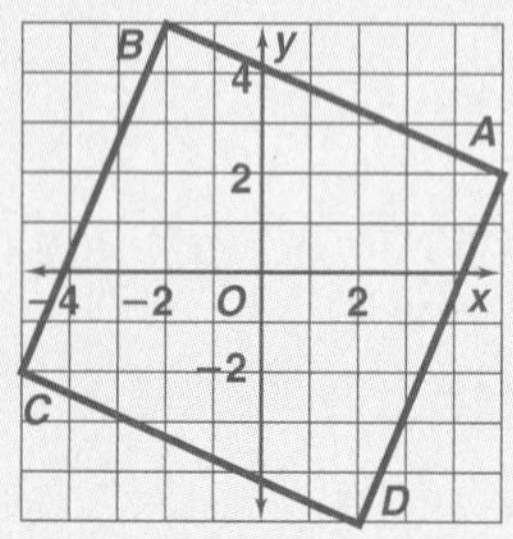

38. [graph: points J, H, K on coordinate grid; axes labeled x, y; −4, −2, O, 2, 4]

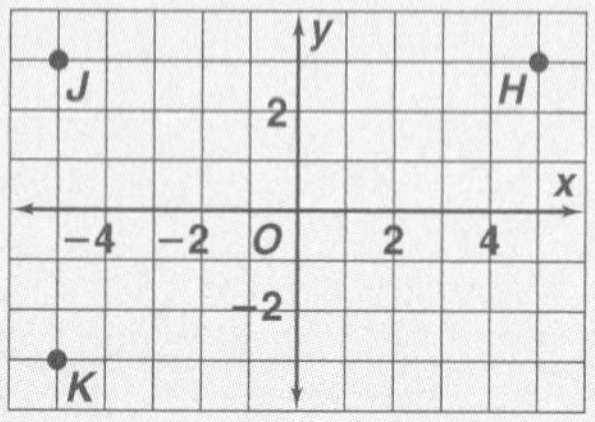

Checkpoint page 143

7. Images and preimages under translations, reflections, and rotations are congruent to each other. Translations and rotations do not affect orientation. Reflection reverses orientation.

18. *Standardized Test Prep* Which figure is *not* the image of the figure at the left under a congruence transformation? D

A. 

B. 

C. 

D. 

E. 

19. *Astronomy* Refer to Example 3. Suppose Earth's motion around the sun, like the moon's motion around Earth, could be described by the type of rotation in this lesson. How would life on Earth be different? Answers may vary. Sample: On one side of Earth it would always be day; on the other, always night.

20. a. *Coordinate Geometry* Graph $A(5, 2)$, then graph B, the image of A under a 90° rotation about O (the origin). (*Hint:* Consider the slope of $\overline{OA}$.) a–c. See margin.
    b. Graph C, the image of A under a 180° rotation about O.
    c. Graph D, the image of A under a 270° rotation about O.
    d. What type of quadrilateral is $ABCD$? Explain. Square; its sides are ≅ and its angles are ≅.

21. $\overline{M'N'}$ is the rotation image of $\overline{MN}$ about point E. Name all the congruent angles and segments in the diagram. $\overline{MN} \cong \overline{M'N'}$, $\overline{ME} \cong \overline{M'E}$, $\overline{EN} \cong \overline{EN'}$, $\angle MEN \cong \angle M'EN'$, $\angle MNE \cong \angle M'N'E$, $\angle EMN \cong \angle EM'N'$, $\angle MEM' \cong \angle NEN'$

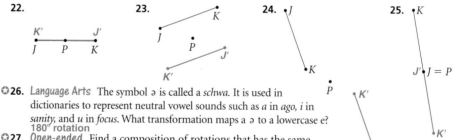

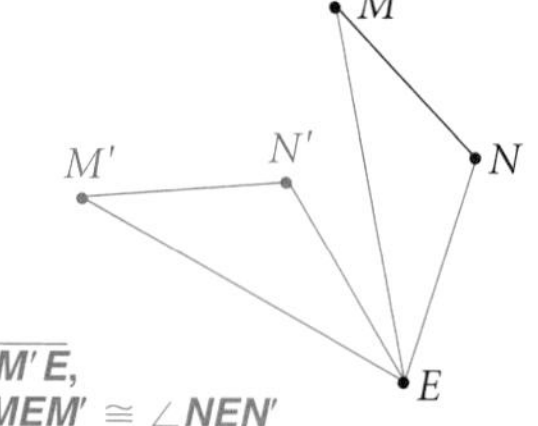

Copy each figure, then draw the image of $\overline{JK}$ under a 180° rotation about P.

22. [figure: K′ J′ above J P K on a segment]

23. 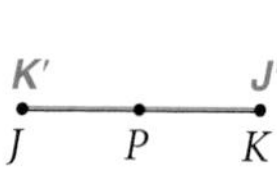

24. 

25. 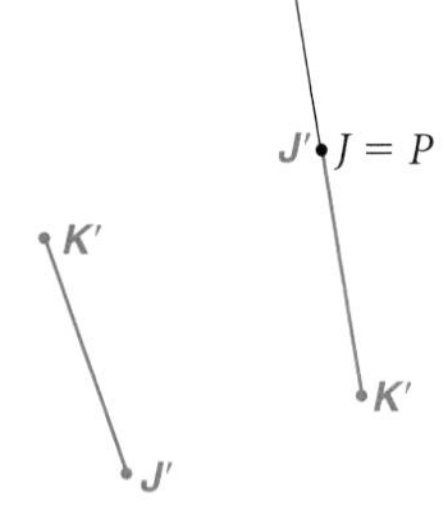

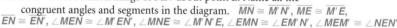

26. *Language Arts* The symbol ə is called a *schwa.* It is used in dictionaries to represent neutral vowel sounds such as *a* in *ago, i* in *sanity,* and *u* in *focus.* What transformation maps a ə to a lowercase e? 180° rotation

27. *Open-ended* Find a composition of rotations that has the same effect as a 360° rotation about a point X. Sample: a 288° rotation and a 72° rotation

Native American Art **Find the measure of the rotation about C that maps Q to X.**

28. 90

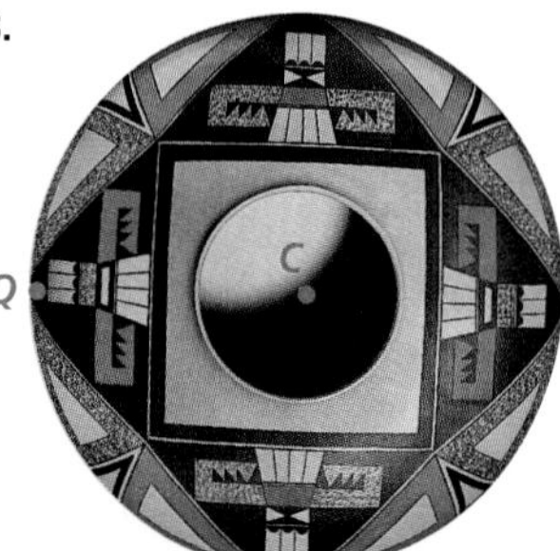

29. 108

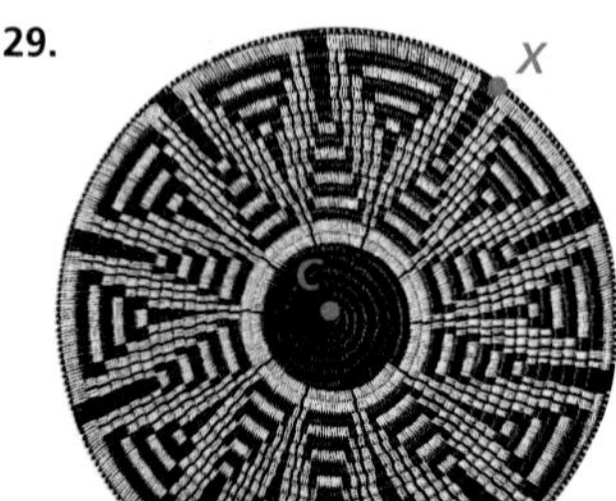

30. 225

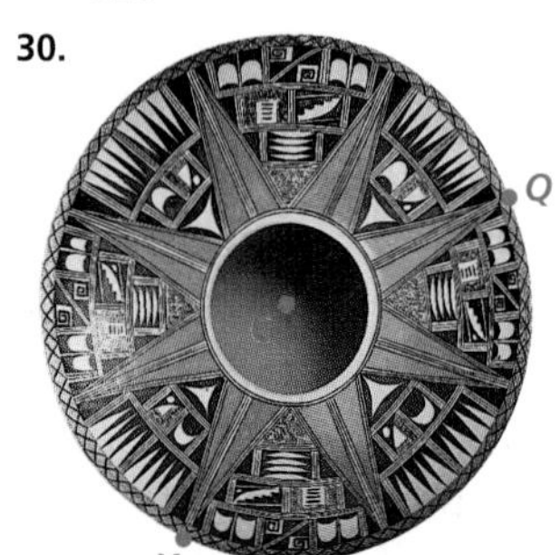

GETTING READY FOR LESSON 3-4 This exercise illustrates Theorem 3-2 (a composition of reflections in two intersecting lines is a rotation),which is presented in Lesson 3-4.

Wrap Up

THE BIG IDEA Ask students: *Draw the preimage and image of a triangle under a rotation. Then describe the rotation by naming the center of rotation and the angle of rotation.*

RETEACHING ACTIVITY Students locate rotation images of figures by tracing and rotating the preimage. (Reteaching worksheet 3-3)

Exercises CHECKPOINT

In this Checkpoint, your students will assess their own progress in Lessons 3-1 to 3-3.

Exercise 8 Remind students that not all transformations are isometries.

Chapter Project — *Find Out by Modeling*

Some frieze patterns can also be mapped onto themselves by a 180° rotation. Use tracing paper to make a copy of each pattern. Rotate your copy to help you determine whether the pattern can be mapped onto itself by a 180° rotation. Mark the centers of rotation on your copy.

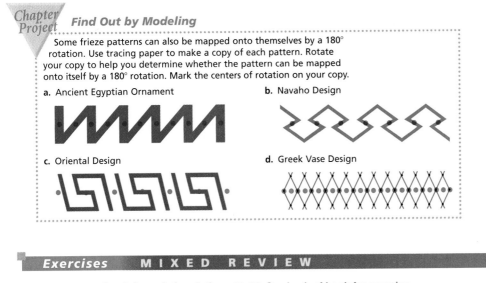

a. Ancient Egyptian Ornament

b. Navaho Design

c. Oriental Design

d. Greek Vase Design

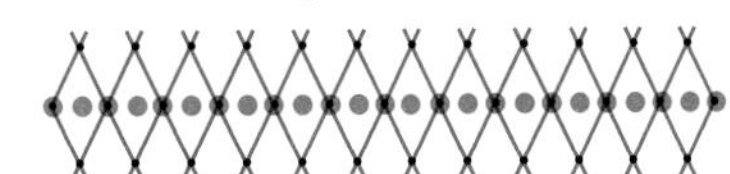

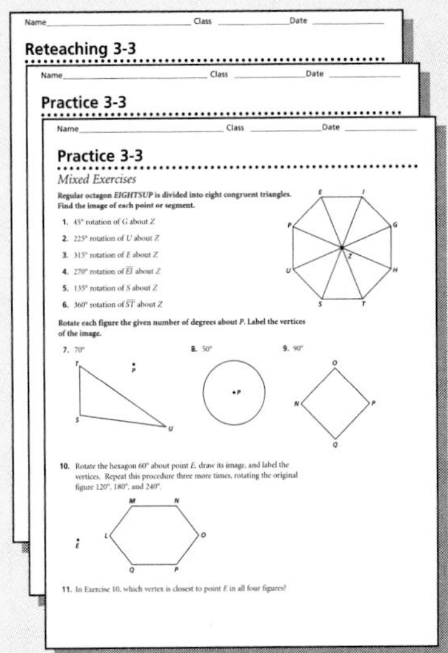

Name ____ Class ____ Date ____

Reteaching 3-3

Name ____ Class ____ Date ____

Practice 3-3

Name ____ Class ____ Date ____

Practice 3-3

Mixed Exercises

Regular octagon *EIGHTSUP* is divided into eight congruent triangles. Find the image of each point or segment.

1. 45° rotation of G about Z
2. 225° rotation of U about Z
3. 315° rotation of E about Z
4. 270° rotation of $\overline{EI}$ about Z
5. 135° rotation of S about Z
6. 360° rotation of $\overline{ST}$ about Z

Rotate each figure the given number of degrees about P. Label the vertices of the image.

7. 70°
8. 50°
9. 90°

10. Rotate the hexagon 60° about point E, draw its image, and label the vertices. Repeat this procedure three more times, rotating the original figure 120°, 180°, and 240°.

11. In Exercise 10, which vertex is closest to point E in all four figures?

Exercises MIXED REVIEW

Create a separate sketch for each description. 31–36. See back of book for samples.

31. skew lines
32. nonsimilar kites
33. parallel planes
34. similar trapezoids
35. perpendicular lines
36. nonsimilar rhombuses

37. **Writing** Determine whether a triangle with vertices (3, 2), (−1, 1), and (2, −1) is a right triangle. Explain how you know. Sample: No; the slopes of the sides are $\frac{1}{4}$, $-\frac{2}{3}$, and 3. No sides are ⊥ because the slopes are not negative reciprocals of each other.

Getting Ready for Lesson 3-4

38. **Coordinate Geometry** Graph $H(5, 3)$ and J, its reflection image in the y-axis. Then graph K, the reflection image of J in the x-axis. Describe a rotation that maps H to K. See margin p. 142 for graph; 180° rotation about (0, 0)

Exercises CHECKPOINT

Find the image of $T(3, 4)$ under each transformation.

1. reflection in the x-axis (3, −4)
2. rotation of 90° about (0, 0) (−4, 3)
3. translation ⟨−2, 7⟩ (1, 11)
4. rotation of 270° about (0, 0) (4, −3)
5. translation ⟨1, −5⟩ (4, −1)
6. reflection in the line $y = x$ (4, 3)

7. **Writing** Explain how translations, reflections, and rotations affect the congruence and orientation of figures. See margin p. 142.

8. a. List the corresponding sides for the transformation shown.
b. Is the transformation an isometry? Explain.
8a. $\overline{AD}$ and $\overline{A'D'}$, $\overline{AF}$ and $\overline{A'F'}$, $\overline{DF}$ and $\overline{D'F'}$
b. No; the image is not ≅ to the preimage.

Lesson Quiz

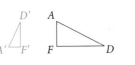

Lesson Quiz is also available in Transparencies.

1. Draw △*CDE* with vertices $C(1, 2)$, $D(3, 8)$, and $E(5, 3)$. Then find its image under a 80° rotation about C. See back of book.
2. Draw $\overline{BK}$ with endpoints $B(-5, -4)$ and $K(-2, 4)$. Then draw its image under a 90° rotation about (0, 0). See back of book.
3. Describe the rotation about the center of a rectangle that maps the rectangle onto itself. 180° or 360°

3-4 Teaching Notes

PROBLEM OF THE DAY

Divide the figure into two congruent pieces. Hint: It cannot be done with a straight line.

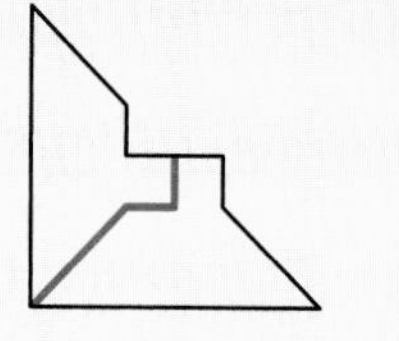

Problem of the Day is also available in Transparencies.

CONNECTING TO PRIOR KNOWLEDGE Have students draw a triangle. Then have them find the image under a reflection in a vertical line, a horizontal line, and another line.

WORK TOGETHER

Students working in groups can experiment by drawing triangles of different sizes and parallel lines at different distances apart. Students can also draw the lines intersecting at different angles.

THINK AND DISCUSS

Students should readily accept Theorems 3-1 and 3-2 without proof after answering Questions 1–2 in the Work Together.

Lesson Planning Options

Prerequisite Skills

- Reflecting figures in lines
- Translating figures

Assignment Options for Exercises On Your Own

To provide flexible scheduling, this lesson can be subdivided into parts.

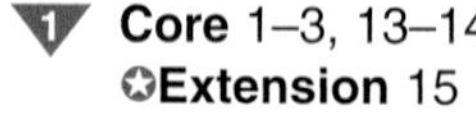

1 **Core** 1–3, 13–14
✪**Extension** 15

2 **Core** 4–12, 16–29
✪**Extension** 30–32

Use Mixed Review to maintain skills.

Resources

Student Edition

Skills Handbook, p. 671
Extra Practice, p. 650
Glossary/Study Guide

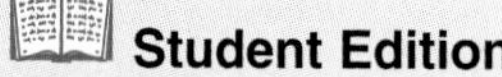

Teaching Resources

Chapter Support File, Ch. 3
- Practice 3-4 (two worksheets)
- Reteaching 3-4

Classroom Manager 3-4
Glossary, Spanish Resources

Transparencies
5, 41, 49

Connections Creative Art . . . and more

3-4 Compositions of Reflections

What You'll Learn

- Showing how reflections are related to the other isometries
- Identifying glide reflections

...And Why

To be able to describe how objects relate to one another

What You'll Need

- straightedge
- lined paper
- graph paper

WORK TOGETHER

- Have each member of your group use a straightedge to draw figures like those at the right on a piece of lined paper. Reflect the triangle in line ℓ_1; then reflect the image in line ℓ_2.

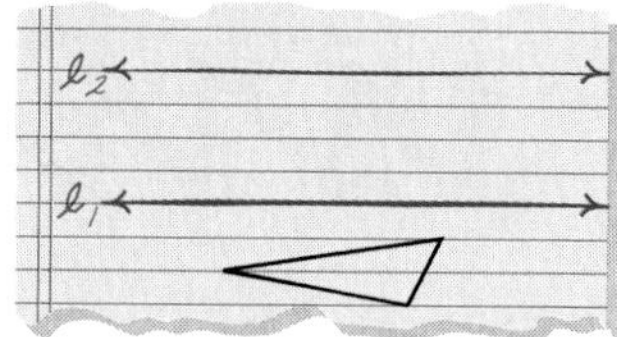

1. Compare results within your group. What transformation that you've studied has the same effect as the composition of two reflections in parallel lines? **a translation**

- Have each member of your group use a straightedge to draw figures like those at the left on a piece of paper. Reflect the triangle in line ℓ_3; then reflect the image in line ℓ_4.

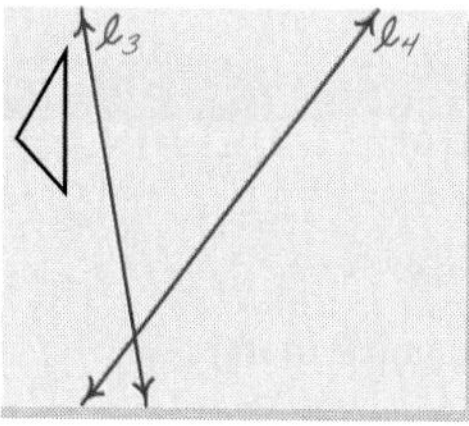

2. Compare results within your group. What transformation that you've studied has the same effect as the composition of two reflections in intersecting lines? **a rotation**

THINK AND DISCUSS

Part 1

Compositions of Two Reflections

The Work Together illustrates the two properties summarized in the theorems below.

Theorem 3-1 A composition of reflections in two parallel lines is a translation.

Theorem 3-2 A composition of reflections in two intersecting lines is a rotation.

The vibrant images of a kaleidoscope are produced by repeated reflections in intersecting mirrors.

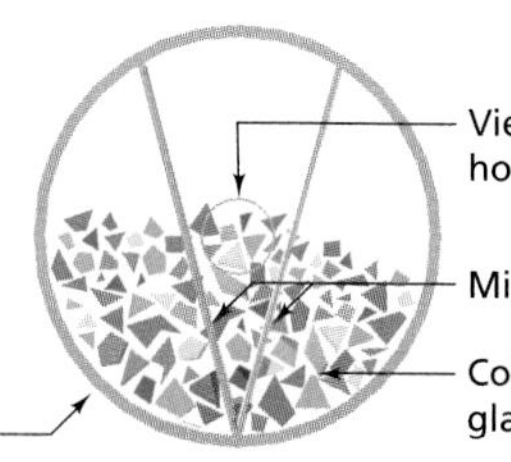

Example 1 **Relating to the Real World** 

Some students may not have seen a kaleidoscope. If possible, bring in a kaleidoscope with which students can experiment or books that show kaleidoscope images.

MAKING CONNECTIONS Sir David Brewster studied to be a minister. After a short time, he left the ministry to study optics (light). Along with making scientific contributions in that field, Brewster's interest in instruments led him to create the first kaleidoscope in 1816.

Example 2

Have students trace the two P's and use paper folding to replicate each reflection.

EXTENSION Have students work in groups to find another pair of reflections that will map the left P onto the right P.

Question 3 You may want to ask students to find two reflections that map one of the P's onto the other in such a way that the first reflection does not have its image of P touching the final image.

CRITICAL THINKING Question 4 Help students see that the point about which the figure is rotated is the intersection of the two reflection lines created by the folds.

Example 1 **Relating to the Real World** 

Creative Art Determine the angle between the mirrors in this kaleidoscope image.

This wedge is repeated 6 times in 360°.

$360° \div 6 = 60°$

Suppose you are given two congruent figures in random positions in a plane. Could you use reflections to map one onto the other? If so, how many reflections would be needed? Example 2 shows that if the figures have the same orientation, only two reflections are needed.

Example 2

Paper folding The two P's at the right are congruent. Use two reflections to map one figure onto the other.

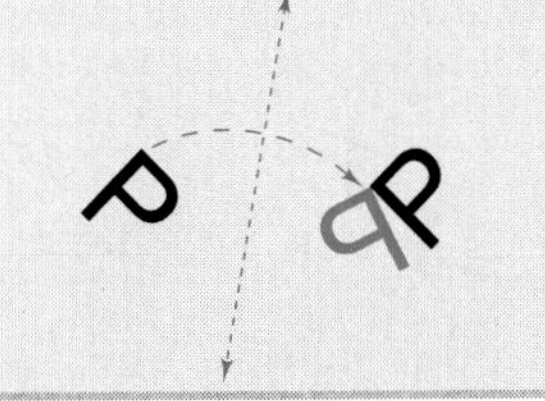

Reflection 1: Pick a point on one P, then fold it onto the corresponding point on the other P.

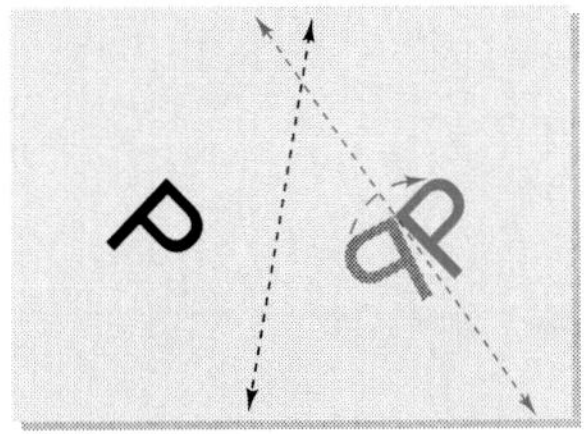

Reflection 2: Fold the two P's that share a point onto one another.

3. **Try This** Trace the two P's in Example 2 in different locations on your paper; then use paper folding to map one figure onto the other. **Check students' work.**
4. *Critical Thinking* What single isometry could be used to map one of the P's onto the other? Explain. **A rotation; a composition of two reflections in intersecting lines is a rotation.**

Additional Examples

FOR EXAMPLE 2

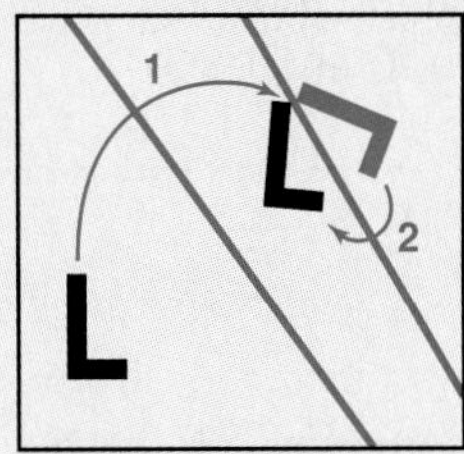

In the diagram, the two L's shown are congruent. Use two reflections to map one L onto the other.

Discussion: *Did you and your classmates reflect in the same lines? in the same order?*

Answers may vary. Sample given above.

FOR EXAMPLE 3

Refer to the diagram in Example 3. Find the image of $\triangle TEX$ under the glide reflection in $\langle 6, -5 \rangle$ and $y = 0$.

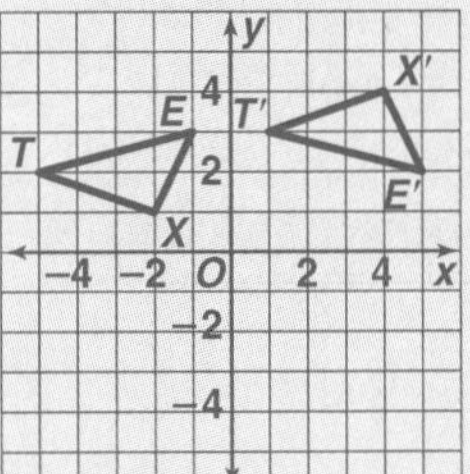

Discussion: *Can you produce the same image using just reflections? If so, how many reflections would be needed?*

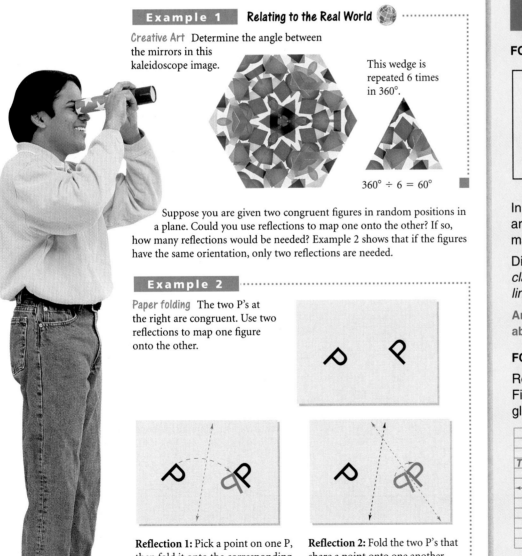

Theorem 3-3 Point out to students that reflecting a figure once in any line results in two figures with the opposite orientation. From Example 2, we know that one of those figures can be mapped onto the other with two reflections.

Have students recall from Theorem 3-2 that the composition of reflections in two intersecting lines is a translation. So it follows that the composition of three reflections in intersecting lines is a composition of a translation and a reflection, also called a glide reflection.

EXTENSION Ask students to find a transformation that is equivalent to the reflection of a figure in three parallel lines.

Example 3

TACTILE LEARNING Students may want to trace $\triangle TEX$ to illustrate the translation, then use paper folding to find the reflection.

Technology Options

For Exercises 7–12, students may use the transformation tools in geometry software to find each image.

Prentice Hall Technology

Software
- Secondary Math Lab Toolkit™
- Computer Item Generator 3-4

CD-ROM
- Multimedia Geometry Lab 3

Internet
- See the Prentice Hall site. (http://www.phschool.com)

146

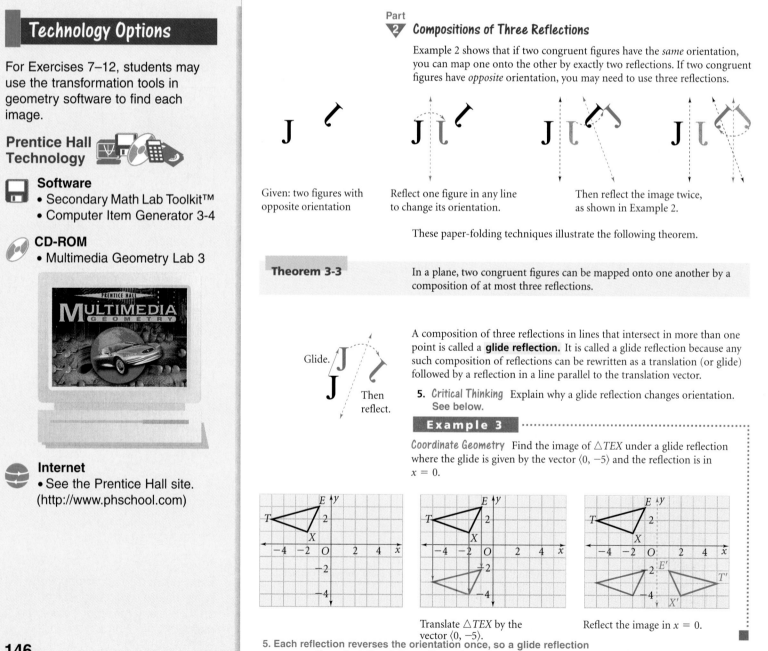

Part 2

Compositions of Three Reflections

Example 2 shows that if two congruent figures have the *same* orientation, you can map one onto the other by exactly two reflections. If two congruent figures have *opposite* orientation, you may need to use three reflections.

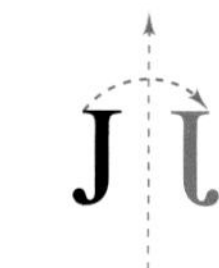

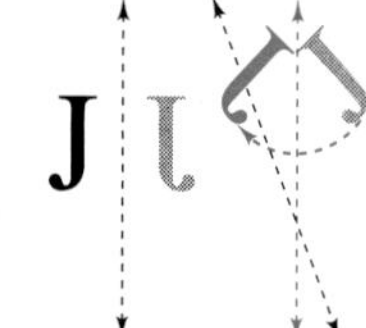

Given: two figures with opposite orientation

Reflect one figure in any line to change its orientation.

Then reflect the image twice, as shown in Example 2.

These paper-folding techniques illustrate the following theorem.

Theorem 3-3 In a plane, two congruent figures can be mapped onto one another by a composition of at most three reflections.

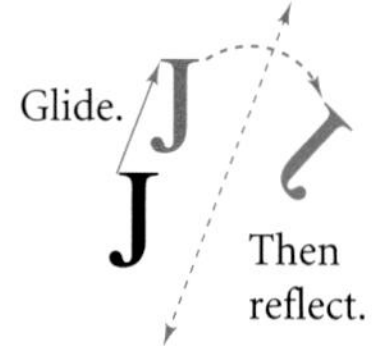

A composition of three reflections in lines that intersect in more than one point is called a **glide reflection.** It is called a glide reflection because any such composition of reflections can be rewritten as a translation (or glide) followed by a reflection in a line parallel to the translation vector.

5. *Critical Thinking* Explain why a glide reflection changes orientation. See below.

Example 3

Coordinate Geometry Find the image of $\triangle TEX$ under a glide reflection where the glide is given by the vector $\langle 0, -5 \rangle$ and the reflection is in $x = 0$.

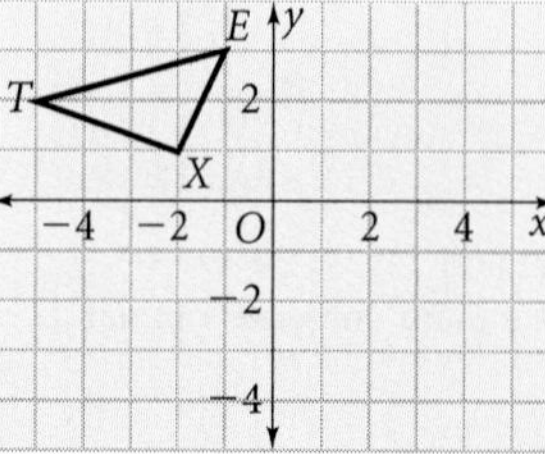

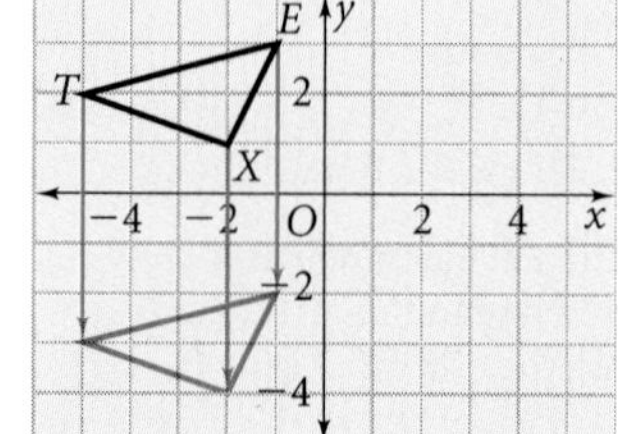

Translate $\triangle TEX$ by the vector $\langle 0, -5 \rangle$.

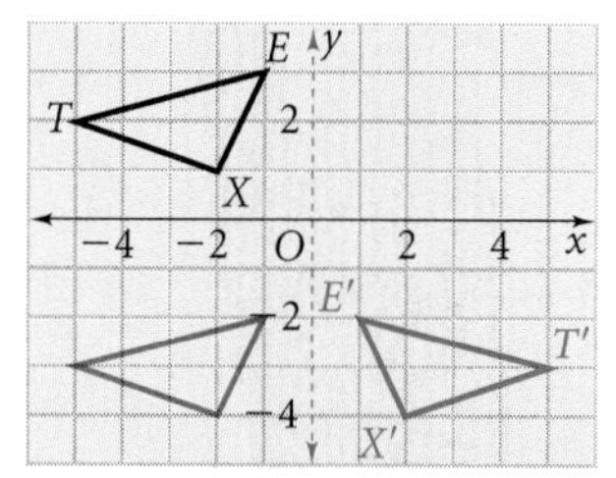

Reflect the image in $x = 0$.

5. Each reflection reverses the orientation once, so a glide reflection reverses the orientation 3 times. Two orientation changes cancel each other.

Theorem 3-4 Have students record the theorem and the diagrams in their notebooks. The diagrams provide a visual explanation of what each transformation does.

AUDITORY LEARNING Have students work with a partner. Have one student describe a composition of isometries and another students classify the result as one of the four isometries given in Theorem 3-4 .

Example 4

DIVERSITY Some students, especially those confused by the vocabulary, may need further explanation. Be sure it is clear to students that the transformation in part a is not a translation and the transformation in part b is not a reflection.

6. Would the result of Example 3 be the same if you reflected $\triangle TEX$ first, then translated it? **yes**

7. **Try This** Find the image of $\triangle TEX$ under a glide reflection given by the vector $\langle 1, 0\rangle$ and a reflection in $y = -2$. **See margin.**

You can map any two congruent figures onto one another by a single reflection, translation, rotation, or glide reflection. These four transformations are the only isometries.

Theorem 3-4
Isometry Classification Theorem

There are only four isometries. They are the following.

reflection

translation

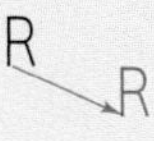

rotation

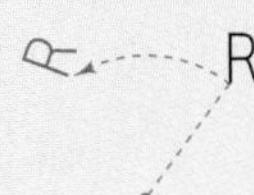

glide reflection

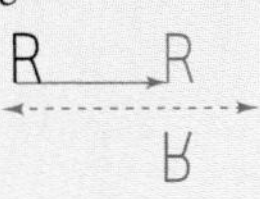

Example 4

Each pair of figures is congruent. What isometry maps one to the other?

a. 

b.  

PROBLEM SOLVING HINT
Use Logical Reasoning.

a. These figures have the same orientation, so the transformation must be either a translation or a rotation. It's obviously not a translation, so it must be a rotation.

b. These figures have opposite orientation, so the transformation must be either a reflection or a glide reflection. Since it's not a reflection, it must be a glide reflection.

Exercises ON YOUR OWN

Creative Art **What is the angle between the mirrors for each kaleidoscope image?**

1. 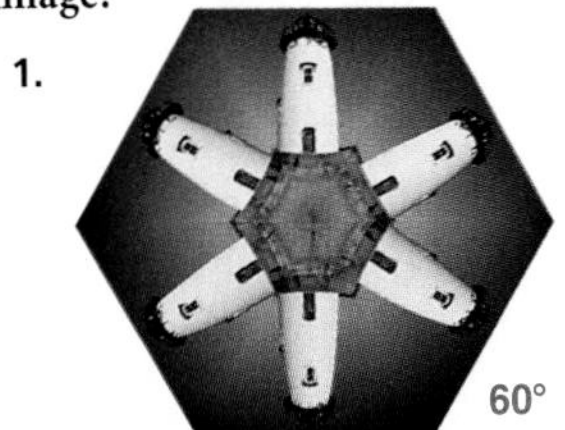 60°

2. 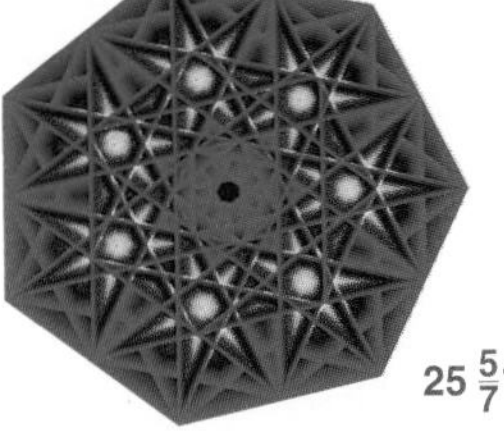 $25\frac{5}{7}°$

3. 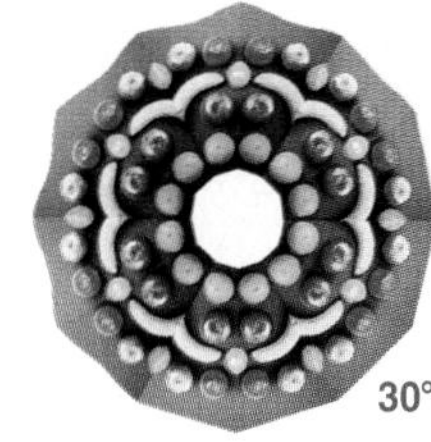 30°

pages 144–147 Think and Discuss

7. 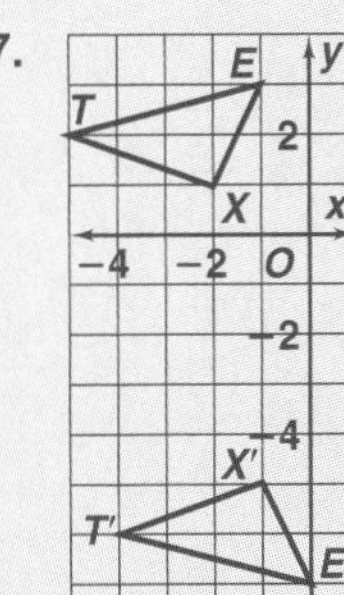

Exercises ON YOUR OWN

Exercises 4–6 Students will best be able to check the orientation of the figures more easily if they rotate their books so that the bottom of each figure is close to them.

Exercises 13–16 Students should observe the number of lines of reflection and their relationship to each other to help determine the type of transformation.

ERROR ALERT! **Exercises 17–20** Some students may assume that the *x*- and *y*-axes are lines of reflection. **Remediation:** Point out to students that the lines are bold because they indicate the axes on the coordinate grid and not necessarily lines of reflection.

pages 147–150 On Your Own

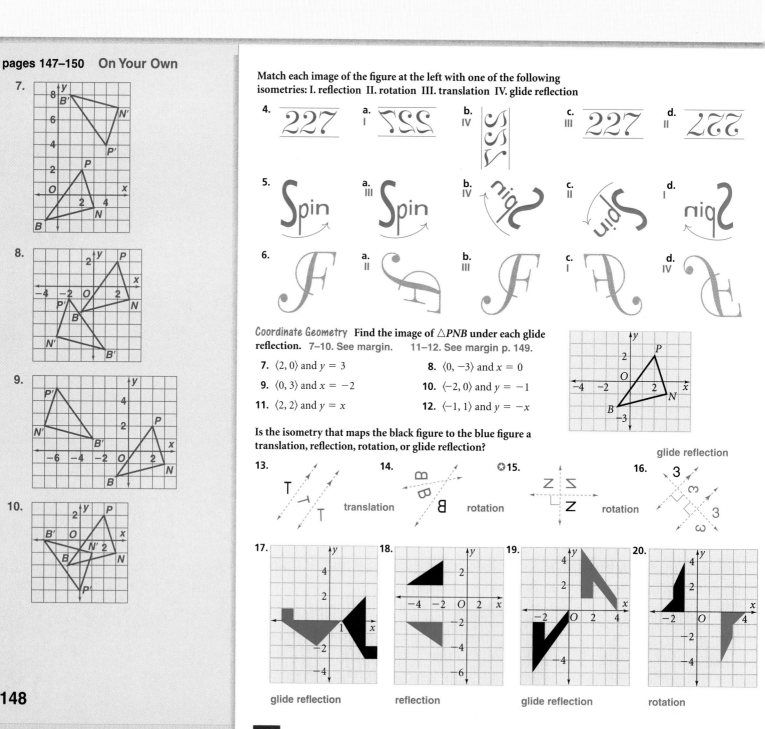

7. 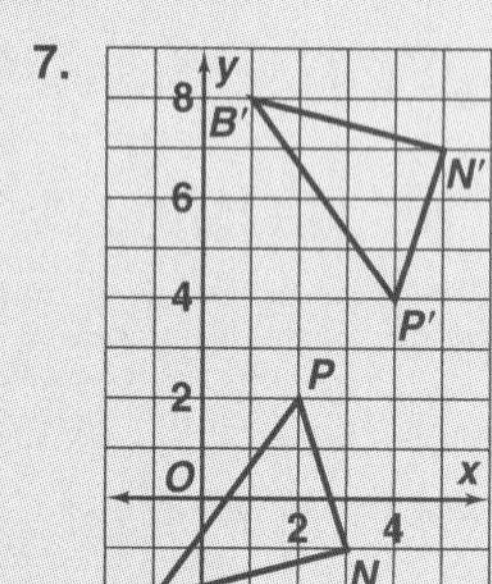

8. 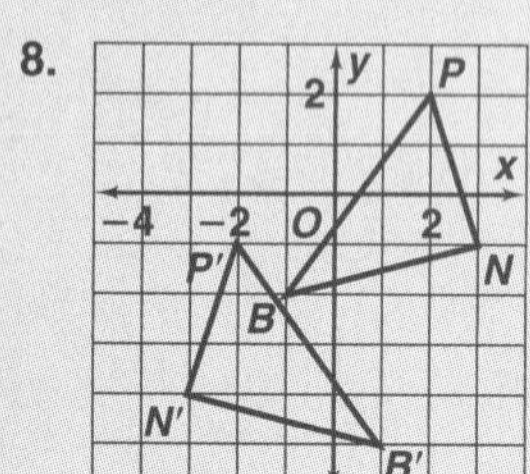

9. 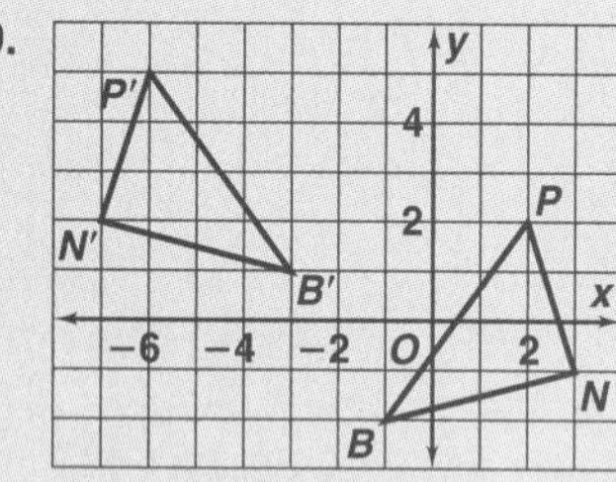

10. 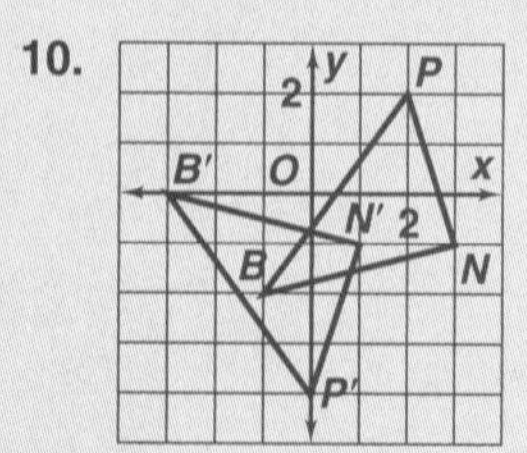

148

Match each image of the figure at the left with one of the following isometries: I. reflection II. rotation III. translation IV. glide reflection

4.  a. I  b. IV 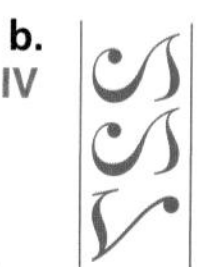 c. III  d. II 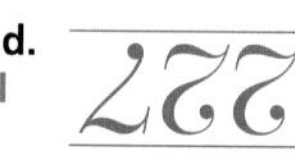

5.  a. III  b. IV  c. II  d. I 

6.  a. II  b. III  c. I 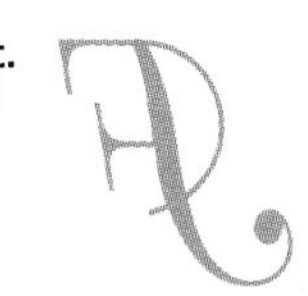 d. IV 

Coordinate Geometry **Find the image of $\triangle PNB$ under each glide reflection.** 7–10. See margin. 11–12. See margin p. 149.

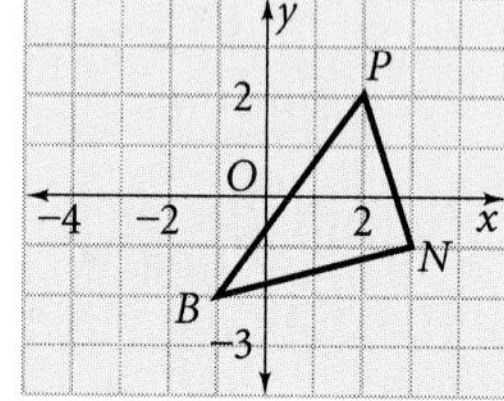

7. $\langle 2, 0\rangle$ and $y = 3$
8. $\langle 0, -3\rangle$ and $x = 0$
9. $\langle 0, 3\rangle$ and $x = -2$
10. $\langle -2, 0\rangle$ and $y = -1$
11. $\langle 2, 2\rangle$ and $y = x$
12. $\langle -1, 1\rangle$ and $y = -x$

Is the isometry that maps the black figure to the blue figure a translation, reflection, rotation, or glide reflection?

13. 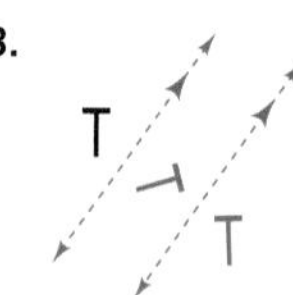 translation

14. 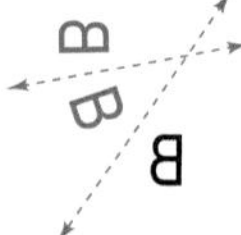 rotation

15. 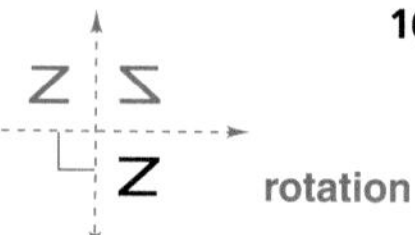 rotation

16. 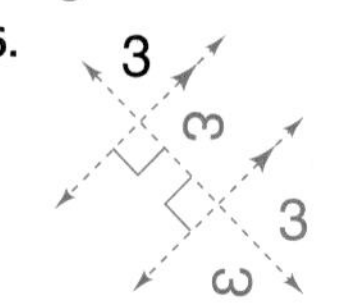 glide reflection

17. 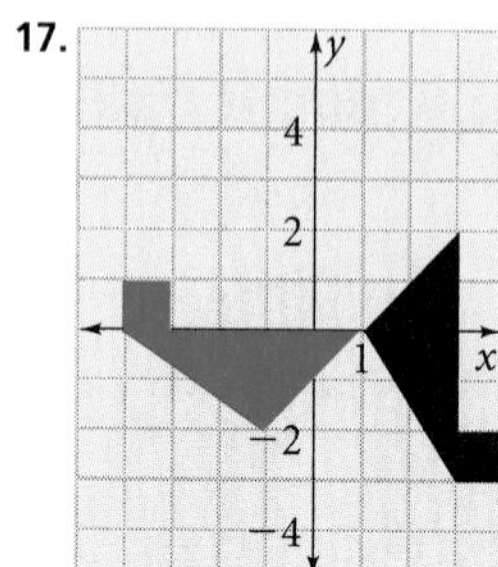 glide reflection

18. reflection

19. 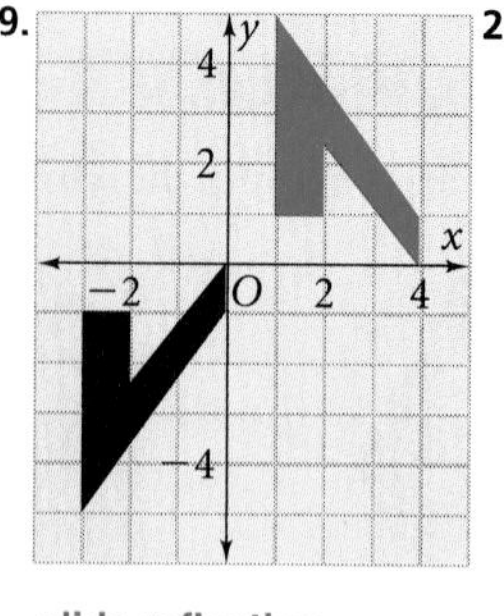 glide reflection

20. 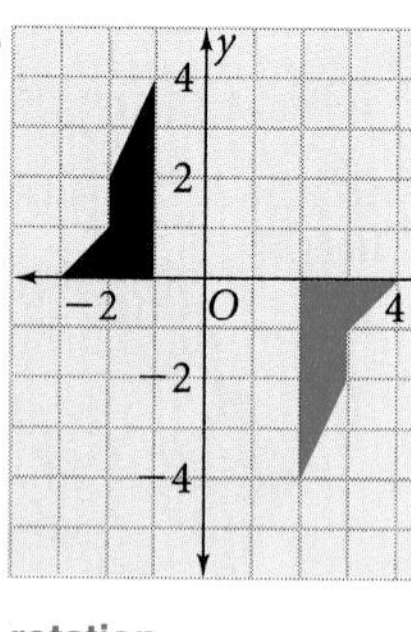 rotation

ALTERNATIVE ASSESSMENT **Exercises 21–28** These exercises can help you assess students' understanding of the four isometries. Students may want to make a cutout of the triangular shape and manipulate it to find each transformation.

Exercise 30 Suggest that students cut the figure from the center of the folded paper and not from the edges to get six distinct figures.

PROBABILITY **Exercise 31** Encourage students to experiment. They should notice that translations and reflections are highly unlikely but that rotations and glide reflections occur with equal frequency.

State whether each mapping is a reflection, rotation, translation, or glide reflection.

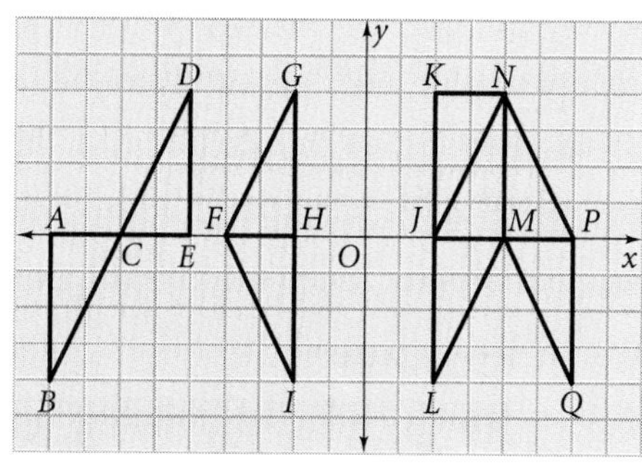

21. $\triangle ABC \rightarrow \triangle EDC$ rotation
22. $\triangle EDC \rightarrow \triangle PQM$ glide reflection
23. $\triangle MNJ \rightarrow \triangle EDC$ translation
24. $\triangle HIF \rightarrow \triangle HGF$ reflection
25. $\triangle PQM \rightarrow \triangle JLM$ reflection
26. $\triangle MNP \rightarrow \triangle EDC$ reflection
27. $\triangle JLM \rightarrow \triangle MNJ$ rotation
28. $\triangle PQM \rightarrow \triangle KJN$ glide reflection

29. *Writing* Reflections and glide reflections are *odd isometries*, while translations and rotations are *even isometries*. Use what you learned in this lesson to explain why these categories make sense. See margin.

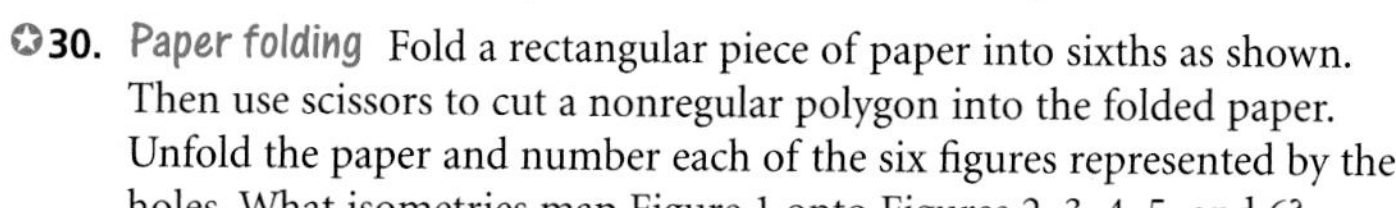

30. *Paper folding* Fold a rectangular piece of paper into sixths as shown. Then use scissors to cut a nonregular polygon into the folded paper. Unfold the paper and number each of the six figures represented by the holes. What isometries map Figure 1 onto Figures 2, 3, 4, 5, and 6? reflection; reflection; rotation; translation; glide reflection

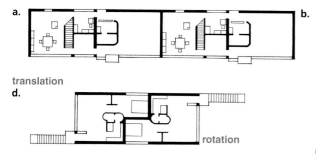

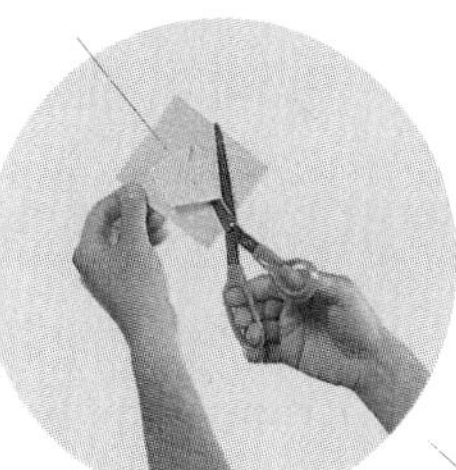

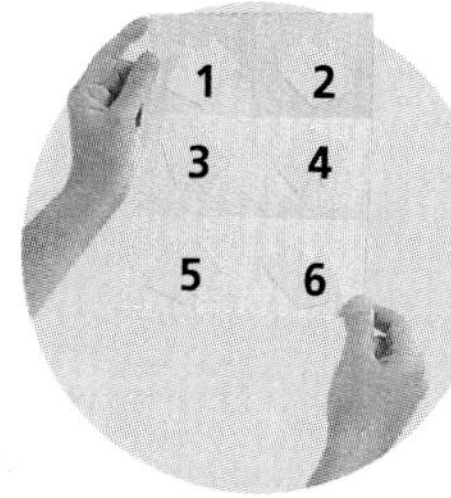

31. *Probability* Suppose you toss two cardboard cutouts of congruent figures into the air so that they land in random positions on the floor. Consider the isometry that maps one of the figures onto the other. Which of the four isometries, if any, are most likely to occur? See below.

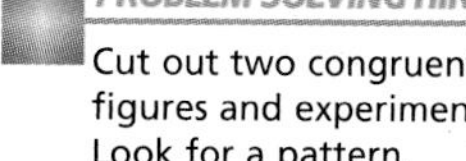

PROBLEM SOLVING HINT

Cut out two congruent figures and experiment. Look for a pattern.

32. *Architecture* These housing plans were created by the Swiss architect Le Corbusier for a development in Pessac, France. They illustrate each of the four isometries. Name the isometry illustrated by each design.

a.

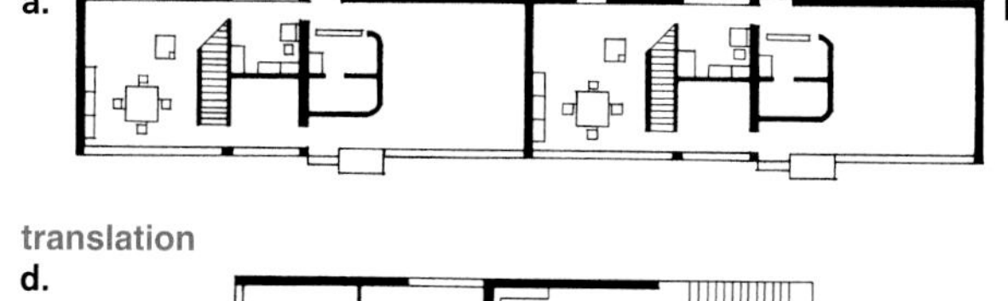

translation

b.

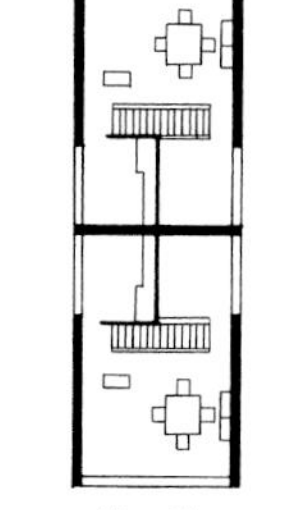

reflection

c.

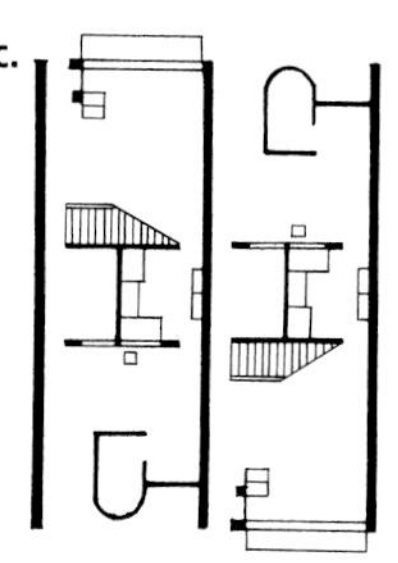

glide reflection

d.

rotation

31. Rotations and glide reflections are equally likely to occur. They are more likely to occur than translations and reflections.

11.

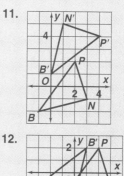

12.

29. **Reflections and glide reflections can be expressed as compositions of odd numbers of reflections. Translations and rotations can be expressed as compositions of even numbers of reflections.**

Chapter Project **FIND OUT BY INVESTIGATING** Students may want to trace carefully part of the design, then translate and reflect it as indicated.

Exercises MIXED REVIEW

Exercises 33–35 Students review reading graphs. Explain to students that ATM stands for "Automated Teller Machine."

GETTING READY FOR LESSON 3-5 These exercises prepare students for identifying rotational symmetry.

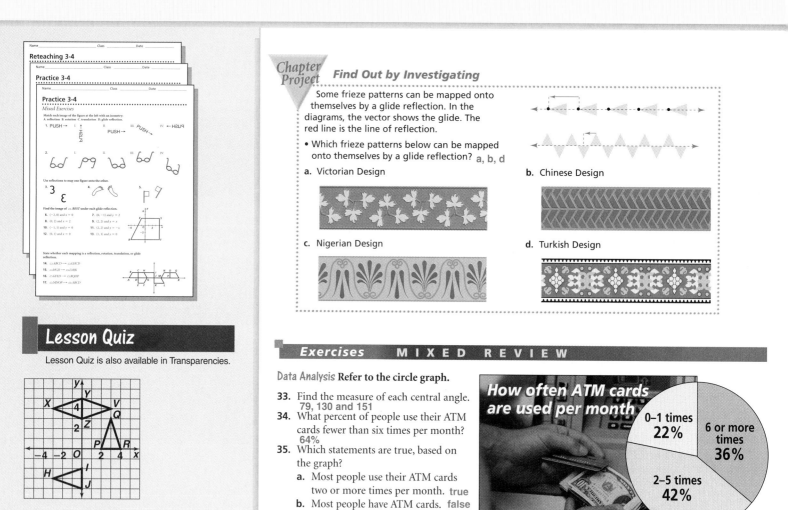

Wrap Up

THE BIG IDEA Ask students: *What composition of reflections has the same effect as a translation? a rotation? a glide reflection?*

RETEACHING ACTIVITY Students use paper-folding to reflect figures in lines. Then they identify transformations that map one figure onto another. (Reteaching worksheet 3-4)

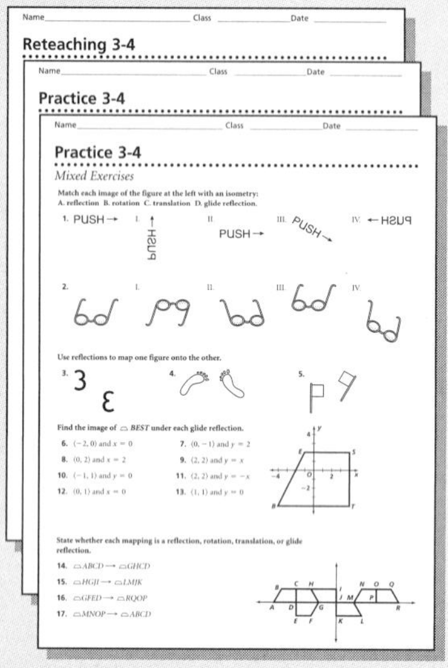

Lesson Quiz

Lesson Quiz is also available in Transparencies.

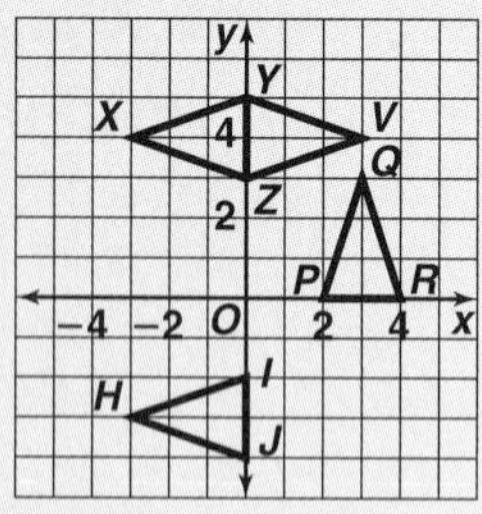

1. Name the type of isometry that maps $\triangle XYZ$ to $\triangle VYZ$. **reflection**
2. Name the type of isometry that maps $\triangle XYZ$ to $\triangle HIJ$. **translation**
3. Name the type of isometry that maps $\triangle XYZ$ to $\triangle QPR$. **glide reflection**

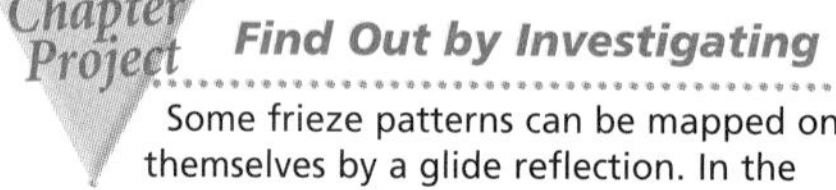

Chapter Project ***Find Out by Investigating***

Some frieze patterns can be mapped onto themselves by a glide reflection. In the diagrams, the vector shows the glide. The red line is the line of reflection.

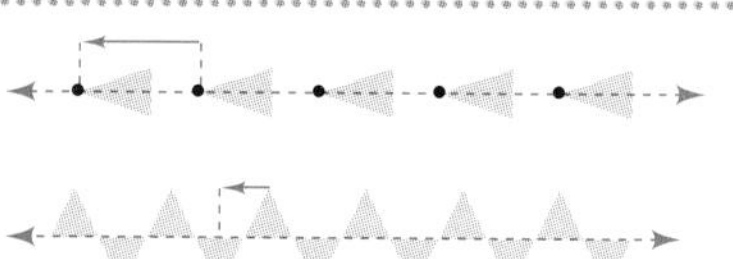

- Which frieze patterns below can be mapped onto themselves by a glide reflection? **a, b, d**

a. Victorian Design

b. Chinese Design

c. Nigerian Design

d. Turkish Design

Exercises MIXED REVIEW

Data Analysis **Refer to the circle graph.**

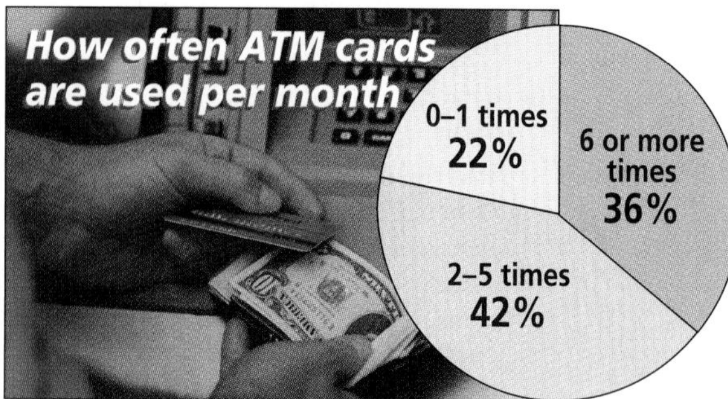

Source: *Research Partnership survey for Cirrus Systems*

33. Find the measure of each central angle. **79, 130 and 151**
34. What percent of people use their ATM cards fewer than six times per month? **64%**
35. Which statements are true, based on the graph?
    a. Most people use their ATM cards two or more times per month. **true**
    b. Most people have ATM cards. **false**
    c. At least 36% of people use their ATM cards one or more times per week. **true**

Getting Ready for Lesson 3-5

Find the image of each figure under the given transformation. **36–38. Each figure maps onto itself.**

36.

Rotation of 60° about O

37.

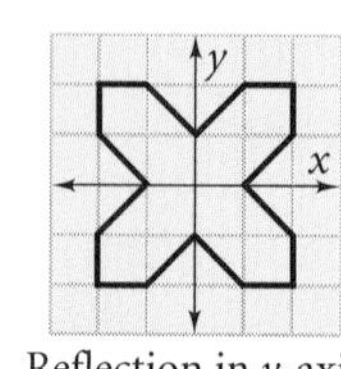

Reflection in y-axis

38.

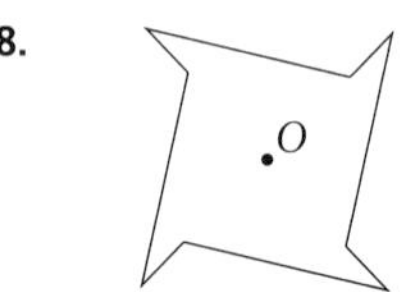

Rotation of 90° about O

Math ToolboX

Students use geometry software to create a symmetrical design. This activity introduces ideas of symmetry which will be presented in Lesson 3-5.

The software allows students to explore the effect of changing the shape of the figure being reflected.

ERROR ALERT! If students draw line segments instead of lines, they may not get six angles as shown in the diagram. **Remediation:** Have students read the directions carefully. Point out that each line should appear to go to the edge of the computer screen.

You may want to display students' designs. Have students observe the variety of designs that can be created using this simple technique.

ADDITIONAL PROBLEM Create a kaleidoscope with six lines of reflection. Draw a line and construct a point on the line. Rotate the figure 30° about the point and repeat until you have six lines. Add a figure to the interior of an angle and reflect it as described in the text.

Materials and Manipulatives

- Geometry software

Transparencies
12

Math ToolboX Technology

Kaleidoscopes

Before Lesson 3-5

The mirrors in a kaleidoscope reflect objects to create a *symmetrical* design. Work in pairs or small groups to create your own kaleidoscope.

Construct

Check students' work.

- Use geometry software. Draw a line and construct a point on the line. Rotate the line 60° about the point. Rotate the image 60° about the point.
- Construct a polygon in the interior of an angle, as shown. Reflect the polygon in the closest line in a clockwise direction. Reflect the image in the next closest line in a clockwise direction. Continue reflecting until the kaleidoscope is filled. Then hide the lines of reflection.

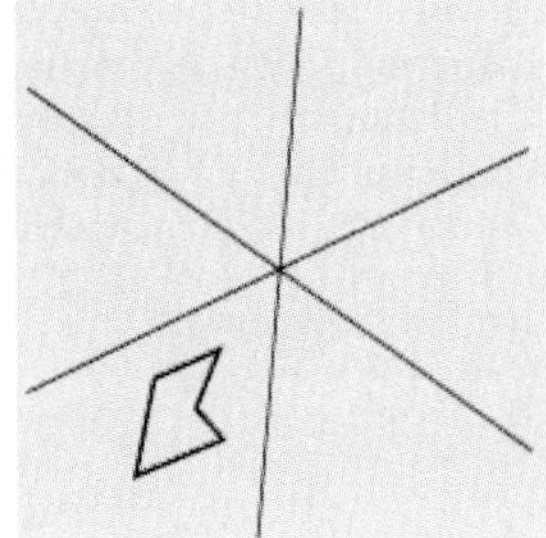

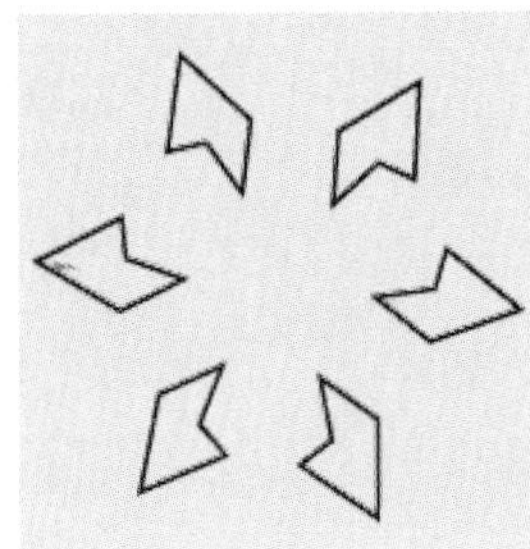

Investigate

- Manipulate the original figure by dragging any of its vertices or selecting and moving it. As the figure is manipulated, what happens to the images? Does the design remain symmetrical? Continue manipulating the original figure until you are satisfied with your design. Print the design and color it. All 6 polygons change in the same way; yes.
- Now add other figures in addition to the original polygon. Reflect these figures to create a more interesting design, as shown at the right. (You may need to temporarily show the hidden lines of reflection.) Print your design and color it. Check students' work.

Extend

Create a kaleidoscope with four lines of reflection. Draw a line and construct a point on the line. Rotate the line 45° about the point and repeat until you have four lines. Add a figure to the interior of an angle and reflect it as described above.

Check students' work.

151

3-5 Teaching Notes

PROBLEM OF THE DAY

These numbers are harponots: 23476, 61258, 83056, 27418. These numbers are not harponots: 16528, 2983, 25638, 18634. Which of these numbers are harponots: 45630, 83290, 14764, 21658 ? 83290, 21658 (A harponot is a 5-digit number with alternating even and odd digits such that the first digit is even and the sum of the digits is 22.)

Problem of the Day is also available in Transparencies.

CONNECTING TO PRIOR KNOWLEDGE Have students sketch a rectangle, then draw a line that bisects opposite sides. Have them reflect the rectangle in the line and discuss how the preimage and image are related.

THINK AND DISCUSS

Discuss with students how the definition of symmetry of a figure relates to the symmetry property of equality and the symmetry property of congruence.

Example 1

To find lines of symmetry, students may want to copy each figure and fold the image onto itself. Another method is to place a mirror or MIRA™ on a suspected line of symmetry and check that the resulting figure is the same as the original figure.

Lesson Planning Options

Prerequisite Skills

- Rotating figures
- Reflecting figures

Assignment Options for Exercises On Your Own

To provide flexible scheduling, this lesson can be subdivided into parts.

1 **Core** 15–18, 30–32
✪**Extension** 14, 40

2 **Core** 1–13, 19–28, 38, 41–46
✪**Extension** 29, 33–37, 39

Use Mixed Review to maintain skills.

Resources

Student Edition
Skills Handbook, p. 678
Extra Practice, p. 650
Glossary/Study Guide

Teaching Resources
Chapter Support File, Ch. 3
- Practice 3-5 (two worksheets)
- Reteaching 3-5

Classroom Manager 3-5
Glossary, Spanish Resources

Transparencies
5, 42

Connections Advertising . . . and more

3-5 Symmetry

What You'll Learn
- Identifying types of symmetry in figures

...And Why
To understand a topic that influences art, dance, and poetry, and is an important tool of scientists

THINK AND DISCUSS

Part 1 **Reflectional Symmetry**

A figure has **symmetry** if there is an isometry that maps the figure onto itself. A plane figure has **reflectional symmetry,** or **line symmetry,** if there is a reflection that maps the figure onto itself. If you fold a figure along a line of symmetry, the halves match exactly.

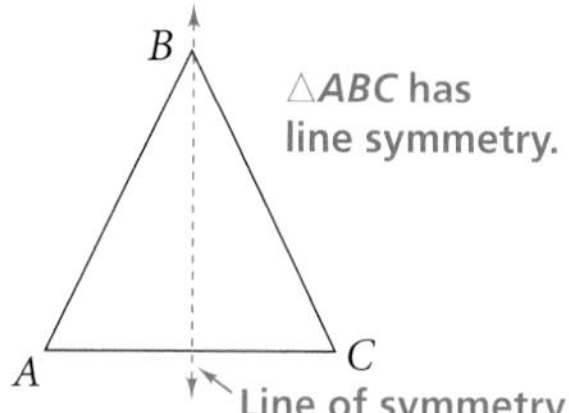

Example 1

Draw the lines of symmetry for each figure.

a. **b.** **c.**

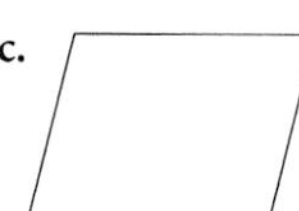

a.
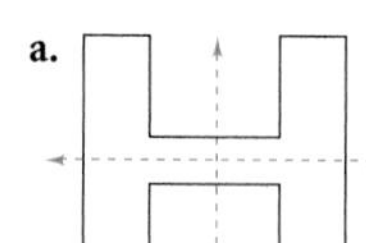

b.
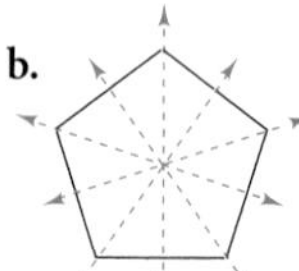

c. This figure has no lines of symmetry.

Symmetry is especially important to left-handers. Because about 95% of people are right-handed, right-handed versions of objects are easier to find (and often less expensive!) than left-handed versions of the same objects.

Paul McCartney of the Beatles used converted right-handed bass guitars until he was given a left-handed Rickenbacker bass in the mid-1960s.

ERROR ALERT! Students may think that a figure that can be cut into two congruent pieces has reflectional symmetry. **Remediation:** Have students trace and cut out the parallelogram in part c. Have them manipulate it to show that it has no reflectional symmetry. Then have them cut it along its diagonal to show that it can be divided into two congruent pieces.

DIVERSITY Help students understand that "95% of people are right-handed" means that one out of twenty people is left-handed. Survey the class to find the number of left-handed people. Discuss the difficulties left-handed people sometimes experience.

ESL *Reflectional symmetry* in three-dimensional objects can also be called *plane symmetry* or, in special cases, *bilateral symmetry.*

MAKING CONNECTIONS Rock collectors, chemists, and geologists use reflectional symmetry of crystals to help identify them. Have students research types of crystals and their symmetries.

Example 2 **Relating to the Real World** 

Students learned to draw top, front, and side views of three-dimensional objects in Lesson 2-7. In this example, only the view that most clearly suggests the plane of symmetry needs to be drawn.

CONNECTING TO STUDENTS' WORLD Have students find reflectional symmetry in three-dimensional objects around them. Have them sketch an orthographic view of the object, including a line that suggests the plane of symmetry.

Left-handed people appreciate reflectional symmetry because objects that have it can be used by both left-handers and right-handers.

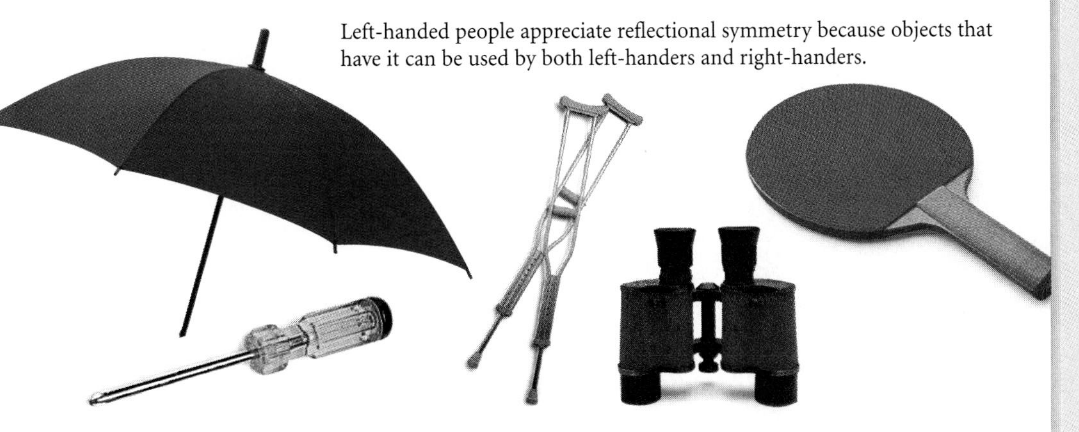

Three-dimensional objects with reflectional symmetry can be divided into two congruent parts by a plane. You can sketch these symmetries in two dimensions by using orthographic views (top, front, or right side).

Example 2 **Relating to the Real World** 

Technical Drawing Show the reflectional symmetries of each object by sketching an orthographic view.

a. 

b. 

a. 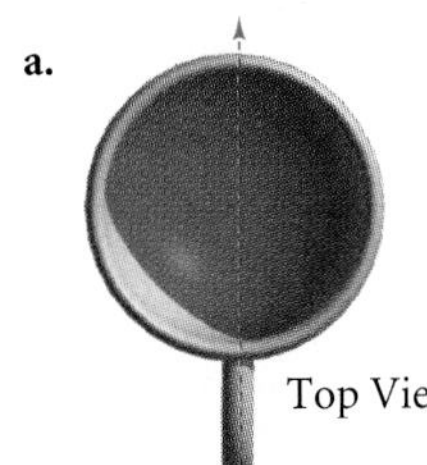

Top View

b. 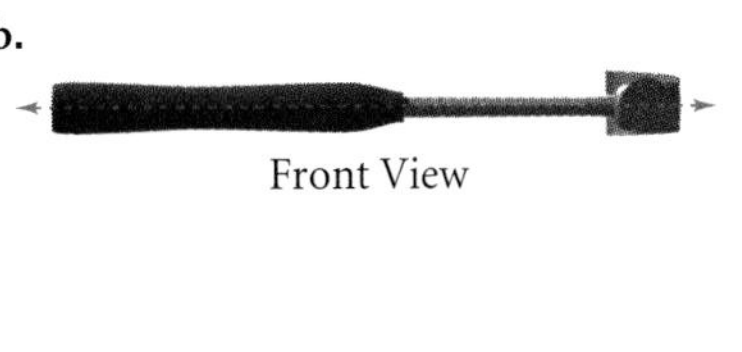

Front View

1. *Critical Thinking* Name an object that has more than one plane of symmetry. **Samples: unlabeled cans; plain drinking glass; starfish**

Additional Examples

FOR EXAMPLE 1

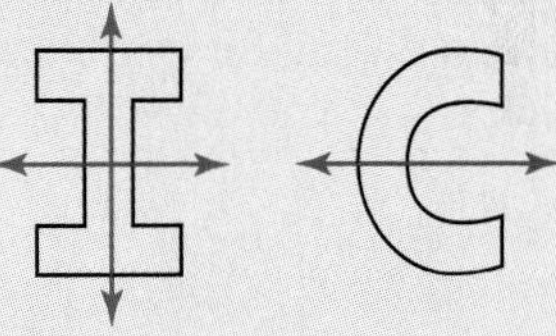

Draw the lines of symmetry for each letter.

Help students see that a figure has rotational symmetry only if the angle of rotation is 180° or less. If the only rotation that maps a figure onto itself is 360°, the figure does not have rotational symmetry.

Example 3

Students can experiment by copying a figure on tracing paper, then choosing different points about which to rotate the figure.

CRITICAL THINKING Although a figure is defined to have rotational symmetry if there is a rotation of 180° or less that maps they figure onto itself, a figure may also be mapped onto itself by a rotation between 180° and 360°. Ask students to name a rotation between 180° and 360° that maps the triangle in part a onto itself.

Question 2 Suggest students look at Example 3 part c and look back at Example 1 part c. Then have students create other such examples. Students can also investigate whether a figure with line symmetry must also have rotational symmetry.

Question 3 Help students understand that a figure with point symmetry has rotational symmetry but that the converse is not always true.

WORK TOGETHER

Many examples that students find will be three-dimensional; thus the suggestion to draw orthographic views. You may want to exclude any examples that you have already mentioned in class.

Technology Options

For Exercises 38–40, students may sketch the graphs of the equations using a graphing calculator or graphing software.

Prentice Hall Technology

Software

- Secondary Math Lab Toolkit™
- Computer Item Generator 3-5

Internet

- See the Prentice Hall site. (http://www.phschool.com)

154

The spinning motion of a lathe ensures that objects created on it have rotational symmetry.

Part 2

Rotational Symmetry

A figure has **rotational symmetry** if there is a rotation of 180° or less that maps the figure onto itself.

Example 3

Which figures have rotational symmetry? For those that do, give the angle of rotation.

a. 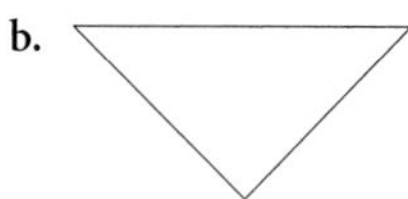 b. c. 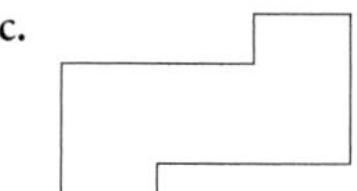

a. 120° b. This figure does not have rotational symmetry. c. 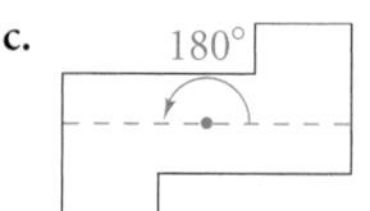

2. If a figure has rotational symmetry, must it also have line symmetry? Explain your answer. **No; figure (c) in Example 3 has rotational symmetry but not line symmetry.**

A rotation of 180° is known as a **half-turn.** If a half-turn maps a plane figure onto itself, the figure has **point symmetry.**

3. **Try This** Which figures have point symmetry?

a.  yes

b. 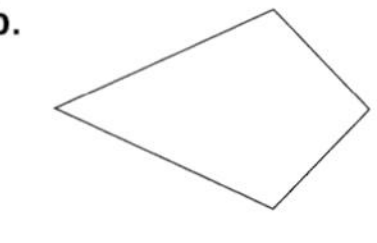 no

c. 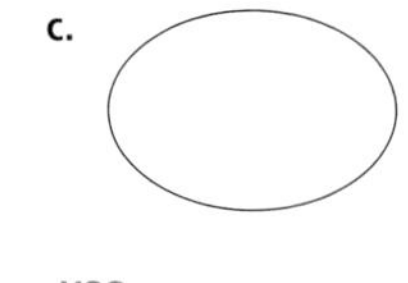 yes

So far, you've looked at figures with reflectional and rotational symmetry. As you may have guessed, figures may also have *translational* or *glide reflectional symmetry*. You will discuss these symmetries in the next lesson.

Type of Symmetry	Points
Reflectional Symmetry	1
Rotational Symmetry of 180°	2
Rotational Symmetry other than 180°	3

WORK TOGETHER

- Work in groups to find examples of symmetrical objects in your classroom. For each object that you find, sketch an orthographic view and list its symmetries. You will have only ten minutes in which to search, so plan your time wisely!
- Determine your group's score by using the chart at the left.

Once the activity is completed, have the group with the most points report their findings to the class. The class should verify the accuracy of the group's sketches and that the symmetries described are correct.

KINESTHETIC LEARNING With the administration's permission, close off a school parking lot. Take students out to the parking lot to analyze hubcap symmetry. Challenge each group to find as many types of symmetry as possible.

Exercises ON YOUR OWN

Exercises 1–8 Students may want to copy the figures and use paper folding, cutouts, or mirrors.

ALTERNATIVE ASSESSMENT **Exercises 9–12** These exercises can help you assess students' understanding of the symmetries found in real-world objects. Have students explain their reasoning to partners.

EXTENSION Exercise 10 If you have block scheduling or an extended period, have students make their own snowflake designs, keeping in mind that snowflakes always have six-fold rotational symmetry.

PATTERNS Exercise 14b Students should see that since a square is a rectangle, the lines of symmetry of a rectangle are also lines of symmetry of a square.

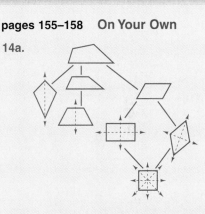

Exercises ON YOUR OWN

What types of symmetry does each figure have? If it has reflectional symmetry, sketch the figure and the line(s) of symmetry. If it has rotational symmetry, state the angle of rotation.

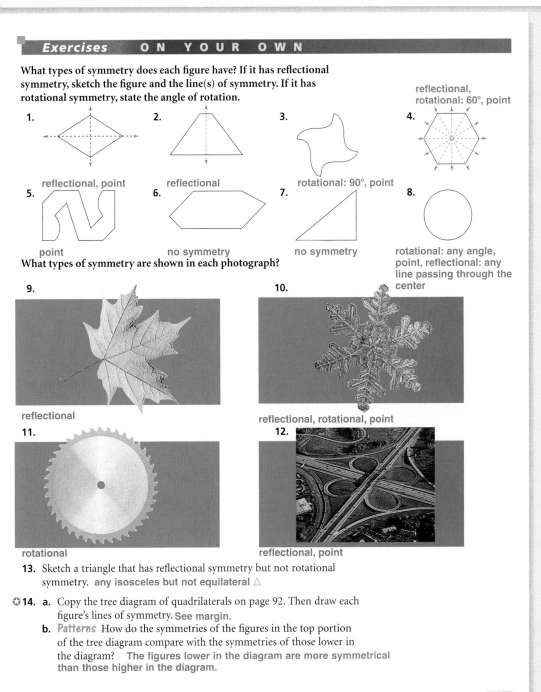

1. reflectional, point
2. reflectional
3. rotational: 90°, point
4. reflectional, rotational: 60°, point
5. point
6. no symmetry
7. no symmetry
8. rotational: any angle, point, reflectional: any line passing through the center

What types of symmetry are shown in each photograph?

9. reflectional
10. reflectional, rotational, point
11. rotational
12. reflectional, point

13. Sketch a triangle that has reflectional symmetry but not rotational symmetry. **any isosceles but not equilateral △**

14. a. Copy the tree diagram of quadrilaterals on page 92. Then draw each figure's lines of symmetry. **See margin.**
    b. *Patterns* How do the symmetries of the figures in the top portion of the tree diagram compare with the symmetries of those lower in the diagram? **The figures lower in the diagram are more symmetrical than those higher in the diagram.**

pages 155–158 On Your Own

14a.

DIVERSITY Exercise 33 This is a good opportunity to discuss different alphabets such as Cyrillic, Korean, and Thai.

OPEN-ENDED Exercise 38 Students may want to enlarge the Venn diagram to have more room to draw figures.

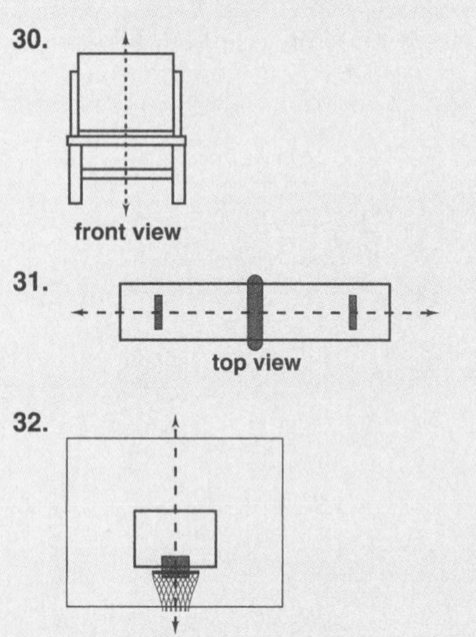

33a.

Language	Horizontal Line	Vertical Line	Point
English	B, C, D, E, H, I, K, O, X	A, H, I, M, O, T, U, V, W, X, Y	H, I, N, O, S, X, Z
Greek	Β, Ε, Η, Θ, Ι, Κ, Ξ, Ο, Σ, Φ, Χ	Α, Δ, Η, Θ, Ι, Λ, Μ, Ξ, Ο, Π, Τ, Υ, Φ, Χ, Ψ, Ω	Ζ, Η, Θ, Ι, Ν, Ξ, Ο, Φ, Χ

b. Answers may vary. Sample: Greek; Greek alphabet has more letters with at least one kind of symmetry and more letters with multiple symmetry.

Each diagram shows a shape folded along a red line of symmetry. Sketch the unfolded figure.

15. 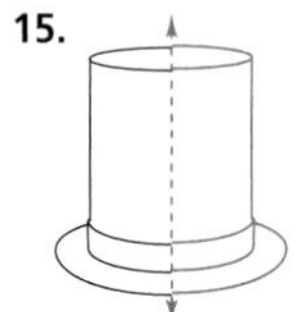

16. 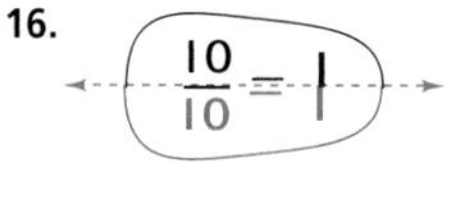

17. 

18. a. The word CODE has a horizontal line of symmetry through its center. Find three other words that have this type of symmetry. **a. Sample: CHECKBOOK, DOCK, HOOD**
b. The word WAXY, when printed vertically, has a vertical line of symmetry. Find three other words that have this type of symmetry. **b. Sample: TOMATO, HOAX, YOUTH**

Advertising **Many automobile manufacturers have symmetrical logos. Describe the symmetry, if any, in each logo.**

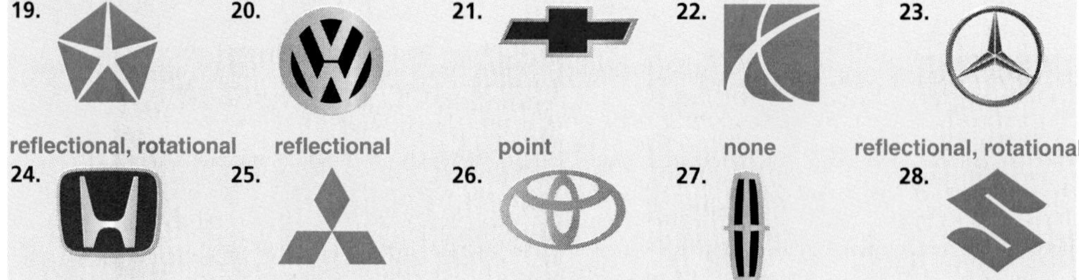

29. *Research* Many company logos are symmetrical. Find three symmetrical logos in the Yellow Pages of your local phone book. Copy each logo, identify the name of the business, and describe the type(s) of symmetry illustrated. **Check students' work.**

Geometry in 3 Dimensions **Show the reflectional symmetries of each object by sketching an orthographic view.** **30–32. See margin.**

30. 31. 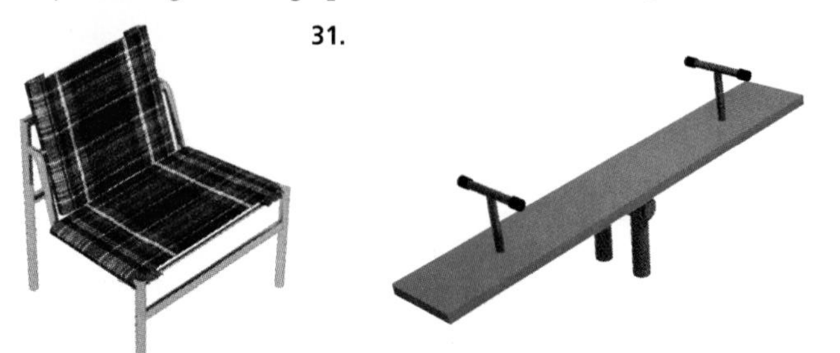

32. 

OPEN-ENDED Exercise 39 The example shown has a horizontal line of symmetry. It is more difficult to write creative equations with a vertical line of symmetry.

COORDINATE GEOMETRY Exercises 44–46 Have students support their responses with sketches. Challenge students to draw one figure with a vertex at (3, 4) that has all three given types of symmetries.

Chapter Project **FIND OUT BY CLASSIFYING** Students may also want to classify the patterns found on pages 137, 143, and 150 by their symmetries.

Exercises MIXED REVIEW

Exercises 47–50 Check that students do not confuse the slope formula with the method for finding a midpoint or with how to find a translation vector that maps one point onto another.

GETTING READY FOR LESSON 3-6 This exercise prepares students to identify figures that tessellate.

33. a. *Languages* Copy the chart at the right. Then use the alphabets below to list the letters in each category. Some letters will appear in more than one category.

b. Which alphabet is more symmetrical? Explain your reasoning. a–b. See margin p. 156.

A B C D E F G H I J K L M N O P Q R S T U V W X Y Z

Α Β Γ Δ Ε Ζ Η Θ Ι Κ Λ Μ Ν Ξ Ο Π Ρ Σ Τ Υ Φ Χ Ψ Ω

Type of Symmetry

Language	Horizontal Line	Vertical Line	Point
English			
Greek			

34. *Writing* Use what you learned in Lesson 3-4 to explain why a figure that has two or more lines of symmetry must also have rotational symmetry. A composition of two reflections in intersecting lines of symmetry is a rotation.

Algebra **Sketch the graph of each equation. Describe the symmetry of each graph.** 35–37. See margin.

35. $y = x^2$ **36.** $y = (x - 2)^2$ **37.** $y = x^3$

38. *Open-ended* Copy the Venn diagram; then draw a figure in each of its six regions that shows that type of symmetry.

line symmetry

rotational symmetry

point symmetry

39. *Open-ended* The equation $\frac{10}{10} - 1 = 0 \div \frac{83}{83}$ is not only true, but also symmetrical. Write four other equations or inequalities that are both true and symmetrical. See below right for samples.

40. a. Is the line that contains the bisector of an angle a line of symmetry of the angle? Explain.

b. Is a bisector of a segment a line of symmetry of the segment? Explain. a–b. See margin.

Each of the logos below is nearly symmetrical. For each logo, describe how you could alter it to make it symmetrical. Then, describe the symmetries of your altered logo. 41–43. See margin.

39. 96 = 96, 18 + 81 = 18 + 81, 88 − 33 = 38 + 8 + 3 + 3 + 3; $\frac{80}{80} = \frac{33}{33}$, 80 + 8 = 88

41.

42.

43.

Coordinate Geometry **A figure has a vertex at (3, 4). If the figure has the given type of symmetry, state the coordinates of another vertex of the figure.**

44. line symmetry in the *y*-axis (−3, 4)

45. line symmetry in the *x*-axis (3, −4)

46. point symmetry in the origin (−3, −4)

35. reflectional in *y*-axis

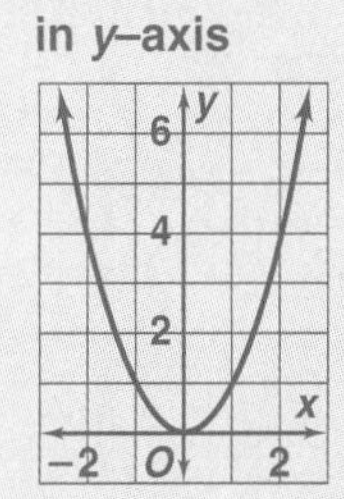

36. reflectional in *x* = 2

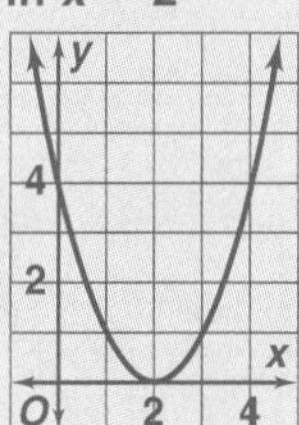

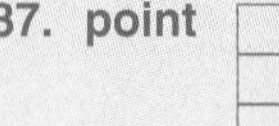

37. point

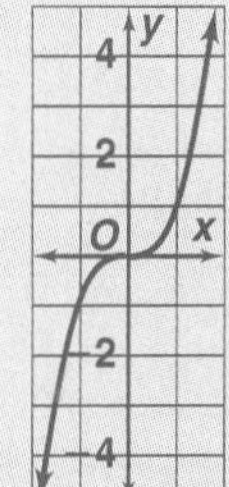

40a. Yes; the bisector divides the angle into 2 ≅ angles with one side of the angle being the reflection of the other.

b. Not necessarily; the bisector divides the segment into 2 ≅ parts but one part cannot be the reflection of the other unless the bisector is the ⊥ bisector.

41. Answers may vary. Sample: Delete the *N*, the *E*, and the shading on the right side of the bells; reflectional symmetry.

42. Answers may vary. Sample: Delete the *S* in the hexagon; reflectional symmetry.

43. Answers may vary. Sample: Fill in the letters in the middle of the logo; rotational symmetry.

Wrap Up

THE BIG IDEA Have students compare and contrast the definitions of *reflectional symmetry, line symmetry, rotational symmetry,* and *point symmetry.*

RETEACHING ACTIVITY Students identify types of symmetries in figures on flags. (Reteaching worksheet 3-1)

Exercises CHECKPOINT

In this Checkpoint, your students will assess their own progress on Lessons 3-4 and 3-5.

Exercises 1–3 Students may want to trace these figures onto another piece of paper to manipulate them.

Exercise 4 Have students draw the figure and its image as well as give the coordinates of the vertices of both.

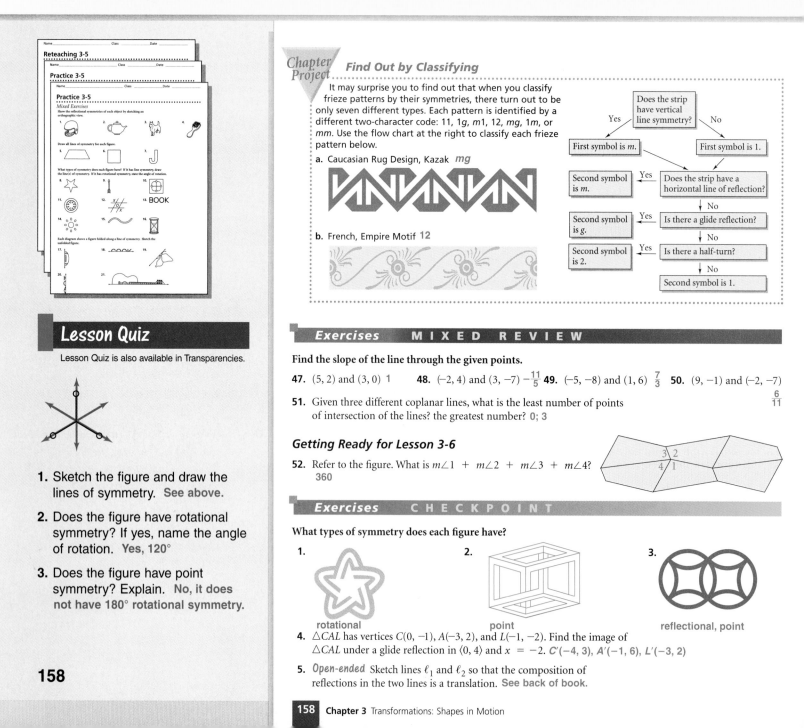

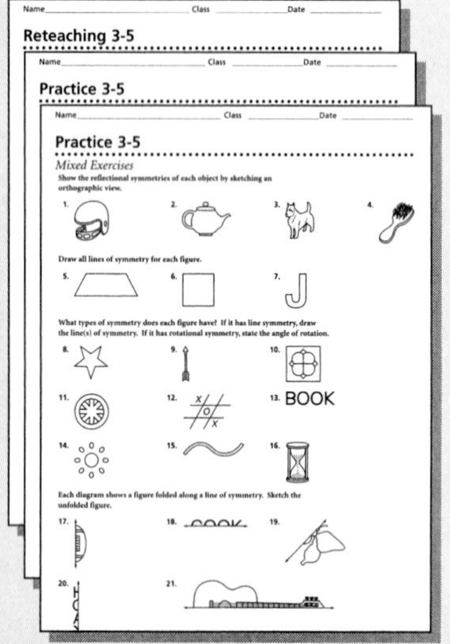
Reteaching 3-5

Practice 3-5

Practice 3-5

Mixed Exercises

Lesson Quiz

Lesson Quiz is also available in Transparencies.

1. Sketch the figure and draw the lines of symmetry. See above.
2. Does the figure have rotational symmetry? If yes, name the angle of rotation. Yes, 120°
3. Does the figure have point symmetry? Explain. No, it does not have 180° rotational symmetry.

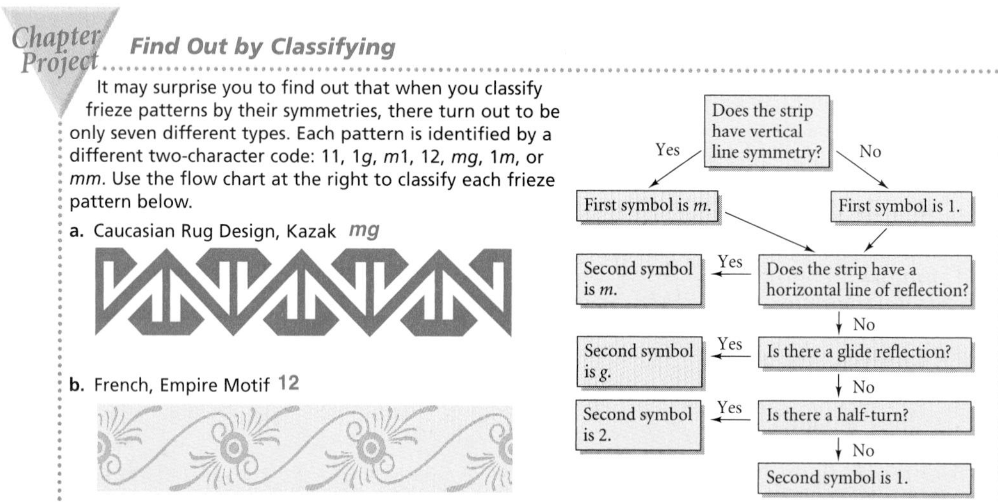

Chapter Project: *Find Out by Classifying*

It may surprise you to find out that when you classify frieze patterns by their symmetries, there turn out to be only seven different types. Each pattern is identified by a different two-character code: 11, 1*g*, *m*1, 12, *mg*, 1*m*, or *mm*. Use the flow chart at the right to classify each frieze pattern below.

a. Caucasian Rug Design, Kazak *mg*

b. French, Empire Motif 12

Exercises MIXED REVIEW

Find the slope of the line through the given points.

47. (5, 2) and (3, 0) 1
48. (−2, 4) and (3, −7) $-\frac{11}{5}$
49. (−5, −8) and (1, 6) $\frac{7}{3}$
50. (9, −1) and (−2, −7) $\frac{6}{11}$

51. Given three different coplanar lines, what is the least number of points of intersection of the lines? the greatest number? 0; 3

Getting Ready for Lesson 3-6

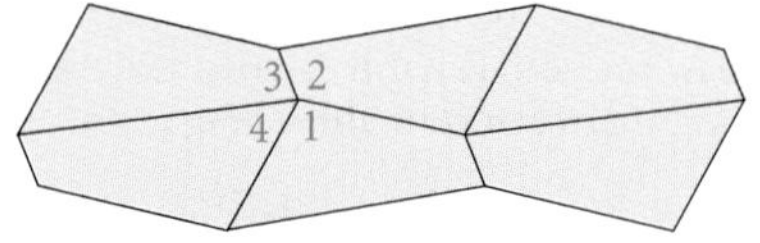

52. Refer to the figure. What is $m\angle 1 + m\angle 2 + m\angle 3 + m\angle 4$? 360

Exercises CHECKPOINT

What types of symmetry does each figure have?

1. rotational

2. 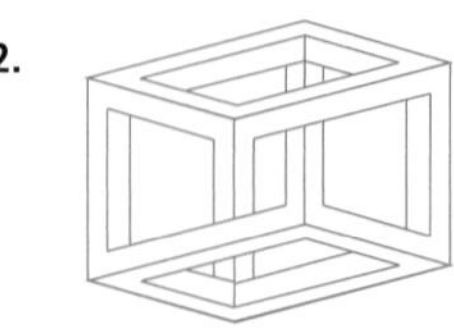
point

3. 
reflectional, point

4. $\triangle CAL$ has vertices $C(0, -1)$, $A(-3, 2)$, and $L(-1, -2)$. Find the image of $\triangle CAL$ under a glide reflection in $\langle 0, 4\rangle$ and $x = -2$. $C'(-4, 3)$, $A'(-1, 6)$, $L'(-3, 2)$

5. *Open-ended* Sketch lines ℓ_1 and ℓ_2 so that the composition of reflections in the two lines is a translation. See back of book.

3-6 Teaching Notes

PROBLEM OF THE DAY

Multiplying 4 × 2178, you get 8712, the reverse of 2178. Find the four-digit number that when multiplied by 9 gives a similar result. 1089

Problem of the Day is also available in Transparencies.

CONNECTING TO PRIOR KNOWLEDGE Have students who have played the game TETRIS™ explain it to others. (Seven tiles are rotated and translated to cover a rectangular playing surface without leaving any gaps.) Ask them to share any techniques or tricks they have learned.

THINK AND DISCUSS p. 159

TACTILE LEARNING If pattern blocks are available, have students create the pavement tiling shown.

Example 1 Relating to the Real World 

CONNECTING TO STUDENTS' WORLD Students will most likely be familiar with Escher prints from calendars, posters, and T-shirts. Ask what they like and dislike about this type of art.

ERROR ALERT! Question 1 Students may have some difficulty seeing a pattern of tiles that is repeated. **Remediation:** Suggest they trace the pattern that they think is being repeated and see if they can cover the picture with it.

Connections Graphic Design . . . and more

3-6 Tessellations

What You'll Learn

- Identifying figures that tessellate
- Identifying symmetries of tessellations

...And Why

To recognize tessellations in nature, architecture, art, and other areas of life

What You'll Need

- scissors
- clear tape
- ruler

Who? The Dutch artist Maurits Cornelis Escher (1898–1972) used transformational geometry in intriguing ways in his work. His work is very popular with the public, scientists, and mathematicians.

THINK AND DISCUSS

Part 1

Identifying Figures that Tessellate

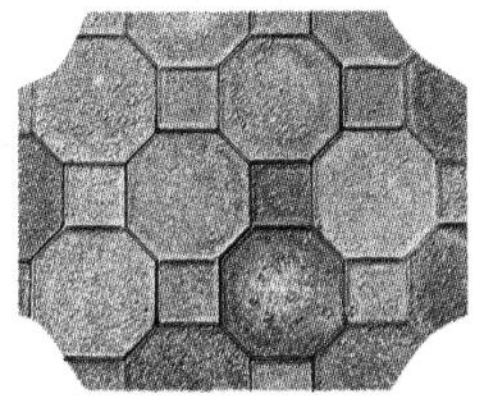

A **tessellation** is a repeating pattern of figures that completely covers a plane without gaps or overlaps. Tessellations are also called **tilings.** A set of figures that can be used to create a tessellation is said to *tessellate.* You can find tessellations in art, nature, and everyday life.

Example 1 Relating to the Real World 

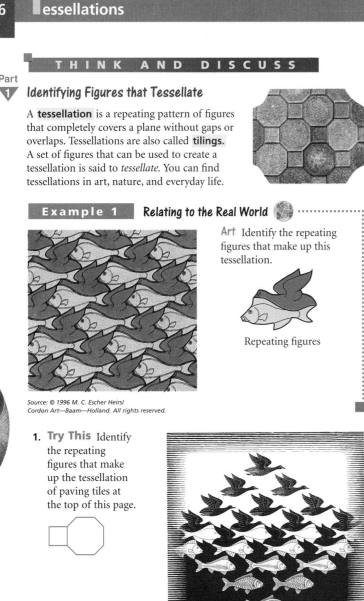

Art Identify the repeating figures that make up this tessellation.

Repeating figures

1. **Try This** Identify the repeating figures that make up the tessellation of paving tiles at the top of this page.

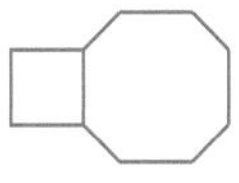

Lesson Planning Options

Prerequisite Skills

- Identifying symmetry
- Finding transformations of figures

Assignment Options for Exercises On Your Own

To provide flexible scheduling, this lesson can be subdivided into parts.

 **Core** 1–3, 10–12, 17–19
✪Extension 13–16

 **Core** 4–9
✪Extension 20

Use Mixed Review to maintain skills.

Resources

 **Student Edition**

Extra Practice, p. 650
Glossary/Study Guide

 **Teaching Resources**

Chapter Support File, Ch. 3
- Practice 3-6 (two worksheets)
- Reteaching 3-6

Classroom Manager 3-6
Glossary, Spanish Resources

 **Transparencies**
1, 7, 42

Students may need some help in understanding the diagrams shown above Question 3. They illustrate that in order for a regular polygon to tessellate the plane, copies of the polygon must be able to be placed so that at a vertex shared by the polygons, the sum of the measures of the angles is 360 and the angles do not overlap. This happens when the angle measure of a regular polygon divides evenly into 360.

CRITICAL THINKING Question 3 You may need to review with students the interior angle measures of regular polygons, $\frac{(n-2) \times 180}{n}$.

Additional Examples

FOR EXAMPLE 1

Refer to page 163, Exercise 5. Identify the repeating figures in the tessellation.

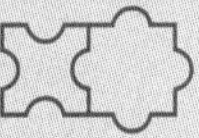

FOR EXAMPLE 2

Refer to the walkway of paving tiles on page 159. List the types of symmetry in the tessellation.

rotational and point symmetry in the dots shown

line symmetry in the bold-faced lines

translational symmetry

glide reflectional symmetry

Because the figures in a tessellation do not overlap or leave gaps, the sum of the measures of the angles around any vertex must be 360.

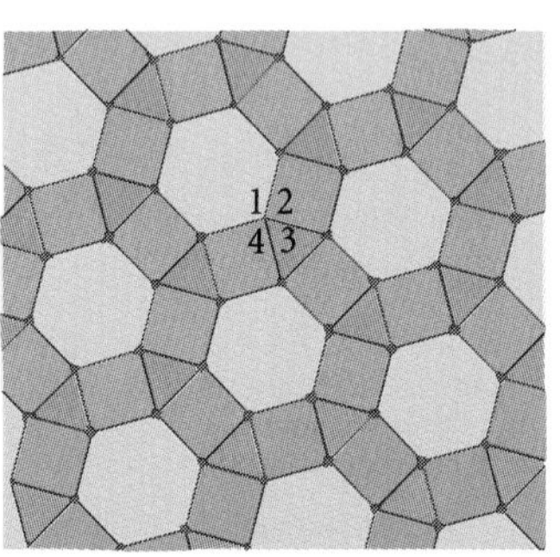

2. a. The tessellation shown consists of regular polygons. Find the measures of angles 1, 2, 3, and 4. **120, 90, 60, 90**
   b. Check your answer to part (a) by making sure that the sum of the measures is 360.

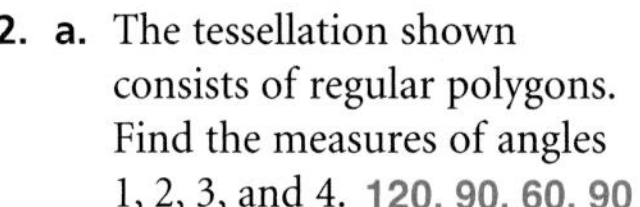

120 + 90 + 60 + 90 = 360 ✓

A **pure tessellation** is a tessellation that consists of congruent copies of one figure. It may surprise you that there are only three pure tessellations made up of regular polygons. To see why this is the case, consider the following diagrams.

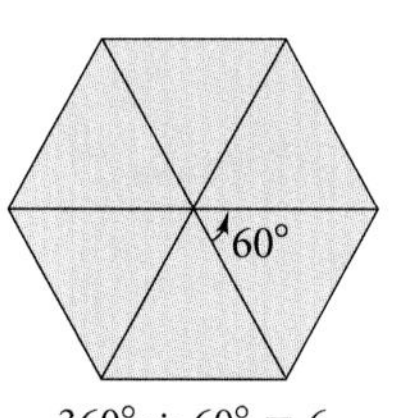

$360° \div 60° = 6$

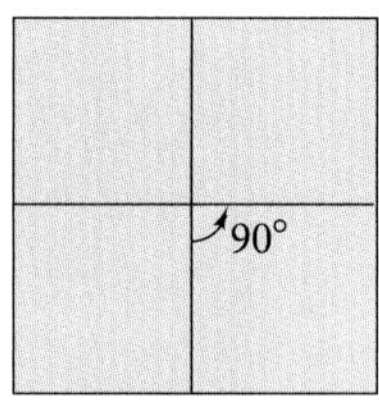

$360° \div 90° = 4$

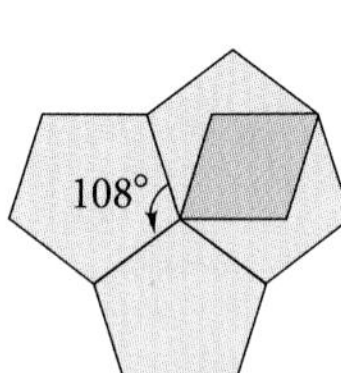

$360° \div 108° \approx 3.3$

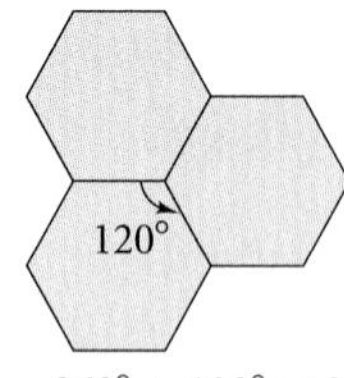

$360° \div 120° = 3$

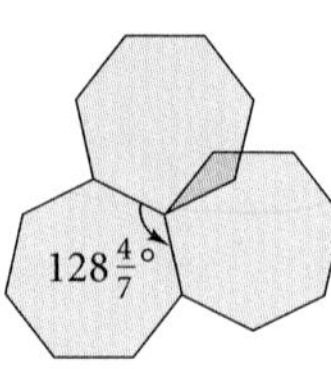

$360° \div 128\frac{4}{7}° \approx 2.8$

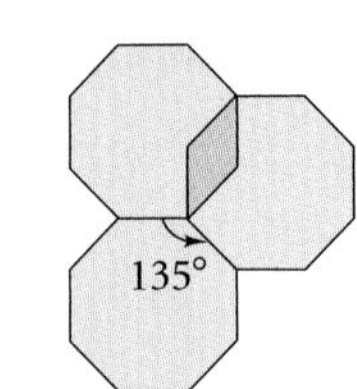

$360° \div 135° \approx 2.6$

3. *Critical Thinking* Explain why no regular polygons with more than six sides tessellate. **See below.**

Regular triangles and quadrilaterals tessellate, but what about other triangles and quadrilaterals? Work in groups to explore this problem.

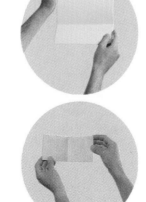

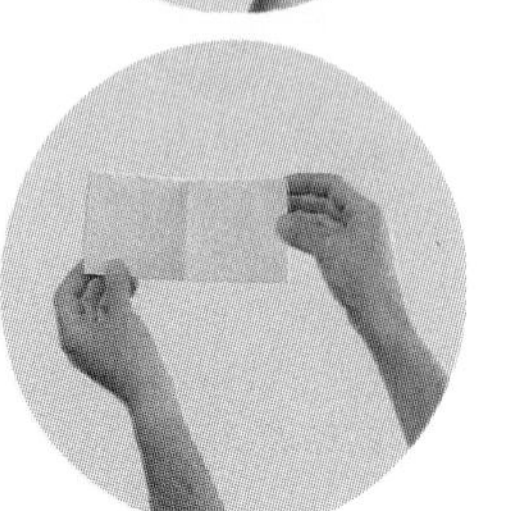

WORK TOGETHER

Step 1: Have each member of your group fold four pieces of paper into sixths, as shown in the photos.

3. A regular polygon with more than 6 sides must have angles greater than 120°, and at least 3 polygons must meet at each vertex. The sum of 3 or more angles greater than 120° cannot be 360°.

WORK TOGETHER p. 160

In Step 2, suggest one member of each group draw an acute triangle, another draw an obtuse triangle, and another draw a right triangle.

Question 4a Students may observe that a triangle can tessellate a plane in more than one way. For example, a tessellation of right triangles can form a large rectangle or a large parallelogram.

In Step 3, students should see already that squares and rectangles will tessellate a plane. Have students draw other types of quadrilaterals, some concave and some convex.

THINK AND DISCUSS p. 161

Remind students that only part of the tessellation is shown in the diagram. The pattern continues in all directions of its plane.

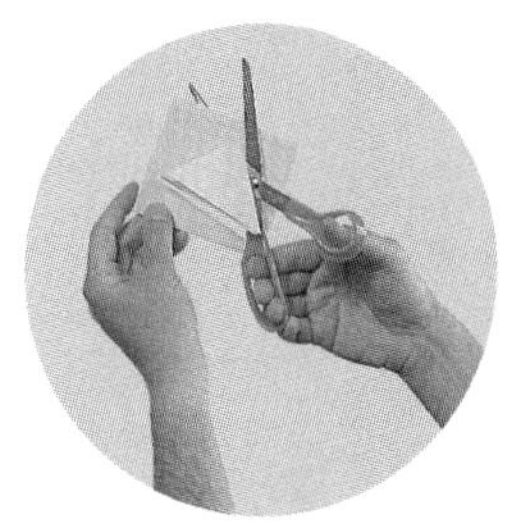

4a. Sample:

b. The sum of the measures of the angles of a triangle is 180. Therefore, 6 triangles meeting at each vertex with 2 of each angle represented will cover the space around the vertex.

Step 2: Draw a triangle on one of the four folded pieces of paper; then cut through all six sheets of paper to create six congruent triangles. Create six more congruent triangles by tracing one of your cutouts onto another folded piece of paper and then cutting out six triangles.

4. a. Try to arrange your twelve congruent triangles into a tessellation. (*Hint:* Arrange vertices so that they meet.) Compare results within your group.
   b. Use what you know about the sum of the measures of the angles of a triangle to explain your results from part (a).
   4a–b. See left.

Step 3: Set your triangles aside. Use the method in Step 2 to create twelve congruent quadrilaterals.

5. a. Try to arrange your twelve congruent quadrilaterals into a tessellation. Compare results within your group.
   b. Use what you know about the sum of the measures of the angles of a quadrilateral to explain your results from part (a).
   a–b. See margin p. 162.

THINK AND DISCUSS

In the Work Together, you discovered the following properties of tessellations.

Theorem 3-5	Every triangle tessellates.
Theorem 3-6	Every quadrilateral tessellates.

Part 2

Tessellations and Symmetry

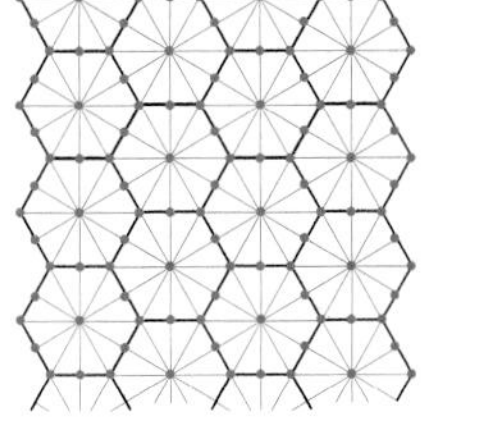

This pure tessellation of regular hexagons has reflectional symmetry in each of the blue lines. It has rotational symmetry centered at each of the red points. The tessellation also has two other types of symmetry—translational symmetry and glide reflectional symmetry.

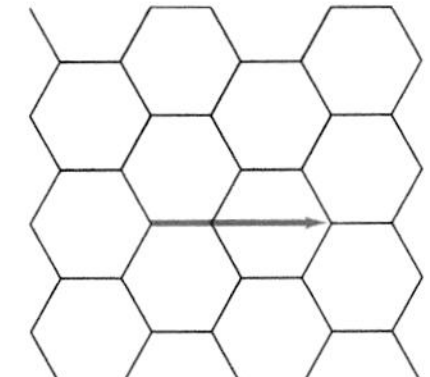

Translational Symmetry

A translation maps the tessellation onto itself.

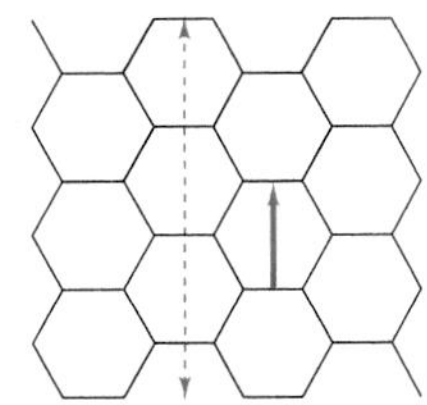

Glide Reflectional Symmetry

A glide reflection maps the tessellation onto itself.

Technology Options

For Exercise 10, students may use a drawing program or geometry software to sketch the two tessellations. Similarly, in Exercises 13–16 students can use geometry software to copy each figure onto a coordinate grid, then create a tessellation.

Prentice Hall Technology

Software
- Secondary Math Lab Toolkit™
- Integrated Math Lab 28
- Computer Item Generator 3-6

Internet
- See the Prentice Hall site. (http://www.phschool.com)

Example 2

Before students determine the symmetries, they should identify the pattern being repeated. You may want to ask why there is no line symmetry or glide reflectional symmetry in part b.

WORK TOGETHER p. 162

Once students have created their figures, have them copy them onto lightweight cardboard and cut them out. They can then trace around the cutouts to create their tessellations.

page 161 Work Together

5a. Sample:

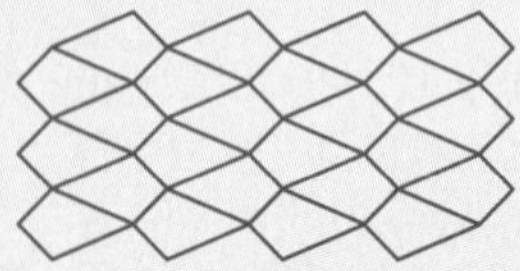

b. The sum of the measures of the angles of a quadrilateral is 360. Four quadrilaterals meeting at a vertex, each represented by a different angle, cover the space around the vertex.

Example 2

List the symmetries of each tessellation.

a.

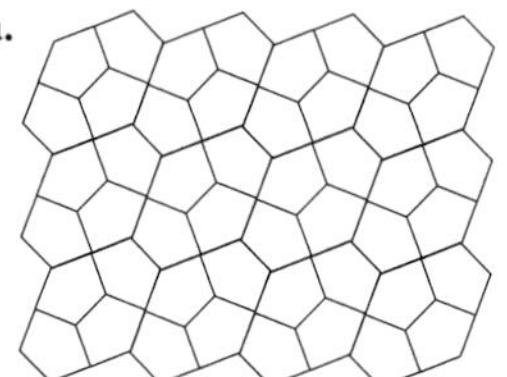

b.

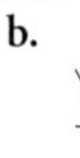

a.

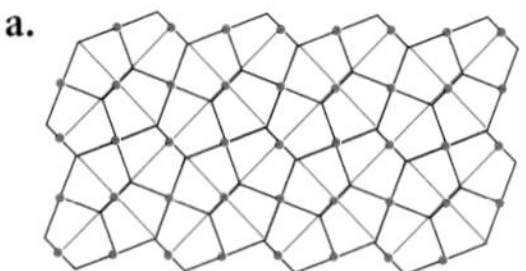

b.

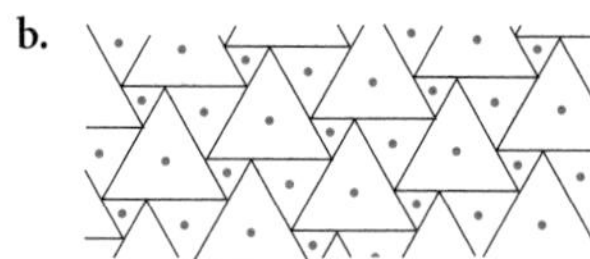

- Line symmetry in the blue lines
- Rotational symmetry in the red points
- Translational symmetry
- Glide reflectional symmetry

- Rotational symmetry in the red points
- Translational symmetry

WORK TOGETHER

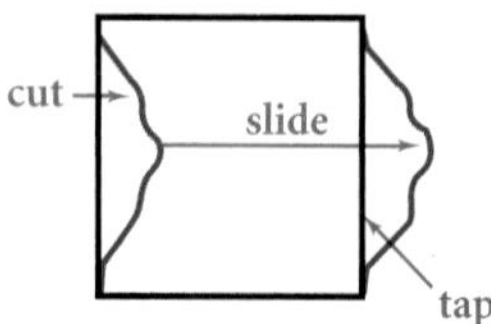

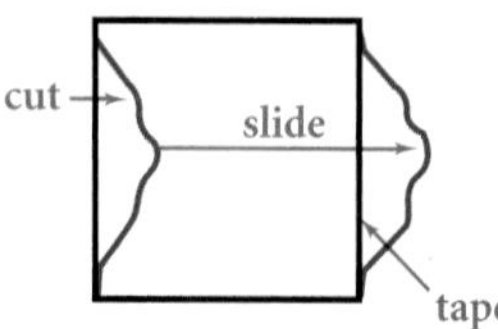

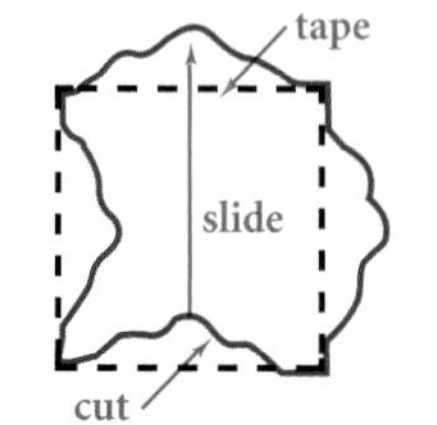

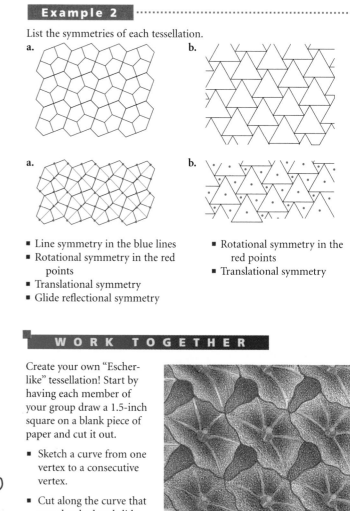

Create your own "Escher-like" tessellation! Start by having each member of your group draw a 1.5-inch square on a blank piece of paper and cut it out.

- Sketch a curve from one vertex to a consecutive vertex.
- Cut along the curve that you sketched and slide the resulting cutout to the opposite side of the square. Tape it in place using clear tape.
- Repeat this process using the remaining two sides of the square.
- Rotate the figure you end up with. What does it look like? A penguin with a hat on? A knight on horseback? A dog with floppy ears? Sketch whatever you come up with on your figure.
- Create a tessellation using your figure.

Exercises ON YOUR OWN

Exercises 1–3 Students can identify the repeating figure using a sketch. Remind students to identify the smallest number of figures that can create the tessellation.

VISUAL LEARNING Exercises 4–9 Students may have greater success if they trace a portion of the tessellation *first*, then use the tracing to find the symmetries.

OPEN-ENDED Exercise 11 Encourage students to find real-world examples such as ceiling tiles rather than examples of Escher prints found in books or on posters. Also point out that the tessellations should be different (i.e. the tessellation in a wire strainer may be the same as the ceiling tile tessellation).

WRITING Exercise 12 Students may wish to use a diagram to illustrate their reasoning.

Exercises ON YOUR OWN

Identify the repeating figure or figures that make up each tessellation. 1–3. See margin.

1. 

Fabric by *Fabric Traditions*

2. 

Arabian design

3. 

Honeycomb

Describe the symmetries of each tessellation. Copy a portion of the tessellation and draw any centers of rotational symmetry or lines of symmetry. 4–9. Also see margin.

4. 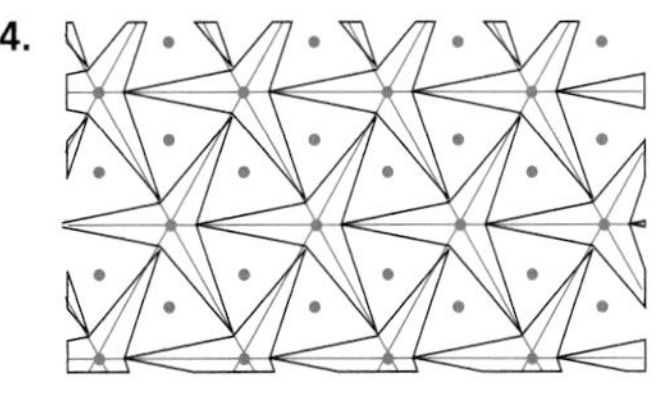

5. 

6. 

7. 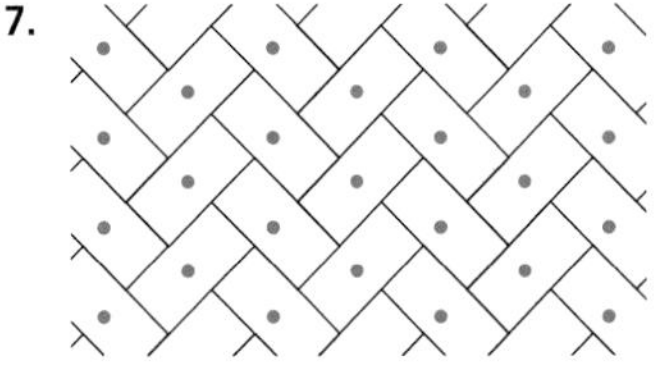

8. 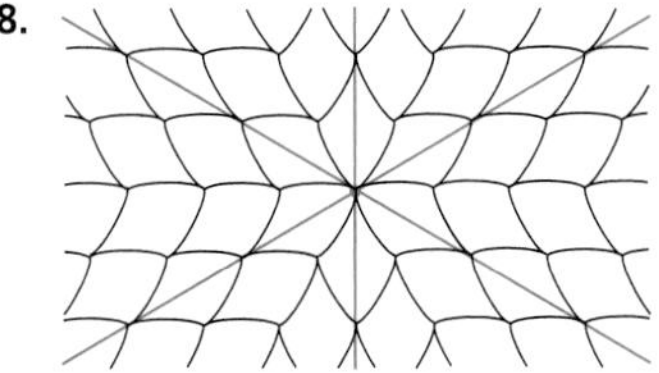

9. 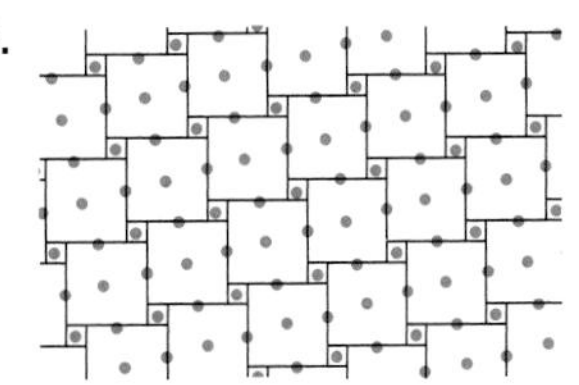

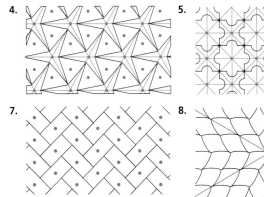

10. The figure shown at the right can be used to tile the plane in several different ways. Make copies of the figure and sketch two different tessellations. See margin.

11. *Open-ended* Find and sketch two examples of tessellations found at home or at school. Check students' work.

12. *Writing* Is it possible to tile the plane with regular decagons? Explain why or why not. No; regular decagons have more than 6 sides. No regular polygon with more than 6 sides tessellates.

pages 163–164 On Your Own

1. 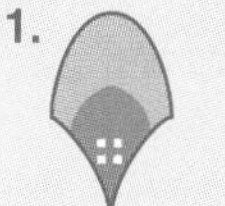
2. 
3. 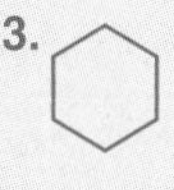
4. rotational, reflectional, glide reflectional, and translational
5. rotational, point, reflectional, glide reflectional, and translational
6. rotational, reflectional, glide reflectional, and translational
7. point and translational
8. rotational and reflectional
9. rotational, point, and translational
10.  

ALTERNATIVE ASSESSMENT **Exercises 13–16** These exercises can help you assess students understanding of tessellations by their ability to create them with irregular polygons. You may want to give students some guidelines as to how large to make their tessellations.

EXTENSION Exercise 20 If students show interest or aptitude for creating tessellations, direct them to more advanced techniques found in other publications or software packages.

Exercises MIXED REVIEW

Exercise 25 Make sure students use the correct symbols and abbreviations when identifying figures in the diagram.

JOURNAL Encourage students to give specific examples to support their reasoning.

GETTING READY FOR LESSON 3-7 This exercise prepares students for finding dilations in Lesson 3-7 by reviewing properties of similar figures.

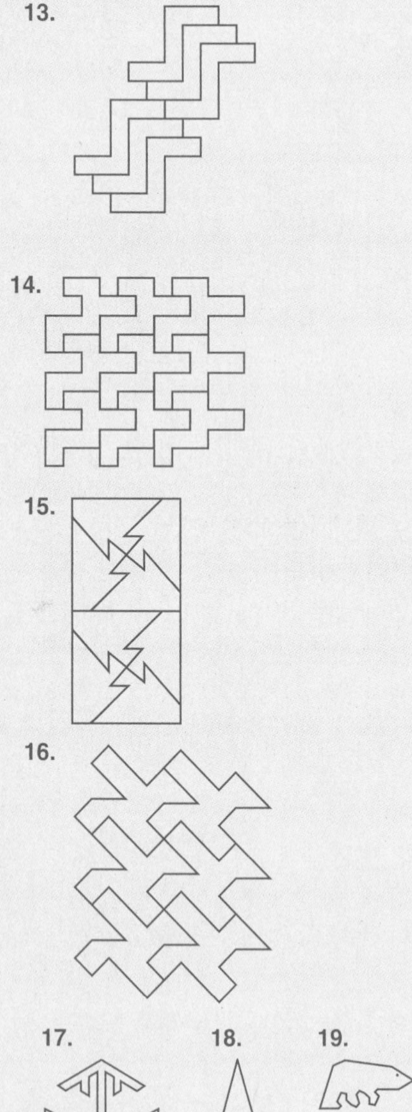

Use each figure to create a tessellation on dot paper. 13–16. See margin.

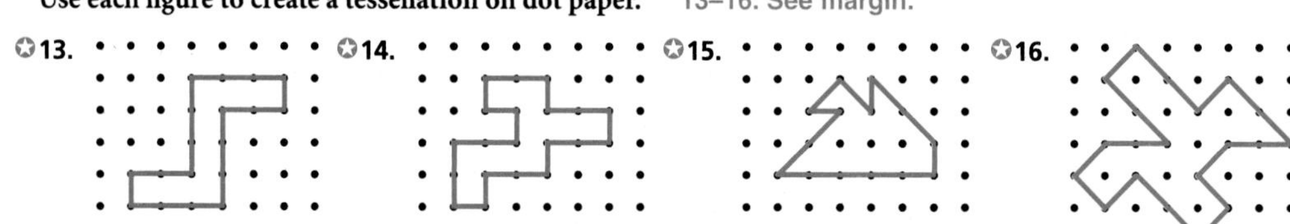

Identify the repeating figure or figures that make up each tessellation. 17–19. See margin.

17.

Mongolian design

18.

Rice wrapped in banana leaves

19.

Design by François Brisse

20. Follow the steps below to create an "Escher-like" tessellation based on a regular hexagon. Check students' work.

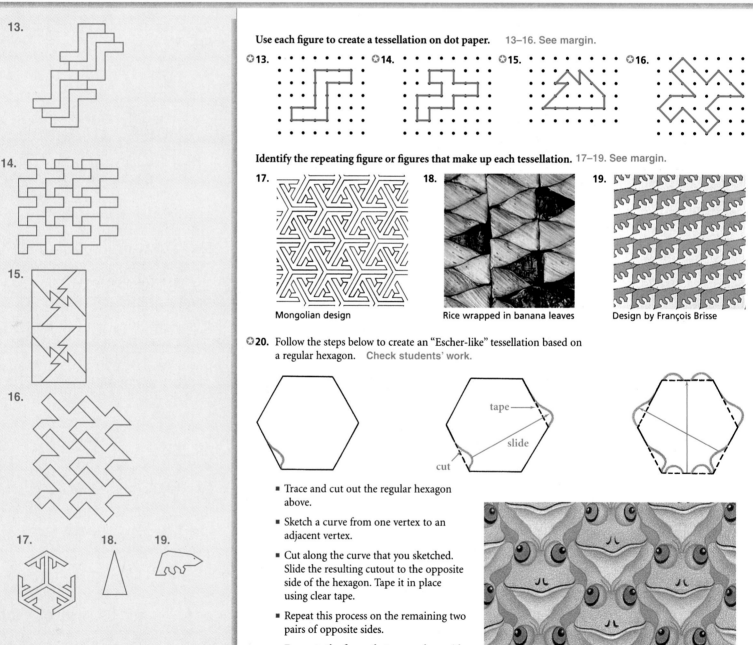

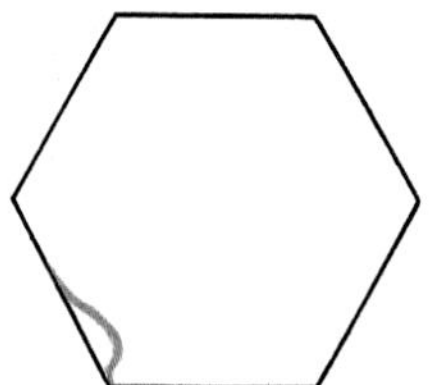

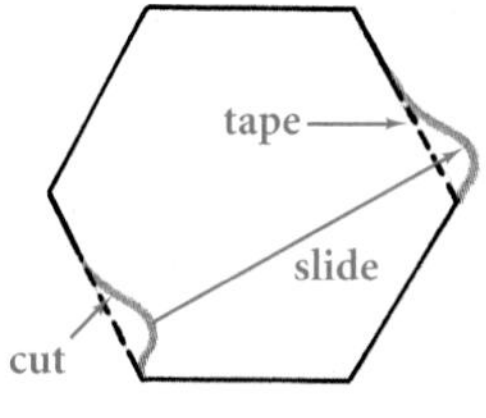

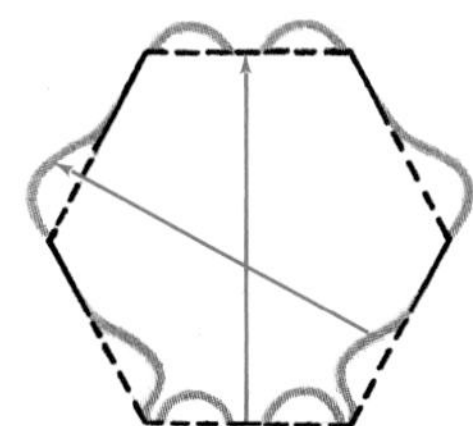

- Trace and cut out the regular hexagon above.
- Sketch a curve from one vertex to an adjacent vertex.
- Cut along the curve that you sketched. Slide the resulting cutout to the opposite side of the hexagon. Tape it in place using clear tape.
- Repeat this process on the remaining two pairs of opposite sides.
- Decorate the figure that you end up with and use it to make a tessellation.

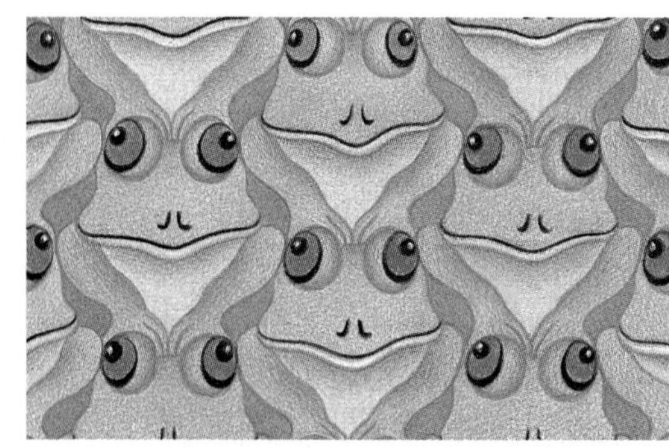

Wrap Up

THE BIG IDEA Ask students: *Describe a tessellation of a quadrilateral that has no reflectional symmetry. What symmetries does the tessellation have?*

RETEACHING ACTIVITY Students copy a figure and create a tessellation. Then they identify the symmetries in the tessellation. (Reteaching worksheet 3-6)

A Point in Time

If you have block scheduling or an extended class period, you may wish to have students investigate these topics:

- Find two other examples of famous mosaics from other cultures. Describe their design, including any patterns or symmetries they have.
- Learn more about Juan O'Gorman, his art, Latin American architecture, and/or Mexican art.
- Research the mosaic used in the Mexico City subway system, which opened in 1968.

Exercises MIXED REVIEW

Classify each triangle by its sides and angles.

21. 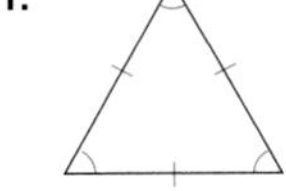
equilateral, equiangular

22. 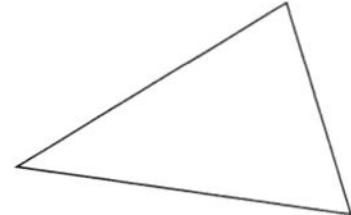
scalene, acute

23.
scalene, right

24. 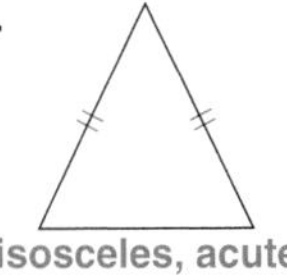
isosceles, acute

25. Given $\odot A$, identify each of the following.

- **a.** a diameter
- **b.** a major arc
- **c.** a minor arc
- **d.** a radius
- **e.** a central angle
- **f.** a pair of adjacent arcs

25a. $\overline{BD}$ b. Sample: $\widehat{BCE}$ c. Sample: $\widehat{ED}$ d. Sample: $\overline{AE}$ e. Sample: $\angle BAE$ f. Sample: $\widehat{BE}$ and $\widehat{ED}$

26. a. Find the measure of an interior angle of a regular 3-gon, 7-gon, and 42-gon. 60, $128\frac{4}{7}$, $171\frac{3}{7}$

b. Find the sum of the measures of the three angles from part (a). 360

Getting Ready for Lesson 3-7

27. In the diagram, $\triangle ABC \sim \triangle DEF$.

- **a.** Find AB and EF. 3; 10
- **b.** Find the scale factor of the enlargement. 2

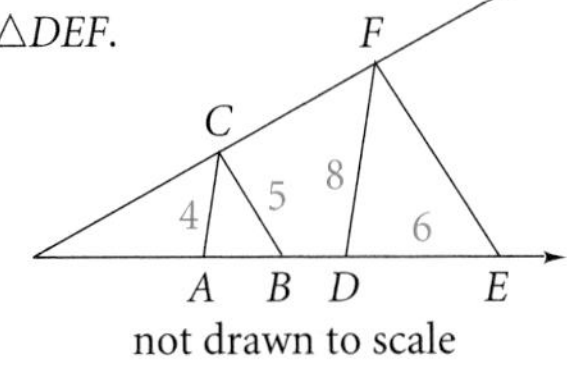
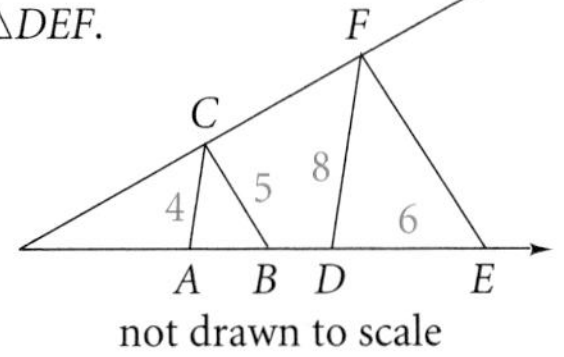
not drawn to scale

SELF ASSESSMENT

For Your Journal

Think about different products that you can buy at a grocery store. How is the idea of tessellation important in the design of containers for products?

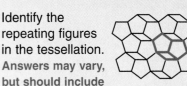

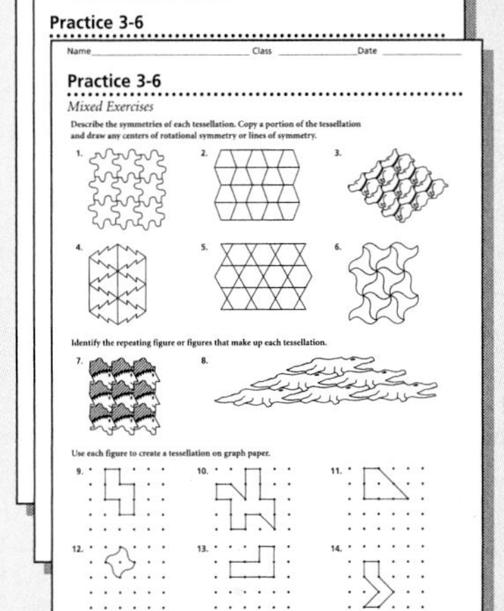

Lesson Quiz

Lesson Quiz is also available in Transparencies.

1. Identify the repeating figures in the tessellation. Answers may vary, but should include a parallelogram and two adjacent pentagons. Sample given above.
2. Describe the types of symmetry of the tessellation. translational symmetry, glide reflectional symmetry, line symmetry in the bold-faced lines, rotational and point symmetry in the dots shown

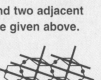

A Point in Time

1500 1600 2000

The Grand Mosaic of Mexico

A mosaic is a picture or decorative design made by setting tiny pieces of glass, stone, or other materials in clay or plaster. A mosaic may be a tessellation. Most mosaics, however, do not have a repeating pattern of figures. The art of constructing mosaics goes back at least 6,000 years to the Sumerians, who used tiles to both decorate and reinforce walls.

The Romans gave us the word *tessellate,* from the Latin *tessellare,* "to pave with tiles." During the second century A.D., Roman architects used 2 million tiles to create the magnificent mosaic of Dionysus in Germany. Large as it was, the Dionysus was less than a third the size of the work created in **1950** by the Mexican artist Juan O'Gorman. O'Gorman's mosaic, which depicts the cultural history of Mexico, is ten stories high and covers all four sides of the library of the National University of Mexico. Constructed of some 7.5 million stones, it is the largest mosaic in the world.

3-7 Teaching Notes

PROBLEM OF THE DAY

On a five-by-five square grid, shade squares so that the grid has rotational symmetry of 90° but no line symmetry. **Answers may vary. Sample given.**

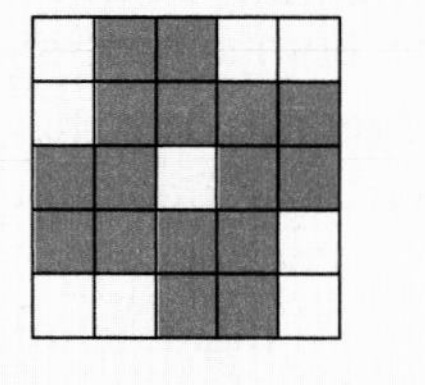

Problem of the Day is also available in Transparencies.

CONNECTING TO PRIOR KNOWLEDGE Discuss with students the relationships between an object and its image in a magnifying glass. Ask them how the size and shape of the object are related to the size and shape of the image.

WORK TOGETHER

ESL Since students with limited English proficiency may have some trouble following the directions, you may want to arrange the groups so that they are with students having strong English skills.

Make sure students read and perform one step at a time. They might want to use a second color to draw and label R', S', T' and $\triangle R'S'T'$.

Lesson Planning Options

Prerequisite Skills

- Determining if figures are similar

Assignment Options for Exercises On Your Own

Core 1–21, 24–28, 32–40

✪**Extension** 22–23, 29–31

Use Mixed Review to maintain skills.

Resources

 **Student Edition**

Skills Handbook, p. 670
Extra Practice, p. 650
Glossary/Study Guide

 **Teaching Resources**

Chapter Support File, Ch. 3
- Practice 3-7 (two worksheets)
- Reteaching 3-7
- Alternative Activity 3-7

Classroom Manager 3-7
Glossary, Spanish Resources

 **Transparencies**
5, 43

What You'll Learn
- Locating dilation images of figures

...And Why

To recognize applications of dilations in maps, photographs, scale models, and architectural blueprints

What You'll Need
- centimeter ruler
- calculator
- graph paper

Connections Human Development . . . and more

3-7 Dilations

WORK TOGETHER

- Have each member of your group draw a triangle and a point outside the triangle. Draw your figures in roughly the same positions as shown in the diagram. Label the triangle $\triangle RST$ and the point C.

- Draw $\overrightarrow{CR}$, $\overrightarrow{CS}$, and $\overrightarrow{CT}$.
- Have each member of your group select a different number n from the set $\{\frac{1}{3}, \frac{1}{2}, 1\frac{1}{2}, 2, 3\}$.
- Measure $\overline{CR}$, $\overline{CS}$, and $\overline{CT}$ to the nearest millimeter. Then calculate $n \cdot CR$, $n \cdot CS$, and $n \cdot CT$.
- Use a ruler to locate point R' on $\overrightarrow{CR}$ so that $CR' = n \cdot CR$. Locate points S' and T' in the same manner. Draw $\triangle R'S'T'$.

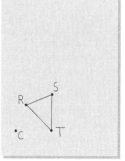

1. Compare corresponding angle measures in triangles $\triangle RST$ and $\triangle R'S'T'$. What do you notice? Compare results within your group. **The corresponding angles are ≅.**
2. Measure the lengths of the sides of $\triangle RST$ and $\triangle R'S'T'$ to the nearest millimeter. Then use a calculator to find the values of the ratios $\frac{R'S'}{RS}$, $\frac{S'T'}{ST}$, and $\frac{T'R'}{TR}$ to the nearest hundredth. What do you notice? **Each ratio is n.**
3. Use your results from Questions 1 and 2 to complete the statement: $\triangle RST$ is __?__ to $\triangle R'S'T'$. **similar**

THINK AND DISCUSS

The transformation that you performed in the Work Together is known as a *dilation.* Every dilation has a center and a scale factor. In the Work Together, the center of the dilation was C. The **scale factor** n described the size change from the original figure to the image. The dimensions of the image were n times that of the preimage. A **dilation** with center C and scale factor n, where $n > 0$, maps a point R to R' in such a way that R' is on $\overrightarrow{CR}$ and $CR' = n \cdot CR$. The center of dilation C is its own image (that is, $C' = C$).

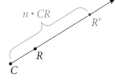

THINK AND DISCUSS

Help students understand the definition of dilation by illustrating it with several examples using actual values for n. Point out the restriction that the values of n must be greater than zero.

CRITICAL THINKING Question 4 This dilation with scale factor 1 is called the identity transformation and is an isometry.

Example 1

In part a, point out that the center of the dilation, X, is on the figure. In part b, the center of the dilation is $O(0, 0)$ and it is inside the figure.

Question 5 Students may want to review the results of the Work Together activity to help them answer the questions.

Example 2 **Relating to the Real World** 

If students compare the height-of-head to height-of-body ratios, they will see that the ratios are not equal.

ALTERNATIVE METHOD Have students copy the diagram but instead of drawing a human figure have them draw a line segment to represent the height of the body and a dotted line segment to represent the height of the head. Then have them find the ratios of the lengths of the dotted segments to the lengths of the solid segments.

This is not a similarity transformation. Do you see why?

The transformation changes shape as well as size. A similarity transformation changes size only.

As you noticed in the Work Together, a dilation maps a figure to a similar figure. A dilation is a **similarity transformation.**

4. *Critical Thinking* Describe the dilation image of a figure when the scale factor is 1. **When the scale factor is 1, the dilation image is the same as the preimage.**

Example 1

Find the scale factor for the dilation that maps the red figure onto the blue figure.

a.

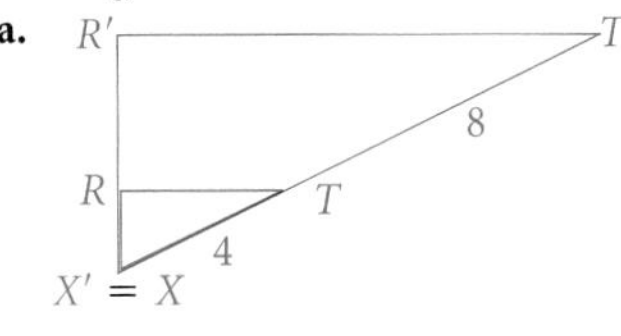

b.

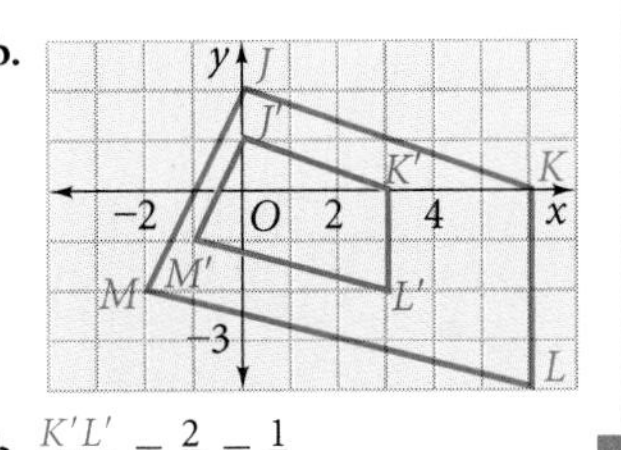

a. $\frac{T'X'}{TX} = \frac{8 + 4}{4} = 3$ **b.** $\frac{K'L'}{KL} = \frac{2}{4} = \frac{1}{2}$

There are two types of dilations. If the image is larger than the original figure, the dilation is an **enlargement.** If the image is smaller than the original figure, the dilation is a **reduction.**

5. What scale factors produce enlargements? reductions? **scale factors greater than 1; scale factors less than 1**

Example 2 **Relating to the Real World** 

6 ft
5 ft
4 ft
3 ft
2 ft
1 ft

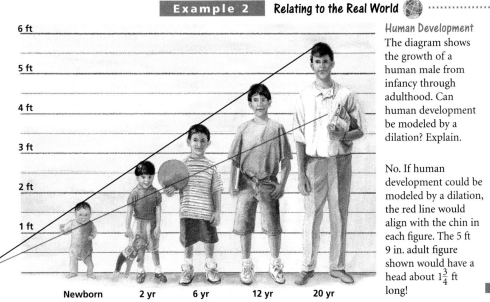

Newborn 2 yr 6 yr 12 yr 20 yr

Human Development The diagram shows the growth of a human male from infancy through adulthood. Can human development be modeled by a dilation? Explain.

No. If human development could be modeled by a dilation, the red line would align with the chin in each figure. The 5 ft 9 in. adult figure shown would have a head about $1\frac{3}{4}$ ft long!

Additional Examples

FOR EXAMPLE 1

Refer to the diagram in Example 1a. If XT is 2 and TT' is 3, find the scale factor for the dilation that maps $\triangle XRT$ to $\triangle X'R'T'$. **2.5**

Discussion: *Can you determine* $\frac{R'X'}{RX}$ *and* $\frac{R'T'}{RT}$*?*

FOR EXAMPLE 3

Refer to the diagram in Example 3. Use matrices to find the image of $\triangle PZG$ under a dilation centered at the origin with scale factor $\frac{3}{2}$.

$$\begin{bmatrix} 3 & -1.5 & 1.5 \\ 0 & 0.75 & -3 \end{bmatrix}$$

Discussion: *Is the dilation an enlargement or a reduction? How do you know?*

VISUAL LEARNING Using the diagrams above Example 3, help students verify that multiplying the coordinates of the point by the scale factor gives the coordinates of its image. The diagrams show that the distance from the origin to the image is n times the distance from the origin to the preimage.

Exercises ON YOUR OWN

ERROR ALERT! **Exercises 1–4** Students who measure imprecisely will produce images that are not congruent to $\triangle TBA$. **Remediation:** Instruct students to use metric rulers to measure from the centers finding the lengths to the nearest millimeter.

Technology Options

Exercises 13–15, students may use graphing calculators to multiply matrices by scalars. For Exercise 19, students may use construction tools in geometry software to construct the dilation image.

Prentice Hall Technology

Software
- Secondary Math Lab Toolkit™
- Computer Item Generator 3-7

Internet
- See the Prentice Hall site. (http://www.phschool.com)

6. $\begin{bmatrix} 1 & -\frac{1}{2} & \frac{1}{2} \\ 0 & \frac{1}{4} & -1 \end{bmatrix}$

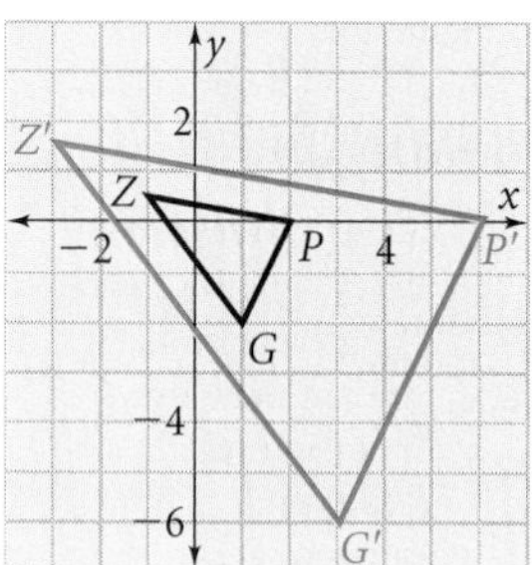

To find the image of a point on the coordinate plane under a dilation with center (0, 0), you multiply the x-coordinate and y-coordinate by the scale factor. Here are two examples.

Scale factor 4
$(x, y) \rightarrow (4x, 4y)$

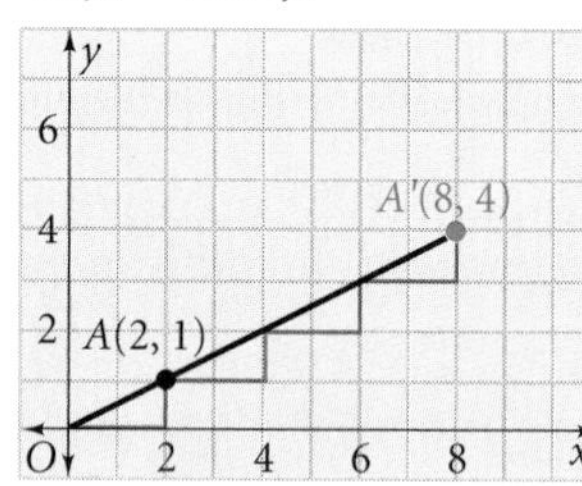

Scale factor $\frac{1}{3}$
$(x, y) \rightarrow (\frac{1}{3}x, \frac{1}{3}y)$

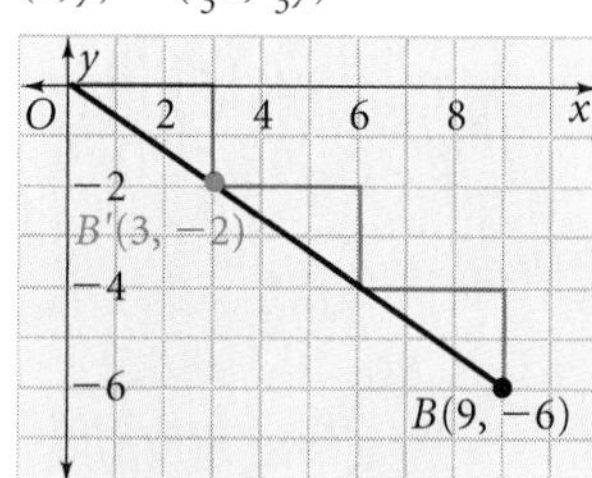

You can use matrices to perform dilations that are centered at the origin.

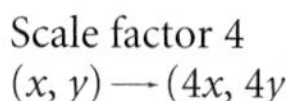

Example 3

Use matrices to find the image of $\triangle PZG$ under a dilation centered at the origin with scale factor 3.

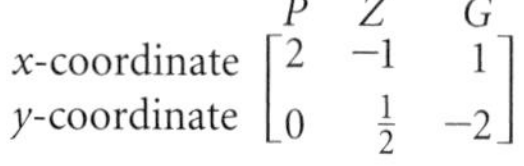

	P	Z	G
x-coordinate	2	−1	1
y-coordinate	0	$\frac{1}{2}$	−2

To find the dilation image of $\triangle PZG$, you multiply all the x-coordinates and y-coordinates by 3.

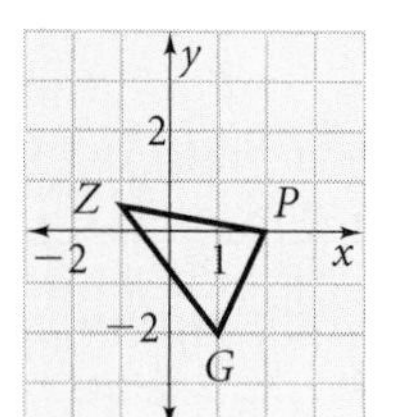

Vertices of Preimage (P Z G) — Vertices of Image (P′ Z′ G′)

$$3 \cdot \begin{bmatrix} 2 & -1 & 1 \\ 0 & \frac{1}{2} & -2 \end{bmatrix} = \begin{bmatrix} 6 & -3 & 3 \\ 0 & \frac{3}{2} & -6 \end{bmatrix}$$

6. **Try This** Use matrices to find the image of $\triangle PZG$ under a dilation centered at the origin with scale factor $\frac{1}{2}$. See left.

The type of multiplication shown in Example 3, in which each entry of a matrix is multiplied by the same number, is called **scalar multiplication.**

Exercises ON YOUR OWN

Copy $\triangle TBA$ and point O. Draw $\triangle T'B'A'$ under the dilation with the given center and scale factor. 1–4. See margin p. 169.

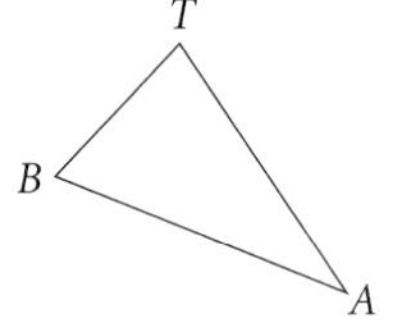

1. Center O, scale factor $\frac{1}{2}$
2. Center B, scale factor 3
3. Center T, scale factor $\frac{1}{3}$
4. Center O, scale factor 2

ALTERNATIVE ASSESSMENT Exercises 5–12 These exercises can be used to help you assess students' understanding of dilations. To find the scale factor, students can find the ratio of the lengths of corresponding sides or the ratio of the distances to the center of dilation of corresponding points.

MAKING CONNECTIONS Exercise 17 The first photographic movie was made in 1877 by Eadweard Muybridge who was hired by the governor of California to prove that at some time in a horse's gallop all four legs are simultaneously off the ground.

The blue figure is a dilation image of the red figure.
(a) Determine whether the dilation is a reduction or an enlargement.
(b) Find the scale factor.

5. 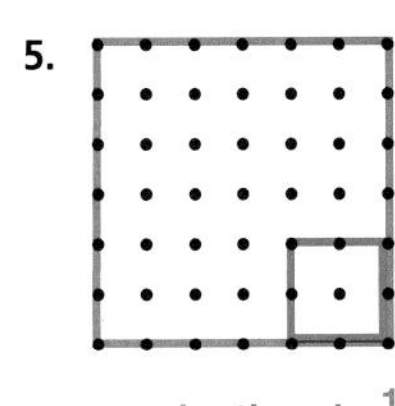

a. reduction b. $\frac{1}{3}$

6. 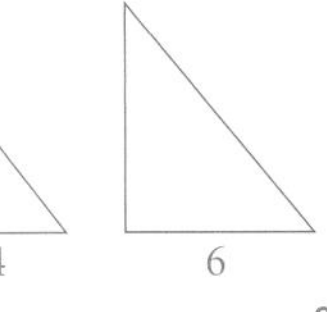

a. enlargement b. $\frac{3}{2}$

7. 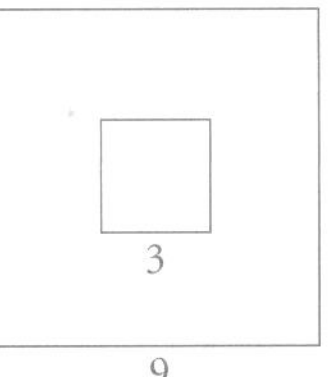

a. enlargement b. 3

8. 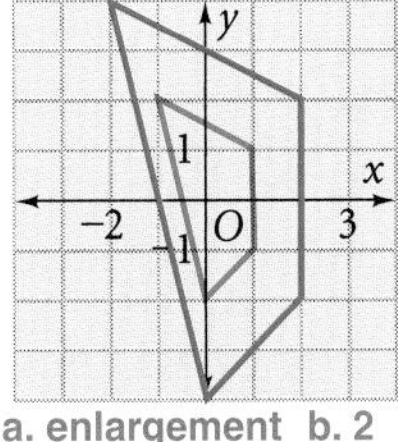

a. enlargement b. 2

9. 2, 4

a. enlargement b. $\frac{3}{2}$

10.

a. reduction b. $\frac{1}{3}$

11. 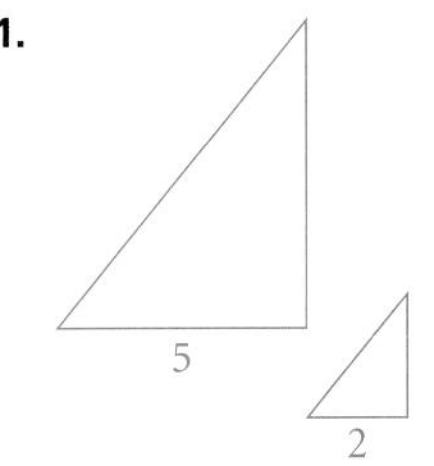

a. reduction b. $\frac{2}{5}$

12. 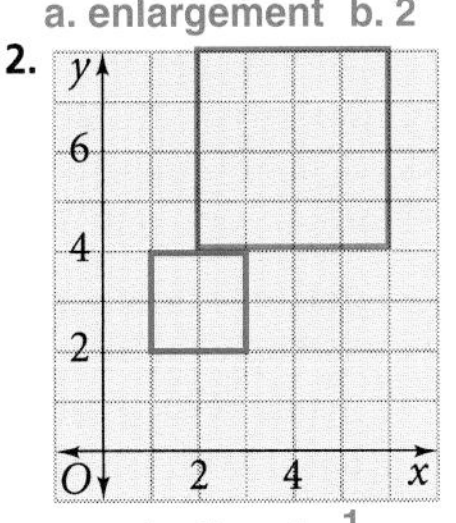

a. reduction b. $\frac{1}{2}$

Use scalar multiplication to find the vertices of $\triangle A'B'C'$ under a dilation with center (0, 0) and the given scale factor. 13–15. See margin.

13. $\begin{matrix} & A & B & C \\ \text{x-coordinate} & 1 & 3 & 5 \\ \text{y-coordinate} & 0 & 2 & 1 \end{matrix}$ scale factor 3

14. $\begin{matrix} & A & B & C \\ \text{x-coordinate} & -2 & 1 & 1 \\ \text{y-coordinate} & -2 & 1 & -1 \end{matrix}$ scale factor $\frac{1}{4}$

15. $\begin{matrix} & A & B & C \\ \text{x-coordinate} & -2 & -4 & -3 \\ \text{y-coordinate} & 0 & -3 & 0 \end{matrix}$ scale factor 2

16. **Entertainment** In the film *Honey, I Blew Up the Kid*, a botched scientific experiment causes a two-year-old boy to grow to a height of 112 ft. If the average height of a two-year-old boy is 3 ft, what is the scale factor of this enlargement? about 37.3

17. **Movies** The projection of a film onto a movie screen is an example of a dilation. Most movies are shot on film that is 35 mm wide. If the width of a movie screen is 12 m, what is the scale factor of this enlargement? about 343

18. A regular triangle with 4-in. sides undergoes a dilation with scale factor 2.5.
a. What are the side lengths of the image? 10 in.
b. What are the angle measures of the image? 60

A giant two-year-old walks through the streets of Las Vegas in a scene from *Honey, I Blew Up the Kid.*

pages 168–171 On Your Own

1. 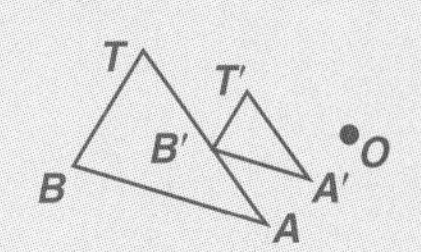

2. 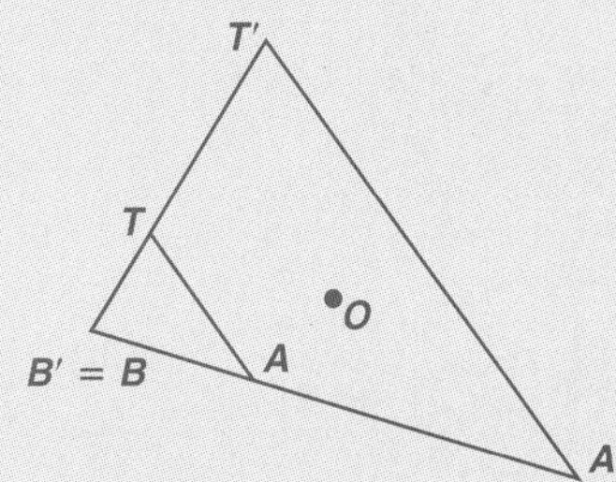

3. T′ = T, B′, A′, B, A

4. 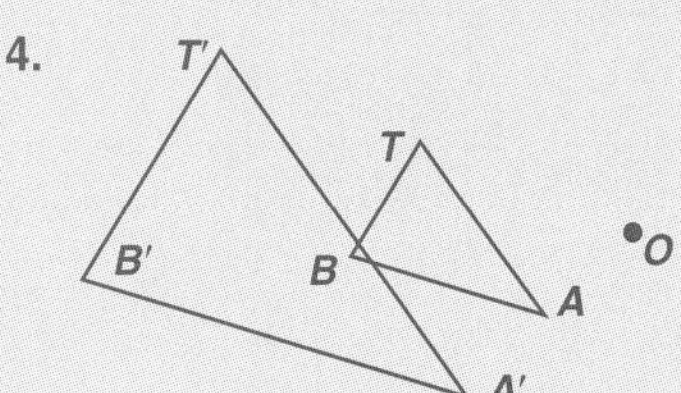

13. $\begin{matrix} A' & B' & C' \end{matrix}$ $\begin{bmatrix} 3 & 9 & 15 \\ 0 & 6 & 3 \end{bmatrix}$

14. $\begin{matrix} A' & B' & C' \end{matrix}$ $\begin{bmatrix} -\frac{1}{2} & \frac{1}{4} & \frac{1}{4} \\ -\frac{1}{2} & \frac{1}{4} & -\frac{1}{4} \end{bmatrix}$

15. $\begin{matrix} A' & B' & C' \end{matrix}$ $\begin{bmatrix} -4 & -8 & -6 \\ 0 & -6 & 0 \end{bmatrix}$

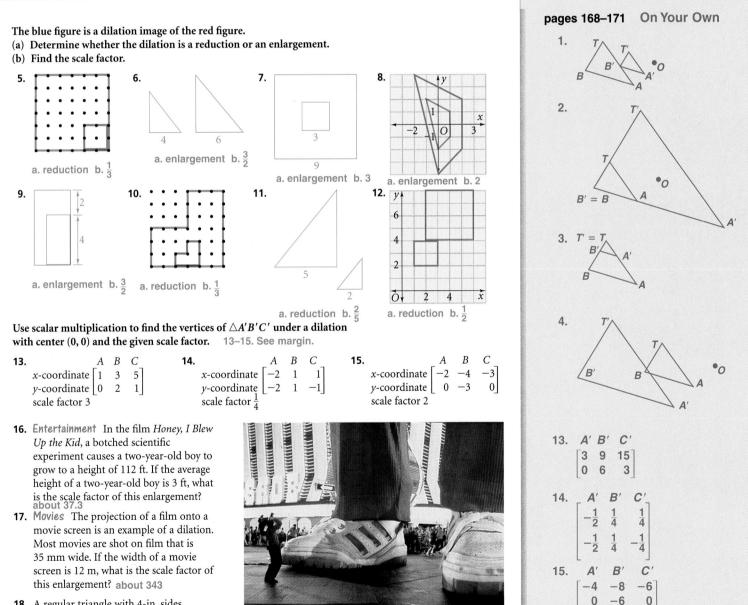

CONNECTING TO STUDENTS' WORLD Exercise 22 Students may be more familiar with a perspective drawing of a road where the median strip and road sides appear to meet in the distance.

CRITICAL THINKING Exercise 23c Help students see that a dilation with a scale factor of -1 produces an image that is congruent to the original figure.

CRITICAL THINKING Exercise 24 Suggest that students draw a diagram showing the two segments. Ask what is true about the orientation of a line segment and its dilation image.

19.

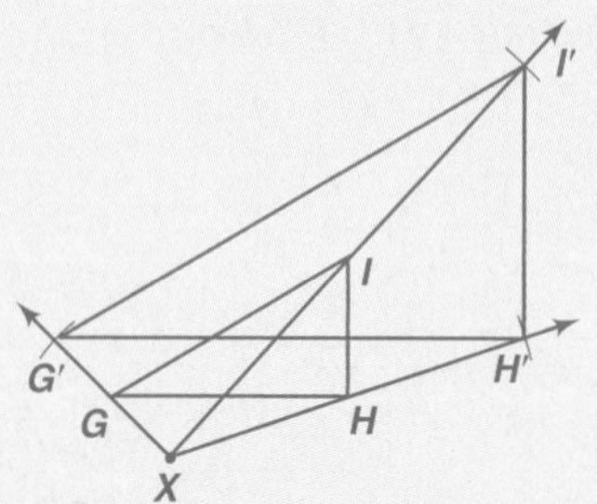

20.

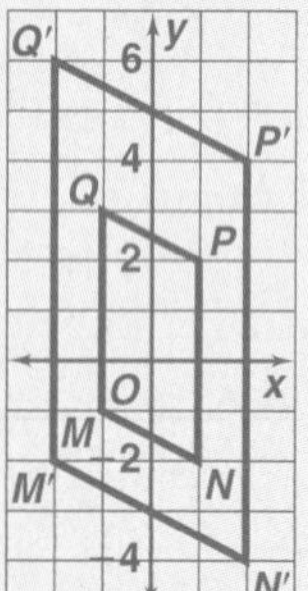

21.

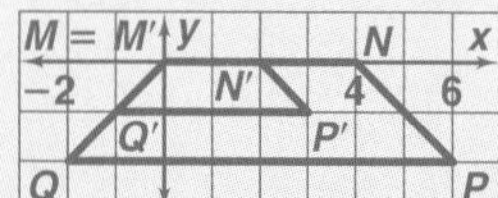

22. The rear of the object is similar to the front with the vanishing point as the center of dilation.

19. *Constructions* Copy $\triangle GHI$ and point X onto your paper. Use a compass and straightedge to construct the image of $\triangle GHI$ under a dilation with center X and scale factor 2. See margin.

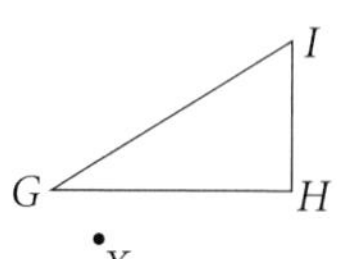

Coordinate Geometry **Graph $MNPQ$ and its image $M'N'P'Q'$ under a dilation with center (0, 0) and the given scale factor.** 20–21. See margin.

20. $M(-1, -1), N(1, -2), P(1, 2), Q(-1, 3)$; scale factor 2

21. $M(0, 0), N(4, 0), P(6, -2), Q(-2, -2)$; scale factor $\frac{1}{2}$

22. *Art* Perspective drawing uses converging lines to give the illusion that an object is three-dimensional. The point at which the lines converge is called the vanishing point. Explain how the type of perspective drawing shown is related to dilations. See margin.

23. Explore what happens if you use a negative scale factor.
   a. Multiply the vertex matrix for $ABCD$ by -3. The result is a vertex matrix for the image of $ABCD$ under a dilation centered at the origin with scale factor -3. a–c. See margin p. 171.
   b. Graph $ABCD$ and $A'B'C'D'$ on the same set of axes.
   c. *Critical Thinking* Compare each point to its image. What conclusion can you draw about the effect of a negative scale factor?

$$\begin{array}{cccc} A & B & C & D \end{array}$$
$$\begin{bmatrix} 2 & -2 & -2 & 2 \\ 2 & 2 & -2 & -2 \end{bmatrix}$$

24. *Critical Thinking* Given $\overline{AB}$ and its dilation image $\overline{A'B'}$, explain how to find the center of dilation. Assume $\overline{AB}$ and $\overline{A'B'}$ are not collinear. See margin p. 171.

Use scalar multiplication to find the vertices of the image of $QRTW$ under a dilation with center (0, 0) and the given scale factor. 25–28. See margin p. 171.

25. scale factor 3
26. scale factor $\frac{1}{2}$
27. scale factor 2
28. scale factor 0.9

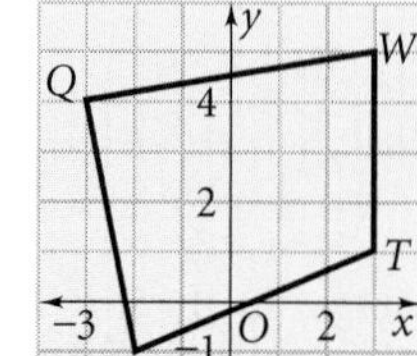

Graphic Design **The designs at the right were created by graphic artist Scott Kim. For each design, (a) describe the location of the center of dilation and (b) find the scale factor for the repeated reductions.**

29.

30.

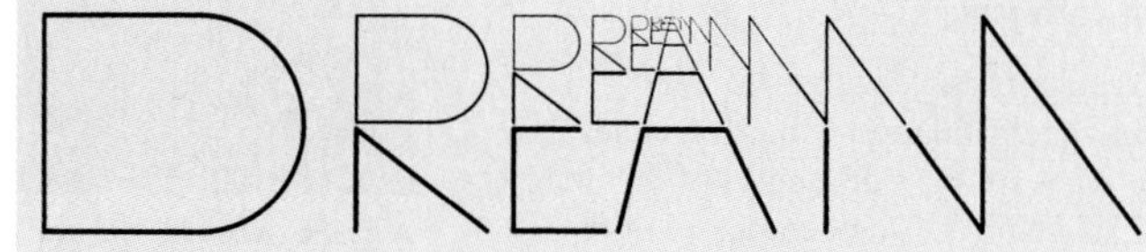

29a. vertex of V
b. $\frac{1}{2}$
30a. vertex of A
b. $\frac{1}{2}$

TECHNOLOGY Exercise 31 Point out to students the designs created using dilations shown in their textbook. Help students see that the first design uses rotations and dilations and the second design uses dilations and translations.

STANDARDIZED TEST TIP Exercise 32 Students may draw a sketch with X in the exterior of $\triangle PLH$ and not realize that it is also possible to draw the diagram with X in the interior of $\triangle PLH$.

Chapter Project FIND OUT BY CREATING Students may want to divide the work by having each group member individually create a design for one of the types. Then the group completes the remaining types together.

31. *Technology* Use geometry software or drawing software to create a design that involves repeated dilations. Print your design and color it. Feel free to use other transformations along with dilations. Check students' work.

32. *Standardized Test Prep* $\triangle P'L'H'$ is the image of $\triangle PLH$ under a dilation with center X and scale factor 3. If P and L lie on $\overline{P'L'}$, what must be true of X? D

A. X is in the exterior of $\triangle PLH$. **B.** X is in the interior of $\triangle PLH$. **C.** X is on $\overline{L'H'}$. **D.** X is on $\overline{PL}$. **E.** $X = H$

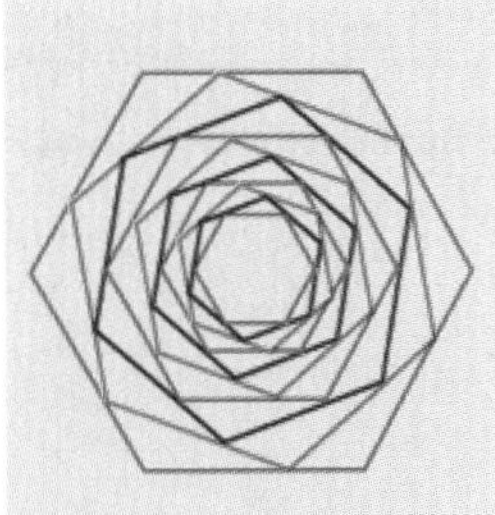

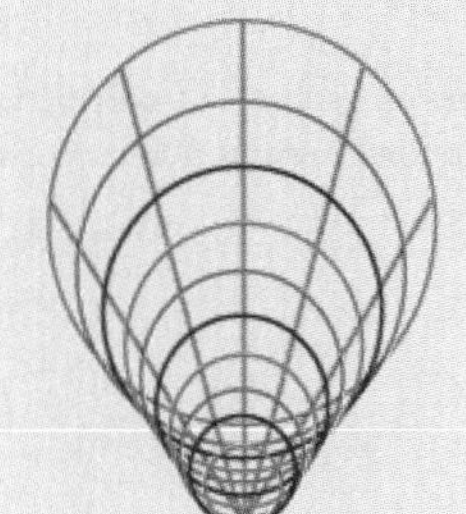

A dilation maps $\triangle HIJ$ to $\triangle H'I'J'$. Find the missing values.

33. $HI = 8$ in.
$IJ = 5$ in.
$HJ = 6$ in.
$H'I' = 16$ in.
$I'J' = ■$ in. 10
$H'J' = ■$ in. 12

34. $HI = 7$ cm
$IJ = 7$ cm
$HJ = ■$ cm 16
$H'I' = 5.25$ cm
$I'J' = ■$ cm 5.25
$H'J' = 12$ cm

35. $HI = ■$ ft 32
$IJ = 30$ ft
$HJ = 24$ ft
$H'I' = 8$ ft
$I'J' = ■$ ft 7.5
$H'J' = 6$ ft

Write *true* or *false*. Explain your answers.

36. A dilation with a scale factor greater than 1 is a reduction. False; a dilation with a scale factor greater than 1 is an enlargement.

37. Under a dilation, corresponding angles of the image and preimage are congruent. True; the image and the preimage are similar.

38. A dilation is an isometry. False; a dilation doesn't map a segment to a ≅ segment unless the scale factor is 1.

39. A dilation changes orientation. False; a dilation does not change orientation.

40. A dilation image cannot have any points in common with its preimage. False; if the center of dilation is on the preimage, it is also on the image.

Chapter Project ***Find Out by Creating***

In previous Find Out questions, you investigated and classified frieze patterns from a variety of cultures. Now you can make your own. Use graph paper, dot paper, geometry or drawing software, or cutouts (such as your pentominoes from the Chapter 2 project). Make at least one frieze pattern for each of the seven types summarized below.

Check students' work.

The Seven Types of Frieze Patterns

Type	Symmetries	Example
11	T	P P P P P P P
12	T, H	Z Z Z Z Z Z Z
*m*1	T, RV	Y Y Y Y Y Y Y
1*g*	T, G	D W D M D W D
1*m*	T, RH, G	D D D D D D D
mg	T, H, RV, G	M W M W M W M
mm	T, H, RV, RH, G	I I I I I I I

Key to Symmetries:
T = Translation
H = Half-turn
RV = Reflection in Vertical Line
RH = Reflection in Horizontal Line
G = Glide reflection

23a. $\begin{matrix} A' & B' & C' & D' \end{matrix}$
$$\begin{bmatrix} -6 & 6 & 6 & -6 \\ -6 & -6 & 6 & 6 \end{bmatrix}$$

b.

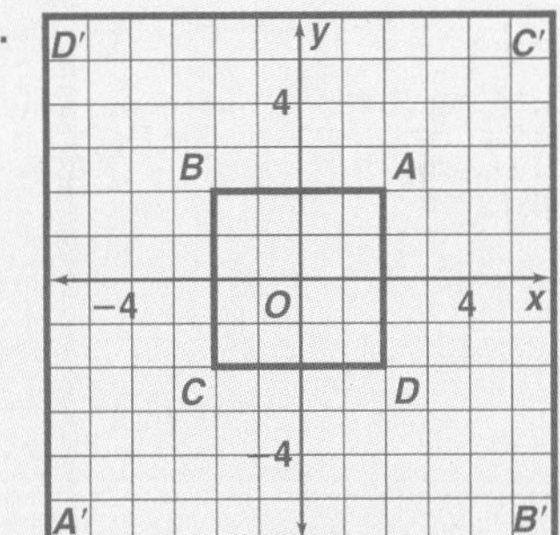

c. The image of a dilation with a negative factor is the image of a dilation with a positive factor with the same absolute value, rotated 180° about the origin.

24. Connect corresponding points A and A' and B and B'. Extend the lines until they intersect.

25. $Q' \; R' \; T \; W'$
$$\begin{bmatrix} -9 & -6 & 9 & 9 \\ 12 & -3 & 3 & 15 \end{bmatrix}$$

26. $Q' \; R' \; T' \; W'$
$$\begin{bmatrix} -1\frac{1}{2} & -1 & 1\frac{1}{2} & 1\frac{1}{2} \\ 2 & -\frac{1}{2} & \frac{1}{2} & 2\frac{1}{2} \end{bmatrix}$$

27. $Q' \; R' \; T \; W'$
$$\begin{bmatrix} -6 & -4 & 6 & 6 \\ 8 & -2 & 2 & 10 \end{bmatrix}$$

28. $Q' \; R' \; T \; W'$
$$\begin{bmatrix} -2.7 & -1.8 & 2.7 & 2.7 \\ 3.6 & -0.9 & 0.9 & 4.5 \end{bmatrix}$$

Exercises MIXED REVIEW

Exercises 41–43 Students find missing angle measures.

PORTFOLIO Share with students the criteria you will use to assess their work in portfolios, as well as how you plan to use the results. Students should understand how the rubrics assess their work, how each piece in the portfolio counts, and how the scores they get in their portfolios will affect their overall evaluation.

Wrap Up

THE BIG IDEA Ask students: *Explain the relationship between the scale factor and the image of a dilation.*

RETEACHING ACTIVITY Students create patterns with dilations of quadrilaterals. (Reteaching worksheet 3-7)

Geometry at Work

For further information about the training necessary to be a graphic artist, contact a local design or technical school. Encourage students to investigate these topics:

- the training necessary to become a graphic designer
- the math and computer skills used by graphic designers
- the type of businesses that hire graphic designers

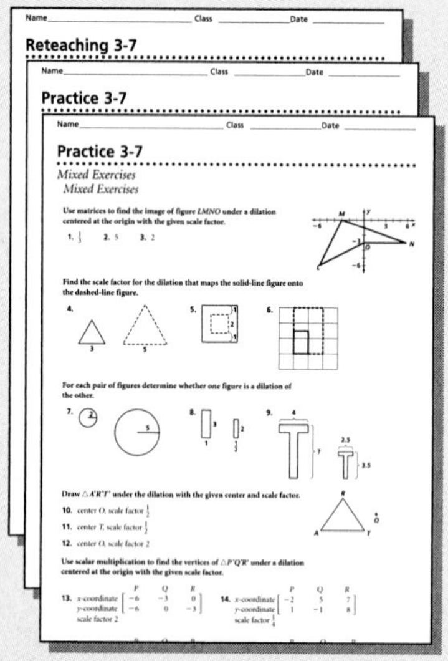

Lesson Quiz

Lesson Quiz is also available in Transparencies.

1. The second figure is the dilation image of the first figure. Find the scale factor of the dilation. 2.5

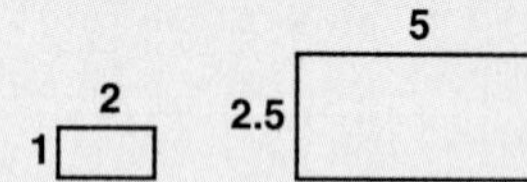

2. Find the image of $\triangle MPQ$ with vertices $M(1, -2)$, $N(4, 0)$ and $Q(1, 2)$ under a dilation with center (0, 0) and a scale factor of 3. $\triangle M'P'Q'$ with vertices $M'(3, -6)$, $N'(12, 0)$ and $Q'(3, 6)$

3. A dilation maps $\triangle CDE$ to $\triangle C'D'E'$. Find the missing values if the scale factor is 2.
   $CD = 4$ $DE = 5$
   $C'D' =$ ___?___ $D'E' =$ ___?___ 8, 10

Exercises MIXED REVIEW

Find the value of each variable.

41. $x = 105$; $y = 75$; $z = 35$

42. 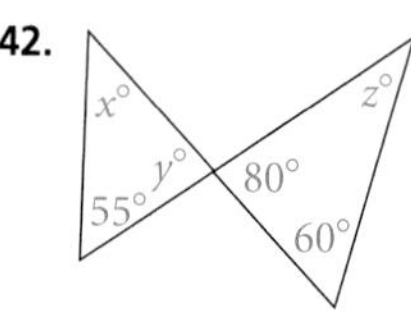

$x = 45$; $y = 80$; $z = 40$

43. 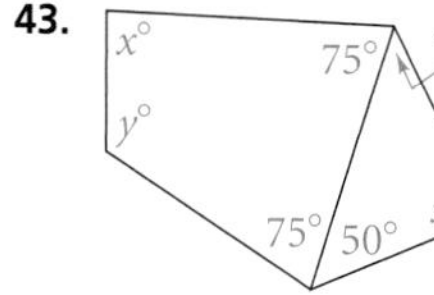

$x = 85$; $y = 125$

Graph each set of points and state which type of quadrilateral it determines.

44. $(-1, -2), (1, 4), (-3, 4), (3, -2)$ parallelogram

45. $(2, -1), (6, 2), (10, -1), (8, 2)$ trapezoid

46. $(-7, 1), (-5, 3), (-2, -4), (0, -2)$ rectangle

47. *Geometry in 3 Dimensions* Planes T and G are parallel, and plane M is perpendicular to plane G. Sketch the three planes. See margin p. 173.

48. Find the coordinates of the midpoint of the segment with endpoints $A(4, 8)$ and $B(-3, -6)$. $\left(\frac{1}{2}, 1\right)$

PORTFOLIO

For your portfolio, select one or two items from your work for this chapter. Here are some possibilities:
- tessellations
- kaleidoscope patterns
- computer-generated designs involving transformations

Explain why you have included each selection.

Geometry at Work

Graphic Artist

Not too long ago, the graphic artist's main tools were the pen and paintbrush. Today, graphic artists are just as likely to have a computer mouse in hand as either of these. Computers have helped graphic artists produce effects that could only be imagined previously. Some of the "special effects" on the cover of this book, for instance, were produced using design software. Computers have also helped lower the cost of producing graphic art, because they allow the artist to work more quickly and to store and transport images easily.

You can find each of the transformations that you've studied in this chapter in software written for graphic artists. At the click of a mouse, the graphic artist rotates, reflects, translates, dilates, and creates!

Mini Project: Use a computer drawing program to create a new logo for your school's stationery. Try to use transformations in your logo.

Finishing the Chapter Project

PROJECT DAY You may wish to plan a project day on which students share their completed projects. Encourage groups to explain their processes as well as their products.

PROJECT NOTEBOOK Have students review their project work and bring their notebooks up to date.

- Have students review the sketches, classifications, and designs needed for the project.
- Ask groups to share any insights they found when completing the project, such as how they identify different transformations.

SCORING RUBRIC

3 Student demonstrates a clear understanding of transformations by correctly identifying isometries in frieze patterns. Designs are neat, accurate, and illustrate the correct transformations. Classifications are accurate and complete.

2 Student demonstrates a general understanding of transformations by identifying with minor mistakes isometries in frieze patterns. Designs are neat and usually illustrate the correct transformations. Classifications are complete with few inaccuracies.

1 Student completes all sketches and designs but with major errors. Classifications are complete but inaccurate.

0 Major elements are incomplete or missing.

Finishing the Chapter Project

CHAPTER PROJECT

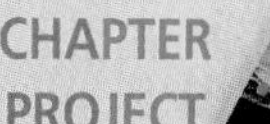

Find Out questions and activities on pages 137, 143, 150, 158, and 171 will help you complete your project. Prepare a frieze pattern display. Include a brief explanation of frieze patterns as well as your original designs for each of the seven types of frieze patterns. Find more examples of frieze patterns from various cultures, as well as examples from buildings, clothing, and other places in your home, school, and community. Classify each example into one of the seven categories, and include them in your display.

Reflect and Revise

Ask a classmate to review your display with you. Together, check that your diagrams and explanations are clear and your information accurate. Have you used geometric terms correctly? Is the display attractive, organized, and complete? Have you included material that no one else has included? Revise your work as needed. Consider doing more research.

Follow Up

Use logical reasoning and what you've learned about transformations to explain why there are no more than seven different frieze patterns. List all other possible combinations of symmetries and show how each can be ruled out.

For More Information

Appleton, Le Roy H. *American Indian Design and Decoration*. New York: Dover, 1971.

Hargittai, István and Magdolna. *Symmetry: A Unifying Concept.* Berkeley, California: Ten Speed Press, 1994.

Schuman, Jo Miles. *Art from Many Hands: Multicultural Art Projects for Home and School*. Englewood Cliffs, New Jersey: Prentice Hall, 1981.

Stevens, Peter S. *Handbook of Regular Patterns: An Introduction to Symmetry in Two Dimensions*. Cambridge, Massachusetts: MIT, 1981.

page 172 Mixed Review

47.

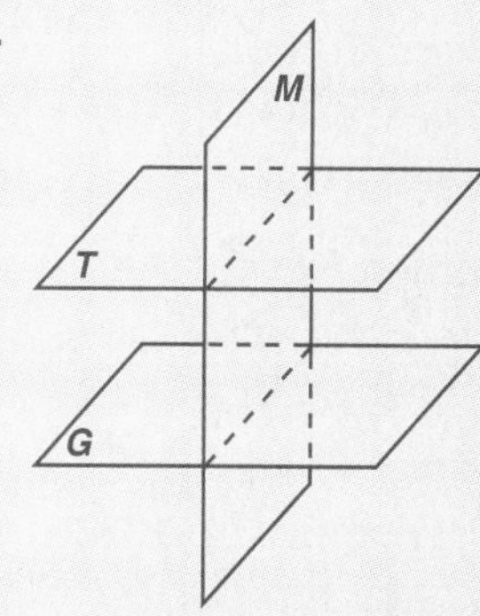

Wrap Up

HOW AM I DOING? Have students work in small groups. Ask each group to make a short presentation describing one of the transformations presented in this chapter and its properties. Each presentation must include a visual aid and a sample problem.

KEY TERMS The numbers in parentheses direct students to the pages where the terms are used or defined. Students should be able to (1) write a simple explanation of each term, (2) illustrate the term with a diagram, or (3) show an example that uses the term.

COORDINATE GEOMETRY Exercises 1–4 Remind students they can use paper folding, MIRA™, or measuring to draw the images.

STANDARDIZED TEST TIP Exercise 9 Help students see that choices A, C, and D can be eliminated immediately because they are in the second and third quadrants.

Resources

Student Edition

Extra Practice, p. 636
Glossary/ Study Guide

Teaching Resources

Study Skills Handbook
Glossary, Spanish Resources

Wrap Up pages 174–177

1.

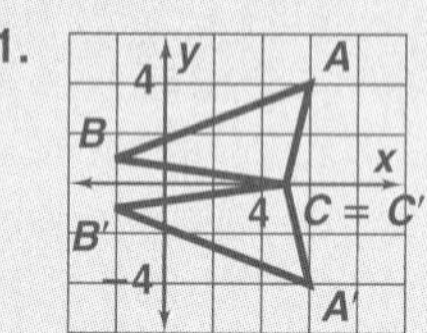

2.

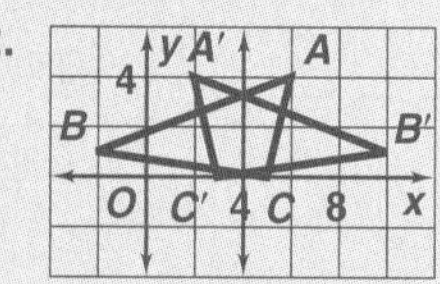

3.

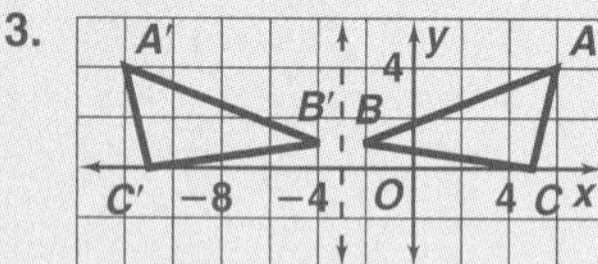

4.

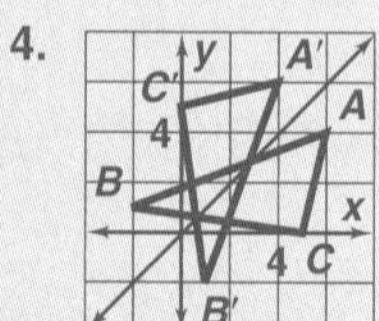

3 Wrap Up

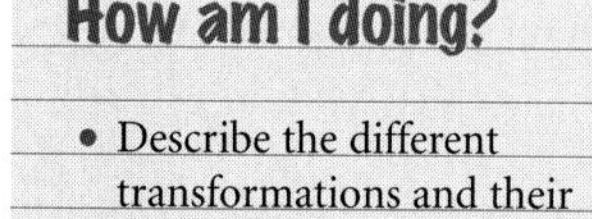

How am I doing?

- Describe the different transformations and their properties.
- State the different types of symmetry and draw examples of each.

Key Terms

composition (p. 135)
dilation (p. 166)
enlargement (p. 167)
entry (p. 131)
frieze pattern (p. 137)
glide reflection (p. 146)
glide reflectional symmetry (p. 161)
half-turn (p. 154)
image (p. 124)
isometry (p. 124)
line symmetry (p. 152)
map (p. 124)
matrix (p. 131)
orientation (p. 126)
point symmetry (p. 154)
preimage (p. 124)
prime notation (p. 124)
pure tessellation (p. 160)
reduction (p. 167)
reflection (p. 126)
reflectional symmetry (p. 152)
rotation (p. 139)
rotational symmetry (p. 154)
scalar multiplication (p. 168)
scale factor (p. 166)
similarity transformation (p. 167)
strip pattern (p. 137)
symmetry (p. 152)
tessellation (p. 159)
tiling (p. 159)
transformation (p. 124)
translation (p. 132)
translational symmetry (p. 161)

Reflections 3-1

A **transformation** is a change made to the position, shape, or size of a figure. An **isometry** is a transformation in which the original figure and its image are congruent. The diagram shows a **reflection** of B to B' in line r. A reflection is an isometry that changes a figure's orientation.

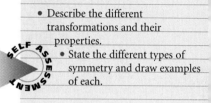

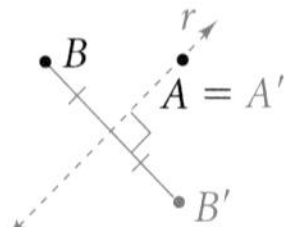

Coordinate Geometry **Given points $A(6, 4)$, $B(-2, 1)$, and $C(5, 0)$, draw $\triangle ABC$ and its reflection image in the given line.** 1–4. See margin.

1. the x-axis
2. $x = 4$
3. $x = -3$
4. $y = x$

Trace each figure, then find its reflection image in line j.

5.

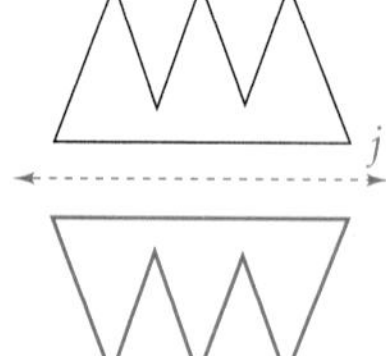

6.

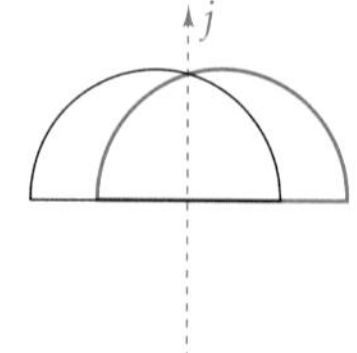

7.

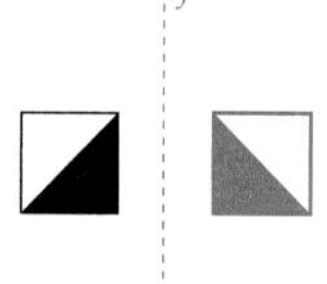

8.

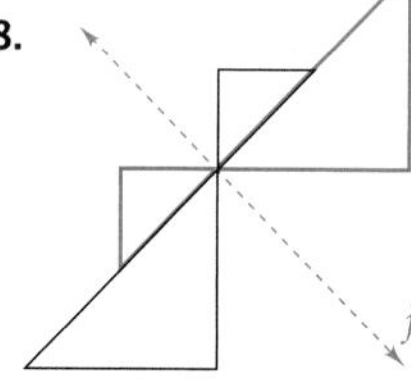

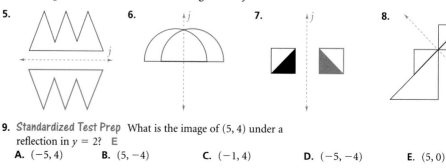

9. *Standardized Test Prep* What is the image of (5, 4) under a reflection in $y = 2$? E

A. $(-5, 4)$ **B.** $(5, -4)$ **C.** $(-1, 4)$ **D.** $(-5, -4)$ **E.** $(5, 0)$

Exercises 11–12 Make sure students do not try to use scalar multiplication of matrices as they did with dilations.

Translations 3-2

A **translation** is a transformation that moves points the same distance and in the same direction. A translation is an isometry that does not change orientation. You can use vectors and matrices to describe a translation.

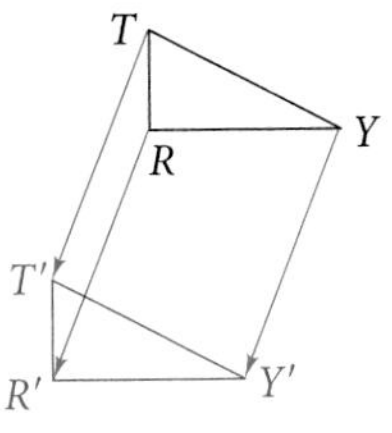

Under a **composition** of two transformations, the second transformation is performed on the image of the first.

10. ***Open-ended*** Draw a figure in the fourth quadrant. Draw a translation vector under which the figure would move to the second quadrant.
See margin for sample.

Use matrix addition to find the image of each figure under the given translation.

11. $\triangle ABC$ with vertices $A(5, 9)$, $B(4, 3)$, $C(1, 2)$
Translation: $\langle 2, 3\rangle$ $A'(7, 12)$, $B'(6, 6)$, $C'(3, 5)$

12. $\triangle RST$ with vertices $R(0, -4)$, $S(-2, -1)$, $T(-6, 1)$
Translation: $\langle -4, 7\rangle$
$R'(-4, 3)$, $S'(-6, 6)$, $T'(-10, 8)$

Find a single translation that has the same effect as each composition of translations.

13. $\langle 4, 8\rangle$ followed by $\langle -2, 0\rangle$
$\langle 2, 8\rangle$

14. $\langle -5, -7\rangle$ followed by $\langle 3, 6\rangle$
$\langle -2, -1\rangle$

15. $\langle 10, -9\rangle$ followed by $\langle 1, 5\rangle$
$\langle 11, -4\rangle$

Rotations 3-3

The diagram shows a **rotation** of point V about point R through $x°$. A rotation is an isometry that does not change orientation.

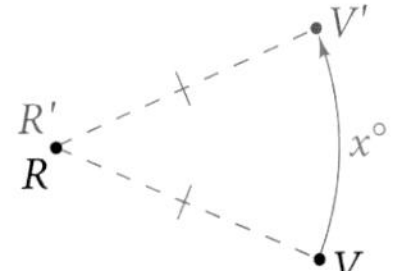

Copy each figure and point *P*. Rotate the figure the given number of degrees about *P*. Label the vertices of the image.

16. 180°

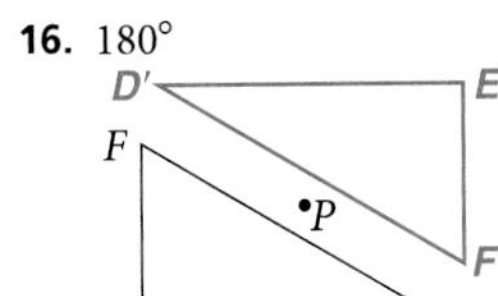

17. 135°

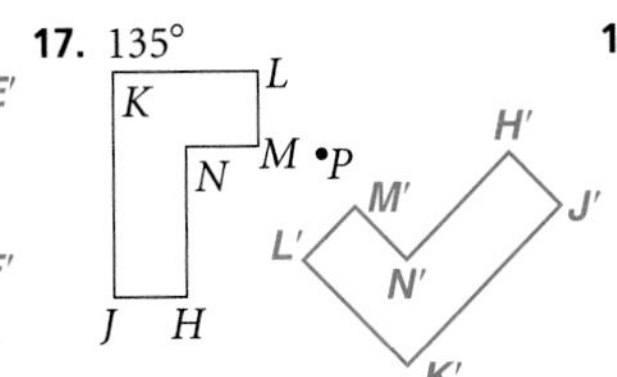

18. 60°

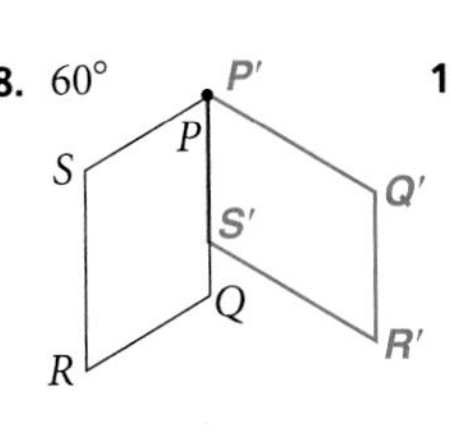

19. 90°

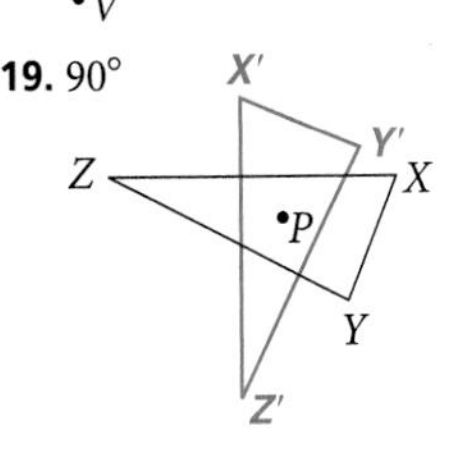

Find the image of each point under a 90° rotation about the origin.

20. $(5, 2)$
$(-2, 5)$

21. $(0, 3)$
$(-3, 0)$

22. $(-4, 1)$
$(-1, -4)$

23. $(7, 0)$
$(0, 7)$

24. $(-2, -8)$
$(8, -2)$

25. $(0, 0)$
$(0, 0)$

Compositions of Reflections 3-4

A composition of reflections in two parallel lines is a translation. A composition of reflections in two intersecting lines is a rotation. The diagram shows a **glide reflection.** The only four isometries are reflection, translation, rotation, and glide reflection.

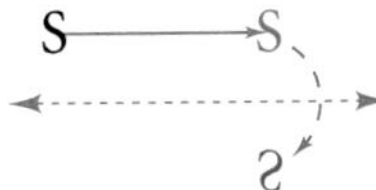

10.

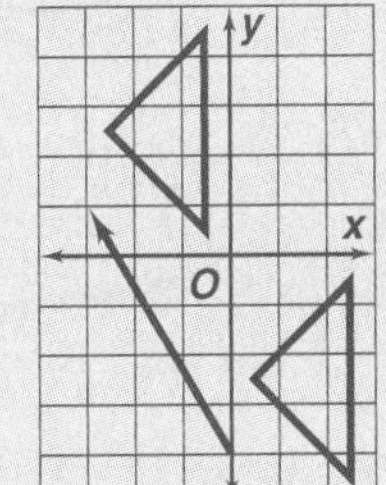

Exercises 26–27 Students will be best able to check the orientation of the figures if they rotate their books so the bottom of each figure is close to them.

ALTERNATIVE ASSESSMENT **Exercises 29–31** Students' ability to recognize reflectional and rotational symmetries will reveal their understanding of the reflection and rotation isometries.

Remind students that the new mathematical terms in this chapter are defined in the Glossary/Study Guide in the back of the book.

Match each image of the figure at the left with one of the following isometries. I. reflection II. rotation III. translation IV. glide reflection

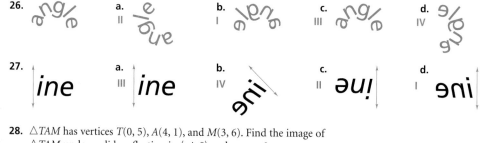

26. angle **a.** II  **b.** I **c.** III  **d.** IV

27. ine **a.** III ine **b.** IV 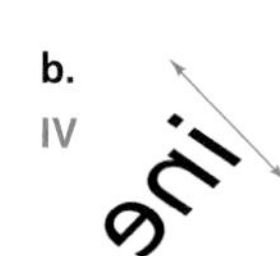 **c.** II **d.** I

28. $\triangle TAM$ has vertices $T(0, 5)$, $A(4, 1)$, and $M(3, 6)$. Find the image of $\triangle TAM$ under a glide reflection in $\langle -4, 0 \rangle$ and $y = -2$.
$T'(-4, -9)$, $A'(0, -5)$, $M'(-1, -10)$

Symmetry 3-5

A figure has **symmetry** if there is an isometry that maps the figure onto itself. A plane figure has **reflectional symmetry,** or **line symmetry,** if there is a line in which the figure is reflected onto itself. A figure has **rotational symmetry** if there is a rotation of 180° or less that maps the figure onto itself. If a plane figure can be mapped onto itself by a rotation of 180° (a **half-turn**), it has **point symmetry.**

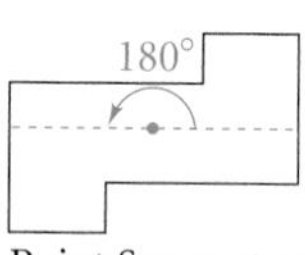

Point Symmetry

What type(s) of symmetry does each figure have? If it has rotational symmetry, state the angle of rotation.

29. 
reflectional

30. 
72° rotational

31. 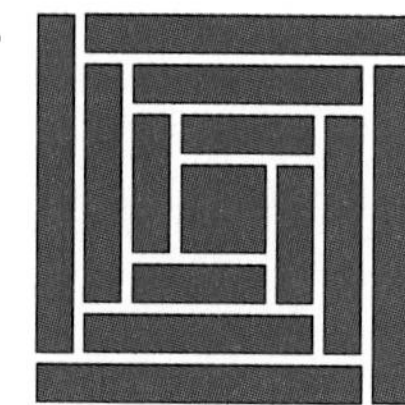
90° rotational, point

Tessellations 3-6

A **tessellation**, or **tiling**, is a repeating pattern of figures that completely covers a plane without gaps or overlaps. Every triangle and quadrilateral tessellates. Tessellations can have many kinds of symmetries, including **translational symmetry** and **glide reflectional symmetry.**

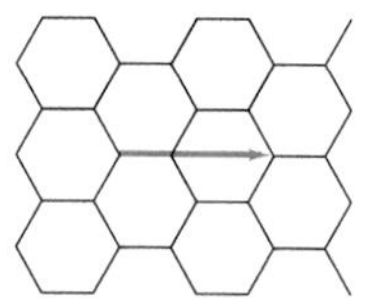
Translational Symmetry
A translation maps the tessellation onto itself.

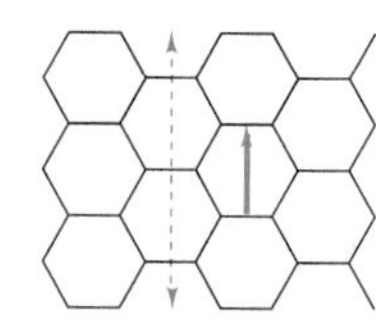
Glide Reflectional Symmetry
A glide reflection maps the tessellation onto itself.

Getting Ready for Chapter 4

Students may work these exercises independently or in small groups. The skills previewed will help prepare students for studying properties of triangles.

In Exercises 32–34, (a) identify the repeating figure(s) that make up each tessellation, and (b) describe the symmetries of each tessellation. 32–34. See margin.

32. 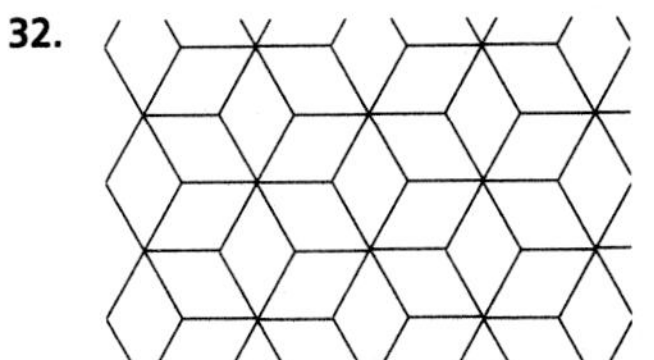 **33.**  **34.** 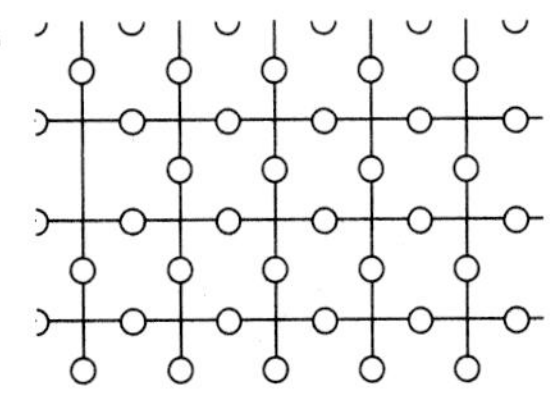

Dilations 3-7

The diagram shows a **dilation** with center C and **scale factor** n. A dilation is a **similarity transformation** because it maps figures to similar figures. When the scale factor is greater than 1, the dilation is an **enlargement.** When the scale factor is less than 1, the dilation is a **reduction.** In the coordinate plane, you can use **scalar multiplication** to find the image of a figure under a dilation centered at the origin.

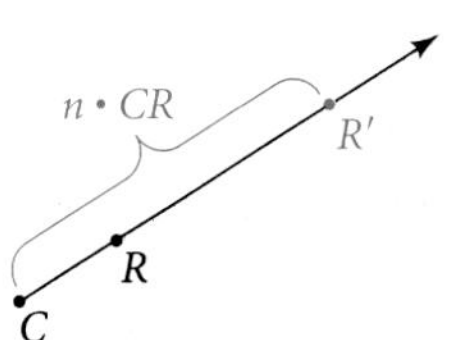

Use matrices to find the image of each set of points under a dilation centered at the origin with the given scale factor. 35–38. See margin.

35. $M(-3, 4), A(-6, -1), T(0, 0), H(3, 2)$; scale factor 5

36. $A(7, -1), N(-4, -3), D(0, 2)$; scale factor 2

37. $W(4, 5), I(2, 6), T(3, 8), H(0, 7)$; scale factor 3

38. $F(-4, 0), U(5, 0), N(-2, -5)$; scale factor $\frac{1}{2}$

39. Writing Explain how each of the five transformations you studied in this chapter affects the orientation of a figure and its image. Rotations, dilations and translations preserve orientation. Reflections and glide reflections reverse orientation.

Getting Ready for CHAPTER 4

Find the coordinates of the midpoint of the segment with the given endpoints.

40. $C(3, 5)$ and $D(1, 11)$ (2, 8)

41. $E(6, 7)$ and $F(-4, 7)$ (1, 7)

42. $T(5, 8)$ and $W(5, 0)$ (5, 4)

Classify each triangle by its sides and angles.

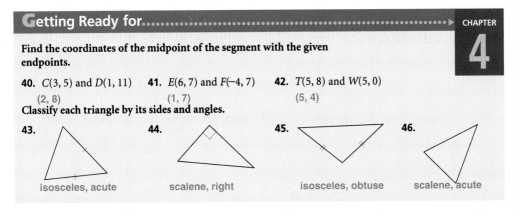

43. 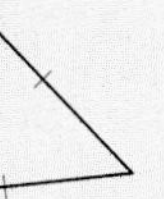
isosceles, acute

44. 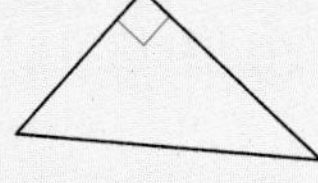
scalene, right

45. 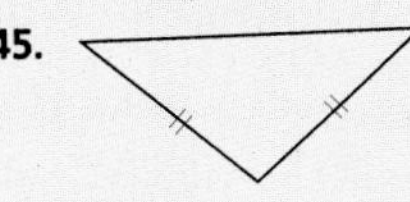
isosceles, obtuse

46. 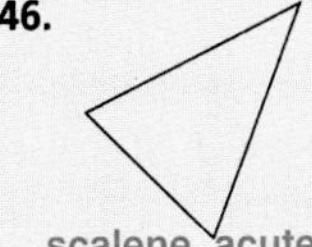
scalene, acute

32a. 

b. rotational, point, reflectional, translational, glide reflectional

33a. □ and △

b. point, reflectional, translational, glide reflectional

34a. 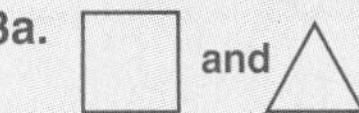

b. rotational, point, reflectional, translational, glide reflectional

35. $\begin{matrix} M' & A' & T' & H' \end{matrix}$
$\begin{bmatrix} -15 & -30 & 0 & 15 \\ 20 & -5 & 0 & 10 \end{bmatrix}$

36. $\begin{matrix} A' & N' & D' \end{matrix}$
$\begin{bmatrix} 14 & -8 & 0 \\ -2 & -6 & 4 \end{bmatrix}$

37. $\begin{matrix} W' & I' & T' & H' \end{matrix}$
$\begin{bmatrix} 12 & 6 & 9 & 0 \\ 15 & 18 & 24 & 21 \end{bmatrix}$

38. $\begin{matrix} F' & U' & N' \end{matrix}$
$\begin{bmatrix} -2 & 2\frac{1}{2} & -1 \\ 0 & 0 & -2\frac{1}{2} \end{bmatrix}$

Assessment

ENHANCED MULTIPLE CHOICE QUESTIONS are more complex than traditional multiple choice questions, which assess only one skill. Enhanced multiple choice questions assess the processes that students use, as well as the end results. The questions are written so that students use more than one strategy to solve the problem. Using multiple strategies is encouraged by the National Council of Teachers of Mathematics (NCTM). **Exercise 21 is** an enhanced multiple choice question.

FREE RESPONSE QUESTIONS do not give answer choices. Some exercises have more than one possible answer. Students need to give only one correct response. **Exercises 1–13, 18–20, and 22–24** are free response questions.

WRITING EXERCISES allow students to describe how they think about and understand the concepts they have learned. **Exercise 14** is a writing exercise.

OPEN-ENDED PROBLEMS allow for more than one solution. Students must construct their own responses instead of choosing from possible answers. The students' responses will help you determine the depth of their understanding and any possible areas of difficulty. **Exercises 15–17** are open-ended problems.

Resources

Teaching Resources

Chapter Support File, Ch. 3
- Chapter assessment, Forms A and B
- Alternative Assessment

Chapter Assessment, Spanish Resources

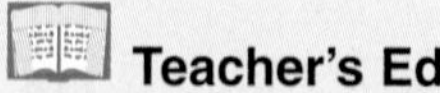

Teacher's Edition

See also p. 122E for assessment options

Software

Computer Item Generator

Assessment page 178

1. $A'(-11, 0)$, $B'(-9, -2)$, $C'(-11, -5)$, $D'(-15, -1)$
2. $A'(-3, 8)$, $B'(-5, 6)$, $C'(-3, 3)$, $D'(1, 7)$
3. $A'(0, 3)$, $B'(2, 1)$, $C'(5, 3)$, $D'(1, 7)$
4. $A'(2, 0)$, $B'\left(\frac{2}{3}, -1\frac{1}{3}\right)$, $C'\left(2, -3\frac{1}{3}\right)$, $D'\left(4\frac{2}{3}, -\frac{2}{3}\right)$
5. $A'(-3, 3)$, $B'(-1, 1)$, $C'(-3, -2)$, $D'(-7, 2)$
6. $A'(0, 3)$, $B'(-2, 1)$, $C'(-5, 3)$, $D'(-1, 7)$
7. $A'(0, -3)$, $B'(-2, -1)$, $C'(-5, -3)$, $D'(-1, -7)$
8. $A'(15, 0)$, $B'(5, -10)$, $C'(15, -25)$, $D'(35, -5)$
9. $A'(1, 10)$, $B'(-1, 12)$, $C'(1, 15)$, $D'(5, 11)$

18. rotational, point, reflectional, translational, glide reflectional

178

3 Assessment

Coordinate Geometry **Find the coordinates of the vertices of the image of *ABCD* under each transformation.**

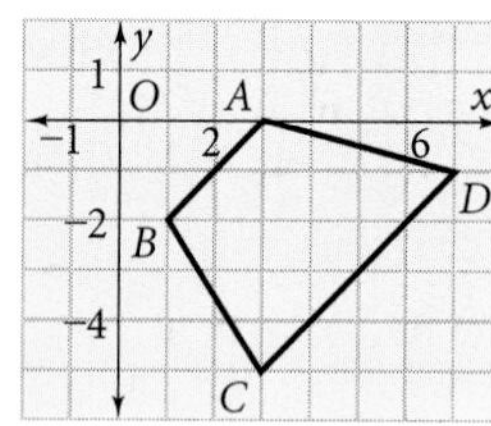

1. reflection in $x = -4$ 1–9. See margin.
2. translation $\langle -6, 8\rangle$
3. rotation of 90° about the point (0, 0)
4. dilation with scale factor $\frac{2}{3}$ centered at the origin
5. glide reflection in $\langle 0, 3\rangle$ and $x = 0$
6. reflection in $y = x$
7. rotation of 270° about the point (0, 0)
8. dilation with scale factor 5 centered at (0, 0)
9. glide reflection in $\langle -2, 0\rangle$ and $y = 5$

What type of transformation has the same effect as each composition of transformations?

10. translation $\langle 4, 0\rangle$ followed by reflection in $y = -4$ glide reflection
11. translation $\langle 4, 8\rangle$ followed by $\langle -2, 9\rangle$ translation
12. reflection in $y = 7$, then in $y = 3$ translation
13. reflection in $y = x$, then in $y = 2x + 5$ rotation
14. *Writing* Line *m* intersects $\overline{UH}$ at *N*, and $UN = NH$. Must *H* be the reflection image of *U* in line *m*? Explain why or why not. See back of book.

Open-ended **Sketch a figure that has each type of symmetry.** 15–17. See back of book for samples.

15. reflectional 16. rotational 17. point

18. Describe the symmetries of this tessellation. Copy a portion of the tessellation and draw any centers of rotational symmetry or lines of symmetry.

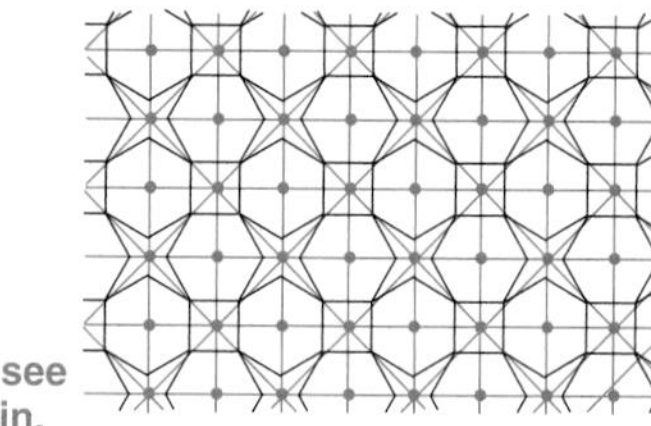

Also see margin.

What type(s) of symmetry does each figure have?

19. rotational, reflectional
20. rotational, point, reflectional

21. *Standardized Test Prep* Which of the following letters does *not* tessellate? C

A. V B. H C. K D. L E. E

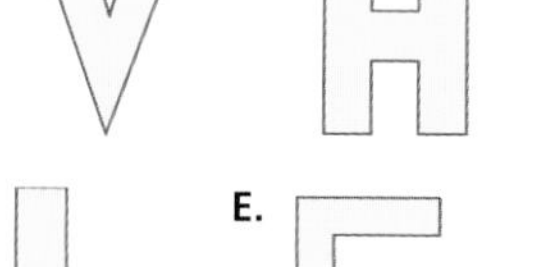

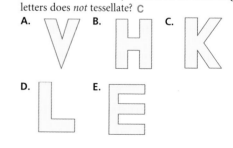

Find the image of △*ABC* under a dilation with center (0, 0) and the given scale factor. 22–24. See back of book.

22. $A(2, 4)$, $B(3, 7)$, $C(5, 1)$; scale factor 4
23. $A(0, 0)$, $B(-3, 2)$, $C(1, 7)$; scale factor $\frac{1}{2}$
24. $A(-2, 2)$, $B(2, -2)$, $C(3, 4)$; scale factor 3

Preparing for Standardized Tests

Standardized tests, such as those administered for state assessment, the SAT, or the ACT, include regular math questions, quantitative comparison questions, open-ended problems, and free response questions (which the SAT calls *grid-ins*).

MULTIPLE CHOICE QUESTIONS are followed by five answer choices, one of which is correct. **Exercises 1–8** are multiple choice questions.

QUANTITATIVE COMPARISON QUESTIONS ask students to compare two quantities. **Exercises 9 and 10** are quantitative comparison questions.

FREE RESPONSE QUESTIONS do not give answer choices. Students must provide one correct answer on their own. **Exercises 11 and 12** are free response questions.

OPEN-ENDED PROBLEMS allow for more than one solution. Students must construct their own responses instead of choosing a single answer. The responses students give will help you determine the depth of their understanding and what difficulties, if any, they are experiencing. This section has no open-ended problem.

STANDARDIZED TEST TIP **Exercise 4** Help students see that comparing the slopes is the most effective approach, not drawing a diagram.

3 Preparing for Standardized Tests

For Exercises 1–10, choose the correct letter.

1. What is the image of $(-3, 8)$ reflected in $y = 4$? E
   A. $(3, 8)$ B. $(3, -8)$ C. $(-3, -8)$
   D. $(11, 8)$ E. $(-3, 0)$

2. Which angles could an obtuse triangle have? B
   I. a right angle II. two acute angles
   III. an obtuse angle IV. two vertical angles
   A. I and II B. II and III C. III and IV
   D. I and IV E. none of the above

3. What is the image of $(4, 5)$ rotated 270° about the origin? D
   A. $(-5, 4)$ B. $(-4, -5)$ C. $(-5, -4)$
   D. $(5, -4)$ E. none of the above

4. Which lines are perpendicular to $y = 2x - 4$? C
   I. $y = \frac{1}{2}x + 6$ II. $y = 0.5x + 11$
   III. $y = 2x + 7$ IV. $y = -0.5x - 1$
   A. I and II B. III only C. IV only
   D. II and IV E. I, II, and IV

5. The point $(2, 7)$ is reflected in the y-axis, then translated by $\langle 0, -7 \rangle$. Where is its image? A
   A. x-axis B. third quadrant
   C. fourth quadrant D. origin
   E. first quadrant

6. Which figure does *not* tessellate? C
   A. B.
   C.  D.  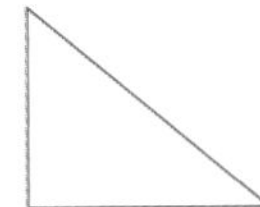
   E. none of the above

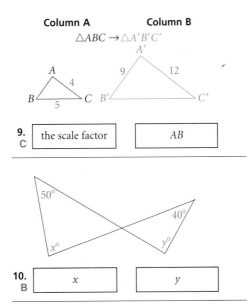

7. Calculator What is the distance between the points $(3, 5)$ and $(-4, -9)$? A
   A. 15.7 B. 4.1 C. 6.1
   D. 15 E. 21

8. What is the midpoint of the segment with endpoints $(0, -4)$ and $(-4, 7)$? C
   A. $(-4, 3)$ B. $(-2, 3)$ C. $(-2, \frac{3}{2})$
   D. $(-4, \frac{3}{2})$ E. $(2, -3)$

Compare the boxed quantity in Column A with the boxed quantity in Column B. Choose the best answer.

A. The quantity in Column A is greater.
B. The quantity in Column B is greater.
C. The two quantities are equal.
D. The relationship cannot be determined on the basis of the information supplied.

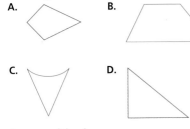

	Column A	Column B
	$\triangle ABC \rightarrow \triangle A'B'C'$ (AB = 5, AC = 4; A'B' = 9, A'C' = 12)	
9. C	the scale factor	AB
10. B	x	y

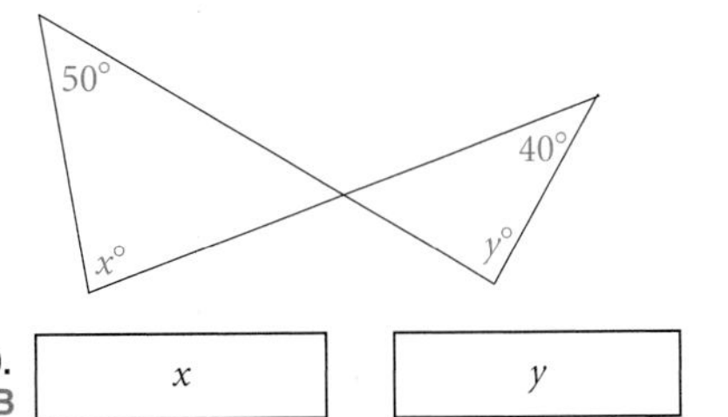

Find each answer.

11. Which transformations are isometries? reflection, rotation, translation, glide reflection
12. You are building a scale model of a building. The front of the actual building will be 60 ft wide and 100 ft tall. The front of your model is 3 ft by 5 ft. What is the scale factor of the reduction? $\frac{1}{20}$

Resources

Teaching Resources

Chapter Support File, Ch. 3
- Standardized Test Practice
- Cumulative Review

Teacher's Edition

See also p. 122E for assessment options.

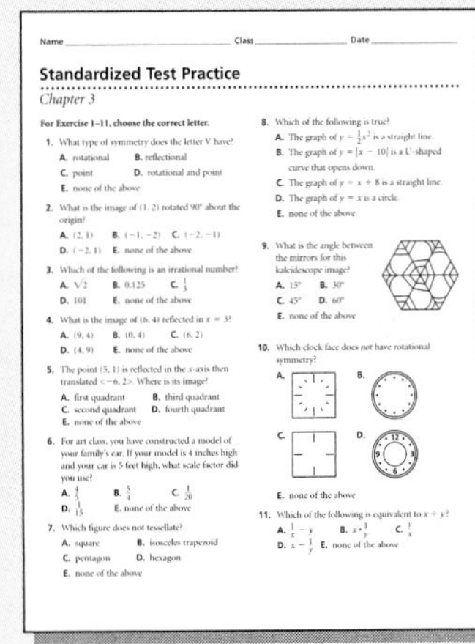
Name ______ Class ______ Date ______

Standardized Test Practice

Chapter 3

For Exercise 1–11, choose the correct letter.

1. What type of symmetry does the letter V have?
   A. rotational B. reflectional C. point D. rotational and point E. none of the above
2. What is the image of $(1, 2)$ rotated 90° about the origin?
   A. $(2, 1)$ B. $(-1, -2)$ C. $(-2, -1)$ D. $(-2, 1)$ E. none of the above
3. Which of the following is an irrational number?
   A. $\sqrt{2}$ B. 0.125 C. $\frac{1}{3}$ D. 101 E. none of the above
4. What is the image of $(6, 4)$ reflected in $x = 3$?
   A. $(9, 4)$ B. $(0, 4)$ C. $(6, 2)$ D. $(4, 9)$ E. none of the above
5. The point $(5, 1)$ is reflected in the x-axis then translated $\langle -6, 2 \rangle$. Where is its image?
   A. first quadrant B. third quadrant C. second quadrant D. fourth quadrant E. none of the above
6. For art class, you have constructed a model of your family's car. If your model is 4 inches high and your car is 5 feet high, what scale factor did you use?
   A. $\frac{4}{5}$ B. $\frac{5}{4}$ C. $\frac{1}{20}$ D. $\frac{1}{15}$ E. none of the above
7. Which figure does not tessellate?
   A. square B. isosceles trapezoid C. pentagon D. hexagon E. none of the above
8. Which of the following is true?
   A. The graph of $y = \frac{1}{2}x^2$ is a straight line.
   B. The graph of $y = |x - 10|$ is a U-shaped curve that opens down.
   C. The graph of $y = x + 8$ is a straight line.
   D. The graph of $y = x$ is a circle.
   E. none of the above
9. What is the angle between the mirrors for this kaleidescope image?
   A. 15° B. 30° C. 45° D. 60° E. none of the above
10. Which clock face does *not* have rotational symmetry?
   A. B. C. D. E. none of the above
11. Which of the following is equivalent to $x \div y$?
   A. $\frac{1}{x} - y$ B. $x \cdot \frac{1}{y}$ C. $\frac{y}{x}$ D. $x - \frac{1}{y}$ E. none of the above

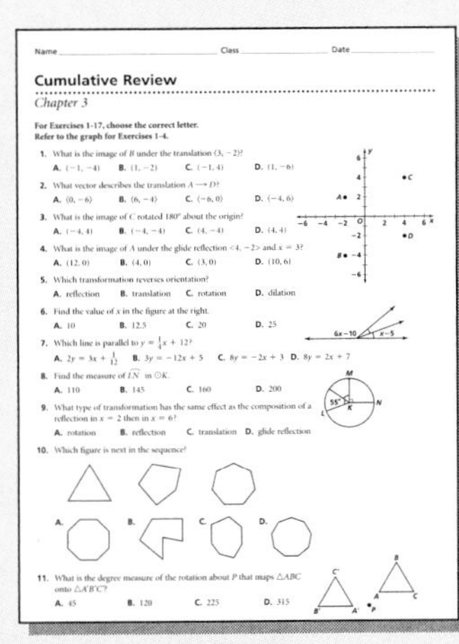
Name ______ Class ______ Date ______

Cumulative Review

Chapter 3

For Exercises 1-17, choose the correct letter.
Refer to the graph for Exercises 1-4.

1. What is the image of B under the translation $\langle 3, -2 \rangle$?
   A. $(-1, -4)$ B. $(1, -2)$ C. $(-1, 4)$ D. $(1, -6)$
2. What vector describes the translation $A \rightarrow D$?
   A. $\langle 0, -6 \rangle$ B. $\langle 6, -4 \rangle$ C. $\langle -6, 0 \rangle$ D. $\langle -4, 6 \rangle$
3. What is the image of C rotated 180° about the origin?
   A. $(-4, 4)$ B. $(-4, -4)$ C. $(4, -4)$ D. $(4, 4)$
4. What is the image of A under the glide reflection $\langle 4, -2 \rangle$ and $x = 3$?
   A. $(12, 0)$ B. $(4, 0)$ C. $(3, 0)$ D. $(10, 6)$
5. Which transformation reverses orientation?
   A. reflection B. translation C. rotation D. dilation
6. Find the value of x in the figure at the right.
   A. 10 B. 12.5 C. 20 D. 25
7. Which line is parallel to $y = \frac{1}{4}x + 12$?
   A. $2y = 3x + \frac{1}{12}$ B. $3y = -12x + 5$ C. $8y = -2x + 3$ D. $8y = 2x + 7$
8. Find the measure of $\overparen{LN}$ in $\odot K$.
   A. 110 B. 145 C. 160 D. 200
9. What type of transformation has the same effect as the composition of a reflection in $x = 2$ then in $x = 6$?
   A. rotation B. reflection C. translation D. glide reflection
10. Which figure is next in the sequence?
   A. B. C. D.
11. What is the degree measure of the rotation about P that maps $\triangle ABC$ onto $\triangle A'B'C'$?
   A. 45 B. 120 C. 225 D. 315

CHAPTER 4

Triangle Relationships

To accommodate flexible scheduling, some lessons are divided into parts. Assignment Options are given in the Lesson Planning Options for each lesson.

PACING OPTIONS

This chart suggests pacing only for the core lessons and their parts, and it is provided merely as a possible guide. It will help you determine how much time you have in your schedule to cover other features, such as the Chapter Project, Math Toolboxes, Wrap Up, and Assessment.

	1 Class Period	1 Class Period	1 Class Period	1 Class Period	1 Class Period	1 Class Period	1 Class Period	1 Class Period	1 Class Period
Traditional (40–45 min class periods)	4-1 Part 1	4-1 Part 2	4-2	4-3	4-4	4-5	4-6 Part 1	4-6 Part 2	4-7 Part 1
Two-Year Geometry (40–45 min class periods)	4-1 Part 1	4-1 Part 2	4-2	4-2	4-3	4-3	Tool-box	4-4	4-4
Block Scheduling (90 min class periods)	4-1 Parts 1, 2	4-2	4-3	4-4	4-5	4-6 Parts 1, 2	4-7 Parts 1, 2	4-8 Parts 1, 2	

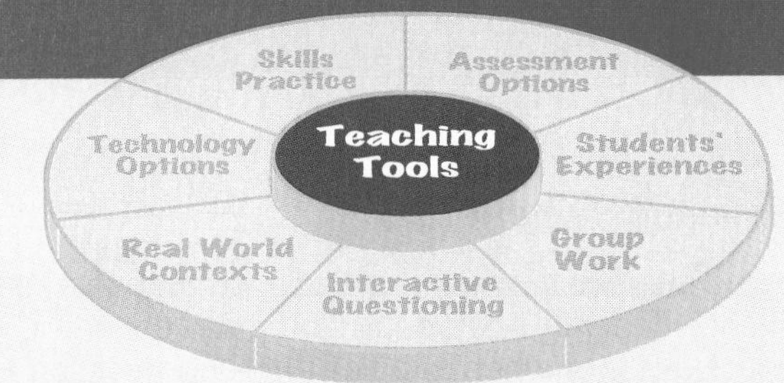

What Students Will Learn and Why

In this chapter, students build on their logical reasoning skills, learned in Chapter 1, by learning how to write and interpret different types of conditional statements, to use different styles of proofs to write convincing arguments, and to write convincing arguments using indirect reasoning. To solve problems they use and apply properties of isosceles triangles, midsegments, and inequalities involving triangle side lengths and angle measures. Finally, students use properties of angle bisectors, perpendicular bisectors, altitudes, and medians to solve locus problems. Students become better problem solvers and logical thinkers, and they come to understand how geometric figures are used in architecture, design, and transportation.

Discussing the Chapter/Building on Experience

The concept map below relates chapter topics to real-world applications. You and your class may wish to add to the map or develop maps of your own. The center oval describes the topic of the chapter. The next level displays topics within the lessons. The outer ovals reflect applications of the content. As you and your class build a concept map, invite students to discuss applications with which they are familiar.

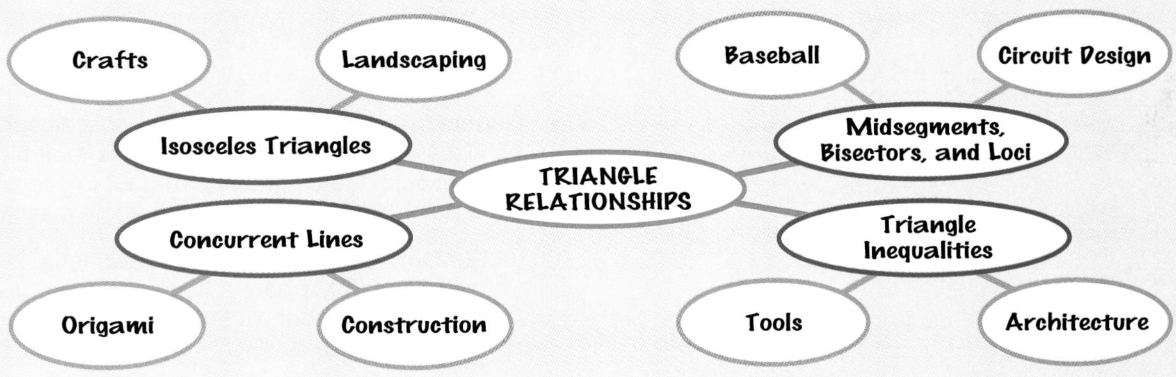

1 Class Period	1 Class Period	1 Class Period	1 Class Period	1 Class Period	1 Class Period	1 Class Period	1 Class Period	1 Class Period	1 Class Period	1 Class Period
4-7 2	4-8 1	4-8 2								
4-5	4-5	Tool-box	4-6 1	4-6 2	4-6 2	4-7 1	4-7 2	Tool-box	4-8 1	4-8 2

Interactive Questioning Tips

A question is interactive when there is "give and take" between the questioner (teacher or student) and the respondent. In Think and Discuss or when a critical thinking question is asked, it is important to involve different students each time, even if it means calling on students who do not volunteer. If a particular student is known to be shy, help him or her by starting out with an easy question as a confidence builder. In Lesson 4-5, students are asked to explain their strategy for the game *What's My Number.* This is an opportunity to involve many students.

Skills Practice

Every lesson provides skill practice with Try This exercises, Exercises On Your Own, and Exercises Mixed Review. The Student Edition includes Checkpoints (pp. 206, 225) and Cumulative Review (p. 239). In the Teacher's Edition, the Lesson Planning Options section for each lesson lists Prerequisite Skills students should know for that lesson. At the back of the Student Edition is the Skills Handbook—mini-lessons on math your students may need to review. The Chapter Support File for Chapter 4 in the Teaching Resources box includes two Practice worksheets per lesson, a worksheet for two Checkpoints, and worksheets for Cumulative Review and Standardized Test Preparation.

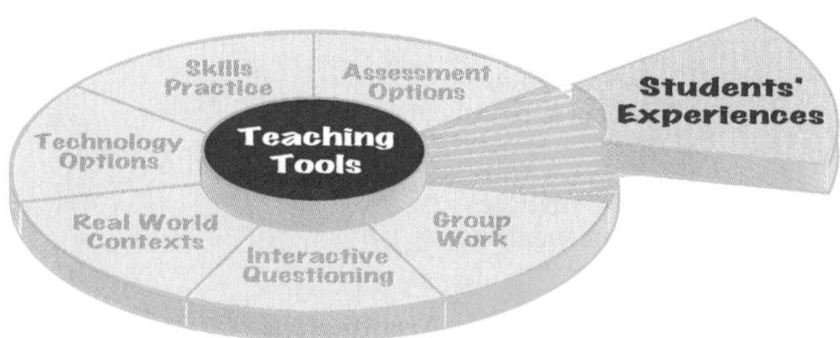

Diverse Learning and Teaching Styles

In your Teacher's Edition, you will find suggestions as to how you can help students complete mathematical tasks in Chapter 4 by reinforcing various learning styles. Here are some examples.

- **Visual learning** students identify isosceles triangles in the classroom (p. 188), draw triangles to apply theorems (p. 216), copy the diagrams of a pool to see why the center is the point of concurrency of the angle bisectors (p. 228)
- **Tactile learning** students use straws to build a model of a swing set (p. 203), create a flexible triangle using popsicle sticks (p. 215), cut out circles and tape straws along diameters (p. 221)
- **Auditory learning** students work in groups to read through solutions (p. 202), remember the meaning of terms by their prefixes (p. 228)
- **Kinesthetic learning** students demonstrate properties of a perpendicular bisector (p. 220)

Alternative Activity for Lesson 4-2

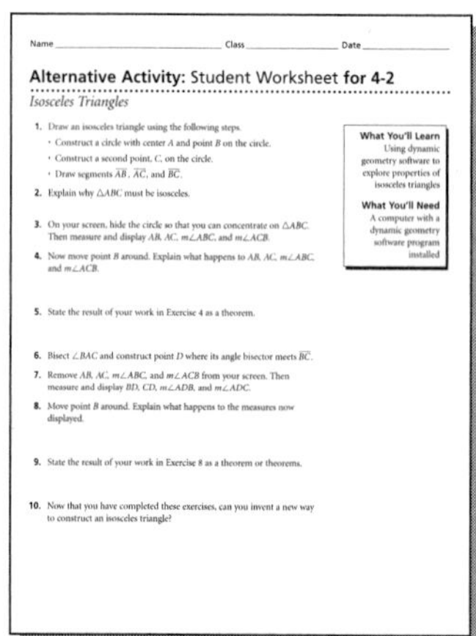
Alternative Activity: Student Worksheet for 4-2

Isosceles Triangles

for use with Theorems 4-1 and 4-2, uses geometry software to explore and establish properties of isosceles triangles.

Alternative Activity for Lesson 4-6

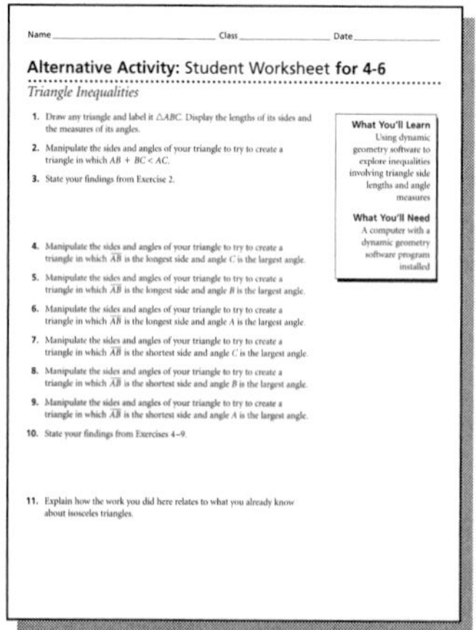
Alternative Activity: Student Worksheet for 4-6

Triangle Inequalities

for use with the Work Together, Example 1, and Example 3, uses geometry software to build triangles and explore the inequalities relating sides and the angles opposite them.

Alternative Activity for Lesson 4-7

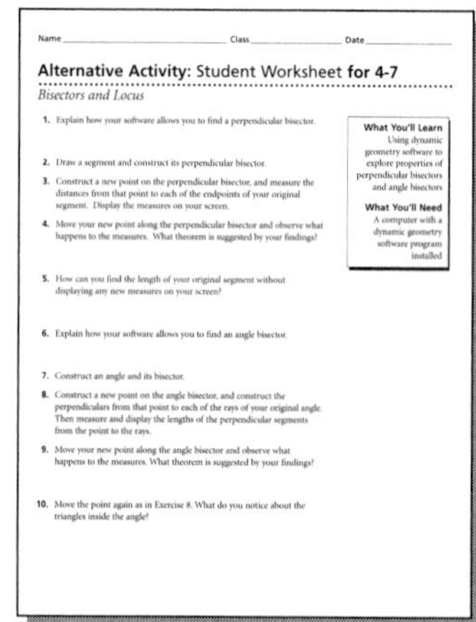
Alternative Activity: Student Worksheet for 4-7

Bisectors and Locus

for use with the Work Together and Examples, uses geometry software to draw, measure, and manipulate angle bisectors and perpendicular bisectors to establish equidistance theorems.

Skills Practice
Assessment Options
Teaching Tools
Technology Options
Students' Experiences
Real World Contexts
Interactive Questioning
Group Work

Cooperative Learning Tips

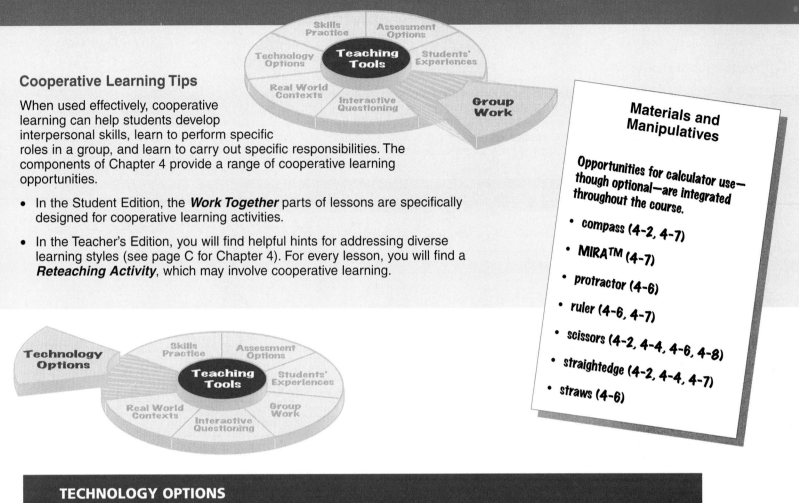

When used effectively, cooperative learning can help students develop interpersonal skills, learn to perform specific roles in a group, and learn to carry out specific responsibilities. The components of Chapter 4 provide a range of cooperative learning opportunities.

- In the Student Edition, the ***Work Together*** parts of lessons are specifically designed for cooperative learning activities.
- In the Teacher's Edition, you will find helpful hints for addressing diverse learning styles (see page C for Chapter 4). For every lesson, you will find a ***Reteaching Activity***, which may involve cooperative learning.

Materials and Manipulatives

Opportunities for calculator use—though optional—are integrated throughout the course.

- compass (4-2, 4-7)
- MIRA™ (4-7)
- protractor (4-6)
- ruler (4-6, 4-7)
- scissors (4-2, 4-4, 4-6, 4-8)
- straightedge (4-2, 4-4, 4-7)
- straws (4-6)

Technology Options
Skills Practice
Assessment Options
Teaching Tools
Students' Experiences
Real World Contexts
Interactive Questioning
Group Work

TECHNOLOGY OPTIONS

Technology Tools		Chapter Project	4-1	4-2	4-3	4-4	4-5	4-6	4-7	4-8
Calculator		Numerous opportunities throughout for students to use scientific calculators.								
Software	Secondary Math Lab Toolkit™		✔	✔	✔	✔	✔	✔	✔	✔
	Integrated Math Lab					✔				✔
	Computer Item Generator		✔	✔	✔	✔	✔	✔	✔	✔
	Student Edition					✔T		✔		✔T
Video	Video Field Trip	✔								
CD-ROM	Multimedia Geometry Lab			✔		✔		✔	✔	
Internet		See the Prentice Hall site. (http://www.phschool.com)								

✔T indicates Math Toolbox.

The Prentice Hall Geometry program offers you a rich variety of technology options. Be assured that all these options are provided as a means of enriching the program and are not essential for the successful completion of the course.

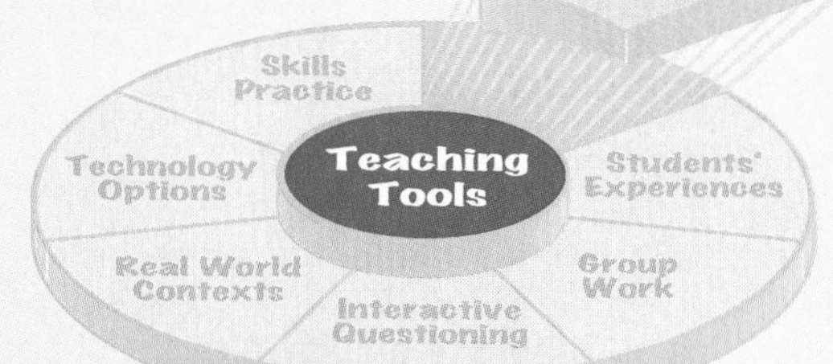

Assessment Options

The Prentice Hall Geometry Program provides you with many options. From these options, you may choose instructional materials and techniques appropriate for your students, or those necessary to meet your district's curriculum requirements. As the chart indicates, the program also supports your teaching efforts by offering you many choices for assessment.

ASSESSMENT OPTIONS

Assessment Support Materials	Chapter Project	4-1	4-2	4-3	4-4	4-5	4-6	4-7	4-8	Chapter End
Chapter Project	▲■	▲■		▲■	▲■			▲■		▲■
Checkpoints					●▲■			●▲■		
Writing Assignment		▲	▲■	▲	▲■●		▲■	●▲	▲■	●▲
Chapter Assessment										▲●
Alternative Assessment		■	■	■	■	■	■	■	■	●■
Cumulative Review										●▲■
Standardized Test Prep			▲■	▲■	▲■	▲	▲■	▲■		▲●
Computer Item Generator	Can be used to create custom-made practice or assessment at any time.									

▲ = Student Edition ■ = Teacher's Edition ● = Teaching Resources

Checkpoints

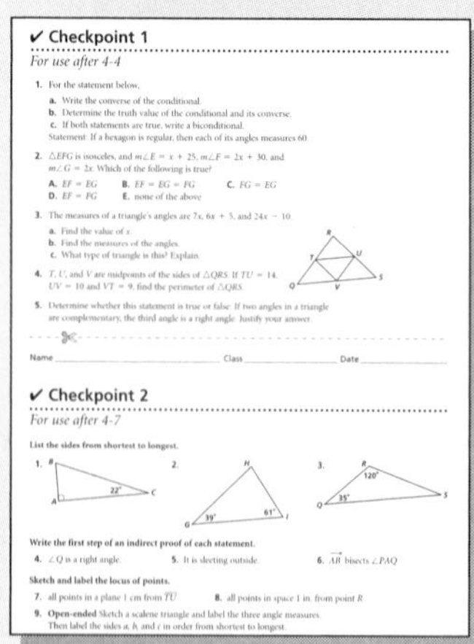

Alternative Assessment

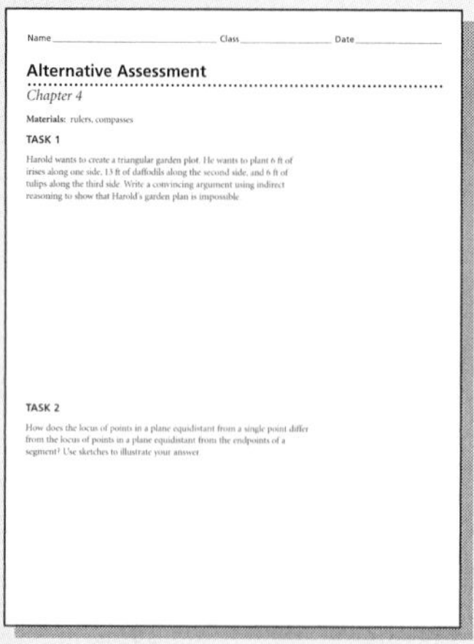

Chapter Assessment

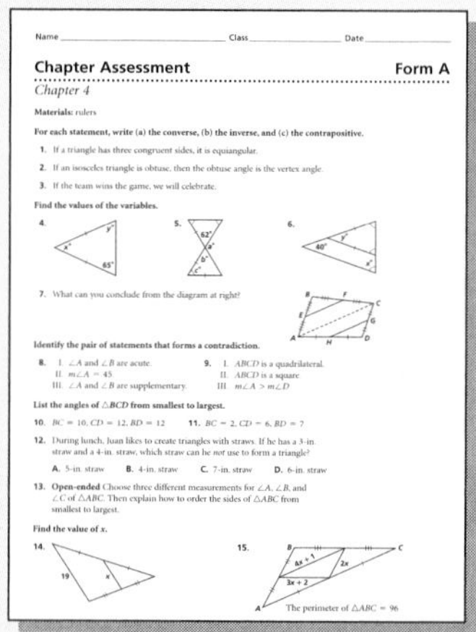

Available in both Form A and Form B

Making the Right Connections

Mathematics is imbedded in nearly every walk of life. The National Council of Teachers of Mathematics (NCTM) encourages educators to recognize these connections and to emphasize them for the purpose of better educating students for success in life and in a global economy. The ***Connections*** chart below highlights these connections for Chapter 4.

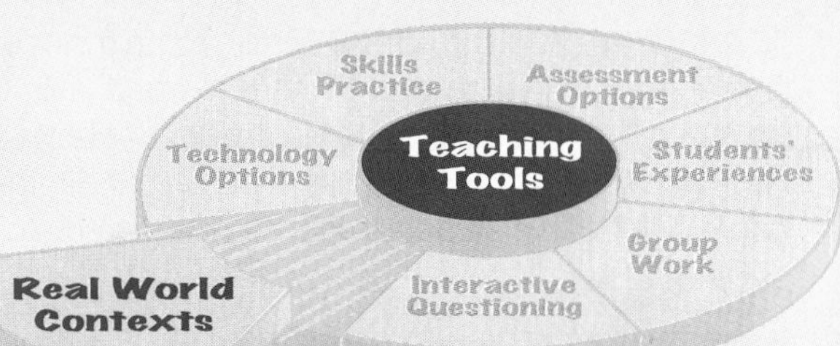

CONNECTIONS

Lesson	Interdisciplinary Connections	Career Prep	Other Real World Connections	Math Integration	NCTM Standards
Chapter Project	Language Arts		Puzzles Riddles		Problem Solving Connections
4-1	Literature Chemistry	Advertising	Advertisements	Algebra Coordinate Geometry Probability	Algebra Communication Problem Solving Reasoning
4-2	Art	Landscaping	Crafts Architecture Graphic Arts Communications	Algebra Coordinate Geometry	Algebra Connections Communications Problem Solving
4-3	Literature	Writing	Punch Clock Passport	Logical Reasoning Coordinate Geometry	Reasoning Communication Problem Solving
4-4	Art	Architecture Surveying	Swimming Creative Arts	Coordinate Geometry Algebra	Coordinate Geometry Connections Communication Problem Solving
4-5	Literature		Mysteries Consumer Issues Drawbridges	Coordinate Geometry Probability	Reasoning Connections Communication Problem Solving
4-6		Architecture	Landscaping Tools	Geometry in 3 Dimensions Probability	Reasoning Connections Communication Problem Solving
4-7	History	City Planning	National Landmarks Baseball Jet Vapors	Coordinate Geometry Logical Reasoning	Connections Communication Problem Solving
4-8	History	Park Design Recreation	Origami	Coordinate Geometry Geometry in 3 Dimensions	Connections Coordinate Geometry Communication Problem Solving

CHAPTER 4 Triangle Relationships

CONNECTING TO PRIOR LEARNING To help students see how logical reasoning is related to the real world, ask: *You want to entertain nine friends three at a time, over twelve school days. How would you arrange it so that no two students are invited on the same day?* (Have students choose nine names to represent friends.)

CULTURAL CONNECTIONS While the origin of logic puzzles dates back to ancient Greece, they were made popular in England in the 19th century by Charles L. Dodgson, also known as Lewis Carroll, the author of the Alice-in-Wonderland classic, *Through the Looking Glass.* Ask students to share some of their favorite riddles and brain teasers with the class.

INTERDISCIPLINARY CONNECTIONS Help students see that the logical thinking skills they develop studying geometric proofs have implications in many diverse fields, such as law, journalism, computer programming, and engineering.

ABOUT THE PROJECT The Chapter Project gives students the opportunity to explore ways of solving logic puzzles and to create their own mind benders. In the Find Out questions found throughout the chapter, students make lists of possible solutions and analyze them, drawing diagrams to organize their reasoning.

Technology Options

Prentice Hall Technology

Video

- Video Field Trip 4, "Brain Twisters," a look at how video game developers deal with problems in logic

CHAPTER 4 Triangle Relationships

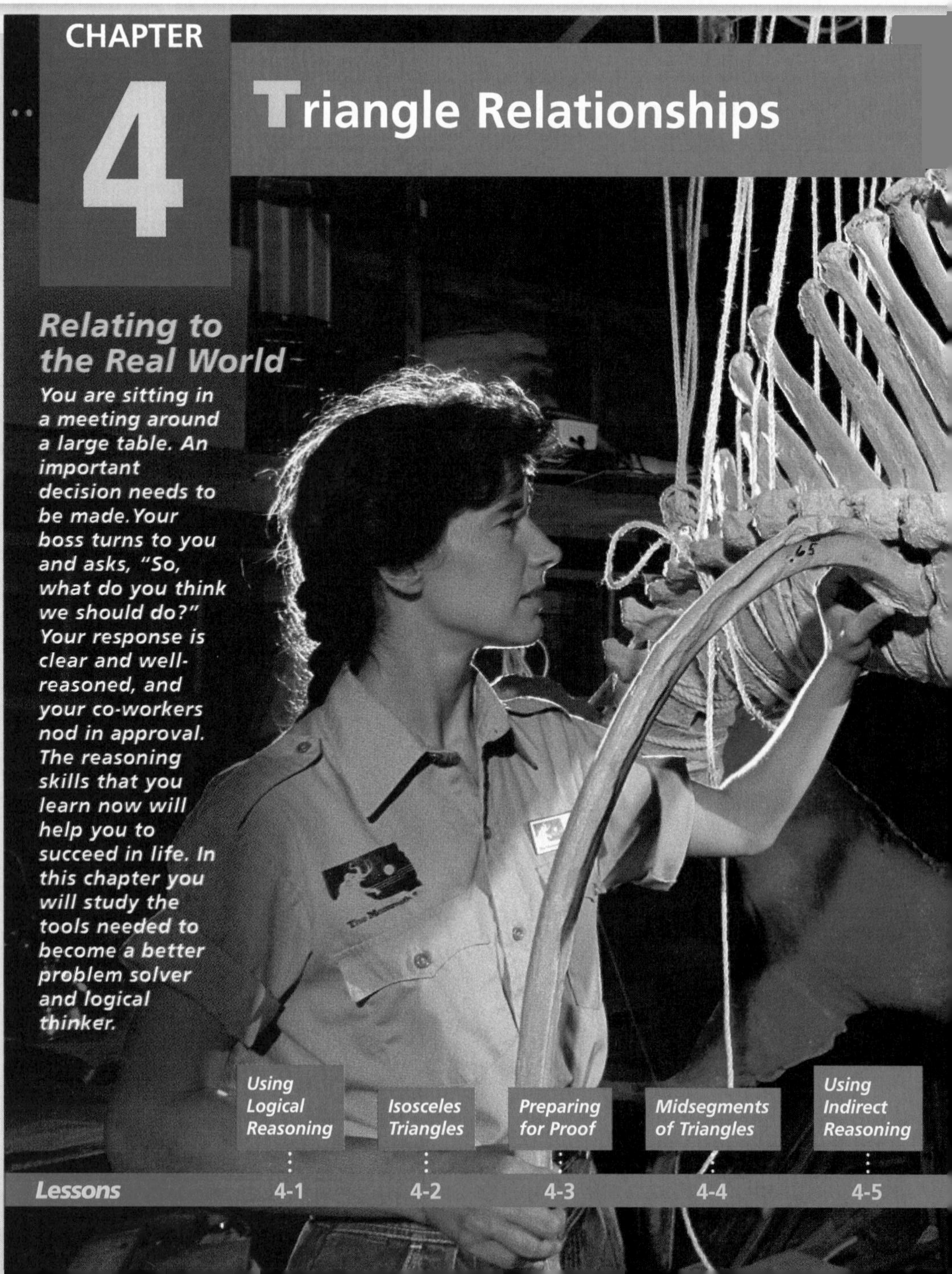

Relating to the Real World

You are sitting in a meeting around a large table. An important decision needs to be made. Your boss turns to you and asks, "So, what do you think we should do?" Your response is clear and well-reasoned, and your co-workers nod in approval. The reasoning skills that you learn now will help you to succeed in life. In this chapter you will study the tools needed to become a better problem solver and logical thinker.

Lessons	4-1	4-2	4-3	4-4	4-5
	Using Logical Reasoning	*Isosceles Triangles*	*Preparing for Proof*	*Midsegments of Triangles*	*Using Indirect Reasoning*

Launching the Project

PROJECT NOTEBOOK Encourage students to keep all project-related materials in a separate folder or notebook. **See Chapter Project and Scoring Rubric in Chapter Support File.**

- Have students work in groups to solve the following riddle. Then discuss the strategies groups used to find the answer. Find two integers that satisfy all the following conditions:
  1. Both integers are even.
  2. The sum of the integers is negative.
  3. The product of the integers is –96.
  4. Neither integer is a perfect square.
  5. Neither integer is a factor of the other.
  6. Neither integer is a cube. **6 and −16**

- Have students work in groups to solve the following puzzle. Then discuss the strategies groups used to find the answer. Invert a triangle of ten pennies (one penny in the top row, two pennies in the second row, three pennies in the third row, and four pennies in the bottom row) by moving only three pennies. **Put the outer two pennies from the bottom row in the second row, one on either side of the row. Place the penny from the top row below the two pennies left in the bottom row.**

TRACKING THE PROJECT You may wish to have students read Finishing the Chapter Project on page 233 to help them get an overview of the project. Set benchmark deadlines for students to show their work in progress.

CHAPTER PROJECT

PUZZLING PIECES

A paleontologist makes sense of the past by piecing together fossils. By using logical reasoning, she makes a few bones tell the story of an entire species. That feeling of discovery—that sense of "aha!"—has driven people throughout history to use logic to solve puzzles.

In your project for this chapter, you will explore ways of solving logic puzzles. You will also create your own puzzles. You will see how logic, though used for amusement, is the backbone of mathematics—a powerful tool for determining truth.

To help you complete the project:

▼ **p. 187** *Find Out by Listing*
▼ **p. 198** *Find Out by Organizing*
▼ **p. 205** *Find Out by Analyzing*
▼ **p. 225** *Find Out by Writing*
▼ **p. 233** *Finishing the Project*

▼Project Resources

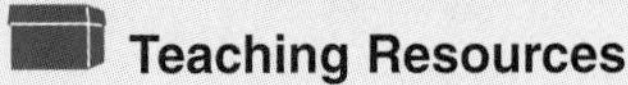

Teaching Resources

Chapter Support File, Ch. 4
- Chapter Project Manager and Scoring Rubric

Transparencies
50

▼Using the Rubric

Sharing the scoring rubric for the project with your students will alert them to your expectations before they begin work on the project.

As students complete each Find Out question in the chapter, you may wish to have them evaluate their own work or a partner's work based on the scoring rubric. Students should have the opportunity to revise their work after it has been reviewed.

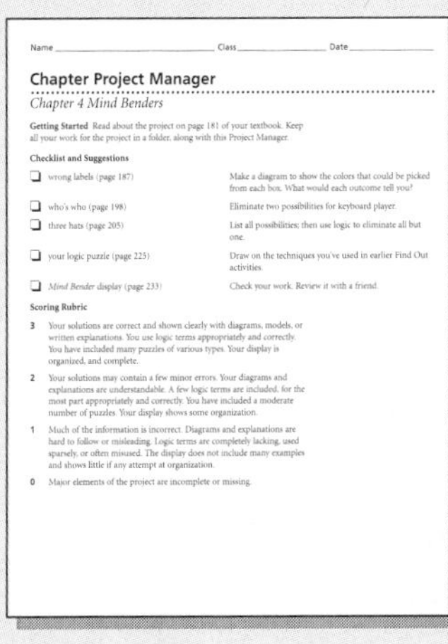

Name ____________ Class ________ Date ________

Chapter Project Manager

Chapter 4 Mind Benders

Getting Started Read about the project on page 181 of your textbook. Keep all your work for the project in a folder, along with this Project Manager.

Checklist and Suggestions

❑ wrong labels (page 187)	Make a diagram to show the colors that could be picked from each box. What would each outcome tell you?
❑ who's who (page 198)	Eliminate two possibilities for keyboard player.
❑ three hats (page 205)	List all possibilities; then use logic to eliminate all but one.
❑ your logic puzzle (page 225)	Draw on the techniques you've used in earlier Find Out activities.
❑ *Mind Bender* display (page 233)	Check your work. Review it with a friend.

Scoring Rubric

3 Your solutions are correct and shown clearly with diagrams, models, or written explanations. You use logic terms appropriately and correctly. You have included many puzzles of various types. Your display is organized, and complete.

2 Your solutions may contain a few minor errors. Your diagrams and explanations are understandable. A few logic terms are included, for the most part appropriately and correctly. You have included a moderate number of puzzles. Your display shows some organization.

1 Much of the information is incorrect. Diagrams and explanations are hard to follow or misleading. Logic terms are completely lacking, used sparsely, or often misused. The display does not include many examples and shows little if any attempt at organization.

0 Major elements of the project are incomplete or missing.

4-1 Teaching Notes

PROBLEM OF THE DAY

Three ships leave from Boston for France on the same day. The round trip takes the first ship 12 days, the second 16 days, and the third 20 days. How many days will elapse before all three ships again leave Boston on the same day? (Assume continuous round-trip activities for all three ships.) 240 days

Problem of the Day is also available in Transparencies.

CONNECTING TO PRIOR KNOWLEDGE Give students examples of if-then statements and have them decide if they are true or false. Examples include: If an angle is a right angle, then its measure is 90°. If a polygon has seven sides, then it is a hexagon. If a figure is reflected over two lines, then the transformation is a translation.

THINK AND DISCUSS

If-then statements are often symbolized as "if p, then q" or "$p \Rightarrow q$" where p represents the hypothesis and q represents the conclusion.

Example 1

Make sure students see that the "if" and "then" are not part of the hypothesis and the conclusion.

Lesson Planning Options

Prerequisite Skills

- Understanding properties of polygons
- Understanding transformations

Assignment Options for Exercises On Your Own

To provide flexible scheduling, this lesson can be subdivided into parts.

1 **Core** 1–10
Extension 27

2 **Core** 11–26, 28–31
Extension 32–35

Use Mixed Review to maintain skills.

Resources

Student Edition
Skills Handbook, p. 664
Extra Practice, p. 651
Glossary/Study Guide

Teaching Resources
Chapter Support File, Ch. 4
- Practice 4-1 (two worksheets)
- Reteaching 4-1

Classroom Manager 4-1
Glossary, Spanish Resources

Transparencies
20, 51, 55

Connections Literature . . . and more

4-1 Using Logical Reasoning

What You'll Learn

- Writing and interpreting different types of conditional statements

...And Why

To help you analyze situations and become a better problem solver

THINK AND DISCUSS

Part 1

Conditionals and Converses

- If Raúl's major is bagpipe, then he attends Carnegie-Mellon University.
- If a second goes by, then Earth has moved another $18\frac{1}{2}$ mi along its orbit.
- If a movie is scary, then the concession stands sell more popcorn.
- If you are not completely satisfied, then your money will be refunded.

1. You make and hear *if-then* statements like these many times each day. What are some *if-then* statements you have heard? Check students' work.

Another name for an *if-then statement* is a **conditional.** Every conditional has two parts. The part following *if* is the **hypothesis,** and the part following *then* is the **conclusion.**

Example 1

Identify the hypothesis and conclusion in this statement:

If it is February, then there are only 28 days in the month.

Hypothesis: It is February.
Conclusion: There are only 28 days in the month.

If you want double the love, then buy a pair.

2. **Try This** Identify the hypothesis and conclusion in the photo caption at the left. You want double the love; buy a pair.

When you determine whether a conditional is true or false, you determine its **truth value.** To show that a conditional is false, you need to find only one *counterexample* for which the hypothesis is true and the conclusion is false. The conditional in Example 1 is false because during a leap year February has 29 days.

3. Find a counterexample for this conditional: If the name of a state contains the word *New*, then the state borders an ocean. New Mexico does not border an ocean.

Many sentences can be written as conditionals. For example, the sentence

Quadrilaterals have four sides.

can be rewritten in if-then form as

If a polygon is a quadrilateral, then it has four sides.

Help students see that a conditional statement cannot be called true by finding one or more examples where it is true. A conditional needs to be proven true. Proving conditionals will be investigated further in Lesson 4-3.

Question 3 You may want to display a map for students to check which states border oceans.

Have students practice writing statements as conditionals. Use the theorems and postulates from Chapters 1–3 as examples. Also give students examples of statements that cannot be rewritten as conditionals, such as questions and commands.

Example 2

ERROR ALERT! When writing the converse of a conditional, students may also interchange the "if" and the "then."

Remediation: Have students write "if" and "then" first, leaving space in between, then interchange and write the hypothesis and the conclusion.

Question 4 Have students investigate the truth value of conditionals and their converses. They should find that the converse of a true conditional can be false and the converse of a false conditional can be true.

Using symbol notation, the converse of "if *p*, then *q*" ("$p \Rightarrow q$") is "if *q*, then *p*" ("$q \Rightarrow p$"). A biconditional statement is represented by "*p* iff *q*" or "$p \Leftrightarrow q$."

The **converse** of a conditional interchanges the hypothesis and conclusion.

Example 2

Write the converse of this statement: If a polygon is a quadrilateral, then it has four sides.

Conditional: If a polygon is a quadrilateral, then it has four sides.

Converse: If a polygon has four sides, then it is a quadrilateral.

Literature Notice that both statements in Example 2 have the same truth value. This is *not* true of all conditionals and their converses, as Alice discovers in this passage from Lewis Carroll's *Alice's Adventures in Wonderland.*

The Hatter opened his eyes very wide on hearing this; but all he *said* was "Why is a raven like a writing-desk?"

"Come, we shall have some fun now!" thought Alice. "I'm glad they've begun asking riddles—I believe I can guess that," she added aloud.

"Do you mean that you think you can find out the answer to it?" said the March Hare.

"Exactly so," said Alice.

"Then you should say what you mean," the March Hare went on.

"I do," Alice hastily replied; "at least—at least I mean what I say—that's the same thing, you know."

"Not the same thing a bit!" said the Hatter. "Why, you might just as well say that 'I see what I eat' is the same thing as 'I eat what I see'!"

The Hatter's statement "I see what I eat" can be rewritten in if-then form as "If I eat it, then I see it." The converse, "I eat what I see," can be rewritten as "If I see it, then I eat it."

4. Are the truth values for the Hatter's statement and its converse the same? Explain. **No; you see everything you eat, but you do not eat everything you see.**

Part 2

Biconditionals, Inverses, and Contrapositives

When a conditional and its converse are true, you can combine them as a **biconditional.** The conditionals from Example 2 can be combined as

If a polygon is a quadrilateral, then it has four sides, *and* if a polygon has four sides, then it is a quadrilateral.

This long sentence can be shortened by using the phrase *if and only if:*

A polygon is a quadrilateral *if and only if* it has four sides.

Additional Examples

FOR EXAMPLE 1

Identify the hypothesis and conclusion of this statement: If it is 12:00, then the sun has gone down. **Hypothesis: It is 12:00. Conclusion: The sun has gone down.**

Discussion: *What is the truth value of the conditional?*

FOR EXAMPLE 2

Write the converse of this statement: If two lines are vertical, then they are parallel. **If two lines are parallel, then they are vertical.**

Discussion: *Are the truth values of the conditional and its converse the same?*

FOR EXAMPLE 3

Write the two statements that make up the definition: A number is even if and only if it is divisible by 2. **If a number is even, then it is divisible by 2. If a number is divisible by 2, then it is even.**

FOR EXAMPLE 4

Write the inverse and contrapositive of the statement: If a number is divisible by 10, then it is divisible by 5. **Inverse: If a number is not divisible by 10, then it is not divisible by 5. Contrapositive: If a number is not divisible by 5, then it is not divisible by 10.**

Example 3

ESL Have students notice that when a converse is written, sometimes the wording of the hypothesis and the conclusion is changed slightly. Point out that "its measure is 90" became "the measure of an angle is 90."

Question 5 Help students understand that the negation of a true statement is false and the negation of a false statement is true.

Using symbol notation, the negation of p is represented by "$\sim p$." The inverse of "if p, then q" is represented by "if $\sim p$, then $\sim q$" ("$\sim p \Rightarrow \sim q$") and the contrapositive by "if $\sim q$, then $\sim p$" ("$\sim q \Rightarrow \sim p$").

Example 4

ALTERNATIVE METHOD Note that the contrapositive is found by going to the original statement and negating, then interchanging the hypothesis and conclusion. This is taking the converse of the inverse. The contrapositive can also be found by taking the inverse of the converse.

CRITICAL THINKING Question 7 Have students compare answers with a partner. Then have them find the truth value of the statements. Ask students if the truth values of the statements are related.

Have students draw a Venn diagram for the conditional in Question 7 and use it to explain the truth value of the inverse and contrapositive.

Technology Options

Prentice Hall Technology

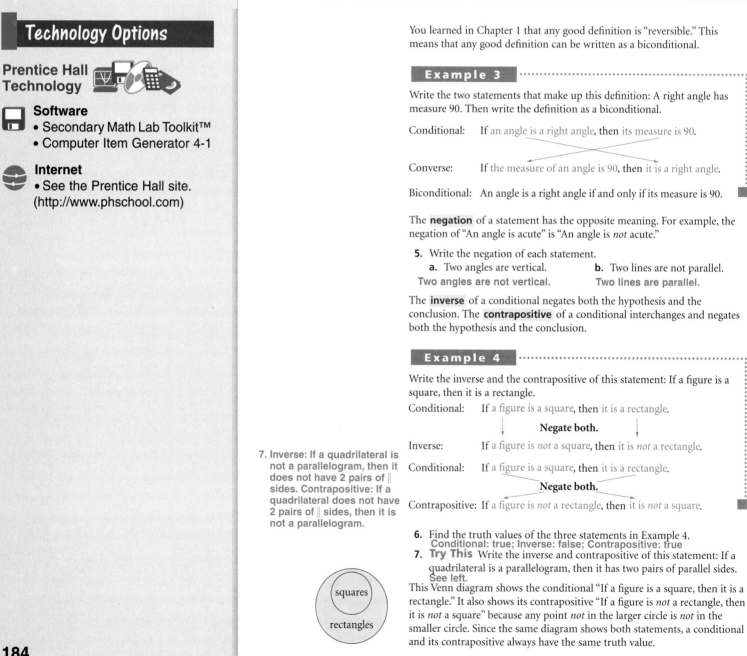

Software
- Secondary Math Lab Toolkit™
- Computer Item Generator 4-1

Internet
- See the Prentice Hall site. (http://www.phschool.com)

184

7. Inverse: If a quadrilateral is not a parallelogram, then it does not have 2 pairs of ∥ sides. Contrapositive: If a quadrilateral does not have 2 pairs of ∥ sides, then it is not a parallelogram.

You learned in Chapter 1 that any good definition is "reversible." This means that any good definition can be written as a biconditional.

Example 3

Write the two statements that make up this definition: A right angle has measure 90. Then write the definition as a biconditional.

Conditional: If an angle is a right angle, then its measure is 90.

Converse: If the measure of an angle is 90, then it is a right angle.

Biconditional: An angle is a right angle if and only if its measure is 90.

The **negation** of a statement has the opposite meaning. For example, the negation of "An angle is acute" is "An angle is *not* acute."

5. Write the negation of each statement.
   a. Two angles are vertical. **Two angles are not vertical.**
   b. Two lines are not parallel. **Two lines are parallel.**

The **inverse** of a conditional negates both the hypothesis and the conclusion. The **contrapositive** of a conditional interchanges and negates both the hypothesis and the conclusion.

Example 4

Write the inverse and the contrapositive of this statement: If a figure is a square, then it is a rectangle.

Conditional: If a figure is a square, then it is a rectangle.

Negate both.

Inverse: If a figure is *not* a square, then it is *not* a rectangle.

Conditional: If a figure is a square, then it is a rectangle.

Negate both.

Contrapositive: If a figure is *not* a rectangle, then it is *not* a square.

6. Find the truth values of the three statements in Example 4. **Conditional: true; Inverse: false; Contrapositive: true**
7. **Try This** Write the inverse and contrapositive of this statement: If a quadrilateral is a parallelogram, then it has two pairs of parallel sides. **See left.**

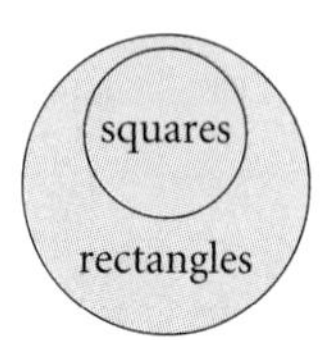

This Venn diagram shows the conditional "If a figure is a square, then it is a rectangle." It also shows its contrapositive "If a figure is *not* a rectangle, then it is *not* a square" because any point *not* in the larger circle is *not* in the smaller circle. Since the same diagram shows both statements, a conditional and its contrapositive always have the same truth value.

ESL Students may have trouble differentiating the meanings of the terms *converse* and *inverse,* and the terms *conditional* and *biconditional.* You may want to display a poster with explanations and examples of each.

VISUAL LEARNING Students can see how the dark and light boxes change places in the Summary of Conditionals depending on the type of statement.

Exercises ON YOUR OWN

Exercises 2–5 Make sure students do not underline "if" and "then" as part of the hypothesis and conclusion.

Exercises 6–9 You may also want students to give an example that satisfies each statement so they can see that examples can be found to satisfy false statements.

Summary of Conditionals

Statement	Form	Example
conditional	If ■, then ■.	If an angle is a straight angle, then its measure is 180.
converse	If ■, then ■.	If the measure of an angle is 180, then it is a straight angle.
inverse	If *not* ■, then *not* ■.	If an angle is *not* a straight angle, then its measure is *not* 180.
contrapositive	If *not* ■, then *not* ■.	If the measure of an angle is *not* 180, then it is *not* a straight angle.
biconditional	■ if and only if ■.	An angle is a straight angle if and only if its measure is 180.

Exercises ON YOUR OWN

1. Identify the hypothesis and conclusion in the cartoon. You send in a proof-of-purchase label; they send you a get-well card.

FRANK AND ERNEST By BOB THAVES

For Exercises 2–5: (a) Rewrite each statement in if-then form. (b) Underline the hypothesis once and the conclusion twice.

2. Glass objects are fragile.
   If an object is made of glass, then it is fragile.
3. $3x - 7 = 14$ implies that $3x = 21$.
   If $3x - 7 = 14$, then $3x = 21$.
4. Numbers that have 2 as a factor are even.
   If a number has 2 as a factor, then it is even.
5. An isosceles triangle has two congruent sides.
   If a triangle is isosceles, then it has two congruent sides.

Find a counterexample for each statement.

6. If it is not a weekday, then it is Saturday.
   Sunday is not a weekday.
7. Odd integers less than 10 are prime.
   1 and 9 are not prime.
8. If you live in a country that borders the United States, then you live in Canada.
   Mexico borders the United States.
9. If you play a sport with a ball and bat, then you play baseball.
   Softball and cricket are sports played with a ball and a bat.
10. a. *Open-ended* Write a conditional with the same truth value as its converse.
    b. Write a conditional whose converse has the opposite truth value.
    a–b. See margin.

pages 185–187 On Your Own

10a. Sample: If a polygon has three sides, then it is a triangle.
b. Sample: If a quadrilateral has four ≅ sides, then it is a square.
11a. If you grow, then you will eat all of your vegetables.
b. If you do not eat all of your vegetables, then you will not grow.
c. If you do not grow, then you will not eat all of your vegetables.
12a. If a figure has rotational symmetry, then it has point symmetry.
b. If a figure does not have point symmetry, it does not have rotational symmetry.
c. If a figure does not have rotational symmetry, then it does not have point symmetry.
13a. If a △ has a 90° angle, then it is a rt. △.
b. If a △ is not a rt. △, then it does not have a 90° angle.
c. If a △ does not have a 90° angle, then it is not a rt. △.
14a. If a quadrilateral is not a rhombus, then it has exactly 2 ≅ sides.
b. If a quadrilateral does not have exactly 2 ≅ sides, then it is a rhombus.
c. If a quadrilateral is a rhombus, then it does not have exactly two ≅ sides.

Exercises 11–18 Check that students find the inverse and contrapositive of the given conditional, and *not* of the converse.

Exercise 24 Remind students that two non-adjacent angles can be complementary.

DIVERSITY Exercise 27 Take this opportunity to discuss ads for alcohol, cigarettes, clothes, and cars that use misleading advertising to appeal to people's need for acceptance, admiration, and popularity.

ALTERNATIVE ASSESSMENT Exercises 32–35 These exercises can help you assess students' understanding of conditionals and contrapositives. Have students check their responses with a partner and discuss any discrepancies until they can agree on a response.

15a. If 2 segments have the same length, then they are ≅.

b. If 2 segments are not ≅, then they have different lengths.

c. If 2 segments have different lengths, then they are not ≅.

16a. If you will not get paid, then you do not work.

b. If you work, then you will get paid.

c. If you will get paid, you work.

17a. If the sum of the measures of the angles of a polygon is 540, then it is a pentagon.

b. If a polygon is not a pentagon, then the sum of the measures of its angles is not 540.

c. If the sum of the measures of angles of a polygon is not 540, then it is not a pentagon.

18a. If the contrapositive of a conditional statement is false, then the conditional is false.

b. If a conditional statement is true, then its contrapositive is true.

c. If the contrapositive of a conditional statement is true, then the conditional statement is true.

19a. If you have a passport, then you travel from the U.S. to Kenya.

b. true; false

For each statement, write (a) the converse, (b) the inverse, and (c) the contrapositive. 11–14. See margin p. 185. 15–18. See margin.

11. If you eat all of your vegetables, then you will grow.

12. *Transformations* If a figure has point symmetry, then it has rotational symmetry.

13. If a triangle is a right triangle, then it has a 90° angle.

14. If a quadrilateral has exactly two congruent sides, then it is not a rhombus.

15. If two segments are congruent, then they have the same length.

16. If you do not work, you will not get paid.

17. If a polygon is a pentagon, then the sum of the measures of its angles is 540.

18. If a conditional statement is false, then its contrapositive is false.

For Exercises 19–26: (a) Write the converse of each statement. (b) Determine the truth value of the statement and its converse. (c) If both statements are true, write a biconditional. 19. See margin. 20–26. See back of book.

19. If you travel from the United States to Kenya, then you have a passport.

20. *Coordinate Geometry* If a point is in the first quadrant, then its coordinates are positive.

21. *Chemistry* If a substance is water, then its chemical formula is H_2O.

22. *Transformations* If a figure has two lines of symmetry, then it has rotational symmetry.

23. *Coordinate Geometry* If two nonvertical lines are parallel, then their slopes are equal.

24. If two angles are complementary, then the sum of their measures is 90.

25. If you are in Indiana, then you are in Indianapolis.

26. *Probability* If the probability that an event will occur is 1, then the event is certain to occur.

✪**27. a.** *Consumer Issues* Advertisements often suggest conditional statements. For example, an ad might imply that if you don't buy a product, you won't be popular. What conditional is implied in the ad at the right?

b. *Research* Find magazine ads that use conditionals effectively. Make a poster to display these ads.

a–b. See back of book.

For a few extra bucks,
you could've had
TREADMASTERS.
JUST MARRIED
TREADMASTER TIRES

Write the two conditionals that make up each biconditional. 28–29. See back of book.

28. A swimmer wins a race if and only if she swims the fastest.

29. A number is divisible by 3 if and only if the sum of its digits is divisible by 3.

30. Two angles are congruent if and only if they have the same measure. If two angles have the same measure, then they are ≅; if two angles are ≅, then they have the same measure.

Chapter Project FIND OUT BY LISTING Have students work in groups. Students can list the possible contents for each box and then find the different combinations for all three boxes. Checking the number of red and blue hats in the combinations will help students narrow their choices.

Exercises MIXED REVIEW

Exercises 36–39 You may want students to find the equation of each line.

GETTING READY FOR LESSON 4-2 These exercises prepare students to use and apply the properties of isosceles triangles.

Wrap Up

THE BIG IDEA Ask students: *Explain how to find the converse, inverse, and contrapositive of a conditional. Give an example to support your explanations.*

RETEACHING ACTIVITY Students write conditionals relating to sports, hobbies, school, and mathematics. Then they write the converse, inverse, and contrapositive for each of their conditionals and for each of their partner's conditionals. (Reteaching worksheet 4-1)

31. Writing Jynona knows that vertical angles are congruent. She thinks the converse is also true. Is she correct? Explain.
No; two ≅ adjacent angles are a counterexample.

For each Venn diagram: (a) Write a conditional statement. (b) Write the contrapositive of the conditional.

32. 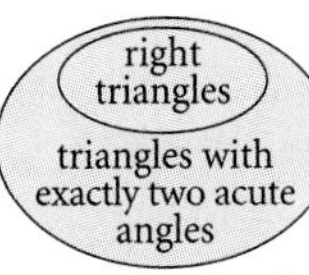

33. 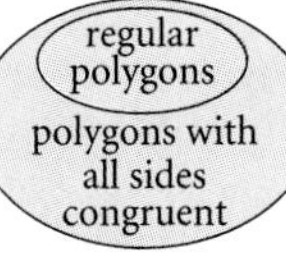

34. 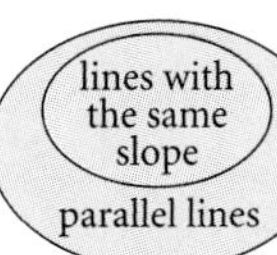

35. 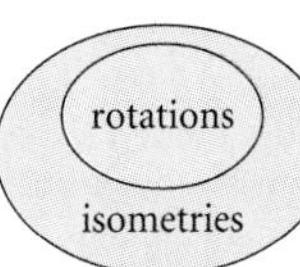

32–35. See back of book.

Chapter Project **Find Out by Listing**

Three red hats and three blue hats are packed in three boxes, with two hats to a box. The boxes are all labeled incorrectly. To determine what each box actually contains, you may select one hat from one box, without looking at the contents of that box. Explain how this will allow you to determine the contents of each box. (*Hint:* List all possible solutions; then use logic to solve.) See back of book.

Exercises MIXED REVIEW

Coordinate Geometry **Sketch a line with the given slope containing the given point.** 36–38. See back of book.

36. $m = \frac{1}{2}, (2, -6)$ **37.** $m = 1, (0, 5)$ **38.** $m = -2, (-3, 6)$ **39.** $m = \frac{1}{3}, (0, 0)$

39. 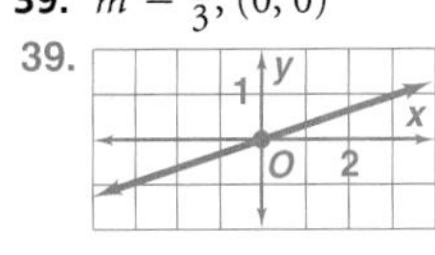

40. An angle's measure is 10 more than its supplement. Find the measures of both angles. 95; 85

41. Transformational Geometry Locate the coordinates of the image of $\triangle ABC$ with vertices $A(0, 3)$, $B(-4, -6)$, $C(6, 1)$ under a 180° rotation about the origin. $A'(0, -3)$, $B'(4, 6)$, $C'(-6, -1)$

Getting Ready for Lesson 4-2

Find the value of *x*.

42. 105 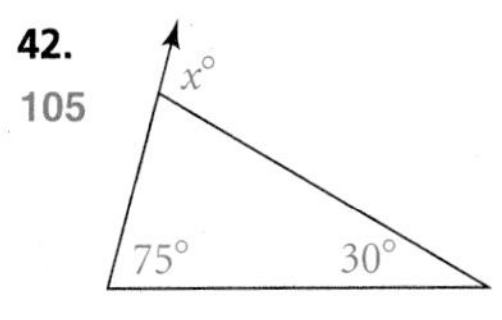

43. 35 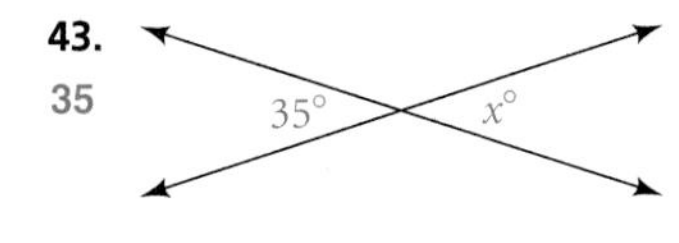

44. 40 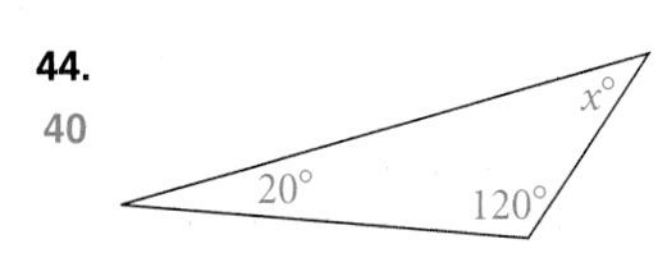

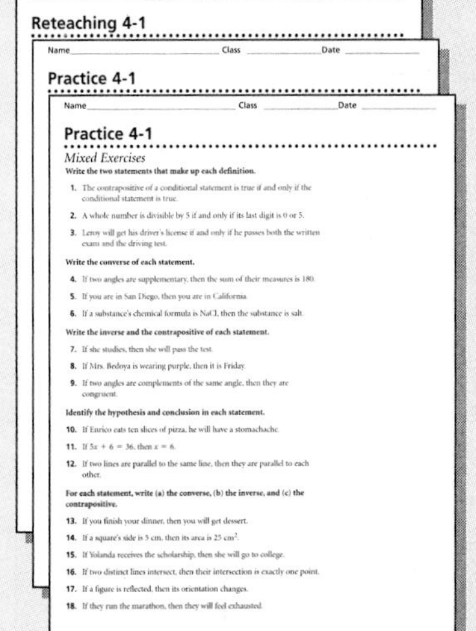
Reteaching 4-1
Practice 4-1
Practice 4-1
Mixed Exercises

Lesson Quiz

Lesson Quiz is also available in Transparencies.

Exercises 1–4, use this statement: If a triangle is scalene, then no two sides are congruent.

1. Identify the hypothesis and the conclusion. Hypothesis: A triangle is scalene. Conclusion: No two sides are congruent.
2. Write the converse. If no two sides of a triangle are congruent, then it is scalene.
3. Write the inverse. If a triangle is not scalene, then two sides are congruent.
4. Write the contrapositive. If two sides of a triangle are congruent, then it is not scalene.

4-2 Teaching Notes

PROBLEM OF THE DAY

Show how a teacher can arrange twelve students in six rows with three students in each row so the teacher is equidistant from each row.

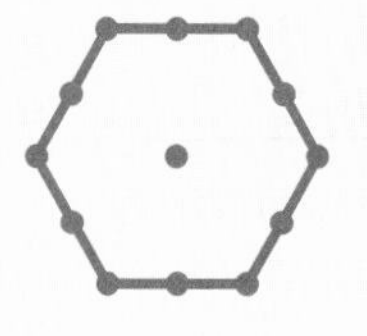

Problem of the Day is also available in Transparencies.

CONNECTING TO PRIOR KNOWLEDGE Draw the following triangles on the board and have students classify them according to their angles and sides.

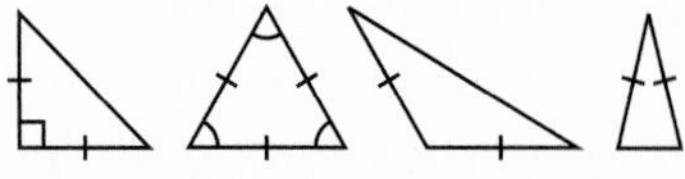

WORK TOGETHER

Before students begin this activity, have them review Constructions 1 and 2 and the Example of Lesson 1-6.

Students may have trouble identifying the opposite sides and angles. Illustrate for students that the side opposite an angle is intersected by a ray from the vertex in the interior of the angle.

THINK AND DISCUSS

ESL **VISUAL LEARNING** Begin by having students identify isosceles triangles in the classroom. Then draw isosceles triangles in different positions and have students practice naming the bases, legs, base angles, and vertex angles.

Lesson Planning Options

Prerequisite Skills

- Constructing congruent segments and angles
- Finding measures of interior and exterior angles of polygons

Assignment Options for Exercises On Your Own

Core 1–15, 20–33, 35–40

✪**Extension** 16–19, 34

Use Mixed Review to maintain skills.

Resources

Student Edition

Extra Practice, p. 651

Glossary/Study Guide

Teaching Resources

Chapter Support File, Ch. 4

- Practice 4-2 (two worksheets)
- Reteaching 4-2
- Alternative Activity 4-2

Classroom Manager 4-2

Glossary, Spanish Resources

Transparencies

5, 51

Connections  Landscaping . . . and more

4-2 Isosceles Triangles

What You'll Learn

- Using and applying properties of isosceles triangles

...And Why

To understand a geometric figure used in the designs of many buildings and bridges

What You'll Need

- straightedge
- compass
- scissors

TECHNOLOGY HINT

The Work Together could be done using geometry software.

WORK TOGETHER

Have each member of your group construct a different isosceles triangle and then cut it out. Be sure to include acute and obtuse triangles.

- Label the triangle $\triangle ABC$, with A and B opposite the congruent sides.
- Bisect $\angle C$ by folding the triangle so that the congruent sides overlap. Label the intersection of the fold line and $\overline{AB}$ as point D.

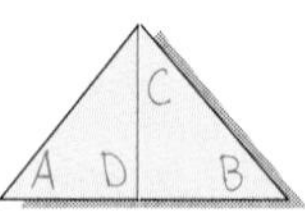

1. What do you notice about $\angle A$ and $\angle B$? Compare results within your group. $\angle A \cong \angle B$
2. a. What types of angles do $\angle CDA$ and $\angle CDB$ appear to be? right angles
   b. What do you notice about $\overline{AD}$ and $\overline{DB}$? $\overline{AD} \cong \overline{DB}$
   c. Use your answers to parts (a) and (b) to complete the statement: $\overline{CD}$ is the __?__ of $\overline{AB}$. $\perp$ bisector

- Construct a new triangle that has two congruent angles. Cut out the triangle and label it $\triangle EFG$, where $\angle E \cong \angle F$.

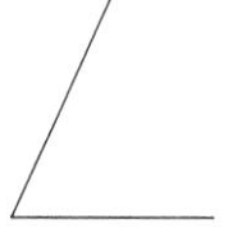

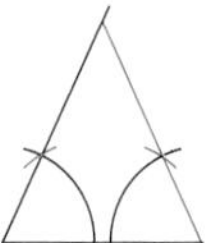

3. Fold the triangle so that the congruent angles overlap.
   a. What do you notice about $\overline{EG}$ and $\overline{FG}$? Compare results within your group. $\overline{EG} \cong \overline{FG}$
   b. What type of triangle is $\triangle EFG$? isosceles

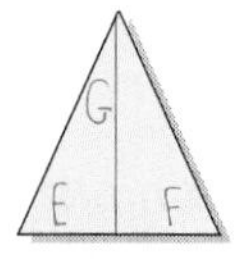

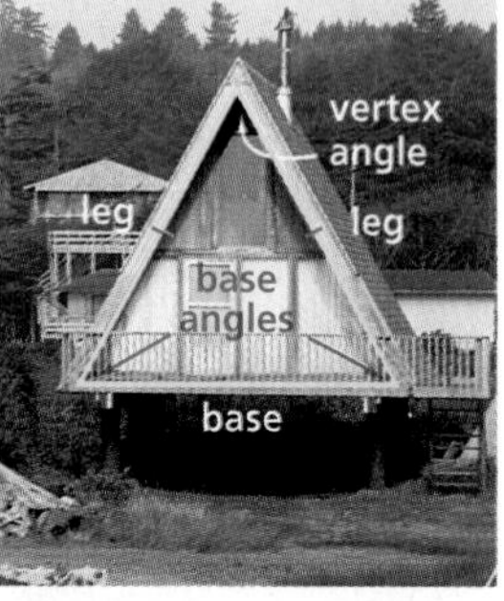

THINK AND DISCUSS

Isosceles triangles are common in the real world. You can find them in structures such as bridges and buildings. The congruent sides of an isosceles triangle are the **legs.** The third side is the **base.** The two congruent sides form the **vertex angle.** The other two angles are the **base angles.**

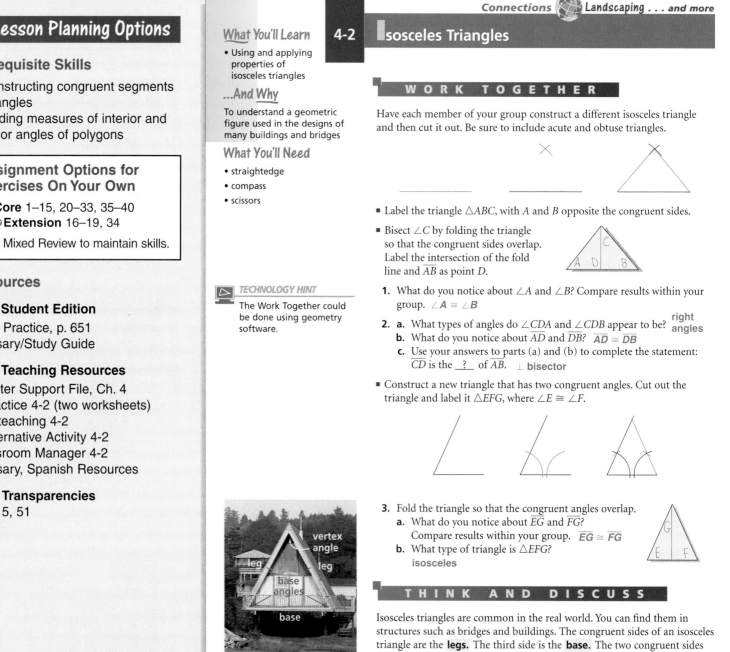

Converse of Isosceles Triangle Theorem Have students compare the hypothesis and conclusion of this theorem to those of the Isosceles Triangle Theorem.

Example 1

ERROR ALERT! Some students may think $x = m\angle LMN$. **Remediation:** Point out to students that the disjointed arcs between $\angle LMO$ and $\angle OMN$ are used to represent two different congruent angles and not one large angle.

Question 5 To find *x*, students can solve an equation as in Example 1. However, students may use the results from Example 1 to reason that since $m\angle N$ is 20 less than $m\angle N$ in Example 1, *x* must be 20 more.

Example 2

For part a, students may want to draw $\triangle RTS$ without points *U*, *V*, or *W* to see that $\angle R$ and $\angle S$ are its base angles.

Your observations from the Work Together suggest the following theorems. The proofs of these theorems involve properties of congruent triangles that you will study in Chapter 8.

Theorem 4-1 Isosceles Triangle Theorem

If two sides of a triangle are congruent, then the angles opposite those sides are also congruent.

If $\overline{AC} \cong \overline{BC}$, then $\angle A \cong \angle B$.

Theorem 4-2

The bisector of the vertex angle of an isosceles triangle is the perpendicular bisector of the base.

If $\overline{AC} \cong \overline{BC}$ and $\overline{CD}$ bisects $\angle ACB$, then $\overline{CD} \perp \overline{AB}$ and $\overline{CD}$ bisects $\overline{AB}$.

Theorem 4-3 Converse of Isosceles Triangle Theorem

If two angles of a triangle are congruent, then the sides opposite the angles are congruent.

If $\angle A \cong \angle B$, then $\overline{AC} \cong \overline{BC}$.

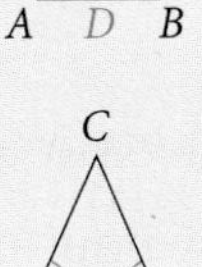

4. Write the Isosceles Triangle Theorem and its converse as a biconditional. 2 sides of a △ are ≅ if and only if the angles opp. those sides are ≅.

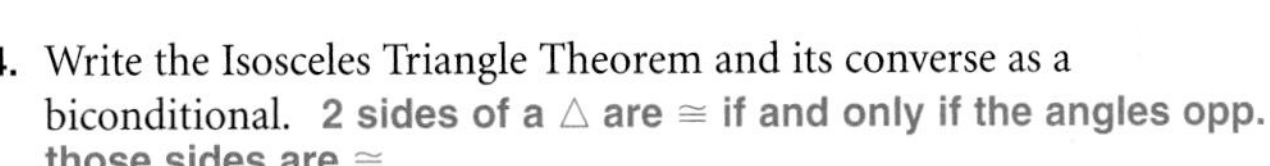

Example 1

Algebra Find the values of *x* and *y*.

By Theorem 4-2, you know that $\overline{MO} \perp \overline{LN}$. So $y = 90$. Because the triangle is isosceles, $\angle L \cong \angle N$. So $m\angle N = 63$.

$m\angle N + x + y = 180$	Triangle Angle-Sum Theorem
$63 + x + 90 = 180$	Substitution
$x = 27$	Subtract 153 from each side.

So $x = 27$ and $y = 90$.

5. **Try This** Suppose $m\angle L = 43$. Find the values of *x* and *y*. 47; 90

Example 2

Complete each statement. Explain your answers.

a. $\overline{RT} \cong$? b. $\overline{RU} \cong$? c. $\overline{VW} \cong$?

a. $\overline{RT} \cong \overline{ST}$ because $\angle R \cong \angle S$.

b. $\overline{RU} \cong \overline{VU}$ because $\angle R \cong \angle RVU$.

c. $\overline{VW} \cong \overline{SW}$ because $\angle WVS \cong \angle S$.

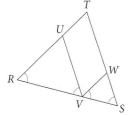

Additional Examples

FOR EXAMPLE 1

Refer to the diagram in Example 1. If $m\angle L = 52$, find the values of *x* and *y*. $x = 38$, $y = 90$

FOR EXAMPLE 2

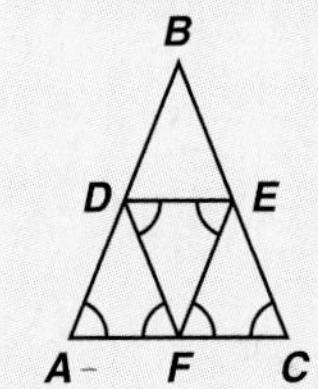

$\overline{AB} \cong$? $\overline{BC}$

$\overline{FD} \cong$? $\overline{DA}$ or $\overline{FE}$

$\overline{CE} \cong$? $\overline{FE}$

FOR EXAMPLE 3

Refer to the diagram in Example 3. Imagine that a segment is drawn to connect the sides of the angle marked *x*. Find the measures of the other two angles of the triangle. The measure of each angle would be 30.

Point out that while the terms "equilateral" and "equiangular" can be used interchangeably for triangles, this is not true for other polygons. For example, squares and rectangles are both equiangular but only the square is equilateral.

Question 8 Some students may write, "A triangle is equilateral if and only if it is equiangular," while others may write, "A triangle is equiangular if and only if it is equilateral." Discuss why these are both correct.

Example 3

ERROR ALERT! Some students may assume the hexagon is regular and use the Polygon Interior Angle-Sum Theorem to find *x*. **Remediation:** Point out that, although the hexagon is equilateral, you do not know it is equiangular.

EXTENSION Have students collect other landscape designs from gardening and landscaping books and magazines. Have them sketch the designs and describe them using geometric terms.

Technology Options

For Exercise 10, students may use graphing utilities to investigate possible locations for the third vertex of the triangle. For Exercise 34, students may create their own designs using drawing or geometry software, then print and decorate them.

Prentice Hall Technology 

Software
- Secondary Math Lab Toolkit™
- Computer Item Generator 4-2

CD-ROM
- Multimedia Geometry Lab 4

Internet
- See the Prentice Hall site. (http://www.phschool.com)

190

QUICK REVIEW

An equilateral triangle has three congruent sides. An equiangular triangle has three congruent angles.

7a–b. The sides are ≅; if 2 ∠s of a △ are ≅, then the sides opposite them are ≅.

6. a. Choose two sides of $\triangle EFG$. What must be true about the angles opposite these sides? Why?
   b. Repeat part (a) with a different pair of sides.
   c. What is true about the angles of an equilateral triangle? The three angles are ≅.

6a–b. The angles are ≅; base ∠s of an isosceles △ are ≅.

7. a. Choose two angles of $\triangle MNO$. What must be true about the sides opposite these angles? Why?
   b. Repeat part (a) with a different pair of angles.
   c. What is true about the sides of an equiangular triangle? 3 sides are ≅.

Your observations from Questions 6 and 7 are summarized below.

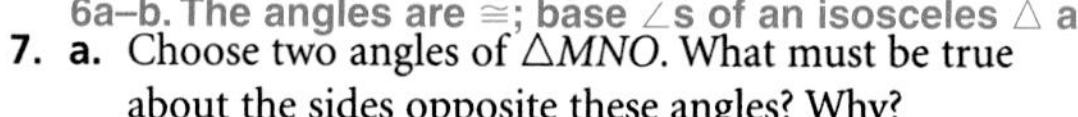

Corollary to Isosceles Triangle Theorem

If a triangle is equilateral, then it is equiangular.

If $\overline{XY} \cong \overline{YZ} \cong \overline{ZX}$, then $\angle X \cong \angle Y \cong \angle Z$.

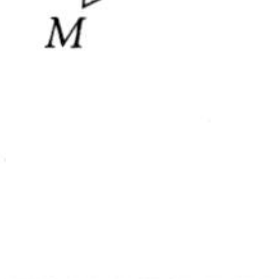

Corollary to Converse of Isosceles Triangle Theorem

If a triangle is equiangular, then it is equilateral.

If $\angle X \cong \angle Y \cong \angle Z$, then $\overline{XY} \cong \overline{YZ} \cong \overline{ZX}$.

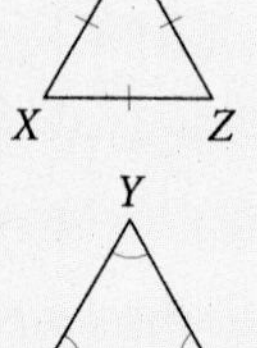

8. Use the corollaries above to write a biconditional.
   A triangle is equilateral if and only if it is equiangular.

Example 3 **Relating to the Real World** 

Landscaping A landscaper is building a raised bed garden to fit in the hexagonal space in the diagram. The path around the garden consists of rectangles and equilateral triangles. What is the measure of the angle marked *x*?

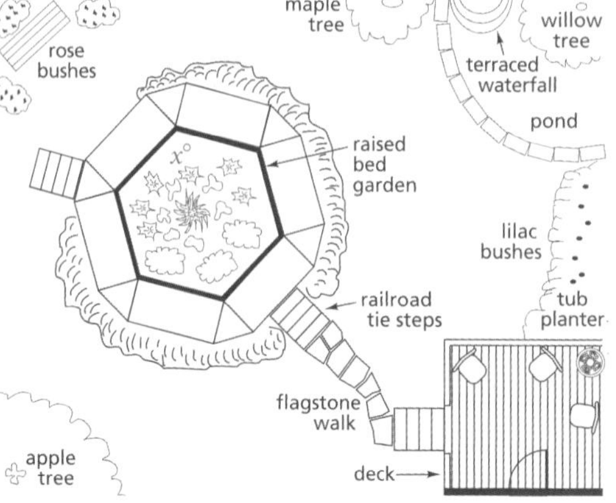

Each angle of a rectangle measures 90. Each angle of an equilateral triangle measures 60. (Why?)

$$x + 90 + 60 + 90 = 360$$
$$x = 120$$

The measure of the angle is 120.

Exercises ON YOUR OWN

MAKING CONNECTIONS Exercise 9 The world's tallest cathedral spire, measuring 528 feet, is on the Protestant Cathedral of Ulm in Germany. Construction began in 1377 but was not completed until 1890.

CRITICAL THINKING Exercise 10 You may want to draw an isosceles right triangle and discuss with students which angles are the base angles.

COORDINATE GEOMETRY Exercise 11 Be sure that students consider points that lie in Quadrants 1 and 4.

CONNECTING TO STUDENTS' WORLD Exercise 16 Have students collect logos from clubs, sports teams, clothing, record labels, etc. Then have them highlight and name geometric figures used in the logos.

Exercises ON YOUR OWN

Algebra **Find the values of x and y.**

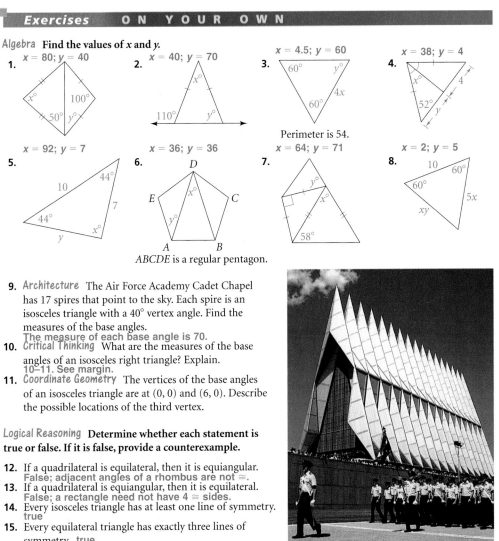

1. $x = 80$; $y = 40$

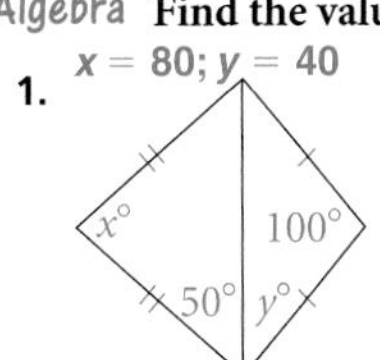

2. $x = 40$; $y = 70$

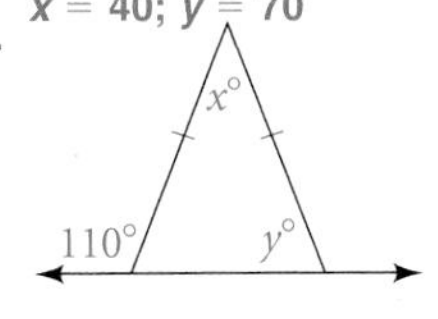

3. $x = 4.5$; $y = 60$

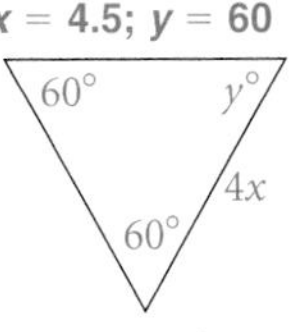

Perimeter is 54.

4. $x = 38$; $y = 4$

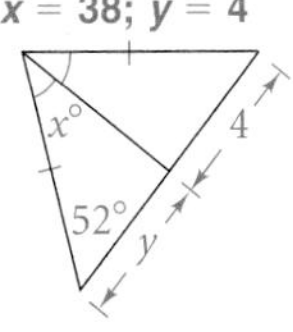

5. $x = 92$; $y = 7$

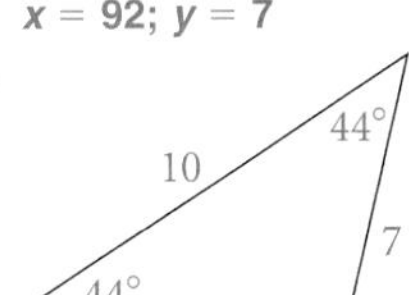

6. $x = 36$; $y = 36$

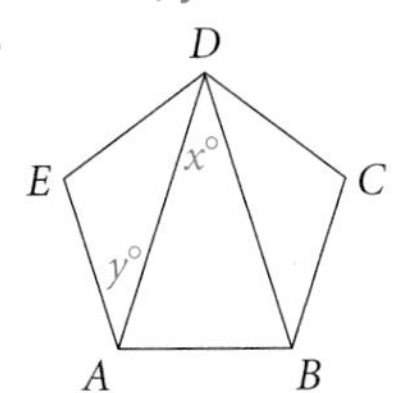

ABCDE is a regular pentagon.

7. $x = 64$; $y = 71$

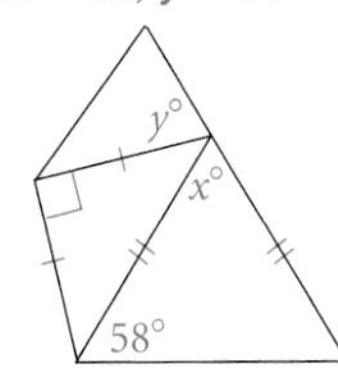

8. $x = 2$; $y = 5$

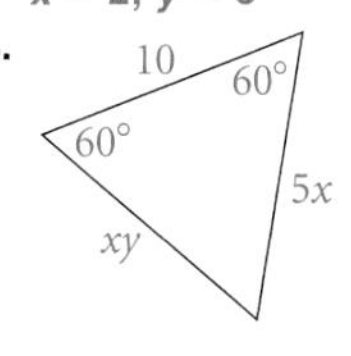

9. Architecture The Air Force Academy Cadet Chapel has 17 spires that point to the sky. Each spire is an isosceles triangle with a 40° vertex angle. Find the measures of the base angles.
The measure of each base angle is 70.

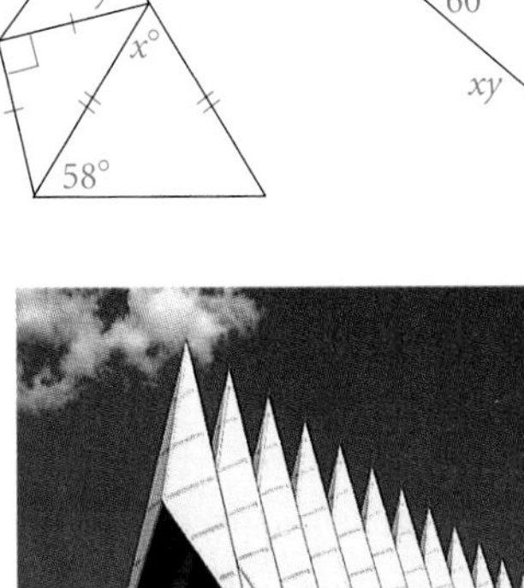

10. Critical Thinking What are the measures of the base angles of an isosceles right triangle? Explain.
10–11. See margin.
11. Coordinate Geometry The vertices of the base angles of an isosceles triangle are at (0, 0) and (6, 0). Describe the possible locations of the third vertex.

Logical Reasoning **Determine whether each statement is true or false. If it is false, provide a counterexample.**

12. If a quadrilateral is equilateral, then it is equiangular.
False; adjacent angles of a rhombus are not ≅.
13. If a quadrilateral is equiangular, then it is equilateral.
False; a rectangle need not have 4 ≅ sides.
14. Every isosceles triangle has at least one line of symmetry.
true
15. Every equilateral triangle has exactly three lines of symmetry. true

16. Graphic Arts The logo of the National Council of Teachers of Mathematics is shown at the right.
    a. Trace the logo onto your paper. Highlight an obtuse isosceles triangle in the design and then find its angle measures. a–b. See margin.
    b. Open-ended Repeat part (a) for each of the following figures: kite, pentagon, hexagon.

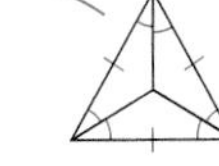

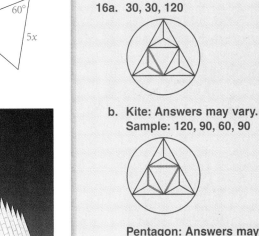

The triangles in the logo have these congruent sides and angles.

pages 191–193 On Your Own

10. 45; if x is the measure of a base angle, then the sum of the measures of the base angles is given by $2x = 180 - 90$. So $x = 45$.

11. The 3rd vertex must be on the ⊥ bisector of the base, the line $x = 3$.

16a. 30, 30, 120

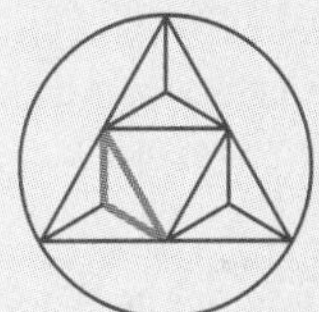

b. Kite: Answers may vary. Sample: 120, 90, 60, 90

Pentagon: Answers may vary. Sample: 120, 120, 120, 90, 90

Hexagon: Answers may vary. Sample: 120, 120, 120, 120, 120, 120

Exercises 17–18 Have students work with partners. Remind them to check that the product of the slopes of the lines through the sides of the right angle is –1.

WRITING Exercise 20 Be sure that students explain the conditional, and not the converse. You may want to ask them if the converse is true.

ALTERNATIVE ASSESSMENT Exercises 26–32 These exercises can help you assess students' understanding of the properties of isosceles triangles by observing their ability to apply the theorems and corollaries presented in this lesson to find missing angle measures and side lengths.

Exercise 27 Help students see that the larger triangle is equilateral because each side is made up of two congruent segments.

Exercise 28 Before students can find x, they need to find the measures of the angles of a regular hexagon.

Exercise 32 Students should see that $\triangle OED$ is an isosceles triangle because all radii of $\odot O$ are congruent.

20. Yes; if a $\triangle$ has at least 2 $\cong$ sides, it is isosceles. An equiangular $\triangle$ is equilateral and has 3 $\cong$ sides, so it is isosceles.

34a.

page 193 Mixed Review

46. Answers may vary. Samples: $m\angle M = m\angle O$ because $MN = NO$; $m\angle M = m\angle O = 45$ because $m\angle M + m\angle O = 180 - m\angle N = 90$.

47. $\overline{DF} \parallel \overline{EG}$ because in a plane, 2 lines $\perp$ to a 3rd line are $\parallel$.

48. Answers may vary. Samples: $m\angle LJM = m\angle JLM = m\angle LJK = m\angle JLK = 45$ because base $\angle$s of an isoceles $\triangle$ are $\cong$ and the vertex angle of each $\triangle$ is a rt. angle. $\angle MJK$ and $\angle KLM$ are rt. $\angle$s by the Angle Addition Post. $JKLM$ is a square by def. of square.

Coordinate Geometry **For each pair of points, there are six points that could be the third vertex of an isosceles right triangle. Find the coordinates of each point.**

17. (0, 0) and (5, 5) **18.** (2, 3) and (5, 6)
17–18. See right.

19. *Algebra* A triangle has angle measures $x + 15$, $3x - 35$, and $4x$.
  a. Find the value of x. **25**
  b. Find the measure of each angle. **40, 40, 100**
  c. What type of triangle is it? Why? **Isosceles; the $\triangle$ has 2 $\cong$ angles.**

20. *Writing* If a triangle is equiangular, is it also isosceles? Explain. **See margin.**

21. a. *Communications* In the diagram, what type of triangle is formed by the cable pairs and the ground? **21a. isosceles**
  b. What are the two different base lengths of the triangles? **900 ft; 1100 ft**
  c. How is the tower related to each of the triangles?
Answers may vary. Sample: The tower is the $\perp$ bisector of the base.

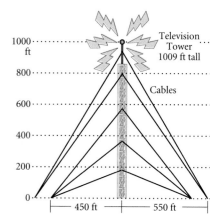

Television Tower 1009 ft tall
Cables
1000 ft
800
600
400
200
0
450 ft
550 ft
Tower cables extend to both widths.

Find each value.

22. If $m\angle L = 58$, then $m\angle LKJ = \blacksquare$. **64**

23. If $JL = 5$, then $ML = \blacksquare$. **2.5**

24. If $m\angle JKM = 48$, then $m\angle J = \blacksquare$. **42**

25. If $m\angle J = 55$, then $m\angle JKM = \blacksquare$. **35**

17. (0, 5), (5, 0), (0, 10), (10, 0), (–5, 5), (5, –5)
18. (–1, 6), (2, 6), (2, 9), (5, 0), (5, 3), (8, 3)

Choose **Use mental math, pencil and paper, or a calculator to find the values of the variables.**

26. **6**

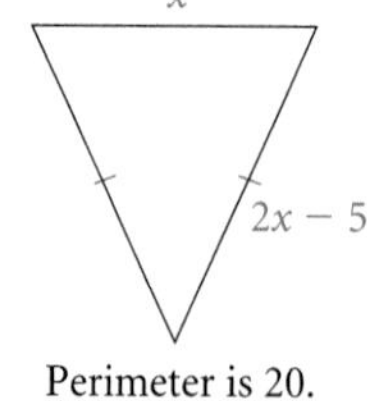

Perimeter is 20.

27. **60**

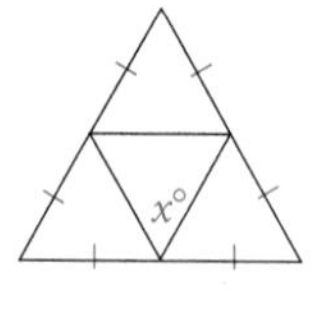

28. **30**

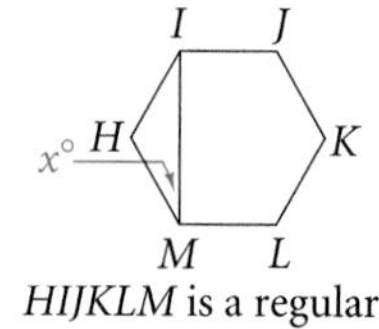

$HIJKLM$ is a regular hexagon.

29. **50**

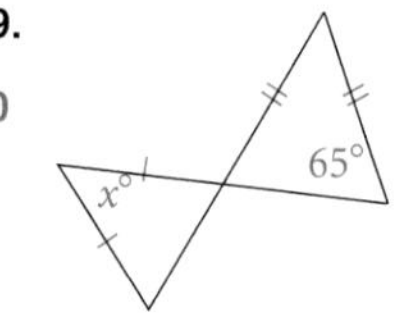

30. **x = 60; y = 30**

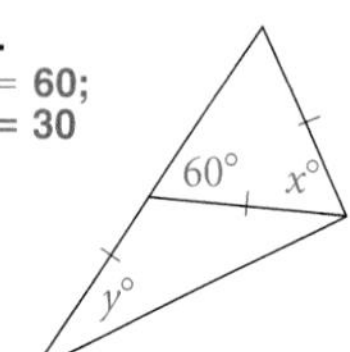

31. **120**

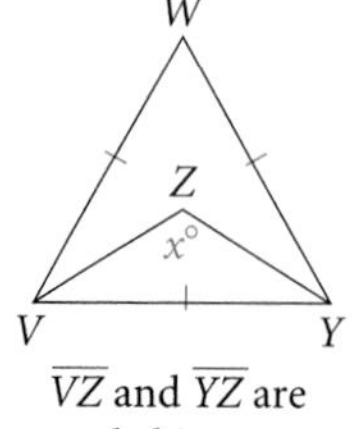

$\overline{VZ}$ and $\overline{YZ}$ are angle bisectors.

32. **110**

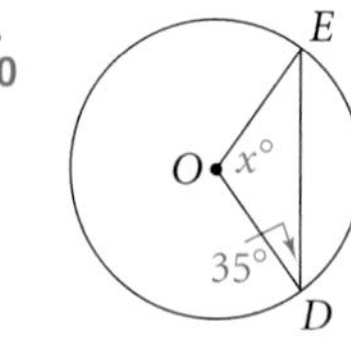

$\overline{OD}$ and $\overline{OE}$ are radii.

33. **70**

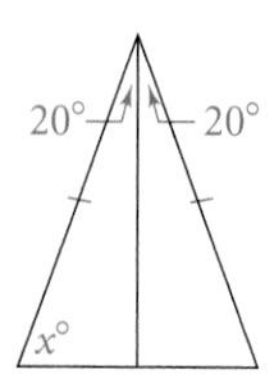

Exercise 34 Help students see that the quadrilaterals inscribed within the circle are squares.

STANDARDIZED TEST TIP **Exercise 36** Suggest students draw a line through the side shared by both polygons. Then students should see that $m\angle SHA$ equals the sum of 90 and the measure of one exterior angle of the hexagon.

Exercises MIXED REVIEW

Exercise 44 Have students graph both lines to check their answers.

GETTING READY FOR LESSON 4-3 These exercises prepare students to justify statements in proofs.

Wrap Up

THE BIG IDEA Ask students: *Describe all the properties of isosceles triangles you have learned thus far.*

RETEACHING ACTIVITY Students use and apply properties of isosceles triangles to find missing angle measures. (Reteaching worksheet 4-2)

34. Crafts This design is used in Hmong crafts and in Islamic and Mexican tiles. To create it, the artist starts by drawing a circle and four equally spaced diameters.

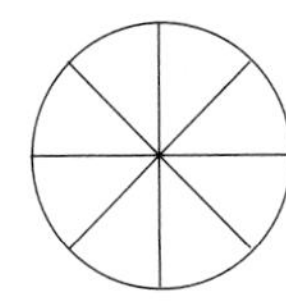

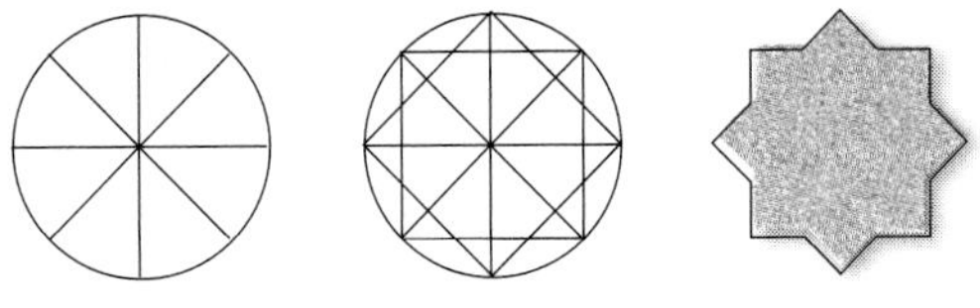

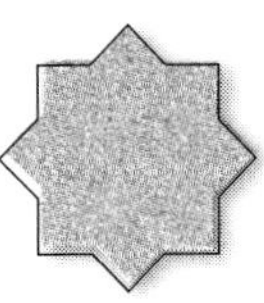

Step 1 Step 2 Step 3

a. How many different sizes of isosceles right triangles can you find in Step 2? Trace an example of each onto your paper. **5 different triangles; see margin p. 192 for diagram.**

b. For each size of triangle that you traced, count the number of times it appears in the diagram. **8, 8, 16, 8, and 16 times, respectively**

35. Critical Thinking Patrick defines the base of an isosceles triangle as "the bottom side of an isosceles triangle." Is his definition a good one? Explain why or why not. **No; the base is the side opposite the vertex angle.**

36. Standardized Test Prep A square and a regular hexagon are placed so that they have a common side. Find $m\angle HAS$. **C**

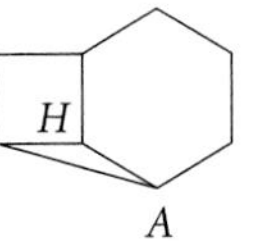

A. 9 B. 10 C. 15 D. 20 E. 30

Algebra **Find the values of *m* and *n*.**

37.

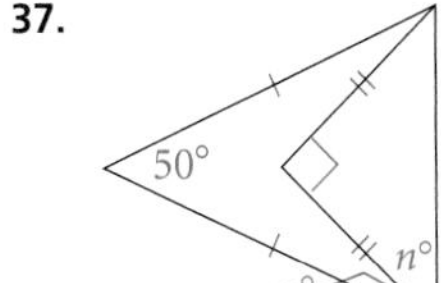

$m = 20$; $n = 45$

38.

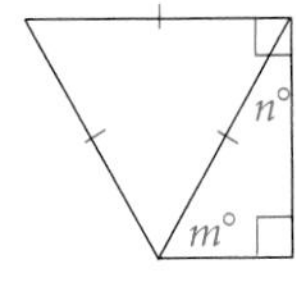

$m = 60$; $n = 30$

39.

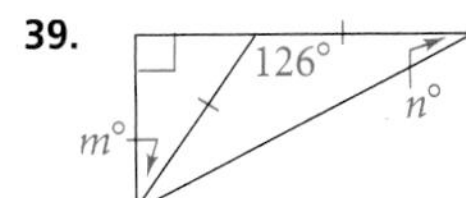

$m = 36$; $n = 27$

40.

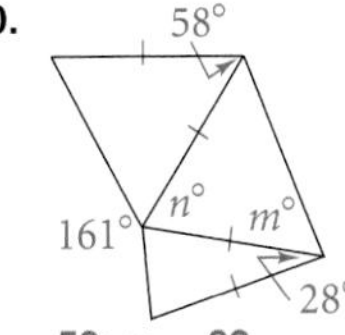

$m = 59$; $n = 62$

Exercises MIXED REVIEW

Coordinate Geometry **The endpoints of a diameter of a circle are given. Find the coordinates of the center and the length of a radius.**

41. (3, 8), (−1, 2) **(1, 5); $\sqrt{13}$**

42. (−2, 5), (−5, 2) **(−3.5, 3.5); $\frac{3}{2}\sqrt{2}$**

43. (3, 7), (−2, 6) **(0.5, 6.5); $\frac{1}{2}\sqrt{26}$**

44. Coordinate Geometry Find the equation of the line that passes through (0, 4) and is parallel to $y = -3x - 5$. **$y = -3x + 4$**

45. Find the number of sides of a regular polygon whose exterior angles measure 15°. **24 sides**

Getting Ready for Lesson 4-3

What can you conclude from each diagram? Justify your answers. **46–48. See margin p. 192.**

46. (diagram: O, P, M, N)

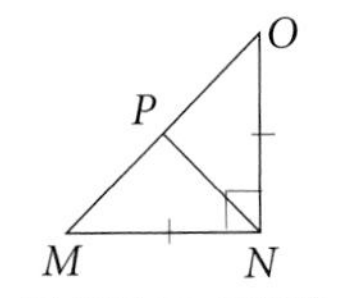

$\angle MNP \cong \angle ONP$

47.

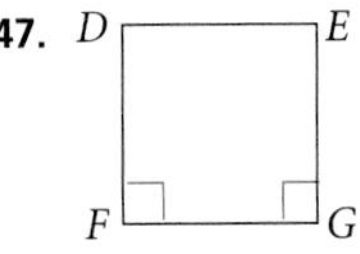

48.

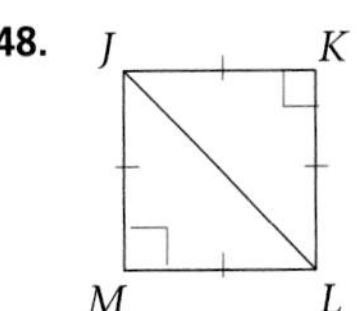

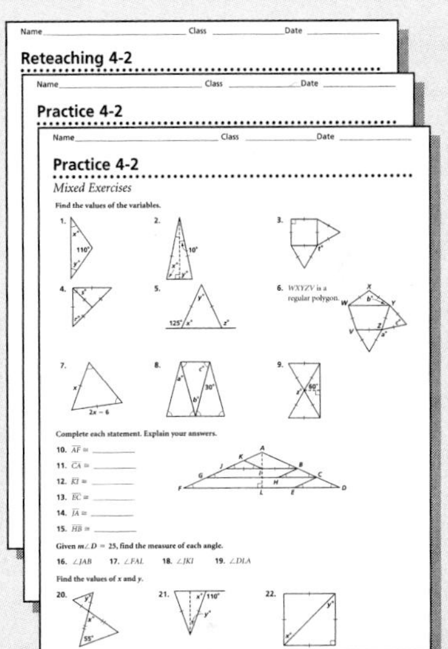
Reteaching 4-2

Practice 4-2

Practice 4-2
Mixed Exercises

Lesson Quiz

Lesson Quiz is also available in Transparencies.

1. Draw a right isosceles triangle. Label its vertex angle, base angles, legs, and base. **Answers will vary. Sample:**

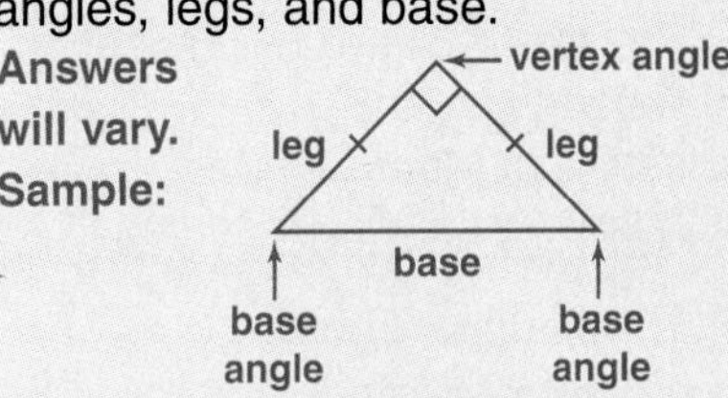

2. The measure of one of the base angles of an isosceles triangle is 55. Find the measures of the other two angles. **55, 70**

3. The measure of an exterior angle drawn from the vertex angle of an isosceles triangle is 112. Find the measures of the angles of the triangle. **68, 56, 56**

4-3 Teaching Notes

PROBLEM OF THE DAY

3 chocolates	3 creams	2 chocolates 1 cream

Somehow the labels on the candy boxes got mixed up so that no label is correct. What is the least number of pieces you can test to determine which label belongs to which box? **one from the box labeled "2 chocolates and 1 cream"**

Problem of the Day is also available in Transparencies.

CONNECTING TO PRIOR KNOWLEDGE Ask students to use the diagram to justify the following statements: $m\angle 1 + m\angle 4 = 180$, $m\angle 4 = m\angle 2 + m\angle 3$, and $\triangle ABC$ is a right triangle.

DIVERSITY Take this opportunity to discuss the different places of birth of students. Display a map of the world on a bulletin board and use pushpins to indicate the different locations.

Lesson Planning Options

Prerequisite Skills

- Understanding properties of equality and congruence

Assignment Options for Exercises On Your Own

Core 1–7, 10–15, 17–18
Extension 8–9, 16

Use Mixed Review to maintain skills.

Resources

Student Edition
Skills Handbook, p. 664
Extra Practice, p. 651
Glossary/Study Guide

Teaching Resources
Chapter Support File, Ch. 4
- Practice 4-3 (two worksheets)
- Reteaching 4-3

Classroom Manager 4-3
Glossary, Spanish Resources

Transparencies
52

4-3 Preparing for Proof

What You'll Learn

- Using different styles of proofs to write convincing arguments

...And Why

To help you think logically

THINK AND DISCUSS

In everyday life, proof takes many forms.

A passport is proof of your citizenship when traveling in foreign countries.

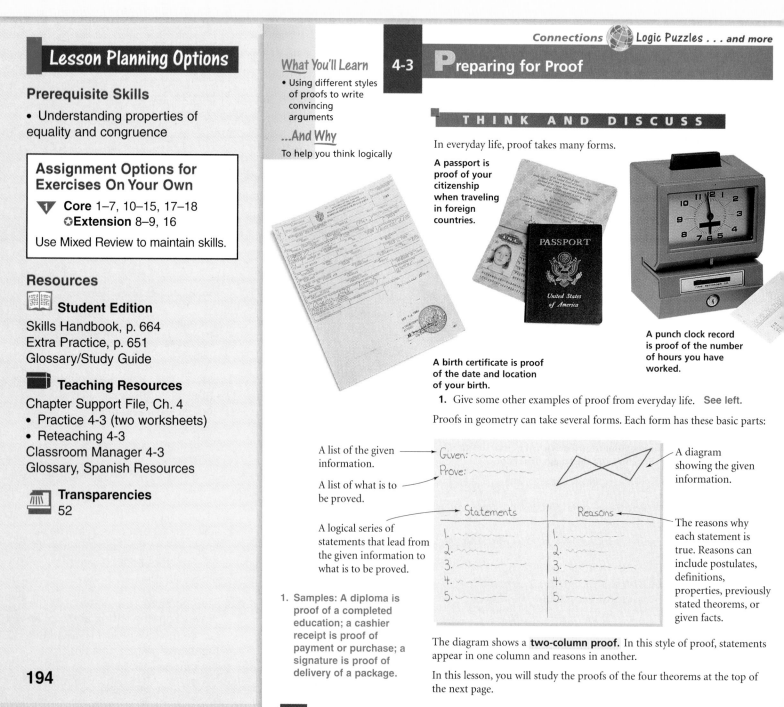

A birth certificate is proof of the date and location of your birth.

A punch clock record is proof of the number of hours you have worked.

1. Give some other examples of proof from everyday life. **See left.**

Proofs in geometry can take several forms. Each form has these basic parts:

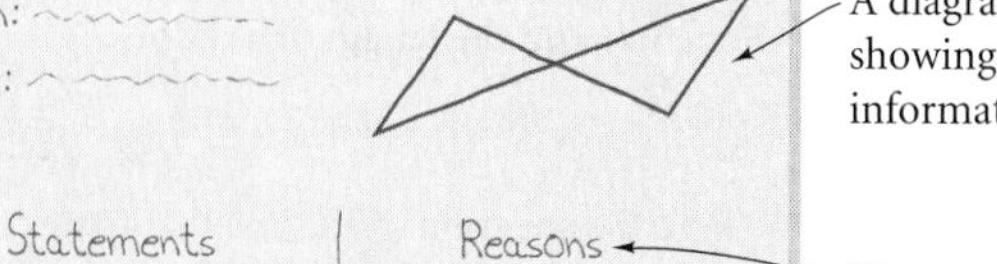

A list of the given information.

A list of what is to be proved.

A diagram showing the given information.

A logical series of statements that lead from the given information to what is to be proved.

The reasons why each statement is true. Reasons can include postulates, definitions, properties, previously stated theorems, or given facts.

1. Samples: A diploma is proof of a completed education; a cashier receipt is proof of payment or purchase; a signature is proof of delivery of a package.

The diagram shows a **two-column proof.** In this style of proof, statements appear in one column and reasons in another.

In this lesson, you will study the proofs of the four theorems at the top of the next page.

To emphasize the need for proof, have students investigate this statement: For $n = 1, 2, 3, ...,$ $n^2 + n + 41$ always produces a prime number. Students will find it interesting that, although this statement is true for $n = 1, 2, 3, ..., 40$, it is false for $n = 41$.

ERROR ALERT! Students with poor writing and organizational skills may have difficulty setting up a two-column proof. **Remediation:** You may want to provide students with a template which leaves room for them to fill in the "Given," "Prove," "Diagram," "Statements," and "Reasons."

TACTILE LEARNING Have students draw and cut out a large right triangle. Have them tear off the non-right angles and place them over the right angle to show that together the two angles form a 90° angle.

Example

Use this proof to help students see that the steps for writing a proof are similar to the steps they use to solve word problems. Emphasize that before students begin a proof, they should understand what they need to prove, then plan what postulates, theorems, and definitions they can use to prove it. When the proof is complete, students should check that their conclusion matches what they are trying to prove.

Theorem 4-4	If a triangle is a right triangle, then the acute angles are complementary.
Theorem 4-5	If two angles of one triangle are congruent to two angles of another triangle, then the third angles are congruent.
Theorem 4-6	All right angles are congruent.
Theorem 4-7	If two angles are congruent and supplementary, then each is a right angle.

In a proof of a theorem, the *Given* information and the figure relate to the hypothesis of the theorem. You *Prove* the conclusion of the theorem.

Theorem 4-4
If a triangle is a right triangle, then the acute angles are complementary.

Hypothesis
Given: $\triangle EFG$ with right angle $\angle F$
Prove: $\angle E$ and $\angle G$ are complementary.
Conclusion

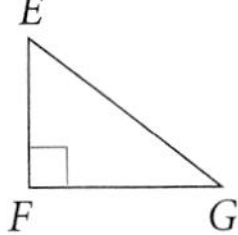

Two-Column Proof of Theorem 4-4

Statements	Reasons
1. $\angle F$ is a right angle.	1. Given
2. $m\angle F = 90$	2. Def. of right angle
3. $m\angle E + m\angle F + m\angle G = 180$	3. Triangle Angle-Sum Thm.
4. $m\angle E + 90 + m\angle G = 180$	4. Substitution
5. $m\angle E + m\angle G = 90$	5. Subtraction Prop. of Equality
6. $\angle E$ and $\angle G$ are complementary.	6. Def. of complementary angles

In a **paragraph proof,** the statements and reasons appear in sentences within a paragraph.

Example

Write a paragraph proof for Theorem 4-5.

Given: $\angle X \cong \angle Q$ and $\angle Y \cong \angle R$
Prove: $\angle Z \cong \angle S$

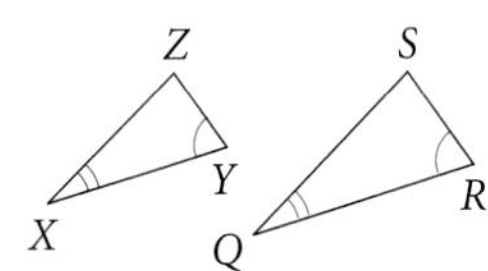

Paragraph Proof
By the Triangle Angle-Sum Theorem, $m\angle X + m\angle Y + m\angle Z = 180$ and $m\angle Q + m\angle R + m\angle S = 180$. By substitution, $m\angle X + m\angle Y + m\angle Z = m\angle Q + m\angle R + m\angle S$. We are given that $\angle X \cong \angle Q$ and $\angle Y \cong \angle R$ (or $m\angle X = m\angle Q$ and $m\angle Y = m\angle R$). Subtracting equal quantities from both sides of the equation leaves $m\angle Z = m\angle S$, so $\angle Z \cong \angle S$.

Additional Examples

FOR EXAMPLE

Write a two-column proof for Theorem 4-5.

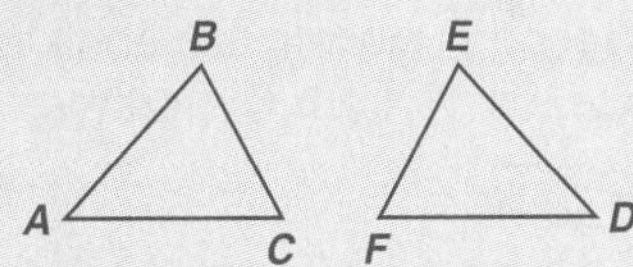

Given: $\angle A \cong \angle D$; $\angle B \cong \angle E$
Prove: $\angle C \cong \angle F$

1. $\angle A \cong \angle D$; $\angle B \cong \angle E$ (given)
2. $m\angle A = m\angle D$; $m\angle B = m\angle E$ (def. of congruence)
3. $m\angle A + m\angle B + m\angle C = 180$; $m\angle D + m\angle E + m\angle F = 180$ (Triangle Angle-Sum Theorem)
4. $m\angle A + m\angle B + m\angle C = m\angle D + m\angle E + m\angle F$ (Transitive Prop. of Equality)
5. $m\angle A + m\angle B + m\angle C = m\angle A + m\angle B + m\angle F$ (substitution)
6. $m\angle C = m\angle F$ (Subtraction Prop. of Equality)
7. $\angle C \cong \angle F$ (def. of congruence)

WORK TOGETHER

DIVERSITY Students who have difficulties with writing sometimes cannot write as quickly as they can think and may lose their train of thought when writing proofs. For this activity and for some of the exercises, you may want to pair strong writers with weaker ones.

Question 2 Check that students use complete sentences and that each statement is justified with a reason.

Question 3 Be sure that students recognize which part of each sentence in the paragraph proof is the statement and which part is the reason.

Exercises ON YOUR OWN

Exercises 1–6 There can be more than one conclusion drawn from each drawing. However, make sure that students do not conclude statements that can only be justified by appearance.

Technology Options

Prentice Hall Technology

Software
- Secondary Math Lab Toolkit™
- Computer Item Generator 4-3

Internet
- See the Prentice Hall site. (http://www.phschool.com)

196

WORK TOGETHER

Work in pairs.

2. Rewrite this two-column proof of Theorem 4-6 as a paragraph proof. See below.

Given: $\angle X$ and $\angle Y$ are right angles.

Prove: $\angle X \cong \angle Y$

X Y

Two-Column Proof

Statements	Reasons
1. $\angle X$ and $\angle Y$ are right angles.	1. Given
2. $m\angle X = 90$, $m\angle Y = 90$	2. Def. of right angles
3. $m\angle X = m\angle Y$, or $\angle X \cong \angle Y$	3. Substitution

3. Rewrite this paragraph proof of Theorem 4-7 as a two-column proof. See margin p. 197.

Given: $\angle W$ and $\angle V$ are congruent and supplementary.

Prove: $\angle W$ and $\angle V$ are right angles.

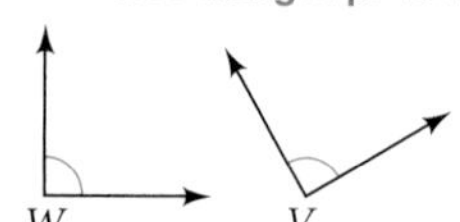

Paragraph Proof

$\angle W$ and $\angle V$ are congruent and supplementary, so $m\angle W = m\angle V$ and $m\angle W + m\angle V = 180$. Substituting $m\angle W$ for $m\angle V$ gives $m\angle W + m\angle W = 180$. Therefore, $m\angle W = 90$. Since $\angle W \cong \angle V$, $m\angle V = 90$, too. Thus both angles are right angles.

2. By def. of rt. angles $m\angle X = 90$ and $m\angle Y = 90$. $m\angle X = m\angle Y$ by substitution, so $\angle X \cong \angle Y$.

Exercises ON YOUR OWN

What can you conclude from each diagram? Justify your answers. 1–6. See back of book.

1.

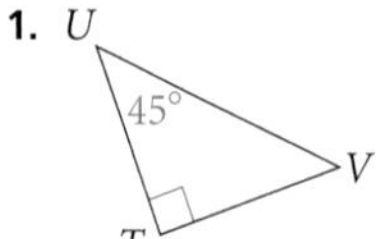

2.

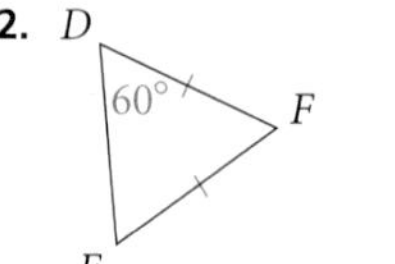

3.

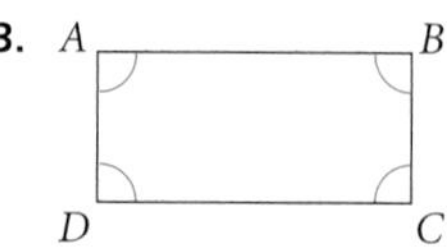

4. A, B, D, C

5.

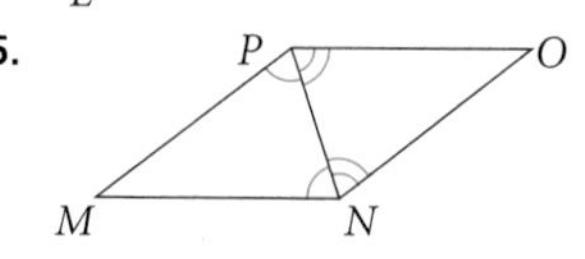

6.

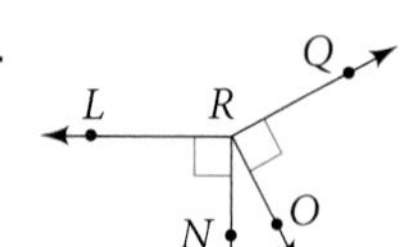

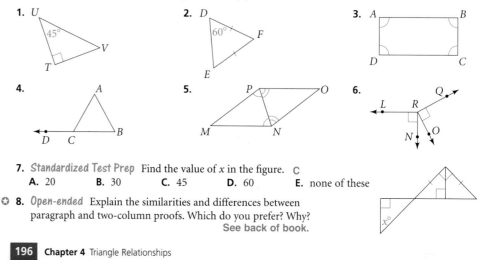

7. *Standardized Test Prep* Find the value of x in the figure. C
A. 20 **B.** 30 **C.** 45 **D.** 60 **E.** none of these

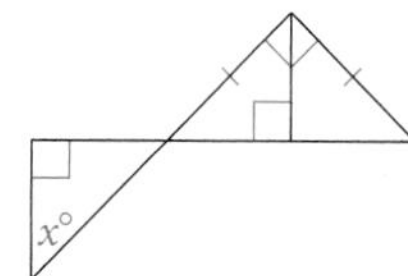

8. *Open-ended* Explain the similarities and differences between paragraph and two-column proofs. Which do you prefer? Why? See back of book.

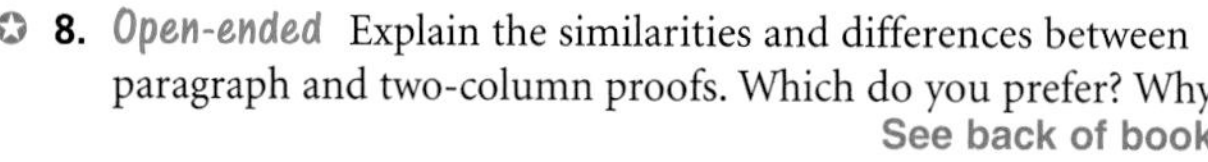

STANDARDIZED TEST TIP **Exercise 7** Students can solve for *x* using properties of angles and triangles, or they can eliminate choices by substituting each value of *x* into the diagram, getting contradictions with incorrect angle measures.

Exercise 8 Depending on learning styles, different students may prefer different proof formats. Students should be familiar with both formats presented in this lesson, but in future lessons you may want to allow students the opportunity to use the proof format with which they feel more comfortable.

Exercise 10 Have students notice that the statement in the "Given" is not necessarily the first statement in the proof.

Exercises 13–14 You might want to agree upon conventions for abbreviating common words used in the "Reasons" column of a proof such as ∠ for angle, def. for definition, ≅ for congruent, etc.

9. **Writing** Russell Black Elk found this multiple-choice question in a puzzle book. Solve the puzzle and explain your solution.
E; see margin for explanation.

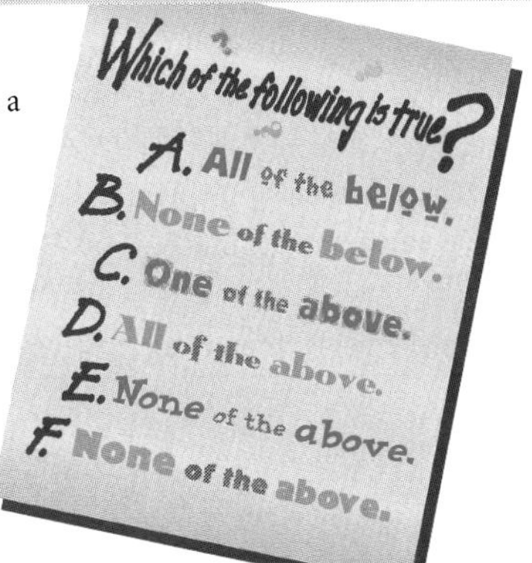

Which of the following is true?
A. All of the below.
B. None of the below.
C. One of the above.
D. All of the above.
E. None of the above.
F. None of the above.

10. Rewrite this paragraph proof as a two-column proof.

Given: $\angle 1 \cong \angle 4$

Prove: $\angle 2 \cong \angle 3$

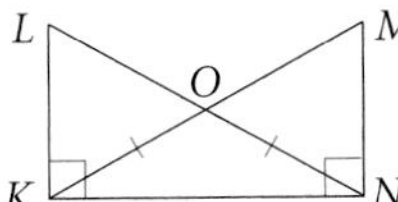

$\angle 1$ and $\angle 2$ are vertical angles, as are $\angle 3$ and $\angle 4$. Vertical angles are congruent, so $\angle 1 \cong \angle 2$ and $\angle 3 \cong \angle 4$. We are given that $\angle 1 \cong \angle 4$. By the Transitive Property of Congruence, $\angle 2 \cong \angle 4$ and $\angle 2 \cong \angle 3$. See margin.

Refer to the diagrams to complete each statement.

11. a. $\angle OKN \cong$ ___?___
b. $\angle LKO \cong$ ___?___
c. $\angle LOK \cong$ ___?___

L M O K N

11a. $\angle ONK$ b. $\angle MNO$ c. $\angle MON$

12. a. $m\angle USR =$ ___?___ 58
b. $m\angle RUS =$ ___?___ 64
c. $m\angle SUQ =$ ___?___ 116
d. $m\angle USQ =$ ___?___ 32
e. $m\angle QST =$ ___?___ 90

Q U R 58° T S

13. **Preparing for Proof** The reasons given in this proof are correct, but they are in the wrong order. List them in the correct order.

Given: $m\angle AOB = m\angle BOC$ d, f, b, a, c, e

Prove: $\overleftrightarrow{OA} \perp \overleftrightarrow{OB}$

B A O C

Statements	Reasons
1. $m\angle AOB = m\angle BOC$	a. Division Prop. of Equality
2. $m\angle AOB + m\angle BOC = 180$	b. Substitution
3. $m\angle AOB + m\angle AOB = 180$ or $2(m\angle AOB) = 180$	c. Def. of right angle
4. $m\angle AOB = 90$	d. Given
5. $\angle AOB$ is a right angle.	e. Def. of perpendicular lines
6. $\overleftrightarrow{OA} \perp \overleftrightarrow{OB}$	f. Angle Addition Postulate

14. **Preparing for Proof** Rewrite this proof as a paragraph proof.

Given: $\overline{XZ} \cong \overline{YZ}$ and $\overline{XW} \cong \overline{YW}$ See margin.

Prove: $m\angle 1 = m\angle 2$

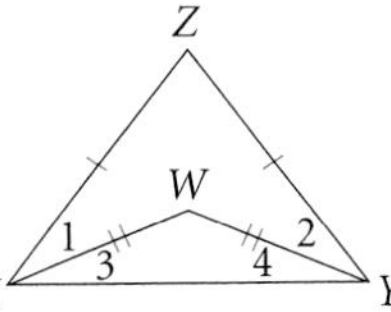

Statements	Reasons
1. $\overline{XZ} \cong \overline{YZ}$	1. Given
2. $\angle ZXY \cong \angle ZYX$ or $m\angle ZXY = m\angle ZYX$	2. Base ∠s of an isosceles △ are ≅.
3. $\overline{XW} \cong \overline{YW}$	3. Given
4. $\angle 3 \cong \angle 4$ or $m\angle 3 = m\angle 4$	4. Base ∠s of an isosceles △ are ≅.
5. $m\angle ZXY = m\angle 1 + m\angle 3$; $m\angle ZYX = m\angle 2 + m\angle 4$	5. Angle Addition Postulate
6. $m\angle 1 + m\angle 3 = m\angle 2 + m\angle 4$	6. Substitution
7. $m\angle 1 = m\angle 2$	7. Subtraction Prop. of Equality

page 196 Work Together

3. 1. $\angle W$ and $\angle V$ are supp. (Given)
2. $\angle W \cong \angle V$ (Given)
3. $m\angle W + m\angle V = 180$ (Def. supp. angles)
4. $m\angle W + m\angle W = 180$ (Substitution)
5. $m\angle W = 90$ (Multiplication Prop. of =)
6. $m\angle V = 90$ (Substitution)
7. $\angle W$ and $\angle W$ are rt. angles (Def. rt. angle)

9. E; assume (A) is T. Then (B–F) are all T. But (B) is F if (C–F) are T. So the assumption that (A) is T must be F and (A) is F. Assume (B) is T. Then (C–F) are F. But (C) is T if (B) is T, so the assumption that (B) is T must be F and (B) is F. Since (A) and (B) are F, (C) is F. Since (A–C) are F, (D) is F. Since (A–D) are F, (E) is T. Since (E) is T, (F) is F.

10. 1. $\angle 1 \cong \angle 2$ (Vert. ∠s are ≅)
2. $\angle 1 \cong \angle 4$ (Given)
3. $\angle 2 \cong \angle 4$ (Trans. Prop. of ≅)
4. $\angle 3 \cong \angle 4$ (Vert. ∠s are ≅.)
5. $\angle 2 \cong \angle 3$ (Trans. Prop. of ≅)

14. You are given that $\triangle XYZ$ is an isosceles △. $\angle ZXY \cong \angle ZYX$ or $m\angle ZXY = m\angle ZYX$ because base ∠s of an isosceles △ are ≅. Similarly, $\angle 3 \cong \angle 4$ or $m\angle 3 = m\angle 4$. $m\angle ZXY = m\angle 1 + m\angle 3$ and $m\angle ZYX = m\angle 2 + m\angle 4$ by the Angle Addition Post. By Substitution, $m\angle 1 + m\angle 3 = m\angle 2 + m\angle 4$. Subtracting = quantities from each side yields $m\angle 1 = m\angle 2$.

ALTERNATIVE ASSESSMENT **Exercise 15** This exercise can help you assess students' ability to reason logically. Students have the choice of using a paragraph proof or a two-column proof to organize their explanations.

Exercise 16 Students may not see the error in this proof if they do not remember that division by zero is undefined.

Chapter Project FIND OUT BY ORGANIZING You may want to start off with solving a similar type of puzzle with the class. For example, ask students to determine which person is the artist, the dancer, and the soccer player from the following clues: Kim is taller than the artist. Mike and the soccer player have practice on Monday. Ann, the tallest of the three, is in the same grade as the dancer.

Exercises MIXED REVIEW

Exercises 19–20 You may want to have students work with a partner. Students should check their answers by making sure that the sum of the measures of the angles is about 360.

GETTING READY FOR LESSON 4-4 This exercise prepares students to use properties of the midsegments of triangles.

page 199 Mixed Review

20a. False; less than half the adults want students to save or invest the money.

b. False; the diagram makes no reference to parents.

c. True; more than half the adults, 81%, said the students should not spend the money as they please.

21a.

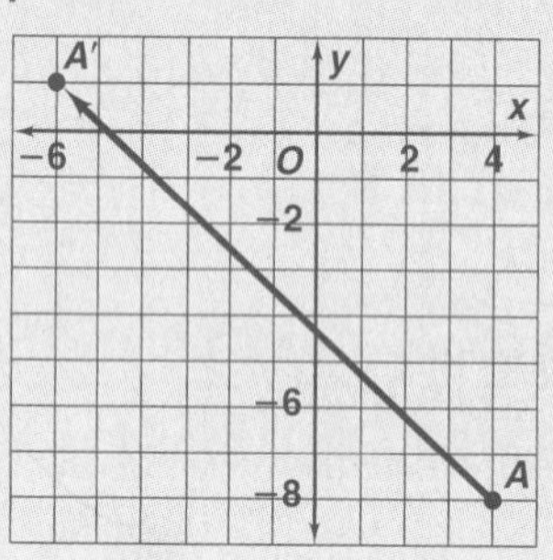

198

15. *Logical Reasoning* Explain why this statement is true:
If $m\angle 1 + m\angle 2 = 180$ and $m\angle 2 + m\angle 3 = 180$, then $\angle 1 \cong \angle 3$.

By Substitution, $m\angle 1 + m\angle 2 = m\angle 2 + m\angle 3$. Subtracting = quantities from each side yields $m\angle 1 = m\angle 3$.

16. *Logical Reasoning* Explain why this proof is invalid.

Given: $a = b$

Prove: $1 = 2$

You cannot use the Division Prop. of = because $b - a = 0$.

Statements	Reasons
1. $a = b$	1. Given
2. $ab = b^2$	2. Multiplication Prop. of Equality
3. $ab - a^2 = b^2 - a^2$	3. Subtraction Prop. of Equality
4. $a(b - a) = (b + a)(b - a)$	4. Distributive Property
5. $a = b + a$	5. Division Prop. of Equality
6. $a = a + a$	6. Substitution
7. $a = 2a$	7. Distributive Property
8. $1 = 2$	8. Division Prop. of Equality

17. Supply the reasons to complete this proof of the Corollary to the Isosceles Triangle Theorem stated on page 190.

Given: $\triangle ABC$ with $\overline{AB} \cong \overline{BC} \cong \overline{CA}$

Prove: $\angle A \cong \angle B$, $\angle B \cong \angle C$, and $\angle A \cong \angle C$

B
A
C

Statements	Reasons
1. $\overline{AB} \cong \overline{BC} \cong \overline{CA}$	a. ?
2. $\angle A \cong \angle C$	b. ?
3. $\angle C \cong \angle B$	c. ?
4. $\angle A \cong \angle B$	d. ?

a. Given;
b. Isosceles Triangle Thm.;
c. Isosceles Triangle Thm.;
d. Transitive Prop. of ≅

18. Complete this paragraph proof.

Given: $\angle PST \cong \angle PRQ$

Prove: $\triangle PSR$ is isosceles.

P
T S R Q

$m\angle PST + m\angle PSR = 180$ and $m\angle PRQ + m\angle PRS = 180$ by the **a.** ? Postulate. By the **b.** ? , $\angle PST$ and $\angle PSR$, as well as $\angle PRQ$ and $\angle PRS$, are supplementary. We are given that **c.** ? . By the Congruent Supplements Thm., **d.** ? . If two ∠s of a △ are ≅, the sides opposite them are ≅, so **e.** ? . By **f.** ? , $\triangle PSR$ is isosceles.

a. Angle Addition
b. def. of supplementary angles
c. $\angle PST \cong \angle PRQ$
d. $\angle PSR \cong \angle PRS$ e. $\overline{PS} \cong \overline{PR}$
f. def. of isosceles △

Chapter Project **Find Out by Organizing**

A drummer, guitarist, and keyboard player named Amy, Bob, and Carla are in a band. Use the clues to determine which instrument each plays.

Carla and the drummer wear different-colored shirts.
The keyboard player is older than Bob.
Amy, the youngest band member, lives next door to the guitarist.

You can solve this type of logic puzzle by eliminating possibilities. Make a grid. Put an X in a box once you eliminate it as a possibility.

Instrument	Amy	Bob	Carla
Drums			
Guitar			
Keyboard			

Amy is the drummer; Bob is the guitarist; Carla is the keyboard player.

Wrap Up

THE BIG IDEA Ask students: *Describe two styles of proof and the types of reasons that can be used to justify a statement in a proof.*

RETEACHING Students practice writing two-column proofs by filling in missing statements and reasons of a partially completed proof. (Reteaching worksheet 4-3)

A Point in Time

If you have block scheduling or an extended class period, you may wish to have students investigate these topics:

- Find a mystery written by Agatha Christie, Sherlock Holmes, or another author using logical reasoning.
- Write your own detective story using logical reasoning to solve a mystery.
- Investigate what type of education and skills are required to become a mystery writer.
- Watch either of the films, *Murder on the Orient Express* or *Death on the Nile*, and present a movie review to the class.

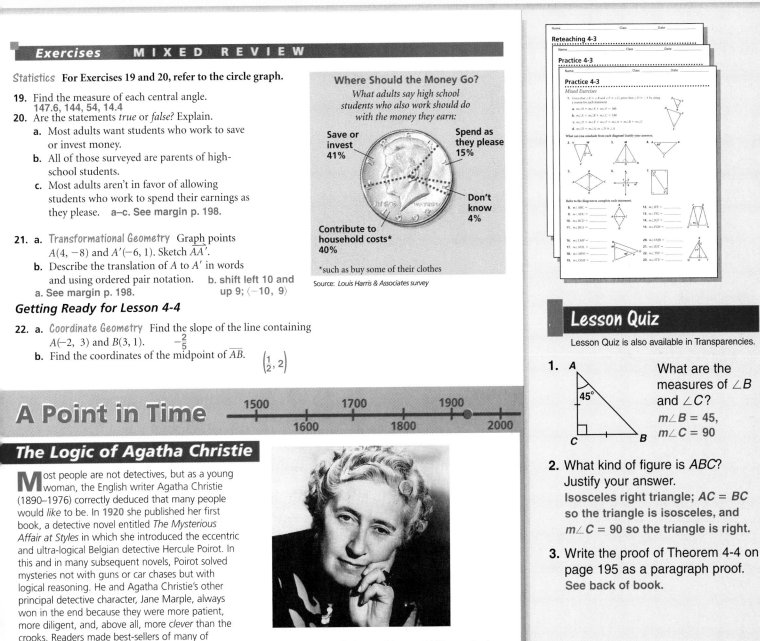

Exercises MIXED REVIEW

Statistics **For Exercises 19 and 20, refer to the circle graph.**

19. Find the measure of each central angle. **147.6, 144, 54, 14.4**

20. Are the statements *true* or *false?* Explain.
- **a.** Most adults want students who work to save or invest money.
- **b.** All of those surveyed are parents of high-school students.
- **c.** Most adults aren't in favor of allowing students who work to spend their earnings as they please. **a–c. See margin p. 198.**

Where Should the Money Go?

What adults say high school students who also work should do with the money they earn:

Save or invest 41%

Spend as they please 15%

Don't know 4%

Contribute to household costs* 40%

*such as buy some of their clothes

Source: *Louis Harris & Associates survey*

21. a. *Transformational Geometry* Graph points $A(4, -8)$ and $A'(-6, 1)$. Sketch $\overrightarrow{AA'}$.

b. Describe the translation of A to A' in words and using ordered pair notation. **b. shift left 10 and up 9; $\langle -10, 9 \rangle$**

a. See margin p. 198.

Getting Ready for Lesson 4-4

22. a. *Coordinate Geometry* Find the slope of the line containing $A(-2, 3)$ and $B(3, 1)$. $-\frac{2}{5}$

b. Find the coordinates of the midpoint of $\overline{AB}$. $\left(\frac{1}{2}, 2\right)$

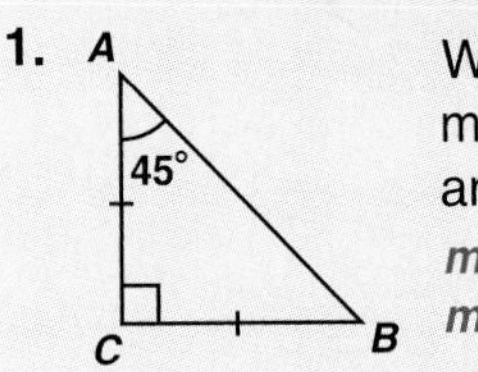

Lesson Quiz

Lesson Quiz is also available in Transparencies.

1. What are the measures of $\angle B$ and $\angle C$? (Figure: triangle ABC with 45° at A, right angle at C.)
$m\angle B = 45$, $m\angle C = 90$

2. What kind of figure is ABC? Justify your answer.
Isosceles right triangle; $AC = BC$ so the triangle is isosceles, and $m\angle C = 90$ so the triangle is right.

3. Write the proof of Theorem 4-4 on page 195 as a paragraph proof.
See back of book.

A Point in Time

1500 1600 1700 1800 1900 2000

The Logic of Agatha Christie

Most people are not detectives, but as a young woman, the English writer Agatha Christie (1890–1976) correctly deduced that many people would *like* to be. In **1920** she published her first book, a detective novel entitled *The Mysterious Affair at Styles* in which she introduced the eccentric and ultra-logical Belgian detective Hercule Poirot. In this and in many subsequent novels, Poirot solved mysteries not with guns or car chases but with logical reasoning. He and Agatha Christie's other principal detective character, Jane Marple, always won in the end because they were more patient, more diligent, and, above all, more *clever* than the crooks. Readers made best-sellers of many of Christie's 78 detective novels. Many of her novels, including *Murder on the Orient Express* and *Death on the Nile*, have been adapted into popular films.

To date, her books have sold some 2 billion copies in 44 languages, making Agatha Christie by far the world's top-selling writer of fiction.

Math ToolboX

Students use geometry software to investigate the properties of the midsegment of a triangle. They discover that the midsegment is parallel to a side of the triangle and is half its length. These properties of a midsegment will be proved in Lesson 4-4.

Geometry software allows students to manipulate the triangle by dragging on a vertex to see certain properties of midsegments hold for all types of triangles.

Construct

ERROR ALERT! Students may try to take a short cut and approximate the placement of the midpoints D and E.

Remediation: Check that students use construction or measurement to find the midpoints.

Extend

Have students manipulate $\triangle ABC$ so it is right, acute, obtuse, and equilateral.

ADDITIONAL PROBLEM Have students measure AD, DB, AB, AE, EC, and AC. Then have them compare the ratios $\frac{AD}{DB}$ to $\frac{AE}{EC}$ and $\frac{AD}{AB}$ to $\frac{AE}{AC}$. Have students list all their conjectures about the segments.

Materials and Manipulatives

- Geometry software

Math ToolboX — Technology

Investigating Midsegments

Before Lesson 4-4

Work in pairs or small groups.

Construct

Use geometry software to draw a triangle. Label it $\triangle ABC$. Construct the midpoints of $\overline{AB}$ and $\overline{AC}$, label them D and E, respectively, and then connect them with a *midsegment*.
Check students' work.

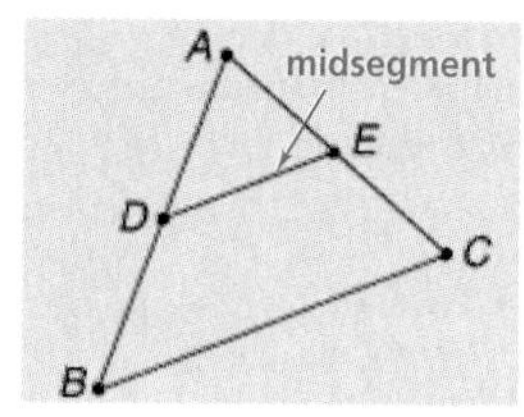

Investigate

- Measure the lengths of $\overline{DE}$ and $\overline{BC}$. Calculate $\frac{DE}{BC}$.
- Measure the slopes of $\overline{DE}$ and $\overline{BC}$.
- Manipulate the triangle and observe the lengths and slopes of the segments.

Check students' work.

Conjecture

List all your **conjectures** about a midsegment.
The midsegment is $\parallel$ to a side of the $\triangle$ and is half its length.

Extend

- Construct the other two midsegments in $\triangle ABC$. Measure the angles of the four triangles determined by the three midsegments. How do they compare to the angles of the original triangle? Make **conjectures.** See below.
- Measure the sides of the four triangles. Make a **conjecture** about the four triangles determined by the midsegments of a triangle. Make a **conjecture** about the relationship between the original triangle and the four triangles. The sides of the midsegment $\triangle$ are each $\frac{1}{2}$ of the corr. side of the orig. $\triangle$; the 4 $\triangle$s are $\cong$; the 4 $\triangle$s are $\sim$ to the orig. $\triangle$.
- Measure the areas of the four triangles formed by the midsegments of a triangle. Measure the area of the original triangle. Make a **conjecture** about the areas. Do the same for perimeter. The area of each smaller $\triangle$ is $\frac{1}{4}$ the area of the orig. $\triangle$; the perimeter of each smaller $\triangle$ is $\frac{1}{2}$ the perimeter of the orig. $\triangle$.

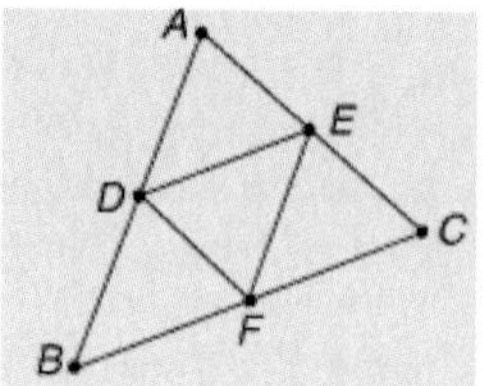

Opp. angles of the orig. $\triangle$ and the midsegment $\triangle$ have $=$ measures; corr. angles in the 4 smaller $\triangle$s have $=$ measures.

200

4-4 Teaching Notes

PROBLEM OF THE DAY

A frog at the bottom of a 40-ft well jumps up three feet every day and every night falls back down two feet. How many days will it take the frog to get out of the well? 38 days

Problem of the Day is also available in Transparencies.

CONNECTING TO PRIOR KNOWLEDGE Ask students to find the midpoint and length of a segment with endpoints $A(-5, 3)$ and $B(2, 3)$. Then have them show that the segment is parallel to a line containing $(-2, -1)$ and $(4, -1)$.

WORK TOGETHER

Have students label the vertices in the interior of the triangles so that when they cut the triangles out, the vertices will be labeled on the cut-out figures.

ERROR ALERT! Because of the orientation of $\overline{AC}$, students may not see why folding A onto C marks the midpoint of $\overline{AC}$. **Remediation:** Demonstrate with a piece of rectangular paper how folding the corners of a side onto each other folds the paper in half.

Connections Architecture . . . and more

4-4 Midsegments of Triangles

What You'll Learn

- Using properties of midsegments to solve problems

...And Why

- To help you find lengths and distances indirectly

What You'll Need

- scissors
- straightedge

WORK TOGETHER

Have each member of your group draw and cut out a large scalene triangle. Be sure to include right, acute, and obtuse triangles.

- Label the vertices of your triangle A, B, and C.
- Fold A onto C to find the midpoint of $\overline{AC}$. Do the same for $\overline{BC}$. Label the midpoints L and N, then draw $\overline{LN}$.

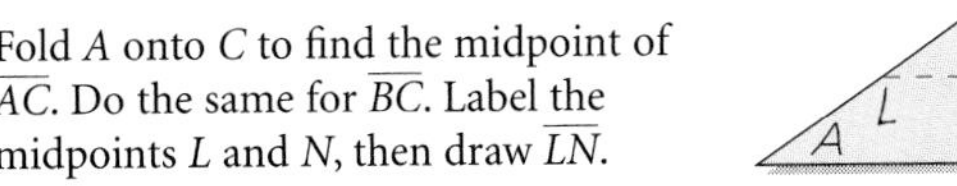

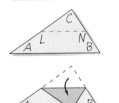

- Fold your triangle on $\overline{LN}$.
- Fold A to C. Do the same for B.

1. a. What type of quadrilateral does the folded triangle appear to form? a. rectangle
   b. What does this tell you about $\overline{LN}$ and $\overline{AB}$? b. $\overline{LN} \parallel \overline{AB}$
2. How does LN compare to AB? Explain. $LN = \frac{1}{2}AB$; when folded, A meets B, so the resulting side of the rectangle is $\frac{1}{2}AB$.
3. Make a **conjecture** about how the segment joining the midpoints of two sides of a triangle is related to the third side of the triangle.

   The segment is half as long as and $\parallel$ to the 3rd side.

THINK AND DISCUSS

The segment you constructed in the Work Together is a midsegment. A **midsegment** of a triangle is a segment connecting the midpoints of two of its sides.

Theorem 4-8 Triangle Midsegment Theorem — If a segment joins the midpoints of two sides of a triangle, then the segment is parallel to the third side and half its length.

You can prove the Triangle Midsegment Theorem by using coordinate geometry and algebra. This style of proof is called a *coordinate proof.* You begin the proof by placing a triangle in a convenient spot on the coordinate plane. You then choose variables for the coordinates of the vertices.

Lesson Planning Options

Prerequisite Skills

- Using the midpoint and distance formulas
- Finding the slopes of parallel lines

Assignment Options for Exercises On Your Own

Core 1–5, 8–16

✪**Extension** 6–7, 17

Use Mixed Review to maintain skills.

Resources

Student Edition

Skills Handbook, pp. 674, 678
Extra Practice, p. 651
Glossary/Study Guide

Teaching Resources

Chapter Support File, Ch. 4
- Practice 4-4 (two worksheets)
- Reteaching 4-4

Classroom Manager 4-4
Glossary, Spanish Resources

Transparencies
5, 52, 56

THINK AND DISCUSS

Theorem 4-8 is proved using a coordinate proof. Before working through the proof with students, you may want to check the validity of the theorem using numerical values for the coordinates. Students are asked to make their own numerical example in Question 4.

Discuss with students why variables are chosen instead of numbers as coordinates for the vertices in the proof. Help students see that locating the triangle at the origin does not affect the outcome of the proof but makes the computations easier.

CRITICAL THINKING Ask students to explain how you can reason from the fact that R and S have the same y-coordinates that the slope of $\overline{RS}$ equals zero.

Example 1

AUDITORY LEARNING Have students work in groups to read through the solution to Example 1. Then ask for volunteers to explain in their own words how to find AB and other volunteers to explain how to find CD.

CRITICAL THINKING **Question 5** Ask students if they used theorems, postulates, or definitions to justify their answers.

Additional Examples

FOR EXAMPLE 1

Refer to the diagram in Example 1. If $AB = 7$, find EG and DC.
EG = 14, *DG* = 7

Discussion: *If △FAB is an equilateral triangle, what can you say about △FEG?*

FOR EXAMPLE 2

Refer to the diagrams in Example 2. If the distance across the lake is 288 ft, how many strides would DeAndre have paced in Step 5?
48 strides

QUICK REVIEW

Midpoint Formula:
$\left(\frac{x_1 + x_2}{2}, \frac{y_1 + y_2}{2}\right)$

Distance Formula:
$\sqrt{(x_2 - x_1)^2 + (y_2 - y_1)^2}$

For practice with simplifying radicals, see Skills Handbook page 674.

Coordinate Proof of Theorem 4-8

Given: R is the midpoint of $\overline{OP}$.
S is the midpoint of $\overline{QP}$.

Prove: $\overline{RS} \parallel \overline{OQ}$ and $RS = \frac{1}{2}OQ$

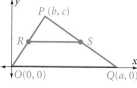

- Use the Midpoint Formula to find the coordinates of R and S.

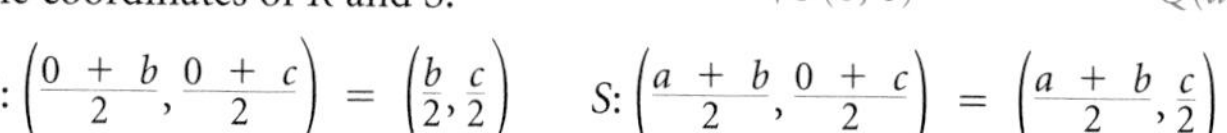

$R: \left(\frac{0+b}{2}, \frac{0+c}{2}\right) = \left(\frac{b}{2}, \frac{c}{2}\right) \quad S: \left(\frac{a+b}{2}, \frac{0+c}{2}\right) = \left(\frac{a+b}{2}, \frac{c}{2}\right)$

- To prove that $\overline{RS}$ and $\overline{OQ}$ are parallel, show that their slopes are equal. Because the y-coordinates of R and S are the same, the slope of $\overline{RS}$ is zero. The same is true for $\overline{OQ}$. Therefore, $\overline{RS} \parallel \overline{OQ}$.
- Use the Distance Formula to find RS and OQ.

$$RS = \sqrt{\left(\frac{a+b}{2} - \frac{b}{2}\right)^2 + \left(\frac{c}{2} - \frac{c}{2}\right)^2}$$

$$= \sqrt{\left(\frac{a}{2} + \frac{b}{2} - \frac{b}{2}\right)^2 + 0^2} = \sqrt{\left(\frac{a}{2}\right)^2} = \frac{a}{2} = \frac{1}{2}a$$

$$OQ = \sqrt{(a-0)^2 + (0-0)^2}$$

$$= \sqrt{a^2 + 0^2} = a$$

Therefore, $RS = \frac{1}{2}OQ$.

4. Select numerical values for the coordinates of P and Q.
   a. Use the Midpoint Formula to find the coordinates of R and S.
   b. **Verify** that $RS = \frac{1}{2}OQ$ for the values you chose.
   c. **Verify** that $\overline{RS} \parallel \overline{OQ}$ for the values you chose.

4a. Sample: for $P(4, 8)$ and $Q(6, 0)$, $R(2, 4)$, $S(5, 4)$
b. For sample in part (a), $RS = 3$, $OQ = 6$, $RS = \frac{1}{2}OQ$ ✓
c. For sample in part (a), slope of $\overline{RS} = 0$, slope of $\overline{OQ} = 0$ ✓

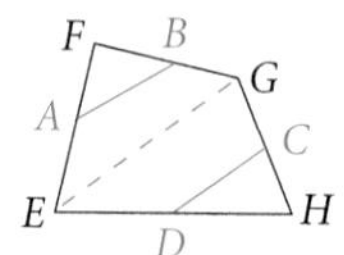

Example 1

In quadrilateral $EFGH$, the points A, B, C, and D are midpoints and $EG = 18$ cm. Find AB and CD.

Consider △EFG. By the Triangle Midsegment Theorem, $AB = \frac{1}{2}EG$. Using the same reasoning for △EHG, you get $CD = \frac{1}{2}EG$. Because $EG = 18$ cm, $\frac{1}{2}EG = 9$ cm. Therefore, $AB = CD = 9$ cm.

5. *Critical Thinking* Is $\overline{AB} \parallel \overline{CD}$? **Justify** your answer.
6. **Try This** $FH = 25$ cm. Find BC and AD.
7. *Critical Thinking* What type of quadrilateral is $ABCD$? Explain.

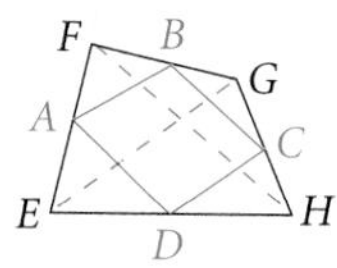

5. Yes; $\overline{AB} \parallel \overline{EG}$ and $\overline{CD} \parallel \overline{EG}$; 2 lines ∥ to a 3rd line are ∥.
6. $BC = AD = 12.5$ cm
7. $ABCD$ is a parallelogram because its opp. sides are ∥.

Example 2 **Relating to the Real World** 

ESL To help students see how the Triangle Midsegment Theorem is being applied, ask leading questions, such as "Why did DeAndre not just measure the distance across the lake?" and "Why did he mark 35 paces on one side of the lake and 118 paces on the other side?"

TACTILE LEARNING If you have block scheduling or an extended class period, have students use straws or popsicle sticks to build a scale model of a swing set so that the "sides" of the swing set are isosceles triangles with a support bar at the midpoint of the sides of the triangles. Ask students to explain how they found the length of the support bar.

You can use the Triangle Midsegment Theorem to find lengths of segments that might otherwise be difficult to measure.

Example 2 **Relating to the Real World** 

Indirect Measurement DeAndre swims the length of a lake and wants to know the distance he swam. Here is what he does to find out.

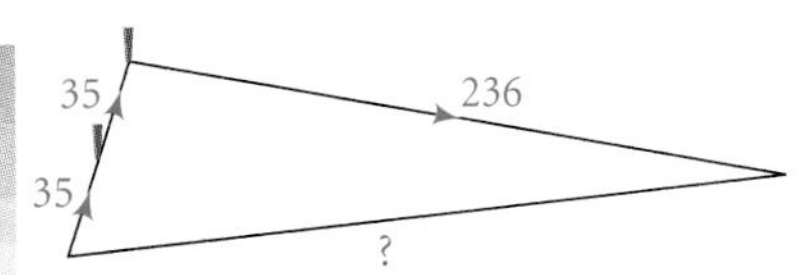

Step 1: From the edge of the lake, he paces 35 strides and sets a stake.

Step 2: He paces 35 more strides in the same direction and sets another stake.

Step 3: He paces to the other end of the lake, counting 236 strides.

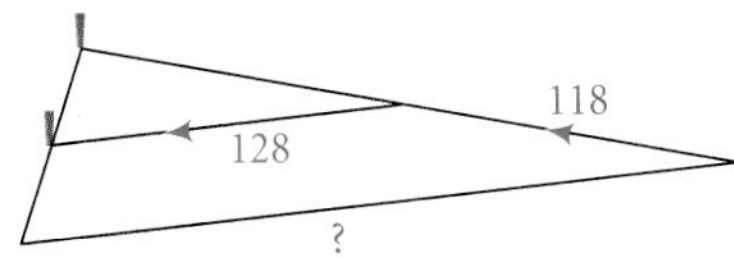

Step 4: He paces half the distance to the second stake (118 strides).

Step 5: He paces to the first stake, counting 128 strides.

If DeAndre's stride averages 3 ft, about how far did he swim?

$2(128 \text{ strides}) = 256 \text{ strides}$ — Triangle Midsegment Theorem

$256 \text{ strides} \times \frac{3 \text{ ft}}{1 \text{ stride}} = 768 \text{ ft}$ — Convert strides to feet.

DeAndre swam approximately 768 ft.

Technology Options

For Exercise 5, students may use geometry software to plot the triangle and calculate the midpoints of the sides. For Exercise 7, students may draw the figure using geometry software and investigate the effects of transformations using transformation tools.

Prentice Hall Technology 

Software
- Secondary Math Lab Toolkit™
- Integrated Math Lab 29
- Computer Item Generator 4-4

CD-ROM
- Multimedia Geometry Lab 4

Internet
- See the Prentice Hall site. (http://www.phschool.com)

Exercises ON YOUR OWN

Mental Math **Find the value of x.**

1. 9

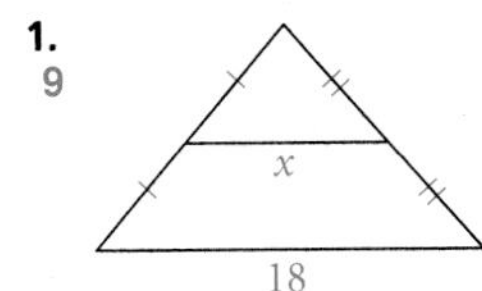

2. 11

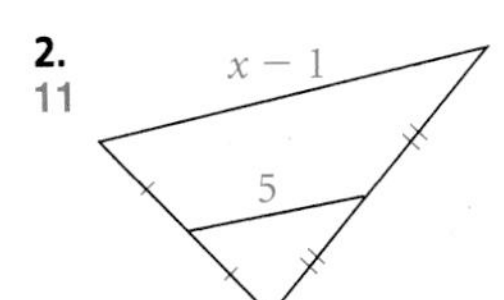

3. 31

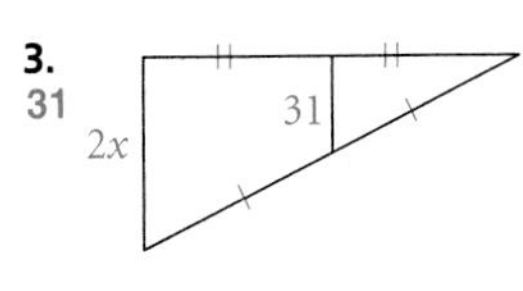

Exercises ON YOUR OWN

Exercise 4b Make sure that students find the perimeter of $\triangle HIJ$ and not $\triangle HFG$.

Exercise 5b Because $\overline{HJ}$ and $\overline{EF}$ are neither horizontal nor vertical, students need to calculate their slopes to show that the two segments are parallel.

MAKING CONNECTIONS Exercise 6 The Rock and Roll Hall of Fame opened on September 1, 1995, in Cleveland, Ohio. Among its many exhibits are Buddy Holly's high school diploma, a 1968 leather stage outfit and a guitar once worn by Elvis, and John Lennon's Sergeant Pepper jacket.

ERROR ALERT! **Exercise 7b** Students may think only of the isometries. **Remediation:** Review the transformations studied in Chapter 3: reflections, translations, rotations, and dilations.

Exercise 8 An alternative activity is presented in the Toolbox on page 200, where students explore this problem using geometry software.

ALTERNATIVE ASSESSMENT **Exercises 9–14** These exercises can help you assess students' understanding of the Triangle Midsegment Theorem by having students identify the midsegment and use it to find missing side lengths. Have students work in pairs or small groups.

pages 203–205 On Your Own

7a. Answers may vary. Sample:

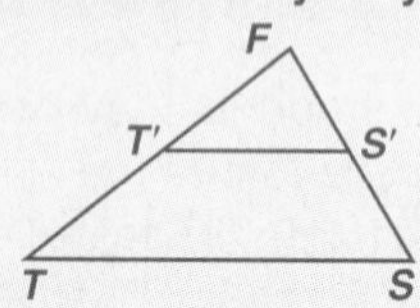

b. Dilation with center F and scale factor $\frac{1}{2}$.

c. The triangles are $\sim$.

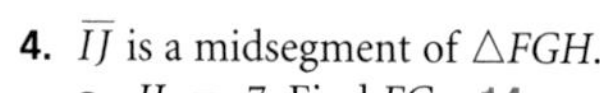

4. $\overline{IJ}$ is a midsegment of $\triangle FGH$.

a. $IJ = 7$. Find FG. 14

b. $FH = 13$ and $GH = 10$. Find the perimeter of $\triangle HIJ$. 18.5

5. *Coordinate Geometry* The coordinates of the vertices of a triangle are $E(1, 2)$, $F(5, 6)$, and $G(3, -2)$.

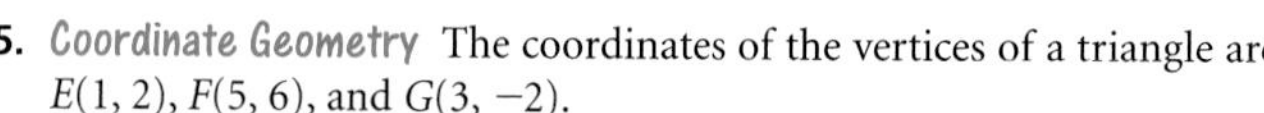

a. Find the coordinates of H, the midpoint of $\overline{EG}$, and J, the midpoint of $\overline{FG}$. $H(2, 0)$; $J(4, 2)$

b. Verify that $\overline{HJ} \parallel \overline{EF}$. slope of $\overline{HJ} = 1$, slope of $\overline{EF} = 1$ ✔

c. Verify that $HJ = \frac{1}{2}EF$. $HJ = 2\sqrt{2}$, $EF = 4\sqrt{2}$, $HJ = \frac{1}{2}EF$

6. *Architecture* The triangular face of the Rock and Roll Hall of Fame in Cleveland, Ohio, is isosceles. The length of the base is 229 ft 6 in. The face consists of smaller triangles determined by the midsegments. What is the length of the base of the highlighted triangle? 57 ft 4.5 in.

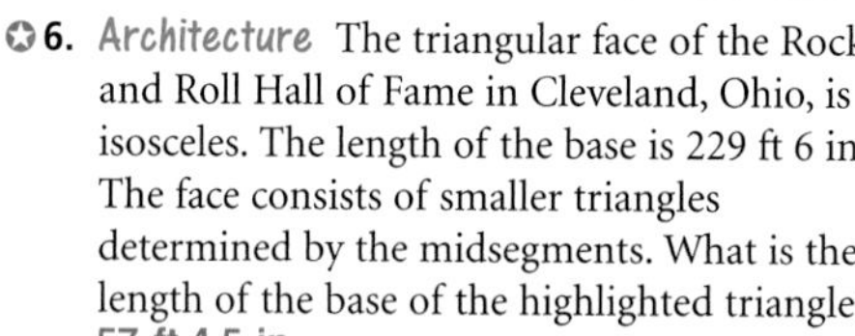

7. a. Draw a triangle and label it $\triangle FST$. Then draw the midsegment opposite $\overline{ST}$.

b. *Transformational Geometry* Describe a transformation of $\triangle FST$ that produces the same diagram as in part (a).

c. What does your answer to part (b) tell you about the triangles formed in part (a)? See margin.

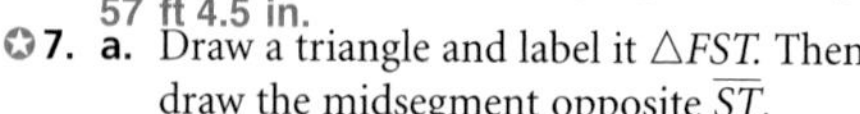

8. *Open-ended* Draw a triangle and its three midsegments. Compare the four triangles determined by the midsegments. Repeat the experiment with a different triangle. Make a **conjecture** about your observations. Answers may vary. Sample: The 4 triangles are $\cong$.

Choose **Use mental math, pencil and paper, or a calculator to find the values of the variables.**

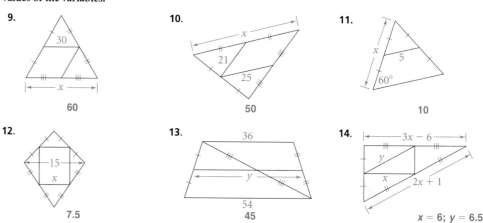

9.

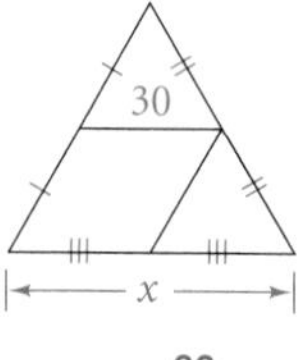

60

10.

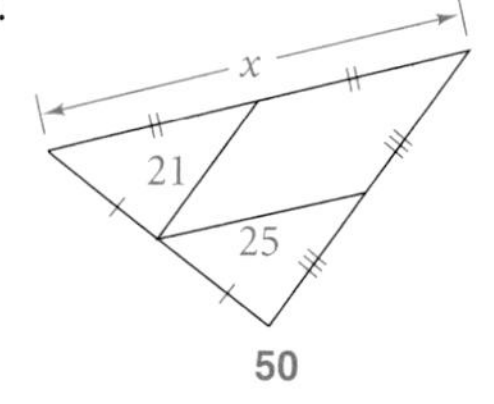

50

11.

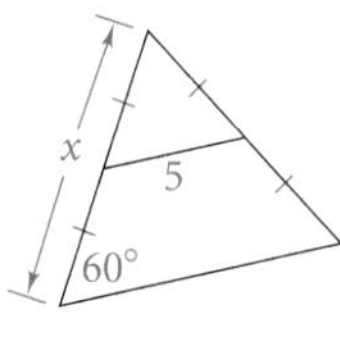

10

12.

15
x

7.5

13.

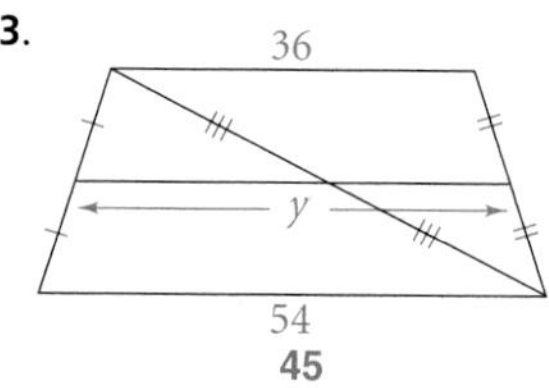

45

14.

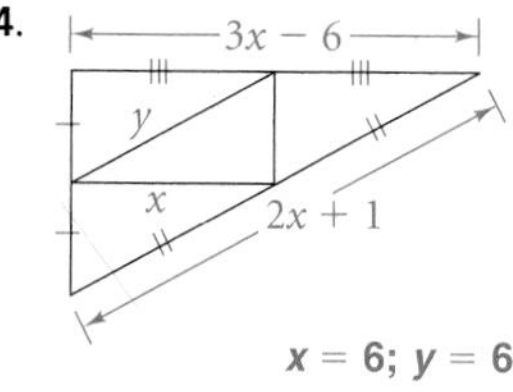

$x = 6$; $y = 6.5$

CONNECTING TO STUDENTS' WORLD Exercise 15 Have students collect kite designs from books or create their own kite designs. (They should be designed so they can fly!) Then have them describe the geometric properties of their designs.

Chapter Project **FIND OUT BY ANALYZING** Have students work in groups of three or four. Students may want to enact the situation labeling three pieces of paper with R and two with B and using the paper as their hats.

15. *Creative Arts* Marita is designing a kite for a competition. She plans to use a decorative ribbon to connect the midpoints of the sides of the kite. The diagonals of the kite measure 64 cm and 90 cm. Find the amount of ribbon she will need. **154 cm**

16. *Preparing for Proof* This is a proof that the midsegments of an equilateral triangle form an equilateral triangle. The reasons given in the proof are correct, but they are in the wrong order. List them in the correct order. **(1) e or g, (2) a or d, (3) b, (4) e or g, (5) f, (6) c, (7) a or d**

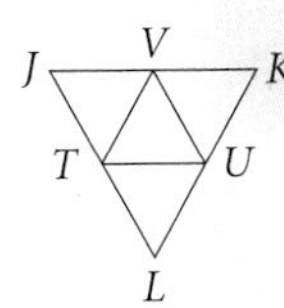

Given: Equilateral $\triangle JKL$ with midpoints T, U, and V

Prove: $\triangle TUV$ is equilateral.

Statements	Reasons
1. $\triangle JKL$ is equilateral.	a. Def. of equilateral triangle
2. $JK = KL = JL$	b. Multiplication Prop. of Equality
3. $\frac{1}{2}JK = \frac{1}{2}KL = \frac{1}{2}JL$	c. Substitution
4. T, U, and V are midpoints.	d. Def. of equilateral triangle
5. $TU = \frac{1}{2}JK$; $UV = \frac{1}{2}JL$; $TV = \frac{1}{2}KL$	e. Given
6. $TU = UV = TV$	f. Triangle Midsegment Thm.
7. $\triangle TUV$ is equilateral.	g. Given

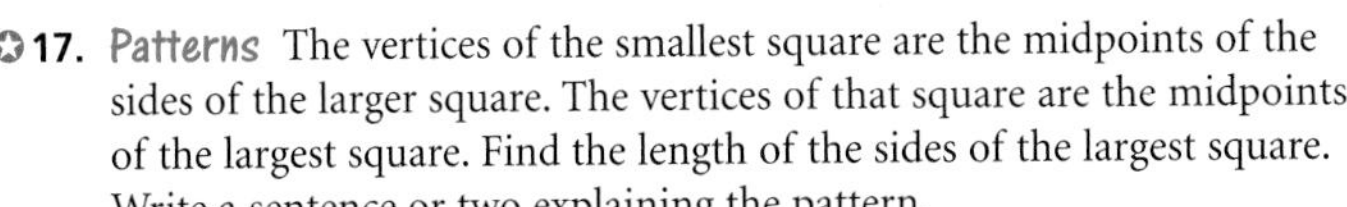

17. *Patterns* The vertices of the smallest square are the midpoints of the sides of the larger square. The vertices of that square are the midpoints of the largest square. Find the length of the sides of the largest square. Write a sentence or two explaining the pattern.

1 cm

17. 2 cm; the length of a side of the largest square = the length of the diagonal of the middle square. The length of the diagonal of that square is twice the length of the sides of the smallest square.

Chapter Project

Find Out by Analyzing

See margin.

Try your powers of logic on this new version of an old puzzle.

Alan, Ben, and Cal are seated as shown with their eyes closed. Three hats are placed on their heads from a box they know contains 3 red and 2 blue hats. They open their eyes and look forward.

Alan says, "I cannot deduce what color hat I'm wearing."

Hearing that, Ben says, "I cannot deduce what color I'm wearing, either."

Cal then says, "I know what color I'm wearing!"

How does Cal know what color his hat is? (*Hint*: Use one of the strategies you used to solve the previous two puzzles on pages 187 and 198.)

Find Out By Analyzing

Red; if Alan saw 2 blue hats, he would have known that he had a red hat. So at least 1 hat in front of him must be red. If Ben saw a blue hat, he would have known that he had a red hat. Cal's hat must not be blue.

Checkpoint page 206

1a. **If the measure of at least one of the angles of a triangle is 60, then the triangle is equilateral.**

2a. **If all the angles of a polygon are ≅, then the polygon is regular.**

3. **A converse reverses the hypothesis and the conclusion. The truth value of a converse does not depend on the truth value of the original statement. A contrapositive reverses and negates the hypothesis and the conclusion of the original statement. The truth values of a statement and its contrapositive are the same.**

Exercises MIXED REVIEW

JOURNAL Students may want to make a table showing properties that apply to all triangles, then those that just apply to special triangles such as right triangles, isosceles triangles, and equilateral triangles.

GETTING READY FOR LESSON 4-5 These exercises prepare students to use indirect reasoning to write arguments.

Wrap Up

THE BIG IDEA Ask students: *Restate the Triangle Midsegment Theorem in your own words. Include a diagram and give an example of how it can be used to solve a problem.*

RETEACHING ACTIVITY Students draw triangles and find their midsegments. Then they use properties of midsegments to find the lengths of sides of the triangles. (Reteaching worksheet 4-4)

Exercises CHECKPOINT

In this Checkpoint, your students will assess their own progress on Lessons 4-1 to 4-4.

STANDARDIZED TEST TIP **Exercise 4** Students need to set different pairs of sides equal to see if there is a value of x that makes them the same length.

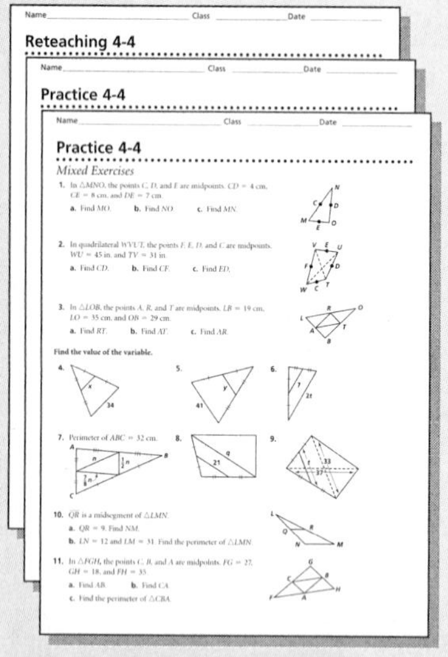

Lesson Quiz

Lesson Quiz is also available in Transparencies.

$\overline{DE}$ and $\overline{EF}$ are midsegments. $DE = 7$ and $AB = 10$.

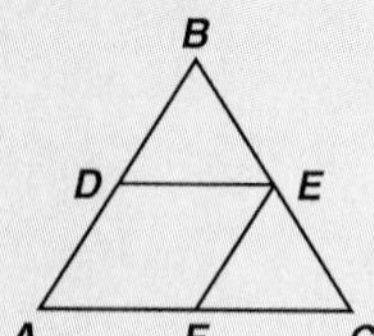

1. Find AC. 14
2. Find EF. 5
3. What is the perimeter of $ADEF$? 24 units
4. What kind of quadrilateral is $ADEF$? parallelogram

206

Exercises MIXED REVIEW

Coordinate Geometry **Find the distance between the given points.**

18. $B(0, 9)$ and $E(4, 9)$ 4
19. $V(8, -7)$ and $W(4, -4)$ 5
20. $A(3, 2)$ and $N(-1, 0)$ $2\sqrt{5}$
21. **Transformational Geometry** State the coordinates of the point (6, 2) after a rotation of 90° about the origin. (–2, 6)
22. **Standardized Test Prep** A circle and a square lie in a plane. What is the maximum number of points of intersection of the figures?
    A. one B. two C. four D. six E. eight
    E

Getting Ready for Lesson 4-5

Write the negation of each statement. 23–26. See right.

23. Lines m and n intersect.
24. The integer x is odd.
25. $\triangle ABC$ is scalene.
26. $\overline{AB} \parallel \overline{KM}$
27. A given angle is neither acute, right, nor obtuse. What is its measure? Explain how you know.
    180; it must be a straight angle.

23. Lines m and n do not intersect.
24. The integer x is even.
25. $\triangle ABC$ is isosceles.
26. $\overline{AB} \nparallel \overline{KM}$

FOR YOUR JOURNAL

Make a list of the properties of triangles you've learned so far in this chapter. Include a diagram to illustrate each property. Add to your list as you continue with the chapter.

Exercises CHECKPOINT

For Exercises 1 and 2: (a) Write the converse of each conditional.
(b) Determine the truth value of the conditional and its converse.
(c) If both statements are true, write a biconditional.

1a–2a. See margin p. 205.

1. If a triangle is equilateral, then the measure of at least one of its angles is 60.
   1b. true; false
2. If a polygon is regular, then its angles are congruent.
   2b. true; false
3. **Writing** Explain the difference between a converse and a contrapositive. See margin p. 205.
4. **Standardized Test Prep** $\triangle ABC$ is isosceles, and $AC = 3x$, $AB = 2x + 30$, and $BC = 3x + 40$. Which of the following is true? C
   A. $\angle A \cong \angle B$ B. $\angle A \cong \angle C$ C. $\angle B \cong \angle C$
   D. $\angle A \cong \angle B \cong \angle C$ E. none of the above
5. The measures of the angles of a triangle are $6x$, $7x - 9$, and $8x$.
   a. **Algebra** Find the value of x. 9
   b. What are the measures of the angles? 54, 54, 72
   c. What type of triangle is this? Explain. Isosceles; the triangle has 2 ≅ angles.
6. Determine whether this statement is true or false: If a triangle is obtuse, then it is not isosceles. **Justify** your answer.
   See right.
7. M, N, O, and P are midpoints of the sides of trapezoid $ABCD$. $AC = BD = 18$. Find the perimeter of $MNOP$. 36

6. False; a triangle with angles 30°, 30°, 120° is an obtuse isosceles triangle.

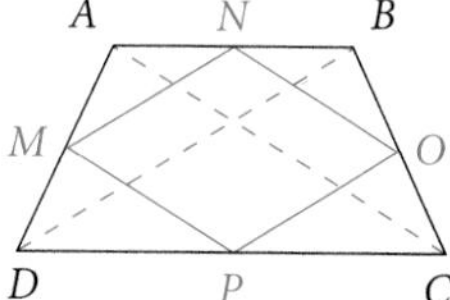

4-5 Teaching Notes

PROBLEM OF THE DAY

A farmer has a large field with six hay stacks in one corner, half as many in another corner, twice as many in another corner, and four in a fourth corner. As the hay stacks are collected in the center of the field, one stack is scattered into the wind. How many hay stacks does the farmer have now? 24

Problem of the Day is also available in Transparencies.

CONNECTING TO PRIOR KNOWLEDGE Ask: *In which year did Elizabeth Robinson win the 100-meter dash in the Olympics?*

a. *1935* **b.** *1944* **c.** *1928* **d.** *1896*

Discuss how students can use indirect reasoning to narrow the possible answer choices down to c. (1935 was not an Olympic year. Olympics were not held in 1944 due to World War II. In 1896, women did not participate.)

THINK AND DISCUSS

VISUAL LEARNING Help students see that they used indirect reasoning to solve the Find Out by Organizing problem on page 198 by using X's to eliminate possibilities until only one possibility remained.

Example 1 Relating to the Real World 

ERROR ALERT! Students sometimes write the opposite of phrases such as "$25 or more" and "more than $20" as "$25 or less" and "no less than $20," respectively. **Remediation:** Help students see that, for example, "$25 or more" includes $25 as a possibility so its opposite should not.

Connections  Consumer Issues . . . and more

4-5 Using Indirect Reasoning

What You'll Learn

- Writing convincing arguments by using indirect reasoning

...And Why

To help you in real-life situations in which proving something directly isn't possible

THINK AND DISCUSS

Suppose that your brother tells you, "Susan called a few minutes ago." You have two friends named Susan, and you know that one of them is at play rehearsal. You deduce that the other Susan must be the caller.

This type of reasoning is called indirect reasoning. In **indirect reasoning,** all possibilities are considered and then all but one are proved false. The remaining possibility must be true. Mathematical proofs involving indirect reasoning usually follow the pattern in the following example.

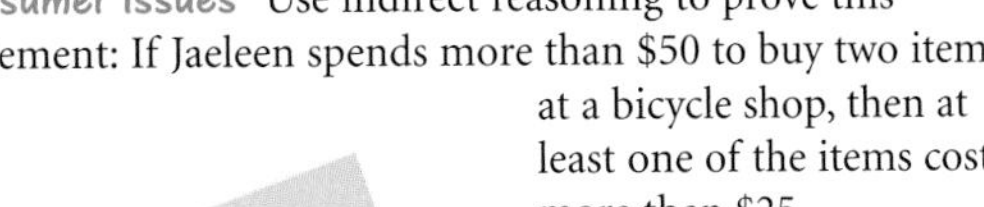

Example 1 Relating to the Real World 

Consumer Issues Use indirect reasoning to prove this statement: If Jaeleen spends more than $50 to buy two items at a bicycle shop, then at least one of the items costs more than $25.

Given: The cost of two items is more than $50.
Prove: At least one of the items costs more than $25.

- Begin by assuming that the opposite of what you want to prove is true. That is, assume that neither item costs more than $25.
- This means that both items cost $25 or less. This, in turn, means that the two items together cost $50 or less. This contradicts the given information that the amount spent is more than $50. So, the assumption that neither item costs more than $25 must be incorrect.
- Therefore, at least one of the items costs more than $25.

bicycle helmet

bicycle safety light

Lesson Planning Options

Prerequisite Skills

- Writing the opposite of statements

Assignment Options for Exercises On Your Own

Core 1–24
Extension 25–27

Use Mixed Review to maintain skills.

Resources

Student Edition
Skills Handbook, p. 664
Extra Practice, p. 651
Glossary/Study Guide

Teaching Resources
Chapter Support File, Ch. 4
- Practice 4-5 (two worksheets)
- Reteaching 4-5

Classroom Manager 4-5
Glossary, Spanish Resources

Transparencies
53

Students may not feel as comfortable with the validity of indirect proofs as they do with direct proofs. Point out that the method of indirect proof is based on the fact that a statement is either true or false and that a statement cannot be true and false at the same time.

DIVERSITY Students with poor writing and organizational skills may be overwhelmed at the thought of writing an indirect proof. Have students write the explanation of each step in their own words on an index card. Then have them turn each index card over after writing that step in their proofs.

Example 2

Some students have difficulty understanding the logic of indirect proof. Help these students understand why $m\angle N = 0$ means that $\triangle LMN$ does not exist so the assumption made is false.

Question 3 Help students set up a template on which to write their proofs. Label a paper with the key words "Given," "Prove," "Step 1," "Step 2," and "Step 3," and leave space for students to fill in the missing information.

Additional Examples

FOR EXAMPLE 1

Use indirect reasoning to prove this statement: If a movie was shown 25 times in seven days and was not shown more than four times in any one day, then it was shown at least once a day. **Given: A movie was shown 25 times in seven days and was not shown more than four times in any one day. Prove: The movie was shown at least once a day. Assume the movies was not shown at least once a day. This means that the movie was shown 25 times in six days or less. But this contradicts the given information that the movie was not shown more than four times a day ($6 \times 4 = 24$). Therefore, the movie was shown at least once a day.**

Discussion: *Describe in your own words the steps you used to prove the statement.*

FOR EXAMPLE 2

Write an indirect proof to show that a pentagon cannot have more than four acute angles. **See back of book.**

Discussion: *What theorems did you use in your reasoning?*

1a. Assume that quadrilateral *TRWX* has four acute angles.
b. Assume the integer *n* is not divisible by 5.
c. Assume the shoes cost more than \$20.

3. Assume that a ▱ with 3 rt. angles is not a rectangle. Then the 4th angle must be either obtuse or acute. If the angle is obtuse, then its measure is > 90 and the sum of the measures of the angles is > 360. If the angle is acute, then its measure is < 90 and the sum of the angle measures is < 360. Both cases contradict the fact that the sum of angle measures of a quadrilateral = 360. Therefore, the initial assumption is false. So a ▱ with 3 rt. angles must be a rectangle.

The three parts of the proof in Example 1 are summarized below.

Writing an Indirect Proof

Step 1: Assume that the opposite of what you want to prove is true.

Step 2: Use logical reasoning to reach a contradiction of an earlier statement, such as the given information or a theorem. Then state that the assumption you made was false.

Step 3: State that what you wanted to prove must be true.

1. Write the first step of an indirect proof of each statement.
   a. Quadrilateral *TRWX* does not have four acute angles.
   b. An integer n is divisible by 5.
   c. The shoes cost no more than \$20.
2. Identify the pair of statements that form a contradiction.
   a. I. $\triangle ABC$ is acute. **II and III**
      II. $\triangle ABC$ is scalene.
      III. $\triangle ABC$ is equiangular.
   b. I. $m\angle 1 + m\angle 2 = 180$
      II. $m\angle 1 - m\angle 2 = m\angle 2$
      III. $m\angle 1 \leq m\angle 2$ **II and III**
   c. I. Both items that Val bought cost more than \$10.
      II. Val spent \$34 for the two items. **II and III**
      III. Neither of the two items that Val bought cost more than \$15.

Example 2

Write an indirect proof.

Given: $\triangle LMN$
Prove: $\triangle LMN$ has at most one right angle.

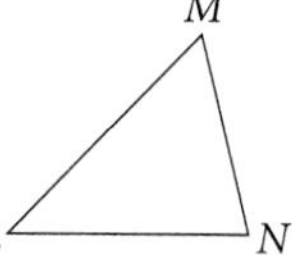

Indirect Proof

Step 1: Assume $\triangle LMN$ has more than one right angle. That is, assume that $\angle L$ and $\angle M$ are both right angles.

Step 2: If $\angle L$ and $\angle M$ are both right angles, then $m\angle L = m\angle M = 90$. According to the Triangle Angle-Sum Theorem, $m\angle L + m\angle M + m\angle N = 180$. Substitution gives $90 + 90 + m\angle N = 180$. Solving leaves $m\angle N = 0$. This means that there is no $\triangle LMN$, which contradicts the given statement. So the assumption that $\angle L$ and $\angle M$ are both right angles must be false.

Step 3: Therefore, $\triangle LMN$ has at most one right angle. ■

3. **Try This** Use indirect reasoning to show that a parallelogram with three right angles is a rectangle. **See left above.**

WORK TOGETHER

Have students keep a list of the questions asked and then discuss with the class the ones that best enable them to narrow down the answer.

Question 4 Have students describe strategies for asking questions and strategies for choosing a number that is harder to guess than others.

Exercises ON YOUR OWN

Exercises 5–6 Review with students the notation used to negate the math symbols $\cong$, $=$, $>$, $<$, and $\|$.

MAKING CONNECTIONS Exercise 11 The oldest drawbridge in the United States is the Missouri River Bridge in Omaha, Nebraska, built in 1893. The swing bridge is 519 ft long.

WORK TOGETHER

Play *What's My Number* in groups of three or four. Here's how to play.

- One member of the group chooses a number from 1 to 20.
- The remaining members ask yes-or-no questions about the number until they know what the number is.
- The person answering the questions records the number of questions required to guess the number.

Play the game at least three times, rotating roles with each game.

4. **Critical Thinking** Describe the best strategy for playing *What's My Number* to a friend who is just learning to play it.
   Answers may vary. Sample: At each step, divide the range of possible numbers as nearly in half as possible.

Exercises ON YOUR OWN

Write the first step of an indirect proof of each statement.

1. It is raining outside.
   Assume it is not raining outside.
2. $\angle J$ is not a right angle.
   Assume $\angle J$ is a rt. angle.
3. $\triangle PEN$ is isosceles.
   Assume $\triangle PEN$ is scalene.
4. At least one angle is obtuse.
   Assume none of the angles is obtuse.
5. $\overline{XY} \cong \overline{AB}$
   Assume $\overline{XY} \ncong \overline{AB}$.
6. $m\angle 2 > 90$
   Assume $m\angle 2 \leq 90$.

Identify the pair of statements that forms a contradiction.

7. I. $\triangle PQR$ is equilateral.
   II. $\triangle PQR$ is a right triangle.
   III. $\triangle PQR$ is isosceles.
   I and II
8. I. $ABCD$ is a parallelogram.
   II. $ABCD$ is a trapezoid.
   III. $ABCD$ has two acute angles.
   I and II
9. I. ℓ and m are skew.
   II. ℓ and m do not intersect.
   III. ℓ is parallel to m.
   I and III
10. I. $\overline{FG} \parallel \overline{KL}$
    II. $\overline{FG} \perp \overline{KL}$
    III. $\overline{FG} \cong \overline{KL}$
    I and II

What conclusion follows from each pair of statements?

11. There are three types of drawbridges: bascule, lift, and swing. This drawbridge does not swing or lift.
    This bridge is a bascule.
12. If this were the day of the party, our friends would be home. No one is home.
    The party is not today.
13. Every air traffic controller in the world speaks English on the job. Sumiko does not speak English.
    Sumiko is not an air traffic controller.
14. If two nonvertical lines are perpendicular, then the product of their slopes is -1. The product of the slopes of nonvertical lines ℓ and n is not -1.
    The lines ℓ and n are not $\perp$.

Technology Options

Prentice Hall Technology

Software
- Secondary Math Lab Toolkit™
- Computer Item Generator 4-5

Internet
- See the Prentice Hall site. (http://www.phschool.com)

Exercise 15 You may want to allow time for students to share their proofs with partners. Then have students revise their proofs based on the comments received from their partners.

Exercises 19–22 For students having difficulty writing indirect proofs, you may want to provide an outline as in Exercise 16 and have students fill in the blanks.

ALTERNATIVE ASSESSMENT Exercises 23–24 These exercises help you assess students' ability to write an indirect proof. Have students work with a partner and suggest that they model the proof given in Example 2.

CONNECTING TO STUDENTS' WORLD Exercise 25 Have students work in groups to create a similar story problem. They can make themselves or their friends the characters in the problem and use familiar locations.

pages 209–211 On Your Own

19. Assume that the driver had not applied the brakes. Then the wheels would not have locked and there would be no skid marks. There are skid marks. Therefore, the assumption is false. The driver had applied the brakes.
20. If the temp. outside is above 32°F, water on the sidewalk cannot freeze. There is ice forming on the sidewalk. Therefore, the assumption is false. The temp. is 32°F or below.
21. Assume the polygon is a hexagon. Then the sum of measures of its interior angles is 720. But the sum of measures of the polygon's interior angles is 900, not 720. Therefore, the assumption is false. The polygon is not a hexagon.
22. Assume a quadrilateral has 4 acute angles. The measure of each acute angle is < 90. Then the sum of the measures of the angles is < 360. The sum of interior angles of a quadrilateral $= 360$. Therefore, the assumption is false. A quadrilateral cannot have more than 3 acute angles.

15. Given $\triangle ABC$ with $BC > AC$, use indirect reasoning to show that $\angle A \ncong \angle B$. Assume $\angle A \cong \angle B$. Then $\triangle ABC$ is isosceles with $BC = AC$. This contradicts the assumption. Therefore, $\angle A \ncong \angle B$.

16. *Preparing for Proof* Complete this indirect proof that every quadrilateral contains at least one right or acute angle.

Assume that a quadrilateral does not contain **a.** __?__. That is, assume that the measure of each of the angles is greater than **b.** __?__. The sum of the measures of the four angles, then, is greater than **c.** __?__. By the **d.** __?__ Theorem, however, the sum of the measures of the interior angles of a quadrilateral is **e.** __?__. This contradicts **f.** __?__, so the assumption that **g.** __?__ is false. Therefore, **h.** __?__.

a. a rt. or acute angle b. 90 c. 360 d. Polygon Interior Angle-Sum e. 360 f. preceding statement g. a quadrilateral does not contain an acute or a rt. angle h. a quadrilateral contains at least one rt. or acute angle

17. *Standardized Test Prep* Which of the following represents the measure of an interior angle of a regular polygon? E

A. 30 **B.** 50 **C.** 70 **D.** 100 **E.** 140

PROBLEM SOLVING HINT

Use indirect reasoning. Eliminate all incorrect answer choices. The remaining choice must be correct.

18. Earlene lives near a noisy construction site at which work ends promptly at 5:00 each weekday. Earlene thinks, "Today is Tuesday. If it were before 5:00, I would hear construction noise, but I don't hear any. So it must be later than 5:00."

a. What does Earlene prove? It is later than 5:00.
b. What assumption does she make? It is before 5:00.
c. What fact contradicts the assumption? She does not hear any noise from the construction site.

For Exercises 19–25, write a convincing argument that uses indirect reasoning. 19–22. See margin. 23–24. See back of book.

19. Fresh skid marks appear behind a green car at the scene of an accident. Show that the driver of the green car applied the brakes.

20. Ice is forming on the sidewalk in front of Toni's house. Show that the temperature outside must be 32°F or less.

21. The sum of the measures of the interior angles of a polygon is 900. Show that the polygon is not a hexagon.

22. Show that a quadrilateral can have at most three acute angles.

23. An obtuse triangle cannot contain a right angle.

Given: $\triangle PQR$ with obtuse $\angle Q$

Prove: $m\angle P \neq 90$

24. If a triangle is isosceles, then a base angle is not a right angle.

Given: $\overline{BC} \cong \overline{AC}$

Prove: $\angle B$ is not a right angle.

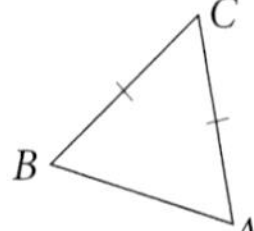

25. Mr. Pitt is a suspect in a robbery. Here are the facts:

- A robbery occurred in Charlotte, North Carolina, at 1:00 A.M. on April 9.
- A hotel clerk in Maine saw Mr. Pitt at 12:05 A.M. on April 9.
- Mr. Pitt has an identical twin brother who was in Chicago during the time the robbery took place.
- Mr. Pitt has receipts for purchases made in Maine on April 8.

Show that Mr. Pitt was not the robber.

Mr. Pitt was in Maine on April 8 and stayed there at least until 12:05 A.M. Assume Mr. Pitt is the robber. Then he took < 55 min to travel from Maine to Charlotte. It is not possible to travel from Maine to Charlotte in 55 min or less. Therefore, Mr. Pitt is not the robber.

Exercises MIXED REVIEW

Exercise 32a When students use the terms to write six conditionals, they will not all be true.

Exercise 33 Students may want to draw a diagram of the transformation. They can use any isometry, but suggest that a translation is the easiest.

GETTING READY FOR LESSON 4-6 These exercises prepare students to solve problems using inequalities involving triangle side lengths.

Wrap Up

THE BIG IDEA Ask students: *Explain in your own words the three steps of writing an indirect proof.*

RETEACHING ACTIVITY Students use indirect reasoning to arrange the statements of an indirect proof in the correct order. Then they write an indirect proof. (Reteaching worksheet 4-5)

26. **Open-ended** Describe a real-life situation in which you used an indirect argument to convince someone of your point of view. Outline your argument. Check students' work.

27. **Mysteries** In Arthur Conan Doyle's story "The Sign of the Four," Sherlock Holmes talks to his sidekick Watson about how a culprit enters a room that has only four entrances: a door, a window, a chimney, and a hole in the roof.

"You will not apply my precept," he said, shaking his head. "How often have I said to you that when you have eliminated the impossible, whatever remains, *however improbable,* must be the truth? We know that he did not come through the door, the window, or the chimney. We also know that he could not have been concealed in the room, as there is no concealment possible. Whence, then, did he come?"

How did the culprit enter the room? Explain. The hole in the roof; of 5 possibilities, 4 have been eliminated.

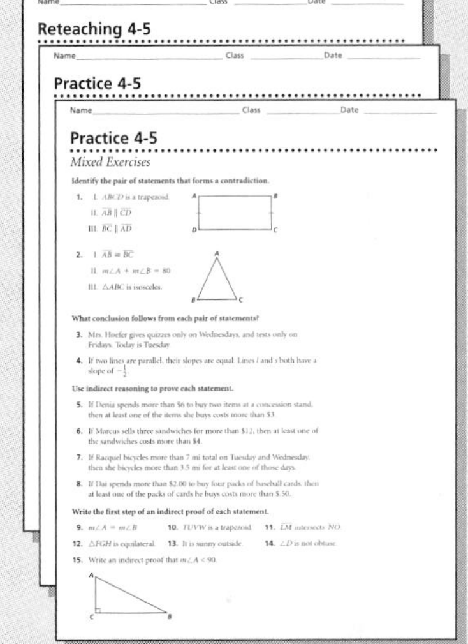

Name ______ Class ______ Date ______

Reteaching 4-5

Name ______ Class ______ Date ______

Practice 4-5

Name ______ Class ______ Date ______

Practice 4-5

Mixed Exercises

Identify the pair of statements that forms a contradiction.

1. I. $ABCD$ is a trapezoid.
   II. $\overline{AB} \parallel \overline{CD}$
   III. $\overline{BC} \parallel \overline{AD}$

2. I. $\overline{AB} \cong \overline{BC}$
   II. $m\angle A + m\angle B = 80$
   III. $\triangle ABC$ is isosceles.

What conclusion follows from each pair of statements?

3. Mrs. Hoefer gives quizzes only on Wednesdays, and tests only on Fridays. Today is Tuesday.
4. If two lines are parallel, their slopes are equal. Lines l and s both have a slope of $-\frac{1}{2}$.

Use indirect reasoning to prove each statement.

5. If Denia spends more than \$6 to buy two items at a concession stand, then at least one of the items she buys costs more than \$3.
6. If Marcus sells three sandwiches for more than \$12, then at least one of the sandwiches costs more than \$4.
7. If Racquel bicycles more than 7 mi total on Tuesday and Wednesday, then she bicycles more than 3.5 mi for at least one of those days.
8. If Dai spends more than \$2.00 to buy four packs of baseball cards, then at least one of the packs of cards he buys costs more than \$.50.

Write the first step of an indirect proof of each statement.

9. $m\angle A = m\angle B$
10. $TUVW$ is a trapezoid.
11. $\overline{EM}$ intersects $\overline{NO}$.
12. $\triangle FGH$ is equilateral.
13. It is sunny outside.
14. $\angle D$ is not obtuse.
15. Write an indirect proof that $m\angle A < 90$.

Exercises MIXED REVIEW

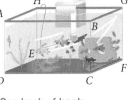

28–31. Answers may vary. Samples are given.

Geometry in 3 Dimensions **Refer to the diagram for Exercises 28–31.**

A B C D E F G H

28. Name two parallel planes. $ABCD$ and $EFGH$

29. Name two intersecting planes. $ABCD$ and $BCFG$

30. Name two skew lines. $\overleftrightarrow{AB}$ and $\overleftrightarrow{DE}$

31. Name four coplanar points. A, B, C, and D

32. a. Use the words *square, rhombus,* and *parallelogram* to write six conditionals in the form "If a figure is a __?__, then it is a __?__." a. See back of book.

b. **Probability** What is the probability that a conditional chosen at random from among the six is true? $\frac{1}{2}$

c. **Probability** What is the probability that the converse of a randomly chosen statement from part (a) is true? $\frac{1}{2}$

d. **Probability** What is the probability that the contrapositive of a randomly chosen statement from part (a) is true? $\frac{1}{2}$

33. **Transformational Geometry** An isometry maps $LEFT \longrightarrow BURN$. Which statement is *not* necessarily true? B

A. $EF = UR$ **B.** $\angle TLE \cong \angle BUR$ **C.** $\angle F \cong \angle R$
D. $LF = BR$ **E.** $FT = RN$

Getting Ready for Lesson 4-6

Coordinate Geometry **Graph the triangles whose vertices are given. List the sides in order from shortest to longest.**

34. $A(5, 0), B(0, 8), C(0, 0)$ $\overline{AC}, \overline{BC}, \overline{AB}$

35. $P(2, 4), Q(-5, 1), R(0, 0)$ $\overline{PR}, \overline{QR}, \overline{PQ}$

36. $G(3, 0), H(4, 3), J(8, 0)$ $\overline{GH}, \overline{HJ} \cong \overline{GJ}$

Lesson Quiz

Lesson Quiz is also available in Transparencies.

1. Identify the pair of statements that forms a contradiction.
   I. $m\angle A + m\angle B = 90$
   II. $\angle A$ and $\angle B$ are acute
   III. $\triangle ABC$ is an acute triangle.
   I and III

2. What conclusion can you draw from the following pair of statements? If the sum of the measures of two angles is 90, the angles are complementary. The measure of one of two angles is 100. **The angles are not complementary.**

3. Write a convincing argument that uses indirect reasoning to show $\sqrt{10} \neq 5$. **Assume $\sqrt{10} = 5$. Then $\sqrt{10}^2 = 5^2$ and $10 = 25$. But $10 \neq 25$, so $\sqrt{10} \neq 5$.**

Math ToolboX

Students review how to use the Properties of Inequality to solve inequalities containing variables. Students will use these skills to solve problems about triangle side lengths and angle measures in Lesson 4-6.

Review the Properties of Inequality with students. Give several examples using numerical values for a, b, c, and d. Remind students that the Addition Property shows subtraction ($a - b = a + (-b)$) and the Multiplication Property shows division $\left(\frac{a}{b} = a\left(\frac{1}{b}\right)\right)$.

ERROR ALERT! Students sometimes change the direction of the inequality sign when they add or subtract a negative number from both sides. **Remediation:** Use a number line to illustrate that subtracting positive and negative numbers from both sides of an inequality does not change the direction of the inequality sign.

Example

Have students check the solution by picking values less than 3 and substituting them into the original inequality.

ADDITIONAL PROBLEM Have students make up an inequality similar to those in the exercises for each of the following solutions: $x < -3$, $x < \frac{1}{2}$, $x \leq 20$, and $x \geq -14$.

Math ToolboX — Algebra Review

Solving Inequalities

Before Lesson 4-6

The solutions of an inequality are all the numbers that make the inequality true. Below is a review of the Properties of Inequality. To solve inequalities you will use the Addition and Multiplication Properties of Inequality.

Properties of Inequality

For all real numbers a, b, c, and d:

Addition	If $a > b$ and $c \geq d$, then $a + c > b + d$.
Multiplication	If $a > b$ and $c > 0$, then $ac > bc$. If $a > b$ and $c < 0$, then $ac < bc$.
Transitive	If $a > b$ and $b > c$, then $a > c$.
Comparison	If $a = b + c$ and $c > 0$, then $a > b$.

Example

Solve $-6x + 7 > 25$.

$-6x + 7 - 7 > 25 - 7$ ← Add -7 to each side (or subtract 7 from each side).

$\frac{-6x}{-6} < \frac{18}{-6}$ ← Multiply each side by $-\frac{1}{6}$ (or divide each side by -6). Remember to reverse the order of the inequality.

$x < -3$ ← Simplify.

Solve each inequality.

1. $7x - 13 \leq -20$ $x \leq -1$
2. $3z + 8 > 16$ $z > 2\frac{2}{3}$
3. $-2x + 5 < 16$ $x > -5\frac{1}{2}$
4. $8y + 2 \geq -14$ $y \geq -2$
5. $5a + 1 \leq 91$ $a \leq 18$
6. $-x - 2 > 17$ $x < -19$
7. $-4z - 10 < -12$ $z > \frac{1}{2}$
8. $9x - 8 \geq 82$ $x \geq 10$
9. $6n + 3 \leq -18$ $n \leq -3\frac{1}{2}$
10. $c + 13 > 34$ $c > 21$
11. $3x - 5x + 2 < 12$ $x > -5$
12. $x - 19 < -78$ $x < -59$
13. $-n - 27 \leq 92$ $n \geq -119$
14. $-9t + 47 < 101$ $t > -6$
15. $8x - 4 + x > -76$ $x > -8$
16. $2(y - 5) > -24$ $y > -7$
17. $8b + 3 \geq 67$ $b \geq 8$
18. $-3(4x - 1) \geq 15$ $x \leq -1$
19. $r - 9 \leq -67$ $r \leq -58$
20. $\frac{1}{2}(4x - 7) \geq 19$ $x \geq 11\frac{1}{4}$
21. $5x - 3x + 2x < -20$ $x < -5$
22. $9x - 10x + 4 < 12$ $x > -8$
23. $-3x - 7x \leq 97$ $x \geq -9.7$
24. $8y - 33 > -1$ $y > 4$
25. $4a + 17 \geq 13$ $a \geq -1$
26. $-4(5z + 2) > 20$ $z < -1\frac{2}{5}$
27. $x + 78 \geq -284$ $x \geq -362$

4-6 Teaching Notes

PROBLEM OF THE DAY

Two face clocks show five o'clock. One clock gains one minute each hour while the other loses 1 minute each hour. In how many hours will both clocks again show the identical time? 360 hours

Problem of the Day is also available in Transparencies.

CONNECTING TO PRIOR KNOWLEDGE Have students solve each of the following inequalities for x. Then have volunteers present their solutions to the class.

$3x - 7 < 5$ $\quad -2x + 4 < 6$ $\quad \frac{x}{4} + 5 > 1$

WORK TOGETHER p. 213

As students try to form triangles, emphasize that the ends of the straws must meet. Provide the following illustration to point out what is not considered a triangle.

ALTERNATIVE METHOD Have students use a compass or drawing software to try to construct triangles with different combinations of the lengths, keeping track of their results in a table.

Connections Architecture . . . and more

4-6 Triangle Inequalities

What You'll Learn

- Using inequalities involving triangle side lengths and angle measures to solve problems

...And Why

To use triangle inequalities in solving real-world problems when only some measures of a triangle are known

What You'll Need

scissors, straws, ruler, protractor

WORK TOGETHER

Work in groups of three. Have each member of your group cut straws into 2-, 3-, 4-, 5-, and 6-in. segments.

- Have each member pick three segments at random and test whether they form a triangle. Continue picking segments until you find three sets of segments that form a triangle and three that do not form a triangle. Record your results in a table like the one shown.

Lengths of Segments			Triangle
No. 1	No. 2	No. 3	Formed?
2	3	4	Yes
2	3	5	No
5	4	3	Yes

1. Pick a row of data that yields a triangle. Compare each quantity.
   a. Segment 1 + Segment 2 ? Segment 3 >
   b. Segment 1 + Segment 3 ? Segment 2 >
   c. Segment 2 + Segment 3 ? Segment 1 >
2. Pick a row of data that does *not* yield a triangle. Use it to complete parts (a)–(c) of Question 1. >, >, and =, or >, >, and < (in any order)
3. Patterns Compare the results of Questions 1 and 2 within your group. Look for a pattern. Write a **conjecture** about the sum of the lengths of two sides of a triangle compared to the length of the third side.

3. The sum of the lengths of any two sides of △ is > the length of the 3rd side.

Lesson Planning Options

Prerequisite Skills

- Solving Inequalities

Assignment Options for Exercises On Your Own

To provide flexible scheduling, this lesson can be subdivided into parts.

 **Core** 1–8, 23
✪**Extension** 31–34

 **Core** 9–22, 24, 27–30
✪**Extension** 25–26, 35–36

Use Mixed Review to maintain skills.

Resources

 **Student Edition**

Skills Handbook, p. 679
Extra Practice, p. 651
Glossary/Study Guide

 **Teaching Resources**

Chapter Support File, Ch. 4
- Practice 4-6 (two worksheets)
- Reteaching 4-6
- Alternative Activity 4-6

Classroom Manager 4-6
Glossary, Spanish Resources

 **Transparencies**

5, 53, 57

THINK AND DISCUSS p. 214

Question 4 Ask students for other real-world examples where they applied the Triangle Inequality Theorem without knowing it. For example, ask them if they have ever crossed a street diagonally.

Example 1

Help students understand that they do not have to check all combinations of sides. Checking that the sum of the lengths of the shorter two sides is greater than the length of the third side is sufficient.

WORK TOGETHER p. 214

Question 6 Point out that the letters *a, b, c, A, B,* and *C* are positioned on the triangle so that *a* is opposite $\angle A$, *b* is opposite $\angle B$, and *c* is opposite $\angle C$.

Question 7 Challenge students to test their conjectures by trying to draw counterexamples.

Additional Examples

FOR EXAMPLE 1

Is it possible for a triangle to have sides with the given lengths? Explain.

a. 2 in., 5 in., 8 in. **No; $2 + 5 \not> 8$.**

b. 4 m, 6 m, 9 m **Yes; $4 + 6 > 9$, $6 + 9 > 4$, and $4 + 9 > 6$.**

Discussion: *Describe how you could change the lengths in part a so a triangle could be formed.*

FOR EXAMPLE 2

A landscape architect is designing a triangular deck with sides 15 ft, 12 ft, and 18 ft. She wants to place flowering plants in the corner with the smallest angle. In which corner should she place the plants? **The corner opposite the 12-ft side**

Discussion: *Describe possible lengths of a triangle where the shortest side is 15 ft.*

214

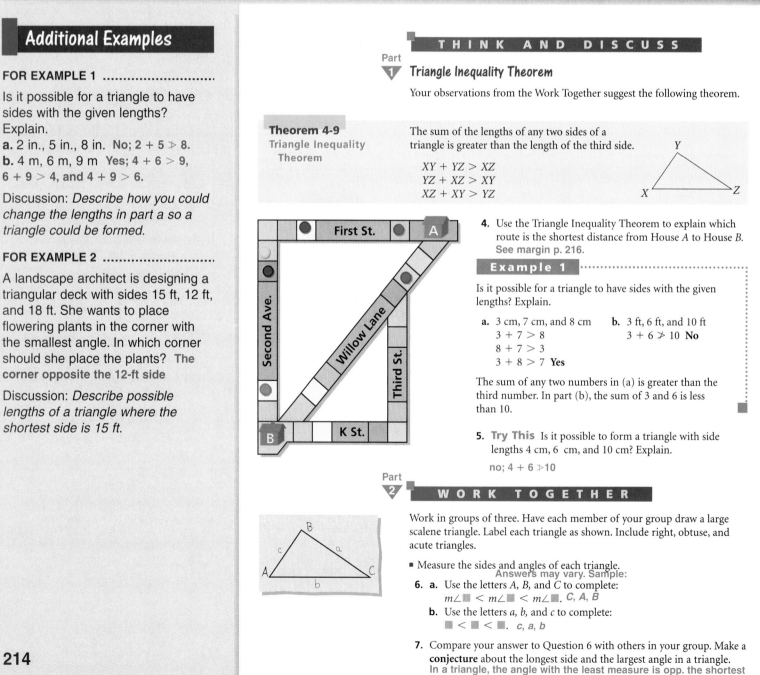

THINK AND DISCUSS

Part 1

Triangle Inequality Theorem

Your observations from the Work Together suggest the following theorem.

Theorem 4-9
Triangle Inequality Theorem

The sum of the lengths of any two sides of a triangle is greater than the length of the third side.

$XY + YZ > XZ$
$YZ + XZ > XY$
$XZ + XY > YZ$

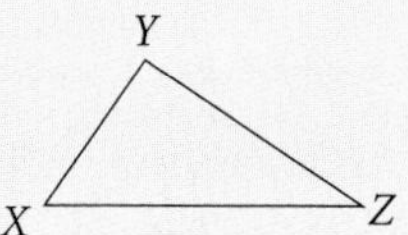

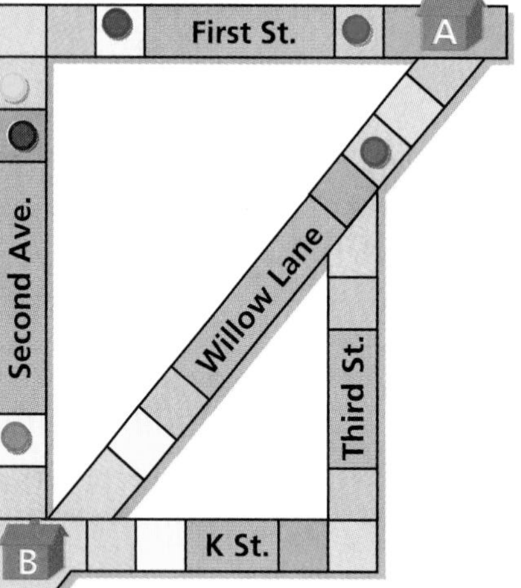

4. Use the Triangle Inequality Theorem to explain which route is the shortest distance from House *A* to House *B*. **See margin p. 216.**

Example 1

Is it possible for a triangle to have sides with the given lengths? Explain.

a. 3 cm, 7 cm, and 8 cm
$3 + 7 > 8$
$8 + 7 > 3$
$3 + 8 > 7$ **Yes**

b. 3 ft, 6 ft, and 10 ft
$3 + 6 \not> 10$ **No**

The sum of any two numbers in (a) is greater than the third number. In part (b), the sum of 3 and 6 is less than 10.

5. **Try This** Is it possible to form a triangle with side lengths 4 cm, 6 cm, and 10 cm? Explain.
no; $4 + 6 \not> 10$

Part 2

WORK TOGETHER

B
c a
A C
b

Work in groups of three. Have each member of your group draw a large scalene triangle. Label each triangle as shown. Include right, obtuse, and acute triangles.

- Measure the sides and angles of each triangle.

Answers may vary. Sample:

6. **a.** Use the letters *A, B,* and *C* to complete: $m\angle\blacksquare < m\angle\blacksquare < m\angle\blacksquare$. **C, A, B**
   b. Use the letters *a, b,* and *c* to complete: $\blacksquare < \blacksquare < \blacksquare$. **c, a, b**

7. Compare your answer to Question 6 with others in your group. Make a **conjecture** about the longest side and the largest angle in a triangle. **In a triangle, the angle with the least measure is opp. the shortest side. The angle with the greatest measure is opp. the longest side.**

THINK AND DISCUSS p. 215

ERROR ALERT! Theorem 4-10 Students may confuse the side opposite an angle with a side adjacent to the angle. **Remediation:** Have students copy $\triangle XYZ$ as shown in the text and use colored pencils to color-code each angle and its opposite side.

TACTILE LEARNING Have students create a flexible triangle using two popsicle sticks held together at one end by a brad and at the other end by an elastic band to make the third side. Students can manipulate the length of the side made by the elastic band and observe how the measure of the angle opposite it changes.

Example 2 Relating to the Real World 

Question 8 Have students construct a triangle with the given side length and measure the angles to check their answers.

Theorem 4-11 Point out to students that the negation of $BC > AC$ is $BC = AC$ or $BC < AC$. Both cases need to be proven false in the indirect proof.

THINK AND DISCUSS

Inequalities Relating Sides and Angles

Your observations in the Work Together lead to Theorems 4-10 and 4-11.

Theorem 4-10

If two sides of a triangle are not congruent, then the larger angle lies opposite the longer side.

If $XZ > XY$, then $m\angle Y > m\angle Z$.

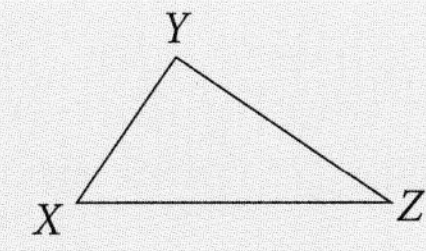

You will justify Theorem 4-10 in Exercise 35.

Example 2 Relating to the Real World 

Architecture A landscape architect is designing a triangular deck. She wants to place benches in the two largest corners. In which corners should she place the benches?

The two largest corners are opposite the two longest sides, 27 ft and 21 ft.

8. **Try This** The sides of a triangle are 14 in., 7 in., and 8 in. long. The smallest angle is opposite which side? 7 in.

Theorem 4-11

If two angles of a triangle are not congruent, then the longer side lies opposite the larger angle.

Indirect Proof of Theorem 4-11

Given: $m\angle A > m\angle B$
Prove: $BC > AC$

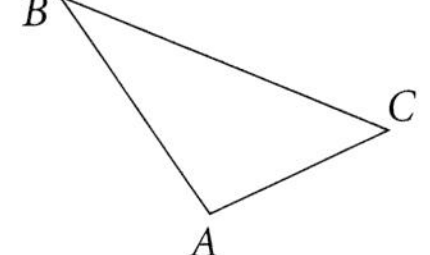

Step 1: Assume $BC \not> AC$. That is, assume $BC < AC$ or $BC = AC$.

Step 2: If $BC < AC$, then $m\angle A < m\angle B$ (Theorem 4-10). That contradicts the given fact that $m\angle A > m\angle B$. Therefore, the assumption that $BC < AC$ must be false.

If $BC = AC$, then $m\angle A = m\angle B$ (Isosceles Triangle Theorem). This also contradicts the given fact that $m\angle A > m\angle B$. Therefore the assumption that $BC = AC$ must be false.

Step 3: Therefore, $BC > AC$ must be true.

Technology Options

For Exercises 1–8, students may use geometry software to try to construct each triangle. For Exercise 25, students may perform the activity described using geometry software.

Prentice Hall Technology 

 **Software**
- Secondary Math Lab Toolkit™
- Computer Item Generator 4-6

 **CD-ROM**
- Multimedia Geometry Lab 4

 **Internet**
- See the Prentice Hall site. (http://www.phschool.com)

Example 3

VISUAL LEARNING To help students see that Theorem 4-10 and 4-11 only apply to one triangle, draw $\triangle XYZ$ similar to $\triangle TUV$. Show that $\angle U < \angle Z$ does not imply that $\overline{TV} < \overline{XY}$.

Exercises ON YOUR OWN

ALTERNATIVE ASSESSMENT **Exercises 1–8** These exercises can be used to assess students' understanding of the Triangle Inequality Theorem. Have students work with partners to suggest a change to one of the side lengths where a triangle cannot be formed so that a triangle can be formed.

Exercises 13–14 Students may need to sketch and label each triangle in order to recognize which segment is opposite each angle.

GEOMETRY IN 3 DIMENSIONS Exercise 22 If possible, provide students with a three-dimensional model of a pyramid to manipulate.

page 214 Think and Discuss

4. Willow Lane; the length of Willow Lane is less than the sum of lengths of First St. and Second Ave. Also, the length of Willow Lane between Third St. and K St. is less than the sum of the lengths of Third St. and K St.

pages 216–218 On Your Own

22. Answers may vary. Sample: For $\triangle PTB$. $\angle T$ is a rt. angle, so the other 2 angles are acute. Then the side opp. $\angle T$ is the longest side in the $\triangle$. Therefore, $PT < PB$. Similarly, PT is $<$ the length of each of the other 3 sides.

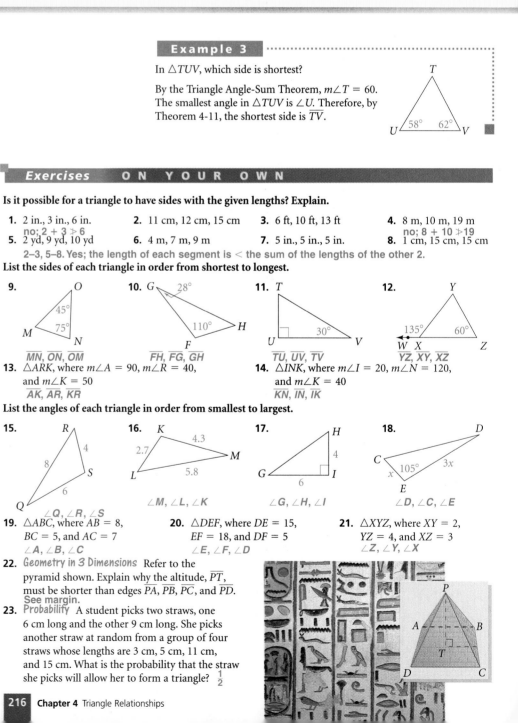

216

Example 3

In $\triangle TUV$, which side is shortest?

By the Triangle Angle-Sum Theorem, $m\angle T = 60$. The smallest angle in $\triangle TUV$ is $\angle U$. Therefore, by Theorem 4-11, the shortest side is $\overline{TV}$.

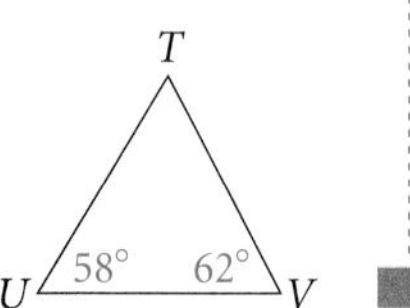

Exercises ON YOUR OWN

Is it possible for a triangle to have sides with the given lengths? Explain.

1. 2 in., 3 in., 6 in. no; $2 + 3 \not> 6$
2. 11 cm, 12 cm, 15 cm
3. 6 ft, 10 ft, 13 ft
4. 8 m, 10 m, 19 m no; $8 + 10 \not> 19$
5. 2 yd, 9 yd, 10 yd
6. 4 m, 7 m, 9 m
7. 5 in., 5 in., 5 in.
8. 1 cm, 15 cm, 15 cm

2–3, 5–8. Yes; the length of each segment is $<$ the sum of the lengths of the other 2.

List the sides of each triangle in order from shortest to longest.

9. 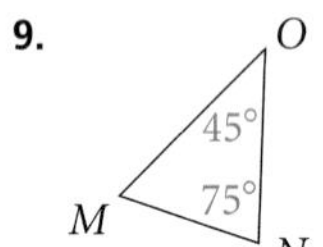

$\overline{MN}, \overline{ON}, \overline{OM}$

10. 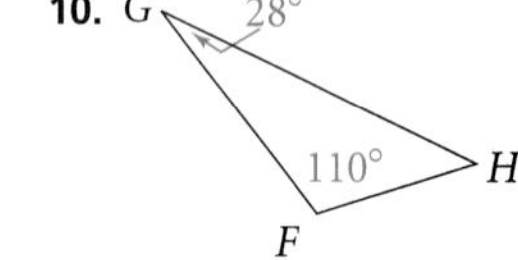

$\overline{FH}, \overline{FG}, \overline{GH}$

11. 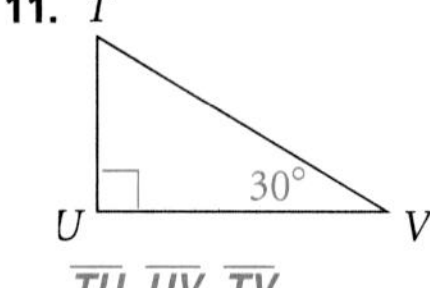

$\overline{TU}, \overline{UV}, \overline{TV}$

12. 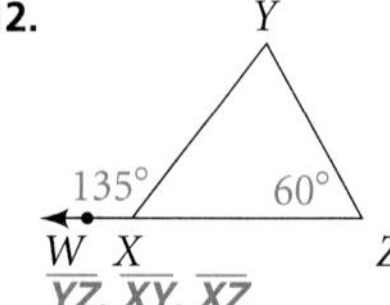

$\overline{YZ}, \overline{XY}, \overline{XZ}$

13. $\triangle ARK$, where $m\angle A = 90$, $m\angle R = 40$, and $m\angle K = 50$ $\overline{AK}, \overline{AR}, \overline{KR}$

14. $\triangle INK$, where $m\angle I = 20$, $m\angle N = 120$, and $m\angle K = 40$ $\overline{KN}, \overline{IN}, \overline{IK}$

List the angles of each triangle in order from smallest to largest.

15. R, S, Q; sides 4, 8, 6
$\angle Q, \angle R, \angle S$

16. K, M, L; sides 4.3, 2.7, 5.8
$\angle M, \angle L, \angle K$

17. 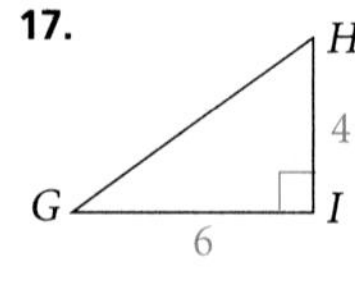

$\angle G, \angle H, \angle I$

18. 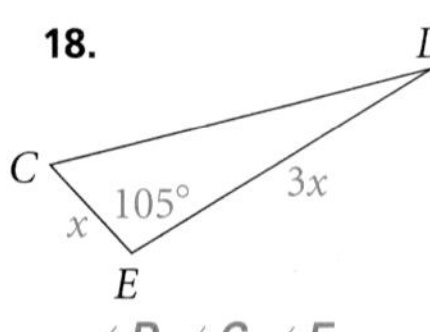

$\angle D, \angle C, \angle E$

19. $\triangle ABC$, where $AB = 8$, $BC = 5$, and $AC = 7$ $\angle A, \angle B, \angle C$

20. $\triangle DEF$, where $DE = 15$, $EF = 18$, and $DF = 5$ $\angle E, \angle F, \angle D$

21. $\triangle XYZ$, where $XY = 2$, $YZ = 4$, and $XZ = 3$ $\angle Z, \angle Y, \angle X$

22. *Geometry in 3 Dimensions* Refer to the pyramid shown. Explain why the altitude, $\overline{PT}$, must be shorter than edges $\overline{PA}$, $\overline{PB}$, $\overline{PC}$, and $\overline{PD}$. See margin.

23. *Probability* A student picks two straws, one 6 cm long and the other 9 cm long. She picks another straw at random from a group of four straws whose lengths are 3 cm, 5 cm, 11 cm, and 15 cm. What is the probability that the straw she picks will allow her to form a triangle? $\frac{1}{2}$

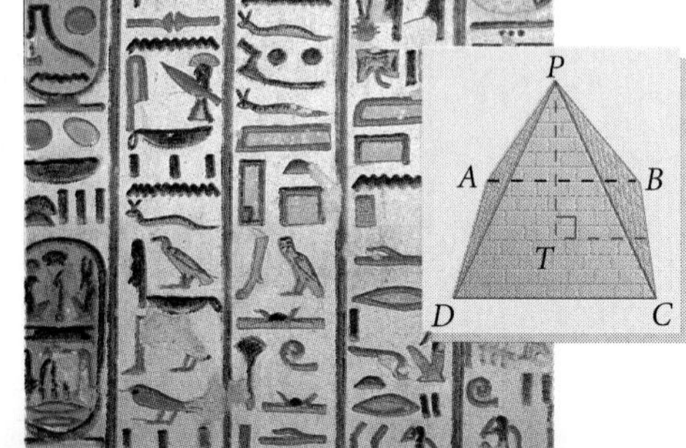

PROBABILITY Exercise 23 Suggest that students make a chart, as they did in the Work Together on page 213, listing the possible combinations of side lengths and the results.

STANDARDIZED TEST TIP Exercise 24 A common error is for students to pair $a°$ with 15 and $b°$ with 16.

TECHNOLOGY Exercise 25 In part a, have students copy the spreadsheet and add two columns "$m\angle FAC$ __?__ $m\angle HDE$" and "FC __?__ HE," to keep track of the comparisons for each row.

Exercise 30 Make sure that students do not conclude that $XY = WZ$ because $m\angle XWY = m\angle WZY$.

24. *Standardized Test Prep* Compare the quantities in Columns A and B. Select the best answer. **A**

Column A	Column B
a	b

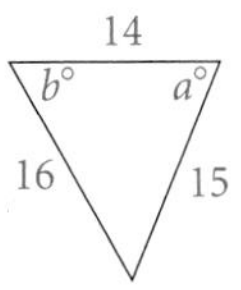

A. The quantity in Column A is greater.
B. The quantity in Column B is greater.
C. The quantities are equal.
D. The relationship cannot be determined from the information given.

25. *Technology* Darren used geometry software to draw $\triangle ACF$ and $\triangle DEH$ so that $\overline{AC} \cong \overline{DE}$ and $\overline{AF} \cong \overline{DH}$. He then manipulated point H to collect the data in the spreadsheet. $<,<;\ <,<;\ <,<;\ >,>;\ >,>$

a. Compare these values for each row of the spreadsheet.
$m\angle FAC$ __?__ $m\angle HDE$ $\qquad$ FC __?__ HE

b. *Patterns* What pattern do you notice in part (a)?

c. The pattern that you noticed is stated as the Hinge Theorem. Complete the theorem:
Hinge Theorem *If two sides of one triangle are congruent to two sides of another triangle, and the included angle of the first triangle is greater than the included angle of the second triangle, then* __?__.

b–c. See margin.

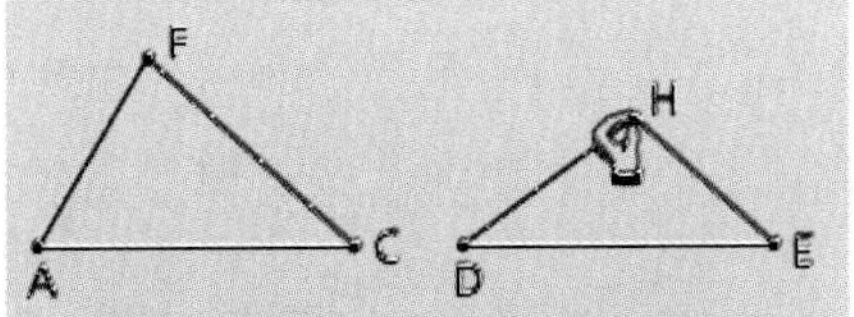

	∠FAC	∠HDE	FC	HE
1	58.3	104.3	3.21	4.98
2	58.3	94.2	3.21	4.64
3	58.3	65.2	3.21	3.50
4	58.3	50.7	3.21	2.88
5	58.3	34.7	3.21	2.18

26. *Critical Thinking* Pliers, scissors, and many other tools are hinged. When the angle between the blades of a pair of scissors increases, what happens to the distance between the tips of the blades? Explain how this relates to the Hinge Theorem in Exercise 25. **See margin.**

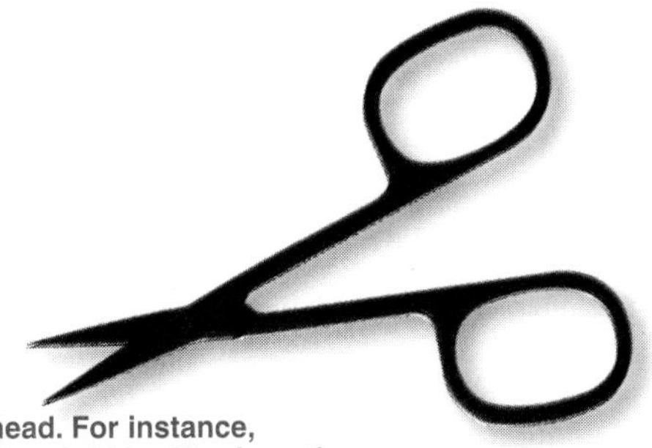

27. *Critical Thinking* The Shau family is crossing Kansas on Highway 70. A sign reads "Topeka 110 miles, Wichita 90 miles." Avi says, "I didn't know that it was only 20 miles from Topeka to Wichita." Explain to Avi why the distance between the two cities doesn't have to be 20 miles. **The 2 cities may not be both straight ahead. For instance, Topeka might be 110 mi east, and Wichita might be 90 mi south.**

Critical Thinking **Which segment is the shortest?**

28. $\overline{RS}$

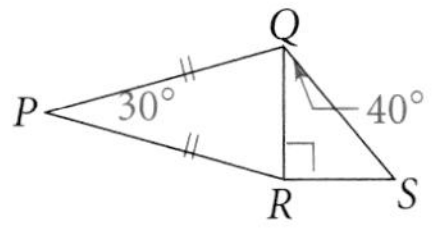

29. $\overline{CD}$

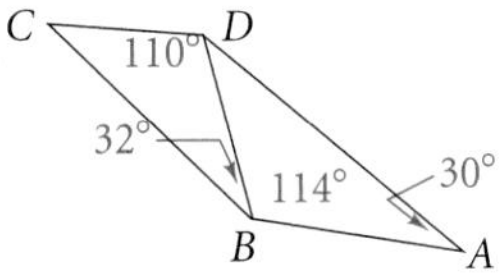

30. $\overline{XY}$

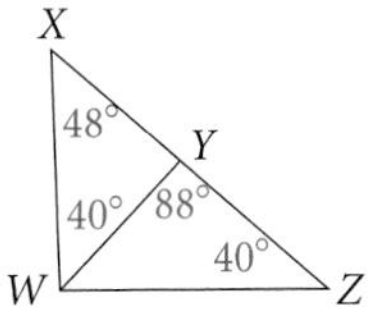

The lengths of two sides of a triangle are given. Write an inequality to represent the range of values for *z*, the length of the third side.

31. 8 ft, 12 ft $\quad$ **$4 < z < 20$**

32. 5 in., 16 in. $\quad$ **$11 < z < 21$**

33. 6 cm, 6 cm $\quad$ **$0 < z < 12$**

34. x, y, where $x \geq y$ $\quad$ **$x - y < z < x + y$**

25b. The directions of each pair of inequalities match.

c. The 3rd side of the 1st triangle is longer than the 3rd side of the 2nd triangle.

26. The distance increases; the hinge and the tips of the scissors form a triangle with 2 sides of fixed length.

36. By Triangle Angle-Sum Thm., $m\angle P + m\angle PAT + m\angle PTA = 180$. $m\angle PTA = 90$, so $m\angle P + m\angle PAT = 90$. Then $m\angle PAT < 90$. Therefore, $m\angle PTA > m\angle PAT$. Since the longer side lies opp. the larger angle, $PA > PT$.

Exercise 36 Students may have already been using this corollary unconsciously when measuring the distance between a point and a line.

Exercises MIXED REVIEW

Exercise 37 Students can use a graph to find the coordinates of *S′* and *Y′* or find the direction vector and add its coordinates to the coordinates of *S* and *Y*.

JOURNAL Encourage students to do more than just restate the theorems. Ask them to explain in their own words the key points in the lesson, and to organize them in a way that makes most sense to them.

GETTING READY FOR LESSON 4-7 These exercises prepare students for solving locus problems.

Wrap Up

THE BIG IDEA Ask students: *Suppose you are asked to make a triangle with side lengths 5 cm, 12 cm, and 13 cm. Is it possible? If yes, explain which angle would be the largest.*

RETEACHING ACTIVITY Each student draws an obtuse, an acute, and an equilateral triangle. Then each student exchanges triangles with a partner and describes the relationship between the sides and angles of the partner's triangles. (Reteaching worksheet 4-6)

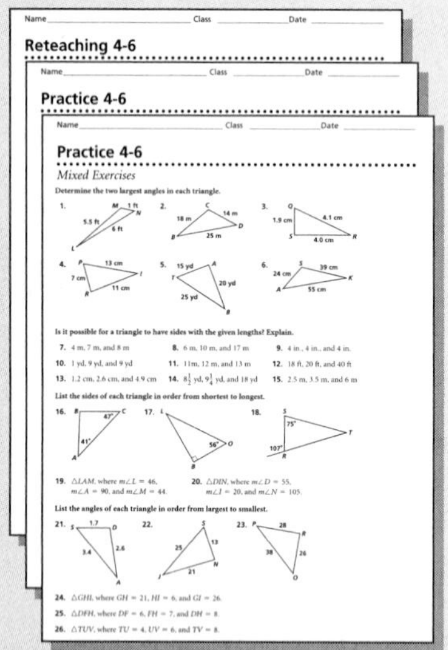
Reteaching 4-6
Practice 4-6
Practice 4-6
Mixed Exercises

Lesson Quiz

Lesson Quiz is also available in Transparencies.

1. Is it possible for a triangle to have sides with lengths 5 ft, 8 ft, and 2 ft? Explain. **No, by the Triangle Inequality Theorem, the sum of the lengths of any two sides of a triangle is greater than the length of the third side. 5 + 2 < 8 so a triangle cannot be formed.**
2. $m\angle B = 60$, $m\angle K = 20$, and $m\angle R = 100$. List the sides of $\triangle BKR$ in order from the shortest to the longest. **$\overline{BR}$, $\overline{KR}$, $\overline{BK}$**
3. $GT = 5$, $TE = 8$, and $GE = 12$. List the angles of $\triangle GTE$ in order from smallest to largest. **$\angle E$, $\angle G$, $\angle T$**

35. **Preparing for Proof** Theorem 4-10 states: If two sides of a triangle are not congruent, then the larger angle lies opposite the longer side. To prove this theorem, begin with $\triangle TOY$, with $OY > TY$. Find P on $\overline{OY}$ so that $\overline{TY} \cong \overline{PY}$. Draw $\overline{TP}$. Supply a reason for each statement.

Given: $OY > TY$ and $\overline{TY} \cong \overline{PY}$

Prove: $m\angle OTY > m\angle 3$

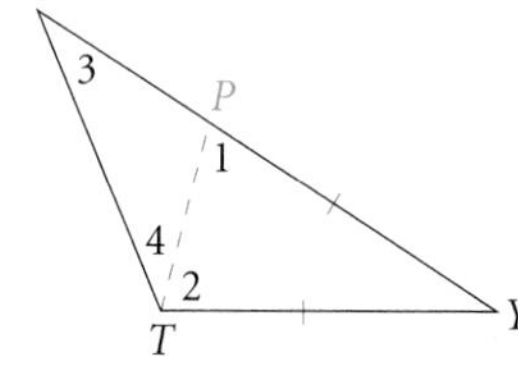

Statements	Reasons
1. $\overline{YP} \cong \overline{YT}$	a. ? Given
2. $m\angle 1 = m\angle 2$	b. ? Isosceles Triangle Thm.
3. $m\angle OTY = m\angle 4 + m\angle 2$	c. ? Angle Addition Post.
4. $m\angle OTY > m\angle 2$	4. Comparison Prop. of Ineq. (p. 212)
5. $m\angle OTY > m\angle 1$	d. ? Substitution
6. $m\angle 1 = m\angle 3 + m\angle 4$	e. ? Exterior Angle Thm.
7. $m\angle 1 > m\angle 3$	7. Comparison Prop. of Ineq.
8. $m\angle OTY > m\angle 3$	f. ? Transitive Prop. of Inequality

36. **Logical Reasoning** A corollary to Theorem 4-11 states: The perpendicular segment from a point to a line is the shortest segment from the point to the line. Show that $PA > PT$, given that $\overline{PT} \perp \overline{TA}$. See margin p. 217.

Exercises MIXED REVIEW

37. **Transformational Geometry** $\triangle SKY$ has vertices $S(-1, 0)$, $K(3, 8)$, and $Y(5, 4)$. A translation maps K to $K'(2, 1)$. Find the coordinates of the images of S and Y under this translation. **$S'(-2, -7)$, $Y'(4, -3)$**

38. **Open-ended** Use a rhombus to create a tessellation. **See below right.**

39. Find the measure of an interior angle and an exterior angle of a regular 15-gon. **156; 24**

Getting Ready for Lesson 4-7

Describe the set of red points in terms of their distance from the set of blue points.

40.

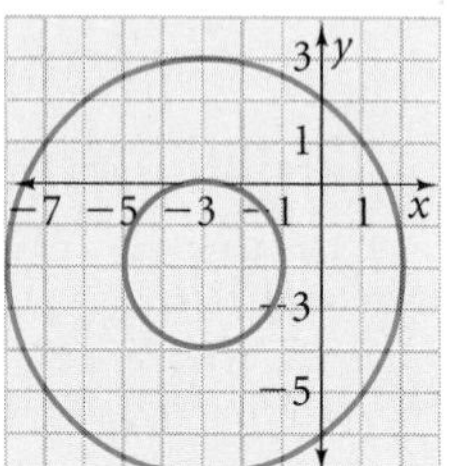

The set of red pts. is 3 units from the set of blue pts.

41.

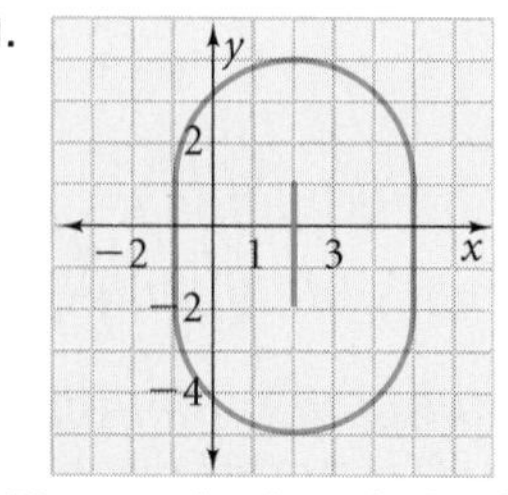

The set of red pts. is 3 units from the set of blue pts.

FOR YOUR JOURNAL

Write a summary of the key points of this lesson. Include diagrams with your summary where appropriate.

38.

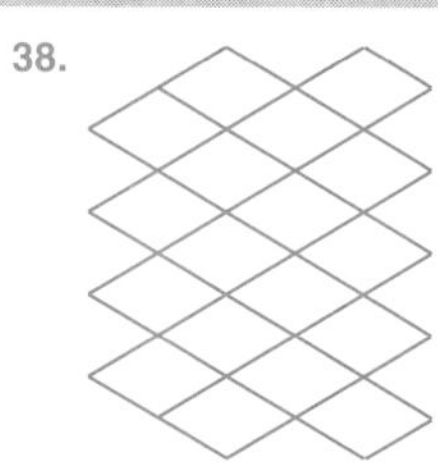

4-7 Teaching Notes

PROBLEM OF THE DAY

Substitute a different number for each letter to make the following statement true:

```
  HALF
+ HALF
 WHOLE
```

Possible answer: 9703 + 9703 = 19,406

Problem of the Day is also available in Transparencies.

CONNECTING TO PRIOR KNOWLEDGE Have students describe all the objects that are one foot away and six feet away from them. Make sure they describe objects in all directions including above and below them.

WORK TOGETHER

Have students work with a partner. One students can do the drawing and measuring and the other can record the answers to the questions.

EXTENSION Have students review the triangles they drew in the Work Together. Ask them to explain the relationship between the location of the vertex on the perpendicular bisector and the angles of the triangle.

THINK AND DISCUSS

ESL **Question 6** As students write the biconditional, check that they understand the meaning of the term "equidistant." They may want to rewrite this word as "equally distant."

Connections Landmarks . . . and more

4-7 Bisectors and Locus

What You'll Learn

- Using properties of angle bisectors and perpendicular bisectors
- Solving locus problems

...And Why

To learn methods used by circuit designers and many other professionals who solve problems in which stated conditions must be met

What You'll Need

straightedge, compass, ruler, MIRA™

TECHNOLOGY HINT

The Work Together could be done using geometry software.

4b. To construct the ⊥ bisector of a segment, you find 2 pts. that are equidistant from the endpts. The line through these pts. is the ⊥ bisector.

6. A pt. is on the ⊥ bisector of a segment if and only if it is equidistant from the endpts. of the segment.

WORK TOGETHER

- Draw a segment and construct its perpendicular bisector by using a straightedge and a compass or a MIRA™.
- Draw a point on the perpendicular bisector and then draw segments connecting this point to the endpoints of the segment.

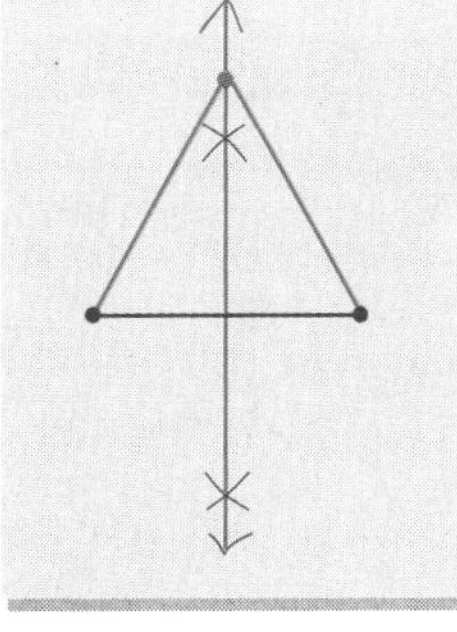

1. Compare the lengths of the segments. What do you notice? The lengths are =.
2. Repeat this process with some other points. Does what you noticed still hold true? yes
3. Use what you discovered to complete this statement: If a point is on the perpendicular bisector of a segment, then __?__. it is equidistant from the endpts. of the segment
4. a. Write the converse of the statement you completed in Question 3.
   b. Explain how the converse is related to the method you use to construct a perpendicular bisector. See left.
   4a. If a point is equidistant from the endpts. of a segment, then it is on the ⊥ bisector of the segment.

THINK AND DISCUSS

Part 1

Perpendicular Bisectors and Locus

The properties you discovered in the Work Together are summarized in the following theorems.

Theorem 4-12 Perpendicular Bisector Theorem

If a point is on the perpendicular bisector of a segment, then it is equidistant from the endpoints of the segment.

Theorem 4-13 Converse of Perpendicular Bisector Theorem

If a point is equidistant from the endpoints of a segment, then it is on the perpendicular bisector of the segment.

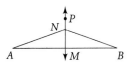

5. a. Given that $AN = BN$, what can you conclude about point N? N is a pt. on the ⊥ bisector of $\overline{AB}$.
   b. Given that $\overleftrightarrow{MP}$ is the perpendicular bisector of $\overline{AB}$, what can you conclude about AN and BN? about $\triangle ABN$? $AN = BN$; $\triangle ABN$ is an isosceles △.
6. Rewrite the two theorems as a single biconditional statement. See left above.

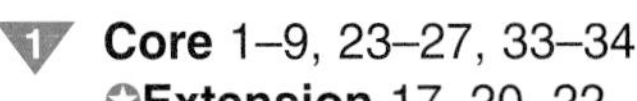

Lesson Planning Options

Prerequisite Skills

- Constructing perpendicular bisectors
- Drawing angle bisectors

Assignment Options for Exercises On Your Own

To provide flexible scheduling, this lesson can be subdivided into parts.

1 **Core** 1–9, 23–27, 33–34
✪**Extension** 17–20, 22

2 **Core** 10–16, 21, 28–32
✪**Extension** 35–37

Use Mixed Review to maintain skills.

Resources

Student Edition

Skills Handbook, p. 660
Extra Practice, p. 651
Glossary/Study Guide

Teaching Resources

Chapter Support File, Ch. 4
- Practice 4-7(two worksheets)
- Reteaching 4-7
- Alternative Activity 4-7

Classroom Manager 4-7
Glossary, Spanish Resources

Transparencies
20, 54

KINESTHETIC LEARNING The following activity will help demonstrate the properties of a perpendicular bisector. Have two students stand in opposite corners of the classroom. Stand on the perpendicular bisector of the segment joining the two students. Ask the class to describe your distance from the students. Move along and off the perpendicular bisector and have students discuss how your distance from the students changes.

Example 1 **Relating to the Real World**

Help students see that the intersection of the red segment and line *m* is the point that is the shortest equal distance from the landmarks. As you move away from the point of intersection along line *m*, the distance between the landmarks remains equal but gets longer.

Point out to students that the term "locus" comes from the Latin word for location and that its plural is "loci" (pronounced low-sigh).

Example 2

ERROR ALERT! Some students may think that point *C* is part of the locus. **Remediation:** Point out that *C* does not meet the condition "set of all points 1 cm from *C*."

Additional Examples

FOR EXAMPLE 2

Draw a point. Label it *B*. Sketch the locus of points in a plane that are 2 cm from point *B*. **Students' sketches should be a circle with center *B* and radius 2 cm.**

Discussion: *How would your sketch change if the locus contained all the points 2 cm or less from point B?*

FOR EXAMPLE 3

What is the common name for the part of a baseball field between the foul lines and beyond the infield? **outfield**

Discussion: *Describe the locations of other common places on a baseball field.*

220

9. 1 cm V C

7. Given isosceles triangle $\triangle URI$ with vertex angle $\angle R$, what does Theorem 4-13 tell you about point *R*? **R is on the $\perp$ bisector of $\overline{UI}$.**

Example 1 **Relating to the Real World** 

National Landmarks Find the set of points in Washington, D.C., that are equidistant from the Jefferson Memorial and the White House.

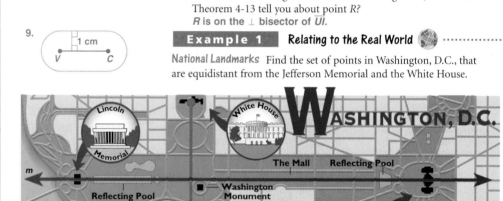

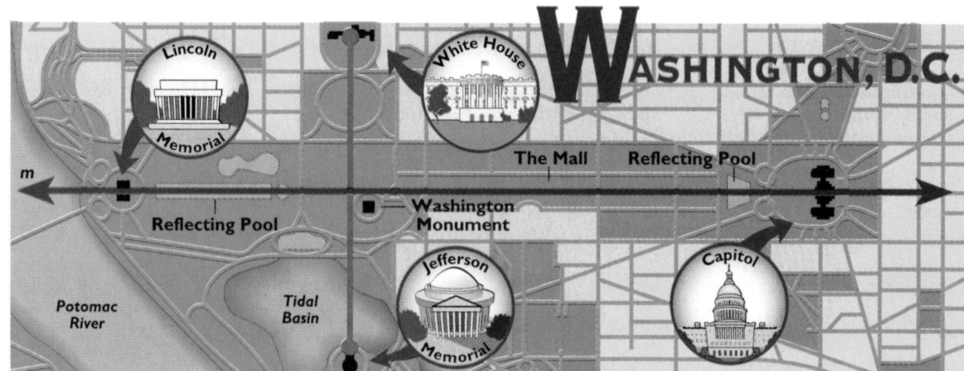

The red segment connects the Jefferson Memorial and the White House. All points on the perpendicular bisector *m* of this segment are equidistant from its endpoints. The perpendicular bisector passes through some of Washington's most famous landmarks.

8. For which landmarks does line *m* appear to be a line of symmetry? **the Lincoln Memorial, the U.S. Capitol, the Reflecting Pool**

Example 1 involves the concept of locus. A **locus** is a set of points that meets a stated condition. In Example 1, the condition is "equidistant from the Jefferson Memorial and the White House." The locus is the perpendicular bisector of the segment connecting the two landmarks.

Who? Benjamin Banneker (1731–1806) was an American astronomer, farmer, mathematician, and surveyor. In 1791, Banneker assisted in laying out the boundaries of Washington, D.C.

Example 2

Sketch the locus of points in a plane that are 1 cm from point *C*.

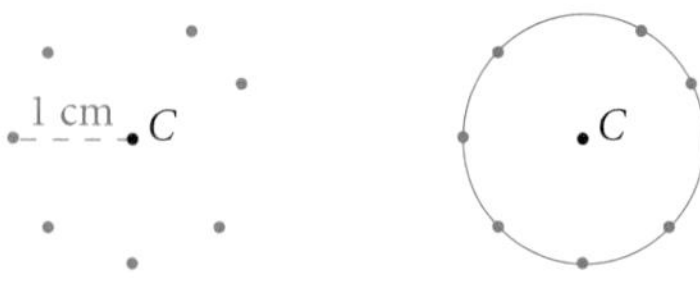

Locate several points 1 cm from *C*. Keep doing so until you see a pattern. The locus is a circle with center *C* and radius 1 cm.

9. **Try This** Sketch the locus of points in a plane that are 1 cm from a segment $\overline{VC}$. **See left above.**

TACTILE LEARNING **Question 10** Have students cut out large circles and tape straws along their diameters. By rotating the straw around, students will see that the circle traces out a sphere.

Help students see that a locus in a plane can be a two-dimensional figure and a locus in space can be a three-dimensional figure.

Question 11 You may want to suggest that students use the triangle inequalities from Lesson 4-6.

WORK TOGETHER p. 221

Have students work with a partner. Make sure students refer to the diagrams to help them see how to create the angle bisector and perpendicular segments.

10. What would the locus be in Example 2 if the words "in a plane" were replaced with "in space"?
The locus in space is a sphere of radius 1 cm with center C.

As the answer to Question 10 implies, a locus of points in a plane and a locus of points in space can be quite different. For example, consider this condition: all points 3 cm from line ℓ.

11.
By Triangle Angle-Sum Thm., $m\angle A + m\angle ABC + m\angle ACB = 180$. $m\angle ABC = 90$, so $m\angle ACB + m\angle A = 90$. Then $m\angle ACB < 90$ and $m\angle A < 90$. Therefore, $m\angle ACB < m\angle ABC$. Since the longer side lies opp. the larger angle, $AB < AC$.

The locus in a plane looks like this . . .

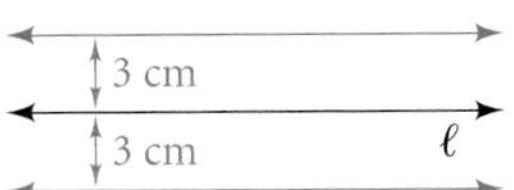

The locus is two parallel lines, each 3 cm from line ℓ.

The locus in space looks like this . . .

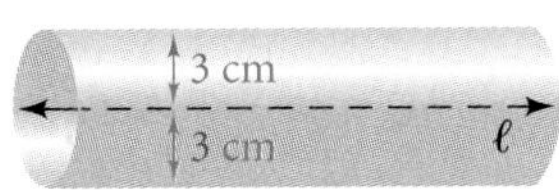

The locus is an endless cylinder with radius 3 cm and center-line ℓ.

QUICK REVIEW

To bisect an angle using paper folding, fold the paper so that the sides of the angle overlap.

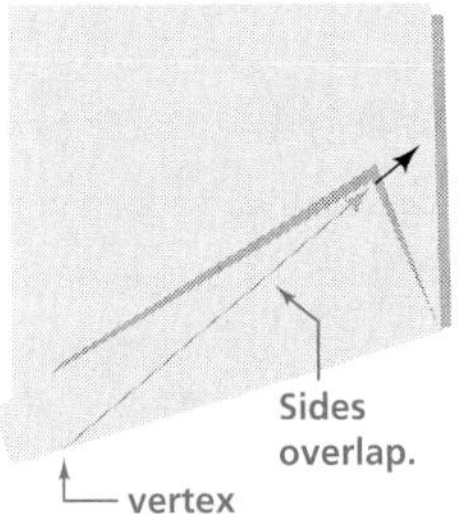

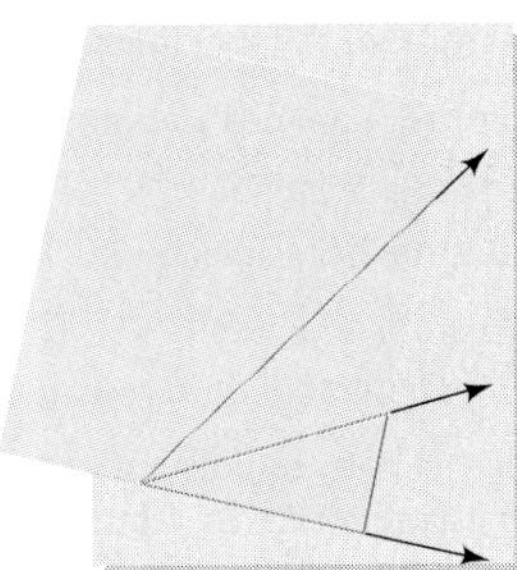

Part 2

Angle Bisectors and Locus

The Work Together below involves the distance from a point to a line. The **distance from a point to a line** is the length of the perpendicular segment from the point to the line.

11. Let C be any point on line n other than B. Show that $AB < AC$.
See left.

WORK TOGETHER

- Draw an angle and use paper folding to create its bisector.
- Draw a point on the bisector. Use the corner of a piece of paper to create perpendicular segments from both sides of the angle to the point.

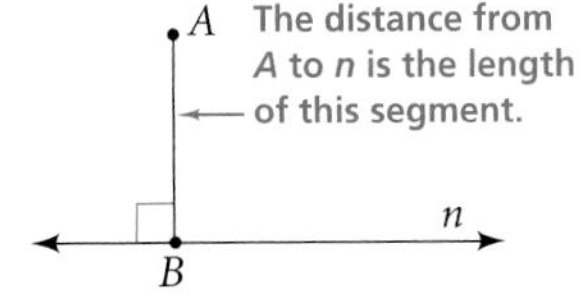

12. Measure the lengths of the two segments you drew. What do you notice? The lengths are =.

13. Repeat with two other points. Does what you noticed still hold true?
yes

14. Use what you discovered to complete the statement: If a point is on the bisector of an angle, then __?__.
the point is equidistant from the sides of the angle

Technology Options

For Exercises 1–12, students may sketch each locus using geometry software. For Exercises 23–28, students may use geometry software to sketch each locus on a coordinate plane.

Prentice Hall Technology

Software
- Secondary Math Lab Toolkit™
- Computer Item Generator 4-7

CD-ROM
- Multimedia Geometry Lab 4

Internet
- See the Prentice Hall site. (http://www.phschool.com)

THINK AND DISCUSS

ALTERNATIVE ASSESSMENT **Question 15** To assess students' understanding of the difference between Theorems 4-14 and 4-15, have students justify each conclusion with the appropriate theorem.

Example 3 **Relating to the Real World**

When a locus problem has two parts that must be satisfied, emphasize that students should find the points that satisfy each condition individually, then look at where the loci intersect.

VISUAL LEARNING Students may benefit from sketching the locus of points for each condition on separate pieces of tracing paper and laying them over each other to see where they intersect.

CONNECTING TO STUDENTS' WORLD Have students describe a location on a sports field, in a band formation, on a dance team, and so on, as a locus with two parts.

pages 223–225 On Your Own

1.

2.

3.

4.

5.

6.

7.

8.

9.

THINK AND DISCUSS

The property that you discovered in the Work Together is stated below. Its converse, which also is true, follows it.

Theorem 4-14 Angle Bisector Theorem	If a point is on the bisector of an angle, then it is equidistant from the sides of the angle.
Theorem 4-15 Converse of Angle Bisector Theorem	If a point in the interior of an angle is equidistant from the sides of the angle, then it is on the angle bisector.

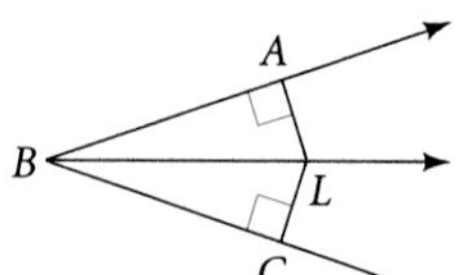

15. **a.** Given that $m\angle ABL = m\angle CBL$, what can you conclude about AL and CL? $AL = CL$

b. Given that $AL = CL$, what can you conclude about $m\angle ABL$ and $m\angle CBL$? $m\angle ABL = m\angle CBL$

16. What is the locus of all points in the interior of an angle that are equidistant from the sides of the angle? the angle bisector

Sometimes the condition in a locus problem has more than one part.

Example 3 **Relating to the Real World** 

Sports What is a common name for the part of a baseball field that is equidistant from the foul lines and 60 ft 6 in. from home plate?

There are two parts to the condition stated in the problem.

Part 1: Equidistant from the foul lines

The red angle bisector contains all points equidistant from the foul lines.

Part 2: 60 ft 6 in. from home plate

The blue arc contains all points 60 ft 6 in. from home plate.

The pitcher's plate is both equidistant from the foul lines and 60 ft 6 in. from home plate.

Exercises ON YOUR OWN

Exercises 4, 5 and 12 Students may have difficulty sketching three-dimensional figures. Suggest they use descriptions to clarify their drawings.

COORDINATE GEOMETRY Exercise 14 This exercise helps students make the connection between algebra skills and geometry concepts.

STANDARDIZED TEST TIP **Exercise 16** Students may not realize that a radius can be drawn to any point on the circle and thus any point on the circle is two units from the origin.

LOGICAL REASONING Exercise 20 Have students work in small groups to discuss Rosie's reasoning. Suggest that they use sketches to illustrate their thinking.

Exercises ON YOUR OWN

Sketch and label each locus. 1–9. See margin p. 222. 10–12. See margin.

1. all points in a plane 4 cm from a point X
2. all points in a plane 1 in. from a line $\overleftrightarrow{UV}$
3. all points in a plane 1 in. from a segment $\overline{UV}$
4. all points in space 3 cm from a point F
5. all points in space a distance a from a line $\overleftrightarrow{DE}$
6. all points in a plane 1 in. from a circle with radius 0.5 in.
7. all points in a plane equidistant from two parallel lines
8. all points in a plane equidistant from the endpoints of $\overline{PQ}$
9. all points in space equidistant from two parallel lines
10. all points in a plane equidistant from $\overleftrightarrow{MN}$ and $\overleftrightarrow{OP}$ where $\overleftrightarrow{MN} \perp \overleftrightarrow{OP}$
11. all points in a plane 3 cm from $\overline{GH}$ and 5 cm from G, where $GH = 4.5$ cm
12. all points equidistant from two parallel planes

13. Find the locus of points equidistant from the sides of $\angle JKL$ and on $\odot C$.
13. The locus is the two points at which the bisector of $\angle JKL$ intersects $\odot C$.

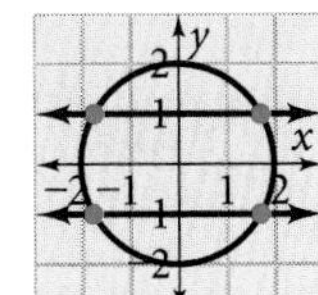

14. *Coordinate Geometry* Write an equation for the locus of points equidistant from (2, −3) and (6, 1). $y = -x + 3$

15. *Sports* What is the common name for the part of a baseball field that is equidistant from first and third bases and 127 ft from home plate? second base

16. *Standardized Test Prep* The highlighted points are the locus of points on the coordinate plane that are C
    - A. 2 units from the origin and 1 unit from the y-axis.
    - B. 1 unit from the origin and 2 units from the y-axis.
    - C. 2 units from the origin and 1 unit from the x-axis.
    - D. 1 unit from the origin and 2 units from the x-axis.
    - E. none of the above

17. a. What is the locus of the tip of the minute hand on a clock?
    b. What is the locus of the tip of the hour hand on a clock?
    a. a circle b. a (smaller) circle

18. *Open-ended* The smoke trails of the jets show the paths that they travel. Find a picture from a book or magazine or draw a sketch that shows an object and its path. Check students' work.

19. *Open-ended* Give two examples of locus from everyday life, one in a plane and one in space. See margin.

20. *Logical Reasoning* Rosie says that it is impossible to find a point equidistant from three collinear points. Is she correct? Explain your thinking.

See margin.

10.

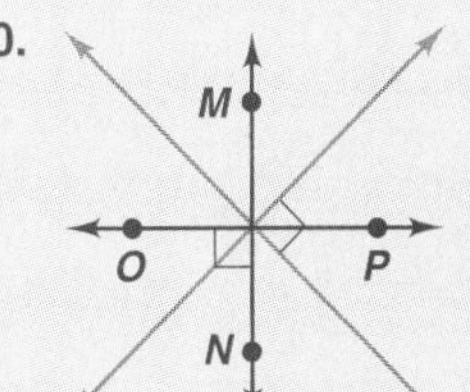

11.

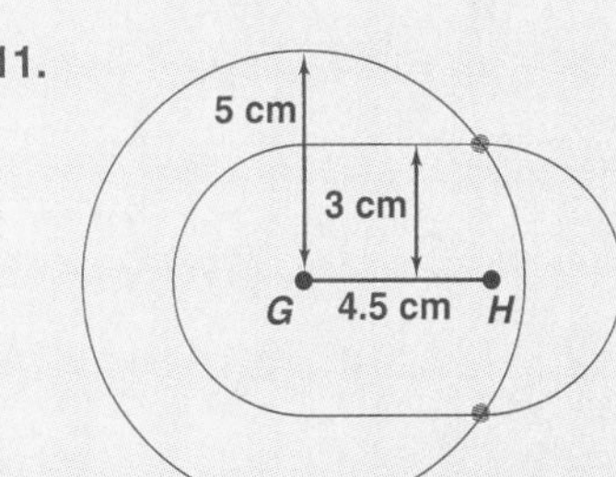

12.

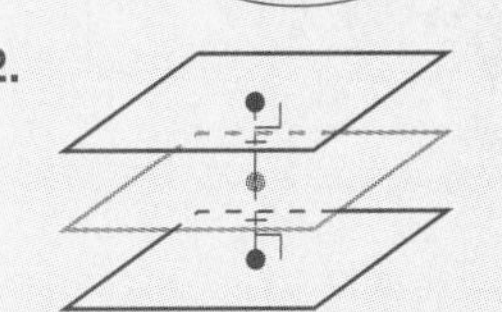

19. Sample: The 50-yd line is the locus of all the pts. on a football field equidistant from the endlines; a soap bubble is the locus of all pts. at a given distance from its center.

20. Yes; the locus of pts. equidistant from the 1st and 2nd pts. is the ⊥ bisector of the segment connecting these pts. The locus of pts. equidistant from the 2nd and 3rd pts. is the ⊥ bisector of the segment connecting them. The 2 segments are collinear. So the 2 bisectors are ⊥ to a line. Therefore, the bisectors are ∥ and do not intersect. This means that there are no pts. in the locus.

CONNECTING TO STUDENTS' WORLD Exercise 21 Have students bring in local maps. Have them write locus problems with two parts to describe different locations on the map. Then have them exchange problems and maps and have other students find the locations.

OPEN-ENDED Exercise 22 While there are many correct answers, make sure that students' examples are accurate in terms of size and not just in terms of shape.

COORDINATE GEOMETRY Exercises 23–28 Suggest that students plot a few points satisfying each condition before describing all the points in the locus.

Exercises 35–37 A locus can be used to describe a path. Before students begin these exercises, discuss an example with students such as the locus of points in the path of a ball thrown into the air which is a parabola.

Chapter Project **FIND OUT BY WRITING** Have students work in groups to generate ideas for puzzles. After students complete their puzzles, have the group evaluate them for clarity, organization, and accuracy.

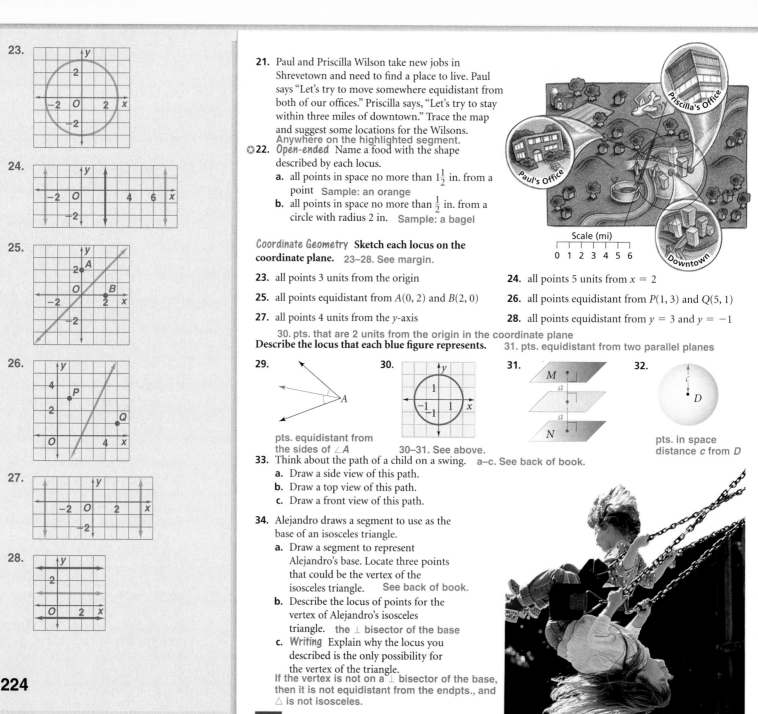

23.

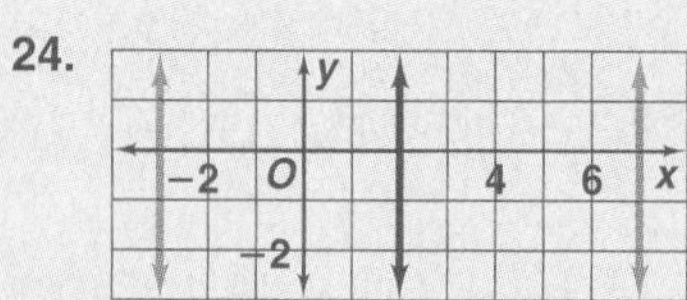

24.

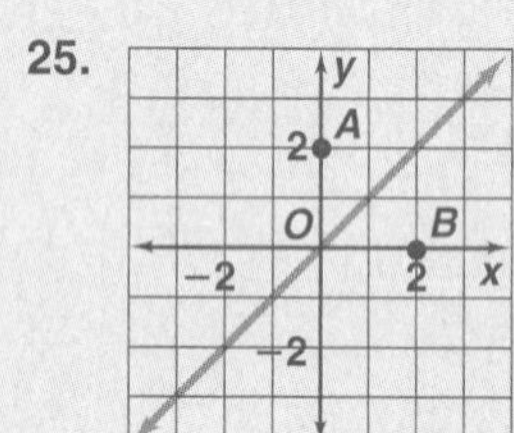

25.

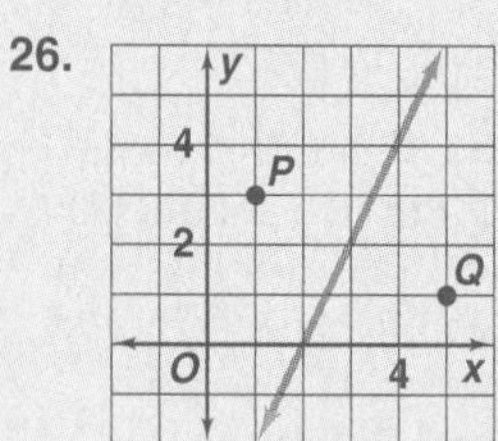

26.

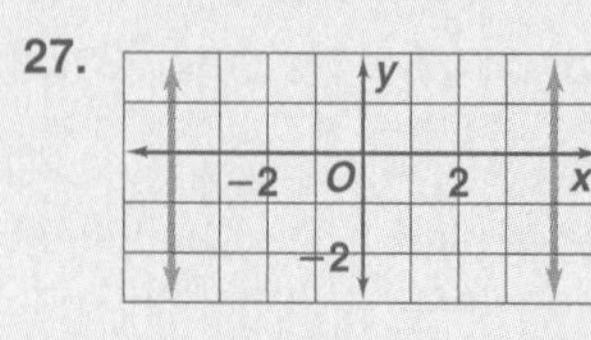

27.

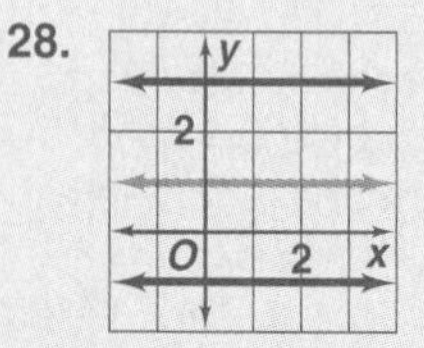

28.

224

21. Paul and Priscilla Wilson take new jobs in Shrevetown and need to find a place to live. Paul says "Let's try to move somewhere equidistant from both of our offices." Priscilla says, "Let's try to stay within three miles of downtown." Trace the map and suggest some locations for the Wilsons. Anywhere on the highlighted segment.

22. *Open-ended* Name a food with the shape described by each locus.

a. all points in space no more than $1\frac{1}{2}$ in. from a point Sample: an orange

b. all points in space no more than $\frac{1}{2}$ in. from a circle with radius 2 in. Sample: a bagel

Coordinate Geometry **Sketch each locus on the coordinate plane.** 23–28. See margin.

23. all points 3 units from the origin

24. all points 5 units from $x = 2$

25. all points equidistant from $A(0, 2)$ and $B(2, 0)$

26. all points equidistant from $P(1, 3)$ and $Q(5, 1)$

27. all points 4 units from the y-axis

28. all points equidistant from $y = 3$ and $y = -1$

Describe the locus that each blue figure represents.

29.

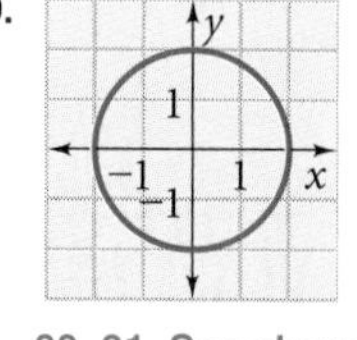

pts. equidistant from the sides of $\angle A$

30.

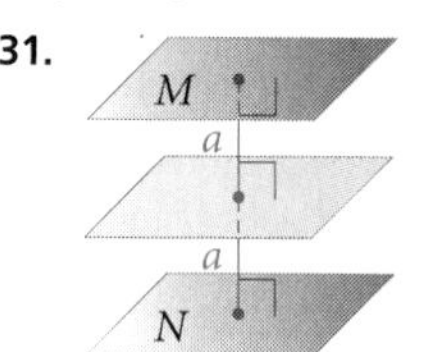

30. pts. that are 2 units from the origin in the coordinate plane

31.

31. pts. equidistant from two parallel planes

30–31. See above.

32.

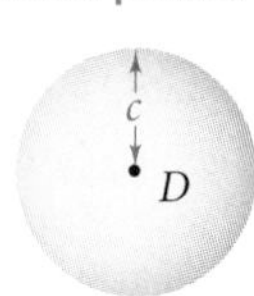

pts. in space distance c from D

33. Think about the path of a child on a swing. a–c. See back of book.

a. Draw a side view of this path.

b. Draw a top view of this path.

c. Draw a front view of this path.

34. Alejandro draws a segment to use as the base of an isosceles triangle.

a. Draw a segment to represent Alejandro's base. Locate three points that could be the vertex of the isosceles triangle. See back of book.

b. Describe the locus of points for the vertex of Alejandro's isosceles triangle. the ⊥ bisector of the base

c. *Writing* Explain why the locus you described is the only possibility for the vertex of the triangle.

If the vertex is not on a ⊥ bisector of the base, then it is not equidistant from the endpts., and △ is not isosceles.

Exercises MIXED REVIEW

Exercises 38–40 Students review how to name arcs of a circle.

GETTING READY FOR LESSON 4-8 These exercises help students review how to construct midpoints and bisectors.

Wrap Up

THE BIG IDEA Ask students: *Define perpendicular bisector and angle bisector using loci.*

RETEACHING ACTIVITY Students work with partners to identify points in the classroom that are described by loci. (Reteaching worksheet 4-7)

Exercises CHECKPOINT

In this Checkpoint, your students will assess their own progress on Lessons 4-5 to 4-7.

Exercises 1–3 Students may want to begin by listing angles from smallest to largest.

OPEN-ENDED Exercise 4 Make sure students write the opposite of the conclusion, and not of the hypothesis.

Sketch each path.

35. the swimmer's left foot

36. a doorknob as the door opens

37. a knot in the middle of a jump rope as the rope is being used

35–37. See back of book.

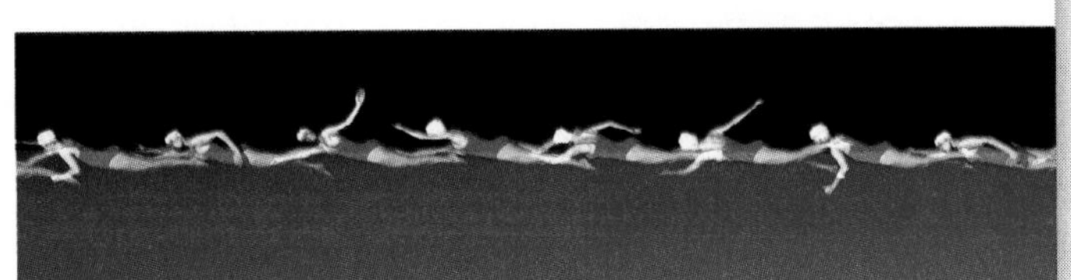

Chapter Project *Find Out by Writing*

Make up a logic puzzle in which the solver must use clues to match the people, places, or things you describe. Have a classmate solve your puzzle. If necessary, refine your puzzle based on input from your classmate.

Check students' work.

Exercises MIXED REVIEW

Identify the following in ⊙*O*.

38. a central angle and its intercepted arc $\angle COB$ and $\overset{\frown}{BC}$ or $\angle COA$ and $\overset{\frown}{AC}$

39. two major arcs $\overset{\frown}{CBA}$, $\overset{\frown}{CAB}$

40. a pair of adjacent arcs $\overset{\frown}{AC}$, $\overset{\frown}{CB}$

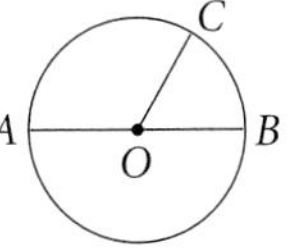

Getting Ready for Lesson 4-8

Constructions **Draw a large triangle. Construct each figure.** 41–42. See back of book.

41. an angle bisector

42. a midpoint of a side

43. a perpendicular bisector of a side Same construction as in Exercise 42.

Exercises CHECKPOINT

List the sides from shortest to longest.

1. 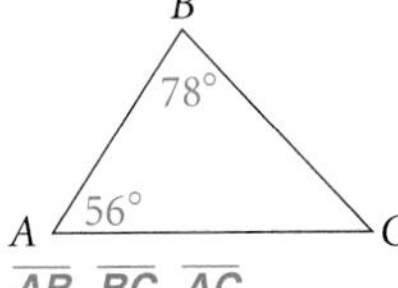

$\overline{AB}$, $\overline{BC}$, $\overline{AC}$

2. 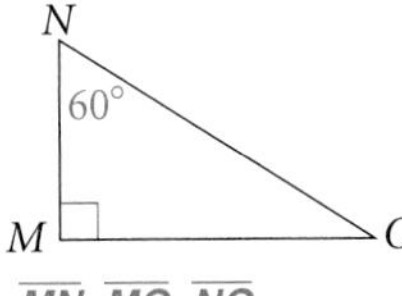

$\overline{MN}$, $\overline{MO}$, $\overline{NO}$

3. 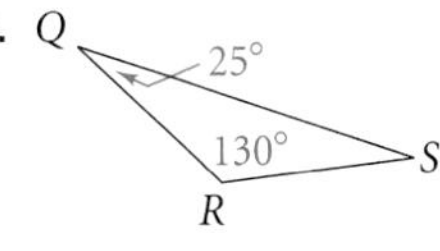

$\overline{QR} \cong \overline{RS}$, $\overline{QS}$

4. *Open-ended* Write a conditional that is true. Then write the first step of an indirect proof for your conditional. Sample: If $x = |x|$, then $x \geq 0$; assume $x < 0$.

Write the first step of an indirect proof of each statement.

5. February has fewer than 30 days. Assume February has at least 30 days.

6. A pentagon has at most three right angles. Assume pentagon has at least 4 rt. angles.

Sketch and label the locus of points. 7–8. See back of book.

7. all points in a plane a distance *d* from a line $\overleftrightarrow{PR}$

8. all points in space 1 in. from a plane

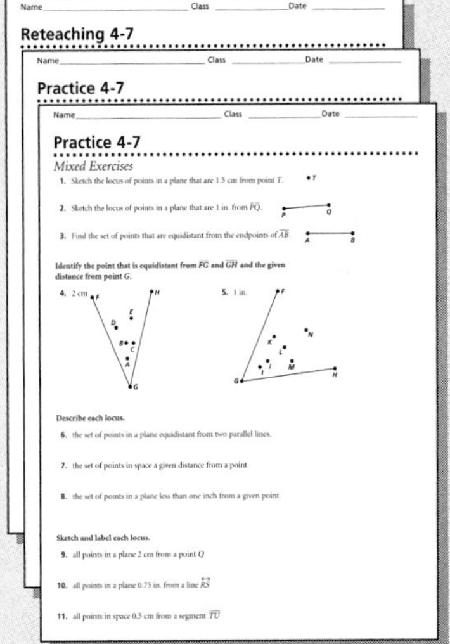

Lesson Quiz

Lesson Quiz is also available in Transparencies.

1. Sketch and label the locus of all points in a plane 1 in. from a segment $\overline{AB}$.

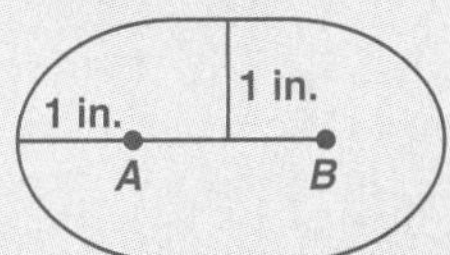

2. Sketch and label the locus of all points in space 3 cm from a line $\overleftrightarrow{XY}$. Locus should be an endless cylinder with radius 3 cm and center line $\overleftrightarrow{XY}$.

3. Sketch the locus of all points equidistant from (−2, 3) and (−6, 5) on the coordinate plane. Locus should be the a line through (−4, 4) with slope 2.

Math Toolbox

Students explore the special segments in a triangle. They see that the perpendicular bisectors of the sides, angle bisectors, altitudes, and medians of a triangle each intersect at a point.

Geometry software enables students to see that certain properties of these special segments remain true no matter how the triangles are manipulated.

Construct

Question 3 Make sure that students understand that the altitude is not always on the interior of the triangle. Draw an obtuse angle and an external altitude.

Investigate

ERROR ALERT! Students may confuse the results they got in Questions 1–4. **Remediation:** Have students sketch the results of their constructions in Questions 1–4.

ADDITIONAL PROBLEM Draw $\triangle JKL$. Construct the angle bisectors for each angle and label them as shown.

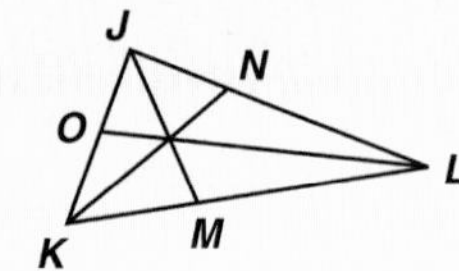

Find the product $\frac{JN}{NL} \cdot \frac{LM}{MK} \cdot \frac{KO}{OJ}$. What do you notice?

Materials and Manipulatives

- Geometry software

Math Toolbox — Technology

Exploring Special Segments in Triangles

Before Lesson 4-8

Work in pairs or small groups.

Construct

Use geometry software. 1–4. Check students' work.

1. Construct a triangle and the three perpendicular bisectors of its sides.
2. Construct a triangle and its three angle bisectors.
3. Construct a triangle. Construct a line through a vertex of the triangle that is perpendicular to the line containing the side opposite that vertex. Similarly, draw the perpendiculars from the other two vertices. Since an *altitude* of a triangle is the segment from a vertex to the line containing the opposite side, the three lines you have drawn contain the three altitudes of the triangle.

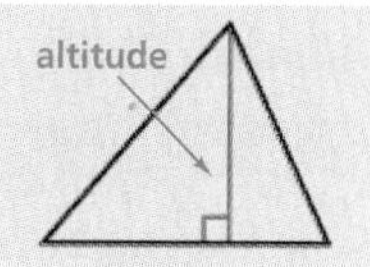

4. Construct a triangle. Construct the midpoint of a side of the triangle and draw the segment from the midpoint to the opposite vertex. This segment is called a *median* of the triangle. Construct the other two medians.

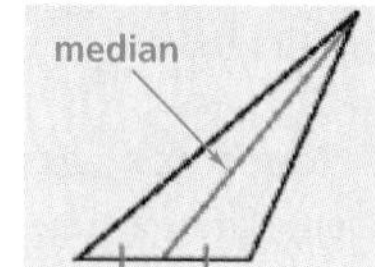

Investigate

Check students' work.

- What do you notice about the lines, rays, or segments that you constructed in each triangle?
- Manipulate the triangles. Does the property still hold in the manipulated triangles?

Conjecture

Each set of lines intersects at a single pt.

List your **conjectures** about the angle bisectors, the perpendicular bisectors, the lines containing the altitudes, and the medians of a triangle.

Extend

- In what types of triangles do the perpendicular bisectors of the sides intersect inside the triangle? on the triangle? outside the triangle? acute △; right △; obtuse △
- Describe the triangles for which the lines containing the altitudes, the angle bisectors, or the medians intersect inside, on, or outside the triangles. The medians and angle bisectors always intersect inside the △. Altitudes intersect inside the △ for acute △s, at a vertex for right △s, and outside the △ for obtuse △s.

226

4-8 Teaching Notes

PROBLEM OF THE DAY

Jose, Daniel, Gina, and Carlita are all friends. Their ages are 26, 29, 32, and 35. Gina is married to the oldest person. Jose who is younger than Gina, is not the youngest. Who is married to whom and what are their ages? Jose (29) and Carlita (26), Daniel (35) and Gina (32)

Problem of the Day is also available in Transparencies.

CONNECTING TO PRIOR KNOWLEDGE Review with students the definitions of angle bisector and perpendicular bisector. Have students describe the three ways they can find each (paper folding, construction, and measurement).

WORK TOGETHER

ERROR ALERT! Step 6 Students may not see the relationship between the perpendicular bisectors of the obtuse triangle if they only look at the parts of the bisectors that lie in the interior of the triangles. **Remediation:** Have students trace the *lines* created by the folds.

THINK AND DISCUSS

ESL Help students understand the difference between collinear and concurrent. Students should be familiar with the term "point of intersection" as the point where two lines meet. Point out that the term "point of concurrency" is used for the point where *three or more* lines meet.

Connections  Recreation . . . and more

4-8 Concurrent Lines

What You'll Learn

- Identifying properties of perpendicular bisectors, angle bisectors, altitudes, and medians of a triangle

...And Why

To understand the points of concurrency that are used in architecture, construction, and transportation

What You'll Need

- scissors

WORK TOGETHER

Step 1: Each member of your group should draw and cut out five triangles: two acute, two right, and one obtuse. Make them big enough so that they are easy to fold.

Step 2: Use paper folding to create the angle bisectors of each angle of an acute triangle. What do you notice about the angle bisectors?

Step 3: Repeat Step 2 with a right and an obtuse triangle. Does what you discovered still hold true?

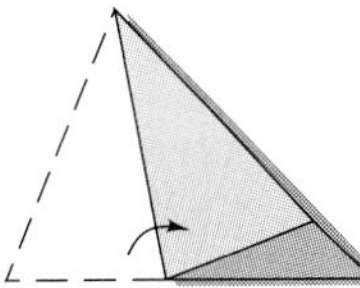

Folding an Angle Bisector

1. Make a **conjecture** about the bisectors of the angles of a triangle. The angle bisectors intersect at a point.

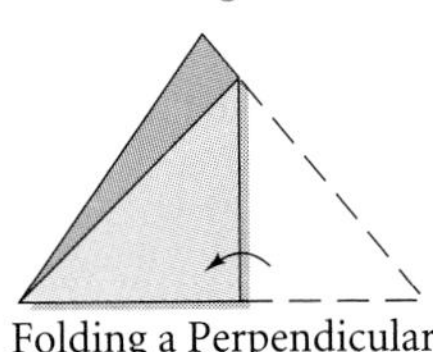

Folding a Perpendicular Bisector

Step 4: Use paper folding to create the perpendicular bisectors of each of the sides of an acute triangle. What do you notice?

Step 5: Repeat Step 4 with a right triangle. What do you notice?

Step 6: Draw an obtuse triangle in the middle of a piece of paper (do not cut it out!), then repeat Step 4 with this triangle. What do you notice?

2. Make a **conjecture** about the perpendicular bisectors of the sides of a triangle. The $\perp$ bisectors of the sides intersect at a pt.

THINK AND DISCUSS

Part 1

Perpendicular Bisectors and Angle Bisectors

When three or more lines intersect in one point, they are **concurrent.** The point at which they are concurrent is the **point of concurrency.** Your explorations in the Work Together lead to the following theorems.

Theorem 4-16	The perpendicular bisectors of the sides of a triangle are concurrent at a point equidistant from the vertices.
Theorem 4-17	The bisectors of the angles of a triangle are concurrent at a point equidistant from the sides.

Lesson Planning Options

Prerequisite Skills

- Understanding the definitions of perpendicular and bisector
- Finding equations of lines

Assignment Options for Exercises On Your Own

To provide flexible scheduling, this lesson can be subdivided into parts.

1. **Core** 6–9 (a), 13–14, 16
   Extension 18
2. **Core** 1–5, 6–9 (b), 10–12, 15
   Extension 17

Use Mixed Review to maintain skills.

Resources

 **Student Edition**

Skills Handbook, pp. 660, 678
Extra Practice, p. 651
Glossary/Study Guide

Teaching Resources

Chapter Support File, Ch. 4
- Practice 4-8 (two worksheets)
- Reteaching 4-8

Classroom Manager 4-8
Glossary, Spanish Resources

 **Transparencies**
54, 58

The point of concurrency of the perpendicular bisectors is called the *circumcenter.* The point of concurrency of angle bisectors is called the *incenter.*

Theorem 4-16 In groups, have students read through the paragraph proof given on page 228. Then ask them to rewrite it in their own words. Students may want to elaborate on some of the statements and reasons to clarify the proof. For example, they may want to state explicitly the Converse of the Perpendicular Bisector Theorem.

Example 1 **Relating to the Real World** 

DIVERSITY Be aware that some students have never lived in or even seen houses with yards, especially yards big enough for a swimming pool.

VISUAL LEARNING To help students see why the center of the pool is chosen to be the point of concurrency of the angle bisectors, have them copy the diagram and choose other points as the center. Using a compass, have them draw circles as large as possible within the triangle. They should see that they cannot find a larger circle.

ESL **AUDITORY LEARNING** Students can remember the meanings of the terms "circumscribe" and "inscribe" by their prefixes "circum-" meaning "around" and "in-" meaning "within." Review other words with these prefixes and their meanings, such as circumference, circumvent, inside, and interior.

Additional Examples

FOR EXAMPLE 1

Draw an acute triangle. Then find a point on the interior of the triangle that is equidistant from each side. **Sketches will vary. Point should be the intersection of the angle bisectors.**

Discussion: *What theorem did you use to find the point?*

FOR EXAMPLE 2

Find the center of the circle that circumscribes $\triangle CDE$ with vertices $C(0, -6)$, $D(0, 0)$, and $E(-8, 0)$. **$(-4, -3)$**

Discussion: *How can you find the radius of the circle?*

FOR EXAMPLE 3

a. Use paper folding to create the altitudes from each of the three vertices of an obtuse triangle. **Check students' work.**

b. Use paper folding to create the three medians of an obtuse triangle. **Check students' work.**

Discussion: *Describe the difference between the altitude of an acute triangle and the altitude of an obtuse triangle.*

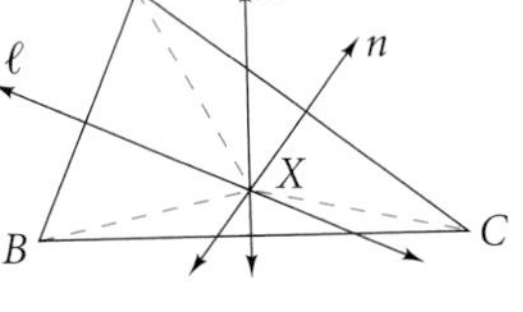

Paragraph Proof of Theorem 4-16

Given: Lines ℓ, m, and n are perpendicular bisectors of the sides of $\triangle ABC$. X is the intersection of lines ℓ and m.

Prove: Line n contains point X, and X is equidistant from A, B, and C.

Since m is the perpendicular bisector of $\overline{BC}$, $BX = CX$. Similarly, since ℓ is the perpendicular bisector of $\overline{AB}$, $AX = BX$. By substitution, $AX = CX$. So by the Converse of the Perpendicular Bisector Theorem, X is on line n. Since $AX = BX = CX$, X is equidistant from A, B, and C.

Example 1 **Relating to the Real World** 

Recreation The Jacksons want to install a circular pool in their backyard. They want the pool to be as large as possible. Where would the largest possible pool be located?

The point of concurrency of the angle bisectors is equidistant from the sides of the triangular yard (Theorem 4-17). If any other point were chosen as the center of the pool, it would be closer to at least one of the sides of the yard, and the pool would have to be smaller. ■

As Example 1 suggests, the points of concurrency in Theorems 4-16 and 4-17 have some interesting properties related to circles.

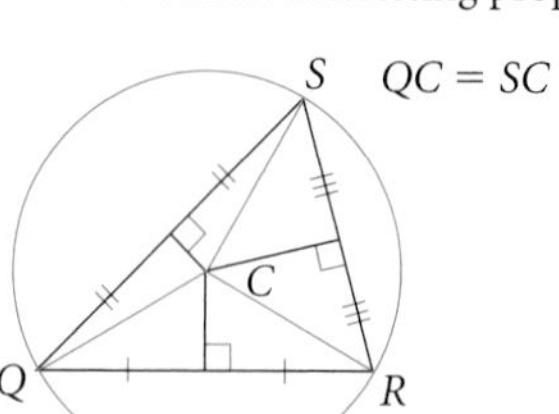

Point C, called the *circumcenter,* is equidistant from the vertices of $\triangle QRS$. The circle is *circumscribed* around the triangle.

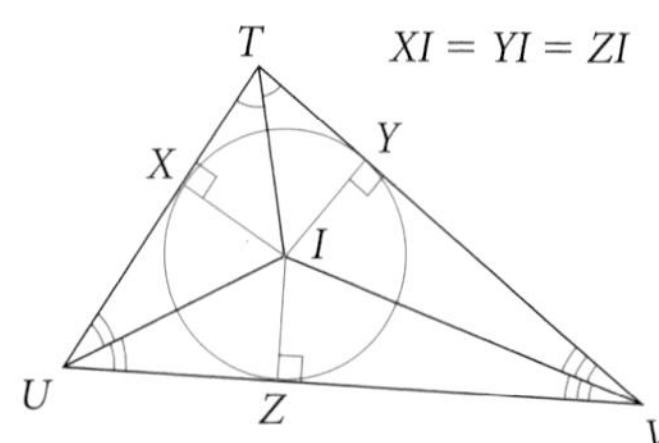

Point I, called the *incenter,* is equidistant from the sides of $\triangle TUV$. The circle is *inscribed* in the triangle.

Example 2

ERROR ALERT! Students may not understand why the point of concurrency of the perpendicular bisectors of the sides is used rather than the point of concurrency of the angle bisectors to find the center of the circle. **Remediation:** Reinforce that when a circle is circumscribed around a triangle, the vertices of the triangle lie on the circle. The point of concurrency of the perpendicular bisectors of the sides of the triangle is equidistant from the vertices and therefore equidistant from the circle.

TACTILE LEARNING Have students cut out four triangles, fold and label each of the four segments (angle bisectors, perpendicular bisectors, altitudes, and medians), then make a poster to display them.

Example 2

Coordinate Geometry Find the center of the circle that circumscribes $\triangle OPS$.

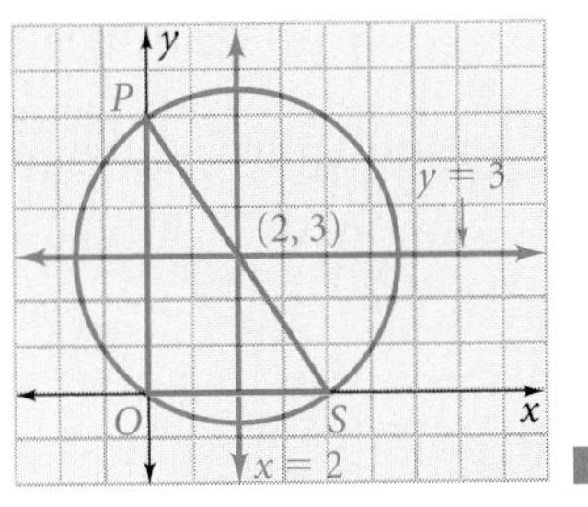

Two of the perpendicular bisectors of the sides of the triangle are $x = 2$ and $y = 3$. These lines intersect at (2, 3). This point is the center of the circle.

3. The 3rd ⊥ bisector passes through the pt. of intersection of the 1st two.

3. *Critical Thinking* Explain why it was not necessary to find the third perpendicular bisector in Example 2.

4. **Try This** Find the center of the circle that circumscribes the triangle with vertices (0, 0), (−8, 0), and (0, 6). (−4, 3)

Part 2

Medians and Altitudes

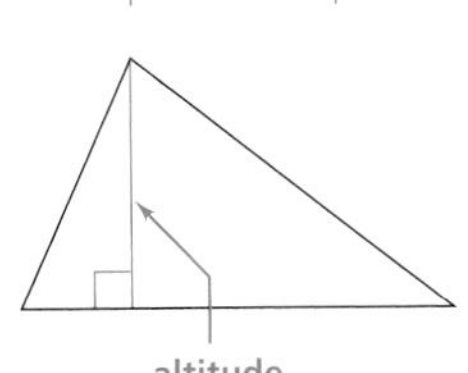

altitude

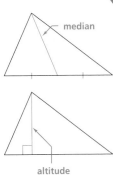

Two other special segments of a triangle are medians and altitudes. The **median of a triangle** is a segment whose endpoints are a vertex and the midpoint of the side opposite the vertex. The **altitude of a triangle** is a perpendicular segment from a vertex to the line containing the side opposite the vertex.

Unlike angle bisectors and medians, an altitude of a triangle may lie outside the triangle. Consider the following diagrams.

Acute Triangle: Altitude is inside.

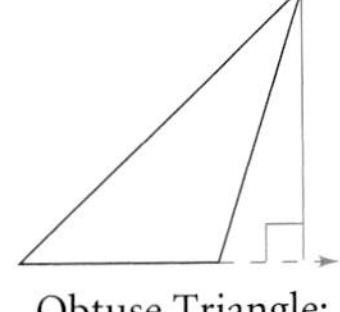

Right Triangle: Altitude is a side.

Obtuse Triangle: Altitude is outside.

You can use paper folding to find altitudes and medians.

To find an altitude . . .

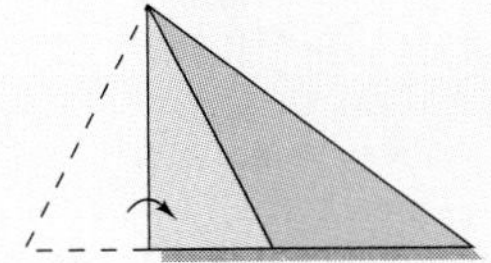

Fold so that a side overlaps itself and the fold contains a vertex.

To find a median . . .

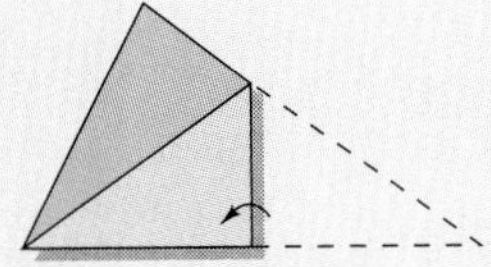

Fold one vertex to another to find the midpoint of a side,

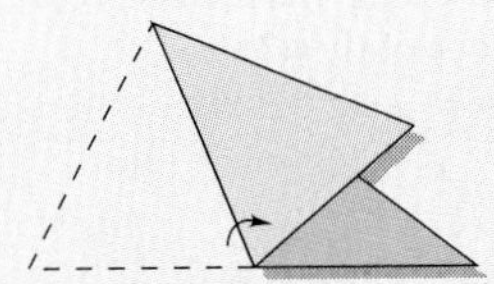

then fold from the midpoint to the opposite vertex.

Technology Options

For Exercise 14, students may use geometry software to construct the triangle and circumscribe it with a circle. Then students can manipulate the triangle and see how the circle changes.

Prentice Hall Technology

Software
- Secondary Math Lab Toolkit™
- Integrated Math Lab 30
- Computer Item Generator 4-8

Internet
- See the Prentice Hall site. (http://www.phschool.com)

Example 3

EXTENSION If you have block scheduling or an extended class period, have students also find the altitudes and medians from each of the three vertices of both a right and an obtuse triangle.

The point of concurrency of the lines containing the altitudes of a triangle is called the *orthocenter*. The point of concurrency of the medians is called the *centroid*.

Question 5 Help students see that in a right triangle, two of the sides are altitudes and in an obtuse triangle, two of the altitudes lie outside the triangle.

EXTENSION For the point of concurrency for medians, have students investigate where on a median the point lies. They may discover that the point of concurrency divides the median in a ratio of 2:1.

The orange triangle shows the paper-folded medians.
The blue triangle shows the paper-folded altitudes.

Example 3

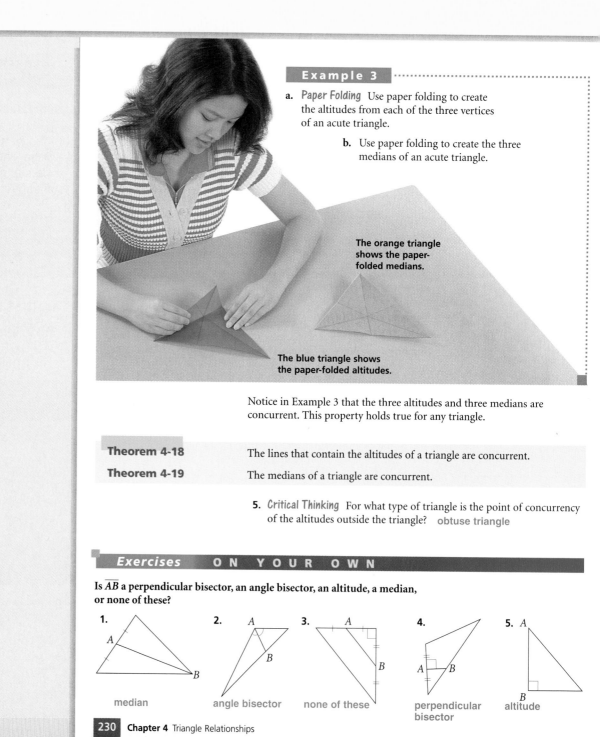

a. *Paper Folding* Use paper folding to create the altitudes from each of the three vertices of an acute triangle.

b. Use paper folding to create the three medians of an acute triangle.

Notice in Example 3 that the three altitudes and three medians are concurrent. This property holds true for any triangle.

Theorem 4-18 The lines that contain the altitudes of a triangle are concurrent.

Theorem 4-19 The medians of a triangle are concurrent.

5. *Critical Thinking* For what type of triangle is the point of concurrency of the altitudes outside the triangle? obtuse triangle

Exercises ON YOUR OWN

Is $\overline{AB}$ a perpendicular bisector, an angle bisector, an altitude, a median, or none of these?

1. A B

median

2. 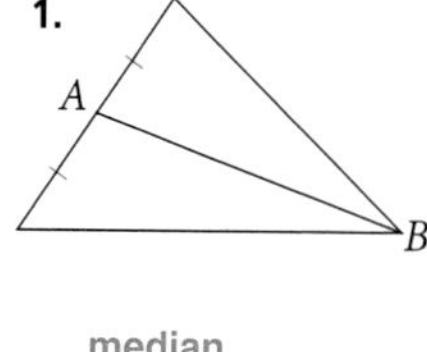

angle bisector

3. 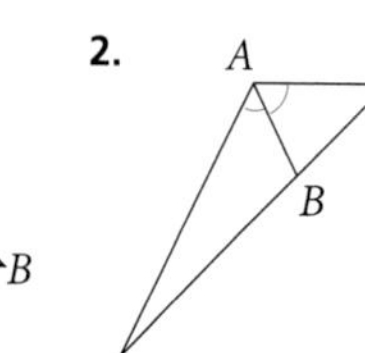

none of these

4. 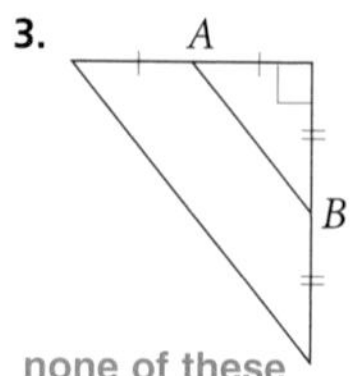

perpendicular bisector

5. 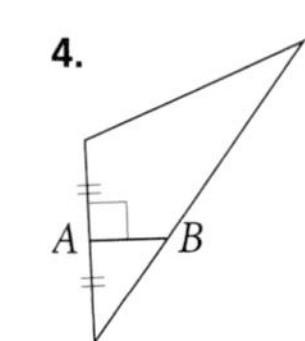

altitude

Exercises ON YOUR OWN

Exercises 6–9 Students should understand from Question 3 that they need only to find the point of intersection of two of the perpendicular bisectors and the altitudes.

EXTENSION Exercise 12 Have students investigate the points of concurrency for the special segments and lines using isosceles and equilateral triangles.

ALTERNATIVE ASSESSMENT **Exercise 13** This exercise can help you assess students' understanding of Theorems 4-16 and 4-17. Have students work with a partner. Ask them to explain how they found the location for the drinking fountain.

ERROR ALERT! **Exercise 16** Students may shade the center of the circle and part of the perpendicular bisectors of the sides. **Remediation:** Remind students how to shade all the points less than a given number on a number line or all the points on the interior of a circle with a given radius.

For each triangle, give the coordinates of the point of concurrency of (a) the perpendicular bisectors of the sides and (b) the altitudes.

6. 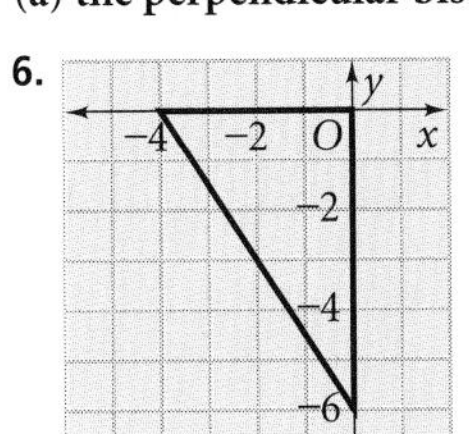

a. (– 2, – 3) b. (0, 0)

7. 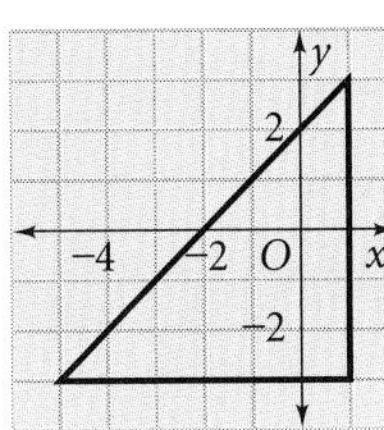

a. (–2, 0) b. (1, – 3)

8. 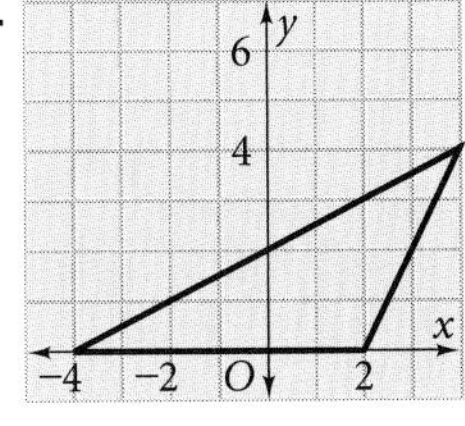

a. (–1, 4) b. (4, –4)

9. 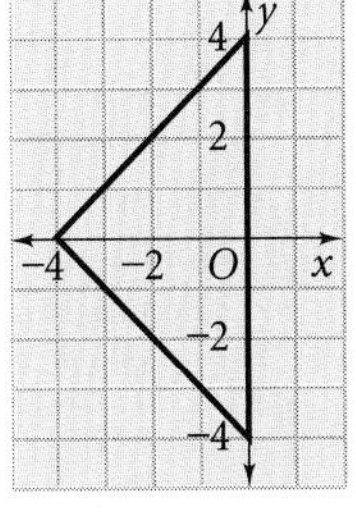

a. (0, 0) b. (– 4, 0)

The points of concurrency for the lines and segments listed in I–IV have been drawn on the triangles. Match the points with the lines and segments.

I. perpendicular bisectors of sides

II. angle bisectors

III. medians

IV. altitudes

10. A, B, C, D — ID, IIB, IIIC, IVA

11. A, B, C, D — IA, IIC, IIIB, IVD

12. History of Mathematics Leonard Euler proved in 1765 that for any triangle, three of the four points of concurrency are collinear. The line that contains these three points is known as *Euler's Line*. Refer to Exercises 10 and 11 to determine which point of concurrency does *not* lie on Euler's Line. the pt. of concurrency of the angle bisectors

13. Park Design Where should park officials place a drinking fountain in Altgeld Park so that it is equidistant from the tennis court, the playground, and the volleyball court? See below.

Altgeld Park — Playground, Tennis Court, Volleyball Court

14. Open-ended Draw a triangle and construct the perpendicular bisectors of two of its sides. Then construct the circle that circumscribes the triangle. See margin.

15. Coordinate Geometry $\triangle DEF$ has vertices $D(0, 0)$, $E(12, 0)$, and $F(0, 12)$. $x = 0, y = 0, y = x$
   a. Find the equations of the lines that contain the three altitudes.
   b. Find the equations of the three perpendicular bisectors of the sides.
   c. Writing Are any of the lines in parts (a) and (b) the same? Explain.

b. $x = 6$, $y = 6$, $y = x$ c. See margin.

16. Locus Three students are seated at uniform distances around a circular table. Copy the diagram and shade the points on the table that are closer to Moesha than to Jan or Chandra.

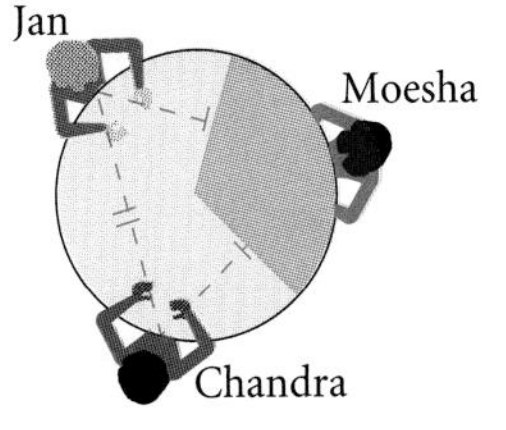

13. the pt. of concurrency of the ⊥ bisectors of segments connecting the 3 areas

pages 230–232 On Your Own

14. Sample:

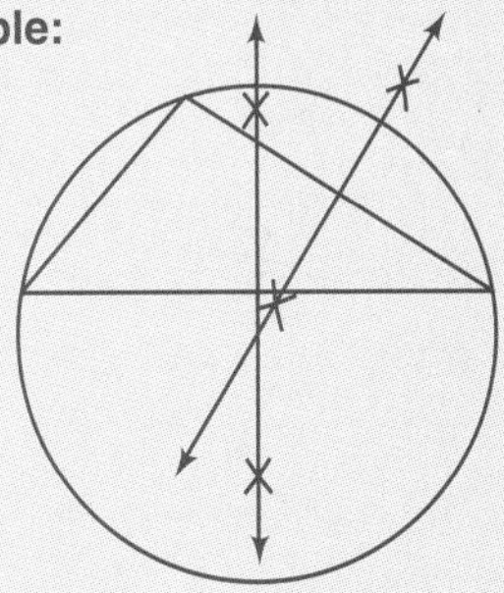

15c. The line $y = x$; since the altitude from D bisects the base of isosceles $\triangle DEF$, the altitude is also the ⊥ bisector of the base.

Exercise 18 Have students compare this proof with the proof of Theorem 4-16 on page 228. Ask students to point out the differences in the "Given" and "Prove" statements as well as in the arguments.

Exercises MIXED REVIEW

ESTIMATION Exercises 19–21 Students can use a corner of a piece of paper to estimate if an angle is greater than or less than 90°.

SELF ASSESSMENT **PORTFOLIO** Share with students the criteria you will use to assess their work in portfolios, as well as how you plan to use the results. Students should understand how the rubrics assess their work, how each piece in the portfolio counts, and how the scores they get in their portfolios will affect their overall evaluation.

Wrap Up

THE BIG IDEA Ask students: *Summarize what you have learned about the special segments related to a triangle. Use diagrams and include all the properties of the segments.*

RETEACHING ACTIVITY Students draw obtuse, acute, and right triangles. Then they use protractors and straightedges to find the points of concurrency of the lines containing the altitudes. (Reteaching worksheet 4-8)

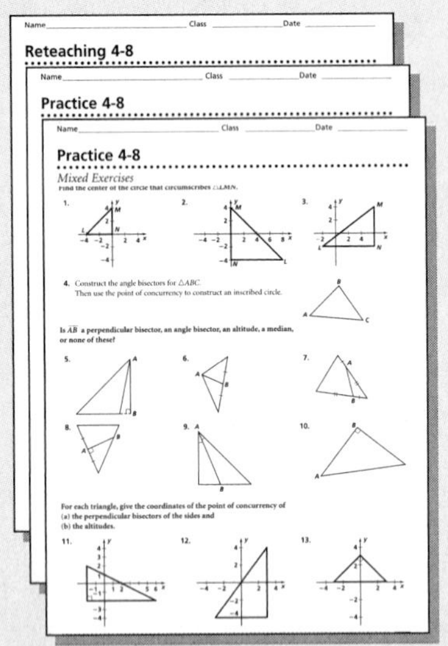
Reteaching 4-8

Practice 4-8

Practice 4-8

Mixed Exercises

Find the center of the circle that circumscribes △LMN.

4. Construct the angle bisectors for △ABC. Then use the point of concurrency to construct an inscribed circle.

Is AB a perpendicular bisector, an angle bisector, an altitude, a median, or none of these?

For each triangle, give the coordinates of the point of concurrency of (a) the perpendicular bisectors of the sides and (b) the altitudes.

Lesson Quiz

Lesson Quiz is also available in Transparencies.

$\triangle PQR$ has vertices $P(2, 0)$, $Q(10, 0)$ and $R(2, 8)$.

1a. Draw and label the bisector of angle R. See back of book.

b. Draw and label the median with endpoint at Q. See back of book.

2. Find the point of concurrency of the altitudes. (2, 0)

3. Find the center of the circle that circumscribes $\triangle PQR$. (6, 4)

232

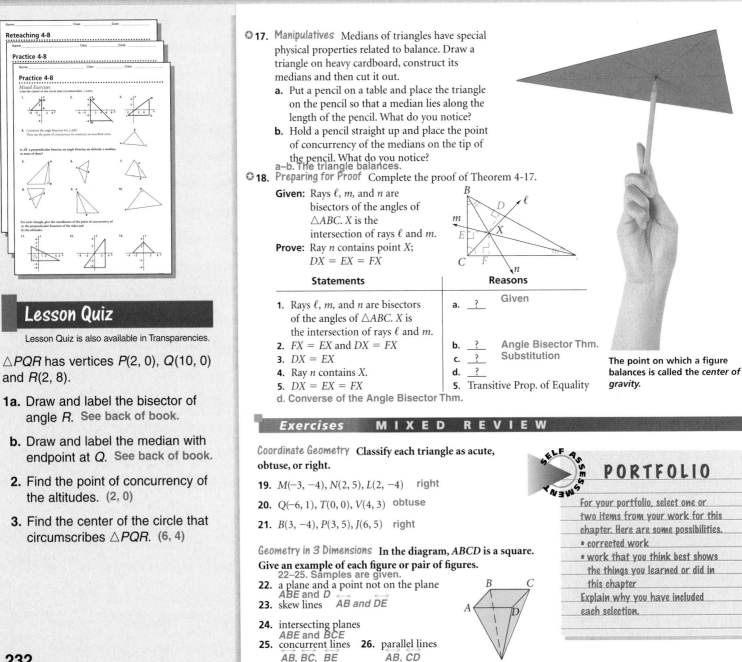

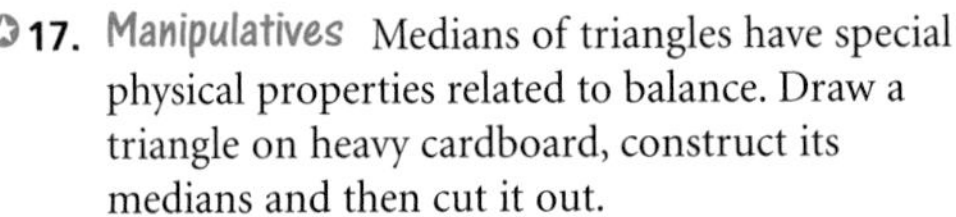

17. *Manipulatives* Medians of triangles have special physical properties related to balance. Draw a triangle on heavy cardboard, construct its medians and then cut it out.

a. Put a pencil on a table and place the triangle on the pencil so that a median lies along the length of the pencil. What do you notice?

b. Hold a pencil straight up and place the point of concurrency of the medians on the tip of the pencil. What do you notice?

a–b. The triangle balances.

The point on which a figure balances is called the *center of gravity.*

18. *Preparing for Proof* Complete the proof of Theorem 4-17.

Given: Rays ℓ, m, and n are bisectors of the angles of $\triangle ABC$. X is the intersection of rays ℓ and m.

Prove: Ray n contains point X; $DX = EX = FX$

Statements	Reasons
1. Rays ℓ, m, and n are bisectors of the angles of $\triangle ABC$. X is the intersection of rays ℓ and m.	a. ? Given
2. $FX = EX$ and $DX = FX$	b. ? Angle Bisector Thm.
3. $DX = EX$	c. ? Substitution
4. Ray n contains X.	d. ?
5. $DX = EX = FX$	5. Transitive Prop. of Equality

d. Converse of the Angle Bisector Thm.

Exercises MIXED REVIEW

Coordinate Geometry **Classify each triangle as acute, obtuse, or right.**

19. $M(-3, -4)$, $N(2, 5)$, $L(2, -4)$ right

20. $Q(-6, 1)$, $T(0, 0)$, $V(4, 3)$ obtuse

21. $B(3, -4)$, $P(3, 5)$, $J(6, 5)$ right

Geometry in 3 Dimensions **In the diagram, $ABCD$ is a square. Give an example of each figure or pair of figures.**

22–25. Samples are given.

22. a plane and a point not on the plane ABE and D

23. skew lines $\overleftrightarrow{AB}$ and $\overleftrightarrow{DE}$

24. intersecting planes ABE and BCE

25. concurrent lines $\overleftrightarrow{AB}$, $\overleftrightarrow{BC}$, $\overleftrightarrow{BE}$

26. parallel lines $\overleftrightarrow{AB}$, $\overleftrightarrow{CD}$

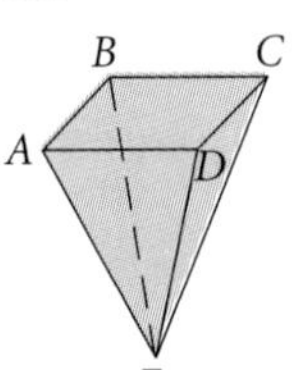

SELF ASSESSMENT **PORTFOLIO**

For your portfolio, select one or two items from your work for this chapter. Here are some possibilities.
- corrected work
- work that you think best shows the things you learned or did in this chapter

Explain why you have included each selection.

Finishing the Chapter Project

PROJECT DAY You may wish to plan a project day on which students share their completed projects. Encourage groups to explain their process as well as their product.

PROJECT NOTEBOOK Have students review their project work and bring their notebooks up to date.

- Have students review their puzzles and solutions in their displays.
- Ask groups to share any insights they found when completing the project, such as shortcuts or strategies they used in solving and creating logic problems.

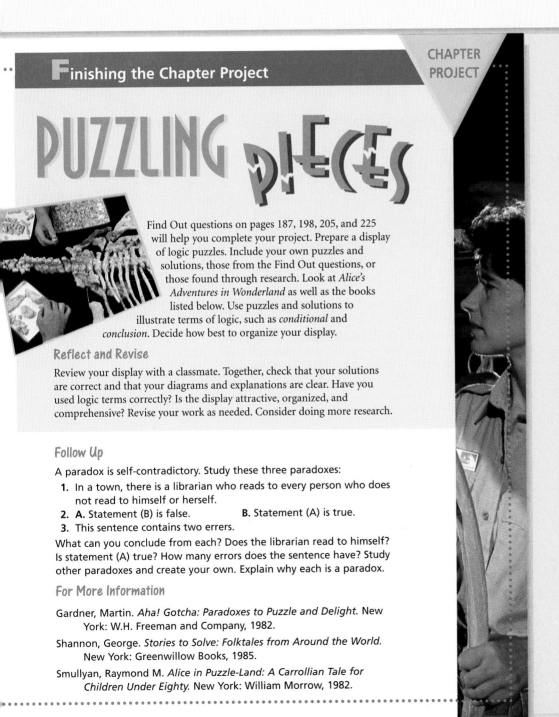

SCORING RUBRIC

3 Student's solutions are correct. Diagrams and explanations are clear. Logic terms are used correctly. Display is attractive, organized, and comprehensive. Research is evident.

2 Student's solutions contain minor flaws. Diagrams and explanations are clear. Logic terms are used correctly with a few exceptions. Display is attractive, complete, and has some organizational structure.

1 Student's solutions have errors. Diagrams are complete but some explanations are confusing. Logic terms are not always used appropriately. Display is complete but lacks organization.

0 Major elements are incomplete or missing.

Finishing the Chapter Project

CHAPTER PROJECT

PUZZLING PIECES

Find Out questions on pages 187, 198, 205, and 225 will help you complete your project. Prepare a display of logic puzzles. Include your own puzzles and solutions, those from the Find Out questions, or those found through research. Look at *Alice's Adventures in Wonderland* as well as the books listed below. Use puzzles and solutions to illustrate terms of logic, such as *conditional* and *conclusion*. Decide how best to organize your display.

Reflect and Revise

Review your display with a classmate. Together, check that your solutions are correct and that your diagrams and explanations are clear. Have you used logic terms correctly? Is the display attractive, organized, and comprehensive? Revise your work as needed. Consider doing more research.

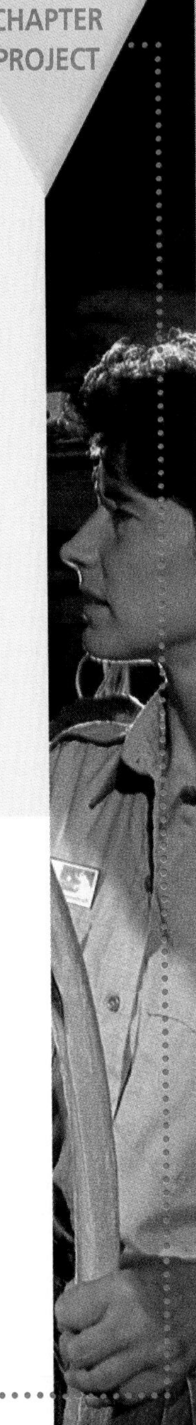

Follow Up

A paradox is self-contradictory. Study these three paradoxes:

1. In a town, there is a librarian who reads to every person who does not read to himself or herself.
2. **A.** Statement (B) is false. **B.** Statement (A) is true.
3. This sentence contains two errers.

What can you conclude from each? Does the librarian read to himself? Is statement (A) true? How many errors does the sentence have? Study other paradoxes and create your own. Explain why each is a paradox.

For More Information

Gardner, Martin. *Aha! Gotcha: Paradoxes to Puzzle and Delight.* New York: W.H. Freeman and Company, 1982.

Shannon, George. *Stories to Solve: Folktales from Around the World.* New York: Greenwillow Books, 1985.

Smullyan, Raymond M. *Alice in Puzzle-Land: A Carrollian Tale for Children Under Eighty.* New York: William Morrow, 1982.

Wrap Up

HOW AM I DOING? Have students work in small groups. Ask each group to make a short presentation explaining the properties of midsegments of triangles. Each presentation must include a visual aid and a sample problem.

KEY TERMS The numbers in parentheses direct students to the pages where the terms are used or defined. Students should be able to (1) write a simple explanation of each term, (2) illustrate the term with a diagram, or (3) show an example that uses the term.

Exercises 1–4 Remind students to make the appropriate changes in the wording when they write the converses of the conditionals.

Resources

Student Edition

Extra Practice, p. 637
Glossary/Study Guide

Teaching Resources

Students Study Survival Handbook
Glossary, Spanish Resources

4 Wrap Up

How am I doing?

- State three ideas from this chapter that you think are important. Explain your choices.
- Describe the different styles of proof.

Key Terms

altitude of a triangle (p. 229)
base (p. 188)
base angle (p. 188)
biconditional (p. 183)
conclusion (p. 182)
concurrent (p. 227)
conditional (p. 182)
contrapositive (p. 184)
converse (p. 183)
distance from a point to a line (p. 221)
hypothesis (p. 182)
indirect reasoning (p. 207)
inverse (p. 184)
legs (p. 188)
locus (p. 220)
median of a triangle (p. 229)
midsegment (p. 201)
negation (p.184)
point of concurrency (p. 227)
paragraph proof (p. 195)
truth value (p. 182)
two-column proof (p. 194)
vertex angle (p. 188)

Using Logical Reasoning 4-1

An *if-then statement* is a **conditional.** The part following *if* is the **hypothesis,** and the part following *then* is the **conclusion.** You find its **truth value** when you determine if a conditional is true or false.

Statement	Form	Example
conditional	If ■, then ■.	If a polygon is a triangle, then it has three sides.
converse	If ■, then ■.	If a polygon has three sides, then it is a triangle.
inverse	If *not* ■, then *not* ■.	If a polygon is *not* a triangle, then it does *not* have three sides.
contrapositive	If *not* ■, then *not* ■.	If a polygon does *not* have three sides, then it is *not* a triangle.
biconditional	■ if and only if ■.	A polygon is a triangle if and only if it has three sides.

For Exercises 1–4: (a) Write the converse. (b) Determine the truth value of the conditional and its converse. (c) If both statements are true, write a biconditional.

1. If you are in Australia, then you are south of the equator.
   a. If you are south of the equator, then you are in Australia. b. true; false
2. If an angle is obtuse, then its measure is greater than 90 and less than 180. a. If the measure of an angle is > 90 and < 180, then the angle is obtuse.
   b. true; true c. An angle is obtuse if and only if its measure is > 90 and < 180.
3. If it is snowing, then it is cold outside.
   a. If it is cold outside, then it is snowing. b. true; false
4. If a figure is a square, then its sides are congruent.
   a. If the sides of a figure are ≅, then it is a square. b. true; false
5. *Open-ended* Write a conditional and then write its contrapositive.
   Sample: If Boris plays the piano, then he plays chess; if Boris does not play chess, then he does not play the piano.

Exercises 6–9 Make sure students differentiate between when *x* is a side length and when it is an angle measure.

ERROR ALERT! **Exercise 11** Students may rewrite the proof using Exercise 10 with the reasons in the wrong order. **Remediation:** Be sure they write the proof using the *solution* to Exercise 10.

Isosceles Triangles 4-2

If two sides of a triangle are congruent, then the angles opposite those sides are also congruent. The bisector of the vertex angle of an isosceles triangle is the perpendicular bisector of the base. If two angles of a triangle are congruent, then the sides opposite the angles are congruent.

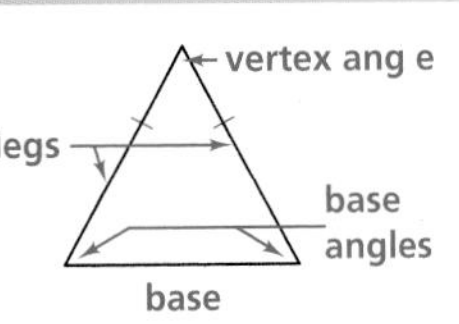

Find the values of *x* and *y*.

6. 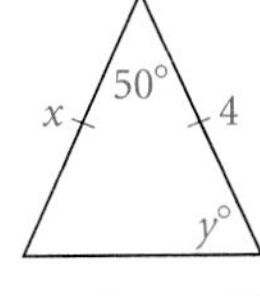

$x = 4$; $y = 65$

7. 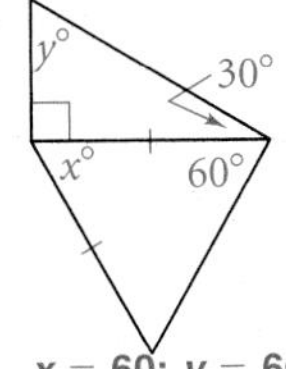

$x = 60$; $y = 60$

8. 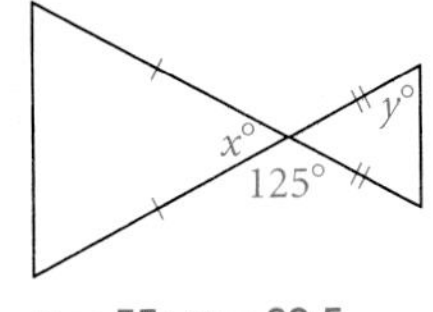

$x = 55$; $y = 62.5$

9. 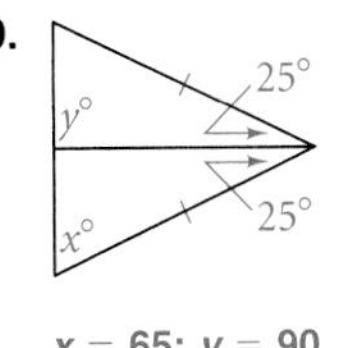

$x = 65$; $y = 90$

Midsegments of Triangles 4-3, 4-4

There are different types of proofs, including the **paragraph proof** and the **two-column proof.**

A **midsegment** of a triangle is a segment that connects the midpoints of its sides. The midsegment connecting two sides of a triangle is parallel to the third side and half its length.

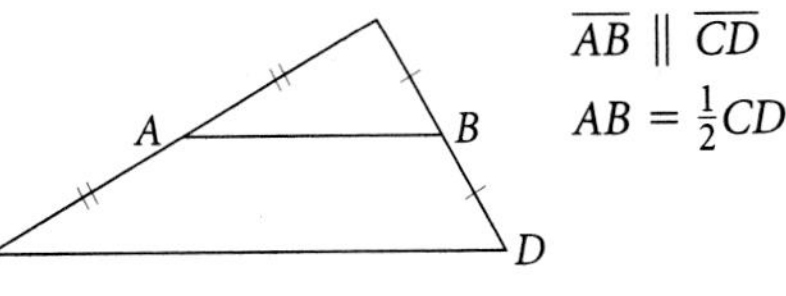

$\overline{AB} \parallel \overline{CD}$

$AB = \frac{1}{2}CD$

10. Preparing for Proof The reasons given in this proof are correct, but they are in the wrong order. List them in the correct order.
Given: $\triangle BCA \cong \triangle CDE$ d, c, a, b
$\triangle CDE \cong \triangle EGF$
Prove: $\overline{AF} \parallel \overline{BG}$

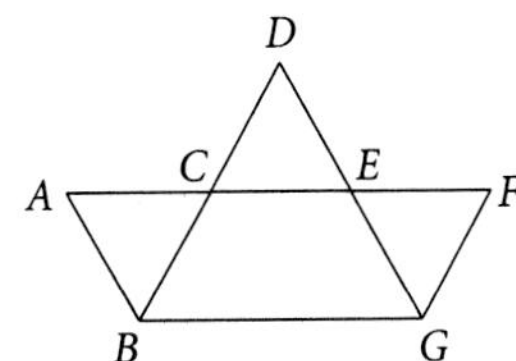

Statements	Reasons
1. $\triangle BCA \cong \triangle CDE$ $\triangle CDE \cong \triangle EGF$	a. Def. of midpoint
2. $\overline{BC} \cong \overline{CD}$, $\overline{DE} \cong \overline{EG}$	b. Triangle Midsegment Thm.
3. C is the midpoint of $\overline{BD}$. E is the midpoint of $\overline{DG}$.	c. Def. of congruent polygons
4. $\overline{AF} \parallel \overline{BG}$	d. Given

11. By def., if the triangles are ≅, then their corres. sides are ≅. So $\overline{BC} \cong \overline{CD}$ and $\overline{DE} \cong \overline{EG}$. By def., *C* is the midpt. of $\overline{BD}$ and *E* is the midpt. of $\overline{DG}$. By the Triangle Midsegment Thm., $\overline{AF} \parallel \overline{BG}$.

11. Writing Rewrite the proof above as a paragraph proof. See right.

What can you conclude from each diagram? Justify your answers. 12–14. See margin.

12. 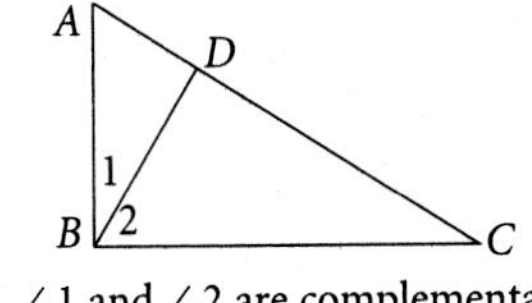

$\angle 1$ and $\angle 2$ are complementary.

13. 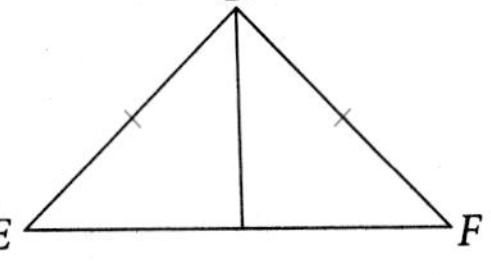

14. 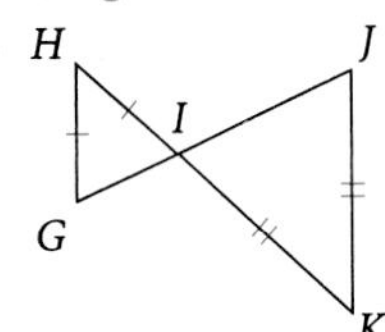

Wrap Up pages 234–237

12. Answers may vary. Sample: $\angle ABC$ is a rt. angle by def. of complementary angles and the Angle Addition Post. $\angle A$ and $\angle C$ are complementary because acute angles of a rt. △ are complementary.

13. $\angle E \cong \angle F$ because base ∠s of an isosceles △ are ≅.

14. Answers may vary. Samples: $\angle HIG \cong \angle JIK$ because they are vert. angles. $\angle HIG \cong \angle G$ and $\angle JIK \cong \angle J$ because base ∠s of an isosceles △ are ≅.

Exercises 18–21 Have students work with a partner. Have partners take turns writing out their indirect reasoning.

ALTERNATIVE ASSESSMENT **Exercises 26–29** To assess students' understanding of loci, give them sketches of loci and ask them to describe them in words.

Remind students that the new mathematical terms in this chapter are defined in the Glossary/Study Guide in the back of the book.

19. Assume that both numbers are odd. The product of 2 odd numbers is always odd, which contradicts the fact that their product is even. So the assumption that both numbers are odd is false, and at least 1 must be even.

20. Assume that a triangle has 2 or more obtuse angles. By def., the measure of each of these angles is > 90. Then the sum of angle measures of the △ is > 180. By the Triangle Angle-Sum Thm., the sum of angle measures of a △ is 180. Therefore the assumption was false, and a △ has no more than 1 obtuse angle.

21. Assume 1 angle of an equilateral △ is obtuse. Then its measure is > 90 and < 180. By the Isosceles Triangle Thm., the remaining angles are each ≅ to the 1st angle. By def. of ≅ angles and the Transitive Prop. of =, the measures of the 3 angles are =, and all the angles are obtuse. Then the sum of the measures of the angles is > 270. But the sum of the measures of angles of a △ is 180. Therefore, the assumption is false. An equilateral △ cannot have an obtuse angle.

Algebra **Find the value of x.**

15.

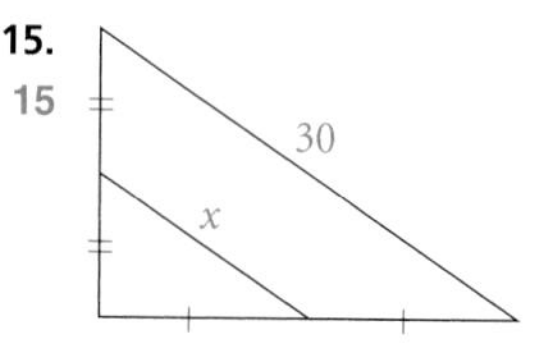

16.

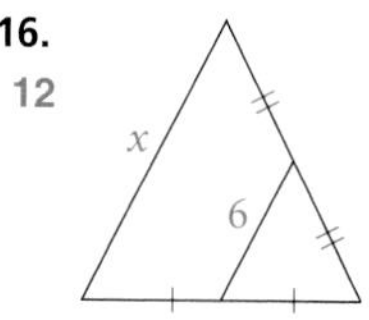

17.

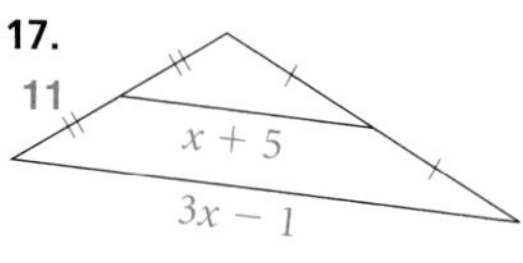

Using Indirect Reasoning 4-5

To use **indirect reasoning**, consider all possibilities and then prove all but one false. The remaining possibility must be true.

There are three steps in an indirect proof.

Step 1: Assume the opposite of what you want to prove is true.
Step 2: Use logical reasoning to reach a contradiction of an earlier statement, such as the given information or a theorem. Then state that the assumption you made was false.
Step 3: State that what you wanted to prove must be true.

18. Assume that the room had been painted with oil-based paint. Then the brushes would be rinsing in paint thinner, but they are not. So the assumption is false. The room must not have been painted with oil-based paint.

Write a convincing argument that uses indirect reasoning. 19–21. See margin.

18. Mary walks into a newly-painted room and finds 2 paint brushes rinsing in water. Show that the room was not painted with oil-based paint. See above right.

19. The product of two numbers is even. Show that at least one of the two numbers must be even.

20. Show that a triangle can have at most one obtuse angle.

21. Show that an equilateral triangle cannot have an obtuse angle.

Triangle Inequalities 4-6

The sum of the lengths of any two sides of a triangle is greater than the length of the third side. If two sides of a triangle are not congruent, the larger angle lies opposite the larger side.

List the angles and sides in order from smallest to largest.

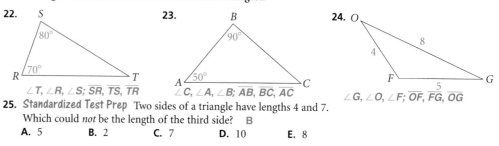

22. S, 80°, R, 70°, T

$\angle T, \angle R, \angle S; \overline{SR}, \overline{TS}, \overline{TR}$

23.

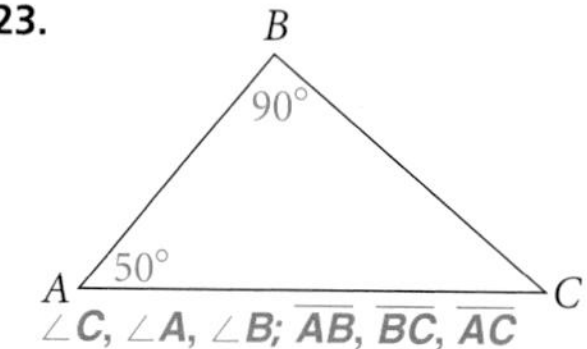

$\angle C, \angle A, \angle B; \overline{AB}, \overline{BC}, \overline{AC}$

24.

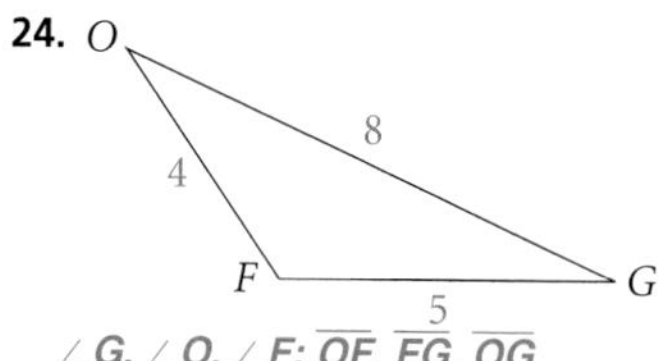

$\angle G, \angle O, \angle F; \overline{OF}, \overline{FG}, \overline{OG}$

25. *Standardized Test Prep* Two sides of a triangle have lengths 4 and 7. Which could *not* be the length of the third side? B

A. 5 **B.** 2 **C.** 7 **D.** 10 **E.** 8

Getting Ready for Chapter 5

Students may work these exercises independently or in small groups. The skills previewed will help prepare students for measuring figures in a plane.

Bisectors and Locus 4-7

A point is on the perpendicular bisector of a segment if and only if it is equidistant from the endpoints of the segment. A point is on the bisector of an angle if and only if it is equidistant from the sides of the angle. A set of points that meet a stated condition is a **locus**.

Sketch and label the locus of points.

26. all points in a plane 2 cm from a circle with radius 1 cm

27. all points in a plane equidistant from two points

28. all points in space a distance a from $\overline{DS}$

29. all points in space a distance b from a point P
See below right.

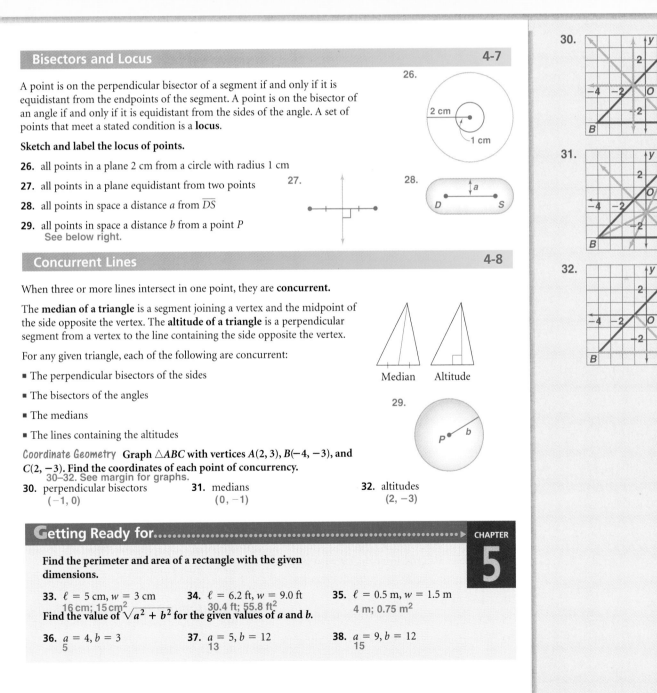

26.
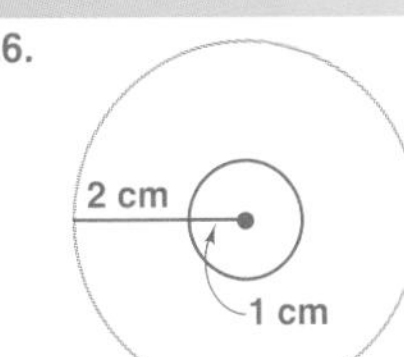

27.

28.

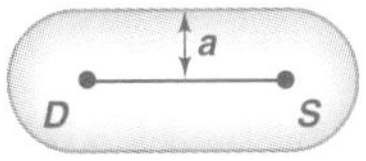

Concurrent Lines 4-8

When three or more lines intersect in one point, they are **concurrent.**

The **median of a triangle** is a segment joining a vertex and the midpoint of the side opposite the vertex. The **altitude of a triangle** is a perpendicular segment from a vertex to the line containing the side opposite the vertex.

For any given triangle, each of the following are concurrent:

- The perpendicular bisectors of the sides
- The bisectors of the angles
- The medians
- The lines containing the altitudes

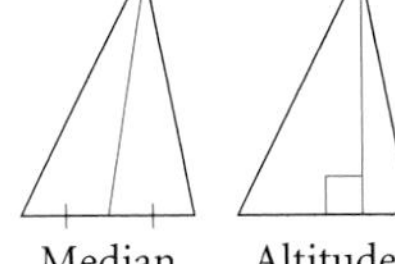
Median Altitude

29.
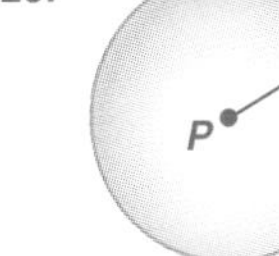

Coordinate Geometry **Graph $\triangle ABC$ with vertices $A(2, 3)$, $B(-4, -3)$, and $C(2, -3)$. Find the coordinates of each point of concurrency.**
30–32. See margin for graphs.

30. perpendicular bisectors
$(-1, 0)$

31. medians
$(0, -1)$

32. altitudes
$(2, -3)$

Getting Ready for........ CHAPTER 5

Find the perimeter and area of a rectangle with the given dimensions.

33. $\ell = 5$ cm, $w = 3$ cm
16 cm; 15 cm^2

34. $\ell = 6.2$ ft, $w = 9.0$ ft
30.4 ft; 55.8 ft^2

35. $\ell = 0.5$ m, $w = 1.5$ m
4 m; 0.75 m^2

Find the value of $\sqrt{a^2 + b^2}$ for the given values of a and b.

36. $a = 4, b = 3$
5

37. $a = 5, b = 12$
13

38. $a = 9, b = 12$
15

30.
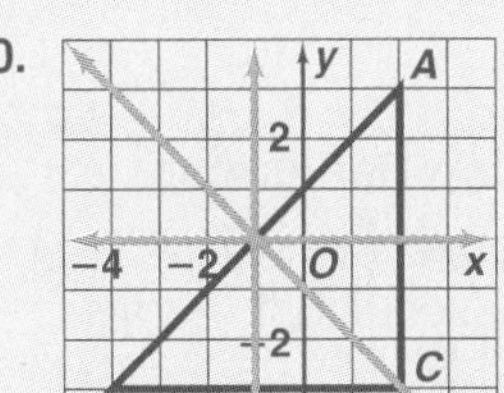

31.
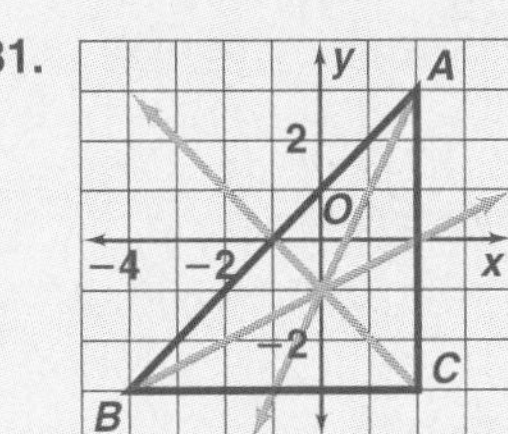

32.
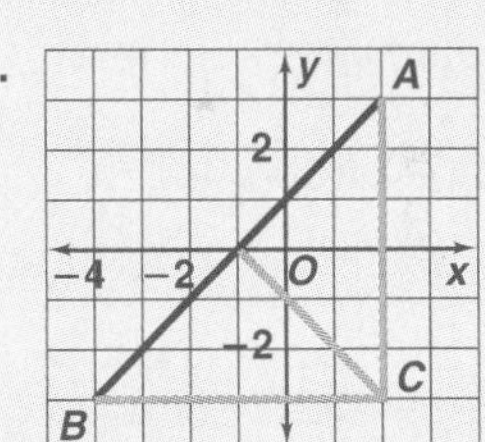

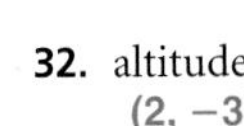

Assessment

ENHANCED MULTIPLE CHOICE QUESTIONS are more complex than traditional multiple choice questions, which assess only one skill. Enhanced multiple choice questions assess the processes that students use, as well as the end results. The questions are written so that students use more than one strategy to solve the problem. Using multiple strategies is encouraged by the National Council of Teachers of Mathematics (NCTM). **Exercise 25** is an enhanced multiple choice question.

FREE RESPONSE QUESTIONS do not give answer choices. Some exercises have more than one possible answer. Students need to give only one correct response. **Exercises 1–11, 13–16, and 18–24** are free response questions.

WRITING EXERCISES allow students to describe how they think about and understand the concepts they have learned. **Exercise 17** is a writing exercise.

OPEN-ENDED PROBLEMS allow for more than one solution. Students must construct their own responses instead of choosing from possible answers. The students' responses will help you determine the depth of their understanding and any possible areas of difficulty. **Exercises 12** is an open-ended problem.

Resources

Teaching Resources

Chapter Support File, Ch. 4
- Chapter Assessment, Forms A and B
- Alternative Assessment

Chapter Assessment, Spanish Resources

Teacher's Edition

See also p. 180E for assessment options

Software
- Computer Item Generator

Assessment page 238

1a. If a polygon is an octagon, then it has 8 sides.

b. If a polygon does not have 8 sides, then it is not an octagon.

c. If a polygon is not an octagon, then it does not have 8 sides.

2a. If it is an even-numbered year, then it is a leap year.

b. If it is not a leap year, then it is not an even-numbered year.

c. If it is not an even-numbered year, then it is not a leap year.

3a. If it is not summer, then it is snowing.

b. If it is not snowing, then it is summer.

c. If it is summer, then it is not snowing.

6. Answers may vary. Sample: $\overline{DE} \parallel \overline{BC}$, $DE = \frac{1}{2}BC$; Triangle Midsegment Thm.

4 Assessment

For each statement, write (a) the converse, (b) the inverse, and (c) the contrapositive. 1–3. See margin.

1. If a polygon has eight sides, then it is an octagon.
2. If it is a leap year, then it is an even-numbered year.
3. If it is snowing, then it is not summer.

Algebra **Find the values of x and y.**

4.

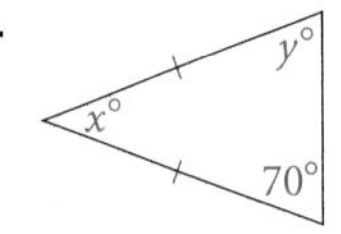

$x = 40$; $y = 70$

5.

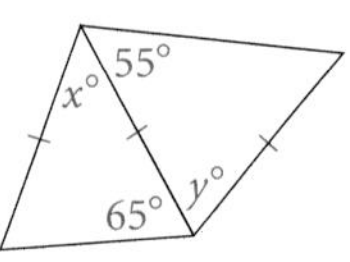

$x = 50$; $y = 70$

6. What can you conclude from the diagram? Justify your answer.

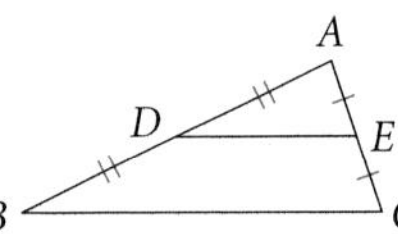

See margin.

Identify the pair of statements that forms a contradiction.

7. I. $\triangle PQR$ is a right triangle. I and II
   II. $\triangle PQR$ is an obtuse triangle.
   III. $\triangle PQR$ is scalene.
8. I. $\angle DAS \cong \angle CAT$ II and III
   II. $\angle DAS$ and $\angle CAT$ are vertical.
   III. $\angle DAS$ and $\angle CAT$ are adjacent.

List the angles of $\triangle ABC$ from smallest to largest.

9. $AB = 9, BC = 4, AC = 12$ $\angle A, \angle C, \angle B$
10. $AB = 10, BC = 11, AC = 9$ $\angle B, \angle C, \angle A$
11. $AB = 3, BC = 9, AC = 7$ $\angle C, \angle B, \angle A$
12. *Open-ended* Write three lengths that cannot be the lengths of sides of a triangle. Explain your answer. Sample: 4 cm, 5 cm, and 10 cm; $4 + 5 \not> 10$

List the sides of each triangle in order from smallest to largest.

13.

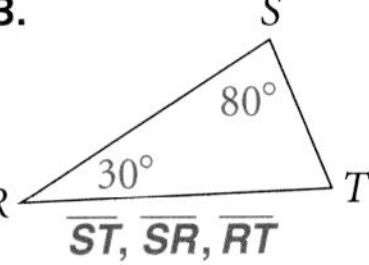

$\overline{ST}, \overline{SR}, \overline{RT}$

14. $\overline{KV}, \overline{MV}, \overline{KM}$

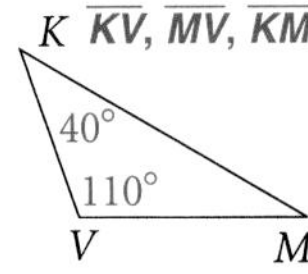

Find the value of x.

15. 6.5

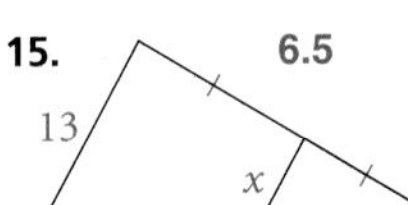

16. 12

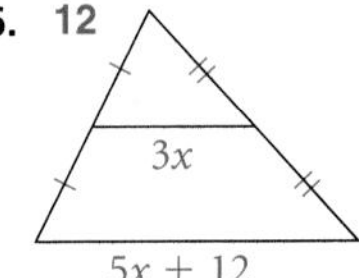

17. *Writing* Use indirect reasoning to explain why the following statement is true: If an isosceles triangle is obtuse, then the obtuse angle is the vertex angle. See back of book.

Coordinate Geometry **Sketch each locus on a coordinate plane.** 18–21. See back of book.

18. all points 6 units from the origin
19. all points 3 units from the line $y = -2$
20. all points equidistant from points (2, 4) and (0, 0)
21. all points equidistant from the axes

Sketch each figure. Determine whether the point of concurrency is in the interior, exterior, or on the triangle.

22. acute triangle, perpendicular bisectors interior
23. obtuse triangle, medians interior
24. right triangle, altitudes on the triangle
25. *Standardized Test Prep* $\triangle ABC$ has vertices $A(2, 5)$, $B(2, -3)$, and $C(10, -3)$. Which point of concurrency is at (6, 1)? C
    A. angle bisectors
    B. altitudes
    C. perpendicular bisectors
    D. medians
    E. none of the above

Cumulative Review

Item	Review Topic	Chapter
1	Triangles	2
2, 6, 8	Transformations	3
3	Patterns and Inductive Reasoning	1
4, 12	Using Logical Reasoning	4
5	Classifying Quadrilaterals	2
7	Midsegments of Triangles	4
9	Polygons	2
10	Angles	1
11	Perpendicular Lines in the Coordinate Plane	2
13	Basic Constructions	1
14	Locus	4

4 Cumulative Review

For Exercises 1–11, choose the correct letter.

1. Which could be the measures of the angles of a triangle? E
   I. 37, 89, 54 II. 125, 45, 10
   III. 100, 75, 15 IV. 60, 60, 60
   A. I only B. IV only C. I and II
   D. II and IV E. I, II, and IV

2. $\triangle DEB$ has vertices $D(3, 7)$, $E(1, 4)$, and $B(-1, 5)$. In which quadrants is the image of $\triangle DEB$ under a 90° rotation about the origin? B
   A. I and II B. II and III C. III and IV
   D. I and IV E. none of the above

3. What is the next term in the sequence 1000, 200, 40, 8, . . . ? A
   A. 1.6 B. 3 C. 4 D. 0.16
   E. none of the above

4. What is the converse of the statement "If a strawberry is red, then it is ripe"? B
   A. If a strawberry is not red, then it is not ripe.
   B. If a strawberry is ripe, then it is red.
   C. A strawberry is ripe if and only if it is red.
   D. If a strawberry is not ripe, then it is not red.
   E. A strawberry is not ripe if and only if it is not red.

5. Which quadrilateral cannot contain four right angles? B
   A. square B. trapezoid C. rectangle
   D. rhombus E. parallelogram

6. A dilation centered at the origin maps $(-3, 6)$ to $(-9, 18)$. Which of the following does *not* represent the same dilation? C
   A. $(0, 5) \longrightarrow (0, 15)$ B. $(1, -4) \longrightarrow (3, -12)$
   C. $(4, 3) \longrightarrow (9, 12)$ D. $(6, 2) \longrightarrow (18, 6)$
   E. $(-2, -7) \longrightarrow (-6, -21)$

7. What is the length of a midsegment parallel to the side of a triangle 6 cm long? A
   A. 3 cm B. 9 cm C. 12 cm
   D. 15 cm E. none of the above

8. What is the image of $(6, -9)$ under the translation $\langle 5, -2 \rangle$? A
   A. $(11, -11)$ B. $(11, -7)$ C. $(1, 11)$
   D. $(-1, -11)$ E. none of the above

9. What type of polygon is shown? C

   A. triangle B. quadrilateral C. hexagon
   D. octagon E. none of the above

Compare the boxed quantity in Column A with the boxed quantity in Column B. Choose the best answer.

A. The quantity in Column A is greater.
B. The quantity in Column B is greater.
C. The two quantities are equal.
D. The relationship cannot be determined from the information given.

	Column A	Column B	
	$\angle CDB$ and $\angle RDM$ are vertical angles.		
10.	$m\angle CDB$	$m\angle BDR$	D
	Lines ℓ and t are perpendicular.		
11.	the slope of ℓ	the slope of t	D

Find each answer.

12. Open-ended Write a conditional that has the same truth value as its converse. Sample: If a polygon has fewer than 4 sides, then it is a $\triangle$.

13. Construct a right triangle. Then construct the bisectors of two of its angles. See back of book.

14. Coordinate Geometry Find the locus of points in a plane equidistant from the lines $y = x$ and $y = -x$. the coordinate axes

Resources

Teaching Resources

Chapter Support File, Ch. 4
- Cumulative Review
- Standardized Test Practice

Teacher's Edition

See also p. 180E for assessment options

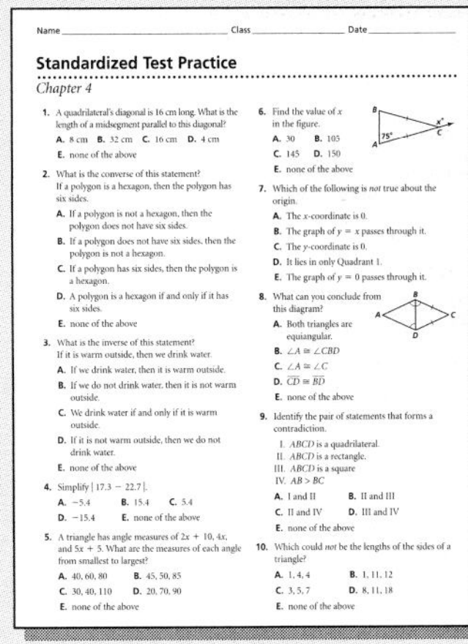
Name Class Date
Standardized Test Practice
Chapter 4

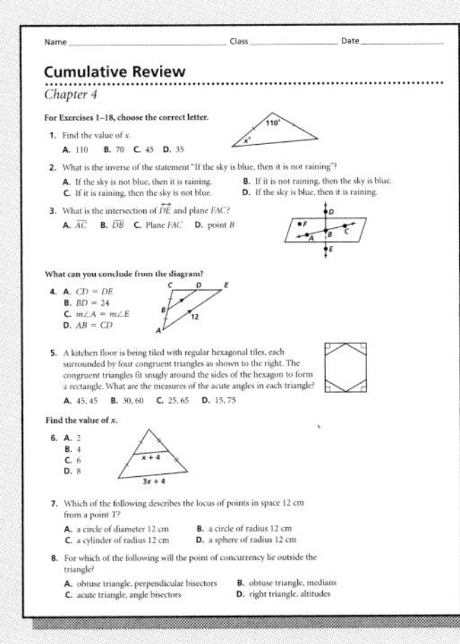
Name Class Date
Cumulative Review
Chapter 4

CHAPTER 5 Measuring in the Plane

To accommodate flexible scheduling, some lessons are divided into parts. Assignment Options are given in the Lesson Planning Options for each lesson.

PACING OPTIONS

This chart suggests pacing only for the core lessons and their parts, and it is provided merely as a possible guide. It will help you determine how much time you have in your schedule to cover other features, such as the Chapter Project, Math Toolboxes, Wrap Up, and Assessment.

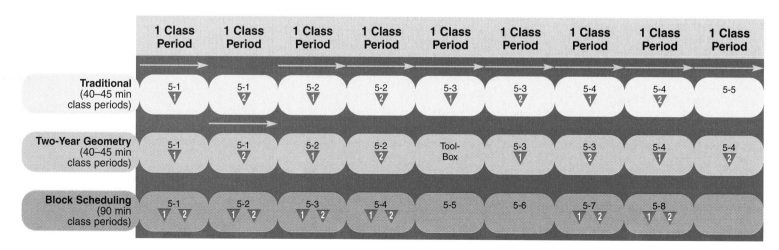

	1 Class Period	1 Class Period	1 Class Period	1 Class Period	1 Class Period	1 Class Period	1 Class Period	1 Class Period	1 Class Period
Traditional (40–45 min class periods)	5-1 Part 1	5-1 Part 2	5-2 Part 1	5-2 Part 2	5-3 Part 1	5-3 Part 2	5-4 Part 1	5-4 Part 2	5-5
Two-Year Geometry (40–45 min class periods)	5-1 Part 1	5-1 Part 2	5-2 Part 1	5-2 Part 2	Tool-Box	5-3 Part 1	5-3 Part 2	5-4 Part 1	5-4 Part 2
Block Scheduling (90 min class periods)	5-1 Parts 1, 2	5-2 Parts 1, 2	5-3 Parts 1, 2	5-4 Parts 1, 2	5-5	5-6	5-7 Parts 1, 2	5-8 Parts 1, 2	

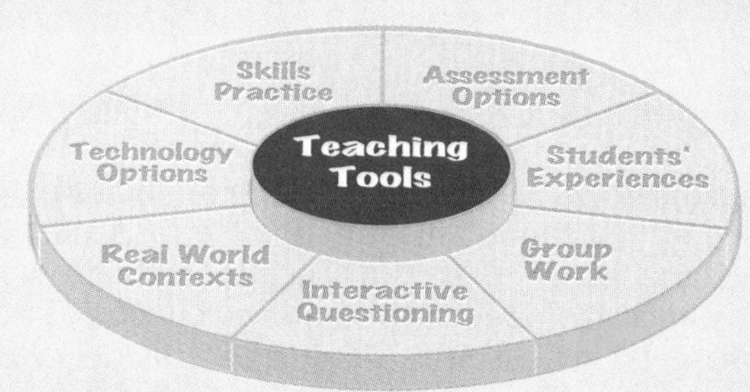

What Students Will Learn and Why

In this chapter, students build on their knowledge of triangles and quadrilaterals, learned in Chapter 2, by learning to find the area and perimeter of parallelograms, triangles, trapezoids, and regular polygons. Students study the Pythagorean Theorem, its converse, and the properties of 30°-60°-90° triangles. Finally, students learn to find circumference, arc length, and area of circles, sectors, and segments of circles. The concepts in this chapter are used by architects, race car designers, and in many other careers.

Discussing the Chapter/Building on Experience

The concept map below relates chapter topics to real-world applications. You and your class may wish to add to the map or develop maps of your own. The center oval describes the topic of the chapter. The next level displays topics within the lessons. The outer ovals reflect applications of the content. As you and your class build a concept map, invite students to discuss applications with which they are familiar.

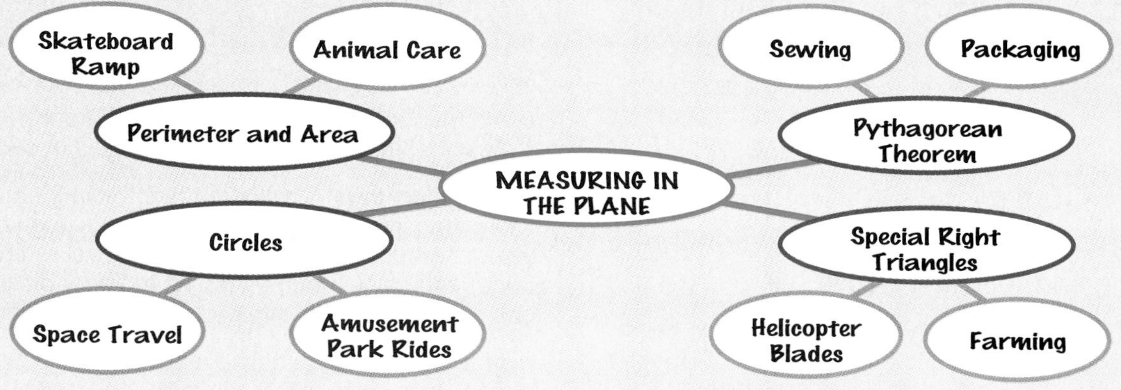

1 Class Period	1 Class Period	1 Class Period	1 Class Period	1 Class Period	1 Class Period	1 Class Period	1 Class Period	1 Class Period	1 Class Period	1 Class Period
5-6	5-7 ▽1	5-7 ▽2	5-8 ▽1	5-8 ▽2						
5-5	5-5	5-6	5-6	5-7 ▽1	5-7 ▽2	5-8 ▽1	5-8 ▽2	Tool-Box		

Tips and Tools

Interactive Questioning Tips

A question is interactive when there is "give and take" between the questioner (teacher or student) and the respondent. In Think and Discuss or when a critical thinking question is asked, it is important to allow for varying conceptual tempos among students. In Lesson 5-7, Example 3, students are asked to explain if it is possible for two arcs of different circles to have the same measure but different lengths.While some students may have an immediate response, others may need more time to consider all the elements involved, and that should certainly be encouraged. Don't rush students.

Skills Practice

Every lesson provides skill practice with Try This exercises, Exercises On Your Own, and Exercises Mixed Review. The Student Edition includes Checkpoints (pp. 268, 284) and Preparing for Standardized Tests (p. 299). In the Teacher's Edition, the Lesson Planning Options section for each lesson lists Prerequisite Skills students should know for that lesson. At the back of the Student Edition is the Skills Handbook—mini-lessons on math your students may need to review. The Chapter Support File for Chapter 5 in the Teaching Resources box includes two Practice worksheets per lesson, a worksheet for two Checkpoints, and worksheets for Cumulative Review and Standardized Test Preparation.

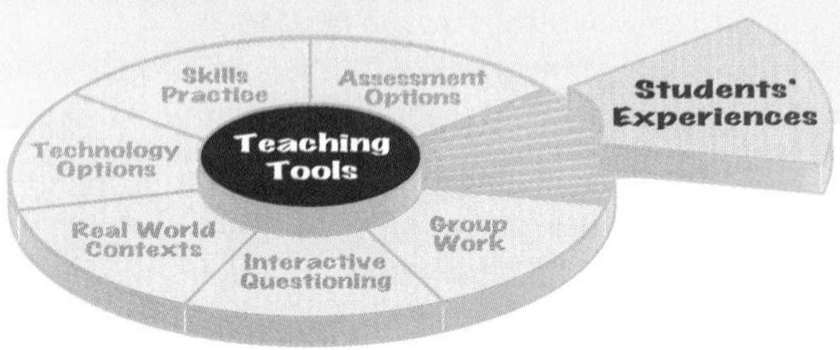

Diverse Learning and Teaching Styles

In your Teacher's Edition, you will find suggestions as to how you can help students complete mathematical tasks in Chapter 5 by reinforcing various learning styles. Here are some examples.

- **Visual learning** use geometry software to draw triangles and label their angle measures and side lengths (p. 258), use a map to approximate the area of trapezoid-shaped states (p. 270), find real-world examples of sectors (p. 286)
- **Tactile learning** investigate the formula for arc length using the circular objects from the Work Together (p. 281), work in groups to approximate the measurement of two large rectangles made by taping together pieces of graph paper (p. 286)
- **Auditory learning** practice repeating aloud formulas for the area of rectangles, parallelograms, and triangles (p. 251)
- **Kinesthetic learning** use measuring tape to find the dimensions and calculate the area of the school parking lot (p. 252)

Alternative Activity for Lesson 5-2

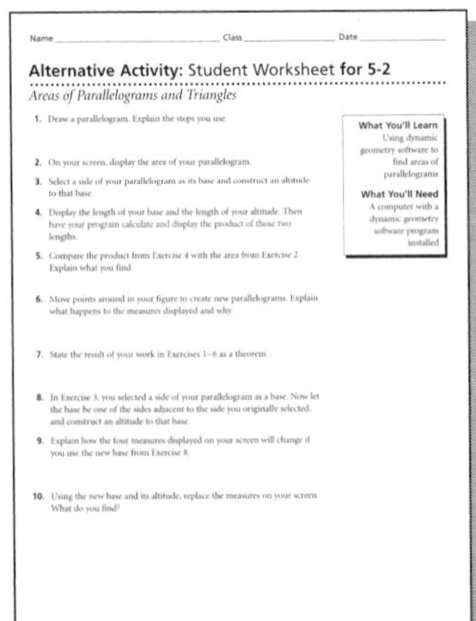
Name ______ Class ______ Date ______

Alternative Activity: Student Worksheet for 5-2

Areas of Parallelograms and Triangles

1. Draw a parallelogram. Explain the steps you use.
2. On your screen, display the area of your parallelogram.
3. Select a side of your parallelogram as its base and construct an altitude to that base.
4. Display the length of your base and the length of your altitude. Then have your program calculate and display the product of those two lengths.
5. Compare the product from Exercise 4 with the area from Exercise 2. Explain what you find.
6. Move points around in your figure to create new parallelograms. Explain what happens to the measures displayed and why.
7. State the result of your work in Exercises 1–6 as a theorem.
8. In Exercise 3, you selected a side of your parallelogram as a base. Now let the base be one of the sides adjacent to the side you originally selected, and construct an altitude to that base.
9. Explain how the four measures displayed on your screen will change if you use the new base from Exercise 8.
10. Using the new base and its altitude, replace the measures on your screen. What do you find?

What You'll Learn Using dynamic geometry software to find areas of parallelograms

What You'll Need A computer with a dynamic geometry software program installed

for use with theorem 5-2, Example 1, and Example 2, uses geometry software to explore the formula for area of a parallelogram.

Alternative Activity for Lesson 5-3

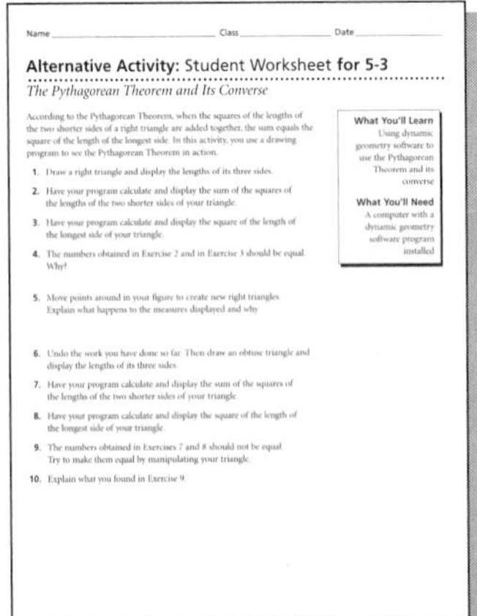
Name ______ Class ______ Date ______

Alternative Activity: Student Worksheet for 5-3

The Pythagorean Theorem and Its Converse

According to the Pythagorean Theorem, when the squares of the lengths of the two shorter sides of a right triangle are added together, the sum equals the square of the length of the longest side. In this activity, you use a drawing program to see the Pythagorean Theorem in action.

1. Draw a right triangle and display the lengths of its three sides.
2. Have your program calculate and display the sum of the squares of the lengths of the two shorter sides of your triangle.
3. Have your program calculate and display the square of the length of the longest side of your triangle.
4. The numbers obtained in Exercise 2 and in Exercise 3 should be equal. Why?
5. Move points around in your figure to create new right triangles. Explain what happens to the measures displayed and why.
6. Undo the work you have done so far. Then draw an obtuse triangle and display the lengths of its three sides.
7. Have your program calculate and display the sum of the squares of the lengths of the two shorter sides of your triangle.
8. Have your program calculate and display the square of the length of the longest side of your triangle.
9. The numbers obtained in Exercises 7 and 8 should not be equal. Try to make them equal by manipulating your triangle.
10. Explain what you found in Exercise 9.

What You'll Learn Using dynamic geometry software to use the Pythagorean Theorem and its converse

What You'll Need A computer with a dynamic geometry software program installed

for use with Think and Discuss, Example 1, and Example 2, uses geometry software to explore the Pythagorean Theorem by drawing and manipulating right and non-right triangles.

Alternative Activity for Lesson 5-7

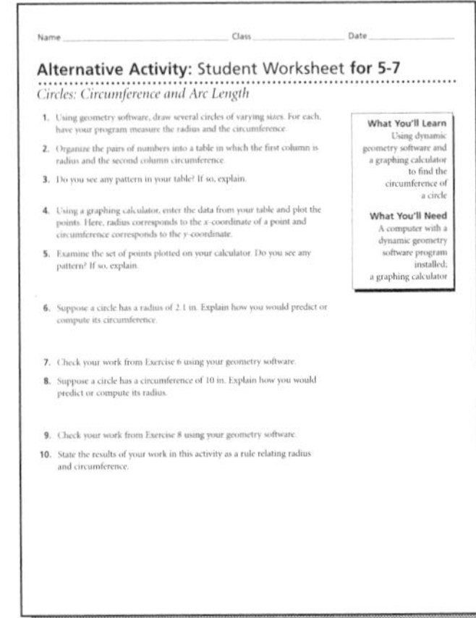
Name ______ Class ______ Date ______

Alternative Activity: Student Worksheet for 5-7

Circles: Circumference and Arc Length

1. Using geometry software, draw several circles of varying sizes. For each, have your program measure the radius and the circumference.
2. Organize the pairs of numbers into a table in which the first column is radius and the second column circumference.
3. Do you see any pattern in your table? If so, explain.
4. Using a graphing calculator, enter the data from your table and plot the points. Here, radius corresponds to the x-coordinate of a point and circumference corresponds to the y-coordinate.
5. Examine the set of points plotted on your calculator. Do you see any pattern? If so, explain.
6. Suppose a circle has a radius of 2.1 in. Explain how you would predict or compute its circumference.
7. Check your work from Exercise 6 using your geometry software.
8. Suppose a circle has a circumference of 10 in. Explain how you would predict or compute its radius.
9. Check your work from Exercise 8 using your geometry software.
10. State the results of your work in this activity as a rule relating radius and circumference.

What You'll Learn Using dynamic geometry software and a graphing calculator to find the circumference of a circle

What You'll Need A computer with a dynamic geometry software program installed; a graphing calculator

for use with Work Together and Think and Discuss, uses geometry software to explore the relationship between radius and circumference and develop a formula for circumference.

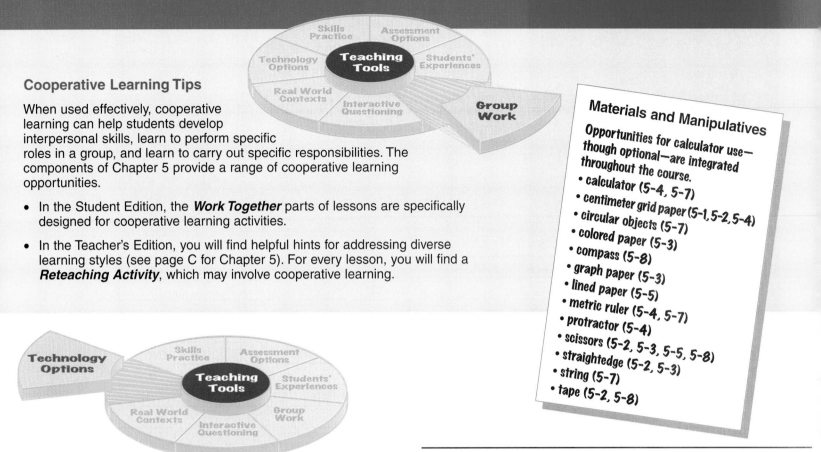

Cooperative Learning Tips

When used effectively, cooperative learning can help students develop interpersonal skills, learn to perform specific roles in a group, and learn to carry out specific responsibilities. The components of Chapter 5 provide a range of cooperative learning opportunities.

- In the Student Edition, the ***Work Together*** parts of lessons are specifically designed for cooperative learning activities.
- In the Teacher's Edition, you will find helpful hints for addressing diverse learning styles (see page C for Chapter 5). For every lesson, you will find a ***Reteaching Activity***, which may involve cooperative learning.

Materials and Manipulatives

Opportunities for calculator use—though optional—are integrated throughout the course.

- calculator (5-4, 5-7)
- centimeter grid paper (5-1, 5-2, 5-4)
- circular objects (5-7)
- colored paper (5-3)
- compass (5-8)
- graph paper (5-3)
- lined paper (5-5)
- metric ruler (5-4, 5-7)
- protractor (5-4)
- scissors (5-2, 5-3, 5-5, 5-8)
- straightedge (5-2, 5-3)
- string (5-7)
- tape (5-2, 5-8)

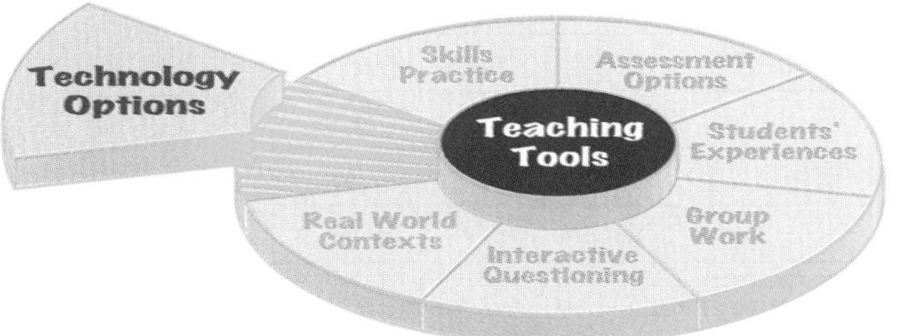

Numerous opportunities throughout for students to use scientific calculators.

TECHNOLOGY OPTIONS

Technology Tools		Chapter Project	5-1	5-2	5-3	5-4	5-5	5-6	5-7	5-8
Calculator		Numerous opportunities throughout for students to use scientific calculators.								
Software	Secondary Math Lab Toolkit™		✔	✔	✔	✔	✔	✔	✔	✔
	Integrated Math Lab			✔					✔	
	Computer Item Generator		✔	✔	✔	✔	✔	✔	✔	✔
	Student Edition		✔	✔						✔T
Video	Video Field Trip	✔								
CD-ROM	Multimedia Geometry Lab		✔		✔			✔		✔
Internet		See the Prentice Hall site. (http://www.phschool.com)								

✔T indicates Math Toolbox.

The Prentice Hall Geometry program offers you a rich variety of technology options. Be assured that all these options are provided as a means of enriching the program and are not essential for the successful completion of the course.

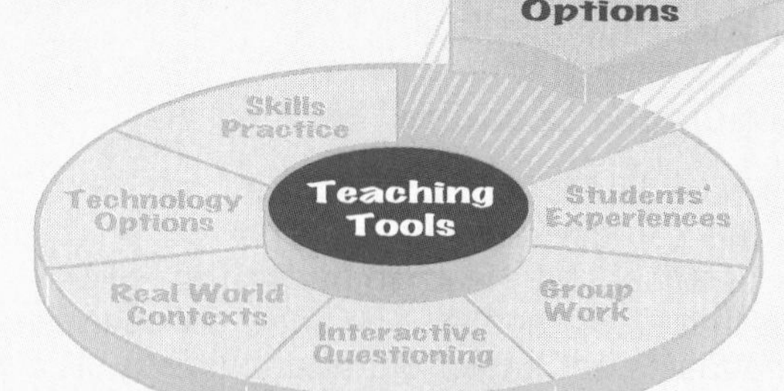

Assessment Options

The Prentice Hall Geometry Program provides you with many options. From these options, you may choose instructional materials and techniques appropriate for your students, or those necessary to meet your district's curriculum requirements. As the chart indicates, the program also supports your teaching efforts by offering you many choices for assessment.

ASSESSMENT OPTIONS

Assessment Support Materials	Chapter Project	5-1	5-2	5-3	5-4	5-5	5-6	5-7	5-8	Chapter End
Chapter Project	▲■●	▲■	▲■			▲■			▲■	▲■
Checkpoints					●▲■			●▲■		
Self-Assessment		▲■			▲■				▲■	
Writing Assignment		▲■	▲		●▲■		▲■	▲●■	▲■	▲●
Chapter Assessment										▲●
Alternative Assessment		■	■	■	■	■	■	■	■	■●
Cumulative Review										●
Standardized Test Prep		▲■		▲	▲■		▲	▲■		▲■●
Computer Item Generator	Can be used to create custom-made practice or assessment at any time.									

▲ = Student Edition ■ = Teacher's Edition ● = Teaching Resources

Checkpoints

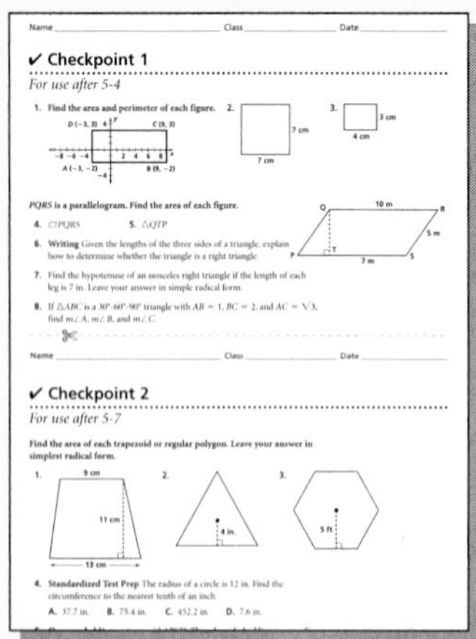

Name ______ Class ______ Date ______

✔ Checkpoint 1

For use after 5-4

1. **Find the area and perimeter of each figure.** 2. 3.

PQRS **is a parallelogram. Find the area of each figure.**

4. ▱*PQRS* 5. △*QTP*

6. **Writing** Given the lengths of the three sides of a triangle, explain how to determine whether the triangle is a right triangle.

7. Find the hypotenuse of an isosceles right triangle if the length of each leg is 7 in. Leave your answer in simple radical form.

8. If △*ABC* is a 30°-60°-90° triangle with $AB = 1$, $BC = 2$, and $AC = \sqrt{3}$, find $m\angle A$, $m\angle B$, and $m\angle C$.

Name ______ Class ______ Date ______

✔ Checkpoint 2

For use after 5-7

Find the area of each trapezoid or regular polygon. Leave your answer in simplest radical form.

1. 2. 3.

4. **Standardized Test Prep** The radius of a circle is 12 in. Find the circumference to the nearest tenth of an inch.

A. 37.7 in. B. 75.4 in. C. 452.2 in. D. 7.6 in.

Alternative Assessment

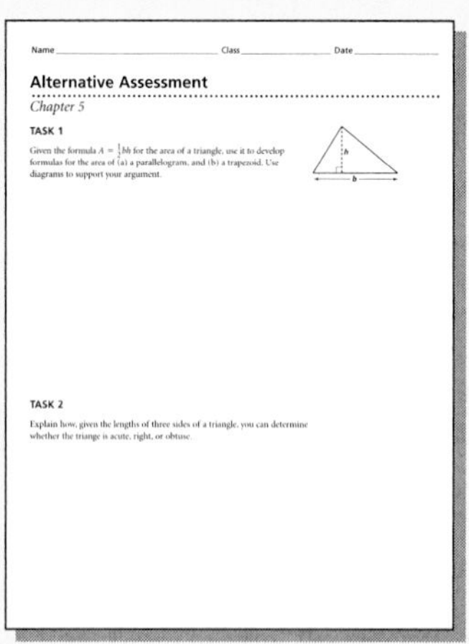

Name ______ Class ______ Date ______

Alternative Assessment

Chapter 5

TASK 1

Given the formula $A = \frac{1}{2}bh$ for the area of a triangle, use it to develop formulas for the area of (a) a parallelogram, and (b) a trapezoid. Use diagrams to support your argument.

TASK 2

Explain how, given the lengths of three sides of a triangle, you can determine whether the triange is acute, right, or obtuse.

Chapter Assessment

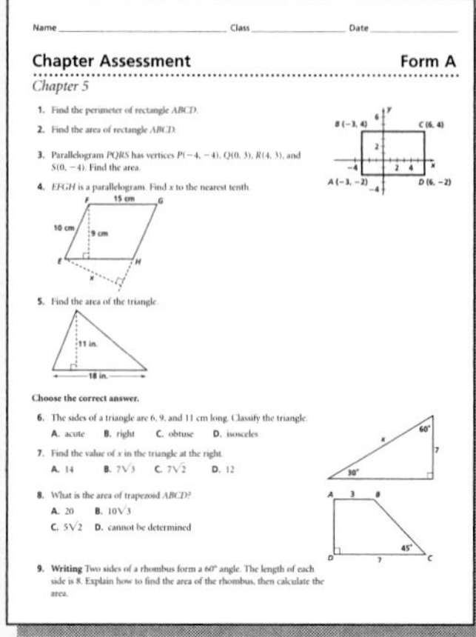

Name ______ Class ______ Date ______

Chapter Assessment **Form A**

Chapter 5

1. Find the perimeter of rectangle *ABCD*.
2. Find the area of rectangle *ABCD*.
3. Parallelogram *PQRS* has vertices $P(-4, -4)$, $Q(0, 3)$, $R(4, 3)$, and $S(0, -4)$. Find the area.
4. *EFGH* is a parallelogram. Find *x* to the nearest tenth.
5. Find the area of the triangle.

Choose the correct answer.

6. The sides of a triangle are 6, 9, and 11 cm long. Classify the triangle.
A. acute B. right C. obtuse D. isosceles
7. Find the value of *x* in the triangle at the right.
A. 14 B. $7\sqrt{3}$ C. $7\sqrt{2}$ D. 12
8. What is the area of trapezoid *ABCD*?
A. 20 B. $10\sqrt{3}$ C. $5\sqrt{2}$ D. cannot be determined
9. **Writing** Two sides of a rhombus form a 60° angle. The length of each side is 8. Explain how to find the area of the rhombus, then calculate the area.

Available in both Form A and Form B

Making the Right Connections

Mathematics is imbedded in nearly every walk of life. The National Council of Teachers of Mathematics (NCTM) encourages educators to recognize these connections and to emphasize them for the purpose of better educating students for success in life and in a global economy. The ***Connections*** chart below highlights these connections for Chapter 5.

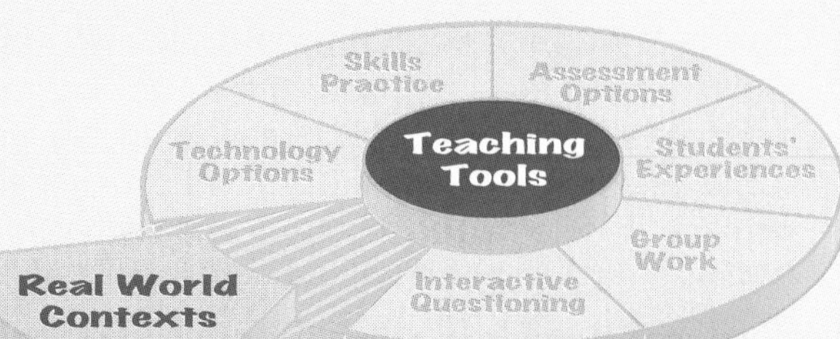

CONNECTIONS

Lesson	Interdisciplinary Connections	Career Prep	Other Real World Connections	Math Integration	NCTM Standards
Chapter Project	History	Textile Manufacturing	Quilting Fabric Making		Connections Problem Solving
5-1	Science	Animal Science Design Tiling	Animal Care Safe Stairs Carpeting Tiling Gardening	Coordinate Geometry	Communication Problem Solving
5-2		Architecture	Landscaping	Coordinate Geometry Probability	Connections Algebra Communication Problem Solving
5-3	History		Boundaries Packaging Satellites Sewing	Algebra Coordinate Geometry Geometry in 3 Dimensions	Connections Algebra Communication Problem Solving
5-4		Design Farming	Baseball Diamonds Helicopter Blades	Algebra Geometry in 3 Dimensions	Algebra Connections Communication Problem Solving
5-5	Geography		Crafts Skateboard Ramp	Algebra Geometry in 3 Dimensions	Algebra Connections Communication Problem Solving
5-6		Engineering	Racing Cars and Boats Gazebo Satellites	Coordinate Geometry	Connections Algebra Reasoning Communication Problem Solving
5-7		Metal Working Automobile Manufacturing	Amusement Park Rides Space Travel	Coordinate Geometry	Algebra Connections Communication Problem Solving
5-8	Archaeology Biology	Food Preparation	Dart Board Animal Habitat Cake Making		Connections Communication Problem Solving

CHAPTER 5 Measuring in the Plane

CONNECTING TO PRIOR LEARNING Discuss with students how perimeter and area are used by the following people: home decorators (in carpeting, tiling, and arranging furniture), carpenters (in estimating the amount of materials to buy), and farmers (in determining the sizes and shapes of fields to minimize erosion and maximize the amount of crops planted).

CULTURAL CONNECTIONS Until the twentieth century only natural materials, such as animal hair, plant fibers, or the products of silkworms, were used to make fabrics. Many of these materials can be found only in warmer climates in places like India, Egypt, and parts of the Americas. Ask students what impact the development of synthetic fibers, such as rayon and polyester, has had on the U.S. economy.

INTERDISCIPLINARY CONNECTIONS Until the late 1800s, fabric making was done by skilled artisans. During the 19th century, powered textile mills were developed in England and the United States, and Eli Whitney invented the cotton gin. In the twentieth century, textile manufacturing has become fully automated in the United States. Have students research the effects technology has had on the evolution of the textile industry.

Technology Options

Prentice Hall Technology

Video
Video Field Trip 5, "Designing Patterns," a look at designing in the fashion industry with Jhane Barnes in New York

CHAPTER 5 Measuring in the Plane

Relating to the Real World

From architects to race car designers, many careers make use of the concepts you will learn in this chapter. You will find the perimeters and areas of polygons and circles. You will also study one of the most famous theorems in geometry: the Pythagorean Theorem.

Lessons	
5-1	*Understanding Perimeter and Area*
5-2	*Areas of Parallelograms and Triangles*
5-3	*The Pythagorean Theorem and Its Converse*
5-4	*Special Right Triangles*
5-5	*Areas of Trapezoids*

ABOUT THE PROJECT Students explore patchwork techniques used by Native Americans and American pioneers. Then they use these techniques to design their own quilts.

Launching The Project

PROJECT NOTEBOOK Encourage students to keep all project-related materials in a separate folder or notebook. **See Chapter Project Manager and Scoring Rubric in Chapter Support File.**

- Have students who are familiar with patchwork quilts describe how patterns are designed and how quilts are made.
- Some students may own quilts that they are willing to bring to school to show classmates.

TRACKING THE PROJECT You may wish to have students read Finishing the Chapter Project on page 292 to help them get an overview of the project. Set benchmark deadlines for students to show their work in progress.

CHAPTER PROJECT

And Sew On

Throughout history people in all corners of the world have used patterns in their clothing, rugs, wall hangings, and blankets. Some of these articles were symbols of wealth and power. Today, textiles and fabrics still reflect social identity and cultural expression.

In your project for this chapter, you will explore patchwork techniques used by Native Americans and American pioneers. You will use these techniques to design your own quilt.

To help you complete the project:

- p. 248 *Find Out by Modeling*
- p. 254 *Find Out by Creating*
- p. 273 *Find Out by Researching*
- p. 290 *Find Out by Calculating*
- p. 292 *Finishing the Project*

Areas of Regular Polygons 5-6

Circles: Circumference and Arc Length 5-7

Areas of Circles, Sectors, and Segments of Circles 5-8

Project Resources

Teaching Resources

Chapter Support File, Ch. 5
- Chapter Project Manager and Scoring Rubric

Transparencies
59

Using the Rubric

Sharing the scoring rubric for the project with your students will alert them to your expectations before they begin work on the project.

As students complete each Find Out question in the chapter, you may wish to have them evaluate their own work or a partner's work based on the scoring rubric. Students should have the opportunity to revise their work after it has been reviewed.

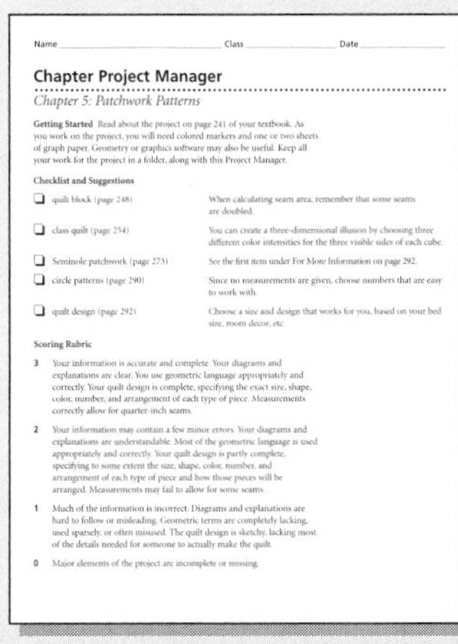

Name ________ Class ________ Date ________

Chapter Project Manager

Chapter 5: Patchwork Patterns

Getting Started Read about the project on page 241 of your textbook. As you work on the project, you will need colored markers and one or two sheets of graph paper. Geometry or graphics software may also be useful. Keep all your work for the project in a folder, along with this Project Manager.

Checklist and Suggestions

❑ quilt block (page 248)	When calculating seam area, remember that some seams are doubled.
❑ class quilt (page 254)	You can create a three-dimensional illusion by choosing three different color intensities for the three visible sides of each cube.
❑ Seminole patchwork (page 273)	See the first item under For More Information on page 292.
❑ circle patterns (page 290)	Since no measurements are given, choose numbers that are easy to work with.
❑ quilt design (page 292)	Choose a size and design that works for you, based on your bed size, room decor, etc.

Scoring Rubric

3 Your information is accurate and complete. Your diagrams and explanations are clear. You use geometric language appropriately and correctly. Your quilt design is complete, specifying the exact size, shape, color, number, and arrangement of each type of piece. Measurements correctly allow for quarter-inch seams.

2 Your information may contain a few minor errors. Your diagrams and explanations are understandable. Most of the geometric language is used appropriately and correctly. Your quilt design is partly complete, specifying to some extent the size, shape, color, number, and arrangement of each type of piece and how those pieces will be arranged. Measurements may fail to allow for some seams.

1 Much of the information is incorrect. Diagrams and explanations are hard to follow or misleading. Geometric terms are completely lacking, used sparsely, or often misused. The quilt design is sketchy, lacking most of the details needed for someone to actually make the quilt.

0 Major elements of the project are incomplete or missing.

5-1 Teaching Notes

PROBLEM OF THE DAY

In how many different ways can half the triangular regions in the square be shaded? (Rotations and reflections of patterns are not considered different.) 13

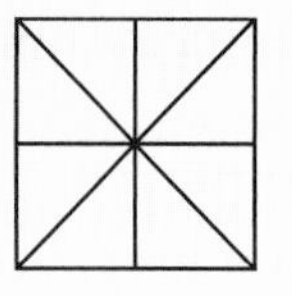

Problem of the Day is also available in Transparencies.

CONNECTING TO PRIOR KNOWLEDGE Review with students the properties of squares, rectangles, and parallelograms. Have students use calculators to find the perimeter of rectangles with dimensions $\sqrt{7}$ cm by $\sqrt{13}$ cm, $\sqrt{21}$ in. by $\sqrt{21}$ in., and $\sqrt{37}$ m by $\sqrt{5}$ m.

WORK TOGETHER

As students complete Questions 1–5, they may be surprised to find no relationship between the area and the perimeter of a rectangle. They might possibly conclude for the three examples given that the perimeter of a rectangle in units is always greater than or equal to its area in square units. Ask students to find a counterexample for this hypothesis.

THINK AND DISCUSS

Discuss the meaning of the formulas for the perimeter of a square and rectangle. Emphasize that memorization without understanding will lead to confusion later in the chapter when students learn other formulas.

Lesson Planning Options

Prerequisite Skills

- Finding perimeter of polygons
- Finding distance between points in the coordinate plane

Assignment Options for Exercises On Your Own

To provide flexible scheduling, this lesson can be subdivided into parts.

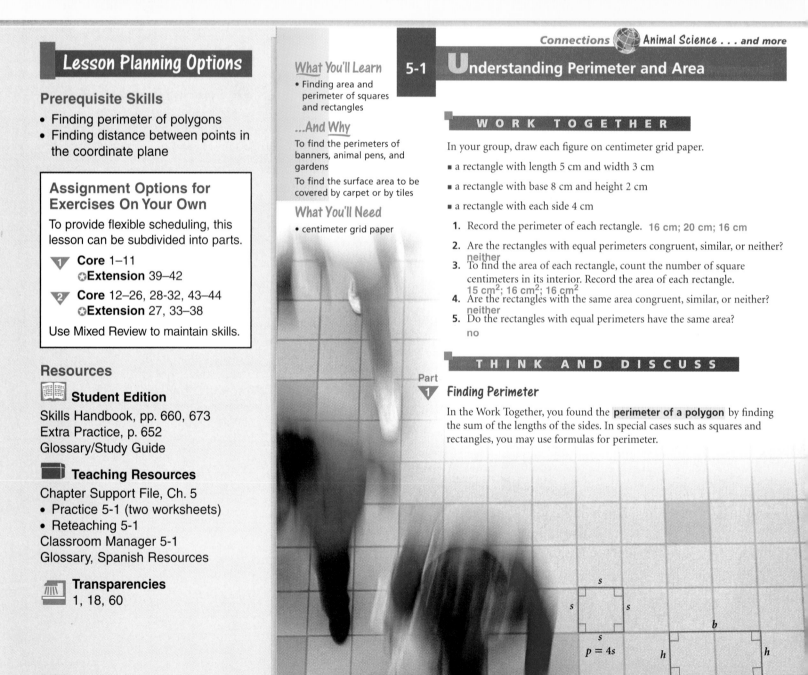

Core 1–11
Extension 39–42

Core 12–26, 28-32, 43–44
Extension 27, 33–38

Use Mixed Review to maintain skills.

Resources

Student Edition

Skills Handbook, pp. 660, 673
Extra Practice, p. 652
Glossary/Study Guide

Teaching Resources

Chapter Support File, Ch. 5
- Practice 5-1 (two worksheets)
- Reteaching 5-1

Classroom Manager 5-1
Glossary, Spanish Resources

Transparencies
1, 18, 60

Connections  Animal Science . . . and more

5-1 Understanding Perimeter and Area

What You'll Learn
- Finding area and perimeter of squares and rectangles

...And Why

To find the perimeters of banners, animal pens, and gardens

To find the surface area to be covered by carpet or by tiles

What You'll Need
- centimeter grid paper

WORK TOGETHER

In your group, draw each figure on centimeter grid paper.

- a rectangle with length 5 cm and width 3 cm
- a rectangle with base 8 cm and height 2 cm
- a rectangle with each side 4 cm

1. Record the perimeter of each rectangle. 16 cm; 20 cm; 16 cm
2. Are the rectangles with equal perimeters congruent, similar, or neither? neither
3. To find the area of each rectangle, count the number of square centimeters in its interior. Record the area of each rectangle. 15 cm^2; 16 cm^2; 16 cm^2
4. Are the rectangles with the same area congruent, similar, or neither? neither
5. Do the rectangles with equal perimeters have the same area? no

THINK AND DISCUSS

Part 

Finding Perimeter

In the Work Together, you found the **perimeter of a polygon** by finding the sum of the lengths of the sides. In special cases such as squares and rectangles, you may use formulas for perimeter.

Question 6 You may also want to ask students the following: *Can you use the formula for the perimeter of a rectangle to find the perimeter of a square? Explain.*

Example 1

ESTIMATION Encourage students to begin by estimating *AC* using the grid. You may want to tell them that the diagonal of a unit square is about 1.4 units. Then discuss how they can use estimation to check if their solutions are reasonable.

Help students understand that the size of a square unit depends on the unit used. Have students compare the sizes of a square centimeter, a square inch, a square foot, and a square meter.

CRITICAL THINKING Postulate 5-2 Remind students that they discovered in the Work Together that the converse of this postulate is not true for rectangles. Ask students for what type of quadrilateral the converse is true and why.

Postulate 5-3 Check that students apply this postulate when finding area, not perimeter. Use the figure given in Question 9 to show that the sum of the perimeters of the region *is not* the sum of the perimeters of the nonoverlapping regions.

Question 8c Have students use the results to find the number of square inches in a rectangle with dimensions three feet by two feet. Check that students multiply 6 ft^2 by $\frac{144 \text{ in.}^2}{1 \text{ ft}^2}$, not $\frac{12 \text{ in.}}{1 \text{ ft}}$.

---

6. Can you use the formula for the perimeter of a square to find the perimeter of any rectangle? Explain.
No; a square is a special kind of rectangle.

You can use the Distance Formula to find perimeter in the coordinate plane.

Example 1

Coordinate Geometry Find the perimeter of $\triangle ABC$.

Find the length of each side. Add the lengths to find the perimeter.

$AB = 5 - (-1) = 6$

$BC = 6 - (-2) = 8$

$AC = \sqrt{(5 - (-1))^2 + (6 - (-2))^2}$ Use the Distance Formula.

$= \sqrt{6^2 + 8^2} = \sqrt{100} = 10$

$AB + BC + AC = 6 + 8 + 10 = 24$

The perimeter of $\triangle ABC$ is 24 units.

7. **Try This** Graph the quadrilateral with vertices $K(-3, -3)$, $L(1, -3)$, $M(1, 4)$, and $N(-3, 1)$. Find the perimeter of *KLMN*.
See margin p. 245.

Part 2

Finding Area

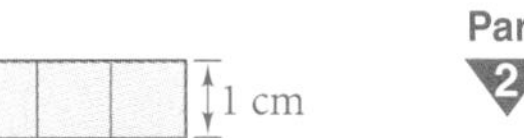

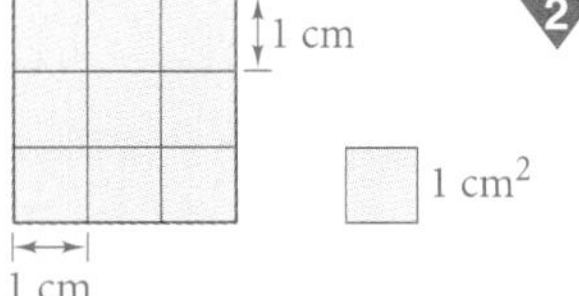

The **area of a polygon** is the number of square units enclosed by the polygon. The blue square at the left encloses nine smaller red squares. Each red square has sides 1 cm long and is called a square centimeter. By counting square centimeters, you see that the blue square has area 9 cm^2.

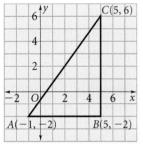

Postulate 5-1 The area of a square is the square of the length of a side.

$A = s^2$

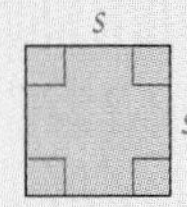

Postulate 5-2 If two figures are congruent, their areas are equal.

Postulate 5-3 The area of a region is the sum of the areas of its nonoverlapping parts.

8. a. **Try This** What is the area of a square whose sides are 12 in. long? 144 in.^{2}
b. What is the area of a square whose sides are 1 ft long? 1 ft^2
c. How many square inches are in a square foot? 144

9b–c. See margin p. 245.

9. a. By counting squares, find the area of the polygon outlined in blue. 30 in.^{2}
b. Use Postulate 5-1 to find the area of each square outlined in red.
c. How does the sum of your answers to part (b) compare to your answer to part (a)? Which postulate does this **verify**?

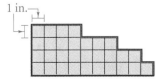

Additional Examples

FOR EXAMPLE 1

Find the perimeter of $\triangle XYZ$ with coordinates $X(-3, 3)$, $Y(0, -1)$, and $Z(-3, -1)$. 12 units

Discussion: *What is the perimeter of the image of $\triangle XYZ$ under a reflection in the y-axis?*

FOR EXAMPLE 2

A rectangular store sign is 4 yards long and 4 feet wide. What is its area in square feet? 48 ft^2

Discussion: *How many square yards is the area of the store sign? Explain.*

FOR EXAMPLE 3

You have 48 feet of fencing. You want to fence a rectangular section. What are the dimensions of the rectangle with the maximum area? 12 ft by 12 ft

Theorem 5-1 Students may not be familiar with labeling the sides of a rectangle as *height* and *base.* Point out that a rectangle is a special type of parallelogram with four right angles, and the height of a rectangle is always equal to a side of the rectangle.

Example 2 Relating to the Real World 

ERROR ALERT! Some students may disregard the units and calculate the area by multiplying 2 by 4. **Remediation:** Copy the diagram and add lines to show 8 rectangular regions with dimensions 1 yd by 1 ft. Have students continue to add lines until the rectangle is divided into squares. Discuss the dimensions of each square, the total number of squares, and how the diagram relates to the worked-out example.

Example 3 Relating to the Real World 

Help students see that the graph shows all possible values for *b* and *h.* Discuss why the integer values are of most significance because fencing is usually purchased by the foot.

Technology Options

For Exercise 34, students may use computers or graphing calculators to sketch the different rectangles.

Prentice Hall Technology 

Software
- Secondary Math Lab Toolkit™
- Computer Item Generator 5-1

CD-ROM
- Multimedia Geometry Lab 5

Internet
- See the Prentice Hall site. (http://www.phschool.com)

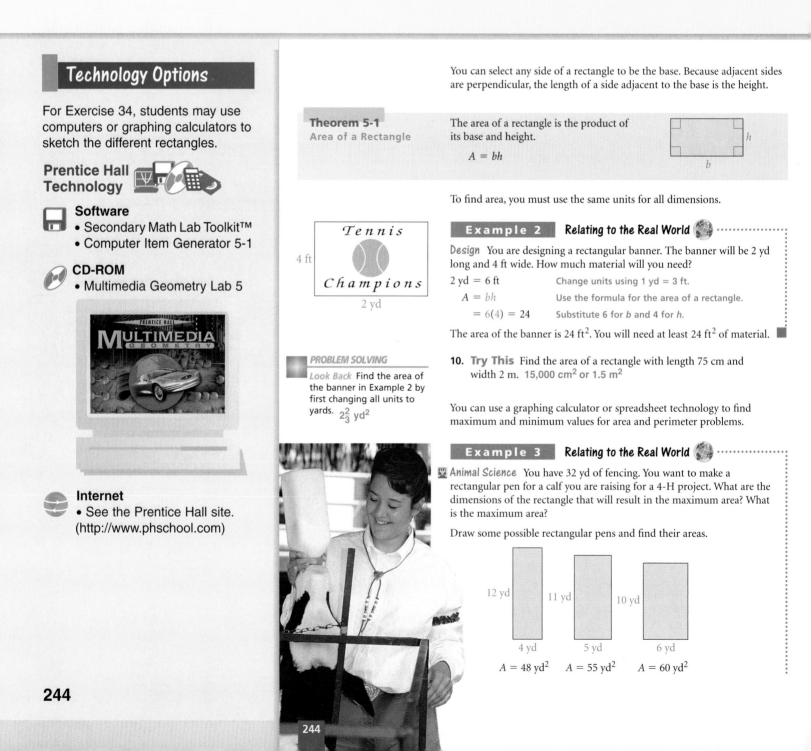

You can select any side of a rectangle to be the base. Because adjacent sides are perpendicular, the length of a side adjacent to the base is the height.

Theorem 5-1
Area of a Rectangle

The area of a rectangle is the product of its base and height.

$A = bh$

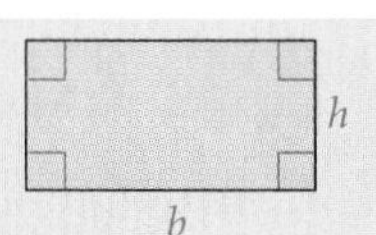

To find area, you must use the same units for all dimensions.

Example 2 Relating to the Real World 

Design You are designing a rectangular banner. The banner will be 2 yd long and 4 ft wide. How much material will you need?

$2 \text{ yd} = 6 \text{ ft}$	Change units using 1 yd = 3 ft.
$A = bh$	Use the formula for the area of a rectangle.
$= 6(4) = 24$	Substitute 6 for *b* and 4 for *h*.

The area of the banner is 24 ft^2. You will need at least 24 ft^2 of material.

PROBLEM SOLVING

Look Back Find the area of the banner in Example 2 by first changing all units to yards. $2\frac{2}{3}$ yd^2

10. Try This Find the area of a rectangle with length 75 cm and width 2 m. 15,000 cm^2 or 1.5 m^2

You can use a graphing calculator or spreadsheet technology to find maximum and minimum values for area and perimeter problems.

Example 3 Relating to the Real World 

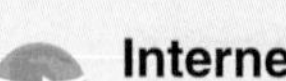

Animal Science You have 32 yd of fencing. You want to make a rectangular pen for a calf you are raising for a 4-H project. What are the dimensions of the rectangle that will result in the maximum area? What is the maximum area?

Draw some possible rectangular pens and find their areas.

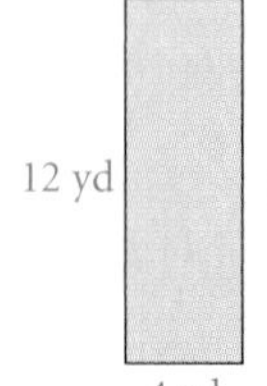

$A = 48 \text{ yd}^2$ $A = 55 \text{ yd}^2$ $A = 60 \text{ yd}^2$

Question 12 The generalization of the answer from Example 3 can be made on the assumption that the base and height are not restricted to integral values. Have students try the same problem with 30 feet of fencing. You can get the maximum area by enclosing a square with side length 7.5 ft.

Exercises ON YOUR OWN

Exercises 1–3 These examples provide an opportunity to discuss choosing appropriate units of measure. For example, the perimeter of the cover of a book is best measured using centimeters or inches, while the perimeter of a house or building is best measured using feet, yards, or meters.

Exercises 6–7 Although finding the perimeter of nonrectangular figures was not reviewed in the lesson, students should not have difficulty applying the definition of perimeter given on page 242 to these figures.

VISUAL LEARNING Exercises 8–11 Some students may want to draw the rectangles in these exercises and other rectangles described in the exercise set on grid paper before calculating perimeters and areas. Encourage students to label the sides of their drawings with the appropriate units.

	A	B	C
1	b	h = 16 − b	A = bh
2	1	15	15
3	2	14	28
4	3	13	39
5	...	...	...

Create a spreadsheet to find area. Choose values for b from 0 to 15.

Make a graph of the spreadsheet values. Graph values of b on the horizontal axis and values of A on the vertical axis. Connect the points with a smooth curve.

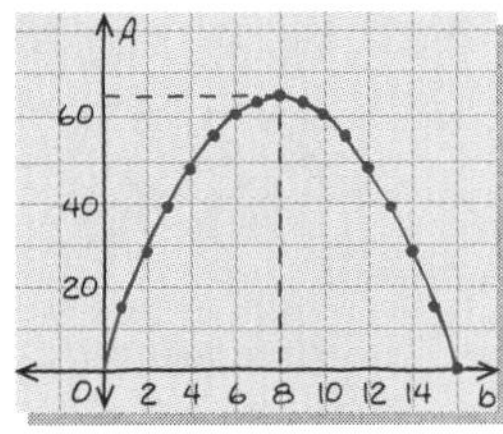

The maximum value occurs at $b = 8$. When $b = 8$, $h = 8$ and $A = 64$.

To have the maximum area for your calf, you should fence a square with sides 8 yd long. The maximum area is 64 yd^2.

11. Subtract $2b$ from each side; then divide each side by 2.

11. *Critical Thinking* Show how the equation $h = 16 - b$ was derived from the formula $2b + 2h = 32$.

12. Use the answer to Example 3. Make a **conjecture** by completing this statement: If you have a fixed amount of fencing to enclose a rectangle, you can get the maximum area by enclosing a __?__. **square**

Exercises ON YOUR OWN

Estimation **Estimate the perimeter of each item.** 1–3. Answers may vary. Samples are given.

1. the cover of this book **about 40 in.**

2. the cover of your notebook **about 42 in.**

3. a classroom bulletin board **about 20 ft**

Mental Math **Find the perimeter of each figure.**

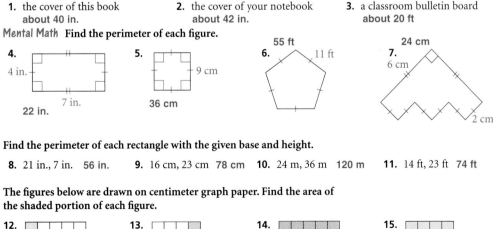

4.

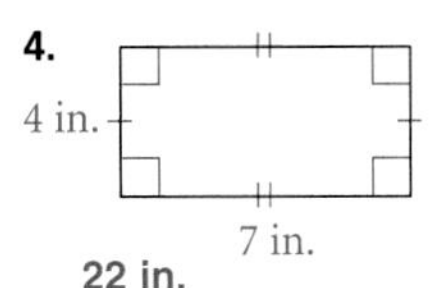

22 in.

5.

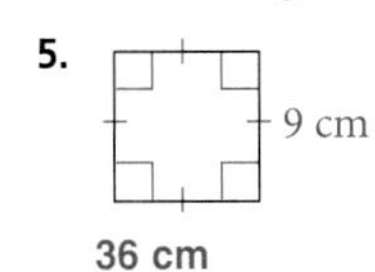

36 cm

6. **55 ft**

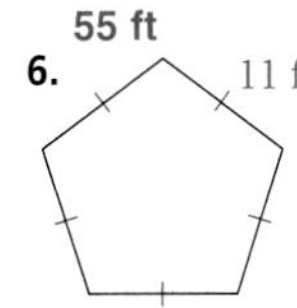

7. **24 cm**

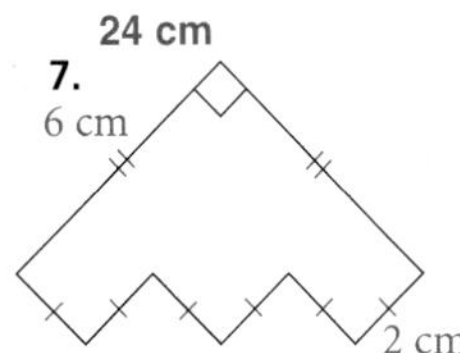

Find the perimeter of each rectangle with the given base and height.

8. 21 in., 7 in. **56 in.**

9. 16 cm, 23 cm **78 cm**

10. 24 m, 36 m **120 m**

11. 14 ft, 23 ft **74 ft**

The figures below are drawn on centimeter graph paper. Find the area of the shaded portion of each figure.

12.

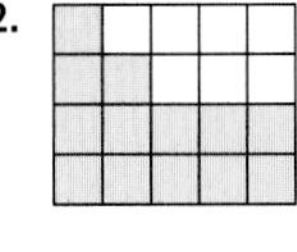

13 cm^2

13.

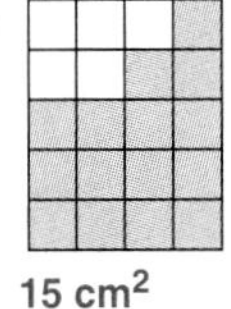

15 cm^2

14.

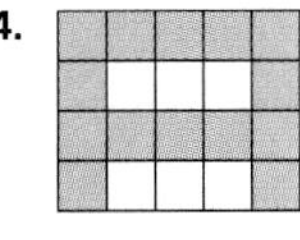

14 cm^2

15.

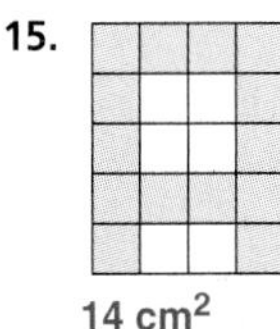

14 cm^2

pages 242–245 Think and Discuss

7.

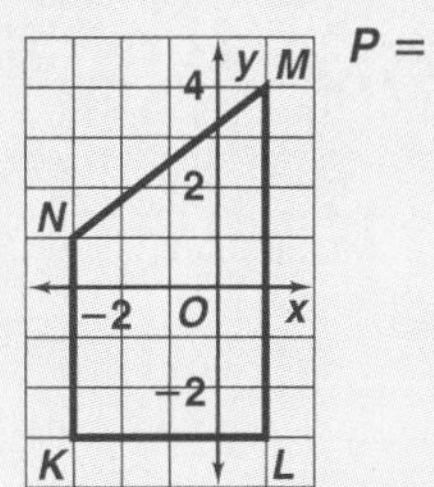

9b. 16 in.^{2} + 9 in.^{2} + 4 in.^{2} + 1 in.^{2} = 30 in.^{2}

c. They are =; Postulate 5-3: the area of a region is the sum of the areas of its non-overlapping parts.

COORDINATE GEOMETRY Exercises 16–19 Students can find the area by finding the base and height of the rectangle and multiplying or by counting the number of unit squares on the grid. Encourage students to use both methods as a way to check their work.

COORDINATE GEOMETRY Exercise 21 Make sure students connect the vertices in the order they are listed and then complete the polygon by connecting the last point to the first. In part c, there are many ways to divide the polygon into rectangles. Students may want to add a line between *D* and *G* and find the area of *ABCH* minus the area of *DEFG*.

Exercise 27 Make sure students understand how much carpet is needed to cover "from the bottom of the first riser to the top of the sixth riser." Students will need this length to answer part a and part b.

MAKING CONNECTIONS Exercise 27 The spiral staircase in the Mapco-White County Coal Mine in Carni, Illinois is 1103 feet deep and has 1520 steps. Ask students to find the height of a riser if they are all the same height. about 8.7 in.

pages 245–248 On Your Own

21a, c.

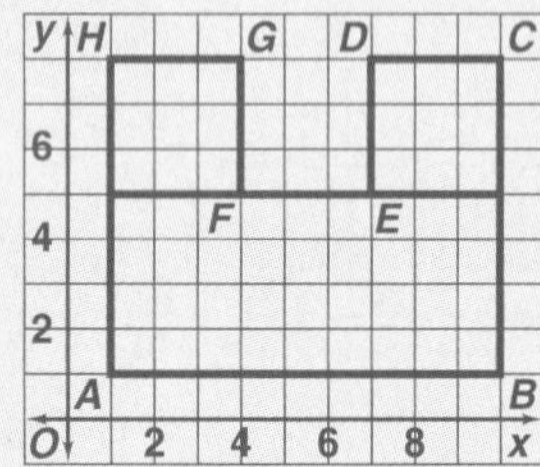

34b.

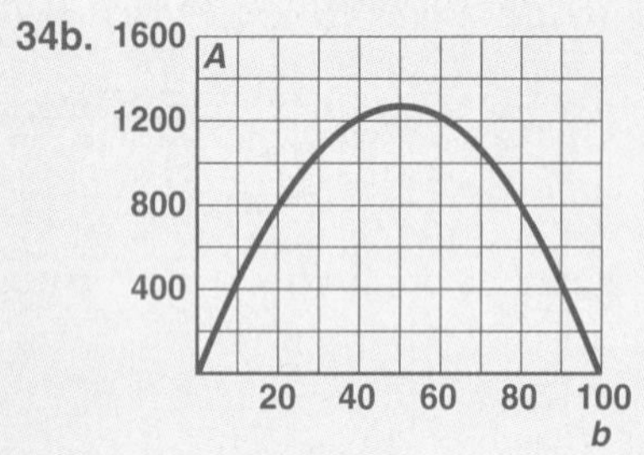

Coordinate Geometry **Graph each rectangle *ABCD* and find its area.**

16. $A(0, 0), B(0, 4), C(5, 4), D(5, 0)$ 20 units^2
17. $A(1, 4), B(1, 7), C(5, 7), D(5, 4)$ 12 units^2
18. $A(-3, 2), B(-2, 2), C(-2, -2), D(-3, -2)$ 4 units^2
19. $A(-2, -6), B(-2, -3), C(3, -3), D(3, -6)$ 15 units^2

20. A rectangle is 11 cm wide. Its area is 176 cm^2. What is the length of the rectangle? 16 cm

21. *Coordinate Geometry* Points $A(1, 1)$, $B(10, 1)$, $C(10, 8)$, $D(7, 8)$, $E(7, 5)$, $F(4, 5)$, $G(4, 8)$, and $H(1, 8)$ are the coordinates of the vertices of polygon *ABCDEFGH*. a, c. See margin.
    a. Draw the polygon on graph paper.
    b. Find the perimeter of the polygon. 38 units
    c. Divide the polygon into rectangles.
    d. Find the area of the polygon. 54 units^2

22. The perimeter of a rectangle is 40 cm and the base is 12 cm. What is the area? 96 cm^2

23. A square and a rectangle have equal areas. The rectangle is 64 cm by 81 cm. What is the perimeter of the square? 288 cm

Find the area of each rectangle with the given base and height.

24. 4 ft 6 in., 4 in. 216 in.^{2}
25. 1 yd 18 in., 4 yd 6 yd^2
26. 2 ft 3 in., 6 in. 162 in.^{2}

Building Safe Stairs

Since falls are a major cause of injury, it makes sense to be concerned about the safety of stairs. According to John Templer, the world's foremost authority on stairs, steps with a 7-in. riser and an 11-in. tread form the safest possible stairs.

Prior to his investigations, Francois Blondel's formula, dated 1675, had recommended that stair measurements conform to the formula 2(riser) + tread = 25.5 in.

Source: *Smithsonian*

27. *Carpeting* You use John Templer's dimensions to build a stairway with six steps. You want to carpet the stairs with a 3-ft wide runner from the bottom of the first riser to the top of the sixth riser.
    a. Find the area of the runner. 3492 in.^{2} or $24\frac{1}{4}$ ft^2
    b. Since a roll of carpet is 12 ft across, a rectangle of carpet that measures 3 ft by 12 ft is cut from the roll to make the runner. How many square feet of the material will be wasted? $11\frac{3}{4}$ ft^2
    c. The carpet costs \$17.95/yd^2. You must pay for the entire piece that is cut. Find the cost of the carpet. \$71.80
    d. Binding for the edge of the runner costs \$1.75/yd. How much will the binding cost if the two long edges of the runner are bound? \$9.43

ESL Exercises 28–31 Discuss with students the meanings of the terms "edging," "basement," "wallpaper," and "weatherstripping." Depending on your geographical area, students may be more familiar with some of these terms than others. Point out examples of the terms found in the school, if possible.

CONNECTING TO STUDENTS' WORLD Exercise 32 Have students measure the length and width of the classroom, the gymnasium, the cafeteria, or a hallway. Then have them determine how many square tiles of a given dimension it would take to cover the floor.

TECHNOLOGY Exercise 33b Ask students to use the results of their spreadsheet to draw a graph that shows *all* the possible perimeters.

ALTERNATIVE ASSESSMENT Exercises 35–38 These exercises will help you evaluate students' understanding of area and their ability to apply Postulates 5-3 and Theorem 5-1. Have students compare with a partner their answers and their methods for solving. Note that figures can be divided into rectangular regions in more than one way.

OPEN-ENDED Exercise 43 Some students may experience difficulty if they try to find just two squares with the same total area as an 11-in. by 11-in. square. Have students read the directions carefully.

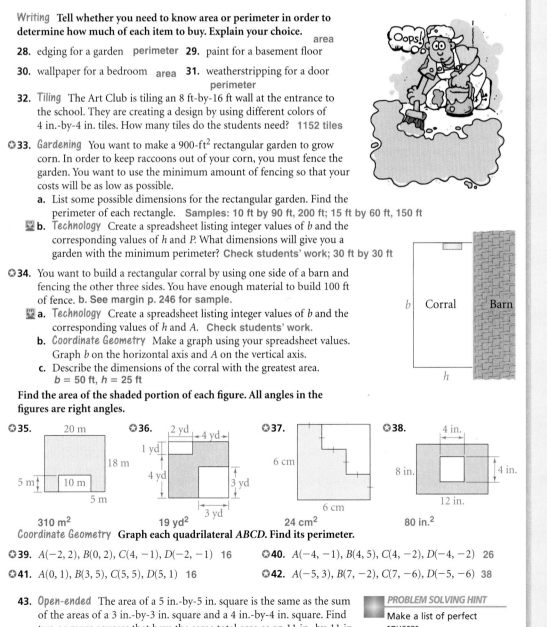

Writing **Tell whether you need to know area or perimeter in order to determine how much of each item to buy. Explain your choice.**

28. edging for a garden **perimeter**
29. paint for a basement floor **area**
30. wallpaper for a bedroom **area**
31. weatherstripping for a door **perimeter**

32. *Tiling* The Art Club is tiling an 8 ft-by-16 ft wall at the entrance to the school. They are creating a design by using different colors of 4 in.-by-4 in. tiles. How many tiles do the students need? **1152 tiles**

33. *Gardening* You want to make a 900-ft^2 rectangular garden to grow corn. In order to keep raccoons out of your corn, you must fence the garden. You want to use the minimum amount of fencing so that your costs will be as low as possible.
    a. List some possible dimensions for the rectangular garden. Find the perimeter of each rectangle. **Samples: 10 ft by 90 ft, 200 ft; 15 ft by 60 ft, 150 ft**
    b. *Technology* Create a spreadsheet listing integer values of b and the corresponding values of h and P. What dimensions will give you a garden with the minimum perimeter? **Check students' work; 30 ft by 30 ft**

34. You want to build a rectangular corral by using one side of a barn and fencing the other three sides. You have enough material to build 100 ft of fence. **b. See margin p. 246 for sample.**
    a. *Technology* Create a spreadsheet listing integer values of b and the corresponding values of h and A. **Check students' work.**
    b. *Coordinate Geometry* Make a graph using your spreadsheet values. Graph b on the horizontal axis and A on the vertical axis.
    c. Describe the dimensions of the corral with the greatest area. **b = 50 ft, h = 25 ft**

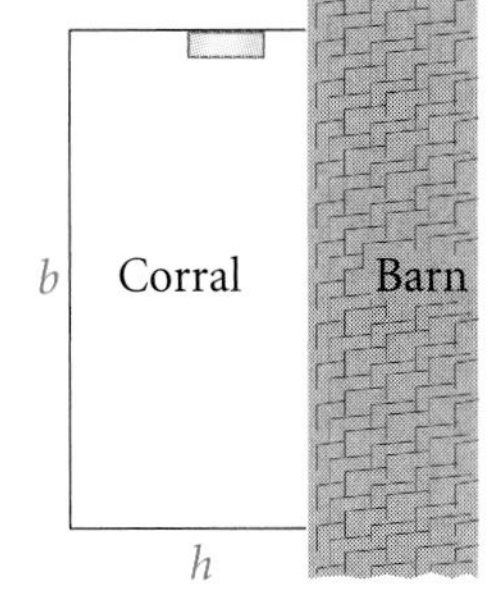

Find the area of the shaded portion of each figure. All angles in the figures are right angles.

35. 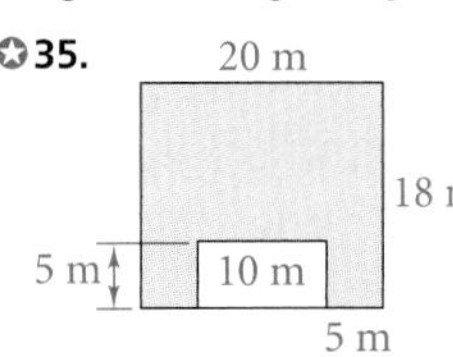

310 m^2

36. 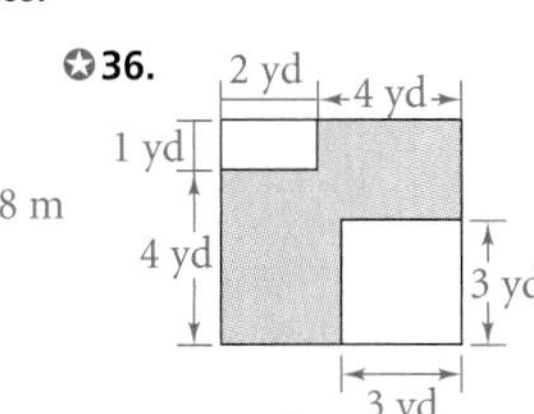

19 yd^2

37. 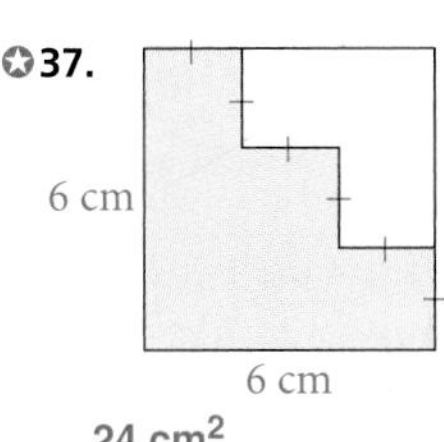

24 cm^2

38. 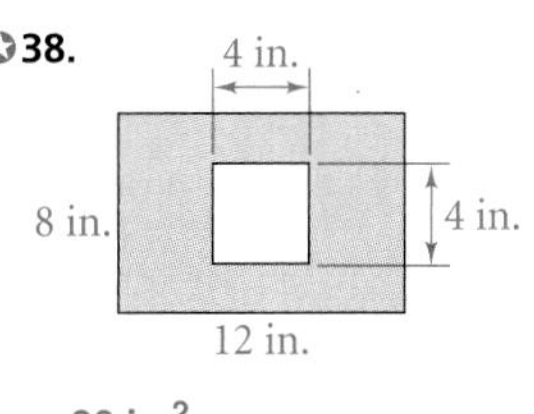

80 $in.^2$

Coordinate Geometry **Graph each quadrilateral $ABCD$. Find its perimeter.**

39. $A(-2, 2), B(0, 2), C(4, -1), D(-2, -1)$ **16**
40. $A(-4, -1), B(4, 5), C(4, -2), D(-4, -2)$ **26**
41. $A(0, 1), B(3, 5), C(5, 5), D(5, 1)$ **16**
42. $A(-5, 3), B(7, -2), C(7, -6), D(-5, -6)$ **38**

43. *Open-ended* The area of a 5 in.-by-5 in. square is the same as the sum of the areas of a 3 in.-by-3 in. square and a 4 in.-by-4 in. square. Find two or more squares that have the same total area as an 11 in.-by-11 in. square. **Samples: 2 in.-by-2 in., 6 in.-by-6 in., 9 in.-by-9 in.; 6 in.-by-6 in., 6 in.-by-6 in., 7 in.-by-7 in.**

PROBLEM SOLVING HINT
Make a list of perfect squares.

Chapter Project FIND OUT BY MODELING Have students work in small groups to complete this activity. One student may want to hold the small squares together while another staples them. Watch that students staple the second pair of squares so that they form a 2 by 2 square.

Exercises MIXED REVIEW

Exercises 45–47 Students can graph the segment and the midpoint as a way to check their answers.

SELF ASSESSMENT JOURNAL Ask students to include the units of measurement for area and perimeter and a diagram illustrating each. Make sure their examples are different from those found in the lesson.

GETTING READY FOR LESSON 5-2 These exercises prepare students to find the areas of triangles.

Wrap Up

THE BIG IDEA Ask students: *Describe in your own words why the formulas for the area and perimeter of a rectangle "work."*

RETEACHING ACTIVITY Students sketch all the possible rectangles with integral dimensions and an area of 60 square units. (Reteaching worksheet 5-1)

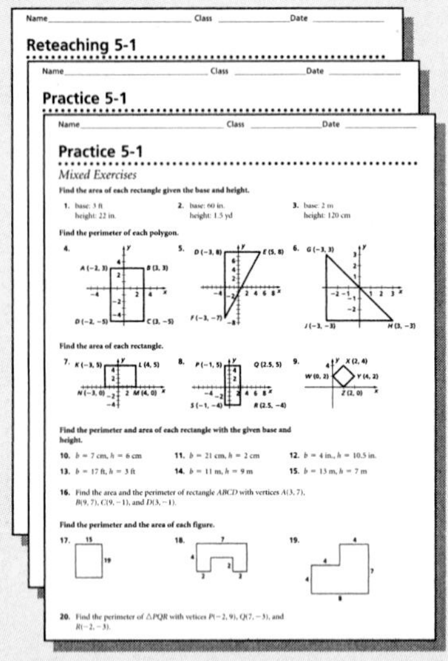
Reteaching 5-1

Practice 5-1

Practice 5-1

Mixed Exercises

Lesson Quiz

Lesson Quiz is also available in Transparencies.

1. Find the perimeter of a rectangle with base 15 in. and height 13 in. 56 in.
2. Find the area of a rectangle with vertices (−2, 4), (−2, −2), (3, 4), and (3, −2). 30 square units
3. You have 96 feet of fencing. You want to fence a rectangular region in such a way that it has the maximum area. What are the dimensions of the region? 24 ft by 24 ft

44. *Standardized Test Prep* The length of a rectangle is increased by 50% and the width is decreased by 50%. How is the area affected? B

A. increased by 25% **B.** decreased by 25% **C.** increased by 50%
D. decreased by 50% **E.** unchanged

Chapter Project *Find Out by Modeling*

You can create a quilt by sewing together congruent squares to form blocks. To model a quilt block, cut four 3 in.-by-3 in. squares out of $\frac{1}{4}$-in. graph paper. Place one square on top of another and make a seam by stapling the two squares together $\frac{1}{4}$ in. from one of the edges. Unfold the squares and press the seam flat in the back.
Repeat this with the two other squares. Then place the two sections on top of each other. Staple a $\frac{1}{4}$-in. seam from one end to the other. Unfold and press the seams back.

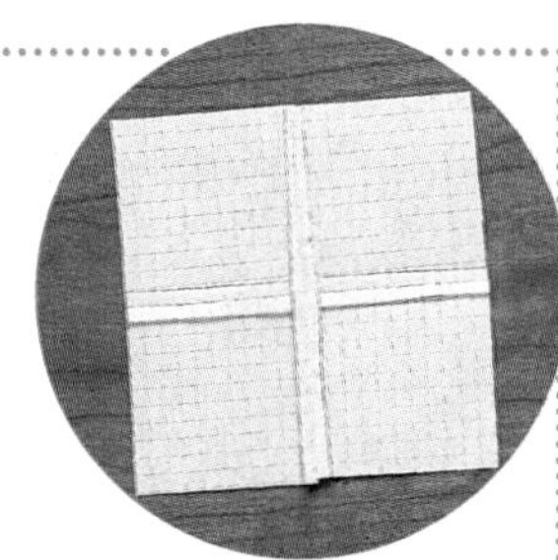

- What is the total area of the four paper squares that you started with? 36 in.^{2}
- What is the area of your finished quilt block? 30.25 in.^{2}

Exercises MIXED REVIEW

Coordinate Geometry **Find the coordinates of the midpoint of a segment with the given endpoints.**

45. $A(4, 1), B(7, 9)$ **46.** $G(0, 3), H(3, 8)$ **47.** $R(-2, 7), S(-6, -1)$

45. (5.5, 5) 46. (1.5, 5.5) 47. (−4, 3)

Write the converse of each conditional.

48. If you make a touchdown, then you score six points. If you score 6 pts., then you make a touchdown.
49. If it is Thanksgiving, then it is November. If it is November, then it is Thanksgiving.
50. If a figure is a square, then it is a rectangle. If a figure is a rectangle, then it is a square.
51. A triangle has two sides with lengths 3 m and 5 m. What is the range of possible lengths for the third side? between 2 m and 8 m

SELF ASSESSMENT FOR YOUR JOURNAL

Explain the difference between area and perimeter. Use examples to show how and when each type of measurement might be used.

Getting Ready for Lesson 5-2

Each rectangle is divided into two congruent triangles. Find the area of each triangle.

52. 6 units^2
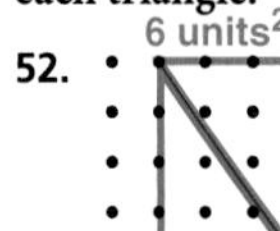

53. 2 units^2
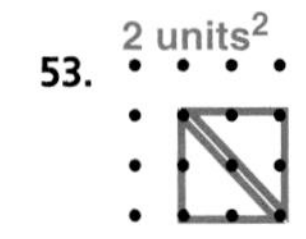

54. 3 units^2
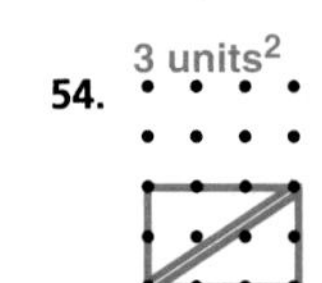

55. 8 units^2
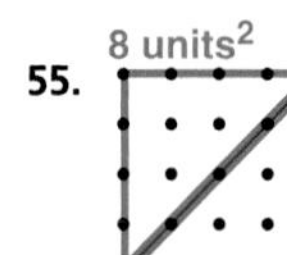

PROBLEM OF THE DAY

Suppose a U.S. flag is 65 in. long and 39 in. wide. Each of the four short stripes has a length of 39 in. What fractional part of the flag is red? about 41.5 % or $\frac{27}{65}$

Problem of the Day is also available in Transparencies.

CONNECTING TO PRIOR KNOWLEDGE Draw a parallelogram, a rectangle, a square, and a rhombus. Have students name each figure in as many ways as they can.

WORK TOGETHER p. 249

Suggest that students cut their rectangles along grid lines. This will facilitate measuring the bases, heights, and lengths. Help students see that the slope of the cut they make to form the triangle does not affect the type of figure that results, nor does cutting from one of the shorter sides to the other.

Make sure that students include in their lists of similarities that their rectangles and parallelograms have equal base lengths, heights, and areas. This will help them see why Theorem 5-2 is true.

Connections Architecture . . . and more

5-2 Areas of Parallelograms and Triangles

What You'll Learn

- Finding areas of parallelograms and triangles

...And Why

To solve design problems in architecture and landscaping

What You'll Need

- centimeter grid paper
- straightedge
- scissors
- tape

WORK TOGETHER

Have each member of your group cut out a different rectangle from centimeter grid paper.

- Record the base, height, and area of each rectangle.
- Cut out a triangle from one side of the rectangle as shown below. Tape it to the opposite side to form a parallelogram.

1. Compare each original rectangle with the parallelogram formed. With your group, list all the ways the rectangle and the parallelogram are the same and all the ways they are different. See below.

THINK AND DISCUSS

Part 1 **Areas of Parallelograms**

In the Work Together, you cut a rectangle into two pieces and used the pieces to form another parallelogram. The area of the parallelogram was the same as the area of the rectangle. This suggests the following theorem.

Theorem 5-2 Area of a Parallelogram

The area of a parallelogram is the product of any base and the corresponding height.

$A = bh$

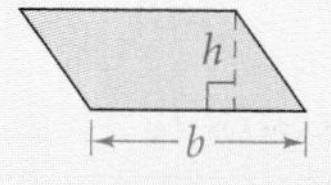

1. Answers may vary. Sample: One pair of opp. sides of the rectangle is ≅ to one pair of opp. sides of the ▱. Their heights and areas are =. The angles of the rectangle are ≇ to the angles of the ▱.

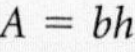

Lesson Planning Options

Prerequisite Skills

- Understanding parallelograms and triangles

Assignment Options for Exercises On Your Own

To provide flexible scheduling, this lesson can be subdivided into parts.

1 **Core** 4, 5, 7, 16–18
✪**Extension** 33, 34

2 **Core** 1–3, 6, 8–15, 19–28
✪**Extension** 29–32, 35, 36

Use Mixed Review to maintain skills.

Resources

Student Edition

Skills Handbook, p. 673
Extra Practice, p. 652
Glossary/Study Guide

Teaching Resources

Chapter Support File, Ch. 5
- Practice 5-2 (two worksheets)
- Reteaching 5-2
- Alternative Activity 5-2

Classroom Manager 5-2
Glossary, Spanish Resources

Transparencies
1, 8, 60

THINK AND DISCUSS p. 249

ESL Students may be confused by the use of the terms *base* and *height* in this lesson. Review their definitions and confirm that students understand that *base* and *height* can be used interchangeably with *length* and *width* when referring to rectangles. Also clarify any false understanding that the horizontal side is always the *base* or *length*.

Question 2 It may help students to turn their papers so the base to which they are going to draw an altitude is horizontal. Remind students that the altitude may not always be in the interior of the figure. Suggest that students review Part 2 of Lesson 4-8 on page 229.

Example 1

ERROR ALERT! Some students may multiply the height by the noncorresponding base. **Remediation:** Point out that although any side can be the base, the height that corresponds to that base must be perpendicular to that base.

Example 2

ERROR ALERT! Some students may think that the base corresponding to height $\overline{CF}$ is $\overline{AF}$ rather than $\overline{AD}$. **Remediation:** Help students see that the base of a parallelogram is a side of the parallelogram and that it is extended to draw the height. You may want to have students use a dotted line rather than a solid line to extend the base.

Additional Examples

FOR EXAMPLE 1

What is the area of parallelogram *GHIJ* with vertices $G(-4, -2)$, $H(3, -2)$, $I(5, 3)$, and $J(-2, 3)$. **35 square units**

Discussion: *Give the coordinates of a rectangle with the same area.*

FOR EXAMPLE 2

Refer to the diagram in Example 2. If $AD = 5$ in., $DE = 4$ in., and $AB = 6$ in., find *CF*. **4.8 in.**

FOR EXAMPLE 3

Refer to the formula in Example 3. How much force is exerted by a 65 mi/h wind blowing directly against the end of the building shown below? **about 8551 pounds**

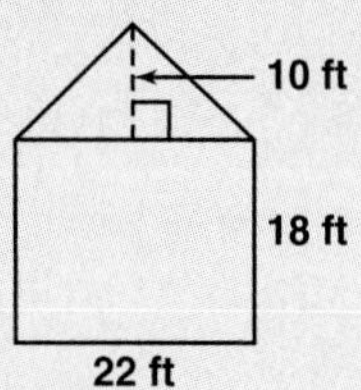

You can choose any side to be a **base** of a parallelogram. An **altitude** is any segment perpendicular to the line containing the base drawn from the side opposite the base. The **height** is the length of the altitude.

2. Draw any parallelogram and draw altitudes to two adjacent sides. **See margin p. 252.**

Example 1

Coordinate Geometry What is the area of ▱*PQRS* with vertices $P(1, 2)$, $Q(6, 2)$, $R(8, 5)$, and $S(3, 5)$?

Graph ▱*PQRS*. If you choose $\overline{PQ}$ as the base, then the height is 3.

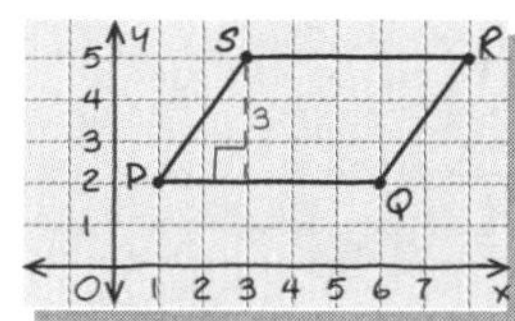

$$b = PQ = 5$$
$$h = 3$$
$$A = bh = 5(3) = 15$$

▱*PQRS* has area 15 square units.

3. **Try This** What is the area of ▱*EFGH* with vertices $E(-4, 3)$, $F(0, 3)$, $G(1, -2)$, and $H(-3, -2)$? **20 units²**

You can use the area formula to find missing dimensions in a parallelogram.

Example 2

In ▱*ABCD*, $\overline{DE}$ and $\overline{CF}$ are altitudes. Find *CF* to the nearest tenth.

Find the area of ▱*ABCD*. Then use the area formula to find *CF*.

$A = bh$
$= 10(12)$ — Use base *AB* and height *DE*.
$= 120$

The area of ▱*ABCD* is 120 in.^{2}.

$A = bh$
$120 = 13(CF)$ — Use base *AD* and height *CF*.
$CF = \frac{120}{13}$ — Divide each side by 13.
≈ 9.2

$\overline{CF}$ is about 9.2 in. long.

4. **Try This** A parallelogram has sides 15 cm and 18 cm. The altitude perpendicular to the line containing the 15 cm side is 9 cm long. Sketch the parallelogram. Then find the length of the altitude perpendicular to the line containing the 18-cm side. **7.5 cm**

Some students may choose to solve the problem in Example 2 more directly by solving the equation 10(12) =13(*CF*). Point out how this is essentially the same as shown in the example.

WORK TOGETHER p. 251

ALTERNATIVE METHOD Draw any $\triangle PQR$. Connect the midpoints of $\overline{PQ}$ and $\overline{PR}$. Then drop a perpendicular from *P* to the new segment. Cut out the two triangles and rearrange the three pieces to form a rectangle. The area of the rectangle, which equals the area of the triangle, is $b(\frac{h}{2})$ or $\frac{1}{2}bh$.

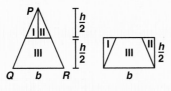

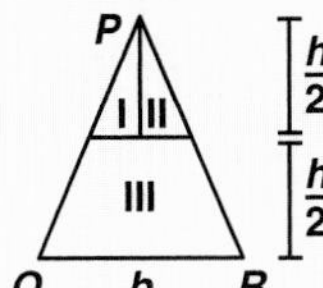

THINK AND DISCUSS p. 251

AUDITORY LEARNING Have students practice repeating aloud the formulas for the area of a rectangle, parallelogram, and triangle. Remind students who say "area equals one-half base times height" that the base and height must refer to perpendicular segments.

Example 3 Relating to the Real World 

DIVERSITY Depending on your geographical area, hurricanes may or may not be a threat. Students may want to share experiences they may have had with hurricanes, tornadoes, and earthquakes. Discuss the precautions one takes when living in areas with a high incidence of these potentially catastrophic events.

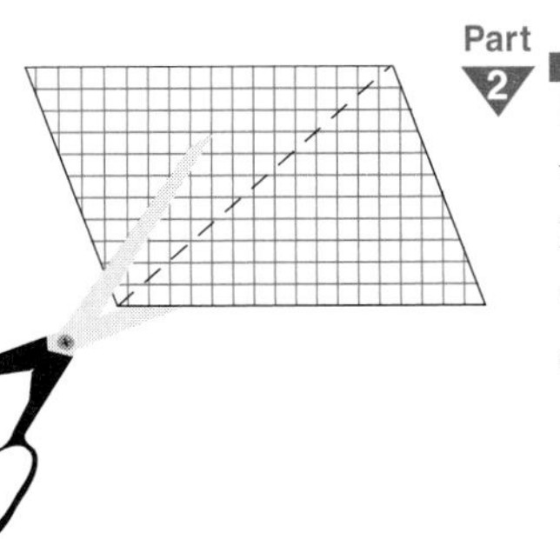

Part 2

WORK TOGETHER

Work in groups. Have each member of your group cut out a different parallelogram from centimeter grid paper.

- Record the base, height, and area of each parallelogram.
- Cut each parallelogram along a diagonal as shown, forming two triangles.

5. How does the area of each triangle compare to the area of the parallelogram? **The area of each △ is half the area of the ▱.**

THINK AND DISCUSS

Areas of Triangles

In the Work Together, you cut a parallelogram into two congruent triangles of equal area. This suggests the following theorem.

Theorem 5-3
Area of a Triangle

The area of a triangle is half the product of any base and the corresponding height.

$$A = \frac{1}{2}bh$$

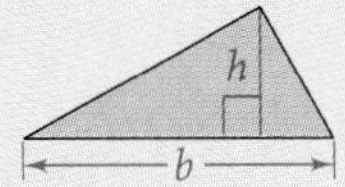

You can choose any side to be a **base** of a triangle. The corresponding **height** is the length of an altitude drawn to the line containing that base.

Example 3 Relating to the Real World 

Architecture When designing a building, an architect must be sure that the building can stand up to hurricane force winds, which have a velocity of 73 mi/h or more. The formula $F = 0.004Av^2$ gives the force *F* in pounds exerted by a wind blowing against a flat surface. *A* is the area of the surface in square feet, and *v* is the wind velocity in miles per hour. How much force is exerted by a 73 mi/h wind blowing directly against the side of this building?

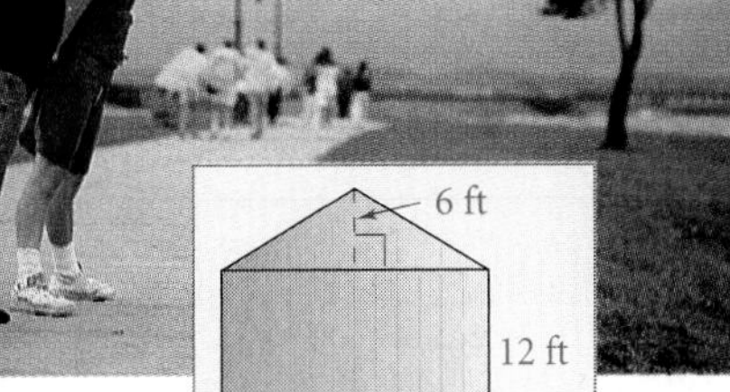

Find the area of the side of the building.

triangle area $= \frac{1}{2}bh = \frac{1}{2}(20)6 = 60 \text{ ft}^2$

rectangle area $= bh = 20(12) = 240 \text{ ft}^2$

area of end of building $= 60 + 240 = 300 \text{ ft}^2$

$F = 0.004Av^2$ Use the formula for force.

$= 0.004(300)(73)^2$ Substitute 300 for *A* and 73 for *v*.

$= 6394.8$

The force is about 6400 lb.

Technology Options

Students may use geometry software to draw the triangles in Exercise 28. Suggest they draw one triangle with area 12 square units, then drag its vertices to create other triangles with the same area. Students may also replicate the activity described in Exercise 29.

Prentice Hall Technology 

 **Software**
- Secondary Math Lab Toolkit™
- Integrated Math Lab 31
- Computer Item Generator 5-2

 **Internet**
- See the Prentice Hall site. (http://www.phschool.com)

Exercises ON YOUR OWN

Exercises 4–6 The areas of these figures can be found by using the results of Exercises 1–3. Suggest that students calculate the areas in more than one way in order to verify their answers.

ALTERNATIVE ASSESSMENT **Exercises 16–18** These exercises can help you assess students' understanding of the area of a parallelogram. Check that students correctly identify a base and its corresponding height in each parallelogram.

KINESTHETIC LEARNING Exercise 19 If you have block scheduling or an extended class period, get permission to close off a certain area of the school parking lot. Have students use measuring tape to find the dimensions and calculate the area of the section. Have them draw a diagram and write an explanation of how they found the measurements and calculated the area.

pages 249–250 Think and Discuss

2.

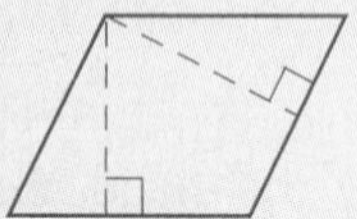

pages 252–254 On Your Own

19a. Answers may vary. Sample:
(1) Find the area of 31 ft-by-50 ft rectangle and subtract the area of 2 △s.

(2) Find the area of each small ▱. Multiply by 4 and add the area of the 15 ft-by-50 ft rectangle.

252

Exercises ON YOUR OWN

Find the area of each figure.

1. ▱$ABJF$ **15 units²**
2. △BDJ **6 units²**
3. △DKJ **6 units²**
4. ▱$BDKJ$ **12 units²**
5. ▱$ADKF$ **27 units²**
6. △BCJ **3 units²**

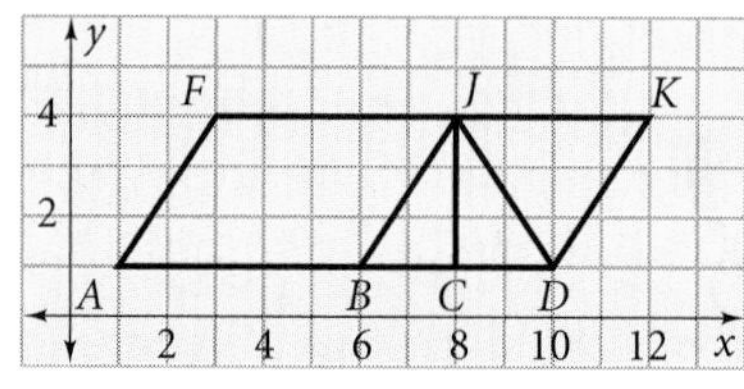

7. The area of a parallelogram is 24 in.² and the height is 6 in. Find the length of the base. **4 in.**
8. An isosceles right triangle has area of 98 cm². Find the length of each leg. **14 cm**

Find the area of each shaded region.

9.
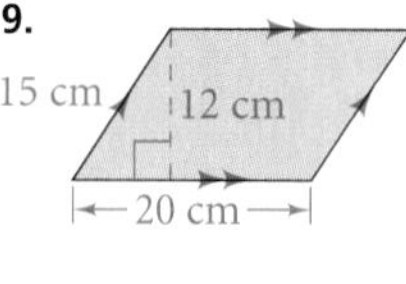

240 cm²

10.
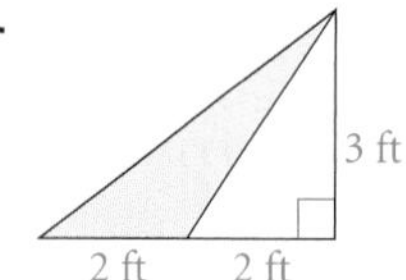

3 ft²

11.
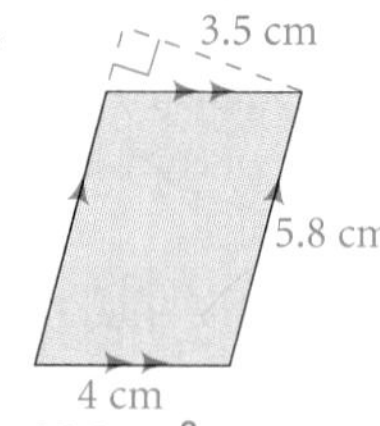

20.3 cm²

12.
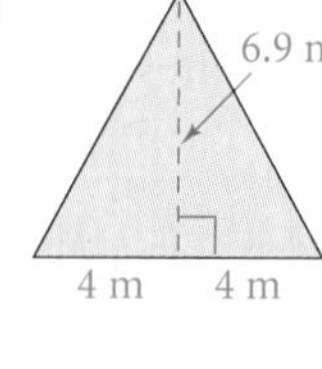

27.6 m²

Coordinate Geometry **(a) Graph the lines. (b) Find the area of the triangle enclosed by the lines.**

13. $y = x, x = 0$, and $y = 7$ **24.5 units²**
14. $y = x + 2, y = 2, x = 6$ **18 units²**
15. $y = -\frac{1}{2}x + 3, y = 0, x = -2$ **16 units²**

Find the value of h in each parallelogram.

16.
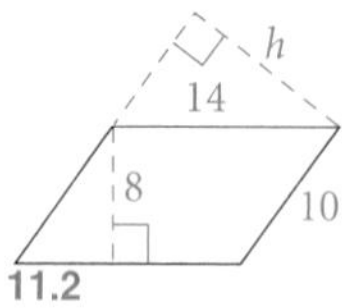

11.2

17.
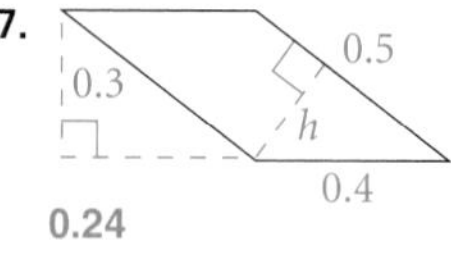

0.24

18.
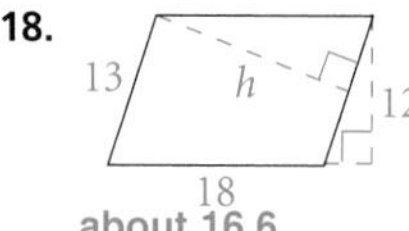

about 16.6

19. *Landscaping* Taisha's Bakery has a plan for a 50 ft-by-31 ft parking lot. The four parking spaces are congruent parallelograms, the driving area is a rectangle, and the two unpaved areas for flowers are congruent triangles.
    a. *Writing* Explain two different ways to find the area of the region that must be paved. **See margin.**
    b. **Verify** your answer to part (a) by using each method to find the area. **1390 ft²**

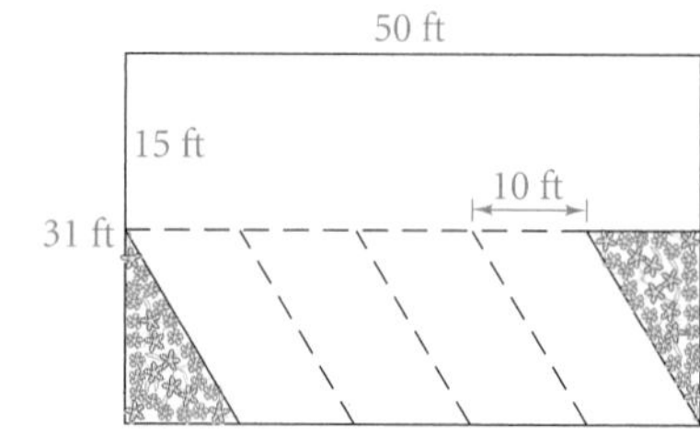

20. *Algebra* In a triangle, a base and the corresponding height are in the ratio 3 : 2. The area is 108 in.². Find the base and the corresponding height. **18 in.; 12 in.**

ESTIMATION Exercises 21–23 Encourage students to estimate the area of each figure by counting the number of grid squares and parts of squares. Then have them use their estimates to check if their answers are reasonable.

PROBABILITY Exercise 24 Help students make the distinction between theoretical probability:

$$P = \frac{\text{number of favorable outcomes}}{\text{number of possible outcomes}}$$

and geometric probability:

$$P = \frac{\text{area of selected region}}{\text{area of entire region}}.$$

MAKING CONNECTIONS Exercise 30 Heron, also known as Hero, invented the first turbine, called an aeolipile, around 200 B.C. He filled a flask with water, then heated it. Steam released from two spouts at the side of the flask caused the flask to spin.

CRITICAL THINKING Exercise 32 Ask students to give real-world examples where Heron's formula may be more helpful in finding the area of a triangle than $A = \frac{1}{2}bh$. One example is finding the area of a "triangular" shape like a pond where you know the distance along each side.

Find the area of each figure.

21. 8 units^2

22. 9 units^2

23. 8 units^2

24. *Probability* Ann drew these three figures on a grid. A fly landed at random at a point on the grid.

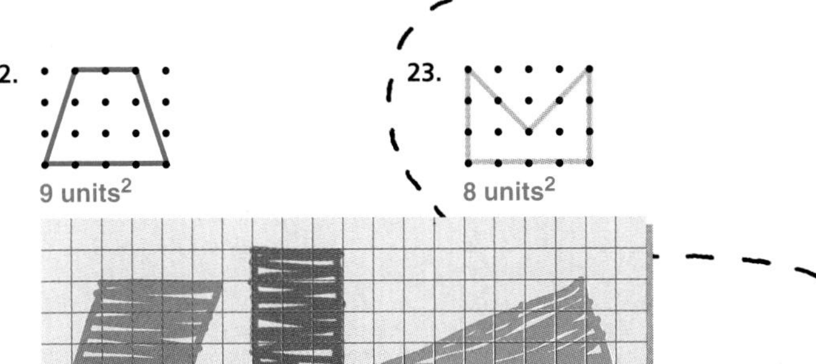

a. Is the fly more likely to have landed on one of the figures or on the blank grid? Explain.

b. Suppose you know the fly landed on one of the figures. Is the fly more likely to have landed on one figure than on another? Explain.

a–b. See margin.

Find the area of each figure.

25.

312.5 ft^2

26.

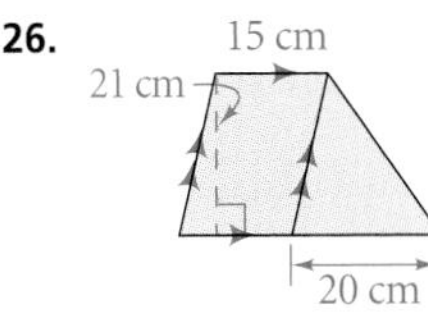

525 cm^2

27.

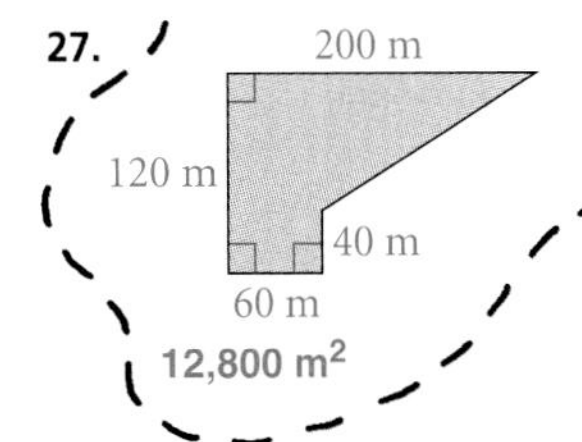

12,800 m^2

28. *Open-ended* Using graph paper, draw an acute triangle, an obtuse triangle, and a right triangle, each with area 12 units^2. See margin for sample.

29. *Technology* Juanita used geometry software to create the figure at the right. She drew segment $\overline{AB}$, chose point C, and constructed line k parallel to $\overline{AB}$ through point C. Then Juanita chose point D on line k. Next she dragged point D along line k to form different triangles. How do the areas of the triangles compare? Explain. The areas of the △s are =; they have the same bases and = heights.

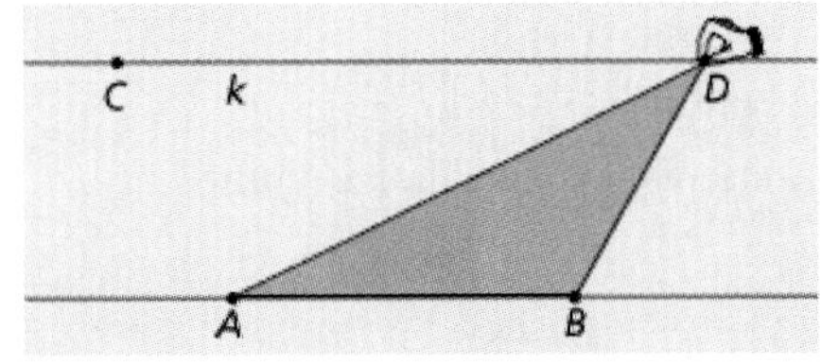

The ancient Greek mathematician Heron is most famous for his formula for the area of a triangle in terms of its sides *a*, *b*, and *c*.

$$A = \sqrt{s(s-a)(s-b)(s-c)}, \text{ where } s = \tfrac{1}{2}(a+b+c)$$

Use Heron's formula and a calculator to find the area of each triangle. Round your answer to the nearest whole number.

30. $a = 8$ in., $b = 9$ in., $c = 10$ in. 34 in.^{2}

31. $a = 15$ m, $b = 17$ m, $c = 21$ m 126 m^2

32. a. Use Heron's formula to find the area of the triangle at the right.

b. **Verify** your answer to part (a) by using the formula $A = \frac{1}{2}bh$.

a. 54 in.^{2} b. Check students' work.

15 in. 9 in. 12 in.

24a. Blank grid; the area not shaded is > the area shaded.

b. No; the figures have = area.

28.

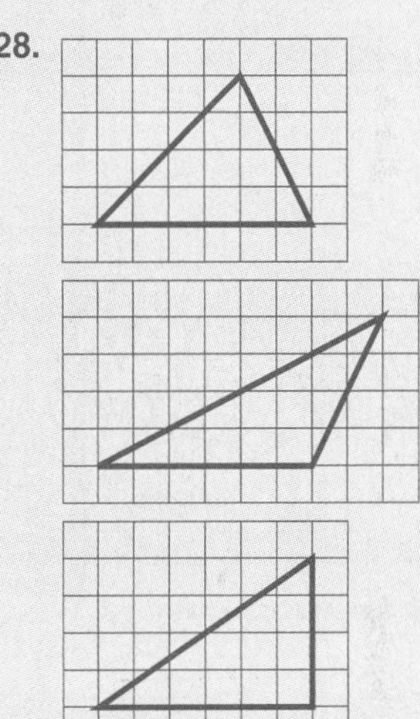

Chapter Project **FIND OUT BY CREATING** Depending on the size of the groups, students may want to make additional blocks so they can create a larger quilt. Encourage students to create their own designs. Depending on materials available, students can use crayons, markers, water colors, or colored construction paper to make their designs.

Exercises MIXED REVIEW

TRANSFORMATIONS Exercises 37–40 Have students copy the grid and the figure. Then have them draw each image in addition to giving its coordinates.

GETTING READY FOR LESSON 5-3 These exercises prepare students for solving problems using the Pythagorean Theorem.

Wrap Up

THE BIG IDEA Ask students: *Explain how the formula for the area of a rectangle can be used to find the formulas for the area of a parallelogram and the area of a triangle.*

RETEACHING ACTIVITY Students draw obtuse, acute, and right triangles on grid paper with an area of 12 square units. Then they find the area of other triangles. (Reteaching worksheet 5-2)

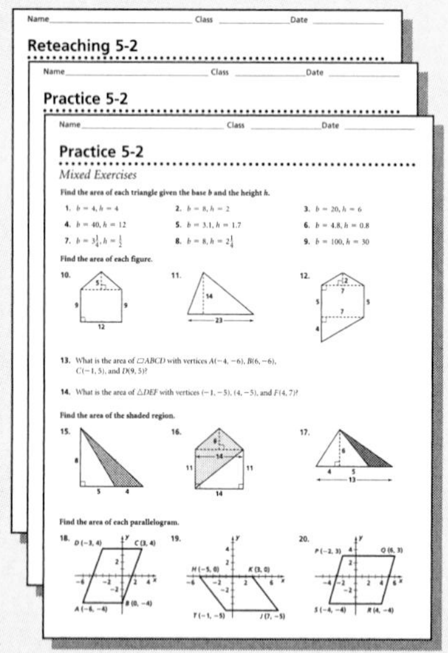

Lesson Quiz

Lesson Quiz is also available in Transparencies.

1. Find the area of parallelogram *ABCD* with vertices $A(1, 0)$, $B(5, 0)$, $C(4, 4)$ and $D(-1, 4)$. 16 square units
2. Find the area of a triangle enclosed by the lines $y = 0$, $y = 2x$, and $x = 4$. 16 square units
3. Find the area of the figure. 120 cm^2

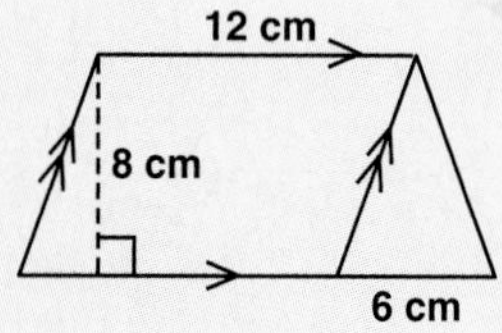

Coordinate Geometry **The vertices of a polygon are given. Graph each polygon and find its area.**

33. $A(3, 9), B(8, 9), C(2, -3), D(-3, -3)$ 60 $units^2$

34. $E(1, 1), F(4, 5), G(11, 5), H(8, 1)$ 28 $units^2$

35. $M(-2, -5), L(1, -5), N(2, -2)$ 4.5 $units^2$

36. $R(1, 2), S(1, 6), T(4, 1)$ 6 $units^2$

Chapter Project — *Find Out by Creating*

Your class can model a quilt by using the quilt blocks your classmates created in the *Find Out* activity on page 248. Here is one suggestion for a design.

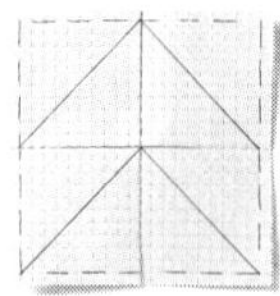

On each block, mark off a $\frac{1}{4}$-in. border for seams. Draw the four diagonals pictured.

Staple four blocks together in a row, keeping the orientation shown at the left throughout the row. Do this until you have four rows.

Staple the rows together, turning the second and fourth row upside down. Color the blocks to create a three-dimensional illusion.

Exercises MIXED REVIEW

Transformations **Find the coordinates of the images of *A, B, C,* and *D* after each transformation.**

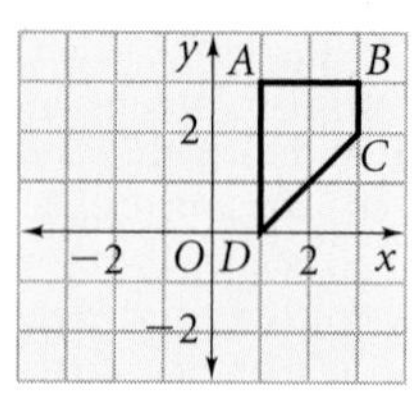

37. reflection in the line $x = 1$
    $A'(1, 3), B'(-1, 3), C'(-1, 2), D'(1, 0)$
38. translation $\langle -4, -7 \rangle$
    $A'(-3, -4), B'(-1, -4), C'(-1, -5), D'(-3, -7)$
39. rotation 180° about the point $(0, 0)$
    $A'(-1, -3), B'(-3, -3), C'(-3, -2), D'(-1, 0)$
40. Find the coordinates of the midpoint of the segment joining $P(-2, -3)$ and $Q(9, 12)$. (3.5, 4.5)

Getting Ready for Lesson 5-3

Square the lengths of the sides of each triangle. What do you notice?

41.

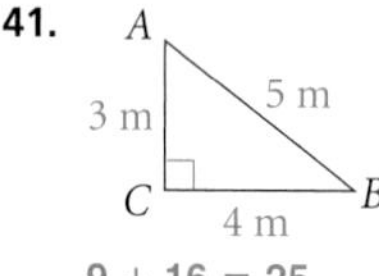

$9 + 16 = 25$

42.

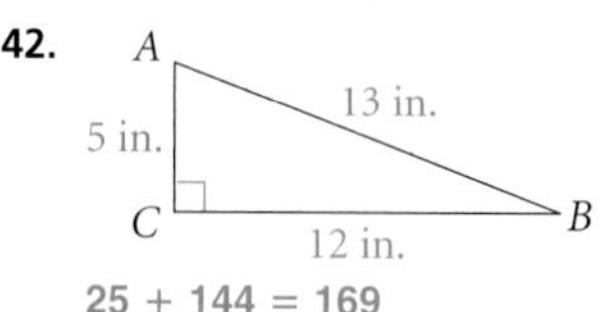

$25 + 144 = 169$

43.

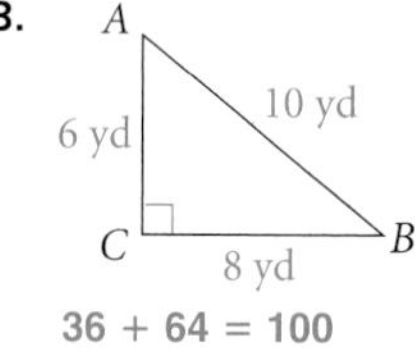

$36 + 64 = 100$

Math ToolboX

Students review how to simplify radical expressions. Students will use this skill in Lesson 5-3 when they apply the Pythagorean Theorem.

Example 1

Some students may want to simplify radicals such as $\sqrt{8}$ and $\sqrt{294}$ before multiplying or dividing by another radical. While this is acceptable, point out that it is not necessary and is sometimes less efficient because the resulting product or quotient may still need to be simplified.

Example 2

ERROR ALERT! Some students may rewrite $\sqrt{\frac{4}{3}}$ as $\frac{\sqrt{4}}{3}$. **Remediation:** Have students use a calculator to approximate the two expressions to show that they are not equivalent. Then have them approximate $\frac{\sqrt{4}}{\sqrt{3}}$ to verify that it is equivalent to $\sqrt{\frac{4}{3}}$.

ADDITIONAL PROBLEM Have students simplify the expressions $\sqrt{15} \cdot \sqrt{30}$ and $\sqrt{42} \div \sqrt{12}$. $3\sqrt{50}$; $\frac{\sqrt{14}}{2}$

Math ToolboX — Algebra Review

Simplifying Radicals

Before Lesson 5-3

You can multiply and divide numbers that are under radical signs.

Example 1

Simplify the expressions $\sqrt{2} \cdot \sqrt{8}$ and $\sqrt{294} \div \sqrt{3}$.

$\sqrt{2} \cdot \sqrt{8} = \sqrt{2 \cdot 8}$ — Write both numbers under one radical.

$= \sqrt{16}$ — Simplify the expression under the radical.

$= 4$ — Factor out perfect squares and simplify.

$$\sqrt{294} \div \sqrt{3} = \sqrt{\frac{294}{3}} = \sqrt{98} = \sqrt{49 \cdot 2} = 7\sqrt{2}$$

A radical expression is in simplest radical form when all the following are true.

- The number under the radical sign has no perfect square factors other than 1.
- The number under the radical sign does not contain a fraction.
- The denominator does not contain a radical expression.

Example 2

Write $\sqrt{\frac{4}{3}}$ in simplest form.

$\sqrt{\frac{4}{3}} = \frac{\sqrt{4}}{\sqrt{3}}$ — Rewrite the single radical as the quotient of two radicals.

$= \frac{2}{\sqrt{3}}$ — Simplify.

$= \frac{2}{\sqrt{3}} \cdot \frac{\sqrt{3}}{\sqrt{3}}$ — Multiply by a form of 1 to rationalize the denominator.

$= \frac{2\sqrt{3}}{3}$

Simplify each expression.

1. $\sqrt{5} \cdot \sqrt{10}$ $5\sqrt{2}$
2. $\sqrt{243}$ $9\sqrt{3}$
3. $\sqrt{128} \div \sqrt{2}$ 8
4. $\sqrt{\frac{125}{4}}$ $\frac{5\sqrt{5}}{2}$
5. $\sqrt{6} \cdot \sqrt{8}$ $4\sqrt{3}$
6. $\frac{\sqrt{36}}{\sqrt{3}}$ $2\sqrt{3}$
7. $\frac{\sqrt{144}}{\sqrt{2}}$ $6\sqrt{2}$
8. $\sqrt{3} \cdot \sqrt{12}$ 6
9. $\sqrt{72} \div \sqrt{2}$ 6
10. $\sqrt{169}$ 13
11. $24 \div \sqrt{8}$ $6\sqrt{2}$
12. $\sqrt{300} \div \sqrt{5}$ $2\sqrt{15}$

255

5-3 Teaching Notes

PROBLEM OF THE DAY

Lines *m* and *n* are parallel. Which of the triangles *ABC*, *ABD*, or *ABE* has the greatest area? the least area?

The areas are the same.

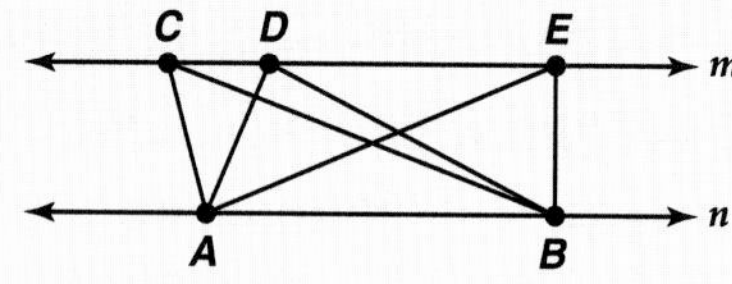

Problem of the Day is also available in Transparencies.

CONNECTING TO PRIOR KNOWLEDGE Ask students if the following can be the lengths of sides of a triangle. If yes, ask them to identify the lengths of the sides opposite the greatest and smallest angles.

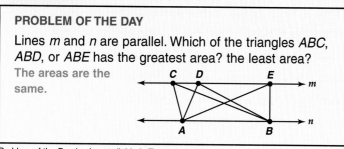

a. 3, 4, 5 **b.** 4, 7, 12 **c.** 5, 6, 10 **d.** 7, 7, 14

WORK TOGETHER

Emphasize that students should draw and cut the rectangles, triangles, and squares with precision. Students may want to tape together the pieces they form so they can place the squares on top of each other and compare areas.

Question 3 Ask students to explain their reasoning. Help them see how their conclusions are related to the lengths of the sides of the right triangles cut from the rectangle.

Lesson Planning Options

Prerequisite Skills

- Simplifying radicals

Assignment Options for Exercises On Your Own

To provide flexible scheduling, this lesson can be subdivided into parts.

1 **Core** 1–10, 23–32
Extension 37, 46–50

2 **Core** 11–22, 33–36, 38–45, 56–58
Extension 51–55

Use Mixed Review to maintain skills.

Resources

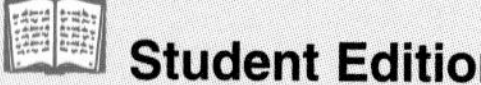

Student Edition

Skills Handbook, p. 674
Extra Practice, p. 652
Glossary/Study Guide

Teaching Resources

Chapter Support File, Ch. 5
- Practice 5-3 (two worksheets)
- Reteaching 5-3
- Alternative Activity 5-3

Classroom Manager 5-3
Glossary, Spanish Resources

Transparencies
5, 61, 64

Connections Recreation . . . and more

5-3 The Pythagorean Theorem and Its Converse

What You'll Learn

- Using the Pythagorean Theorem and its converse

...And Why

To solve problems involving boundaries, packaging, and satellites

What You'll Need

scissors, graph paper, colored paper, straightedge

WORK TOGETHER

Work in groups. Using graph paper, draw any rectangle. Label the sides *a* and *b*. Cut four rectangles with length *a* and width *b* from the graph paper. Then cut each rectangle on its diagonal, *c*, forming eight congruent triangles.

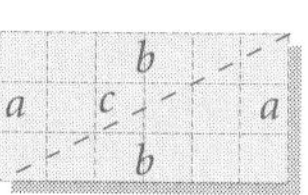

Cut three squares from the colored paper, one with sides of length *a*, one with sides of length *b*, and one with sides of length *c*.

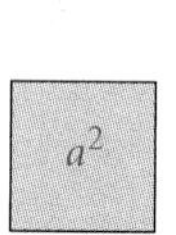

Separate the pieces into groups.

Group 1: four triangles and the two smaller squares

Group 2: four triangles and the largest square

Arrange the pieces of each group to form a square.

1. Write an algebraic expression for the area of each of the squares you formed. $a^2 + b^2 + 2ab$; $c^2 + 2ab$
2. How do the areas of the two squares you formed compare? The areas are =.
3. What can you conclude about the areas of the squares you cut from colored paper? The area of the largest square is = to the sum of the areas of the smaller squares.
4. Express your conclusion as an algebraic equation. $c^2 = a^2 + b^2$

THINK AND DISCUSS

Part 1

The Pythagorean Theorem

hypotenuse

legs

In a right triangle, the side opposite the right angle is the longest side. It is the **hypotenuse.** The other two sides are the **legs of a right triangle.**

THINK AND DISCUSS

MAKING CONNECTIONS The Work Together presented one justification of the Pythagorean Theorem. Students will prove this theorem in a different way in Exercise 46. Students may be surprised to learn that there are at least 360 proofs of the Pythagorean Theorem. One such proof dates from 1876 and is credited to President James A. Garfield. It is shown on page 273.

Students may already be familiar with the Pythagorean Theorem and may be able to recite "$a^2 + b^2 = c^2$." Have students practice stating the theorem using words.

Sometimes the rounding directions given in a lesson may be in conflict with what students have learned about significant digits in science. Students should follow the rounding directions given for an exercise and should not be concerned about significant digits.

Example 1 Relating to the Real World 

Discuss the fact that, while an equation of the form $x^2 = a$ has two solutions, one positive and one negative, the negative solution is discarded, since all distances in geometry are positive.

Point out to students that when using most scientific calculators to approximate a square root, they should first enter the number, then press the square root key.

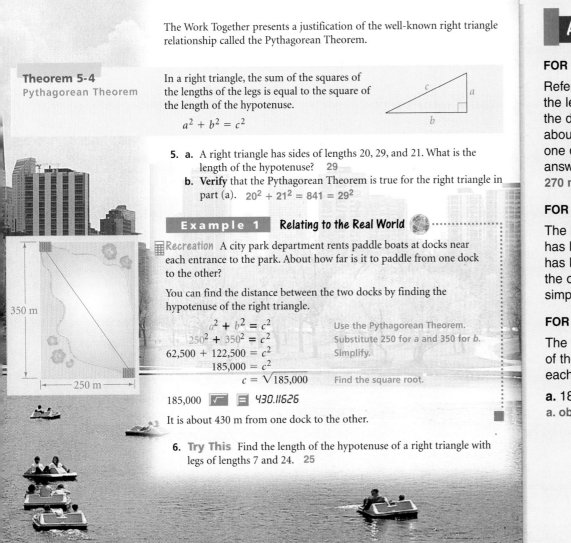

The Work Together presents a justification of the well-known right triangle relationship called the Pythagorean Theorem.

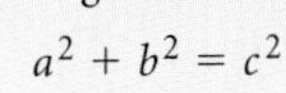

Theorem 5-4
Pythagorean Theorem

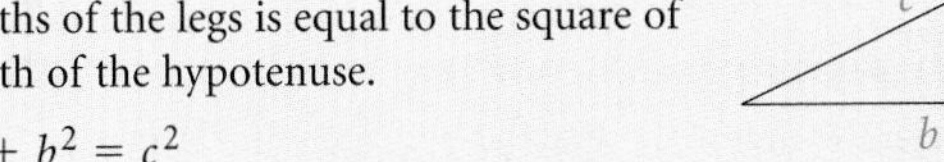

In a right triangle, the sum of the squares of the lengths of the legs is equal to the square of the length of the hypotenuse.

$$a^2 + b^2 = c^2$$

5. **a.** A right triangle has sides of lengths 20, 29, and 21. What is the length of the hypotenuse? 29
   b. **Verify** that the Pythagorean Theorem is true for the right triangle in part (a). $20^2 + 21^2 = 841 = 29^2$

Example 1 Relating to the Real World 

Recreation A city park department rents paddle boats at docks near each entrance to the park. About how far is it to paddle from one dock to the other?

You can find the distance between the two docks by finding the hypotenuse of the right triangle.

$a^2 + b^2 = c^2$	Use the Pythagorean Theorem.
$250^2 + 350^2 = c^2$	Substitute 250 for *a* and 350 for *b*.
$62{,}500 + 122{,}500 = c^2$	Simplify.
$185{,}000 = c^2$	
$c = \sqrt{185{,}000}$	Find the square root.

185,000  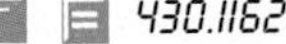 430.11626

It is about 430 m from one dock to the other.

6. **Try This** Find the length of the hypotenuse of a right triangle with legs of lengths 7 and 24. 25

Additional Examples

FOR EXAMPLE 1

Refer to the diagram in Example 1. If the lengths of the streets connecting the docks are 175 m and 200 m, about how far is it to paddle from one dock to the other? Round your answer to the nearest ten meters.
270 m

FOR EXAMPLE 2

The hypotenuse of a right triangle has length 16 cm and one of its legs has length 10 cm. Find the length of the other leg. Leave your answer in simplest radical form. **$2\sqrt{39}$ cm**

FOR EXAMPLE 3

The numbers represent the lengths of the sides of a triangle. Classify each as acute, obtuse, or right.

a. 18, 22, 35 **b.** 24, 45, 51
a. obtuse **b. right**

257

Example 2

ERROR ALERT! Some students may let $a = 20$ and $b = 8$, not differentiating between legs and hypotenuse.
Remediation: Point out that the standard notation is to let a and b represent the legs and c the hypotenuse. Remind students that the hypotenuse is always the longest side and opposite the right angle.

CRITICAL THINKING Question 8 Ask students how a triangle whose sides form a Pythagorean triple and a triangle whose sides are a multiple of that triple are related. Students should remember that the second triangle is a dilation of the first and that the two triangles are similar.

VISUAL LEARNING If you have block scheduling or an extended class period, have students use geometry software to draw triangles labeling their angle measures and side lengths. Then have them calculate squares of the sides and drag the vertices until the squares of the two smallest sides equal the square of the largest side. They should find that they have a right triangle.

Technology Options

For Exercises 11–22, students may check their answers by using geometry software to draw the triangles with the given side lengths and then measure the angles.

Prentice Hall Technology

Software
- Secondary Math Lab Toolkit™
- Computer Item Generator 5-3

CD-ROM
- Multimedia Geometry Lab 5

Internet
- See the Prentice Hall site. (http://www.phschool.com)

QUICK REVIEW

A radical expression is in simplest radical form when all the following are true.
- The number under the radical sign has no perfect square factors other than 1.
- The number under the radical sign does not contain a fraction.
- The denominator does not contain a radical expression.

Sometimes you will leave your answer in simplest radical form.

Example 2

Find the value of x. Leave your answer in simplest radical form.

Use the Pythagorean Theorem.

$a^2 + b^2 = c^2$
$8^2 + x^2 = 20^2$ Substitute.
$64 + x^2 = 400$ Simplify.
$x^2 = 336$ Subtract 64 from each side.
$x = \sqrt{336}$ Find the square root.
$x = \sqrt{16(21)}$ Simplify.
$x = 4\sqrt{21}$

For practice with radical expressions, see Skills Handbook page 674.

7. Try This The hypotenuse of a right triangle has length 12. One leg has length 6. Find the length of the other leg in simplest radical form. $6\sqrt{3}$

When the lengths of the sides of a right triangle are integers, the integers form a **Pythagorean triple.** Here are some common Pythagorean triples.

3, 4, 5   5, 12, 13   8, 15, 17   7, 24, 25

8. Open-ended Choose an integer. Multiply each number of a Pythagorean triple by that integer. **Verify** that the result is a Pythagorean triple. **Sample: 5, 12, 13; 10, 24, 26; $10^2 + 24^2 = 676 = 26^2$ ✓**

Part 2

The Converse of the Pythagorean Theorem

You can use the Converse of the Pythagorean Theorem to determine whether a triangle is a right triangle.

Theorem 5-5 Converse of the Pythagorean Theorem

If the square of the length of one side of a triangle is equal to the sum of the squares of the lengths of the other two sides, then the triangle is a right triangle.

Czech-American mathematician Olga Taussky-Todd (1906–1995) studied Pythagorean triangles. In 1970, she won the Ford Prize for her research.

The Converse of the Pythagorean Theorem leads to the inequalities below. You can use them to determine whether a triangle is obtuse or acute.

In $\triangle ABC$ with longest side c,
if $c^2 > a^2 + b^2$, then the triangle is obtuse, and
if $c^2 < a^2 + b^2$, then the triangle is acute.

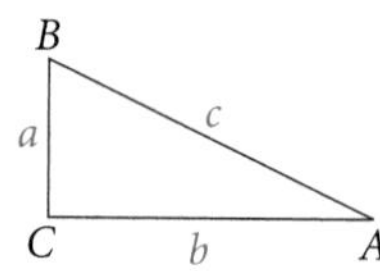

Example 3

Make sure students understand that the Converse of the Pythagorean Theorem can help them classify triangles, provided the three lengths form a triangle. However, it does not indicate if three lengths actually do form a triangle. For example, 5, 4, and 10 may appear to the be lengths of sides of an obtuse triangle ($10^2 > 5^2 + 4^2$), but a triangle cannot be formed with sides measuring 5, 4, and 10 ($5 + 4 < 10$).

Exercises ON YOUR OWN

CRITICAL THINKING Exercises 4 and 7 Most students will recognize that the altitude bisects the base of each triangle. Ask students to justify their reasoning. (Since the vertex from which the altitude is drawn is equidistant from the endpoints, it must lie on the perpendicular bisector.)

CONNECTING TO STUDENTS' WORLD Exercise 10 Have students measure the diagonal length of a baseball diamond on a local baseball field and use the length to calculate the distance between the bases.

The Pythagorean Theorem is named for Pythagoras, a Greek mathematician who lived in the sixth century B.C. We now know that the Babylonians, Egyptians, and Chinese were aware of this relationship before Pythagoras.

The diagram below illustrates an ancient Greek proof of the Pythagorean Theorem for an isosceles right triangle.

Example 3

The numbers represent the lengths of the sides of a triangle. Classify each triangle as acute, obtuse, or right.

a. 13, 84, 85

$85^2 \stackrel{?}{=} 13^2 + 84^2$	Compare c^2 to $a^2 + b^2$. Substitute the length
$7225 \stackrel{?}{=} 169 + 7056$	of the longest side for c.
$7225 = 7225$	$c^2 = a^2 + b^2$

The triangle is a right triangle.

b. 6, 11, 14

$14^2 \stackrel{?}{=} 6^2 + 11^2$	Compare c^2 to $a^2 + b^2$. Substitute the length
$196 \stackrel{?}{=} 36 + 121$	of the longest side for c.
$196 > 157$	$c^2 > a^2 + b^2$

The triangle is an obtuse triangle.

9. Try This A triangle has sides of lengths 7, 8, and 9. Classify the triangle as acute, obtuse, or right. acute

Exercises ON YOUR OWN

Algebra **Find the value of x. Leave your answer in simplest radical form.**

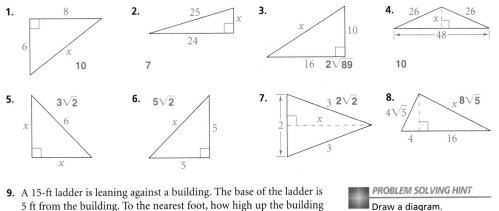

1.
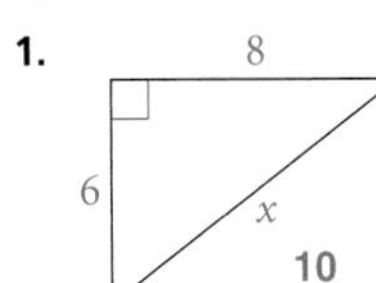

10

2.
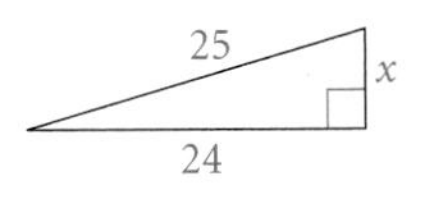

7

3.
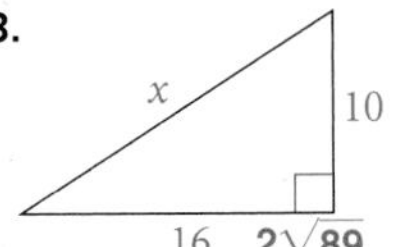

$2\sqrt{89}$

4.
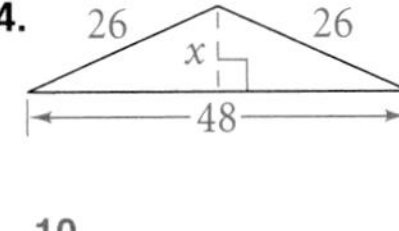

10

5. $3\sqrt{2}$
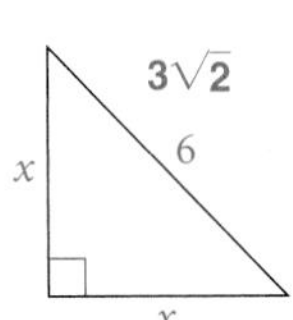

6. $5\sqrt{2}$
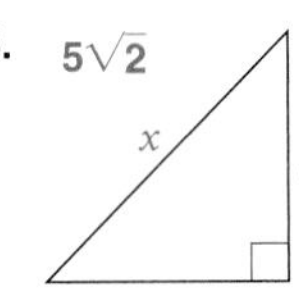

7.
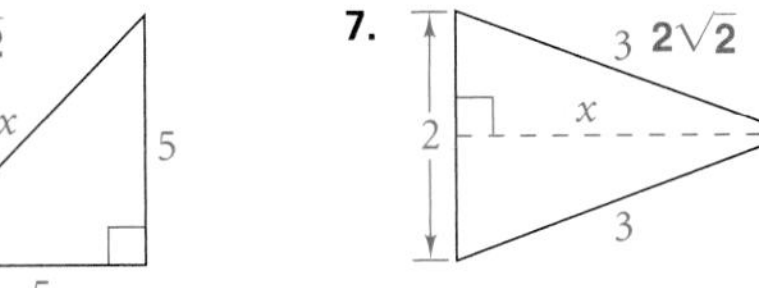

$2\sqrt{2}$

8.
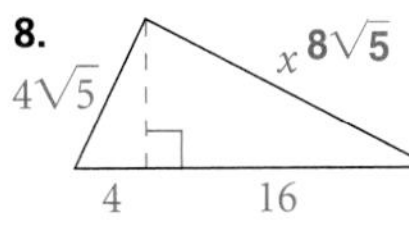

$8\sqrt{5}$

9. A 15-ft ladder is leaning against a building. The base of the ladder is 5 ft from the building. To the nearest foot, how high up the building does the ladder reach? 14 ft

PROBLEM SOLVING HINT
Draw a diagram.

10. A brick walkway forms the diagonal of a square playground. The walkway is 24 m long. To the nearest tenth of a meter, how long is a side of the playground? 17.0 m

ERROR ALERT! Exercise 14 Some students may compare the sum of the squares of the first two lengths listed to the square of the third length and classify the triangle as obtuse. **Remediation:** Reinforce that students should compare the sum of the squares of the shortest two lengths to the square of the longest length.

Exercises 17 and 22 Make sure students understand which are the shortest two lengths. Review with students how to estimate square roots, i.e. $\sqrt{3}$ is between $\sqrt{1}$ and $\sqrt{4}$ so it is between 1 and 2.

RESEARCH Exercise 23b Students should be able to find this information in an encyclopedia.

OPEN-ENDED Exercise 24 One way students can solve this problem is to use areas.

ESL Exercise 31 Students may not be familiar with the terms "embroider" and "embroidery hoop." If possible, bring to class a piece of embroidery and an embroidery hoop. (Check with the art teacher or the home economics teacher.) Ask students what these items are called in their native languages.

pages 259–262 On Your Own

23a. The surveyor could stretch the rope to form a △ with the sides containing 3, 4, and 5 intervals.

b. Construction of the Aswan High Dam permits flood control.

24.

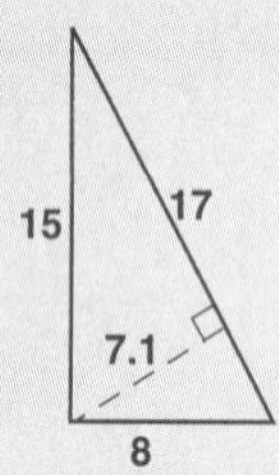

Choose Use mental math, paper and pencil, or a calculator. The lengths of the sides of a triangle are given. Classify each triangle as acute, right, or obtuse.

11. 15, 8, 21 obtuse
12. 12, 16, 20 right
13. $2, 2\frac{1}{2}, 3$ acute
14. 30, 34, 16 right
15. 0.3, 0.4, 0.6 obtuse
16. 11, 12, 15 acute
17. $\sqrt{3}, 2, 3$ obtuse
18. 1.8, 8, 8.2 right
19. 20, 21, 28 acute
20. 31, 23, 12 obtuse
21. 30, 40, 50 right
22. $\sqrt{11}, \sqrt{7}, 4$ acute

23. **Ancient Egypt** Each year the Nile River overflowed its banks and deposited fertile silt on the valley farmlands. Although the flood was helpful to farmers, it often destroyed boundary markers. Egyptian surveyors used a rope with knots at 12 equal intervals to help reconstruct boundaries.
    a. **Writing** Explain how a surveyor could use this rope to form a right angle.
    b. **Research** Find out why the Nile no longer floods as it did in ancient Egypt.
    a–b. See margin.

24. **Open-ended** Draw a right triangle with three sides that are integers. Draw the altitude to the hypotenuse. Label the lengths of the three sides and the altitude. See margin for sample.

Calculator Use the triangle at the right. Find the missing length to the nearest tenth.

25. $a = 3, b = 7, c = ■$ 7.6
26. $a = 1.2, b = ■, c = 3.5$ 3.3
27. $a = ■, b = 23, c = 30$ 19.3
28. $a = 0.7, b = ■, c = 0.8$ 0.4
29. $a = 8, b = 8, c = ■$ 11.3
30. $a = ■, b = 9, c = 18$ 15.6

c, b, a

31. **Sewing** You want to embroider a square design. You have an embroidery hoop with a 6-in. diameter. Find the largest value of x such that the entire square will fit in the hoop. Round to the nearest tenth. 4.2 in.

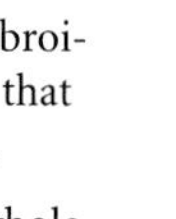

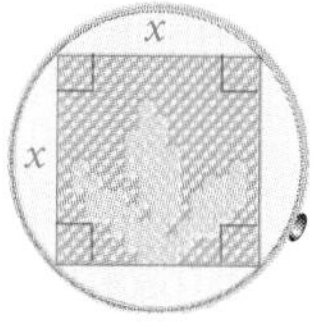

32. A rectangle has 10-in. diagonals and the lengths of its sides are whole numbers. Use the problem-solving strategy *Guess and Test* to find the perimeter of the rectangle. 28 in.

Find the area of each figure. Leave your answer in simplest radical form.

33.

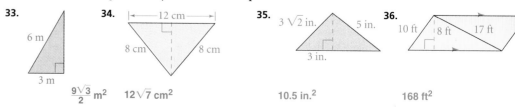

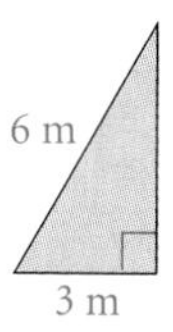

$\frac{9\sqrt{3}}{2}$ m²

34.

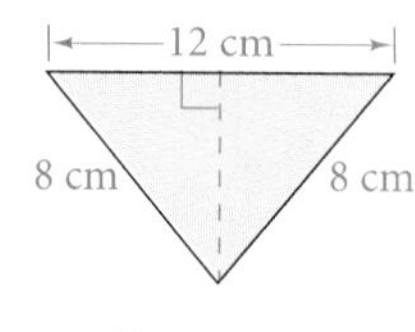

$12\sqrt{7}$ cm²

35. $3\sqrt{2}$ in., 5 in., 3 in.

10.5 in.²

36.

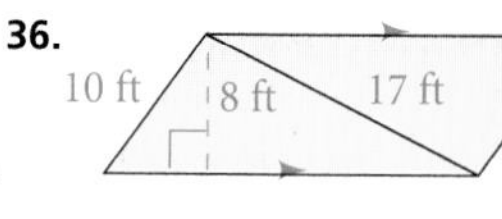

168 ft²

ALTERNATIVE ASSESSMENT **Exercises 33–36** These exercises can help you assess students' ability to use the Pythagorean Theorem to find the altitudes of triangles and parallelograms in order to apply the area formulas. Students can work in pairs alternating roles as solver and checker.

LOGICAL REASONING **Exercise 46** You may want to review with students how to expand the binomial $(b - a)^2$.

37. *Coordinate Geometry* You can use the Pythagorean Theorem to prove the Distance Formula. Let points $P(x_1, y_1)$ and $Q(x_2, y_2)$ be the endpoints of the hypotenuse of a right triangle.

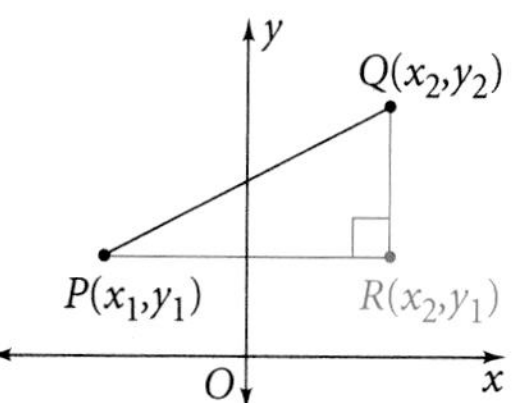

a. Write an algebraic expression to complete each of the following: $PR = \blacksquare$ and $QR = \blacksquare$. $|x_2 - x_1|$; $|y_2 - y_1|$

b. By the Pythagorean Theorem, $PQ^2 = PR^2 + QR^2$. Rewrite this statement, substituting the algebraic expressions you found for PR and QR in part (a). $PQ^2 = (x_2 - x_1)^2 + (y_2 - y_1)^2$

c. Complete the proof by finding the square root of each side of the equation that you wrote in part (b). $PQ = \sqrt{(x_2 - x_1)^2 + (y_2 - y_1)^2}$

Find a third number so that the three numbers form a Pythagorean triple.

38. 9, 41 40 **39.** 14, 48 50 **40.** 60, 61 11 **41.** 8, 17 15

42. 20, 21 29 **43.** 13, 85 84 **44.** 12, 37 35 **45.** 63, 65 16

46. *Logical Reasoning* You can use the diagram at the right to prove the Pythagorean Theorem.

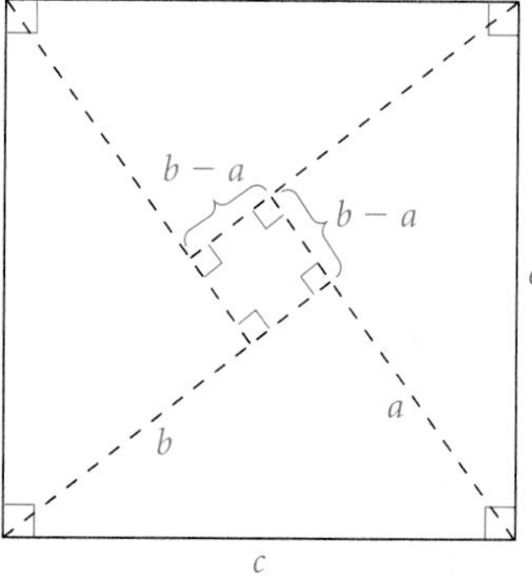

a. Find the area of the large square in terms of c. c^2

b. Find the area of the large square in terms of a and b by finding the area of the four triangles and the small square.

c. Write an equation setting your answers to part (a) and part (b) equal to each other. Complete the proof by simplifying the equation. $c^2 = 2ab + (b - a)^2$; $c^2 = a^2 + b^2$

b. $2ab + (b - a)^2$

Calculator **The figures below are drawn on centimeter graph paper. Find the perimeter of each shaded figure to the nearest tenth.**

47.
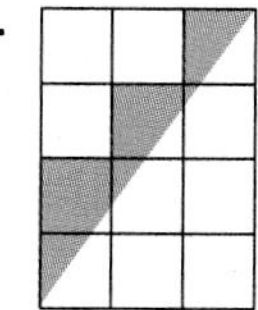
12 cm

48.
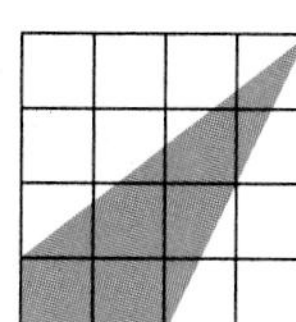
12.5 cm

49.
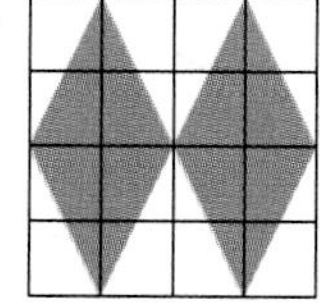
17.9 cm

50.
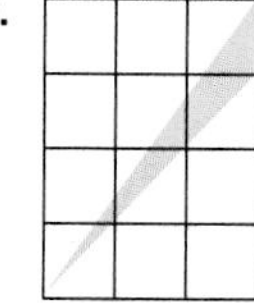
10.2 cm

51. *Geometry in 3 Dimensions* The box at the right is a rectangular solid.

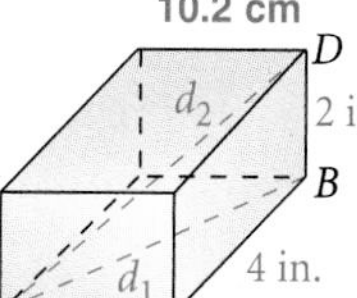

a. Use $\triangle ABC$ to find the length of the diagonal of the base, d_1. 5 in.

b. Use $\triangle ABD$ to find the length of the diagonal of the box, d_2. See below.

c. You can **generalize** steps in parts (a) and (b). Use the fact that $AC^2 + BC^2 = d_1^2$ and $d_1^2 + BD^2 = d_2^2$ to write a one-step formula to find d_2. $d_2 = \sqrt{AC^2 + BC^2 + BD^2}$

d. *Calculator* Use the formula you wrote to find the length of the longest fishing pole you can pack in a box with dimensions 18 in., 24 in., and 16 in. 34 in.

b. $\sqrt{29}$ in. or about 5.4 in.

GEOMETRY IN 3 DIMENSIONS Exercises 52–55 Some students will have difficulty visualizing these segments. If possible, create a 3-dimensional coordinate system using straws. Use toothpicks to show the line segments.

EXTENSION Exercise 57 Have students review the Fibonacci Sequence from Exercise 16 of Lesson 1-1. Let x, y, z, and w represent four consecutive Fibonacci numbers. If $a = xw$, $b = 2yz$, and $c = zw - xy$, then a, b, and c form a Pythagorean triple. Have students check this for three sets of four consecutive Fibonacci numbers.

Exercises MIXED REVIEW

Exercises 59–61 Remind students to copy the figures and not to write in the textbook.

GETTING READY FOR LESSON 5-4 These exercises prepare students to use the properties of 45°-45°-90° triangles and 30°-60°-90° triangles.

Wrap Up

THE BIG IDEA Ask students: *Rephrase the Pythagorean Theorem in your own words. Then give two examples of how it can be used to solve real-world problems.*

RETEACHING ACTIVITY Students prove the Pythagorean Theorem by building squares on each side of a right triangle and comparing the areas of the squares. (Reteaching worksheet 5-3)

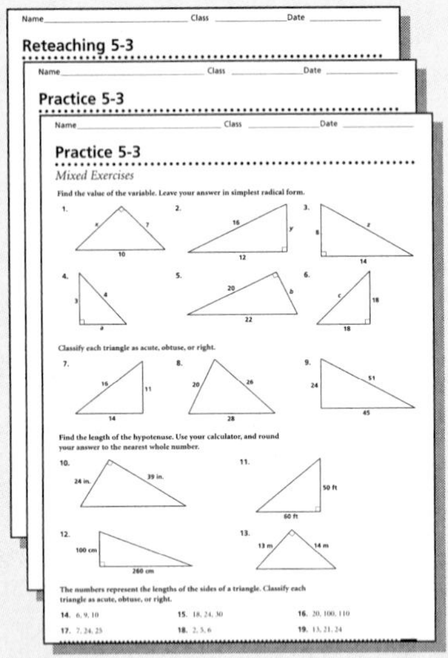

Lesson Quiz

Lesson Quiz is also available in Transparencies.

For Exercises 1–2, leave your answers in simplest radical form.

1. A right triangle has legs of length 8 cm and 14 cm. Find the length of the hypotenuse. $2\sqrt{65}$ cm
2. A right triangle has a hypotenuse of length 18 in. and a leg of length 12 in. Find the length of the other leg. $6\sqrt{5}$ in.
3. The lengths of the sides of a triangle are given. Classify each triangle as acute, right, or obtuse.
   a. 21, 72, 75 **b.** 45, 56, 40
   a. right b. acute

262

Geometry in 3 Dimensions **Points $P(x_1, y_1, z_1)$ and $Q(x_2, y_2, z_2)$ are points in a three-dimensional coordinate system. Use the following formula to find PQ. Leave your answer in simplest radical form.**

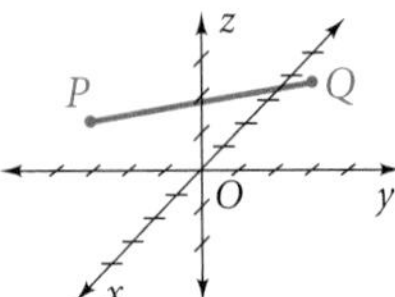

$$d = \sqrt{(x_2 - x_1)^2 + (y_2 - y_1)^2 + (z_2 - z_1)^2}$$

52. $P(0, 0, 0)$, $Q(1, 2, 3)$ $\sqrt{14}$ **53.** $P(0, 0, 0)$, $Q(-3, 4, -6)$ $\sqrt{61}$

54. $P(-1, 3, 5)$, $Q(2, 1, 7)$ $\sqrt{17}$ **55.** $P(3, -4, 8)$, $Q(-1, 6, 2)$ $2\sqrt{38}$

56. *Space* The Hubble Space Telescope is orbiting Earth 600 km above Earth's surface. Earth's radius is about 6370 km. Use the Pythagorean Theorem to find the distance, x, from the telescope to Earth's horizon. Round your answer to the nearest ten kilometers. 2830 km

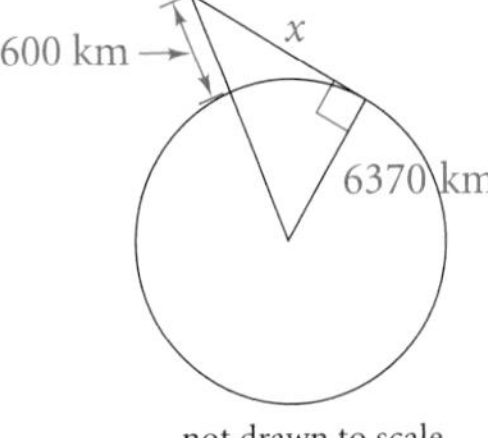

not drawn to scale

57. a. The ancient Greek philosopher Plato used the expressions $2n$, $n^2 - 1$, and $n^2 + 1$ to produce Pythagorean triples. Choose any integer greater than 1. Substitute for n and evaluate the three expressions. Sample: $n = 4$; 8, 15, 17

b. Verify that your answers to part (a) form a Pythagorean triple.
b. $8^2 + 15^2 = 289 = 17^2$

58. *Standardized Test Prep* $\triangle ABC$ has perimeter 20 in. What is its area? D

A. 12 in.^{2} **B.** 16 in.^{2} **C.** 24 in.^{2}
D. $8\sqrt{5}$ in.^{2} **E.** $16\sqrt{5}$ in.^{2}

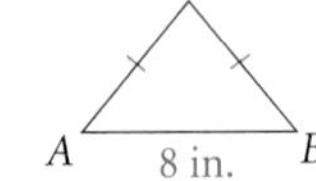

Exercises MIXED REVIEW

Sketch each figure after a counterclockwise rotation of 90° about C.

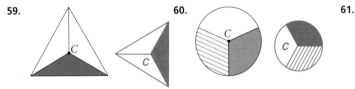

59.

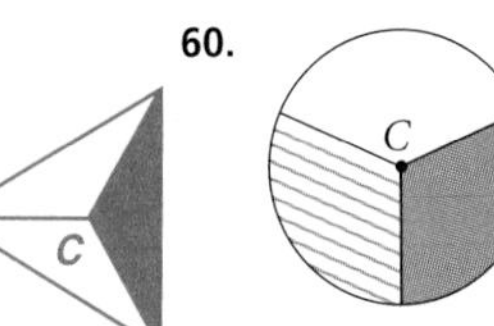

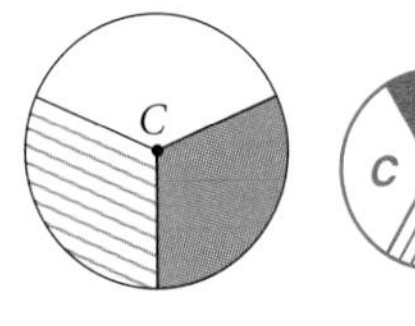

60.

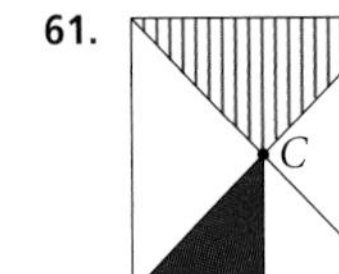

61.

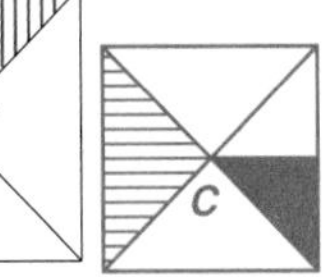

62. An angle is 87°. What is the measure of its complement? 3

Getting Ready for Lesson 5-4

Use a protractor to find the measures of the angles of each triangle.

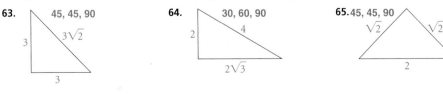

63. 45, 45, 90

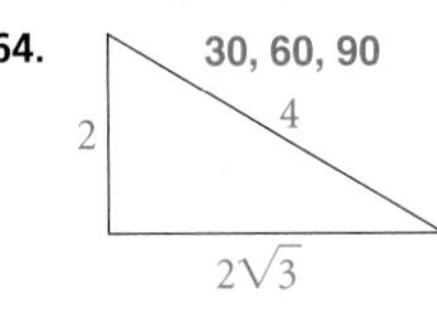

64. 30, 60, 90

65. 45, 45, 90

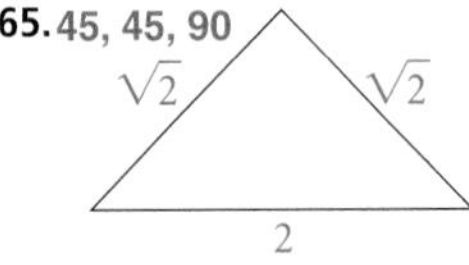

5-4 Teaching Notes

PROBLEM OF THE DAY

One Pythagorean triple is 8, 15, 17. Find at least two other Pythagorean triples that have 15 as one of the numbers. 15, 20, 25; 15, 36, 39; 15, 112, 113

Problem of the Day is also available in Transparencies.

CONNECTING TO PRIOR KNOWLEDGE Ask students to use the Pythagorean Theorem to find the missing lengths of the following right triangles if *a*, *b*, and *c* represent the lengths of the sides.

a. $a = 1, b = \underline{\ ?\ }, c = \sqrt{2}$ **b.** $a = 1, b = \sqrt{3}, c = \underline{\ ?\ }$
c. $a = 3, b = \underline{\ ?\ }, c = 6$ **d.** $a = 4, b = 4, c = \underline{\ ?\ }$

WORK TOGETHER p. 263

Have students work in groups of at least four students. Groups may want to exchange results and check that their conjectures hold true for other groups' results. Have students double-check any answer that does not seem to fit the pattern.

THINK AND DISCUSS p. 263

Question 4 The figures in parts a–c show isosceles right triangles in different orientations. Have students identify the legs and hypotenuse of each. Part c may be especially tricky since students observed a pattern in the Work Together where the length of the hypotenuse contains $\sqrt{2}$.

Connections  Sports . . . and more

5-4 Special Right Triangles

What You'll Learn

- Using the properties of 45°-45°-90° and 30°-60°-90° triangles

...And Why

To study figures in real life, including baseball diamonds and helicopter blades, which use special right triangles

What You'll Need

- centimeter grid paper
- metric ruler
- calculator
- protractor

WORK TOGETHER

Work in a group. Have each person draw a different isosceles right triangle on centimeter grid paper. Choose integer values for the lengths of the legs.

- Record the length of each leg. Then use the Pythagorean Theorem to find the length of the hypotenuse. Leave your answers in simplest radical form.
- Organize your group's data in a table like the one below. Look for a pattern relating the side lengths of each triangle.

Triangle	Leg Length	Hypotenuse Length
Triangle 1	■	■
Triangle 2	■	■

- Make a **conjecture** about the relationship between the lengths of the legs and the length of the hypotenuse of an isosceles right triangle.

THINK AND DISCUSS

Part  1

45°-45°-90° Triangles

1. What do you know about the measures of the acute angles of an isosceles right triangle? Each angle's measure is 45.
2. If the measures of the angles of a triangle are 45, 45, and 90, why are the legs of the triangle congruent? Use the Converse of the Isosceles Triangle Theorem.

Another name for an isosceles right triangle is a 45°-45°-90° triangle.

3. **a.** Use the Pythagorean Theorem to solve for *y* in terms of *x*. Leave your answer in simplest radical form. $y = x\sqrt{2}$
   b. Do the results of part (a) agree with the pattern you found in the Work Together? yes

4. Find the value of each variable *without* using the Pythagorean Theorem.

a. $9\sqrt{2}$

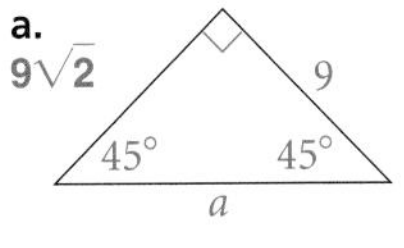

b. 25

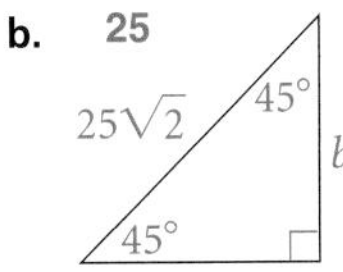

c. 4

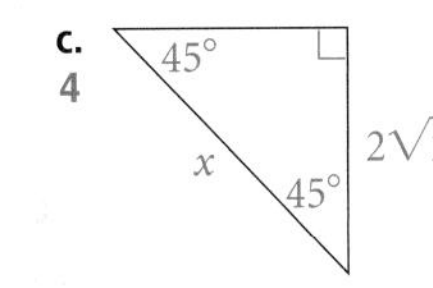

Lesson Planning Options

Prerequisite Skills

- Applying the Pythagorean Theorem
- Rationalizing the denominator

Assignment Options for Exercises On Your Own

To provide flexible scheduling, this lesson can be subdivided into parts.

 **Core** 1–2, 5–6, 24
Extension 27

 **Core** 3–4, 7–23
Extension 25–26

Use Mixed Review to maintain skills.

Resources

 **Student Edition**

Skills Handbook, p. 674
Extra Practice, p. 652
Glossary/Study Guide

Teaching Resources

Chapter Support File, Ch. 5
- Practice 5-4 (two worksheets)
- Reteaching 5-4

Classroom Manager 5-4
Glossary, Spanish Resources

 **Transparencies**

5, 61, 65

45°-45°-90° TRIANGLE THEOREM Another way this theorem can be stated is that in a 45°-45°-90° triangle, the lengths of the sides are in the ratio $1 : 1 : \sqrt{2}$.

Example 1 **Relating to the Real World** 

TACTILE LEARNING Have students check the answer by cutting out a 90-mm by 90-mm square, folding it along its diagonal, and measuring the length of the diagonal to the nearest millimeter.

MAKING CONNECTIONS Some students may be surprised to discover that Abner Doubleday did not invent baseball in 1839. Baseball evolved from the British games cricket and rounders. Two earlier games similar to baseball were "town ball" and the "New York game" played in the 1820's.

WORK TOGETHER p. 264

After students make their lists describing $\triangle ABC$, $\triangle ABD$, and $\triangle CBD$, you may want to put on the board a master list compiled from individual groups' lists. Have students add to their lists characteristics or properties that other groups noticed which they did not.

Additional Examples

FOR EXAMPLE 1

A softball diamond is a square where the distance from base to base is 60 ft. To the nearest foot, how far does a person at second base throw to home plate? 85 ft

Discussion: *If the pitcher's plate is located 40 feet from home plate, is it closer to second base or to home plate?*

FOR EXAMPLE 2

Find the value of each variable.

a.

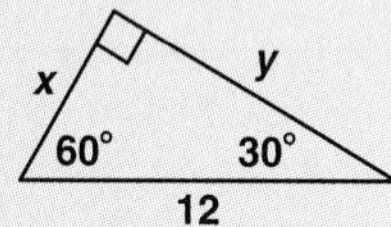

b.

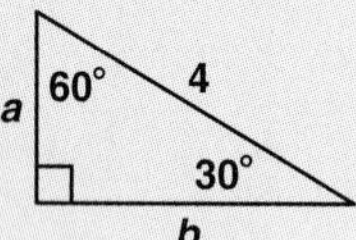

a. $x = 6$, $y = 6\sqrt{3}$, b. $a = 2$, $b = 2\sqrt{3}$

FOR EXAMPLE 3

Refer to the diagram in Example 3. If the sides of the rhombus are 8 cm long, how many square centimeters of colored glass will be needed for the panel? Round your answer to the nearest square centimeter. 55 cm²

The pattern you observed in the Work Together (and generalized in Question 3) is the basis of the following theorem.

Theorem 5-6
45°-45°-90° Triangle Theorem

In a 45°-45°-90° triangle, both legs are congruent and the length of the hypotenuse is $\sqrt{2}$ times the length of a leg.

$$\text{hypotenuse} = \sqrt{2} \cdot \text{leg}$$

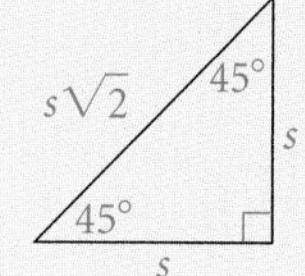

Example 1 **Relating to the Real World** 

Sports A baseball diamond is a square. The distance from base to base is 90 ft. To the nearest foot, how far does the second baseman throw a ball to home plate?

The distance d from second base to home plate is the length of the hypotenuse of a 45°-45°-90° triangle.

$d = 90\sqrt{2}$ hypotenuse $= \sqrt{2} \cdot$ leg

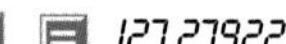

The distance from second base to home plate is about 127 ft.

5. a. *Calculator* Find $\sqrt{2}$ to the nearest thousandth. 1.414
   b. *Mental Math* Use the answer to part (a) to estimate the length of a diagonal of a square with sides 100 ft long. 141.4 ft

WORK TOGETHER

Work with a group.

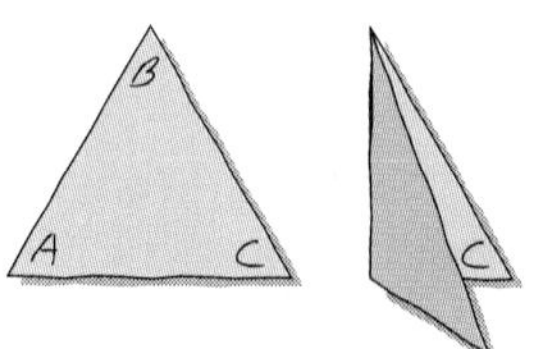

- Draw an equilateral triangle with sides 6 cm long and cut it out. Label the vertices *A*, *B*, and *C*. Fold vertex *A* onto vertex *C* as shown at the left. Unfold the triangle and label the fold-line $\overline{BD}$.
- With your group, make a list of everything you know about $\triangle ABC$, $\triangle ABD$, and $\triangle CBD$, their angles and their sides.

6. Name a pair of congruent triangles. $\triangle ABD$, $\triangle CBD$
7. a. Find $m\angle A$, $m\angle ADB$, and $m\angle ABD$. 60; 90; 30
   b. Name $\triangle ABD$ using its angle measures. $\triangle ABD$ is a 30°-60°-90° $\triangle$.
8. a. Complete: $\overline{DB}$ is the __?__ of $\overline{AC}$. ⊥ bisector
   b. If $AB = 6$, what is AD? 3
   c. Use the Pythagorean Theorem to find BD in simplest radical form.
   d. Find the ratios $\frac{AB}{AD}$ and $\frac{BD}{AD}$. 2; $\sqrt{3}$ c. $3\sqrt{3}$

THINK AND DISCUSS p. 265

Students may need to be reminded that the shortest side of a triangle is always opposite the smallest angle. Point out that in a 30°-60°-90° triangle, the shortest side is always opposite the 30° angle.

30°-60°-90° Triangle Theorem Another way this theorem can be stated is that in a 30°-60°-90° triangle, the lengths of the sides are in a ratio of $1 : \sqrt{3} : 2$.

You may want to have students refer to Example 2 of the Math Toolbox on page 255 to review how to rationalize a denominator before beginning Example 2b.

Example 2

ERROR ALERT! **Part b** When students are not told which is the shortest leg, they will often apply the ratios of the sides incorrectly. **Remediation:** It may help students to remember that when going from a shorter side to a longer side, you multiply and that when going from a longer side to a shorter side, you divide.

THINK AND DISCUSS

30°-60°-90° Triangles

The ratios you found in Question 8 part (d) suggest the following theorem about 30°-60°-90° triangles.

Theorem 5-7
30°-60°-90° Triangle Theorem

In a 30°-60°-90° triangle, the length of the hypotenuse is twice the length of the shorter leg. The length of the longer leg is $\sqrt{3}$ times the length of the shorter leg.

hypotenuse = 2 · shorter leg

longer leg = $\sqrt{3}$ · shorter leg

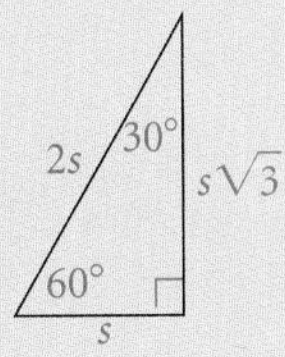

Justification:

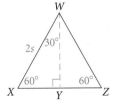

W, 2s, 30°, 60°, 60°, X, Y, Z

Refer to $\triangle WXZ$ at the left. Since $\overline{WY}$ is the perpendicular bisector of $\overline{XZ}$, $XY = \frac{1}{2}XZ$. That means that if $XW = 2s$, then $XY = s$.

$XY^2 + YW^2 = XW^2$	Use the Pythagorean Theorem.
$s^2 + YW^2 = (2s)^2$	Substitute s for XY and $2s$ for XW.
$YW^2 = 4s^2 - s^2$	Subtract s^2 from each side.
$YW^2 = 3s^2$	
$YW = s\sqrt{3}$	Find the square root of each side.

Example 2

Algebra Find the value of each variable.

a.

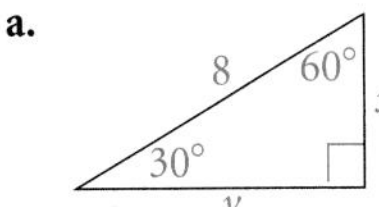

a. $8 = 2x$	hypotenuse = 2 · shorter leg
$x = 4$	
$y = x\sqrt{3}$	longer leg = $\sqrt{3}$ · shorter leg
$y = 4\sqrt{3}$	Substitute 4 for x.

b.

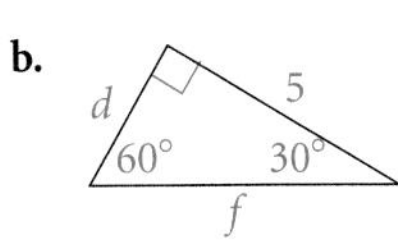

b. $5 = d\sqrt{3}$	longer leg = $\sqrt{3}$ · shorter leg
$d = \frac{5}{\sqrt{3}} \cdot \frac{\sqrt{3}}{\sqrt{3}} = \frac{5\sqrt{3}}{3}$	Simplify.
$f = 2d$	hypotenuse = 2 · shorter leg
$f = 2 \cdot \frac{5\sqrt{3}}{3} = \frac{10\sqrt{3}}{3}$	Substitute $\frac{5\sqrt{3}}{3}$ for d.

9. **Try This** The shorter leg of a 30°-60°-90° triangle has length $\sqrt{6}$. What are the lengths of the other two sides? Leave your answers in simplest radical form. $3\sqrt{2}, 2\sqrt{6}$

Technology Options

Prentice Hall Technology

Software
- Secondary Math Lab Toolkit™
- Computer Item Generator 5-4

Internet
- See the Prentice Hall site. (http://www.phschool.com)

Example 3 Relating to the Real World

Some students will have difficulty applying the 30°-60°-90° Triangle Theorem. Confusion may arise over which side, *x* or *h*, to solve for first. Point out that since the theorem describes the sides in relation to the shortest side, their first step should be to find the value of the shortest side.

ESL **Exercise 9** Students may be unfamiliar with the term "conveyor belt" and may think it is some kind of waist belt. Discuss conveyor belts students may have seen at a grocery store or at the airport. All students may be confused by "angle with the ground" and may need help setting up the diagram.

Exercises ON YOUR OWN

Exercises 1–8 Students can check their answers by using the Pythagorean Theorem. A quick way to check if the lengths are reasonable is to check that the longest side is opposite the largest angle and the shortest side is opposite the smallest angle.

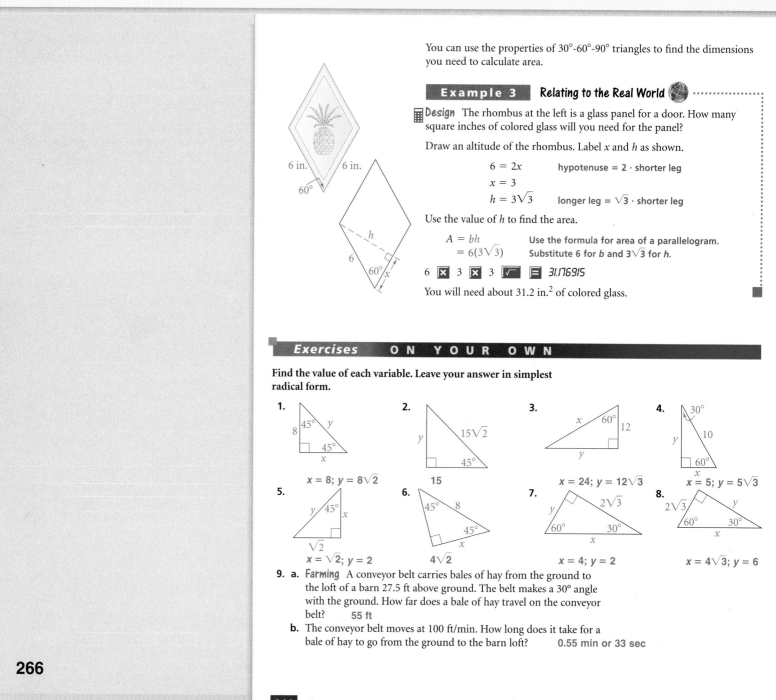

You can use the properties of 30°-60°-90° triangles to find the dimensions you need to calculate area.

Example 3 Relating to the Real World

Design The rhombus at the left is a glass panel for a door. How many square inches of colored glass will you need for the panel?

Draw an altitude of the rhombus. Label x and h as shown.

$6 = 2x$ hypotenuse = 2 · shorter leg

$x = 3$

$h = 3\sqrt{3}$ longer leg = $\sqrt{3}$ · shorter leg

Use the value of h to find the area.

$A = bh$ Use the formula for area of a parallelogram.

$= 6(3\sqrt{3})$ Substitute 6 for b and $3\sqrt{3}$ for h.

6 ⊠ 3 ⊠ 3 √ = 31.176915

You will need about 31.2 in.^{2} of colored glass.

Exercises ON YOUR OWN

Find the value of each variable. Leave your answer in simplest radical form.

1. $x = 8$; $y = 8\sqrt{2}$

2. 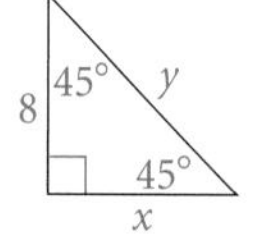
15

3. 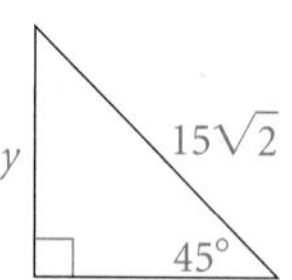
$x = 24$; $y = 12\sqrt{3}$

4. 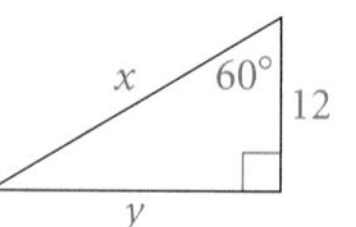
$x = 5$; $y = 5\sqrt{3}$

5. 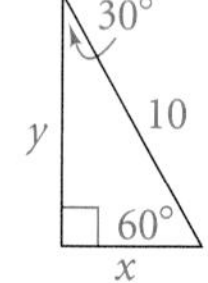
$x = \sqrt{2}$; $y = 2$

6. $4\sqrt{2}$

7. 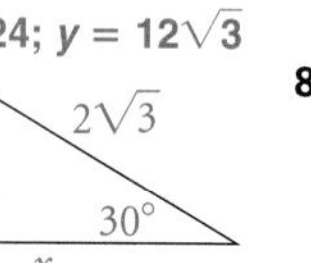
$x = 4$; $y = 2$

8. 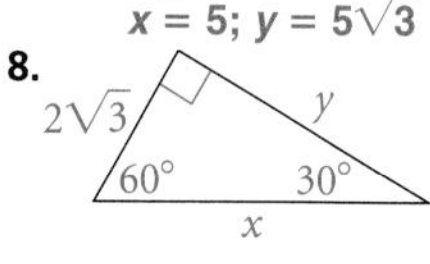
$x = 4\sqrt{3}$; $y = 6$

9. a. **Farming** A conveyor belt carries bales of hay from the ground to the loft of a barn 27.5 ft above ground. The belt makes a 30° angle with the ground. How far does a bale of hay travel on the conveyor belt? **55 ft**

   b. The conveyor belt moves at 100 ft/min. How long does it take for a bale of hay to go from the ground to the barn loft? **0.55 min or 33 sec**

ALTERNATIVE ASSESSMENT Exercises 10–13 These exercises can help you assess students' understanding of the 45°-45°-90° Triangle Theorem and the 30°-60°-90° Triangle Theorem. You may want to have students compare answers with a partner, then work together to correct any answers which they do not agree on.

STANDARDIZED TEST TIP Exercise 19 Tell students that it is a good habit to look at the answer choices before attempting to solve the problem. In this case, it is clear that, since choices A and C have two of the same lengths, one of them cannot give the sides of a 30°-60°-90° triangle.

Exercise 24 You may want to point out to students that it is not necessary to simplify radicals before using a calculator to find an approximation. In fact, it is often easier if they do not simplify first.

OPEN-ENDED Exercise 25 You may want to have students check their group members' problems and solutions for accuracy.

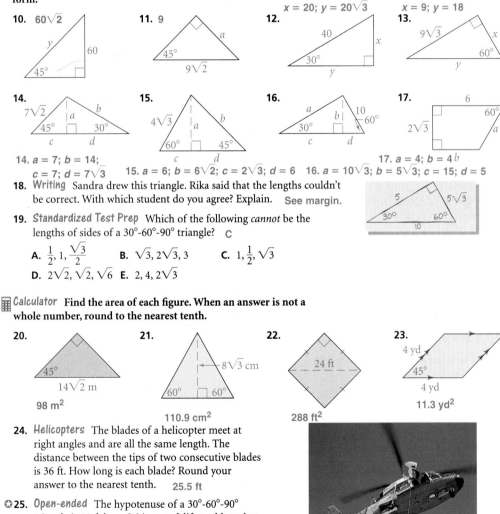

Find the value of each variable. Leave your answer in simplest radical form.

10.  $60\sqrt{2}$

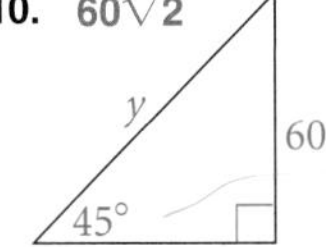

11. 9

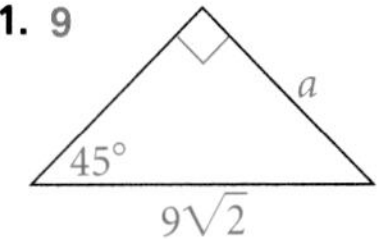

12. $x = 20;\ y = 20\sqrt{3}$

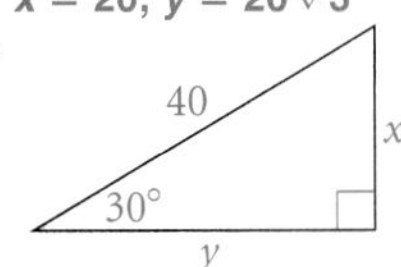

13. $x = 9;\ y = 18$

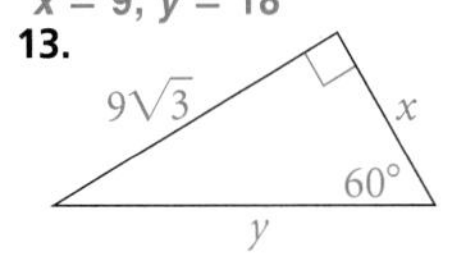

14.

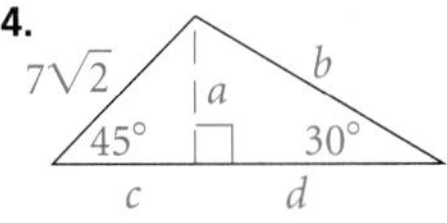

15.

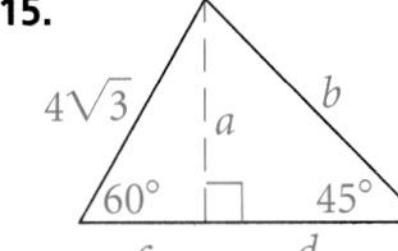

16.

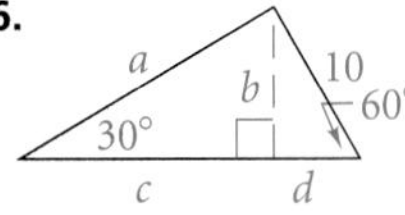

17.

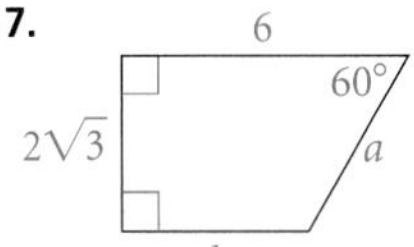

14. $a = 7;\ b = 14;\ c = 7;\ d = 7\sqrt{3}$ 15. $a = 6;\ b = 6\sqrt{2};\ c = 2\sqrt{3};\ d = 6$ 16. $a = 10\sqrt{3};\ b = 5\sqrt{3};\ c = 15;\ d = 5$ 17. $a = 4;\ b = 4$

18. *Writing* Sandra drew this triangle. Rika said that the lengths couldn't be correct. With which student do you agree? Explain. See margin.

5, $5\sqrt{3}$, 30°, 60°, 10

19. *Standardized Test Prep* Which of the following *cannot* be the lengths of sides of a 30°-60°-90° triangle? C

A. 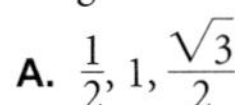 $\frac{1}{2}, 1, \frac{\sqrt{3}}{2}$ B. $\sqrt{3}, 2\sqrt{3}, 3$ C. $1, \frac{1}{2}, \sqrt{3}$
D. $2\sqrt{2}, \sqrt{2}, \sqrt{6}$ E. $2, 4, 2\sqrt{3}$

Calculator **Find the area of each figure. When an answer is not a whole number, round to the nearest tenth.**

20.

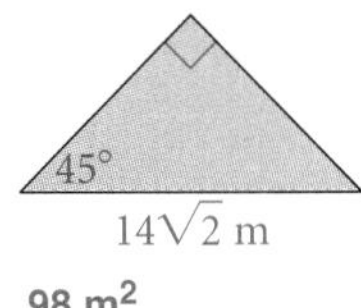

98 m^2

21.

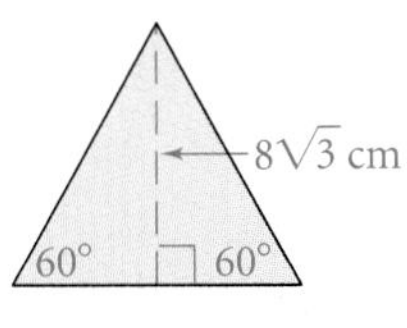

110.9 cm^2

22.

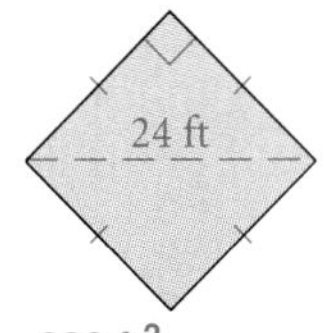

288 ft^2

23. 4 yd, 45°, 4 yd

11.3 yd^2

24. *Helicopters* The blades of a helicopter meet at right angles and are all the same length. The distance between the tips of two consecutive blades is 36 ft. How long is each blade? Round your answer to the nearest tenth. 25.5 ft

25. *Open-ended* The hypotenuse of a 30°-60°-90° triangle is 12 ft long. Write a real-life problem that you can solve using this triangle. Show your solution. See margin.

26. A rhombus has a 60° angle and sides 5 cm long. What is its area? Round your answer to the nearest tenth. 21.7 cm^2

pages 266–268 On Your Own

18. Rika; Sandra marked the shorter leg as opposite the acute angle with greater measure.

25. Sample: A garden is shaped like an equilateral △ with 12-ft sides. The entrance is the midpoint of one side and there is a bench at the opposite vertex. You need to build a straight cobblestone path from the entrance to the bench. How long is the path?

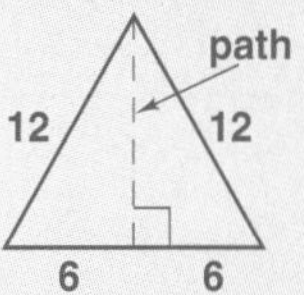

length of path = $6\sqrt{3} = 10.4$ ft

Checkpoint page 268

8.

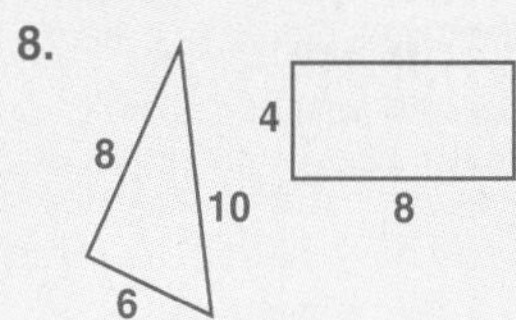

GEOMETRY IN 3 DIMENSIONS Exercise 27 Point out that this is a special case of Exercise 51 on page 261, finding the diagonal of a rectangular solid.

Exercises MIXED REVIEW

Exercise 30 Students may want to review the Math Toolbox on page 89.

JOURNAL Suggest that students organize their summary using a bulleted list to describe the characteristics of each triangle.

GETTING READY FOR LESSON 5-5 These exercises prepare students for finding the area of a trapezoid.

Wrap Up

THE BIG IDEA Ask students: *How can you find the lengths of a 45°-45°-90° triangle and of a 30°-60°-90° triangle if you are only given the length of the shortest side?*

RETEACHING ACTIVITY Students draw a 30°-60°-90° triangle, measure its sides, and compare their results with the 30°-60°-90° Triangle Theorem. (Reteaching worksheet 5-4)

Exercises CHECKPOINT

In this Checkpoint, your students will assess their own progress in Lessons 5-1 to 5-4.

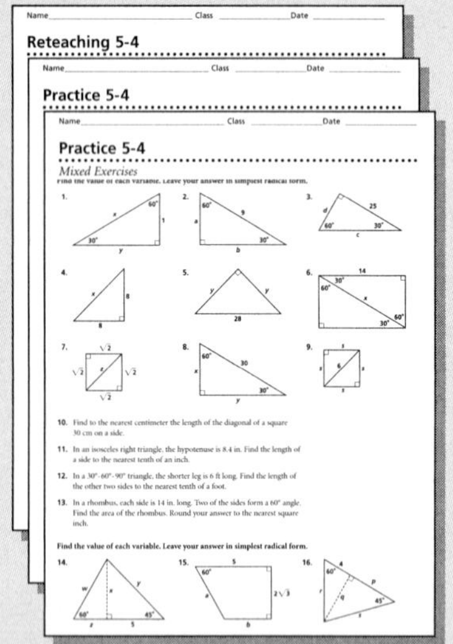

Lesson Quiz

Lesson Quiz is also available in Transparencies.

1. One leg of a 45°-45°-90° triangle has length 3 cm. Find the length of the hypotenuse. $3\sqrt{2}$ **cm**
2. The shorter leg of a 30°-60°-90° triangle has length 5 in. Find the lengths of the other leg and the hypotenuse. **leg: $5\sqrt{3}$ in.; hypotenuse: 10 in.**
3. The hypotenuse of a 30°-60°-90° triangle has a length 22 m. Find the lengths of the legs of the triangle. **shorter leg: 11 m; longer leg: $11\sqrt{3}$ m**

268

27. a. *Geometry in 3 Dimensions* Find the length d, in simplest radical form, of the diagonal of a cube with sides 1 unit long. $\sqrt{3}$ **units**
    b. Find the length d of the diagonal of a cube with sides 2 units long. $2\sqrt{3}$ **units**
    c. *Generalize* Find the length d of the diagonal of a cube with sides s units long. $s\sqrt{3}$ **units**

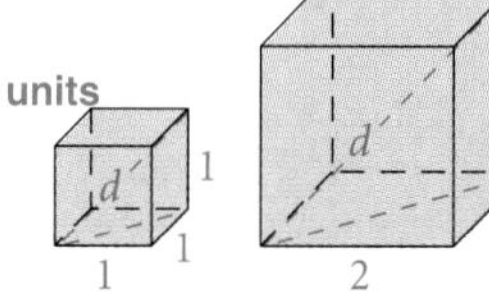

Exercises MIXED REVIEW

Find the slope of $\overline{AB}$.

28. $A(1, 0), B(-2, 3)$ -1
29. $A(-5, 4), B(-1, 8)$ 1
30. Find the equation of the line with slope $\frac{1}{2}$ containing the point $(-2, 5)$. $y = \frac{1}{2}x + 6$

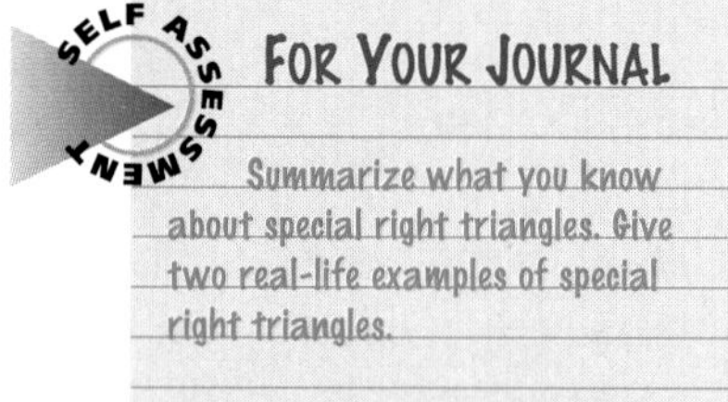

FOR YOUR JOURNAL
Summarize what you know about special right triangles. Give two real-life examples of special right triangles.

Getting Ready For Lesson 5-5

Find the area and perimeter of each trapezoid to the nearest tenth.

31. 32.

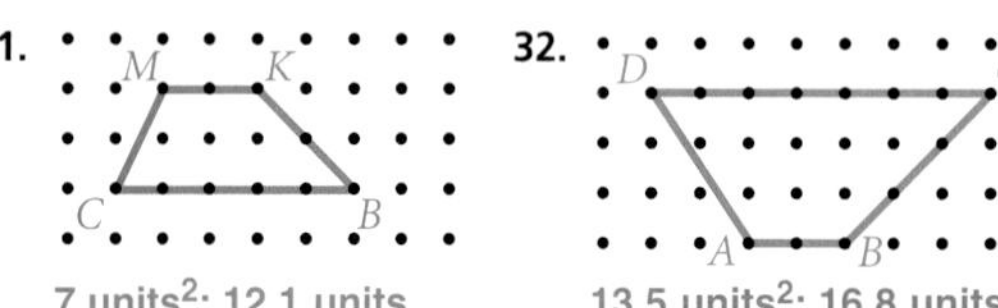

31. 7 units^2; 12.1 units
32. 13.5 units^2; 16.8 units

Exercises CHECKPOINT

Find the area and perimeter of each figure.

1. 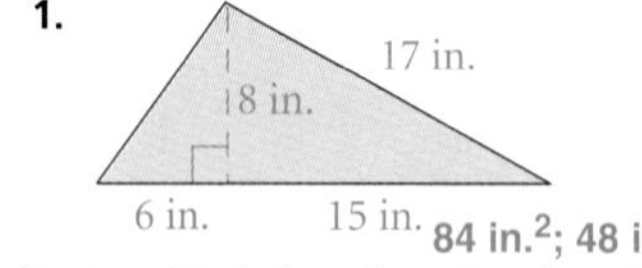

84 in.^{2}; 48 in.

2. 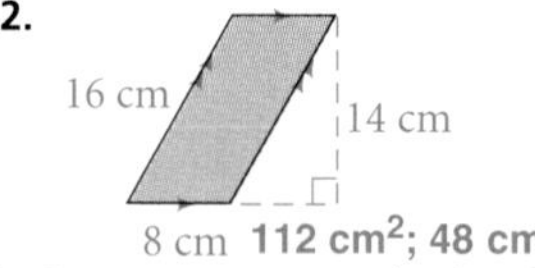

112 cm^2; 48 cm

3. 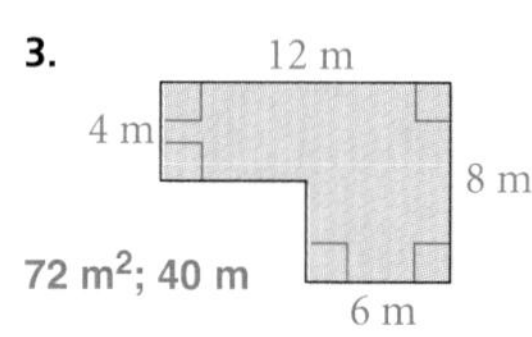

72 m^2; 40 m

Algebra **Find the value of each variable. Leave your answer in simplest radical form.**

4. 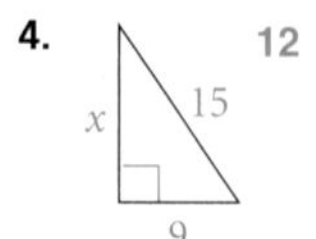

12

5. 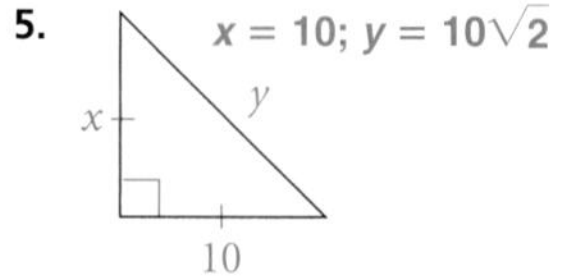

$x = 10$; $y = 10\sqrt{2}$

6. 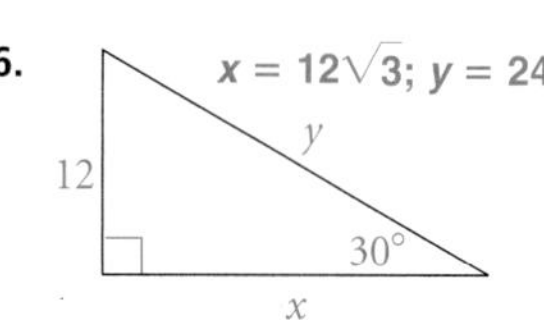

$x = 12\sqrt{3}$; $y = 24$

7. *Standardized Test Prep* Which numbers could represent the lengths of the sides of an acute triangle? **B**
   A. 3, 4, 5 **B.** 6, 8, 9 **C.** 14, 45, 50 **D.** 5, 12, 13 **E.** 5, 9, 13
8. *Open-ended* Sketch a rectangle and a triangle with the same perimeter. Label the lengths of the sides of the figures. **See margin p. 267 for sample.**

PROBLEM OF THE DAY

Each triangle is a 45°-45°-90° triangle. $AB = 1$. Find BC. 16

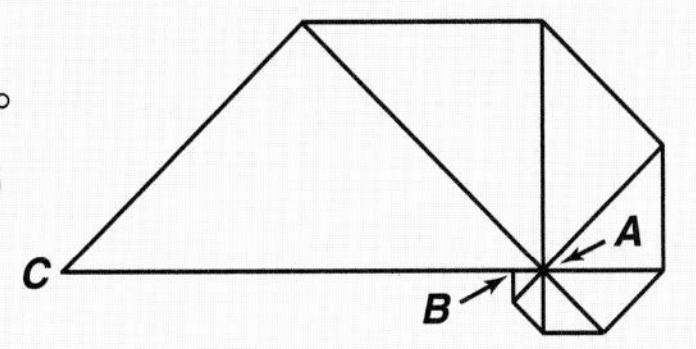

Problem of the Day is also available in Transparencies.

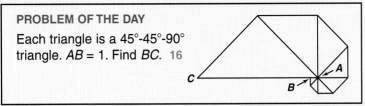

CONNECTING TO PRIOR KNOWLEDGE Draw an isosceles trapezoid, a trapezoid with two right angles, and two other trapezoids in different orientations on the board. Ask students to name the figures and describe their similarities and differences.

WORK TOGETHER

Have group members draw different trapezoids. Students who draw trapezoids with two right angles may be surprised that their two trapezoids form a rectangle. (They can also be arranged to form a non-rectangular parallelogram.) Make sure students see that a parallelogram is always formed no matter what the size or shape of the trapezoid.

THINK AND DISCUSS

Theorem 5-8 The area of a trapezoid can also be expressed as "the average of the lengths of the bases times the height."

Connections 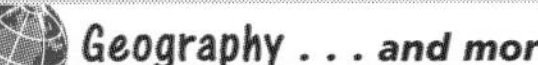 Geography . . . and more

5-5 Areas of Trapezoids

What You'll Learn
- Finding the areas of trapezoids

...And Why

To approximate the areas of irregular figures

What You'll Need
- lined paper
- scissors

WORK TOGETHER

Work in groups. Fold a piece of lined paper in half along one of the lines. On two lines of the paper, draw parallel segments of different lengths. Connect the endpoints of the segments to form a trapezoid. Cut through both layers of the folded paper, so that you will have two congruent trapezoids. Label b_1, b_2, and h for each trapezoid.

- Arrange the congruent trapezoids to form a parallelogram as shown at the left below.

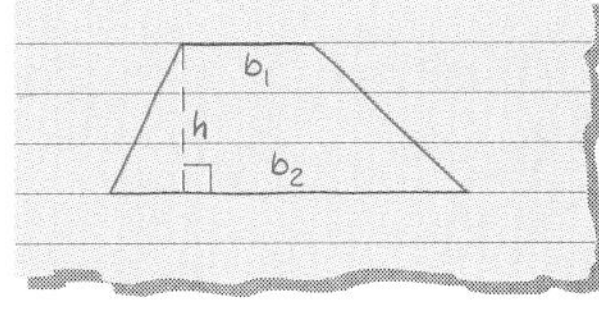

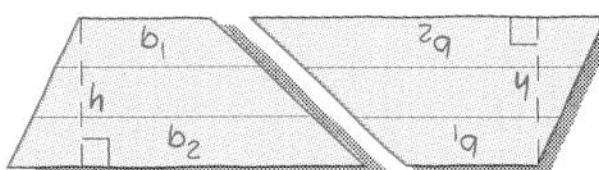

1. a. Write an expression for the length of the base of the parallelogram. $b_1 + b_2$
   b. Write an expression for the area of the parallelogram using b_1, b_2, and h. $(b_1 + b_2)h$
2. How does the area of each trapezoid compare to the area of the parallelogram? The area of each trapezoid is half the area of the ▱.
3. Use your answers to Questions 1 and 2 to write a formula for the area of each trapezoid. $\frac{1}{2}h(b_1 + b_2)$

THINK AND DISCUSS

In a trapezoid, the parallel sides are the **bases.** The nonparallel sides are the **legs.** The **height** h is the perpendicular distance between the two parallel bases.

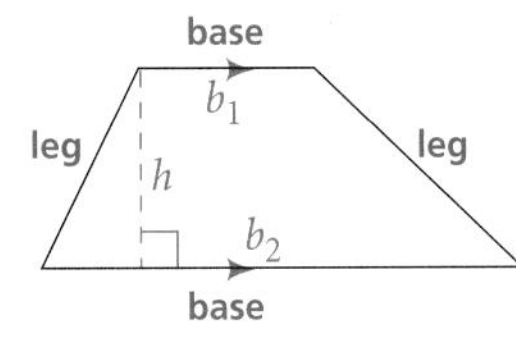

Your observations in the Work Together suggest the following theorem.

Theorem 5-8
Area of a Trapezoid

The area of a trapezoid is half the product of the height and the sum of the lengths of the bases.

$$A = \frac{1}{2}h(b_1 + b_2)$$

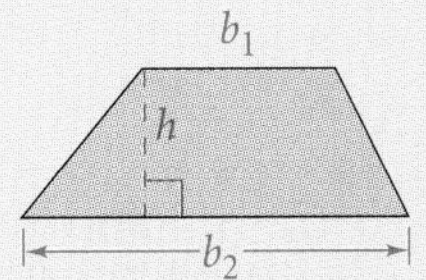

4. *Critical Thinking* When finding the area of a trapezoid, does it make a difference which base is labeled b_1 and which base is labeled b_2? Explain. no; $b_1 + b_2 = b_2 + b_1$

Lesson Planning Options

Prerequisite Skills
- Applying the Pythagorean Theorem
- Finding the area of parallelograms

Assignment Options for Exercises On Your Own

Core 1–5, 7–21
✪**Extension** 6, 22–23

Use Mixed Review to maintain skills.

Resources

 **Student Edition**

Skills Handbook, p. 673
Extra Practice, p. 652
Glossary/Study Guide

Teaching Resources

Chapter Support File, Ch. 5
- Practice 5-5 (two worksheets)
- Reteaching 5-5
- Alternative Activity 5-5

Classroom Manager 5-5
Glossary, Spanish Resources

Transparencies
1, 18, 62

ERROR ALERT! Some students may assume that the bases are always the horizontal sides and that the altitude is always vertical. **Remediation:** Draw trapezoids in different orientations and have students identify the bases and height.

EXTENSION The median of a trapezoid is a segment joining the legs at their midpoints. Its length is one-half the sum of the lengths of the bases. Have students rewrite the formula for the area of a trapezoid in terms of its median m and height h. **$A = mh$**

Example 1 **Relating to the Real World**

VISUAL LEARNING If you have block scheduling or an extended class period, have students use a map to approximate the areas of other trapezoid-shaped states such as North Dakota and Connecticut. Then have them research the actual areas.

Example 2

Have students check the answer by finding the areas of the triangle and the rectangle formed when the altitude is drawn.

You may want to make a poster displaying the area formulas presented in this chapter. Have students copy the contents of the poster onto index cards which they can use when working on the exercises at home.

Additional Examples

FOR EXAMPLE 1

Find the area of a trapezoid with height 42 in. and bases with lengths 121 in. and 145 in. **5586 in.^{2}**

Discussion: *One student found the area by multiplying 266 by 21. Another found the area by multiplying 42 by 133. Another student multiplied 42 by 266, then divided by two. Which student is correct?*

FOR EXAMPLE 2

Refer to the diagram for Example 2. If $SR = 21$ cm and $PQ = 25$ cm, find the area of trapezoid $PQRS$. **$92\sqrt{3}$ cm^2**

Discussion: *Do the lengths of $\overline{SR}$ and $\overline{PQ}$ affect the relationship between the sides of $\triangle PSE$?*

270

250 mi
Mammoth Springs
Fort Smith
Little Rock
242 mi
Arkansas R.
Mississippi R.
190 mi

Example 1 **Relating to the Real World** 

Geography Approximate the area of Arkansas by finding the area of the trapezoid shown.

$A = \frac{1}{2}h(b_1 + b_2)$ — Use the area formula for a trapezoid.

$= \frac{1}{2}(242)(190 + 250)$ — Substitute.

$= 53{,}240$

The area of Arkansas is about 53,240 mi^2.

5. **Try This** Find the area of a trapezoid with height 7 cm and bases 12 cm and 15 cm. **94.5 cm^2**

Sometimes properties of special right triangles can help you find the area of a trapezoid.

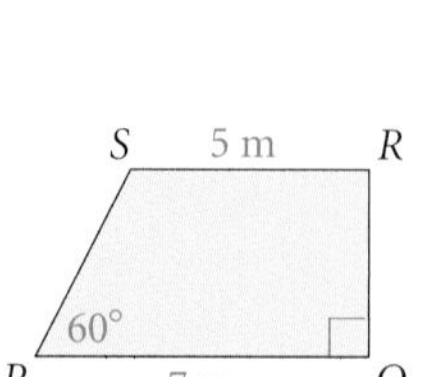

Example 2

Find the area of trapezoid $PQRS$. Leave your answer in simplest radical form.

You can draw an altitude that divides the trapezoid into a rectangle and a 30°-60°-90° triangle. Find h.

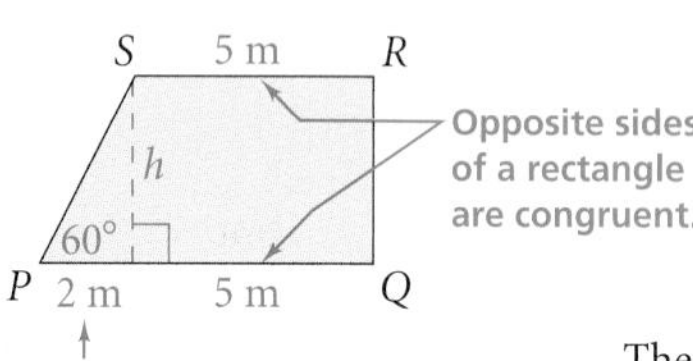

$h = 2\sqrt{3}$ — longer leg = shorter leg · $\sqrt{3}$

$A = \frac{1}{2}h(b_1 + b_2)$ — Use the area formula for a trapezoid.

$= \frac{1}{2}(2\sqrt{3})(5 + 7)$ — Substitute.

$= 12\sqrt{3}$ — Simplify.

The area of trapezoid $PQRS$ is $12\sqrt{3}$ m^2.

6. Suppose $m\angle P = 45$. Find the area of trapezoid $PQRS$. **12 m^2**

Exercises ON YOUR OWN

Exercises 3 and 5 Students may want to turn the book so that the bases of the trapezoid are horizontal.

DIVERSITY Exercise 6 Assign each group a different country. Have them approximate its area using a map. Ask students to explain which shape(s) they used: triangle, rectangle, parallelogram, trapezoid, or a combination of shapes. Then have them research cultural and historical information about the country. Choose countries where students, their parents, or their grandparents have lived.

ERROR ALERT! Exercise 7 Some students will correctly divide 80 by 40 but forget to multiply the result by 2.

Remediation: Have students substitute the value of $(b_1 + b_2)$ in the trapezoid area formula and solve for h. Then suggest they check their value of h by calculating the area using the values of b_1, b_2, and h and seeing if it equals 80 ft^2.

ESL Exercise 12 Some students may be unfamiliar with the term "rain gutter." If there are houses with rain gutters close to the school, take students to see them. If not, see if a hardware store will let you borrow a piece of one to bring to class. (You could assign this as an extra credit project.)

ALTERNATIVE METHOD Exercise 13 Have students draw any trapezoid and an altitude that cuts it into a triangle and a parallelogram. Then ask them to justify the trapezoid area formula using the area formulas of a parallelogram and triangle.

Exercises ON YOUR OWN

Find the area of each trapezoid.

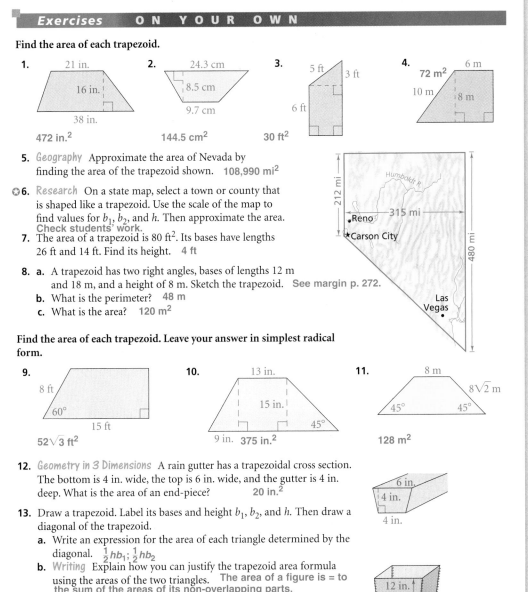

1. 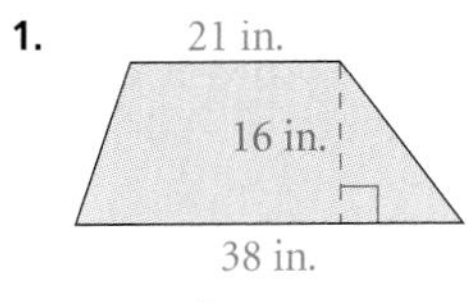

472 in.^{2}

2. 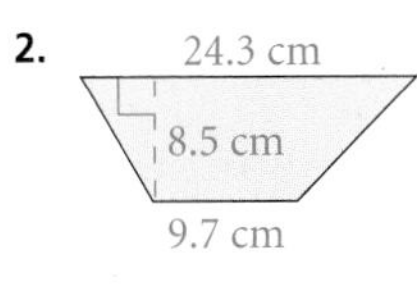

144.5 cm^2

3. 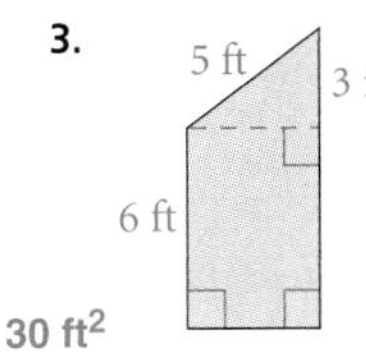

30 ft^2

4. 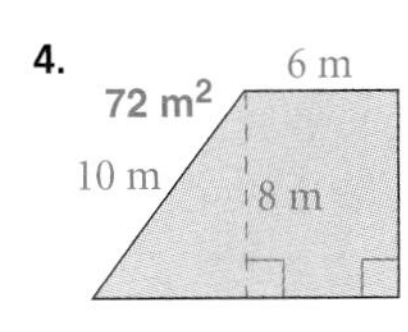

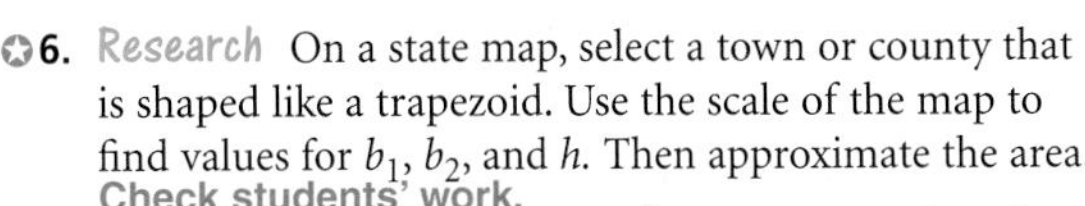

5. *Geography* Approximate the area of Nevada by finding the area of the trapezoid shown. **108,990 mi^2**

6. *Research* On a state map, select a town or county that is shaped like a trapezoid. Use the scale of the map to find values for b_1, b_2, and h. Then approximate the area. **Check students' work.**

7. The area of a trapezoid is 80 ft^2. Its bases have lengths 26 ft and 14 ft. Find its height. **4 ft**

8. a. A trapezoid has two right angles, bases of lengths 12 m and 18 m, and a height of 8 m. Sketch the trapezoid. **See margin p. 272.**
   b. What is the perimeter? **48 m**
   c. What is the area? **120 m^2**

212 mi
Humboldt R.
315 mi
Reno
Carson City
480 mi
Las Vegas

Find the area of each trapezoid. Leave your answer in simplest radical form.

9. 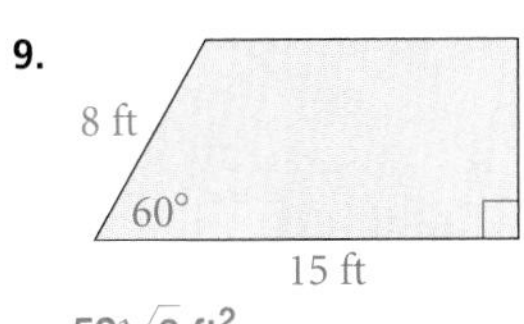

$52\sqrt{3}$ ft^2

10. 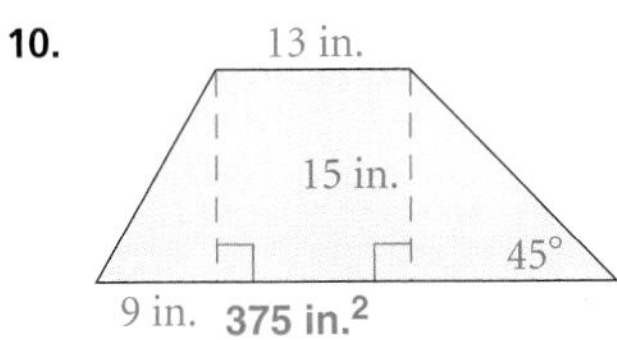

375 in.^{2}

11. 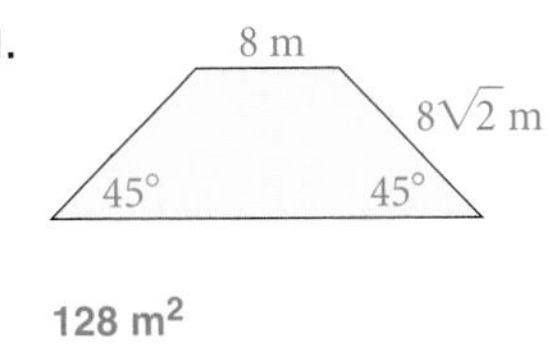

128 m^2

12. *Geometry in 3 Dimensions* A rain gutter has a trapezoidal cross section. The bottom is 4 in. wide, the top is 6 in. wide, and the gutter is 4 in. deep. What is the area of an end-piece? **20 in.^{2}**

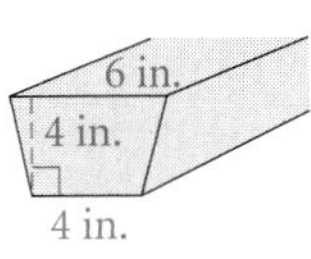

13. Draw a trapezoid. Label its bases and height b_1, b_2, and h. Then draw a diagonal of the trapezoid.
    a. Write an expression for the area of each triangle determined by the diagonal. **$\frac{1}{2}hb_1$; $\frac{1}{2}hb_2$**
    b. *Writing* Explain how you can justify the trapezoid area formula using the areas of the two triangles. **The area of a figure is = to the sum of the areas of its non-overlapping parts.**

14. *Open-ended* Draw a trapezoid. Measure its height and the lengths of its bases. Find its area. **Check students' work.**

15. *Crafts* You plan to lace together four isosceles trapezoids and a square to make the trash basket shown. How much material will you need? **669 in.^{2}**

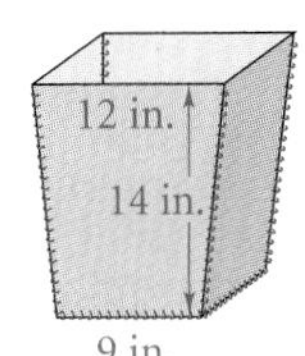

Technology Options

For Exercise 22, students may want to graph the lines using geometry software.

Prentice Hall Technology 

 **Software**
- Secondary Math Lab Toolkit™
- Computer Item Generator 5-5

 **Internet**
- See the Prentice Hall site. (http://www.phschool.com)

ALTERNATIVE ASSESSMENT Exercise 16 This exercise can help you assess students' ability to use the trapezoid area formula to find the length of the legs of a trapezoid. Have students work in groups on this problem. You may want to give them a hint that they should use the trapezoid area formula and the Pythagorean Theorem.

ALGEBRA Exercise 17 The hint suggests using $2x$ and $4x$ so students can avoid using fractions. Using x and $2x$ is also acceptable.

MAKING CONNECTIONS Exercise 23 The area of a trapezoid is used in calculus to approximate the area of non-polygonal regions. For example, to approximate the area under the piece of the curve shown below, you could find the sum of the areas of trapezoids T_1, T_2, T_3, T_4 and T_5.

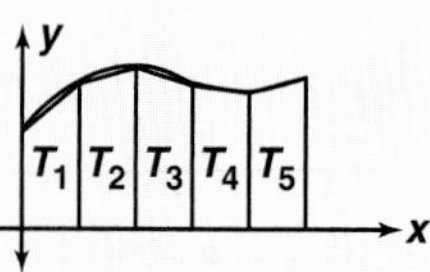

Exercises MIXED REVIEW

Exercises 24–27 Ask students to explain their reasoning.

GETTING READY FOR LESSON 5-6 These exercises prepare students for finding the areas of regular polygons.

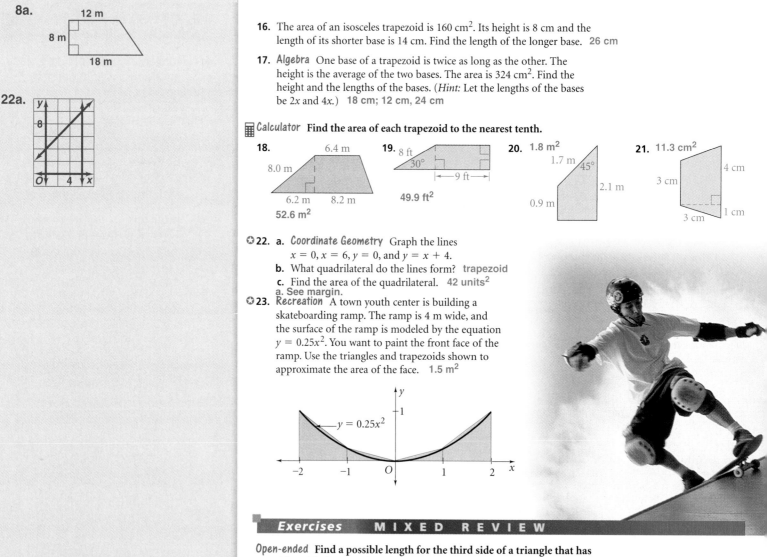

8a.

12 m

8 m

18 m

22a.

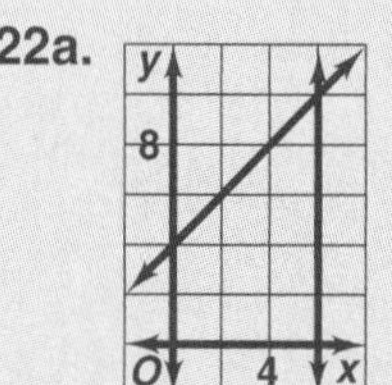

16. The area of an isosceles trapezoid is 160 cm^2. Its height is 8 cm and the length of its shorter base is 14 cm. Find the length of the longer base. 26 cm

17. *Algebra* One base of a trapezoid is twice as long as the other. The height is the average of the two bases. The area is 324 cm^2. Find the height and the lengths of the bases. (*Hint:* Let the lengths of the bases be $2x$ and $4x$.) 18 cm; 12 cm, 24 cm

Calculator **Find the area of each trapezoid to the nearest tenth.**

18. 19.

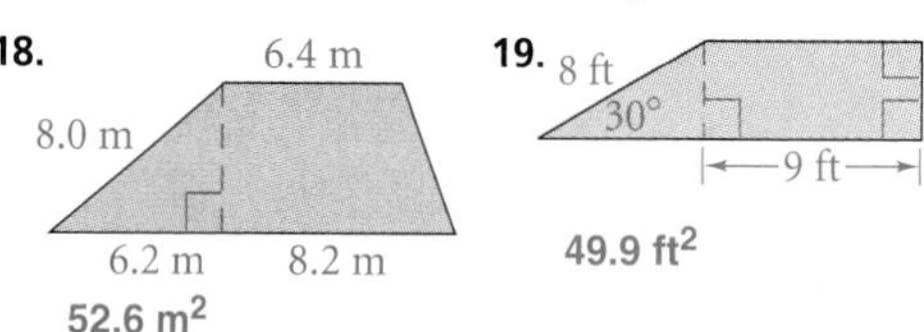

18. 52.6 m^2 19. 49.9 ft^2

20. 1.8 m^2

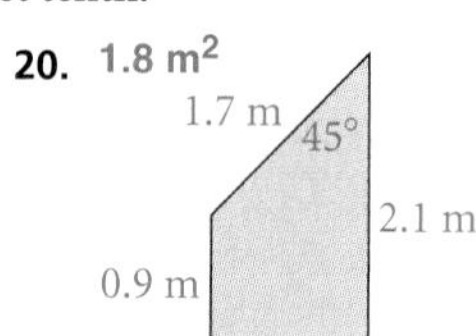

21. 11.3 cm^2

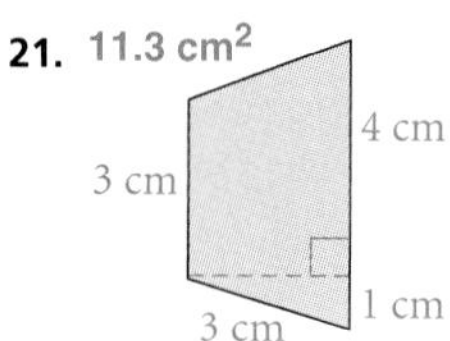

22. a. *Coordinate Geometry* Graph the lines $x = 0, x = 6, y = 0$, and $y = x + 4$. a. See margin.
b. What quadrilateral do the lines form? trapezoid
c. Find the area of the quadrilateral. 42 $units^2$

23. *Recreation* A town youth center is building a skateboarding ramp. The ramp is 4 m wide, and the surface of the ramp is modeled by the equation $y = 0.25x^2$. You want to paint the front face of the ramp. Use the triangles and trapezoids shown to approximate the area of the face. 1.5 m^2

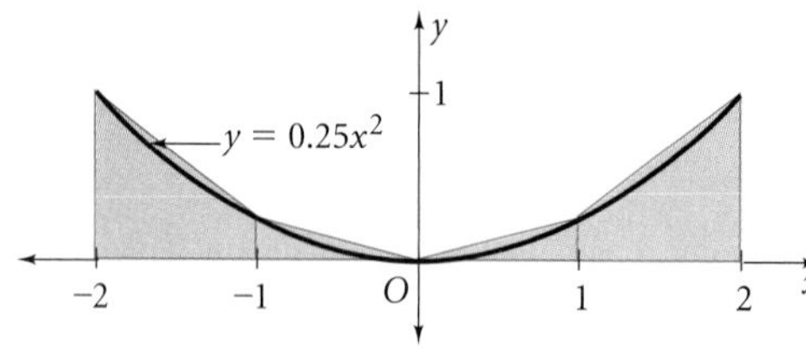

Exercises MIXED REVIEW

Open-ended **Find a possible length for the third side of a triangle that has two sides with the given lengths.**

24. 7 cm, 10 cm between 3 cm and 17 cm
25. 2 in., 8 in. between 6 in. and 10 in.
26. 13 mm, 6 mm between 7 mm and 19 mm
27. 4 ft, 9 ft between 5 ft and 13 ft

28. *Locus* Describe the locus of points in a plane equidistant from the sides of an angle. What is another name for this locus? a line passing through the vertex and forming ≅ angles with the sides of the orig. angle; angle bisector

Chapter Project **FIND OUT BY RESEARCHING** Students can find other patchwork designs used by Seminoles by looking in books on quilting at the local library or contacting a local quilting guild.

Wrap Up

THE BIG IDEA Have students define the parts of a trapezoid, including diagrams, and rephrase the trapezoid area formula in their own words.

RETEACHING ACTIVITY Students draw a trapezoid with area 48 cm^2 on grid paper. Then they find the areas of other trapezoids. (Reteaching worksheet 5-5)

A Point in Time

If you have block scheduling or an extended class period you may wish to have students investigate these topics:

- How was President Garfield employed before he became president? How long did he serve in office? How did he die? **President of Hiram College, general, congressman; about a year; he was assassinated by Charles Guiteau.**
- Research the proofs of the Pythagorean Theorem credited to Babylonian, Hindu, and Chinese mathematicians.

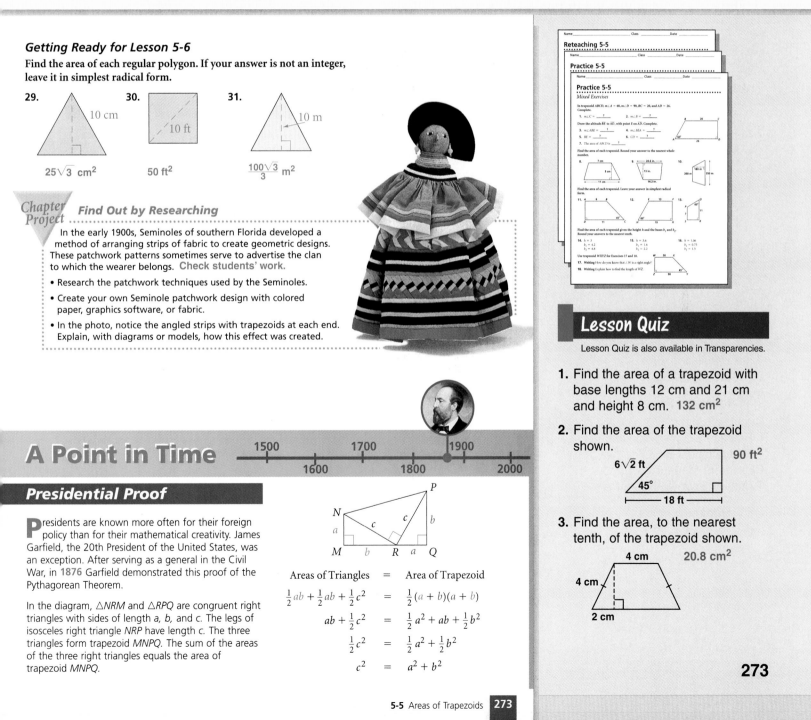

Getting Ready for Lesson 5-6

Find the area of each regular polygon. If your answer is not an integer, leave it in simplest radical form.

29.

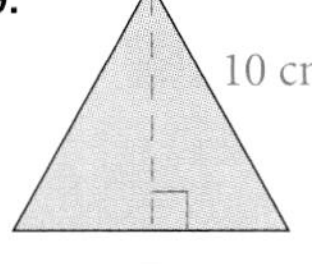

$25\sqrt{3}$ cm^2

30.

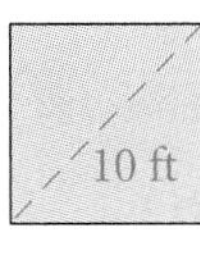

50 ft^2

31.

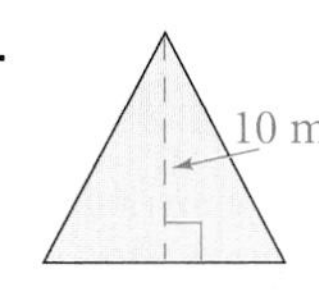

$\frac{100\sqrt{3}}{3}$ m^2

Chapter Project ***Find Out by Researching***

In the early 1900s, Seminoles of southern Florida developed a method of arranging strips of fabric to create geometric designs. These patchwork patterns sometimes serve to advertise the clan to which the wearer belongs. **Check students' work.**

- Research the patchwork techniques used by the Seminoles.
- Create your own Seminole patchwork design with colored paper, graphics software, or fabric.
- In the photo, notice the angled strips with trapezoids at each end. Explain, with diagrams or models, how this effect was created.

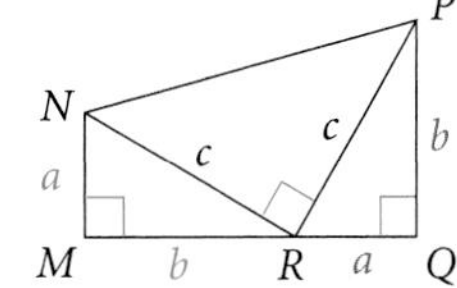

A Point in Time

1500 1600 1700 1800 1900 2000

Presidential Proof

Presidents are known more often for their foreign policy than for their mathematical creativity. James Garfield, the 20th President of the United States, was an exception. After serving as a general in the Civil War, in **1876** Garfield demonstrated this proof of the Pythagorean Theorem.

In the diagram, $\triangle NRM$ and $\triangle RPQ$ are congruent right triangles with sides of length *a, b,* and *c*. The legs of isosceles right triangle *NRP* have length *c*. The three triangles form trapezoid *MNPQ*. The sum of the areas of the three right triangles equals the area of trapezoid *MNPQ*.

Areas of Triangles	=	Area of Trapezoid
$\frac{1}{2}ab + \frac{1}{2}ab + \frac{1}{2}c^2$	=	$\frac{1}{2}(a + b)(a + b)$
$ab + \frac{1}{2}c^2$	=	$\frac{1}{2}a^2 + ab + \frac{1}{2}b^2$
$\frac{1}{2}c^2$	=	$\frac{1}{2}a^2 + \frac{1}{2}b^2$
c^2	=	$a^2 + b^2$

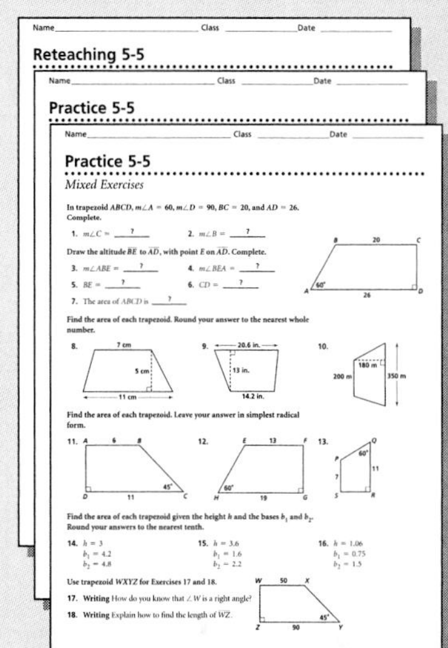

Name______ Class ______ Date ______

Reteaching 5-5

Name______ Class ______ Date ______

Practice 5-5

Name______ Class ______ Date ______

Practice 5-5

Mixed Exercises

In trapezoid *ABCD*, $m\angle A = 60$, $m\angle D = 90$, $BC = 20$, and $AD = 26$. Complete.

1. $m\angle C =$ __?__
2. $m\angle B =$ __?__

Draw the altitude $\overline{BE}$ to $\overline{AD}$, with point *E* on $\overline{AD}$. Complete.

3. $m\angle ABE =$ __?__
4. $m\angle BEA =$ __?__
5. $BE =$ __?__
6. $CD =$ __?__
7. The area of *ABCD* is __?__

Find the area of each trapezoid. Round your answer to the nearest whole number.

8. 7 cm, 5 cm, 11 cm
9. 20.6 in., 13 in., 14.2 in.
10. 200 m, 180 m, 350 m

Find the area of each trapezoid. Leave your answer in simplest radical form.

11. A 6 B, D 11 C, 45°
12. E 13 F, H 19 G, 60°
13. P, Q, 60°, 7, 11, S, R

Find the area of each trapezoid given the height *h* and the bases b_1 and b_2. Round your answers to the nearest tenth.

14. $h = 3$, $b_1 = 4.2$, $b_2 = 4.8$
15. $h = 3.6$, $b_1 = 1.6$, $b_2 = 2.2$
16. $h = 1.06$, $b_1 = 0.75$, $b_2 = 1.5$

Use trapezoid *WXYZ* for Exercises 17 and 18.

17. **Writing** How do you know that $\angle W$ is a right angle?
18. **Writing** Explain how to find the length of $\overline{WZ}$.

Lesson Quiz

Lesson Quiz is also available in Transparencies.

1. Find the area of a trapezoid with base lengths 12 cm and 21 cm and height 8 cm. **132 cm^2**
2. Find the area of the trapezoid shown. **90 ft^2**

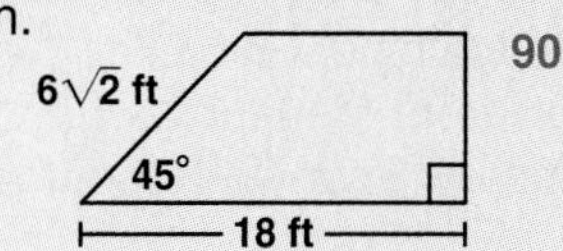

3. Find the area, to the nearest tenth, of the trapezoid shown. **20.8 cm^2**

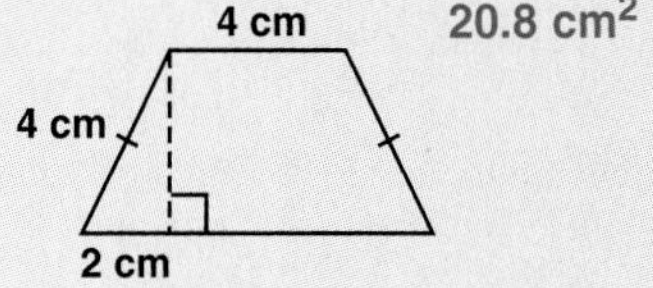

5-6 Teaching Notes

PROBLEM OF THE DAY

Six squares are made with 17 toothpicks. Remove 6 toothpicks to leave two squares. Answers will vary. Sample given.

Problem of the Day is also available in Transparencies.

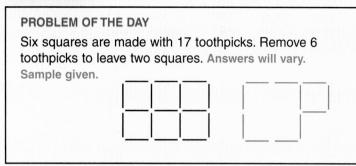

CONNECTING TO PRIOR KNOWLEDGE Present students with the following diagram. Ask them what they can say about $\overline{AD}$, $\overline{DB}$, $\angle ACD$, and $\angle DCB$ and why.

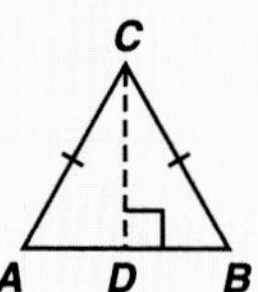

THINK AND DISCUSS

ESL Students may be unfamiliar with the word *circumscribe*. Help them break it into its prefix *circum* which means "around" and its root *scribe* which means "to write."

Lesson Planning Options

Prerequisite Skills

- Recognizing characteristics of regular polygons
- Applying special right triangle theorems

Assignment Options for Exercises On Your Own

Core 1–18, 20, 22–26

✪Extension 19, 21

Use Mixed Review to maintain skills.

Resources

Student Edition

Skills Handbook, pp. 673, 674
Extra Practice, p. 652
Glossary/Study Guide

Teaching Resources

Chapter Support File, Ch. 5
- Practice 5-6 (two worksheets)
- Reteaching 5-6

Classroom Manager 5-6
Glossary, Spanish Resources

Transparencies
13, 18, 62, 66

274

Connections Racing Cars and Boats . . . *and more*

5-6 Areas of Regular Polygons

What You'll Learn
- Finding areas of regular polygons

...And Why

To find amounts of materials used in manufacturing and in architecture

A regular polygon is any polygon that is both equilateral and equiangular.

THINK AND DISCUSS

You can circumscribe a circle about any regular polygon. The **center** of a regular polygon is the center of the circumscribed circle. The **radius** of a regular polygon is the distance from the center to a vertex. The **apothem** of a regular polygon is the perpendicular distance from the center to a side.

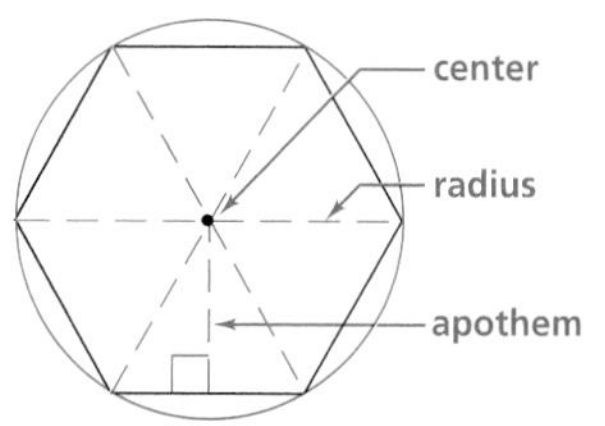

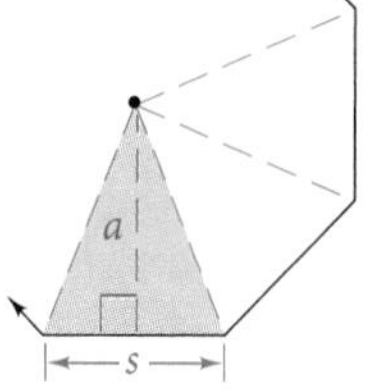

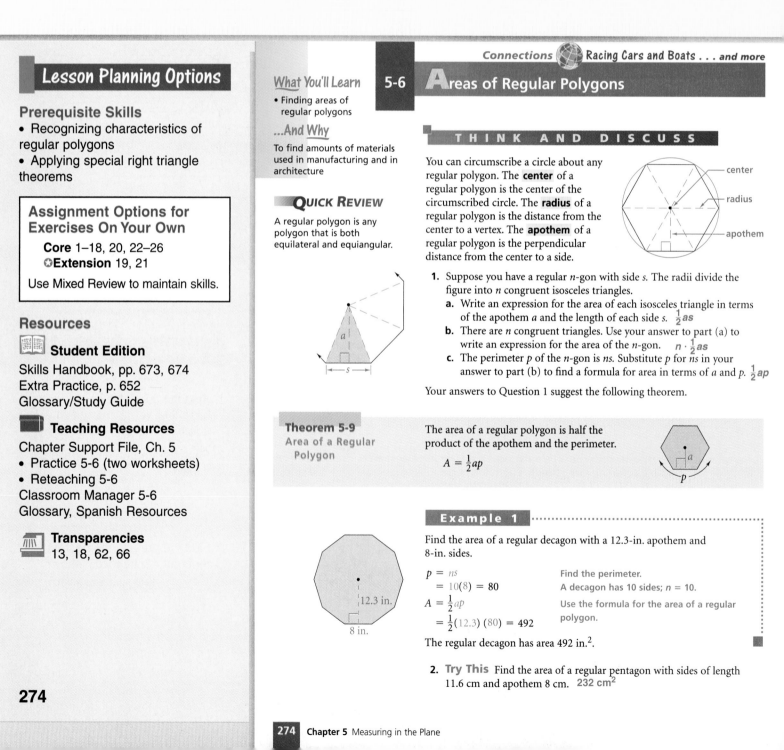

1. Suppose you have a regular n-gon with side s. The radii divide the figure into n congruent isosceles triangles.
   a. Write an expression for the area of each isosceles triangle in terms of the apothem a and the length of each side s. $\frac{1}{2}as$
   b. There are n congruent triangles. Use your answer to part (a) to write an expression for the area of the n-gon. $n \cdot \frac{1}{2}as$
   c. The perimeter p of the n-gon is ns. Substitute p for ns in your answer to part (b) to find a formula for area in terms of a and p. $\frac{1}{2}ap$

Your answers to Question 1 suggest the following theorem.

Theorem 5-9
Area of a Regular Polygon

The area of a regular polygon is half the product of the apothem and the perimeter.

$$A = \frac{1}{2}ap$$

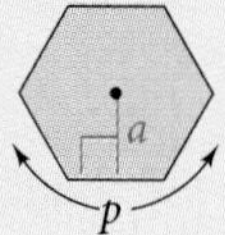

Example 1

Find the area of a regular decagon with a 12.3-in. apothem and 8-in. sides.

$p = ns$ — Find the perimeter.

$= 10(8) = 80$ — A decagon has 10 sides; $n = 10$.

$A = \frac{1}{2}ap$ — Use the formula for the area of a regular polygon.

$= \frac{1}{2}(12.3)(80) = 492$

The regular decagon has area 492 in.^{2}.

2. **Try This** Find the area of a regular pentagon with sides of length 11.6 cm and apothem 8 cm. 232 cm^2

Question 1c Depending on the order of the variables in students' answers to parts a and b, they may have difficulty with the substitution. Help them see that, by the Commutative Property of Multiplication, they can rewrite their expressions as $\frac{1}{2}ans$, and then substitute p for ns.

CRITICAL THINKING Ask students to explain why the apothem is a perpendicular bisector and why a radius bisects an angle of the polygon. These concepts will be used throughout the lesson to find the lengths of radii, apothems, and sides.

Example 1

VISUAL LEARNING Also have students compute the area using the method described in Questions 1 a and b: copy the diagram, triangulate the decagon, find the area of one triangle, then multiply the area by the number of triangles. Discuss with students which method requires less work.

EXTENSION It should be obvious that a tessellation of a square can be used to fill a larger square. Students may want to investigate whether a tessellation of a hexagon can be used to fill a larger hexagon.

Example 2 **Relating to the Real World** 

Students may be confused seeing the term radius used without seeing a circle. You may want to copy the hexagon and circumscribe it.

Help students see that the apothem, radius, and half of a side of a regular hexagon form a 30°-60°-90° triangle.

QUICK REVIEW

Regular polygons that tessellate are triangles, squares, and hexagons.

Engineers use regular polygons that tessellate because they fill the plane without wasting space. You can use special right triangles to find their areas.

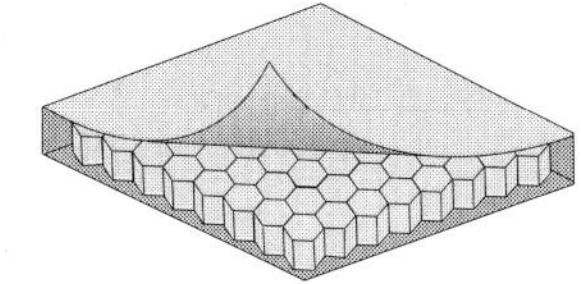

Example 2 **Relating to the Real World** 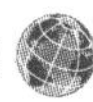

30° 60° a 10 mm 5 mm

Racing Cars and boats used for racing need to be strong and durable, yet lightweight. One material that designers use to build body shells is a honeycomb of regular hexagonal prisms sandwiched between two layers of outer material. The honeycomb is plastic and provides strength and resilience without adding a lot of weight. The figure at the left is a cross section of one hexagonal cell.

The radii of a regular hexagon form six 60° angles at the center. So, you can use a 30°-60°-90° triangle to find the apothem a.

$a = 5\sqrt{3}$	longer leg = $\sqrt{3}$ · shorter leg
$p = ns$	Find the perimeter of the hexagon.
$= 6(10) = 60$	Substitute 6 for n and 10 for s.
$A = \frac{1}{2}ap$	Find the area.
$= \frac{1}{2}(5\sqrt{3})(60)$	Substitute.

0.5 [×] 5 [×] 3  [×] 60 [=] 259.80762

The area is about 260 mm^2.

3. **Estimation** About how many hexagonal cells are in a 10 cm by 10 cm square panel? **about 40 cells**
4. **Try This** The apothem of a regular hexagon is 15 ft. Find the area of the hexagon. **about 779 ft^2**

Additional Examples

FOR EXAMPLE 1

Find the area of a regular heptagon with a 9.4-in. apothem and 9-in. sides. **296.1 in.^{2}**

FOR EXAMPLE 2

The length of a radius of a regular hexagon tile is 8 cm. Find the area of the tile to the nearest tenth. **166.3 cm^2**

Discussion: *How many floor tiles would you need to cover an 8-m by 10-m floor?*

FOR EXAMPLE 3

The apothem of an equilateral triangle is 7 cm. Find the area of the triangle to the nearest tenth. **254.6 cm^2**

275

Example 3

Help students see why that the apothem, radius, and half of a side of an equilateral triangle form a 30°-60°-90° triangle.

PROBLEM SOLVING The altitude of an equilateral triangle is the longer leg of a 30°-60°-90° triangle. Help students sketch and label the equilateral triangle shown below.

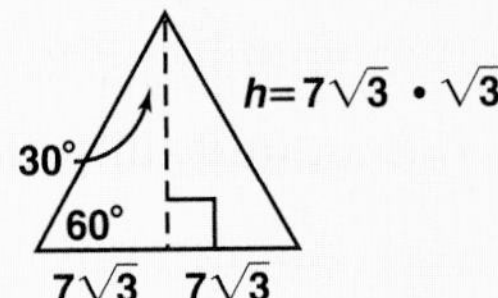

ERROR ALERT! Question 5 Some students may think that the apothem and the radius form a 30°-60°-90° triangle with half of the side as is true of a hexagon and an equilateral triangle. **Remediation:** Point out that each angle of the square is 90°, so the radius bisects it into two 45° angles.

Exercises ON YOUR OWN

Exercises 1–3 Students may want to copy the figures into their notebooks and replace the numbers with the correct angle measures.

Exercises 7–10 Students can refer to Exercises 1–3 (or their notebooks) to see how to use a 30°-60°-90° triangle or a 45°-45°-90° triangle to find the missing lengths of regular polygons.

Technology Options

For Exercise 14, students may create their design using drawing or geometry software.

Prentice Hall Technology

Software
- Secondary Math Lab Toolkit™
- Computer Item Generator 5-6

CD-ROM
- Multimedia Geometry Lab 5

Internet
- See the Prentice Hall site. (http://www.phschool.com)

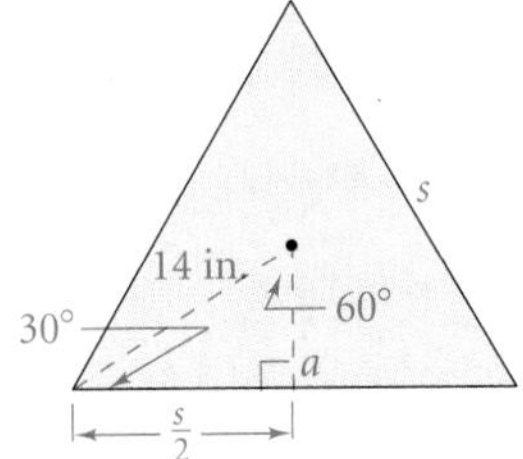

Use 30°-60°-90° △ to find the base and the height, $s = 14\sqrt{3}$ and $h = 21$. So the area is $\frac{1}{2}bh = 147\sqrt{3}$.

PROBLEM SOLVING

Look Back Check the solution to Example 3 by finding the area of the triangle using a different formula.

Example 3

Find the area of an equilateral triangle with radius 14 in. Leave your answer in simplest radical form.

You can use a 30°-60°-90° triangle to find the apothem a and the length of a side s.

$a = 7$	hypotenuse = 2 · shorter leg
$\frac{s}{2} = 7\sqrt{3}$	longer leg = $\sqrt{3}$ · shorter leg
$s = 14\sqrt{3}$	
$p = ns$	Find the perimeter.
$p = 3(14\sqrt{3})$	Substitute 3 for n and $14\sqrt{3}$ for s.
$= 42\sqrt{3}$	
$A = \frac{1}{2}ap$	Use the formula for area of a regular polygon.
$= \frac{1}{2}(7)(42\sqrt{3})$	Substitute 7 for a and $42\sqrt{3}$ for p.
$= 147\sqrt{3}$	

The area of the triangle is $147\sqrt{3}$ in.^{2}.

5. **Try This** Find the area of a square with radius 4 in. 32 in.^{2}

Exercises ON YOUR OWN

Each regular polygon has radii and an apothem as shown. Find the measure of each numbered angle.

1. 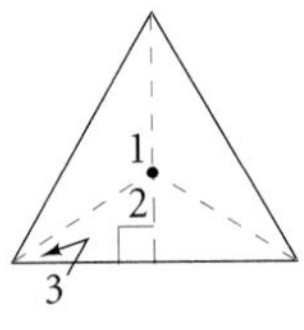

120; 60; 30

2. 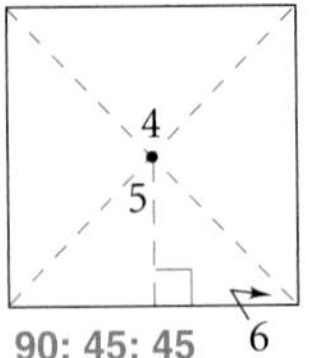

90; 45; 45

3. 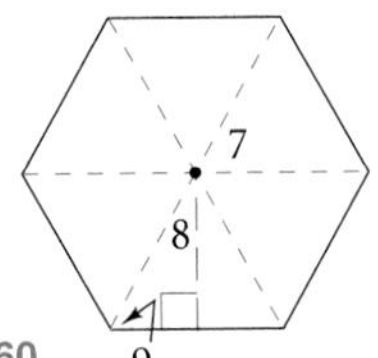

60; 30; 60

4. A regular pentagon has apothem 24.3 cm and side 35.4 cm. Find its area to the nearest tenth. 2150.6 cm^2

5. A regular octagon has apothem 60.5 in. and side 50 in. Find its area. 12,100 in.^{2}

6. The apothem of a regular decagon is 19 m. Each side is 12.4 m. Find its area. 1178 m^2

Calculator **Find the area of each regular polygon to the nearest tenth.**

7. 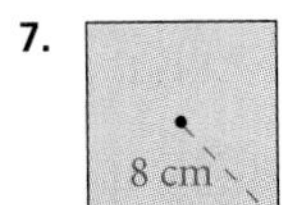

128 cm^2

8. 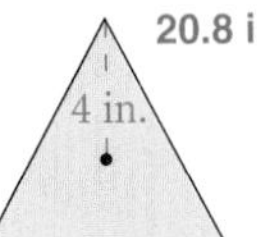

20.8 in.^{2}

9. 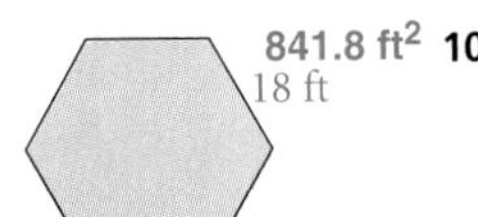

841.8 ft^2

10. 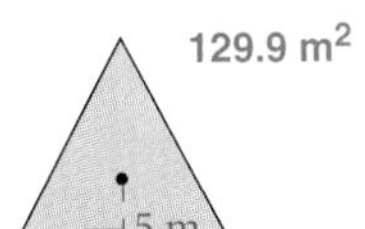

129.9 m^2

Exercise 12 Have students work in groups to formulate a plan for finding the lengths. You may want to suggest that they let *s* represent the length of a side. One plan might be to use the special right triangles to write expressions for the areas of each figure, set each area equal to 36, and solve for *s*.

WRITING Exercise 13 Ask students to name the theorem which they use in their explanation. Also have them draw several polygons labeling the measures of the radii and apothems.

OPEN-ENDED Exercises 14 Students may want to color and/or decorate their designs, which you may then display on a bulletin board in the classroom.

ALTERNATIVE ASSESSMENT Exercises 15–18 You can use these exercises to help you assess students' ability to use special right triangles in finding the lengths necessary to calculate the area of a regular polygon. Encourage students to use estimation to check that their answers are reasonable.

11. *Architecture* The floor of this gazebo is a regular octagon. Each side is 8 ft long, and its apothem is 9.7 ft. To the nearest tenth, find the area of the floor. **310.4 ft^2**

12. *Calculator* The area of a regular polygon is 36 in.^{2}. Find the length of a side if the polygon has the given number of sides. Round your answer to the nearest tenth.

a. 3 **9.1 in.** b. 4 **6 in.** c. 6 **3.7 in.**

d. *Estimation* Suppose the polygon is a pentagon. What would you expect the length of its side to be? Explain. **See margin.**

13. *Writing* Explain why the radius of a regular polygon cannot be less than the apothem. **The radius is the hypotenuse of a rt. △ with the apothem as one of its legs.**

14. *Open-ended* Create a design using equilateral triangles and regular hexagons that have sides of the same length. Find the area of the completed design. **See margin for sample.**

Find the area of each regular polygon with the given radius or apothem. Leave your answer in simplest radical form.

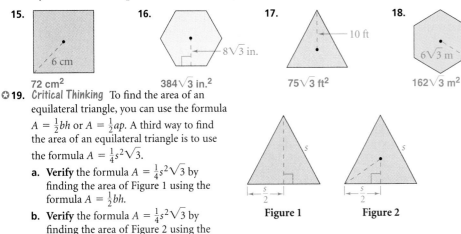

15.

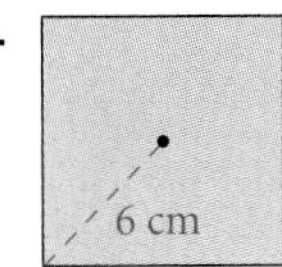

72 cm^2

16.

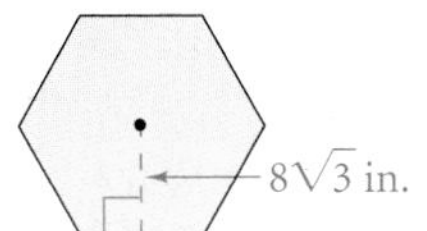

$384\sqrt{3}$ in.^{2}

17.

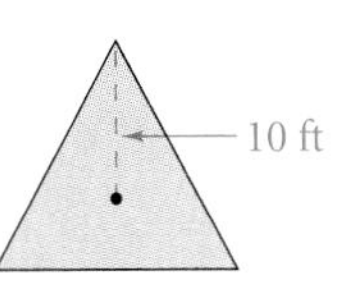

$75\sqrt{3}$ ft^2

18.

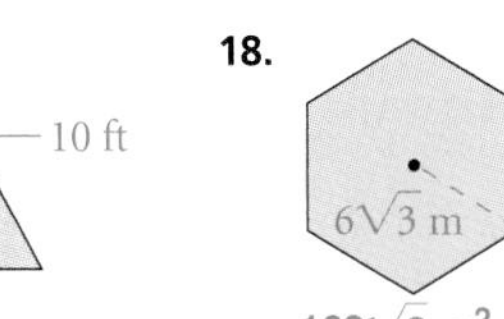

$162\sqrt{3}$ m^2

19. *Critical Thinking* To find the area of an equilateral triangle, you can use the formula $A = \frac{1}{2}bh$ or $A = \frac{1}{2}ap$. A third way to find the area of an equilateral triangle is to use the formula $A = \frac{1}{4}s^2\sqrt{3}$.

a. **Verify** the formula $A = \frac{1}{4}s^2\sqrt{3}$ by finding the area of Figure 1 using the formula $A = \frac{1}{2}bh$.

b. **Verify** the formula $A = \frac{1}{4}s^2\sqrt{3}$ by finding the area of Figure 2 using the formula $A = \frac{1}{2}ap$. **a–b. See margin.**

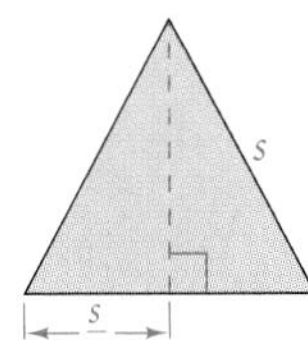

Figure 1

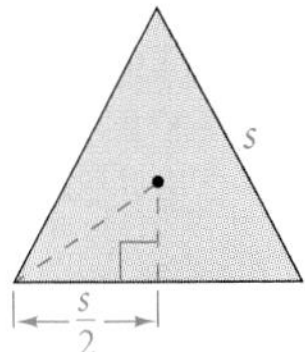

Figure 2

20. *Standardized Test Prep* A square and an equilateral triangle share a common side. What is the ratio of the area of the triangle to the area of the square? **C**

A. $1 : \sqrt{2}$ B. $\sqrt{2} : \sqrt{3}$ C. $\sqrt{3} : 4$ D. $\sqrt{2} : 1$ E. $\sqrt{3} : 1$

pages 276–278 On Your Own

12d. Answers may vary. Sample: about 4 in.; the length of a side of a pentagon should be between 3.7 in. and 6 in.

14.

$\frac{35}{2}\sqrt{3}$ unit^2

19a. $h = \frac{\sqrt{3}}{2}s$

$A = \frac{1}{2}hs = \left(\frac{1}{2} \cdot \frac{\sqrt{3}}{2}\right)s^2$

$A = \frac{\sqrt{3}}{4}s^2$

b. $a = \frac{\sqrt{3}}{6}s$

$A = \frac{1}{2}ap = \frac{1}{2}\left(\frac{\sqrt{3}}{6}s\right) \cdot 3s$

$A = \frac{\sqrt{3}}{4}s^2$

page 278 Mixed Review

27.

28.

29.

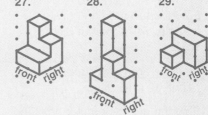

Exercises MIXED REVIEW

Exercises 27–29 Students will need isometric dot paper.

Exercise 30 Ask students to explain how they found the angle measures.

GETTING READY FOR LESSON 5-7 These exercises prepare students to find circumference and arc length.

Wrap Up

THE BIG IDEA Ask students: *Describe how to find the area of a regular polygon. Define any new terms used in your description.*

RETEACHING ACTIVITY Students verify the 45°-45°-90° Triangle Theorem by drawing a square and comparing the lengths of its side, apothem, and radius. (Reteaching worksheet 5-6)

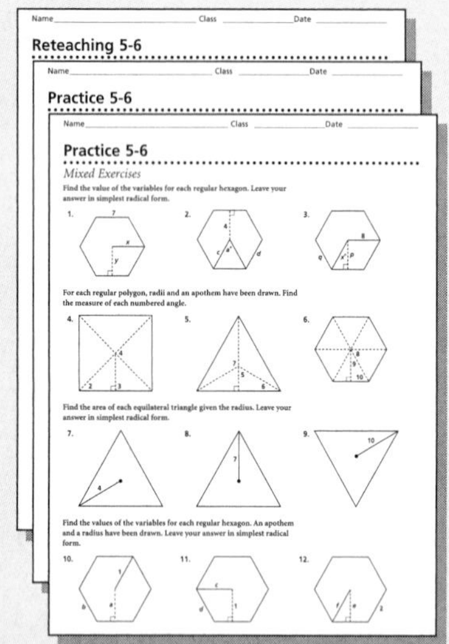

Reteaching 5-6

Practice 5-6

Practice 5-6

Mixed Exercises

Lesson Quiz

Lesson Quiz is also available in Transparencies.

For Exercises 1–4, leave answers in simplest radical form, if necessary.

1. Find the area of a regular octagon with apothem 11.3 in. and side length 9.4 in. 424.88 in.^{2}
2. Find the area of an equilateral triangle with apothem 6 cm. $108\sqrt{3}$ cm^2
3. Find the area of a square with radius 10 in. 200 in.^{2}
4. Find the area of regular hexagon with side length 12 ft. $216\sqrt{3}$ ft^2

21. *Coordinate Geometry* A regular octagon with center at the origin and radius 4 is graphed in the coordinate plane.

a. Since V_2 lies on the line $y = x$, its x- and y-coordinates are equal. Use the Distance Formula to find the coordinates of V_2 to the nearest tenth. a. (2.8, 2.8)

b. Use the coordinates of V_2 and the formula $A = \frac{1}{2}bh$ to find the area of $\triangle V_1OV_2$ to the nearest tenth.

c. Use your answer to part (b) to find the area of the octagon to the nearest tenth.

b. 5.6 units^2 c. 44.8 units^2

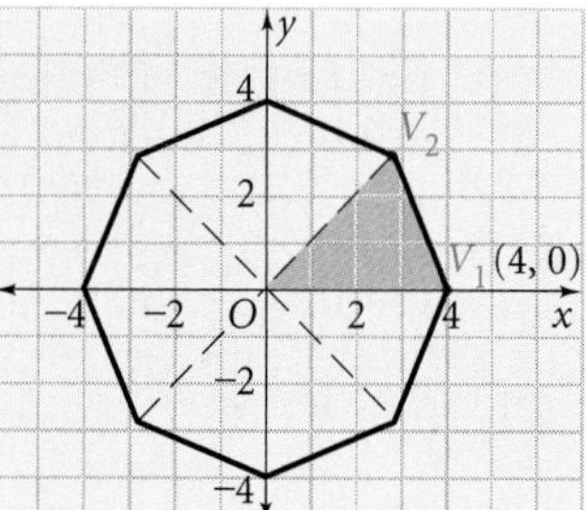

22. *Satellites* One of the smallest satellites ever developed is in the shape of a pyramid. Each of the four faces of the pyramid is an equilateral triangle with sides about 13 cm long. What is the area of one equilateral triangular face of the satellite? Round your answer to the nearest tenth. 73.2 cm^2

Find the area of each regular polygon. If your answer is not an integer, you may leave it in simplest radical form.

23.

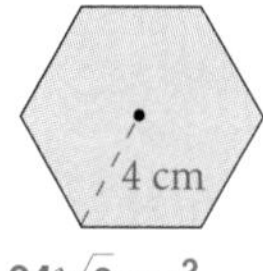

$24\sqrt{3}$ cm^2

24.

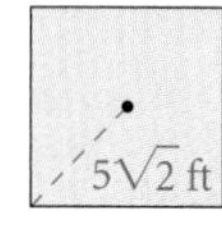

100 ft^2

25.

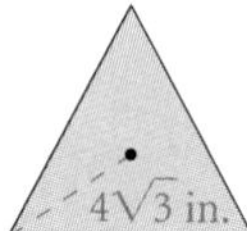

$36\sqrt{3}$ in.^{2}

26.

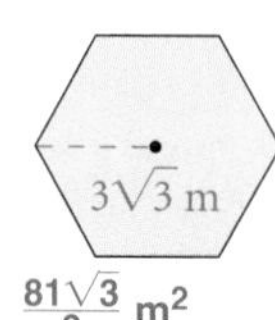

$\frac{81\sqrt{3}}{2}$ m^2

Exercises MIXED REVIEW

Create an isometric drawing for each foundation drawing. 27–29. See margin p. 277.

27.

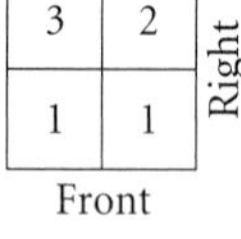

28.

5		
1	3	2

Right

Front

29.

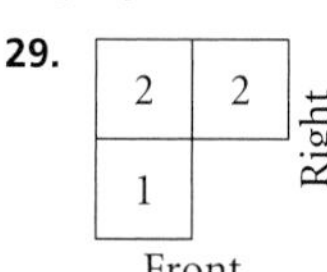

30. The measure of an angle is three more than twice the measure of its supplement. Find the measure of the angle. 121

Getting Ready for Lesson 5-7

Calculator **Evaluate each expression. Round your answer to the nearest hundredth.**

31. $2\pi r$ for $r = 4$ 25.13

32. πd for $d = 7.3$ 22.93

33. $2\pi r$ for $r = 5$ 31.42

34. πd for $d = 11.8$ 37.07

5-7 Teaching Notes

PROBLEM OF THE DAY

How can a doughnut be cut into equal pieces with three cuts of a knife? **Cut the doughnut lengthwise through its center, then cut it vertically, then horizontally.**

Problem of the Day is also available in Transparencies.

CONNECTING TO PRIOR KNOWLEDGE Draw the following circle on the board. Have student give an example of each arc and its measure.

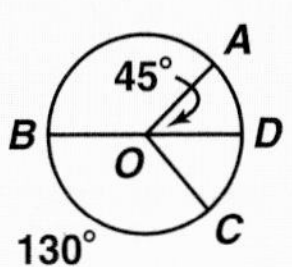
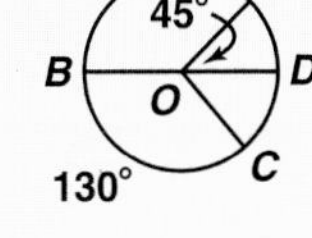

a. minor arc
b. major arc
c. semicircle

WORK TOGETHER

Have students measure objects that vary in size. If time allows, have students measure more than one object and/or collect data from other groups before making conjectures.

THINK AND DISCUSS

Example 1

ERROR ALERT! Some students may not differentiate between radius and diameter and use the incorrect formula.
Remediation: Review the definitions of diameter and radius. Also draw a circle showing a diameter labeled as two radii.

Connections Automobiles . . . and more

5-7 Circles: Circumference and Arc Length

What You'll Learn

- Finding the circumference of a circle and the length of an arc

...And Why

To solve problems involving auto safety, metalworking, and amusement park rides

What You'll Need

- circular objects
- string
- metric ruler
- calculator

WORK TOGETHER

Work in groups. Each member of your group should have one circular object such as a juice can or a jar lid.

- Measure the diameter of each circle to the nearest millimeter.
- Find the circumference of each circle by wrapping a string around each object. Straighten the string and measure its length to the nearest tenth of a centimeter.
- Organize your group's data in a table like the one below. Calculate the ratio $\frac{\text{circumference}}{\text{diameter}}$ to the nearest hundredth.

Name of Object	Circumference (C)	Diameter (d)	$\frac{C}{d}$
jelly-jar lid	19.6 cm	6.2 cm	3.16

1. Make a **conjecture** about the relationship between the circumference and the diameter of a circle. **The circumference is about 3 times the diameter.**

THINK AND DISCUSS

Part 1 

Circumference

The ratios you found in the Work Together are estimates of the number **pi** (π), the ratio of the circumference of a circle to its diameter.

Theorem 5-10 Circumference of a Circle

The circumference of a circle is π times the diameter.

$C = \pi d$ or $C = 2\pi r$

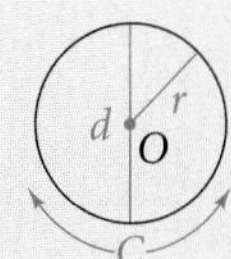

Example 1

Find the circumference of $\odot A$ and $\odot B$. Leave your answer in terms of π.

a.

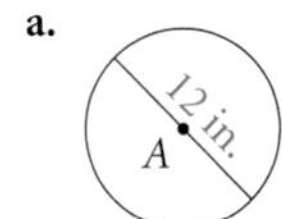

$C = \pi d$
$C = 12\pi$ in.

b.

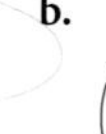

$C = 2\pi r$
$C = 2 \cdot \pi \cdot 5.3$
$C = 10.6\pi$ cm

2. **Try This** What is the radius of a circle with circumference 18π m? **9 m**

Lesson Planning Options

Prerequisite Skills

- Finding arc measures

Assignment Options for Exercises On Your Own

To provide flexible scheduling, this lesson can be subdivided into parts.

1 **Core** 1–8
Extension 26–27

2 **Core** 9–22, 24–25
Extension 23

Use Mixed Review to maintain skills.

Resources

Student Edition

Skills Handbook, pp. 660, 673
Extra Practice, p. 652
Glossary/Study Guide

Teaching Resources

Chapter Support File, Ch. 5
- Practice 5-7 (two worksheets)
- Reteaching 5-7
- Alternative Activity 5-7

Classroom Manager 5-7
Glossary, Spanish Resources

Transparencies

12, 63

DIVERSITY Tell students that the most decimal places to which π has been calculated is 2,260,321,336 by Gregory Volfovich and David Volfovich Chudnovsky in 1991, on their homemade computer in New York City. Also tell them that Hiroyuki Goto, 21, of Tokyo, Japan, recited π to 42,195 places on February 18, 1995. Then have them discuss why someone would want to do these calculations and memorizations. Help students see that some people enjoy these challenges.

ESTIMATION Make sure students understand that π is a constant, not a variable. Help them see that they can estimate the circumference of a circle by finding $6 \times r$ or $3 \times d$.

ESL Some students may confuse the term *circumference* with the term *circumscribe*, which they learned in Lesson 5-6. Emphasize that circumference is "the length around a circle" and circumscribe is a verb meaning "to draw around."

Example 2 **Relating to the Real World**

Discuss with students the meaning of the term "turning circle" and check that students understand the diagram. Help them see the connections to their previous study of rotations.

Point out to students that the circumferences of the outer circle and the inner circle are both written in terms of π. This makes subtraction easier and rounding errors are not introduced. Also point out that, depending on whether the π key or 3.14 is used, answers may vary slightly. Remind students that, even on a calculator, the π key gives only an approximation of π.

Additional Examples

FOR EXAMPLE 1

Find the circumference of the following circles. Leave your answers in terms of π.

a. a circle with diameter 16 cm

b. a circle with radius 4 in.

a. 16π cm   b. 8π in.

Discussion: *If the ratio of the diameters of two circles is 2:1, what is the ratio of their circumferences?*

FOR EXAMPLE 2

The radii of two concentric circles are 4.5 cm and 5.2 cm. How much greater is the circumference of the larger circle than that of the smaller circle? 1.4π

Discussion: *If the radius of a circle is increased by 1, how much does its circumference increase?*

FOR EXAMPLE 3

The diameter of a circle is 12 cm.

a. $\overset{\frown}{AB}$ has measure 60. Find its length. 2π

b. $\overset{\frown}{ACD}$ has measure 210. Find its length. 7π

Since the number π is irrational, you cannot write it as a decimal. You can use 3.14, $\frac{22}{7}$, or the π key on your calculator as approximations for π.

Two circles that lie in the same plane and have the same center are **concentric circles.**

Example 2 **Relating to the Real World**

16.1 ft
4.7 ft

Automobiles A manufacturer advertises that a new car has a turning radius of only 16.1 ft. The distance between the two front tires is 4.7 ft. How much farther do the outside tires have to travel in making a complete circle than the tires on the inside?

The outside and inside tires travel on concentric circles. The radius of the outer circle is 16.1 ft. To find the radius of the inner circle, you must subtract 4.7 ft.

circumference of outer circle $= 2\pi(16.1) = 32.2\pi$

radius of the inner circle $= 16.1 - 4.7 = 11.4$ ft

circumference of inner circle $= 2\pi(11.4) = 22.8\pi$

The difference in the two distances is $32.2\pi - 22.8\pi = 9.4\pi$.

9.4 [×] [π] [=] 29.530971

The outside tires travel about 29.5 ft farther than the inside tires.

3. Try This The diameter of a bicycle wheel is 26 in. To the nearest whole number, how many revolutions does the wheel make when the bicycle travels 100 yd? 44 revolutions

280

Question 3 Help students understand that as a bicycle makes one revolution, the distance the bicycle has traveled is the circumference of the wheel. Also check that students correctly convert yards to inches.

CONNECTING TO STUDENTS' WORLD Question 3 Have students measure the diameter of their bicycle tire or of a friend's bicycle tire. Have them calculate the number of revolutions the tire will make over a given distance.

Emphasize the difference between arc length and arc measure. Students may want to think of arc length as "distance" and arc measure as "amount of turn." Discuss real-world examples to illustrate the need for both measures.

Example 3

CRITICAL THINKING Ask students to explain why "$\pi(16)$" is used in part a and "$2\pi(15)$" is used in part b.

TACTILE LEARNING If you have block scheduling or an extended class period, have students investigate the formula for arc length using the circular objects from the Work Together as follows. Mark the endpoints of an arc. Roll the object along a ruler to measure the arc to the nearest millimeter. Then calculate the arc length by measuring the central angle and then using the formula. Compare the results.

Part 2

Arc Length

In Chapter 2 you found the measure of an arc in degrees. You can also find the **arc length,** which is a fraction of a circle's circumference.

An arc of 60° represents $\frac{60}{360}$ or $\frac{1}{6}$ of the circle. Its arc length is $\frac{1}{6}$ the circumference of the circle.

This observation suggests the following generalization.

Theorem 5-11
Arc Length

The length of an arc of a circle is the product of the ratio $\frac{\text{measure of the arc}}{360}$ and the circumference of the circle.

length of $\widehat{AB} = \frac{m\widehat{AB}}{360} \cdot 2\pi r$

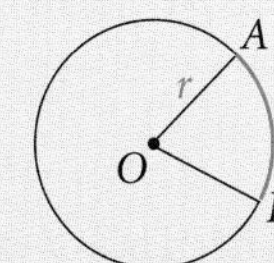

Example 3

Find the length of the arc shown in red on each circle. Leave your answer in terms of π.

a.

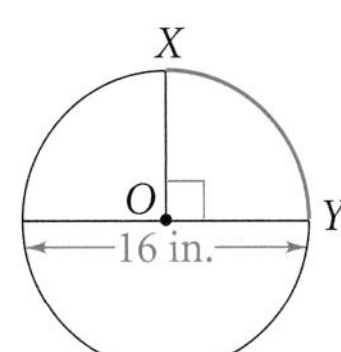

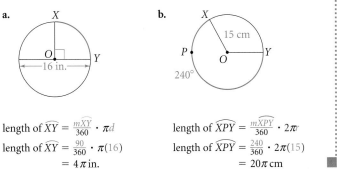

length of $\widehat{XY} = \frac{m\widehat{XY}}{360} \cdot \pi d$

length of $\widehat{XY} = \frac{90}{360} \cdot \pi(16)$

$= 4\pi$ in.

b.

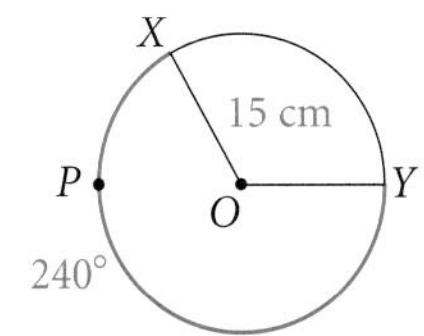

length of $\widehat{XPY} = \frac{m\widehat{XPY}}{360} \cdot 2\pi r$

length of $\widehat{XPY} = \frac{240}{360} \cdot 2\pi(15)$

$= 20\pi$ cm

4. **Try This** Find the length of a semicircle with radius 1.3 m. Leave your answer in terms of π. **1.3π m**
5. **Critical Thinking** Is it possible for two arcs of different circles to have the same measure, but different lengths? Support your answer with an example. **Yes; see margin p. 282 for diagram.**
6. **Critical Thinking** Is it possible for two arcs of different circles to have the same length but have different measures? Support your answer with an example. **Yes; see margin p. 282 for diagram.**

Your answers to Questions 5 and 6 illustrate that for arcs to be congruent two things must be true. **Congruent arcs** are arcs that have the same measure and are in the same circle or in congruent circles.

Technology Options

Students may use a graphing program to solve Exercise 14.

Prentice Hall Technology

Software
- Secondary Math Lab Toolkit™
- Integrated Math Lab 32
- Computer Item Generator 5-7

Internet
- See the Prentice Hall site. (http://www.phschool.com)

Exercises ON YOUR OWN

Exercises 5–8 You may want to have all students use the π key so that all students' answers should be the same.

Mental Math Exercises 10–12 Suggest students use mental math to answer these exercises.

ALTERNATIVE ASSESSMENT **Exercise 13** This exercise can be used to help you assess students' understanding of circumference by noting their ability to find the diameter and radius of a circle given its circumference.

OPEN-ENDED **Exercise 18** You may want to suggest to students having difficulty with this problem that they consider drawing concentric circles.

pages 279–281 Think and Discuss

5. Sample:

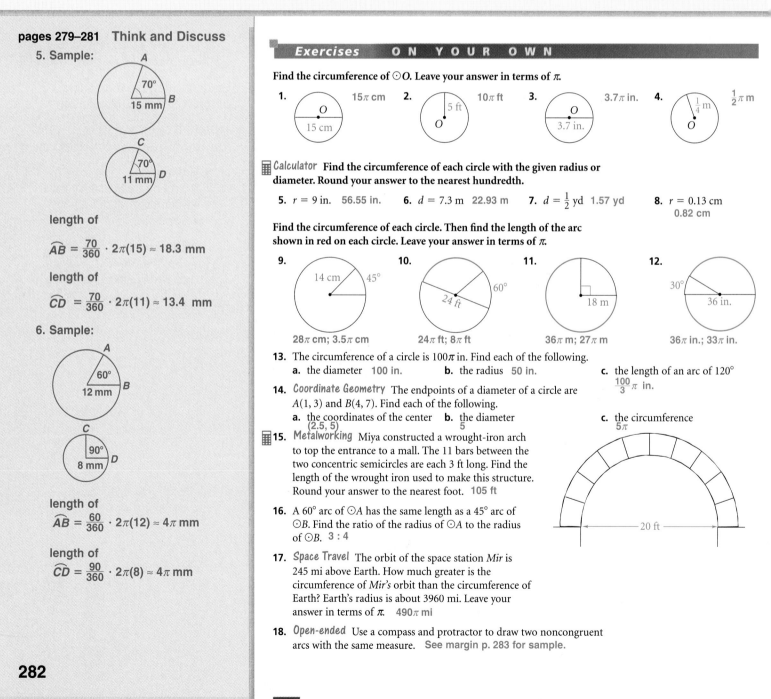

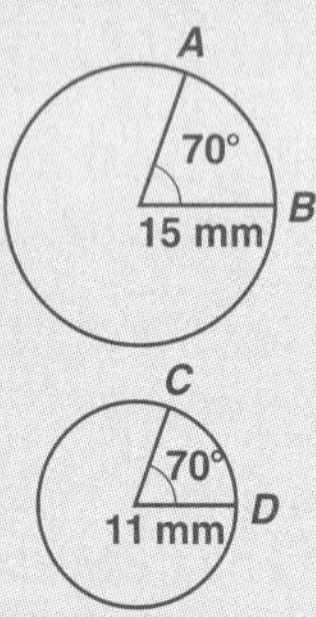

length of

$\widehat{AB} = \frac{70}{360} \cdot 2\pi(15) \approx 18.3$ mm

length of

$\widehat{CD} = \frac{70}{360} \cdot 2\pi(11) \approx 13.4$ mm

6. Sample:

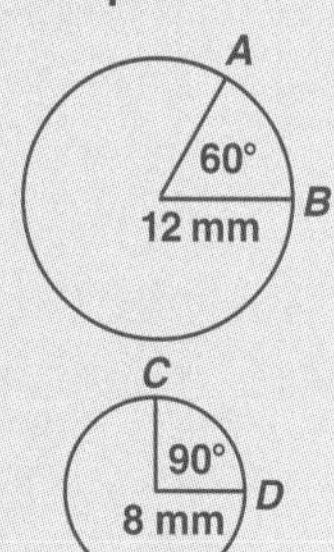

length of

$\widehat{AB} = \frac{60}{360} \cdot 2\pi(12) \approx 4\pi$ mm

length of

$\widehat{CD} = \frac{90}{360} \cdot 2\pi(8) \approx 4\pi$ mm

282

Exercises ON YOUR OWN

Find the circumference of $\odot O$. Leave your answer in terms of π.

1. 15 cm (diameter) — 15π cm
2. 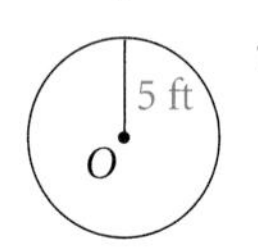

10π ft
3. 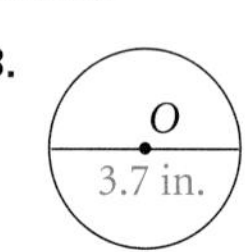

3.7π in.
4. 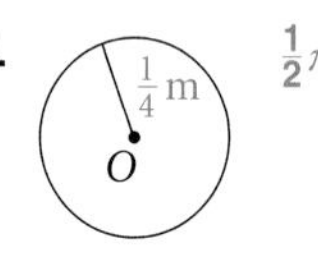

$\frac{1}{2}\pi$ m

Calculator **Find the circumference of each circle with the given radius or diameter. Round your answer to the nearest hundredth.**

5. $r = 9$ in. 56.55 in.
6. $d = 7.3$ m 22.93 m
7. $d = \frac{1}{2}$ yd 1.57 yd
8. $r = 0.13$ cm 0.82 cm

Find the circumference of each circle. Then find the length of the arc shown in red on each circle. Leave your answer in terms of π.

9. 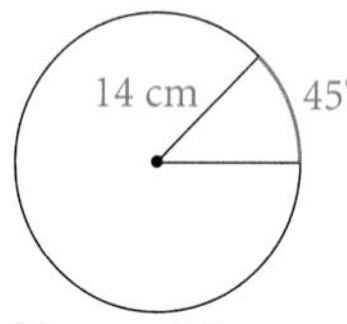

28π cm; 3.5π cm
10. 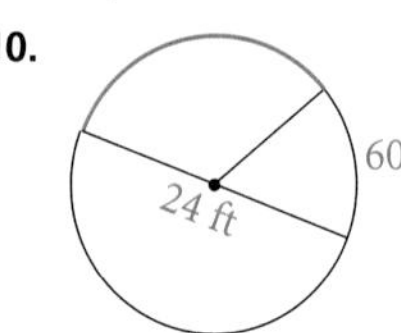

24π ft; 8π ft
11. 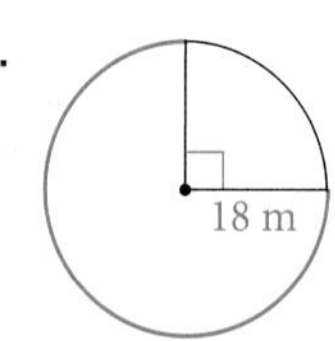

36π m; 27π m
12. 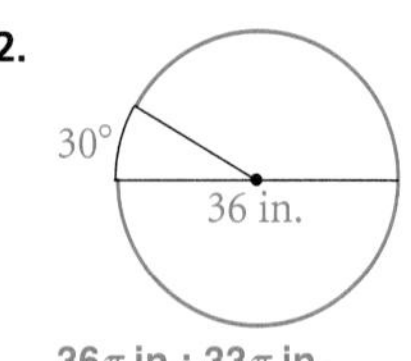

36π in.; 33π in.

13. The circumference of a circle is 100π in. Find each of the following.
    a. the diameter 100 in.
    b. the radius 50 in.
    c. the length of an arc of 120° $\frac{100}{3}\pi$ in.
14. **Coordinate Geometry** The endpoints of a diameter of a circle are $A(1, 3)$ and $B(4, 7)$. Find each of the following.
    a. the coordinates of the center (2.5, 5)
    b. the diameter 5
    c. the circumference 5π
15. **Metalworking** Miya constructed a wrought-iron arch to top the entrance to a mall. The 11 bars between the two concentric semicircles are each 3 ft long. Find the length of the wrought iron used to make this structure. Round your answer to the nearest foot. 105 ft

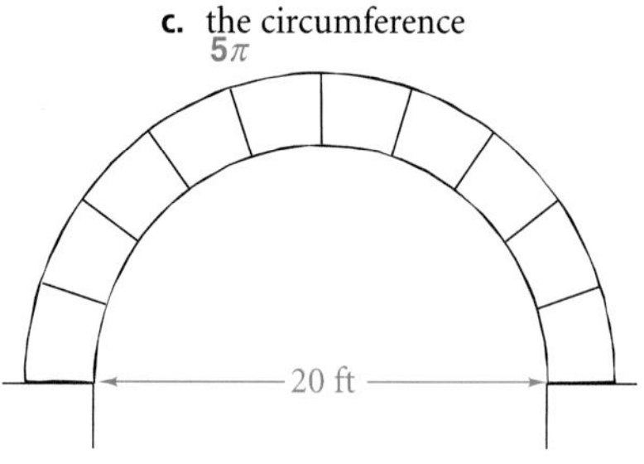

16. A 60° arc of $\odot A$ has the same length as a 45° arc of $\odot B$. Find the ratio of the radius of $\odot A$ to the radius of $\odot B$. 3 : 4
17. **Space Travel** The orbit of the space station *Mir* is 245 mi above Earth. How much greater is the circumference of *Mir's* orbit than the circumference of Earth? Earth's radius is about 3960 mi. Leave your answer in terms of π. 490π mi
18. **Open-ended** Use a compass and protractor to draw two noncongruent arcs with the same measure. See margin p. 283 for sample.

Exercise 23 Help students see this problem from more than one perspective by having them discuss how they found the answer.

STANDARDIZED TEST TIP **Exercise 24** Point out to students that leaving their work in terms of π saves computation time.

CARTOON **Exercise 26** Make sure that students understand the explanation in the cartoon. Ask them to think of other examples where two objects spin in concentric circles at different speeds. One example is a pair of ice skaters skating in a circle. The ice skater on the outside of the circle must skate faster than the ice skater on the inside of the circle.

Calculator **Find the length of the arc shown in red on each circle. Round your answer to the nearest hundredth.**

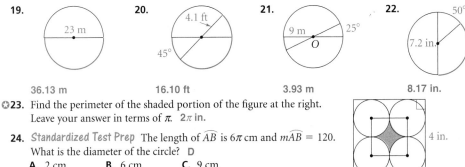

19. 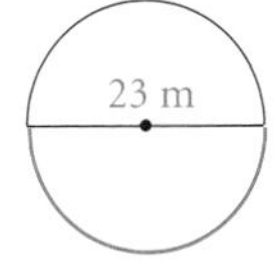
23 m
36.13 m

20. 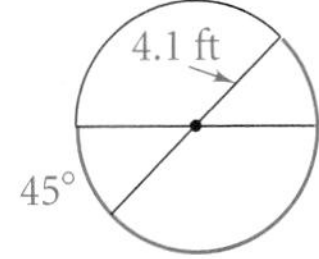
4.1 ft
45°
16.10 ft

21. 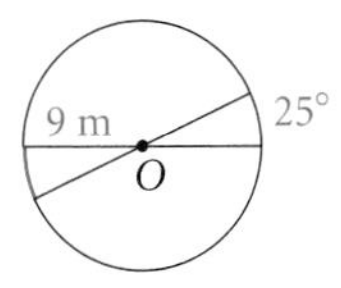
9 m
25°
O
3.93 m

22. 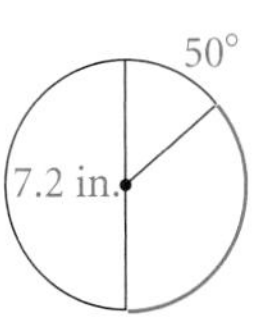
50°
7.2 in.
8.17 in.

23. Find the perimeter of the shaded portion of the figure at the right. Leave your answer in terms of π. **2π in.**

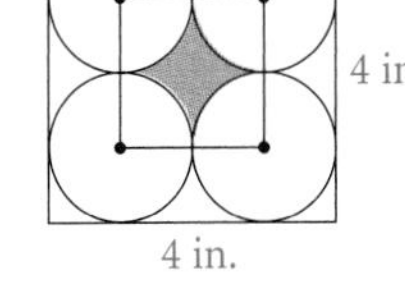
4 in.
4 in.

24. *Standardized Test Prep* The length of $\widehat{AB}$ is 6π cm and $m\widehat{AB} = 120$. What is the diameter of the circle? **D**
    A. 2 cm
    B. 6 cm
    C. 9 cm
    D. 18 cm
    E. 24 cm

25. *Coordinate Geometry* Find the length of a semicircle with endpoints (3, 7) and (3, −1). Round your answer to the nearest tenth. **12.6**

CALVIN AND HOBBES by Bill Watterson

PLAYING A RECORD? I'LL SHOW YOU SOMETHING INTERESTING.
© 1990 Universal Press Syndicate
6-28

COMPARE A POINT ON THE LABEL WITH A POINT ON THE RECORD'S OUTER EDGE. THEY BOTH MAKE A COMPLETE CIRCLE IN THE SAME AMOUNT OF TIME, RIGHT?
YEAH...

BUT THE POINT ON THE RECORD'S EDGE HAS TO MAKE A BIGGER CIRCLE IN THE SAME TIME, SO IT GOES FASTER. SEE, TWO POINTS ON ONE DISK MOVE AT TWO SPEEDS, EVEN THOUGH THEY BOTH MAKE THE SAME REVOLUTIONS PER MINUTE!

Cartoon **Use what you learned from Calvin's father to answer the following questions.**

26. In one revolution, how much farther does a point 10 cm from the center of the record travel than a point 3 cm from the center? Round your answer to the nearest hundredth. **43.98 cm**

27. *Writing* Kendra and her mother plan to ride the merry-go-round. Two horses on the merry-go-round are side by side. For a more exciting ride, should Kendra sit on the inside or the outside? Explain your reasoning. **See margin.**

pages 282–283 On Your Own

18. Sample:

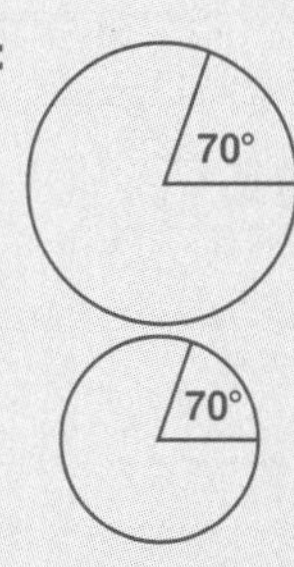
70°
70°

27. Outside; the outside horse is further away from the center than the inside horse. It moves faster because, in a given amount of time, it covers a greater distance.

page 284 Mixed Review

28. 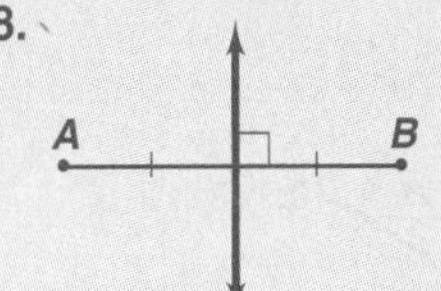
A
B

29. 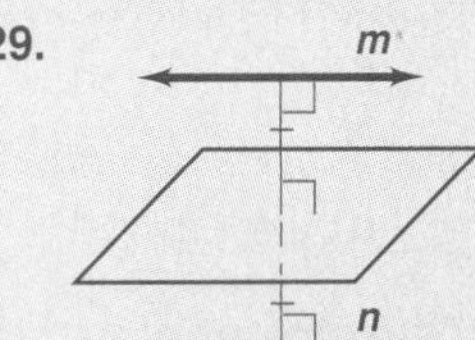
m
n

Exercises MIXED REVIEW

TRANSFORMATIONS Exercise 30 You may want students to include a graph with their answer.

GETTING READY FOR LESSON 5-8 These exercises prepare students to find the area of a circle.

Wrap Up

THE BIG IDEA Ask students: *Explain how you find the length of an arc. Define any new vocabulary you use in your explanation.*

RETEACHING ACTIVITY Students draw a circle and an arc. Then they calculate the length of the arc and measure its length using string. (Reteaching worksheet 5-7)

Exercises CHECKPOINT

In this Checkpoint, your students will assess their own progress in Lessons 5-5 to 5-7.

Exercises 2–3 Students who have trouble with these exercises should review their answers to Exercises 1 and 3 on page 276 and also review special right triangles.

WRITING Exercise 10 Check that students use geometry vocabulary correctly in their explanations.

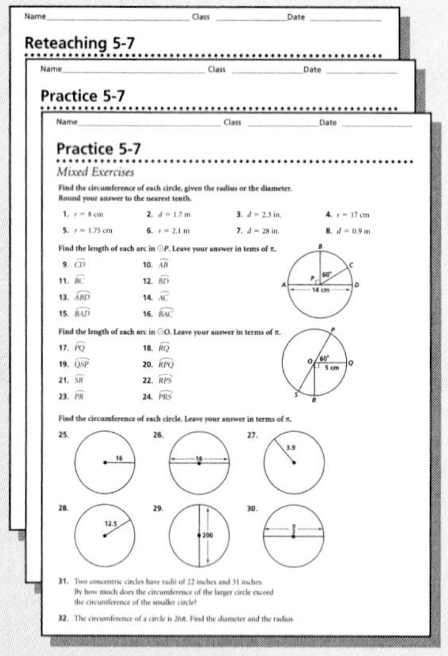
Reteaching 5-7
Practice 5-7
Practice 5-7
Mixed Exercises

Lesson Quiz

Lesson Quiz is also available in Transparencies.

For Exercises 1–4, leave your answers in terms of π.

1. Find the circumference of a circle with radius 2.7 in. **5.4π in.**
2. Find the radius of a circle with circumference 10.2π cm. **5.1 cm**
3. A circle has a diameter of length 9 cm. Find the length of $\widehat{AC}$ on the circle if $\widehat{AC}$ measures 45°. **$\frac{9\pi}{8}$ cm**
4. A circle has a radius of length 18 cm. Find the length of $\widehat{QRS}$ on the circle if $\widehat{QRS}$ measures 270°. **27π cm**

Exercises MIXED REVIEW

Locus **Sketch and label each locus.** 28–29. See margin p. 283.

28. all points in a plane equidistant from points A and B
29. all points in space equidistant from parallel lines m and n

30. *Transformations* A triangle has vertices $A(3, 2)$, $B(4, 1)$, and $C(4, 3)$. Find the coordinates of the image of the triangle under a glide reflection in $\langle 0, 1\rangle$ and $x = 0$. $A'(-3, 3)$, $B'(-4, 2)$, $C'(-4, 4)$

Getting Ready for Lesson 5-8

Estimation **A circle is drawn on three different grids. Use the scale of each grid to estimate the area of each circle in square inches.** 31–33. Estimates may vary slightly.

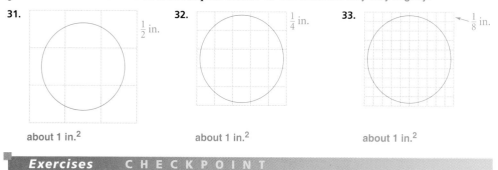

31. $\frac{1}{2}$ in. — about 1 in.^{2}
32. $\frac{1}{4}$ in. — about 1 in.^{2}
33. $\frac{1}{8}$ in. — about 1 in.^{2}

Exercises CHECKPOINT

Find the area of each trapezoid or regular polygon. Leave your answer in simplest radical form.

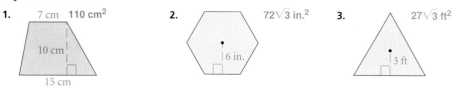

1. 7 cm, 10 cm, 15 cm — 110 cm^2
2. 6 in. — $72\sqrt{3}\text{ in.}^2$
3. 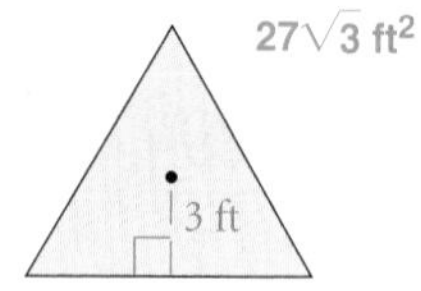

$27\sqrt{3}\text{ ft}^2$

Calculator **Find the circumference of a circle with the given radius. Round your answer to the nearest hundredth.**

4. 8 in. 50.27 in.
5. 2 m 12.57 m
6. 5 ft 31.42 ft
7. 1.4 km 8.80 km
8. 9 mm 56.55 mm

9. In a circle of radius 18 mm, $m\widehat{AB} = 45$. Find the length of $\widehat{AB}$. Leave your answer in terms of π. 4.5π mm

10. *Writing* Explain at least two ways to find the area of an equilateral triangle. Use an example to illustrate your explanation. Answers may vary. See back of book for sample.

5-8 Teaching Notes

PROBLEM OF THE DAY

If the points shown are equally spaced, and if each arc measures 180, find the length of the path along the arcs from *A* to *B*. 6.5π

A B

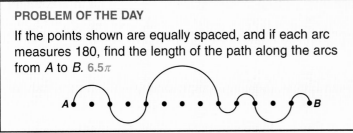

Problem of the Day is also available in Transparencies.

CONNECTING TO PRIOR KNOWLEDGE Draw a circle and a diameter. Label it 12 cm. Ask students to identify the following:

a. d **b.** r **c.** $2r$ **d.** r^2

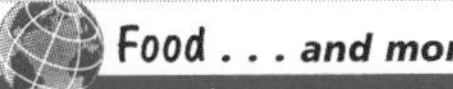

WORK TOGETHER

DIVERSITY It is important that students cut the circle and its wedges carefully so that the resulting figure will look like a parallelogram. Students who have physical or visual difficulties may have trouble and should be paired with students who can help them fold and cut accurately.

THINK AND DISCUSS

ERROR ALERT! Theorem 5-12 Some students will confuse doubling the radius with squaring the radius. **Remediation:** Point out that squaring a number means multiplying the number by itself. Then have students practice several examples.

Connections Food . . . and more

5-8 Areas of Circles, Sectors, and Segments of Circles

What You'll Learn

- Computing the areas of circles, sectors, and segments of circles

...And Why

To solve real-world problems in food preparation, archaeology, and biology

What You'll Need

- compass
- scissors
- tape

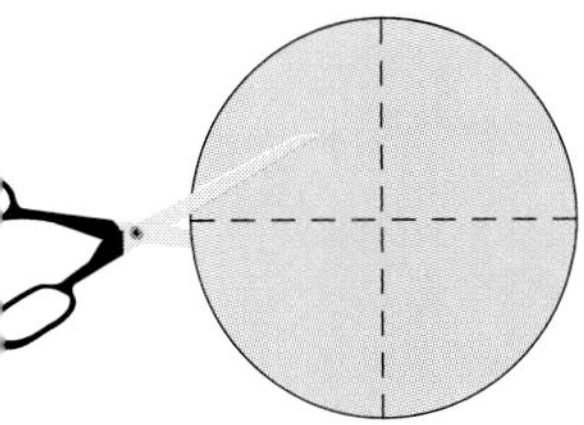

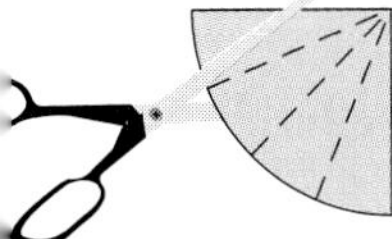

WORK TOGETHER

Work in groups. Have each member of your group use a compass to draw a large circle. Fold the circle in half horizontally and vertically. Cut the circle into four wedges on the fold lines. Then fold each wedge into quarters. Cut each wedge on the fold lines. You will have 16 wedges. Tape the wedges to a piece of paper to form the figure below.

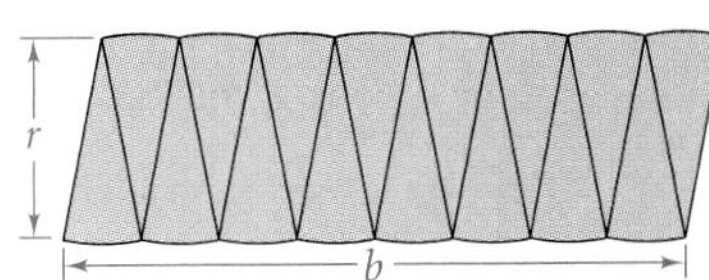

1. How does the area of the figure compare with the area of the circle? They are =.
2. The base of the figure is formed by arcs of the circle. Write an equation relating the length of the base b to the circumference C of the circle. $b = \frac{1}{2}C$
3. Write an equation for the length of the base b in terms of the radius r of the circle. $b = \pi r$
4. If you increase the number of wedges, the figure you create becomes more and more like a rectangle with base b and height r. Write an expression for the area of the rectangle in terms of r. πr^2

THINK AND DISCUSS

Part 1

Areas of Circles

Your observations in the Work Together suggest the following theorem.

Theorem 5-12
Area of a Circle

The area of a circle is the product of π and the square of the radius.

$A = \pi r^2$

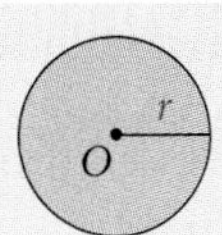

5. **Try This** What is the area of a circle with radius 15 cm? Leave your answer in terms of π. 225π cm^2

Lesson Planning Options

Prerequisite Skills

- Finding areas of parallelograms
- Finding the measures of arcs

Assignment Options for Exercises On Your Own

To provide flexible scheduling, this lesson can be subdivided into parts.

 1 **Core** 1–10
Extension 11

2 **Core** 12–23, 28–29
Extension 24–27

Use Mixed Review to maintain skills.

Resources

Student Edition
Skills Handbook, pp. 670, 673
Extra Practice, p. 652
Glossary/Study Guide

Teaching Resources
Chapter Support File, Ch. 5
- Practice 5-8 (two worksheets)
- Reteaching 5-8

Classroom Manager 5-8
Glossary, Spanish Resources

Transparencies
12, 63, 67

Example 1 Relating to the Real World 

TACTILE LEARNING Have students work in groups to make two large rectangles by taping together four pieces of one-inch graph paper, being careful to align the grid lines. Then have them draw a 10-in. circle and a 12-in. circle on each. Ask students to approximate the number of square inches in each circle. Have them compare their approximations with $25\pi \approx 78.5$ and $36\pi \approx 113.1$

EXTENSION An interesting extension to this problem is: *If a small slice is one-eighth of a small pizza, how many small slices would equal the amount of pizza in a medium pizza?* about $11\frac{1}{2}$

CONNECTING TO STUDENTS' WORLD Question 6 Have students contact a local pizza restaurant to find out the diameters and prices of a small and a large pizza. Have them determine which pizza is a better buy. Discuss how the pizza problem assumes consistent thickness, which may or may not be the case in real life.

VISUAL LEARNING Use physical models if possible. Trivial Pursuit™ pieces are good models of sectors. Have students brainstorm other real-world examples of sectors such as a piece of pie, a piece of watermelon, or the section between two hands on a clock.

Theorem 5-13 Have students compare the similarities and differences between finding the length of an arc and finding the area of a sector.

Additional Examples

FOR EXAMPLE 1

A goat is tied with a rope 8 m long. How much more area does the goat have access to if the 8-m rope is replaced with a 9-m rope? Round your answer to the nearest meter.

area of 8-m grazing circle $= 8^2\pi = 64\pi$

area of 9-m grazing circle $= 9^2\pi = 81\pi$

difference in area $= 17\pi \approx 53$

The goat has an additional 53 m².

FOR EXAMPLE 2

A circle has diameter 14 in. What is the area of a sector bounded by an 80° arc? Round your answer to the nearest tenth. 34.2 in.²

FOR EXAMPLE 3

A circle has radius 8 cm. Find the area of a segment of the circle bounded by a 120° arc. Round your answer to the nearest tenth.

area of sector $= \frac{120}{360}(64\pi) = \frac{64\pi}{3}$

area of triangle $= \frac{1}{2}(8\sqrt{3} \times 4) = 16\sqrt{3}$

area of segment $= \frac{64\pi}{3} - 16\sqrt{3} \approx 39.3$

39.3 cm²

Example 1 Relating to the Real World

Food The diameter of a small pizza is 10 in. How much more pizza do you get if you order a medium pizza with diameter 12 in.?

radius of small pizza $= \frac{10}{2} = 5$ $\quad r = \frac{d}{2}$

radius of medium pizza $= \frac{12}{2} = 6$ $\quad r = \frac{d}{2}$

Use the formula for the area of a circle.

area of small pizza $= \pi(5)^2 = 25\pi$ $\quad A = \pi r^2$

area of medium pizza $= \pi(6)^2 = 36\pi$ $\quad A = \pi r^2$

difference in area $= 36\pi - 25\pi = 11\pi$

11 [×] [π] [=] 34.557519

The medium pizza has about 35 in.² more pizza than the small pizza.

See margin p. 288.

6. Suppose the small pizza in Example 1 costs $5.00 and the medium pizza costs $6.00. Which pizza is a better buy? Explain your answer.

Part 2 Sectors and Segments

A **sector of a circle** is the region bounded by two radii and their intercepted arc. A slice of pizza is an example of a sector of a circle. You name a sector using one endpoint of the arc, the center of the circle, and the other endpoint of the arc. Sector *XOY* is at the left.

The area of a sector is a fractional part of the area of a circle. The ratio of a sector's area to a circle's area is $\frac{\text{measure of the arc}}{360}$.

Theorem 5-13 Area of a Sector of a Circle

The area of a sector of a circle is the product of the ratio $\frac{\text{measure of the arc}}{360}$ and the area of the circle.

Area of sector $AOB = \frac{m\overset{\frown}{AB}}{360} \cdot \pi r^2$

A, r, O, B

Example 2

Have students estimate the area of the sector as a little less than one-fourth the area of the circle, $\frac{1}{4}(400\pi)$, and compare the estimate to the solution.

Question 7 Students may have difficulty with the calculations because $\frac{125}{360}$ does not simplify to a simple fraction. Have students write down the keystrokes they would use and then compare them with others. Students should see that there is more than one correct way to enter the keystrokes. Discuss how this illustrates the Commutative Property.

ERROR ALERT! Some students may be confused by the terms *segment* and *segment of a circle.* **Remediation:** Point out how the terms are related (a segment of a circle is formed by a line segment and an arc) and how they are different (a line segment has length and a segment of a circle has area).

Example 3

Point out that sometimes the term *segment* refers to a segment of a circle. Students can use the context in which the term is used and the diagram to determine whether the word *segment* refers to a line segment or a segment of a circle.

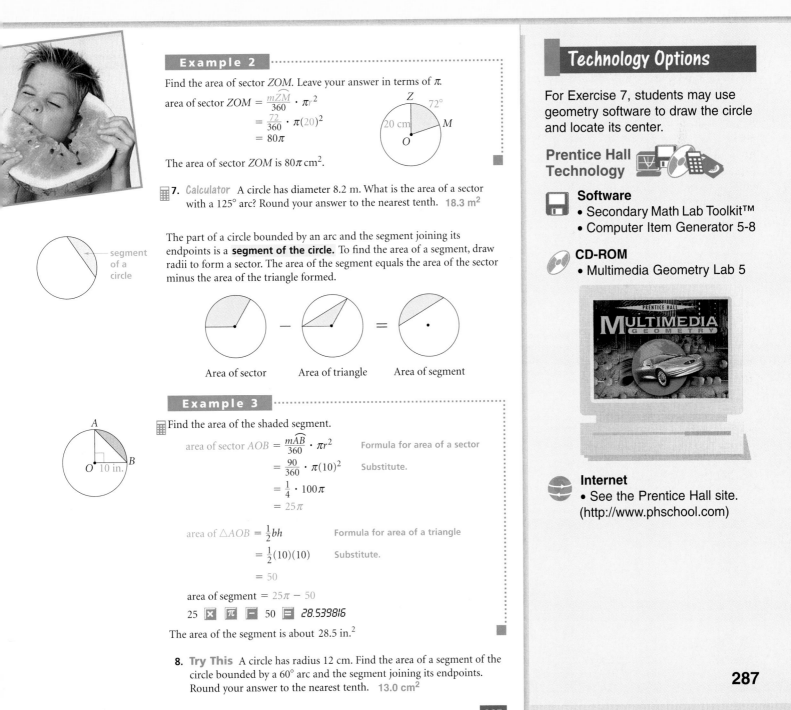

Example 2

Find the area of sector ZOM. Leave your answer in terms of π.

$$\text{area of sector } ZOM = \frac{m\overset{\frown}{ZM}}{360} \cdot \pi r^2$$
$$= \frac{72}{360} \cdot \pi(20)^2$$
$$= 80\pi$$

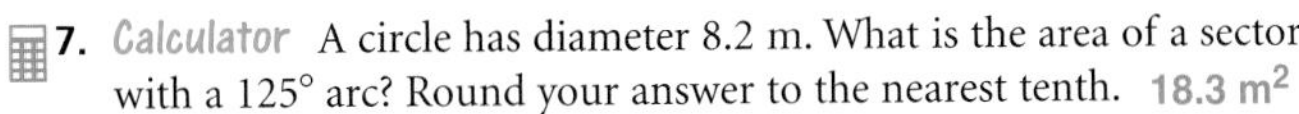

The area of sector ZOM is 80π cm^2.

7. Calculator A circle has diameter 8.2 m. What is the area of a sector with a 125° arc? Round your answer to the nearest tenth. 18.3 m^2

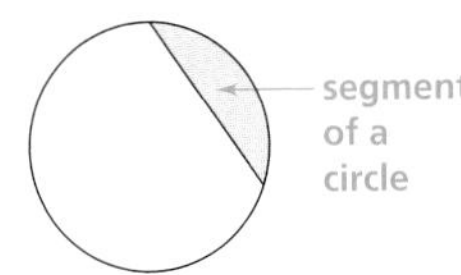

The part of a circle bounded by an arc and the segment joining its endpoints is a **segment of the circle.** To find the area of a segment, draw radii to form a sector. The area of the segment equals the area of the sector minus the area of the triangle formed.

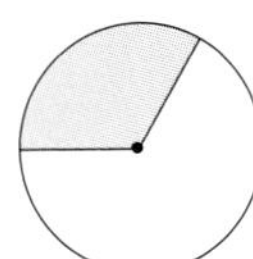

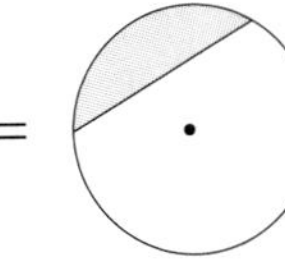

Area of sector — Area of triangle = Area of segment

Example 3

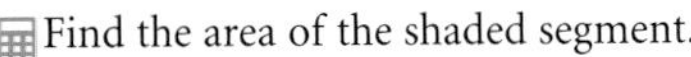

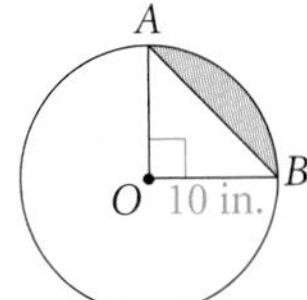

Find the area of the shaded segment.

$$\text{area of sector } AOB = \frac{m\overset{\frown}{AB}}{360} \cdot \pi r^2 \quad \text{Formula for area of a sector}$$
$$= \frac{90}{360} \cdot \pi(10)^2 \quad \text{Substitute.}$$
$$= \frac{1}{4} \cdot 100\pi$$
$$= 25\pi$$

$$\text{area of } \triangle AOB = \frac{1}{2}bh \quad \text{Formula for area of a triangle}$$
$$= \frac{1}{2}(10)(10) \quad \text{Substitute.}$$
$$= 50$$

$$\text{area of segment} = 25\pi - 50$$

25 [×] [π] [−] 50 [=] 28.539816

The area of the segment is about 28.5 in.^{2}

8. **Try This** A circle has radius 12 cm. Find the area of a segment of the circle bounded by a 60° arc and the segment joining its endpoints. Round your answer to the nearest tenth. 13.0 cm^2

Technology Options

For Exercise 7, students may use geometry software to draw the circle and locate its center.

Prentice Hall Technology

Software
- Secondary Math Lab Toolkit™
- Computer Item Generator 5-8

CD-ROM
- Multimedia Geometry Lab 5

Internet
- See the Prentice Hall site. (http://www.phschool.com)

Exercises ON YOUR OWN

Exercises 1–4 Use these exercises to check that students substitute r, not d, into πr^2 and correctly evaluate r^2. In Exercise 3, some students may have trouble finding one-half of $\frac{3}{4}$.

Exercise 5 Have students explain how they found the diameter. Make sure that they take the square root of 225 before doubling it.

Exercise 11 Help students see that the radius of the circle that the diver can cover is the shorter leg of the right triangle formed by the diver's line and a line perpendicular to the floor of the ocean.

ESTIMATION Exercises 12–15 Encourage students to use estimation to check the reasonableness of their answers.

ESL Exercise 16 Some students will not know what a dartboard is. Draw a sketch on the board of a dartboard with concentric circles and one with sectors. Ask students what they are called in their native languages.

pages 285–287 Think and Discuss

6. Medium; the cost per $in.^2$ is about 6 cents for the small pizza and about 5 cents for the medium pizza.

Exercises ON YOUR OWN

Find the area of each circle. Leave your answers in terms of π.

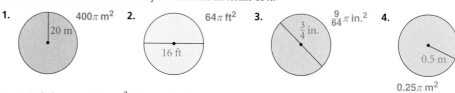

1. 20 m — 400π m^2

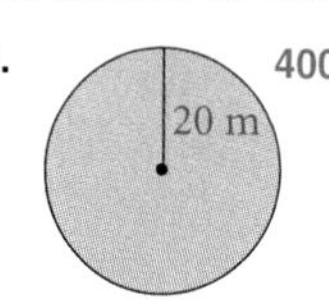

2. 16 ft — 64π ft^2
3. $\frac{3}{4}$ in. — $\frac{9}{64}\pi$ $in.^2$
4. 0.5 m — 0.25π m^2

5. A circle has area 225π m^2. What is its diameter? 30 m
6. How many circles with radius 4 in. will have the same total area as a circle with radius 12 in.? 9
7. *Coordinate Geometry* The endpoints of a diameter of $\odot A$ are (2, 1) and (5, 5). Find the area of $\odot A$. Leave your answer in terms of π. 6.25π $units^2$

Calculator Find the area of each circle. Round your answer to the nearest hundredth.

8. $r = 7$ ft — 153.94 ft^2
9. $d = 8.3$ m — 54.11 m^2
10. $d = 0.24$ cm — 0.05 cm^2

11. *Archaeology* Off the coast of Sweden, divers are working to bring up artifacts from a ship that sank several hundred years ago. The line to a diver is 100 ft long, and the diver is working at a depth of 80 ft. What is the area of the circle that the diver can cover? Round your answer to the nearest square foot. 11,310 ft^2

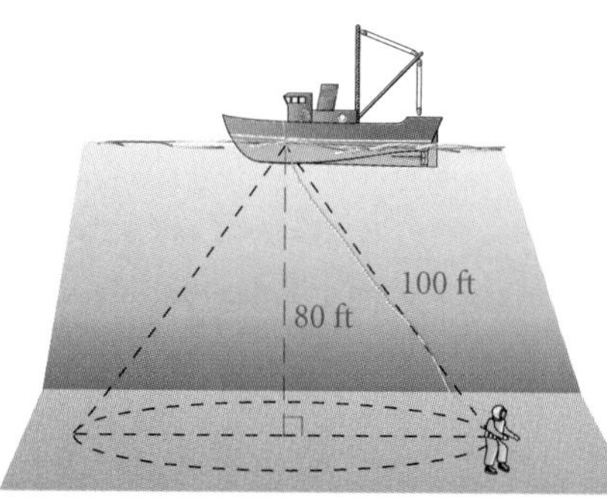

Find the area of each shaded sector of a circle. Leave your answer in terms of π.

12. 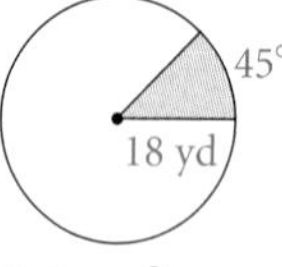

40.5π yd^2

13. 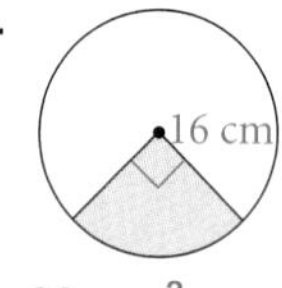

64π cm^2

14. 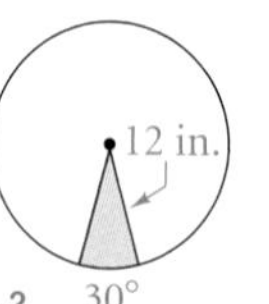

12π $in.^2$

15. 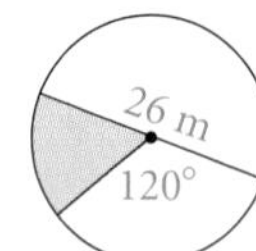

$\frac{169}{6}\pi$ m^2

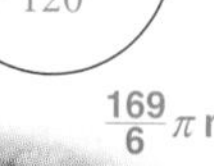

16. *Games* A dartboard has a diameter of 20 in. and is divided into 20 congruent sectors. Find the area of one sector. Round your answer to the nearest tenth. 15.7 $in.^2$
17. *Animal Habitats* In the Pacific Northwest, a red fox has a circular home range with a radius of about 718 m. To the nearest thousand, about how many square meters are in a red fox's home range? 1,620,000 m^2

ALTERNATIVE ASSESSMENT **Exercises 18–21** These exercises can be used to help you assess students' understanding of the objectives of this lesson: computing areas of circles, sectors, and segments. Have students write the formula(s) they use for each problem.

Exercises 24–27 This set of exercises can be a nice group activity. Have students work together on a plan for solving each exercise.

Calculator **Find the area of each shaded segment of a circle. Round your answer to the nearest hundredth.**

18. 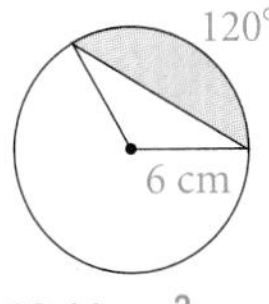

$22.11\ \text{cm}^2$

19. 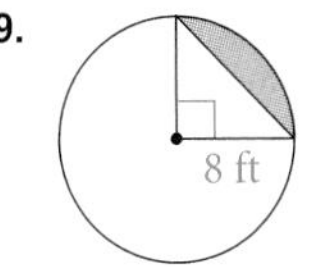

$18.27\ \text{ft}^2$

20. 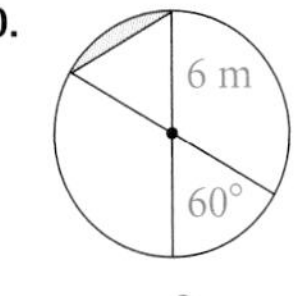

$3.26\ \text{m}^2$

21. 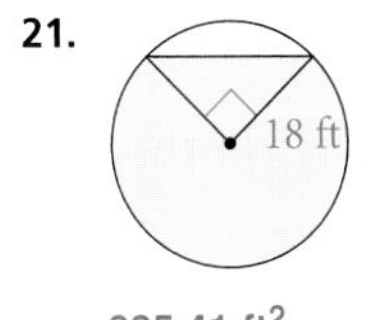

$925.41\ \text{ft}^2$

22. Writing The American Institute of Baking suggests a technique for cutting and serving a tiered cake. The tiers of a cake have the same height and have diameters 8 in. and 13 in. The top layer and the circle directly under it are cut into 8 pieces and the exterior ring of the 13-inch layer is cut into 12 pieces. Which piece would be biggest, a top, bottom-inside, or bottom-outside piece? Explain your answer. See margin.

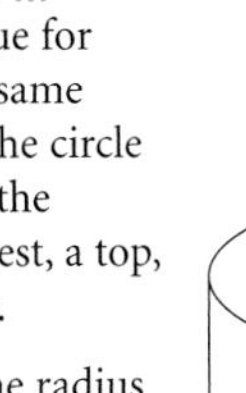

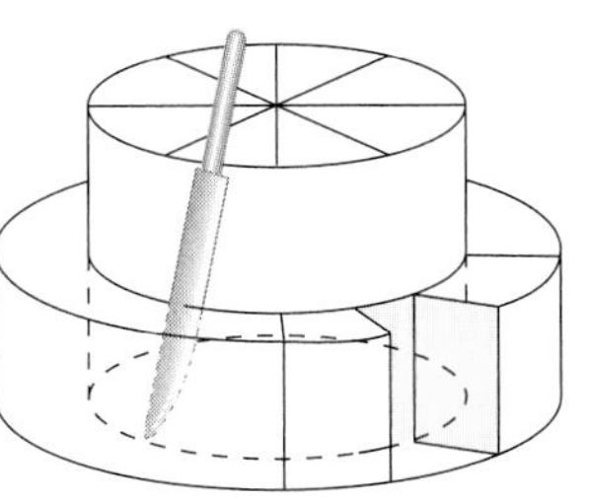

23. A sector of a circle with a 90° arc has area 36π in.^{2}. What is the radius of the circle? 12 in.

Find the area of the shaded figure. Leave your answer in terms of π.

24. 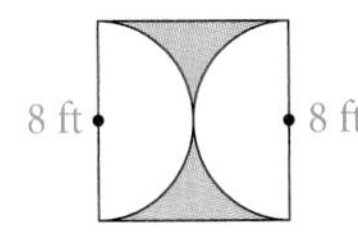

$(64 - 16\pi)\ \text{ft}^2$

25. 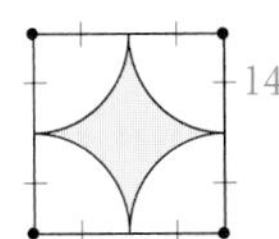

$(784 - 196\pi)\ \text{in.}^2$

26. 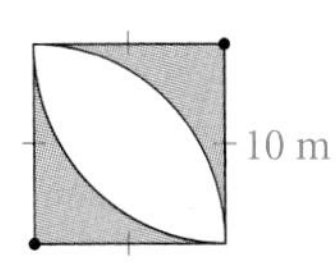

$(200 - 50\pi)\ \text{m}^2$

27. 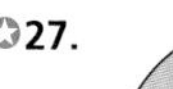
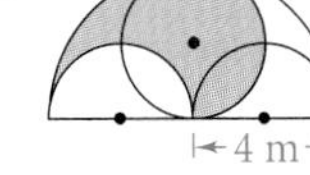

$4\pi\ \text{m}^2$

28. Open-ended Draw a diagram for a sector of a circle such that the sector has area $16\pi\ \text{cm}^2$. Label the radius of the circle and the measure of the arc of the sector. See margin for sample.

29. An 8 ft-by-10 ft floating dock is anchored in the middle of a pond. The bow of a canoe is tied to one corner of the dock with a 10-ft rope.
    a. Sketch a diagram of the area in which the bow of the canoe can travel.
    b. Write a plan for finding the area. a–b. See margin.
    c. Find the area. Round your answer to the nearest square foot. about 239 ft^2

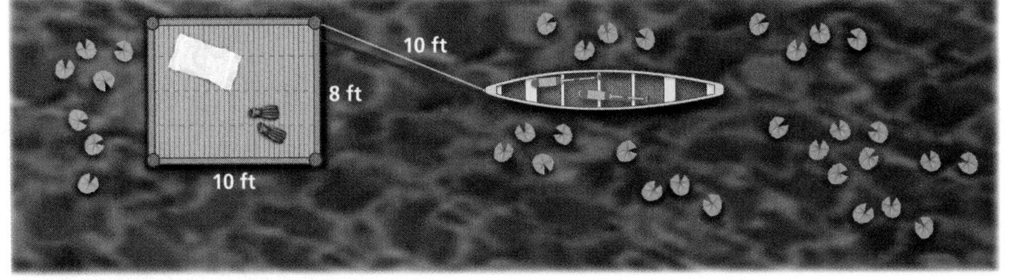

pages 288–290 On Your Own

22. Bottom-outside; since the heights of all the pieces are the same, the piece with the greater base area has the greater volume. The area of a top and a bottom-inside piece is ≈ 6.3 in.^{2}; the area of a bottom-outside piece is ≈ 6.9 in^2.

28. 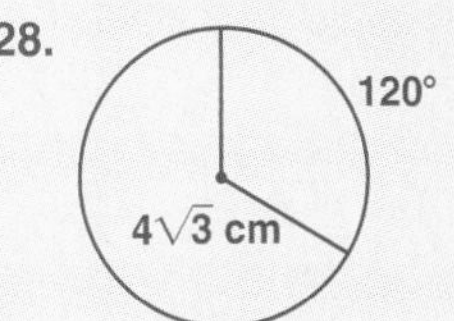

29a. 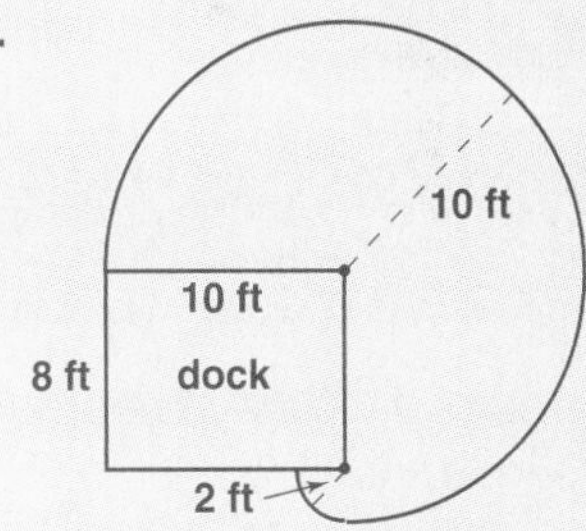

b. the area of $\frac{3}{4}$ circle with radius 10 ft and $\frac{1}{4}$ circle with radius 2 ft

Chapter Project **FIND OUT BY CALCULATING** Have students work in groups to discuss a plan for finding the percents. One plan might be to let the side of each square be 8, then find the ratio of the area of the square minus the area of circle to the area of square for each.

Exercises MIXED REVIEW

DATA ANALYSIS Exercises 30–32 Review with students why the vertical scale is drawn with a "zig zag" at the bottom.

SELF ASSESSMENT PORTFOLIO Share with students the criteria you will use to assess their work in portfolios, as well as how you plan to use the results. Students should understand how the rubrics assess their work, how each piece in the portfolio counts, and how the scores they get in their portfolios will affect their overall evaluation.

Wrap Up

THE BIG IDEA Ask students to define in their own words *sector* and *segment of a circle.* Then have them explain how to find the area of each.

RETEACHING ACTIVITY Students draw a circle on grid paper and estimate its area. Then they calculate its area using the formula for the area of a circle. (Reteaching worksheet 5-8)

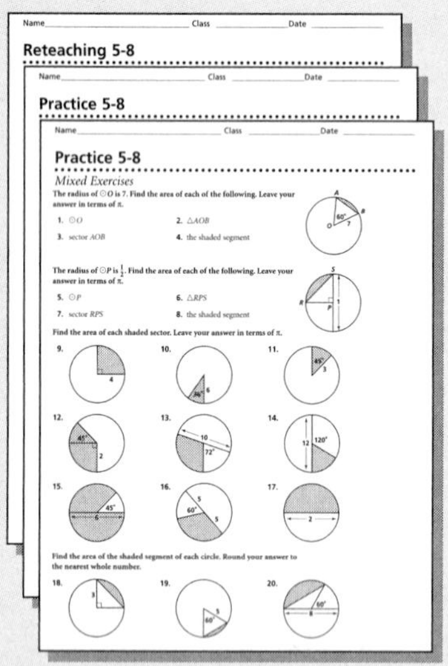

Lesson Quiz

Lesson Quiz is also available in Transparencies.

For Exercises 1–2, leave your answers in terms of π.

1. Find the area of a circle with diameter 22 m. 121π m^2
2. A circle has radius 4 in. Find the area of a sector bounded by a 75° arc. $\frac{10\pi}{3}$ in.^{2}
3. A circle has diameter 10 m. Find the area of a segment bounded by a 90° arc. Round your answer to the nearest tenth. 7.1 m^2
4. Find the diameter of a circle with area 169π cm^2. 26 cm

Chapter Project *Find Out by Calculating*

The circles on this quilt were sewn onto the background cloth. Cutting circles from rectangles leaves some waste. Explore whether you can reduce waste by using smaller circles.

- Compare the percent of material wasted when the shaded circles are cut from squares A, B, and C below. Each method wastes the same amount of material.

A. 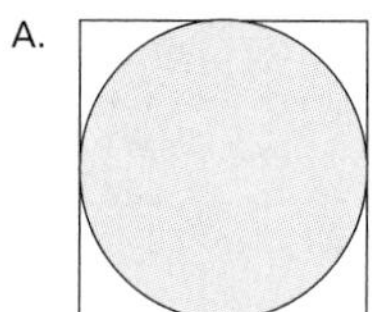 B. 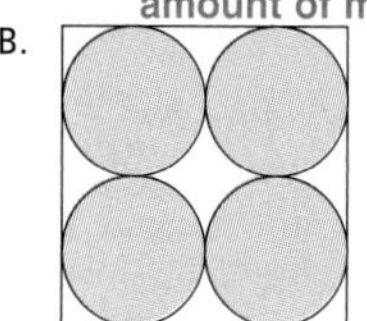 C. 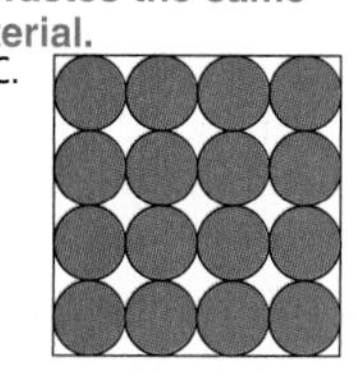

- Estimate how many times longer it would take to cut out the 16 circles from square C than the 1 circle from square A. Support your estimate with calculations.

4 times as long; a circle in C has $\frac{1}{4}$ of the circumference of a circle in A, but there are 16 circles in C.

Exercises MIXED REVIEW

Data Analysis **Use the line graph for Exercises 30–32.** 30–32. Answers may vary slightly.

30. In 1990, how much did the average person spend on media such as printed material, videos, and recordings? $380
31. How much has spending increased from 1990 to 1994? $90
32. **Predict** how much the average person will spend on media in the year 2000. Sample: $625

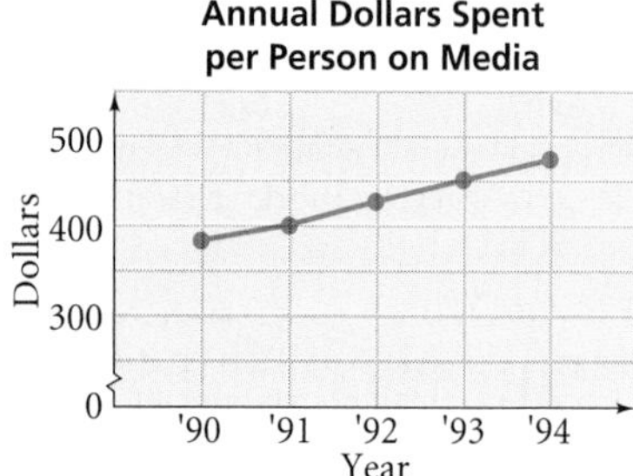

33. What is the area of a 30°-60°-90° triangle with hypotenuse 12 cm? Leave your answer in simplest radical form. $18\sqrt{3}$ cm^2

The measures of two angles of a triangle are given. Find the measure of the third angle. Then classify the triangle by its sides and angles.

34. 54°, 108°
35. 72°, 36°
36. 36°, 54°
37. 78°, 34°
38. 60°, 60°
39. 90°, 45°

34. 18; scalene, obtuse
35. 72; isosceles, acute
36. 90; scalene, right
37. 68; scalene, acute
38. 60; equilateral, acute
39. 45; isosceles, right

SELF ASSESSMENT PORTFOLIO

For your portfolio, select one or two items from your work for this chapter. Here are some possibilities.
- corrected work
- a journal entry

Explain why you have included each selection.

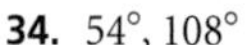

Math ToolboX

Students investigate the ratio of the perimeters and areas of inscribed regular polygons to the circumferences and areas of the circles in which they are inscribed.

The software allows students to increase the number of sides of the inscribed regular polygon easily, to find the measurements and ratios accurately, and to manipulate the size of the circle.

Investigate

ERROR ALERT! Some students may change the size of the circle without changing the size of the triangle. **Remediation:** Make sure that the vertices of the triangle remain on the circle.

Students may want to compare their results with other pairs or groups before making their conjectures.

Extend

Introduce the idea of limits by discussing the ratios $\frac{\text{perimeter}}{\text{circumference}}$ and $\frac{\text{polygon area}}{\text{circle area}}$ as the number of sides become infinitely large.

ADDITIONAL PROBLEM Ask students to use geometry software to find the triangle with the largest area that can be inscribed in a circle. Many will be surprised to find it is an equilateral triangle and not an obtuse triangle.

Math ToolboX Technology

Exploring Area and Circumference

After Lesson 5-8

A polygon that is *inscribed* in a circle has all its vertices on the circle. Work in pairs or small groups. Investigate the ratios of the perimeters and areas of inscribed regular polygons to the circumference and area of the circle in which they are inscribed. Begin by making a table like this.

Regular Polygon			Circle		Ratios	
Sides	Perimeter	Area	Circumference	Area	$\frac{\text{Perimeter}}{\text{Circumference}}$	$\frac{\text{Polygon Area}}{\text{Circle Area}}$
3						

Construct

Use geometry software to construct a circle. Find its circumference and area and record them in your table. Inscribe an equilateral triangle in the circle. Your software may be able to do this for you automatically, or you can construct three points on the circle and move them so they are approximately evenly spaced on the circle. Then draw the triangle. Check students' work.

Investigate

Use your geometry software to measure the perimeter and area of the triangle and to calculate the ratios $\frac{\text{triangle perimeter}}{\text{circle circumference}}$ and $\frac{\text{triangle area}}{\text{circle area}}$. Record the results.

Manipulate the circle to change its size. Do the ratios you calculated stay the same or change? The ratios do not change with size.

Now inscribe a square in a circle and fill in your table for a polygon of four sides. Do the same for a regular pentagon.

Conjecture

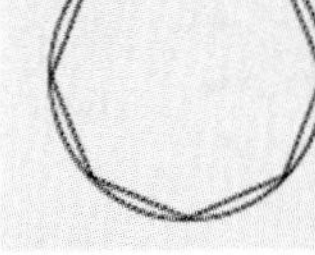

What will happen to the ratios $\frac{\text{perimeter}}{\text{circumference}}$ and $\frac{\text{polygon area}}{\text{circle area}}$ as you increase the number of sides of the polygon?
As the number of sides increases, each ratio comes closer to 1.

Extend

- Extend your table to include polygons of 12 sides. Does your conjecture still hold? Compare the two columns of ratios in your table. How do they differ? Yes; the ratio of perimeter to circumference gets closer to 1 faster than the ratio of the areas.
- Estimate the perimeter and area of a polygon of 100 sides that is inscribed in a circle with a radius of 10 cm. about 63 cm; about 314 cm^2

Materials and Manipulatives

- Geometry software

Finishing the Chapter Project

PROJECT DAY You may wish to plan a project day during which students share their completed projects. Encourage groups to explain their processes as well as their products.

PROJECT NOTEBOOK Have students review their project work and bring their notebooks up to date.

- Have students show the models of quilts and the patchwork designs they made and explain the techniques they used to create them.
- Ask groups to share any insights they found when completing the project, such as how they used geometric shapes to design their quilt patterns.

SCORING RUBRIC

3 Student's quilt design is complete. Diagrams are clear. Explanations and information are accurate. Display is attractive, organized, and comprehensive. Additional research is evident.

2 Student's quilt design is complete. Diagrams are clear. Explanations and information are accurate with only a few minor flaws. Display is attractive, organized, and comprehensive.

1 Student's quilt design is complete but the diagrams are not clear. Explanations and information contain flaws. Display needs organization and could be more comprehensive.

0 Major elements are incomplete or missing.

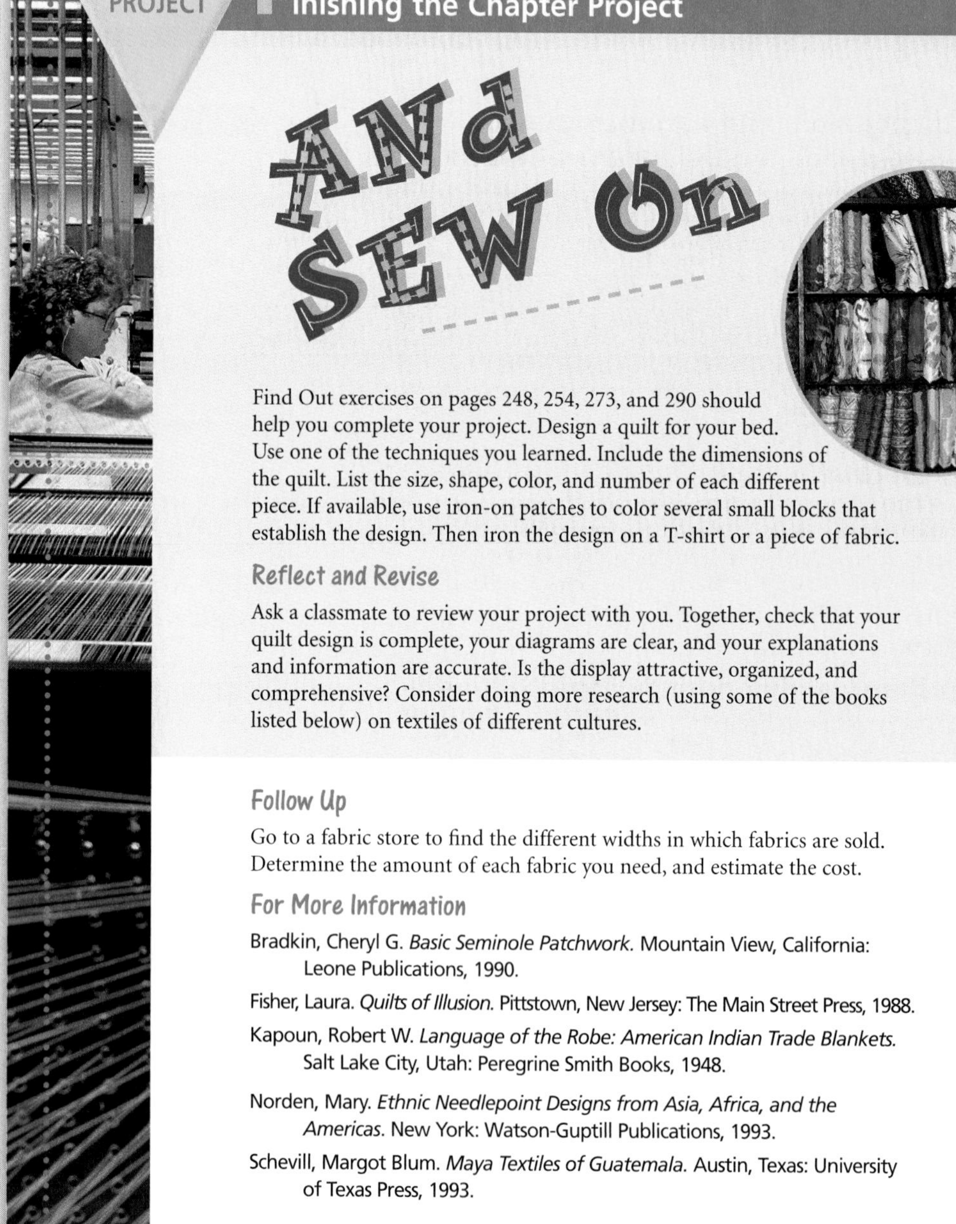

CHAPTER PROJECT

Finishing the Chapter Project

And Sew On

Find Out exercises on pages 248, 254, 273, and 290 should help you complete your project. Design a quilt for your bed. Use one of the techniques you learned. Include the dimensions of the quilt. List the size, shape, color, and number of each different piece. If available, use iron-on patches to color several small blocks that establish the design. Then iron the design on a T-shirt or a piece of fabric.

Reflect and Revise

Ask a classmate to review your project with you. Together, check that your quilt design is complete, your diagrams are clear, and your explanations and information are accurate. Is the display attractive, organized, and comprehensive? Consider doing more research (using some of the books listed below) on textiles of different cultures.

Follow Up

Go to a fabric store to find the different widths in which fabrics are sold. Determine the amount of each fabric you need, and estimate the cost.

For More Information

Bradkin, Cheryl G. *Basic Seminole Patchwork.* Mountain View, California: Leone Publications, 1990.

Fisher, Laura. *Quilts of Illusion.* Pittstown, New Jersey: The Main Street Press, 1988.

Kapoun, Robert W. *Language of the Robe: American Indian Trade Blankets.* Salt Lake City, Utah: Peregrine Smith Books, 1948.

Norden, Mary. *Ethnic Needlepoint Designs from Asia, Africa, and the Americas.* New York: Watson-Guptill Publications, 1993.

Schevill, Margot Blum. *Maya Textiles of Guatemala.* Austin, Texas: University of Texas Press, 1993.

Wrap Up

HOW AM I DOING? Have students work in small groups. Ask each group to make a short presentation explaining how to find the area of a different polygon. Each presentation must include a visual aid and a sample problem.

KEY TERMS The numbers in parentheses direct students to the pages where the terms are used or defined. Students should be able to (1) write a simple explanation of each term, (2) illustrate the term with a diagram, or (3) show an example that uses the term.

Exercise 3 Most students will divide this figure into two rectangles to find the area. Check that students do not count the segment they added as part of the perimeter.

5 Wrap Up

How am I doing?

- State three ideas from this chapter that you think are important. Explain your choices.
- Explain how to find the area of different polygons.

Key Terms

altitude (p. 250)
apothem (p. 274)
arc length (p. 281)
area of a circle (p. 285)
area of a parallelogram (p. 249)
area of a polygon (p. 243)
area of a rectangle (p. 244)
area of a square (p. 243)
area of a trapezoid (p. 269)
area of a triangle (p. 251)
base (pp. 250, 251, 269)
center (p. 274)
circumference of a circle (p. 279)
concentric circles (p. 280)
congruent arcs (p. 281)
Converse of the Pythagorean Theorem (p. 258)
45°-45°-90° triangle (p. 264)
height (pp. 250, 251, 269)
hypotenuse (p. 256)
legs of a right triangle (p. 256)
legs of a trapezoid (p. 269)
perimeter of a polygon (p. 242)
pi (p. 279)
Pythagorean Theorem (p. 257)
Pythagorean triple (p. 258)
radius (p. 274)
sector of a circle (p. 286)
segment of a circle (p. 287)
30°-60°-90° triangle (p. 265)

Understanding Perimeter and Area — 5-1

The **perimeter of a polygon** is the sum of the lengths of its sides.

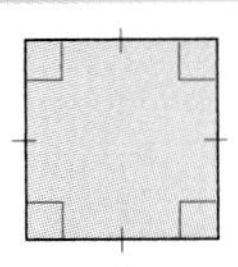

The formula for the perimeter of a square is $P = 4s$. The formula for the perimeter of a rectangle is $P = 2b + 2h$.

The **area of a polygon** is the number of square units it encloses. The area of a region is the sum of the area of its nonoverlapping parts. If two figures are congruent, their areas are equal.

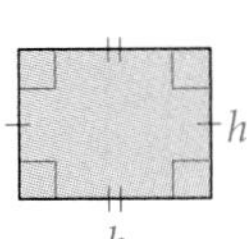

The formula for the **area of a square** is $A = s^2$. The formula for the **area of a rectangle** is $A = bh$.

Find the perimeter and area of each figure.

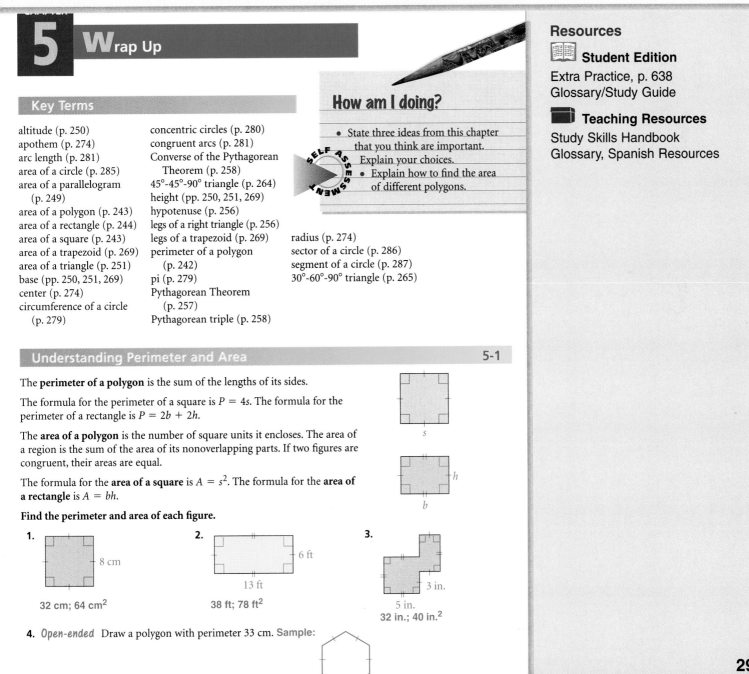

1. 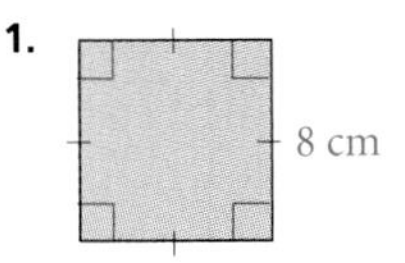

32 cm; 64 cm^2

2. 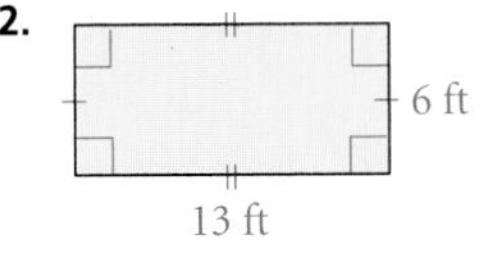

38 ft; 78 ft^2

3. 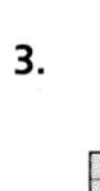 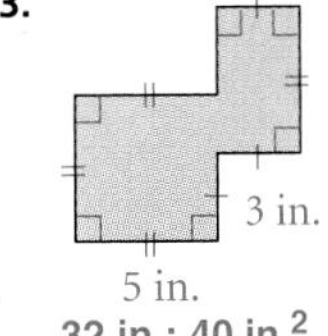

32 in.; 40 in.^{2}

4. *Open-ended* Draw a polygon with perimeter 33 cm. Sample:

Resources

Student Edition

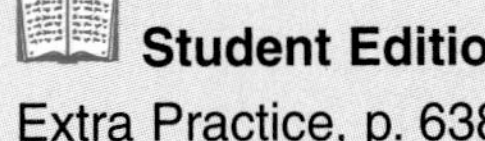
Extra Practice, p. 638

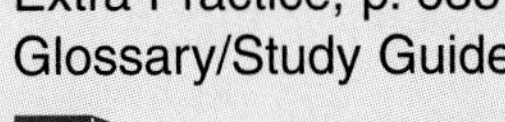
Glossary/Study Guide

Teaching Resources

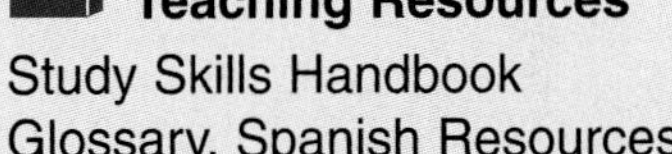
Study Skills Handbook
Glossary, Spanish Resources

Exercises 5–7 Make sure students understand which figures have a factor of one-half in the area formula.

ERROR ALERT! **Exercises 8–10** Some students may want to use special right triangles. **Remediation:** Point out that the measures of the acute angles cannot be determined.

Areas of Parallelograms and Triangles 5-2

You can find the area of a parallelogram or a triangle if you know the **base** and **height**. The **area of a parallelogram** is $A = bh$. The **area of a triangle** is $A = \frac{1}{2}bh$.

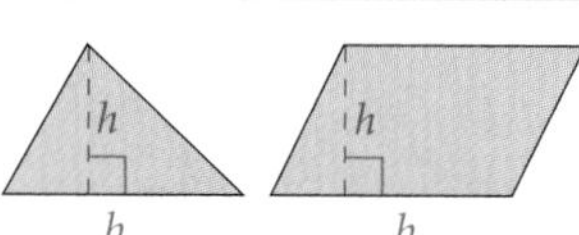

Find the area of each figure.

5. 10 m²

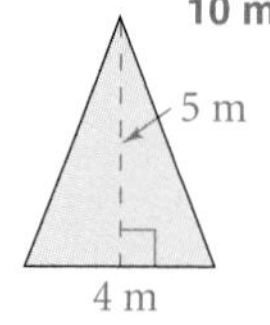

6. 90 in.²

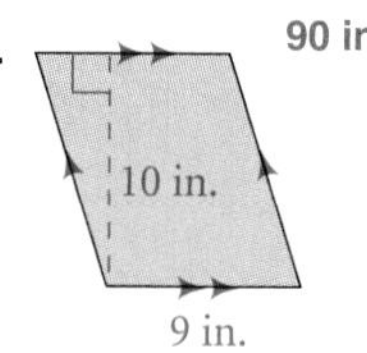

7. 33 ft²

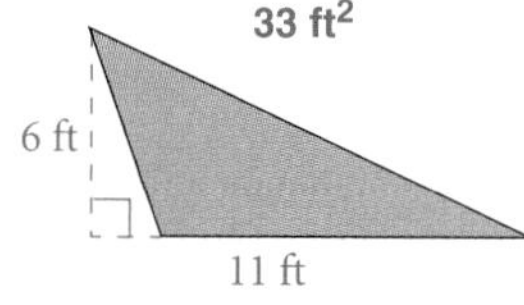

The Pythagorean Theorem and Its Converse 5-3

The **Pythagorean Theorem** states that in a right triangle the sum of the squares of the lengths of the legs equals the square of the length of the hypotenuse, or $a^2 + b^2 = c^2$.

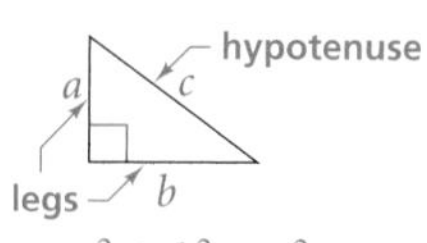

Positive integers a, b, and c form a **Pythagorean triple** if $a^2 + b^2 = c^2$.

The **Converse of the Pythagorean Theorem** states that if the square of the length of one side of a triangle is equal to the sum of the squares of the lengths of the other two sides, then the triangle is a right triangle.

In a triangle with longest side c, if $c^2 > a^2 + b^2$, the triangle is obtuse, and if $c^2 < a^2 + b^2$, the triangle is acute.

Find each value of *x*. If your answer is not an integer, you may leave it in simplest radical form.

8.

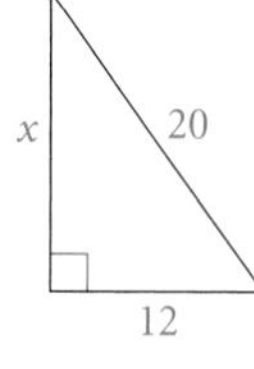

16

9.

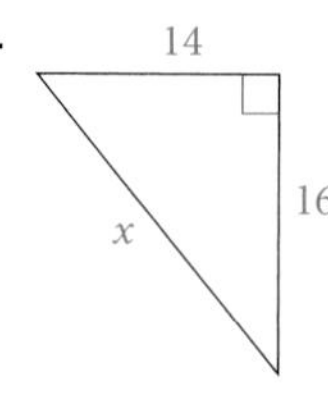

$2\sqrt{113}$

10.

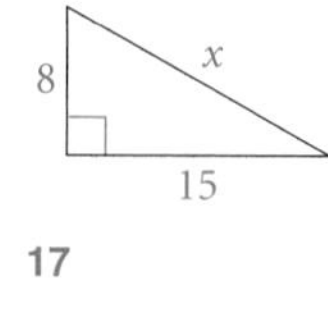

17

Special Right Triangles 5-4

In a **45°-45°-90° triangle,** both legs are congruent and the length of the hypotenuse is $\sqrt{2}$ times the length of a leg.

In a **30°-60°-90° triangle,** the length of the hypotenuse is twice the length of the shorter leg. The length of the longer leg is $\sqrt{3}$ times the length of the shorter leg.

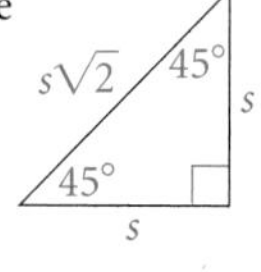

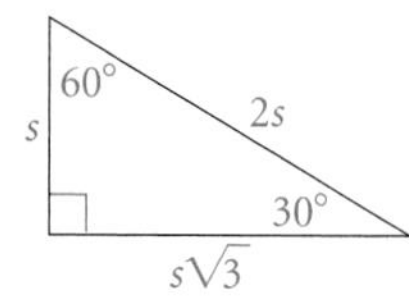

Exercises 11 and 13 Help students see why they cannot use the Pythagorean Theorem to find the missing side lengths. (Only one side length is given.)

ALTERNATIVE ASSESSMENT **Exercises 19–21** You can use these exercises to help you assess students' understanding of special right triangles as well as area of regular polygons. Students will need to use special right triangles to find the lengths of the apothem and side of each regular polygon.

Find the value of each variable. If your answer is not an integer, you may leave it in simplest radical form.

11. 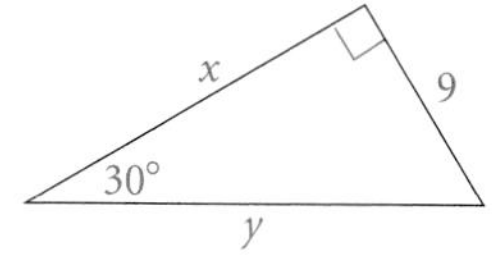

$x = 9\sqrt{3}$; $y = 18$

12. 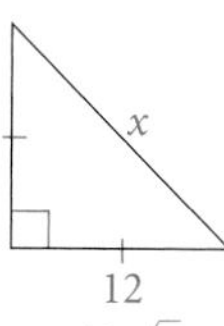

$x = 12\sqrt{2}$

13. 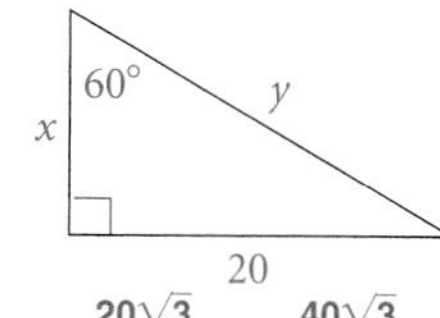

$x = \frac{20\sqrt{3}}{3}$; $y = \frac{40\sqrt{3}}{3}$

14. *Standardized Test Prep* A triangle has sides with lengths 4, 4, and $4\sqrt{2}$. What kind of triangle is it? **E**

A. acute isosceles
B. scalene right
C. equilateral
D. obtuse right
E. isosceles right

Areas of Trapezoids 5-5

The two parallel sides of a trapezoid are **bases.** The nonparallel sides are **legs.** The **height** is the perpendicular distance between the two bases. The **area of a trapezoid** is $A = \frac{1}{2}h(b_1 + b_2)$.

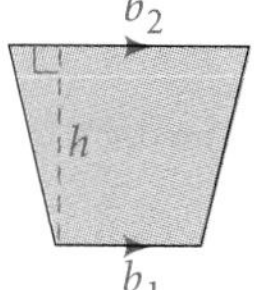

Find the area of each trapezoid. If your answer is not an integer, you may leave it in simplest radical form.

15. 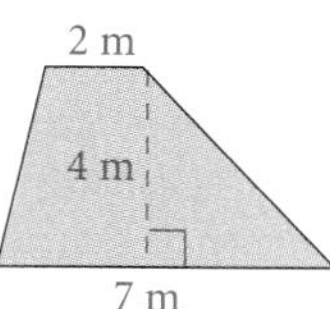

18 m^2

16. 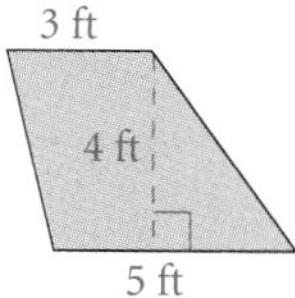

16 ft^2

17. 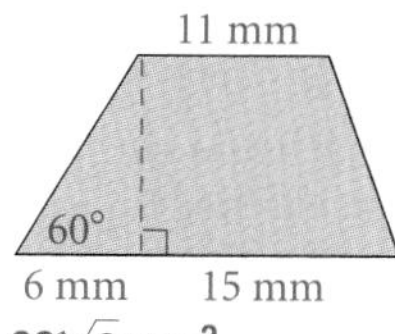

$96\sqrt{3}\text{ mm}^2$

18. *Writing* Explain how the formula for the area of a trapezoid is related to the formula for the area of a triangle. **Every trapezoid can be divided into 2 △s with height h and bases b_1 and b_2.**

Areas of Regular Polygons 5-6

The **center** of a regular polygon is the center of its circumscribed circle. The **radius** is the distance from the center to a vertex. The **apothem** is the perpendicular distance from the center to a side. The area of a regular polygon with apothem a and perimeter p is $A = \frac{1}{2}ap$.

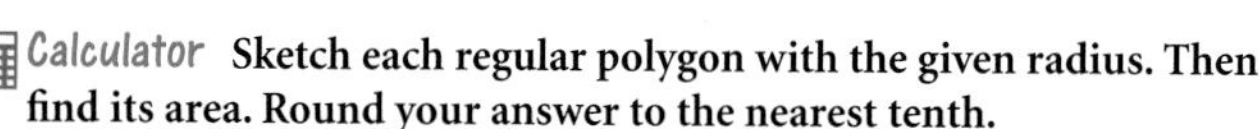

Calculator **Sketch each regular polygon with the given radius. Then find its area. Round your answer to the nearest tenth.**

19. triangle; radius 4 in. **20.8 in.^{2}**

20. square; radius 8 mm **128 mm^2**

21. hexagon; radius 7 cm **127.3 cm^2**

Exercises 25–27 Have students work in groups to discuss how to find the area of each shaded region. In Exercise 25, ask students if there's a "shortcut" to finding the area of the shaded region.

Remind students that the new mathematical terms in this chapter are defined in the Glossary/Study Guide in the back of the book.

Getting Ready For Chapter 6

Students may work these exercises independently or in small groups. The skills previewed will help prepare students for studying solids.

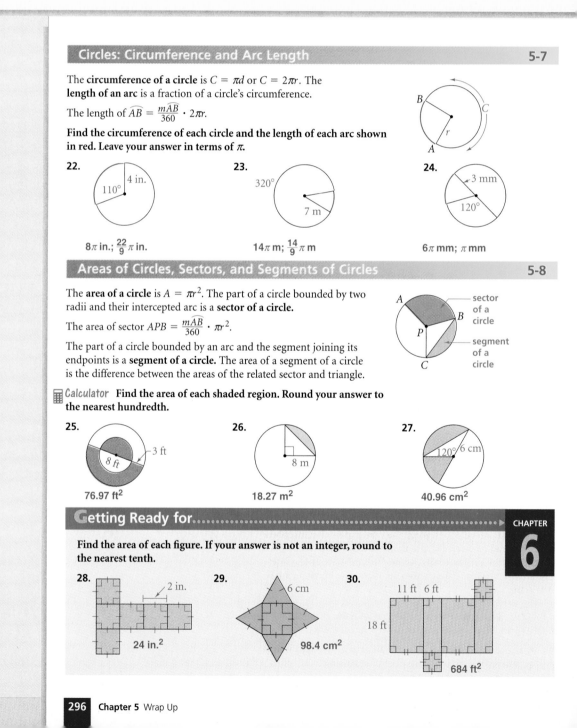

Circles: Circumference and Arc Length 5-7

The **circumference of a circle** is $C = \pi d$ or $C = 2\pi r$. The **length of an arc** is a fraction of a circle's circumference.

The length of $\widehat{AB} = \frac{m\widehat{AB}}{360} \cdot 2\pi r$.

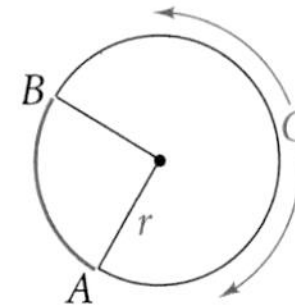

Find the circumference of each circle and the length of each arc shown in red. Leave your answer in terms of π.

22.

8π in.; $\frac{22}{9}\pi$ in.

23.
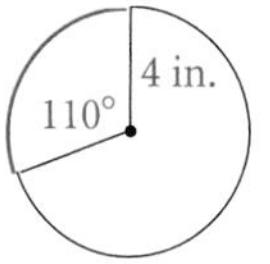

14π m; $\frac{14}{9}\pi$ m

24.
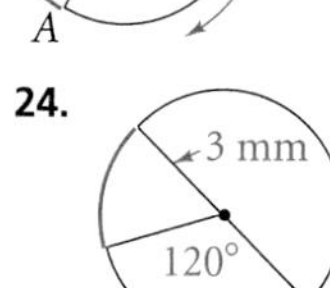

6π mm; π mm

Areas of Circles, Sectors, and Segments of Circles 5-8

The **area of a circle** is $A = \pi r^2$. The part of a circle bounded by two radii and their intercepted arc is a **sector of a circle.**

The area of sector $APB = \frac{m\widehat{AB}}{360} \cdot \pi r^2$.

The part of a circle bounded by an arc and the segment joining its endpoints is a **segment of a circle.** The area of a segment of a circle is the difference between the areas of the related sector and triangle.

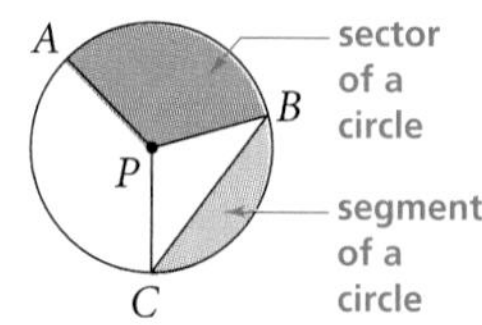

Calculator **Find the area of each shaded region. Round your answer to the nearest hundredth.**

25.
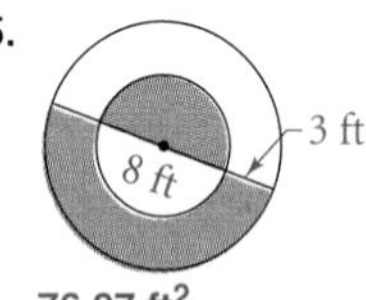

76.97 ft^2

26.
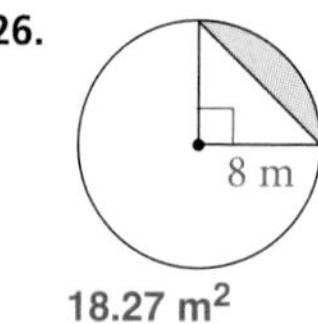

18.27 m^2

27.
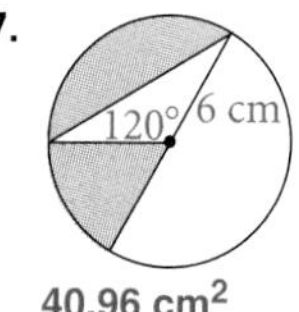

40.96 cm^2

Getting Ready for CHAPTER 6

Find the area of each figure. If your answer is not an integer, round to the nearest tenth.

28.
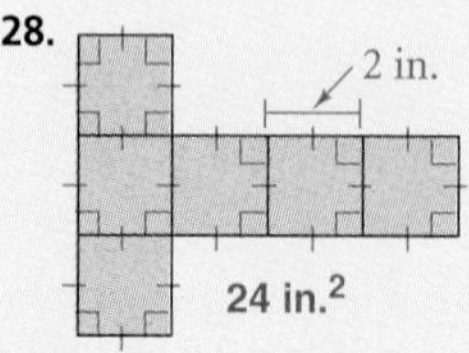

24 $in.^2$

29.
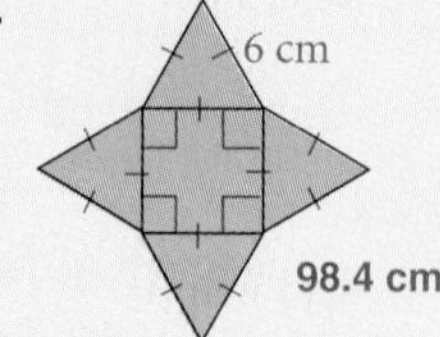

98.4 cm^2

30.
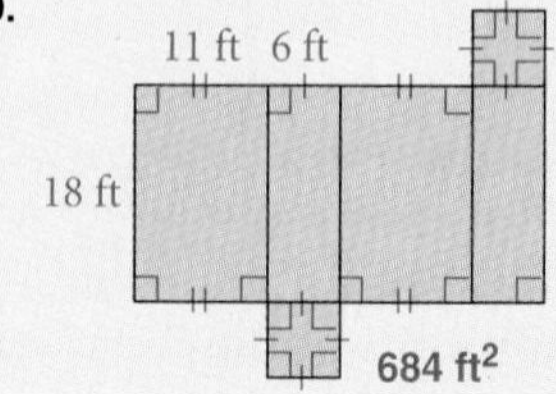

684 ft^2

Assessment

ENHANCED MULTIPLE CHOICE QUESTIONS are more complex than traditional multiple choice questions, which assess only one skill. Enhanced multiple choice questions assess the processes that students use, as well as the end results. The questions are written so that students use more than one strategy to solve the problem. Using multiple strategies is encouraged by the National Council of Teachers of Mathematics (NCTM). **Exercises 17 and 30** are enhanced multiple choice questions.

FREE RESPONSE QUESTIONS do not give answer choices. Some exercises have more than one possible answer. Students need to give only one correct response. **Exercises 1–10, 12–16, 18–24, 26–29, 31–38, and 40–42** are free response questions.

WRITING EXERCISES allow students to describe how they think about and understand the concepts they have learned. **Exercise 25** is a writing exercise.

OPEN-ENDED PROBLEMS allow for more than one solution. Students must construct their own responses instead of choosing from possible answers. The students' responses will help you determine the depth of their understanding and any possible areas of difficulty. **Exercises 11 and 39** are open-ended problems.

5 Assessment

Find the perimeter of each figure.

1. 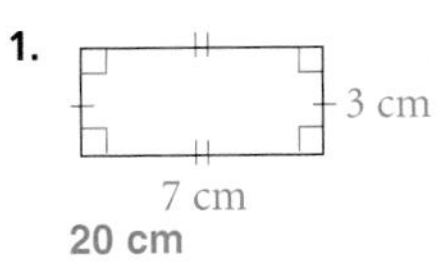

20 cm

2. 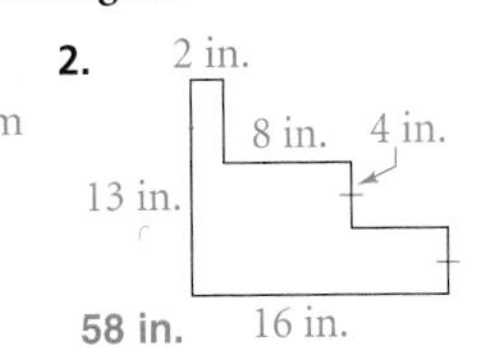

58 in.

3. You have 64 ft of fencing. What are the dimensions of the rectangle of greatest area you could enclose? 16 ft by 16 ft

Find the area of each figure. If your answer is not an integer, round to the nearest tenth.

4. 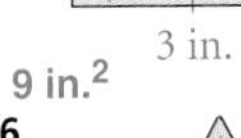

9 in.^{2}

5. 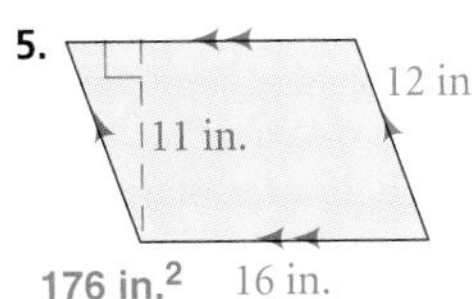

176 in.^{2}

6. 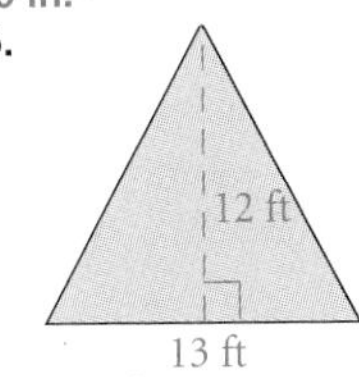

78 ft^2

7. 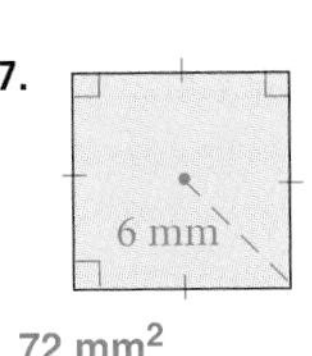

72 mm^2

8. 8 m, 9 m, 60°
62.4 m^2

9. 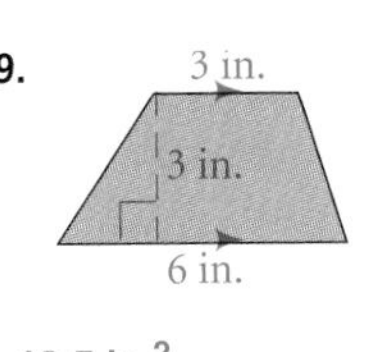

13.5 in.^{2}

10. *Coordinate Geometry* A quadrilateral has vertices at $A(0, 7)$, $B(-2, 7)$, $C(-2, 0)$, and $D(0, 0)$. Find the area and perimeter of $ABCD$. 14 units^2; 18 units

11. *Open-ended* An equilateral triangle, a square, and a regular pentagon all have the same perimeter. What can this perimeter be if all figures have sides that are integers?
any multiple of 60

Find the area of each regular polygon. Round to the nearest tenth.

12. 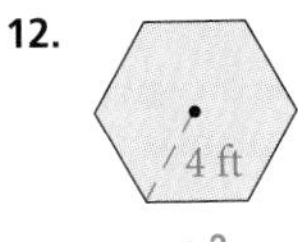

41.6 ft^2

13. 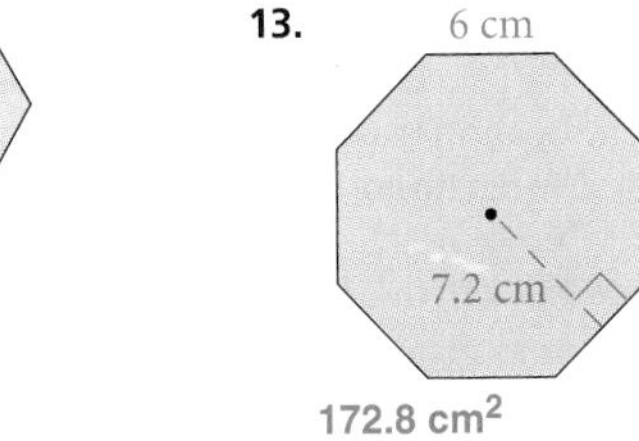

172.8 cm^2

The lengths of two sides of a right triangle are given. Find the length of the third side. Leave your answers in simplest radical form.

14. one leg 9, other leg 6 $3\sqrt{13}$
15. one leg 12, hypotenuse 17 $\sqrt{145}$
16. hypotenuse 20, leg 10 $10\sqrt{3}$

17. *Standardized Test Prep* Which integers form Pythagorean triples? E
I. 15, 36, 39
II. 6, 8, 10
III. 16, 30, 34
IV. 10, 12, 14
A. I only B. IV only C. II and III
D. III and IV E. I, II, and III

Find the values of the variables. Leave your answers in simplest radical form.

18. 7, 11, x
$x = \sqrt{170}$

19. 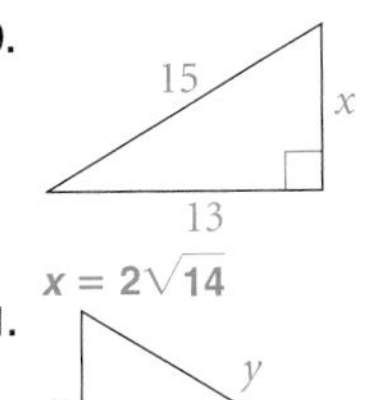

$x = 2\sqrt{14}$

20. 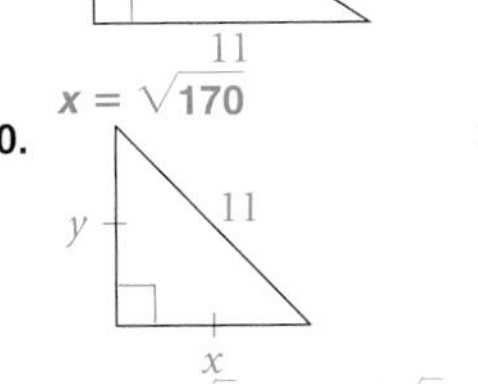

$x = \frac{11\sqrt{2}}{2}$; $y = \frac{11\sqrt{2}}{2}$

21. 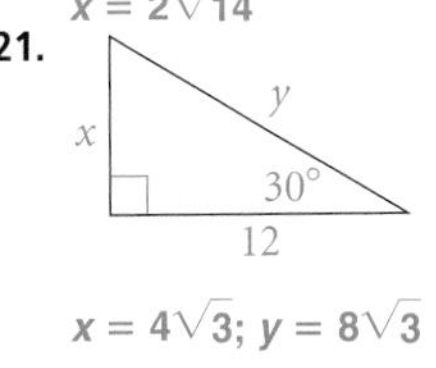

$x = 4\sqrt{3}$; $y = 8\sqrt{3}$

Resources

Teaching Resources
Chapter Support File, Ch. 5
- Chapter Assessment, Forms A and B
- Alternative Assessment

Chapter Assessment, Spanish Resources

Teacher's Edition
See also p. 240E for assessment options

Software
Computer Item Generator

Assessment pages 297–298

25. The ratio of the length of the longer leg to the length of the shorter leg is $\sqrt{3} : 1$. The ratio of the length of the hypotenuse to the length of the shorter leg is $2 : 1$. Find the length of the shorter leg first, then use it to find the remaining lengths.

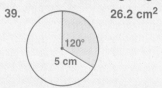

39. 26.2 cm^2

120°
5 cm

Preparing for Standardized Tests page 299

11. No; if an altitude is outside the △, then the △ is obtuse and the altitude is from an acute angle vertex. The altitude from the other acute angle vertex is also outside the △.

13. Compare the square of the largest number with the sum of squares of the other 2 numbers. If they are =, then the △ is a rt. △. For example, 4, 5, 6 is not a rt. △: $4^2 + 5^2 \neq 6^2$; 7, 24, 25 is a rt. △: $7^2 + 24^2 = 25^2$.

14.

3 cm

6 cm

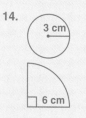

The lengths of three sides of a triangle are given. Describe each triangle as acute, right, or obtuse.

22. 9 cm, 10 cm, 12 cm acute

23. 8 m, 15 m, 17 m right

24. 5 in., 6 in., 10 in. obtuse

25. *Writing* Explain how you can use the length of the shorter side of a 30°-60°-90° triangle to find the lengths of the other two sides. See margin.

Find the length of each arc shown in red. Leave your answers in terms of π.

26. 5 in., 120° — $\frac{10}{3}\pi$ in.

27. 3 cm — 1.5π cm

28. 10 m, 60° — $\frac{10}{3}\pi$ m

29. 7 ft, 45° — $\frac{21\pi}{4}$ ft

30. *Standardized Test Prep* Which length is greatest? C
    - A. the diagonal of a 4-in. square
    - B. the diameter of a circle with 3-in. radius
    - C. the circumference of a circle with 2-in. radius
    - D. the length of a semicircle of a circle with diameter 6 in.
    - E. the perimeter of a 2 in.-by-3 in. rectangle

Find the area and circumference of a circle with the given radius or diameter. Leave your answers in terms of π.

31. $r = 4$ cm
32. $d = 10$ in.
33. $d = 7$ ft
34. $r = 12$ m

31. 16π cm^2; 8π cm 32. 25π $in.^2$; 10π in.
33. 12.25π ft^2; 7π ft 34. 144π m^2; 24π m

Calculator **Find the area of each shaded region. Round your answer to the nearest hundredth.**

35. 36.

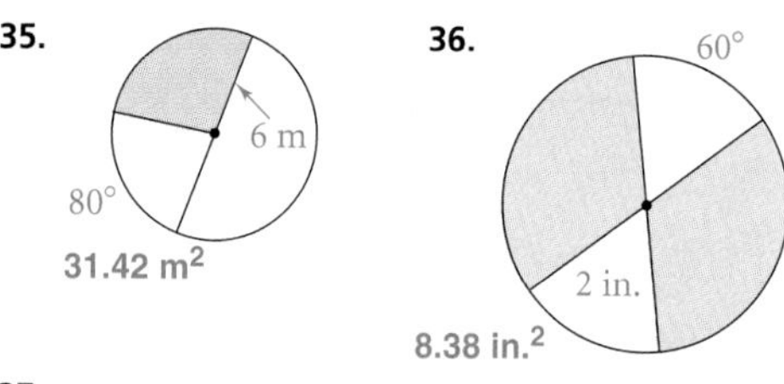

35. 31.42 m^2 36. 8.38 $in.^2$

37. 38.

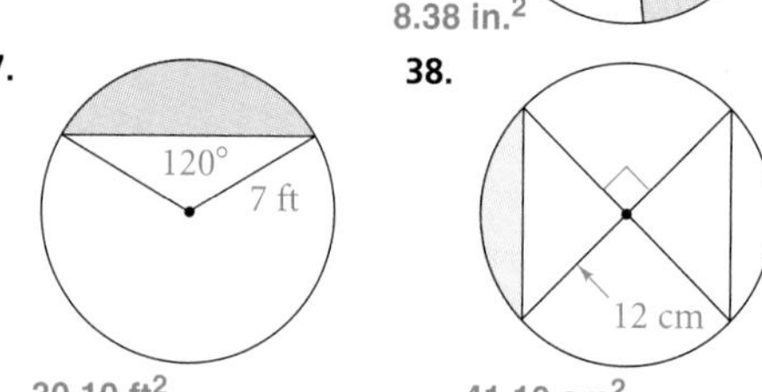

37. 30.10 ft^2 38. 41.10 cm^2

39. *Open-ended* Use a compass to draw a circle. Shade a sector of the circle and find its area. See margin for sample.

Find the area of each figure. Leave your answer in terms of π.

40. 41.

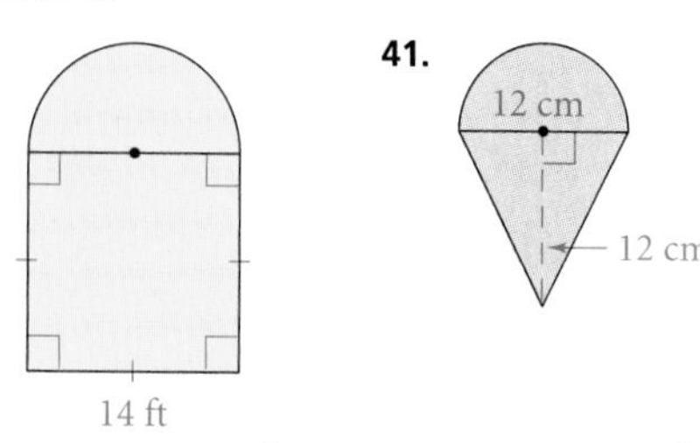

40. $(196 + 24.5\pi)$ ft^2 41. $(72 + 18\pi)$ cm^2

42. *Sports* Netball players in different positions are restricted to different parts of the court. A wing defense can play in the center third and in her own goal third, except in the semicircle around the net. How much area does she have to play in? Round your answer to the nearest tenth. 2931.2 ft^2

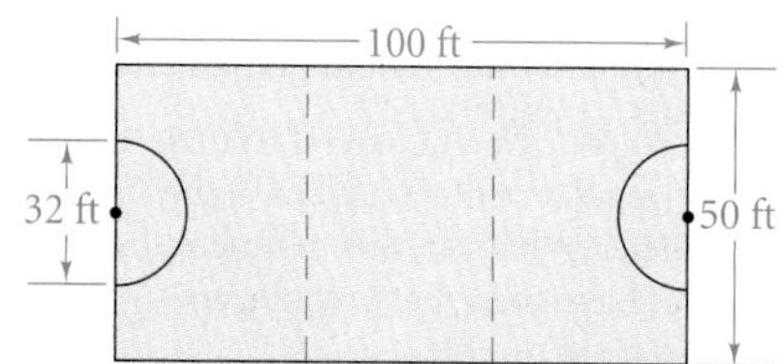

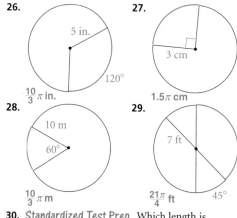

Preparing for Standardized Tests

Standardized tests, such as those administered for state assessment, the SAT, or the ACT, include regular math questions, quantitative comparison questions, open-ended problems, and free response questions (which the SAT calls *grid-ins*).

MULTIPLE CHOICE QUESTIONS are followed by five answer choices, one of which is correct. **Exercises 1–8** are multiple choice questions.

QUANTITATIVE COMPARISON QUESTIONS ask students to compare two quantities. **Exercises 9 and 10** are quantitative comparison questions.

FREE RESPONSE QUESTIONS do not give answer choices. Students must provide one correct answer on their own. **Exercises 11 and 12** are free response questions.

OPEN-ENDED PROBLEMS allow for more than one solution. Students must construct their own responses instead of choosing a single answer. The responses students give will help you determine the depth of their understanding and what difficulties, if any, they are experiencing. **Exercise 14** is an open-ended problem.

STANDARDIZED TEST TIP **Exercise 3** A common error is for students to compare the sum of the given sides to the third side and forget to compare other combinations of sides. In this example, these students may choose a. They notice that $6 + 3 \not> 12$ and $6 + 3 \not> 9$ but they fail to see that $3 + 1 \not> 6$.

5 Preparing for Standardized Tests

For Exercises 1–10, choose the correct letter.

1. What is the area of a rectangle with vertices at (−2, 5), (3, 5), (3, −1), and (−2, −1)? A
   A. 30 **B.** 25 **C.** 4 **D.** 24 **E.** 56

2. An isosceles triangle has two angles measuring 49 and 82. What is the measure of the third angle? B
   A. 82 **B.** 49 **C.** 51
   D. 8 **E.** none of the above

3. The lengths of two sides of a triangle are 6 cm and 3 cm. What *cannot* be the length of the third side? E
   I. 12 cm **II.** 9 cm **III.** 5 cm **IV.** 1 cm
   A. I and II **B.** II and III **C.** III and IV
   D. I and IV **E.** I, II, and IV

4. What is the circumference of a circle with radius 5 ft? C
   A. 5π ft **B.** 25π ft **C.** 10π ft
   D. 125π ft **E.** 15π ft

5. The length of the hypotenuse of an isosceles right triangle is 8 in. What is the length of one leg? B
   A. 4 in. **B.** $4\sqrt{2}$ in. **C.** $8\sqrt{2}$ in.
   D. 2 in. **E.** none of the above

6. Which figure has area 30 ft^2? D

A.

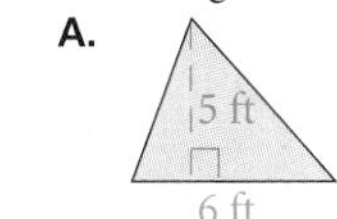

B.

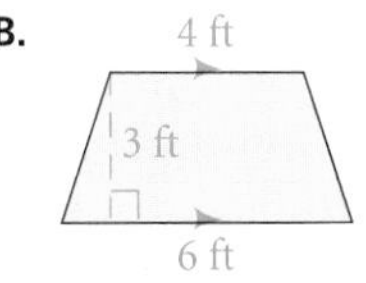

C.

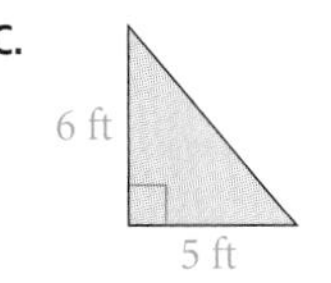

D.

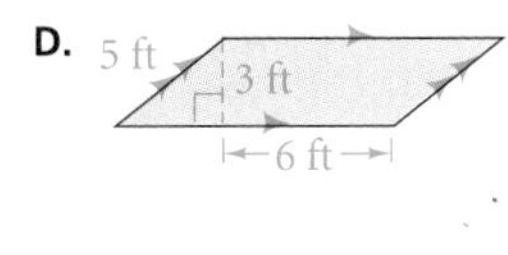

E. none of the above

7. Which *cannot* be the perimeter of an equilateral triangle with integer side lengths? C
   A. 36 m **B.** 48 m **C.** 16 m **D.** 24 m **E.** 9 m

8. $\overline{DE}$ is a midsegment of $\triangle ABC$. Find DE. A

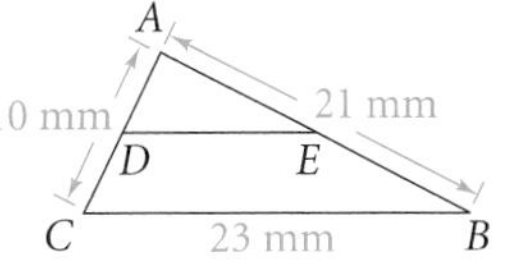

A. 11.5 mm **B.** 11 mm **C.** 10.5 mm
D. 10 mm **E.** 5 mm

Compare the boxed quantity in Column A with the boxed quantity in Column B. Choose the best answer.

A. The quantity in Column A is greater.
B. The quantity in Column B is greater.
C. The two quantities are equal.
D. The relationship cannot be determined on the basis of the information supplied.

	Column A	Column B	
	perimeter of square $RSTV = 12x$		
9.	side of $RSTV$	$3x$	C
10.	RT	RV	A

11. Critical Thinking Is it possible to sketch a triangle in which exactly one of the altitudes is outside the triangle? Explain. See margin p.298.

12. The area of a circle is 144π cm^2. What is the area of a sector with a 90° arc? 36π cm^2

13. Writing Explain how to use the Converse of the Pythagorean Theorem to determine if three numbers can represent the lengths of the sides of a right triangle. Include an example. See margin p. 298.

14. Open-ended Draw a circle. Then draw a second circle with a sector with a 90° arc so that the area of the sector equals the area of the first circle. See margin p. 298 for sample.

Resources

Teaching Resources

Chapter Support File, Ch. 5
- Standardized Test Practice
- Cumulative Review

Teacher's Edition

See also p. 240E for assessment options

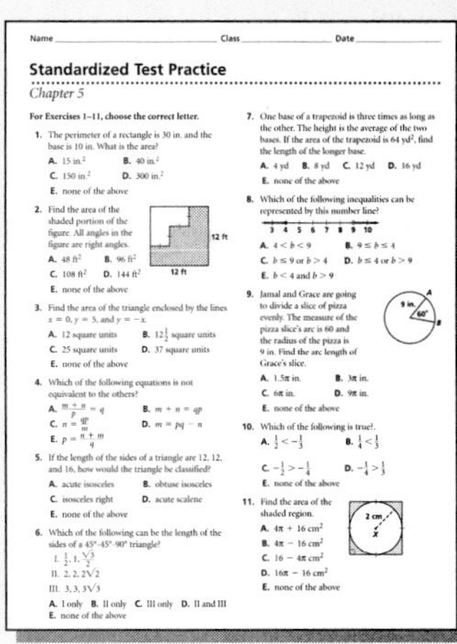

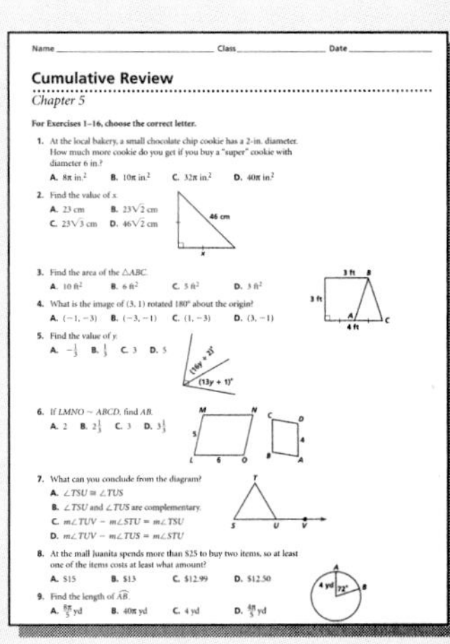

CHAPTER 6

Measuring in Space

To accommodate flexible scheduling, some lessons are divided into parts. Assignment Options are given in the Lesson Planning Options for each lesson.

PACING OPTIONS

This chart suggests pacing only for the core lessons and their parts, and it is provided merely as a possible guide. It will help you determine how much time you have in your schedule to cover other features, such as the Chapter Project, Math Toolboxes, Wrap Up, and Assessment.

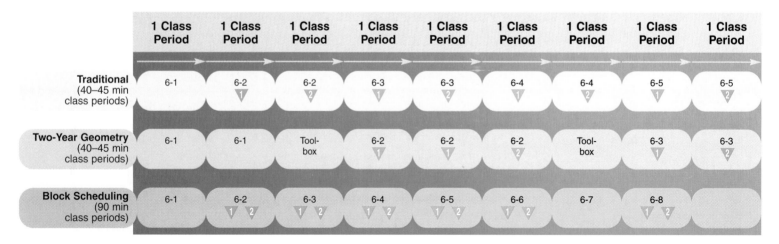

	1 Class Period	1 Class Period	1 Class Period	1 Class Period	1 Class Period	1 Class Period	1 Class Period	1 Class Period	1 Class Period
Traditional (40–45 min class periods)	6-1	6-2 Part 1	6-2 Part 2	6-3 Part 1	6-3 Part 2	6-4 Part 1	6-4 Part 2	6-5 Part 1	6-5 Part 2
Two-Year Geometry (40–45 min class periods)	6-1	6-1	Toolbox	6-2 Part 1	6-2 Part 1	6-2 Part 2	Toolbox	6-3 Part 1	6-3 Part 2
Block Scheduling (90 min class periods)	6-1	6-2 Parts 1, 2	6-3 Parts 1, 2	6-4 Parts 1, 2	6-5 Parts 1, 2	6-6 Parts 1, 2	6-7	6-8 Parts 1, 2	

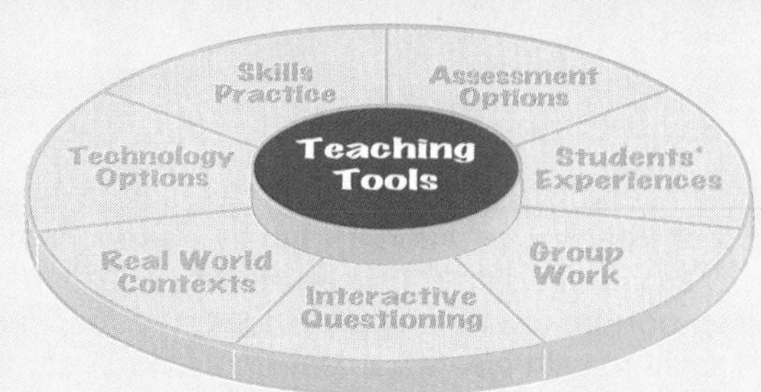

What Students Will Learn and Why

In this chapter, students build on their knowledge of figures in the plane, learned in Chapters 1–5, by learning to measure figures in space. They learn to recognize nets of various space figures and how to find the surface area and volume of prisms, cylinders, pyramids, cones, and spheres. Then students learn how to recognize composite space figures and find their surface areas and volumes. Finally, they learn how to use geometric models to find the probability of events. Concepts learned in this chapter will help students describe everyday objects they see, such as office buildings, water towers, and video cassette cases.

Discussing the Chapter/Building on Experience

The concept map below relates chapter topics to real-world applications. You and your class may wish to add to the map or develop maps of your own. The center oval describes the topic of the chapter. The next level displays topics within the lessons. The outer ovals reflect applications of the content. As you and your class build a concept map, invite students to discuss applications with which they are familiar.

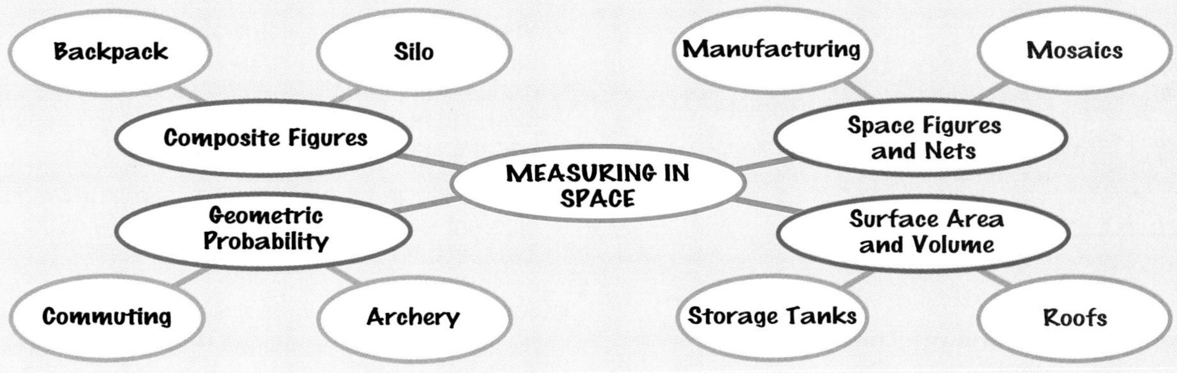

1 Class Period	1 Class Period	1 Class Period	1 Class Period	1 Class Period	1 Class Period	1 Class Period	1 Class Period	1 Class Period	1 Class Period	1 Class Period
6-6 ▼1	6-6 ▼2	6-7	6-8 ▼1	6-8 ▼2						
6-4 ▼1	6-4 ▼2	6-5 ▼1	6-5 ▼1	6-5 ▼2	6-6 ▼1	6-6 ▼2	6-7	6-7	6-8 ▼1	6-8 ▼2

Interactive Questioning Tips

A question is interactive when there is "give and take" between the questioner (teacher or student) and the respondent. In Think and Discuss or when a critical thinking question is asked, it is important to encourage a student to respond in a manner consistent with his or her learning style. A student who is primarily a visual learner might be encouraged to go to the chalkboard and illustrate with a diagram a point that he or she is trying to make. For example, in Lesson 6-2, students are asked to explain the reasoning for the design of CD packaging.

Skills Practice

Every lesson provides skill practice with Try This exercises, Exercises On Your Own, and Exercises Mixed Review. The Student Edition includes Checkpoints (pp. 322, 343) and Cumulative Review (p. 359). In the Teacher's Edition, the Lesson Planning Options section for each lesson lists Prerequisite Skills students should know for that lesson. At the back of the Student Edition is the Skills Handbook—mini-lessons on math your students may need to review. The Chapter Support File for Chapter 6 in the Teaching Resources box includes two Practice worksheets per lesson, a worksheet for two Checkpoints, and worksheets for Cumulative Review and Standardized Test Preparation.

Diverse Learning and Teaching Styles

In your Teacher's Edition, you will find suggestions as to how you can help students complete mathematical tasks in Chapter 6 by reinforcing various learning styles. Here are some examples.

- **Visual learning** create pyramids and discuss their features (p. 316), use stacks of papers, index cards, and /or coins to explain the term *cross section* and Cavalieri's Principle (p. 324), study the relationship between the base of a pyramid and the surface area of a sphere (p. 338)
- **Tactile learning** measure the height and radius of cones of different sizes (p. 318), investigate how many cones of rice it takes to fill a cylinder (p. 332)
- **Auditory learning** write and verbalize formulas to help with retention (p. 318), remember that the area of a triangle is $\frac{1}{2}$ the area of a rectangle in 2 dimensions and the volume of a pyramid is $\frac{1}{3}$ the volume of a prism in 3 dimensions (p. 331)
- **Kinesthetic learning** make a game board and toss coins to experiment with probability (p. 350)

Alternative Activity for Lesson 6-2

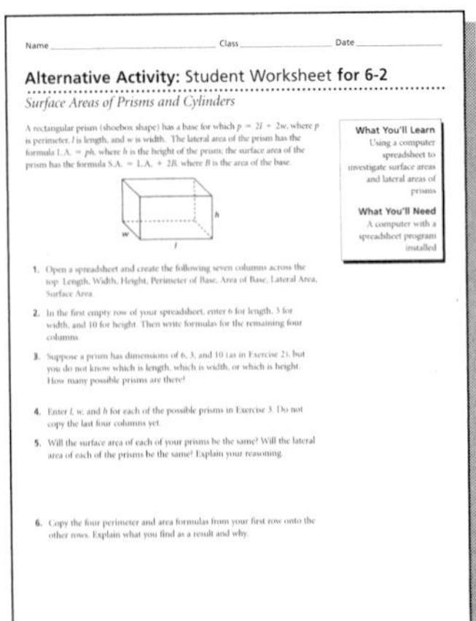

Name ______ Class ______ Date ______

Alternative Activity: Student Worksheet **for 6-2**

Surface Areas of Prisms and Cylinders

A rectangular prism (shoebox shape) has a base for which $p = 2l + 2w$, where p is perimeter, l is length, and w is width. The lateral area of the prism has the formula L.A. = ph, where h is the height of the prism; the surface area of the prism has the formula S.A. = L.A. + $2B$, where B is the area of the base.

What You'll Learn Using a computer spreadsheet to investigate surface areas and lateral areas of prisms

What You'll Need A computer with a spreadsheet program installed

1. Open a spreadsheet and create the following seven columns across the top: Length, Width, Height, Perimeter of Base, Area of Base, Lateral Area, Surface Area.
2. In the first empty row of your spreadsheet, enter 6 for length, 3 for width, and 10 for height. Then write formulas for the remaining four columns.
3. Suppose a prism has dimensions of 6, 3, and 10 (as in Exercise 2), but you do not know which is length, which is width, or which is height. How many possible prisms are there?
4. Enter l, w, and h for each of the possible prisms in Exercise 3. Do not copy the last four columns yet.
5. Will the surface area of each of your prisms be the same? Will the lateral area of each of the prisms be the same? Explain your reasoning.
6. Copy the four perimeter and area formulas from your first row onto the other rows. Explain what you find as a result and why.

for use with theorem 6-1 and Example 1, uses geometry software to explore surface area and lateral area of right rectangular prisms.

Alternative Activity for Lesson 6-4

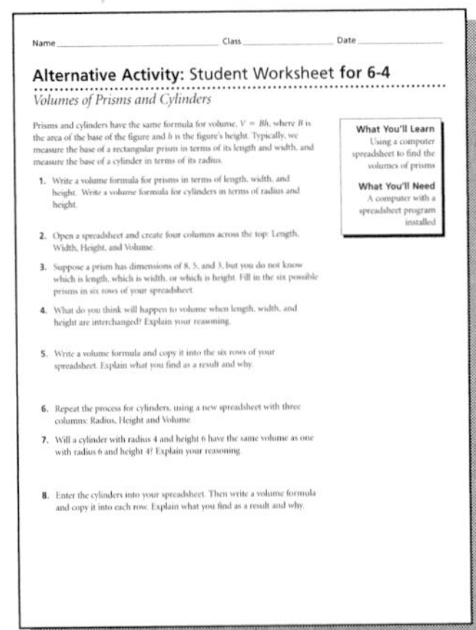

Name ______ Class ______ Date ______

Alternative Activity: Student Worksheet **for 6-4**

Volumes of Prisms and Cylinders

Prisms and cylinders have the same formula for volume, $V = Bh$, where B is the area of the base of the figure and h is the figure's height. Typically, we measure the base of a rectangular prism in terms of its length and width, and measure the base of a cylinder in terms of its radius.

What You'll Learn Using a computer spreadsheet to find the volumes of prisms

What You'll Need A computer with a spreadsheet program installed

1. Write a volume formula for prisms in terms of length, width, and height. Write a volume formula for cylinders in terms of radius and height.
2. Open a spreadsheet and create four columns across the top: Length, Width, Height, and Volume.
3. Suppose a prism has dimensions of 8, 5, and 3, but you do not know which is length, which is width, or which is height. Fill in the six possible prisms in six rows of your spreadsheet.
4. What do you think will happen to volume when length, width, and height are interchanged? Explain your reasoning.
5. Write a volume formula and copy it into the six rows of your spreadsheet. Explain what you find as a result and why.
6. Repeat the process for cylinders, using a new spreadsheet with three columns: Radius, Height and Volume.
7. Will a cylinder with radius 4 and height 6 have the same volume as one with radius 6 and height 4? Explain your reasoning.
8. Enter the cylinders into your spreadsheet. Then write a volume formula and copy it into each row. Explain what you find as a result and why.

for use with theorems 6-6 and 6-7, Example 1, and Example 2, uses geometry software to explore volume of rectangular prisms and cylinders.

Alternative Activity for Lesson 6-5

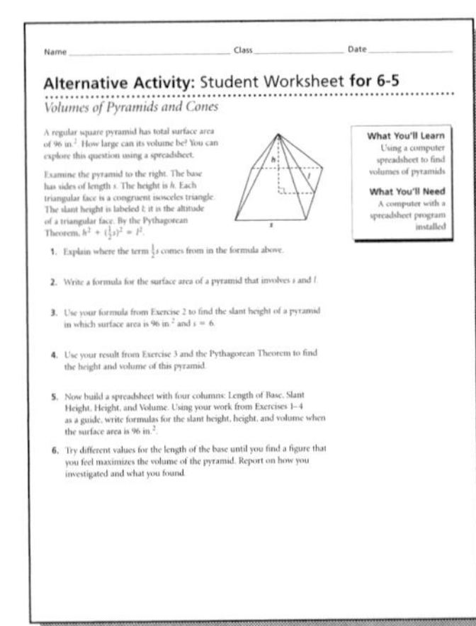

Name ______ Class ______ Date ______

Alternative Activity: Student Worksheet **for 6-5**

Volumes of Pyramids and Cones

A regular square pyramid has total surface area of 96 in.^{2} How large can its volume be? You can explore this question using a spreadsheet.

Examine the pyramid to the right. The base has sides of length s. The height is h. Each triangular face is a congruent isosceles triangle. The slant height is labeled l; it is the altitude of a triangular face. By the Pythagorean Theorem, $h^2 + (\frac{1}{2}s)^2 = l^2$.

What You'll Learn Using a computer spreadsheet to find volumes of pyramids

What You'll Need A computer with a spreadsheet program installed

1. Explain where the term $\frac{1}{2}s$ comes from in the formula above.
2. Write a formula for the surface area of a pyramid that involves s and l.
3. Use your formula from Exercise 2 to find the slant height of a pyramid in which surface area is 96 in.^{2} and $s = 6$.
4. Use your result from Exercise 3 and the Pythagorean Theorem to find the height and volume of this pyramid.
5. Now build a spreadsheet with four columns: Length of Base, Slant Height, Height, and Volume. Using your work from Exercises 1–4 as a guide, write formulas for the slant height, height, and volume when the surface area is 96 in.^{2}.
6. Try different values for the length of the base until you find a figure that you feel maximizes the volume of the pyramid. Report on how you investigated and what you found.

for use with theorem 6-8, Example 1, and Example 2, uses geometry software to explore volume of pyramids and creates a formula for the surface area of the pyramids.

Cooperative Learning Tips

When used effectively, cooperative learning can help students develop interpersonal skills, learn to perform specific roles in a group, and learn to carry out specific responsibilities. The components of Chapter 6 provide a range of cooperative learning opportunities.

- In the Student Edition, the ***Work Together*** parts of lessons are specifically designed for cooperative learning activities.
- In the Teacher's Edition, you will find helpful hints for addressing diverse learning styles (see page C for Chapter 6). For every lesson, you will find a ***Reteaching Activity***, which may involve cooperative learning.

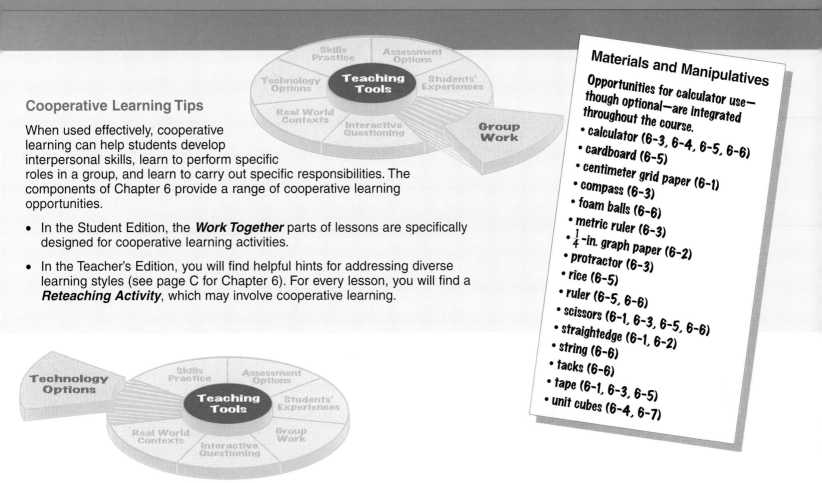

Materials and Manipulatives

Opportunities for calculator use—though optional—are integrated throughout the course.

- calculator (6-3, 6-4, 6-5, 6-6)
- cardboard (6-5)
- centimeter grid paper (6-1)
- compass (6-3)
- foam balls (6-6)
- metric ruler (6-3)
- $\frac{1}{4}$-in. graph paper (6-2)
- protractor (6-3)
- rice (6-5)
- ruler (6-5, 6-6)
- scissors (6-1, 6-3, 6-5, 6-6)
- straightedge (6-1, 6-2)
- string (6-6)
- tacks (6-6)
- tape (6-1, 6-3, 6-5)
- unit cubes (6-4, 6-7)

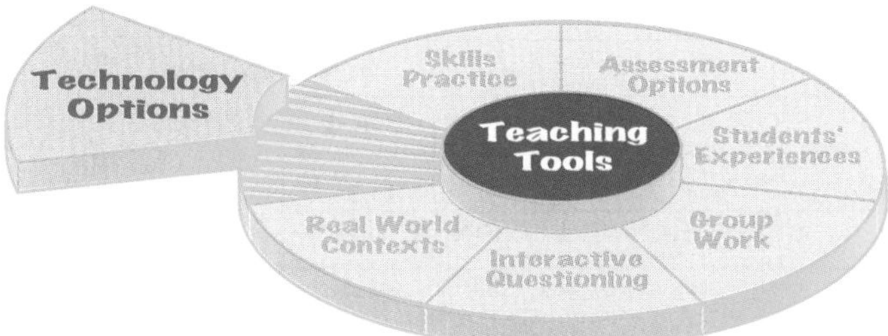

TECHNOLOGY OPTIONS

Technology Tools		Chapter Project	6-1	6-2	6-3	6-4	6-5	6-6	6-7	6-8
Calculator		Numerous opportunities throughout for students to use scientific calculators.								
Software	Secondary Math Lab Toolkit™		✔	✔	✔	✔	✔	✔	✔	✔
	Integrated Math Lab					✔				✔
	Computer Item Generator		✔	✔	✔	✔	✔	✔	✔	✔
	Student Edition			✔T						
Video	Video Field Trip	✔								
CD-ROM	Multimedia Geometry Lab		✔		✔		✔	✔		
Internet		See the Prentice Hall site. (http://www.phschool.com)								

✔T indicates Math Toolbox.

The Prentice Hall Geometry program offers you a rich variety of technology options. Be assured that all these options are provided as a means of enriching the program and are not essential for the successful completion of the course.

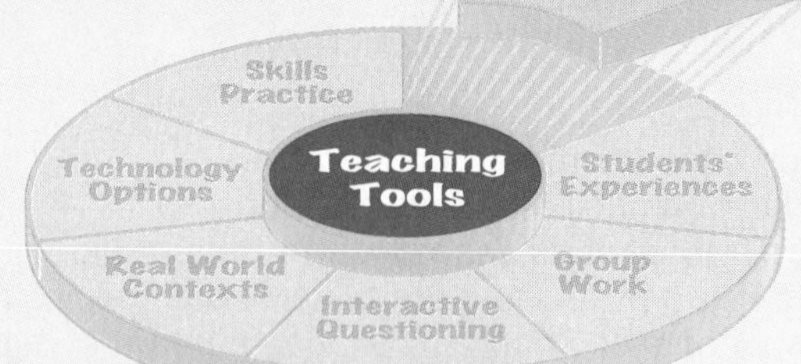

Assessment Options

The Prentice Hall Geometry Program provides you with many options. From these options, you may choose instructional materials and techniques appropriate for your students, or those necessary to meet your district's curriculum requirements. As the chart indicates, the program also supports your teaching efforts by offering you many choices for assessment.

ASSESSMENT OPTIONS

Assessment Support Materials	Chapter Project	6-1	6-2	6-3	6-4	6-5	6-6	6-7	6-8	Chapter End
Chapter Project	▲■●	▲■	▲■		▲■	▲■				▲■
Checkpoints				▲■●			▲■●			
Self-Assessment			▲■		▲■	▲■		▲■	▲■	▲■
Writing Assignment		▲	▲■	▲●	▲■	▲■	▲■●	▲■	▲■	▲●
Chapter Assessment										▲●
Alternative Assessment		■	■	■	■	■	■	■	■	■●
Cumulative Review										▲■●
Standardized Test Prep			▲■	▲	▲■		▲■		▲■	●
Chapters 1–6 Assessment										●
Computer Item Generator	Can be used to create custom-made practice or assessment at any time.									

▲ = Student Edition ■ = Teacher's Edition ● = Teaching Resources

Checkpoints

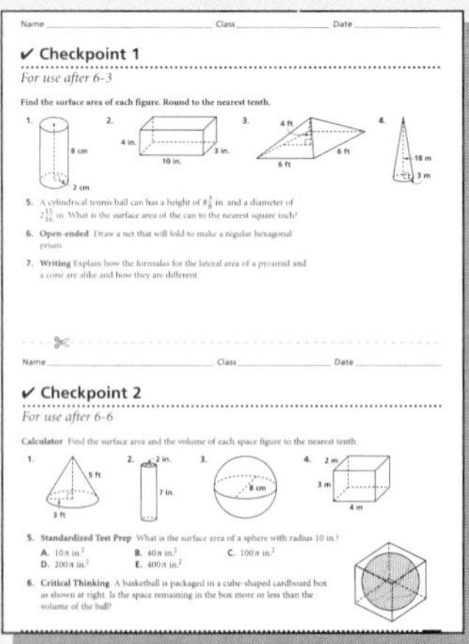
Checkpoint 1
For use after 6-3

Checkpoint 2
For use after 6-6

Alternative Assessment

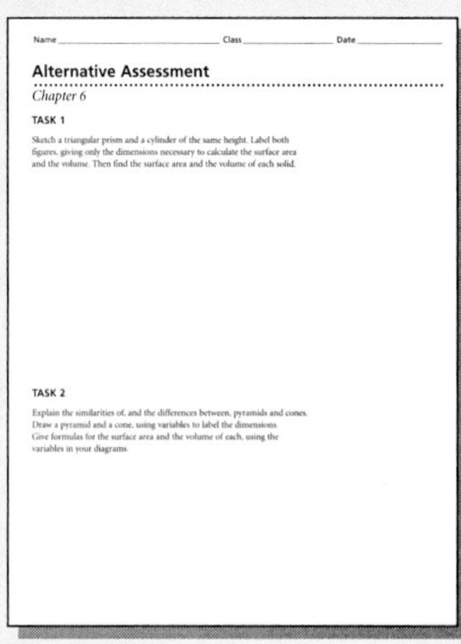
Alternative Assessment
Chapter 6

TASK 1

TASK 2

Chapter Assessment

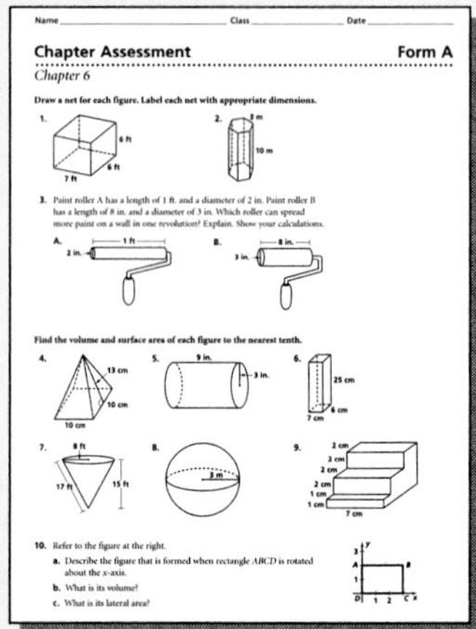
Chapter Assessment Form A
Chapter 6

Available in both Form A and Form B

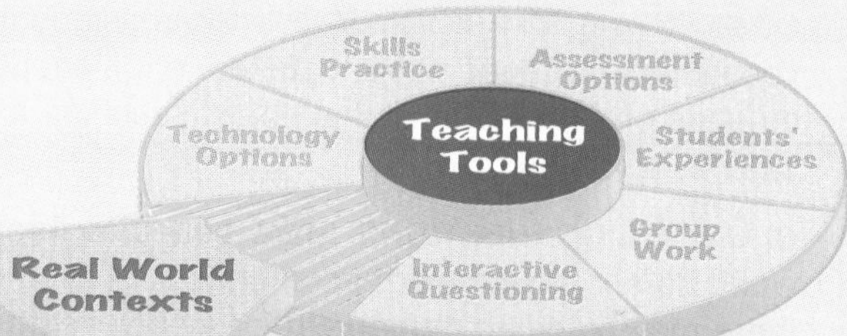

Making the Right Connections

Mathematics is imbedded in nearly every walk of life. The National Council of Teachers of Mathematics (NCTM) encourages educators to recognize these connections and to emphasize them for the purpose of better educating students for success in life and in a global economy. The ***Connections*** chart below highlights these connections for Chapter 6.

CONNECTIONS

Lesson	Interdisciplinary Connections	Career Prep	Other Real World Connections	Math Integration	NCTM Standards
Chapter Project	Economics	Design Manufacturing			Connection Problem Solving
6-1	History Biology	Manufacturing	Textiles Cracker Box		Connections Communication Problem Solving
6-2	History	Design Machinery	CD Cases Video Cassette Boxes Frieze Patterns	Algebra Geometry in 3 Dimensions Coordinate Geometry	Connections Communication Problem Solving
6-3	Social Studies	Manufacturing Architecture	Great Pyramid of Giza Tower Roofs Hourglass	Algebra Coordinate Geometry	Connections Communication Problem Solving
6-4	Geography	Environmental Engineer Plumbing	Aquarium Tanks Water-Supply Tunnel Landscaping	Geometry in 3 Dimensions	Connections Communication Problem Solving
6-5		Architecture	Teepee Transamerica Building	Algebra Coordinate Geometry	Connections Communication Problem Solving
6-6	Science Geography	Manufacturing	Soccer Balls Ball of String Meteorology	Algebra Coordinate Geometry Geometry in 3 Dimensions	Connections Communication Problem Solving
6-7		Manufacturing Engineering	Silo Backpack Carpentry	Algebra Coordinate Geometry	Connections Communication Problem Solving
6-8	Astronomy		Commuting Dart Game Archery Sonar Sub		Probability Communication Problem Solving

CHAPTER 6 Measuring in Space

CONNECTING TO PRIOR LEARNING Ask students to use vocabulary from geometry to describe the shapes of the sides or faces of three-dimensional objects such as a desk, a filing cabinet, or a flag pole.

CULTURAL CONNECTIONS Many countries throughout the world do not have supermarket chains. In such countries, there may be different markets for meats, fish, produce, and dry goods. Ask students what the advantages and disadvantages are of being able to buy all their groceries at one large supermarket. Have students who have lived in or visited countries outside the United States share with the class their knowledge of bazaars and markets.

INTERDISCIPLINARY CONNECTIONS There are approximately 23,000 supermarkets in the United States. Supermarkets represent only 10% of U.S. food stores, but supermarkets sell 70% of the food. Students might be interested in researching the history of supermarkets and superstores in the United States.

Technology Options

Prentice Hall Technology

Video
Video Field Trip 6, "The Perfect Cut," an introduction to the work of diamond cutters

CHAPTER 6 Measuring in Space

Relating to the Real World

What types of space objects do you observe each day? As you ride down the street, you might pass by an office building, a water tower, or a house with a dormer window. At the grocery store, you see a variety of boxes, containers, cans, and bottles on the shelves. You can describe many space objects as prisms, cylinders, cones, pyramids, or combinations of these. In this chapter you will learn how to find the surface areas and volumes of space objects.

ABOUT THE PROJECT Students explore designs of packages and what a manufacturer might consider when designing the packaging of a product. Then they design and construct their own package.

Launching the Project

PROJECT NOTEBOOK Encourage students to keep all project-related materials in a separate folder or notebook. See Chapter Project Manager and Scoring Rubric in Chapter Support File.

- Ask students: *Why are the drinks you buy at a fast food restaurant sold in cups that are wider at the top than at the bottom? Why are books rectangular and not round or trapezoid-shaped? Why are many toys in packages unassembled?*
- Ask students if the package design of any products they use has changed (toothpaste containers, soft drink containers, juice boxes). Why do they think the packaging has been changed?

TRACKING THE PROJECT You may wish to have students read Finishing the Chapter Project on page 353 to help them get an overview of the project. Set benchmark deadlines for students to show their work in progress.

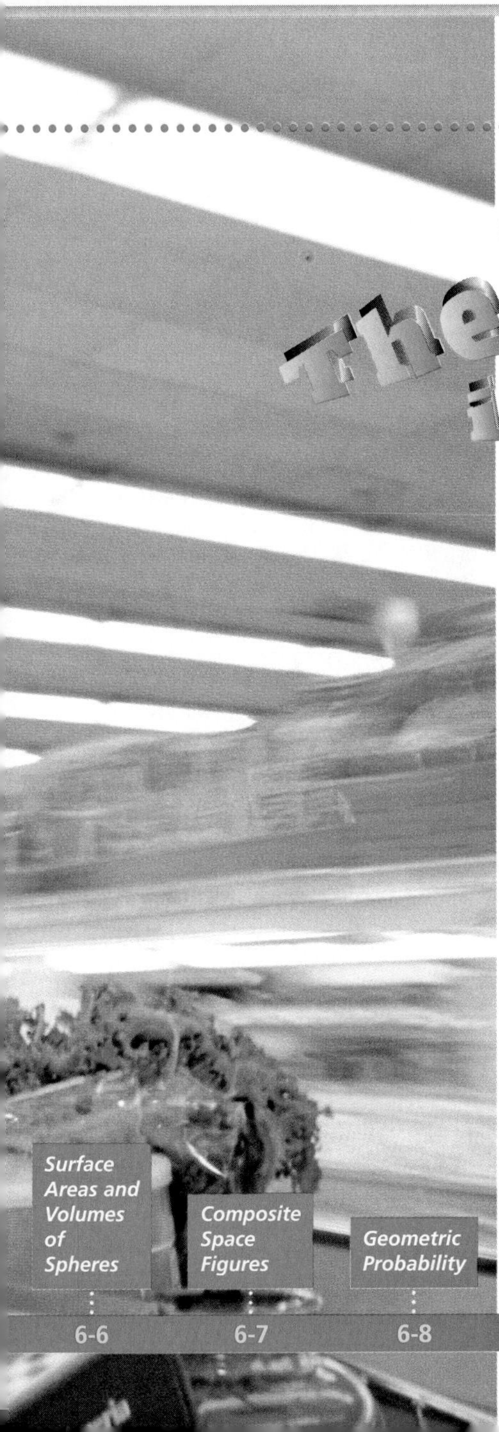

CHAPTER PROJECT

The Place is Packed

Walk into any supermarket and look at the shapes lining the shelves. Bottles of ketchup are tapered like cones. Boxes of cereal stand tall and wide but not too deep. Cylindrical cans of tuna are short and wide. Manufacturers consider dozens of factors before determining which shape will best suit the consumer and boost the company's profits.

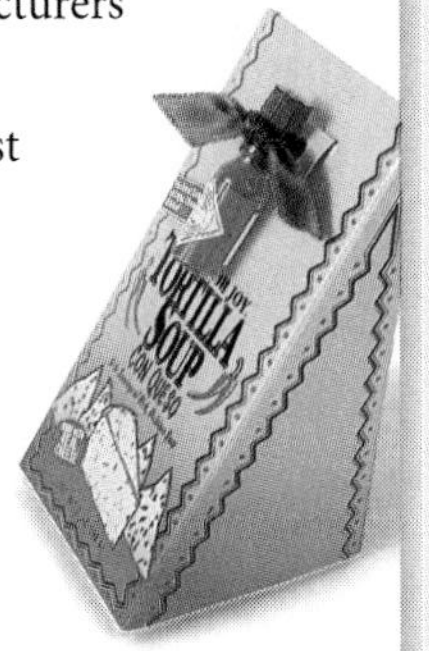

In this chapter project, you will explore package design and uncover some of the reasons for the shapes that manufacturers have chosen. You will also design and construct your own package. You will see how spatial sense and business sense go hand in hand to determine the shapes of things you use every day.

To help you complete the project:

Surface Areas and Volumes of Spheres 6-6

Composite Space Figures 6-7

Geometric Probability 6-8

Project Resources

Teaching Resources

Chapter Support File, Ch. 6
- Chapter Project Manager and Scoring Rubric

Transparencies
68

Using the Rubric

Sharing the scoring rubric for the project with your students will alert them to your expectations before they begin work on the project.

As students complete each Find Out question in the chapter, you may wish to have them evaluate their own work or a partner's work based on the scoring rubric. Students should have the opportunity to revise their work after it has been reviewed.

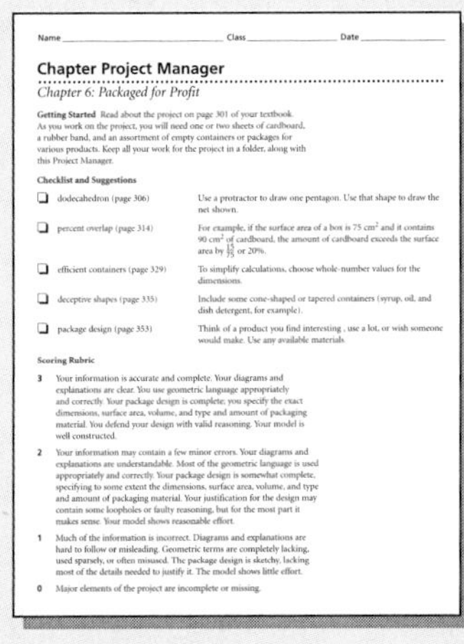

Name ______ Class ______ Date ______

Chapter Project Manager

Chapter 6: Packaged for Profit

Getting Started Read about the project on page 301 of your textbook. As you work on the project, you will need one or two sheets of cardboard, a rubber band, and an assortment of empty containers or packages for various products. Keep all your work for the project in a folder, along with this Project Manager.

Checklist and Suggestions

❑ dodecahedron (page 306)	Use a protractor to draw one pentagon. Use that shape to draw the net shown.
❑ percent overlap (page 314)	For example, if the surface area of a box is 75 cm^2 and it contains 90 cm^2 of cardboard, the amount of cardboard exceeds the surface area by $\frac{15}{75}$ or 20%.
❑ efficient containers (page 329)	To simplify calculations, choose whole-number values for the dimensions.
❑ deceptive shapes (page 335)	Include some cone-shaped or tapered containers (syrup, oil, and dish detergent, for example).
❑ package design (page 353)	Think of a product you find interesting , use a lot, or wish someone would make. Use any available materials.

Scoring Rubric

3 Your information is accurate and complete. Your diagrams and explanations are clear. You use geometric language appropriately and correctly. Your package design is complete; you specify the exact dimensions, surface area, volume, and type and amount of packaging material. You defend your design with valid reasoning. Your model is well constructed.

2 Your information may contain a few minor errors. Your diagrams and explanations are understandable. Most of the geometric language is used appropriately and correctly. Your package design is somewhat complete, specifying to some extent the dimensions, surface area, volume, and type and amount of packaging material. Your justification for the design may contain some loopholes or faulty reasoning, but for the most part it makes sense. Your model shows reasonable effort.

1 Much of the information is incorrect. Diagrams and explanations are hard to follow or misleading. Geometric terms are completely lacking, used sparsely, or often misused. The package design is sketchy, lacking most of the details needed to justify it. The model shows little effort.

0 Major elements of the project are incomplete or missing.

6-1 Teaching Notes

PROBLEM OF THE DAY

A rectangle encloses a triangle and a quarter circle. Find the area of the shaded region to the nearest tenth. 91.5 in.^{2}

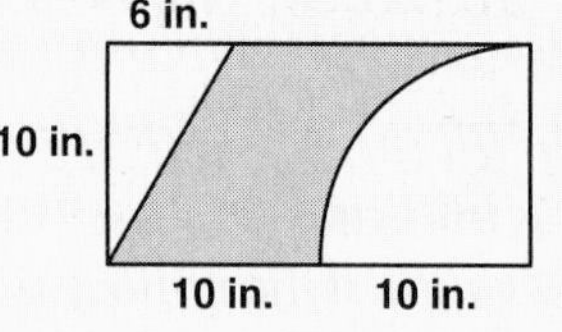

Problem of the Day is also available in Transparencies.

CONNECTING TO PRIOR KNOWLEDGE Ask students to give examples of three-dimensional objects in the classroom. Have them describe the objects using geometric terms. Then have them create a classification system for the objects using "objects with a square side," "objects with a circular side," "objects that have points," etc.

THINK AND DISCUSS p. 302

ESL VISUAL LEARNING Make sure students understand the difference between "polyhedron" and "polygon." Have available models of different polyhedrons and cutouts of different polygons for students to manipulate.

ERROR ALERT! Some students may think that spheres and cylinders are polyhedrons. **Remediation:** Emphasize that the surfaces of polyhedrons are polygons.

WORK TOGETHER p. 302

Provide students with centimeter grid paper to use for the nets. Have students keep their models to use in the next Work Together on page 303.

Lesson Planning Options

Prerequisite Skills

- Recognizing polygons

Assignment Options for Exercises On Your Own

Core 1–16
✪Extension 17

Use Mixed Review to maintain skills.

Resources

 **Student Edition**

Skills Handbook, pp. 660, 662, 673
Extra Practice, p. 653
Glossary/Study Guide

Teaching Resources

Chapter Support File, Ch. 6
- Practice 6-1 (two worksheets)
- Reteaching 6-1

Classroom Manager 6-1
Glossary, Spanish Resources

 **Transparencies** 2, 7, 69

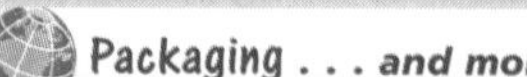

6-1 Space Figures and Nets

What You'll Learn
- Recognizing nets of various space figures

...And Why

To help you visualize the faces of space figures that you encounter in everyday life

What You'll Need

straightedge, centimeter grid paper, scissors, tape

THINK AND DISCUSS

As you can see in the photo below, most buildings are polyhedrons. A **polyhedron** is a three-dimensional figure whose surfaces are polygons. The polygons are the **faces** of the polyhedron. An **edge** is a segment that is the intersection of two faces. A **vertex** is a point where edges intersect.

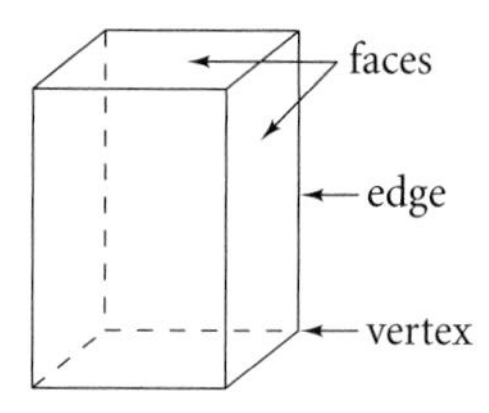

1. a. **Try This** How many faces does the polyhedron below have? 5
   b. How many edges does it have? 9
   c. How many vertices does it have? 6

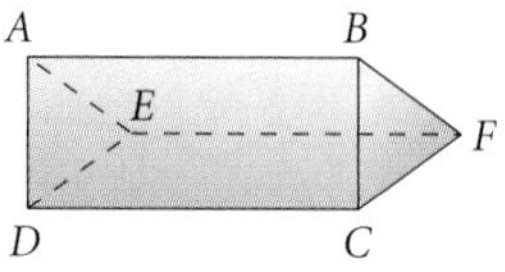

A **net** is a two-dimensional pattern that you can fold to form a three-dimensional figure. Packagers use nets to design boxes.

 Grace Chisholm Young (1868–1944) was the first woman to officially receive a doctorate in Germany. In her *First Book of Geometry,* she provides nets to cut out and fold to help students visualize theorems in solid geometry.

WORK TOGETHER

- Working in a group, draw a larger copy of this net on grid paper. Cut it out and fold it to make a cube.

2. a. Describe the faces of the cube. They are ≅ squares.
   b. Write a definition of cube. See back of book.

- Draw a larger copy of this net on grid paper. Cut it out and fold it to make a pyramid.

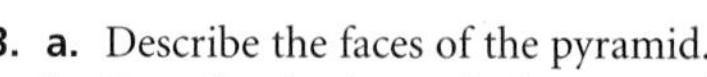

3. a. Describe the faces of the pyramid.
   b. Describe the faces of other pyramids you have seen.
   c. Complete this definition: A pyramid is a polyhedron whose base is a polygon and whose other faces are __?__. triangles

3a. 1 face is a square. The other 4 are △s.

b. Sample: 1 base is a hexagon, 6 faces are △s.

DIVERSITY Students with fine motor difficulties may have trouble cutting and folding nets. It may be easier for students to cut and tape the nets if they make their copies very large.

Question 3b Provide students with models of pyramids that have triangular, square, and hexagonal bases.

THINK AND DISCUSS p. 303

Example *Relating to the Real World* 

Question 4 Help students see that there are many nets for the same polyhedron. The net depends on how the polyhedron is "unfolded."

CONNECTING TO STUDENTS' WORLD Have each student bring in an empty cereal, pasta, tissue, or other type of box to cut into a net. Remember to have them cut off any overlapping sections.

WORK TOGETHER p. 303

Give students centimeter grid paper to use for their nets. Students will also need the cube and pyramid models they made in the Work Together on page 302.

Question 6 The objective is for students to derive the formula $E = F + V - 2$. Note that this is equivalent to $F + V = E + 2$.

THINK AND DISCUSS

Example *Relating to the Real World* 

Packaging Draw a net for the graham cracker box. Label the net with the appropriate dimensions.

20 cm
7 cm
14 cm

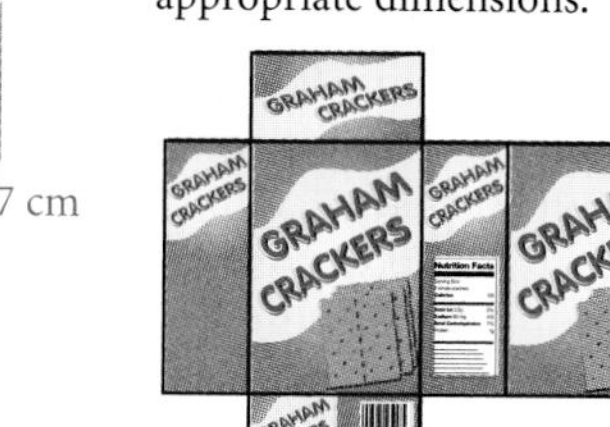

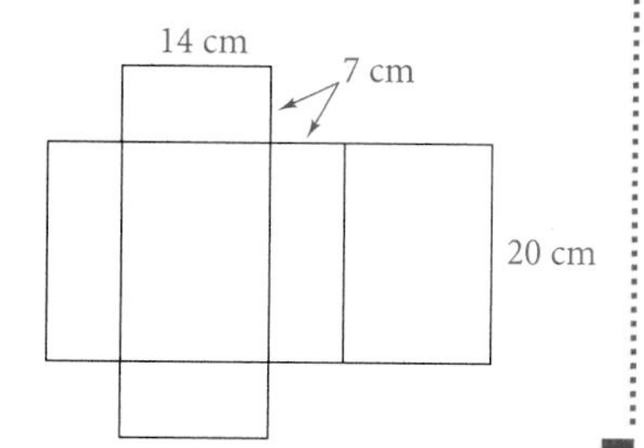

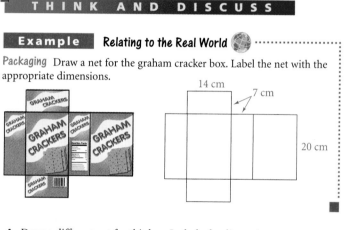

4. Draw a different net for this box. Include the dimensions. See back of book.

WORK TOGETHER

Work in a group to draw larger copies of the nets below. Use the nets to make three-dimensional models.

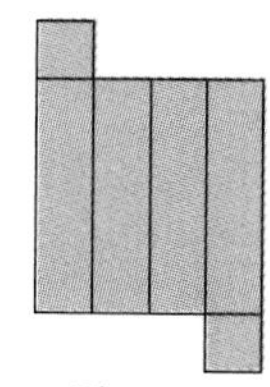
Figure 1

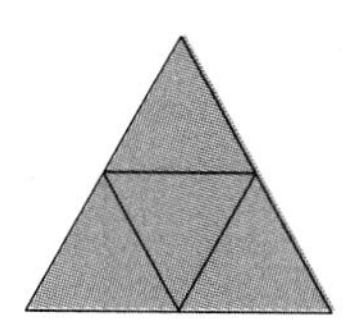
Figure 2

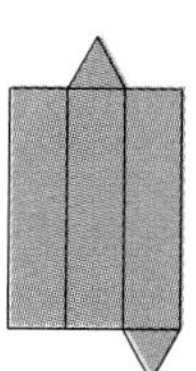
Figure 3

5. Complete the table below, using these three models and the cube and pyramid you made for the Work Together on page 302.

Polyhedron	Number of Faces (F)	Number of Vertices (V)	Number of Edges (E)
Cube	6	8	12
Pyramid	5	5	8
Figure 1	6	8	12
Figure 2	4	4	6
Figure 3	5	6	9

6. Look for a pattern in your table. Write a formula for E in terms of F and V. Then, compare your results with those of other groups. Euler discovered that this relationship is true for any polyhedron. This formula is known as Euler's Formula. $E = F + V - 2$

Additional Examples

FOR EXAMPLE

Draw a net for the cereal box. Label the net with the appropriate dimensions.

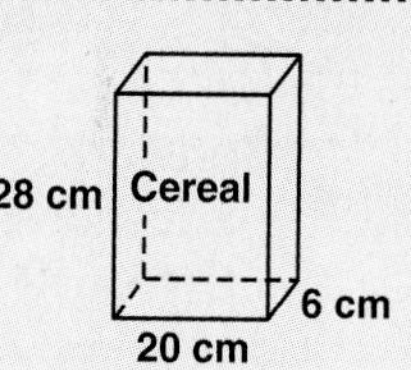

Answers will vary. Sample:

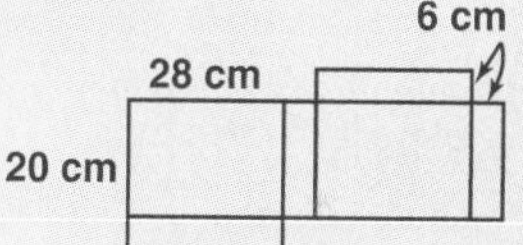

Draw a net for the tissue box. Label the net with the appropriate dimensions.

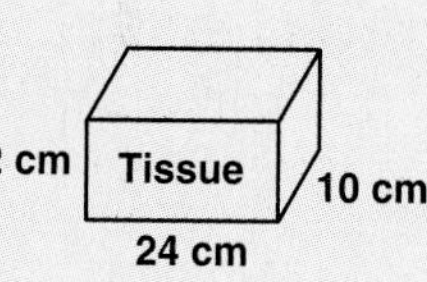

Answers will vary. Sample:

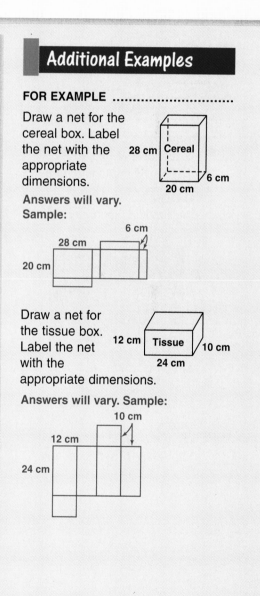

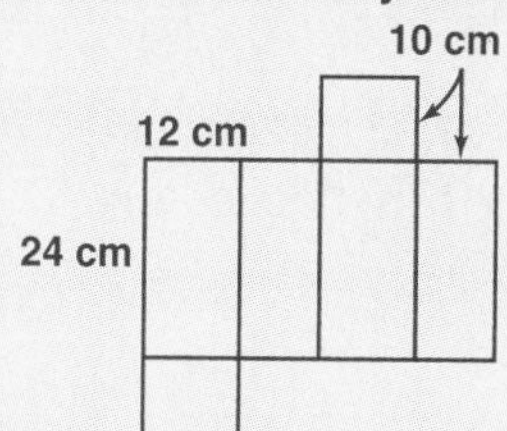

Exercises ON YOUR OWN

Exercises 1–7 Students may want to make larger copies of the nets, cut them out, and fold them to make the polyhedrons.

ALTERNATIVE ASSESSMENT **Exercises 3–7** You may want to assess students' understanding of nets by drawing five figures similar to those shown in Exercises 3–7 and have students make a net for each figure.

DIVERSITY **Exercise 8** Have students research geometric figures in the textiles of native cultures and have them present their findings to the class.

Technology Options

Prentice Hall Technology

Software

- Secondary Math Lab Toolkit™
- Computer Item Generator 6-1

CD-ROM

- Multimedia Geometry Lab 6

Internet

- See the Prentice Hall site. (http://www.phschool.com)

Exercises ON YOUR OWN

1. Which nets will fold to make a cube? A, B, D

A. 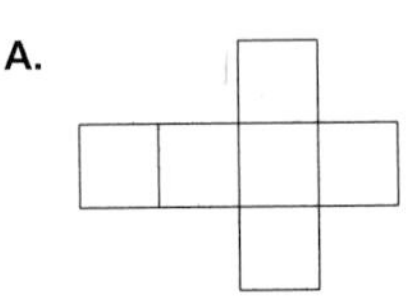
B. 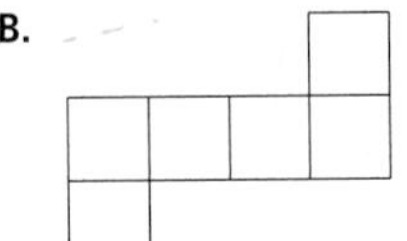
C. 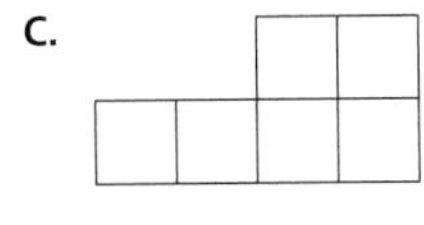
D. 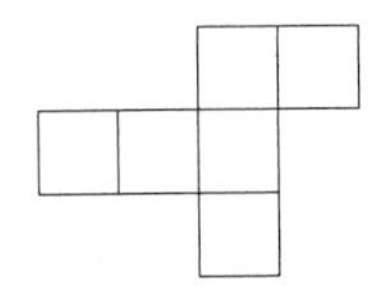

2. Which nets will fold to make a pyramid with a square base? A, B, D

A. 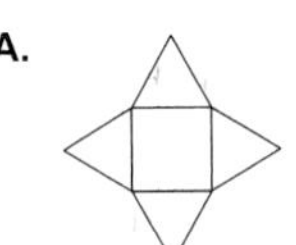
B. 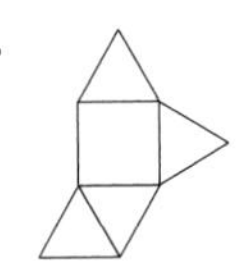
C. 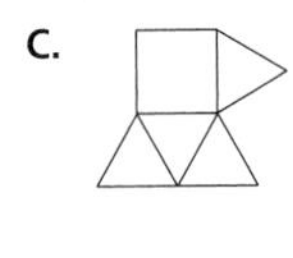
D. 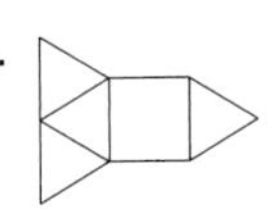

Match each three-dimensional figure with its net.

3. B 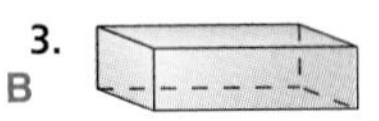
4. D 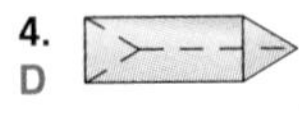
5. E 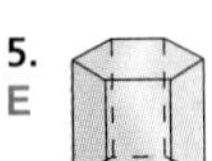
6. C 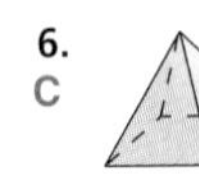
7. A 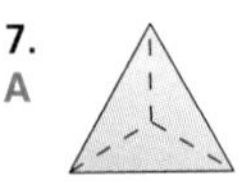

A. 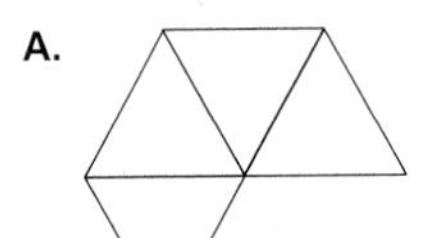
B. 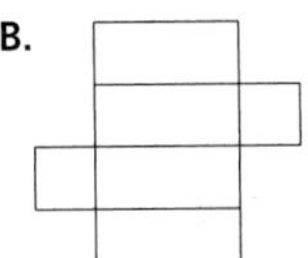
C. 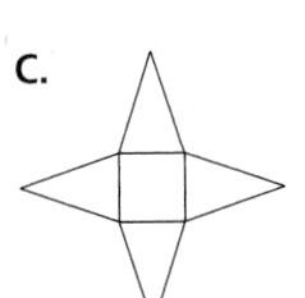
D. 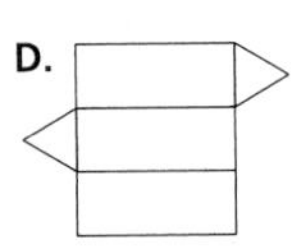
E. 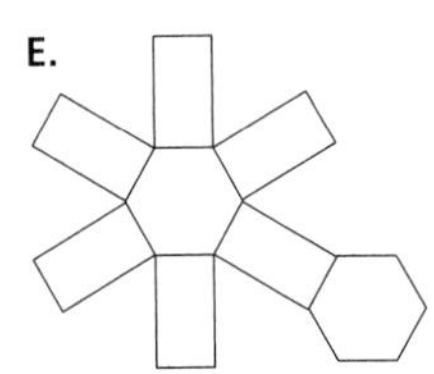

See below.

8. The fourth-century Andean textile at the right is now on display at the Museum of Fine Arts, Boston, Massachusetts.
   a. Which of the three outlined figures could be nets for the same polyhedron?
   b. Describe this polyhedron.

   a. Fig. 2 and Fig. 3
   b. a cube

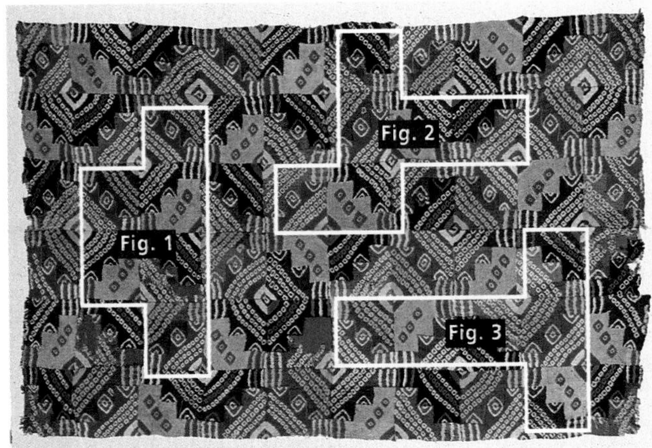

EXTENSION Exercise 13 A hexomino piece is formed by connecting six squares so that each square shares at least one side with another square. Have students work in groups to discover all possible hexominoes which fold to form cubes.

Exercise 14 Encourage students to use a template for an equilateral triangle and a square with the same side length to draw each net. Then they can cut the nets out and check that they fold to form pyramids.

RESEARCH Exercise 17 You may ask students to research Platonic Solids or Archimedean Solids as an extra credit project.

CRITICAL THINKING Exercise 17b Ask students why the Platonic Solids are named as they are.

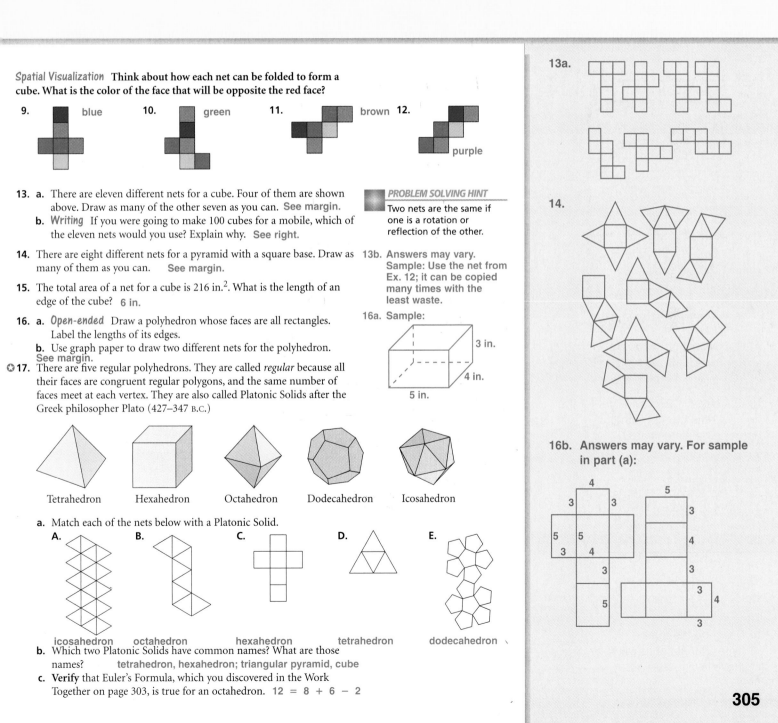

Spatial Visualization **Think about how each net can be folded to form a cube. What is the color of the face that will be opposite the red face?**

9. 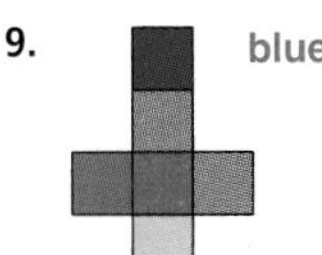 blue

10. 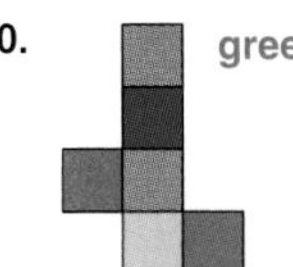 green

11. 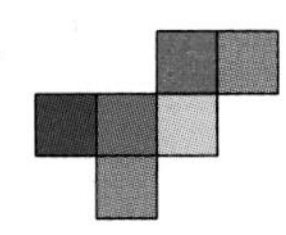 brown

12. 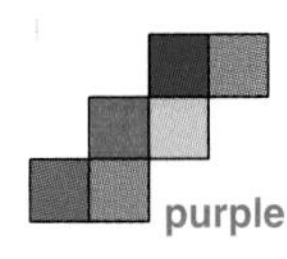 purple

13. a. There are eleven different nets for a cube. Four of them are shown above. Draw as many of the other seven as you can. See margin.

b. *Writing* If you were going to make 100 cubes for a mobile, which of the eleven nets would you use? Explain why. See right.

14. There are eight different nets for a pyramid with a square base. Draw as many of them as you can. See margin.

15. The total area of a net for a cube is 216 in.^{2}. What is the length of an edge of the cube? 6 in.

16. a. *Open-ended* Draw a polyhedron whose faces are all rectangles. Label the lengths of its edges.

b. Use graph paper to draw two different nets for the polyhedron. See margin.

17. There are five regular polyhedrons. They are called *regular* because all their faces are congruent regular polygons, and the same number of faces meet at each vertex. They are also called Platonic Solids after the Greek philosopher Plato (427–347 B.C.)

PROBLEM SOLVING HINT

Two nets are the same if one is a rotation or reflection of the other.

13b. Answers may vary. Sample: Use the net from Ex. 12; it can be copied many times with the least waste.

16a. Sample:

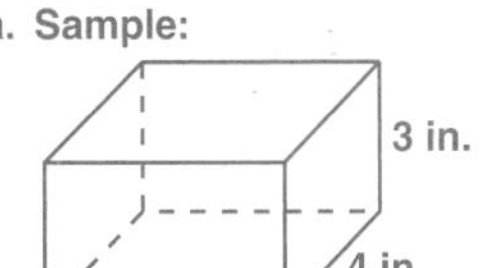
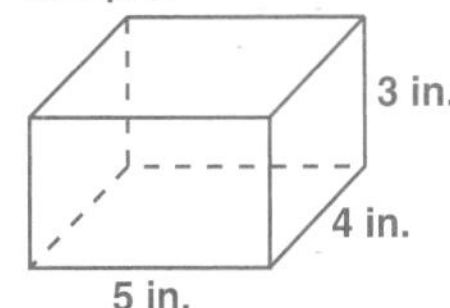

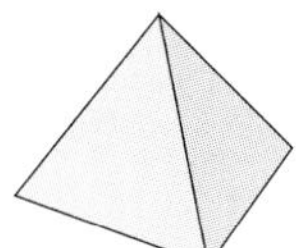
Tetrahedron

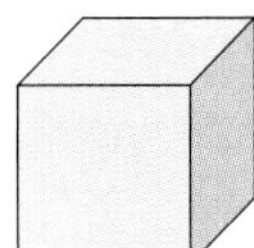
Hexahedron

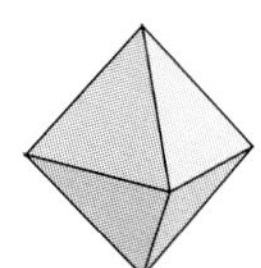
Octahedron

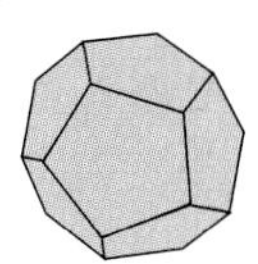
Dodecahedron

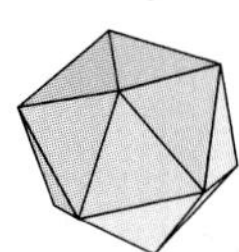
Icosahedron

a. Match each of the nets below with a Platonic Solid.

A. 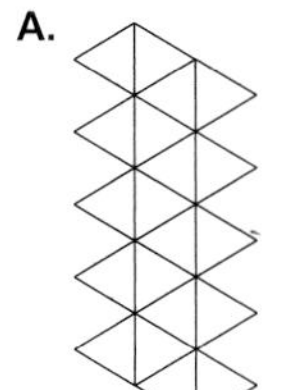 icosahedron

B. 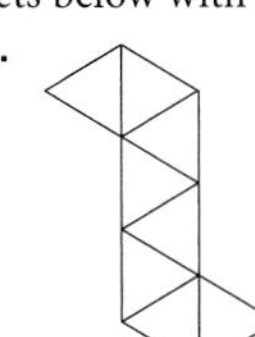 octahedron

C. 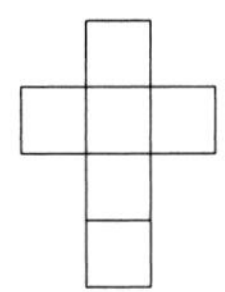 hexahedron

D. 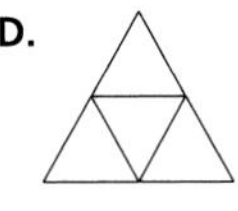 tetrahedron

E. 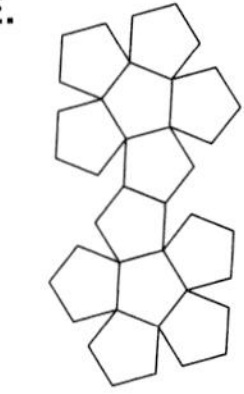 dodecahedron

b. Which two Platonic Solids have common names? What are those names? tetrahedron, hexahedron; triangular pyramid, cube

c. Verify that Euler's Formula, which you discovered in the Work Together on page 303, is true for an octahedron. $12 = 8 + 6 - 2$

13a.

14.

16b. Answers may vary. For sample in part (a):

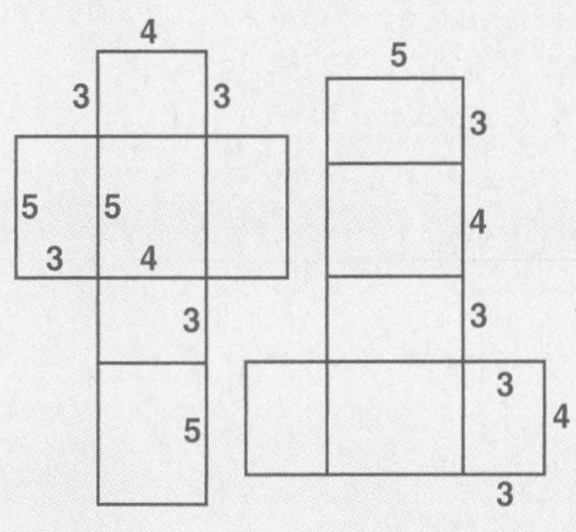

Chapter Project **FIND OUT BY DOING** You may want to provide students with a template for them to copy. Students may want to color or decorate their nets before forming the dodecahedron.

Exercises MIXED REVIEW

OPEN-ENDED Exercise 19 Have students classify the triangles they draw by their sides and angles.

Exercise 20 Students will need a compass and a straightedge.

GETTING READY FOR LESSON 6-2 These exercises prepare students to find the surface area of a solid.

Wrap Up

THE BIG IDEA Ask students to state the relationship between the vertices, edges, and faces of a polyhedron. Have them give two real-world examples of polyhedrons and show that their vertices, edges, and faces satisfy this formula.

RETEACHING ACTIVITY Students draw nets for a right triangular prism and count the number of vertices, faces, and edges. (Reteaching worksheet 6-1)

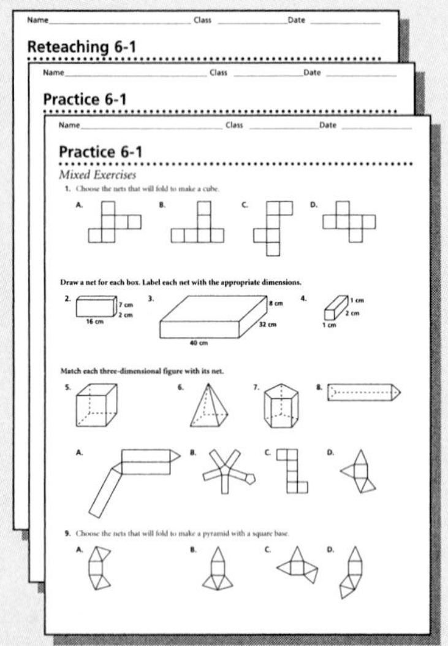

Lesson Quiz

Lesson Quiz is also available in Transparencies.

In Exercises 1–2, draw a net for the figure. Label the net with the appropriate dimensions.

1. See back of book.

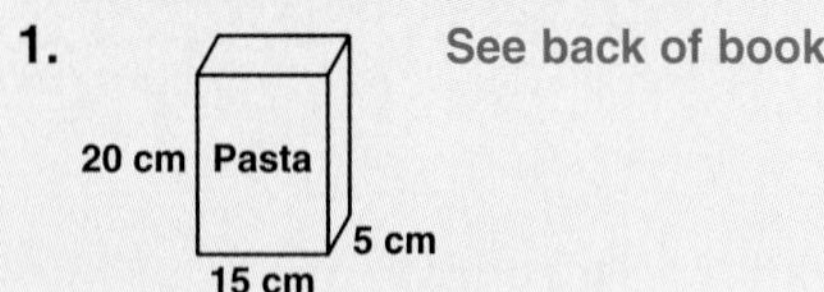

2. See back of book.

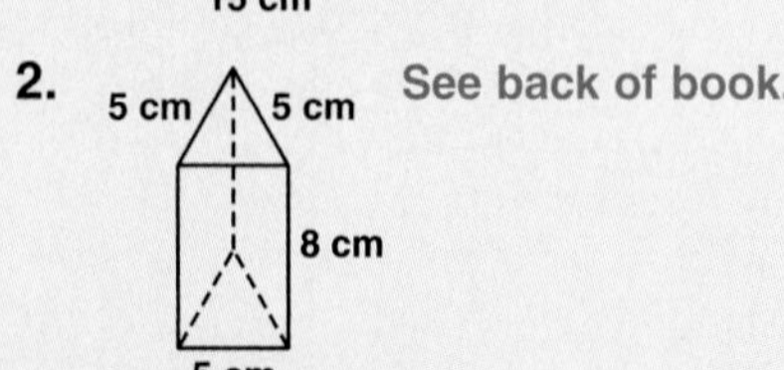

3. Describe the three-dimensional figure with the following net.

a pyramid with a hexagonal base

Chapter Project — Find Out by Doing

With one or two sheets of cardboard and a rubber band, you can make a pop-up version of one of the Platonic Solids.

- Draw and cut out two larger copies of this net. All of the faces are congruent regular pentagons.
- Fold along the dotted lines and then flatten again.
- Place one net on top of the other as shown. (The flaps of the top pattern should fold downward and the flaps of the bottom upward.) Hold the patterns flat and stretch a rubber band (shown in red) over and under the protruding vertices. Watch the flat patterns pop into a dodecahedron. Check students' work.

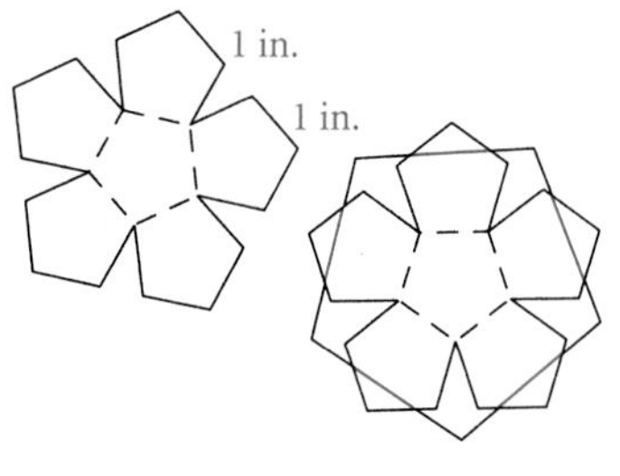

Exercises MIXED REVIEW

18. a. *Biology* The size of a jaguar's territory depends on how much food is available. Where there is a lot of food, such as in a forest, jaguars have circular territories about 3 mi in diameter. Use $\pi \approx 3$ to **estimate** the area of such a region. about 6.75 mi^2
    b. Where food is less available, a jaguar may need up to 200 mi^2. **Estimate** the radius of this circular territory. about 8 mi
19. *Open-ended* Draw a triangle that has no lines of symmetry. sample: a scalene triangle
20. *Constructions* Copy $\overline{TR}$. Construct its perpendicular bisector. See margin p.307

    T ———— R
21. In $\triangle ABC$, $AC = 20$, $AB = 18$, and $BC = 13$. Which angle of the triangle has the greatest measure? $\angle B$

Getting Ready for Lesson 6-2

Find the area of each net.

22. 96 cm^2

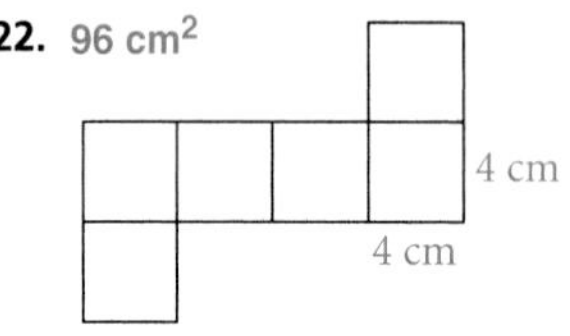

23. 40π cm^2

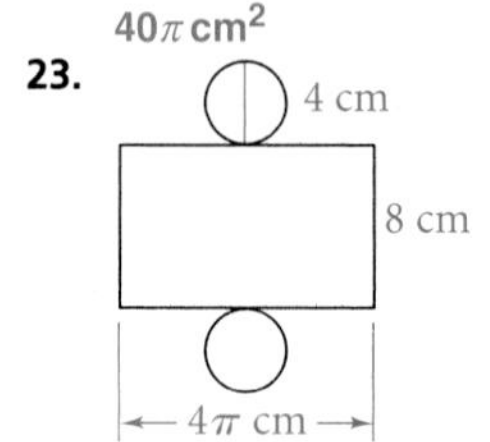

24. $36\sqrt{3}$ m^2

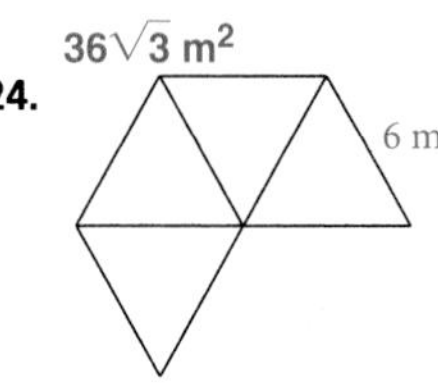

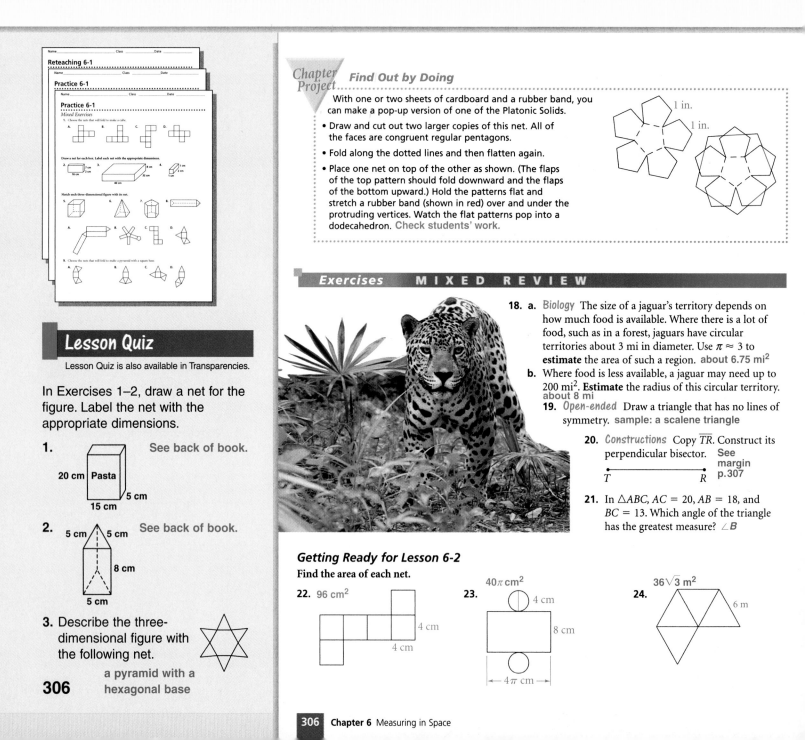

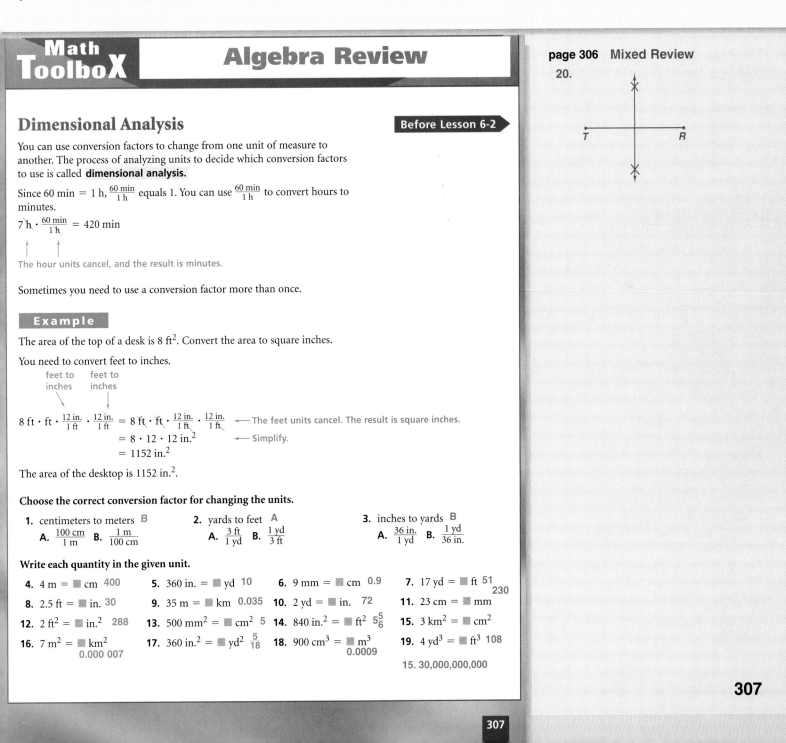

Math ToolboX

Students review how to convert from one unit of measure to another. Students will use this skill when finding the surface area and volume of solids.

Example

ALTERNATIVE APPROACH Some students may want to use the conversion factor $\frac{144 \text{ in.}^2}{1 \text{ ft}^2}$ as follows.

$8 \text{ ft}^2 \cdot \frac{144 \text{ in.}^2}{1 \text{ ft}^2} = 1152 \text{ in.}^2$

You may want to review with students the meaning of the prefixes *kilo-*, *centi-*, and *milli-*.

Exercises 1–3 Make sure students understand that the units being converted *from* should be in the denominator and the units being converted *to* should be in the numerator.

ERROR ALERT! **Exercise 13** Some students will multiply 500 mm^2 by the conversion factor $\frac{1 \text{ cm}}{10 \text{ mm}}$. **Remediation:** Help students see that in order to cancel out mm^2 which means mm · mm, they need to multiply by $\frac{1 \text{ cm}}{10 \text{ mm}} \cdot \frac{1 \text{ cm}}{10 \text{ mm}}$, or $\frac{1 \text{ cm}^2}{100 \text{ mm}^2}$

ALTERNATIVE ASSESSMENT Ask students to complete each statement with >, <, or =.

1. 25 ft^2 __?__ 3 yd^2 <
2. 10 m^2 __?__ 10,000 cm^2 >
3. 10 cm^2 __?__ 1000 mm^2 =
4. 100 in.^{2} __?__ 1 ft^2 <

Math ToolboX Algebra Review

Dimensional Analysis

Before Lesson 6-2

You can use conversion factors to change from one unit of measure to another. The process of analyzing units to decide which conversion factors to use is called **dimensional analysis.**

Since 60 min = 1 h, $\frac{60 \text{ min}}{1 \text{ h}}$ equals 1. You can use $\frac{60 \text{ min}}{1 \text{ h}}$ to convert hours to minutes.

$7 \text{ h} \cdot \frac{60 \text{ min}}{1 \text{ h}} = 420 \text{ min}$

The hour units cancel, and the result is minutes.

Sometimes you need to use a conversion factor more than once.

Example

The area of the top of a desk is 8 ft^2. Convert the area to square inches.

You need to convert feet to inches.

feet to inches, feet to inches

$8 \text{ ft} \cdot \text{ft} \cdot \frac{12 \text{ in.}}{1 \text{ ft}} \cdot \frac{12 \text{ in.}}{1 \text{ ft}} = 8 \text{ ft} \cdot \text{ft} \cdot \frac{12 \text{ in.}}{1 \text{ ft}} \cdot \frac{12 \text{ in.}}{1 \text{ ft}}$ ← The feet units cancel. The result is square inches.

$= 8 \cdot 12 \cdot 12 \text{ in.}^2$ ← Simplify.

$= 1152 \text{ in.}^2$

The area of the desktop is 1152 in.^{2}.

Choose the correct conversion factor for changing the units.

1. centimeters to meters B
   A. $\frac{100 \text{ cm}}{1 \text{ m}}$ B. $\frac{1 \text{ m}}{100 \text{ cm}}$
2. yards to feet A
   A. $\frac{3 \text{ ft}}{1 \text{ yd}}$ B. $\frac{1 \text{ yd}}{3 \text{ ft}}$
3. inches to yards B
   A. $\frac{36 \text{ in.}}{1 \text{ yd}}$ B. $\frac{1 \text{ yd}}{36 \text{ in.}}$

Write each quantity in the given unit.

4. 4 m = ■ cm 400
5. 360 in. = ■ yd 10
6. 9 mm = ■ cm 0.9
7. 17 yd = ■ ft 51
8. 2.5 ft = ■ in. 30
9. 35 m = ■ km 0.035
10. 2 yd = ■ in. 72
11. 23 cm = ■ mm 230
12. 2 ft^2 = ■ in.^{2} 288
13. 500 mm^2 = ■ cm^2 5
14. 840 in.^{2} = ■ ft^2 $5\frac{5}{6}$
15. 3 km^2 = ■ cm^2
16. 7 m^2 = ■ km^2 0.000 007
17. 360 in.^{2} = ■ yd^2 $\frac{5}{18}$
18. 900 cm^3 = ■ m^3 0.0009
19. 4 yd^3 = ■ ft^3 108

15. 30,000,000,000

page 306 Mixed Review

20.

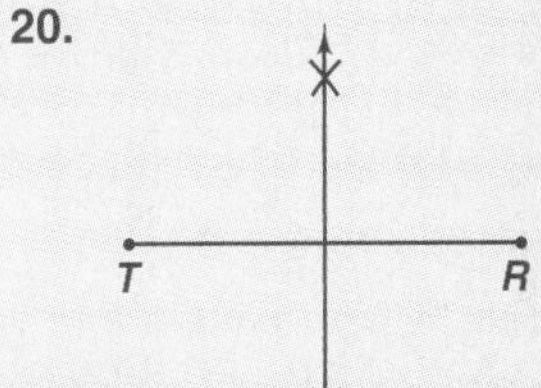

6-2 Teaching Notes

PROBLEM OF THE DAY

A cube with side length 3 units is painted on the outside, then cut into 27 unit cubes. Describe how many faces are painted on each of the unit cubes. **8 with three faces painted, 12 with two faces painted, 6 with one face painted, 1 with no faces painted**

Problem of the Day is also available in Transparencies.

CONNECTING TO PRIOR KNOWLEDGE Ask students to find the area of each of the following nets.

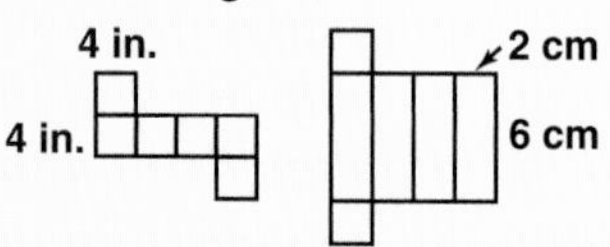

WORK TOGETHER

You may want to bring in old and new CD cases for students to look at before beginning this activity.

Have students begin by carefully taping together four pieces of $\frac{1}{4}$-in. grid paper to form a 23-in. by 16-in. rectangle.

DIVERSITY This activity provides a good opportunity for students to share what music they listen to. Students may want to bring in and play music from their native countries. Encourage students to be tolerant and respectful of other people's preferences in music.

Lesson Planning Options

Prerequisite Skills

- Finding perimeter and area of polygons
- Finding circumference and area of circles

Assignment Options for Exercises On Your Own

To provide flexible scheduling, this lesson can be subdivided into parts.

1 **Core** 1–5, 7 14–16, 22–23
Extension 17

2 **Core** 6, 8–13, 18–21, 24–26
Extension 27

Use Mixed Review to maintain skills.

Resources

Student Edition

Skills Handbook, pp. 660, 667, 673
Extra Practice, p. 653
Glossary/Study Guide

Teaching Resources

Chapter Support File, Ch. 6
- Practice 6-2 (two worksheets)
- Reteaching 6-2
- Alternative Activity 6-2

Classroom Manager 6-2
Glossary, Spanish Resources

Transparencies

15, 16, 18, 69, 73

Connections  Machinery . . . *and more*

6-2 Surface Areas of Prisms and Cylinders

What You'll Learn

- Investigating the surface areas and lateral areas of prisms and cylinders

...And Why

To use surface areas of objects in daily life, from CD cases and videocassette boxes to buildings and storage tanks

What You'll Need

- straightedge
- $\frac{1}{4}$-in. graph paper

WORK TOGETHER

In 1993 the music recording industry changed the size of compact disc packaging. The change to smaller packaging was made in response to the concerns of major recording artists who were worried about the effects of wasted packaging on the environment. Nets for the two packages are shown.

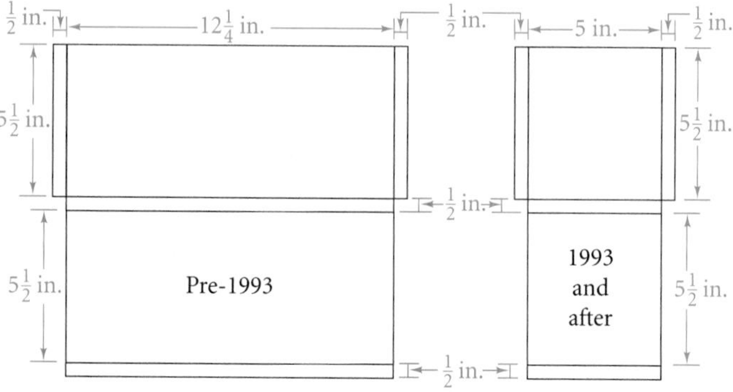

3. Answers may vary. Sample: 2 orig. packages were exactly the same size as 1 vinyl record, so they could fit in the record bins easily.

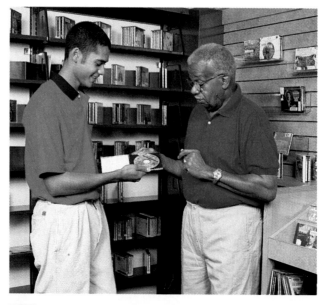

Work with a group. Draw nets on graph paper for each of the two packages.

1. a. What is the area of the net for the pre-1993 CD packaging? $152\frac{1}{2}$ in.^{2}
   b. What is the area of the net for the new, smaller CD packaging? $65\frac{1}{2}$ in.^{2}
   c. How many square inches of packaging are saved by using the smaller packaging? 87 in.^{2}
2. How many pairs of congruent rectangles are in each net? 3 pairs; 3 pairs
3. ***Critical Thinking*** Why do you think the earlier packaging was so large? See above left.

THINK AND DISCUSS

ESL The new vocabulary in this lesson may be overwhelming to some students. You may want to make and display a poster of a prism and a cylinder labeling their parts. Emphasize that the *base of a prism* is a face but the *base of a polygon* is a side.

Question 4 Ask students to explain how a prism is named. Help them see that a prism is classified according to its base.

Have students use the three figures above Question 5 to practice identifying bases, lateral faces, and altitudes. Point out that in the first figure, any pair of opposite faces could be considered the bases.

ERROR ALERT! Some students may think that a right triangular prism is a prism with a base that is a right triangle. **Remediation:** Point out that when "right" describes a prism, the lateral faces are rectangles. Provide physical models and/or draw sketches of right triangular prisms with bases that are not right triangles.

Have students use the diagram at the bottom of the page to give the area of each lateral face. Help students see that $ah + bh + ch + dh = (a + b + c + d)h = ph.$

THINK AND DISCUSS

Part 1

Lateral Areas and Surface Areas of Prisms

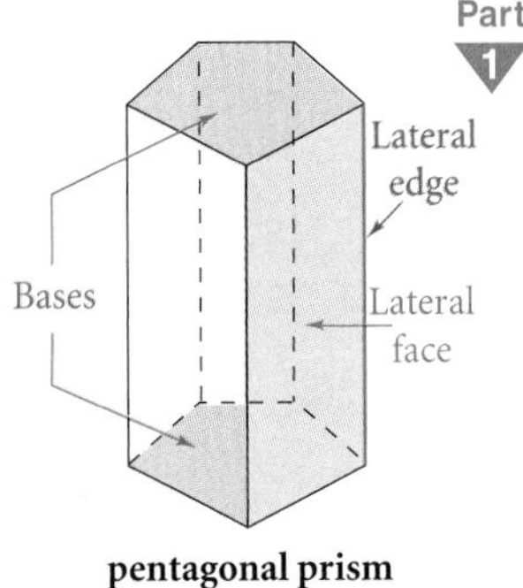

pentagonal prism

The CD packages in the Work Together are examples of rectangular prisms. A **prism** is a polyhedron with two congruent, parallel **bases.** The other faces are **lateral faces.** A prism is named for the shape of its bases.

4. Match each prism with one of the following names: triangular prism, rectangular prism, hexagonal prism, octagonal prism.

a. 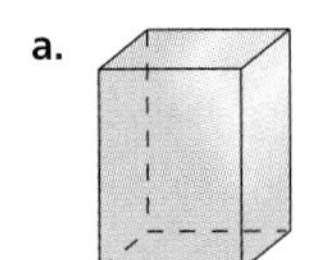
rectangular prism

b. 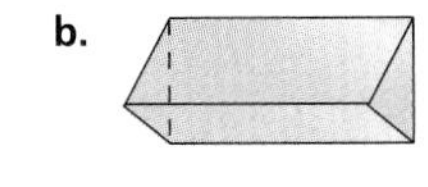
triangular prism

c. 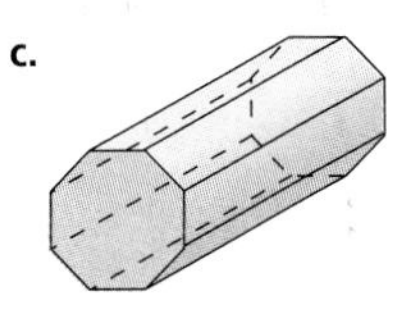
octagonal prism

An **altitude** of a prism is a perpendicular segment that joins the planes of the bases. The **height** *h* of the prism is the length of an altitude. A prism may be either *right* or *oblique.* In a **right prism** the lateral faces are rectangles and a lateral edge is an altitude. In this book you may assume that a prism is a right prism unless you are told otherwise.

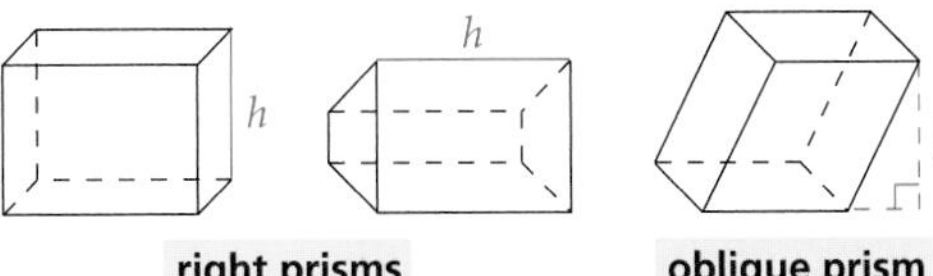

right prisms — oblique prism

5. *Open-ended* Draw a right triangular prism and an oblique triangular prism. Draw and label an altitude in each figure. See margin p. 311.

The **lateral area** of a prism is the sum of the areas of the lateral faces. The **surface area** is the sum of areas of the lateral faces and the two bases. You can also find these areas by using formulas.

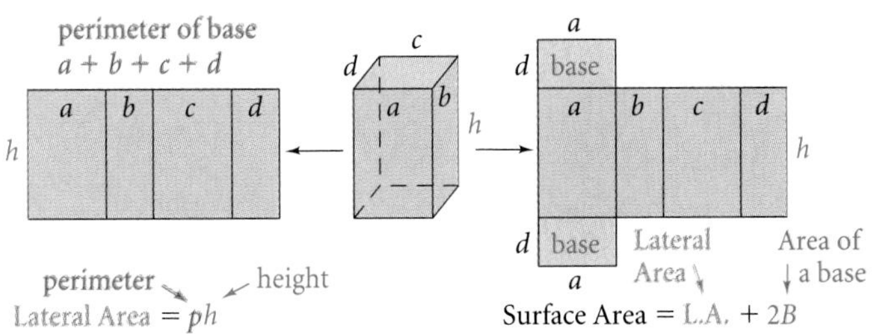

Additional Examples

FOR EXAMPLE 1

A right triangular prism has a height of 5 cm. Its base is an equilateral triangle with side length 2 cm and height $\sqrt{3}$ cm. Find (a) the lateral area and (b) the surface area of the prism. Round your answers to the nearest tenth. **a. 30 cm² b. 33.5 cm²**

FOR EXAMPLE 2

A cylindrical cement pipe has length 500 ft and diameter 3 ft. If you are to paint the exterior of the pipe, how many square feet will you paint? Round your answer to the nearest square foot. **4712 ft²**

Discussion: *If the pipe is 6 in. thick, explain how to find the surface area of the interior of the pipe.*

Theorem 6-1 Make sure that students distinguish between lowercase b and uppercase B. Uppercase B, used in the formula for surface area, refers to the area of a base of the prism, while lowercase b refers to the length of a side of a polygon.

Example 1

Discuss with students the process used to solve each problem. First, the appropriate formula is written. Then, values are substituted for variables and the expression is simplified. Encourage students to use this process. Writing the formulas each time they are used will help students remember them and will reinforce which measures are required.

CRITICAL THINKING Question 6 Ask students to use the formula for the surface area of a right prism to write a special formula for the surface area of a cube.

S.A. $= 4s(s) + 2(s^2) = 6s^2$

Point out that the third cylinder shown on the bottom of the page is called an oblique cylinder. Because the bases of all cylinders are circles, cylinders are not classified as prisms are.

Technology Options

Prentice Hall Technology

Software
- Secondary Math Lab Toolkit™
- Computer Item Generator 6-2

Internet
- See the Prentice Hall site. (http://www.phschool.com)

Theorem 6-1
Lateral and Surface Areas of a Right Prism

The lateral area of a right prism is the product of the perimeter of the base and the height.

$$\text{L.A.} = ph$$

The surface area of a right prism is the sum of the lateral area and the areas of the two bases.

$$\text{S.A.} = \text{L.A.} + 2B$$

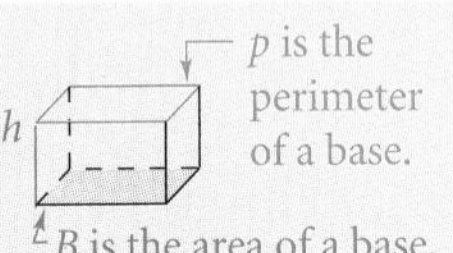

Example 1

Find (a) the lateral area and (b) the surface area of the prism.

The hypotenuse of the triangular base is 5 cm, because the sides form a Pythagorean triple.

a. L.A. $= ph$ — Use the formula for Lateral Area.
$= 12 \cdot 6$ — $p = 3 + 4 + 5 = 12$ cm
$= 72$

The lateral area of the prism is 72 cm^2.

b. S.A. $=$ L.A. $+ 2B$ — Use the formula for Surface Area.
$= 72 + 2(6)$ — $B = \frac{1}{2}(3 \cdot 4) = 6\ \text{cm}^2$
$= 84$

The surface area of the prism is 84 cm^2.

6. **Try This** A **cube** is a prism with square faces. Suppose a cube has edges 5 in. long. What is its lateral area? its surface area?
100 in.^2; 150 in.^2

Part 2

Lateral Areas and Surface Areas of Cylinders

Like a prism, a **cylinder** has two congruent parallel bases. However, the bases of a cylinder are circles. An **altitude** of a cylinder is a perpendicular segment that joins the planes of the bases. The **height** h of a cylinder is the length of an altitude.

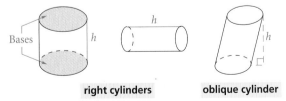

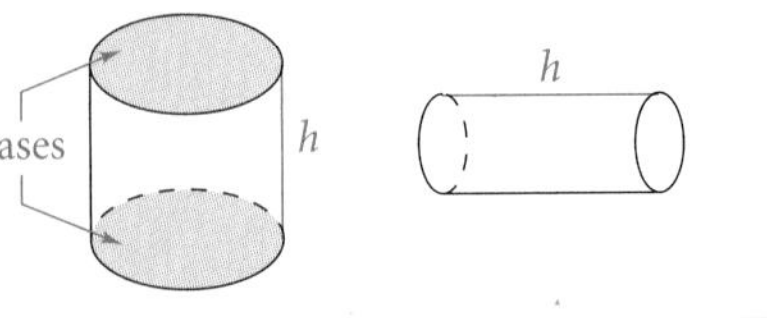

right cylinders **oblique cylinder**

In this book you may assume that a cylinder is a *right* cylinder, like the first two cylinders above, unless you are told otherwise.

TACTILE LEARNING If you have block scheduling or an extended class period, provide students with paper or cardboard cylinders which they can "unroll." Before "unrolling" the cylinders, have students color the edges of the bases. When they "unroll" the cylinder, they will see that each edge they colored is a side of the rectangular region.

Theorem 6-2 Some students may prefer to remember the lateral area of a right cylinder as L.A. = Ch, which is similar to the formula L.A. = ph for prisms.

Example 2 **Relating to the Real World** 

Discuss with students why lateral area is found and not surface area. Provide students with other real-world examples, such as finding the surface area of a cylindrical fence post, a barrel with no top, or a pipe, and ask them to identify what part of they surface area they need to find.

You may want to make a poster of a prism, labeling the base and height, and include the formulas for finding the lateral area and the surface area. Make a similar poster of a cylinder. You can add the formulas for volume after Lesson 6-4. Students can copy the information on index cards, drawing the figure on one side, and writing the formulas on the other.

To find the lateral area of a cylinder, visualize "unrolling" it. The area of the resulting rectangle is the **lateral area** of the cylinder. The **surface area** of a cylinder is the sum of the lateral area and the areas of the two circular bases. You can find formulas for these areas by looking at a net for a cylinder.

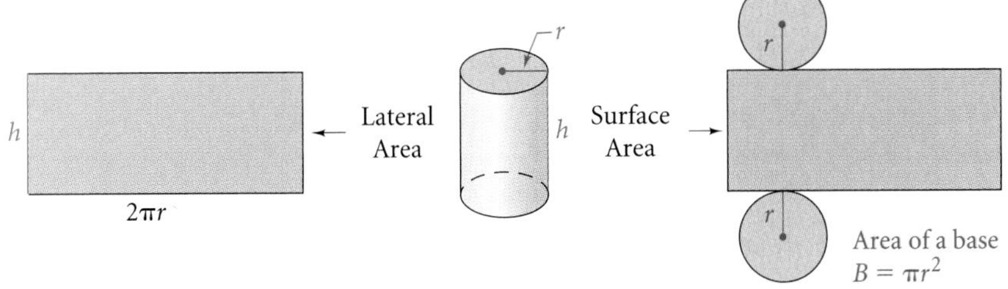

Theorem 6-2
Lateral and Surface Areas of a Right Cylinder

The lateral area of a right cylinder is the product of the circumference of the base and the height of the cylinder.

$$\text{L.A.} = 2\pi rh, \text{ or L.A.} = \pi dh$$

The surface area of a right cylinder is the sum of the lateral area and the areas of the two bases.

$$\text{S.A.} = \text{L.A.} + 2B$$

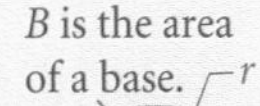

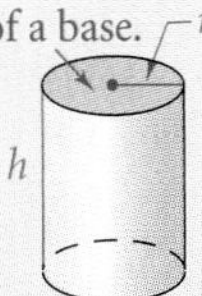

7. **Try This** The radius of the base of a cylinder is 4 in. and its height is 6 in.
   a. Find the lateral area of the cylinder in terms of π. **48π in.^{2}**
   b. Find the surface area of the cylinder in terms of π. **80π in.^{2}**

Example 2 **Relating to the Real World** 

Machinery The wheel of the steamroller at the left is a cylinder. How many square feet does a single revolution of the wheel cover? Round your answer to the nearest square foot.

The area covered is the lateral area of a cylinder that has a diameter of 5 ft and a height of 7.2 ft.

$\text{L.A.} = \pi dh$ — **Use the formula for Lateral Area of a cylinder.**

$= \pi(5)(7.2)$ — **Substitute.**

$= 36\pi$ — **Simplify.**

36 × π = 113.09734

A single revolution of this steamroller wheel covers about 113 ft^2.

8. **Estimation** Use $\pi \approx 3$ to estimate the lateral area and surface area of a cylinder with height 10 cm and radius 10 cm.
   about 600 cm^2; about 1200 cm^2

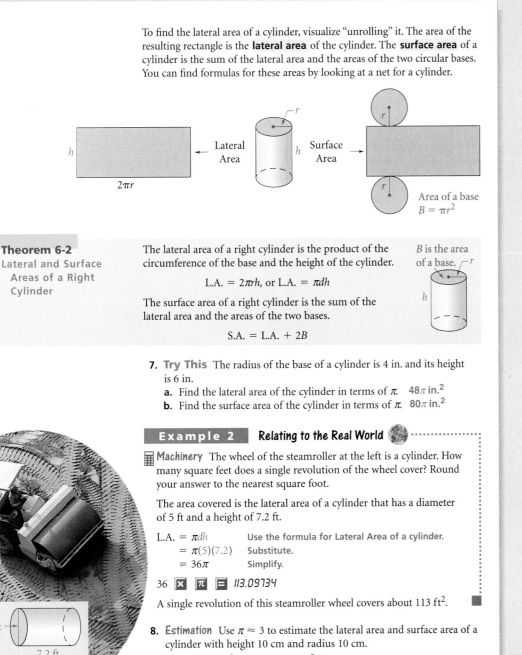

pages 309–311 Think and Discuss

5.

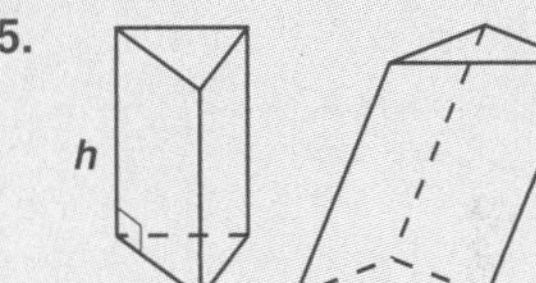

Exercises ON YOUR OWN

Exercises 1–4 If possible, provide students with cubes with which they can replicate the figures and count the number of squares on the surface of each.

ALTERNATIVE ASSESSMENT **Exercise 9** This exercise can help you assess students' understanding of prisms and surface area. Have students work in small groups. Each student can perform every calculation, then they can compare answers. Students will need to use the 30°-60°-90° Triangle Theorem to find the area of the hexagonal base.

ERROR ALERT! **Exercise 13** Students may calculate the surface area of the straw, adding the area of the bases to the lateral area. **Remediation:** Bring in straws and have students describe the surface of a straw.

Exercise 14 You may want to bring in a video cassette tape box so students can see which end is open.

pages 312–314 On Your Own

16.

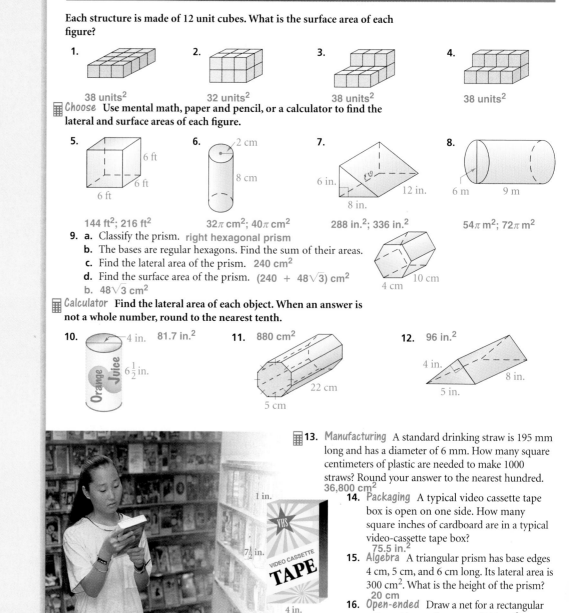

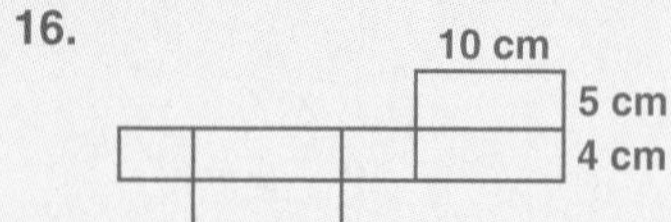

Exercises ON YOUR OWN

Each structure is made of 12 unit cubes. What is the surface area of each figure?

1.  38 units^2

2. 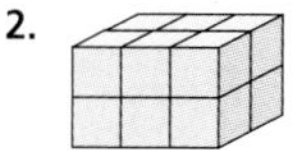 32 units^2

3. 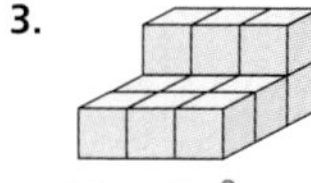 38 units^2

4. 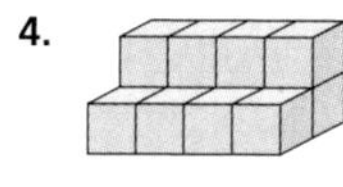 38 units^2

Choose **Use mental math, paper and pencil, or a calculator to find the lateral and surface areas of each figure.**

5. 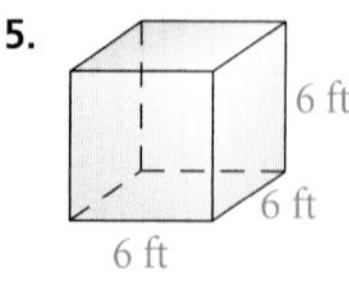

144 ft^2; 216 ft^2

6. 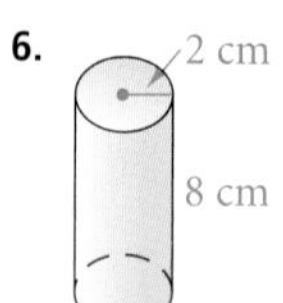

$32\pi\text{ cm}^2$; $40\pi\text{ cm}^2$

7. 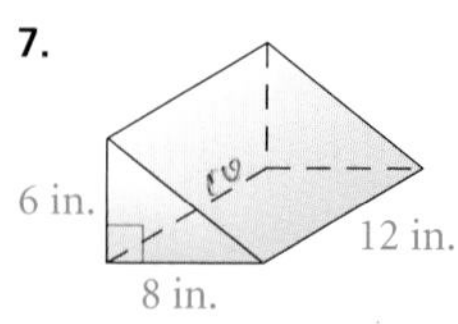

288 in.^2; 336 in.^2

8. 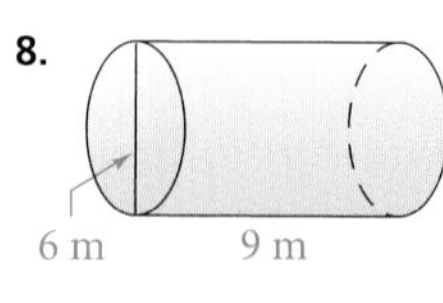

$54\pi\text{ m}^2$; $72\pi\text{ m}^2$

9. a. Classify the prism. right hexagonal prism
   b. The bases are regular hexagons. Find the sum of their areas.
   c. Find the lateral area of the prism. 240 cm^2
   d. Find the surface area of the prism. $(240 + 48\sqrt{3})\text{ cm}^2$
   b. $48\sqrt{3}\text{ cm}^2$

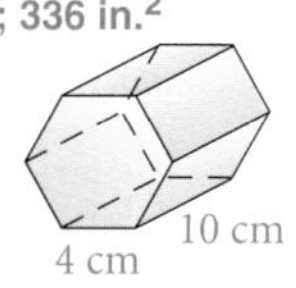

Calculator **Find the lateral area of each object. When an answer is not a whole number, round to the nearest tenth.**

10. 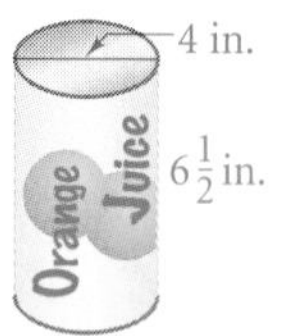

81.7 in.^2

11. 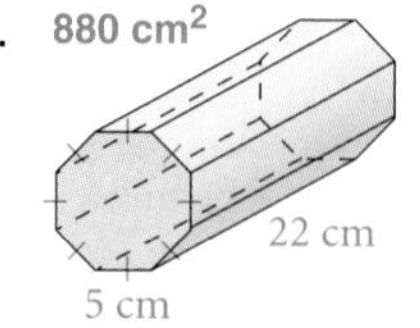

880 cm^2

12. 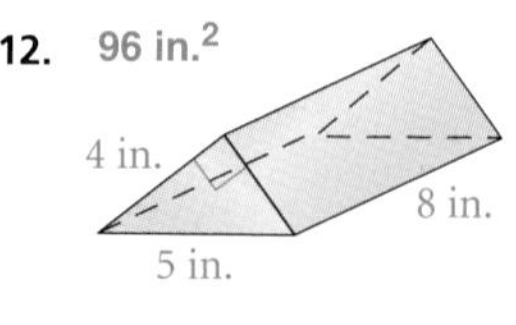

96 in.^2

13. *Manufacturing* A standard drinking straw is 195 mm long and has a diameter of 6 mm. How many square centimeters of plastic are needed to make 1000 straws? Round your answer to the nearest hundred. $36{,}800\text{ cm}^2$

14. *Packaging* A typical video cassette tape box is open on one side. How many square inches of cardboard are in a typical video-cassette tape box? 75.5 in.^2

1 in.
VHS
$7\frac{1}{2}$ in.
VIDEO CASSETTE TAPE
4 in.

15. *Algebra* A triangular prism has base edges 4 cm, 5 cm, and 6 cm long. Its lateral area is 300 cm^2. What is the height of the prism? 20 cm

16. *Open-ended* Draw a net for a rectangular prism with a surface area of 220 cm^2. See margin.

GEOMETRY IN 3 DIMENSIONS Exercise 17 Students can use the corner of a room to visualize three dimensions. The edges of the ceiling can represent the x- and y- axes and the edge where the two walls meet can represent the z-axis.

COORDINATE GEOMETRY Exercise 24 Students can rotate an index card around a fixed point to help them visualize the space figure. By taping a pencil to an edge of the card, students can trace the base of the figure as they rotate the card.

STANDARDIZED TEST TIP Exercise 25 A common error is for students to assume that the area is doubled. Suggest that they calculate the surface area of a cube with side lengths 1 unit and a cube with side length 2 units.

ALGEBRA Exercise 26 If students have trouble getting started, suggest that they let $r =$ radius and $9 - r =$ height.

Exercise 27 Students may want to review the definition of frieze pattern and examples on page 137 of Chapter 3.

17. a. *Geometry in 3 Dimensions* List the three coordinates (x, y, z) for vertices A, B, C, and D of the rectangular prism. See below.
    b. What is AB? 5 c. What is BC? 3 d. What is CD? 4
    e. What is the surface area of the prism? 94 units^2

    17a. A (3, 0, 0), B (3, 5, 0), C (0, 5, 0), D (0, 5, 4)

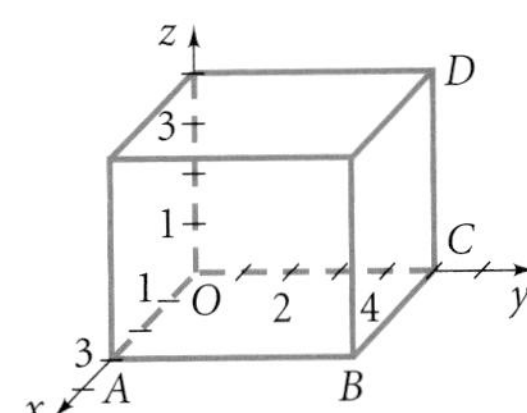

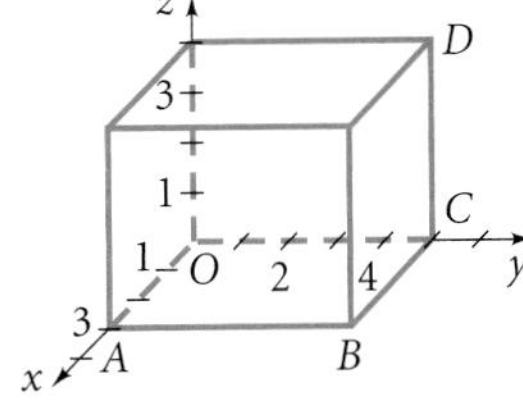

18. *Estimation* Estimate the surface area of a cube with edges 4.95 cm long. about 150 cm^2
19. *Writing* Explain how a cylinder and a prism are alike and how they are different. See margin.

Calculator **Find the surface area of each figure. When an answer is not a whole number, round to the nearest tenth.**

20. 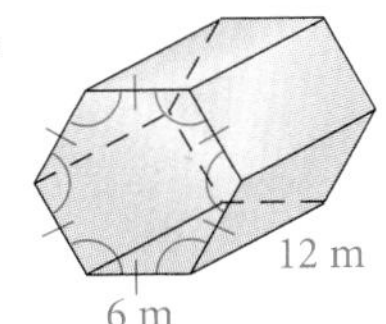

70.7 cm^2

21. 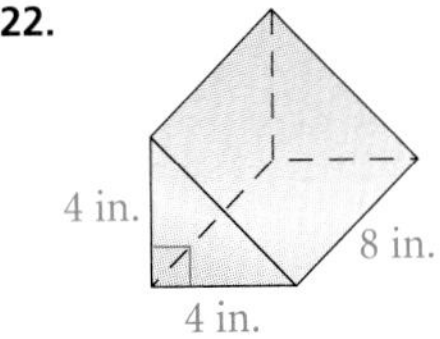

619.1 m^2

22. 4 in., 8 in., 4 in.
125.3 in.^{2}

23. 29 cm, 6.5 cm, 19 cm
1726 cm^2

24. a. *Coordinate Geometry* Suppose the rectangle shown at the right is rotated 360° about the y-axis. What space figure will the rotating rectangle generate? right cylinder
    b. Find the surface area of this figure in terms of π. 48π
    c. What will be the surface area in terms of π if the rectangle is rotated 360° about the x-axis? 24π

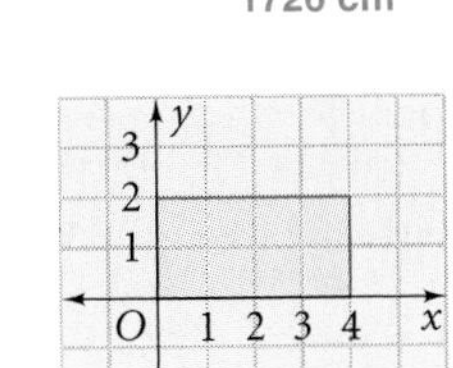

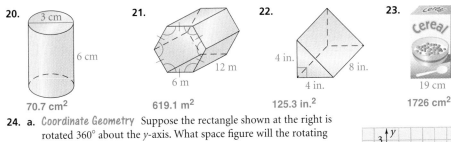

25. *Standardized Test Prep* If the radius and height of a cylinder are both doubled, then the surface area is ▪. D
    A. the same B. doubled C. tripled D. quadrupled
    E. not enough information given to determine the amount of change in the surface area
26. *Algebra* The sum of the height and radius of a cylinder is 9 m. The surface area of the cylinder is 54π m^2. Find the height and radius. 6 m; 3 m
27. *Frieze Patterns* From about 3500 B.C. to 2500 B.C., Sumerians etched cylindrical stones to form seals. They used the imprint from rotating the seal to make an official signature. These seals make interesting frieze patterns.
    a. Two and one-quarter revolutions of a cylinder created the frieze pattern at the right. What are the dimensions of the cylinder? Round to the nearest tenth.
    b. What type of transformation appears in the frieze pattern?

    a. $r = 0.7$ cm, $h = 4$ cm
    b. a translation

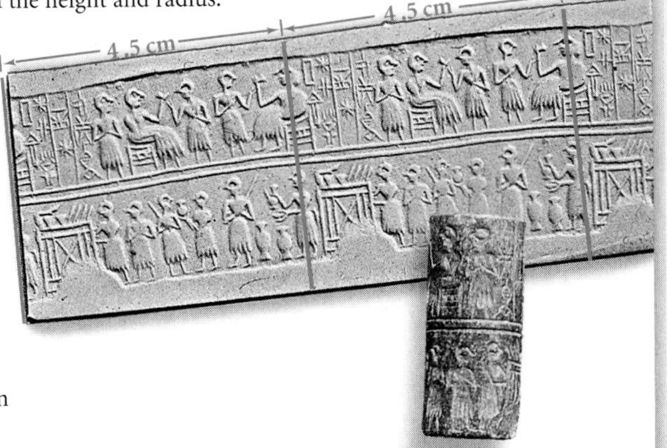

19. Answers may vary. Sample: Each is a 3-dimensional object with 2 ∥ and ≅ bases. These bases are circles in a cylinder and polygons in a prism.

313

Chapter Project **FIND OUT BY MEASURING** Check that the containers students collect can be cut open. As they cut them open, make sure that they are careful not to cut off any of the overlapping pieces. Remind students to omit the overlapping sections in calculating the surface area of the container, but to include them in their calculations of the total area of the packaging.

Exercises MIXED REVIEW

Exercises 31–33 Have students include a graph with their answer.

Exercise 34 Students can review biconditionals in Lesson 4-1.

SELF ASSESSMENT **JOURNAL** Students may want to make two lists, one for products packaged in cylindrical containers, and another for products packaged in boxes shaped like prisms.

GETTING READY FOR LESSON 6-3 These exercises prepare students to find the slant height of a pyramid.

Wrap Up

THE BIG IDEA Ask students: *Explain how to find the surface area of both a prism and a cylinder.*

RETEACHING ACTIVITY Students copy and cut out a net and fold it to make a prism. Then they calculate its lateral area and surface area. (Reteaching worksheet 6-2)

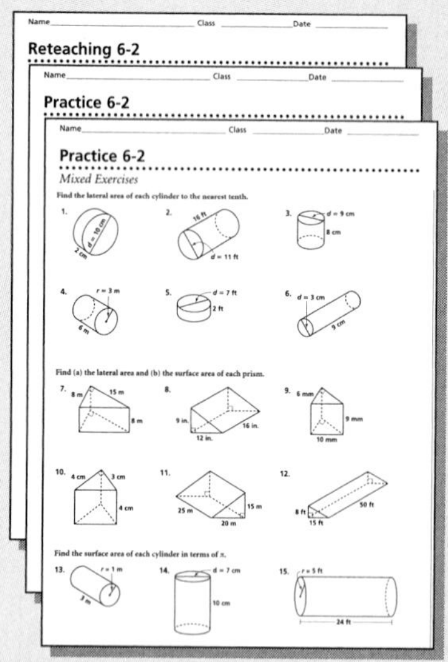
Reteaching 6-2

Practice 6-2

Practice 6-2
Mixed Exercises
Find the lateral area of each cylinder to the nearest tenth.

Find (a) the lateral area and (b) the surface area of each prism.

Find the surface area of each cylinder in terms of π.

Lesson Quiz

Lesson Quiz is also available in Transparencies.

1. The length of a side of a cube is 8 cm. Find the surface area of the cube. 384 cm^2
2. A length of each side of the base of a right hexagonal prism is 5 in. The height of the prism is 12 in. Find the lateral area. 360 in.^2
3. The radius of a cylinder is 9 in. The height of the cylinder is 25 in. Find the surface area of the cylinder to the nearest tenth. 1922.7 in.^2
4. The base of a right rectangular prism has length 15 ft and width 8 ft. The height of the prism is 20 ft. Find the surface area. 1160 ft^2

Chapter Project ***Find Out by Measuring***

Collect some empty cardboard containers shaped like prisms and cylinders.

- Measure each container and calculate its surface area.
- Flatten each container by carefully separating the places where it has been glued together. Find the total area of the packaging material used.
- For each container, find the percent by which the area of the packaging material exceeds the surface area of the container.

1. How does an unfolded and flattened prism-shaped package differ from a net for a prism?
2. Compare the percents you calculated. What did you find out about the amount of extra material needed for prism-shaped containers? for cylindrical containers?
3. Why would a manufacturer be concerned about the surface area of a package? about the amount of material used to make the package? Check students' work.

Exercises MIXED REVIEW

Find the area of each figure. You may leave answers in simplest radical form.

28.
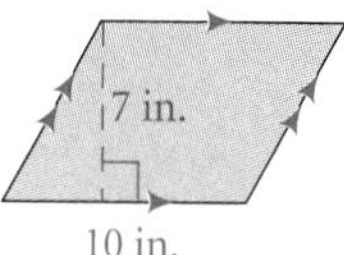

29.
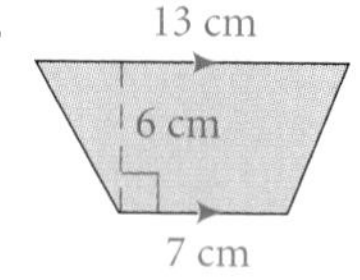

30.
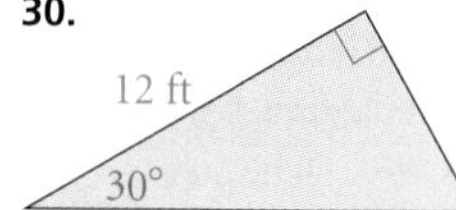

Transformations **Find the coordinates of the images of points $B(-4, 2)$, $I(0, -3)$, and $G(1, 0)$ under each reflection.**

31. in the y-axis **32.** in the x-axis **33.** in the line $x = 4$

34. Write a definition for a trapezoid. Write your definition as a biconditional.

Getting Ready for Lesson 6-3

Calculator **Use a calculator to find the length of each hypotenuse to the nearest tenth.**

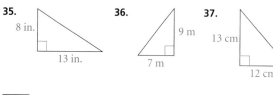

35. 8 in., 13 in. **36.** 9 m, 7 m **37.** 13 cm, 12 cm

SELF ASSESSMENT **FOR YOUR JOURNAL**

Give examples of products that are usually packaged in cylindrical containers. Then give examples of products that are usually packaged in boxes that are prisms. Explain why you think manufacturers choose particular container shapes.

Math ToolboX

Students investigate the surface area of rectangular prisms with the same volume but different base lengths. Students apply the formulas for surface area and volume that they learned in Lesson 6-2.

By using a spreadsheet, students can quickly calculate the surface areas of prism with different side lengths. The results are organized in a table for easy comparison, and computational errors are avoided.

Investigate

ERROR ALERT! Some students may incorrectly input the formulas into the spreadsheet. **Remediation:** Have students check that their spreadsheet is set up correctly by calculating by hand the height and surface area for the first value they enter in Column A.

Help students see that the values for the side of the base can be larger than 100 or less than 1.

ADDITIONAL PROBLEM If a cylinder has a volume of 100 cm^3, what integral dimensions would give the smallest surface area? $r = 1, h = \frac{100}{\pi}$

Materials and Manipulatives

- Spreadsheet software

Transparencies
15, 16

Math ToolboX Technology

Exploring Surface Area

After Lesson 6-2

Work in pairs or small groups.

Input

Use your spreadsheet program to investigate the surface areas of rectangular prisms with square bases. Consider square prisms with a volume of 100 cm^3 and see how the surface area (S.A.) changes as the length of the side (s) of a base changes.

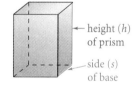

height (h) of prism

side (s) of base

The volume of a prism equals the area of a base times its height ($V = Bh$). Therefore, the height of the prism equals the volume divided by the area of the base ($h = \frac{V}{B} = \frac{V}{s^2}$). The surface area of a square prism equals two times the area of the base plus four times the area of a face (S.A. $= 2B + 4sh = 2s^2 + 4sh$). Set up your spreadsheet as follows.

	A	B	C
1	Square Prisms with a Volume of 100 cm^3		
2			
3	sides (s) of base	height (h) of prism	Surface Area (S.A.)
4		= 100/A4^2	= 2*A4^2+4*A4*B4

Investigate

Copy the formulas down several rows and enter different values for the length of the side of the base in Column A. How small can the surface area be? How large can it be? **about 130 cm^2; arbitrarily large**

Conjecture

Which dimensions give a very large surface area? Which dimensions give the smallest surface area? How do the side of the base and the height compare in the prism of smallest surface area? What is the shape of the square prism that has the smallest surface area? **either a large side length or a large height; $s = h \approx 4.6$ cm; length of side of base = height; cube**

Extend

- If a square prism has a volume of 1000 cm^3, what dimensions would give the smallest surface area? **10 cm-by-10 cm-by-10 cm**

315

6-3 Teaching Notes

PROBLEM OF THE DAY

What is the smallest diameter of a log from which you can cut a 10-cm square post. $10\sqrt{2}$ cm

Problem of the Day is also available in Transparencies.

CONNECTING TO PRIOR KNOWLEDGE Give students the following net for a square pyramid. Ask them to identify the solid and find the area of the net.

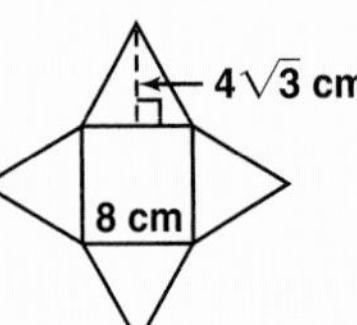

THINK AND DISCUSS

VISUAL LEARNING As you discuss the features of a pyramid, have physical models available for students. You can create pyramids from nets or make them with straws or pipe cleaners. For each pyramid, have students measure the slant height and the length of an edge of the base.

ERROR ALERT! Some students will have trouble differentiating between the height and slant height of a pyramid. **Remediation:** Reinforce that the height of a pyramid is perpendicular to the base of the pyramid. Also, it may help them to think of the slant height as the distance they would travel walking up the center of a pyramid wall.

Lesson Planning Options

Prerequisite Skills

- Finding perimeter and area of polygons
- Finding circumference and area of circles

Assignment Options for Exercises On Your Own

To provide flexible scheduling, this lesson can be subdivided into parts.

1. **Core** 2, 4, 5, 7, 13, 15, 27–28 ✪**Extension** 25, 30
2. **Core** 1, 3, 6, 8–10, 12, 14, 16–24, 26 ✪**Extension** 11, 29

Use Mixed Review to maintain skills.

Resources

Student Edition

Skills Handbook, pp. 660, 673
Extra Practice, p. 653
Glossary/Study Guide

Teaching Resources

Chapter Support File, Ch. 6
- Practice 6-3 (two worksheets)
- Reteaching 6-3

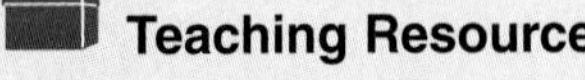
Classroom Manager 6-3
Glossary, Spanish Resources

Transparencies

15, 16, 18, 70, 74

316

Connections Social Studies . . . and more

6-3 Surface Areas of Pyramids and Cones

What You'll Learn

- Finding the lateral areas and surface areas of pyramids and cones

...And Why

To find the lateral areas of pyramids, such as the Great Pyramid at Giza, and of conical tower roofs

What You'll Need

calculator, metric ruler, compass, protractor, scissors, tape

THINK AND DISCUSS

Part 1

Lateral Areas and Surface Areas of Pyramids

Many Egyptian pharaohs built pyramids as burial tombs. The Fourth Dynasty, 2615–2494 B.C., was the age of the great pyramids. The builders knew and understood the mathematical properties of a pyramid.

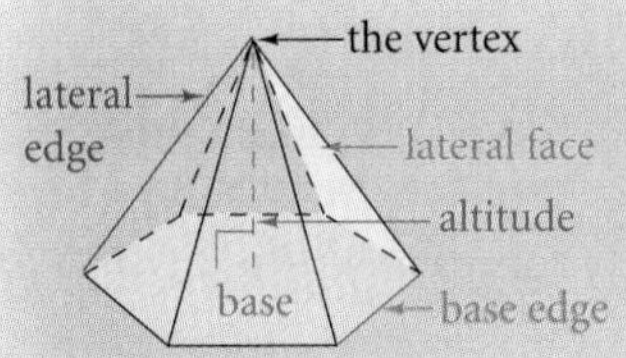

A **pyramid** is a polyhedron in which one face (the **base**) can be any polygon and the other faces (the **lateral faces**) are triangles that meet at a common vertex (called the **vertex** of the pyramid). You can name a pyramid by the shape of its base. The **altitude** of a pyramid is the perpendicular segment from the vertex to the plane of the base. The length of the altitude is the **height** h of the pyramid.

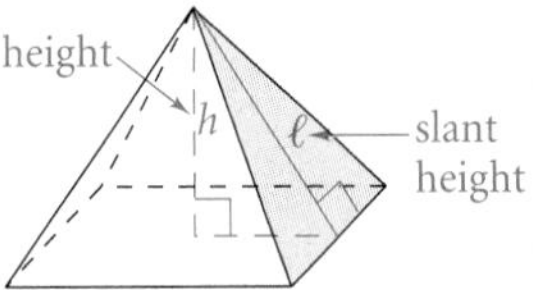

A **regular pyramid** is a pyramid whose base is a regular polygon. The lateral faces are congruent isosceles triangles. The **slant height** ℓ is the length of the altitude of a lateral face of the pyramid. In this book, you can assume a pyramid is regular unless you are told otherwise.

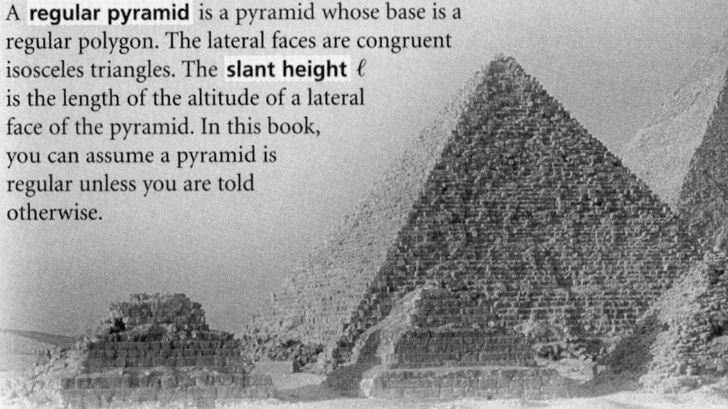

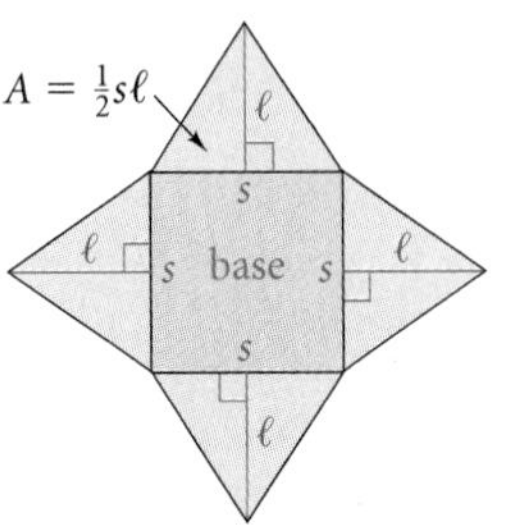

You can find a formula for the lateral area of a pyramid by looking at its net. The **lateral area** is the sum of the areas of the congruent lateral faces.

$$\text{L.A.} = 4(\tfrac{1}{2}s\ell) \quad \text{The area of each lateral face is } \tfrac{1}{2}s\ell.$$
$$= \tfrac{1}{2}(4s)\ell \quad \text{Commutative Property of Multiplication}$$
$$= \tfrac{1}{2}p\ell \quad \text{The perimeter } p \text{ of the base is } 4s.$$

To find the **surface area** of a pyramid, add the area of its base to its lateral area.

Students may be curious why l is used to represent slant height rather than s. Remind them that s is used to represent the length of a side of a polygon.

Theorem 6-3 Point out that this theorem is only true for regular pyramids. If the pyramid is not regular, the slant height could be different on each lateral face.

CRITICAL THINKING Ask students how the formula for the surface area of a prism and the formula for the surface area of a regular pyramid are alike and how they are different.

Example 1 **Relating to the Real World** 

Help students see that knowing the length of a side and the height of a regular pyramid is sufficient to find the lateral area. They can use the Pythagorean Theorem and, in some cases, the special right triangle theorems to find the slant height.

CRITICAL THINKING Ask students how the slant height of a regular pyramid compares to its height.

Theorem 6-3
Lateral and Surface Areas of a Regular Pyramid

The lateral area of a regular pyramid is half the product of the perimeter of the base and the slant height.

$$\text{L.A.} = \frac{1}{2}p\ell$$

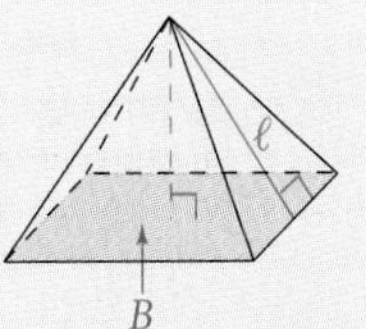

The surface area of a regular pyramid is the sum of the lateral area and the area of the base.

$$\text{S.A.} = \text{L.A.} + B$$

1. **Try This** A regular hexagonal pyramid has base edges 60 m long and slant height 35 m. Find the perimeter of its base and its lateral area. 360 m; 6300 m²

Sometimes the slant height of a pyramid is not given. You must calculate it before you can find the lateral or surface area.

Example 1 **Relating to the Real World** 

Social Studies The Great Pyramid at Giza, Egypt, was built about 2580 B.C. as a final resting place for Pharaoh Khufu. At the time it was built, its height was about 481 ft. Each edge of the square base was about 756 ft long. What was the lateral area of the pyramid?

- The legs of right $\triangle ABC$ are the height of the pyramid and the apothem of the base. The height of the pyramid is 481 ft. The apothem of the base is $\frac{756}{2}$, or 378 ft. You can use the Pythagorean Theorem to find the slant height ℓ.

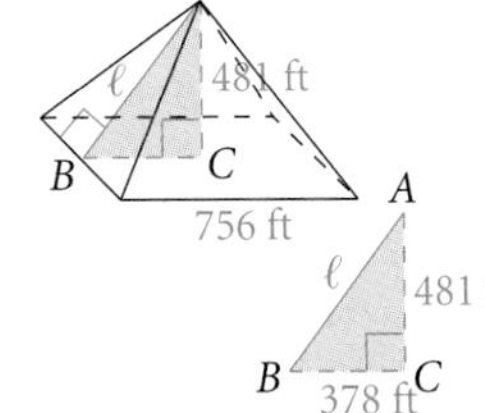

$\ell^2 = AC^2 + BC^2$

$\ell^2 = 481^2 + 378^2$

$\ell = \sqrt{481^2 + 378^2}$ Find the square root of each side.

- Now use the formula for the lateral area of a pyramid. The perimeter of the base is approximately $4 \cdot 756$, or 3024 ft.

$\text{L.A.} = \frac{1}{2}p\ell$

$= \frac{1}{2}(3024)(611.75567)$ Substitute.

0.5 × 3024 × 611.75567 = 924974.57

The lateral area of the Great Pyramid at Giza was about 925,000 ft².

2. **Try This** Find the surface area of the Great Pyramid at Giza. about 1,500,000 ft²

Additional Examples

FOR EXAMPLE 1

The Transamerica Building in San Francisco is a pyramid. The length of each edge of the square base is 149 ft and the slant height of the pyramid is 800 ft. What is the lateral area of the pyramid? **238,400 ft²**

FOR EXAMPLE 2

The radius of the base of a cone is 12 in. The slant height is 30 in. Find the lateral area in terms of π. **360π in.²**

Discussion: *Is the lateral area of a cone with radius 30 in. and slant height 12 in. greater or less than the lateral area of the cone in Additional Example 2? Explain.*

TACTILE LEARNING Provide students with nets of cones of different sizes. Have them cut them out and tape them together. Then have them measure the slant height, the height, and the radius of each.

Theorem 6-4 Have students compare Theorems 6-3 and 6-4. Some students may prefer to remember the lateral area of a cone as: L.A. $= \frac{1}{2}Cl$.

CRITICAL THINKING Ask students how the lateral area of a right cone compares to the area of its base.

Example 2

Some students may have difficulty visualizing a right triangle inside a cone. If possible, make a transparent cone (using a blank transparency). Then draw the slant height with a marker on the transparency and use straws or pipe cleaners for the height and base.

AUDITORY LEARNING Encourage students not only to write the formula used to solve a problem, but also to verbalize it. This will help with retention.

You may want to make two more posters showing a pyramid and a cone, its parts, and area formulas. Have students make two more index cards with the figures on one side and the formulas on the other.

Technology Options

Prentice Hall Technology

Software

- Secondary Math Lab Toolkit™
- Computer Item Generator 6-3

CD-ROM

- Multimedia Geometry Lab 6

Internet

- See the Prentice Hall site. (http://www.phschool.com)

Part 2

Lateral Areas and Surface Areas of Cones

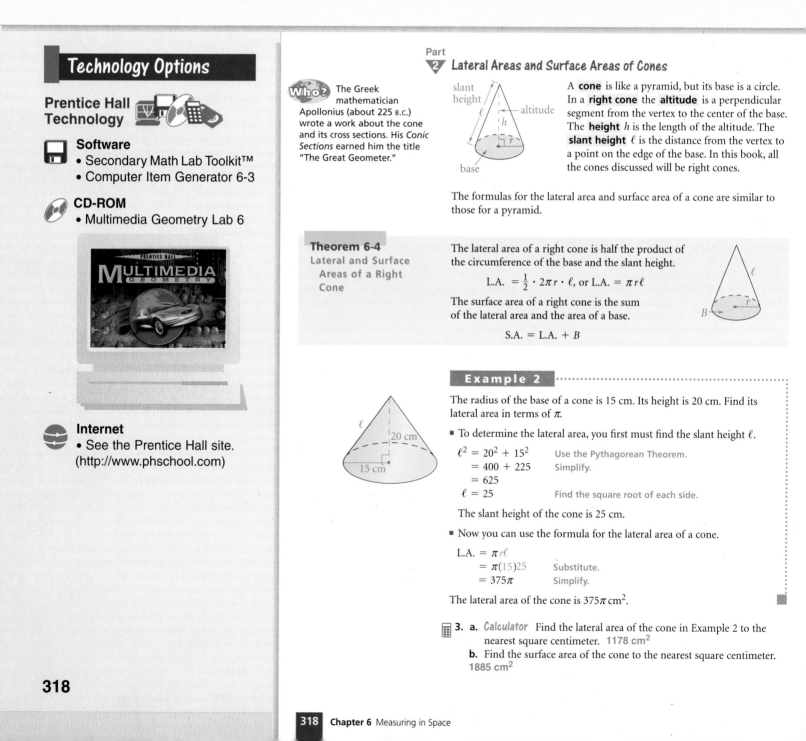

Who? The Greek mathematician Apollonius (about 225 B.C.) wrote a work about the cone and its cross sections. His *Conic Sections* earned him the title "The Great Geometer."

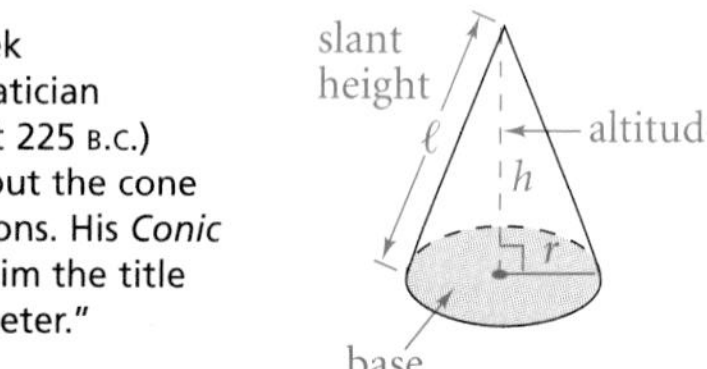

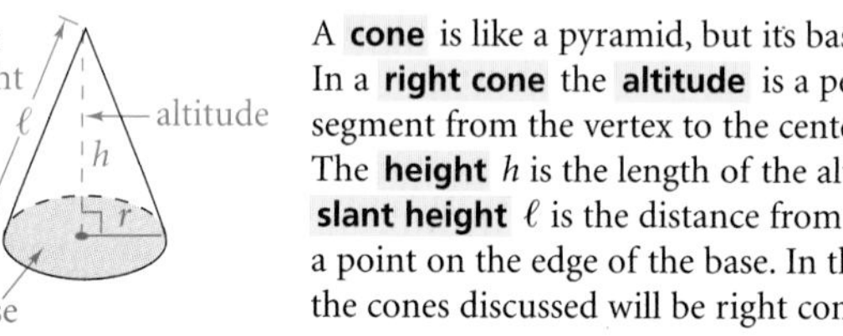

A **cone** is like a pyramid, but its base is a circle. In a **right cone** the **altitude** is a perpendicular segment from the vertex to the center of the base. The **height** h is the length of the altitude. The **slant height** ℓ is the distance from the vertex to a point on the edge of the base. In this book, all the cones discussed will be right cones.

The formulas for the lateral area and surface area of a cone are similar to those for a pyramid.

Theorem 6-4
Lateral and Surface Areas of a Right Cone

The lateral area of a right cone is half the product of the circumference of the base and the slant height.

$$\text{L.A.} = \frac{1}{2} \cdot 2\pi r \cdot \ell, \text{ or L.A.} = \pi r \ell$$

The surface area of a right cone is the sum of the lateral area and the area of a base.

$$\text{S.A.} = \text{L.A.} + B$$

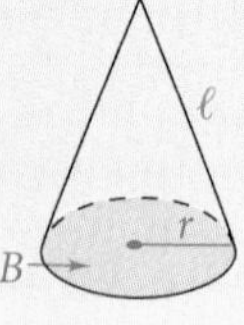

Example 2

The radius of the base of a cone is 15 cm. Its height is 20 cm. Find its lateral area in terms of π.

- To determine the lateral area, you first must find the slant height ℓ.

$\ell^2 = 20^2 + 15^2$ — Use the Pythagorean Theorem.
$= 400 + 225$ — Simplify.
$= 625$
$\ell = 25$ — Find the square root of each side.

The slant height of the cone is 25 cm.

- Now you can use the formula for the lateral area of a cone.

L.A. $= \pi r \ell$
$= \pi(15)25$ — Substitute.
$= 375\pi$ — Simplify.

The lateral area of the cone is 375π cm^2.

3. a. *Calculator* Find the lateral area of the cone in Example 2 to the nearest square centimeter. 1178 cm^2
   b. Find the surface area of the cone to the nearest square centimeter. 1885 cm^2

WORK TOGETHER

Check that students understand that the slant height of each cone is 8 cm and that the circumference of the base of the cone equals the length of the arc of the shaded region.

DIVERSITY Students who are physically challenged may not be able to do the cutting, folding, and taping in this activity. Make sure that they participate as much as possible so they feel included in the activity.

Exercises ON YOUR OWN

CONNECTING TO STUDENTS' WORLD Exercises 5–8 Have students collect pyramid-shaped and cone-shaped objects. Then have them find the appropriate measures and calculate the surface area of each.

	C	r	L.A.
1	8π	4	32π
2	10π	5	40π
3	12π	6	48π

WORK TOGETHER

- Work in a group. Use a compass to draw three congruent circles with radii 8 cm. Use a protractor to draw the shaded sectors shown below.

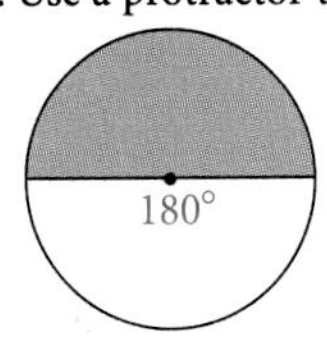

Figure 1

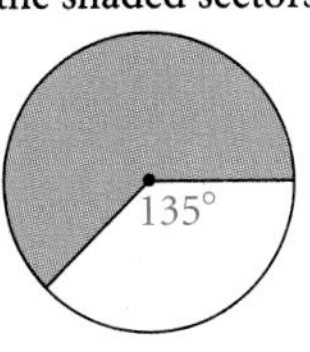

Figure 2

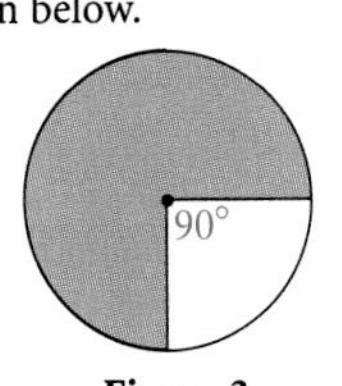

Figure 3

Cone	C	r	L.A.
1	■	■	■
2	■	■	■
3	■	■	■

- Cut out the sectors. Tape the radii of each sector together, without overlapping, to form a cone without a base.

4. Find the slant height of each cone. 8 cm; 8 cm; 8 cm
5. Find the circumference C and radius r of each cone. Then find the lateral area of each cone. Record your results in a table like the one shown at the left. See above left.

Exercises ON YOUR OWN

Choose **Use mental math, pencil and paper, or a calculator to find the slant height of each figure.**

1. 17 cm

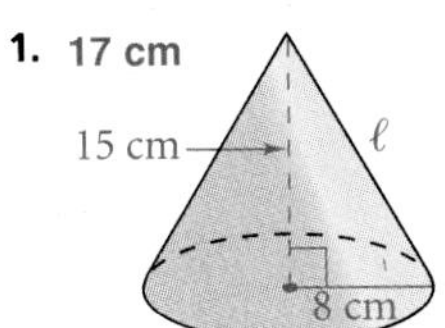

2. 50 m

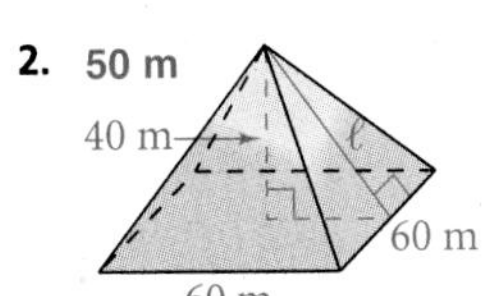

3. 12.8 m

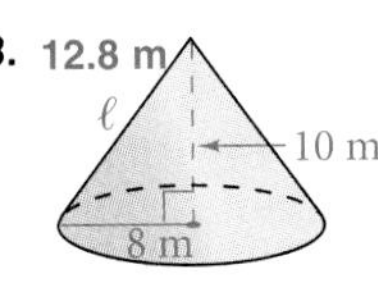

4. 10 cm

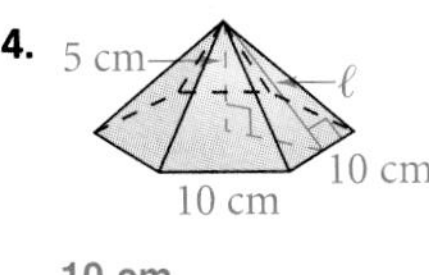

Find the lateral area of each figure. You may leave answers in terms of π.

5. 264 in.^{2}

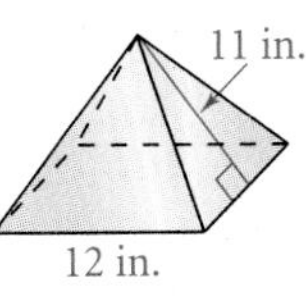

6. 24π ft^2

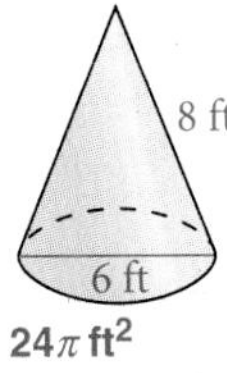

7. 80 in.^{2}

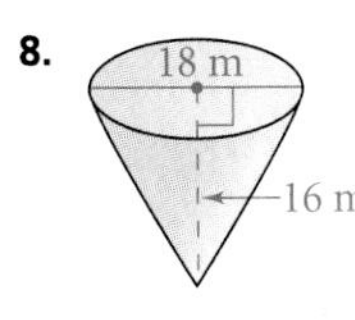

8. about 165π m^2

(18 m, 16 m)

9. *Writing* How are a cone and a pyramid alike? How are they different? See margin.
10. *Architecture* The roof of the tower in a castle is shaped like a cone. The height of the roof is 30 ft and the radius of the base is 15 ft. What is the area of the roof? Round your answer to the nearest tenth. 1580.6 ft^2

pages 319–321 On Your Own

9. Answers may vary. Sample: A cone and a pyramid are 3-dimensional figures with only 1 base. The base of a cone is a circle. The base of a pyramid is a polygon, and the lateral faces are △s.

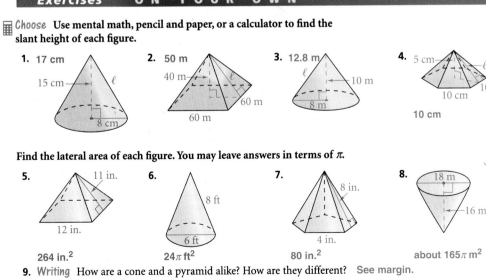

ESL Exercise 12 Students may be unfamiliar with the term "hourglass." If possible, bring one in for students to see. (If you cannot find an hourglass, bring in an egg timer or similar timer from a board game.)

OPEN-ENDED Exercise 15 If students have trouble getting started, suggest they begin by choosing a shape for the base of the pyramid (an equilateral triangle, a square, etc.) and its side length. Then they can substitute for p and solve $48 = \frac{1}{2}pl$ for l.

COORDINATE GEOMETRY Exercise 16 Have students cut an index card along its diagonal. Then have them tape the legs of one of the resulting right triangles to straws. By rotating the straw, students can visualize the figures formed.

ALTERNATIVE ASSESSMENT Exercises 21–24 These exercises can help you assess students' understanding of the formulas for the surface area of pyramids and cones. Have students write the formula they use for each problem. Check that they give their answers in appropriate units.

11. $(\ell + r)r\pi = \ell r\pi + \pi r^2 =$ L.A. $+ B$; Anita's formula needs fewer keystrokes than the L.A. $+ B$ formula.

12. Cylinder; the lateral area of the cylinder is 48π in.^{2} and the lateral area of the 2 cones is 30π in.^{2}

15. S.A. $= 64$ cm^2

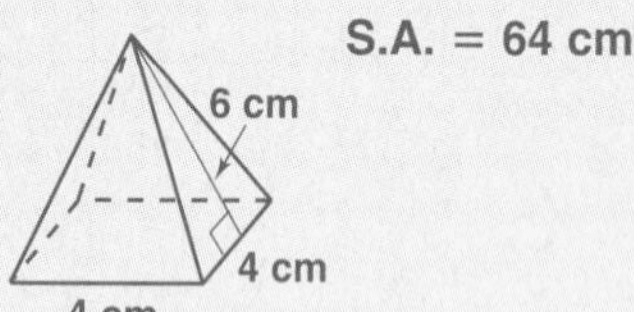

11. *Critical Thinking* Anita says that when she uses her calculator to find the surface area of a cone she uses the formula S.A. $= (\ell + r)r\pi$. Explain why this formula works. Why do you think Anita uses this formula? **See margin.**

12. *Manufacturing* The hourglass shown at the right is made by connecting two glass cones inside a glass cylinder. Which has more glass, the two cones or the cylinder? Explain. **See margin.**

13. A regular square pyramid has base edges 10 in. long and height 4 in. Sketch the pyramid and find its surface area. Round your answer to the nearest tenth. **228.1 in.^{2}**

14. *Algebra* The lateral area of a cone is 48π in.^{2}. The radius is 12 in. Find the slant height. **4 in.**

15. *Open-ended* Draw a pyramid with a lateral area of 48 cm^2. Label its dimensions. Then find its surface area. **See margin for samples.**

16. a. *Coordinate Geometry* Describe the figure that is formed when the right triangle at the right is rotated 360° about the x-axis. Find its lateral area. Leave your answer in terms of π. **right cone; 15π**

b. What is the lateral area of the figure formed when the triangle is rotated 360° about the y-axis? Leave your answer in terms of π. **20π**

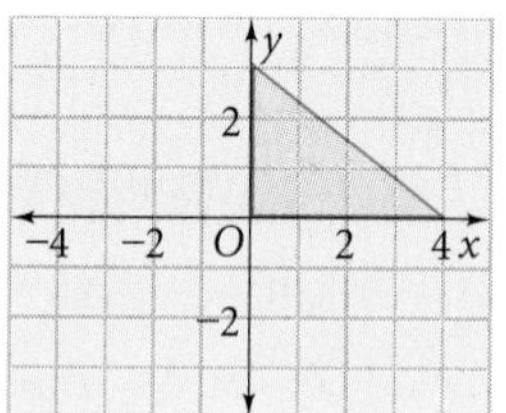

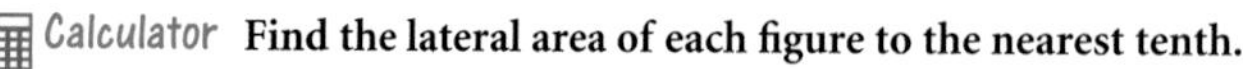

Calculator **Find the lateral area of each figure to the nearest tenth.**

17.

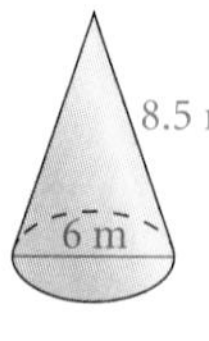

80.1 m^2

18.

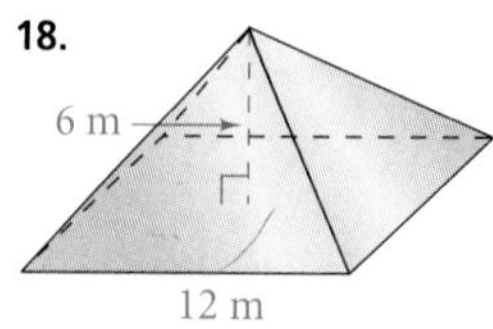

203.6 m^2

19.

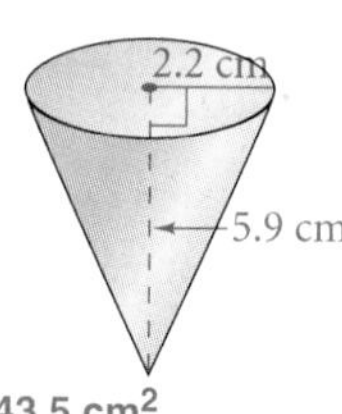

43.5 cm^2

20.

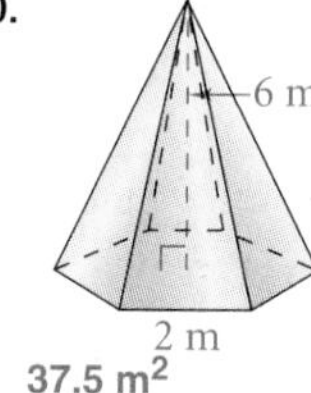

37.5 m^2

Calculator **Find the surface area of each figure to the nearest tenth.**

21.

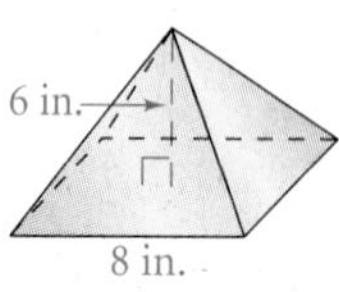

179.4 in.^{2}

22.

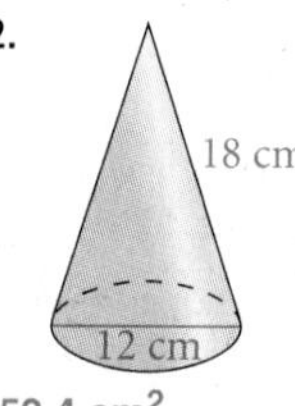

452.4 cm^2

23.

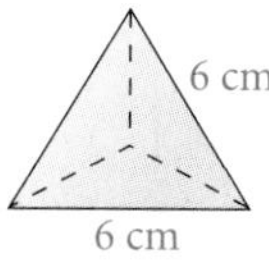

62.4 cm^2

24.

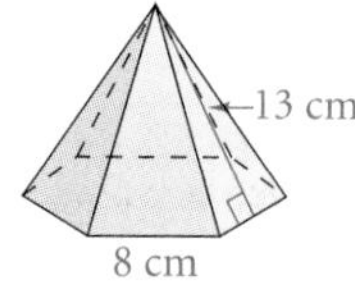

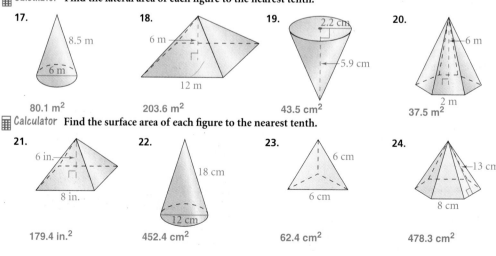

478.3 cm^2

Exercise 25 This exercise can be done with a sealed business envelope but using a dollar bill is more fun. If students find the area of the dollar bill, have them measure in centimeters (l = 15.2 cm, w = 6.5 cm).

MAKING CONNECTIONS Exercise 27 The oldest pyramids were built approximately 150 years before the Great Pyramids in Giza. The first pyramid, a tomb for King Zoser, was a step pyramid consisting of a base, called a *mastaba,* and six diminishing terraces centered one on top of another.

RESEARCH Exercise 30 Students should be able to find this information in an encyclopedia. Encourage them to include sketches or photos of Egyptian and Mexican pyramids in their reports.

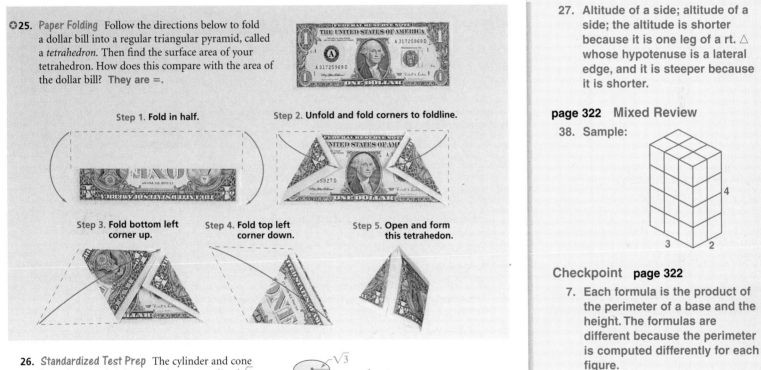

25. Paper Folding Follow the directions below to fold a dollar bill into a regular triangular pyramid, called a *tetrahedron.* Then find the surface area of your tetrahedron. How does this compare with the area of the dollar bill? **They are =.**

Step 1. **Fold in half.**

Step 2. **Unfold and fold corners to foldline.**

Step 3. **Fold bottom left corner up.**

Step 4. **Fold top left corner down.**

Step 5. **Open and form this tetrahedon.**

26. Standardized Test Prep The cylinder and cone have the same height 1 and the same radius $\sqrt{3}$. How does the lateral area x of the cylinder compare with the lateral area y of the cone? **A**

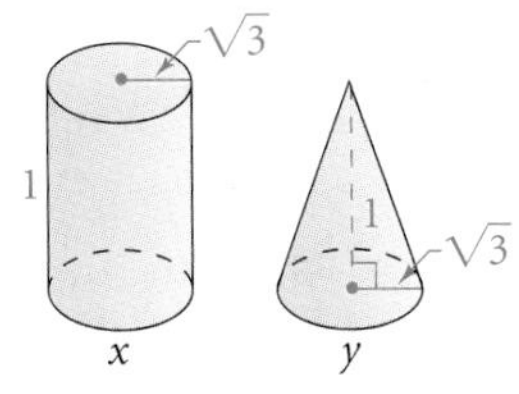

A. $x = y$ B. $x = 2y$ C. $x > 2y$
D. $x < 2y$ E. cannot be determined

27. Writing Suppose you could climb to the top of the Great Pyramid in Egypt. Which route would be shorter, a route along a lateral edge or along the altitude of a side? Which of these routes is steeper? Explain your answers. **See margin.**

28. Algebra The lateral area of a pyramid with a square base is 240 ft². Its base edges are 12 ft long. Find the height of the pyramid. **8 ft**

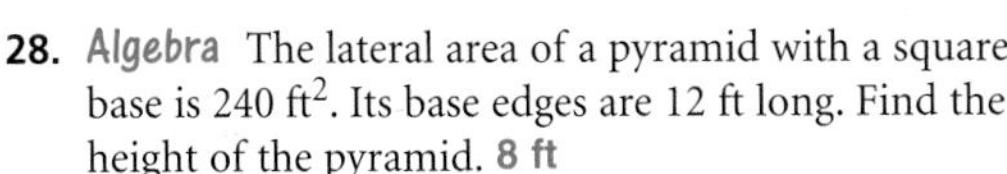

29. Algebra The surface area of a cone is 24π cm² and the lateral area is 15π cm². Find the slant height and the height of the cone. **5 cm; 4 cm**

30. Research Find out about ancient Mexican and Egyptian pyramids. How are they alike? How are they different? **Summarize** your findings in a short report. **Check students' work.**

Pyramid of the Sun, Teotihuacán, Mexico

27. Altitude of a side; altitude of a side; the altitude is shorter because it is one leg of a rt. △ whose hypotenuse is a lateral edge, and it is steeper because it is shorter.

page 322 Mixed Review

38. Sample:

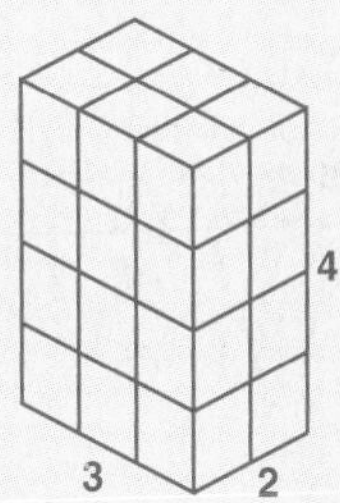

Checkpoint page 322

7. Each formula is the product of the perimeter of a base and the height. The formulas are different because the perimeter is computed differently for each figure.

Exercises MIXED REVIEW

Exercises 31–33 Have students include a graph of the triangles with their answers.

Exercises 34–35 Students can review how to find converses in Lesson 4-1.

GETTING READY FOR LESSON 6-4 These exercises prepare students to find the volume of prisms.

Wrap Up

THE BIG IDEA Ask students: *Explain how to find the surface areas of a pyramid and a cone.*

RETEACHING ACTIVITY Students draw a net of a regular square pyramid, cut it out, and tape it together. Then they find its surface area. (Reteaching worksheet 6-3)

Exercises CHECKPOINT

In this Checkpoint, your students will assess their own progress in Lessons 6-1 to 6-3.

Exercises 1–4 Suggest that students first write the appropriate formula, then substitute the appropriate values and simplify.

OPEN-ENDED Exercise 6 Challenge students to name the regular triangular pyramid in another way.

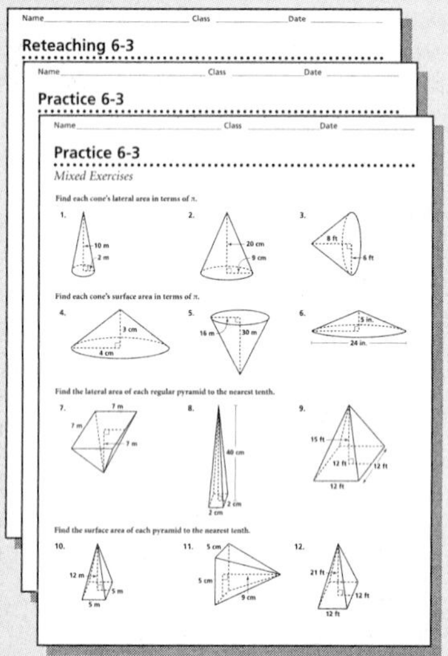

Lesson Quiz

Lesson Quiz is also available in Transparencies.

1. The length of a base edge of a square pyramid is 10 cm. The slant height of the pyramid is 15 cm. Find the surface area. **400 cm²**
2. The diameter of a cone is 24 m and the slant height is 20 m. Find the surface area of the cone to the nearest tenth. **1206.4 m²**
3. The length of an edge of the base of a square pyramid is 8 ft. The height of the pyramid is 3 ft. Find the surface area. **144 ft²**
4. The diameter of a cone is 10 cm and the height is 12 cm. Find the surface area of the cone to the nearest tenth. **282.7 cm²**

Exercises MIXED REVIEW

Coordinate Geometry **Find the lengths of the sides of triangles with the given vertices. Then classify each triangle by its sides.**

31. $A(0, 4), B(-3, 0), C(3, 0)$ **$AB = 5$, $BC = 6$, $AC = 5$; isosceles**
32. $K(5, 0), L(1, 4), M(1, -1)$ **$KL = 4\sqrt{2}$, $LM = 5$, $KM = \sqrt{17}$; scalene**
33. $W(-2, 7), X(-3, -2), Y(0, 4)$ **$WX = \sqrt{82}$, $XY = 3\sqrt{5}$, $YW = \sqrt{13}$; scalene**

Write the converse of each statement. Determine whether the converse is true or false. If false, give a counterexample.

34. If two lines are skew, then they do not intersect. **If 2 lines do not intersect, then they are skew; false; 2 || lines.**
35. If two angles are complementary, then the sum of their measures is 90. **If the sum of measures of 2 angles is 90, then they are complementary; true.**
36. *Transformations* Which letters of the alphabet can be rotated less than 360° and still look like the preimage? State each letter and the angle(s) of rotation. **H, I, N, O, S, X, Z; all can be rotated 180°.**

Getting Ready for Lesson 6-4

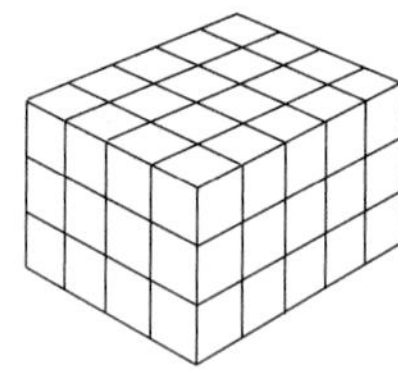

37. There are no hidden holes in the structure at the right. How many cubes make up this structure? **60 cubes**
38. *Open-ended* Sketch a prism made with 24 unit cubes. Label its dimensions. **See margin p. 321.**
39. A cube is made of 27 unit cubes. What are its dimensions? **3 by 3 by 3**

Exercises CHECKPOINT

Calculator **Find the surface area of each figure. When an answer is not a whole number, round to the nearest tenth.**

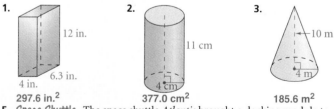

1. 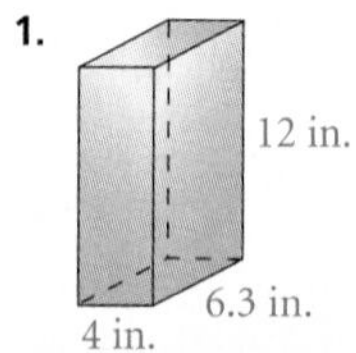

297.6 in.²

2. 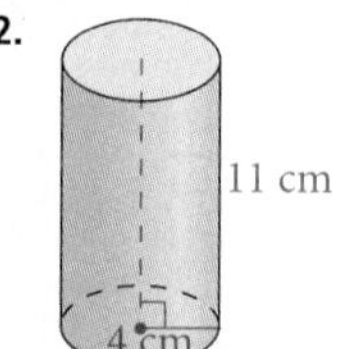

377.0 cm²

3. 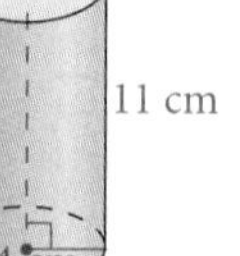

185.6 m²

4. 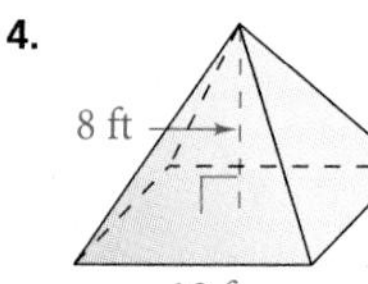

288.7 ft²

5. *Space Shuttle* The space shuttle *Atlantis* brought a docking module to the space station *Mir*. The module is a cylinder with an 8-ft diameter and a height of 15 ft. What is the surface area of the docking module? Round your answer to the nearest tenth. **477.5 ft²**
6. *Open-ended* Draw a net for a regular triangular pyramid. **Sample:**

7. *Writing* Explain how the formulas for the lateral area of a prism and a cylinder are alike and how they are different. **See margin p. 321.**

6-4 Teaching Notes

PROBLEM OF THE DAY

The corners on a cube are cut off. How many edges does the new figure have? 36

Problem of the Day is also available in Transparencies.

CONNECTING TO PRIOR KNOWLEDGE Present students with the following bases of prisms and ask them to calculate the area of each.

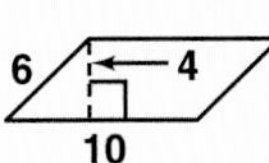

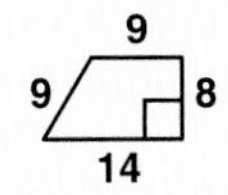

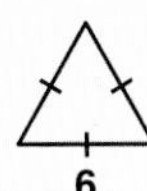

WORK TOGETHER

Students should discover that volume can be found by multiplying the area of the base of the prism by its height. If unit cubes are not available, sugar cubes may be used.

Question 7 Students may have made a similar observation in the Math Toolbox on page 315, where they found the dimensions of prisms with the same volume.

Connections Landscaping . . . and more

6-4 Volumes of Prisms and Cylinders

What You'll Learn

- Finding the volumes of prisms and cylinders

...And Why

To find the space needed to store packages and the amount of water needed to fill an aquarium

What You'll Need

- unit cubes
- calculator

WORK TOGETHER

Work with a group. Explore the volume of a prism with unit cubes.

1. Make a single-layer rectangular prism that is 4 cubes long and 2 cubes wide. The prism will be 4 units by 2 units by 1 unit. How many cubes are in the prism? 8
2. Add a second layer to your prism to make a prism 4 units by 2 units by 2 units. How many cubes are in this prism? 16
3. Add a third layer to your prism to make a prism 4 units by 2 units by 3 units. How many cubes are in this prism? 24
4. How many cubes would be in the prism if you added two additional layers of cubes for a total of 5 layers? 40
5. How many cubes would be in the prism if there were 10 layers? 80
6. Compare a prism 2 cubes long by 3 cubes wide and 4 layers high with the prism in Question 3. What do you notice? Each prism contains = number of cubes.
7. Compare a prism 3 cubes long by 4 cubes wide and 2 layers high with the prisms in Questions 3 and 6. What do you notice? Each prism contains = number of cubes.

Lesson Planning Options

Prerequisite Skills

- Finding the area of polygons and circles
- Applying the special right triangle theorems

Assignment Options for Exercises On Your Own

To provide flexible scheduling, this lesson can be subdivided into parts.

1 **Core** 2, 3, 6–12
Extension 19–20, 25

2 **Core** 1, 4, 5, 13–18, 21, 24
Extension 22–23

Use Mixed Review to maintain skills.

Resources

Student Edition

Skills Handbook, pp. 660, 673
Extra Practice, p. 653
Glossary/Study Guide

Teaching Resources

Chapter Support File, Ch. 6
- Practice 6-4 (two worksheets)
- Reteaching 6-4
- Alternative Activity 6-4

Classroom Manager 6-4
Glossary, Spanish Resources

Transparencies

15, 16, 18, 70, 75

THINK AND DISCUSS

ERROR ALERT! **Question 8** Some students may multiply by 3 (since there are 3 feet in a yard) and conclude that $1 \text{ yd}^3 = 3 \text{ ft}^3$. **Remediation:** Refer students to the Math Toolbox on page 307 to review how to convert units. Help students see that to convert from cubic yards to cubic feet, they can multiply as follows:

$$1 \text{ yd}^3 \cdot \frac{3 \text{ ft}}{1 \text{ yd}} \cdot \frac{3 \text{ ft}}{1 \text{ yd}} \cdot \frac{3 \text{ ft}}{1 \text{ yd}} = 27 \text{ ft}^3.$$

ESL **VISUAL LEARNING Theorem 6-5** Use a stack of paper, index cards, and/or coins to explain the term *cross section* and to illustrate Cavalieri's Principle. Although oblique cylinders are not used in this book, the coin model will help students see that this principle applies to cylinders as well as to prisms.

Students are already familiar with the relationship between the area of a parallelogram and the area of a rectangle. Discuss with students how this is like the relationship between the volume of an oblique prism and the volume of a right prism.

Theorem 6-6 Make sure students understand that the formula for the volume of a prism applies to all prisms but that the formula for surface area of a prism applies to right prisms only.

Students may already be familiar with the formula for the volume of a "box" ($V = lwh$). Help students see how this formula is consistent with $V = Bh$.

Additional Examples

FOR EXAMPLE 1

Find the volume of each prism. Round your answer to the nearest tenth, if necessary.

a. a rectangular prism with height 10 cm and a base with length 15 cm and width 12 cm 1800 cm^3

b. a triangular prism with height 12 in. and a base that is an equilateral triangle with side length 5 in. 129.9 in.^3

Discussion: *Give the dimensions of a triangular prism with the same volume as the rectangular prism in part a.*

FOR EXAMPLE 2

A cylindrical oil tank has a diameter of 120 ft and a height of 50 ft. About how many gallons of oil can the tank hold? Round your answer to the nearest thousand gallons.
4,230, 000 gallons

Discussion: *Can two tanks, each with diameter 60 ft and height 50 ft hold more, less, or the same amount of oil as the tank in Additional Example 2? Explain.*

THINK AND DISCUSS

Part 1

Volumes of Prisms

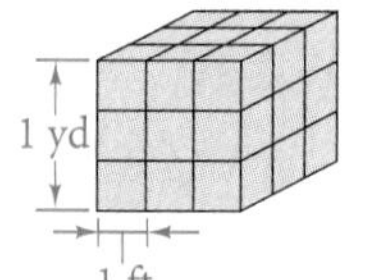

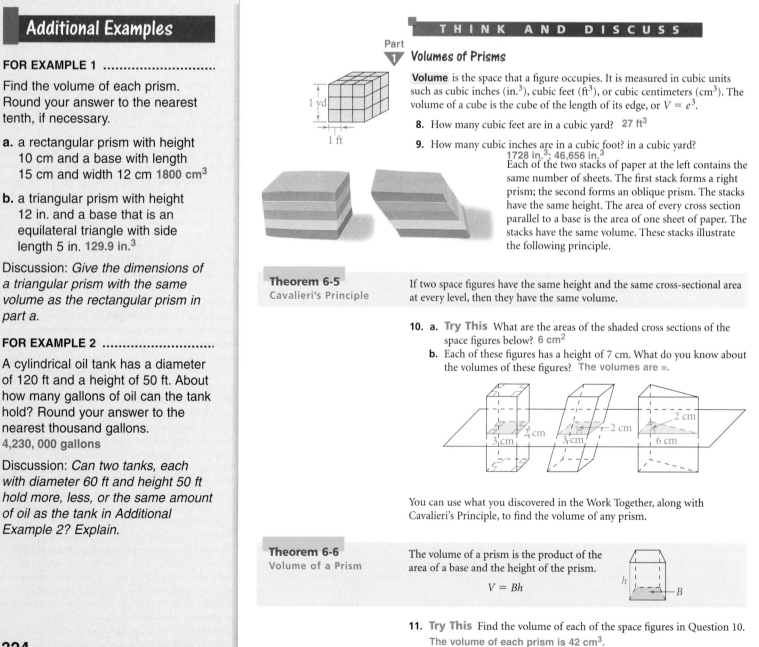

Volume is the space that a figure occupies. It is measured in cubic units such as cubic inches (in.^3), cubic feet (ft^3), or cubic centimeters (cm^3). The volume of a cube is the cube of the length of its edge, or $V = e^3$.

8. How many cubic feet are in a cubic yard? 27 ft^3
9. How many cubic inches are in a cubic foot? in a cubic yard? 1728 in.^3; $46{,}656 \text{ in.}^3$

Each of the two stacks of paper at the left contains the same number of sheets. The first stack forms a right prism; the second forms an oblique prism. The stacks have the same height. The area of every cross section parallel to a base is the area of one sheet of paper. The stacks have the same volume. These stacks illustrate the following principle.

Theorem 6-5
Cavalieri's Principle

If two space figures have the same height and the same cross-sectional area at every level, then they have the same volume.

10. a. **Try This** What are the areas of the shaded cross sections of the space figures below? 6 cm^2
    b. Each of these figures has a height of 7 cm. What do you know about the volumes of these figures? The volumes are =.

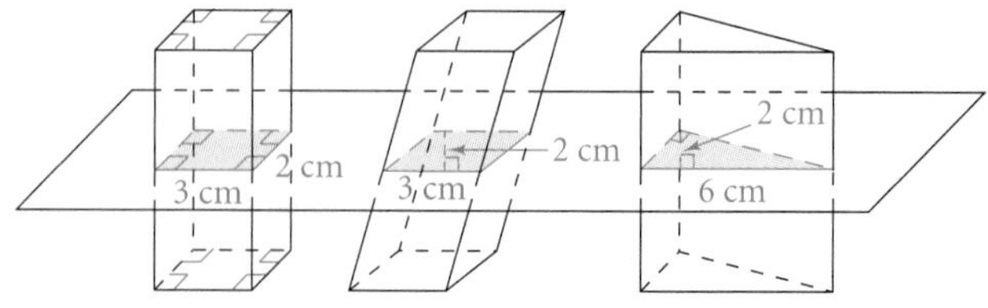

You can use what you discovered in the Work Together, along with Cavalieri's Principle, to find the volume of any prism.

Theorem 6-6
Volume of a Prism

The volume of a prism is the product of the area of a base and the height of the prism.

$$V = Bh$$

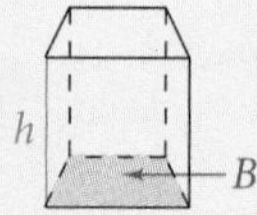

11. **Try This** Find the volume of each of the space figures in Question 10. The volume of each prism is 42 cm^3.

Question 11 Point out to students that the volume of all space figures, not just rectangular prisms, is measured in cubic units.

Example 1

ERROR ALERT! In Part b, students may have trouble identifying the height of a prism when the height is not vertical. **Remediation:** Remind students that the height of a prism is the perpendicular distance between the bases. Then have them practice identifying bases and altitudes of prisms that are in different orientations.

You may need to review with students how to find the height of an equilateral triangle.

Theorem 6-7 Have students compare Theorems 6-6 and 6-7. Have them observe that they need to remember just one formula for the volume of prisms and cylinders, $V = Bh$. When the figure is a prism, B will be the area of a polygon. When the figure is a cylinder, B will be the area of a circle.

EXTENSION Have students form two cylinders using $8\frac{1}{2}$-in. by 11-in. paper, one with the height $8\frac{1}{2}$ in. and the other with the height 11 in. Ask students to guess which has the greater volume, then calculate the volumes to test their guesses. Most students will guess incorrectly that the volumes are equal. **$8\frac{1}{2}$ in. height: $V = 81.8$ in.^{3}; 11 in. height: $V = 63.2$ in.^{3}**

Example 1

Find the volume of each prism.

a.

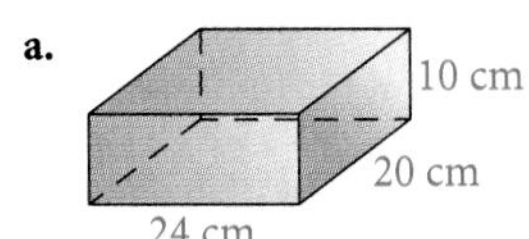

b.

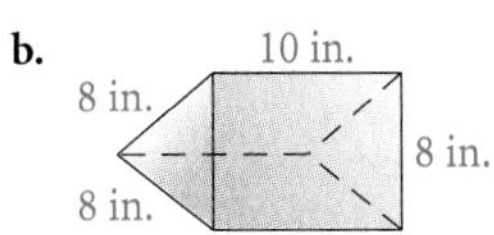

a. $V = Bh$ — Use the formula for volume.

$= 480 \cdot 10$ — $B = 24 \cdot 20 = 480$ cm^2

$= 4800$ — Simplify.

The volume of the rectangular prism is 4800 cm^3.

b. The base of the triangular prism is an equilateral triangle. An altitude of the triangle divides it into two 30°-60°-90° triangles.

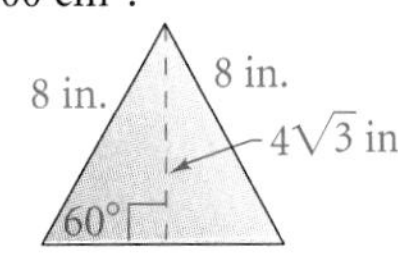

$V = Bh$ — Use the formula for volume.

$= 16\sqrt{3} \cdot 10$ — $B = \frac{1}{2} \cdot 8 \cdot 4\sqrt{3} = 16\sqrt{3}$ in.^{2}

$= 160\sqrt{3}$ — Simplify.

The volume of the triangular prism is $160\sqrt{3}$ in.^{3}.

12. Try This The volume of a triangular prism is 1860 cm^3. Its base is a right triangle with legs 24 cm and 10 cm long. **See left.**

a. Draw and label a diagram.
b. Find the area of the base of the prism.
c. Find the height of the prism.

13. Try This Find the volume of this oblique prism with rectangular bases. **550 in.^{3}**

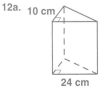

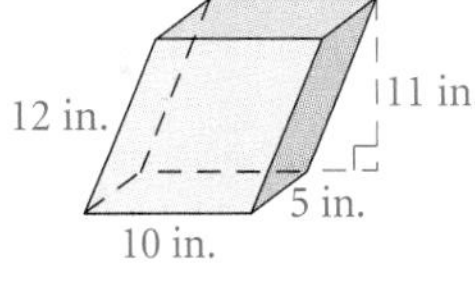

12a. 10 cm, 24 cm

b. 120 cm^2

c. 15.5 cm

Part 2

Volumes of Cylinders

The formula for the volume of a cylinder is similar to the formula for the volume of a prism.

Theorem 6-7
Volume of a Cylinder

The volume of a cylinder is the product of the area of a base and the height of the cylinder.

$$V = Bh, \text{ or } V = \pi r^2 h$$

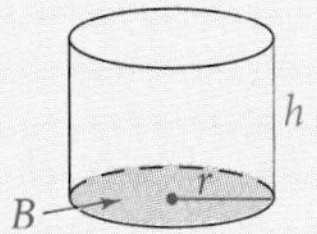

Technology Options

Students may construct the table in the Find Out by Analyzing activity using a spreadsheet.

Prentice Hall Technology

Software
- Secondary Math Lab Toolkit™
- Integrated Math Lab 33
- Computer Item Generator 6-4

Internet
- See the Prentice Hall site. (http://www.phschool.com)

Example 2 **Relating to the Real World** 

Students may need further explanation why the volume is multiplied by 12^3 to convert cubic feet to cubic inches. Show them that in order to cancel ft^3, they must multiply by $\frac{12 \text{ in.}}{1 \text{ ft}} \cdot \frac{12 \text{ in.}}{1 \text{ ft}} \cdot \frac{12 \text{ in.}}{1 \text{ ft}}$ or $\frac{12^3 \text{in.}^3}{1 \text{ ft}^3}$. Refer students who need further review to the Math Toolbox on page 307.

Review with students how to use the y^x key on their calculators to cube a number.

Discuss with students the uncertainty of the last several digits of the answer. While the answer is calculated to the nearest tenth, in real life rounding the answer to the nearest million gallons is more meaningful.

CONNECTING TO STUDENTS' WORLD Have students collect cylindrical juice cans such as tomato juice or pineapple juice cans. Then have them measure the diameter and height and calculate the volume in gallons. Ask how their results compare to what is written on the can.

You may want to add the volume formulas to your posters of a prism, cylinder, pyramid, and cone. Have students add the formulas to their index cards.

Sometimes you need to convert units of measure to solve a problem.

Example 2 **Relating to the Real World** 

Aquarium Tanks The main tank at the Living Seas Aquarium at EPCOT Center in Florida is the largest enclosed tank in the world. It is a cylinder with diameter 203 ft and height 25 ft. About how many million gallons of water does this tank hold? (1 gal ≈ 231 in.^{3})

203 ft

25 ft

- Find the volume of the tank in cubic feet.

$r = \frac{203}{2} = 101.5$ The radius equals half the diameter.

$V = \pi r^2 h$ Use the formula for the volume of a cylinder.

$V = \pi(101.5)^2(25)$ Substitute.

π × 101.5 x² × 25 = 809136.8229

- To convert cubic feet to cubic inches, multiply by 12^3.

809,136.8229 × 12 yˣ 3 = 1398188430

- To find the number of gallons the tank can hold, divide by 231.

1,398,188,430 ÷ 231 = 6052763.766

The main tank can hold about 6 million gallons of water.

For practice with converting measurements, see Skills Handbook, page 667.

14. The main tank at the New England Aquarium in Boston, Massachusetts, has a diameter of 40 ft and is 23 ft deep. a. 216,000 gal
    a. What is the capacity of this tank? Round your answer to the nearest thousand gallons.
    b. How does the size of this tank compare with the size of the one at the Living Seas Aquarium? The New England Aquarium tank is about $\frac{1}{30}$ the size of the Living Seas Aquarium tank.

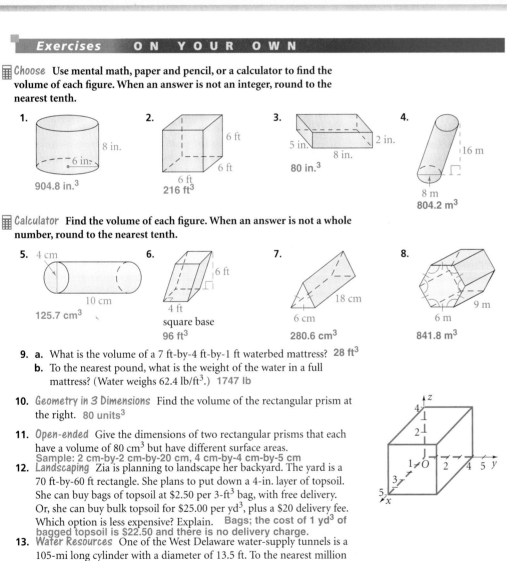

Exercises ON YOUR OWN

Exercises 1–8 Students practice using the formulas for volumes of prisms and cylinders. Remind students to write and say the appropriate formula before finding the volume. Check that students express their answers in the appropriate units.

OPEN-ENDED Exercise 11 Students may want to review the Math Toolbox on page 315 (Exploring Surface Area) before completing this exercise.

Exercise 13 Have students consult the Student Handbook for the conversion of feet to miles.

STANDARDIZED TEST TIP Exercise 14 Students may find it easier to substitute into $V = s^3$ and solve for s.

Exercises ON YOUR OWN

Choose **Use mental math, paper and pencil, or a calculator to find the volume of each figure. When an answer is not an integer, round to the nearest tenth.**

1. 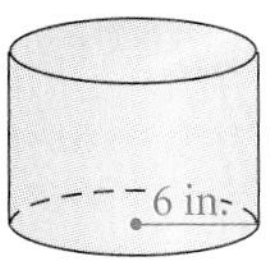 8 in.; 6 in.

904.8 in.^{3}

2.

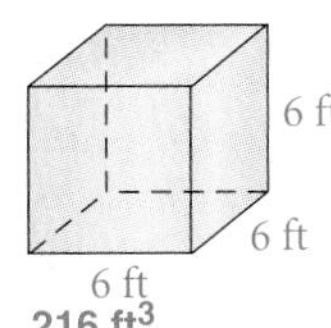

216 ft^3

3.

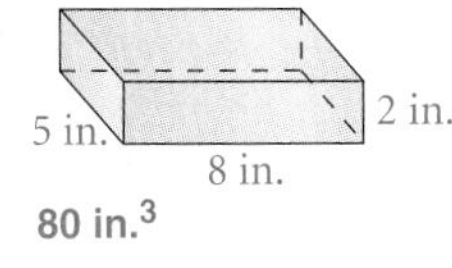

80 in.^{3}

4.

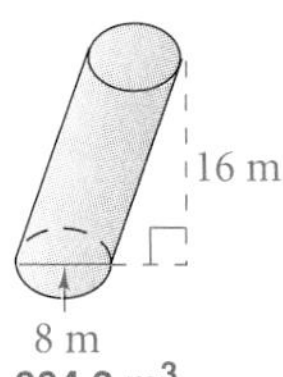

804.2 m^3

Calculator **Find the volume of each figure. When an answer is not a whole number, round to the nearest tenth.**

5. 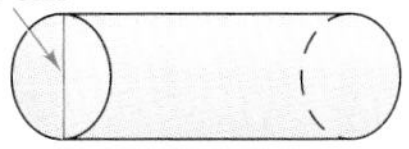 4 cm; 10 cm

125.7 cm^3

6. 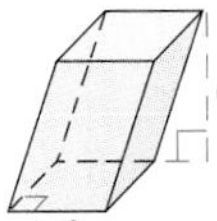 6 ft; 4 ft; square base

96 ft^3

7.

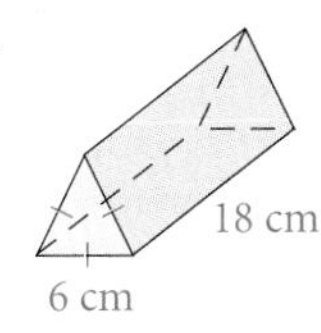

280.6 cm^3

8.

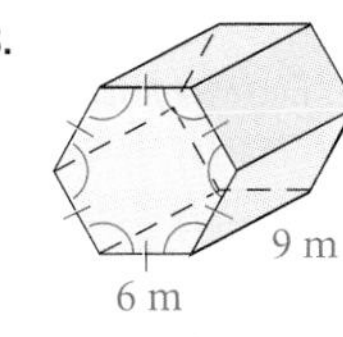

841.8 m^3

9. **a.** What is the volume of a 7 ft-by-4 ft-by-1 ft waterbed mattress? 28 ft^3

b. To the nearest pound, what is the weight of the water in a full mattress? (Water weighs 62.4 lb/ft^3.) 1747 lb

10. *Geometry in 3 Dimensions* Find the volume of the rectangular prism at the right. 80 units^3

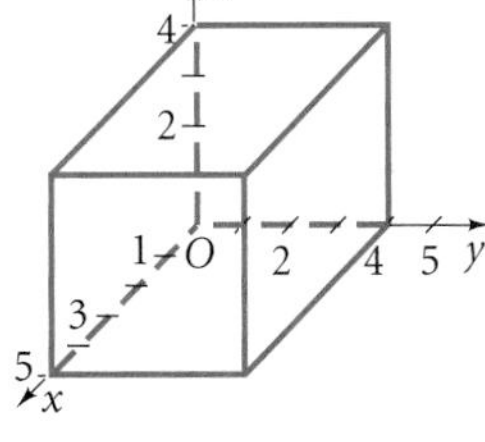

11. *Open-ended* Give the dimensions of two rectangular prisms that each have a volume of 80 cm^3 but have different surface areas.
Sample: 2 cm-by-2 cm-by-20 cm, 4 cm-by-4 cm-by-5 cm

12. *Landscaping* Zia is planning to landscape her backyard. The yard is a 70 ft-by-60 ft rectangle. She plans to put down a 4-in. layer of topsoil. She can buy bags of topsoil at \$2.50 per 3-ft^3 bag, with free delivery. Or, she can buy bulk topsoil for \$25.00 per yd^3, plus a \$20 delivery fee. Which option is less expensive? Explain. Bags; the cost of 1 yd^3 of bagged topsoil is \$22.50 and there is no delivery charge.

13. *Water Resources* One of the West Delaware water-supply tunnels is a 105-mi long cylinder with a diameter of 13.5 ft. To the nearest million cubic feet, how much earth was removed when the tunnel was built?
79 million ft^3

14. *Standardized Test Prep* The volume of a cube is 1000 cm^3. What is its surface area? B

A. 60 cm^2
B. 600 cm^2
C. 100 cm^2
D. about 4630 cm^2
E. cannot be determined

ALTERNATIVE ASSESSMENT Exercises 15–18 These exercises can help you assess students' understanding of the formulas for volume by their ability to manipulate them to find the height of a cylinder or a prism with a given volume. Have students work in small groups or pairs to complete these exercises.

MAKING CONNECTIONS Exercise 20 John Priestly first discovered that green plants affect air in 1772. He observed that placing a candle under a jar extinguished its flame. However, when he placed a sprig of mint under a jar for a few days and then added a candle, the candle burned for a short time.

GEOMETRY IN 3 DIMENSIONS Exercise 25 Students can use the methods suggested on pages 313 and 320 to visualize the figure.

pages 327–329 On Your Own

19c. Answers may vary. Sample: No; the volume of the "improved" cube is $\frac{1}{8}$ the volume of the "ordinary" cube.

Find Out by Analyzing

Answers may vary. Sample:

l	w	h	V	S.A	V : S.A.
6	6	6	216	216	1 : 1
2	3	36	216	372	18 : 31
3	3	24	216	306	36 : 51
4	6	9	216	228	18 : 19

Find the height of each prism or cylinder with the given volume.

15. 5 in.
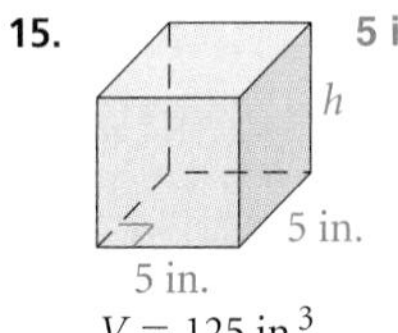

$V = 125$ in.^{3}

16. 3 cm
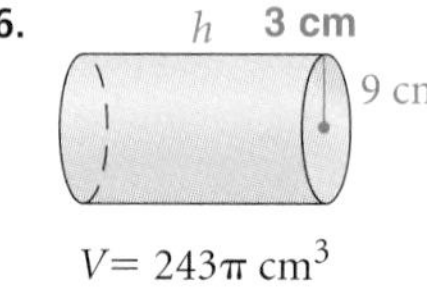

$V = 243\pi$ cm^3

17. 6 ft
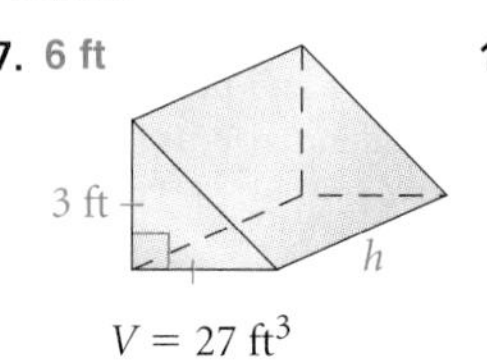

$V = 27$ ft^3

18. 3 m
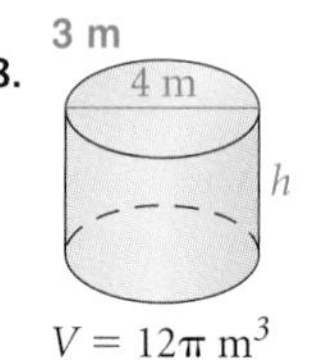

$V = 12\pi$ m^3

19. a. What is the volume of the "ordinary" cube in the cartoon if each edge is 18 in. long? 5832 in.^{3}
b. What is the volume of the "improved" cube if each edge is half as long as an edge of the "ordinary" cube? 729 in.^{3}
c. *Writing* Do you agree with the cartoon statement that the "improved" cube is half the size of the "ordinary" cube? Explain. See margin.

GUINDON © News America Syndicate, 1985

An improved cube (right), half the size of ordinary cubes. It has a convenient carrying handle.

20. *Environmental Engineering* A scientist has suggested that one way to keep indoor air relatively pollution free is to provide two or three pots of flowers such as daisies for every 100 ft^2 of floor space with an 8-ft ceiling. How many pots of daisies would a 35 ft-by-45 ft-by-8 ft classroom need? 32 to 47

21. a. The volume of a cylinder is 600π cm^3. The radius of a base of the cylinder is 5 cm. What is the height of the cylinder? 24 cm
b. The volume of a cylinder is 135π cm^3. The height of the cylinder is 15 cm. What is the radius of a base of the cylinder? 3 cm

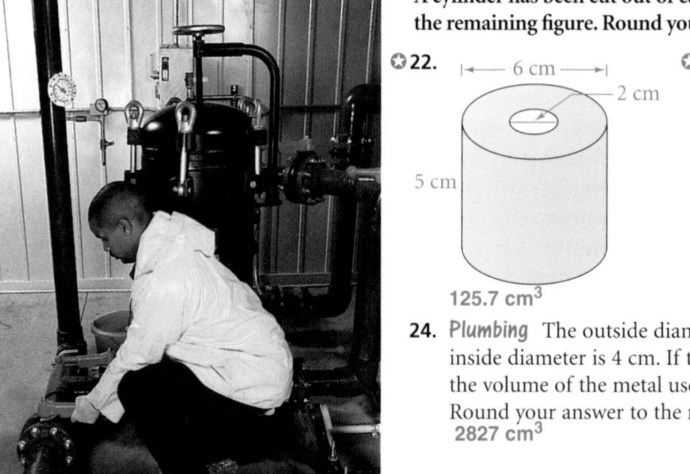

A cylinder has been cut out of each figure. Find the volume of the remaining figure. Round your answer to the nearest tenth.

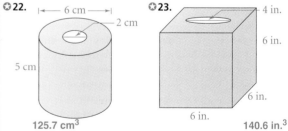

22. 6 cm, 2 cm, 5 cm — 125.7 cm^3

23. 4 in., 6 in., 6 in., 6 in. — 140.6 in.^{3}

24. *Plumbing* The outside diameter of a pipe is 5 cm. The inside diameter is 4 cm. If the pipe is 4 m long, what is the volume of the metal used for this length of pipe? Round your answer to the nearest whole number. 2827 cm^3

FIND OUT BY ANALYZING This activity reinforces the fact that different prisms can have the same volume.

Exercises MIXED REVIEW

Exercises 26–29 Encourage students to use the Triangle Inequality Theorem. Then have them confirm their answers by measuring the lengths of the sides of the triangle.

JOURNAL Students may want to survey friends and relatives to see how they use volume on a daily basis at home and at work.

GETTING READY FOR LESSON 6-5 These exercises prepare students to find the volumes of pyramids and cones.

Wrap Up

THE BIG IDEA Ask students: *Describe how to find the volume of a prism and cylinder. Explain how the methods are the same and how they are different.*

RETEACHING ACTIVITY Students find the volume of part of a pint container and a measuring cup. (Reteaching worksheet 6-4)

25. a. *Geometry in 3 Dimensions* What is the volume, in terms of π, of the cylinder formed if the rectangle at the right is rotated 360° about the x-axis? **16π units^3**
 b. What is the volume, in terms of π, if the rectangle is rotated 360° about the y-axis? **32π units^3**

Chapter Project: *Find Out by Analyzing*

Copy and complete the table below for four *different* rectangular prisms that each have a volume of 216 cm^3. **See margin p. 328.**

Length (cm)	Width (cm)	Depth (cm)	Volume (V) (cm^3)	Surface Area (S.A.) (cm^2)	Ratio V:S.A.
6	6	■	216	■	■
■	■	■	216	■	■

1. Which of the prisms uses the container material most efficiently? least efficiently? Explain. **6 by 6 by 6; 2 by 3 by 36; see right.**
2. Why would a manufacturer be concerned with the ratio of volume to surface area? **to minimize the cost of packaging**
3. Why do you think cereal boxes are not shaped to give the greatest ratio of volume to surface area?

The lower the ratio, the more material is being used to enclose the same volume.

3. Answers may vary. Sample: A cereal box is used for promoting the product, so it needs a large surface area on its front.

Exercises MIXED REVIEW

Draw and label $\triangle ABC$. List the sides from shortest to longest.

26. $\overline{AC}, \overline{BC}, \overline{AB}$
27. $\overline{AC}, \overline{AB}, \overline{BC}$

26. $m\angle A = 67, m\angle B = 34, m\angle C = 79$
27. $m\angle A = 101, m\angle B = 13, m\angle C = 66$
28. $m\angle A = 98, m\angle B = 73, m\angle C = 9$ **$\overline{AB}, \overline{AC}, \overline{BC}$**
29. $m\angle A = 28, m\angle B = 81, m\angle C = 71$ **$\overline{BC}, \overline{AB}, \overline{AC}$**
30. *Critical Thinking* The area of a triangle is 24 cm^2. The longest side of the triangle is 13 cm long. The second longest side is 12 cm long. Is the triangle a right triangle? Explain. **No; the rt. $\triangle$ would have sides 5, 12, 13 and area 30 cm^2.**

Getting Ready for Lesson 6-5

Use the Pythagorean Theorem to find the height h of each space figure.

31. **8 in.**

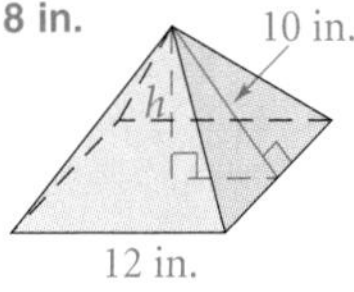

32. **12 cm**

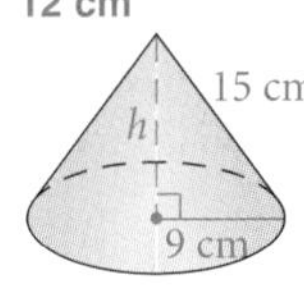

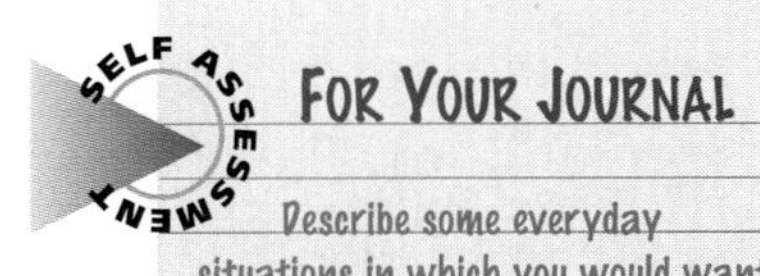

FOR YOUR JOURNAL
Describe some everyday situations in which you would want to know the volumes of prisms.

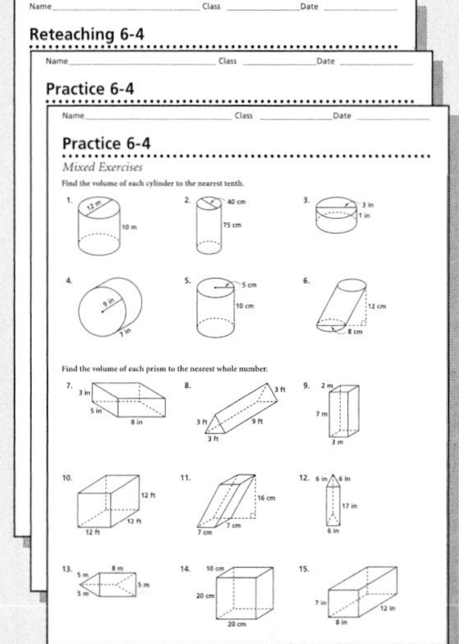

Lesson Quiz

Lesson Quiz is also available in Transparencies.

1. A rectangular prism has height 3 cm, base length 6 cm, and base width 5 cm. Find the volume of the prism. **90 cm^3**
2. A triangular prism has height 24 in. Its base is a right triangle with legs 9 in. and 12 in. Find the volume of the prism. **1296 in.^{3}**
3. A cylinder has height 18 m and diameter 24 m. Find the volume of the cylinder to the nearest cubic meter. **8143 m^3**

6-5 Teaching Notes

PROBLEM OF THE DAY

Arrange eight toothpicks to form a regular octagon, two squares, and eight triangles.

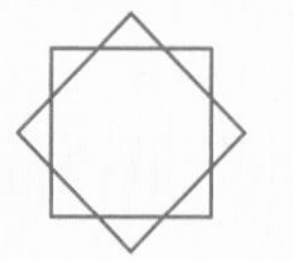

Problem of the Day is also available in Transparencies.

CONNECTING TO PRIOR KNOWLEDGE Have students find the volume of a prism with a square base of length 5 cm and height 8 cm and the volume of a cylinder with a diameter of 5 cm and height 8 cm.

WORK TOGETHER

Students investigate the volume of a pyramid. Have students begin by making a conjecture about the volume of a pyramid relative to the volume of a prism with the same base and height. (Some may make the conjecture that the volume of the pyramid is one-half the volume of the prism.)

Questions 1–2 It is important that students realize that the relationship between the volumes of a prism and a pyramid depends on their having the same base and height.

Lesson Planning Options

Prerequisite Skills

- Finding the area of polygons and circles
- Applying the Pythagorean Theorem

Assignment Options for Exercises On Your Own

To provide flexible scheduling, this lesson can be subdivided into parts.

1. **Core** 3, 7, 10, 15, 16
   Extension 17
2. **Core** 1, 2, 4–6, 8, 9, 11, 13, 14, 19–24
   Extension 12, 18

Use Mixed Review to maintain skills.

Resources

Student Edition

Skills Handbook, pp. 660, 673
Extra Practice, p. 653
Glossary/Study Guide

Teaching Resources

Chapter Support File, Ch. 6
- Practice 6-5 (two worksheets)
- Reteaching 6-5
- Alternative Activity 6-5

Classroom Manager 6-5
Glossary, Spanish Resources

Transparencies
15, 16, 18, 71, 76

What You'll Learn

- Finding volumes of pyramids and cones

...And Why

To solve problems concerning the amount of space in things such as a convention center or a popcorn box

What You'll Need

- cardboard
- ruler
- scissors
- tape
- rice
- calculator

6-5 Volumes of Pyramids and Cones

WORK TOGETHER

You know how to find the volume of a prism. Work in a group to explore the volume of a pyramid.

- Draw the nets shown below on cardboard.
- Cut out the nets and tape them together to make a cube and a regular square pyramid. Each model will have one open face.

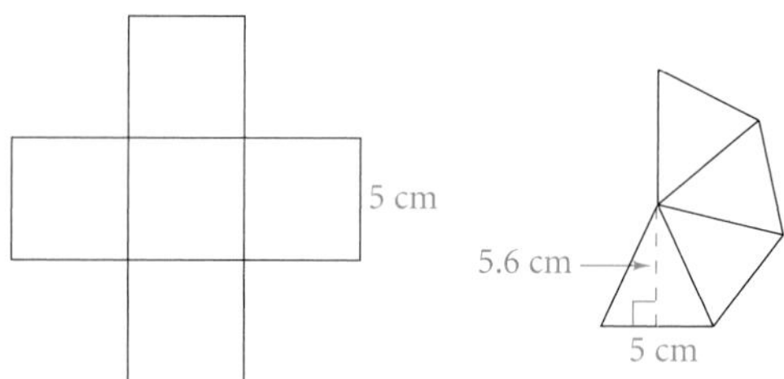

1. Compare the areas of the bases of the cube and the pyramid. The areas are =.
2. Compare the heights of the cube and the pyramid. The heights are =.
3. Fill the pyramid with rice. Then pour the rice from the pyramid into the cube. How many pyramids full of rice does the cube hold? about 3 pyramids
4. The volume of the pyramid is what fractional part of the volume of the cube? $\frac{1}{3}$

THINK AND DISCUSS

ERROR ALERT! **Theorem 6-8** Some students will confuse slant height with height in the formula for the volume of a pyramid. **Remediation:** Reinforce the relationship between the volume of a pyramid and the volume of a prism. Thinking of volume of a pyramid as one-third the volume of a prism should help since slant height was not associated with prisms.

AUDITORY LEARNING It may help students to remember "the area of a triangle is $\frac{1}{2}$ the area of a rectangle in 2 dimensions and the volume of a pyramid is $\frac{1}{3}$ the volume of a prism in 3 dimensions."

Example 1 Relating to the Real World 

Emphasize that the B in the formula for the volume of a pyramid represents the area of the base. In this case, the area of the base is given. In Question 5, students need to calculate the area of the base.

THINK AND DISCUSS

Part 1

Volumes of Pyramids

The Work Together demonstrates the following theorem.

Theorem 6-8
Volume of a Pyramid

The volume of a pyramid is one third the product of the area of the base and the height of the pyramid.

$$V = \frac{1}{3}Bh$$

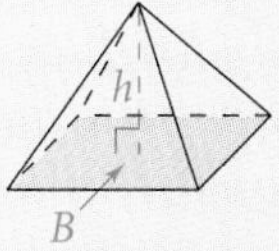

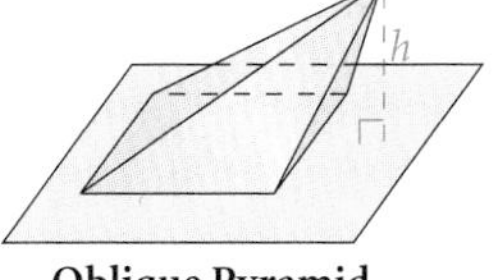

Oblique Pyramid

Because of Cavalieri's Principle, the volume formula is true for all pyramids, including *oblique* pyramids. The **height** h of an oblique pyramid is the length of the perpendicular segment from the vertex to the plane of the base.

Example 1 Relating to the Real World 

Architecture The Pyramid is an arena in Memphis, Tennessee. The area of the base of the Pyramid is about 300,000 ft^2. Its height is 321 ft. What is the volume of the Pyramid?

$V = \frac{1}{3}Bh$ Use the formula for the volume of a pyramid.

$= \frac{1}{3}(300{,}000)(321)$ Substitute.

$= 32{,}100{,}000$ Simplify.

The volume is about 32,100,000 ft^3.

5. **Try This** Find the volume of a regular square pyramid with base edges 12 in. long and height 8 in. 384 in.^{3}

Additional Examples

FOR EXAMPLE 1

Find the volume of a regular square pyramid with base length 15 cm and height 22 cm. **1650 cm^3**

Discussion: *What is the volume of a nonregular square prism with the same dimensions as the pyramid in Additional Example 1?*

FOR EXAMPLE 2

Find the volume of a regular square pyramid with base length 16 m and slant height 10 m. **512 m^3**

Discussion: *If the pyramid were filled with water, could it be poured into a rectangular prism with base length 8 m, base width 6 m, and height 10 m without overflowing?*

FOR EXAMPLE 3

Find the volume of a cone with radius 5 cm and height 8 cm. Round to the nearest tenth. **209.4 cm^3**

Discussion: *How does the volume of the cone compare to the volume of a square pyramid with base length 10 cm and height 8 cm?*

Example 2

Students are accustomed to solving for the slant height (the hypotenuse of the right triangle) in order to find the surface area. Point out that in this example, they are solving for the height which is a leg of the right triangle.

TACTILE LEARNING If you have block scheduling or an extended class period, have students repeat the Work Together activity using cones and cylinders. Provide nets of a cone and a cylinder with the same height and base. Then have students make the figures and investigate how many cones of rice it takes to fill the cylinder.

Example 3

Review the calculator keystrokes with students, especially how to input $\frac{1}{3}$ and $(15)^2$.

EXTENSION Have students investigate frustums made from sections of cones, such as popcorn buckets, megaphones, paper drinking cups, and dog dishes. Have groups research the formulas for the area of frustums made from cones and pyramids and present their results to the class.

Technology Options

For Exercise 11, students may use a spreadsheet to display the possible dimensions.

Prentice Hall Technology 

Software
- Secondary Math Lab Toolkit™
- Computer Item Generator 6-5

CD-ROM
- Multimedia Geometry Lab 6

Internet
- See the Prentice Hall site. (http://www.phschool.com)

To find the volume of a pyramid you need to know its height.

Example 2

Find the volume of a regular square pyramid with base edges 40 ft long and slant height 25 ft.

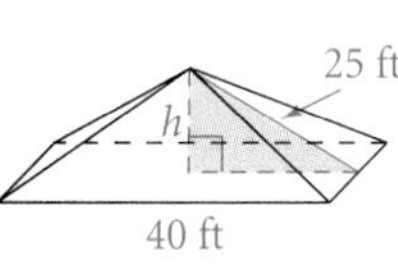

- Find the height of the pyramid.

$25^2 = h^2 + 20^2$ Use the Pythagorean Theorem.
$625 = h^2 + 400$ Simplify.
$h^2 = 225$ Subtract 400 from each side.
$h = 15$ Find the square root of each side.

- Find the volume of the pyramid.

$V = \frac{1}{3}Bh$ Use the formula for volume of a pyramid.
$= \frac{1}{3}(40 \cdot 40)15$ Substitute.
$= 8000$ Simplify.

The volume of the pyramid is 8000 ft^3.

6. **Try This** Find the volume of a regular square pyramid with base edges 24 m long and slant height 13 m. 960 m^3

Part 2

Volumes of Cones

In the Work Together, you discovered that the volume of a pyramid is one third the volume of a prism with the same base and height. You can also find that the volume of a cone is one third the volume of a cylinder with the same base and height.

Theorem 6-9
Volume of a Cone

The volume of a cone is one third the product of the area of the base and the height.

$$V = \frac{1}{3}Bh, \text{ or } V = \frac{1}{3}\pi r^2 h$$

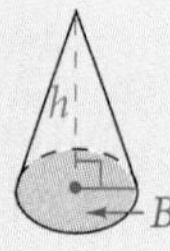

This volume formula applies to all cones, including *oblique* cones.

Exercises ON YOUR OWN

ERROR ALERT! Exercises 1, 2, and 4 Some students may substitute the diameter for the radius in the formula. **Remediation:** Have students identify and write down what r and h equal before they write the formula, then substitute for each variable.

MENTAL MATH Exercise 5 Have students also investigate the volume of a prism when the dimensions of its base are doubled, when the height is doubled, and when the dimensions of the base and the height are both doubled.

DIVERSITY Exercise 6 This exercise provides an opportunity to discuss the rich history of Native Americans. You may want to have groups research different tribes and present their findings to the class. (If possible, choose tribes native to your geographical area.)

Example 3

Find the volume of the oblique cone with diameter 30 ft and height 25 ft. Round to the nearest whole number.

$r = \frac{30}{2} = 15$ — The radius is half the diameter.

$V = \frac{1}{3}\pi r^2 h$ — Use the formula for the volume of a cone.

$= \frac{1}{3}\pi(15)^2 25$ — Substitute.

1 [÷] 3 [×] [π] [×] 15 [x^2] [×] 25 [=] 5890.4862

The volume of the cone is about 5890 ft^3.

7. **Try This** Find the volume of a cone with radius 3 in. and height 8 in. Round to the nearest tenth. 75.4 $in.^3$

Exercises ON YOUR OWN

Calculator **Find the volume of each figure. When an answer is not a whole number, round to the nearest tenth.**

1. 

115.5 $in.^3$

2. 23.0 $in.^3$ 

3. 122.5 $in.^3$ 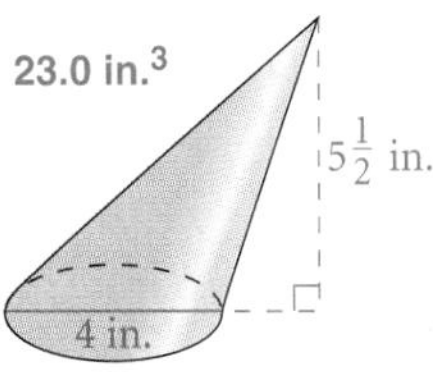

square base

4. 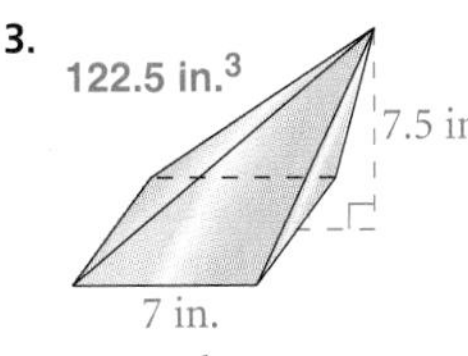

301.6 cm^3

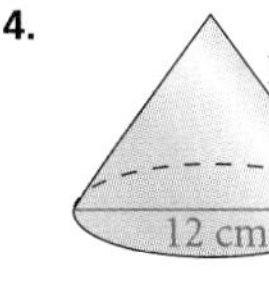

5. a. Mental Math A cone with radius 3 ft and height 10 ft has a volume of 30π ft^3. What is its volume when the radius is doubled? 120π ft^3
   b. What is the volume when the height of the original cone is doubled? 60π ft^3
   c. What is the volume when both the radius and the height of the original cone are doubled? 240π ft^3

6. a. The largest tepee in the United States belongs to a member of the Crow (Native Americans of the Great Plains). It is 43 ft high and 42 ft in diameter. Find its volume to the nearest cubic foot. 19,858 ft^3
   b. How does this compare with the volume of your classroom?
   Check students' work.

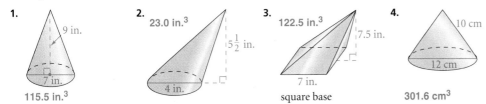

COORDINATE GEOMETRY Exercise 12 Students should now be familiar with this type of problem. If they made a visual model for Exercise 24 in Lesson 6-2, it can also be used for this problem.

CRITICAL THINKING Exercise 13 Ask students how the volume of a cone with radius r and height h compares to the volume of two cones with radii $\frac{r}{2}$ and height h.

Exercise 16 Students will need to use the 30°-60°-90° Triangle Theorem to find the area of the base.

Exercise 17 The Transamerica Building has "wings" for stability. Do not have students include the "wings" when they find the volume.

ESL Exercises 17–18 You may want to pair students with strong English skills with those who are less proficient in English for these word problems.

Find the volume of each figure. You may leave answers in terms of π or in simplest radical form.

7. 300 in.^3

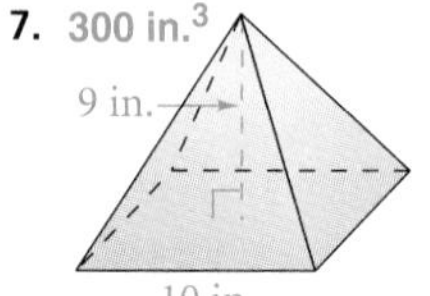

8. $\frac{80}{3}\pi \text{ cm}^3$

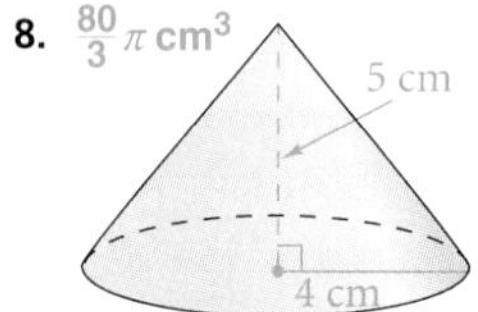

9. $\frac{16}{3}\pi \text{ ft}^3$

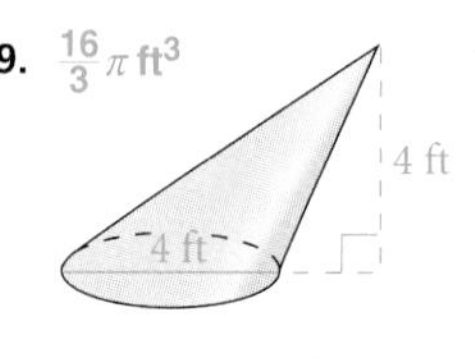

10. $180\sqrt{3} \text{ cm}^3$

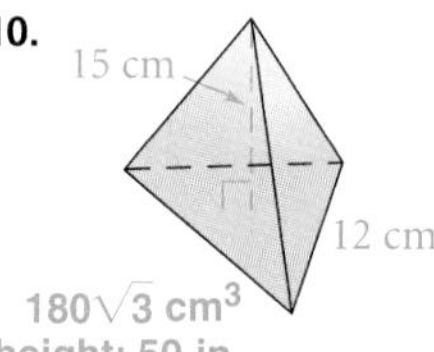

11. *Open-ended* A cone has a volume of $600\pi \text{ in.}^3$. Find two possible sets of dimensions for the height and radius of the cone. Samples: height: 50 in., radius: 6 in.; height: 18 in., radius: 10 in.

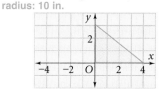

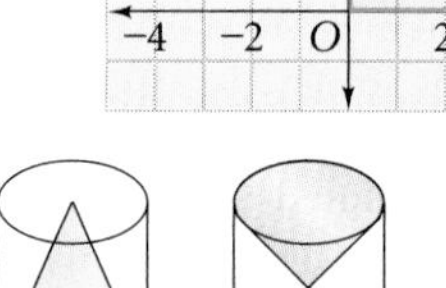

12. a. *Coordinate Geometry* Suppose you rotate the right triangle shown 360° about the x-axis. What is the volume of the resulting cone in terms of π? 12π units^3
    b. Suppose you rotate the triangle 360° about the y-axis. What is the volume in terms of π? 16π units^3

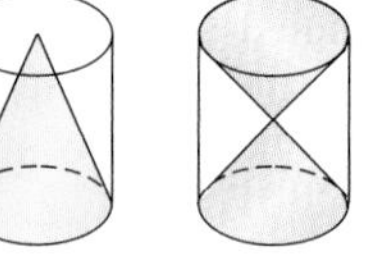

13. The two cylinders pictured at the right are congruent. How does the volume of the larger cone compare to the total volume of the two smaller cones? Explain. They are =.

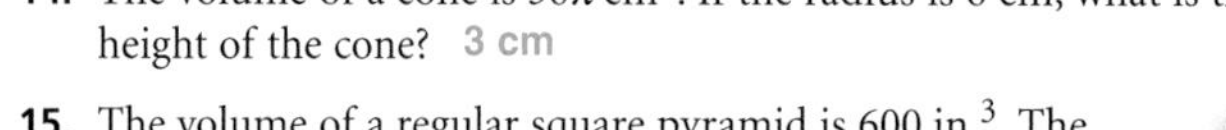

14. The volume of a cone is $36\pi \text{ cm}^3$. If the radius is 6 cm, what is the height of the cone? 3 cm

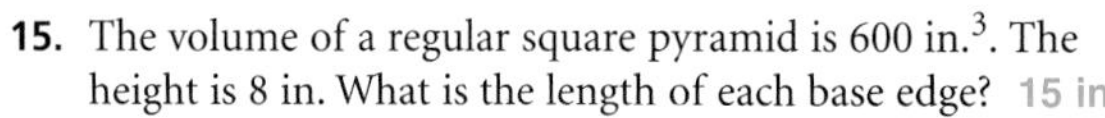

15. The volume of a regular square pyramid is 600 in.^3. The height is 8 in. What is the length of each base edge? 15 in.

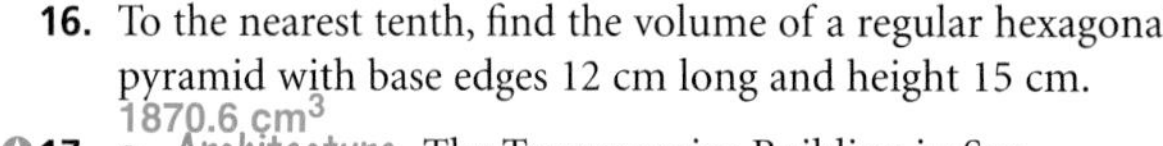

16. To the nearest tenth, find the volume of a regular hexagonal pyramid with base edges 12 cm long and height 15 cm. 1870.6 cm^3

17. a. *Architecture* The Transamerica Building in San Francisco is a pyramid 800 ft tall with a square base 149 ft on each side. What is its volume to the nearest thousand cubic feet? $5{,}920{,}000 \text{ ft}^3$
    b. If the Transamerica Building had been built as a *prism* with the same square base, how tall to the nearest foot would it have to be to have the same volume as the existing building? 267 ft

CRITICAL THINKING Exercise 18 You may want to have students complete this problem in groups. Students can work together to discuss a plan for solving the problem, to check each other's computations, and to discuss the pros and cons of the promotional cone.

ALTERNATIVE ASSESSMENT Exercises 20–23 These exercises can help you assess students' understanding of the volume formulas for a pyramid and a cone by their ability to manipulate the formulas to find the radius or height of the figure. Have students compare their results with a partner and revise their work until their answers agree.

Chapter Project **FIND OUT BY INVESTIGATING** Some students may not be able or willing to go to a supermarket to investigate containers. You may want to provide a variety of containers of different shapes and sizes for students to analyze. You may want to give extra credit to students who bring in containers.

18. *Critical Thinking* A movie theater sells popcorn in cylindrical containers that are 4 in. in diameter and 10 in. high. As a special promotion, the theater plans to sell popcorn in a cone-shaped container for the same price. The diameter of the container will remain the same. The promotional cone will use the same amount of cardboard as the cylindrical container. Do you think this promotional cone is a good value? Why or why not?

Answers may vary. Sample: No; the volume of the cone is smaller than the volume of the cylinder.

19. Which container has the greatest volume? **pyramid**

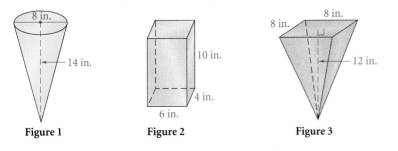

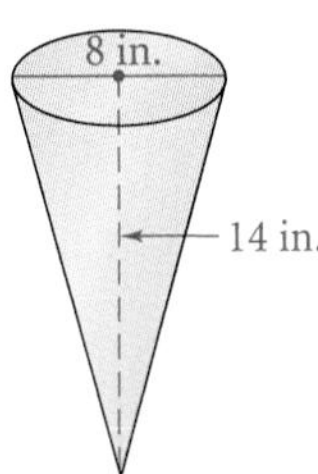

Figure 1

6 in. 10 in. 4 in.

Figure 2

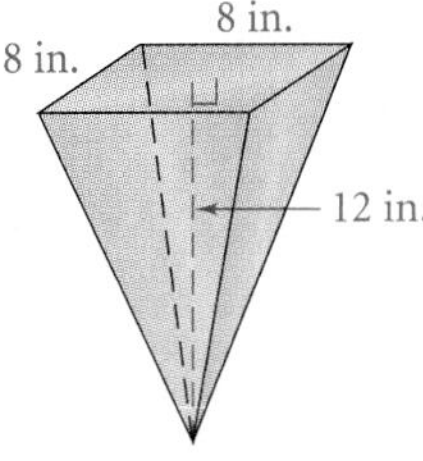

Figure 3

Algebra **Find the value of the variable in each figure. You may leave answers in simplest radical form.**

20. **6**

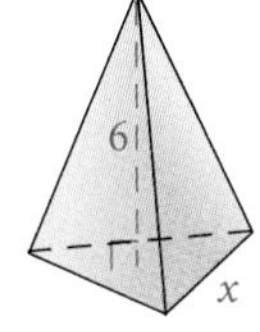

Volume $= 18\sqrt{3}$

21. **3**

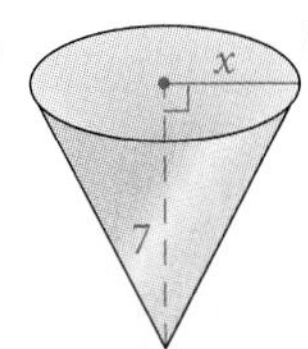

Volume $= 21\pi$

22. **$3\sqrt{2}$**

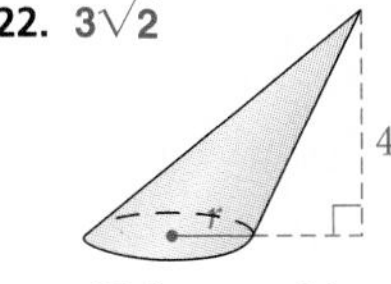

Volume $= 24\pi$

23. **9**

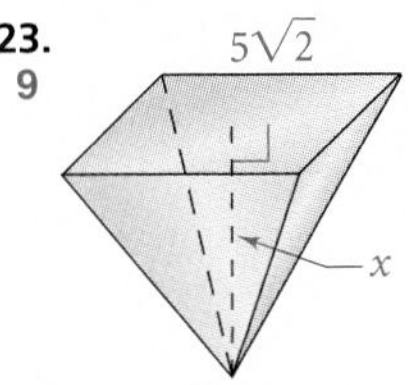

Volume $= 150$

24. *Writing* The figures at the right can be covered by an equal number of straws that are the same length. Describe how Cavalieri's Principle could be adapted to compare the areas of these figures. **See below.**

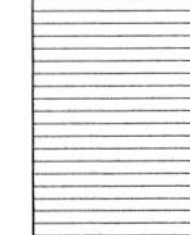

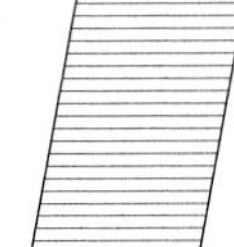

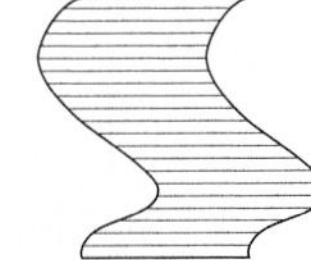

Chapter Project ***Find Out by Investigating***

Do some container shapes seem to give more product for the same money? Go to a supermarket and identify a variety of container shapes. Do some shapes make you think there's more in them than there actually is? What factors do you think a manufacturer considers in deciding the shape of a container? Write a report about your findings. **Check students' work.**

24. **If 2 figures have the same height, and if, at every level, the line ∥ to the base intersects the figures in ≅ segments, then their areas are =.**

Exercises MIXED REVIEW

Exercise 25 Students may want to review the distance formula in Lesson 1-8 and slope in Lesson 2-3.

JOURNAL Check that students use *base, area of base, height, slant height,* and their abbreviations accurately.

GETTING READY FOR LESSON 6-6 These exercises prepare students to measure spheres.

Wrap Up

THE BIG IDEA Ask students: *Explain how the volume formulas for a pyramid and a cone are similar and different.*

RETEACHING ACTIVITY Students calculate the volume of cones and pyramids. (Reteaching worksheet 6-5)

Geometry at Work

For further information about the training necessary to be a packaging engineer, have students contact a local engineering school. You may want to invite a local engineer to class to discuss what they do.

Encourage students to investigate these topics:

- the training necessary to become an engineer
- the math and computer skills used by an engineer
- the different types of engineers and the companies that employ them

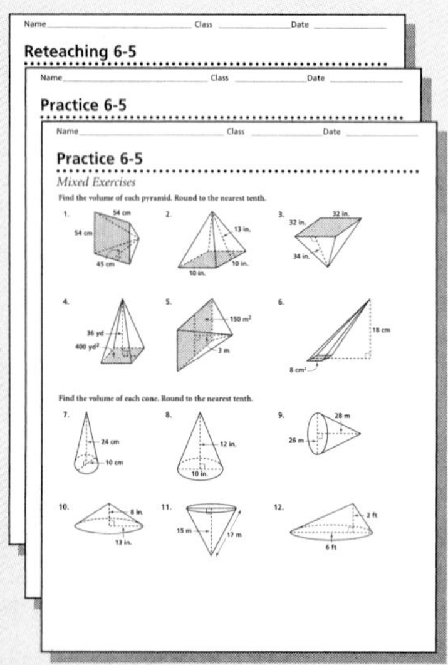
Reteaching 6-5

Practice 6-5

Practice 6-5

Mixed Exercises

Lesson Quiz

Lesson Quiz is also available in Transparencies.

Find the volume of each figure. Round to the nearest tenth, if necessary.

1. a cone with diameter 9 in. and height 16 in. 339.3 in.^3
2. a square pyramid with base length 6 cm and height 9.5 cm 114 cm^3
3. a cone with radius 12 mm and slant height 20 mm 2412.7 mm^3
4. a square pyramid with base length 10 ft and slant height 13 ft 400 ft^3

Exercises MIXED REVIEW

25. The vertices of quadrilateral *ABCD* are $A(-4, -1)$, $B(-1, 3)$, $C(7, -3)$, and $D(4, -7)$.
    a. Use the Distance Formula to find the length of each side. $AB = 5, BC = 10, CD = 5, AD = 10$
    b. Find the slope of each side. See below.
    c. Determine the most accurate name for quadrilateral *ABCD*. rectangle
26. *Movies* The largest permanent movie screen in the world is in Jakarta, Indonesia. It is 96 ft by 70.5 ft. What is its area? 6768 ft^2

FOR YOUR JOURNAL

Explain why finding the volume of a cylinder is like finding the volume of a prism. Then explain why finding the volume of a cone is like finding the volume of a pyramid.

Getting Ready for Lesson 6-6

Calculator **Find the area and circumference of a circle with the given radius. Round answers to the nearest tenth.**

27. 6 in. 113.1 in.^2; 37.7 in.
28. 5 cm 78.5 cm^2; 31.4 cm
29. 2.5 ft 19.6 ft^2; 15.7 ft
30. 1.2 m 4.5 m^2; 7.5 m

Geometry at Work

Packaging Engineer

Each year, more than one trillion dollars in manufactured goods are packaged in some kind of a container. To create each new box, bag, or carton, packaging engineers must balance such factors as safety, environmental impact, and attractiveness against cost of production.

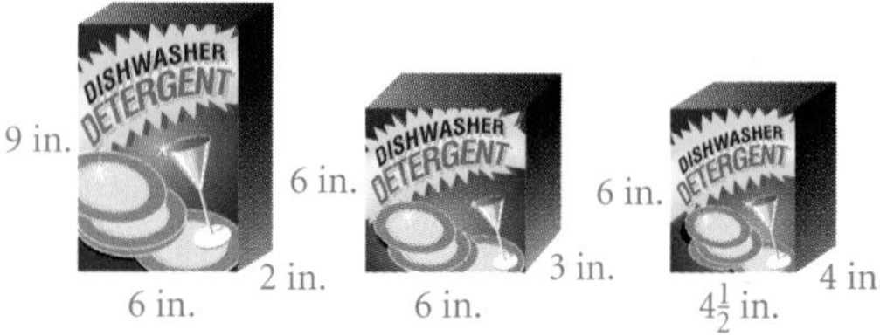

Consider the three boxes of dishwasher detergent. All three boxes have volumes of 108 in.^3, the volume of a standard box of automatic dishwasher detergent. The boxes have different shapes, however, and different surface areas. The box on the left has the greatest surface area and therefore costs the most to produce. Nevertheless, despite the higher cost, the box on the left has become standard. There are many reasons why a company might choose more expensive packaging. In this case, the least expensive package on the right is too difficult for a consumer to pick up and pour. To offset the extra cost, packaging engineers try to choose a package design that will attract enough additional buyers to outweigh the higher cost of production.

Mini Project: Choose a product that you enjoy using. Design and make a new package for the product. Calculate the surface area and volume of your package and describe advantages it has over the current package.

25b. $AB = \frac{4}{3}$, $BC = -\frac{3}{4}$, $CD = \frac{4}{3}$, $AD = -\frac{3}{4}$

6-6 Teaching Notes

PROBLEM OF THE DAY

Margo has a cube, each face painted a different color. In how many ways can she place the numbers 1, 2, 3, 4, 5, and 6 on the cube so that the pairs 1 and 6, 2 and 5, and 3 and 4 are on opposite faces? 48

Problem of the Day is also available in Transparencies.

CONNECTING TO PRIOR KNOWLEDGE Have students calculate the volume of the following:

a. a cylinder with diameter 4 cm and height 16 cm

b. a regular square pyramid with base length 8 in. and height 14 in.

WORK TOGETHER

In this activity, students should discover that it takes twice as much string to cover the curved surface of half a foam ball than to cover the circular region.

ALTERNATIVE METHOD Bring in a beach ball. Have students draw and cut out at least four circles with the same diameter as the ball. Then have them cover the ball with the circles, cutting the circles into pieces and arranging them over the surface of the ball. Students will discover that, after covering the ball with two such circles, it is only about half covered.

Connections  Manufacturing . . . and more

6-6 Surface Areas and Volumes of Spheres

What You'll Learn

- Calculating the surface areas and volumes of spheres

...And Why

To solve real-world problems such as finding the surface area of a soccer ball and the volume of a scoop of ice cream

What You'll Need

- ruler
- scissors
- tacks
- foam balls (cut in half)
- string
- calculator

WORK TOGETHER

How do you compute the surface area of Earth or the amount of leather covering a baseball? Work in a group to explore the surface area of a sphere.

- The surface of half a foam ball consists of two parts—a plane circular region and a curved surface. Place a tack in the center of the circular region. Wind string around the tack covering the entire circular region.
- Once the circular region is covered, cut off any excess string. Measure the length x of string that covered the circular region.
- Place a tack in the center of the curved surface. Wind another string around the tack covering the entire curved surface.
- Once the curved surface is covered, cut off any excess string. Measure the length y of the string that covered the curved surface.

1. a. How do x and y compare? $y > x$

b. Express y as a multiple of x. $y = 2x$

2. a. How much string would you need to cover the entire surface of an uncut foam ball? Express your answer as a multiple of y. $2y$

b. Express your answer to part (a) as a multiple of x. $4x$

3. A string of length x covers an area of πr^2 where r is the radius of the foam ball. Substitute πr^2 for x in the expression you wrote for Question 2(b) to find a formula for the surface area of a sphere. $A = 4\pi r^2$

4. A radius is a segment that has one endpt. at the center and the other endpt. on the sphere.

THINK AND DISCUSS

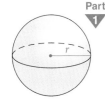

Part 1

Finding the Surface Area of a Sphere

A **sphere** is the set of all points in space equidistant from a given point called the **center.**

4. How would you define a *radius* of a sphere? See above.

5. How would you define a *diameter* of a sphere? a segment passing through the center with endpts. on the sphere

Lesson Planning Options

Prerequisite Skills

- Finding the area of circles
- Understanding cubes and cube roots

Assignment Options for Exercises On Your Own

To provide flexible scheduling, this lesson can be subdivided into parts.

 **Core** 1–4, 16
Extension 14, 26

 **Core** 5–13, 15, 17–18, 22–25, 27
Extension 19–21

Use Mixed Review to maintain skills.

Resources

Student Edition

Skills Handbook, pp. 660, 673
Extra Practice, p. 653
Glossary/Study Guide

Teaching Resources

Chapter Support File, Ch. 6
- Practice 6-6 (two worksheets)
- Reteaching 6-6

Classroom Manager 6-6
Glossary, Spanish Resources

 **Transparencies**
18, 71

THINK AND DISCUSS

Example 1 Relating to the Real World 

Question 6 If possible, bring in a soccer ball so students can see that the sides of the "hexagons" and "pentagons" are curves. This example is a preview of spherical geometry, which will be discussed in Lesson 7-5.

CONNECTING TO STUDENTS' WORLD Have students calculate the surface areas and volumes of other spheres such as a globe, a beach ball, or an orange. They can approximate the radius ($r = \frac{C}{2\pi}$) of each sphere by measuring the circumference of a great circle with a piece of string.

Some students will have trouble following the derivation of the formula for the volume of a sphere. You may want to show in more detail how to get from $\frac{1}{3} \cdot nBr$ to $\frac{1}{3}(4\pi r^2) \cdot r$ to $\frac{1}{3} \cdot 4\pi r^3$.

VISUAL LEARNING The justification of the formula for the volume of a sphere uses the concept of limits. Help students see that as the number of pyramids increases, the size of the base of the pyramid decreases. As this happens, the combined area of the bases becomes closer and closer to the actual surface area of the sphere.

Additional Examples

FOR EXAMPLE 1

Find the surface area of a sphere with diameter 18 in. Round your answer to the nearest tenth. 1017.9 in.^{2}

Discussion: *Describe the dimensions of a cylinder having a smaller surface area than the sphere.*

Find the surface area of a sphere inscribed in a cube with side length 24 cm. Round your answer to the nearest tenth. 1809.6 cm^2

FOR EXAMPLE 2

The volume of a sphere is 904.78 cm^3. What is the surface area of the sphere? Round your answer to the nearest tenth. 452.4 cm^2

Discussion: *How does the surface area of a cube with the same volume compare to the surface area of the sphere?*

The surface area of a sphere is 5026.55 in.^{2}. What is the volume of the sphere? Round your answer to the nearest tenth. 33,510.3 in.^{3}

Your discovery in the Work Together leads to the following theorem.

Theorem 6-10 Surface Area of a Sphere

The surface area of a sphere is four times the product of π and the square of the radius of the sphere.

$$S.A. = 4\pi r^2$$

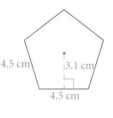

Example 1 Relating to the Real World 

Manufacturing Manufacturers make soccer balls with a radius of 11 cm by sewing together 20 regular hexagons and 12 regular pentagons. Templates for guiding the stitching are shown at the left. Approximate the surface area of a soccer ball to the nearest square centimeter using the following two methods.

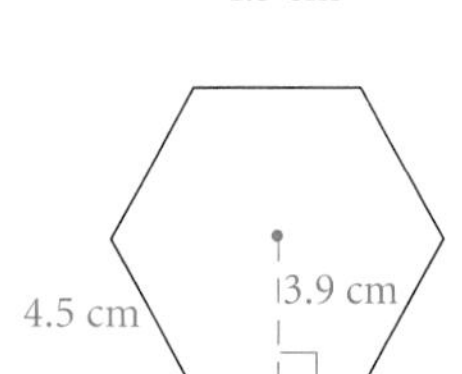

Method 1:
Find the sum of the areas of the pentagons and hexagons.

regular pentagon	regular hexagon
$A = \frac{1}{2}ap$	$A = \frac{1}{2}ap$
$= \frac{1}{2}(3.1)(5 \cdot 4.5)$	$= \frac{1}{2}(3.9)(6 \cdot 4.5)$
$= 34.875$	$= 52.65$

Area of the 12 regular pentagons = (12)(34.875) = 418.5

Area of the 20 regular hexagons = (20)(52.65) = 1053

The sum of the areas of the pentagons and the hexagons is about 1472 cm^2.

Method 2:
Use the formula for the surface area of a sphere.

$S.A. = 4\pi r^2$ Use the formula for surface area.
$= 4 \cdot \pi \cdot 11^2$ Substitute.

4 [×] [π] [×] 11 [x²] [=] 1520.5308

The surface area of the soccer ball is about 1521 cm^2.

6. Compare the answers for the two methods. Explain why they differ. Answers may vary. Sample: Method 2 yields a greater number; the pentagons and hexagons on the ball stretch and curve when the ball is pumped up.

MAKING CONNECTIONS An orange or, in fact, any solid object, need increase only about 25% linearly (i.e., radius, diameter) to double in volume. So, for example, an orange with a diameter of 2.5 in. has twice the volume as an orange with a diameter of 2 in.

ERROR ALERT! **Theorem 6-11** Some students may confuse the formula for the volume of a sphere with the formula for the surface area of a sphere. **Remediation:** To help remember the difference, remind students to picture the surface area of a sphere as four large circles, $4 \cdot \pi r^2$. Also, area is 2-dimensional (r^2) and volume is 3-dimensional (r^3).

You may want to make a poster of a sphere, labeling a radius, diameter, and a great circle. Include the formulas for the surface area and volume. Have students copy the diagram on one side of an index card and the formulas on the other.

RESEARCH Some students may be interested in learning how Cavalieri's Principle can be used to show that the volume of a sphere equals the volume of a cylinder minus the volume of two cones.

Example 2

Make sure students understand each step of the solution. Review how to find the reciprocal of $\frac{4}{3}\pi$ (or $\frac{4\pi}{3}$). Also help them locate and use the cube-root key on their calculators. Some calculators may not have a cube-root key and students will have to use the $\sqrt[x]{y}$ key.

Part 2

Finding the Volume of a Sphere

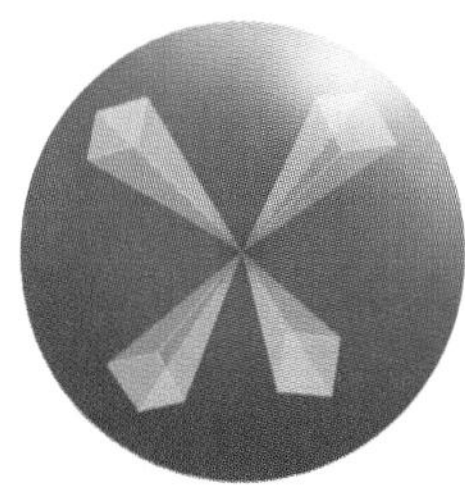

You can fill a sphere with a large number n of small pyramids. The vertex of each pyramid is the center of the sphere. The height of each pyramid is approximately the radius r of the sphere. The sum of the areas of all the bases approximates the surface area of the sphere. You can use this model to derive a formula for the volume of a sphere.

Volume of each pyramid $= \frac{1}{3}Bh$

Sum of the volumes of n pyramids
$= n \cdot \frac{1}{3}Br$ — Substitute r for h.
$= \frac{1}{3} \cdot (nB) \cdot r$
$= \frac{1}{3} \cdot (4\pi r^2) \cdot r$ — Replace nB with the surface area of a sphere.
$= \frac{4}{3}\pi r^3$

The volume of a sphere is $\frac{4}{3}\pi r^3$.

Theorem 6-11
Volume of a Sphere

The volume of a sphere is four thirds the product of π and the cube of the radius of the sphere.

$$V = \frac{4}{3}\pi r^3$$

Example 2

The volume of a sphere is 4849.05 m^3. What is the surface area of the sphere? Round your answer to the nearest tenth.

- Find the radius r.

$V = \frac{4}{3}\pi r^3$	Use the formula for the volume of a sphere.
$4849.05 = \frac{4}{3}\pi r^3$	Substitute.
$4849.05(\frac{3}{4\pi}) = r^3$	Multiply both sides by $\frac{3}{4\pi}$.
$\sqrt[3]{4849.05(\frac{3}{4\pi})} = r$	Find the cube root of each side.

4849.05 [×] 3 [÷] 4 [÷] [π] [=] [$\sqrt[x]{y}$] 3 [=] 10.500001

The radius of the sphere is about 10.5 m.

- Find the surface area of the sphere.

S.A. $= 4\pi r^2$	Use the formula for the surface area of a sphere.
$= 4\pi(10.5)^2$	Substitute.

4 [×] [π] [×] 10.5 [x^2] [=] 1385.4424

The surface area of the sphere is about 1385.4 m^2.

QUICK REVIEW

The *cube root* of x is the number that when *cubed* is x.

Technology Options

Prentice Hall Technology

Software
- Secondary Math Lab Toolkit™
- Computer Item Generator 6-6

CD-ROM
- Multimedia Geometry Lab 6

Internet
- See the Prentice Hall site. (http://www.phschool.com)

MAKING CONNECTIONS Question 9 The shortest distance between any two points on a sphere is the length of the arc of the great circle passing through those two points. Airlines use great circles to plan flight routes because traveling along the path of a great circle decreases travel time and fuel costs.

COORDINATE GEOMETRY Exercise 5 Challenge students to identify a figure that could be rotated around one of the axes to form a hemisphere.

Exercises ON YOUR OWN

Exercises 1–4 Students should not have difficulty with the formulas for surface area. Check that they identify *r* correctly and label their answers in the appropriate units.

7. **Try This** The volume of a sphere is 20,579 in.^{3}. What is the radius of the sphere to the nearest whole number? about 17 in.
8. **Try This** The radius of a sphere is 15 m. What is the volume to the nearest hundred? 14,100 m^3

When a plane and a sphere intersect in more than one point, the intersection is a circle. If the center of the circle is also the center of the sphere, the circle is called a **great circle** of the sphere. The circumference of a great circle is the **circumference of the sphere.** A great circle divides a sphere into two **hemispheres.**

9. *Geography* What is the name of the best-known great circle on Earth? the equator
10. *Geography* Describe the Northern Hemisphere of Earth. the region on the surface of Earth north of the equator

Exercises ON YOUR OWN

Calculator **Find the surface area of each ball to the nearest tenth.**

1. 
$d = 23.9$ cm
1794.5 cm^2

2. 
$d = 68$ mm
14,526.7 mm^2 or 145.3 cm^2

3. 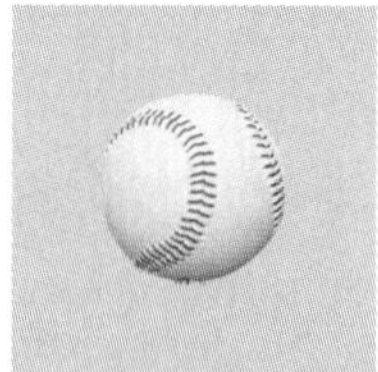
$d = 2\frac{3}{4}$ in.
23.8 in.^{2}

4. 
$d = 1.68$ in.
8.9 in.^{2}

5. *Coordinate Geometry* Find the surface area and volume of the sphere formed by rotating the semicircle at the right 360° about the *x*-axis. Leave your answers in terms of π. 64π units^2; $\frac{256}{3}\pi$ units^3

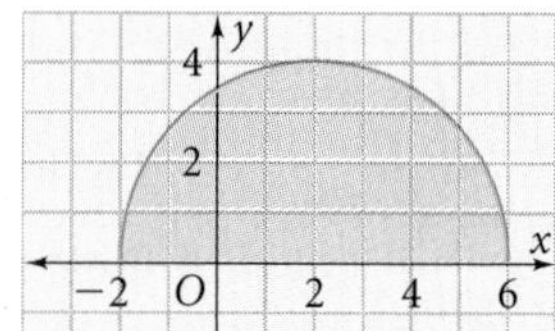

6. A balloon has a 14-in. diameter when it is fully inflated. Half the air is let out of the balloon. Assuming the balloon is a sphere, what is the new diameter? Round your answer to the nearest inch. 11 in.
7. *Meteorology* On July 16, 1882, a massive thunderstorm over Dubuque, Iowa, produced huge hailstones. The diameter of some of the hailstones was 17 in. Ice weighs about 0.033 lb/in.^{3}. What was the approximate weight of these hailstones to the nearest pound? 85 lb

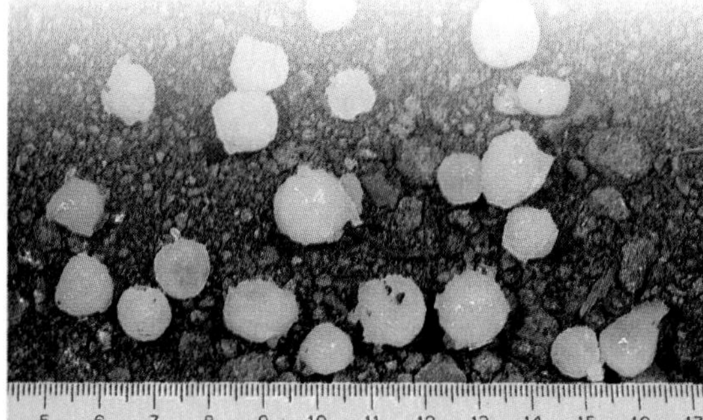

MAKING CONNECTIONS Exercise 12 Bowling dates back to 5200 B.C. where nine stone pins were found in the tomb of an Egyptian boy. In the 4th and 5th centuries, bowling in Germany was a religious ceremony. Participants rolled balls down the church aisles to hit the pin in order to be judged free of sin.

GEOMETRY IN 3 DIMENSIONS Exercise 14 Students should be able to identify the points on the axes 5 units from the center.

MAKING CONNECTIONS Exercise 16 Students may be surprised to learn that the earth is not perfectly spherical. The diameter from the North to South Pole (7900 mi) is 27 miles less than the diameter at the equator (7927 mi). The difference is about $\frac{1}{3}$ of 1%.

Find the volume of each sphere. Leave your answers in terms of π.

8.

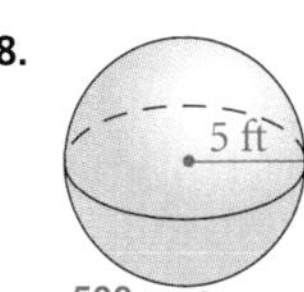

$\frac{500}{3}\pi$ ft^3

9.

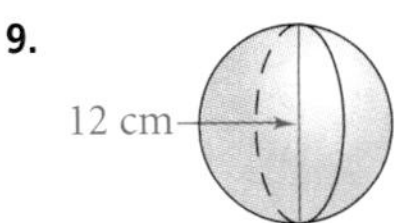

288 π cm^3

10.

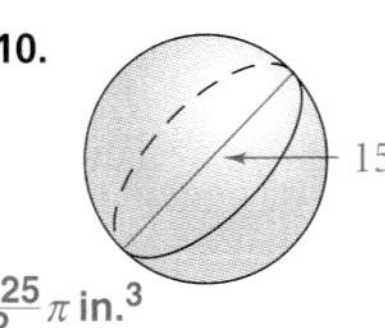

$\frac{1125}{2}\pi$ in.^{3}

11.

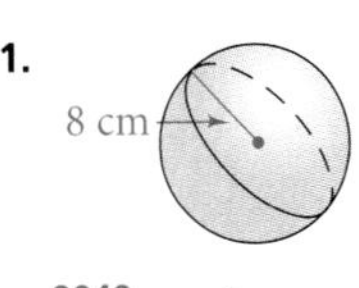

$\frac{2048}{3}\pi$ cm^3

12. *Sports* The circumference of a bowling ball is about 27 in. Find its volume to the nearest tenth. **332.4 in.^{3}**

13. If the sphere of ice cream shown melts, is the cone large enough to hold the melted ice cream? Explain. **No; the volume of the ice cream is $\frac{4}{3}$ times the volume of the cone.**

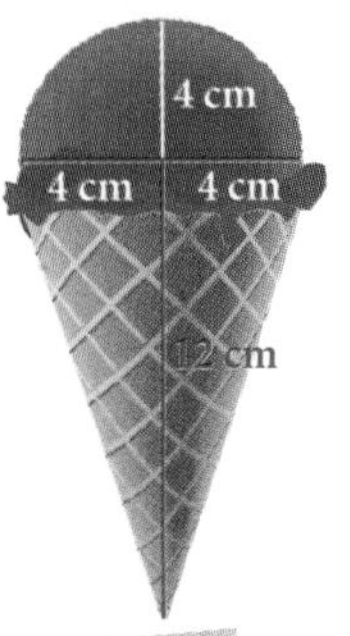

14. *Geometry in 3 Dimensions* The center of a sphere has coordinates $(0, 0, 0)$. The radius of the sphere is 5. **See below for examples.**

a. Name the coordinates of six points on the sphere.

b. Tell whether each of the following points is inside, outside, or on the sphere. (*Hint:* Use the formula from page 262.)
$A(0, -3, 4)$, $B(1, -1, -1)$, $C(4, -6, -10)$
on; inside; outside

Believe It Or Not

J.C. Payne, a Texas farmer, is the world champion string collector. The ball of string he wound over a three-year period has a circumference of 41.5 ft. It weighed 13,000 lb.

Listed in the Guinness Book of Records, the ball of string is now on display in a museum devoted to oddities. It took almost a dozen men with forklift trucks to load the ball onto a truck to move it to the museum.

15. a. What is the volume of the ball of string to the nearest cubic foot? **1207 ft^3**

b. What is the weight of the string per cubic foot? **10.8 $\frac{\text{lb}}{\text{ft}^3}$**

c. If the diameter of the string is 0.1 in., what is the approximate length of the string to the nearest mile? (*Hint:* Think of the unwound string as a long cylinder.) **4191 mi**

CALCULATOR HINT

When answers will be used in later calculations, keep or store them in unrounded form so that rounding errors will not be introduced into the final answer.

16. The radius of Earth is approximately 3960 mi. The area of Australia is about 2,940,000 mi^2.

a. Find the surface area of the Southern Hemisphere. **about 98,530,400 mi^2**

b. *Probability* If a meteorite falls randomly in the Southern Hemisphere, what is the probability that it will fall in Australia? **about 3%**

14a. Samples: (5, 0, 0), (−5, 0, 0), (0, 5, 0), (0, −5, 0), (0, 0, 5), (0, 0, −5), (0, 3, 4), (−4, 0, 3)

ALTERNATIVE ASSESSMENT Exercise 17 You can use these exercises to help you assess students' understanding of volume and surface area of a sphere as well as the volume of a cube. Have students work with a partner taking turns doing the computations.

OPEN-ENDED Exercise 18 If the cylinder and the sphere also have the same radius, ask students how the height of the cylinder is related to the radius of the sphere ($h = \frac{4}{3}r$).

ESL Exercise 25 Students may be unfamiliar with the term *density,* which means mass per unit volume. Discuss with students why objects such as a foam ball, a steel anchor, and a brick with the same volume can have different densities.

WRITING Exercise 27b Students may also want to address how spherical objects are packaged.

pages 340–343 On Your Own

27a. Cube; the edge of the cube is about 1.61 times as long as the radius r of the sphere. The surface area of the cube, about $15.59r^2$, is > surface area of the sphere, about $12.57r^2$.

page 343 Mixed Review

28.

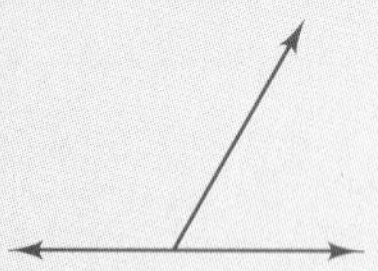

29.

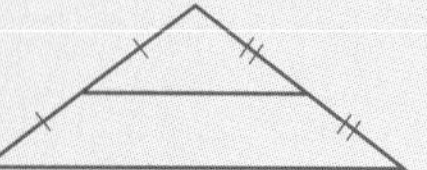

30.

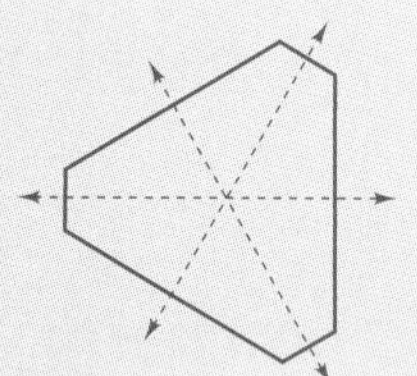

31.

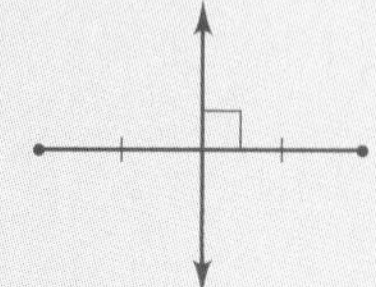

32. 1001, 110110; 1st number has horizontal and vertical lines of symmetry and point symmetry, the 2nd only has the horizontal line of symmetry.

17. The sphere just fits in a cube with edges 6 in. long.
   a. What is the radius of the sphere? 3 in.
   b. What is the volume of the space between the sphere and cube to the nearest tenth? 102.9 in.^{3}

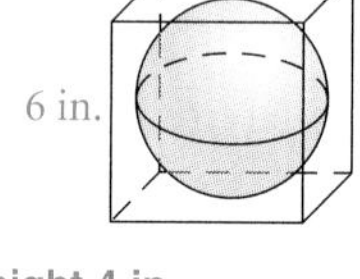

18. *Open-ended* Give the dimensions of a cylinder and a sphere that have the same volume.

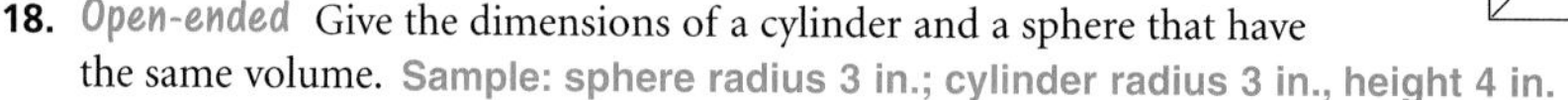

Sample: sphere radius 3 in.; cylinder radius 3 in., height 4 in.

19. The sphere just fits in the cylinder. Archimedes (about 287–212 B.C.) asked to have this figure engraved on his tombstone because he was the first to find the ratio of the volume of the sphere to the volume of the cylinder. What is the ratio that Archimedes discovered? 2 : 3

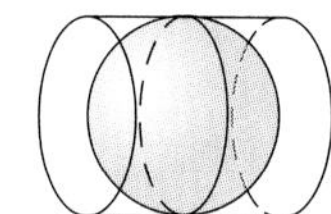

20. Which is greater, the total volume of three balls that each have diameter of 3 in. or the volume of one ball that has a diameter of 8 in.? Explain your answer. See below.

21. A cube with edges 6 in. long just fits in the sphere. The diagonal of the cube is the diameter of the sphere. $6\sqrt{3}$ in.; $3\sqrt{3}$ in.
   a. Find the length of the diagonal of the cube and the radius of the sphere. Leave your answers in simplest radical form.
   b. What is the volume of the space between the sphere and the cube to the nearest tenth? 371.7 in.^{3}

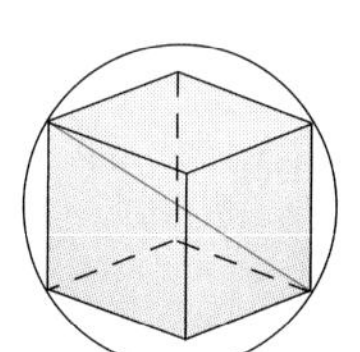

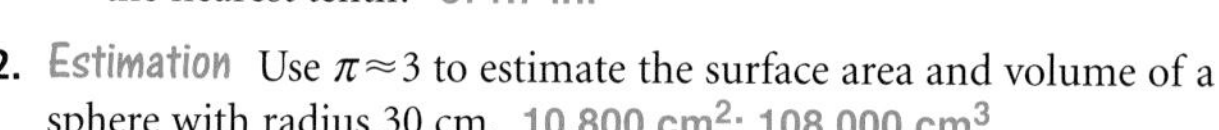

22. *Estimation* Use $\pi \approx 3$ to estimate the surface area and volume of a sphere with radius 30 cm. 10,800 cm^2; 108,000 cm^3

23. *Standardized Test Prep* The cone and sphere just fit in cubes that are the same size. What is the ratio of the volume of the cone to the volume of the sphere? A

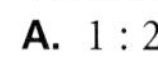

A. 1 : 2   **B.** 1 : 3   **C.** 1 : 4
D. 2 : 3   **E.** cannot be determined

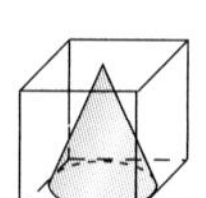

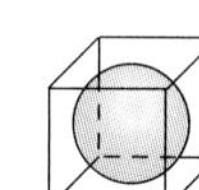

24. a. The number of square meters of surface area of a sphere equals the number of cubic meters of volume. What is the radius of the sphere? 3 m
   b. *Algebra* The ratio of the surface area of a sphere in square meters to its volume in cubic meters is 1 : 5. What is the radius of the sphere? 15 m

25. *Science* The density of steel is about 0.28 lb/in.^{3}. Could you lift a steel ball with radius 4 in.? with radius 6 in.? Explain. See below.

26. A plane that intersects a sphere is 8 cm from the center of the sphere. The radius of the sphere is 17 cm. What is the area of the cross section to the nearest whole number? 707 cm^2

8 cm 17 cm

27. a. *Algebra* If a cube and a sphere have the same volume, which has the greater surface area? Explain. See margin.
   b. *Writing* Explain why spheres are rarely used for packaging.
Answers may vary. Sample: Spheres are very difficult to stack.

20. 8 in. ball; $\frac{256\pi}{3} > \frac{27\pi}{2}$

25. Answers may vary. Sample: No; no; the balls weigh 75 lb and 253 lb, respectively.

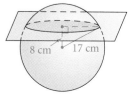

Exercises MIXED REVIEW

OPEN-ENDED Exercise 32 Discuss the symmetries of the two examples given before students begin this exercise.

GETTING READY FOR LESSON 6-7 These exercises prepare students to find the areas of composite space figures.

Wrap Up

THE BIG IDEA Ask students: *Explain how to find the surface area and volume of a sphere.*

RETEACHING ACTIVITY Students discover another way to find the formula for the surface area of a sphere. (Reteaching worksheet 6-6)

Exercises CHECKPOINT

In this Checkpoint, your students will assess their own progress in Lessons 6-2 to 6-6.

STANDARDIZED TEST TIP Exercise 5 Make sure that students check the answer choices first to see that the answer can be left in terms of π.

CRITICAL THINKING Exercise 6 Help students realize that the length of a can is six times the radius of one ball (which is also the radius of the can).

Exercises MIXED REVIEW

Make a sketch for each description. 28–31. See margin p. 342 for samples.

28. a pair of supplementary angles

29. an obtuse triangle and one midsegment

30. a polygon with three lines of symmetry

31. a line segment and its perpendicular bisector

32. *Open-ended* Binary numbers are written with only the digits 0 and 1. These digits can be written so they have both vertical and horizontal lines of symmetry. Using such digits, write two binary numbers that do not have the same symmetries and describe the differences.
See margin p. 342 for sample.

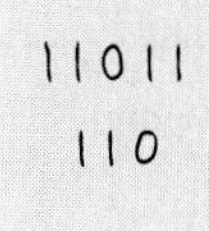

Getting Ready for Lesson 6-7

Calculator **Find the total volume of each pair of figures to the nearest tenth.**

33.

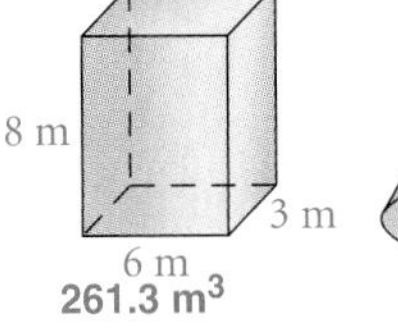

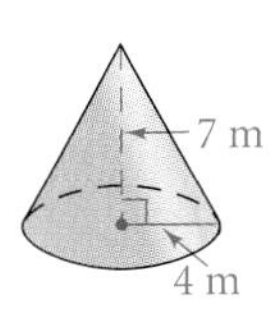

261.3 m^3

34.

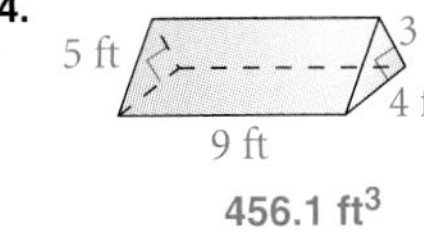

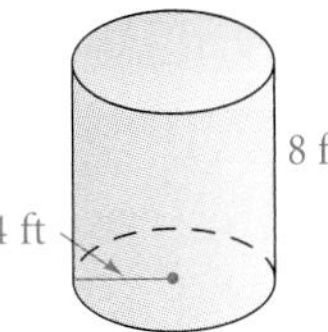

456.1 ft^3

Exercises CHECKPOINT

Calculator **Find the surface area and the volume of each figure to the nearest tenth.**

1. 60.2 ft^2; 22.5 ft^3

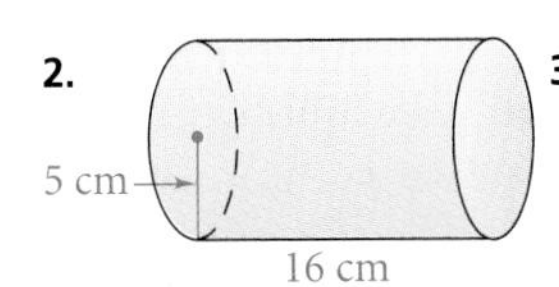

2. 659.7 cm^2; 1256.6 cm^3

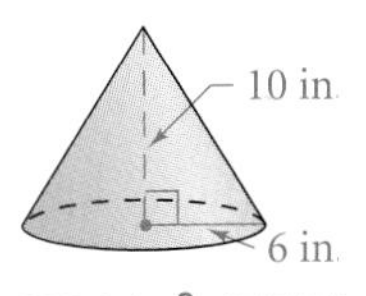

3. 332.9 $in.^2$; 377.0 $in.^3$

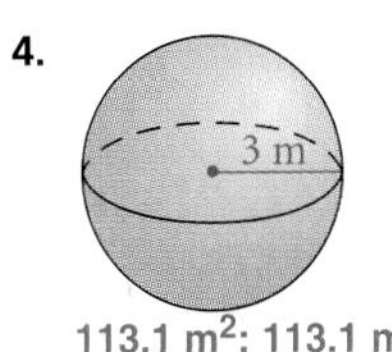

4. 113.1 m^2; 113.1 m^3

5. *Standardized Test Prep* What is the surface area of a sphere with radius 5 in.? C

A. 5π $in.^2$ **B.** 20π $in.^2$ **C.** 100π $in.^2$ **D.** 125π $in.^2$ **E.** $166\frac{2}{3}\pi$ $in.^2$

6. *Critical Thinking* Tennis balls are packaged as shown at the right. Which is greater, the volume of a tennis ball or the space around the three balls? Explain.
The remaining volume is $2\pi r^3$, which is $> \frac{4}{3}\pi r^3$ (volume of one ball).

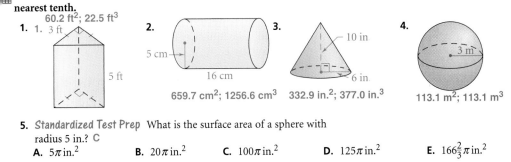

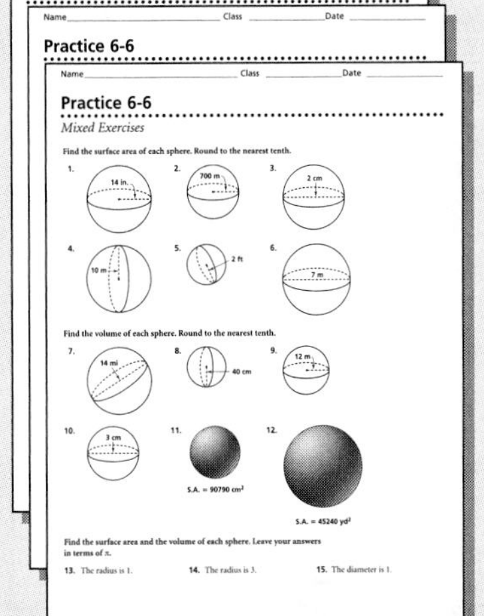

Lesson Quiz

Lesson Quiz is also available in Transparencies.

For Exercises 1–4, round each answer to the nearest tenth, if necessary.

1. Find the surface area of a sphere with radius 3.5 cm. 153.9 cm^2
2. Find the volume of a sphere with diameter 13 in. 1150.3 $in.^3$
3. A sphere has volume 1436.8 ft^3. Find its radius. 7.0 ft
4. A sphere has volume 7238.2 m^3. Find its surface area. 1809.6 m^2

6-7 Teaching Notes

PROBLEM OF THE DAY

A large cube has a surface area of 216 cm^2. What is the total surface area of two smaller cubes whose edges are half as long as those of the large cube? 108 cm^2

Problem of the Day is also available in Transparencies.

CONNECTING TO PRIOR KNOWLEDGE Have students identify three-dimensional objects in the classroom that are not prisms, cylinders, pyramids, or cones. Ask what space figure or figures they resemble.

WORK TOGETHER

TACTILE LEARNING Students will discover that you can find the volume of a composite space figure by adding the volume of its parts, but this is not true for the surface area of a composite space figure.

Question 1 You may want to have students find the surface area and volume in two ways: counting faces of unit cubes and using formulas.

ERROR ALERT! **Question 3** Some students will add the surface areas. **Remediation:** Have students find the surface area by counting the number of faces (unit squares) and comparing that total to the sum of the surface areas. Discuss why they are not the same.

Lesson Planning Options

Prerequisite Skills

- Finding volume of three-dimensional figures
- Finding surface area of three-dimensional figures

Assignment Options for Exercises On Your Own

Core 1–13, 15–17

✪**Extension** 14

Use Mixed Review to maintain skills.

Resources

Student Edition

Skills Handbook, pp. 660, 673
Extra Practice, p. 653
Glossary/Study Guide

Teaching Resources

Chapter Support File, Ch. 6
- Practice 6-7 (two worksheets)
- Reteaching 6-7

Classroom Manager 6-7
Glossary, Spanish Resources

Transparencies

15, 16, 72

6-7 Composite Space Figures

What You'll Learn

- Recognizing composite space figures, which combine two or more simple figures

...And Why

To find the volumes and surface areas of composite space figures such as silos and backpacks

What You'll Need

- unit cubes

WORK TOGETHER

1. Work in a group to build the prisms shown in Figures 1 and 2 using unit cubes. Find the surface area and volume of each prism. 52 units^2, 24 units^3; 22 units^2, 6 units^3
2. What is the sum of the surface areas of the two prisms? What is the sum of their volumes? 74 units^2; 30 units^3

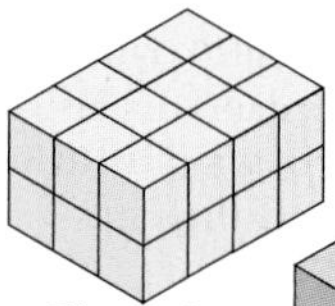

Figure 1

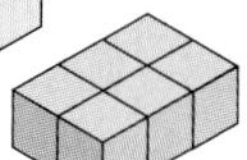

Figure 2

3. Place one prism on top of the other as in Figure 3. Find the surface area and volume of the resulting space figure. 62 units^2; 30 units^3
4. Compare your answers to Questions 2 and 3. How does the relationship of the volumes differ from that of the surface areas? The volume of the combined figures = the sum of the volumes of the prisms; the surface area of the combined figures does not = the sum of the surface areas of the prisms.

Figure 3

THINK AND DISCUSS

You can use what you know about the volumes of three-dimensional figures such as prisms, pyramids, cones, cylinders, and spheres to find the volume of a composite space figure. A **composite space figure** combines two or more of these figures. The volume of a composite space figure is the sum of the volumes of the figures that are combined.

Example 1 Relating to the Real World

Agriculture Find the volume of the grain silo at the left.

The silo combines a cylinder and a hemisphere.

- Volume of the cylinder $= \pi r^2 h = \pi(10)^2(40) = 4000\pi$
- Volume of the hemisphere $= \frac{1}{2}\left(\frac{4}{3}\pi r^3\right) = \frac{2}{3}\pi(10)^3 = \frac{2000\pi}{3}$
- Volume of the composite figure $= 4000\pi + \frac{2000\pi}{3}$

4000 × π + 2000 × π ÷ 3 = 14660.766

The volume of the silo is about 14,700 ft^3.

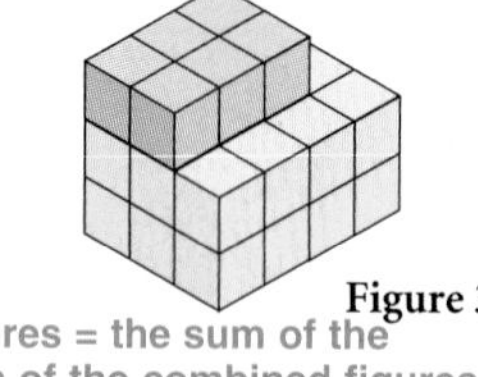

THINK AND DISCUSS

This is a good opportunity to review the three-dimensional figures presented in the chapter and the formulas for finding their volumes and surface areas.

Example 1 Relating to the Real World 

Point out to students the steps used in this problem: identify which figures combine to make the composite space figure, find the volume of each, then find the sum of the volumes.

Question 5b Students can divide the figure into two rectangular prisms by "slicing" the figure horizontally or vertically. In this case, either method produces the same two prisms.

Example 2 Relating to the Real World 

Give students further explanation as to why the height of the prism is 11 in. and the radius of the hemisphere is 6 in.

Question 6 Have students begin by identifying which surfaces this includes, their shapes, and their dimensions.

7a. parts of 3 cones
b. hemisphere, cylinder, cone
c. Answers may vary. Sample: cylinder, 2 cones

5. **Try This** Find the volume of each composite space figure to the nearest whole number.

a. 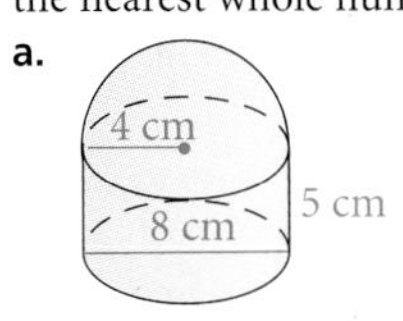

385 cm^3

b.
2 in.
4 in.
2 in.
1 in.
4 in.

12 in.^{3}

You can use geometric figures to approximate the shape of a real-world object. Then you can estimate the volume and surface area of the object.

Example 2 Relating to the Real World 

Estimation What space figures can you use to approximate the shape of the backpack? Use these space figures to estimate the volume of the backpack.

- You can use a prism and half of a cylinder to approximate the shape of the backpack.

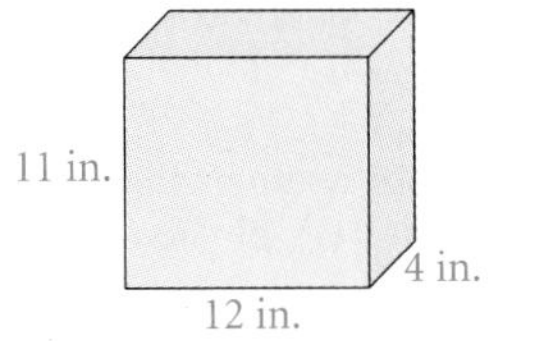

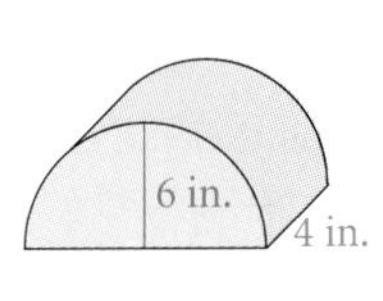

- Volume of the prism $= Bh = (12 \cdot 4)11 = 528$
- Volume of the half cylinder $= \frac{1}{2}(\pi r^2 h) = \frac{1}{2}\pi(6)^2(4)$
$= \frac{1}{2}\pi(36)(4) \approx 226$
- Sum of the two volumes $= 528 + 226 = 754$

The approximate volume of the backpack is 754 in.^{3}.

6. What is the approximate surface area of this backpack? 588 in.^{2}
7. **Try This** Describe the space figures that you can use to approximate the shape of each object. See left.

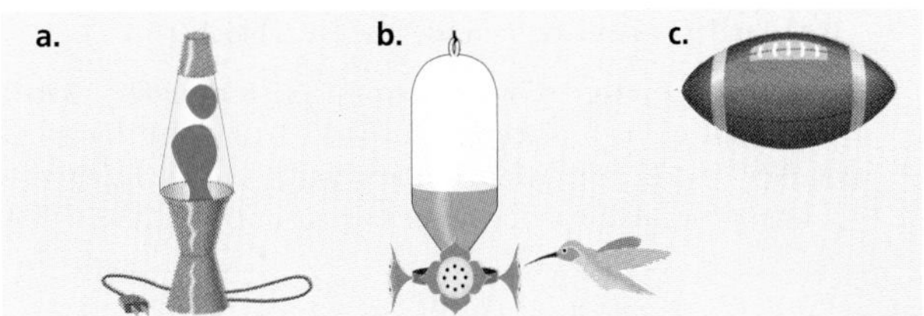

Additional Examples

FOR EXAMPLE 1

Find the volume of the wastebasket. Round to the nearest tenth.
2.6 ft^3

3 ft
1 ft

Discussion: *How could you change the dimensions of the wastebasket so that it could hold at least 4 cubic feet of trash?*

FOR EXAMPLE 2

What space figures can you use to approximate the shape of the mailbox? Use these space figures to estimate the volume of the mailbox.

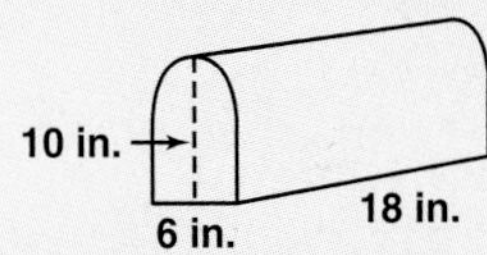

The mailbox combines the volume of half a cylinder and a prism.

Volume of half the cylinder: 254.469

Volume of prism: 756

Sum of the two volumes: 1010.469

The volume of the mailbox is about 1010 in.^{3}.

Discussion: *What is the approximate surface area of the mailbox?*

Exercises ON YOUR OWN

Exercise 2 This figure can be divided into two rectangular prisms either horizontally or vertically. The two methods result in different prisms but the sum of their volumes is the same.

OPEN-ENDED Exercise 4 Have students exchange their figures with a partner and make the missing calculation.

WRITING Exercise 6 Point out that some space figures are composites of more than two shapes.

ALTERNATIVE ASSESSMENT Exercise 7 You can use these exercises to help you assess students' ability to recognize three-dimensional figures generated by rotating two-dimensional figures about an axis. Have students work with a partner to decide how to divide the figure and to find the dimensions of each piece.

WRITING Exercise 11 Refer students to Exercise 17 in Lesson 6-1 on page 305 for illustrations of the Platonic Solids.

Technology Options

Prentice Hall Technology

Software

- Secondary Math Lab Toolkit™
- Computer Item Generator 6-7

Internet

- See the Prentice Hall site. (http://www.phschool.com)

Exercises ON YOUR OWN

Find the volume of each composite space figure. You may leave answers in terms of π.

1. 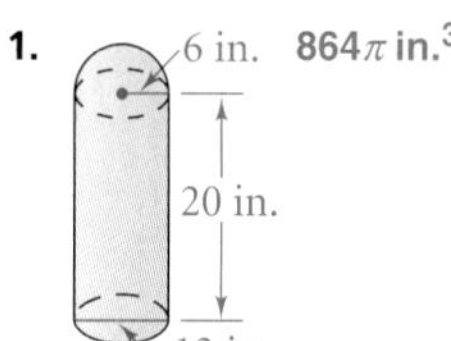

864π in.^{3}

2. 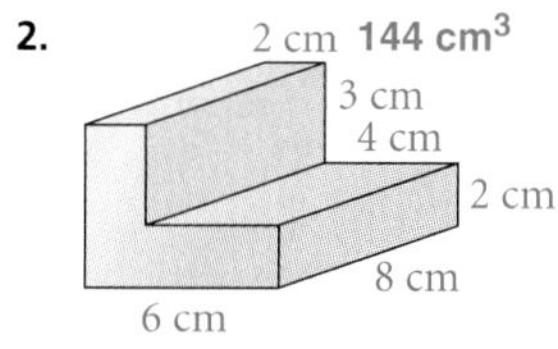

144 cm^3

3. 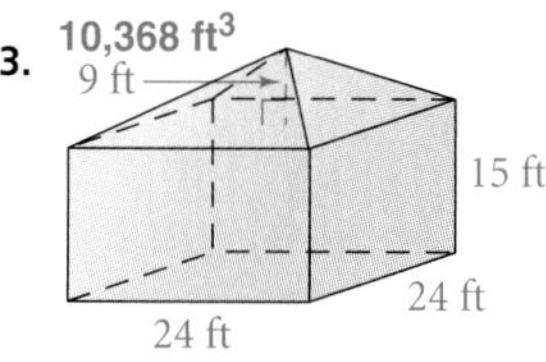

10,368 ft^3

4. **Open-ended** Draw a composite three-dimensional figure, label its dimensions, and find either its surface area or its volume. See back of book for sample.

5. **Manufacturing** Find the volume of the lunch box shown at the right to the nearest cubic inch. 501 in.^{3}

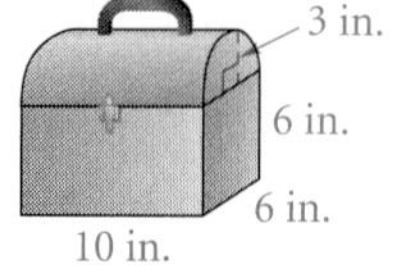

6. **Writing** Describe your home, school, or some other building that is a composite space figure. Explain why it is a composite space figure. Check students' work.

7. a. **Coordinate Geometry** Draw a sketch of the composite space figure formed by rotating this triangle 360° about the x-axis. See back of book.
   b. Find the volume of the figure in terms of π. 32π units^3

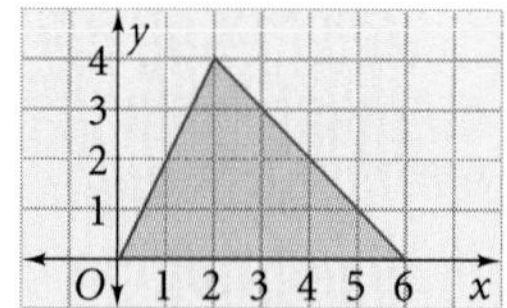

Describe space figures that you can use to approximate the shape of each object. 8–10. Answers may vary. Samples are given.

8. 
sphere, cone

9. 
cone, hemisphere

10. 
parts of 2 pyramids

11. **Writing** Describe how you would find the volume of an octahedron if you know the length of an edge. (See the picture on page 305.) See back of book.

12. In the diagram at the right, what is the volume of the space between the cylinder and the cone to the nearest cubic inch? 335 in.^{3}

13. a. A cylinder is topped with a hemisphere with radius 15 ft. The total volume of the composite figure is 6525π ft^3. Sketch the figure.
    b. **Algebra** Find the height of the cylinder and the height of the composite figure to the nearest whole number. 19 ft; 34 ft

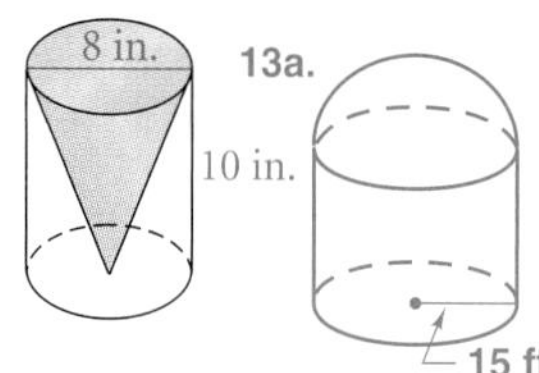

Exercise 15 Some students may confuse the terms "plumb" with "plum." Explain that a "plumb" is a lead weight attached to a line, and is used to measure vertical distance. A "plum", on the other hand, is a variety of fruit.

Exercises MIXED REVIEW

Exercises 18–19 Students may need to review the steps for writing indirect proofs in Lesson 4-5.

JOURNAL Ask students to describe objects that have not yet been discussed in class.

GETTING READY FOR LESSON 6-8 These exercises prepare students to find geometric probabilities.

Wrap Up

THE BIG IDEA Ask students to define *composite space figure* in their own words and explain how to find its surface area and volume.

RETEACHING ACTIVITY Students build a composite space figure with unit cubes, then find its volume. (Reteaching worksheet 6-7)

14. *Coordinate Geometry* Find the surface area of the figure formed by rotating the figure at the right 360° about the y-axis. Leave your answer in terms of π. 20π units^2

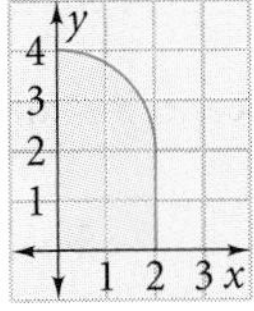

15. *Carpentry* Builders use a plumb bob to establish a vertical line. To the nearest cubic centimeter, find the volume of the plumb bob shown at the right. It combines a hexagonal prism with a pyramid. 73 cm^3

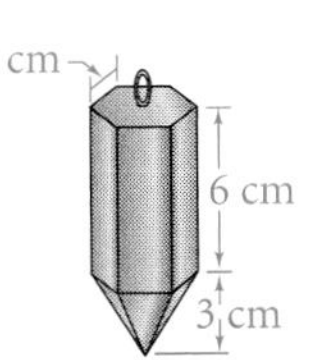

Engineering **Steelworkers use I-beams like the one shown to build bridges and overpasses.**

16. To the nearest cubic foot, find the volume of steel needed to make the beam. 36 ft^3
17. a. To the nearest square foot, what is the surface area of the beam? 237 ft^2
    b. One gallon of paint covers about 450 square feet. How many 1-gallon cans of paint do you need to paint the beam? 1 can

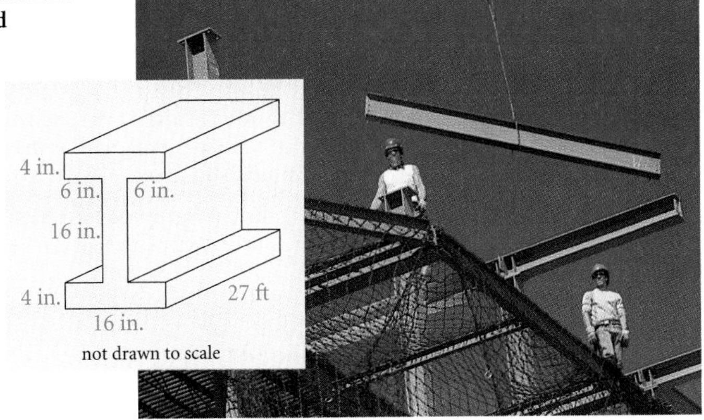

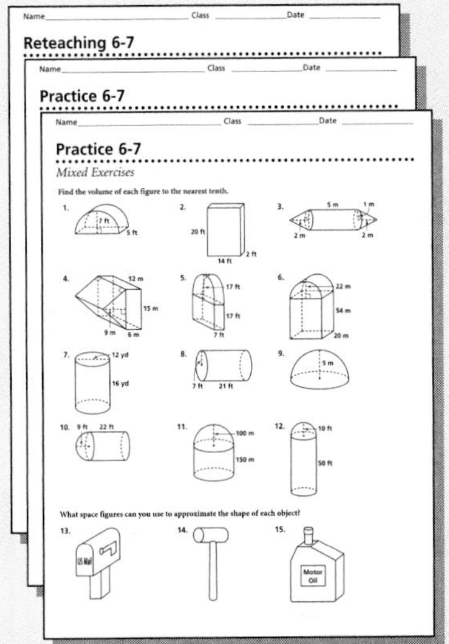

Exercises MIXED REVIEW

Write an indirect proof for each statement.

18. If a triangle is isosceles, then a base angle is not a right angle. See back of book.
19. In $\triangle MNP$, if $MP < MN$, then $\angle P \not\cong \angle N$. See below.
20. *Coordinate Geometry* Find the circumference of a circle if the endpoints of a diameter are (3, 7) and (3, −1). Leave your answer in terms of π. 8π units^2

FOR YOUR JOURNAL

Describe an object in your classroom that is a composite space figure. Explain how you can approximate its volume.

Getting Ready for Lesson 6-8

You roll a number cube. Find each probability.

21. $P(4)$ $\frac{1}{6}$
22. $P(\text{odd number})$ $\frac{1}{2}$
23. $P(\text{prime number})$ $\frac{1}{2}$
24. $P(2 \text{ or } 5)$ $\frac{1}{3}$

19. Assume $\angle P \cong \angle N$. By the Converse of the Isos. Triangle Thm., $\overline{MN} \cong \overline{MP}$, which contradicts the hypothesis. Therefore, $\angle P \not\cong \angle N$.

Lesson Quiz

Lesson Quiz is also available in Transparencies.

Find the volume of each composite figure. Where necessary, leave your answer in terms of π.

1. 108.3 π m^3

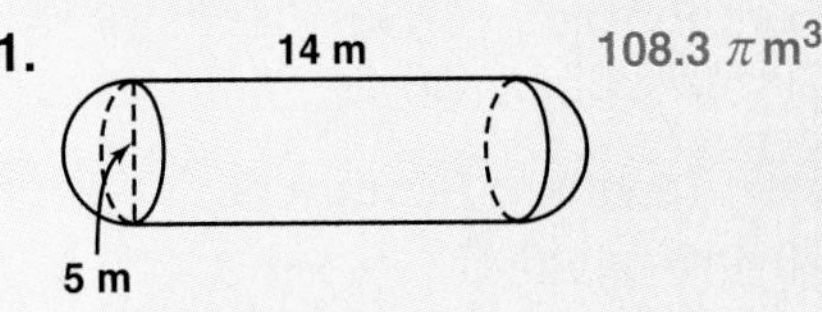

2. 48 in.^{3}

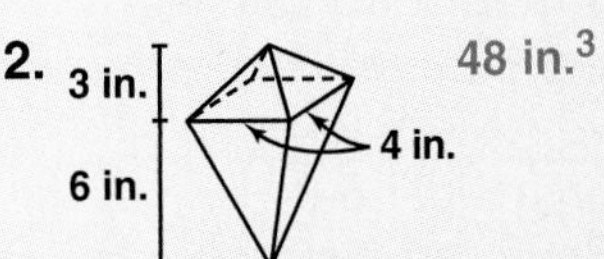

3. 66 ft^3

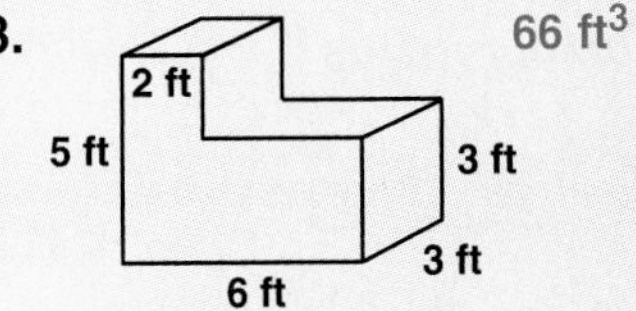

6-8 Teaching Notes

PROBLEM OF THE DAY

If the eight letters in the word GEOMETRY are arranged at random, what is the probability that the first and last letters will be vowels? $\frac{3}{28}$

Problem of the Day is also available in Transparencies.

CONNECTING TO PRIOR KNOWLEDGE Ask students to explain how they would solve the following problem: *A coin is tossed four times. Are you more likely to get two heads and two tails or three heads and one tail?* Review the terms *sample space, possible outcomes*, and *favorable outcomes*.

THINK AND DISCUSS

Two models for geometric probability are presented in this lesson: the segment model and the area model. Make sure students understand the use of each.

Example 1 **Relating to the Real World** 

Have students copy $\overline{AB}$ onto a number line. Then have them use the number line to count the number of minutes between 0 and 15. Point out that their result is the same as the length of $\overline{AR}$: $AR = |15 - 0| = 15$.

Lesson Planning Options

Prerequisite Skills

- Understanding probability
- Finding areas of circles and polygons

Assignment Options for Exercises On Your Own

To provide flexible scheduling, this lesson can be subdivided into parts.

1 **Core** 5, 7, 8, 10
Extension 11

2 **Core** 1–4, 6, 9, 13
Extension 12

Use Mixed Review to maintain skills.

Resources

Student Edition
Skills Handbook, p. 675
Extra Practice, p. 653
Glossary/Study Guide

Teaching Resources
Chapter Support File, Ch. 6
- Practice 6-8 (two worksheets)
- Reteaching 6-8
- Alternative Activity 6-8

Classroom Manager 6-8
Glossary, Spanish Resources

Transparencies
1, 5, 7, 72

348

What You'll Learn

- Using geometric models to find the probability of events

...And Why

To solve probability problems about games, waiting times, and other random events

QUICK REVIEW

The probability of an event is the ratio of the number of favorable outcomes to the number of possible outcomes.

$P(\text{event}) = \frac{\text{favorable outcomes}}{\text{possible outcomes}}$

Connections  Commuting . . . and more

6-8 Geometric Probability

THINK AND DISCUSS

Part 1 **Using a Segment Model**

Mathematicians use models to represent the real world. **Geometric probability** uses geometric figures to represent occurrences of events. Then the occurrences can be compared by comparing measurements of the figures.

Example 1 **Relating to the Real World** 

Commuting Mr. Hedrick's bus runs every 25 minutes. If he arrives at his bus stop at a random time, what is the probability that he will have to wait 10 minutes or more?

Assuming the bus is stopped for a negligible length of time, the 25 minutes between bus arrivals can be represented by $\overline{AB}$.

A B
0 5 10 15 20 25

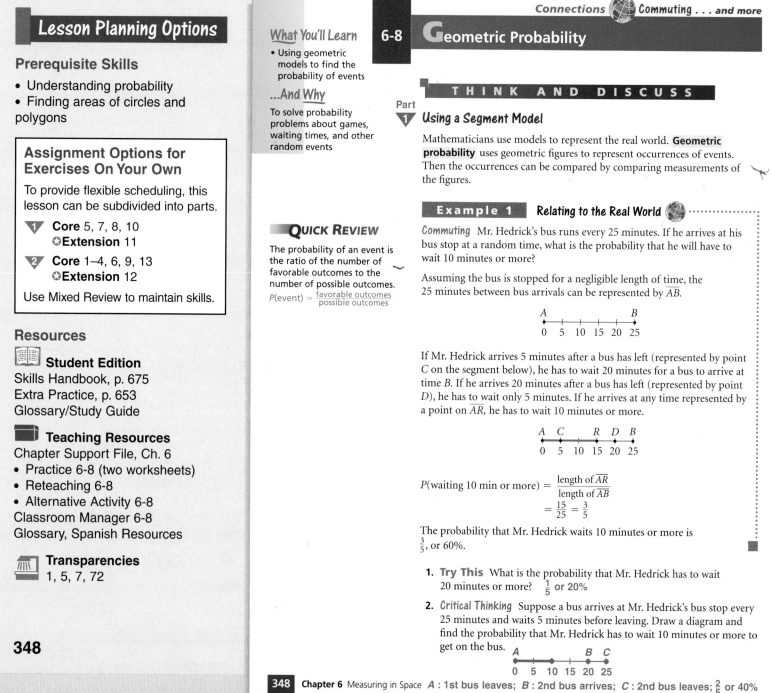

If Mr. Hedrick arrives 5 minutes after a bus has left (represented by point C on the segment below), he has to wait 20 minutes for a bus to arrive at time B. If he arrives 20 minutes after a bus has left (represented by point D), he has to wait only 5 minutes. If he arrives at any time represented by a point on $\overline{AR}$, he has to wait 10 minutes or more.

A C R D B
0 5 10 15 20 25

$$P(\text{waiting 10 min or more}) = \frac{\text{length of } \overline{AR}}{\text{length of } \overline{AB}} = \frac{15}{25} = \frac{3}{5}$$

The probability that Mr. Hedrick waits 10 minutes or more is $\frac{3}{5}$, or 60%.

1. **Try This** What is the probability that Mr. Hedrick has to wait 20 minutes or more? $\frac{1}{5}$ or 20%
2. **Critical Thinking** Suppose a bus arrives at Mr. Hedrick's bus stop every 25 minutes and waits 5 minutes before leaving. Draw a diagram and find the probability that Mr. Hedrick has to wait 10 minutes or more to get on the bus.

A B C
0 5 10 15 20 25

 A : 1st bus leaves; B : 2nd bus arrives; C : 2nd bus leaves; $\frac{2}{5}$ or 40%

ERROR ALERT! Some students may confuse odds $\left(\frac{\text{number of favorable outcomes}}{\text{number of unfavorable outcomes}}\right)$ with probability.
Remediation: Have students study the Quick Review in the side column and the Math Toolbox on page 11 of Chapter 1.

Example 2 *Relating to the Real World*

Make sure that students understand how to derive the equations for *P*(yellow) and *P*(red).

CRITICAL THINKING Question 5 Ask students how the probability relates to the effect doubling the radius has on the area of a circle.

Part 2

Using an Area Model

For some probability situations, you can use an area model.

Example 2 *Relating to the Real World* 

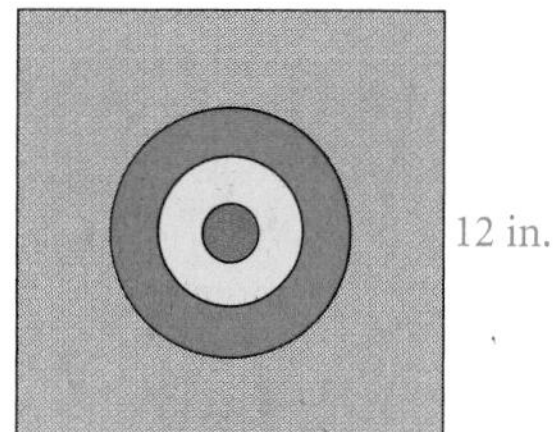

Dart Game At a carnival, you can win prizes if you throw a dart into the blue, yellow, or red regions of a 12 in.-by-12 in. dartboard. The radii of the concentric circles are 1, 2, and 3 inches. Assume that your dart lands on the board and that it is equally likely to land on any point. Find the probability of hitting each colored region.

$$P(\text{blue}) = \frac{\text{blue area}}{\text{area of square}} = \frac{\pi(1)^2}{12^2} = \frac{\pi}{144} \approx 2.2\%$$

Use a calculator.

$$P(\text{yellow}) = \frac{\text{yellow area}}{\text{area of square}} = \frac{\pi(2^2) - \pi(1^2)}{12^2} = \frac{3\pi}{144} \approx 6.5\%$$

$$P(\text{red}) = \frac{\text{red area}}{\text{area of square}} = \frac{\pi(3^2) - \pi(2^2)}{144} = \frac{5\pi}{144} \approx 10.9\%$$

The probability of hitting the blue region is about 2.2%, of hitting the yellow region is about 6.5%, and of hitting the red region is about 10.9%.

5. No; the probability would be quadrupled.

3. **Try This** What is the probability of winning some prize? about 19.6 %
4. **Try This** What is the probability of winning no prize? about 80.4%
5. *Critical Thinking* If the radius of the blue circle were doubled, would the probability of hitting blue be doubled? Explain. See left.

Additional Examples

FOR EXAMPLE 1

Between 6 A.M. and 8 A.M., a commuter train runs every 15 minutes. If you arrive at the train station at a random time, what is the probability that you will have to wait more than 5 minutes? $66\frac{2}{3}\%$

Discussion: *Which is more likely, you will wait more than ten minutes or less than ten minutes?*

FOR EXAMPLE 2

Refer to the diagram in Example 2.

a. What is the probability you will land in the blue or yellow region? ≈ 8.7%

b. What is the probability that you will land in the blue or red region? ≈ 13.1%

FOR EXAMPLE 3

Refer to the diagram in Example 3. What is the probability that the quarter lands within the green circle if it lands on a square with a 10-in. side and the circle had a radius of 2 in.? ≈ 7.4%

Example 3 Relating to the Real World 

VISUAL LEARNING If possible, make physical models to illustrate this example. You may want each group to draw a circle with a 1-in. radius on an 8-in. square then have them measure the radius of a quarter and find the difference between the radius of the circle and the radius of the quarter. Or, perform the measurements on a transparency for the class.

KINESTHETIC LEARNING If you have block scheduling or an extended class period, have students make a game board as described in Example 3 and play the following game. Have each group toss a quarter on the square 100 times. Then have them calculate the experimental probability that it will land in the circle. Compare the experimental probability to the geometric probability found in Example 3.

Exercises ON YOUR OWN

Exercises 1–2 Students can find the probabilities without calculating areas by observing what fraction of the figure is shaded.

Exercise 4 Suggest that students let the radius of the circle equal 1 unit.

Technology Options

Prentice Hall Technology 

 **Software**
- Secondary Math Lab Toolkit™
- Integrated Math Lab 34
- Computer Item Generator 6-8

 **Internet**
- See the Prentice Hall site. (http://www.phschool.com)

350

Some carnival games are more difficult than they appear. Consider the following coin toss game.

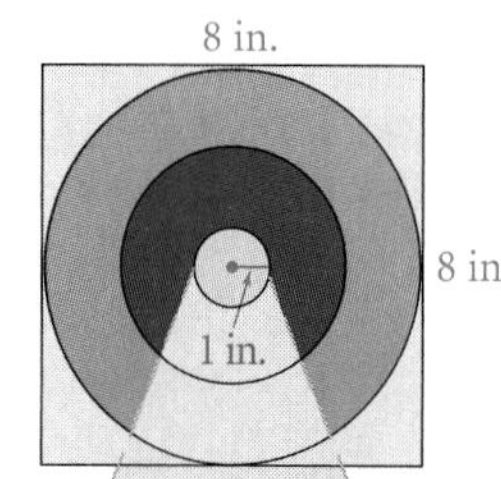

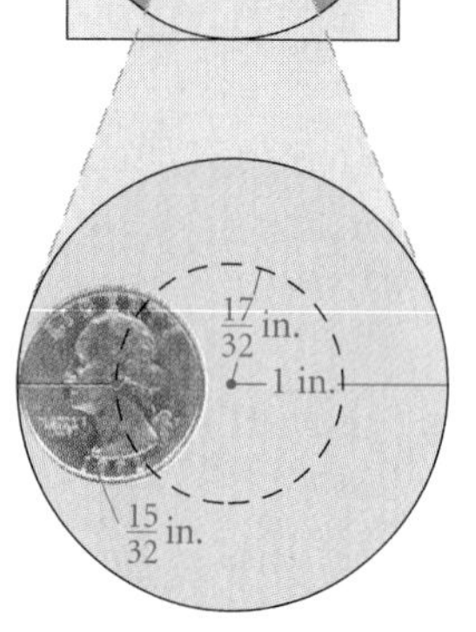

Example 3 Relating to the Real World 

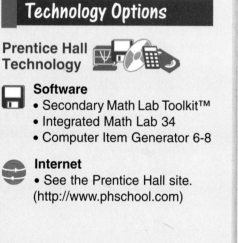

Coin Toss To win a prize, you must toss a quarter so that it lands entirely within a green circle of radius 1 in. The radius of a quarter is $\frac{15}{32}$ in. Suppose that the center of a tossed quarter is equally likely to land at any point within the 8-in. square shown at the left. What is the probability that a quarter will land completely within the green circle?

When a quarter is within the green circle, its center must be more than $\frac{15}{32}$ in. from the edge of the circle. So, the center of the quarter must be less than $\frac{17}{32}$ in. from the center of the green circle. This means that the center of the quarter must be within the dashed circle of radius $\frac{17}{32}$ in. as shown in the diagram.

$$P(\text{quarter within green circle}) = \frac{\text{area of dashed circle}}{\text{area of square}}$$

$$= \frac{\pi\left(\frac{17}{32}\right)^2}{(8)^2} \approx 1.4\%$$

The probability of the quarter landing in the green circle is only about 1.4%.

6. **Try This** Suppose you toss 100 quarters. Would you expect to win a prize? yes

7. a. *Critical Thinking* For every 1000 quarters tossed, about how many prizes would be won? about 14 prizes
   b. Suppose the prize is \$10. About how much profit would the game operator expect for every 1000 quarters tossed? about \$110

Exercises ON YOUR OWN

Darts are thrown at random at each of the boards shown. If a dart hits the board, find the probability that it will land in the shaded area.

1. 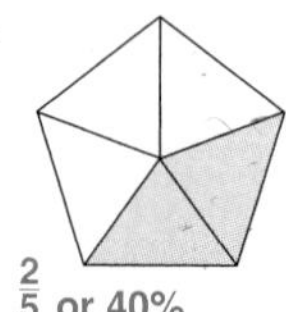
$\frac{2}{5}$ or 40%

2. 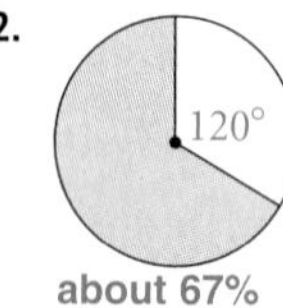

about 67%

3. 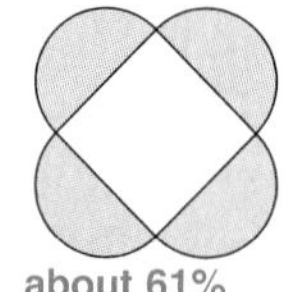
about 61%

4. 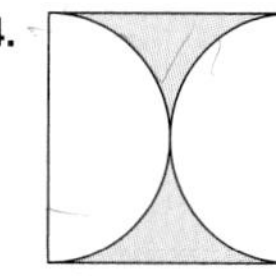
about 21%

5. *Transportation* A rapid transit line runs trains every ten minutes. Draw a geometric model and find the probability that randomly arriving passengers will not have to wait more than four minutes.

40%

Exercises 6–11 Make sure students read the directions and remember to sketch a geometric model for each exercise. You may want to have students work in groups to solve these problems.

ERROR ALERT! **Exercise 8** Some students may use the Pythagorean Theorem instead of the Triangle Inequality Theorem. **Remediation:** Reinforce that the Triangle Inequality Theorem gives criteria for the lengths of sides of triangles in general, while the Pythagorean Theorem gives criteria for the lengths of sides of right triangles only.

ESL **Exercise 9–11** Students may be unfamiliar with the terms "archery," "drawbridge," and "meteorites." Encourage students to look these terms up in a dictionary. If possible, provide illustrations of each.

ALTERNATIVE ASSESSMENT **Exercise 11** The following activity can be used to help you assess students' understanding of geometric probability. Have students research the area of five other countries and calculate the probability that a meteorite landing on Earth will land in one of those countries.

Sketch a geometric model for each exercise and solve.

6. *Ducking Stool* At a fund raiser, volunteers sit above a tank of water hoping that they won't get wet. You can trip the ducking mechanism by throwing a baseball at a metal disk mounted in front of a 1-m square backboard. The volunteer gets wet even if only the edge of the baseball hits the disk. The radius of a baseball is 3.6 cm and the radius of the disk is 8 cm. What is the probability that a baseball that hits the backboard at a random point will hit the disk? about 4.2%

7. Amy made a tape recording of a choir rehearsal. The recording began 21 minutes into the 60-minute tape and lasted 8 minutes. Later she inadvertently erased a 15-minute segment somewhere on the tape.
   a. Make a drawing showing the possible starting times of the erasure. Explain how Amy knows that the erasure did not start after the 45-minute mark.
   b. Make a drawing showing the starting times of the erasure that would erase the entire choir rehearsal. Find the probability that the entire rehearsal was erased.

7a. The erasure must start at least 15 min before the end of the tape.

0 45
0 10 20 30 40 50 60

b. 14 21
0 10 20 30 40 50 60 $\frac{7}{45}$

8. Kimi has a 4-in. straw and a 6-in. straw. She wants to cut the 6-in. straw into two pieces so that the three pieces form a triangle.
   a. If she cuts the straw to get two 3-in. pieces, can she form a triangle? yes
   b. If the two pieces are 1 in. and 5 in., can she form a triangle? no
   c. If Kimi cuts the straw at a random point, what is the probability that she can form a triangle? $\frac{2}{3}$

9. *Archery* An archery target with a radius of 61 cm has five scoring zones of equal widths. The colors of the zones are gold, red, blue, black, and white. The width of each colored zone is 12.2 cm and the radius of the gold circle is also 12.2 cm. If an arrow hits the target at a random point, what is the probability that it hits the gold region? 4%

10. During the summer, the drawbridge over the Quisquam River is raised every half hour to allow boats to pass. It remains open for 5 min. What is the probability that a motorist arriving at the bridge will find it raised? $\frac{1}{6}$

11. *Astronomy* Meteorites (mostly dust-particle size) are continually bombarding Earth. The radius of Earth is about 3960 mi. The area of the United States is about 3,679,245 mi^2. What is the probability that a meteorite landing on Earth will land in the United States? about 1.9%

OPEN-ENDED Exercise 12a Encourage students to consider other shapes like sectors as well as concentric circles when designing their dart boards.

Exercises MIXED REVIEW

CONNECTING TO STUDENTS' WORLD Exercises 14–16 Have students poll the class, their parents, and their teachers on what they like to watch on TV. Then have them collect the data and make a triple bar graph to display it.

SELF ASSESSMENT **PORTFOLIO** Share with students the criteria you will use to assess their work in portfolios, as well as how you plan to use the results. Students should understand how the rubrics assess their work, how each piece in the portfolio counts, and how the scores they get in their portfolios will affect their overall evaluation.

Wrap Up

THE BIG IDEA Ask students to write a problem using geometric probability.

RETEACHING ACTIVITY Students make a probability game and find the geometric probability and experimental probability of a certain outcome. (Reteaching worksheet 6-8)

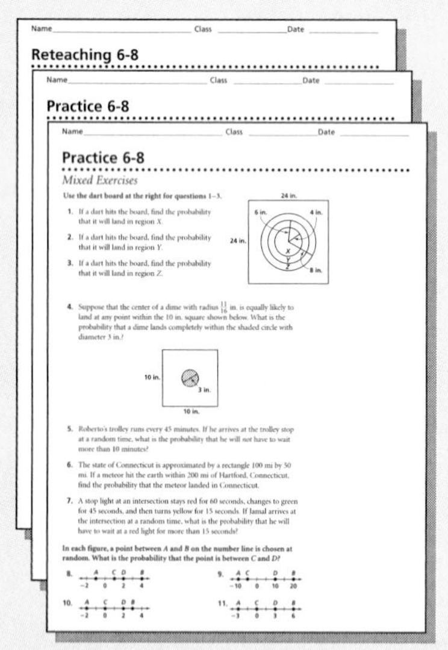
Reteaching 6-8

Practice 6-8

Practice 6-8

Mixed Exercises

Lesson Quiz

Lesson Quiz is also available in Transparencies.

For Exercises 1–2, sketch a geometric model for each exercise and solve.

1. A news radio station gives a weather update every 12 minutes. If you turned on the radio at a random time, what is the probability that you would wait more than 5 minutes to hear the weather update? $58\frac{1}{3}\%$ Models vary. Sample:

0 5 10 12

2. A circle is inscribed in a square with side length 12 cm. What is the probability that the point of a tack dropped onto the square will land outside the circle? ≈ 21.5%; Models vary. Sample:

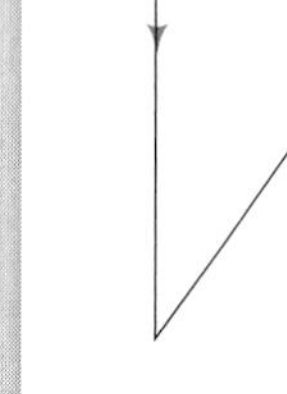

352

12. a. *Open-ended* Design a dartboard game to be used at a charity fair. Specify the size and shape of the regions of the board. **12a-b. Check students' work.**
    b. *Writing* Describe the rules for using your dartboard and the prizes that winners receive. Explain how much money you would expect to raise if the game were played 100 times.

13. *Sonar Sub Search* A ship is trying to locate a disabled remote-controlled research submarine. The captain has determined that the submarine is within a 2000 m-by-2000 m square region. The depth of the ocean in this region is about 6000 m. The ship moves to a position in the center of the square region. Its sonar sends out a signal that covers a conical region. What is the probability that the ship will locate the submarine with the first pulse? **about 26%**

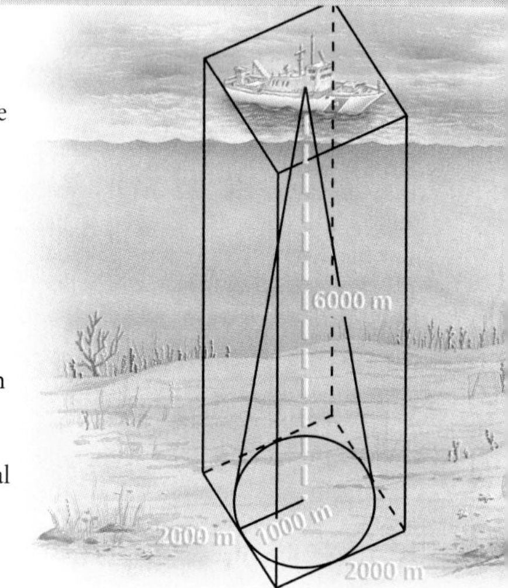

Exercises MIXED REVIEW

Data Analysis **Use the triple bar graph for Exercises 14–16.**

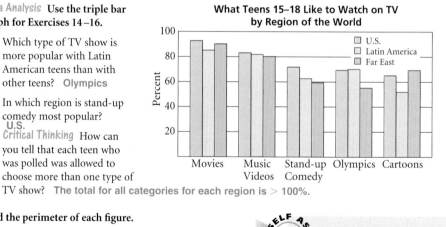

What Teens 15–18 Like to Watch on TV by Region of the World

U.S.
Latin America
Far East

Percent: 20, 40, 60, 80, 100

Movies | Music Videos | Stand-up Comedy | Olympics | Cartoons

14. Which type of TV show is more popular with Latin American teens than with other teens? **Olympics**
15. In which region is stand-up comedy most popular? **U.S.**
16. *Critical Thinking* How can you tell that each teen who was polled was allowed to choose more than one type of TV show? **The total for all categories for each region is > 100%.**

Find the perimeter of each figure.

17. **16 cm** 18. **60 in.**

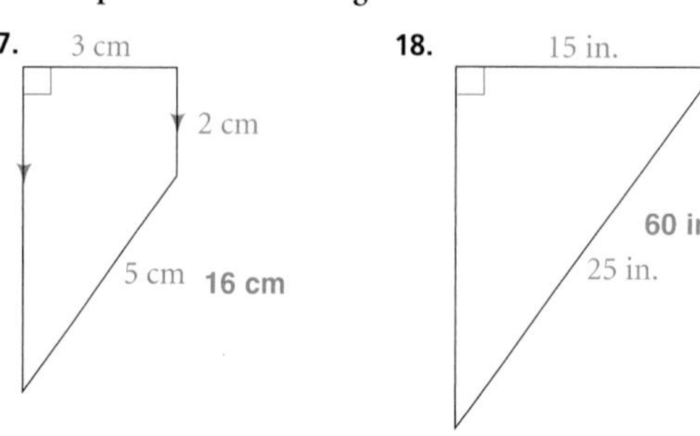

SELF ASSESSMENT **PORTFOLIO**

For your portfolio, select one or two items from your work for this chapter. Some possibilities:
- corrected work
- work that you think best shows the things you did

Explain why you included each selection.

Finishing the Chapter Project

PROJECT DAY You may wish to plan a project day during which students share their completed projects. Encourage groups to explain their processes as well as their products.

PROJECT NOTEBOOK Have students review their project work and bring their notebooks up to date.

- Have students review their package designs along with their measurements and calculations.
- Ask groups to share any insights they found when completing the project, such as how they decided what package design to use.

SCORING RUBRIC

3 Student's package design is complete. Measurements are calculated correctly. Student justifies package design using mathematical and economic arguments. Geometric terms are used correctly. Display is organized and comprehensive.

2 Student's package design is complete. Measurements calculated with few errors. Student justifies package design using some geometric terms. Display is organized.

1 Student's package design is complete but measurements are inaccurate. Student does not sufficiently justify package design or use geometric terms correctly. Display is complete but lacks organization.

0 Major elements are incomplete or missing.

Finishing the Chapter Project
CHAPTER PROJECT
The Place is Packed
Find Out questions on pages 306, 314, 329, and 335 should help you complete your project. Design and construct your own package for a product. Specify the dimensions, surface area, amount and type of packaging material used, and volume of the package. Justify your design with mathematical and economic arguments.
Reflect and Revise
Ask a classmate to review your project with you. Together, check that your package design is complete, your diagrams and explanations clear, and your information accurate. Have you used geometric terms correctly? Have you considered other possible designs? Is the display attractive, organized, and comprehensive? Revise your work as needed.
Follow Up
Find pictures of packaged products in newspaper or magazine advertisements. Identify the shape of each package. Give possible reasons why the manufacturer chose each package design. Display your work on a poster.
For More Information
Botersman, Jack. Paper Capers. New York: Henry Holt and Company, 1986.
Davidson, Patricia, and Robert Willcutt. Spatial Problem Solving with Paper Folding and Cutting. New Rochelle, New York: Cuisenaire Company of America, 1984.
Pearce, Peter. Structure in Nature Is a Strategy for Design. Cambridge, Massachusetts: MIT Press, 1978.
Shell Centre for Mathematical Education. Be a Paper Engineer. Essex, England: Longman Group UK Limited, 1988.
Chapter 6 Finishing the Chapter Project 353

Wrap Up

HOW AM I DOING? Have students work in small groups. Ask each group to make a short presentation explaining how to find the surface area of the different space figures presented in this chapter. Each presentation must include a visual aid and a sample problem.

KEY TERMS The numbers in parentheses direct students to the pages where the terms are used or defined. Students should be able to (1) write a simple explanation of each term, (2) illustrate the term with a diagram, or (3) give an example that uses the term.

STANDARDIZED TEST TIP **Exercise 2** Students can use Euler's formula or just count the edges.

Resources

Student Edition

Extra Practice, p. 639
Glossary/Study Guide

Teaching Resources

Study Skills Handbook
Glossary, Spanish Resources

Wrap Up pages 354–357

1.

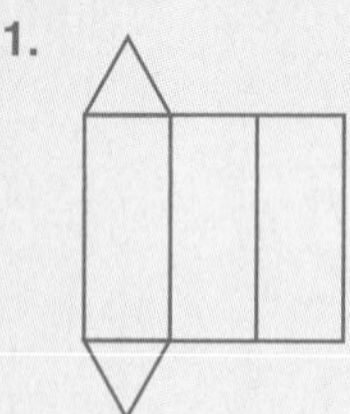

6 Wrap Up

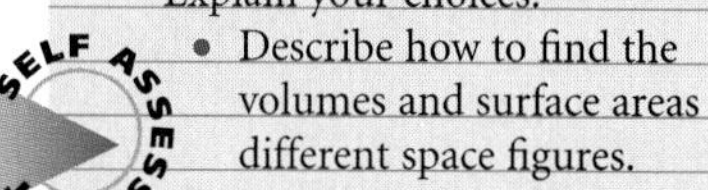

How am I doing?

- State three ideas from this chapter that you think are important. Explain your choices.
- Describe how to find the volumes and surface areas of different space figures.

Key Terms

altitude (pp. 309, 310, 316, 318)
bases (pp. 309, 316)
center (p. 337)
circumference of a sphere (p. 340)
composite space figure (p. 344)
cone (p. 318)
cube (p. 310)
cylinder (p. 310)
edge (p. 302)
faces (p. 302)
geometric probability (p. 348)
great circle (p. 340)
height (pp. 309, 310, 316, 318, 331)
hemisphere (p. 340)
lateral area (pp. 309, 311, 316)
lateral face (pp. 309, 316)
net (p. 302)
oblique cylinder (p. 310)
oblique prism (p. 309)
polyhedron (p. 302)
prism (p. 309)
pyramid (p. 316)
regular pyramid (p. 316)
right cone (p. 318)
right cylinder (p. 310)
right prism (p. 309)
slant height (pp. 316, 318)
sphere (p. 337)
surface area (pp. 309, 311, 316)
vertex (pp. 302, 316)
volume (p. 324)

Space Figures and Nets 6-1

A **polyhedron** is a three-dimensional figure whose surfaces are polygons. The polygons are **faces** of the polyhedron. An **edge** is a segment that is the intersection of two faces. A **vertex** is a point where edges intersect. A **net** is a two-dimensional pattern that folds to form a three-dimensional figure.

1. *Open-ended* Draw a net for the space figure at the right. See margin for sample.
2. *Standardized Test Prep* Which figure has the most edges? D
   - A. rectangular prism
   - B. hexagonal prism
   - C. pentagonal prism
   - D. octagonal prism
   - E. cannot be determined from the information given

Match each three-dimensional figure with its net.

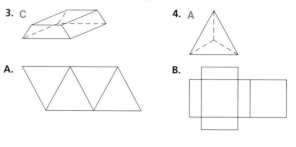

3. C 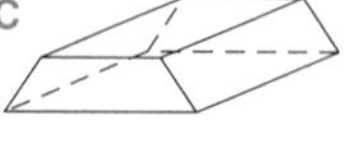

4. A 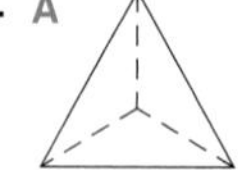

5. B 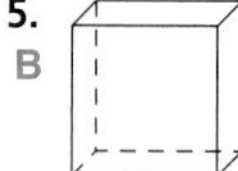

A. 

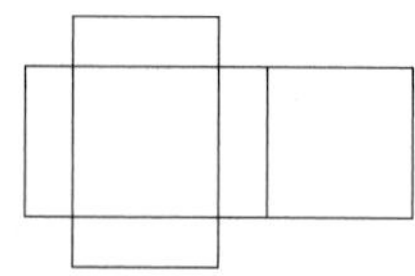

B.

C. 

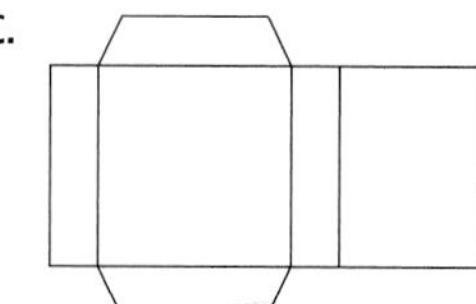

Exercises 10–13 Check that students understand the difference between lateral area and surface area and that they use the proper units to express their answers.

ERROR ALERT! **Exercise 10** Because the lesson on volume came after the lesson on surface area some students may use the height of the figure instead of the slant height when finding the lateral area. **Remediation:** Review the formulas with students and emphasize that they write the formula for each problem.

Surface Areas of Prisms and Cylinders 6-2

The **lateral area** of a **right prism** is the product of the perimeter of the base and the height. The **surface area** of a prism is the sum of the lateral area and the areas of the two bases.

L.A. = ph
S.A. = L.A. + $2B$

p is the perimeter of a base.

B is the area of a base.

The **lateral area** of a **right cylinder** is the product of the circumference of the base and the height of the cylinder. The **surface area** is the sum of the lateral area and the areas of the two bases.

L.A. = $2\pi rh$ or πdh
S.A. = L.A. + $2B$

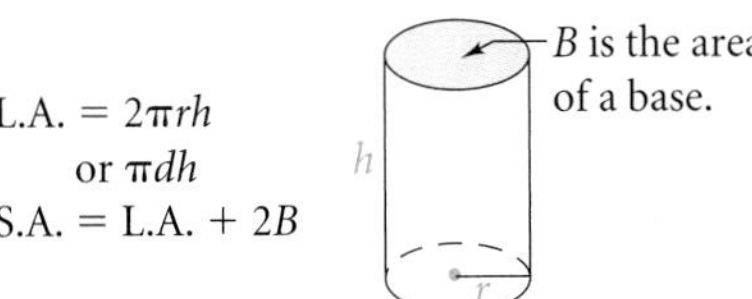

B is the area of a base.

Find the surface area of each figure. You may leave answers in terms of π.

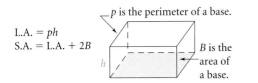

6. 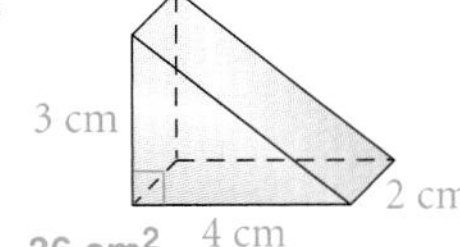

36 cm^2

7. 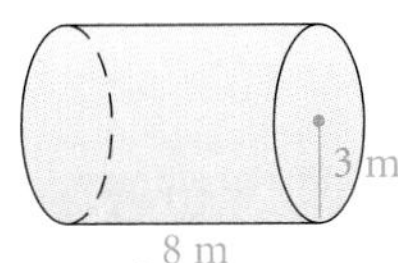

66π m^2

8. 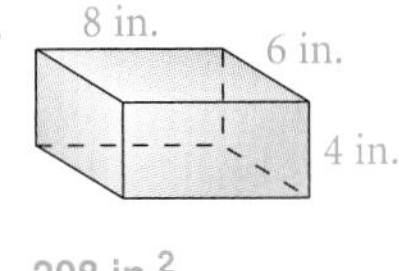

208 in.^{2}

9. 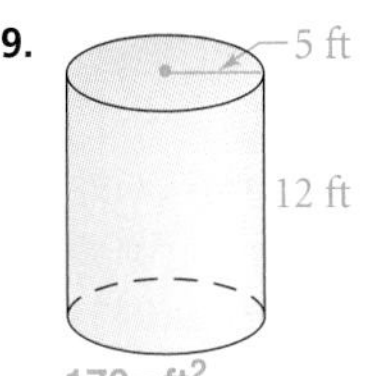

170π ft^2

Surface Areas of Pyramids and Cones 6-3

The **lateral area** of a **regular pyramid** is half the product of the perimeter of the base and the slant height. The **surface area** is the sum of the lateral area and the area of the base.

L.A. = $\frac{1}{2}p\ell$
S.A. = L.A. + B

B is the area of a base.

The **lateral area** of a **right cone** is half the product of the circumference of the base and the slant height. The **surface area** is the sum of the lateral area and the area of the base.

L.A. = $\pi r\ell$
S.A. = L.A. + B

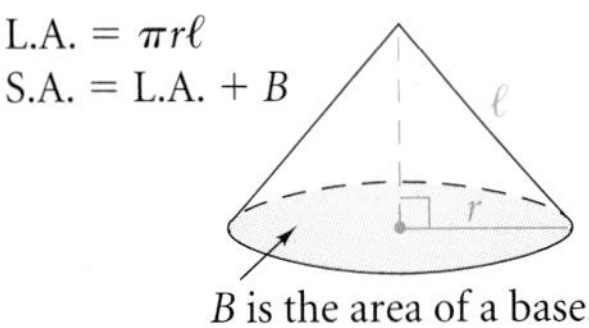

B is the area of a base.

Calculator **Find the lateral area and surface area of each figure. When an answer is not a whole number, round to the nearest tenth.**

10. 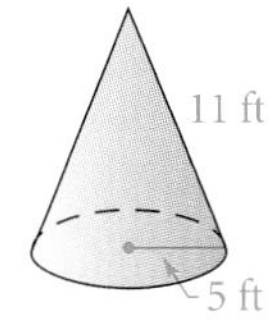

172.8 ft^2; 251.3 ft^2

11. 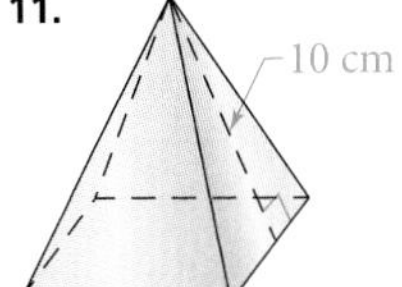

160 cm^2; 224 cm^2

12. 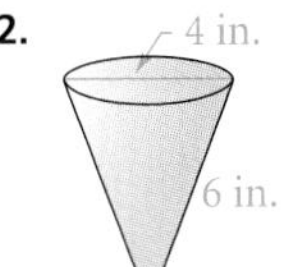

37.7 in.^{2}; 50.3 in.^{2}

13. 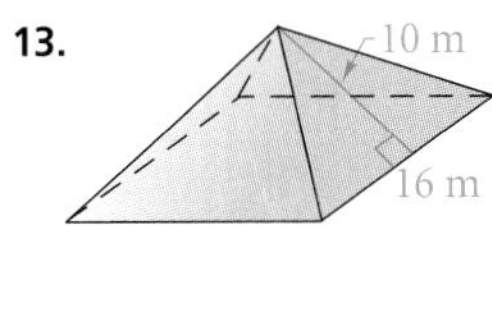

320 m^2; 576 m^2

Exercises 14–17 Remind students that they can learn just one formula for the volume of prisms and cylinders: $V = Bh$.

Exercises 19–22 Check that students use $V = \frac{1}{3}Bh$ and not $V = \frac{1}{2}Bh$.

Volumes of Prisms and Cylinders 6-4

The **volume** of a space figure is the space that the figure occupies. Volume is measured in cubic units.

The **volume** of a **prism** is the product of the area of a base and the height of the prism.

The **volume** of a **cylinder** is the product of the area of a base and the height of the cylinder.

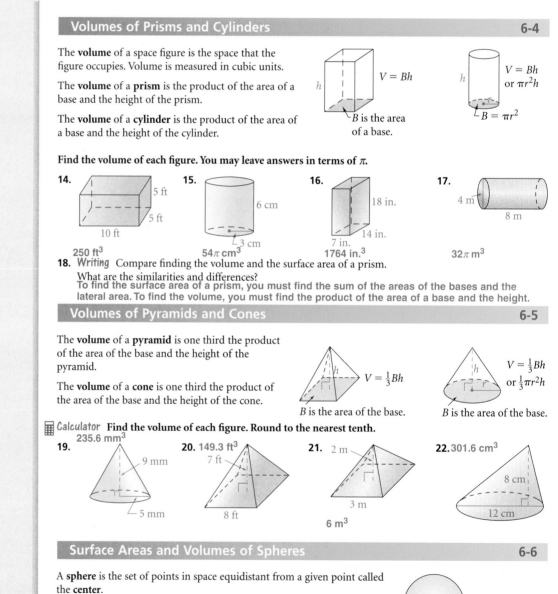

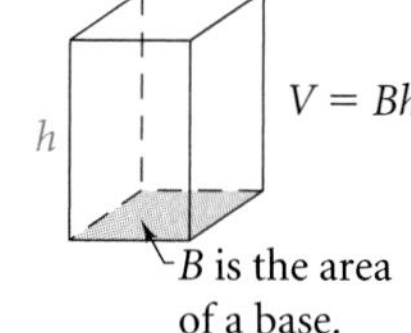

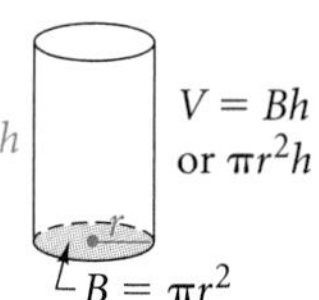

Find the volume of each figure. You may leave answers in terms of π.

14.
250 ft³

15. 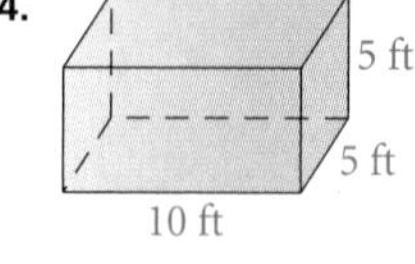

54π cm³

16. 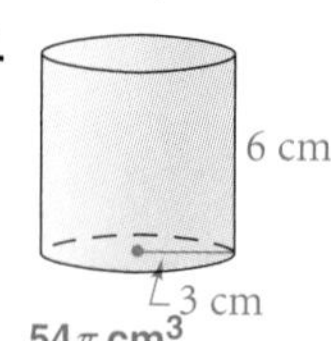

1764 in.³

17. 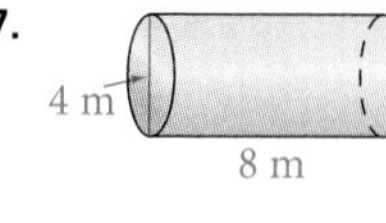

32π m³

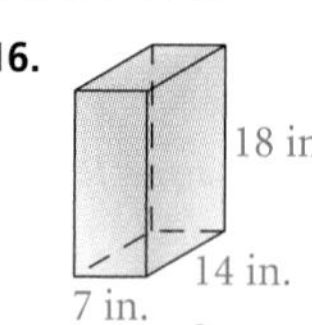

18. *Writing* Compare finding the volume and the surface area of a prism. What are the similarities and differences?
To find the surface area of a prism, you must find the sum of the areas of the bases and the lateral area. To find the volume, you must find the product of the area of a base and the height.

Volumes of Pyramids and Cones 6-5

The **volume** of a **pyramid** is one third the product of the area of the base and the height of the pyramid.

The **volume** of a **cone** is one third the product of the area of the base and the height of the cone.

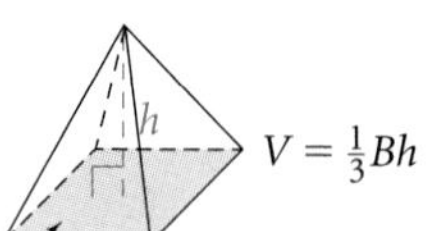

B is the area of the base.

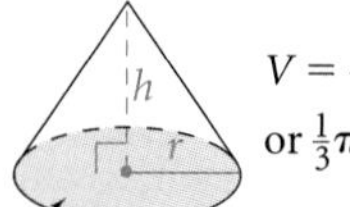

B is the area of the base.

Calculator **Find the volume of each figure. Round to the nearest tenth.**

19. 235.6 mm³

20. 149.3 ft³
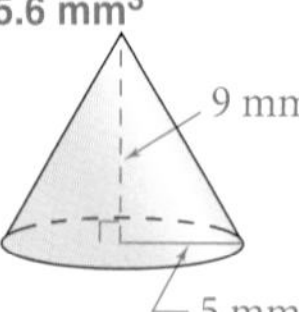

21.
6 m³

22. 301.6 cm³

Surface Areas and Volumes of Spheres 6-6

A **sphere** is the set of points in space equidistant from a given point called the **center**.

The **surface area of a sphere** is four times the product of π and the square of the radius of the sphere. The **volume of a sphere** is $\frac{4}{3}$ the product of π and the cube of the radius of the sphere.

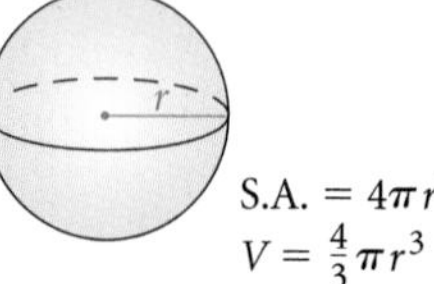

Exercises 23–26 Check that students do not confuse the formulas for surface area and volume.

ALTERNATIVE ASSESSMENT Exercises 28–30 Ask students to sketch other composite figures, choose appropriate measurements, and calculate the volume of each. You may want to specify which figures they should use: a cylinder and a hemisphere, a prism and a pyramid, etc.

Remind students that the new mathematical terms in this chapter are defined in the Glossary/Study Guide in the back of the book.

Getting Ready for Chapter 7

Students may work these exercises independently or in small groups. The skills previewed will help prepare students to study parallel lines.

Calculator **Find the surface area and volume of a sphere with the given radius or diameter. Round answers to the nearest tenth.**

23. $r = 5$ in. **24.** $d = 7$ cm **25.** $d = 4$ ft **26.** $r = 0.8$ ft

23. 314.2 in.^{2}; 523.6 in.^{3}
24. 153.9 cm^2; 179.6 cm^3
25. 50.3 ft^2; 33.5 ft^3
26. 8.0 ft^2; 2.1 ft^3

27. *Sports* The circumference of a lacrosse ball is 8 in. Find its volume to the nearest tenth of a cubic inch. 8.6 in.^{3}

Composite Space Figures 6-7

A **composite space figure** combines two or more space figures. The volume of a composite figure is the sum of the volumes of the combined figures.

Calculator **Find the volume of each figure. When an answer is not a whole number, round to the nearest tenth.**

28.
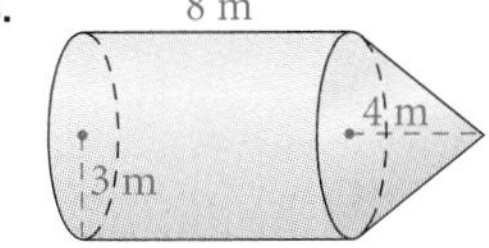

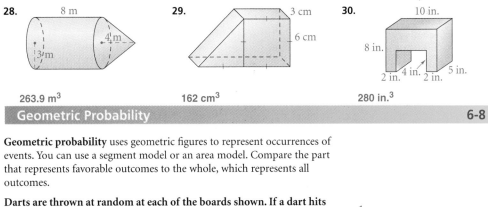

263.9 m^3

29.
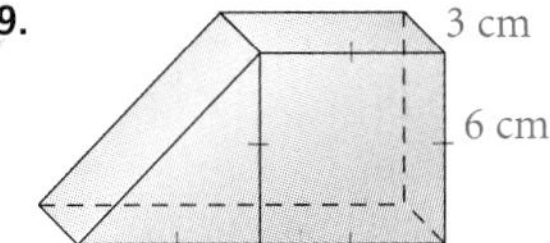

162 cm^3

30.
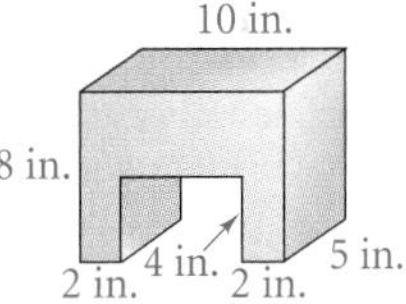

280 in.^{3}

Geometric Probability 6-8

Geometric probability uses geometric figures to represent occurrences of events. You can use a segment model or an area model. Compare the part that represents favorable outcomes to the whole, which represents all outcomes.

Darts are thrown at random at each of the boards shown. If a dart hits the board, find the probability that it will land in the shaded area.

31. $\frac{1}{2}$ or 50%
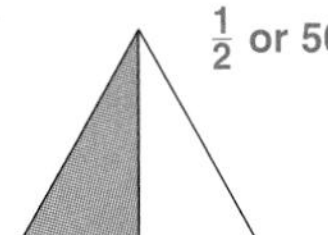

32. $\frac{3}{8}$ or 37.5%
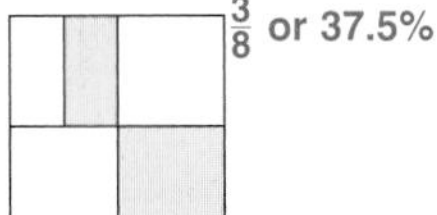

33. $\frac{1}{6}$ or about 16.7%
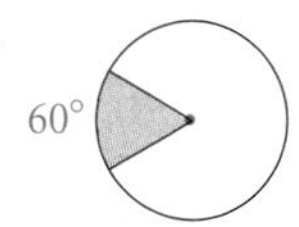

34. *Critical Thinking* If you are modeling probability with a segment, does the length of the segment matter? Explain. No; you model probability by ratio of lengths of segments.

Getting Ready for... CHAPTER 7

Use the rectangular prism at the right.

35. List three pairs of parallel segments.

36. List three pairs of perpendicular segments.

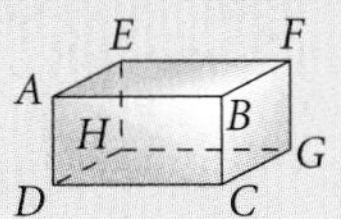

Samples are given.
35. $\overline{AB}, \overline{EF}, \overline{CD}$
36. $\overline{AB}, \overline{BC}, \overline{BF}$

Assessment

ENHANCED MULTIPLE CHOICE QUESTIONS are more complex than traditional multiple choice questions, which assess only one skill. Enhanced multiple choice questions assess the processes that students use, as well as the end results. The questions are written so that students use more than one strategy to solve the problem. Using multiple strategies is encouraged by the National Council of Teachers of Mathematics (NCTM). **Exercise 13** is an enhanced multiple choice question.

FREE RESPONSE QUESTIONS do not give answer choices. Some exercises have more than one possible answer. Students need to give only one correct response. **Exercises 1–9, 11–12, and 15–17** are free response questions.

WRITING EXERCISES allow students to describe how they think about and understand the concepts they have learned. **Exercise 14** is a writing exercise.

OPEN-ENDED PROBLEMS allow for more than one solution. Students must construct their own responses instead of choosing from possible answers. The students' responses will help you determine the depth of their understanding and any possible areas of difficulty. **Exercise 10** is an open-ended problem.

Resources

Teaching Resources
Chapter Support File, Ch. 6
- Chapter Assessment, Forms A and B
- Alternative Assessment

Chapter Assessment, Spanish Resources

Teacher's Edition
See also p. 300E for assessment options

Software
Computer Item Generator

Assessment page 358

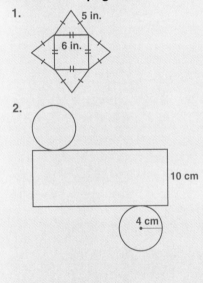

1.
2.

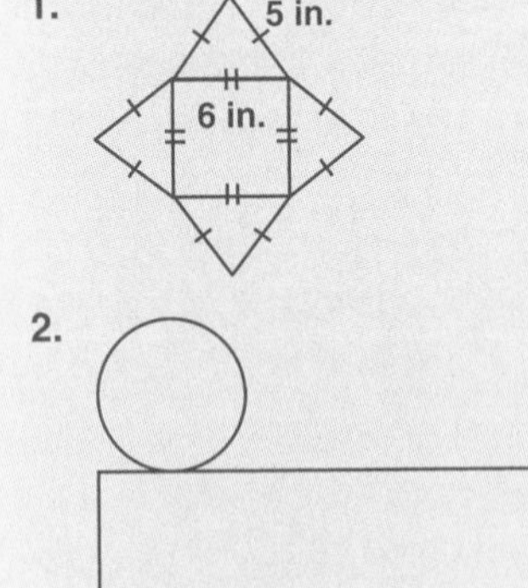

6 Assessment

Draw a net for each figure. Label the net with appropriate dimensions.

1. 

2. 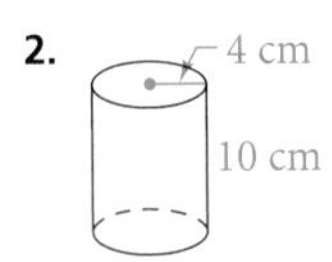

1–2. See margin for samples.

3. a. *Aviation* The "black box" information recorder on an airplane is a rectangular prism. The base is 15 in. by 8 in., and it is 15 in. to 22 in. tall. What are the largest and smallest possible volumes for the box?
   b. Newer flight data recorders are smaller and record more data. A new recorder is 8 in. by 8 in. by 13 in. What is its volume?

3a. 2640 in.^{3}; 1800 in.^{3} b. 832 in.^{3}

Calculator **Find the volume and surface area of each figure. When an answer is not a whole number, round to the nearest tenth.**

4. 4 cm, 11 cm, 5 cm
220 cm^3; 238 cm^2

5. 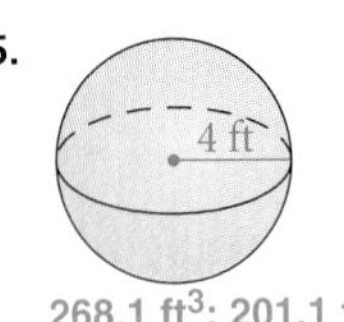

268.1 ft^3; 201.1 ft^2

6. 6 m, 5 m
157.1 m^3; 201.2 m^2

7. 9 in., 8 in.
172.0 in.^{3}; 208 in.^{2}

8. 8 cm, 3 cm
226.2 cm^3; 207.3 cm^2

9. 1 in., 12 in., 6 in.
81.4 in.^{3}; 195.3 in.^{2}

10. *Open-ended* Draw two different space figures that have a volume of 100 in.^{3}. Label the dimensions of each figure. See back of book for sample.

11. a. Describe the figure that is formed when the triangle is rotated 360° about the y-axis.
   b. What is its volume and lateral area in terms of π? 16π units^3; 20π units^2

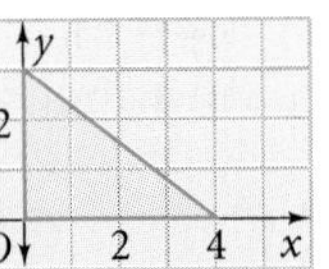

11a. cone

12. How many gallons of paint do you need to paint the walls of a bedroom? The floor is 12 ft by 15 ft and the walls are 7 ft high. One gallon of paint covers about 450 square feet. 1 gal

13. *Standardized Test Prep* Which of these space figures has the greatest volume? B
   A. cube with an edge of 5 cm
   B. cylinder with radius 4 cm and height 4 cm
   C. pyramid with a square base with sides of 6 cm and height 6 cm
   D. cone with radius 4 cm and height 9 cm
   E. rectangular prism with a 5 cm-by-5 cm base and height 6 cm

14. *Writing* Describe a real-world situation in which you would use the volume of an object. Then describe another situation in which you would use the lateral area of an object. See back of book.

15. a. *Estimation* What space figures can you use to approximate the shape of the spring water bottle?
   b. Estimate the volume of the bottle.

(1 in., 6 in., 2 in., Spring Water)

a. a cylinder and a cone
b. approx. 20 in.^{3}

16. *Probability* Every 20 minutes from 4:00 P.M. to 7:00 P.M., a commuter train crosses Main Street. For three minutes a gate stops cars from passing as the train goes by. What is the probability that a motorist driving by during this time will have to stop at the train crossing? 15%

17. *Probability* What is the probability that a dart tossed randomly at this board will hit the shaded area? $\frac{1}{2}$ or 50%

Cumulative Review

Item	Review Topic	Chapter
1	Rotations	3
2	Volume	6
3	Circumference	5
4	Polygons	2
5, 7	Pythagorean Theorem	5
6	Area of a Trapezoid	5
8	Midpoints	1
9	Symmetry	3
10	Angles	1

6 Cumulative Review

For Exercises 1–8, choose the correct letter.

1. Which are rotations of the figure at the right? E

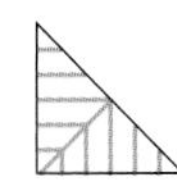

I.  II. 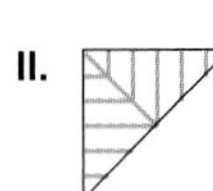

III.  IV. 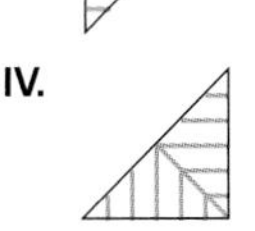

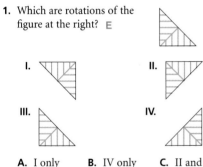

A. I only **B.** IV only **C.** II and IV
D. I, III and IV **E.** I, II, III, and IV

2. What is the volume of the prism? B

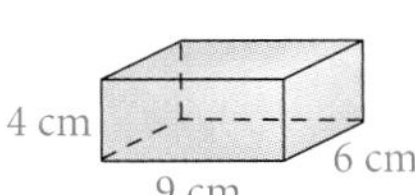

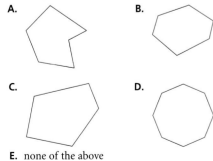

A. 228 cm^3 **B.** 216 cm^3 **C.** 76 cm^3
D. 19 cm^3 **E.** none of the above

3. What is the circumference of a circle with radius 9? C

A. 4.5π **B.** 9π **C.** 18π
D. 81π **E.** none of the above

4. Which figure is *not* a convex polygon? A

A. 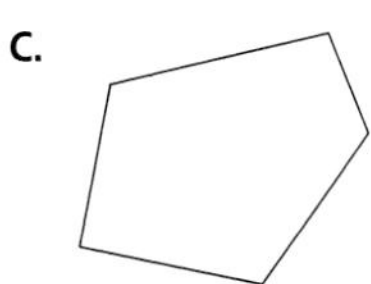 **B.** 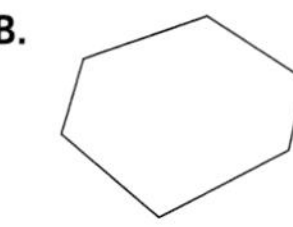

C. 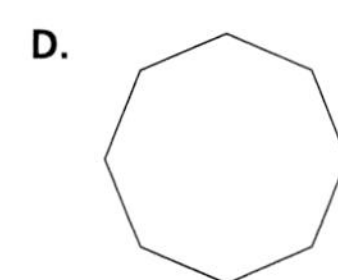 **D.**

E. none of the above

5. The lengths of the hypotenuse and one leg of a right triangle are 10 and 15. Find the length of the other leg to the nearest whole number. D

A. 8 **B.** 9 **C.** 10 **D.** 11 **E.** 12

6. What is the area of the trapezoid? C

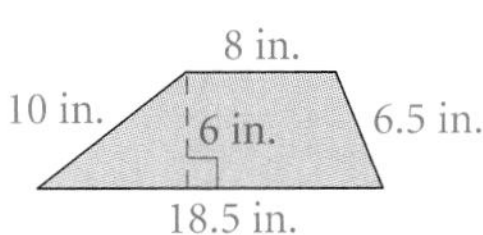

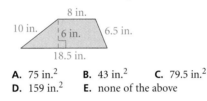

A. 75 $in.^2$ **B.** 43 $in.^2$ **C.** 79.5 $in.^2$
D. 159 $in.^2$ **E.** none of the above

Compare the boxed quantity in Column A with the boxed quantity in Column B. Choose the best answer.

A. The quantity in Column A is greater.
B. The quantity in Column B is greater.
C. The two quantities are equal.
D. The relationship cannot be determined on the basis of the information supplied.

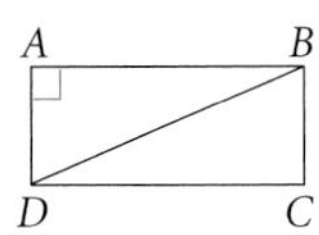

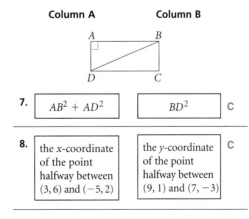

	Column A	Column B	
7.	$AB^2 + AD^2$	BD^2	C
8.	the x-coordinate of the point halfway between $(3, 6)$ and $(-5, 2)$	the y-coordinate of the point halfway between $(9, 1)$ and $(7, -3)$	C

Find each answer.

9. *Open-ended* Sketch a figure with line and point symmetry. See back of book for sample.

10. What is the measure of the angle formed by the minute hand and the hour hand? 120

Resources

 **Teaching Resources**

Chapter Support File, Ch. 6
- Cumulative Review
- Standardized Test Practice

Teacher's Edition

See also p. 300E for assessment options

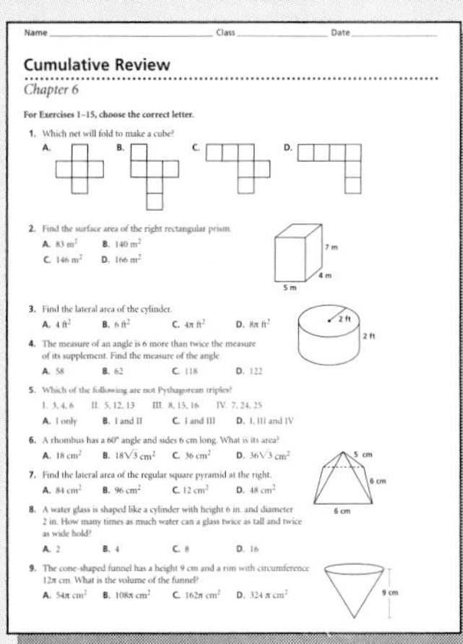

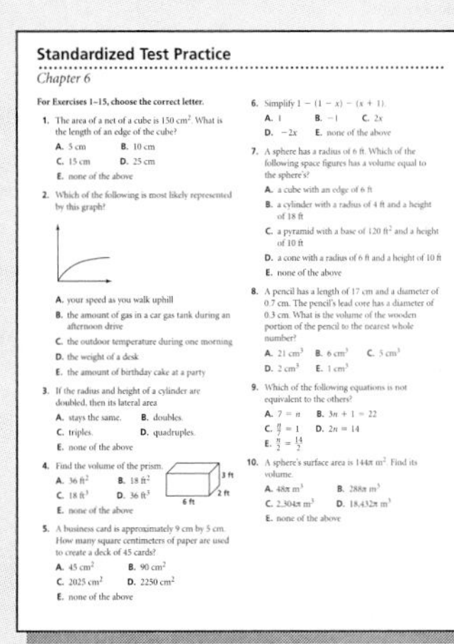

CHAPTER 7 Reasoning and Parallel Lines

To accommodate flexible scheduling, some lessons are divided into parts. Assignment Options are given in the Lesson Planning Options for each lesson.

PACING OPTIONS

This chart suggests pacing only for the core lessons and their parts, and it is provided merely as a possible guide. It will help you determine how much time you have in your schedule to cover other features, such as the Chapter Project, Math Toolboxes, Wrap Up, and Assessment.

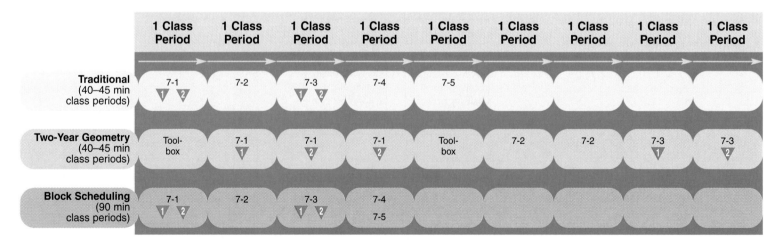

	1 Class Period	1 Class Period	1 Class Period	1 Class Period	1 Class Period	1 Class Period	1 Class Period	1 Class Period	1 Class Period
Traditional (40–45 min class periods)	7-1 Part 1, Part 2	7-2	7-3 Part 1, Part 2	7-4	7-5				
Two-Year Geometry (40–45 min class periods)	Tool-box	7-1 Part 1	7-1 Part 2	7-1 Part 2	Tool-box	7-2	7-2	7-3 Part 1	7-3 Part 2
Block Scheduling (90 min class periods)	7-1 Part 1, Part 2	7-2	7-3 Part 1, Part 2	7-4 7-5					

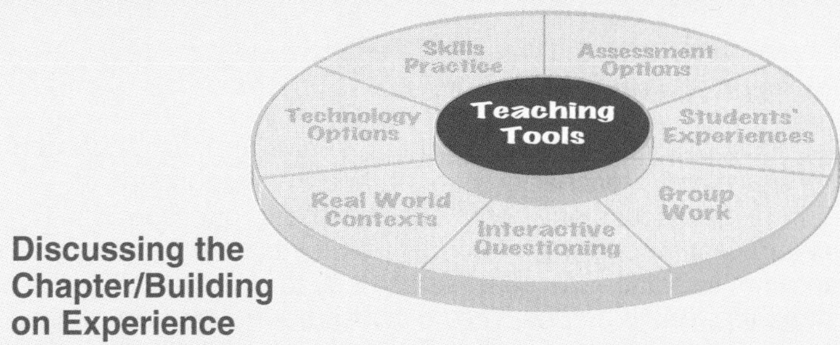

What Students Will Learn and Why

In this chapter, students build on their understanding of parallel and perpendicular lines, learned in Chapter 1. They learn to relate the measures of angles formed by parallel lines and a transversal so that they can recognize conditions that result in parallel lines. They then construct parallel and perpendicular lines. Students also learn to write flow proofs and draw objects in one- and two-point perspective. Finally, students study some of the basic ideas of spherical geometry. The concepts presented in this chapter are applied by architects, builders, and graphic artists.

Discussing the Chapter/Building on Experience

The concept map below relates chapter topics to real-world applications. You and your class may wish to add to the map or develop maps of your own. The center oval describes the topic of the chapter. The next level displays topics within the lessons. The outer ovals reflect applications of the content. As you and your class build a concept map, invite students to discuss applications with which they are familiar.

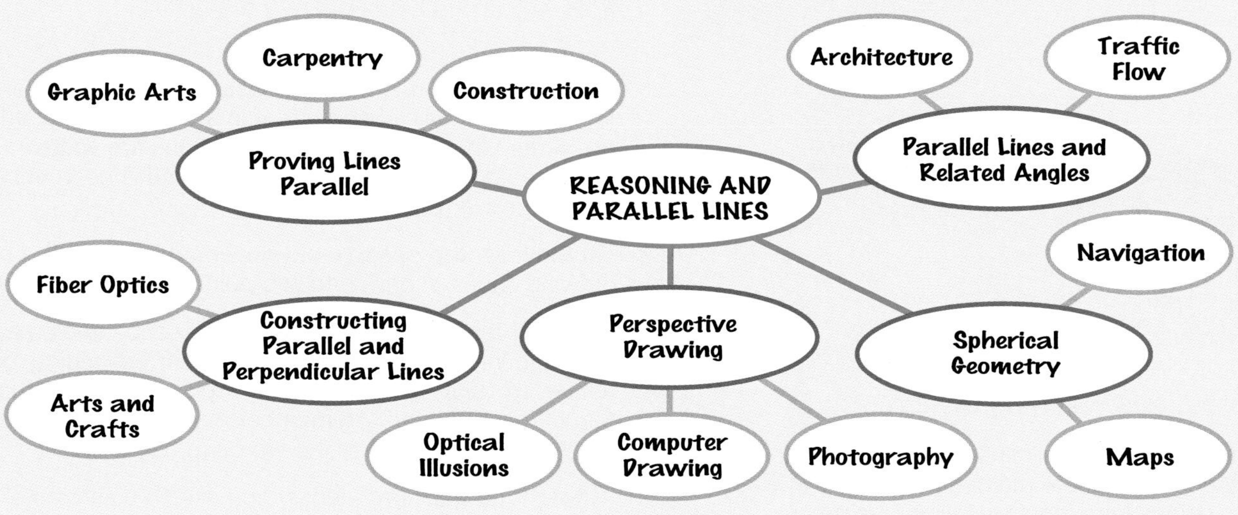

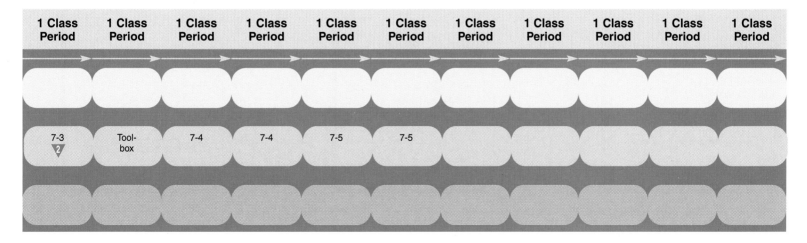

1 Class Period	1 Class Period	1 Class Period	1 Class Period	1 Class Period	1 Class Period	1 Class Period	1 Class Period	1 Class Period	1 Class Period	1 Class Period
7-3 ▽2	Tool-box	7-4	7-4	7-5	7-5					

Interactive Questioning Tips

A question is interactive when there is "give and take" between the questioner (teacher or student) and the respondent. In Think and Discuss or when a critical thinking question is asked, it is important to encourage students to explain their answers in detail. One effective strategy to consider is to have students work in groups. They can discuss the question among themselves, then appoint a spokesperson to give the answer. This promotes active participation and develops high-level thinking skills. For example, in Lesson 7-4, Question 4, students are asked to describe the type of perspective an artist might paint, based on the position of an easel.

Skills Practice

Every lesson provides skill practice with Try This exercises, Exercises On Your Own, and Exercises Mixed Review. The Student Edition includes a Checkpoint (p. 383) and Preparing for Standardized Tests (p. 403). In the Teacher's Edition, the Lesson Planning Options section for each lesson lists Prerequisite Skills students should know for that lesson. At the back of the Student Edition is the Skills Handbook—mini-lessons on math your students may need to review. The Chapter Support File for Chapter 7 in the Teaching Resources box includes two Practice worksheets per lesson, a worksheet for the Checkpoint, and worksheets for Cumulative Review and Standardized Test Preparation.

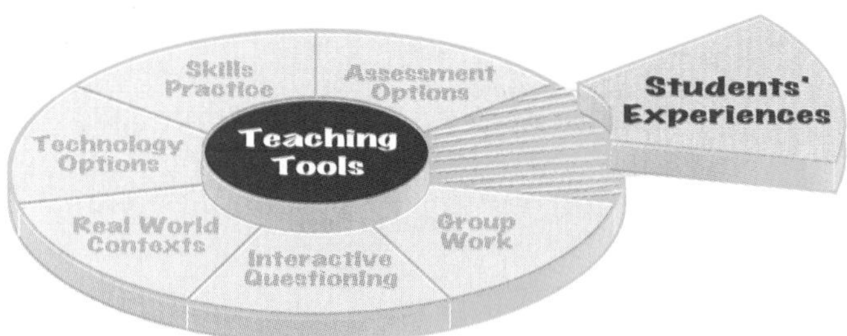

Diverse Learning and Teaching Styles

In your Teacher's Edition, you will find suggestions as to how you can help students complete mathematical tasks in Chapter 7 by reinforcing various learning styles. Here are some examples.

- **Visual learning** use models to illustrate postulates and theorems (p. 364), observe that in a flow proof statements are written in a box and the justifications are written underneath (p. 372), diagram planes and lines to observe the difference (p. 393)
- **Tactile learning** observe physical models (p. 372), practice drawing cubes in one- and two-point perspective (p. 386)
- **Auditory learning** work in pairs to describe angles as alternate interior, same-side interior, corresponding, or neither (p. 365), work in pairs to explain why Constructions 6 and 7 work (p. 380), remember meanings of latitude and longitude by the roots of the words (p. 392)
- **Kinesthetic learning** identify and sketch diagrams of lines on their school building that appear parallel cut by a transversal (p. 367), observe perspective by viewing students of similar size at the opposite end of a field (p. 385)

Alternative Activity for Lesson 7-2

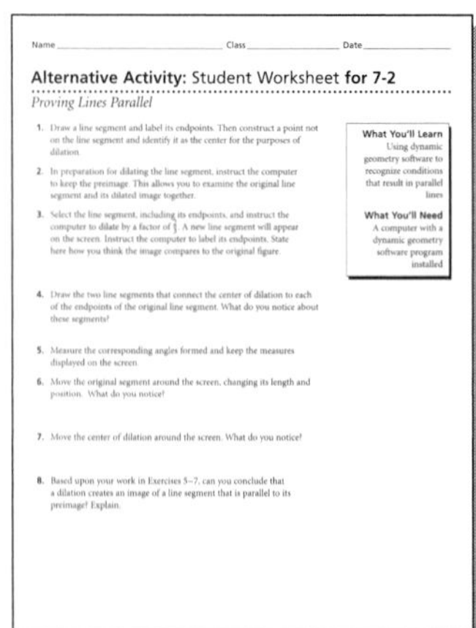

Name ______ Class ______ Date ______

Alternative Activity: Student Worksheet **for 7-2**

Proving Lines Parallel

1. Draw a line segment and label its endpoints. Then construct a point not on the line segment and identify it as the center for the purposes of dilation.
2. In preparation for dilating the line segment, instruct the computer to keep the preimage. This allows you to examine the original line segment and its dilated image together.
3. Select the line segment, including its endpoints, and instruct the computer to dilate by a factor of [illegible]. A new line segment will appear on the screen. Instruct the computer to label its endpoints. State here how you think the image compares to the original figure.
4. Draw the two line segments that connect the center of dilation to each of the endpoints of the original line segment. What do you notice about these segments?
5. Measure the corresponding angles formed and keep the measures displayed on the screen.
6. Move the original segment around the screen, changing its length and position. What do you notice?
7. Move the center of dilation around the screen. What do you notice?
8. Based upon your work in Exercises 5–7, can you conclude that a dilation creates an image of a line segment that is parallel to its preimage? Explain.

What You'll Learn Using dynamic geometry software to recognize conditions that result in parallel lines

What You'll Need A computer with a dynamic geometry software program installed

for use with Example 1, uses geometry software to explore dilations and to investigate the converse of the corresponding angle postulate.

Alternative Activity for Lesson 7-3

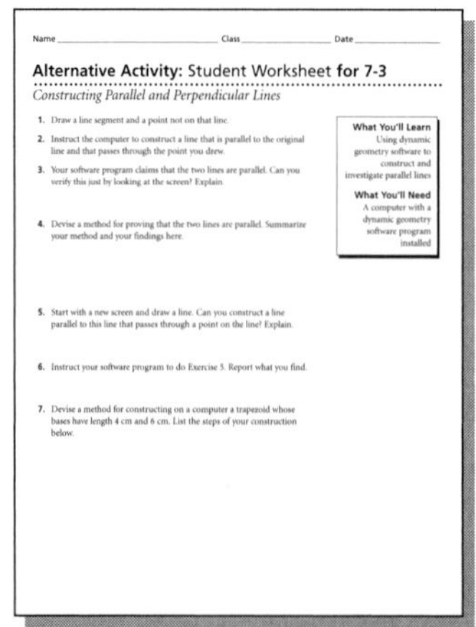

Name ______ Class ______ Date ______

Alternative Activity: Student Worksheet **for 7-3**

Constructing Parallel and Perpendicular Lines

1. Draw a line segment and a point not on that line.
2. Instruct the computer to construct a line that is parallel to the original line and that passes through the point you drew.
3. Your software program claims that the two lines are parallel. Can you verify this just by looking at the screen? Explain.
4. Devise a method for proving that the two lines are parallel. Summarize your method and your findings here.
5. Start with a new screen and draw a line. Can you construct a line parallel to this line that passes through a point on the line? Explain.
6. Instruct your software program to do Exercise 5. Report what you find.
7. Devise a method for constructing on a computer a trapezoid whose bases have length 4 cm and 6 cm. List the steps of your construction below.

What You'll Learn Using dynamic geometry software to construct and investigate parallel lines

What You'll Need A computer with a dynamic geometry software program installed

for use with Think and Discuss and Example 1, uses geometry software to explore parallel lines.

Alternative Activity for Lesson 7-4

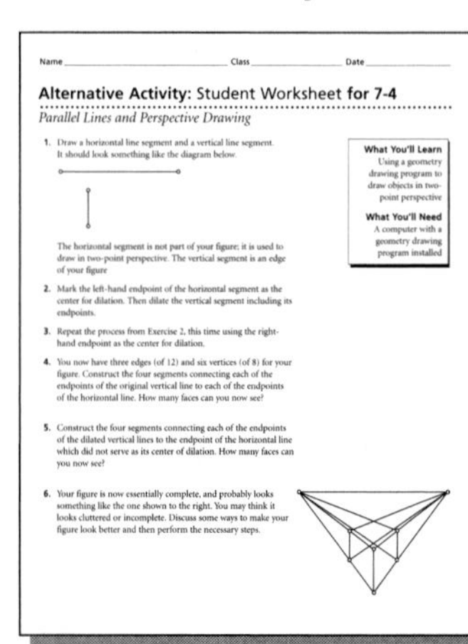

Name ______ Class ______ Date ______

Alternative Activity: Student Worksheet **for 7-4**

Parallel Lines and Perspective Drawing

1. Draw a horizontal line segment and a vertical line segment. It should look something like the diagram below.

   The horizontal segment is not part of your figure; it is used to draw in two-point perspective. The vertical segment is an edge of your figure.
2. Mark the left-hand endpoint of the horizontal segment as the center for dilation. Then dilate the vertical segment including its endpoints.
3. Repeat the process from Exercise 2, this time using the right-hand endpoint as the center for dilation.
4. You now have three edges (of 12) and six vertices (of 8) for your figure. Construct the four segments connecting each of the endpoints of the original vertical line to each of the endpoints of the horizontal line. How many faces can you now see?
5. Construct the four segments connecting each of the endpoints of the dilated vertical lines to the endpoint of the horizontal line which did not serve as its center of dilation. How many faces can you now see?
6. Your figure is now essentially complete, and probably looks something like the one shown to the right. You may think it looks cluttered or incomplete. Discuss some ways to make your figure look better and then perform the necessary steps.

What You'll Learn Using a geometry drawing program to draw objects in two-point perspective

What You'll Need A computer with a geometry drawing program installed

for use with pages 386–387, uses geometry software to construct figures in two-point perspective.

Cooperative Learning Tips

When used effectively, cooperative learning can help students develop interpersonal skills, learn to perform specific roles in a group, and learn to carry out specific responsibilities. The components of Chapter 7 provide a range of cooperative learning opportunities.

- In the Student Edition, the ***Work Together*** parts of lessons are specifically designed for cooperative learning activities.
- In the Teacher's Edition, you will find helpful hints for addressing diverse learning styles (see page C for Chapter 7). For every lesson, you will find a ***Reteaching Activity***, which may involve cooperative learning.

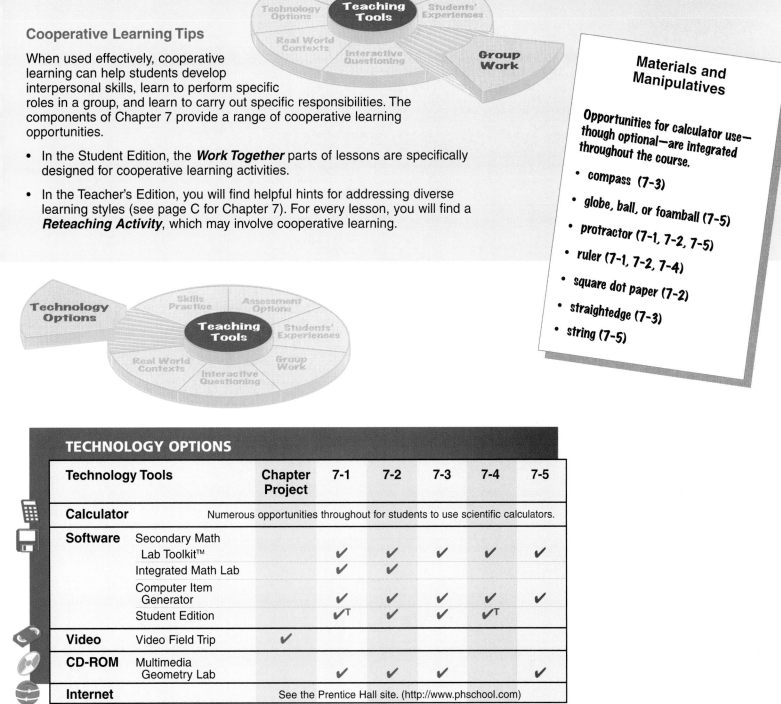

Materials and Manipulatives

Opportunities for calculator use—though optional—are integrated throughout the course.

- compass (7-3)
- globe, ball, or foamball (7-5)
- protractor (7-1, 7-2, 7-5)
- ruler (7-1, 7-2, 7-4)
- square dot paper (7-2)
- straightedge (7-3)
- string (7-5)

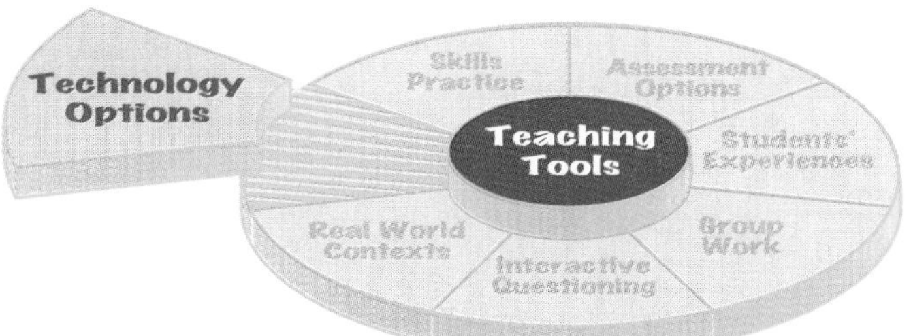

TECHNOLOGY OPTIONS

Technology Tools		Chapter Project	7-1	7-2	7-3	7-4	7-5
Calculator	Numerous opportunities throughout for students to use scientific calculators.						
Software	Secondary Math Lab Toolkit™		✔	✔	✔	✔	✔
	Integrated Math Lab		✔	✔			
	Computer Item Generator		✔	✔	✔	✔	✔
	Student Edition		✔T	✔	✔	✔T	
Video	Video Field Trip	✔					
CD-ROM	Multimedia Geometry Lab		✔	✔	✔		✔
Internet	See the Prentice Hall site. (http://www.phschool.com)						

✔T indicates Math Toolbox.

The Prentice Hall Geometry program offers you a rich variety of technology options. Be assured that all these options are provided as a means of enriching the program and are not essential for the successful completion of the course.

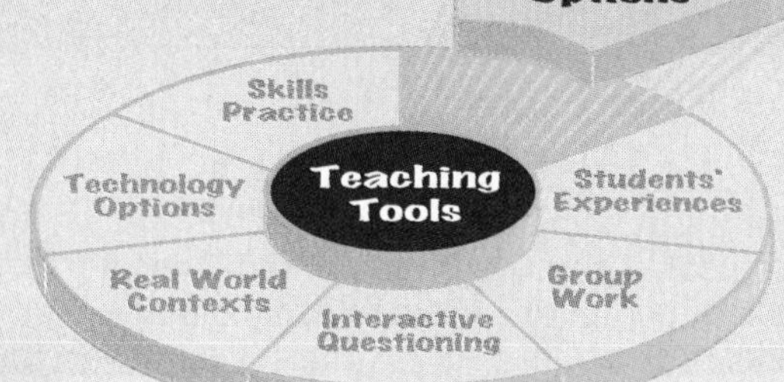

Assessment Options

The Prentice Hall Geometry Program provides you with many options. From these options, you may choose instructional materials and techniques appropriate for your students, or those necessary to meet your district's curriculum requirements. As the chart indicates, the program also supports your teaching efforts by offering you many choices for assessment.

ASSESSMENT OPTIONS

Assessment Support Materials	Chapter Project	7-1	7-2	7-3	7-4	7-5	Chapter End
Chapter Project	▲■●	▲■		▲■	▲■	▲■	▲■
Checkpoints				▲■●			
Self-Assessment							
Writing Assignment		▲■	▲	▲●	▲■	▲■	▲●
Chapter Assessment							▲■●
Alternative Assessment		■	■	■	■	■	■●
Cumulative Review							●
Standardized Test Prep			▲■	▲			▲■●
Computer Item Generator	Can be used to create custom-made practice or assessment at any time.						

▲ = Student Edition ■ = Teacher's Edition ● = Teaching Resources

Checkpoints

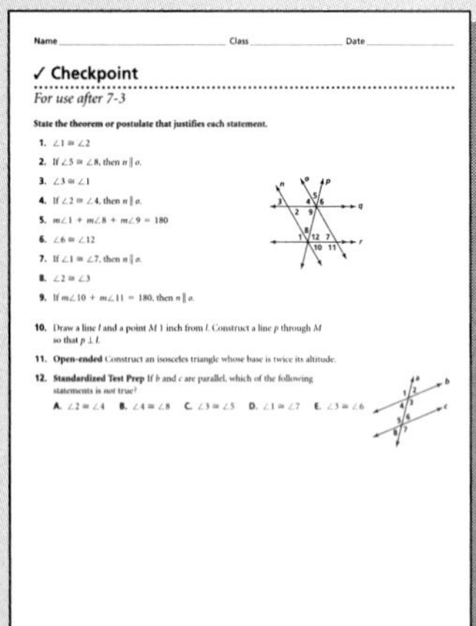
✓ Checkpoint

For use after 7-3

Alternative Assessment

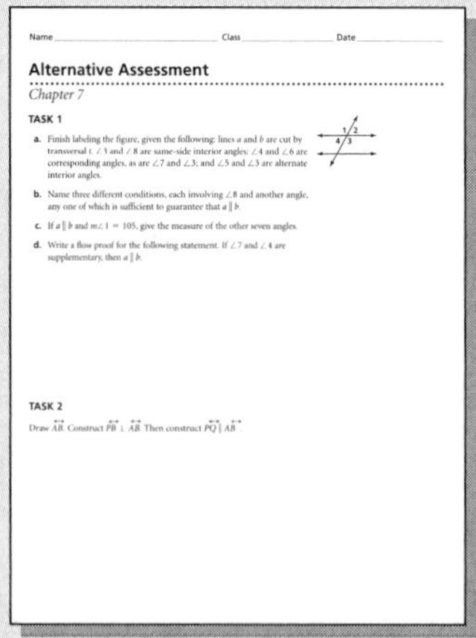
Alternative Assessment

Chapter 7

Chapter Assessment

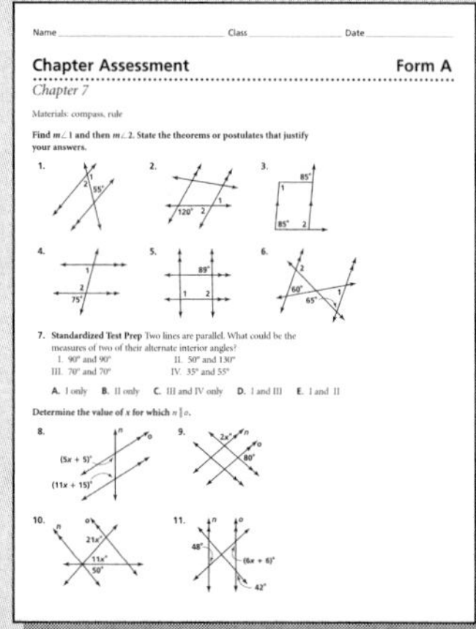
Chapter Assessment Form A

Chapter 7

Available in both Form A and Form B

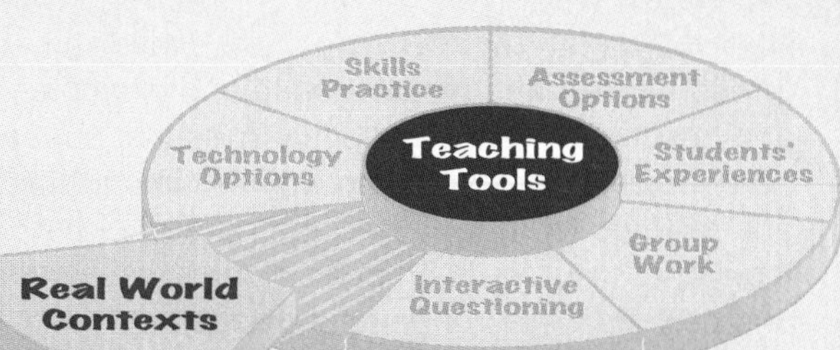

Making the Right Connections

Mathematics is imbedded in nearly every walk of life. The National Council of Teachers of Mathematics (NCTM) encourages educators to recognize these connections and to emphasize them for the purpose of better educating students for success in life and in a global economy. The ***Connections*** chart below highlights these connections for Chapter 7.

CONNECTIONS

Lesson	Interdisciplinary Connections	Career Prep	Other Real World Connections	Math Integration	NCTM Standards
Chapter Project	Economics Sociology	Architecture Construction	Spider Webs Telephone Cables	Algebra	Communication Connections
7-1	History Science Physical Education	Aviation City Planner	Measuring Earth Architecture Traffic Flow Photography	Probability Algebra Transformational Geometry	Problem Solving Communication Connections Reasoning
7-2	Health	Graphic Arts Drafting	Woodworking Carpentry Furniture Olympics	Coordinate Geometry Transformational Geometry	Problem Solving Communication Connections Reasoning
7-3	Computer Science Art	Computer Graphics	Arts and Crafts Fiber Optics Technology	Coordinate Geometry	Problem Solving Communication Connections
7-4	Art Computer Science	Technical Art	Photography Painting Computer Drawing Optical Illusions	Transformational Geometry	Problem Solving Communication Connections
7-5	Geography Social Studies History	Travel Computer Engineering	Maps Navigation	Algebra	Problem Solving Reasoning Structure Communication

CHAPTER 7 Reasoning and Parallel Lines

CONNECTING TO PRIOR LEARNING Have students look through books and magazines to find examples of buildings and houses. Have them identify lines that appear parallel or perpendicular. Ask students why it is important for architects and builders to know if lines are parallel or perpendicular. Ask if anyone has ever been in an older house where the floors and ceilings were not parallel planes.

CULTURAL CONNECTIONS The first telephone signals were transmitted over copper wires. Next radio signals were used to connect parts of the world not accessible by wire. Optical fibers are now replacing wire because a single strand of fiber can transmit 2 billion bits of information per second and can carry 30,000 telephone signals. Ask students how satellite communication is turning the world into a "global village."

INTERDISCIPLINARY CONNECTIONS Telephone networks connect not only telephones but also modems and fax machines around the world. Ask students who are experienced on the Internet to explain to the class how they use a modem to access the Internet and communicate through cyberspace.

Technology Options

Prentice Hall Technology

Video

Video Field Trip 7, "Cyber Map," an interview with one of the authors of Netscape™ software

CHAPTER 7 Reasoning and Parallel Lines

Relating to the Real World

Take a look around. Chances are, you can see an example of parallel lines from where you are sitting. But how can you be sure the lines you see are parallel? Architects and builders use the basic geometric concepts in this chapter to ensure that lines are indeed parallel.

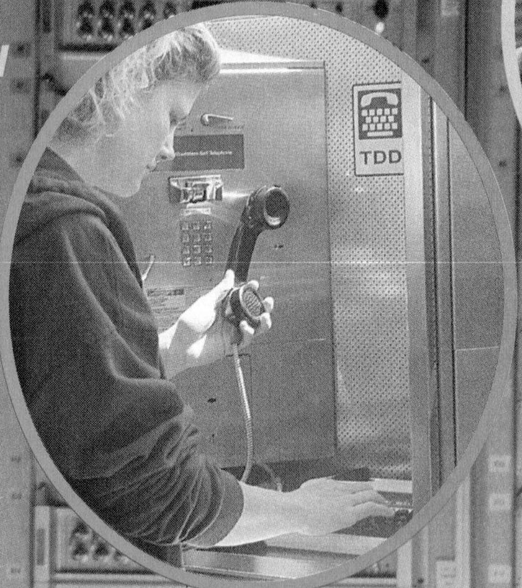

Lessons	7-1	7-2	7-3	7-4	7-5
	Parallel Lines and Related Angles	Proving Lines Parallel	Constructing Parallel and Perpendicular Lines	Parallel Lines and Perspective Drawing	Exploring Spherical Geometry

ABOUT THE PROJECT Students explore simple networks to see how economic and social issues affect their designs. They then design their own networks.

Launching the Project

PROJECT NOTEBOOK Encourage students to keep all project-related materials in a separate folder or notebook. **See Chapter Project Manager and Scoring Rubric in Chapter Support File.**

- Have students bring in local street maps. Have them identify two locations and find the paths along roads they can take from one to the other. Ask which is the shortest path.
- Have students connect their desks with string using the least amount of string possible.

TRACKING THE PROJECT You may wish to have students read Finishing the Chapter Project on page 398 to help them get an overview of the project. Set benchmark deadlines for students to show their work in progress.

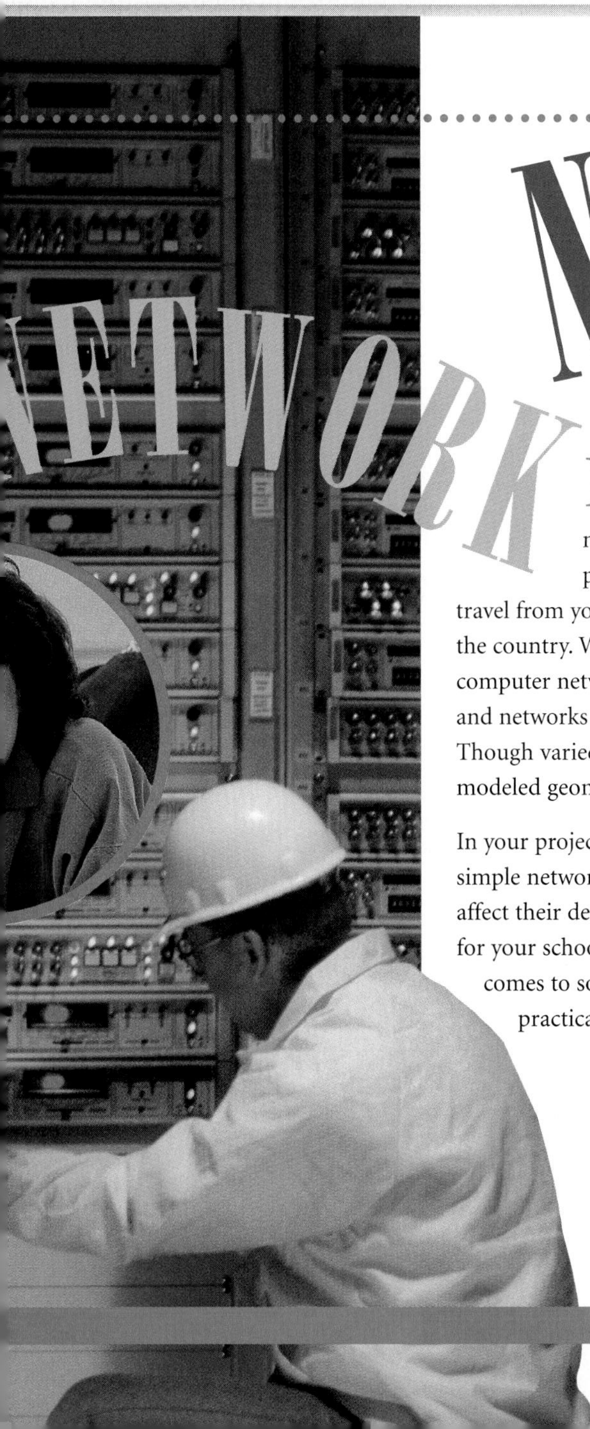

CHAPTER PROJECT

NETWORK NEWS

Like the strands of an immense spider web, unseen cables join your telephone to millions of others. Similarly, your street is part of a vast system of roads enabling you to travel from your house to just about any other house in the country. We live amid telephone, television, and computer networks, networks of highways and hallways, and networks that join airports, bus stops, and people. Though varied in purpose, each of these networks can be modeled geometrically by a collection of connected points.

In your project for this chapter, you will explore some simple networks to see how economic and social issues can affect their design. You will also design your own network for your school or community. You will see that when it comes to solving complex, real-world problems, practicality and mathematics are constant partners.

To help you complete the project:

- **p. 369** *Find Out by Investigating*
- **p. 382** *Find Out by Designing*
- **p. 391** *Find Out by Investigating*
- **p. 396** *Find Out by Modeling*
- **p. 398** *Finishing the Project*

Project Resources

Teaching Resources
Chapter Support File, Ch. 7
- Chapter Project Manager and Scoring Rubric

Transparencies
77

Using the Rubric

Sharing the scoring rubric for the project with your students will alert them to your expectations before they begin work on the project.

As students complete each Find Out question in the chapter, you may wish to have them evaluate their own work or a partner's work based on the scoring rubric. Students should have the opportunity to revise their work after it has been reviewed.

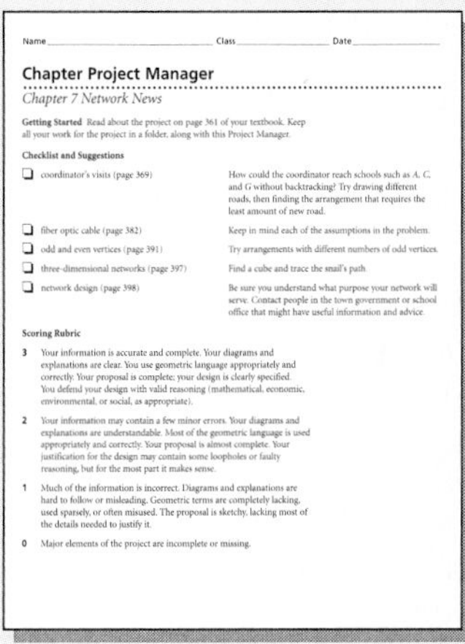

Name ______ Class ______ Date ______

Chapter Project Manager

Chapter 7 Network News

Getting Started Read about the project on page 361 of your textbook. Keep all your work for the project in a folder, along with this Project Manager.

Checklist and Suggestions

❑ coordinator's visits (page 369)	How could the coordinator reach schools such as *A*, *C*, and *G* without backtracking? Try drawing different roads, then finding the arrangement that requires the least amount of new road.
❑ fiber optic cable (page 382)	Keep in mind each of the assumptions in the problem.
❑ odd and even vertices (page 391)	Try arrangements with different numbers of odd vertices.
❑ three-dimensional networks (page 397)	Find a cube and trace the snail's path.
❑ network design (page 398)	Be sure you understand what purpose your network will serve. Contact people in the town government or school office that might have useful information and advice.

Scoring Rubric

3 Your information is accurate and complete. Your diagrams and explanations are clear. You use geometric language appropriately and correctly. Your proposal is complete; your design is clearly specified. You defend your design with valid reasoning (mathematical, economic, environmental, or social, as appropriate).

2 Your information may contain a few minor errors. Your diagrams and explanations are understandable. Most of the geometric language is used appropriately and correctly. Your proposal is almost complete. Your justification for the design may contain some loopholes or faulty reasoning, but for the most part it makes sense.

1 Much of the information is incorrect. Diagrams and explanations are hard to follow or misleading. Geometric terms are completely lacking, used sparsely, or often misused. The proposal is sketchy, lacking most of the details needed to justify it.

0 Major elements of the project are incomplete or missing.

Math ToolboX

Students use geometry software to investigate the relationships among the eight angles formed by a pair of parallel lines and a transversal. These angle relationships will be presented formally in Lesson 7-1.

Using the software enables students to manipulate the lines while parallel lines remaining parallel. They can observe the effect that changing the positions of the lines has on the angle measures.

ERROR ALERT! Students who take a short cut and draw two lines that appear parallel instead of constructing them may not observe any angle relationships because when they manipulate the lines, the parallel lines do not remain parallel.

Remediation: These students need to start over and construct parallel lines.

Conjecture

Students can use numbers to specify certain angles. Even better would be their describing the positions of the angles, such as "between the parallel lines," "on the same side of the transversal," or "above each parallel line."

ADDITIONAL PROBLEM Have students construct two parallel lines and draw a transversal. Then have them construct a line parallel to the transversal. Ask: *What relationships exist among the angles formed? How many different measures are there?*

Materials and Manipulatives

- Geometry software

Transparencies
8, 10

Math ToolboX — Technology

Exploring Parallel Lines and Related Angles

Before Lesson 7-1

Work in pairs or small groups.

Construct

Use geometry software to construct two parallel lines. Make sure that the lines remain parallel when you manipulate them. Construct a point on each line. Then construct the line through these two points. This line is called a *transversal*. Check students' work.

Investigate

Measure each of the eight angles formed by the parallel lines and the transversal and record the measurements. Manipulate the lines and record the new measurements. What relationships do you notice?
$m\angle 1 = m\angle 3 = m\angle 5 = m\angle 7$,
$m\angle 2 = m\angle 4 = m\angle 6 = m\angle 8$

Conjecture

When two parallel lines are intersected by a transversal, what are the relationships among the angles formed? Make as many **conjectures** as possible. Sample: 2 sets of 4 $\cong$ angles are formed.

Extend

Yes; the angles formed by 3 $\|$ lines have a relation similar to the one for the angles formed by 2 $\|$ lines; 2

- Use your software to construct three or more parallel lines. Construct a line that intersects one of the lines. Does it intersect the other lines also? If it does, what relationships exist among the angles formed? How many different measures are there?
- Construct two parallel lines and draw a transversal that is perpendicular to one of the parallel lines. What do you discover?
All the angles formed by these lines are rt. angles.

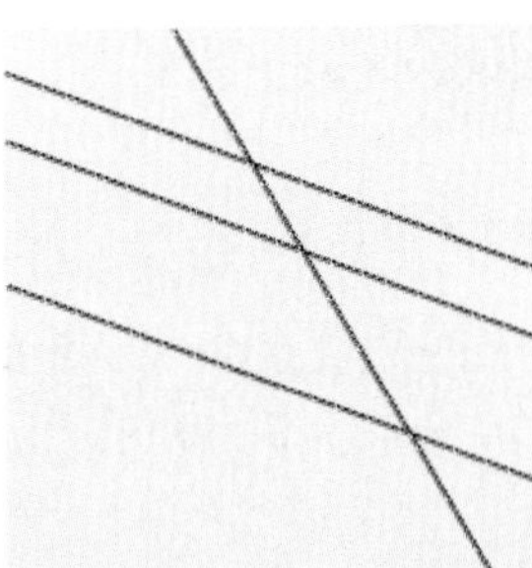

362

7-1 Teaching Notes

PROBLEM OF THE DAY

A regular hexagon is inscribed in a circle. To the nearest percent, what is the probability that a random point within the circle is outside the hexagon? 17%

Problem of the Day is also available in Transparencies.

CONNECTING TO PRIOR KNOWLEDGE Draw the following diagram and ask students to identify all vertical angles, supplementary angles, and adjacent angles.

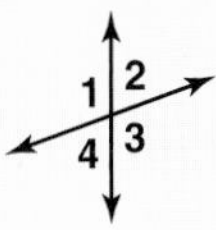

THINK AND DISCUSS p. 363

Question 1 Students may not understand what is meant by the interior and exterior of two lines. Copy the diagram and shade the interior with one color and the exterior with another.

Make sure students understand that pairs of angles can be identified when *any* two lines are cut by a transversal.

Question 3 Use this question to review the terms *adjacent* and *supplementary.*

Example 1 Relating to the Real World 

Help students identify the lines that form ∠1 and ∠2. They may want to trace only those lines onto a piece of paper.

Connections Aviation . . . and more

7-1 Parallel Lines and Related Angles

What You'll Learn

- Identifying pairs of angles formed by two lines and a transversal
- Relating the measures of angles formed by parallel lines and a transversal

...And Why

To understand how parallel lines are used in building, city planning, and construction

What You'll Need

- ruler
- protractor

THINK AND DISCUSS

Part 1

Angles Formed by Intersecting Lines

A **transversal** is a line that intersects two coplanar lines at two distinct points. The diagram shows the eight angles formed by the transversal and the two lines.

1. a. ∠3 and ∠6 are in the *interior* of ℓ and *m*. Name another pair of angles in the interior of ℓ and *m*. Sample: ∠4 and ∠5
   b. Name a pair of angles in the *exterior* of ℓ and *m*. Sample: ∠1 and ∠7
2. a. ∠1 and ∠4 are on *alternate sides* of the transversal *t*. Name another pair of angles on alternate sides of *t*. Sample: ∠5 and ∠8
   b. Name a pair of angles on the *same side* of *t*. Sample: ∠1 and ∠3

You can use the terms in Questions 1 and 2 to describe pairs of angles.

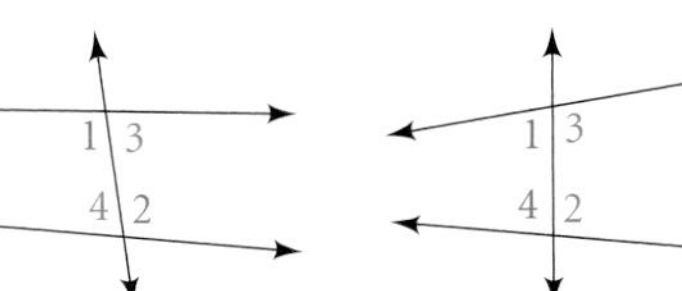

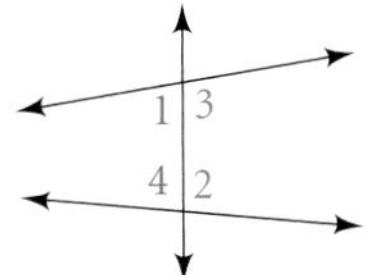

∠1 and ∠2 are **alternate interior angles**, as are ∠3 and ∠4.

∠1 and ∠4 are **same-side interior angles**, as are ∠2 and ∠3.

∠5 and ∠4 are **corresponding angles**, as are ∠6 and ∠2, ∠1 and ∠7, and ∠3 and ∠8.

3. In the diagrams above, ∠1 and ∠3 are not alternate interior angles. What term decribes their positions in relation to each other? adjacent angles

Example 1 Relating to the Real World 

Aviation In the diagram of Lafayette Regional Airport, the black segments are runways and the grey areas are taxiways and terminal buildings. Classify ∠1 and ∠2 as alternate interior angles, same-side interior angles, or corresponding angles.

∠1 and ∠2 are corresponding angles.

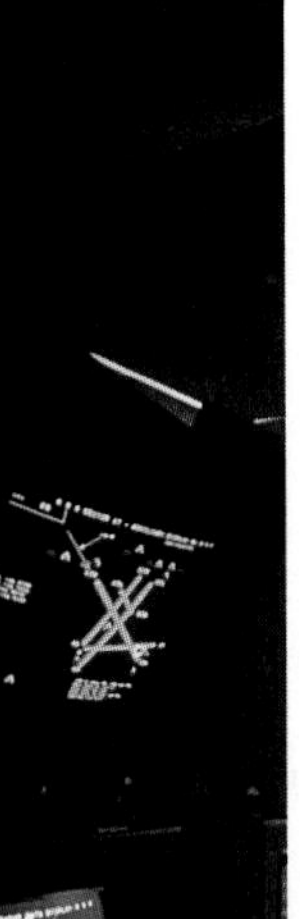

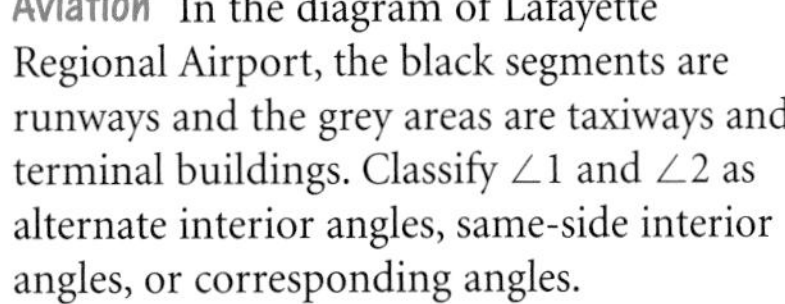

Lafayette Regional Airport
Lafayette, Louisiana

Lesson Planning Options

Prerequisite Skills

- Understanding parallel and perpendicular lines
- Understanding vertical and supplementary angles

Assignment Options for Exercises On Your Own

To provide flexible scheduling, this lesson can be subdivided into parts.

Part 1: **Core** 1–3, 19–27; **Extension** 14–16

Part 2: **Core** 4–13, 17–18, 28–38; **Extension** 39–41

Use Mixed Review to maintain skills.

Resources

Student Edition

Skills Handbook, p. 664
Extra Practice, p. 654
Glossary/Study Guide

Teaching Resources

Chapter Support File, Ch. 7
- Practice 7-1 (two worksheets)
- Reteaching 7-1

Classroom Manager 7-1
Glossary, Spanish Resources

Transparencies
8, 10, 78, 86

WORK TOGETHER

Directions for using geometry software to investigate the angles formed by parallel lines and a transversal are given in the Math Toolbox on page 362.

Check that students state "if two *parallel* lines are cut by a transversal" as the hypothesis of each conjecture they make.

THINK AND DISCUSS

p. 364

VISUAL LEARNING Use models to illustrate the postulate and theorems, such as dividers from cardboard boxes or straws held together by brads. Emphasize that the names of the angle pairs do not depend on the lines being parallel but that the relationships between their measures do.

When writing reasons in proofs, remind students that it is better to write out the statement of the theorem or postulate rather than using its name. Due to space constraints, students may want to use abbreviations for parallel (‖), angles (∠s), and congruent (≅).

Additional Examples

FOR EXAMPLE 1

Classify each pair of angles as alternate interior angles, same-side interior angles, or corresponding angles.

a. ∠4 and ∠2 **b.** ∠3 and ∠4

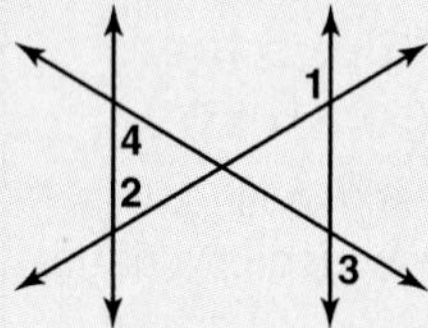

a. same-side interior angles
b. corresponding angles

Discussion: *Identify a pair of alternate interior angles.*

FOR EXAMPLE 2

Write a plan for the following proof.

Given: *PQRS* is a parallelogram.
Prove: ∠1 ≅ ∠3

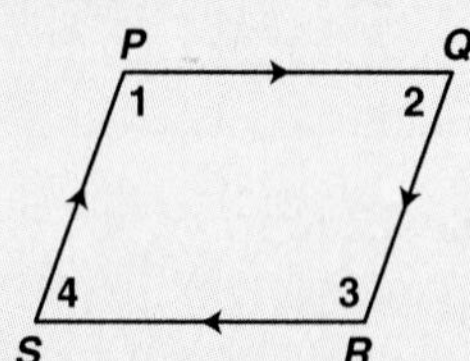

Answers may vary. Sample:
Plan for Proof: To show ∠1 ≅ ∠3, show that ∠1 and ∠2 are supplementary and that ∠2 and ∠3 are supplementary. Then ∠1 ≅ ∠3.

Discussion: *Use the Plan for Proof to write a paragraph proof.*

Part 2

WORK TOGETHER

Work with a partner.

- Draw two parallel lines using lined paper or the two edges of a ruler. Then draw a transversal that intersects the two parallel lines.
- Use a protractor to measure each of the eight angles formed. Record the measures on your drawing.

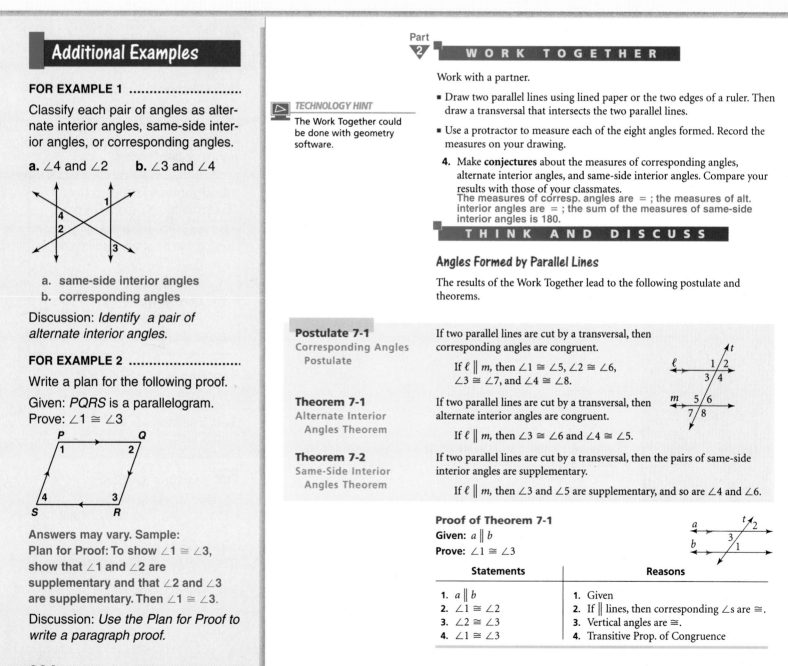

TECHNOLOGY HINT

The Work Together could be done with geometry software.

4. Make **conjectures** about the measures of corresponding angles, alternate interior angles, and same-side interior angles. Compare your results with those of your classmates.
The measures of corresp. angles are = ; the measures of alt. interior angles are = ; the sum of the measures of same-side interior angles is 180.

THINK AND DISCUSS

Angles Formed by Parallel Lines

The results of the Work Together lead to the following postulate and theorems.

Postulate 7-1
Corresponding Angles Postulate

If two parallel lines are cut by a transversal, then corresponding angles are congruent.

If $\ell \parallel m$, then ∠1 ≅ ∠5, ∠2 ≅ ∠6, ∠3 ≅ ∠7, and ∠4 ≅ ∠8.

Theorem 7-1
Alternate Interior Angles Theorem

If two parallel lines are cut by a transversal, then alternate interior angles are congruent.

If $\ell \parallel m$, then ∠3 ≅ ∠6 and ∠4 ≅ ∠5.

Theorem 7-2
Same-Side Interior Angles Theorem

If two parallel lines are cut by a transversal, then the pairs of same-side interior angles are supplementary.

If $\ell \parallel m$, then ∠3 and ∠5 are supplementary, and so are ∠4 and ∠6.

Proof of Theorem 7-1

Given: $a \parallel b$
Prove: ∠1 ≅ ∠3

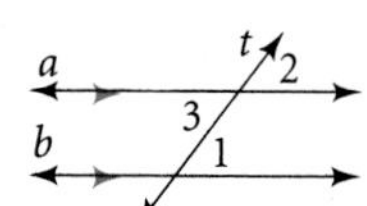

Statements	Reasons
1. $a \parallel b$	1. Given
2. ∠1 ≅ ∠2	2. If ‖ lines, then corresponding ∠s are ≅.
3. ∠2 ≅ ∠3	3. Vertical angles are ≅.
4. ∠1 ≅ ∠3	4. Transitive Prop. of Congruence

Example 2

Discuss with students that a plan for a proof gives the principal statements that they would use in a two-column proof. In the actual proof, each statement must be justified by a reason.

Question 6 Have students state the postulates, theorems, or definitions they use to find the measure of each angle.

AUDITORY LEARNING Have students work with a partner. One student gives the numbers of two angles. Then the other student describes the pair as alternate interior, same side interior, corresponding, or neither. Then have students switch roles.

Example 3 Relating to the Real World

Make sure students follow Eratosthenes' reasoning that if 7.2° is $\frac{1}{50}$ of 360°, then 500 mi is $\frac{1}{50}$ of Earth's circumference.

MAKING CONNECTIONS Students may be surprised to learn that Eratosthenes believed that Earth was round in 200 B.C. because the shape of Earth was still hotly debated at the time of Christopher Columbus in the fifteenth century.

When writing a proof, it is often helpful to start by writing a plan. The plan should describe how you can reason from the given information to what you want to prove.

Example 2

Write a plan for the proof of Theorem 7-2.

Given: $a \parallel b$

Prove: $\angle 1$ and $\angle 2$ are supplementary.

Plan for Proof To show that $m\angle 1 + m\angle 2 = 180$, show that $m\angle 3 + m\angle 2 = 180$ and that $m\angle 1 = m\angle 3$. Then substitute $m\angle 1$ for $m\angle 3$.

5. Use the Plan for Proof to write a two-column proof of Theorem 7-2. See margin p. 366.
6. **Try This** Find the measure of each angle.

   a. $\angle 1$ 110 b. $\angle 2$ 70 c. $\angle 3$ 70
   d. $\angle 4$ 110 e. $\angle 5$ 110 f. $\angle 6$ 70

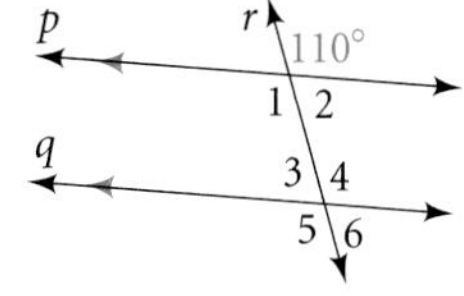

Example 3 Relating to the Real World

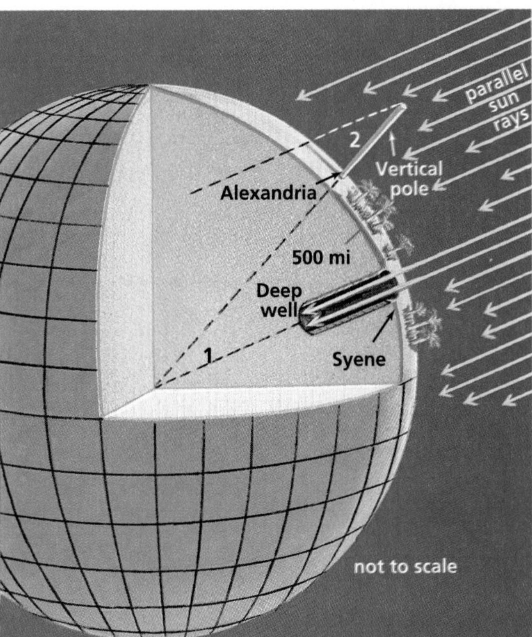

Measuring Earth About 220 B.C., Eratosthenes estimated the circumference of Earth. He achieved this remarkable feat by assuming that Earth is a sphere and that the sun's rays are parallel. He knew that the sun was directly over the town of Syene on the longest day of the year, because sunlight shone directly down a deep well. On that day, he measured the angle of the shadow of a vertical pole in Alexandria, which was 5000 stadia (about 500 miles) north of Syene. How did Eratosthenes know that $\angle 1 \cong \angle 2$? And how could he compute the circumference of Earth knowing $m\angle 1$?

Since $\angle 1$ and $\angle 2$ are alternate interior angles formed by the sun's parallel rays, the angles are congruent. The angle Eratosthenes measured was 7.2°. This is $\frac{1}{50}$ of 360°, so 500 mi is $\frac{1}{50}$ of the circumference of Earth. His estimate of 25,000 mi is very close to the actual value.

Technology Options

For Exercises 38 and 39, students may construct two parallel lines cut by a transversal and investigate the relationship between alternate exterior angles and same-side exterior angles.

Prentice Hall Technology

Software
- Secondary Math Lab Toolkit™
- Integrated Math Lab 35
- Computer Item Generator 7-1

CD-ROM
- Multimedia Geometry Lab 7

Internet
- See the Prentice Hall site. (http://www.phschool.com)

Exercises ON YOUR OWN

Exercises 1–3 Students classify angles that are not necessarily congruent.

Exercises 4–7 Students use the fact that the pairs of lines are parallel to apply the postulate and theorems studied in this lesson.

Exercises 8–13 Have students write out the entire postulate or theorem, not just its name.

OPEN-ENDED Exercise 14 The letters H, A, or N can also be used to illustrate alternate interior angles.

ALTERNATIVE ASSESSMENT Exercise 15 You can use this exercise to help you assess students' ability to identify corresponding angles and alternate interior angles as well as their understanding of translations and rotations. Challenge students to describe a reflection that takes ∠1 onto ∠4 and a glide reflection that takes ∠2 onto ∠7.

WRITING Exercise 16 Students may want to give other examples of words beginning with "trans-" and their meanings.

pages 364–365 Think and Discuss

5. 1. $m\angle 3 + m\angle 2 = 180$ (Angle Add. Post.) 2. $a \parallel b$ (Given) 3. $m\angle 1 = m\angle 3$ (If ∥ lines, then corres. ∠s are ≅.) 4. $m\angle 1 + m\angle 2 = 180$ (Substitution) 5. ∠1 and ∠2 are supplementary. (Def. of supplementary angles)

pages 366–369 On Your Own

1. ∠1 and ∠2: corresponding, ∠3 and ∠4: alt. interior, ∠5 and ∠6: corresponding
2. ∠1 and ∠2: same-side interior, ∠3 and ∠4: corresponding, ∠5 and ∠6: corresponding
3. ∠1 and ∠2: corresponding, ∠3 and ∠4: same-side interior, ∠5 and ∠6: : alt. interior
4. If ∥ lines, then corres. ∠s are ≅.; if ∥ lines, then same-side int. ∠s are supplementary.
5. If ∥ lines, then corres. ∠s are ≅.; if ∥ lines, then same-side int. ∠s are supplementary.
6. If ∥ lines, then same-side int. ∠s are supplementary.); if ∥ lines, then alt. int. ∠s are ≅.
7. If ∥ lines, then same-side int. ∠s are supplementary.; if ∥ lines, then same-side int. ∠s are supplementary.
8. If ∥ lines, then corres. ∠s are ≅.
9. If ∥ lines, then alt. int. ∠s are ≅.
10. If ∥ lines, then same-side int. ∠s are supplementary.

366

Exercises ON YOUR OWN

Classify each pair of angles labeled with the same color as alternate interior angles, same-side interior angles, or corresponding angles. 1–3. See margin.

1. 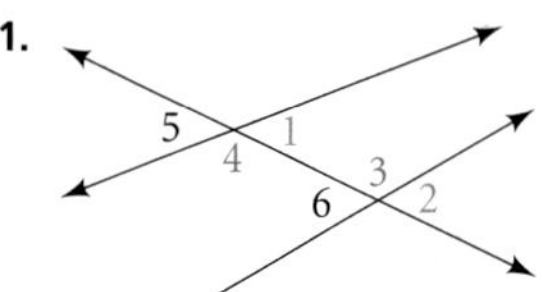

2. 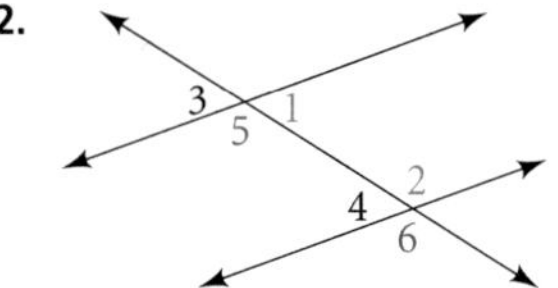

3. 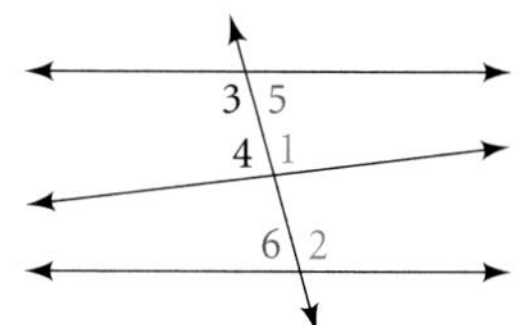

Find $m\angle 1$ and then $m\angle 2$. State the theorems or postulates that justify your answers. 4–7. See margin for sample justifications.

4. 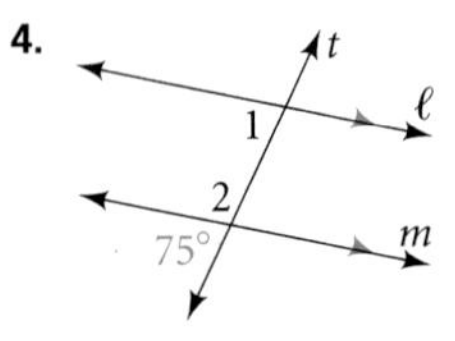

75, 105

5. 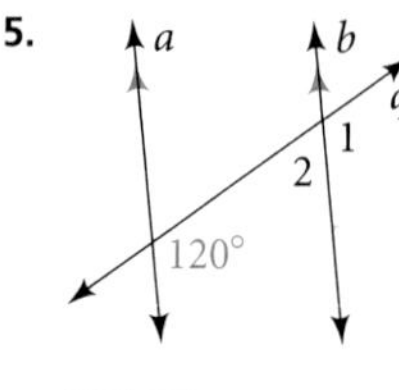

120, 60

6. 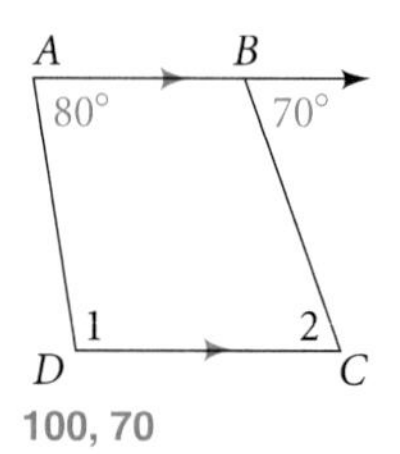

100, 70

7. 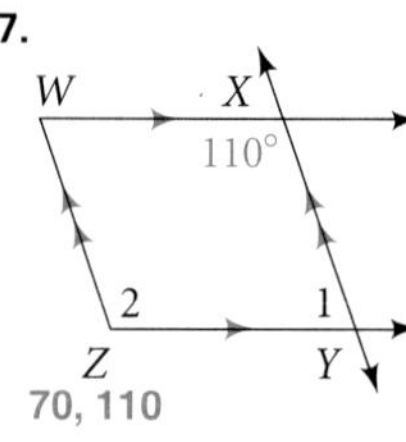

70, 110

State the theorem or postulate that justifies each statement about the figure at the right. 8–13. See margin.

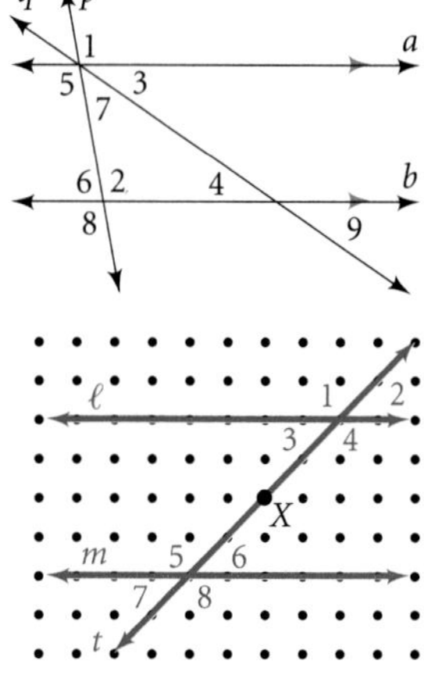

8. ∠1 ≅ ∠2
9. ∠3 ≅ ∠4
10. $m\angle 5 + m\angle 6 = 180$
11. ∠5 ≅ ∠2
12. ∠5 ≅ ∠8
13. ∠3 ≅ ∠9

14. *Open-ended* The letter **Z** illustrates alternate interior angles. Find at least two other letters that illustrate the pairs of angles presented in this lesson. For each letter, show which types of angles are formed. See margin.

15. a. *Transformational Geometry* Lines ℓ and m are parallel, and line t is a transversal. Under the translation ⟨−4, −4⟩, the image of each of the angles ∠1, ∠2, ∠3, and ∠4 is its __?__ angle. corresponding
    b. Under a rotation of 180° in point X, the image of each of the angles ∠3, ∠4, ∠5, and ∠6 is its __?__ angle. alt. interior

16. *Writing* Look up the meaning of the prefix *trans-*. Explain how the meaning of the prefix relates to the word *transversal*. See margin.

17. a. *Probability* Suppose that you pick one even-numbered angle and one odd-numbered angle from the diagram. Find the probability that the two angles are congruent. $\frac{1}{2}$
    b. *Open-ended* Write a probability problem of your own based on the diagram. Then solve it.
    Sample: Suppose you pick 2 even-numbered angles. What is the probability that they are supplementary? $\frac{2}{3}$

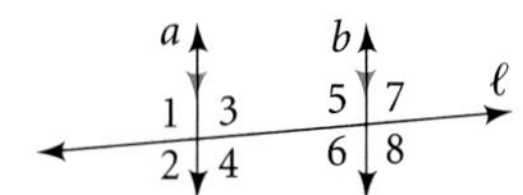

PROBABILITY Exercise 17a Have students work in groups to determine the sample space (sixteen angle pairs), then to check if the angles in each pair are congruent.

KINESTHETIC LEARNING Exercise 18 Take students outside to look at the school building and other surrounding buildings. Have them identify lines on the buildings that appear parallel and are cut by a transversal. Have them sketch the lines and label congruent angles.

ERROR ALERT! **Exercises 19–20** Students may be confused by the four lines in the diagram. **Remediation:** For Exercise 19, have students copy just lines p, ℓ, and m and label the angles they form. For Exercise 20, have students copy just lines ℓ, p, and q and label the angles they form.

Exercises 28–29 Remind students to state the entire theorem or postulate they use to justify a statement.

18. a. Architecture This photograph contains many examples of parallel lines cut by transversals. Given that $a \parallel b$ and $m\angle 1 = 68$, find $m\angle 2$. 68

b. Given that $c \parallel d$ and $m\angle 3 = 42$, find $m\angle 4$. 138

For Exercises 19–27, refer to the diagram below right.

19. Name all pairs of corresponding angles formed by the transversal p and lines ℓ and m. $\angle 1$ and $\angle 9$, $\angle 2$ and $\angle 10$, $\angle 5$ and $\angle 11$, $\angle 6$ and $\angle 12$

20. Name all pairs of alternate interior angles formed by the transversal ℓ and lines p and q. $\angle 2$ and $\angle 7$, $\angle 3$ and $\angle 6$

Name the relationship between $\angle 2$ and each of the given angles. In each case, state which line is the transversal. 22. corresponding, p

21. $\angle 3$ same-side interior angle, ℓ **22.** $\angle 10$ **23.** $\angle 7$ alt. interior, ℓ **24.** $\angle 4$ corresponding, ℓ

Find all angles that have the given relationship to $\angle 6$.

25. alternate interior $\angle 3$, $\angle 9$ **26.** corresponding $\angle 8$, $\angle 12$ **27.** same-side interior $\angle 7$, $\angle 10$

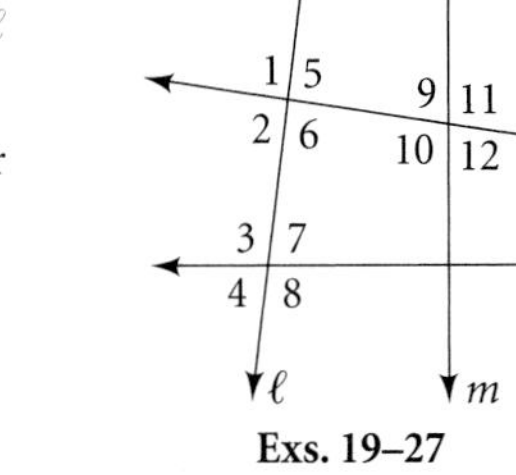

Exs. 19–27

28. Preparing for Proof Supply the reasons to complete this proof.

Given: B is the midpoint of $\overline{AC}$.
E is the midpoint of $\overline{AD}$.

Prove: $\angle 1 \cong \angle 2$

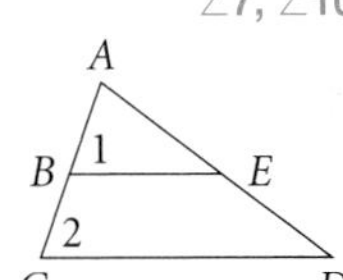
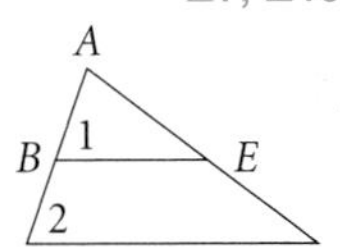

Statements	Reasons
1. B is the midpoint of $\overline{AC}$. E is the midpoint of $\overline{AD}$.	a. ? Given
2. $\overline{BE} \parallel \overline{CD}$	b. ? △ Midsegment Thm.
3. $\angle 1 \cong \angle 2$	c. ? If $\parallel$ lines, then corres. $\angle$s are $\cong$.

29. Preparing for Proof Complete this paragraph proof.

Given: $BERT$ is a parallelogram.

Prove: $\angle 1 \cong \angle 2$

a. $BERT$ is a ▱ b. def. of ▱

We are given that **a.** ? . By **b.** ? , $\overline{ER} \parallel \overline{BT}$. $\angle 1 \cong \angle 2$ because **c.** ? .

E R 1 2 B T

c. if $\parallel$ lines, then alt. int. $\angle$s are $\cong$

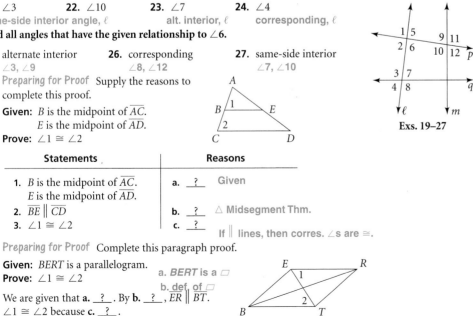

11. If $\parallel$ lines, then alt. int. $\angle$s are $\cong$.

12. If $\parallel$ lines, then corres. $\angle$s are $\cong$.

13. If $\parallel$ lines, then corres. $\angle$s are $\cong$.

14. Samples: N illustrates alt. interior angles; F and E illustrate corres. angles and same-side interior angles.

16. Answers may vary. Sample: In words such as transcontinental and trans-Atlantic, *trans-* means *crossing.* A *transversal* is a line that *crosses* other lines.

39. Conjecture: If 2 lines are $\parallel$, same-side exterior angles formed by these lines and a transversal are supplementary.

1. $a \parallel b$ (Given) 2. $m\angle 4 = m\angle 6$ (If $\parallel$ lines, then corres. $\angle$s are $\cong$.) 3. $m\angle 5 + m\angle 6 = 180$ (Angle Addition Post.) 4. $m\angle 5 + m\angle 4 = 180$ (Substitution) 5. $\angle 4$ and $\angle 5$ are supplementary. (Def. of supplementary angles)

Exercise 37 Help students see that each diagonal of the parallelogram is a transversal.

ESL Exercises 38–40 These exercise require a significant amount of writing. ESL students who understand the reasoning may become discouraged trying to write it down. Pair these students with students more proficient in English. The ESL students can verbalize the steps and their partners can write them down.

Exercises 38–39 You may want to have students add alternate exterior angles and same-side exterior angles to their list of special angles formed by two lines and a transversal.

Chapter Project **FIND OUT BY INVESTIGATING** Have students copy the diagram so they can experiment drawing different routes. Remind them not to write in their books.

40. Because $a \parallel b$ and $\angle 1$ and $\angle 2$ are corres. $\angle$s, $m\angle 1 = m\angle 2$, $m \perp a$, so $m\angle 1 = 90$. By substitution, $m\angle 2 = 90$. Therefore, $m \perp b$ by def. of $\perp$ lines.

41. Answers may vary. Sample: $\perp$ parking does not waste any space but makes it harder to park a car. Slanted parking makes it easier to park a car and makes the direction of traffic clear, but there are fewer parking spaces because some space in each corner is wasted.

Find Out by Investigating

If there is only 1 access road to a school, you must leave via the same road you came on.

200 mi

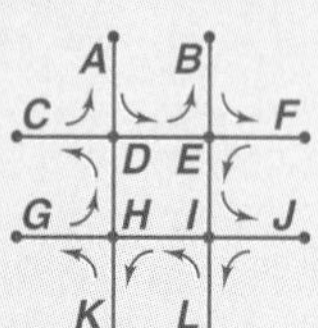

Add $\overline{AB}$, $\overline{CG}$, $\overline{KL}$, $\overline{FJ}$; 120 miles.

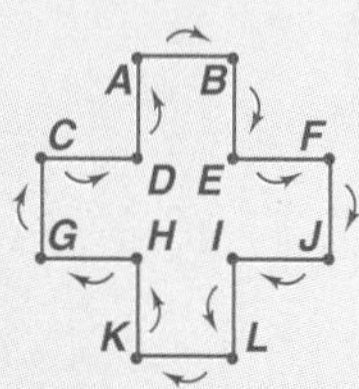

Algebra **Find the values of the variables.**

30. 70

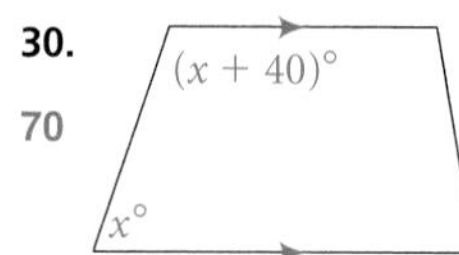

31. 70

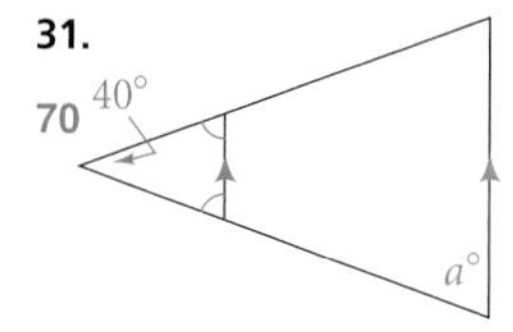

32. 30

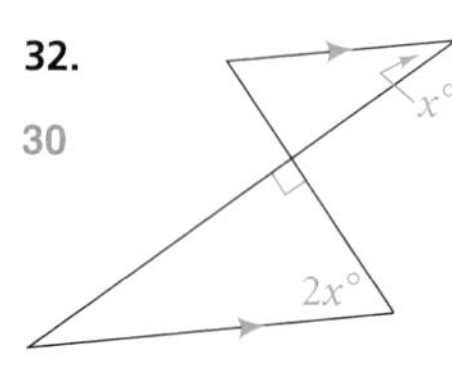

33. 32

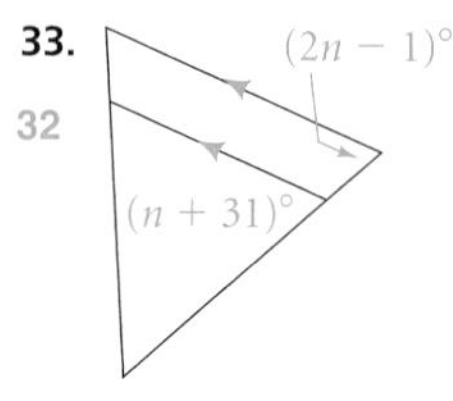

34. 50

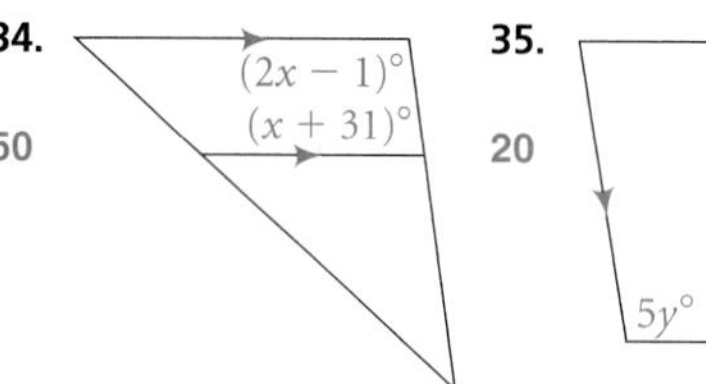

35. 20

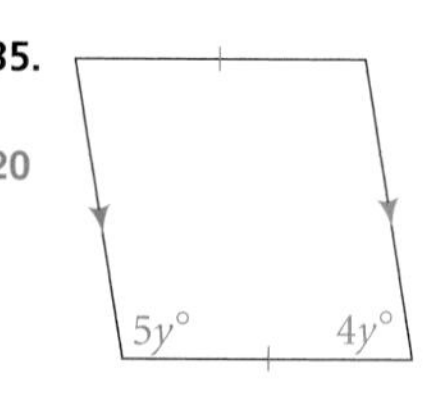

36. 60

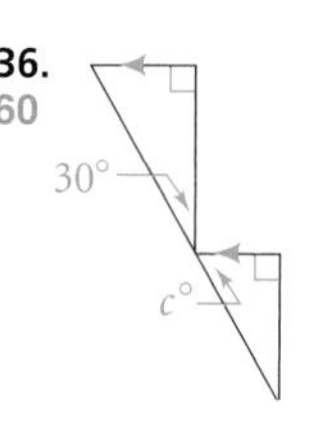

37.

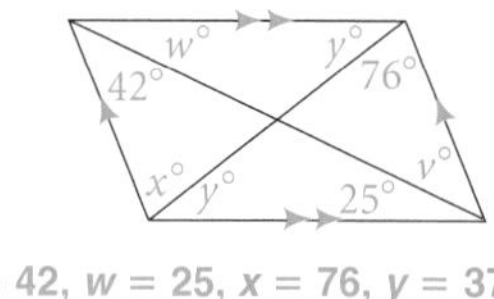

$v = 42$, $w = 25$, $x = 76$, $y = 37$

38. $\angle 1$ and $\angle 3$ are *alternate exterior angles.* Write a two-column proof of this statement: If two parallel lines are cut by a transversal, then alternate exterior angles are congruent.
Given: $a \parallel b$
Prove: $\angle 1 \cong \angle 3$
1. $a \parallel b$ (Given) 2. $\angle 2 \cong \angle 3$ (If $\parallel$ lines, then corres. $\angle$s are $\cong$.) 3. $\angle 1 \cong \angle 2$ (Vert. angles are $\cong$.) 4. $\angle 1 \cong \angle 3$ (Trans. Prop. of $\cong$)
Plan for Proof: Show that $\angle 1 \cong \angle 3$ by showing that both angles are congruent to $\angle 2$.

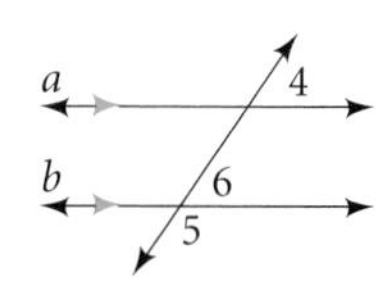

39. *Critical Thinking* $\angle 4$ and $\angle 5$ are *same-side exterior angles.* Make a **conjecture** about the same-side exterior angles formed by two parallel lines and a transversal. Prove your conjecture. See margin p. 367.

40. Use the diagram to write a paragraph proof of this statement: If a transversal is perpendicular to one of two parallel lines, then it is perpendicular to the other line.
Given: $a \parallel b$, $m \perp a$
Prove: $m \perp b$ See margin.

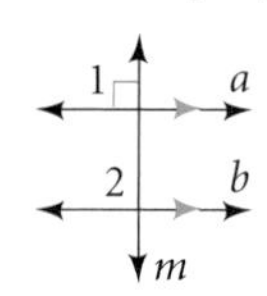
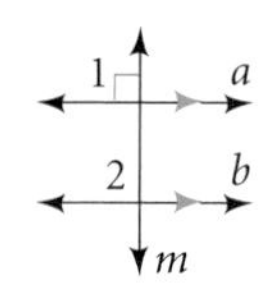
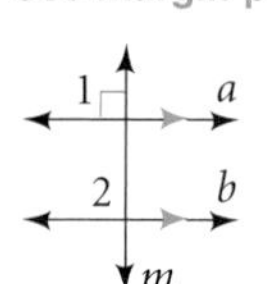

41. *Traffic Flow* You are designing the parking lot for a local shopping area, and are considering the two arrangements shown. Give the advantages and disadvantages of each. See margin.

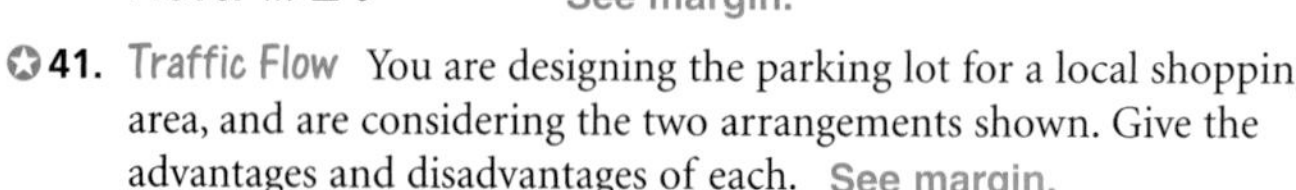

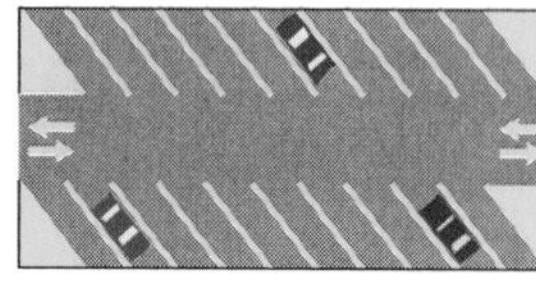

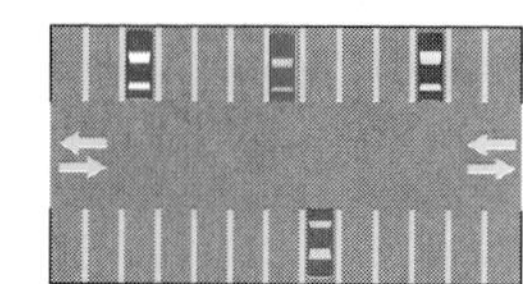

Exercises MIXED REVIEW

CONNECTING TO STUDENTS' WORLD Exercises 46–48 Have students design a similar survey. Get permission for them to distribute it at lunch to male and female students who play musical instruments. Have them collect the data and display it in a double bar graph like the one shown.

Exercise 49 Remind students that the circumference of a sphere is the length of a great circle.

Exercise 50b Have students draw a sketch to show how the pictures would fit on the poster.

GETTING READY FOR LESSON 7-2 These exercises prepare students to write flow proofs.

Wrap Up

THE BIG IDEA Ask students to define the special angle pairs they learned in this lesson and draw an illustration of each.

RETEACHING ACTIVITY Students draw a pair of parallel lines and a transversal. They measure one of the eight angles formed and then find the other seven. (Reteaching worksheet 7-1)

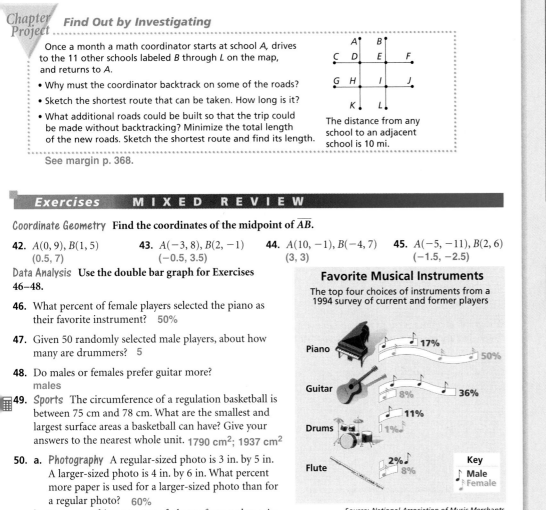

Chapter Project — Find Out by Investigating

Once a month a math coordinator starts at school *A*, drives to the 11 other schools labeled *B* through *L* on the map, and returns to *A*.

- Why must the coordinator backtrack on some of the roads?
- Sketch the shortest route that can be taken. How long is it?
- What additional roads could be built so that the trip could be made without backtracking? Minimize the total length of the new roads. Sketch the shortest route and find its length.

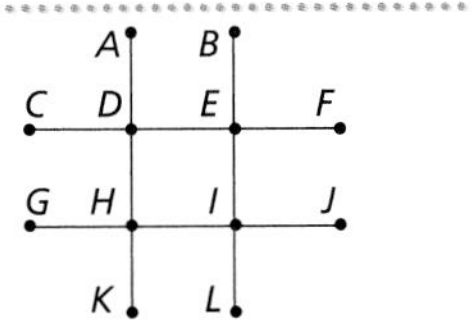

The distance from any school to an adjacent school is 10 mi.

See margin p. 368.

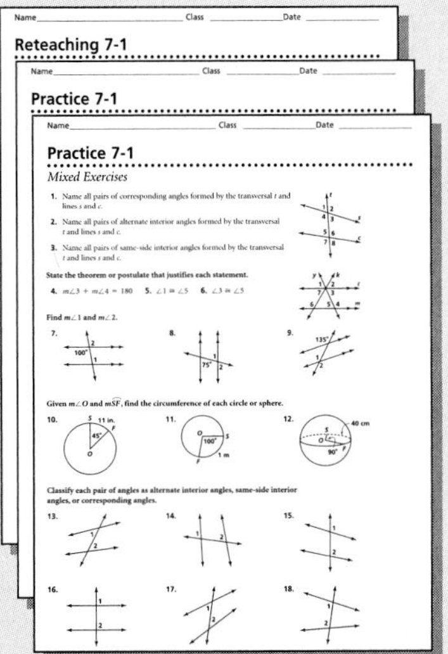

Exercises MIXED REVIEW

Coordinate Geometry **Find the coordinates of the midpoint of $\overline{AB}$.**

42. $A(0, 9), B(1, 5)$ (0.5, 7)

43. $A(-3, 8), B(2, -1)$ (−0.5, 3.5)

44. $A(10, -1), B(-4, 7)$ (3, 3)

45. $A(-5, -11), B(2, 6)$ (−1.5, −2.5)

Data Analysis **Use the double bar graph for Exercises 46–48.**

46. What percent of female players selected the piano as their favorite instrument? 50%

47. Given 50 randomly selected male players, about how many are drummers? 5

48. Do males or females prefer guitar more? males

49. *Sports* The circumference of a regulation basketball is between 75 cm and 78 cm. What are the smallest and largest surface areas a basketball can have? Give your answers to the nearest whole unit. 1790 cm^2; 1937 cm^2

50. **a.** *Photography* A regular-sized photo is 3 in. by 5 in. A larger-sized photo is 4 in. by 6 in. What percent more paper is used for a larger-sized photo than for a regular photo? 60%

b. You are making a poster of photos from a class trip. What is the greatest number of regular-sized photos you can fit on a 2 ft-by-3 ft poster? What is the greatest number of larger-sized photos you can fit? 56 photos; 36 photos

Favorite Musical Instruments

The top four choices of instruments from a 1994 survey of current and former players

Instrument	Male	Female
Piano	17%	50%
Guitar	36%	8%
Drums	11%	1%
Flute	2%	8%

Source: *National Association of Music Merchants*

Getting Ready for Lesson 7-2

Write the converse of each conditional statement.

51. If the sky is blue, then there are no clouds in the sky.
If there are no clouds in the sky, then the sky is blue.

52. If ℓ and *m* are parallel, then corresponding angles ∠1 and ∠2 are congruent.
52. If corres. angles ∠1 and ∠2 are ≅, then ℓ and *m* are ∥.

Lesson Quiz

Lesson Quiz is also available in Transparencies.

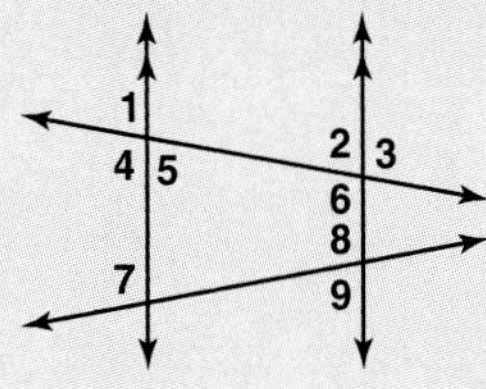

1. Classify each pair of angles as corresponding, alternate interior, or same-side interior.
   a. ∠7 and ∠8 corresponding
   b. ∠6 and ∠8 same-side interior
2. State the postulate or theorem that justifies each statement.
   a. ∠1 ≅ ∠2
   b. $m\angle 5 + m\angle 6 = 180$
   See back of book.

Math ToolboX

Students solve systems of equations in two variables using substitution. They will use this skill in the exercises given in the following lessons.

Example 1

Help students see that the solution of a linear system gives the coordinates of the point where the graphs of the equations intersect. It follows that two equations whose graphs are parallel have no point of intersection and no solution and that two equations whose graphs are the same line have infinitely many solutions.

Example 2

Point out that students need to solve one of the equations for x or y before they can substitute into the second equation.

ERROR ALERT! Students may not understand when a system has infinitely many solutions or no solution. **Remediation:** Make sure students understand that there are infinitely many solutions when a system simplifies to a true statement and there are no solutions when a system simplifies to a false statement.

ADDITIONAL PROBLEM Have students solve the following system of equations which has infinitely many solutions.

$$\begin{cases} 2x + 6y = 10 \\ x = 5 - 3y \end{cases}$$

Transparencies
5, 8, 9, 10

Math ToolboX — Algebra Review

Systems of Linear Equations

After Lesson 7-1

You can solve a system of equations in two variables by using substitution to create a one-variable equation.

Example 1

Solve the system: $y = 3x + 5$
$y = x + 1$

$y = x + 1$ ← Start with one equation.
$3x + 5 = x + 1$ ← Substitute $3x + 5$ for y.
$2x = -4$ ← Solve for x.
$x = -2$

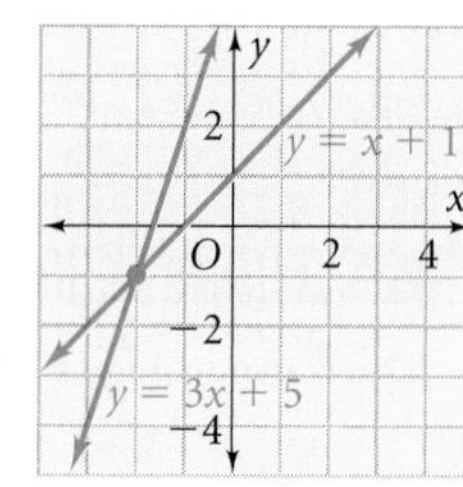

Substitute -2 for x in either equation and solve for y.

$y = x + 1$
$= (-2) + 1 = -1$

Since $x = -2$ and $y = -1$, the solution is $(-2, -1)$.

The graph of a linear system with *no solution* is two parallel lines, and the graph of a linear system with *infinitely many solutions* is one line.

Example 2

Solve the system: $x + y = 3$
$4x + 4y = 8$

$x + y = 3$
$x = 3 - y$ ← Solve the first equation for x.
$4(3 - y) + 4y = 8$ ← Substitute $3 - y$ for x in the second equation.
$12 - 4y + 4y = 8$ ← Simplify.
$12 = 8$ ← False!

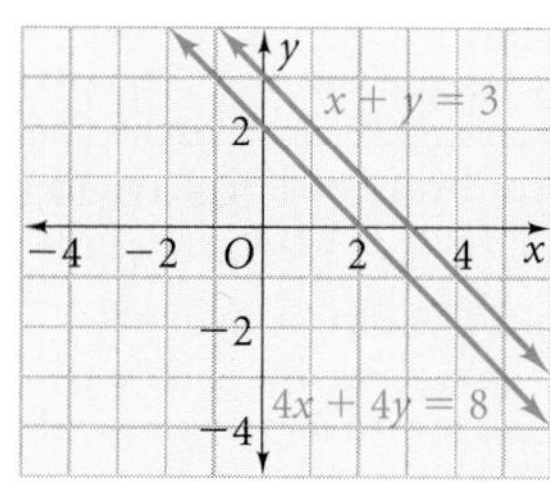

Since $12 = 8$ is a false statement, the system has no solution.

Solve each system of equations.

1. $y = x - 4$, $y = 3x + 2$ (−3, −7)
2. $2x - y = 8$, $x + 2y = 9$ (5, 2)
3. $3x + y = 4$, $-6x - 2y = 12$ no solution
4. $y = -x + 2$, $2y = 4 - 2x$ inf. many solutions
5. $y = 2x + 1$, $y = 3x - 7$ (8, 17)
6. $x - y = 4$, $3x - 3y = 6$ no solution

370

7-2 Teaching Notes

PROBLEM OF THE DAY

In how many different ways, ignoring rotations, can you divide a 4-by-4 square on grid paper into four congruent parts if all the divisions must be along grid lines. 5

Problem of the Day is also available in Transparencies.

CONNECTING TO PRIOR KNOWLEDGE Discuss examples of parallel lines (the lines on a football field or the sides of a street), and why knowing that they are parallel is important.

WORK TOGETHER

Have students work with a partner on this activity.

ALTERNATIVE METHOD Attach three straws to each other with paper clips or brads so that one straw crosses the other two straws. Identify a pair of corresponding angles formed by the straws. Turn the straws until the angles appear congruent. Ask what appears to be true of the straws.

THINK AND DISCUSS

Review the fact that the converse of a statement is written by interchanging the hypothesis with the conclusion.

Example 1

For a quick review of dilations and the properties of similarity transformations, refer students to Lesson 3-7.

Connections Woodworking . . . and more

7-2 Proving Lines Parallel

What You'll Learn

- Recognizing conditions that result in parallel lines
- Writing proofs that involve parallel lines

...And Why

To ensure parallel lines in construction and graphic arts

What You'll Need

- protractor
- ruler
- dot paper

2. $\overleftrightarrow{AB} \parallel \overleftrightarrow{A'C}$

TECHNOLOGY HINT

The Work Together could also be done using geometry software.

WORK TOGETHER

- Draw a segment on dot paper and label it $\overline{AB}$. Draw and label a point C not on $\overleftrightarrow{AB}$. Draw $\overline{BC}$.
- Translate $\angle ABC$ so that the image of B is C. Label the image $\angle A'CC'$.

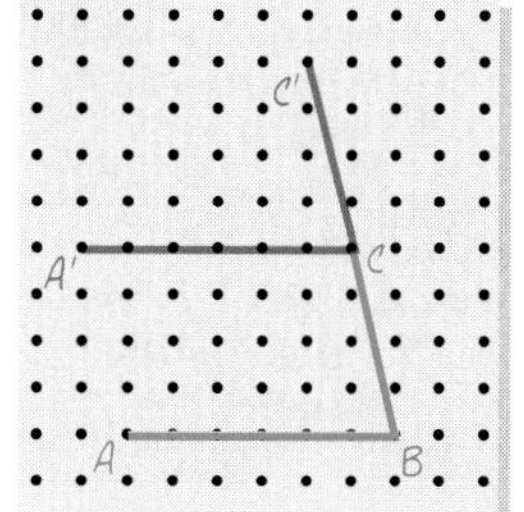

1. What is true of $\angle ABC$ and $\angle A'CC'$? Explain. $\angle ABC \cong \angle A'CC'$; translation is an isometry.
2. What appears to be true of $\overleftrightarrow{AB}$ and $\overleftrightarrow{A'C}$? See left.
3. Use your answers to Questions 1 and 2 to complete this statement: If two lines are cut by a transversal so that a pair of corresponding angles are congruent, then __?__. the lines are ∥

THINK AND DISCUSS

In the Work Together, you discovered that the converse of the Corresponding Angles Postulate is true.

Postulate 7-2 Converse of Corresponding Angles Postulate

If two lines are cut by a transversal so that a pair of corresponding angles are congruent, then the lines are parallel.

If $\angle 1 \cong \angle 2$, then $\ell \parallel m$.

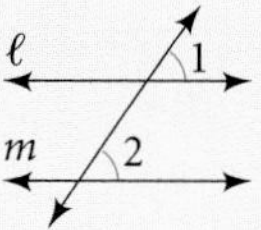

Example 1

Transformational Geometry $\overline{R'A'}$ is the image of $\overline{RA}$ under a dilation centered at X. Show that $\overline{RA} \parallel \overline{R'A'}$.

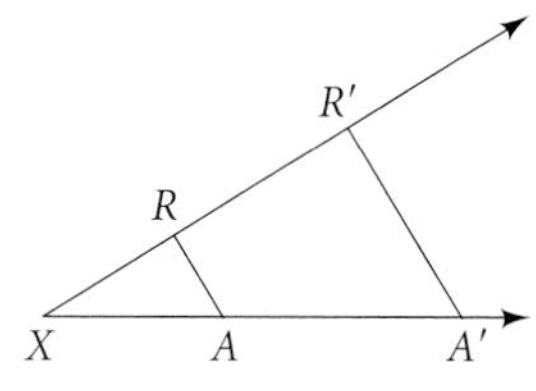

Because a dilation is a similarity transformation, $\triangle XRA \sim \triangle XR'A'$. Corresponding angles of similar polygons are congruent, so $\angle RAX \cong \angle R'A'X$. Since $\overrightarrow{XA'}$ is a transversal of $\overline{RA}$ and $\overline{R'A'}$, by the Converse of the Corresponding Angles Postulate, $\overline{RA} \parallel \overline{R'A'}$.

Lesson Planning Options

Prerequisite Skills

- Understanding the definition of a dilation
- Understanding the characteristics of prisms

Assignment Options for Exercises On Your Own

Core 1–3, 5–28, 30–35

Extension 4, 29, 36–37

Use Mixed Review to maintain skills.

Resources

Student Edition

Skills Handbook, pp. 660, 664
Extra Practice, p. 654
Glossary/Study Guide

Teaching Resources

Chapter Support File, Ch. 7
- Practice 7-2 (two worksheets)
- Reteaching 7-2
- Alternative Activity 7-2

Classroom Manager 7-2
Glossary, Spanish Resources

Transparencies

5, 8, 10, 78

Theorems 7-3 and 7-4 Make sure that students understand the difference between these theorems and the theorems presented in Lesson 7-1.

Discuss with students that the steps of a flow proof can be started at any step. They can even start with the conclusion and work backwards. Once all the steps are written down, arrows are used to show the flow of the statements and reasons.

VISUAL LEARNING Point out that in a flow proof, the statements are written in a box and the justifications are written underneath.

After students know that the Alternate Interior Angles Theorem and its converse are true, have them write the two statements as a biconditional.

Example 2

TACTILE LEARNING If possible, provide a physical model for students. A lightweight cardboard box such as a cereal box or a tissue box can be made to slant. Or, construct the frame of a prism using pipe cleaners or straws and tape.

Additional Examples

FOR EXAMPLE 1

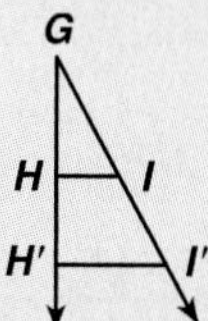

$\overline{H'I'}$ is the image of $\overline{HI}$ under a dilation centered at *G*. Show that $\overline{H'I'} \parallel \overline{HI}$. See back of book.

FOR EXAMPLE 2

Write a paragraph proof.

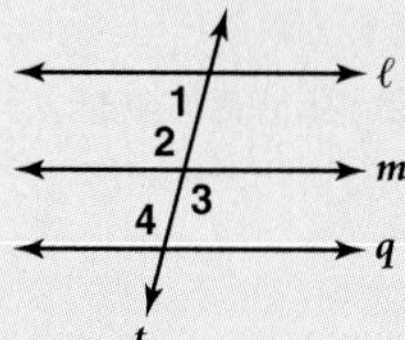

Given: $\angle 1$ and $\angle 2$ are supplementary; $m\angle 3 = m\angle 4$

Prove: $\ell \parallel q$ See back of book.

Discussion: *Write a two-column proof. Which proof do you prefer? Why?*

FOR EXAMPLE 3

What type of quadrilateral can have angles of 72°, 108°, 45°, and 135°? **a trapezoid**

Discussion: *With the given angles, is the quadrilateral necessarily a trapezoid?*

In Lesson 7-1, you proved the Alternate Interior Angles Theorem and the Same-Side Interior Angles Theorem by using the Corresponding Angles Postulate. You can prove the converses of these theorems by using the converse of the postulate.

Theorem 7-3
Converse of Alternate Interior Angles Theorem

If two lines are cut by a transversal so that a pair of alternate interior angles are congruent, then the lines are parallel.

If $\angle 1 \cong \angle 2$, then $\ell \parallel m$.

Theorem 7-4
Converse of Same-Side Interior Angles Theorem

If two lines are cut by a transversal so that a pair of same-side interior angles are supplementary, then the lines are parallel.

If $\angle 2$ and $\angle 4$ are supplementary, then $\ell \parallel m$.

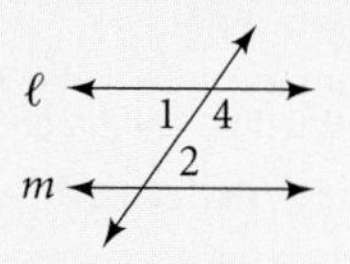

This is a **flow proof** of Theorem 7-3. Arrows show the logical connections between the statements. Reasons are written below the statements.

Flow Proof of Theorem 7-3

Given: $\angle 1 \cong \angle 2$

Prove: $\ell \parallel m$

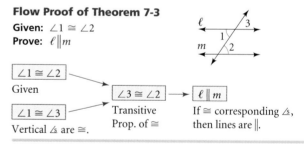

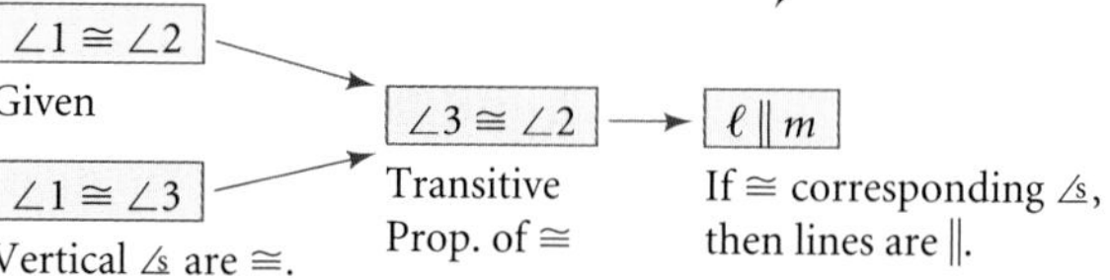

Example 2

Write a paragraph proof.

Given: $\angle BAC$ and $\angle ACD$ are supplementary.
$\angle CDF$ and $\angle DFE$ are supplementary.

Prove: $\overline{AB} \parallel \overline{EF}$

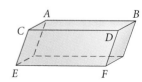

$\angle BAC$ and $\angle ACD$ are supplementary same-side interior angles formed by transversal $\overline{AC}$ with $\overline{AB}$ and $\overline{CD}$. So, $\overline{AB} \parallel \overline{CD}$. Similarly, $\angle CDF$ and $\angle DFE$ are supplementary same-side interior angles formed by transversal $\overline{DF}$ with $\overline{CD}$ and $\overline{EF}$. So, $\overline{CD} \parallel \overline{EF}$. Since $\overline{AB}$ and $\overline{EF}$ are parallel to the same segment, they are parallel to each other (Theorem 2-5).

4. Try This Write a flow proof for Example 2. See margin p. 374.

Example 3

Point out that the trapezoid formed is actually an isosceles trapezoid because the base angles are congruent.

CRITICAL THINKING Ask students to make conjectures about the angles of a parallelogram and the angles of an isosceles trapezoid. Then have them draw an example of each type of figure and measure the angles to test their conjectures.

Example 4 **Relating to the Real World** 

ESL Students may be unfamiliar with the terms "miter box" and "backsaw." The picture should help to illustrate these terms. All students need to understand is that these tools can be used to cut 45° angles.

EXTENSION Have students prove that if two lines are cut by a transversal so that a pair of alternate exterior angles (or same-side exterior angles) are congruent, then the lines are parallel.

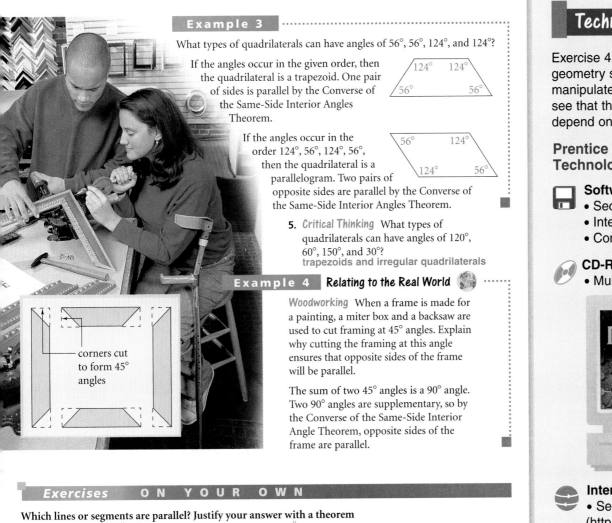

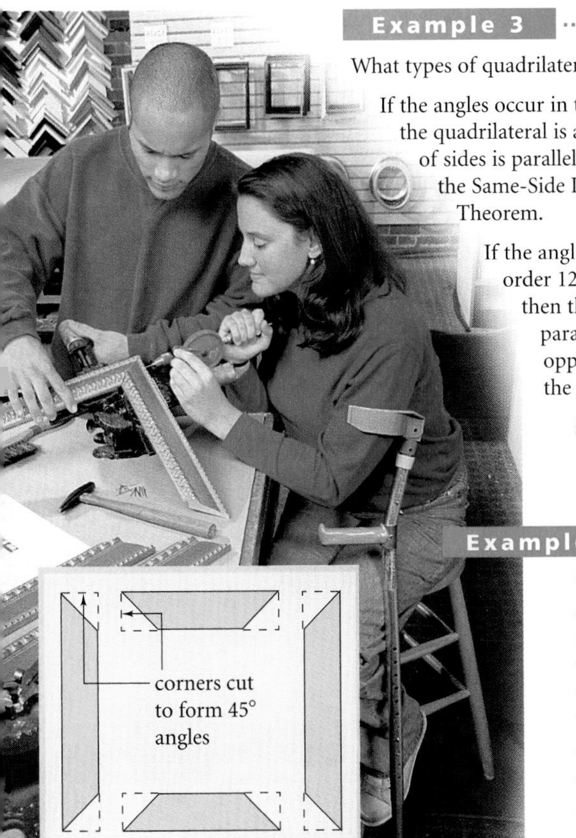

Example 3

What types of quadrilaterals can have angles of 56°, 56°, 124°, and 124°?

If the angles occur in the given order, then the quadrilateral is a trapezoid. One pair of sides is parallel by the Converse of the Same-Side Interior Angles Theorem.

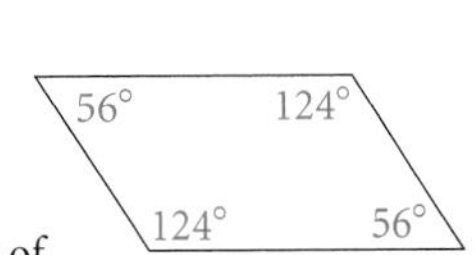

If the angles occur in the order 124°, 56°, 124°, 56°, then the quadrilateral is a parallelogram. Two pairs of opposite sides are parallel by the Converse of the Same-Side Interior Angles Theorem.

5. *Critical Thinking* What types of quadrilaterals can have angles of 120°, 60°, 150°, and 30°? trapezoids and irregular quadrilaterals

Example 4 **Relating to the Real World** 

Woodworking When a frame is made for a painting, a miter box and a backsaw are used to cut framing at 45° angles. Explain why cutting the framing at this angle ensures that opposite sides of the frame will be parallel.

The sum of two 45° angles is a 90° angle. Two 90° angles are supplementary, so by the Converse of the Same-Side Interior Angle Theorem, opposite sides of the frame are parallel.

Technology Options

Exercise 4 can be done using geometry software. Students can manipulate the original triangle to see that the parallelogram does not depend on the type of triangle.

Prentice Hall Technology

Software
- Secondary Math Lab Toolkit™
- Integrated Math Lab 36
- Computer Item Generator 7-2

CD-ROM
- Multimedia Geometry Lab 7

Internet
- See the Prentice Hall site. (http://www.phschool.com)

Exercises ON YOUR OWN

Which lines or segments are parallel? Justify your answer with a theorem or postulate. 2. $\overline{CA} \parallel \overline{HR}$; If ≅ corres. ∠s, then lines are ∥.

1. 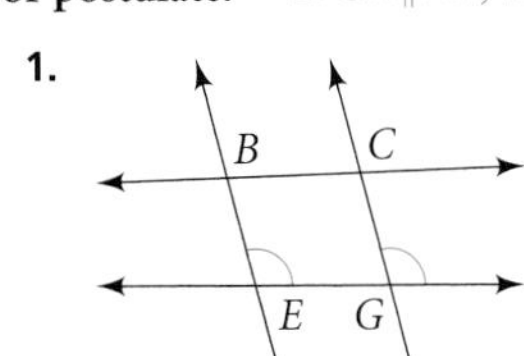

2. 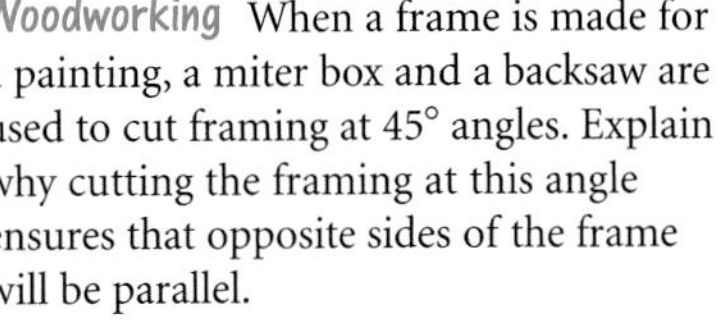
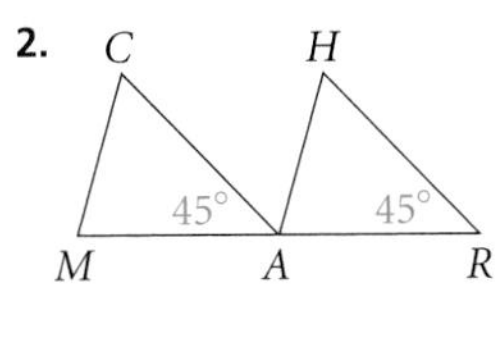

3. 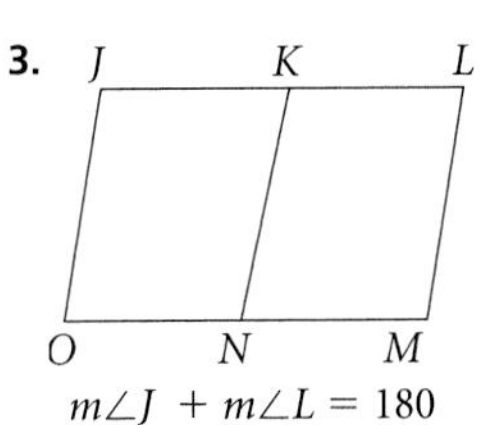

$m\angle J + m\angle L = 180$

$\overleftrightarrow{BE} \parallel \overleftrightarrow{CG}$; If ≅ corres. ∠s, then lines are ∥.

3. $\overline{JO} \parallel \overline{LM}$; If supplementary same-side int. ∠s, then lines are ∥.

Exercises ON YOUR OWN

ALTERNATIVE ASSESSMENT Exercise 4 You can use this exercise to help you assess students' understanding of Theorem 7-3. Check that they recognize that the diagonal is a transversal passing through both pairs of opposite sides and that two pairs of congruent corresponding angles of the triangles form congruent pairs of alternate interior angles.

Exercises 5–14 Make sure that students state the entire theorem or postulate they use to justify their answers.

ERROR ALERT! Exercise 15 Some students may not realize that they are using a theorem when they conclude that $\angle 1 \cong \angle 6$ or $\angle 9 \cong \angle 12$. **Remediation:** Have students review vertical angles in Lesson 1-7.

Exercise 16 Have students use the flow proof on page 372 as a model.

Exercises 17–18 Encourage students to start by writing a plan for each proof. You may want to have students complete these exercises in groups.

pages 371–373 Think and Discuss

4.

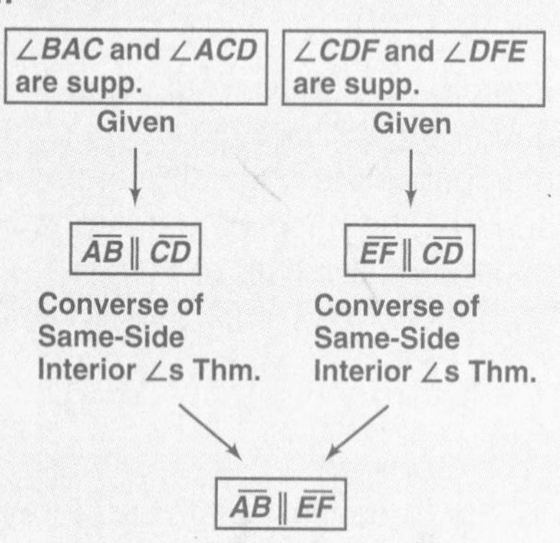

pages 373–376 On Your Own

4. 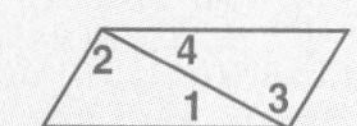

The 2 △s are ≅, so ∠1 ≅ ∠4 and ∠2 ≅ ∠3. These 2 pairs of alt. interior angles are ≅; therefore, opp. sides of the quadrilateral are ∥.

5. If ≅ corres. ∠s, then lines are ∥.
7. If supplementary same-side int. ∠s, then lines are ∥.
9. If ≅ alt. int. ∠s, then lines are ∥.
11. If supplementary same-side int. ∠s, then lines are ∥.
12. If ≅ corres. ∠s, then lines are ∥.
14. If ≅ corres. ∠s, then lines are ∥.

20a. Each of the 2 lines forms a right angle with the same line. All right ∠s are ≅. Then the corres. angles are ≅, so the lines are ∥.

4. *Paper cutting* Use the method shown in the diagram to cut out two congruent triangles. Join the two triangles so that they form a parallelogram. Use what you learned in this lesson to **justify** that the figure is indeed a parallelogram. See margin.

Refer to the diagram. Use the given information to determine which lines, if any, must be parallel. If any lines are parallel, use a theorem or postulate to tell why. 5–14. See margin for reasoning.

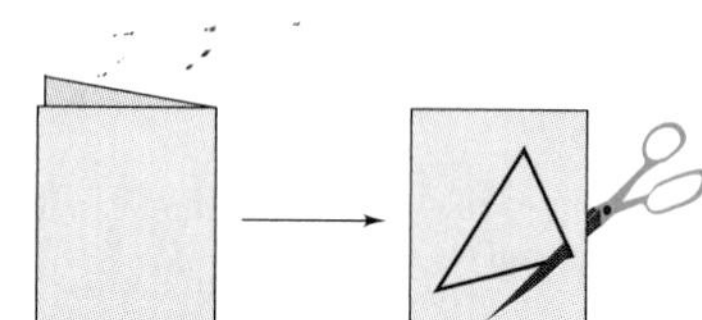

Exs. 5–18

5. $\angle 1 \cong \angle 3$ $a \parallel b$
6. $\angle 1 \cong \angle 6$ no ∥ lines
7. $\angle 6$ is supplementary to $\angle 7$. $a \parallel b$
8. $\angle 11 \cong \angle 7$ no ∥ lines
9. $\angle 5 \cong \angle 10$ $\ell \parallel m$
10. $m\angle 7 = 70, m\angle 9 = 110$ no ∥ lines
11. $\angle 2$ is supplementary to $\angle 3$. $a \parallel b$
12. $\angle 8 \cong \angle 6$ $a \parallel b$
13. $\angle 9 \cong \angle 3$ no ∥ lines
14. $\angle 2 \cong \angle 10$ $\ell \parallel m$

15. If $\angle 1 \cong \angle 12$, what theorems or postulates can you use to show that $\ell \parallel m$? Vertical ∠s are ≅, and if ≅ corres. ∠s, then lines are ∥.

16. *Preparing for Proof* Use this Plan for Proof to write a flow proof. Refer to the diagram at the right. See back of book.

Given: $\ell \parallel m$, $\angle 4 \cong \angle 10$

Prove: $a \parallel b$

Plan for Proof: Show that $a \parallel b$ by showing that the corresponding angles $\angle 2$ and $\angle 4$ are congruent. Show that they are congruent by showing that they are both congruent to $\angle 10$.

Refer to the diagram for Exercises 5–18 to write a flow proof. 17–18. Answers may vary. See back of book.

17. **Given:** $a \parallel b$, $\angle 7 \cong \angle 10$
Prove: $\ell \parallel m$

18. **Given:** $\ell \parallel m$, $\angle 7$ and $\angle 12$ are supplementary.
Prove: $a \parallel b$

19. *Carpentry* A *T-bevel* is a tool used by carpenters to draw congruent angles. By loosening the locking lever, the carpenter can adjust the angle. Explain how the carpenter knows that the two lines that he has drawn using the T-bevel are parallel.
If corres. angles are ≅, then the lines are ∥.

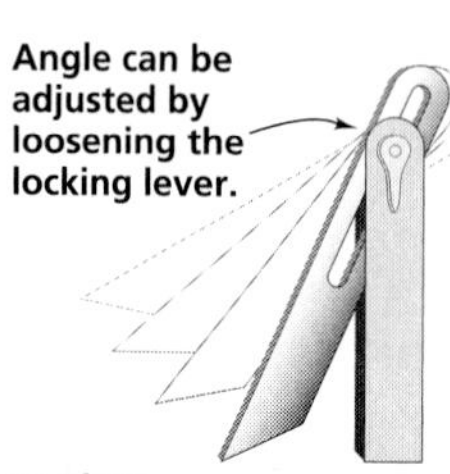

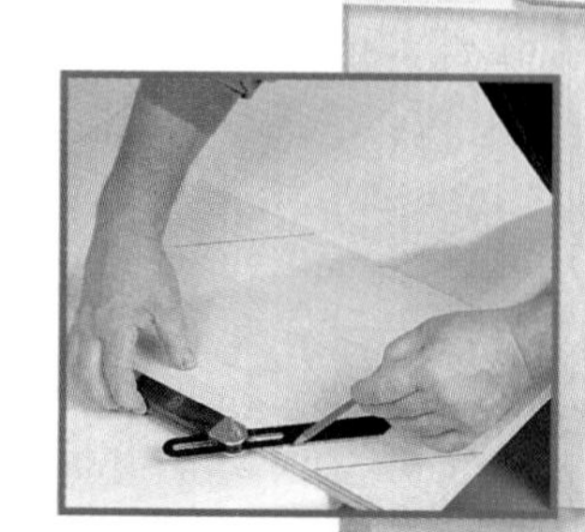

WRITING Exercise 20a This is the converse of Exercise 40 in Lesson 7-1.

GEOMETRY IN 3 DIMENSIONS Exercise 20 b–c Provide physical models for students. Any of the prism models you used in Chapter 6 would work well.

STANDARDIZED TEST TIP Exercise 21 Students need to remember that the sum of the measures of the angles of a quadrilateral is 360.

Exercises 25–27 Ask students to identify the information in the diagrams that they did not use. Discuss how to identify extraneous information.

OPEN-ENDED Exercise 29b Students may want to cut out pictures of furniture from magazines or catalogs and then identify the parallel lines in them.

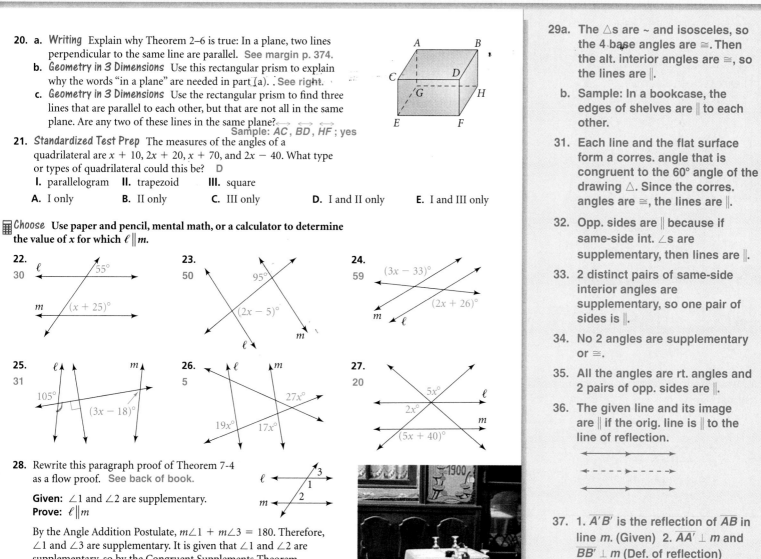

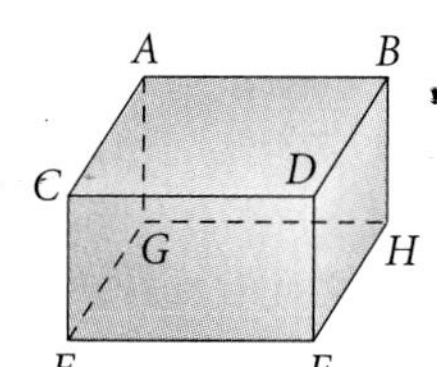

20. **a.** *Writing* Explain why Theorem 2-6 is true: In a plane, two lines perpendicular to the same line are parallel. See margin p. 374.

b. *Geometry in 3 Dimensions* Use this rectangular prism to explain why the words "in a plane" are needed in part (a). See right.

c. *Geometry in 3 Dimensions* Use the rectangular prism to find three lines that are parallel to each other, but that are not all in the same plane. Are any two of these lines in the same plane? Sample: $\overleftrightarrow{AC}$, $\overleftrightarrow{BD}$, $\overleftrightarrow{HF}$; yes

21. *Standardized Test Prep* The measures of the angles of a quadrilateral are $x + 10$, $2x + 20$, $x + 70$, and $2x - 40$. What type or types of quadrilateral could this be? D

I. parallelogram **II.** trapezoid **III.** square

A. I only **B.** II only **C.** III only **D.** I and II only **E.** I and III only

Choose Use paper and pencil, mental math, or a calculator to determine the value of x for which $\ell \parallel m$.

22. 30

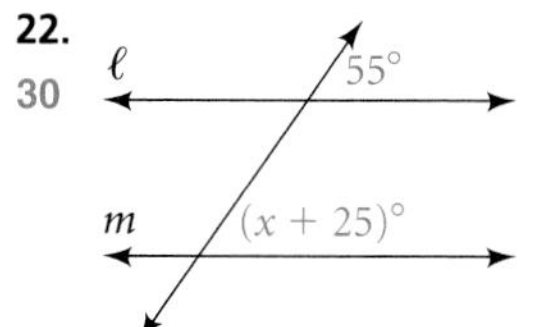

23. 50

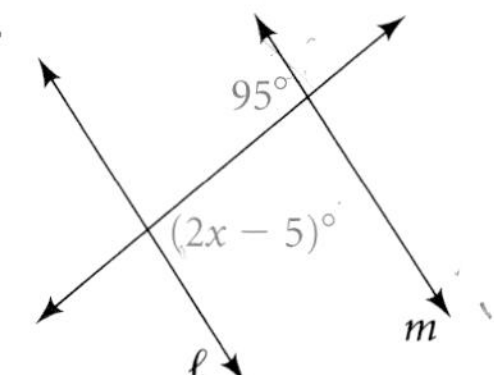

24. 59

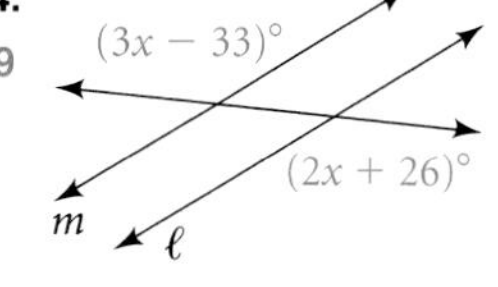
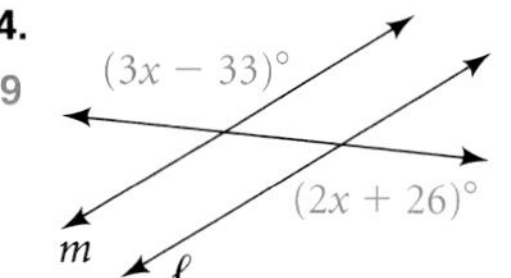

25. 31

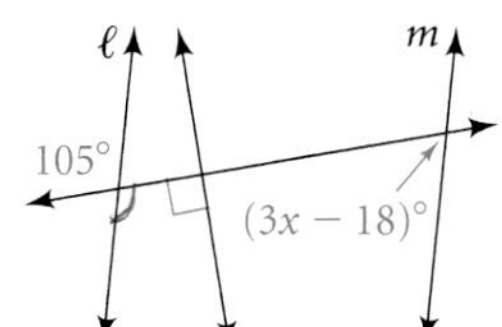

26. 5

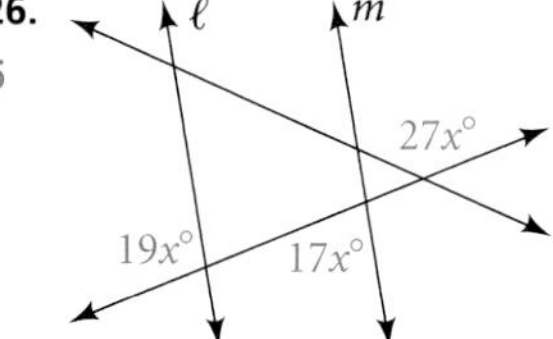

27. 20

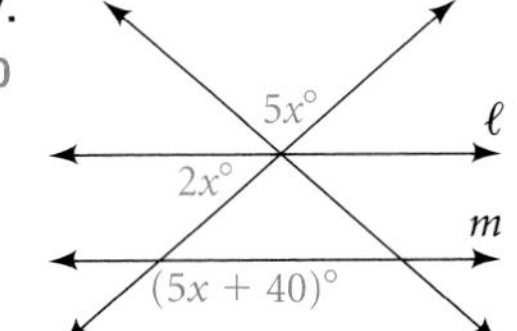

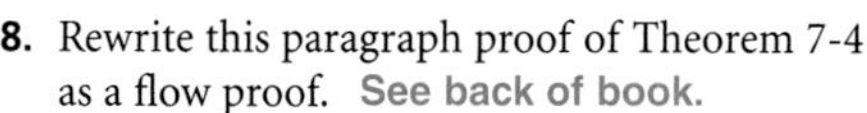

28. Rewrite this paragraph proof of Theorem 7-4 as a flow proof. See back of book.

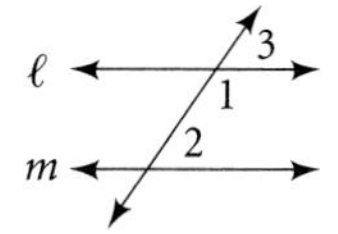

Given: $\angle 1$ and $\angle 2$ are supplementary.
Prove: $\ell \parallel m$

By the Angle Addition Postulate, $m\angle 1 + m\angle 3 = 180$. Therefore, $\angle 1$ and $\angle 3$ are supplementary. It is given that $\angle 1$ and $\angle 2$ are supplementary, so by the Congruent Supplements Theorem, $\angle 2 \cong \angle 3$. $\angle 2$ and $\angle 3$ are corresponding angles, so by the Converse of the Corresponding Angles Postulate, $\ell \parallel m$.

29. **a.** *Furniture* The legs of the chairs shown form similar isosceles triangles. Explain how you know that the seat of the chair is parallel to the ground. a–b. See margin.

b. *Open-ended* Give an example of another type of furniture that shows parallel lines. Include a sketch showing the lines.

29a. The △s are ~ and isosceles, so the 4 base angles are ≅. Then the alt. interior angles are ≅, so the lines are ∥.

b. Sample: In a bookcase, the edges of shelves are ∥ to each other.

31. Each line and the flat surface form a corres. angle that is congruent to the 60° angle of the drawing △. Since the corres. angles are ≅, the lines are ∥.

32. Opp. sides are ∥ because if same-side int. ∠s are supplementary, then lines are ∥.

33. 2 distinct pairs of same-side interior angles are supplementary, so one pair of sides is ∥.

34. No 2 angles are supplementary or ≅.

35. All the angles are rt. angles and 2 pairs of opp. sides are ∥.

36. The given line and its image are ∥ if the orig. line is ∥ to the line of reflection.

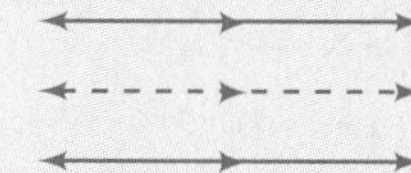

37. 1. $\overline{A'B'}$ is the reflection of $\overline{AB}$ in line m. (Given) 2. $\overline{AA'} \perp m$ and $\overline{BB'} \perp m$ (Def. of reflection) 3. $\overline{AA'} \parallel \overline{BB'}$ (In a plane, 2 lines ⊥ to 3rd are ∥.)

COORDINATE GEOMETRY Exercise 30 Students may want to refer to the Math Toolbox on page 370 for solving systems of equations .

Exercises 32–35 Make sure that students understand how these exercises differ from Example 3. Here the order of the angles is given.

Exercises MIXED REVIEW

Exercises 38–41 Make sure students understand that a semicircular region is a region bounded by a semicircle and a diameter.

Exercise 42 Students may want to research the history of the Olympic torch and present their findings to the class.

GETTING READY FOR LESSON 7-3 These exercises prepare students to construct parallel and perpendicular lines.

Wrap Up

THE BIG IDEA Ask students: *Summarize the various ways you can prove that two lines are parallel.*

RETEACHING ACTIVITY Students fill in the missing steps of a partially completed flow proof. Then they write a flow proof. (Reteaching worksheet 7-2)

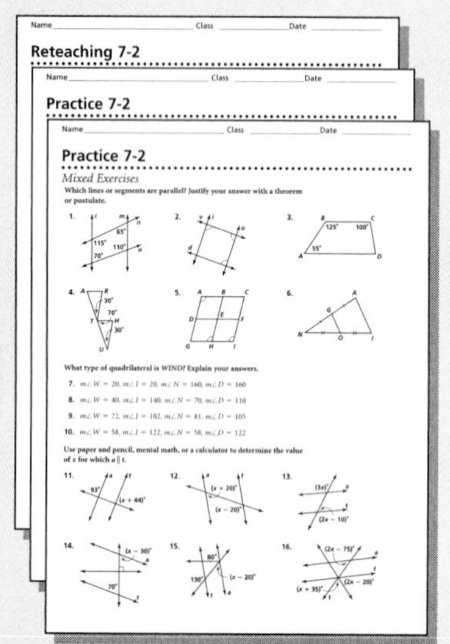

Lesson Quiz

Lesson Quiz is also available in Transparencies.

For Exercises 1–3, use the given information to determine which lines are parallel.

1. $\angle 1 \cong \angle 4$ $r \parallel t$
2. $\angle 7 \cong \angle 4$ $s \parallel t$
3. $\angle 5$ and $\angle 6$ are supplementary. $r \parallel s$
4. Write a paragraph proof.
   Given: $m \parallel n$, $\angle 2 \cong \angle 3$
   Prove: $p \parallel q$

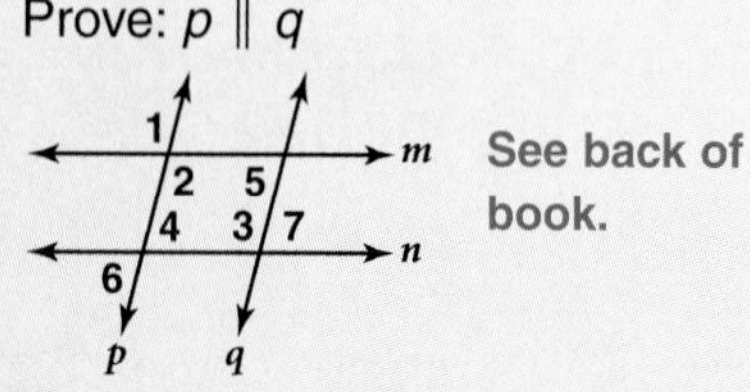

See back of book.

30. *Coordinate Geometry* Given the equations of two lines in the coordinate plane, explain how you can prove that they are parallel. Show that the slopes are =.
31. *Drafting* Explain why the lines shown in the diagram are parallel. See margin p. 375.

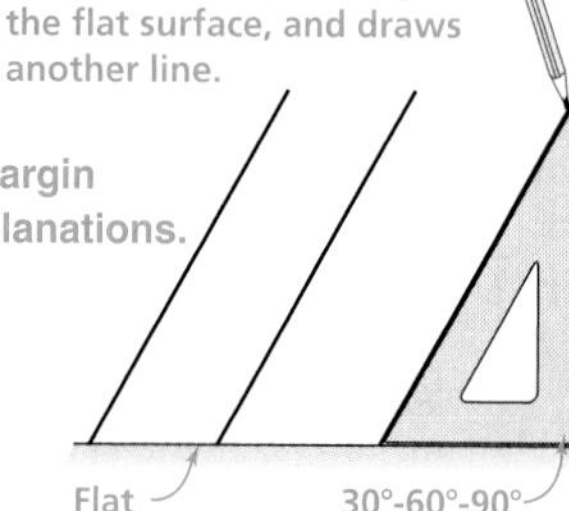

What type of quadrilateral is *PLAN*? Explain your answers. 32–35. See margin p. 375 for explanations.

32. $m\angle P = 72, m\angle L = 108, m\angle A = 72, m\angle N = 108$ parallelogram
33. $m\angle P = 59, m\angle L = 37, m\angle A = 143, m\angle N = 121$ trapezoid
34. $m\angle P = 67, m\angle L = 120, m\angle A = 73, m\angle N = 100$ irregular quadrilateral
35. $m\angle P = 90, m\angle L = 90, m\angle A = 90, m\angle N = 90$ rectangle
36. *Transformations* Under what circumstances will a line be parallel to its image under a reflection? Draw a diagram to support your explanation. See margin p. 375.
37. *Transformations* Write a two-column proof. (*Hint:* Refer to the definition of a reflection in Lesson 3-1.)

    Given: $\overline{A'B'}$ is the reflection image of $\overline{AB}$ in line m.
    Prove: $\overline{AA'} \parallel \overline{BB'}$ See margin p. 375.

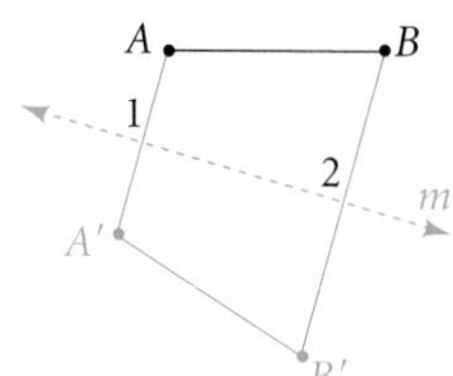

Exercises MIXED REVIEW

Find the area of a semicircular region with the given radius. Round your answer to the nearest tenth.

38. 8 in. 100.5 in.^2
39. 10 cm 157.1 cm^2
40. 4 ft 25.1 ft^2
41. 1.2 m 2.3 m^2
42. a. *Olympics* The torch used for the 1996 Olympic Games in Atlanta is approximately cylindrical. Its length is 32 in., and its diameter is 2.25 in. What is its volume? Round your answer to the nearest whole unit. 127 in.^3
    b. The torch has 22 equally-spaced prongs around the top representing the number of cities that have hosted Olympic Games. How many degrees apart are the prongs? Round your answer to the nearest tenth. 16.4°

Coretta Scott King carried the Olympic torch in 1996.

Getting Ready for Lesson 7-3

Constructions **Draw each figure and then use a compass and straightedge to construct a figure congruent to the one you drew.**

43. an obtuse angle
44. a segment
45. a triangle

43–45. Check students' work.

7-3 Teaching Notes

PROBLEM OF THE DAY

The circumference of the base of a cylinder is 8 in. and the height is 6 in. A spiral stripe is drawn around the cylinder exactly once. It reaches the top directly above the spot where it left the bottom. What is the length of the stripe? 10 in.

Problem of the Day is also available in Transparencies.

CONNECTING TO PRIOR KNOWLEDGE Have students draw an angle, then use a compass and a straightedge to draw an angle congruent to it. Discuss the steps they used.

THINK AND DISCUSS

ESL **VISUAL LEARNING** Demonstrate Construction 5 and the other constructions in this lesson on the board. Have students model each construction at their desks. As you perform each step, verbalize your actions using precise terminology.

Question 1 Point out that constructions must be justified before they can be used in other constructions.

Example 1

Make sure that students draw the segments representing rays longer than the larger segment. In this example, $\overrightarrow{AZ}$ and $\overrightarrow{AB}$ should be drawn with "lengths" greater than *a*.

Connections Technology . . . and more

7-3 Constructing Parallel and Perpendicular Lines

What You'll Learn

- Constructing parallel and perpendicular lines

...And Why

To be able to use parallels and perpendiculars in arts and crafts

What You'll Need

straightedge, compass

THINK AND DISCUSS

Part 1

Constructing Parallel Lines

You can use what you know about corresponding angles and parallel lines to construct parallel lines.

Construction 5
Parallel through a Point Not on a Line

Construct a line parallel to a given line and through a given point not on the line.

Given: Line ℓ and point N not on ℓ

Step 1
Label two points H and J on ℓ. Draw $\overleftrightarrow{HN}$.

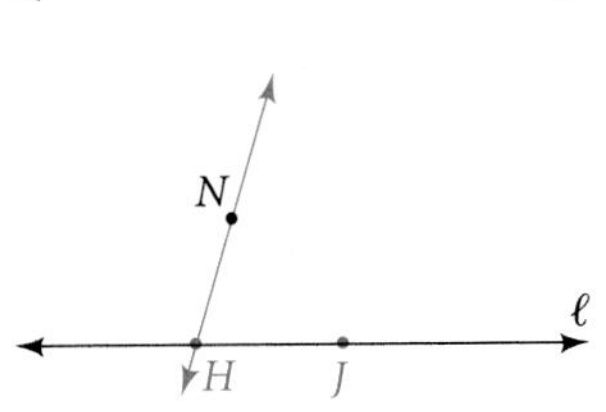

Step 2
Construct $\angle 1$ with vertex at N so that $\angle 1 \cong \angle JHN$ and the two angles are corresponding angles. Label the line you just constructed m.

$\ell \parallel m$

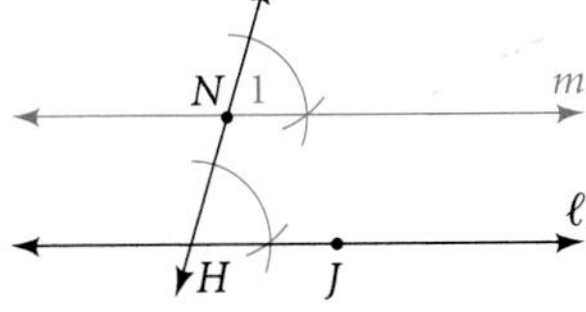

QUICK REVIEW

Instructions for constructing congruent angles are on page 40.

1. Explain why lines ℓ and m are parallel.
If ≅ corres. ∠s, then lines are ∥.

Example 1

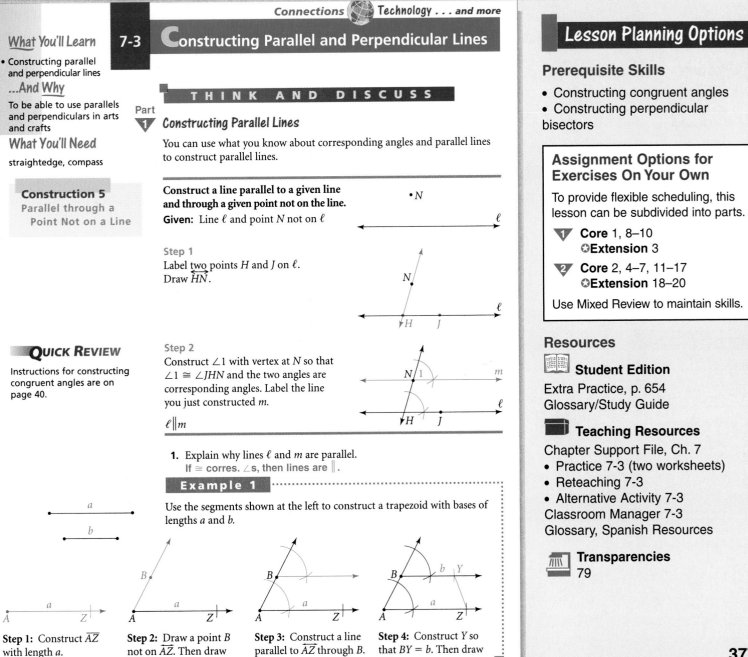

Use the segments shown at the left to construct a trapezoid with bases of lengths a and b.

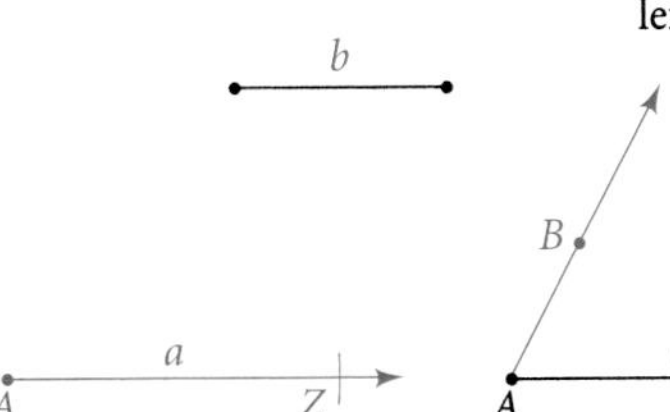

Step 1: Construct $\overline{AZ}$ with length a.

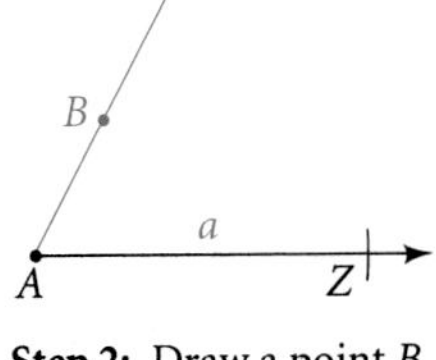

Step 2: Draw a point B not on $\overline{AZ}$. Then draw $\overline{AB}$.

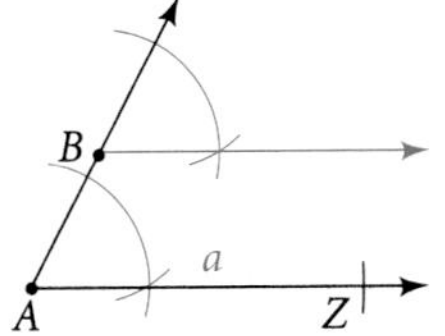

Step 3: Construct a line parallel to $\overline{AZ}$ through B.

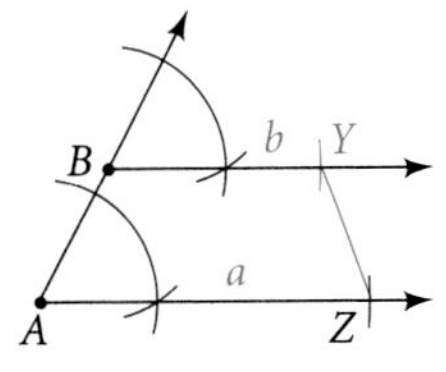

Step 4: Construct Y so that $BY = b$. Then draw $\overline{YZ}$. $ZABY$ is a trapezoid.

Lesson Planning Options

Prerequisite Skills

- Constructing congruent angles
- Constructing perpendicular bisectors

Assignment Options for Exercises On Your Own

To provide flexible scheduling, this lesson can be subdivided into parts.

1 **Core** 1, 8–10
✪**Extension** 3

2 **Core** 2, 4–7, 11–17
✪**Extension** 18–20

Use Mixed Review to maintain skills.

Resources

Student Edition
Extra Practice, p. 654
Glossary/Study Guide

Teaching Resources
Chapter Support File, Ch. 7
- Practice 7-3 (two worksheets)
- Reteaching 7-3
- Alternative Activity 7-3

Classroom Manager 7-3
Glossary, Spanish Resources

Transparencies
79

CRITICAL THINKING Question 3 You may want to have students perform the construction of a perpendicular bisector given on page 42 for practice.

Construction 6 Have students observe that once points *A* and *B* are found, they can use the method for constructing a perpendicular bisector of a segment.

ERROR ALERT! Some students may find that the arcs they draw from points *A* and *B* do not intersect. **Remediation:** Have students open the compass to a wider position after Step 1 and remind them not to squeeze the compass which will change its position.

A paper-folding method for this construction is presented in Exercise 17.

Additional Examples

FOR EXAMPLE 1

Use the segments shown in Example 1 to construct a parallelogram with sides of lengths *a* and *b*.

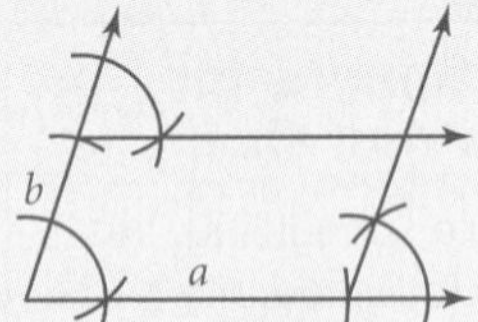

FOR EXAMPLE 2

Use geometry software to construct an isosceles triangle in which the base and the height have the same length.

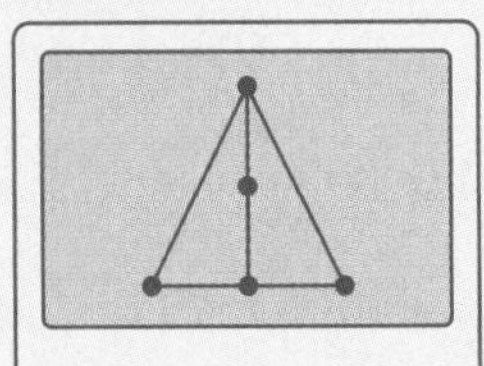

Part 2

Constructing Perpendicular Lines

The two constructions that follow are based on Theorem 4-13: If a point is equidistant from the endpoints of a segment, then it is on the perpendicular bisector of the segment.

2. Explain why $\overleftrightarrow{AB}$ must be the perpendicular bisector of $\overline{CD}$. **2. A and B are equidistant from the endpts. of $\overline{CD}$.**

3. **Critical Thinking** Turn to page 42 and study the method for constructing a perpendicular bisector of a segment. Explain why that construction works. **Intersections of the 2 arcs are equidistant from the endpts. of the segment.**

Construction 6
Perpendicular through a Point on a Line

Construct the perpendicular to a given line at a given point on the line.

Given: Point *P* on line ℓ

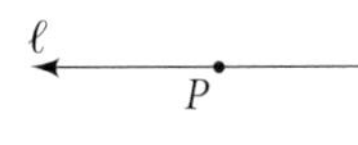

Step 1
Place the compass tip on *P*. Draw arcs intersecting ℓ in two points. Label the points *A* and *B*.

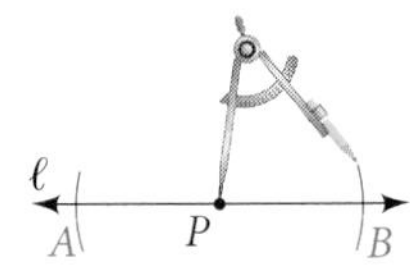

Step 2
Open the compass wider. With the compass tip on *A*, draw an arc above point *P*.

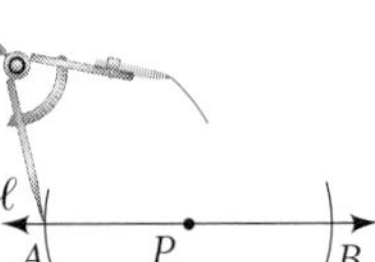

Step 3
Without changing the compass setting, place the compass tip on *B*. Draw an arc that intersects the arc from Step 2. Label the point of intersection *C*.

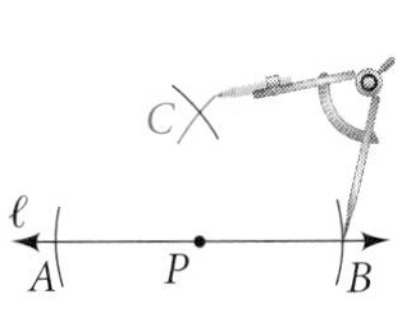

Step 4
Draw $\overleftrightarrow{CP}$.

$\overleftrightarrow{CP} \perp \ell$

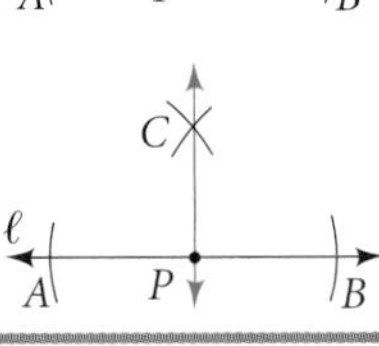

Justification of Construction 6

You constructed *A* and *B* so that $AP = BP$. You constructed *C* so that $AC = BC$. Because *P* and *C* are both equidistant from the endpoints of $\overline{AB}$, $\overleftrightarrow{CP}$ is the perpendicular bisector of $\overline{AB}$. So $\overleftrightarrow{CP} \perp \ell$.

4. **Try This** Draw a line $\overleftrightarrow{EF}$. Construct a line $\overleftrightarrow{FG}$ so that $\overleftrightarrow{EF} \perp \overleftrightarrow{FG}$. **See back of book.**

MAKING CONNECTIONS There are some figures that cannot be constructed. This puzzled Greek mathematicians, and it was not until the nineteenth century that mathematicians proved that you cannot construct a square with the same area as a given circle, a cube with twice the area of a given cube, or an angle one-third the measure of a given angle.

Construction 7 Have students compare Constructions 6 and 7 to see that the only difference is where the compass tip is placed at the start of each construction. The rest of the steps are the same.

American artist Sol LeWitt creates wall-sized drawings that contain geometric figures such as arcs and perpendicular lines. To create arcs, he uses simple, large-scale compasses like the one shown below. He often employs local students to assist in creating his artwork. The two works shown here were on display at the Addison Gallery in Andover, Massachusetts.

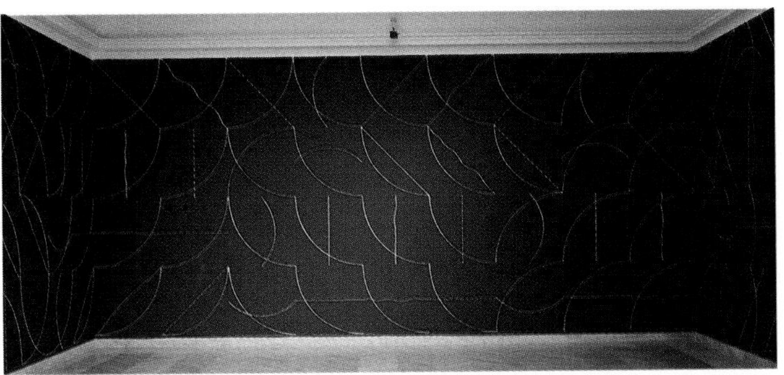

Construction 7
Perpendicular through a Point Not on a Line

Construct the perpendicular to a given line from a given point not on the line.

Given: line ℓ and point R not on ℓ

Step 1
Open your compass to a distance greater than the distance from R to ℓ. With the compass tip on R, draw an arc that intersects ℓ at two points. Label the points E and F.

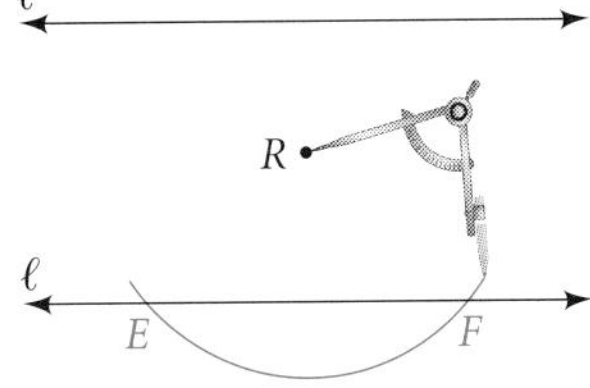

Step 2
Keep the same compass setting. Place the compass point on E and make an arc.

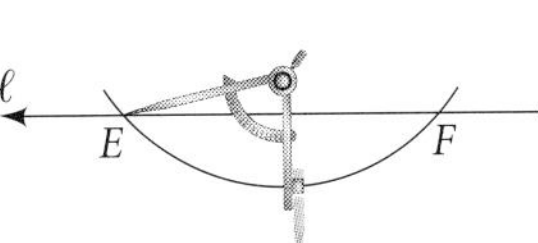

Step 3
Keep the same compass setting. With the compass tip on F, draw an arc that intersects the arc from Step 2. Label the point of intersection G.

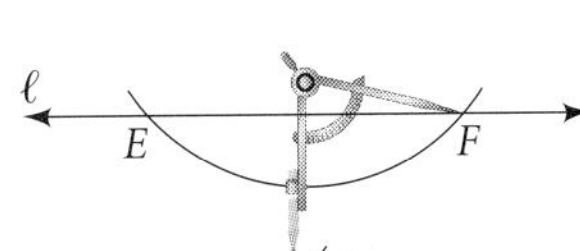

Step 4
Draw $\overleftrightarrow{GR}$.

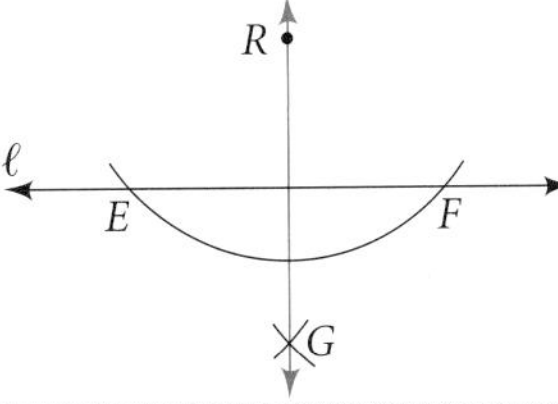

$\overleftrightarrow{GR} \perp \ell$

Technology Options

Any of the constructions in the Exercises On Your Own may be done using construction software. For Exercise 5, students may construct the diagram that is shown.

Prentice Hall Technology

Software
- Secondary Math Lab Toolkit™
- Computer Item Generator 7-3

CD-ROM
- Multimedia Geometry Lab 7

Internet
- See the Prentice Hall site. (http://www.phschool.com)

AUDITORY LEARNING Question 6 Have students work with a partner. Have one student explain why Construction 6 works. Then have the other student explain why Construction 7 works.

Example 2

The diagram shows the construction of a right triangle starting with a leg that is vertical. The same steps can be used to construct a right triangle when the segment in Step 1 is in any position.

Exercises ON YOUR OWN

Exercise 1 Make sure that students have use of a compass and straightedge for this and other exercises in this lesson. You may want to have students work on these exercises in class so they will not need to bring a compass home.

TRANSFORMATIONS Exercise 2 Help students see that they can find the image of $\overline{PQ}$ by first using Construction 7 to draw a line perpendicular to ℓ through P and a line perpendicular to ℓ through Q.

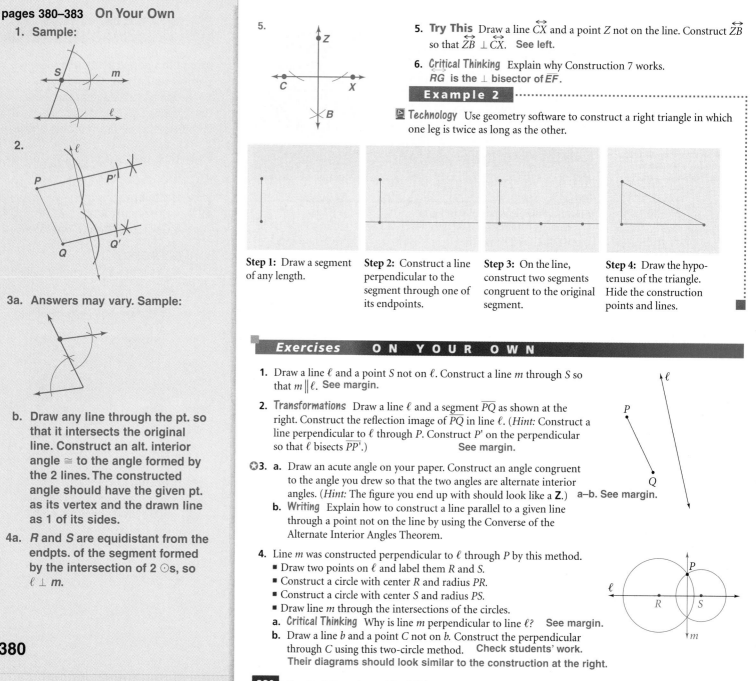

pages 380–383 On Your Own

1. Sample:

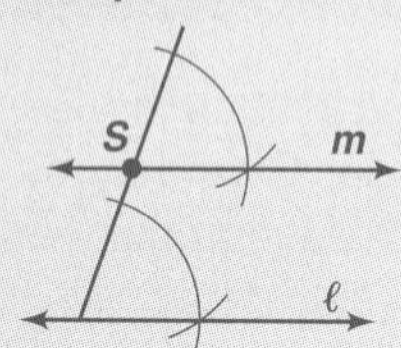

2.

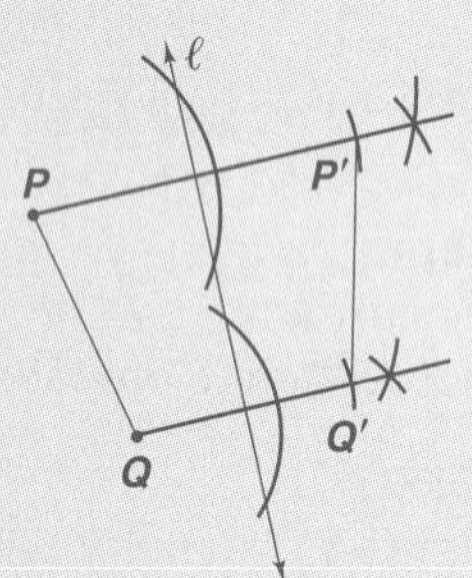

3a. Answers may vary. Sample:

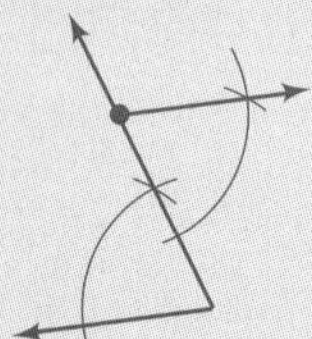

b. Draw any line through the pt. so that it intersects the original line. Construct an alt. interior angle ≅ to the angle formed by the 2 lines. The constructed angle should have the given pt. as its vertex and the drawn line as 1 of its sides.

4a. *R* and *S* are equidistant from the endpts. of the segment formed by the intersection of 2 ⊙s, so $\ell \perp m$.

5.

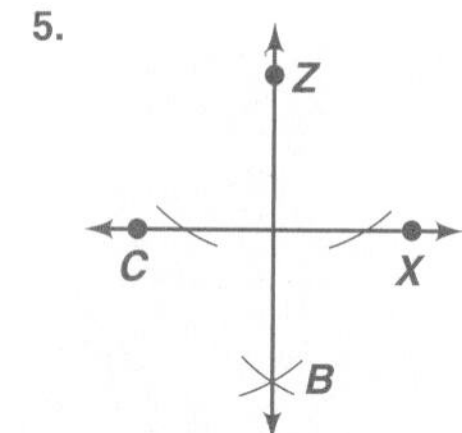

5. **Try This** Draw a line $\overleftrightarrow{CX}$ and a point Z not on the line. Construct $\overleftrightarrow{ZB}$ so that $\overleftrightarrow{ZB} \perp \overleftrightarrow{CX}$. **See left.**

6. **Critical Thinking** Explain why Construction 7 works. **$\overleftrightarrow{RG}$ is the ⊥ bisector of $\overline{EF}$.**

Example 2

Technology Use geometry software to construct a right triangle in which one leg is twice as long as the other.

Step 1: Draw a segment of any length.

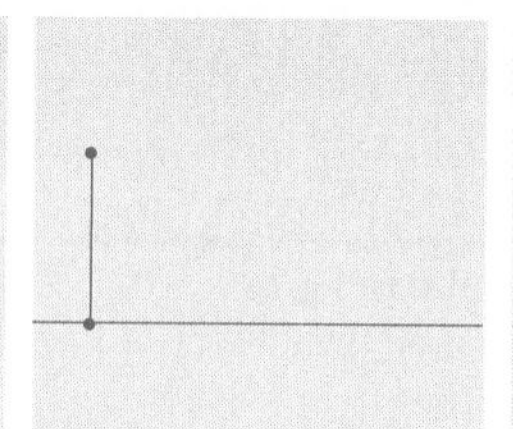

Step 2: Construct a line perpendicular to the segment through one of its endpoints.

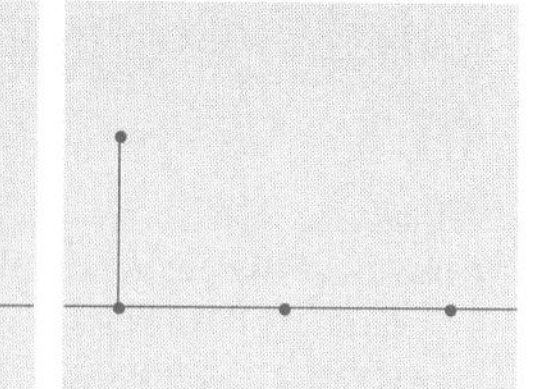

Step 3: On the line, construct two segments congruent to the original segment.

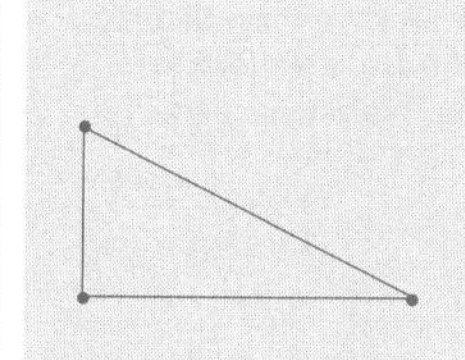

Step 4: Draw the hypotenuse of the triangle. Hide the construction points and lines.

Exercises ON YOUR OWN

1. Draw a line ℓ and a point S not on ℓ. Construct a line m through S so that $m \parallel \ell$. **See margin.**

2. **Transformations** Draw a line ℓ and a segment $\overline{PQ}$ as shown at the right. Construct the reflection image of $\overline{PQ}$ in line ℓ. (*Hint:* Construct a line perpendicular to ℓ through P. Construct P' on the perpendicular so that ℓ bisects $\overline{PP'}$.) **See margin.**

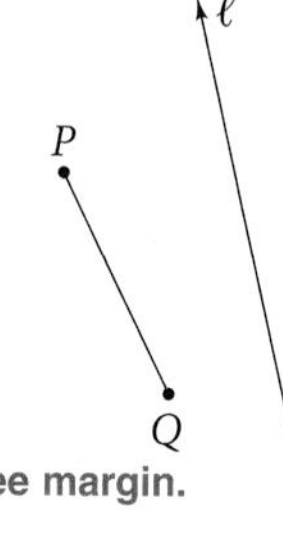

3. a. Draw an acute angle on your paper. Construct an angle congruent to the angle you drew so that the two angles are alternate interior angles. (*Hint:* The figure you end up with should look like a **Z**.) **a–b. See margin.**
   b. **Writing** Explain how to construct a line parallel to a given line through a point not on the line by using the Converse of the Alternate Interior Angles Theorem.

4. Line m was constructed perpendicular to ℓ through P by this method.
   - Draw two points on ℓ and label them R and S.
   - Construct a circle with center R and radius PR.
   - Construct a circle with center S and radius PS.
   - Draw line m through the intersections of the circles.

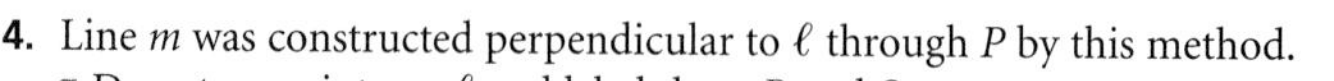

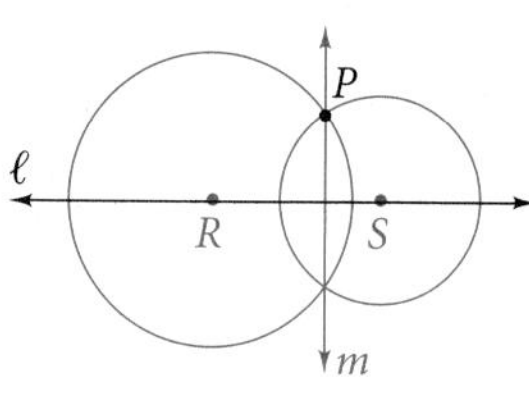

   a. **Critical Thinking** Why is line m perpendicular to line ℓ? **See margin.**
   b. Draw a line b and a point C not on b. Construct the perpendicular through C using this two-circle method. **Check students' work. Their diagrams should look similar to the construction at the right.**

Exercise 5b Students may need a review of symmetry. Refer students to Lesson 3-5.

Exercise 6 Students show by construction that if two lines in a plane are perpendicular to the same line, they are parallel.

Exercises 7–15 Students use the constructions in this lesson to construct quadrilaterals and triangles. You may want to have students work in pairs on these exercises. Check that students do not skip steps in the constructions or try to draw instead of construct.

5. a. Technology In this computer drawing, R and Q are the intersections of $\odot P$ and line n, all three circles are congruent, and line m is determined by the intersection of $\odot Q$ and $\odot R$. Explain why line m must be perpendicular to line n.

b. Symmetry Describe the symmetries of this drawing.
a–b. See below right.

6. a. Draw a line t and a point P on t. Construct a line s through P so that $s \perp t$.

b. Draw a point R that is neither on t nor s. Construct a line q through R so that $q \perp s$.

c. Critical Thinking How are q and t related? Explain.
a–c. See margin.

For Exercises 7–16, use the segments at the right.
7–9. See margin.

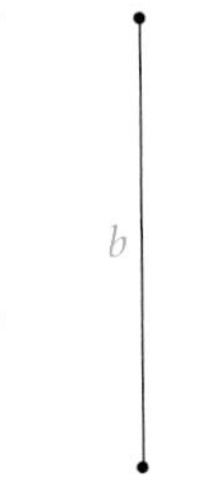

7. Draw a line m. Construct a point C so that the distance from C to m is b. (*Hint:* Construct a perpendicular from a point on the line.)

8. Construct a trapezoid with bases of lengths a and b.

9. Construct an isosceles trapezoid with legs of length a.
10a. See margin.

10. a. Construct a quadrilateral with a pair of parallel sides of length c.

b. What type of quadrilateral does the figure appear to be? parallelogram

11. a. Construct a triangle with side lengths a, b, and c. Label the triangle $\triangle ABC$, where A is opposite the side of length a, and so on.

b. Construct the altitude from C. a–b. See back of book.

12. Construct a right triangle in which the length of a leg is a and the length of the hypotenuse is c. 12–13. Answers may vary. See back of book for samples.

13. Construct a right triangle with legs of lengths b and $\frac{1}{2}b$. See back of book.

14. a. Construct an isosceles right triangle with legs of length b.

b. What is the length of the hypotenuse of this triangle? $b\sqrt{2}$

15. Construct a rectangle with base b and height c. See back of book.

16. Locus Draw a segment of any length. Construct the locus of points in a plane a distance a from the segment. See back of book for sample.

5a. Answers may vary. Sample: The points of intersection of $\odot Q$ and $\odot R$ are equidistant from the endpts. of $\overline{QR}$.

b. The drawing has m as its line of symmetry.

6a–b.

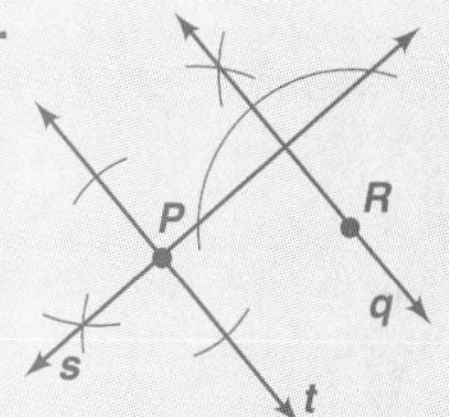

c. They are $\parallel$; in a plane, 2 lines $\perp$ to a 3rd are $\parallel$.

7.

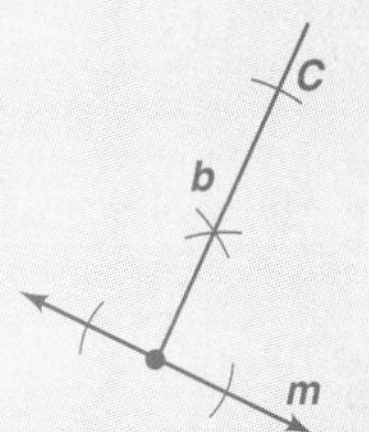

8.

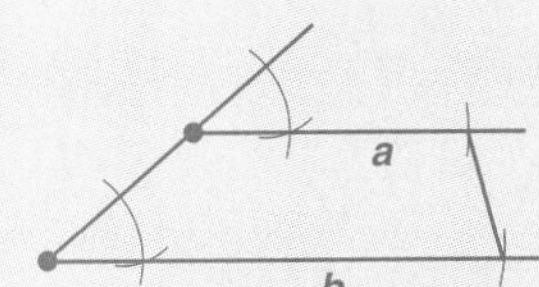

9.

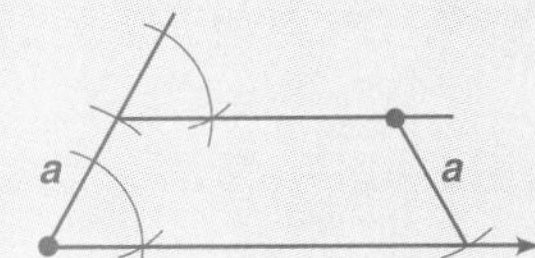

10a.

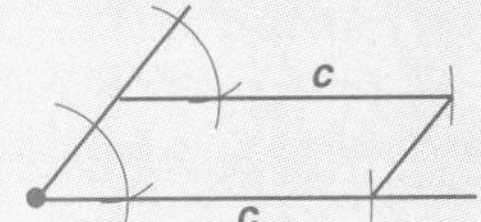

EXTENSION Exercise 17 Also ask students what is true of *m* and *k*. Have them justify their answer.

CRITICAL THINKING Exercise 18 Have students explain how to construct a 45° angle.

ALTERNATIVE ASSESSMENT Exercise 19 This exercise can help you assess students' understanding of constructions by having students perform each construction before they explain how it works.

Chapter Project **FIND OUT BY DESIGNING** Help students see that this problem differs from the Find Out By Investigating problem in Lesson 7-1 because in this activity, the cable does not have to follow the roads.

19a. ①-④: construct 2 ⊥ lines. ⑤: construct a rt. △ with a hypotenuse that is twice the length of a leg.

b. ①-③: construct an equilateral △. ④-⑥: construct the angle bisector.

c. ①-③: construct an equilateral △. ④-⑤: construct the ⊥ bisector of a side.

20a.

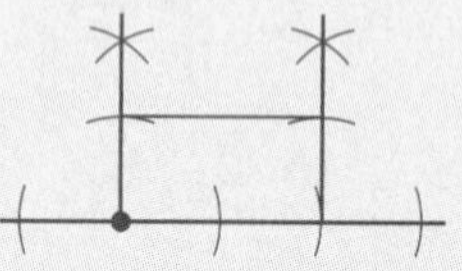

b.

Find Out by Designing

Answers may vary. Sample:

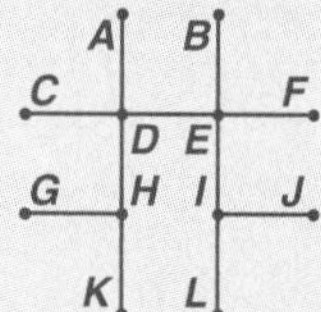

The most efficient design requires 110 mi of cable to link all 12 schools.

17. *Paper Folding* You can use paper folding to create a perpendicular to a given line through a given point. Fold the paper so the line overlaps itself and so the fold line contains the point.
    a. Draw a line *m* and a point *W* not on the line. Use paper folding to create the perpendicular through *W*. Label the fold line *k*.
    b. Use paper folding to create a line perpendicular to *k* through *W*. Label this fold line *p*. **a–b. Check students' work.**
    c. What is true of *p* and *m*? **Justify** your answer. **17c. $p \parallel m$; in a plane, 2 lines ⊥ to 3rd are ∥.**

18. *Critical Thinking* Jane was trying to construct a 45°-45°-90° triangle, but couldn't figure out how to construct a 45° angle. Lenesha told her that she didn't need to know how to construct a 45° angle in order to construct the triangle. What construction procedure do you think Lenesha had in mind? **Construct an isosceles rt. △.**

19. Three methods for constructing a 30°-60°-90° triangle are shown. The numbers indicate the order in which the arcs should be drawn. Explain why each method works. **a–c. See margin.**

a.

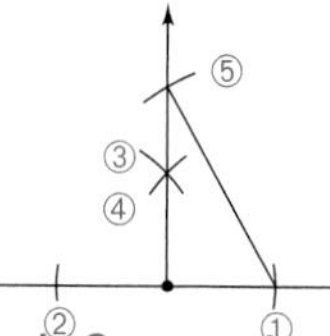

b.

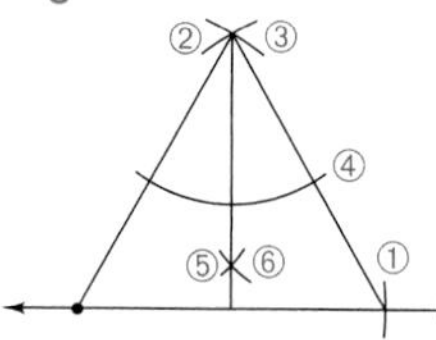

c.

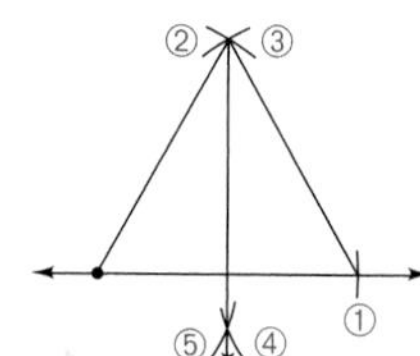

20a–b. See margin.

20. a. *Open-ended* Construct a rectangle whose length is twice its width.
    b. Construct a rectangle whose length is four times its width.
    c. *Critical Thinking* How could you construct a rectangle whose length is 1.5 times its width? (*Hint:* Use a ratio equivalent to 1.5 : 1.) **Construct a rectangle with length 3 units and width 2 units.**

Chapter Project

Find Out by Designing

Design a network of fiber-optic cables to link the 12 schools labeled *A–L* in the diagram. Assume that a computer at each school can be programmed to route a signal from that school to any other school, even if the signal has to pass through other schools on the way. Assume also that a single cable can handle both incoming and outgoing signals—just as a two-lane road handles traffic in both directions. In your design, try to use the fewest miles of cable possible. The cables do not have to coincide with roads. When you've completed your design, compare it with those of your classmates. Describe the design that you recommend and explain your recommendation. **See margin.**

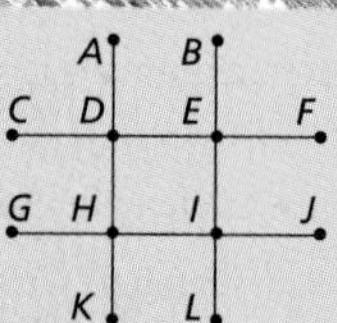

The distance from any school to an adjacent school is 10 mi.

Exercises MIXED REVIEW

COORDINATE GEOMETRY Exercise 24 Students will need to find the slope and then substitute into $y = mx + b$ to solve for b.

GETTING READY FOR LESSON 7-4 These exercises prepare students to draw objects in one- and two-point perspective.

Wrap Up

THE BIG IDEA Ask students: *Explain in your own words how to construct a line perpendicular to a given line through a point not on the line.*

RETEACHING ACTIVITY Students construct right triangles with given side lengths. (Reteaching worksheet 7-3)

Exercises CHECKPOINT

In this Checkpoint, your students will assess their own progress in Lessons 7-1 through 7-3.

Exercises 1–9 Make sure that students state both the hypothesis and conclusion of each theorem and postulate. Check that they use the theorems, postulates, and their converses appropriately.

Exercises MIXED REVIEW

If a triangle can be drawn with sides of the given lengths, will the triangle be acute, right, or obtuse? Explain.

21. 2, 3, 5 Cannot form a △; 2 + 3 = 5

22. 3, 4, 6 22. obtuse; $6^2 > 3^2 + 4^2$

23. 4, 5, 4 23. acute; $5^2 < 4^2 + 4^2$

24. Coordinate Geometry Write the equation of a line through (5, −2) and (4, 3). $y = -5x + 23$

25. You may leave your answers to parts (a–c) in terms of π.

a. A circle has radius 8 cm. Two radii of the circle form a 120° angle. What is the arc length of the intercepted arc? $\frac{16}{3}\pi$ cm

b. What is the area of the entire circle? 64π cm²

c. What is the area of the 120° sector? $\frac{64}{3}\pi$ cm²

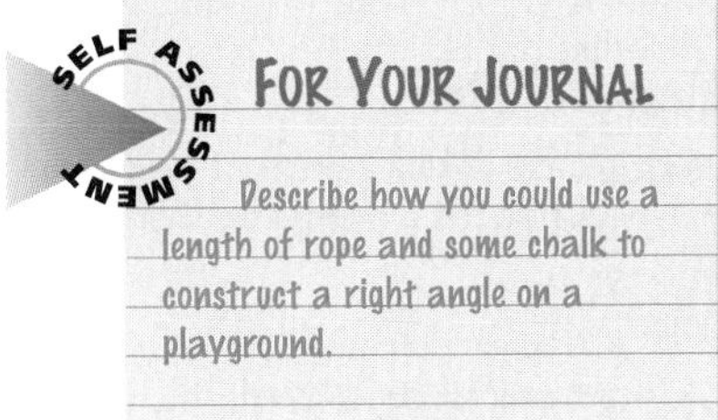

SELF ASSESSMENT
FOR YOUR JOURNAL
Describe how you could use a length of rope and some chalk to construct a right angle on a playground.

Getting Ready for Lesson 7-4

Draw a prism with the given figure as a base. 26–28. See back of book for samples.

26. 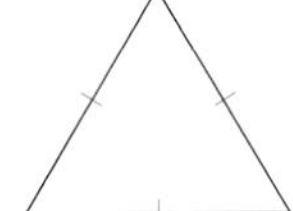

27. 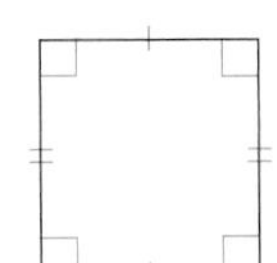

28. 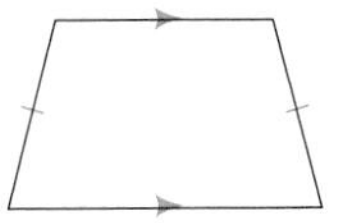

Exercises CHECKPOINT

State the theorem or postulate that justifies each statement. 1–8. See back of book.

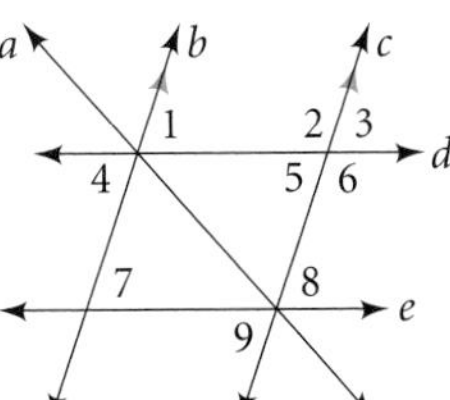

1. $\angle 1 \cong \angle 3$
2. If $\angle 5 \cong \angle 9$, then $d \parallel e$.
3. $m\angle 1 + m\angle 2 = 180$
4. If $\angle 4 \cong \angle 7$, then $d \parallel e$.
5. $\angle 1 \cong \angle 4$
6. $\angle 7 \cong \angle 9$
7. If $\angle 3 \cong \angle 8$, then $d \parallel e$.
8. $\angle 4 \cong \angle 5$
9. If $m\angle 8 + m\angle 6 = 180$, then $d \parallel e$.
   If supplementary same-side int. ∠s, then lines are ∥.
10. Draw a line m and a point D on m. Then construct a line n through D so that $n \perp m$. See back of book for sample.
11. Open-ended Construct a trapezoid with a right angle and with one base twice the length of the other. See back of book for sample.
12. Standardized Test Prep Which of the following statements is *not* always true if two parallel lines m and n are cut by transversal t? C

   A. Corresponding angles are congruent.
   B. Alternate interior angles are congruent.
   C. Exterior angles are congruent.
   D. Four of the eight angles formed are congruent.
   E. Pairs of same-side interior angles are supplementary.

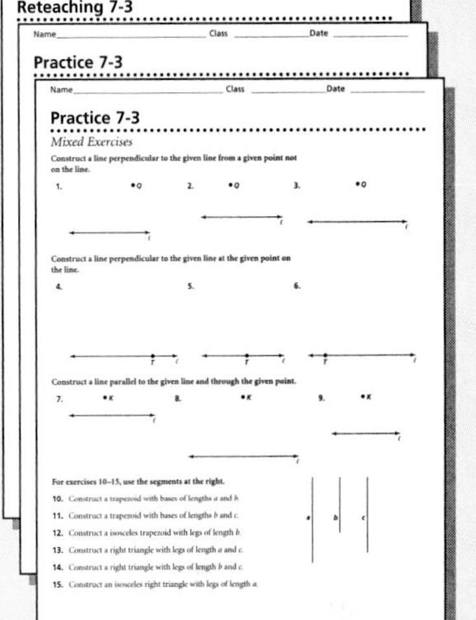
Reteaching 7-3

Practice 7-3

Practice 7-3

Mixed Exercises

Lesson Quiz

Lesson Quiz is also available in Transparencies.

For Exercises 1–3, refer to the diagram.

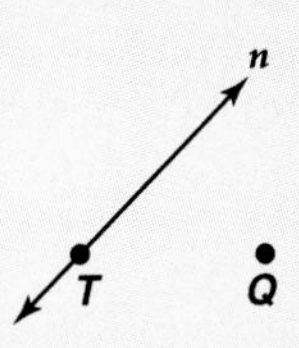

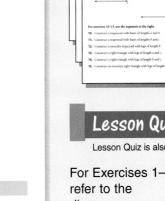

1. Construct a line parallel to n through Q.

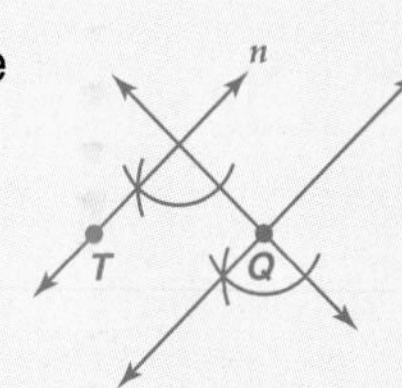

2. Construct the perpendicular to n at T. See back of book.
3. Construct the perpendicular to n from Q. See back of book.

Math ToolboX

Students use geometry software to construct a regular prism with one- point perspective. Students draw objects in one- and two-point perspective in Lesson 7-4.

Using geometry software, students are able to view the prism from different positions by manipulating the point outside the prism. Students can also change the shape of the prism.

Construct

ERROR ALERT! Some students lacking proficiency in using the software may have trouble performing the constructions. **Remediation:** Pair students with a strong understanding of the software with students less proficient in its use.

As students construct their prisms, suggest that they do not construct cubes. The results will not be as interesting.

Investigate

You may want to allow students to check the computer images of other students and compare them to their own.

ALTERNATIVE ASSESSMENT Allow students to construct their own prism, print several different views of it, and explain how they constructed the prism and created each view.

Materials and Manipulatives

- Geometry software

Math ToolboX Technology

Perspective Drawing

Before Lesson 7-4

Work in pairs or small groups using geometry software to construct a rectangular prism in one-point perspective.

Construct

Construct a rectangle *ABCD* for the front of your prism. Start with $\overline{AB}$ and construct perpendiculars at *A* and *B*. Locate point *C* on the perpendicular through *B*. *D* is the intersection of the perpendicular through *C* with the perpendicular through *A*. Hide the lines and construct the segments for the rectangle.

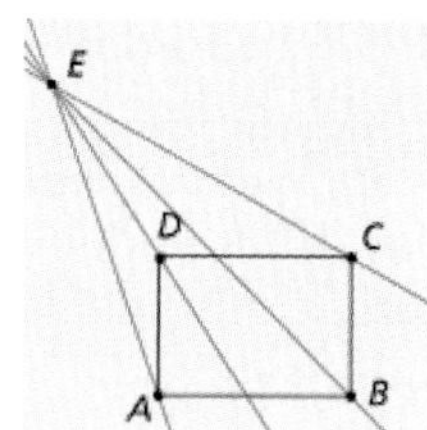

Draw a point *E* outside the rectangle. Construct $\overleftrightarrow{EA}$, $\overleftrightarrow{EB}$, $\overleftrightarrow{EC}$, and $\overleftrightarrow{ED}$.

Now construct the rectangular back of the prism. Locate a point *G* on $\overline{EA}$ and construct a line through *G* parallel to $\overline{AB}$. Construct the intersection *H* of this line with $\overleftrightarrow{EB}$. Construct the line through *H* parallel to $\overline{BC}$. Continue with similar constructions to locate *J* and *K*. Hide all the lines and draw the sides of rectangle *GHJK*.

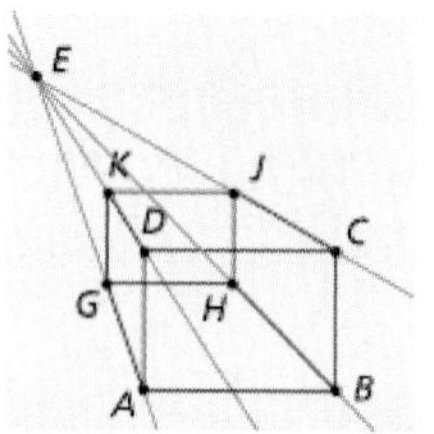

Complete the prism by drawing the remaining edges, $\overline{AG}$, $\overline{BH}$, $\overline{CJ}$, and $\overline{DK}$. Check students' work.

Investigate

Manipulate point *E*. Explore how the position of *E* affects the appearance of the prism. Where is *E* when it seems that you are looking down on the prism and can see its left side? looking directly into the prism? looking up at the prism and can see its right side? Above and to the left; inside *ABCD*; below and to the right.

Manipulate points *G*, *C*, *B*, and *A* to change the shape of the prism.

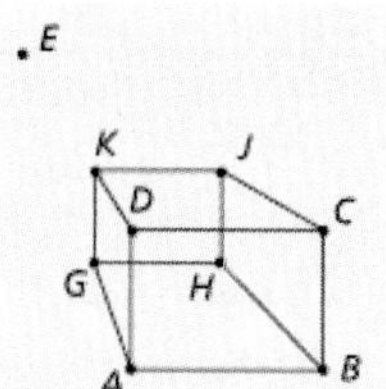

Extend

Draw a house in one-point perspective. Pretend that you are in a helicopter in front of this house and you rise straight up into the sky. Use the software to print several "snapshots" of the house as you would see it from the helicopter. Check students' work.

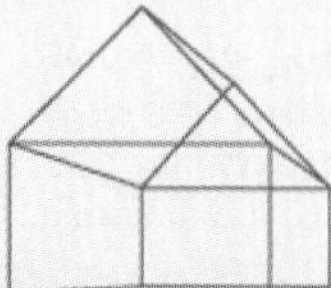
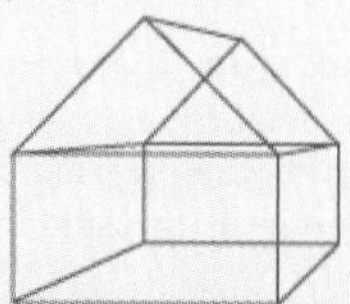
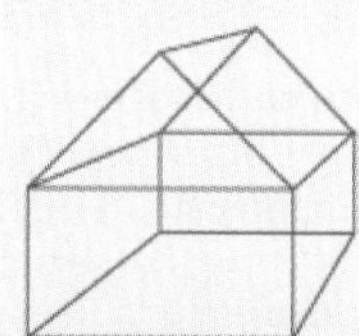
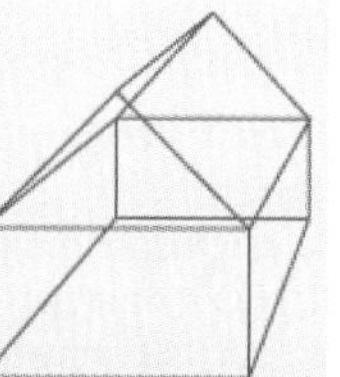

7-4 Teaching Notes

PROBLEM OF THE DAY

Cut the given letter E into five pieces that fit together to form a square.

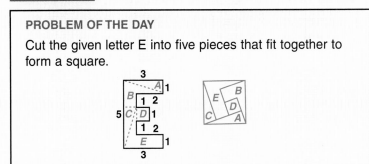

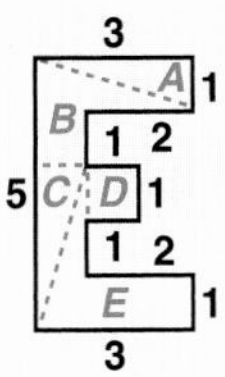

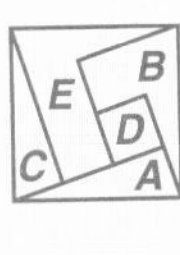

Problem of the Day is also available in Transparencies.

CONNECTING TO PRIOR KNOWLEDGE Have students look through magazines or catalogs to find examples of parallel lines that appear to meet or will meet if extended. Discuss why they appear that way.

THINK AND DISCUSS

ESL KINESTHETIC LEARNING Make sure students understand the term *perspective*. A visual example might help. Take students to one end of a football field. Choose two students of similar height. Have one student stand ten yards away and the other stand at the opposite end of the field. Students should observe that the student standing closer to them appears taller. Discuss why a perspective drawing would show the nearer student taller than the student farther away.

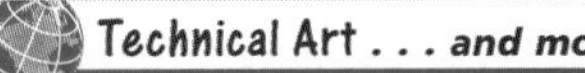

7-4 Parallel Lines and Perspective Drawing

What You'll Learn

- Drawing objects in one- and two-point perspective

...And Why

To create realistic pictures of real-world objects such as buildings

What You'll Need

- ruler

THINK AND DISCUSS

Perspective drawing is a way of drawing objects on a flat surface so that they look the same as they appear to the eye.

Art Techniques for drawing objects in perspective were developed by the ancient Greeks and Romans, but were lost to the Western world until the beginning of the Renaissance in the early 1400s. Renaissance artists used the geometry of perspective to produce works that were far more lifelike and realistic than earlier works.

Before the Renaissance . . .

Artist unknown; English manuscript illumination (c. 1400) depicting Marco Polo setting out from Venice in 1271

The size of objects in pre-Renaissance art had more to do with their importance to the artist than to their positions in space.

After the Renaissance . . .

Jacopo Bellini, *The Palace of Herod,* 15th Century

Bellini's sketchbook contains some of the earliest examples of the application of the principles of perspective drawing.

1. **Discussion** Notice in the painting of Marco Polo's departure from Venice that the ships in the foreground are about the same size as the rowboat behind them. Find other examples of objects that are out of perspective in the painting.

   Sample: People in the rowboat are smaller than people right behind them.

Lesson Planning Options

Prerequisite Skills

- Drawing polygons

Assignment Options for Exercises On Your Own

Core 1–10, 12–16, 18–19
✪**Extension** 11, 17

Use Mixed Review to maintain skills.

Resources

Student Edition

Extra Practice, p. 654
Glossary/Study Guide

Teaching Resources

Chapter Support File, Ch. 7

- Practice 7-4 (two worksheets)
- Reteaching 7-4
- Alternative Activity 7-4

Classroom Manager 7-4
Glossary, Spanish Resources

Transparencies
79, 82, 83

Discuss the value of perspective drawings because it is impossible to draw a three-dimensional object in two dimensions and preserve all lengths, angle measures, and parallel lines.

MAKING CONNECTIONS Fernand Léger (1881–1955), a major figure in the development of cubism, also took an interest in many arts besides painting. He designed sets for ballets and motion pictures. He also worked with ceramics and designed stained glass windows and mosaics.

TACTILE LEARNING Demonstrate the steps for drawing a cube in one- and two-point perspective and have students model them at their desks. Some students may find drawing in perspective confusing but after practice, most will find it fun.

RESEARCH Students who show an interest in perspective drawing may want to do further research on vanishing points and the branch of mathematics called projective geometry.

EXTENSION Have students cut a square out of a piece of poster board. Have them shine a flashlight onto the square so the shadow falls on a flat surface. Ask students to describe the shape of the shadow as they change the position of the flashlight.

Additional Example

FOR EXAMPLE

Refer to Exercises 7–9 on page 389. Is the object drawn in one- or two-point perspective?

7: two, 8: two, 9: one

Discussion: *Explain how you decide if an object is in one- or two-point perspective.*

The work of some modern artists broke from a strict rendering of objects in perspective. The French artist Fernand Léger broke the rules of perspective in this painting in order to call attention to specific colors and shapes.

Léger's paintings during the 1930s made strong visual connections to mechanical objects. Even the people in his paintings tended to have a smooth, mechanical look.

Fernand Léger, *Mother and Child*, 1936

The key to perspective drawing is the use of vanishing points. A **vanishing point** is a point on the "horizon" of a picture where parallel lines "meet." Here is how to draw a cube in **one-point perspective.**

Step 1: Draw a square. Then draw a horizon line and a vanishing point on the line.

Step 2: Lightly draw segments from the vertices of the square to the vanishing point.

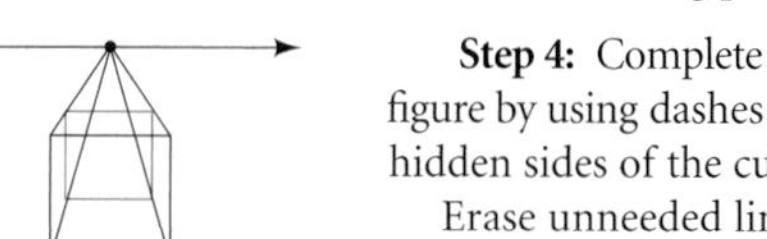

Step 3: Draw a square for the back of the cube. Each vertex should lie on a segment you drew in Step 2.

Step 4: Complete the figure by using dashes for hidden sides of the cube. Erase unneeded lines.

2. **Try This** Draw a shoe box in one-point perspective. See margin p. 388.

Two-point perspective involves the use of two vanishing points.

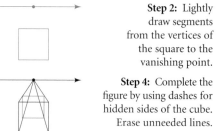

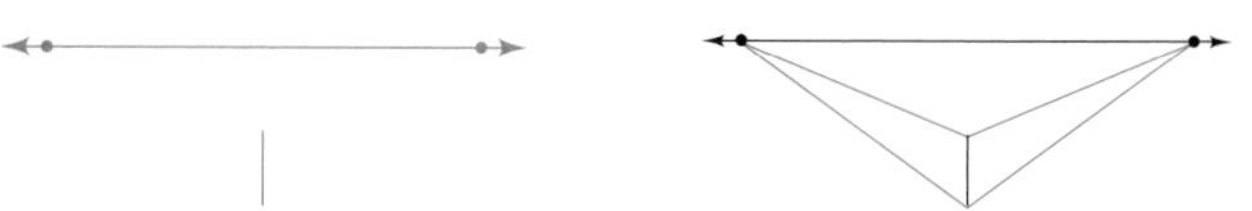

Step 1: Draw a vertical segment. Then draw a horizon line and two vanishing points on the line.

Step 2: Lightly draw segments from the endpoints of the segment to each vanishing point.

Make sure that students do not make any false assumptions when drawing in one- and two-point perspective. For example, they may assume that the vanishing point needs to be above the center of the square in one-point perspective or that the vertical segment must be on the perpendicular bisector of the segment between the two vanishing points in two-point perspective.

In order to draw a cube and not another prism, make sure that the two vertical lines students draw in Step 3 are equidistant from the original vertical segments.

ERROR ALERT! In Step 4 of drawing a cube in two-point perspective, students may not see that they are drawing segments from the endpoints of the segment to the "opposite" vanishing point. **Remediation:** When demonstrating these steps, perform each step in a different color and make sure to verbalize what you are doing.

Example Relating to the Real World 

Make sure students understand that in part a, the lines converge to one vanishing point and in part b, the lines converge to two vanishing points.

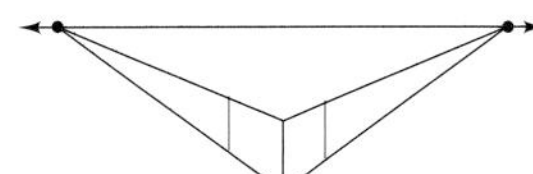

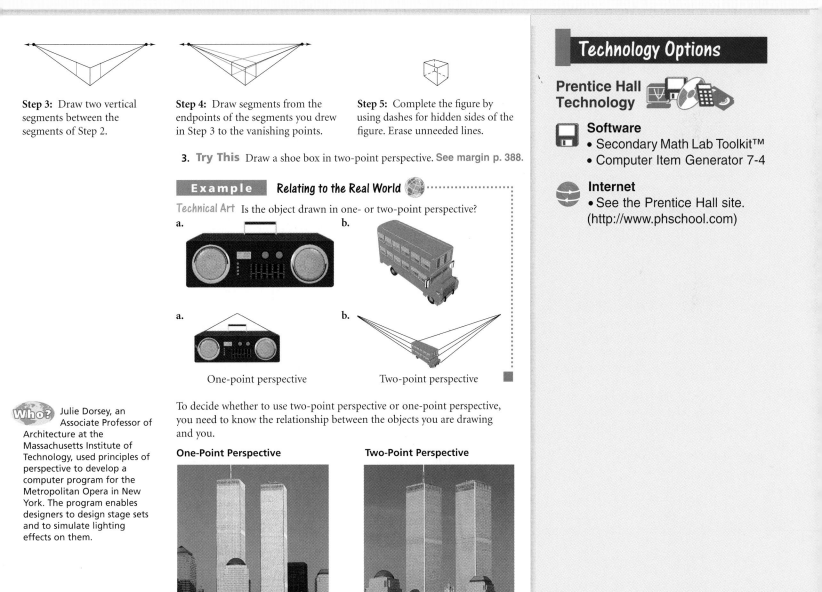

Step 3: Draw two vertical segments between the segments of Step 2.

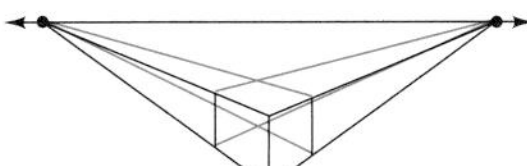

Step 4: Draw segments from the endpoints of the segments you drew in Step 3 to the vanishing points.

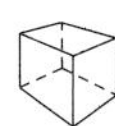

Step 5: Complete the figure by using dashes for hidden sides of the figure. Erase unneeded lines.

3. **Try This** Draw a shoe box in two-point perspective. See margin p. 388.

Example Relating to the Real World 

Technical Art Is the object drawn in one- or two-point perspective?

a. 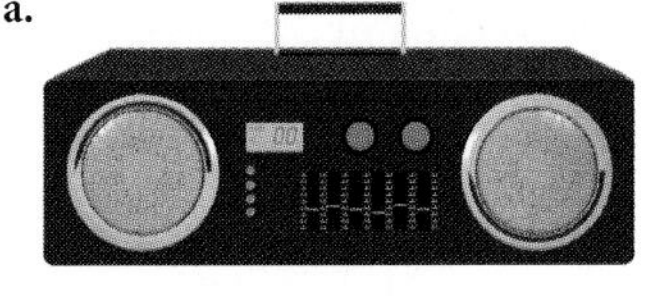 b. 

a. One-point perspective b. Two-point perspective

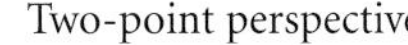

To decide whether to use two-point perspective or one-point perspective, you need to know the relationship between the objects you are drawing and you.

One-Point Perspective

The faces of the buildings are parallel to you, so use one-point perspective.

Two-Point Perspective

None of the faces of the buildings are parallel to you, so use two-point perspective.

Who? Julie Dorsey, an Associate Professor of Architecture at the Massachusetts Institute of Technology, used principles of perspective to develop a computer program for the Metropolitan Opera in New York. The program enables designers to design stage sets and to simulate lighting effects on them.

Technology Options

Prentice Hall Technology 

 **Software**
- Secondary Math Lab Toolkit™
- Computer Item Generator 7-4

 **Internet**
- See the Prentice Hall site. (http://www.phschool.com)

MAKING CONNECTIONS Students interested in photography may enjoy the following project: Have students take pictures of parallel lines from different vantage points, bring in the developed prints, and describe the vanishing points on each.

WORK TOGETHER

Make sure that students in each group start with the same rectangle so that they draw the same "box."

CONNECTING TO STUDENTS' WORLD If you have block scheduling or an extended class period, have students make perspective drawings of a school hallway or the school's football field.

Exercises ON YOUR OWN

ALTERNATIVE ASSESSMENT **Exercises 1–4** You can use these exercises to help you assess students' understanding of one- and two-point perspective by having them copy each figure and identify the vanishing points.

Exercises 5–6 Students may find it fun to enact these scenarios in their homes using similar objects.

pages 385–388 Think and Discuss

2.

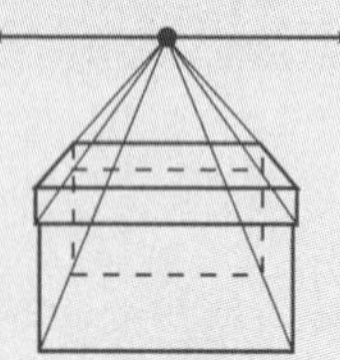

3.

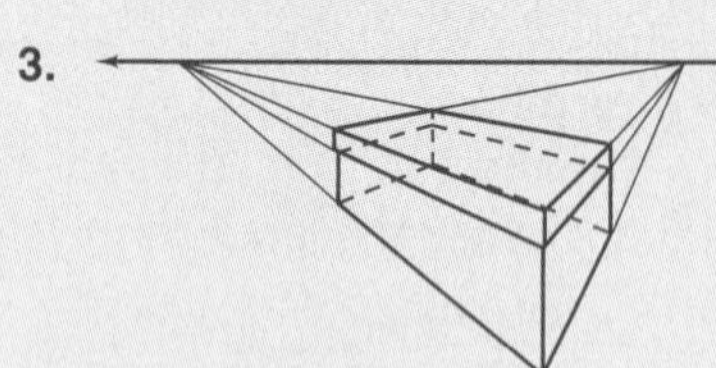

page 388 Work Together

5. If the square shown is the front of the box, the number in each region is the number of sides of the box the "viewer" can see when the vanishing pt. is in that region.

3	2	3
2	1	2
3	2	3

pages 388–391 On Your Own

7.

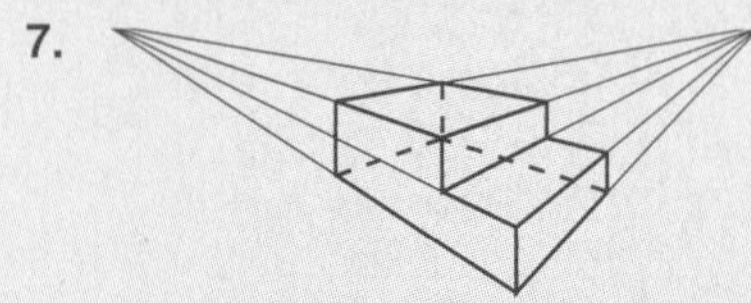

8.

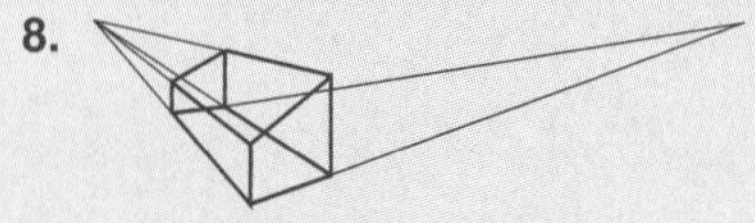

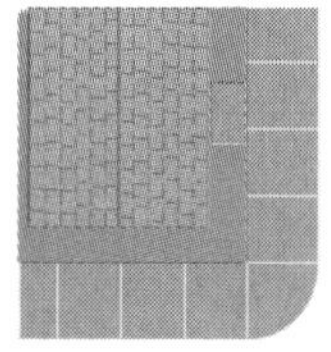

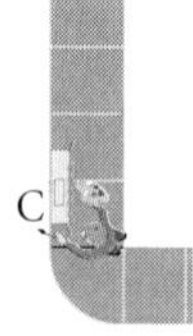

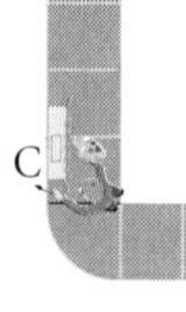

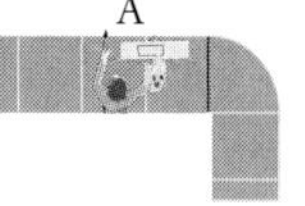

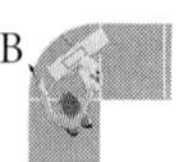

4. *Critical Thinking* Three artists set up easels around a historical building in Paris. Each artist plans to paint a realistic view of the building. Based on the positions of their easels, which type of perspective will each artist's painting show?
Artists A and C's paintings will show 1-pt. perspective; artist B's painting will show 2-pt. perspective.

WORK TOGETHER

Work in groups to explore how the placement of the vanishing point affects a drawing. Have each member of your group draw a box in one-point perspective. Vary the positions of the horizon lines and vanishing points within your group.

5. Where is the vanishing point when the "viewer" can see three sides of the box? two sides? one side?
See margin.

Exercises ON YOUR OWN

Is the object drawn in one- or two-point perspective?

1. 
2-pt. perspective

2. 
1-pt. perspective

3. 
2-pt. perspective

4. 
1-pt. perspective

Study each diagram at the left. Match each position in the diagram to what the viewer would see from that point.

5. 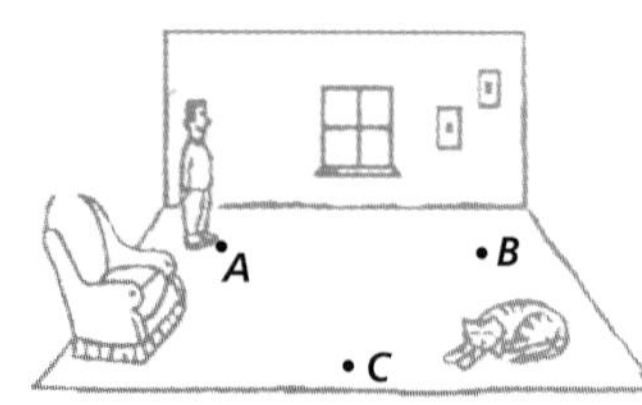

I. **B** 

II. **C** 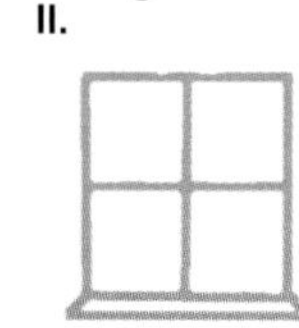

III. **A** 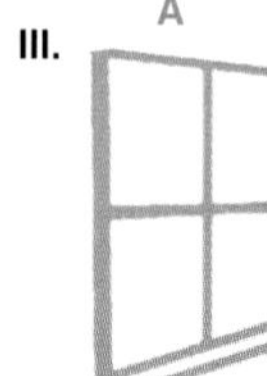

6. 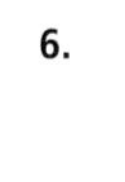

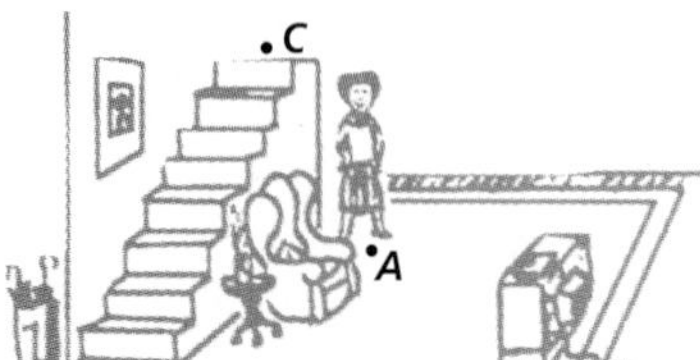

I. **B** 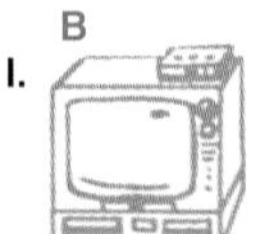

II. **C** 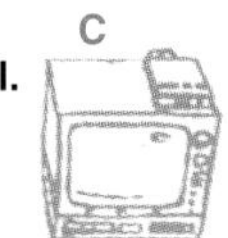

III. **A**

Exercise 10 Students may want to review isometric and orthographic drawings in Lesson 2-7. Ask students which drawing the computer artist starts with.

CRITICAL THINKING Exercise 10 Discuss what happens to the objects' shadows when the lights coincide with the camera. They disappear.

CONNECTING TO STUDENTS' WORLD Exercise 11a Students may enjoy drawing the figures in Exercises 1–4 *not* in proper perspective.

RESEARCH Exercise 11b Students should be able to find information on cubism in any encyclopedia. Suggest that students also research the founders of cubism, Pablo Picasso and Georges Braque.

Copy each prism and locate the vanishing point(s). 7–8. See margin p. 388.

7. 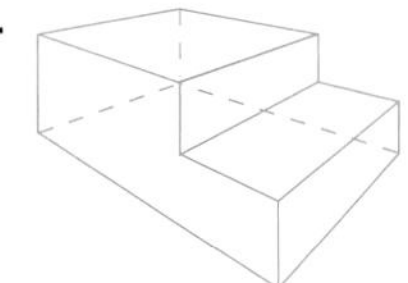

8. 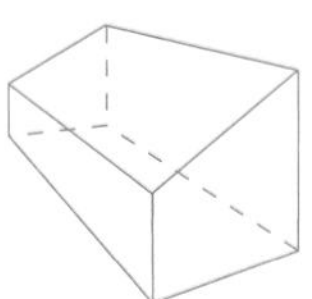

9. 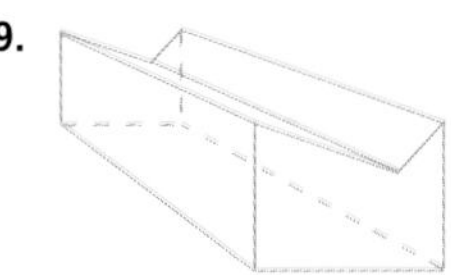

See margin.

A Computer's Perspective

Ray Dream Designer™ is a software program that allows artists to create 3D objects and scenes. The artist starts by drawing top, front, and side views of an object. The program uses this information to assemble a 3D image of the object.

Each object the artist creates is then placed in a scene such as a room or a street. Finally, the artist positions a "camera" and "lights" within the scene. The computer automatically draws all the objects from the viewpoint of the camera.

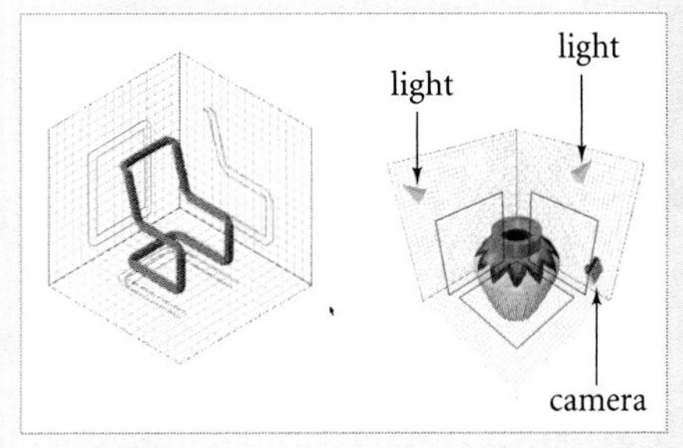

10. Describe the position of the camera for each of these views.

a. 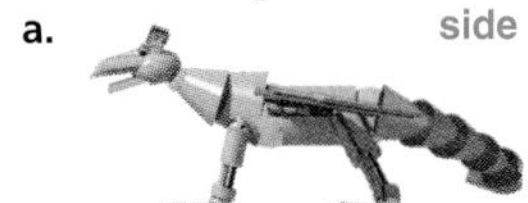 side

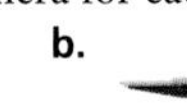

b.  front

c.  top

11. a. Refer to the cartoon to explain why an artist might purposefully paint a scene not in proper perspective.

b. Research Find out about the Cubist movement in painting. What techniques did these artists use? What were they trying to communicate?

a. See margin.
b. Check students' work.

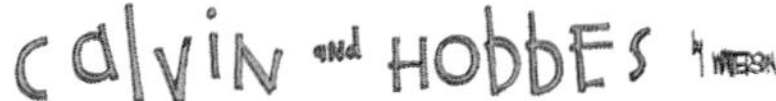

9. (margin figure)

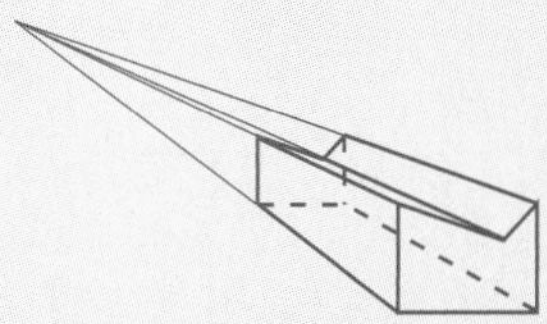

11a. Answers may vary. Sample: The artist is trying to show more than one view of an object, just as we might think of an object in more than one way.

12. Parts of the painting are in perspective, but the painting as a whole is not in perspective.

13. The painting is in perspective. The edges of the road converge to a vanishing point.

14. The students closer to the vanishing pt. appear to be taller.

15. The 4 non-horizontal lines appear to converge at the vanishing pt. So the upper horizontal line appears to be longer.

16. The middle 2 horizontal lines appear to bulge near the vanishing pt.

17. Answers may vary. Sample: ∥ lines converge to vanishing pts., but instead of converging along straight lines, they converge along curved paths. So the images look like they are projected onto the surface of a sphere.

Exercises 14–15 Challenge students to copy the figures and add lines to show that the segments are the same length and the students are the same height.

Exercise 16 Have students copy the diagram and connect the diagonal lines. Ask them how they can use the postulate and theorems in Lesson 7-2 to show the lines are parallel.

DIVERSITY Exercise 17 This exercise provides a good opportunity for the photographers in your class to share what they know about cameras. Discuss careers in photography.

Chapter Project FIND OUT BY INVESTIGATING Students should discover that a network is traceable if all the vertices are even or if exactly two are odd. Make sure students understand even and odd vertices and create enough networks to see this pattern.

18a. Sample: b. Sample:

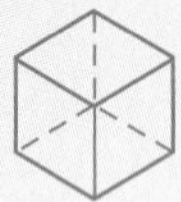

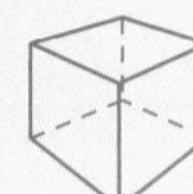

c. In an isometric view, the lines that are ∥ in reality are ∥ in the drawing. In 1-pt. perspective view, only the lines that are ⊥ to the horizon remain ∥. All other lines meet at the vanishing pts.

page 391 Mixed Review

20a. If the acute angles of a △ are complementary, then the △ is a rt. △.

21a. If it is July 4, then it is a national holiday in the United States.

22a. If a figure is a ▱, then it is a rectangle.

Fine Art **Explain how each artist used or did not use perspective.** 12–13. See margin p. 389.

12. Stuart Davis, *New York/Paris No. 2,* 1931

Stuart Davis once wrote "I never ask the question `Does this picture have depth or is it flat?' I consider such a question irrelevant."

13. Richard Estes, *Holland Hotel,* 1984

Richard Estes' paintings are so realistic that they are easily mistaken for photographs.

Optical Illusions **Explain how the concepts you learned in this lesson relate to each of these optical illusions.** 14–16. Answers may vary. See margin p. 389 for samples.

14.

The students appear to be different heights.

15.

The horizontal segments appear to be different lengths.

16.

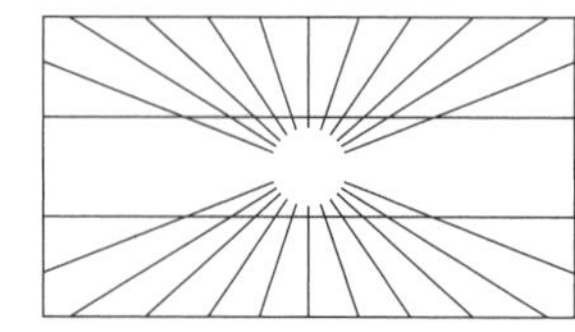

The horizontal lines appear to be curved.

17. Photography This photograph was taken with a type of lens called a *fish-eye lens.* Describe how this type of lens affects parallel lines and vanishing points. See margin p. 389.

18. a. Create an isometric drawing of a box. a–c. See margin.

b. Draw the same box in two-point perspective.

c. Writing Compare how parallel lines appear in each drawing.

Exercises MIXED REVIEW

Exercises 20–22 Have students give a counterexample for each false statement.

JOURNAL Have students share their responses with the class. Create a master list on the board of the disadvantages students describe.

GETTING READY FOR LESSON 7-5 These exercises prepare students to study some of the basic ideas of spherical geometry.

Wrap Up

THE BIG IDEA Ask students: *Describe how to draw a three-dimensional object with one- and two-point perspective.*

RETEACHING ACTIVITY Students draw prisms in one- and two- point perspective and identify vanishing points in their partner's drawings. (Reteaching worksheet 7-4)

19. ***Open-ended*** You can draw block letters in either one-point perspective or two-point perspective. Write your initials in block letters using one-point perspective and two-point perspective. Check students' work.

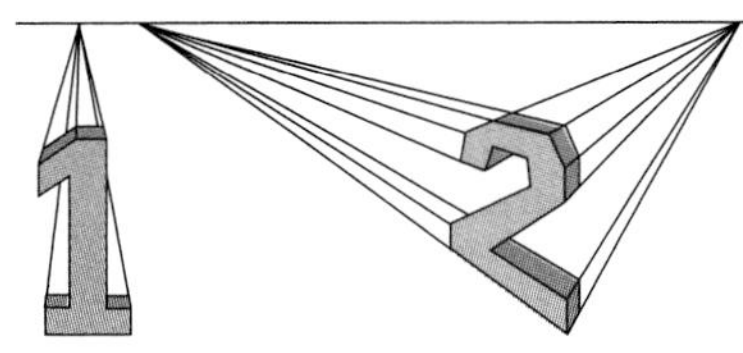

Chapter Project — *Find Out by Investigating*

Each of the points in the two networks at the right is a *vertex* of the network. An *odd vertex* is on an odd number of paths. *O* is an odd vertex. An *even vertex* is on an even number of paths. *E* is an even vertex. odd: 2, even: 2; odd: 4, even: 1

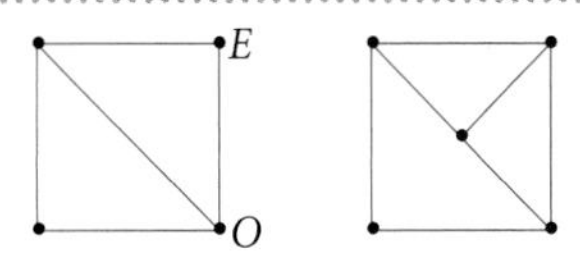

- How many odd and even vertices does each network have?
- Try to trace each network without lifting your pencil from your paper or retracing any path. (You may go over a vertex more than once.) The 1st network is traceable; the 2nd is not.
- Make your own network, and then try to trace it. Record your results in a table like this one. Keep drawing and tracing networks until you see a pattern relating the number of odd and even vertices to whether the network is traceable.

Diagram of Network	Odd Vertices	Even Vertices	Traceable?
	0	5	yes

A network with more than 2 odd vertices is not traceable.

Exercises MIXED REVIEW

In Exercises 20–22: (a) Write the converse of each conditional. (b) Determine the truth value of the conditional and its converse. 20a, 21a, 22a. See margin p. 390.

20. If a triangle is a right triangle, then its acute angles are complementary. b. true; true
21. If it is a national holiday in the United States, then it is July 4. b. false; true
22. If a figure is a rectangle, then it is a parallelogram. b. true; false
23. ***Transformational Geometry*** Describe the image of a circle with center (4, −2) and radius 2 under a dilation with scale factor 3 centered at the origin. a circle with center at (12, −6) and radius 6

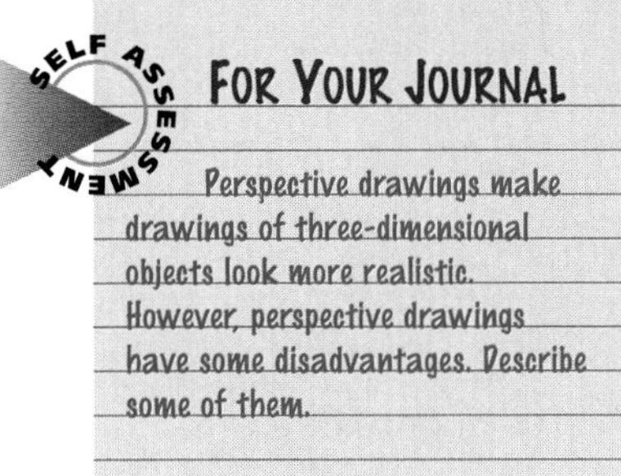

FOR YOUR JOURNAL
Perspective drawings make drawings of three-dimensional objects look more realistic. However, perspective drawings have some disadvantages. Describe some of them.

Getting Ready for Lesson 7-5

Find the sum of the measures of the angles of each spherical triangle.

24. 212

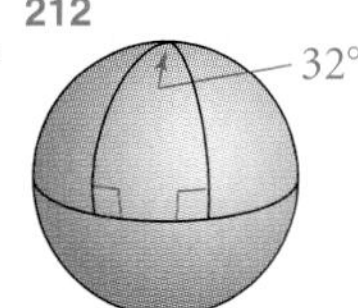

25. 270

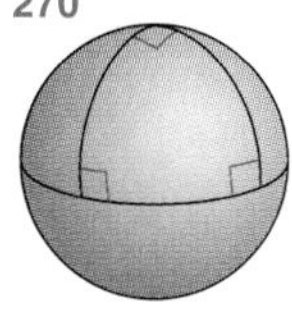

26. 304

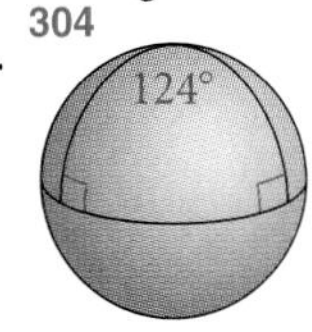

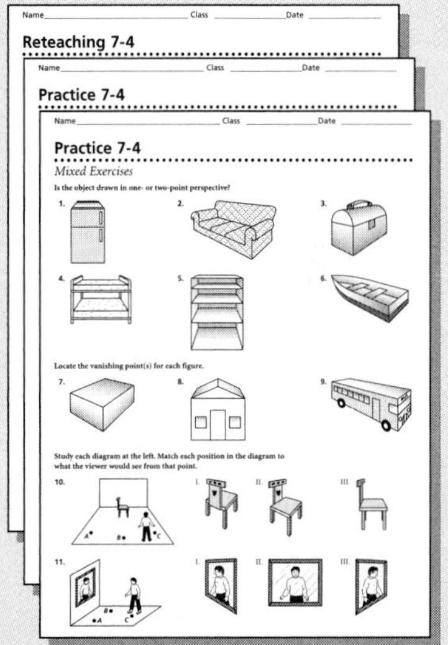

Lesson Quiz

Lesson Quiz is also available in Transparencies.

1. Draw a prism in one-point perspective. Answers may vary. Sample:
2. Draw a prism in two-point perspective. Answers may vary. Sample:

7-5 Teaching Notes

PROBLEM OF THE DAY

A cube has edges of length 5 cm. If a fly lands on a vertex and then walks along the edges, what is the greatest distance the fly could walk before coming to a vertex a second time and without retracing an edge?
just under 40 cm

Problem of the Day is also available in Transparencies.

CONNECTING TO PRIOR KNOWLEDGE Using a globe, ask students to identify a radius, a diameter, and a great circle. Then have students identify the North Pole, the South Pole, the equator, lines of longitude, lines of latitude, and where they live.

WORK TOGETHER

Have students work in groups of four. Provide each with a globe, beach ball, basketball, or volleyball. If students are using a ball, have them mark points on the ball using stickers or tape. Remind them not to write on the balls or globes.

TACTILE LEARNING Students should discover that between two points that are opposite each other, there is no shortest path and between any two points not opposite each other, there is exactly one shortest path.

AUDITORY LEARNING Students can remember that latitude lines go sideways because latitude has the same root as the word lateral (e.g., a lateral pass), whereas the longitude lines run North to South because they are all "long."

Lesson Planning Options

Prerequisite Skills

- Identifying a radius, diameter, and great circle of a sphere

Assignment Options for Exercises On Your Own

Core 1–4, 6–19
✪**Extension** 5, 20

Use Mixed Review to maintain skills.

Resources

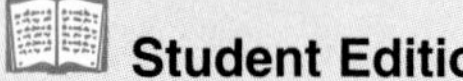
Student Edition

Extra Practice, p. 654
Glossary/Study Guide

Teaching Resources

Chapter Support File, Ch. 7
- Practice 7-5 (two worksheets)
- Reteaching 7-5

Classroom Manager 7-5
Glossary, Spanish Resources

Transparencies
80, 84

Connections Navigation . . . and more

7-5 Exploring Spherical Geometry

What You'll Learn
- Using some of the basic ideas of spherical geometry

...And Why
To better understand the properties of the sphere on which we live

What You'll Need
- globe, ball, or foam ball
- string
- protractor

WORK TOGETHER

1. On a globe or ball, select two points that are opposite each other. That is, select two points that are endpoints of a diameter, such as the North and South poles on a globe. Find the shortest path between the points by holding a string taut between them. Is there one shortest path between the points? no
2. Now hold the string taut between two points that are not opposite one another. Is there one shortest path between the points? yes
3. Form a triangle on a globe or ball by taping string between three points. Use a protractor to estimate the measures of the three angles formed. Is the sum of the measures of the angles of a triangle on a sphere equal to 180? no
4. Now form larger triangles on the globe or ball and measure the three angles. Does the sum seem to depend on the size of the triangle? Explain. yes; the larger the △, the greater the sum.

THINK AND DISCUSS

On this map, it looks like the red segment parallel to the lines of latitude is the shortest path from San Francisco to Tokyo. But on the globe, the red string shows that the shortest path is actually quite different.

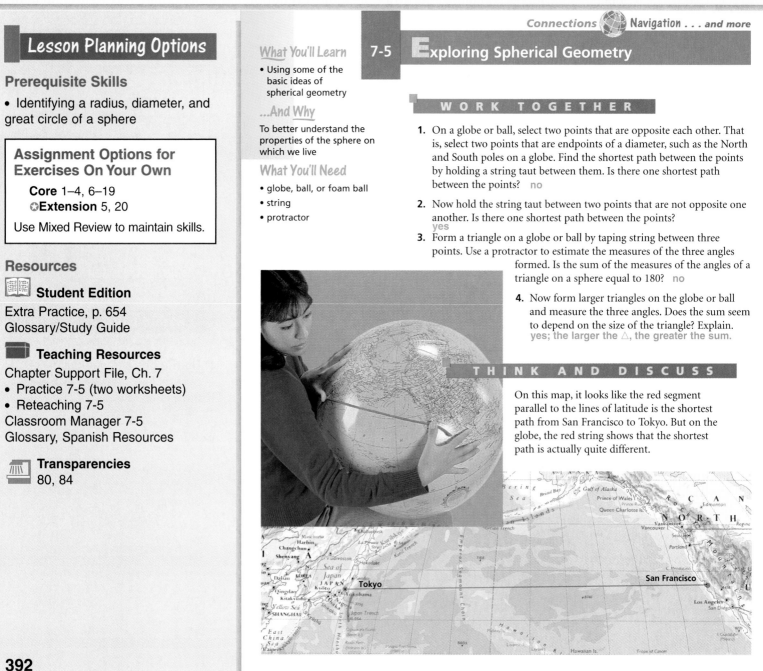

THINK AND DISCUSS

DIVERSITY Bernhard Riemann (1826–1866), a German mathematician, is credited with the development of spherical geometry. Have students research the contributions of other mathematicians from Germany, Russia, and Hungary in the nineteenth century. (See Exercise 20 for suggestions.)

ESL VISUAL LEARNING Students may have trouble understanding that *plane* and *line* can have different meanings in spherical geometry. This concept is especially difficult for ESL students who may have just learned what these terms mean in Euclidean geometry. You may want to make a poster displaying the diagram on page 393. Also have students copy the diagram into their notebooks along with the meanings of the terms.

Example Relating to the Real World 

Make sure students understand that the lines of longitude and the equator are not the only great circles. Make a model or draw a diagram to show other great circles.

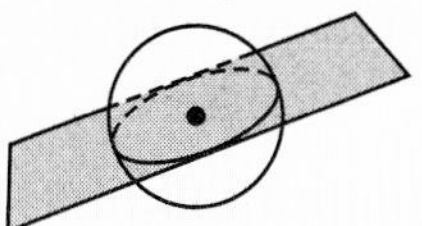

As the travel routes indicate, geometry on a sphere is different from geometry on a plane. The geometry of flat planes, straight lines, and points is called **Euclidean geometry.** In **spherical geometry,** *point* has the same meaning as in Euclidean geometry, but *line* and *plane* do not. In spherical geometry, a "plane" is the surface of a sphere and a "line" is a great circle of a sphere. Recall that a great circle is the intersection of a sphere and a plane that contains the center of the sphere.

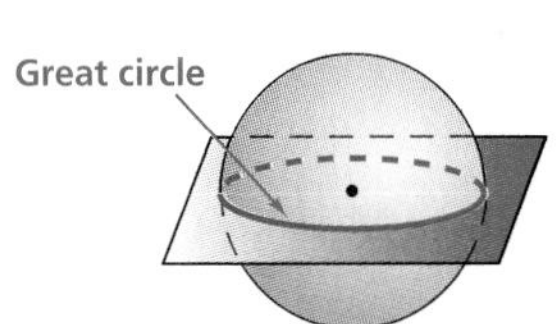

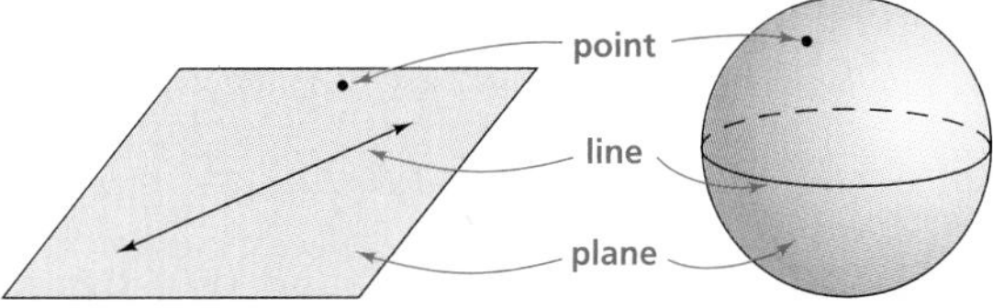

Euclidean Geometry **Spherical Geometry**

Example Relating to the Real World 

Navigation Lines of latitude and longitude are used to identify positions on Earth, much as *x*- and *y*-coordinates identify points on the coordinate plane. Which of these lines are great circles?

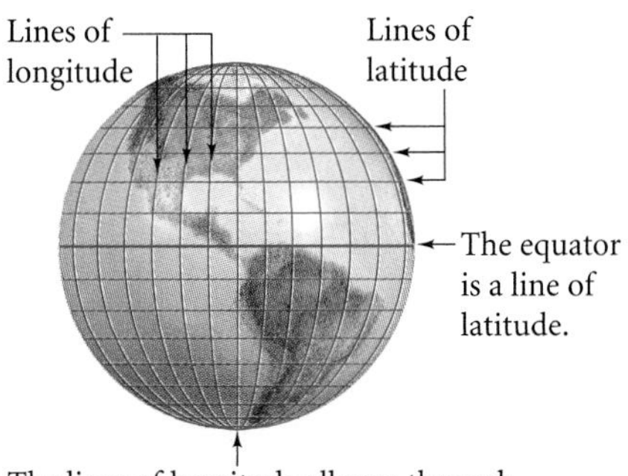

The lines of longitude all pass through the North and South Poles.

All the lines of longitude are great circles. The equator is the only line of latitude that is a great circle. All the other lines of latitude are circles smaller than a great circle.

Who? The physicist Albert Einstein (1879–1955) found that a non-Euclidean geometry was the best model for the paths of light rays over the huge distances of the universe.

You discovered in the Work Together that there are many shortest paths between any two points that are opposite each other on a sphere. You also discovered that there is only one shortest path between two points that are not opposite each other. Each of these shortest paths is an arc of a great circle.

Additional Example

FOR EXAMPLE

Identify the line of latitude and the line of longitude through your city or town. Which of these lines is a great circle? **the longitude line**

Discussion: *How many shortest paths are there from your city or town to Tokyo? to the North Pole?*

Approximate the point on the globe opposite your city or town. How many shortest paths are there between your city or town and this point? **many**

Discussion: *How do you find the shortest path between two points on a globe not opposite each other?*

Question 5 Students will need a globe to answer this question. If each group does not have access to a globe, place one globe at the front of the classroom. Have groups discuss what they need to know about the positions of Tokyo and San Francisco on the globe. Then have them choose one student to go to the globe and check.

MAKING CONNECTIONS Astronomers use coordinate systems to describe locations of objects in the sky. They model the sky using a celestial sphere which has the stars on its surface and the observer at its center. The two angles used to describe the position of a star are similar to the longitude and latitude of a point on the surface of Earth.

Postulate 7-3 Take time to allow students to try to find a counterexample. Let them discover that this postulate does not depend on the position of the line or the point.

ALTERNATIVE ASSESSMENT To assess students' understanding of distance on a sphere, ask each group to identify five pairs of cities with exactly one shortest path between them and then find a pair of cities with more than one shortest path between them.

ERROR ALERT! Postulate 7-4 Some students may argue that two lines of latitude are parallel. **Remediation:** Help students understand that latitude lines (except for the equator) are not lines on a sphere because the plane containing them does not pass through the center of the sphere. Therefore, they are not parallel lines because they are not both lines.

Discuss with students that any great circle passing through the poles meets the great circle at the equator at right angles.

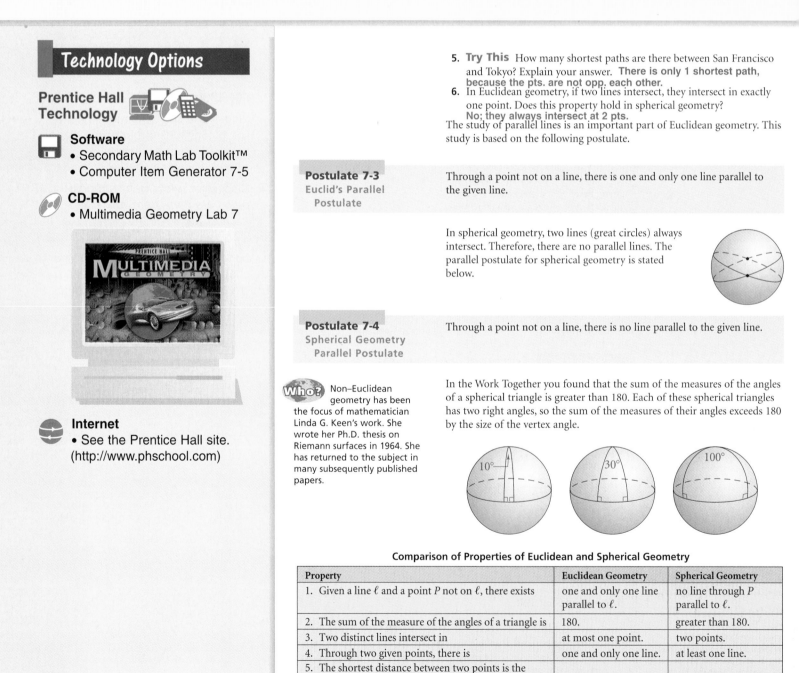

Technology Options

Prentice Hall Technology

Software
- Secondary Math Lab Toolkit™
- Computer Item Generator 7-5

CD-ROM
- Multimedia Geometry Lab 7

Internet
- See the Prentice Hall site. (http://www.phschool.com)

5. **Try This** How many shortest paths are there between San Francisco and Tokyo? Explain your answer. **There is only 1 shortest path, because the pts. are not opp. each other.**
6. In Euclidean geometry, if two lines intersect, they intersect in exactly one point. Does this property hold in spherical geometry? **No; they always intersect at 2 pts.**

The study of parallel lines is an important part of Euclidean geometry. This study is based on the following postulate.

Postulate 7-3
Euclid's Parallel Postulate

Through a point not on a line, there is one and only one line parallel to the given line.

In spherical geometry, two lines (great circles) always intersect. Therefore, there are no parallel lines. The parallel postulate for spherical geometry is stated below.

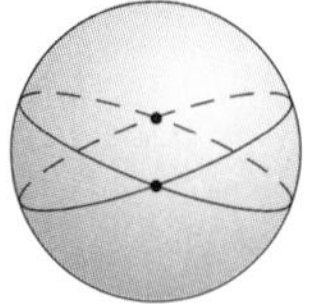

Postulate 7-4
Spherical Geometry Parallel Postulate

Through a point not on a line, there is no line parallel to the given line.

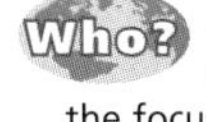

Non–Euclidean geometry has been the focus of mathematician Linda G. Keen's work. She wrote her Ph.D. thesis on Riemann surfaces in 1964. She has returned to the subject in many subsequently published papers.

In the Work Together you found that the sum of the measures of the angles of a spherical triangle is greater than 180. Each of these spherical triangles has two right angles, so the sum of the measures of their angles exceeds 180 by the size of the vertex angle.

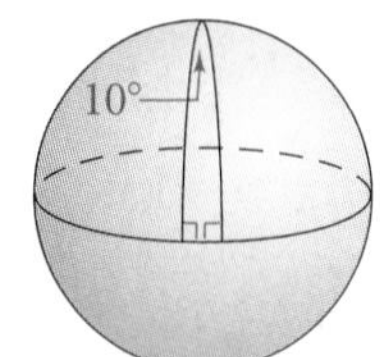

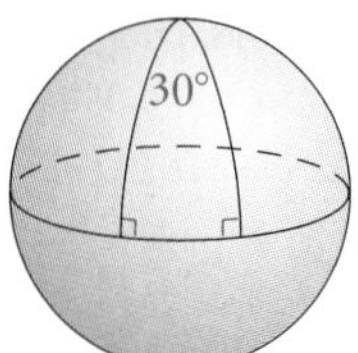

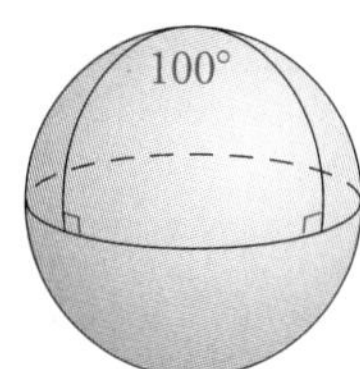

Comparison of Properties of Euclidean and Spherical Geometry

Property	Euclidean Geometry	Spherical Geometry
1. Given a line ℓ and a point P not on ℓ, there exists	one and only one line parallel to ℓ.	no line through P parallel to ℓ.
2. The sum of the measure of the angles of a triangle is	180.	greater than 180.
3. Two distinct lines intersect in	at most one point.	two points.
4. Through two given points, there is	one and only one line.	at least one line.
5. The shortest distance between two points is the length of	a segment.	an arc of a great circle.

The chart at the bottom of page 394 summarizes the differences between Euclidean geometry and spherical geometry presented in this lesson. Make sure students understand each property and can illustrate each with an example or counterexample.

CRITICAL THINKING Ask students to describe a pair of points through which exactly one line passes in spherical geometry.

Exercises ON YOUR OWN

Exercise 4 This problem illustrates that the Segment Addition Postulate in Euclidean geometry is not true in spherical geometry. The distance from Bergen to Montevideo in not the sum of the distances from Bergen to Melbourne and from Melbourne to Montevideo.

Exercises ON YOUR OWN

Draw a sketch to illustrate each property of spherical geometry. 1–3. See margin for sample.

1. There are pairs of points on a sphere through which more than one line can be drawn.
2. A triangle can have more than one right angle.
3. You can draw two equiangular triangles that each have different angle measures.
4. *Geography* Bergen, Norway; Melbourne, Australia; and Montevideo, Uruguay, are on the same great circle. The distance from Bergen to Melbourne is about 9990 miles and the distance from Melbourne to Montevideo is about 7370 miles. Use the fact that the circumference of Earth is about 24,900 miles to find the distance from Montevideo to Bergen. 7540 mi

Bergen, Norway

Montevideo, Uruguay

Melbourne, Australia

5. *Open-ended* Find three locations on a globe that are on a great circle and find the distances between them. Check students' work.

Draw a counterexample to show that the following properties of Euclidean geometry are not true in spherical geometry. 6–11. See margin for sample.

6. Through a point not on line ℓ, there exists one and only one line perpendicular to ℓ.
7. Two coplanar lines that are perpendicular to the same line do not intersect.
8. A triangle can have at most one obtuse angle.
9. If a triangle contains a right angle, then the other two angles in the triangle are complementary.
10. If two angles of one triangle are congruent to two angles of another triangle, then the third angles are congruent.
11. If A, B, and C are three points on a line, then exactly one of the points is between the other two.

pages 395–397 On Your Own

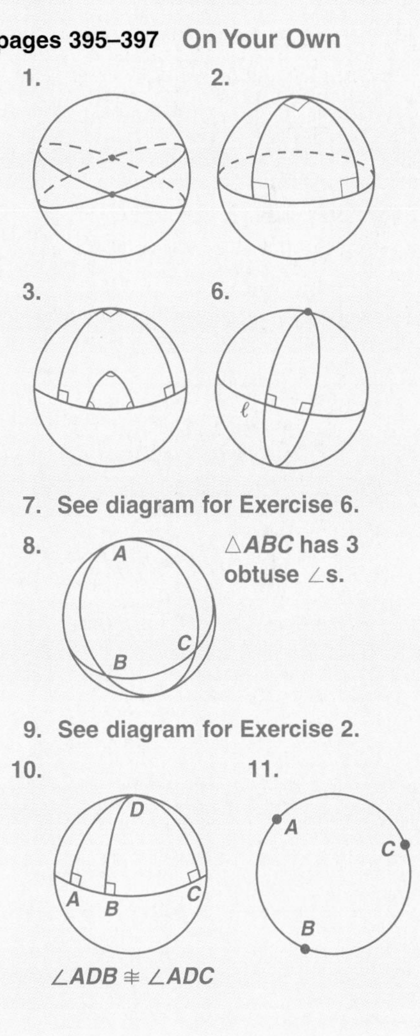

Exercises 15–19 Students will need a globe, ball, or balloon to complete these exercises. Make sure students do not write on the globes or balls but use string and tape to make the figures.

Chapter Project **FIND OUT BY MODELING** Students may want to make a two-dimensional network, like the one shown below, on which they can trace the path.

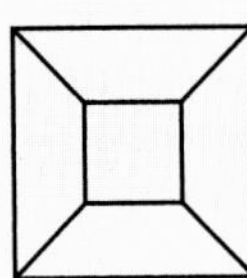

Exercises MIXED REVIEW

Exercises 21–23 Students may want to review Lesson 3-6 for properties of figures that tessellate.

SELF ASSESSMENT **PORTFOLIO** Share with students the criteria you will use to assess their work in portfolios, as well as how you plan to use the results. Students should understand how the rubrics assess their work, how each piece in the portfolio counts, and how the scores they get in their portfolios will affect their overall evaluation.

14a. Euclid's Parallel Postulate

b. alt. int. ∠s are ≅

c. Angle Addition Postulate

d. $m\angle A + m\angle B + m\angle 2 = 180$

page 397 Mixed Review

21.

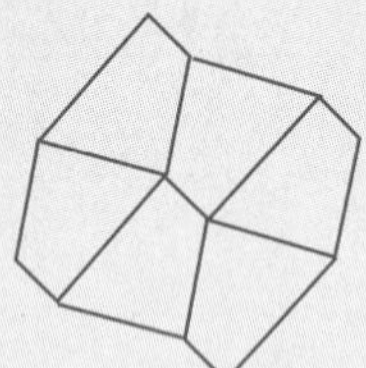

23.

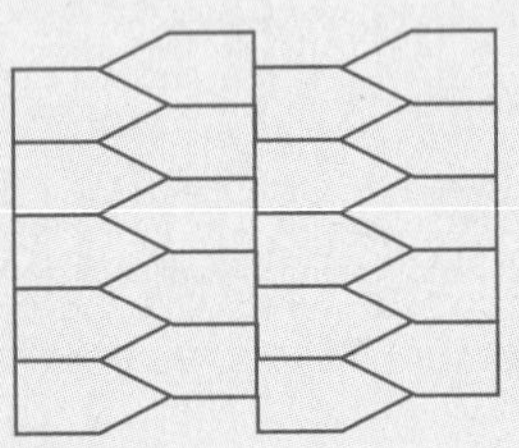

12. *Writing* This figure seems to show parallel lines on a sphere. Explain why they are not parallel lines. At least 1 of the 2 curves is not a great circle, so it is not a line.

13. *Critical Thinking* Does the concept of a *ray* have any meaning in spherical geometry? Explain. See right.

13. No; any "ray" would end up circling back on itself and would therefore be a line.

14. A well-known proof of the Triangle Angle-Sum Theorem is based on the concepts you studied in this chapter. Complete the proof. See margin.

Given: $\triangle ABC$

Prove: $m\angle A + m\angle B + m\angle 2 = 180$

By **a.** ___?___, there is exactly one line through C parallel to $\overleftrightarrow{AB}$. If two parallel lines are cut by a transversal, then **b.** ___?___, so $m\angle A = m\angle 1$ and $m\angle B = m\angle 3$. By **c.** ___?___, $m\angle 1 + m\angle 2 + m\angle 3 = 180$. By Substitution, **d.** ___?___ $= 180$.

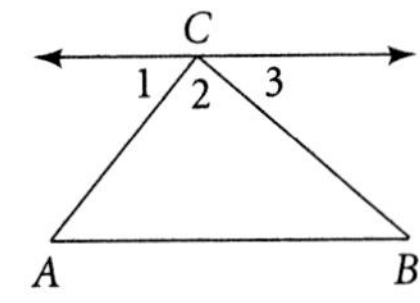

The following statements are true in Euclidean geometry. Make figures on a globe, ball, or balloon to help you decide which statements are false in spherical geometry.

15. Vertical angles are congruent. true

16. An equilateral triangle is equiangular. true

17. The base angles of an isosceles triangle are congruent. true

18. Through a point on a line ℓ there exists one and only one line perpendicular to ℓ. true

19. The measure of an exterior angle of a triangle equals the sum of the measures of its two remote interior angles. false

20. In the 19th century, the Russian mathematician Nickolai Lobachevsky (1793–1856) and the Hungarian mathematician Janos Bolyai (1802–1860) independently developed a geometry that kept all of Euclid's postulates except his parallel postulate. They assumed that, in a plane, more than one parallel can be drawn to a given line through a given point. This geometry can be modeled on a saddle-shaped surface. Lines *a* and *b* are two lines through *X* that do not intersect *c*. So, they are parallel to *c*. Consider a triangle drawn on such a surface. Is the sum of the measures of the angles of this triangle less than, equal to, or greater than 180? < 180

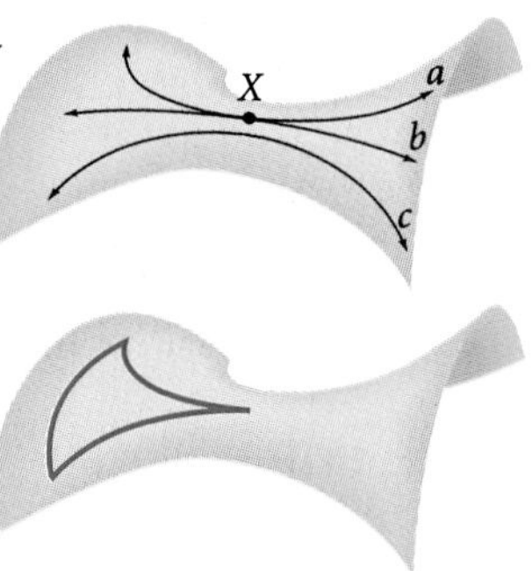

Chapter Project **Find Out by Modeling**

A snail lives in a cubical glass terrarium with edges 1 ft long. How far does the snail have to go to visit all eight vertices of the cube? How far does it have to go to travel along all twelve edges of the cube? 7 ft; 15 ft

Wrap Up

THE BIG IDEA Ask students: *Explain the meanings of line and plane in spherical geometry. Then give two examples of properties in Euclidean geometry that are not true in spherical geometry.*

RETEACHING ACTIVITY Students investigate angles in spherical geometry using a globe or ball. (Reteaching worksheet 7-5)

A Point in Time

If you have block scheduling or an extended class period you may wish to have students investigate these topics:

- Create your own map. Then determine the minimum number of colors needed to color it so that no two regions sharing a boundary are the same color.
- Research how mathematicians determine if two, three, or four colors are needed to color a map. (Actually, mathematicians are still trying to determine an efficient method for determining which maps only require three colors and which maps require four colors.)

Exercises MIXED REVIEW

Does each figure tessellate? If so, create a tessellation with it. 21, 23. See margin p. 396 for tessellation.

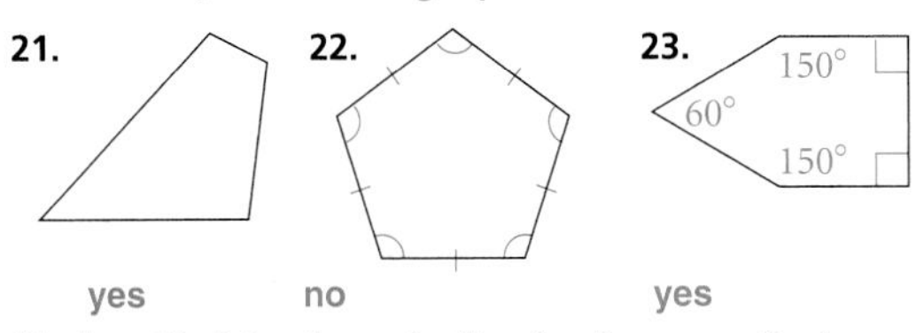

21. yes
22. no
23. yes

Algebra **Find the *slope of a line* that is perpendicular to the line with the given equation.**

24. $y = -3x - 4$ $\frac{1}{3}$
25. $y = \frac{3}{2}x + 6$ $-\frac{2}{3}$
26. $2x - y = 7$ $-\frac{1}{2}$
27. $6x + 2y = -3$ $\frac{1}{3}$
28. The altitude to the hypotenuse of an isosceles right triangle has length 5 cm. What is the area of the triangle? 25 cm^2
29. The measures of two complementary angles are in the ratio of 2 to 3. Find their measures. 36, 54
30. *Standardized Test Prep* A point (x, y) is reflected in a line parallel to the y-axis. Which point could be its reflection image? B
    A. $(2x, 2y)$ **B.** $(-2x, y)$ **C.** $(x, 2y)$ **D.** $(x, -2y)$ **E.** $(2x, -y)$

SELF ASSESSMENT

PORTFOLIO

For your portfolio, select one or two items from your work for this chapter. Here are some possibilities:
- corrected work
- most-improved work
- drawings or models you have made

Explain why you have included each selection.

A Point in Time

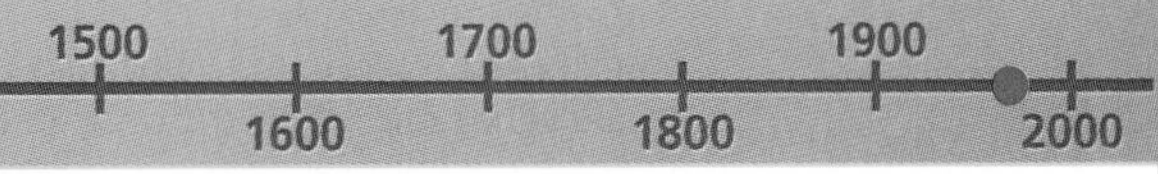

Computer Proofs

Regions that border one another on a map are shaded different colors so that you can tell them apart. Suppose that you wanted to color the regions of a map and, in doing so, use the least number of colors possible. How many would you need? As it turns out, the answer is four. Mathematicians had known this for years, but were unable to *prove* that the minimum number was four.

Then in **1976**, mathematicians Kenneth Appel and Wolfgang Haken found that all maps could be divided into 1936 categories. Using 1000 hours of computer time, they analyzed every category and proved that each could be shaded with four colors. Appel and Haken have shown the value of a computer for proving enormously complex theorems.

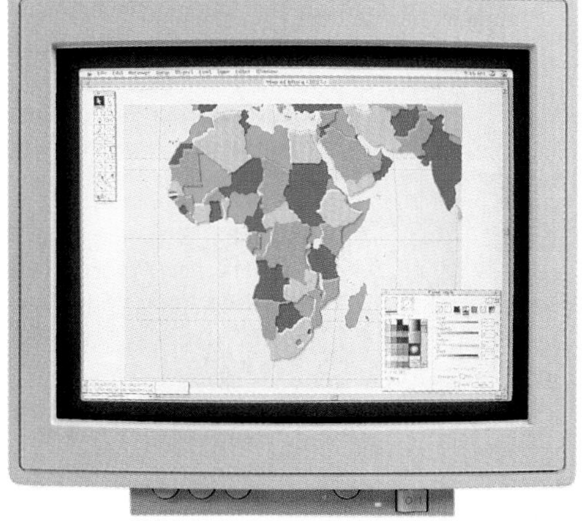

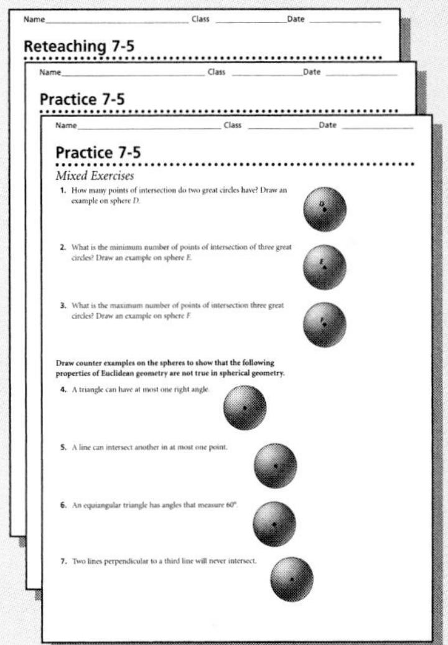

Name ________ Class ________ Date ________

Reteaching 7-5

Name ________ Class ________ Date ________

Practice 7-5

Name ________ Class ________ Date ________

Practice 7-5

Mixed Exercises

1. How many points of intersection do two great circles have? Draw an example on sphere *D*.
2. What is the minimum number of points of intersection of three great circles? Draw an example on sphere *E*.
3. What is the maximum number of points of intersection three great circles? Draw an example on sphere *F*.

Draw counter examples on the spheres to show that the following properties of Euclidean geometry are not true in spherical geometry.

4. A triangle can have at most one right angle.
5. A line can intersect another in at most one point.
6. An equiangular triangle has angles that measure 60°.
7. Two lines perpendicular to a third line will never intersect.

Lesson Quiz

Lesson Quiz is also available in Transparencies.

Decide whether the following statements are true or false in spherical geometry.

1. A triangle can have more than one obtuse angle. true
2. The measures of the angles of an equiangular triangle must be 60°. false
3. If two lines are perpendicular to a third line, then they are parallel. false
4. Two lines can intersect in more than one point. true

Finishing the Chapter Project

PROJECT DAY You may wish to plan a project day during which students share their completed projects. Encourage groups to explain their processes as well as their products.

PROJECT NOTEBOOK Have students review their project work and bring their notebooks up to date.

- Have students share their projects within groups. Ask each group to choose the network most likely to be adopted by the school.
- Have each group present for class selection the network most likely to be adopted by the school.

SCORING RUBRIC

3 Student's network design and proposal are clear and accurate. Project is well-organized and there is evidence that economic, environmental, and social issues were considered in designing the network.

2 Student's network design and proposal are clear and have only minor flaws. Project is organized and there is some evidence that economic, environmental, and social issues were considered in designing the network.

1 Student's network design and proposal are complete but contain errors. Project is organized but there is little evidence that economic, environmental, and social issues were considered in designing the network.

0 Major elements are incomplete or missing.

CHAPTER PROJECT

Finishing the Chapter Project

Network News

Find Out activities on pages 369, 382, 391, and 396 should help you complete your project. Design a network for your school, community, or another group. Here are some ideas.

- Computer network linking all the classrooms in the school
- Network of routes for school buses or city buses
- Fiber-optic network linking all cities with over half a million people

State the purpose of the network and any assumptions you made, such as budget limitations. Prepare a proposal to the decision-making body explaining the economic, environmental, and social benefits of your design.

Reflect and Revise

Ask a classmate to review your work with you. Together, check that your diagrams and explanations are clear and your information accurate. Have you taken into account the efficiency and convenience of your network? Could your project be better organized? Revise your work as needed.

Follow Up

Find out about one of the most famous problems involving networks—the Königsberg Bridge Problem. Describe the problem, its solution, and why the problem is so famous.

For More Information

Garfunkle, Solomon; Lynn Arthur Steen; and Joseph Malkevitch. *For All Practical Purposes: Introduction to Contemporary Mathematics.* New York: W. H. Freeman, 1988.

Jacobs, Harold R. *Mathematics, A Human Endeavor.* New York: W. H. Freeman, 1982.

RouteSmart Street Routing Software. Mineola, New York: Bowne Distinct, 1995.

Wrap Up

HOW AM I DOING? Have students work in small groups. Ask each group to make a short presentation explaining three important ideas from this chapter. Each presentation must include a visual aid and a sample problem.

KEY TERMS The numbers in parentheses direct students to the pages where the terms are used or defined. Students should be able to (1) write a simple explanation of each term, (2) illustrate the term with a diagram, or (3) show an example that uses the term.

Exercises 1–3 Students will need to use the theorems and postulate from Lesson 7-1 along with what they know about supplementary and vertical angles.

STANDARDIZED TEST TIP Exercise 6 Make sure that students do not confuse *complementary* and *supplementary.*

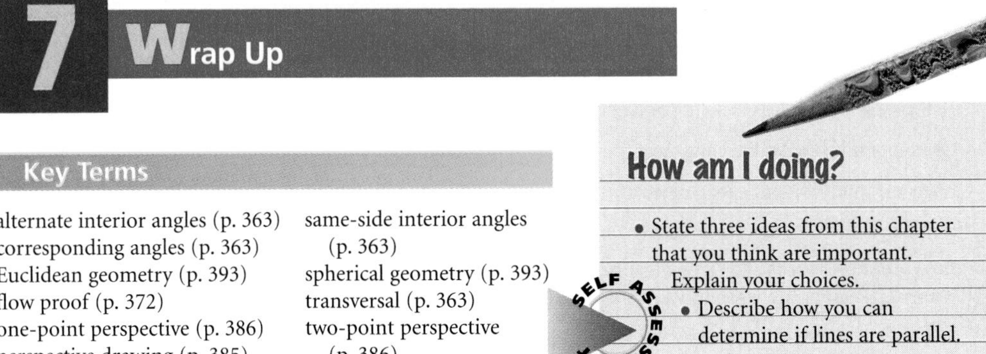

7 Wrap Up

Key Terms

alternate interior angles (p. 363)
corresponding angles (p. 363)
Euclidean geometry (p. 393)
flow proof (p. 372)
one-point perspective (p. 386)
perspective drawing (p. 385)
same-side interior angles (p. 363)
spherical geometry (p. 393)
transversal (p. 363)
two-point perspective (p. 386)
vanishing point (p. 386)

How am I doing?

- State three ideas from this chapter that you think are important. Explain your choices.
- Describe how you can determine if lines are parallel.

Parallel Lines and Related Angles — 7-1

A **transversal** is a line that intersects two coplanar lines at two distinct points. Line t is a transversal of lines ℓ and m. $\angle 1$ and $\angle 4$ are **corresponding angles.** $\angle 3$ and $\angle 4$ are **alternate interior angles.** $\angle 2$ and $\angle 4$ are **same-side interior angles.**

If two parallel lines are cut by a transversal, then the following are true.

- Corresponding angles are congruent.
- Alternate interior angles are congruent.
- Same-side interior angles are supplementary.

Find $m\angle 1$ and then $m\angle 2$. State the theorem or postulate that justifies your answer. 1–3. See margin for sample justifications.

1. 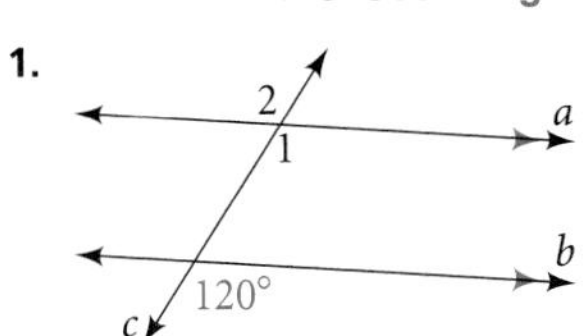

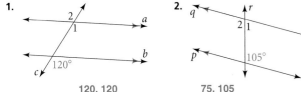

120, 120

2. 75, 105

3. 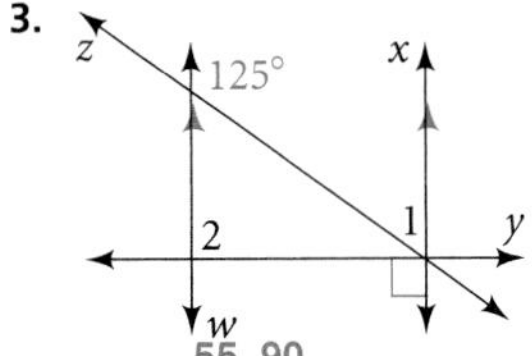

55, 90

4. *Writing* Which angles of a parallelogram must be supplementary? Explain your answer. See margin.

5. *Open-ended* Describe two corresponding angles formed by lines in your classroom. Check students' work.

6. *Standardized Test Prep* If two parallel lines are cut by a transversal, which angles could be complementary? C
   I. alternate interior angles II. same-side interior angles III. corresponding angles
   A. I only B. II only C. I and III only D. II and III only E. I, II, and III

Resources

Student Edition
Extra Practice, p. 642
Glossary/Study Guide

Teaching Resources
Study Skills Handbook
Glossary, Spanish Resources

Wrap Up pages 399–401

1. If ∥ lines, then corres. $\angle$s are $\cong$; vertical $\angle$s are $\cong$.
2. If ∥ lines, then same-side int. $\angle$s are supplementary; if ∥ lines, then alt. int. $\angle$s are $\cong$.
3. If ∥ lines, then same-side int. $\angle$s are supplementary; if ∥ lines, then alt. int. $\angle$s are $\cong$.
4. Consecutive angles; opp. sides are ∥, so same-side interior angles are supplementary.

ALGEBRA Exercises 7–9 Students can check their solutions by substituting the value of x into each expression and finding the measure of each angle.

ERROR ALERT! **Exercise 10** Some students may try to construct the parallelogram so that the opposite sides have lengths a and b. **Remediation:** Remind students that the opposite sides of parallelograms are congruent so a and b must be lengths of adjacent sides.

10.

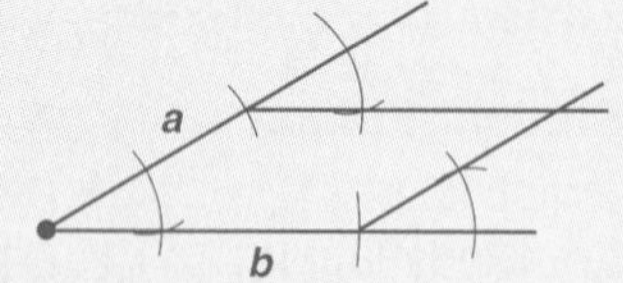

11a.

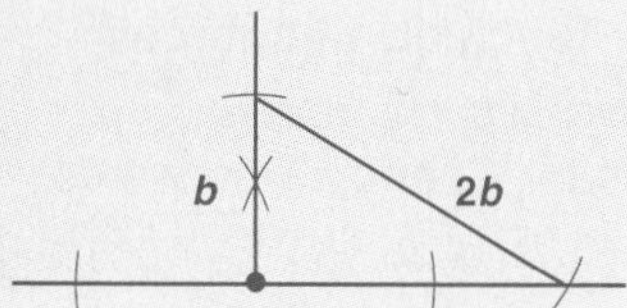

Proving Lines Parallel 7-2

Two lines cut by a transversal are parallel if any of the following are true.

- Corresponding angles are congruent.
- Alternate interior angles are congruent.
- Same-side interior angles are supplementary.

A **flow proof** uses arrows to show the logical connections between the statements. Reasons are written below the statements.

Algebra **Determine the value of x for which $\ell \parallel m$.**

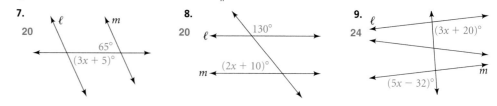

7. 20 (ℓ, m, $65°$, $(3x + 5)°$)

8. 20 (ℓ, m, $130°$, $(2x + 10)°$)

9. 24

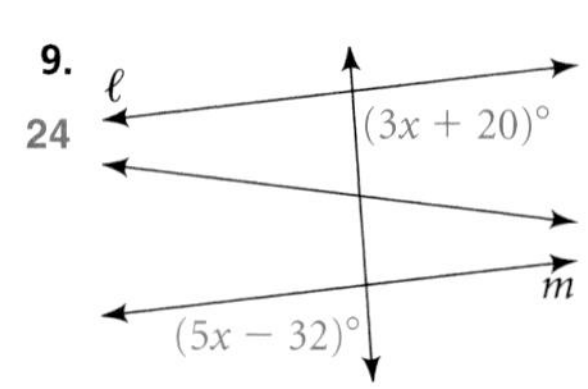

Constructing Parallel and Perpendicular Lines 7-3

You can construct a line parallel to a given line through a given point not on the line. You can also construct the perpendicular to a given line through a given point on the line or through a given point not on the line.

Use the segments at the right.

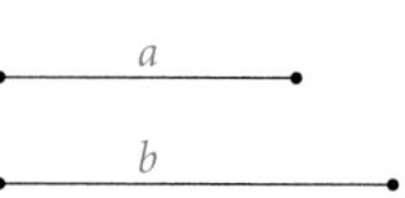

10. Construct a parallelogram with side lengths a and b. See margin.

11. a. Construct a right triangle with a leg of length b and a hypotenuse with length $2b$. See margin.

b. What is the length of the other leg? $b\sqrt{3}$

c. Critical Thinking Find the measure of each angle. 30, 60, 90

Parallel Lines and Perspective Drawing 7-4

You can use **perspective drawing** to draw three-dimensional objects on a flat surface so that they look the same as they appear to the eye. Perspective drawing involves the use of vanishing points. A **vanishing point** is a point on the "horizon" of the drawing where parallel lines "meet." When there is one vanishing point, the drawing is in **one-point perspective.** When the drawing has two vanishing points, it is in **two-point perspective.**

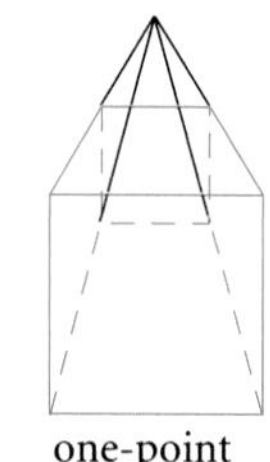
one-point perspective

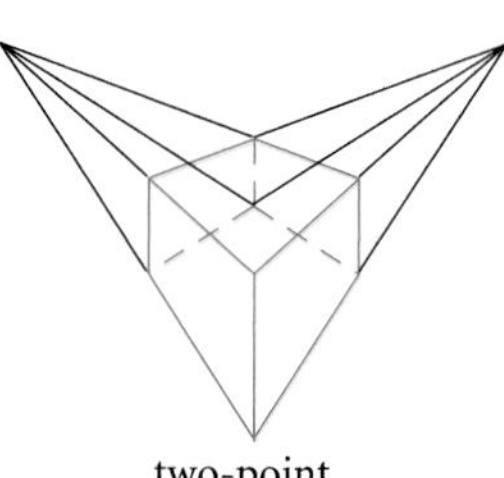
two-point perspective

ALTERNATIVE ASSESSMENT **Exercises 12–14** Another way you can assess students' understanding of perspective drawing is by asking them to draw an object in one- and two-point perspective.

Remind students that the new mathematical terms in this chapter are defined in the Glossary/Study Guide in the back of the book.

Getting Ready for Chapter 8

Students may work these exercises independently or in small groups. The skills previewed will help prepare students to prove triangles congruent.

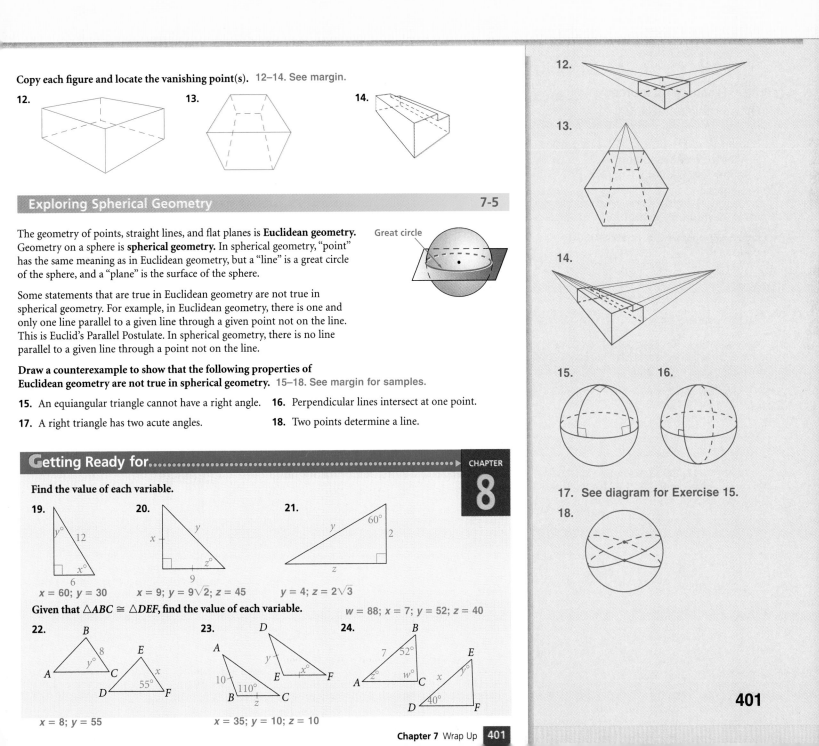

Copy each figure and locate the vanishing point(s). 12–14. See margin.

12.

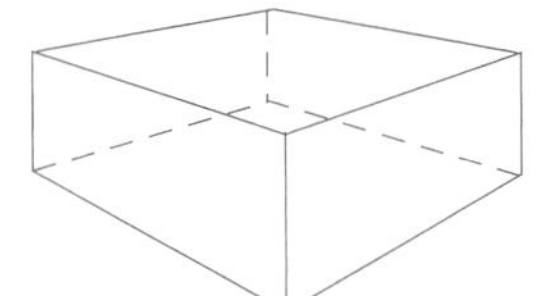

13.

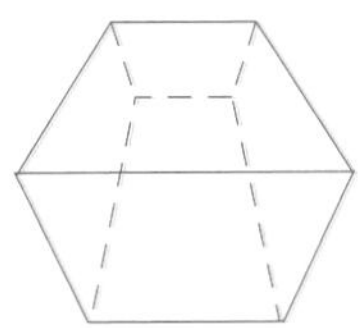

14.

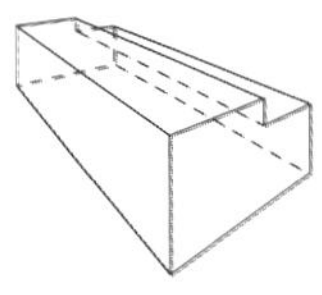

Exploring Spherical Geometry 7-5

The geometry of points, straight lines, and flat planes is **Euclidean geometry.** Geometry on a sphere is **spherical geometry.** In spherical geometry, "point" has the same meaning as in Euclidean geometry, but a "line" is a great circle of the sphere, and a "plane" is the surface of the sphere.

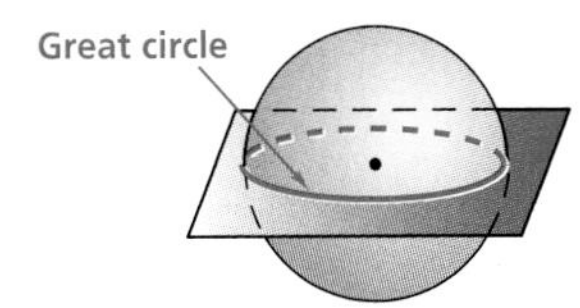

Some statements that are true in Euclidean geometry are not true in spherical geometry. For example, in Euclidean geometry, there is one and only one line parallel to a given line through a given point not on the line. This is Euclid's Parallel Postulate. In spherical geometry, there is no line parallel to a given line through a point not on the line.

Draw a counterexample to show that the following properties of Euclidean geometry are not true in spherical geometry. 15–18. See margin for samples.

15. An equiangular triangle cannot have a right angle.

16. Perpendicular lines intersect at one point.

17. A right triangle has two acute angles.

18. Two points determine a line.

Getting Ready for... CHAPTER 8

Find the value of each variable.

19. $x = 60; y = 30$

20. $x = 9; y = 9\sqrt{2}; z = 45$

21. $y = 4; z = 2\sqrt{3}$

Given that $\triangle ABC \cong \triangle DEF$, find the value of each variable.

22. $x = 8; y = 55$

23. $x = 35; y = 10; z = 10$

24. $w = 88; x = 7; y = 52; z = 40$

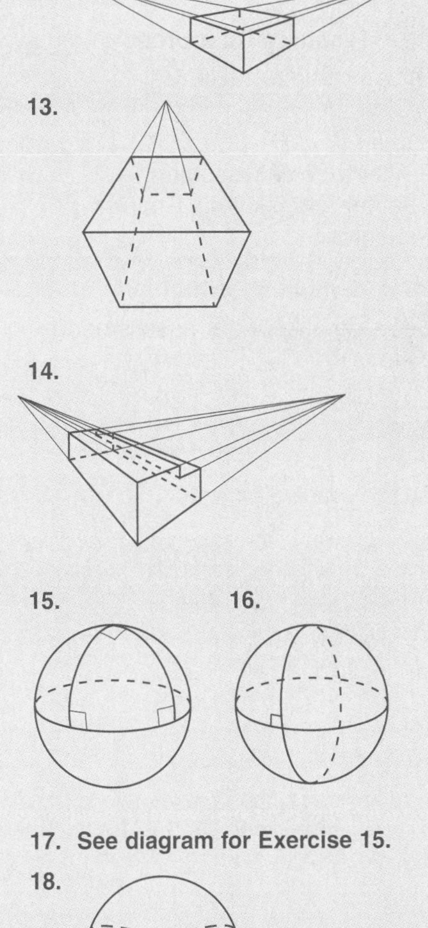

17. See diagram for Exercise 15.

18.

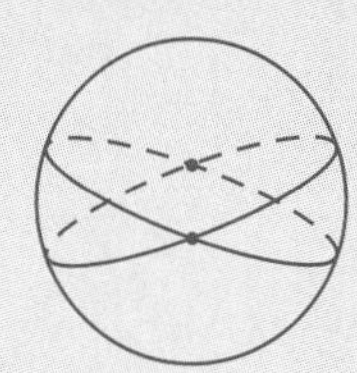

Assessment

ENHANCED MULTIPLE CHOICE QUESTIONS are more complex than traditional multiple choice questions, which assess only one skill. Enhanced multiple choice questions assess the processes that students use, as well as the end results. The questions are written so that students use more than one strategy to solve the problem. Using multiple strategies is encouraged by the National Council of Teachers of Mathematics (NCTM). **Exercise 5** is an enhanced multiple choice question.

FREE RESPONSE QUESTIONS do not give answer choices. Some exercises have more than one possible answer. Students need to give only one correct response. **Exercises 1–4, 6–15, and 17–18** are free response questions.

WRITING EXERCISES allow students to describe how they think about and understand the concepts they have learned. **Exercise 19** is a writing exercise.

OPEN-ENDED PROBLEMS allow for more than one solution. Students must construct their own responses instead of choosing from possible answers. The students' responses will help you determine the depth of their understanding and any possible areas of difficulty. **Exercise 16** is an open-ended problem.

Resources

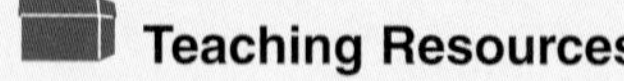

Teaching Resources

Chapter Support File, Ch. 7
- Chapter Assessment, Forms A and B
- Alternative Assessment

Chapter Assessment, Spanish Resources

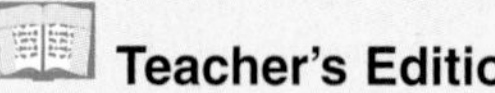

Teacher's Edition

See also p. 360E for assessment options

Software

Computer Item Generator

Assessment page 402

1. If ∥ lines, then corres. ∠s are ≅; if ∥ lines, then alt. int. ∠s are ≅.
2. If ∥ lines, then alt. int. ∠s are ≅; if ∥ lines, then same-side int. ∠s are supplementary.
3. If ∥ lines, then corres. ∠s are ≅; if ∥ lines, then same-side int. ∠s are supplementary.
4. If ∥ lines, then corres. ∠s are ≅; if ∥ lines, then same-side int. ∠s are supplementary.

10.

11.

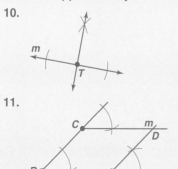

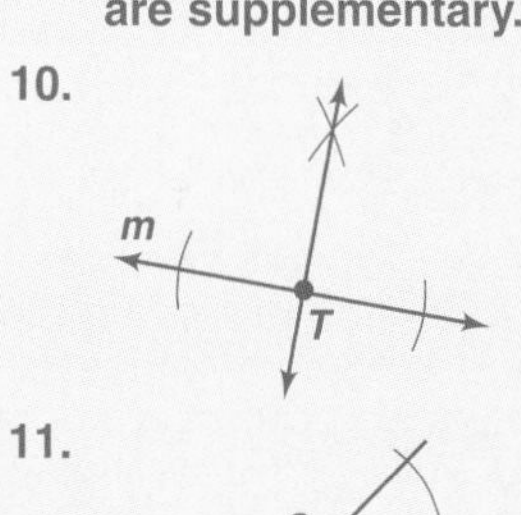

7 Assessment

1–4. See margin for sample justifications.

Find $m\angle 1$, and then $m\angle 2$. State the theorems or postulates that justify your answers.

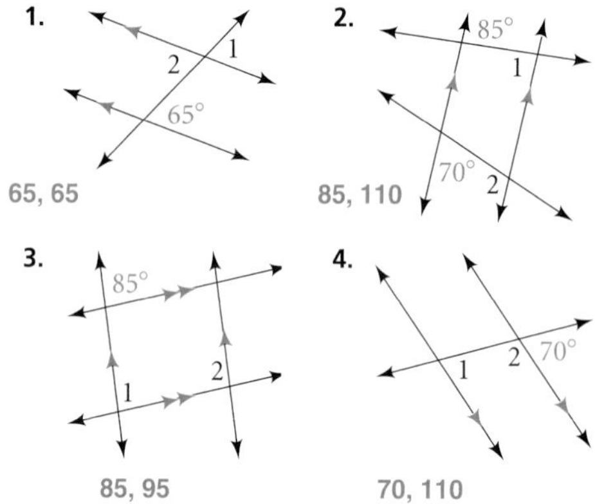

5. *Standardized Test Prep* Two lines are parallel. What could be the measures of two of their same-side interior angles? D
   I. 40 and 140 II. 90 and 90
   III. 60 and 60 IV. 27 and 27

   A. I only B. II only C. II and III
   D. I and II E. I, II, and III

Algebra **Determine the value of x for which $\ell \parallel m$.**

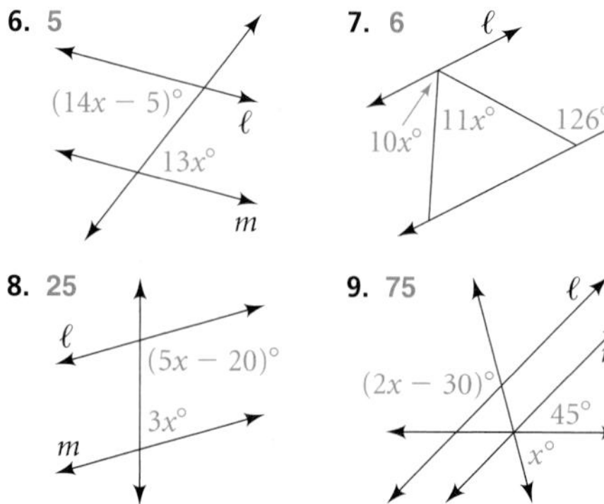

10. Draw a line m and a point T on the line. Construct a line through T perpendicular to m.
    See margin for sample.
11. Draw an angle $\angle ABC$. Then construct line m through C so that $m \parallel \overleftrightarrow{BA}$. Construct D on m so that $ABCD$ is a parallelogram.
    See margin for sample.
12. Construct a rectangle.
    See back of book for sample.

Is each object drawn in one- or two-point perspective?

13. 2-pt. perspective

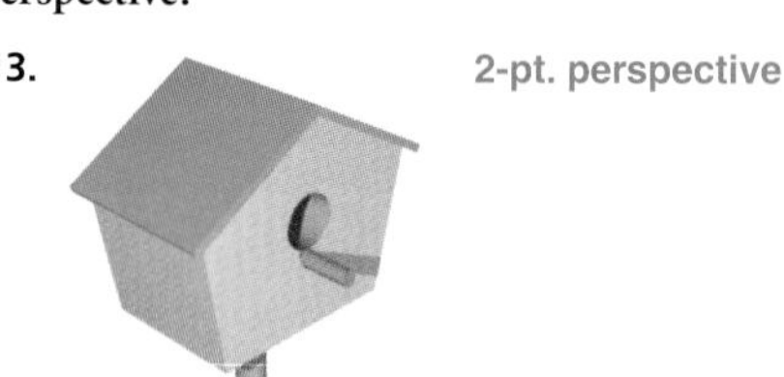

14. 1-pt. perspective

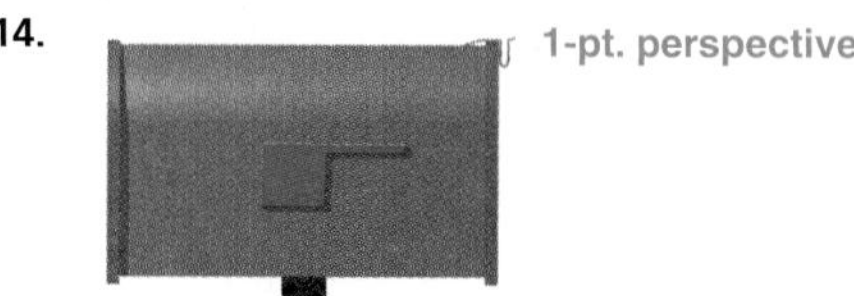

15. 2-pt. perspective

16. *Open-ended* Sketch a three-dimensional object in one-point perspective.
    See back of book for sample.

Draw a counterexample to show that the following properties of Euclidean geometry are not true in spherical geometry.

17. The measures of the angles of an equiangular triangle are 60.
18. Through any two points, there is only one line.
19. *Writing* Describe how the meanings of *point*, *line*, and *plane* differ in spherical geometry and Euclidean geometry. Include a sketch.
    17–19. See back of book for samples.

Preparing for Standardized Tests

Standardized tests, such as those administered for state assessment, the SAT, or the ACT, include regular math questions, quantitative comparison questions, open-ended problems, and free response questions (which the SAT calls *grid-ins*).

MULTIPLE CHOICE QUESTIONS are followed by five answer choices, one of which is correct. **Exercises 1–6** are multiple choice questions.

QUANTITATIVE COMPARISON QUESTIONS ask students to compare two quantities. **Exercises 7–9** are quantitative comparison questions.

FREE RESPONSE QUESTIONS do not give answer choices. Students must provide one correct answer on their own. **Exercise 10** is a free response question.

OPEN-ENDED PROBLEMS allow for more than one solution. Students must construct their own responses instead of choosing a single answer. The responses students give will help you determine the depth of their understanding and what difficulties, if any, they are experiencing. **Exercise 11** is an open-ended problem.

STANDARDIZED TEST TIP **Exercise 6** In order to solve this problem, students will need to remember that an altitude of an isosceles triangle cuts the triangle into two 30°-60°-90° triangles.

7 Preparing for Standardized Tests

For Exercises 1–9, choose the correct letter.

1. What is the surface area of a sphere with radius 7 cm? C

   A. $\frac{196}{3}\pi\text{ cm}^2$ B. $49\pi\text{ cm}^2$ C. $196\pi\text{ cm}^2$
   D. $14\pi\text{ cm}^2$ E. $\frac{1372}{3}\pi\text{ cm}^2$

2. Two of the angles of a triangle on a sphere are right angles. What could be the measure of the third angle? E

   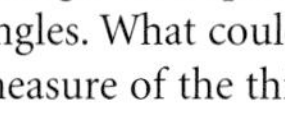

   I. 45 II. 90 III. 135 IV. 180

   A. I and II B. II and III C. III and IV
   D. I and IV E. I, II, and III

3. Which drawing is in two-point perspective? D

   A. 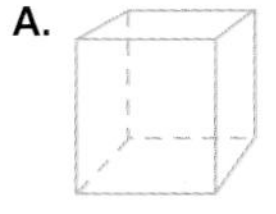

   B. 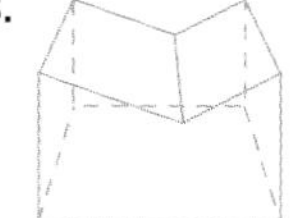
   C. 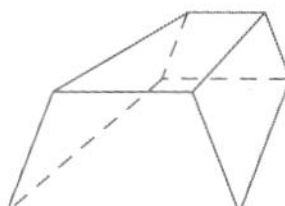
   D. 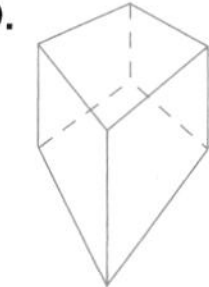

   E. none of the above

4. Which can you use to prove two lines parallel? B
   A. supplementary corresponding angles
   B. congruent alternate interior angles
   C. congruent vertical angles
   D. congruent same-side interior angles
   E. none of the above

5. What kind of symmetry does the figure have? C
   A. 60° rotational symmetry
   B. 90° rotational symmetry
   C. line symmetry
   D. point symmetry
   E. all of the above

6. One leg of an isosceles right triangle is 3 in. long. What is the length of the hypotenuse? B

   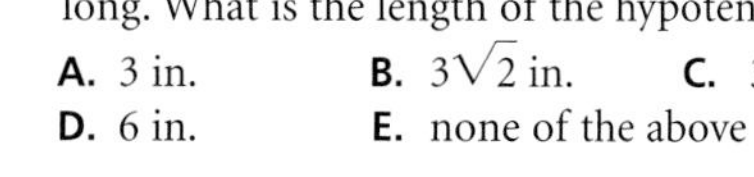

   A. 3 in. B. $3\sqrt{2}$ in. C. $3\sqrt{3}$ in.
   D. 6 in. E. none of the above

Compare the boxed quantity in Column A with the boxed quantity in Column B. Choose the best answer.

A. The quantity in Column A is greater.
B. The quantity in Column B is greater.
C. The two quantities are equal.
D. The relationship cannot be determined on the basis of the information supplied.

	Column A	Column B
7. B	the sum of the measures of the angles of a triangle in Euclidean geometry	the sum of the measures of the angles of a triangle in spherical geometry
8. A	the volume of a cone with radius 8 in. and height 9 in.	the volume of a cylinder with radius 3 in. and height 6 in.
9. B	the number of pairs of corresponding angles formed by two parallel lines and a transversal	the number of pairs of alternate interior angles formed by three parallel lines and a transversal

Find each answer. 10–11. See back of book.

10. A cone has the same radius and height as a cylinder. How are their volumes related?

11. Writing Describe two ways in which a triangle on a sphere differs from a triangle in a plane.

Resources

Teaching Resources

Chapter Support File, Ch. 7
- Standardized Test Practice
- Cumulative Review

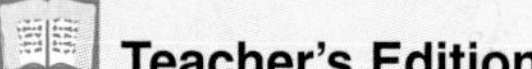

Teacher's Edition

See also p. 360E for assessment options.

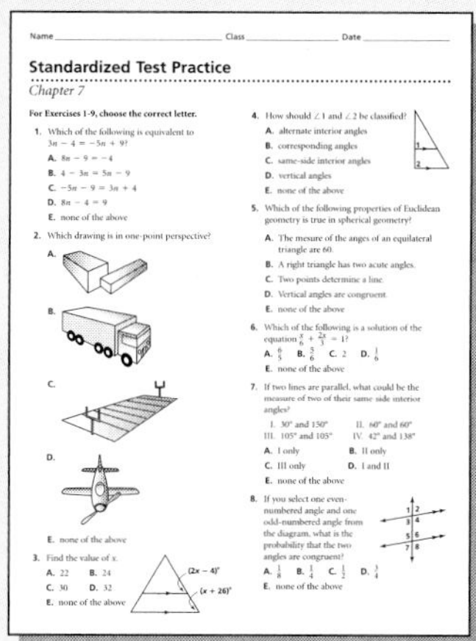

Standardized Test Practice
Chapter 7

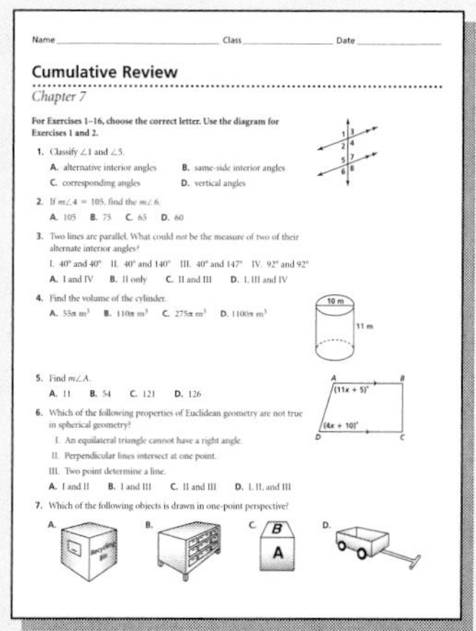

Cumulative Review
Chapter 7

CHAPTER 8

Proving Triangles Congruent

To accommodate flexible scheduling, some lessons are divided into parts. Assignment Options are given in the Lesson Planning Options for each lesson.

8-1 Proving Triangles Congruent: SSS and SAS (pp. 406–412)

Part 1 Using the SSS Postulate

Part 2 Using the SAS Postulate

Key Terms: Side-Angle-Side Postulate, Side-Side-Side Postulate

8-2 Proving Triangles Congruent: AAS and ASA (pp. 414–419)

Part 1 Using the ASA Postulate

Part 2 Using the AAS Theorem

Key Terms: Angle-Angle-Side Theorem, Angle-Side-Angle Postulate

8-3 Congruent Right Triangles (pp. 420–425)

Key Terms: Hypotenuse-Leg Theorem

8-4 Using Congruent Triangles in Proofs (pp. 426–432)

Part 1 Using CPCTC

Part 2 Proving Theorems

Key Terms: CPCTC (corresponding parts of congruent triangles are congruent)

8-5 Using More than One Pair of Congruent Triangles (pp. 433–438)

Part 1 Using Overlapping Triangles in Proofs

Part 2 Using Two Pairs of Congruent Triangles

PACING OPTIONS

This chart suggests pacing only for the core lessons and their parts, and it is provided merely as a possible guide. It will help you determine how much time you have in your schedule to cover other features, such as the Chapter Project, Math Toolboxes, Wrap Up, and Assessment.

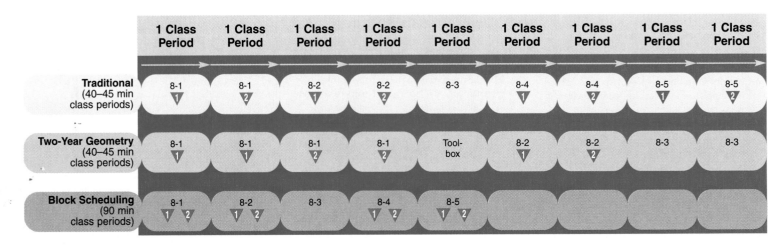

	1 Class Period	1 Class Period	1 Class Period	1 Class Period	1 Class Period	1 Class Period	1 Class Period	1 Class Period	1 Class Period
Traditional (40–45 min class periods)	8-1 Part 1	8-1 Part 2	8-2 Part 1	8-2 Part 2	8-3	8-4 Part 1	8-4 Part 2	8-5 Part 1	8-5 Part 2
Two-Year Geometry (40–45 min class periods)	8-1 Part 1	8-1 Part 1	8-1 Part 2	8-1 Part 2	Tool-box	8-2 Part 1	8-2 Part 2	8-3	8-3
Block Scheduling (90 min class periods)	8-1 Parts 1, 2	8-2 Parts 1, 2	8-3	8-4 Parts 1, 2	8-5 Parts 1, 2				

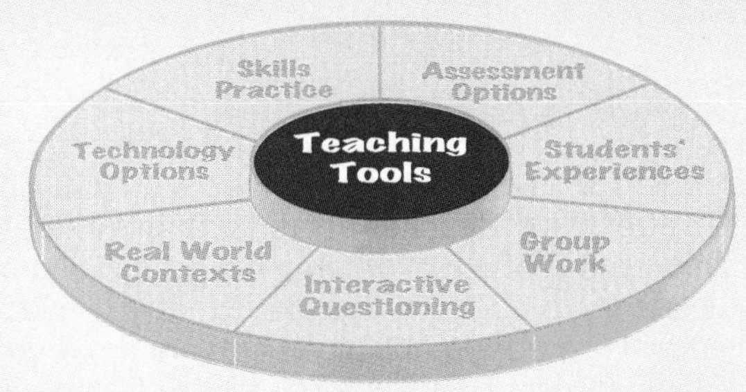

What Students Will Learn and Why

In this chapter, students build on their knowledge of triangles, learned in Chapters 2 and 4. They learn to prove two triangles congruent by the SSS Postulate, SAS Postulate, ASA Postulate, AAS Theorem, and HL Theorem. Students also learn to use triangle congruence and CPCTC to prove that parts of two triangles are congruent. Finally, students learn to identify congruent overlapping triangles and to prove two triangles congruent by first proving two other triangles congruent. Students apply these concepts to indirect measurement and learn how the concepts are applied in engineering and construction.

Discussing the Chapter/Building on Experience

The concept map below relates chapter topics to real-world applications. You and your class may wish to add to the map or develop maps of your own. The center oval describes the topic of the chapter. The next level displays topics within the lessons. The outer ovals reflect applications of the content. As you and your class build a concept map, invite students to discuss applications with which they are familiar.

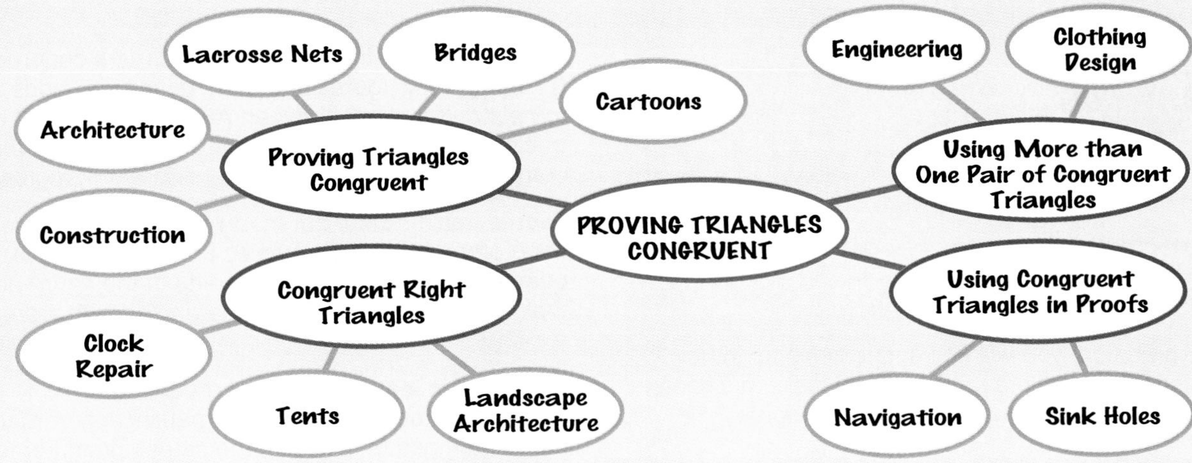

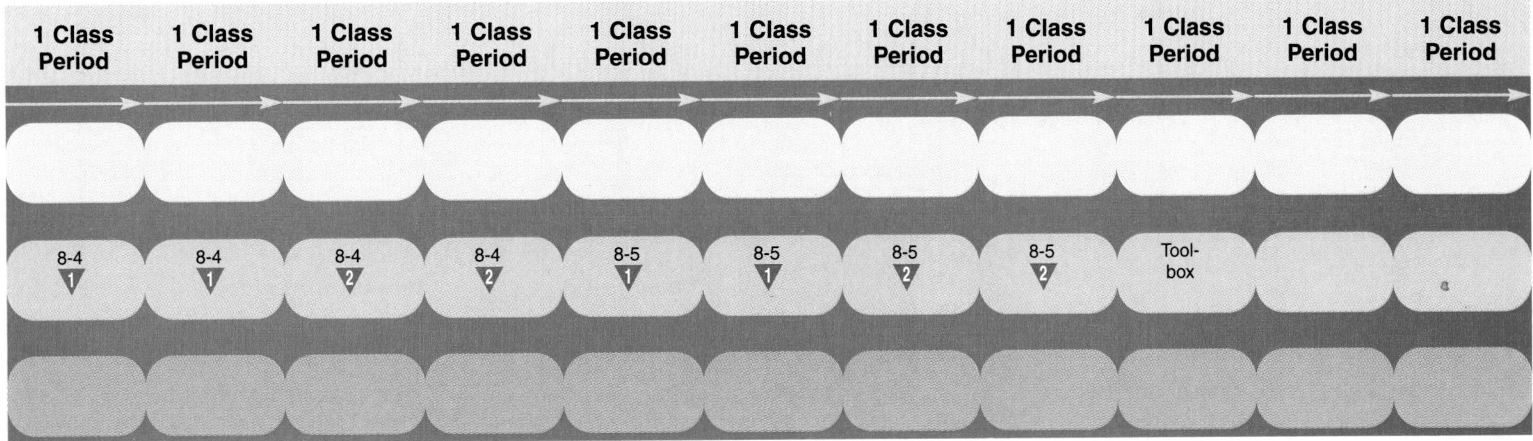

1 Class Period	1 Class Period	1 Class Period	1 Class Period	1 Class Period	1 Class Period	1 Class Period	1 Class Period	1 Class Period	1 Class Period	1 Class Period
8-4 1	8-4 1	8-4 2	8-4 2	8-5 1	8-5 1	8-5 2	8-5 2	Tool-box		

Interactive Questioning Tips

A question is interactive when there is "give and take" between the questioner (teacher or student) and the respondent. In Think and Discuss or when a critical thinking question is asked, try to adjust for the varying ability levels among students by asking questions that are appropriately challenging to the individual. This practice gives all students a chance to succeed and increases the level of participation. In Lesson 8-2, Question 6, students are asked to explain how to use the ASA Postulate. Expect gradations in students' answers.

Skills Practice

Every lesson provides skill practice with Try This exercises, Exercises On Your Own, and Exercises Mixed Review. The Student Edition includes Checkpoints (p. 425) and Cumulative Review (p. 445). In the Teacher's Edition, the Lesson Planning Options section for each lesson lists Prerequisite Skills students should know for that lesson. At the back of the Student Edition is the Skills Handbook—mini-lessons on math your students may need to review. The Chapter Support File for Chapter 7 in the Teaching Resources box includes two Practice worksheets per lesson, a worksheet for two Checkpoints, and worksheets for Cumulative Review and Standardized Test Preparation.

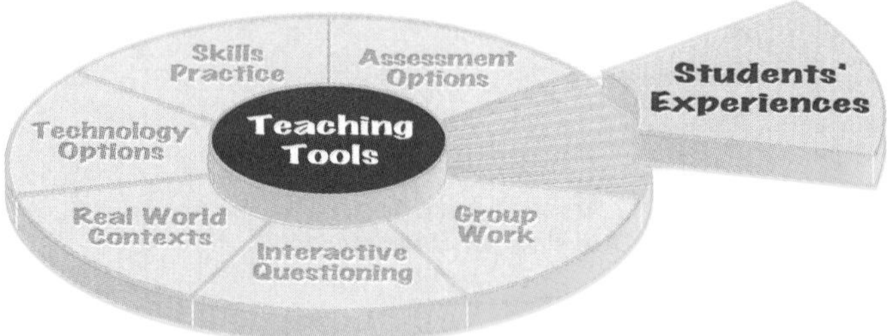

Diverse Learning and Teaching Styles

In your Teacher's Edition, you will find suggestions as to how you can help students complete mathematical tasks in Chapter 8 by reinforcing various learning styles. Here are some examples.

- **Visual learning** trace triangles and mark congruent sides (p. 407), copy figures and mark congruent sides and angles to help differentiate between ASA and AAS (p. 416), use tracing paper to redraw separately overlapping triangles in a complex figure to help visualize discrete triangles (p. 433)
- **Tactile learning** cut out triangles and place them on top of each other so the right angles match up (p. 420), draw the quadrilateral with sides as marked in the figure and justify their answers by measuring the angles with a protractor (p. 429)
- **Kinesthetic learning** use congruent triangles to measure indirectly across a football field, parking lot, or road, and then compare those results with the actual measurement (p. 427)

Alternative Activity for Lesson 8-1

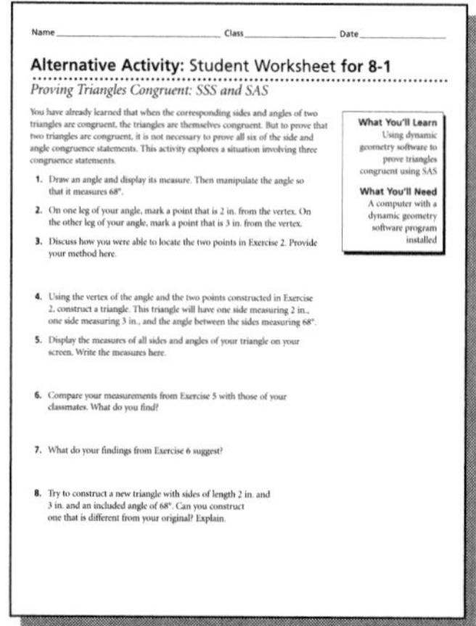
Alternative Activity: Student Worksheet for 8-1

Proving Triangles Congruent: SSS and SAS

for use with the Work Together and Think and Discuss, uses geometry software to explore the SAS Postulate.

Alternative Activity for Lesson 8-2

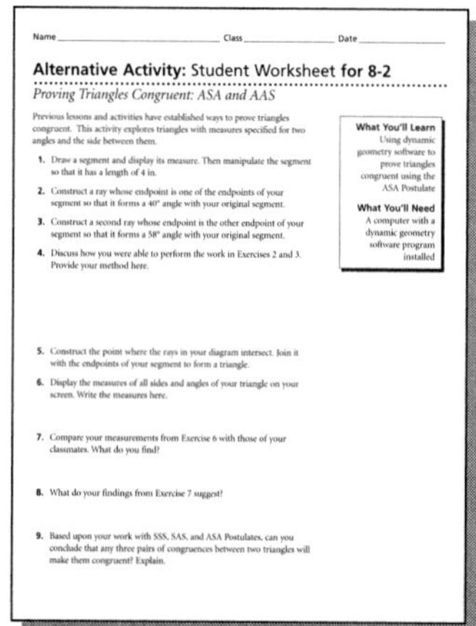
Alternative Activity: Student Worksheet for 8-2

Proving Triangles Congruent: ASA and AAS

for use with the Work Together and Think and Discuss, uses geometry software to explore the ASA postulate.

Alternative Activity for Lesson 8-3

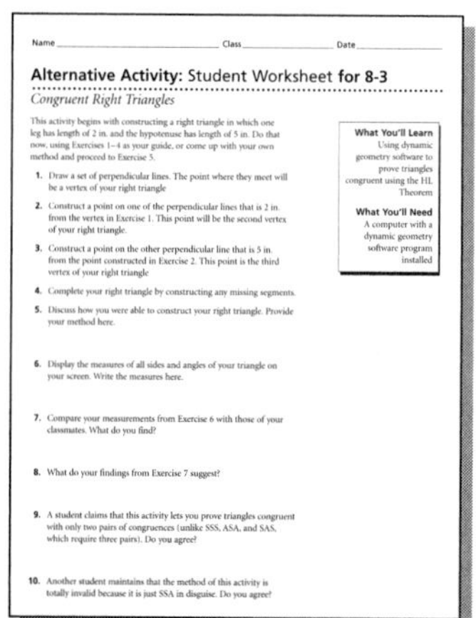
Alternative Activity: Student Worksheet for 8-3

Congruent Right Triangles

for use with the Work Together and Think and Discuss, uses geometry software to explore the HL Theorem.

Skills Practice
Assessment Options
Technology Options
Teaching Tools
Students' Experiences
Real World Contexts
Interactive Questioning
Group Work

Cooperative Learning Tips

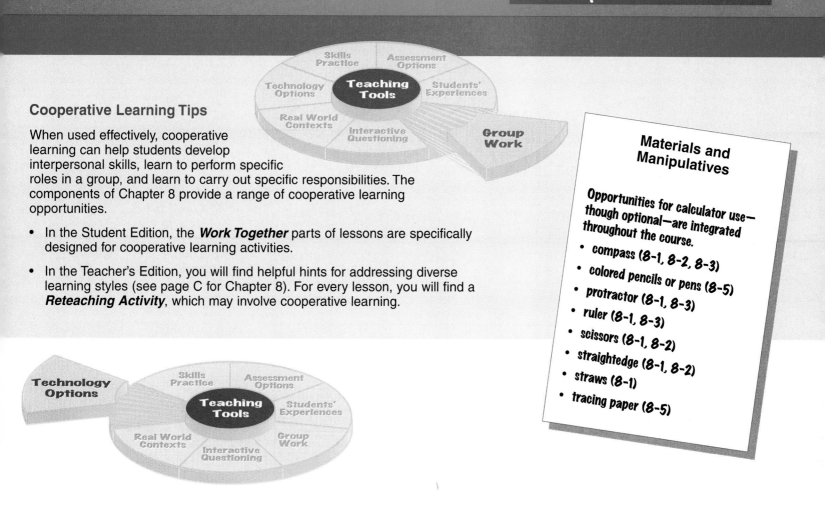

When used effectively, cooperative learning can help students develop interpersonal skills, learn to perform specific roles in a group, and learn to carry out specific responsibilities. The components of Chapter 8 provide a range of cooperative learning opportunities.

- In the Student Edition, the ***Work Together*** parts of lessons are specifically designed for cooperative learning activities.
- In the Teacher's Edition, you will find helpful hints for addressing diverse learning styles (see page C for Chapter 8). For every lesson, you will find a ***Reteaching Activity***, which may involve cooperative learning.

Materials and Manipulatives

Opportunities for calculator use—though optional—are integrated throughout the course.

- compass (8-1, 8-2, 8-3)
- colored pencils or pens (8-5)
- protractor (8-1, 8-3)
- ruler (8-1, 8-3)
- scissors (8-1, 8-2)
- straightedge (8-1, 8-2)
- straws (8-1)
- tracing paper (8-5)

Technology Options
Skills Practice
Assessment Options
Teaching Tools
Students' Experiences
Real World Contexts
Interactive Questioning
Group Work

TECHNOLOGY OPTIONS

Technology Tools		Chapter Project	8-1	8-2	8-3	8-4	8-5
Calculator	Numerous opportunities throughout for students to use scientific calculators.						
Software	Secondary Math Lab Toolkit™		✔	✔	✔	✔	✔
	Integrated Math Lab		✔	✔			
	Computer Item Generator		✔	✔	✔	✔	✔
	Student Edition		✔T				
Video	Video Field Trip	✔					
CD-ROM	Multimedia Geometry Lab		✔	✔	✔		✔
Internet	See the Prentice Hall site. (http://www.phschool.com)						

✔T indicates Math Toolbox.

The Prentice Hall Geometry program offers you a rich variety of technology options. Be assured that all these options are provided as a means of enriching the program and are not essential for the successful completion of the course.

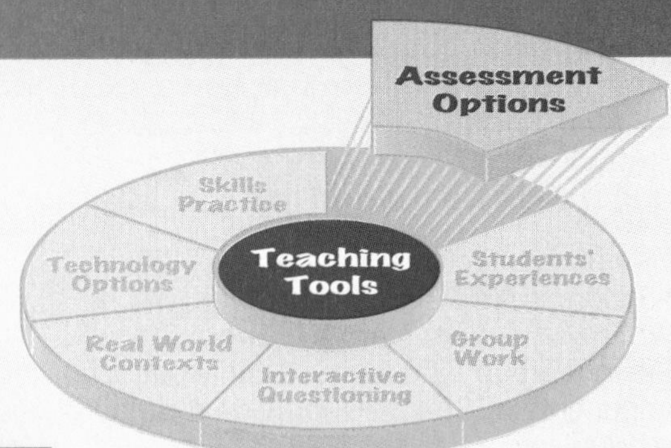

Assessment Options

The Prentice Hall Geometry Program provides you with many options. From these options, you may choose instructional materials and techniques appropriate for your students, or those necessary to meet your district's curriculum requirements. As the chart indicates, the program also supports your teaching efforts by offering you many choices for assessment.

ASSESSMENT OPTIONS

Assessment Support Materials	Chapter Project	8-1	8-2	8-3	8-4	8-5	Chapter End
Chapter Project	▲■●	▲■		▲■	▲■		▲■
Checkpoints				▲■●			
Self-Assessment		▲■	▲■			▲■	▲■
Writing Assignment		▲■	▲■	▲●		▲	●
Chapter Assessment							▲■●
Alternative Assessment		■	■	■	■	■	■●
Cumulative Review							▲■●
Standardized Test Prep			▲■	▲■		▲■	▲■●
Computer Item Generator	Can be used to create custom-made practice or assessment at any time.						

▲ = Student Edition ■ = Teacher's Edition ● = Teaching Resources

Checkpoints

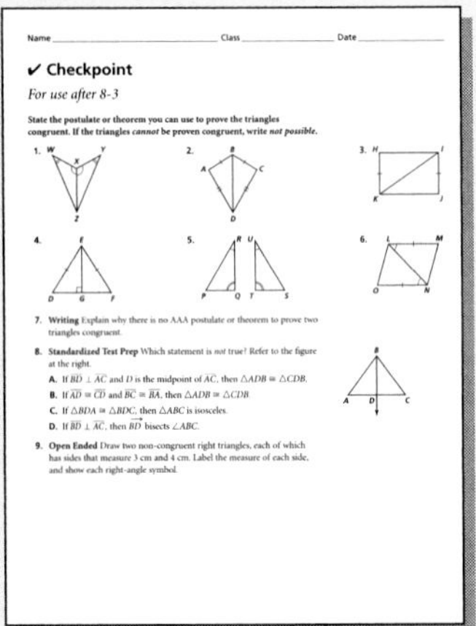
Name Class Date
✔ Checkpoint
For use after 8-3
State the postulate or theorem you can use to prove the triangles congruent. If the triangles *cannot* be proven congruent, write *not possible*.

Alternative Assessment

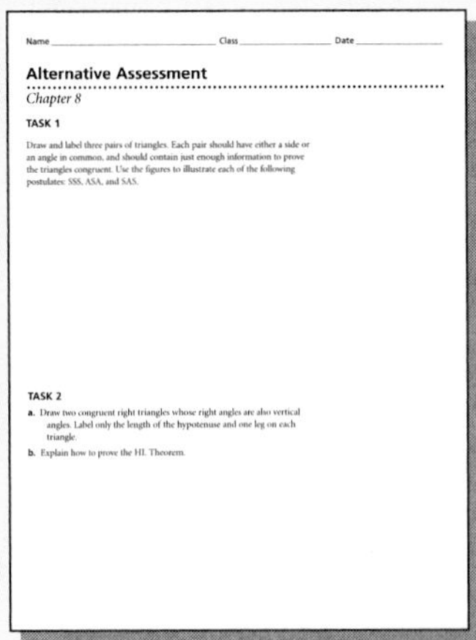
Name Class Date
Alternative Assessment
Chapter 8
TASK 1
TASK 2

Chapter Assessment

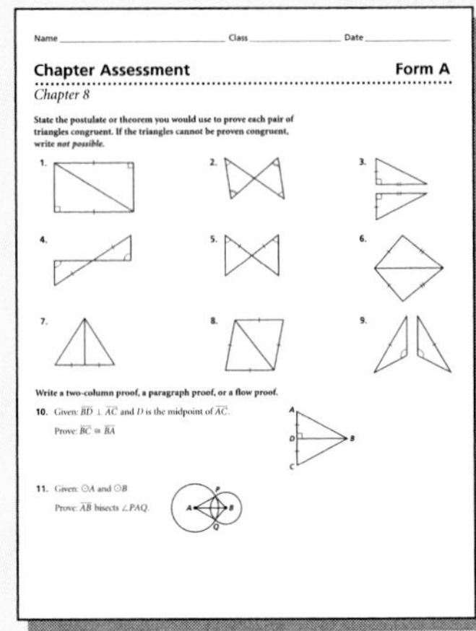
Name Class Date
Chapter Assessment Form A
Chapter 8
State the postulate or theorem you would use to prove each pair of triangles congruent. If the triangles cannot be proven congruent, write *not possible*.
Write a two-column proof, a paragraph proof, or a flow proof.

Available in both Form A and Form B

Making the Right Connections

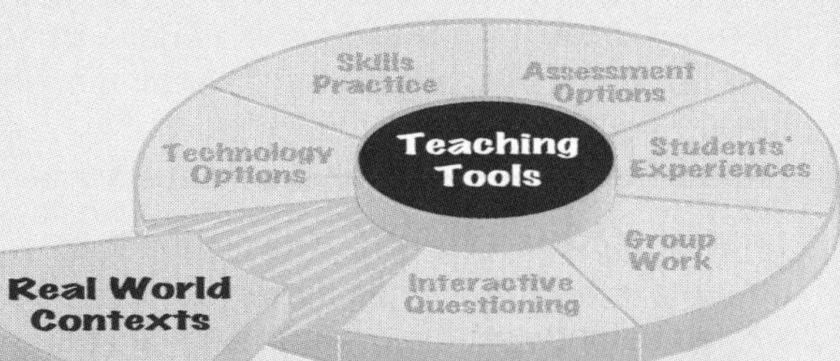

Mathematics is imbedded in nearly every walk of life. The National Council of Teachers of Mathematics (NCTM) encourages educators to recognize these connections and to emphasize them for the purpose of better educating students for success in life and in a global economy. The ***Connections*** chart below highlights these connections for Chapter 8.

CONNECTIONS

Lesson	Interdisciplinary Connections	Career Prep	Other Real World Connections	Math Integration	NCTM Standards
Chapter Project	Home Economics Engineering	Construction	Bridges Quilts		Connections Communication
8-1		Construction	Bridges Cartoons		Communication Problem Solving Reasoning
8-2	History	Die Making	Lacrosse Nets Crystals	Geometry in 3 Dimensions Probability	Communication Problem Solving Reasoning
8-3	History Science	Clock Repair Landscape Architecture	Tents	Geometry in 3 Dimensions Coordinate Geometry	Communication Problem Solving Reasoning
8-4	History		Sinkholes	Data Analysis	Communication Problem Solving Reasoning
8-5	Home Economics	Engineering	Clothing Design	Coordinate Geometry	Communication Problem Solving Reasoning

CHAPTER 8 Proving Triangles Congruent

CONNECTING TO PRIOR LEARNING Have students review the quilt designs they made for the Chapter 5 project. Have them identify figures, especially triangles, that appear congruent. Ask students why they think the figures are congruent.

CULTURAL CONNECTIONS The first bridges were made from tree trunks or large stones thrown across streams, or from twisted bamboo shoots or creepers hung across streams. Today in Japan the Akashi-Kaikyo Bridge, connecting Kobe on the mainland with Awaji on Awaji Island, measures 3910 meters in length with a center span of 1990 meters.

INTERDISCIPLINARY CONNECTIONS The development of the suspension bridge allowed large bodies of water to be spanned. The brooklyn Bridge, designed by John A. Roebling in 1869 and completed in 1883, was the first steel-wired suspension bridge. Ask interested students to present a verbal/visual report on the importance of the arch in bridge constructions: concrete arch, steel arch, continuous truss, simple truss, suspension, longspan cantilever.

ABOUT THE PROJECT Students explore how engineers use triangles to construct safe, strong, stable structures. Then they

Technology Options

Prentice Hall Technology

Video
Video Field Trip 8, "Dome on the Range," a look at the work of a geometric dome designer

CHAPTER 8 Proving Triangles Congruent

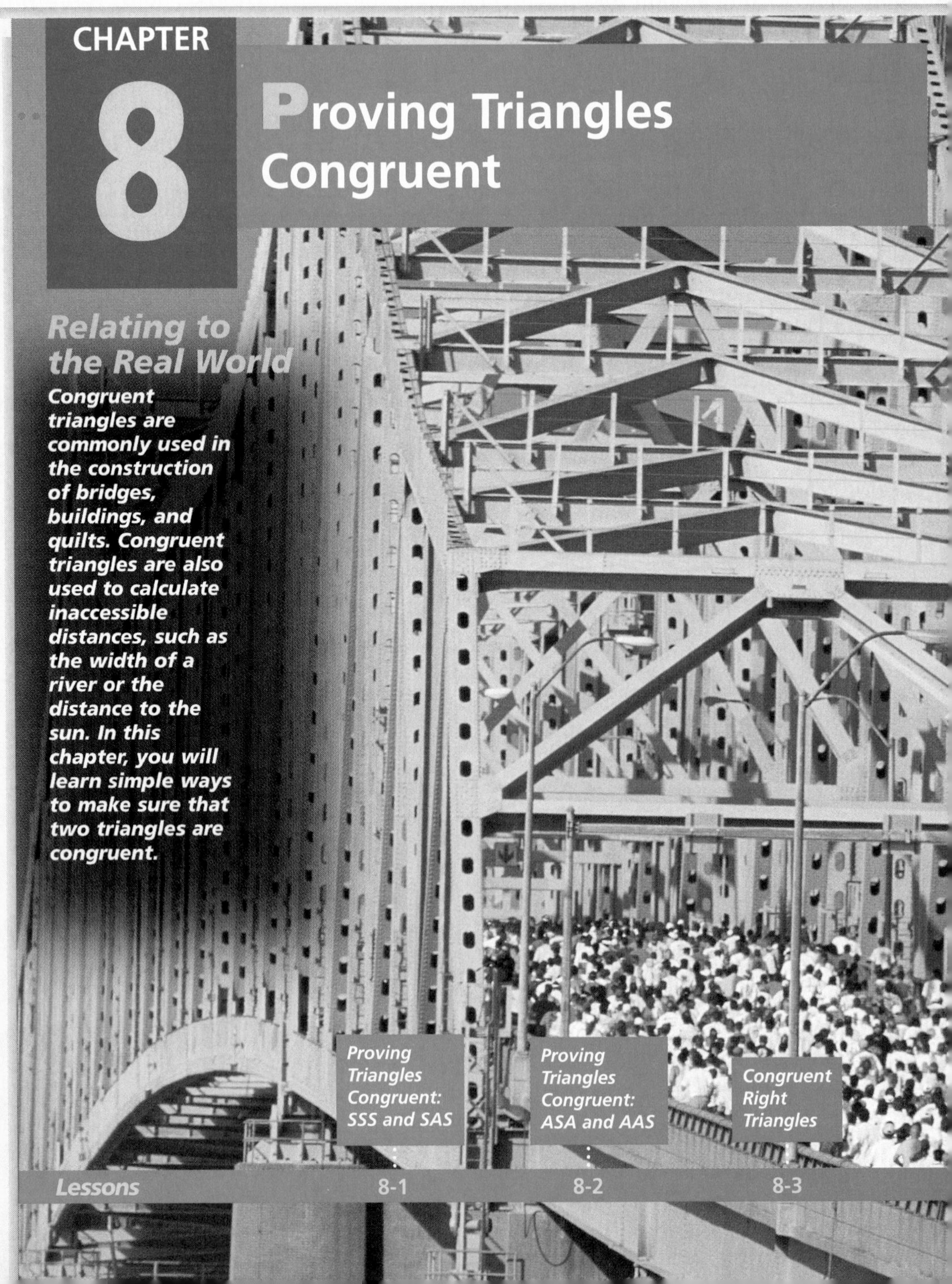

Relating to the Real World

Congruent triangles are commonly used in the construction of bridges, buildings, and quilts. Congruent triangles are also used to calculate inaccessible distances, such as the width of a river or the distance to the sun. In this chapter, you will learn simple ways to make sure that two triangles are congruent.

apply these ideas to build their own bridges using toothpicks or craft sticks.

Launching the Project

PROJECT NOTEBOOK Encourage students to keep all project-related materials in a separate folder or notebook. **See Chapter Project Manager and Scoring Rubric in Chapter Support File.**

- Ask students if they ever built a tower using playing cards. Ask them how they placed the first cards and why.
- Have students study the photographs shown on this page. Discuss why the objects were constructed as they were.

TRACKING THE PROJECT You may wish to have students read Finishing the Chapter Project on page 440 to help them get an overview of the project. Set benchmark deadlines for students to show their work in progress.

CHAPTER PROJECT

Tri Tri Again

Have you ever wondered how bridges stay up? How do such frail-looking frameworks stretch through the air without falling? How can they withstand the twisting forces of hurricane winds and the rumbling weight of trucks and trains? Part of the answer lies in the natural strength of triangles.

In your project for this chapter, you will explore how engineers use triangles to construct safe, strong, stable structures. You will then get a chance to apply these ideas as you design and build your own bridge with toothpicks or craft sticks. You will see how a simple shape can often be the strongest one.

To help you complete the project:

- p. 412 *Find Out by Modeling*
- p. 424 *Find Out by Observing*
- p. 438 *Find Out by Investigating*
- p. 440 *Finishing the Project*

Project Resources

Teaching Resources

Chapter Support File, Ch. 8
- Chapter Project Manager and Scoring Rubric

Transparencies
85

Using the Rubric

Sharing the scoring rubric for the project with your students will alert them to your expectations before they begin work on the project.

As students complete each Find Out question in the chapter, you may wish to have them evaluate their own work or a partner's work based on the scoring rubric. Students should have the opportunity to revise their work after it has been reviewed.

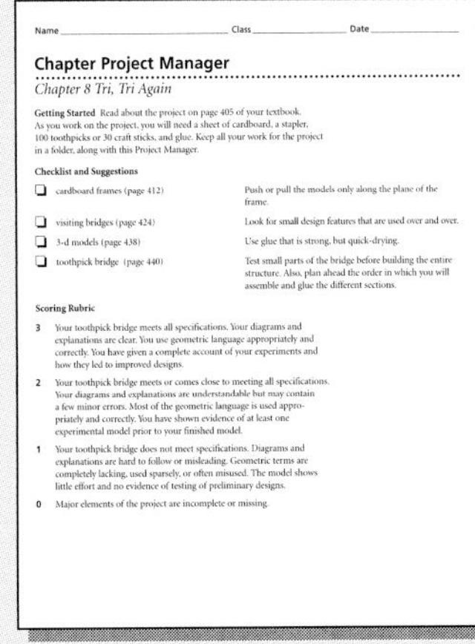

Name ________ Class ________ Date ________

Chapter Project Manager

Chapter 8 Tri, Tri Again

Getting Started Read about the project on page 405 of your textbook. As you work on the project, you will need a sheet of cardboard, a stapler, 100 toothpicks or 30 craft sticks, and glue. Keep all your work for the project in a folder, along with this Project Manager.

Checklist and Suggestions

❑ cardboard frames (page 412)	Push or pull the models only along the plane of the frame.
❑ visiting bridges (page 424)	Look for small design features that are used over and over.
❑ 3-d models (page 438)	Use glue that is strong, but quick-drying.
❑ toothpick bridge (page 440)	Test small parts of the bridge before building the entire structure. Also, plan ahead the order in which you will assemble and glue the different sections.

Scoring Rubric

3 Your toothpick bridge meets all specifications. Your diagrams and explanations are clear. You use geometric language appropriately and correctly. You have given a complete account of your experiments and how they led to improved designs.

2 Your toothpick bridge meets or comes close to meeting all specifications. Your diagrams and explanations are understandable but may contain a few minor errors. Most of the geometric language is used appropriately and correctly. You have shown evidence of at least one experimental model prior to your finished model.

1 Your toothpick bridge does not meet specifications. Diagrams and explanations are hard to follow or misleading. Geometric terms are completely lacking, used sparsely, or often misused. The model shows little effort and no evidence of testing of preliminary designs.

0 Major elements of the project are incomplete or missing.

8-1 Teaching Notes

PROBLEM OF THE DAY

The lengths of the sides of a right triangle are all integers. Two of those integers are primes that differ by 50. Compute the smallest possible length for the third side. **The two sides have length 11 and 61 and the third side has length 60.**

Problem of the Day is also available in Transparencies.

CONNECTING TO PRIOR KNOWLEDGE Draw congruent triangles on the board. Have students identify the congruent parts and then write congruence statements about the triangles.

WORK TOGETHER p. 406

Have students work in groups of four. You may want to cut the straws ahead of time and give each student six pieces of different lengths (including a 2-in., 3-in., and 4-in. piece).

ALTERNATIVE METHOD Have students use geometry software to construct a triangle. Then have them construct another triangle with the same side lengths. Students can then answer Questions 1–2 of the Work Together.

THINK AND DISCUSS p. 406

Review with students the importance of naming corresponding parts in the same order when writing congruence statements for triangles.

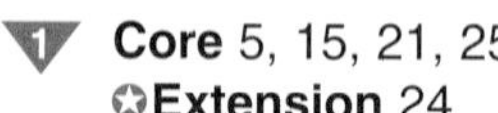

Lesson Planning Options

Prerequisite Skills

- Understanding congruence
- Constructing angles and segments

Assignment Options for Exercises On Your Own

To provide flexible scheduling, this lesson can be subdivided into parts.

1. **Core** 5, 15, 21, 25
   ✪**Extension** 24
2. **Core** 1–4, 6–14, 16–18
   ✪**Extension** 19–20, 22–23

Use Mixed Review to maintain skills.

Resources

Student Edition

Skills Handbook, p. 664
Extra Practice, p. 655
Glossary/Study Guide

Teaching Resources

Chapter Support File, Ch. 8
- Practice 8-1 (two worksheets)
- Reteaching 8-1
- Alternative Activity 8-1

Classroom Manager 8-1
Glossary, Spanish Resources

Transparencies

86, 89

Connections Bridges . . . and more

8-1 Proving Triangles Congruent: SSS and SAS

What You'll Learn

- Proving two triangles congruent using the SSS and SAS postulates

...And Why

To develop an understanding of congruent triangles, which are important in the design and construction of buildings and bridges

What You'll Need

- protractor
- ruler
- straws
- scissors
- compass
- straightedge

WORK TOGETHER

- Have each person in your group use straws to make a triangle with sides 2 in., 3 in., and 4 in. long. Compare your triangles.

1. Make a **conjecture** about two triangles in which three sides of one triangle are congruent to three sides of the other triangle. **They are ≅.**
2. **Verify** your conjecture by selecting other lengths for the sides of a triangle. Have each person in your group make the triangle. Compare your triangles. **Check students' work.**

THINK AND DISCUSS

Part 1

Using the SSS Postulate

In Lesson 2-6, you learned that if two triangles have three pairs of congruent corresponding angles and three pairs of congruent corresponding sides, then the triangles are congruent.

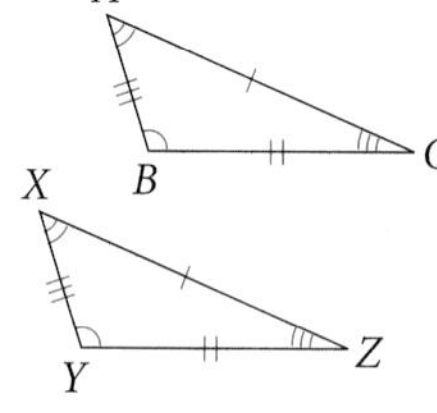

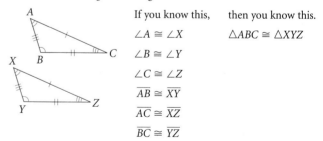

If you know this,	then you know this.
$\angle A \cong \angle X$	$\triangle ABC \cong \triangle XYZ$
$\angle B \cong \angle Y$	
$\angle C \cong \angle Z$	
$\overline{AB} \cong \overline{XY}$	
$\overline{AC} \cong \overline{XZ}$	
$\overline{BC} \cong \overline{YZ}$	

In the Work Together, you discovered that you don't need all six of the congruence statements to ensure that two triangles are congruent. If you know that corresponding sides are congruent, then you know that the triangles are congruent.

Postulate 8-1
Side-Side-Side Postulate (SSS Postulate)

If three sides of one triangle are congruent to three sides of another triangle, then the two triangles are congruent.

$\triangle GHF \cong \triangle PQR$

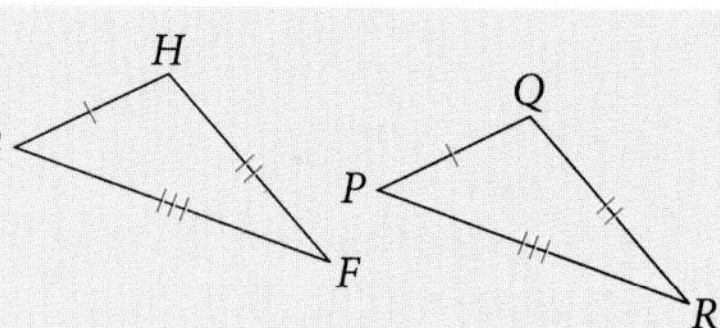

Side-Side-Side Postulate Point out to students that this postulate is abbreviated "SSS Postulate" where "S" stands for "Side."

Example 1 ***Relating to the Real World*** 

VISUAL LEARNING Some students may have difficulty seeing that the three sides are congruent. It may help if they trace $\triangle ABD$ and $\triangle CBD$ separately and then mark the congruent sides.

Point out to students that the proof would be incomplete without Statement 4 in the proof. Make sure students write "SSS Postulate " and not just "SSS" because they will be learning the SSS Similarity Theorem in Lesson 10-2.

Question 4 Remind students not to assume information that is not explicitly stated or which they cannot justify. In this example, $\overline{RK}$ and $\overline{ST}$ may look congruent but cannot be assumed to be congruent.

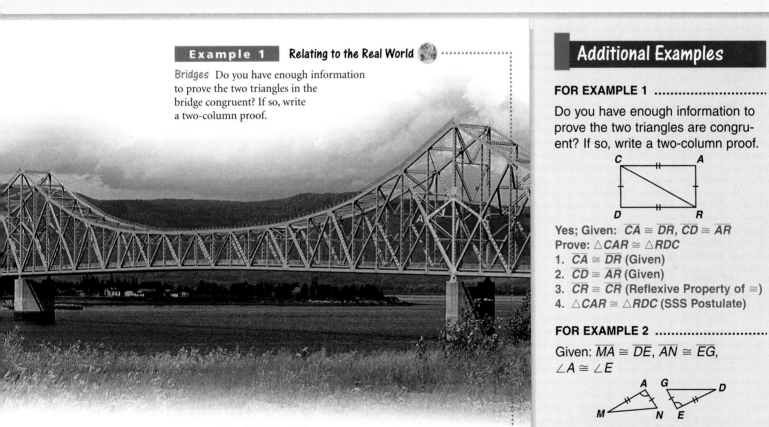

Example 1 ***Relating to the Real World***

Bridges Do you have enough information to prove the two triangles in the bridge congruent? If so, write a two-column proof.

Given: $\overline{AB} \cong \overline{CB}, \overline{AD} \cong \overline{CD}$
Prove: $\triangle ABD \cong \triangle CBD$

Plan for Proof To prove the triangles are congruent, you can use the SSS Postulate. You are given that two pairs of sides are congruent. You can use the Reflexive Property of Congruence to show that $\overline{BD}$ in $\triangle ABD$ is congruent to $\overline{BD}$ in $\triangle CBD$.

Statements	Reasons
1. $\overline{AB} \cong \overline{CB}$	1. Given
2. $\overline{AD} \cong \overline{CD}$	2. Given
3. $\overline{BD} \cong \overline{BD}$	3. Reflexive Property of $\cong$
4. $\triangle ABD \cong \triangle CBD$	4. SSS Postulate

QUICK REVIEW

The Reflexive Property of Congruence tells you that a segment, such as $\overline{BD}$ in this figure, is congruent to itself. It also tells you that an angle is congruent to itself.

3. A two-column proof is just one way to write this proof. Rewrite the proof as a paragraph proof or as a flow proof. See left.

4. **Try This** $\overline{RS} \cong \overline{TK}$. What additional information do you need to prove that $\triangle RSK \cong \triangle TKS$ by the SSS Postulate? $\overline{RK} \cong \overline{TS}$

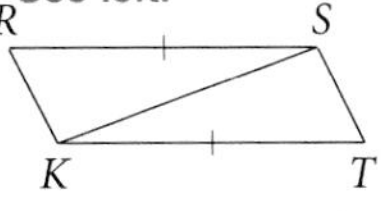

3. Answers may vary. Sample: By Reflexive Prop. of $\cong$, $\overline{BD} \cong \overline{BD}$. Since $\overline{AB} \cong \overline{CB}$ and $\overline{AD} \cong \overline{CD}$, 3 corres. sides of the 2 $\triangle$s are $\cong$. The $\triangle$s are $\cong$ by SSS.

Additional Examples

FOR EXAMPLE 1

Do you have enough information to prove the two triangles are congruent? If so, write a two-column proof.

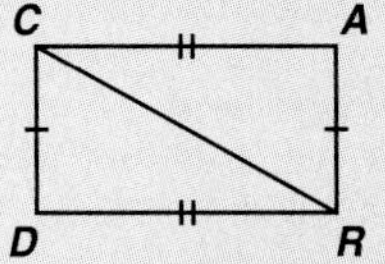

Yes; Given: $\overline{CA} \cong \overline{DR}, \overline{CD} \cong \overline{AR}$
Prove: $\triangle CAR \cong \triangle RDC$
1. $\overline{CA} \cong \overline{DR}$ (Given)
2. $\overline{CD} \cong \overline{AR}$ (Given)
3. $\overline{CR} \cong \overline{CR}$ (Reflexive Property of $\cong$)
4. $\triangle CAR \cong \triangle RDC$ (SSS Postulate)

FOR EXAMPLE 2

Given: $\overline{MA} \cong \overline{DE}, \overline{AN} \cong \overline{EG}$, $\angle A \cong \angle E$

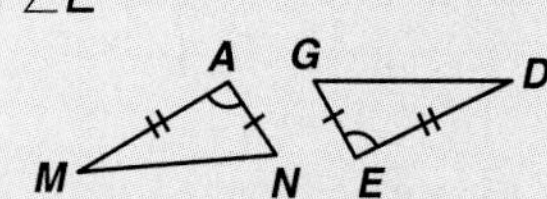

From the given information, can you prove $\triangle MAN \cong \triangle DEG$? Explain.

Yes; $\angle A$ is the included angle between $\overline{MA}$ and $\overline{AN}$ and $\angle E$ is the included angle between $\overline{DE}$ and $\overline{EG}$. These triangles are congruent by the SAS Postulate.

WORK TOGETHER p. 408

It is important that students construct the angles and sides accurately using Constructions 1 and 2 on page 40 in order to get the desired results, two congruent triangles.

ALTERNATIVE METHOD Have students use geometry software to perform the constructions in the Work Together.

THINK AND DISCUSS p. 408

Point out the relationship between the names of the two angles and their included side (the vertices of the angles are the endpoints of the side) and the names of the two sides and their included angle (the endpoint shared by both sides is the vertex of the angle).

ESL Review the word *included* with students. Use the term colloquially: "included in a group," "batteries included," etc. and contrast with *excluded*. Stress the importance of included in the statement of the SAS Postulate.

ERROR ALERT! Question 8 Some students may not understand the significance of the angle being included and may think that choosing any pair of corresponding sides is sufficient. **Remediation:** You may want to provide students with an example of two non-congruent triangles with two congruent sides and a non-included congruent angle.

Technology Options

For Exercises 5 and 24, students may use geometry software to draw the triangles. For Exercise 25, students may use geometry software to draw the quadrilateral.

Prentice Hall Technology

Software
- Secondary Math Lab Toolkit™
- Integrated Math Lab 37
- Computer Item Generator 8-1

CD-ROM
- Multimedia Geometry Lab 8

Internet
- See the Prentice Hall site. (http://www.phschool.com)

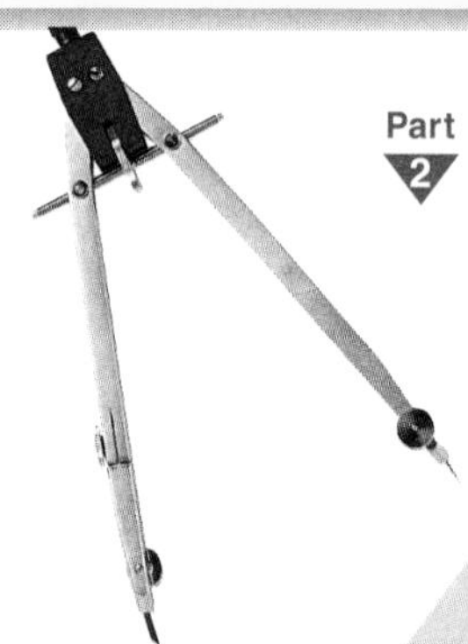

Part 2

WORK TOGETHER

Work in groups of three.

- Have each person use a straightedge to draw one of the following types of triangles: acute, obtuse, right. Make sure that at least one of the triangles is scalene. Label your triangle $\triangle HAM$.
- Exchange triangles within your group. Use a compass and straightedge to construct a copy of $\angle H$. Label the angle $\angle L$.
- On one side of $\angle L$, construct $\overline{LT}$ congruent to $\overline{HM}$. On the other side of $\angle L$, construct $\overline{LE}$ congruent to $\overline{HA}$. Draw $\overline{ET}$, forming $\triangle LET$.
- Cut out the triangles. Place one triangle over the other so that the corresponding parts match.

5. Make a **conjecture.** What seems to be true when an angle of one triangle is congruent to an angle of another triangle, and the two pairs of sides that form these angles are congruent? **The $\triangle$s are $\cong$.**

THINK AND DISCUSS

Using the SAS Postulate

The word *included* is used frequently when referring to the angles and the sides of a triangle.

$\overline{AN}$ is included between $\angle N$ and $\angle A$.

$\angle C$ is included between $\overline{NC}$ and $\overline{AC}$.

6. Which angle is included between $\overline{NC}$ and $\overline{AN}$? **$\angle N$**
7. Which side is included between $\angle C$ and $\angle N$? **$\overline{NC}$**

The conjecture you made in the Work Together suggests another important postulate for proving triangles congruent.

Postulate 8-2
Side-Angle-Side Postulate (SAS Postulate)

If two sides and the included angle of one triangle are congruent to two sides and the included angle of another triangle, then the two triangles are congruent.

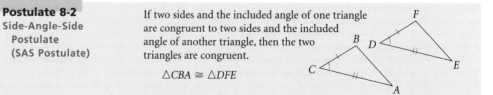

$\triangle CBA \cong \triangle DFE$

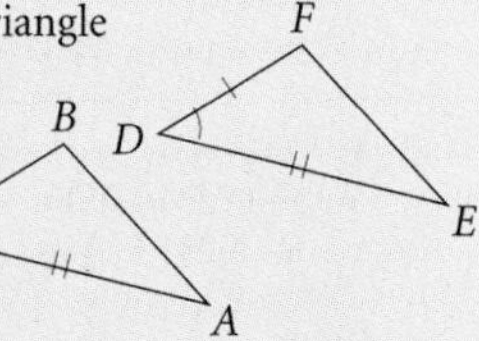

Example 2

Point out that you cannot prove $\triangle RED \cong \triangle CAT$ by the SSS Postulate or the SAS Postulate because you do not know $\overline{DE} \cong \overline{AT}$ or $\angle R \cong \angle C$. This does not mean that they are not congruent, however. To prove they are *not* congruent, you would need to show a pair of corresponding sides or a pair of corresponding angles are *not* congruent.

Question 9 Since all angles and all sides of an equilateral triangle are congruent, students may be confused as to which sides and angles are corresponding. In this example, they can use the triangle congruence statement to determine which sides must correspond.

Question 10 Ask students what kind of triangles $\triangle RED$ and $\triangle CAT$ are and what is special about their angles.

Exercises ON YOUR OWN

Exercises 3–4 Students sometimes are confused when the triangles have different orientations. You may want to ask students to write congruence statements as a way to check their ability to recognize corresponding parts.

---

8. **Try This** What additional information do you need to prove the triangles congruent by the SAS Postulate?

   a.

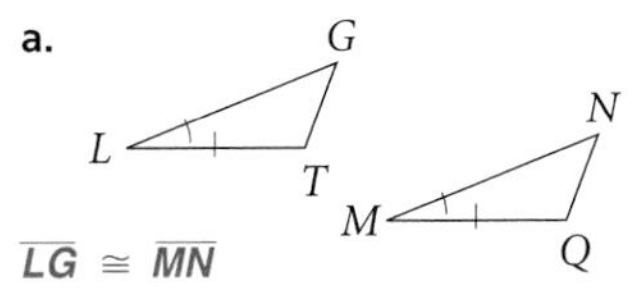

$\overline{LG} \cong \overline{MN}$

   b.

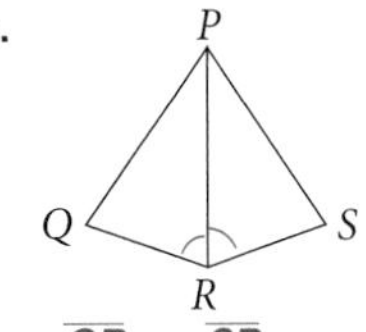

$\overline{QR} \cong \overline{SR}$

Example 2

Given: $\overline{RE} \cong \overline{CA}$, $\overline{RD} \cong \overline{CT}$, $\angle R \cong \angle T$

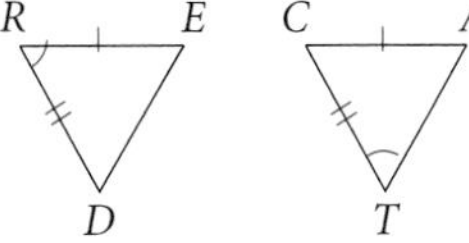

From the information given, can you prove $\triangle RED \cong \triangle CAT$? Explain.

No, there is not enough information to prove $\triangle RED \cong \triangle CAT$. $\angle T$ is not *included* between the congruent sides. $\triangle RED$ may or may not be congruent to $\triangle CAT$.

9. **Try This** In Example 2, suppose you also know that $\triangle CAT$ is equilateral. Can you prove $\triangle RED \cong \triangle CAT$? Explain. **See left.**

9. Yes; an equilateral $\triangle$ is also equiangular, so $\angle C \cong \angle T \cong \angle R$. The $\triangle$s are $\cong$ by SAS.

10. **Try This** Suppose that in Example 2, $RE = CA = RD = CT = 7$ and $m\angle R = m\angle T = 58$. **See margin.**
    a. Sketch each figure, labeling angles and sides with their measures.
    b. Can you prove that $\triangle RED \cong \triangle CAT$? Explain.
    No; since both $\triangle$s are isosceles, $m\angle C = 64$ and the included angles are $\not\cong$.

Exercises ON YOUR OWN

Try to answer these questions without drawing a figure.

1. Which side is included between $\angle X$ and $\angle Z$ in $\triangle XYZ$? $\overline{XZ}$
2. Which angle is included between $\overline{XY}$ and $\overline{XZ}$ in $\triangle XYZ$? $\angle X$

Name the triangle congruence postulate you can use to prove each pair of triangles congruent.

3. SAS

4. SSS

pages 408–409 Think and Discuss

10a.

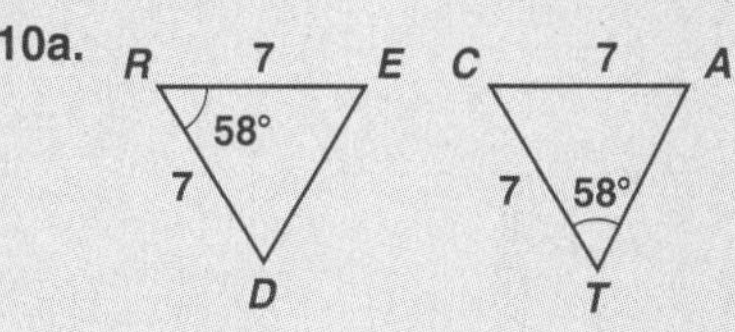

ALTERNATIVE ASSESSMENT Exercises 6–14 Another way to check students' understanding of the SSS and SAS Postulates is to have them draw pairs of triangles with three pairs of corresponding parts. Then have them exchange drawings with a partner and decide if the information given is enough to prove the triangles congruent.

ESL Exercises 6–14 These exercises rely on visual cues and provide a good opportunity to assess ESL students' understanding of the SSS and SAS Postulates.

OPEN-ENDED Exercise 15 Students can use Example 1 and Exercises 3–4 as models. They may want to draw the objects first, then outline the triangles on the figures.

5. ***Critical Thinking*** Suppose a friend insists that since you can prove triangles congruent using the SSS Congruence Postulate, there should be an AAA Congruence Postulate. Draw two triangles that will show that your friend's assumption is incorrect.

Sample:

Decide whether you can use the SSS or SAS Postulate to prove that the triangles below are congruent. If so, write the congruence and identify the postulate. If not, write *not possible.*

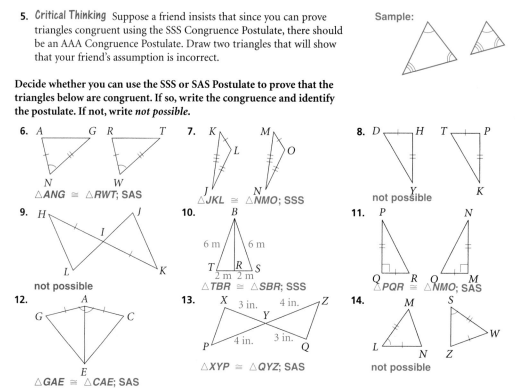

6. $\triangle ANG \cong \triangle RWT$; SAS

7.

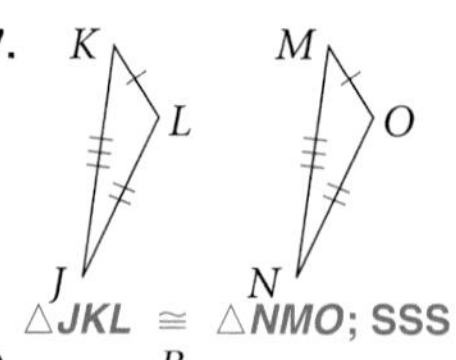

$\triangle JKL \cong \triangle NMO$; SSS

8.

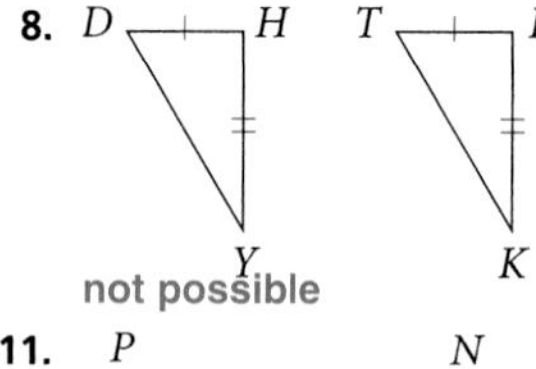

not possible

9. not possible

10. 6 m, 6 m, 2 m, 2 m

$\triangle TBR \cong \triangle SBR$; SSS

11. $\triangle PQR \cong \triangle NMO$; SAS

12. $\triangle GAE \cong \triangle CAE$; SAS

13.

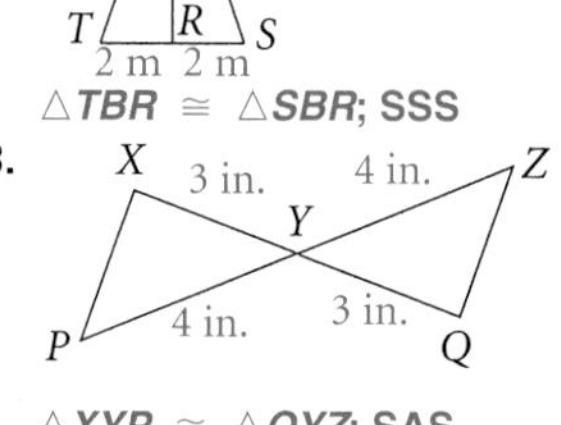

$\triangle XYP \cong \triangle QYZ$; SAS

14.

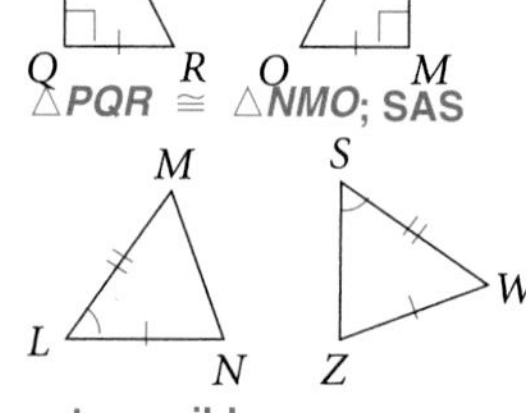

not possible

15. ***Open-ended*** List several places where you have seen congruent triangles used. **Samples: support structures of bridges; scaffolding**

16. ***Preparing for Proof*** Supply the reasons in this proof.

Given: X is the midpoint of $\overline{AG}$ and of $\overline{NR}$.

Prove: $\triangle ANX \cong \triangle GRX$

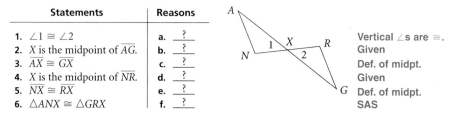

Statements	Reasons
1. $\angle 1 \cong \angle 2$	a. ?
2. X is the midpoint of $\overline{AG}$.	b. ?
3. $\overline{AX} \cong \overline{GX}$	c. ?
4. X is the midpoint of $\overline{NR}$.	d. ?
5. $\overline{NX} \cong \overline{RX}$	e. ?
6. $\triangle ANX \cong \triangle GRX$	f. ?

Vertical $\angle$s are $\cong$.
Given
Def. of midpt.
Given
Def. of midpt.
SAS

17. ***Paper Folding*** Draw an isosceles triangle. Fold the bisector of the vertex angle. Are the two triangles formed congruent? How do you know? **Check students' work; yes; SAS Post.**

Exercise 16 You may want to prepare a handout for students containing the uncompleted proof so they can fill in the blank steps. You may also want to include Exercises 18–20 and 22–23 on the handout.

Exercises 19–20 Encourage students to begin by writing a plan for each proof. You may want to allow class time for students to write the plans in groups and then complete the proofs for homework.

18. Complete the flow proof.
Given: $\overline{AE} \cong \overline{DE}$, $\overline{AB} \cong \overline{DC}$
Prove: $\triangle ABE \cong \triangle DCE$

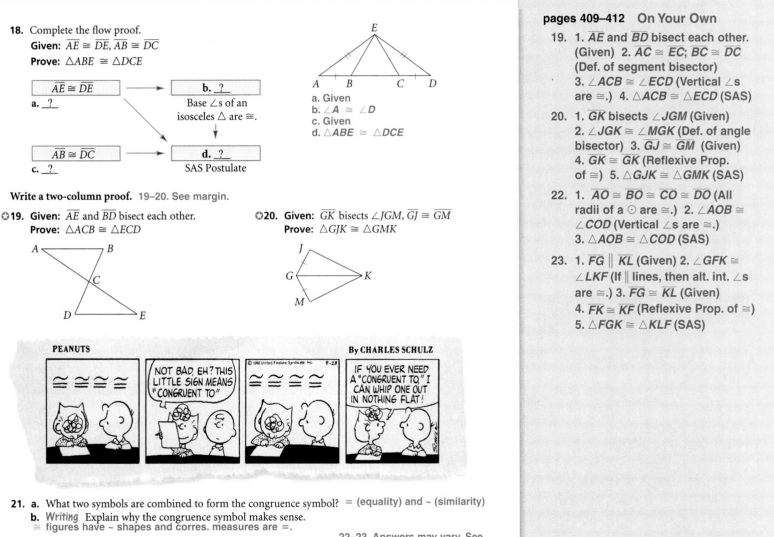

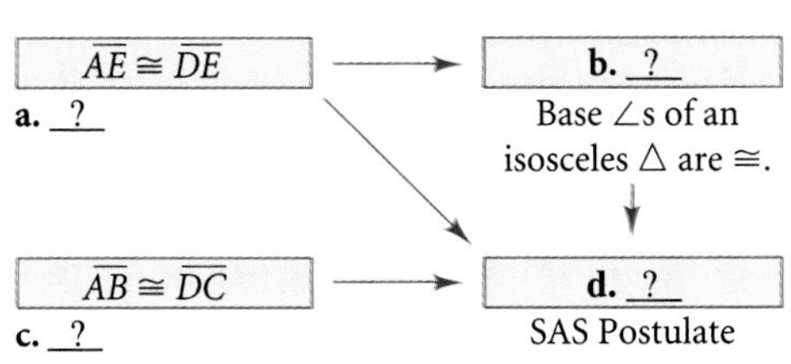

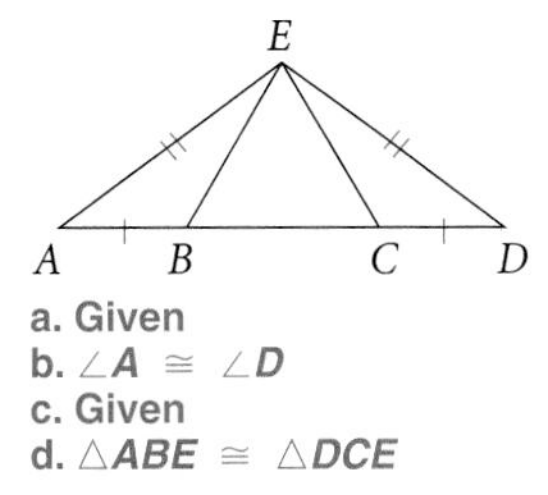

a. Given
b. $\angle A \cong \angle D$
c. Given
d. $\triangle ABE \cong \triangle DCE$

Write a two-column proof. 19–20. See margin.

19. Given: $\overline{AE}$ and $\overline{BD}$ bisect each other.
Prove: $\triangle ACB \cong \triangle ECD$

A B C D E

20. Given: $\overline{GK}$ bisects $\angle JGM$, $\overline{GJ} \cong \overline{GM}$
Prove: $\triangle GJK \cong \triangle GMK$

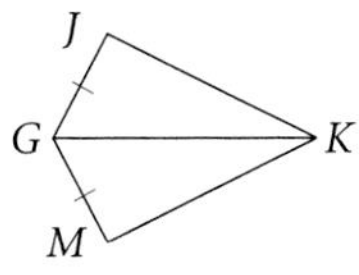

PEANUTS By CHARLES SCHULZ

NOT BAD, EH? THIS LITTLE SIGN MEANS "CONGRUENT TO"

IF YOU EVER NEED A "CONGRUENT TO," I CAN WHIP ONE OUT IN NOTHING FLAT!

21. a. What two symbols are combined to form the congruence symbol? = (equality) and ~ (similarity)

b. *Writing* Explain why the congruence symbol makes sense.
≅ figures have ~ shapes and corres. measures are =.

Choose **Write a two-column proof, a paragraph proof, or a flow proof.** 22–23. Answers may vary. See margin for samples.

22. Given: ⊙O with A, B, C, D on the circle
Prove: $\triangle AOB \cong \triangle COD$

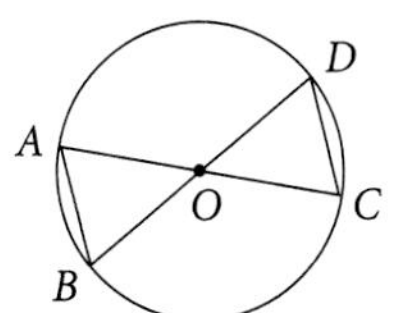

23. Given: $\overline{FG} \parallel \overline{KL}$, $\overline{FG} \cong \overline{KL}$
Prove: $\triangle FGK \cong \triangle KLF$

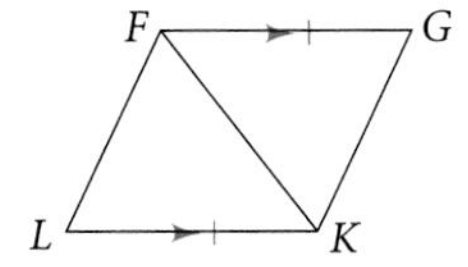

pages 409–412 On Your Own

19. 1. $\overline{AE}$ and $\overline{BD}$ bisect each other. (Given) 2. $\overline{AC} \cong \overline{EC}$; $\overline{BC} \cong \overline{DC}$ (Def. of segment bisector) 3. $\angle ACB \cong \angle ECD$ (Vertical ∠s are ≅.) 4. $\triangle ACB \cong \triangle ECD$ (SAS)

20. 1. $\overline{GK}$ bisects $\angle JGM$ (Given) 2. $\angle JGK \cong \angle MGK$ (Def. of angle bisector) 3. $\overline{GJ} \cong \overline{GM}$ (Given) 4. $\overline{GK} \cong \overline{GK}$ (Reflexive Prop. of ≅) 5. $\triangle GJK \cong \triangle GMK$ (SAS)

22. 1. $\overline{AO} \cong \overline{BO} \cong \overline{CO} \cong \overline{DO}$ (All radii of a ⊙ are ≅.) 2. $\angle AOB \cong \angle COD$ (Vertical ∠s are ≅.) 3. $\triangle AOB \cong \triangle COD$ (SAS)

23. 1. $\overline{FG} \parallel \overline{KL}$ (Given) 2. $\angle GFK \cong \angle LKF$ (If ∥ lines, then alt. int. ∠s are ≅.) 3. $\overline{FG} \cong \overline{KL}$ (Given) 4. $\overline{FK} \cong \overline{KF}$ (Reflexive Prop. of ≅) 5. $\triangle FGK \cong \triangle KLF$ (SAS)

ERROR ALERT! Exercise 24 Students may assume that two of the legs are on each triangle. **Remediation:** You may want to give students the hint that there are three cases they should consider.

Chapter Project **FIND OUT BY MODELING** Students discover that triangles are more stable or rigid than quadrilaterals. Discuss with students real-world examples such as ironing boards, scaffolding, and frames of roofs where triangles are used for stability.

Exercises MIXED REVIEW

Exercises 26–28 Students review how to use the formulas for volume and surface area of spheres, cones, and prisms.

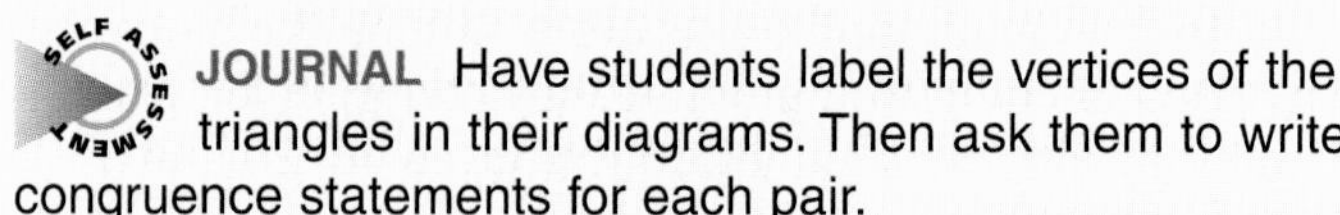

JOURNAL Have students label the vertices of the triangles in their diagrams. Then ask them to write congruence statements for each pair.

GETTING READY FOR LESSON 8-2 These exercises prepare students to explore the ASA Postulate and the AAS Theorem.

Wrap Up

THE BIG IDEA Ask students to describe the differences between the SSS Postulate and the SAS Postulate.

RETEACHING ACTIVITY Students measure sides and angles to show triangles congruent by the SSS and SAS Postulates. (Reteaching worksheet 8-1)

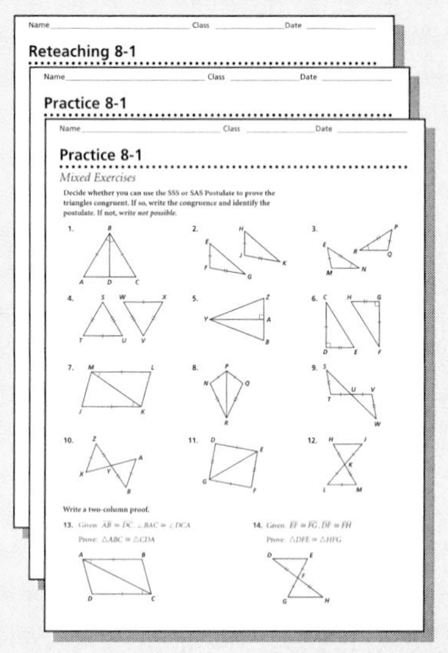

Lesson Quiz

Lesson Quiz is also available in Transparencies.

Name the additional congruent corresponding part needed to prove the triangles congruent by the given postulate.

1. $\triangle TAB \cong \triangle PDG$ by the SSS Postulate: $\overline{TA} \cong \overline{PD}$, $\overline{AB} \cong \overline{DG}$
   $\overline{TB} \cong \overline{PG}$
2. $\triangle WNO \cong \triangle BTZ$ by the SAS Postulate: $\overline{WN} \cong \overline{BT}$, $\overline{ON} \cong \overline{ZT}$
   $\angle N \cong \angle T$
3. Write a two-column proof.

Given: $\overline{YG}$ bisects $\overline{XZ}$, $\overline{YX} \cong \overline{YZ}$
Prove: $\triangle XYG \cong \triangle ZYG$

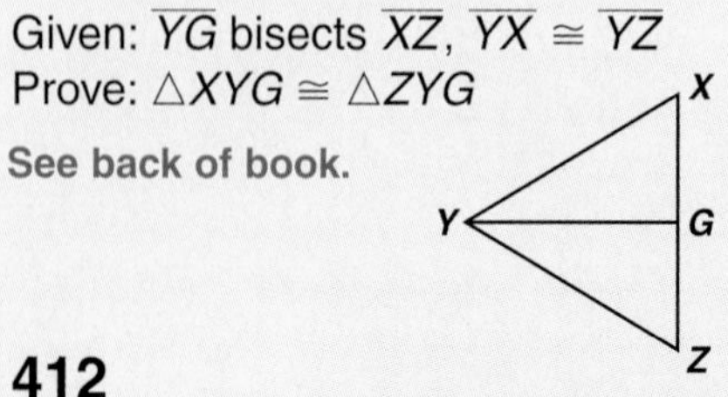

See back of book.

24. *Critical Thinking* Suppose you construct two isosceles triangles so that the four legs are the same length. Can you prove that the triangles are congruent? **Justify** your answer, or give a counterexample.
    No; an equilateral △ and an isosceles rt. △ with ≅ legs are ≇.
25. *Critical Thinking* Janet knows that the four sides of quadrilateral *ABCD* are congruent to the four sides of quadrilateral *EFGH*. Are the two quadrilaterals necessarily congruent? Explain.
    No; their ∠s may not be ≅.

Chapter Project — *Find Out by Modeling*

Many structures have straight beams that meet at *joints*. You can use models to explore ways to strengthen joints.

- Cut seven cardboard strips about 6 in. by $\frac{1}{2}$ in. Make a square frame and a triangular frame. Staple across the joints, as shown.
- With your fingertips, hold each model flat on a desk or table and try to change its shape. Which shape is more stable? triangle
- Cut another cardboard strip and use it to form a brace for the square frame. Is it more rigid? Why do you think the brace works?
  Yes; the brace makes 2 rigid △s.

Exercises MIXED REVIEW

Calculator **Find the volume and surface area of each figure to the nearest tenth.**

26. 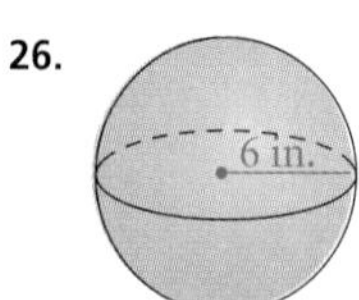

904.8 in.^{3}; 452.4 in.^{2}

27. 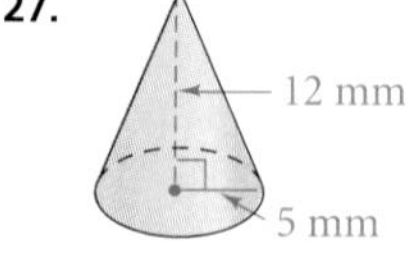

314.2 mm^3; 282.7 mm^2

28. 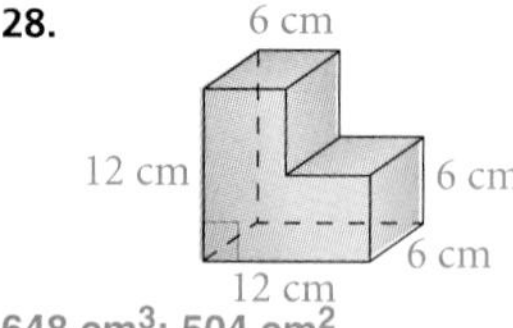

648 cm^3; 504 cm^2

29. One angle of an isosceles triangle is 112°. Find the measures of the other two angles. 34, 34

Getting Ready for Lesson 8-2

30. For $\triangle STP$, which sides are *not* included between $\angle S$ and $\angle T$? $\overline{SP}$ and $\overline{TP}$
31. *Constructions* Draw an obtuse angle on your paper. Label it $\angle 1$. Construct $\angle A$ so that $\angle A \cong \angle 1$. Check students' work.

SELF ASSESSMENT **FOR YOUR JOURNAL**

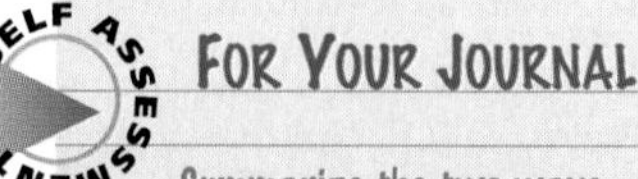

Summarize the two ways that you learned to prove triangles congruent in this lesson. Include diagrams.

Math ToolboX

Students discover that there is no SSA or AAA Postulate. This exploration extends Lesson 8-1 and previews Lesson 8-2 in which students learn the ASA Postulate and AAS Theorem.

The geometry software allows students to construct triangles with congruent angles and sides and then to manipulate them while maintaining the congruences.

ERROR ALERT! Students who are not experienced with the geometry software may have difficulty with the constructions and manipulations. **Remediation:** Pair students with more experience with those with less experience.

Investigate

Help students see that $\angle A$ is a non-included angle relative to sides $\overline{AC}$ and $\overline{CE}$. $\angle E$ is also a non-included angle.

Construct

Make sure students *construct* and not *draw* $\overline{BC}$ and $\overline{DE}$ as parallel segments so that when the positions of sides $\overline{DE}$ and $\overline{BC}$ are changed, the segments remain parallel.

ADDITIONAL PROBLEM Have students construct two triangles with two pairs of corresponding angles and the included side congruent. Then have students construct two triangles with two pairs of corresponding angles and a non-included side congruent. For each pair, ask: *What appears to be true about the triangles?*

Math ToolboX Technology

Exploring SSA and AAA

After Lesson 8-1

Work in pairs or small groups.

Construct

Use geometry software to construct ray $\overrightarrow{AB}$. Draw a circle with center C that intersects $\overrightarrow{AB}$ in two points. Construct $\overline{AC}$. Construct a point E on the circle and construct $\overline{CE}$. Check students' work.

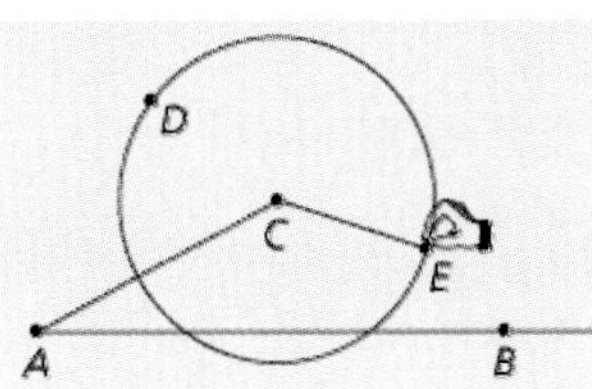

Investigate

Move point E around the circle until E is on $\overrightarrow{AB}$ and forms $\triangle ACE$. Then move E to another point on the circle that is also on $\overrightarrow{AB}$ to form another $\triangle ACE$. In the two triangles, compare the measures of $\angle A$, $\overline{AC}$, and $\overline{CE}$. Are two sides and a nonincluded angle of one triangle congruent to two sides and a nonincluded angle of the other triangle? Are the two triangles congruent? Do you get the same results if you change the size of $\angle A$ and the size of the circle? yes; no; yes

Construct

Construct rays $\overrightarrow{AB}$ and $\overrightarrow{AC}$. Construct $\overline{BC}$ to create $\triangle ABC$. Construct a line parallel to $\overline{BC}$ that intersects $\overrightarrow{AB}$ and $\overrightarrow{AC}$ at points D and E to form $\triangle ADE$. Check students' work.

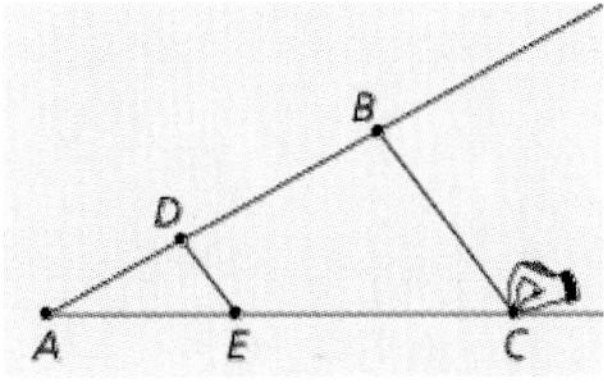

Investigate

Are three angles of $\triangle ABC$ congruent to three angles of $\triangle ADE$? Manipulate the figure to change the positions of sides $\overline{DE}$ and $\overline{BC}$. Do the corresponding angles of the triangles remain congruent? Are the two triangles congruent? Can the two triangles be congruent? yes; yes; no; only when the segments coincide

Conjecture

Do you think there is a SSA congruency theorem? Do you think there is an AAA congruency theorem? Explain your answers.
No; no; the above constructions demonstrate SSA $\triangle$s that are not $\cong$ and AAA $\triangle$s that are not $\cong$.

Extend

Manipulate the first figure you drew so that $\angle A$ is obtuse. Now can the circle intersect $\overrightarrow{AB}$ twice? Can two triangles be formed? Could there be a SSA congruency theorem if the congruent angles are obtuse? no; no; yes

Material and Manipulatives

- Geometry software

8-2 Teaching Notes

PROBLEM OF THE DAY

Four distinct, non-overlapping triangles have been created by six straight lines. Create seven distinct, non-overlapping triangles using six lines.

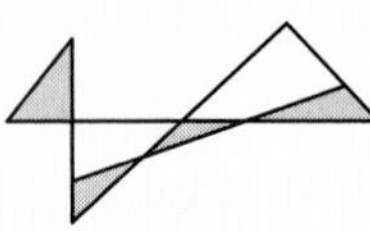

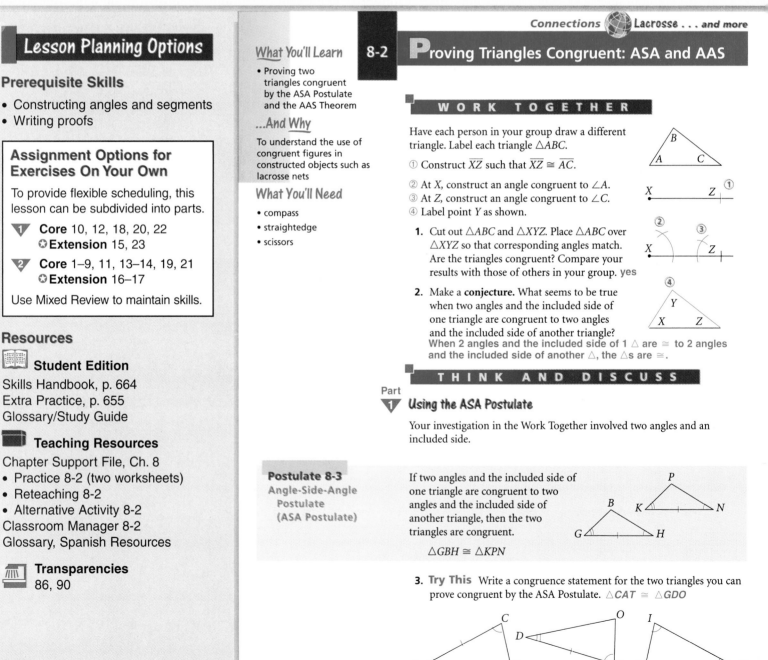

Problem of the Day is also available in Transparencies.

CONNECTING TO PRIOR KNOWLEDGE Draw a pair of triangles with two pairs of angles and the included sides congruent. Ask students to name the congruent corresponding parts.

WORK TOGETHER

Have students work in groups of four. Within each group, students should check each other's constructions to make sure that each step is performed.

ALTERNATIVE METHOD Have students perform the constructions using geometry software. Have them drag one triangle onto the other so that corresponding angles match, then answer Question 2.

Lesson Planning Options

Prerequisite Skills

- Constructing angles and segments
- Writing proofs

Assignment Options for Exercises On Your Own

To provide flexible scheduling, this lesson can be subdivided into parts.

 **Core** 10, 12, 18, 20, 22
Extension 15, 23

 **Core** 1–9, 11, 13–14, 19, 21
Extension 16–17

Use Mixed Review to maintain skills.

Resources

Student Edition
Skills Handbook, p. 664
Extra Practice, p. 655
Glossary/Study Guide

Teaching Resources
Chapter Support File, Ch. 8
- Practice 8-2 (two worksheets)
- Reteaching 8-2
- Alternative Activity 8-2

Classroom Manager 8-2
Glossary, Spanish Resources

 **Transparencies**
86, 90

8-2 Proving Triangles Congruent: ASA and AAS

What You'll Learn

- Proving two triangles congruent by the ASA Postulate and the AAS Theorem

...And Why

To understand the use of congruent figures in constructed objects such as lacrosse nets

What You'll Need

- compass
- straightedge
- scissors

WORK TOGETHER

Have each person in your group draw a different triangle. Label each triangle $\triangle ABC$.

① Construct $\overline{XZ}$ such that $\overline{XZ} \cong \overline{AC}$.

② At X, construct an angle congruent to $\angle A$.
③ At Z, construct an angle congruent to $\angle C$.
④ Label point Y as shown.

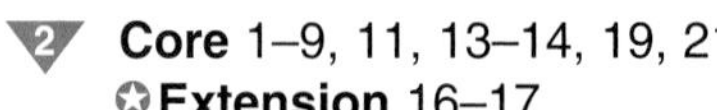

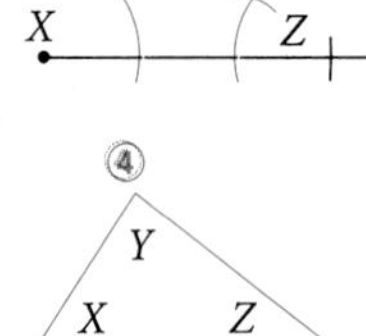

1. Cut out $\triangle ABC$ and $\triangle XYZ$. Place $\triangle ABC$ over $\triangle XYZ$ so that corresponding angles match. Are the triangles congruent? Compare your results with those of others in your group. yes
2. Make a **conjecture.** What seems to be true when two angles and the included side of one triangle are congruent to two angles and the included side of another triangle? When 2 angles and the included side of 1 $\triangle$ are $\cong$ to 2 angles and the included side of another $\triangle$, the $\triangle$s are $\cong$.

THINK AND DISCUSS

Part 1 **Using the ASA Postulate**

Your investigation in the Work Together involved two angles and an included side.

Postulate 8-3 Angle-Side-Angle Postulate (ASA Postulate)

If two angles and the included side of one triangle are congruent to two angles and the included side of another triangle, then the two triangles are congruent.

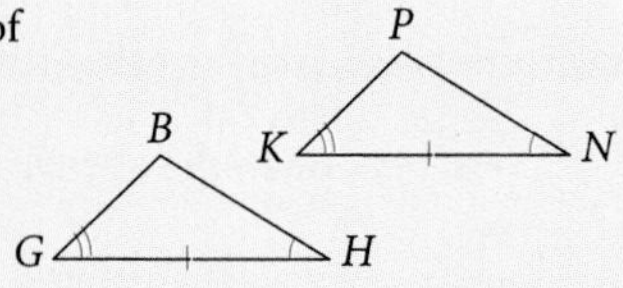

$\triangle GBH \cong \triangle KPN$

3. **Try This** Write a congruence statement for the two triangles you can prove congruent by the ASA Postulate. $\triangle CAT \cong \triangle GDO$

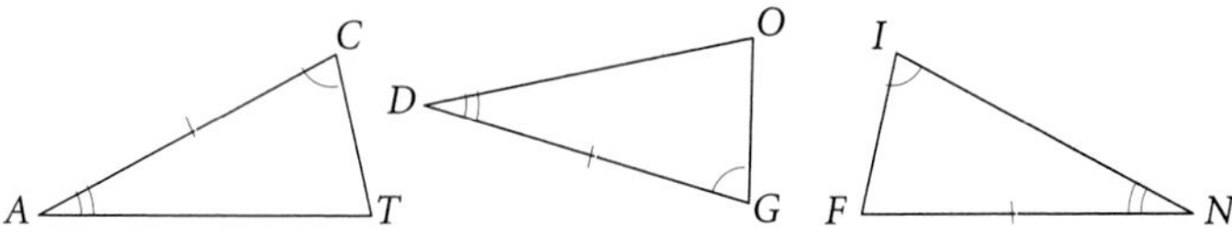

THINK AND DISCUSS

In Lesson 8-1, students learned to identify an angle included between two sides. You may want to review *included side* and give several examples before stating the Angle-Side-Angle Postulate.

Example 1 Relating to the Real World 

When writing a plan for a proof, some students will go into more detail than others. In this example, some students may want to include what is given as part of their plan. Encourage students to write a plan that is clear enough for them to write the proof.

DIVERSITY Lacrosse originated as "baggataway," a game played by North American Indians. It was played by two teams which had up to two hundred men on each side. The senior medicine man from each tribe stood in the goal area. Lacrosse received its modern name from French Canadians who observed that the netted stick used by the Indians resembled a bishop's crosier.

Example 2

Help students see how this proof "flows" from statements to conclusions. Discuss how the two arrows coming from the statement "$\angle B \cong \angle Y$" show that it is used to prove both $\angle C \cong \angle Z$ and $\triangle ABC \cong \triangle XYZ$.

Example 1 Relating to the Real World 

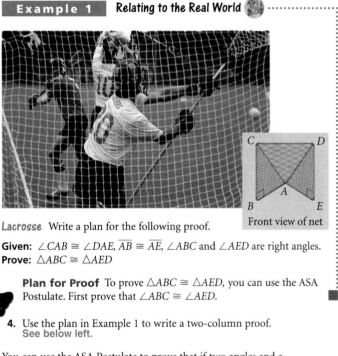

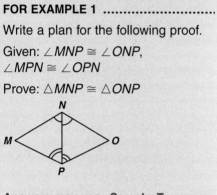

Front view of net

Lacrosse Write a plan for the following proof.

Given: $\angle CAB \cong \angle DAE$, $\overline{AB} \cong \overline{AE}$, $\angle ABC$ and $\angle AED$ are right angles.
Prove: $\triangle ABC \cong \triangle AED$

Plan for Proof To prove $\triangle ABC \cong \triangle AED$, you can use the ASA Postulate. First prove that $\angle ABC \cong \angle AED$.

4. Use the plan in Example 1 to write a two-column proof. See below left.

You can use the ASA Postulate to prove that if two angles and a nonincluded side of one triangle are congruent to two angles and the corresponding nonincluded side of another triangle, then the triangles are congruent.

Example 2

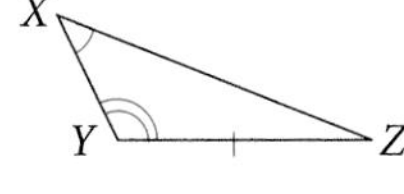

Given: $\angle A \cong \angle X$, $\angle B \cong \angle Y$, $\overline{BC} \cong \overline{YZ}$
Prove: $\triangle ABC \cong \triangle XYZ$

Flow Proof

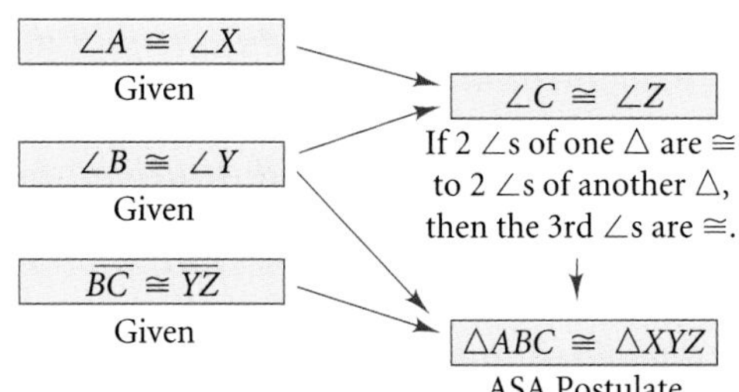

4. 1. $\angle CAB \cong \angle DAE$; $\overline{AB} \cong \overline{AE}$ (Given)
2. $\angle ABC$ and $\angle AED$ are rt. angles. (Given)
3. $\angle ABC \cong \angle AED$ (All rt. $\angle$s are $\cong$.)
4. $\triangle ABC \cong \triangle AED$ (ASA)

Additional Examples

FOR EXAMPLE 1

Write a plan for the following proof.

Given: $\angle MNP \cong \angle ONP$, $\angle MPN \cong \angle OPN$

Prove: $\triangle MNP \cong \triangle ONP$

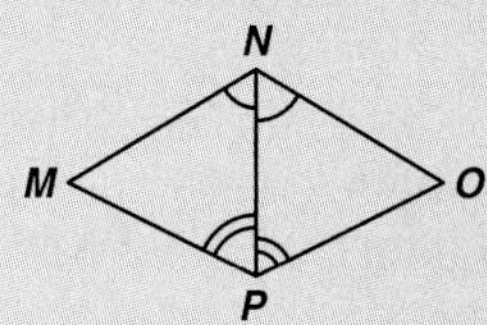

Answers may vary. Sample: To prove $\triangle MNP \cong \triangle ONP$, you can use the ASA Postulate. First prove that $\overline{NP} \cong \overline{NP}$.

FOR EXAMPLE 2

Write a flow proof.

Given: $\overline{PQ} \cong \overline{TS}$, $\angle P \cong \angle S$

Prove: $\triangle PQR \cong \triangle STR$

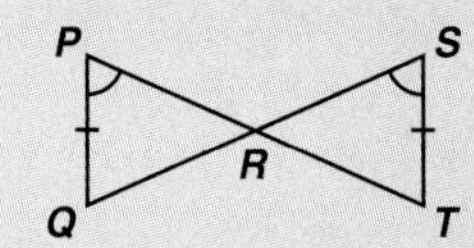

See back of book.

Angle-Angle-Side Theorem Point out that this is a theorem and not a postulate.

ERROR ALERT! Students may think that any three pairs of corresponding congruent parts are sufficient to prove triangles congruent. **Remediation:** Have students investigate SSA and AAA. Refer them to the Math Toolbox on page 413 for a technology investigation of SSA and AAA.

CRITICAL THINKING Question 6 Ask students what additional information is needed to prove the triangles are congruent by ASA.

Exercises ON YOUR OWN

VISUAL LEARNING Exercises 1–8 Students may want to copy the figures and mark the congruent sides and angles in the following way to help them differentiate between ASA and AAS.

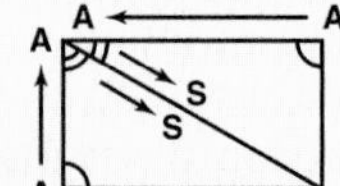

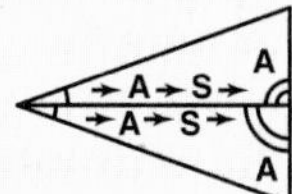

Technology Options

For Exercise 13, students may draw the triangles using geometry software.

Prentice Hall Technology 

Software
- Secondary Math Lab Toolkit™
- Integrated Math Lab 38
- Computer Item Generator 8-2

CD-ROM
- Multimedia Geometry Lab 8

Internet
- See the Prentice Hall site. (http://www.phschool.com)

Part 

Using the AAS Theorem

In Example 2, the ASA Postulate was used in the flow proof to prove the following theorem.

Theorem 8-1 Angle-Angle-Side Theorem (AAS Theorem)

If two angles and a nonincluded side of one triangle are congruent to two angles and the corresponding nonincluded side of another triangle, then the triangles are congruent.

$\triangle DCM \cong \triangle GXT$

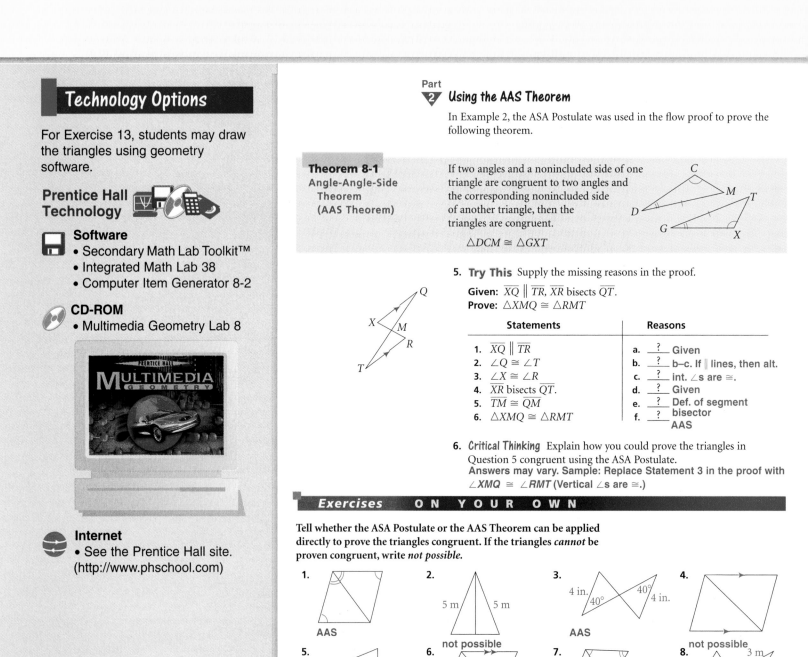

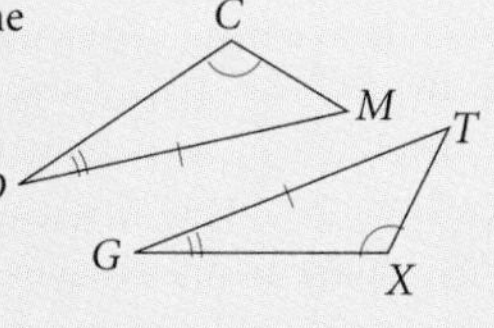

5. **Try This** Supply the missing reasons in the proof.

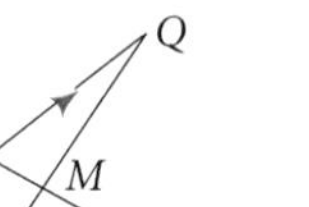

Given: $\overline{XQ} \parallel \overline{TR}$, $\overline{XR}$ bisects $\overline{QT}$.
Prove: $\triangle XMQ \cong \triangle RMT$

Statements	Reasons
1. $\overline{XQ} \parallel \overline{TR}$	a. __?__ Given
2. $\angle Q \cong \angle T$	b. __?__ b–c. If ∥ lines, then alt.
3. $\angle X \cong \angle R$	c. __?__ int. ∠s are ≅.
4. $\overline{XR}$ bisects $\overline{QT}$.	d. __?__ Given
5. $\overline{TM} \cong \overline{QM}$	e. __?__ Def. of segment bisector
6. $\triangle XMQ \cong \triangle RMT$	f. __?__ AAS

6. **Critical Thinking** Explain how you could prove the triangles in Question 5 congruent using the ASA Postulate.
Answers may vary. Sample: Replace Statement 3 in the proof with $\angle XMQ \cong \angle RMT$ (Vertical ∠s are ≅.)

Exercises ON YOUR OWN

Tell whether the ASA Postulate or the AAS Theorem can be applied directly to prove the triangles congruent. If the triangles *cannot* be proven congruent, write *not possible.*

1. 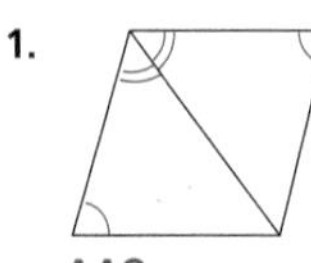
AAS

2. 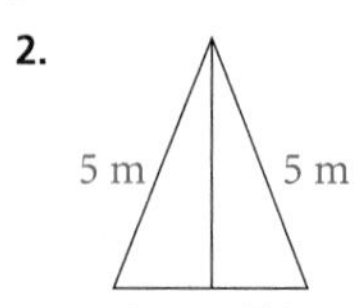

not possible

3. 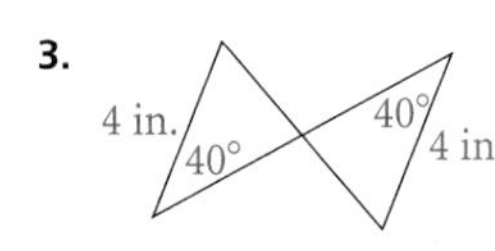

AAS

4. 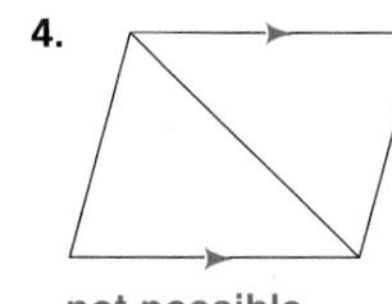
not possible

5. 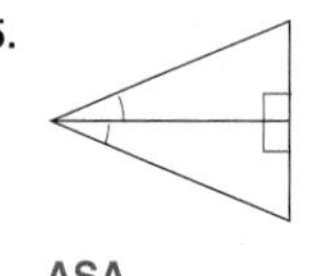
ASA

6. **ASA**

7. **not possible**

8. 3 m, 30°, 30°, 3 m
ASA

Exercises 9–12 Make sure that students do not assume any congruency not stated or not justifiable.

OPEN-ENDED Exercise 13 Students can use many different methods, such as reflection, construction, or measurement, to create the triangles. Depending on the method used, students may use any of the postulates or the theorem from Lessons 8-1 and 8-2.

ALTERNATIVE ASSESSMENT Exercise 14 You can assess students' understanding of different styles of proof by asking them to rewrite this proof as a paragraph proof or a flow proof.

GEOMETRY IN 3 DIMENSIONS Exercise 15 Have students compare answers. They may be surprised that other students used a different postulate or theorem to justify their answers.

Preparing for Proof **What additional information would you need to prove the triangles congruent by the stated postulate or theorem?**

9. AAS Theorem **$\angle D \cong \angle B$**

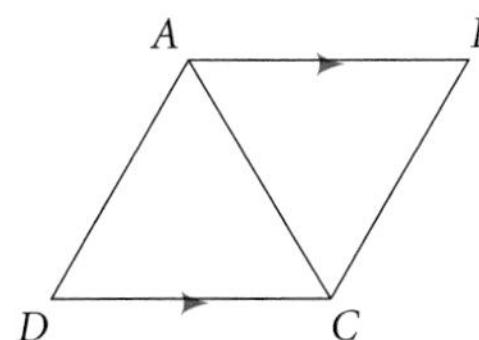

10. ASA Postulate **$\overline{QP} \cong \overline{QT}$**

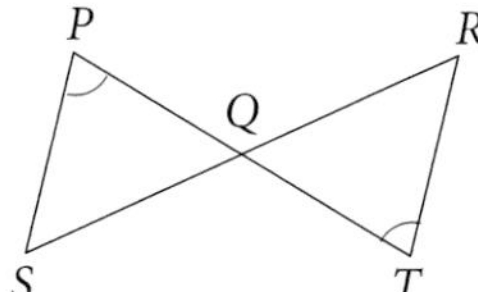

11. AAS Theorem **$\angle M \cong \angle P$**

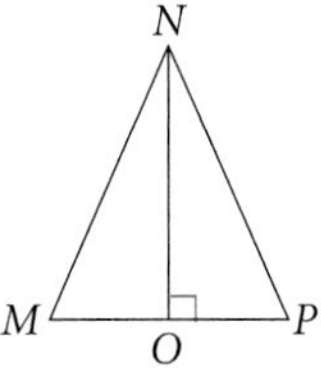

12. SAS Postulate **$\overline{RV} \cong \overline{VT}$**

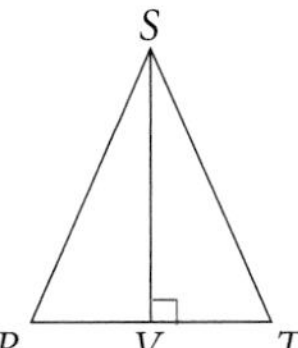

13. a. ***Open-ended*** Draw a triangle. Draw a second triangle that is congruent to the first one and shares a common side with it. **See margin for sample.**

b. Think about how you drew your second triangle. What congruence postulate or theorem did you use to make the second triangle congruent to the first one? **SSS, SAS, or ASA**

14. ***Preparing for Proof*** Supply the missing statements and reasons.

Given: $\overline{PQ} \perp \overline{QS}$, $\overline{RS} \perp \overline{QS}$, T is the midpoint of $\overline{PR}$.
Prove: $\triangle PQT \cong \triangle RST$

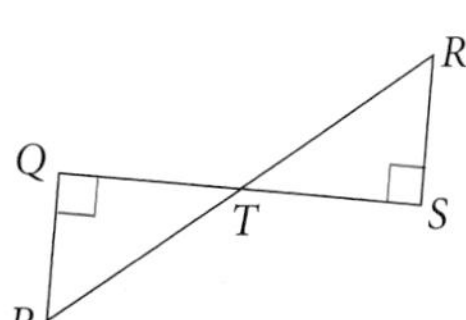

Statements	Reasons
1. $\overline{PQ} \perp \overline{QS}$, $\overline{RS} \perp \overline{QS}$	1. Given
2. $\angle Q$ and $\angle S$ are right angles.	a. __?__ **Def. of $\perp$ lines**
3. $\angle Q \cong \angle S$	b. __?__ **All rt. $\angle$s are $\cong$.**
c. __?__ **$\angle QTP \cong \angle STR$**	4. Vertical angles are $\cong$.
5. T is the midpoint of $\overline{PR}$.	5. Given
6. $\overline{PT} \cong \overline{RT}$	d. __?__ **Def. of midpoint**
7. $\triangle PQT \cong \triangle RST$	e. __?__ **AAS**

15. ***Geometry in 3 Dimensions*** The top portion of this quartz crystal is a hexagonal pyramid. The lateral edges of the pyramid are congruent and the base edges of the pyramid are congruent. Are the triangles that form the lateral faces of the pyramid congruent? **Justify** your answer. **yes; SSS**

pages 416–418 On Your Own

13a.

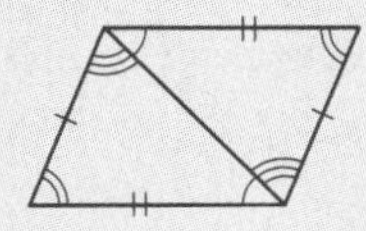

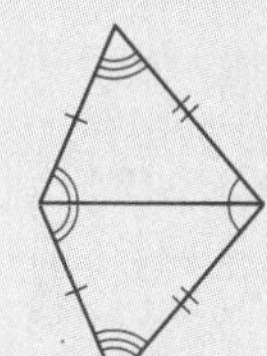

PROBABILITY Exercise 16 Students need to find all the combinations of three statements that can be used to prove the triangles congruent. The most thorough approach would be to list all twenty combinations and then to check each one.

WRITING Exercise 17 Students may want to give an example (or counterexample) to support their reasoning.

Exercises 18–21 Encourage students to write a plan for each proof. You may want to allow time for students to exchange proofs, give feedback, and make corrections.

STANDARDIZED TEST TIP Exercise 22 It may help students to redraw the triangles given in the answer choices separately.

18. 1. $\overline{DH}$ bisects $\angle BDF$ (Given) 2. $\angle BDH \cong \angle FDH$ (Def. of angle bisector) 3. $\overline{DH} \cong \overline{DH}$ (Reflexive Prop. of $\cong$) 4. $\angle 1 \cong \angle 2$ (Given) 5. $\triangle BDH \cong \triangle FDH$ (ASA)

19. 1. $\overline{FG} \parallel \overline{JH}$ (Given) 2. $\angle FGJ \cong \angle HJG$ (If $\parallel$ lines, then alt. int. $\angle$s are $\cong$.) 3. $\angle F \cong \angle H$ (Given) 4. $\overline{JG} \cong \overline{GJ}$ (Reflexive Prop. of $\cong$) 5. $\triangle FGJ \cong \triangle HJG$ (AAS)

20. 1. $\overline{AE} \parallel \overline{BD}$ (Given) 2. $\angle A \cong \angle DBC$ (If $\parallel$ lines, then corres. $\angle$s are $\cong$.) 3. $\angle E \cong \angle D$ (Given) 4. $\overline{AE} \cong \overline{BD}$ (Given) 5. $\triangle AEB \cong \triangle BDC$ (ASA)

21. 1. $\angle MON \cong \angle QOP$ (Vertical $\angle$s are $\cong$.) 2. $\angle N \cong \angle P$ (Given) 3. $\overline{MO} \cong \overline{QO}$ (Given) 4. $\triangle MON \cong \triangle QOP$ (AAS)

page 419 Mixed Review

26.

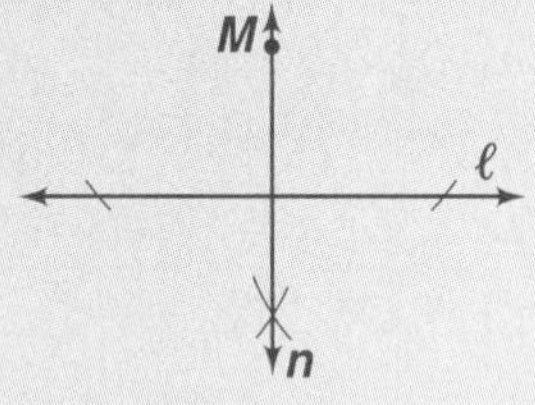

16. Probability Here are six congruence statements about the triangles at the right.

$\angle A \cong \angle X$ $\quad \angle B \cong \angle Y$ $\quad \angle C \cong \angle Z$

$\overline{AB} \cong \overline{XY}$ $\quad \overline{AC} \cong \overline{XZ}$ $\quad \overline{BC} \cong \overline{YZ}$

There are 20 ways to choose groups of three statements from these six statements. What is the probability that a set of three congruence statements chosen at random from the six listed will guarantee that the triangles are congruent? $\frac{13}{20}$

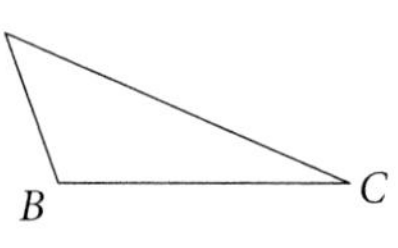

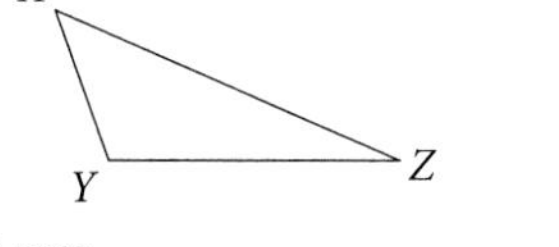

17. Writing Anita claims that it is possible to rewrite any proof that uses the AAS Theorem as a proof that uses the ASA Postulate. Do you agree with Anita? Explain why or why not. **Yes; by Thm. 4-5, if 2 $\angle$s of one $\triangle$ are $\cong$ to 2 $\angle$s of another $\triangle$, then the third $\angle$s are $\cong$.**

Choose **Write a two-column proof, a paragraph proof, or a flow proof.**

18. Given: $\overline{DH}$ bisects $\angle BDF$, $\angle 1 \cong \angle 2$
Prove: $\triangle BDH \cong \triangle FDH$

18–21. Answers may vary. See margin for samples.

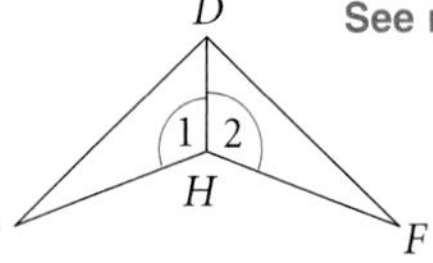

19. Given: $\angle F \cong \angle H$, $\overline{FG} \parallel \overline{JH}$
Prove: $\triangle FGJ \cong \triangle HJG$

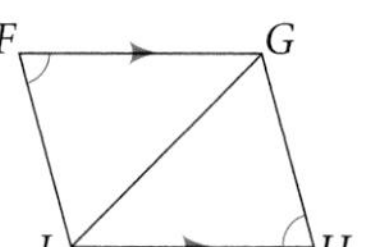

20. Given: $\overline{AE} \parallel \overline{BD}$, $\overline{AE} \cong \overline{BD}$, $\angle E \cong \angle D$
Prove: $\triangle AEB \cong \triangle BDC$

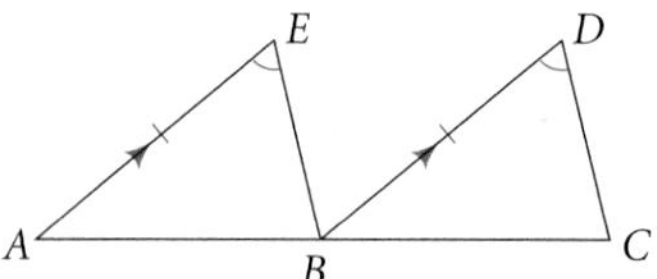

21. Given: $\angle N \cong \angle P$, $\overline{MO} \cong \overline{QO}$
Prove: $\triangle MON \cong \triangle QOP$

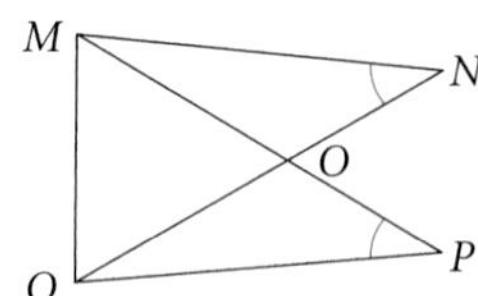

22. Standardized Test Prep Which of the following can you conclude based on the figure at the right? **A**

I. $\triangle ADE$ is isosceles. **II.** $\triangle ABE \cong \triangle DCE$
III. $\triangle BDE$ is isosceles. **IV.** $\angle EBC \cong \angle ECB$

A. I, II, and IV only **B.** I, II, and III only **C.** II, III, and IV only
D. I, III, and IV only **E.** III and IV only

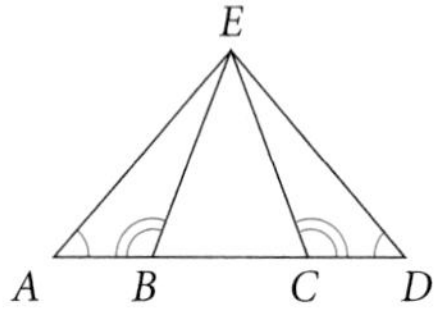

23. Critical Thinking Explain why $\triangle ABC$ cannot be congruent to $\triangle FDE$. **The hypotenuse of a rt. $\triangle$ is longer than each leg. So $FE > 5$ cm and $\overline{FE} \not\cong \overline{AC}$.**

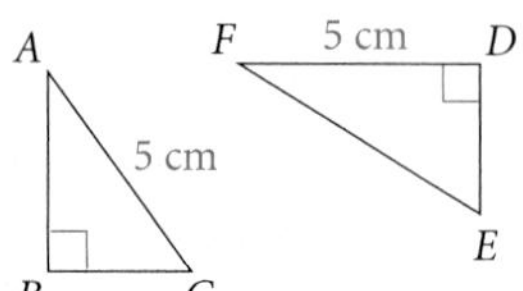

Exercises MIXED REVIEW

JOURNAL Encourage students to include diagrams with their explanations.

GETTING READY FOR LESSON 8-3 These exercises prepare students to investigate congruent right triangles.

Wrap Up

THE BIG IDEA Ask students to explain the differences between the ASA Postulate and the AAS Theorem.

RETEACHING ACTIVITY Students construct pairs of congruent triangles and show they are congruent using the ASA Postulate and AAS Theorem. (Reteaching worksheet 8-2)

Geometry at Work

ESL Make sure students understand that the term "die maker" does not refer to a person who makes number cubes. To clarify, discuss how die making is used in the auto industry.

Encourage students to investigate these topics:

- the education necessary to become a die maker
- the types of businesses that hire die makers
- how die making is used in the automotive industry
- the first automobile to be made using dies
- the technology used by die makers (electrical discharge machines, electrochemical milling, electrochemical grinding, and ultrasonic machining)

Exercises MIXED REVIEW

Coordinate Geometry **Find the coordinates of the midpoint of the segment with the given endpoints.**

24. $(4, 7)$ and $(2, 9)$ **(3, 8)**

25. $(-1, 8)$ and $(5, -8)$ **(2, 0)**

26. *Constructions* Draw a line ℓ and a point M not on ℓ. Construct a line n through M so that $n \perp \ell$. **See margin p. 418 for sample.**

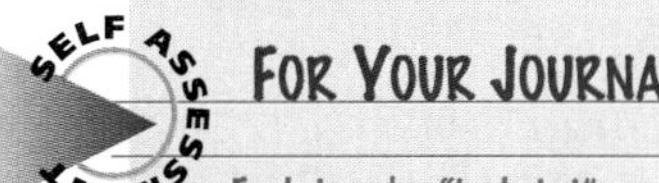

FOR YOUR JOURNAL

Explain why "included" and "nonincluded" are necessary terms in the SAS Postulate, the ASA Postulate, and the AAS Theorem.

Getting Ready for Lesson 8-3

Find the value of each variable. If an answer is not a whole number, leave it in simplest radical form.

27.

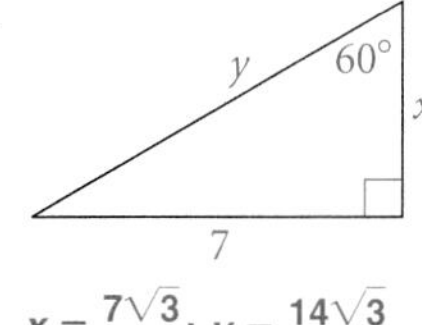

$x = \frac{7\sqrt{3}}{3}$; $y = \frac{14\sqrt{3}}{3}$

28.

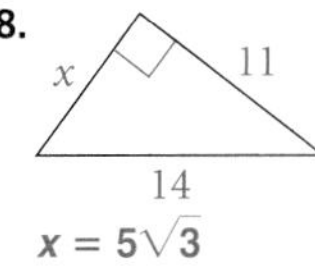

$x = 5\sqrt{3}$

29.

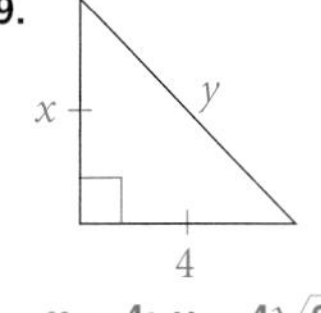

$x = 4$; $y = 4\sqrt{2}$

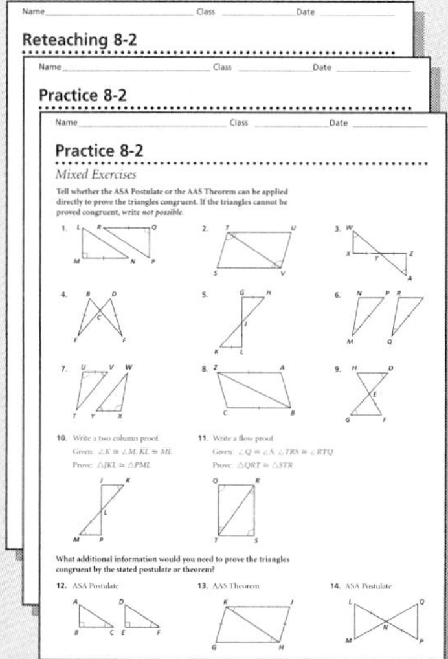

Geometry at Work

Die Maker

Two centuries ago, all manufactured articles were made by hand. Each article produced was slightly different from the others. In 1800, inventor Eli Whitney recognized that manufacturing could be greatly speeded up by using *congruent* parts. Whitney made a *die,* or mold, for each part of a musket he was producing for the U.S. Army. This allowed standard-sized muskets to be put together rapidly, and it ushered in the era of *mass production.*

Today, die makers are highly skilled industrial workers. To create a new product, die makers use metal, plastic, rubber, or other materials to create dies. During manufacture, a part is shaped by its die. This ensures that parts are congruent.

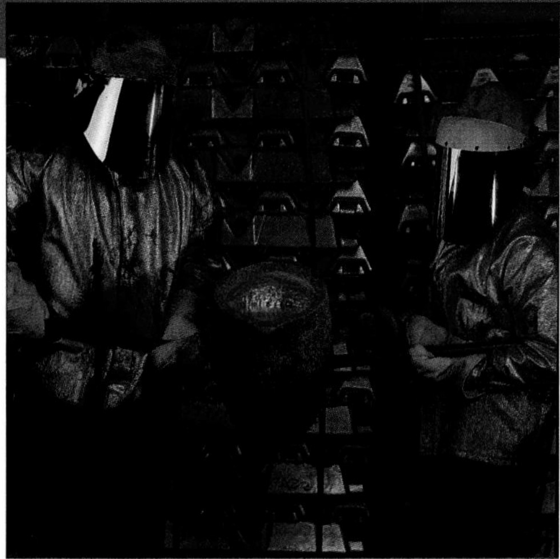

Mini Project: *Research* Write a paragraph on the use of molds and castings to produce congruent parts.

Lesson Quiz

Lesson Quiz is also available in Transparencies.

Tell whether the ASA Postulate or the AAS Theorem can be applied directly to prove the triangles congruent.

1. 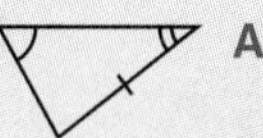 **AAS Theorem**

2. **ASA Postulate**

3. Write a flow proof to prove $\triangle FCD \cong \triangle FED$ using the AAS Theorem. **See back of book.**

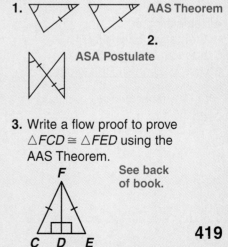

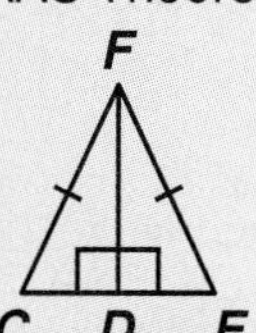
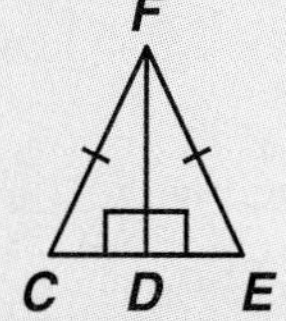

8-3 Teaching Notes

PROBLEM OF THE DAY

A circle is circumscribed about one equilateral triangle and is inscribed in another equilateral triangle. Find the ratio of the areas of the triangles. **1 to 4 (Hint: Draw a diagram and rotate the smaller triangle 180°.)**

Problem of the Day is also available in Transparencies.

CONNECTING TO PRIOR KNOWLEDGE Draw the following pairs of triangles on the board and have students explain why they are congruent.

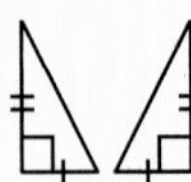
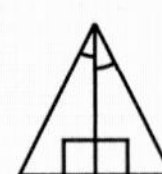
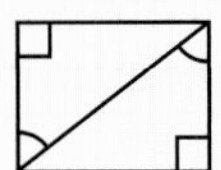

WORK TOGETHER

Have students work in groups of three or four. Students in each group should pick the same values for x and y.

TACTILE LEARNING Question 1 Students may want to cut the triangles out and place them on top of each other so the right angles match up.

THINK AND DISCUSS

Note that the HL Theorem applies only to right triangles and that there is no SSA Theorem that applies to all triangles.

Lesson Planning Options

Prerequisite Skills

- Writing proofs
- Understanding the SSS, ASA, and SAS Postulates and the AAS Theorem

Assignment Options for Exercises On Your Own

Core 1–9, 11–13, 18–20
Extension 10, 14–17

Use Mixed Review to maintain skills.

Resources

Student Edition

Skills Handbook, p. 664
Extra Practice, p. 655
Glossary/Study Guide

Teaching Resources

Chapter Support File, Ch. 8
- Practice 8-3 (two worksheets)
- Reteaching 8-3
- Alternative Activity 8-3

Classroom Manager 8-3
Glossary, Spanish Resources

Transparencies
87

8-3 Congruent Right Triangles

What You'll Learn
- Proving triangles congruent using the HL Theorem

...And Why

To investigate congruence in applications such as fabric for tents

What You'll Need
- compass
- protractor
- ruler

WORK TOGETHER

- As a group, select two numbers from the set {2, 3, 4, 5, 6, 7}. Let x equal the smaller number and y the larger. Have each group member draw a right triangle at the corner of a piece of paper with a leg x in. long and a hypotenuse y in. long. (An example using 5 and 2 is shown.)

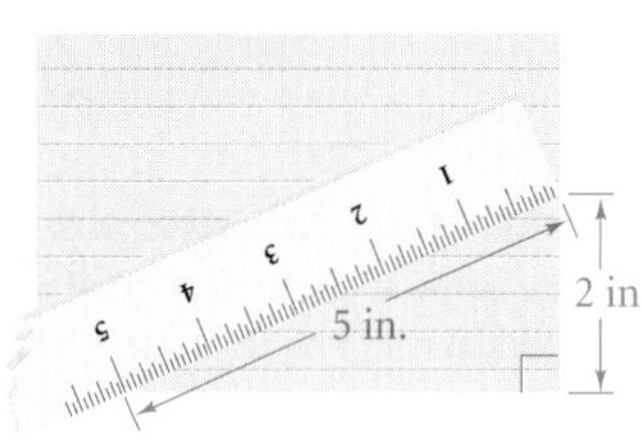

QUICK REVIEW

The hypotenuse of a right triangle is the longest side.

1. Compare triangles within your group and make a **conjecture.** If the hypotenuse and a leg of one right triangle are congruent to the hypotenuse and a leg of another right triangle, then __?__. **the △s are ≅**

- **Verify** your conjecture by selecting two more numbers from the set and creating more right triangles.

THINK AND DISCUSS

In the Work Together, you saw that all triangles formed with a given length for a leg and a given length for a hypotenuse are congruent. This observation leads to the following theorem.

Theorem 8-2
Hypotenuse-Leg Theorem (HL Theorem)

If the hypotenuse and a leg of one right triangle are congruent to the hypotenuse and leg of another right triangle, then the triangles are congruent.

Proof of Theorem 8-2

Given: $\triangle PQR$ and $\triangle XYZ$ are right triangles, $\overline{QR} \cong \overline{YZ}$, and $\overline{PQ} \cong \overline{XY}$

Prove: $\triangle PQR \cong \triangle XYZ$

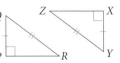

Let $PQ = XY = a$ and $QR = ZY = c$.
By the Pythagorean Theorem, $a^2 + PR^2 = c^2$ and $a^2 + XZ^2 = c^2$. Using the Subtraction Property of Equality, you get $PR^2 = c^2 - a^2$ and $XZ^2 = c^2 - a^2$. So $PR^2 = XZ^2$ and $PR = XZ$. By the SSS Postulate, $\triangle PQR \cong \triangle XYZ$.

ALTERNATIVE METHOD In the proof of Theorem 8-2, the variables a and c are introduced to avoid substitution. If you do not want to introduce new variables, begin the proof as follows: By the Pythagorean Theorem, $PQ^2 + PR^2 = QR^2$ and $XY^2 + XZ^2 = ZY^2$. By substitution, $XY^2 + PR^2 = ZY^2$.Using the Subtraction Property of Equality, you get $PR^2 = ZY^2 - XY^2$ and $XZ^2 = ZY^2 - XY^2$.

Example 1 Relating to the Real World 

Note that in the explanation, $\triangle CPA$ and $\triangle MPA$ are established as right triangles. This is necessary when using the HL Theorem to prove two triangles congruent.

Point out that although only two letters are used to name the HL Theorem, there are three conditions, as stated on page 421.

Example 2

CRITICAL THINKING Ask students to explain why $\angle CBD$, $\angle DBE$, and $\angle ABE$ are right angles.

ALTERNATIVE ASSESSMENT You can assess students' understanding of flow proof by having them work in groups to rewrite the flow proof in Example 2 as a paragraph or two-column proof.

Example 1 Relating to the Real World

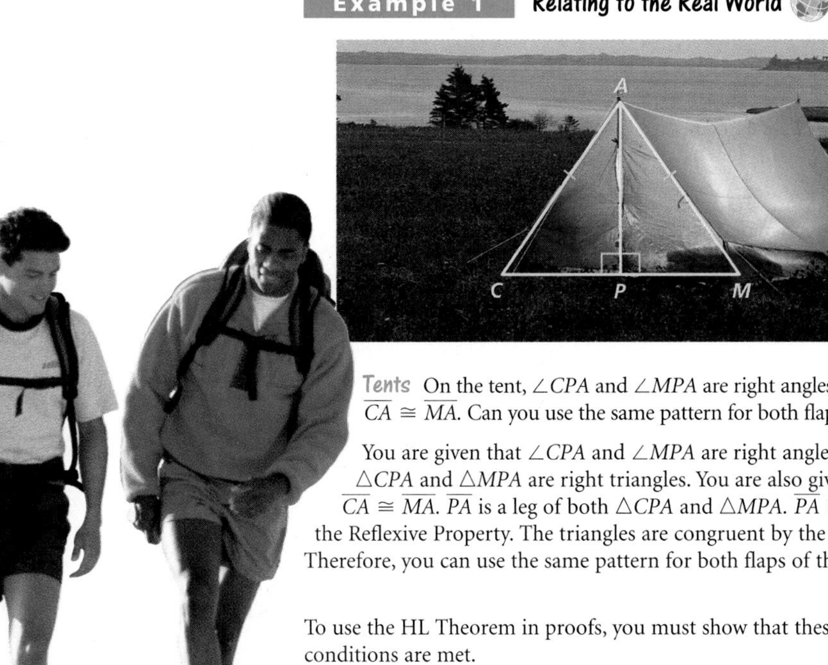

Tents On the tent, $\angle CPA$ and $\angle MPA$ are right angles and $\overline{CA} \cong \overline{MA}$. Can you use the same pattern for both flaps of the tent?

You are given that $\angle CPA$ and $\angle MPA$ are right angles. Therefore, $\triangle CPA$ and $\triangle MPA$ are right triangles. You are also given that $\overline{CA} \cong \overline{MA}$. $\overline{PA}$ is a leg of both $\triangle CPA$ and $\triangle MPA$. $\overline{PA} \cong \overline{PA}$ by the Reflexive Property. The triangles are congruent by the HL Theorem. Therefore, you can use the same pattern for both flaps of the tent.

To use the HL Theorem in proofs, you must show that these three conditions are met.

- There are two right triangles.
- There is one pair of congruent hypotenuses.
- There is one pair of congruent legs.

Example 2

Write a flow proof.

Given: $\overline{CD} \cong \overline{EA}$, $\overline{AD}$ is the perpendicular bisector of $\overline{CE}$.

Prove: $\triangle CBD \cong \triangle EBA$

C A B D E

Flow Proof

- $\overline{AD}$ is the $\perp$ bisector of $\overline{CE}$. (Given) → $\angle CBD$ and $\angle EBA$ are right $\angle$s. (Def. of $\perp$ lines) → $\triangle CBD$ and $\triangle EBA$ are right triangles. (Def. of right triangles) → $\triangle CBD \cong \triangle EBA$ (HL Theorem)
- $\overline{AD}$ is the $\perp$ bisector of $\overline{CE}$. (Given) → B is midpoint of $\overline{CE}$. (Def. of bisector) → $\overline{CB} \cong \overline{EB}$ (Def. of midpoint) → $\triangle CBD \cong \triangle EBA$ (HL Theorem)
- $\overline{CD} \cong \overline{EA}$ (Given) → $\triangle CBD \cong \triangle EBA$ (HL Theorem)

Additional Examples

FOR EXAMPLE 1

From the information given in the diagram, can you prove $\triangle TIA \cong \triangle XIA$? Explain.

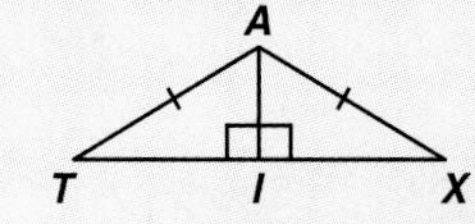

Yes; $\angle TIA$ and $\angle XIA$ are right angles. Therefore, $\triangle TIA$ and $\triangle XIA$ are right triangles. The hypotenuses of the triangles are congruent ($\overline{TA} \cong \overline{XA}$) and a pair of legs are congruent ($\overline{IA} \cong \overline{IA}$). Therefore the triangles are congruent by the HL Theorem.

FOR EXAMPLE 2

Write a flow proof.

Given: $\overline{BD} \perp \overline{AC}$, $\overline{AB} \cong \overline{CB}$

Prove: $\triangle ADB \cong \triangle CDB$

B A D C

See back of book.

CRITICAL THINKING Question 2 Remind students that they can apply the SSS, SAS, and ASA Postulates and the AAS Theorem to right triangles. Some textbooks present LL, HA, and LA Theorems as special cases of the theorem and postulates.

Exercises ON YOUR OWN

STANDARDIZED TEST TIP Exercise 1 Students may want to copy the figure so they can mark the congruent parts on the triangles. In some standardized tests, students are not allowed to mark the question book.

ERROR ALERT! Exercise 2 Students may assume $\angle T$ and $\angle Q$ are right angles. **Remediation:** Remind students that they cannot assume angles to be right or lines to be parallel by visual inspection.

ESL Exercises 2–7 These exercises require recognizing congruent corresponding parts in diagrams and do not involve much reading. These exercises provide a good opportunity to assess ESL students' understanding of proving triangles congruent.

Exercises 3–4 These exercises have two possible answers. The triangles can be proven congruent if either pair of corresponding legs are congruent.

CRITICAL THINKING Exercise 8 Students should find three pairs of congruent right triangles.

Technology Options

For Exercise 11, students may use graphing software to graph the figure. For Exercise 16, students may use geometry software or a drawing program to draw the triangles.

Prentice Hall Technology

Software
- Secondary Math Lab Toolkit™
- Computer Item Generator 8-3

CD-ROM
- Multimedia Geometry Lab 8

Internet
- See the Prentice Hall site. (http://www.phschool.com)

2. *Critical Thinking* Suppose you know that two legs of one right triangle are congruent to two legs of another right triangle. How could you prove the triangles congruent? Explain. Since the rt. angles are ≅, the △s are ≅ by SAS.

3. **Try This** Complete the proof.

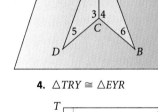

Given: $\overline{WJ} \cong \overline{KZ}$, $\angle JWZ$ and $\angle ZKJ$ right angles.
Prove: $\triangle WJZ \cong \triangle KZJ$

Statements	Reasons
1. $\angle JWZ$ and $\angle ZKJ$ are rt. $\angle$s.	a. ? Given
2. $\triangle WJZ$ and $\triangle KZJ$ are rt. $\triangle$s.	b. ? Def. of rt. △
c. ? $\overline{JZ} \cong \overline{JZ}$	3. Reflexive Property of ≅
d. ? $\overline{WJ} \cong \overline{KZ}$	4. Given
5. $\triangle WJZ \cong \triangle KZJ$	e. ? HL Thm.

Exercises ON YOUR OWN

1. *Standardized Test Prep* Which set of conditions does *not* provide enough information to prove that $\triangle ABC \cong \triangle ADC$? E
   A. $\angle 1 \cong \angle 2$, $\angle 5 \cong \angle 6$
   B. $\overline{AD} \cong \overline{AB}$, $\angle 3$ and $\angle 4$ are right angles.
   C. $\overline{AD} \cong \overline{AB}$, $\overline{DC} \cong \overline{BC}$
   D. $\angle 5 \cong \angle 6$, $\angle 3$ and $\angle 4$ are right angles.
   E. $\overline{AD} \cong \overline{AB}$, $\angle 5 \cong \angle 6$

What additional information would you need to prove the triangles congruent by the HL Theorem?

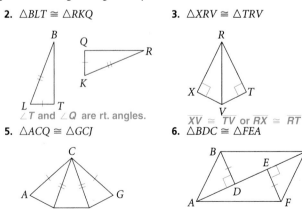

2. $\triangle BLT \cong \triangle RKQ$

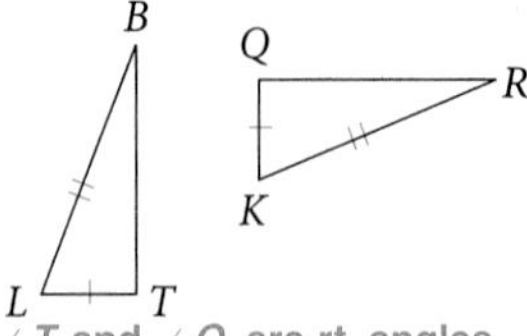

$\angle T$ and $\angle Q$ are rt. angles.

3. $\triangle XRV \cong \triangle TRV$

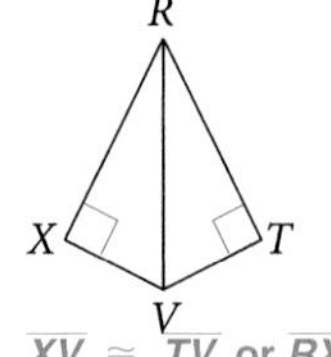

$\overline{XV} \cong \overline{TV}$ or $\overline{RX} \cong \overline{RT}$

4. $\triangle TRY \cong \triangle EYR$

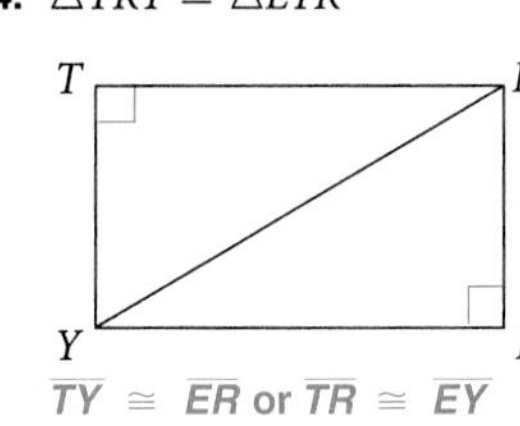

$\overline{TY} \cong \overline{ER}$ or $\overline{TR} \cong \overline{EY}$

5. $\triangle ACQ \cong \triangle GCJ$

$\angle AQC$ and $\angle GJC$ are rt. angles.

6. $\triangle BDC \cong \triangle FEA$

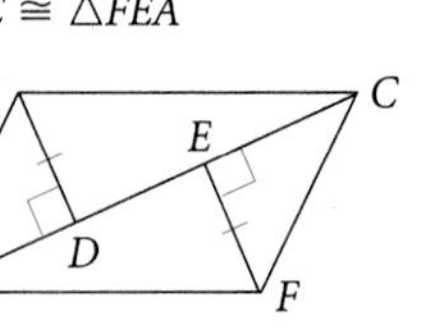

$\overline{BC} \cong \overline{FA}$

7. $\triangle STR \cong \triangle PQN$

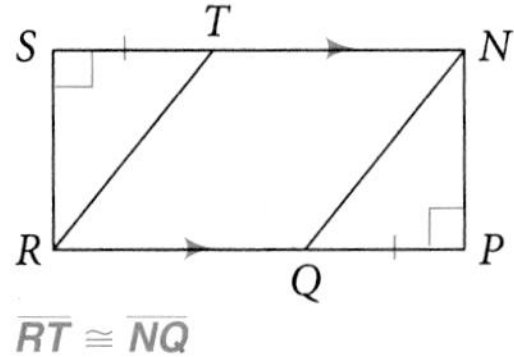

$\overline{RT} \cong \overline{NQ}$

DIVERSITY Exercise 9 Take this opportunity to discuss careers in landscaping and horticulture. Help students see the wide range of skills required in such fields. For example, a landscaper designs landscapes, uses plants to improve air quality in buildings, knows the climate and soil conditions required by different plants, and is an expert in plant diseases. Have students research the educational requirements to become a landscape architect.

COORDINATE GEOMETRY Exercise 11 Students use the relationship between the slopes of perpendicular lines to show that $\triangle EGD$ and $\triangle EGF$ are right triangles.

Exercises 12–13 Encourage students to begin by writing a plan for each proof.

MAKING CONNECTIONS Exercise 14 Aristarchus of Samos is also known for his belief in a heliocentric world system, the view of the universe that places Earth and other planets in motion around the Sun. His beliefs were rejected in favor of a geocentric world system, which places Earth at the center of the universe, until the sixteenth century when Copernicus demonstrated the superiority of the heliocentric system in explaining astronomic observations.

RESEARCH Exercise 14b Students will need to research the distance from the Sun to Earth ($\approx$ 93,000,000 mi.) and from the moon to Earth ($\approx$ 240,000 mi.). They should be able to find this information in an almanac or an encyclopedia.

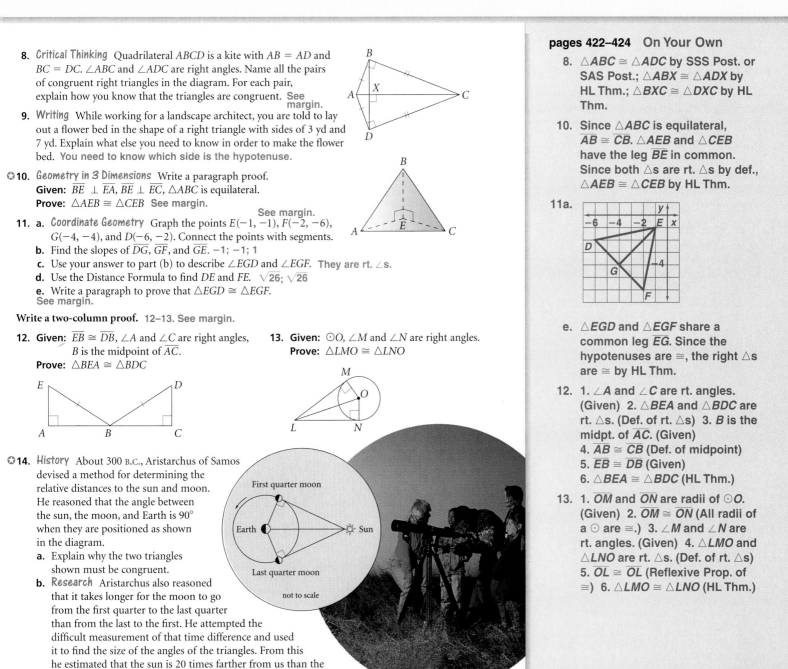

8. *Critical Thinking* Quadrilateral $ABCD$ is a kite with $AB = AD$ and $BC = DC$. $\angle ABC$ and $\angle ADC$ are right angles. Name all the pairs of congruent right triangles in the diagram. For each pair, explain how you know that the triangles are congruent. See margin.

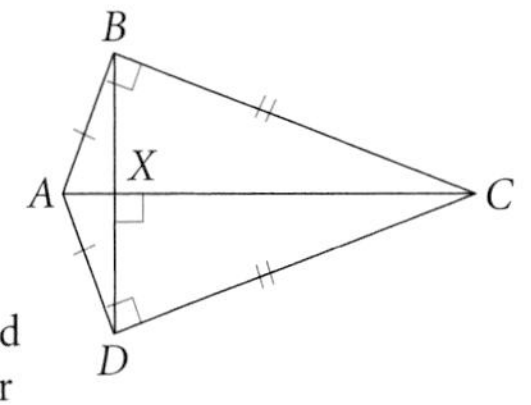

9. *Writing* While working for a landscape architect, you are told to lay out a flower bed in the shape of a right triangle with sides of 3 yd and 7 yd. Explain what else you need to know in order to make the flower bed. You need to know which side is the hypotenuse.

10. *Geometry in 3 Dimensions* Write a paragraph proof.
Given: $\overline{BE} \perp \overline{EA}$, $\overline{BE} \perp \overline{EC}$, $\triangle ABC$ is equilateral.
Prove: $\triangle AEB \cong \triangle CEB$ See margin.

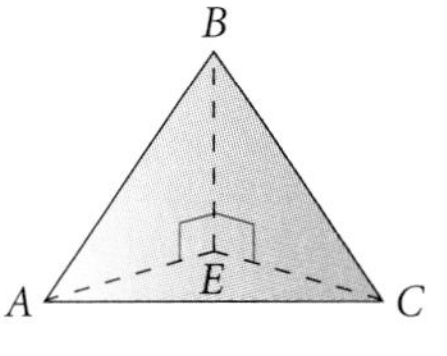

11. a. *Coordinate Geometry* Graph the points $E(-1, -1)$, $F(-2, -6)$, $G(-4, -4)$, and $D(-6, -2)$. Connect the points with segments. See margin.

b. Find the slopes of $\overline{DG}$, $\overline{GF}$, and $\overline{GE}$. -1; -1; 1

c. Use your answer to part (b) to describe $\angle EGD$ and $\angle EGF$. They are rt. $\angle$s.

d. Use the Distance Formula to find DE and FE. $\sqrt{26}$; $\sqrt{26}$

e. Write a paragraph to prove that $\triangle EGD \cong \triangle EGF$. See margin.

Write a two-column proof. 12–13. See margin.

12. Given: $\overline{EB} \cong \overline{DB}$, $\angle A$ and $\angle C$ are right angles, B is the midpoint of $\overline{AC}$.
Prove: $\triangle BEA \cong \triangle BDC$

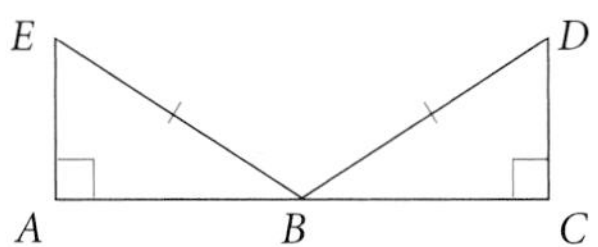

13. Given: $\odot O$, $\angle M$ and $\angle N$ are right angles.
Prove: $\triangle LMO \cong \triangle LNO$

14. *History* About 300 B.C., Aristarchus of Samos devised a method for determining the relative distances to the sun and moon. He reasoned that the angle between the sun, the moon, and Earth is 90° when they are positioned as shown in the diagram.

a. Explain why the two triangles shown must be congruent.

b. *Research* Aristarchus also reasoned that it takes longer for the moon to go from the first quarter to the last quarter than from the last to the first. He attempted the difficult measurement of that time difference and used it to find the size of the angles of the triangles. From this he estimated that the sun is 20 times farther from us than the moon is. How accurate was his estimate?

a–b. See margin p. 424.

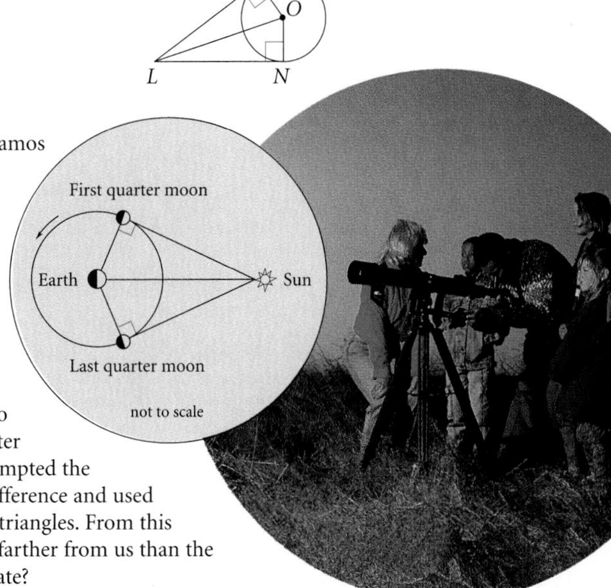

pages 422–424 On Your Own

8. $\triangle ABC \cong \triangle ADC$ by SSS Post. or SAS Post.; $\triangle ABX \cong \triangle ADX$ by HL Thm.; $\triangle BXC \cong \triangle DXC$ by HL Thm.

10. Since $\triangle ABC$ is equilateral, $\overline{AB} \cong \overline{CB}$. $\triangle AEB$ and $\triangle CEB$ have the leg $\overline{BE}$ in common. Since both $\triangle$s are rt. $\triangle$s by def., $\triangle AEB \cong \triangle CEB$ by HL Thm.

11a.

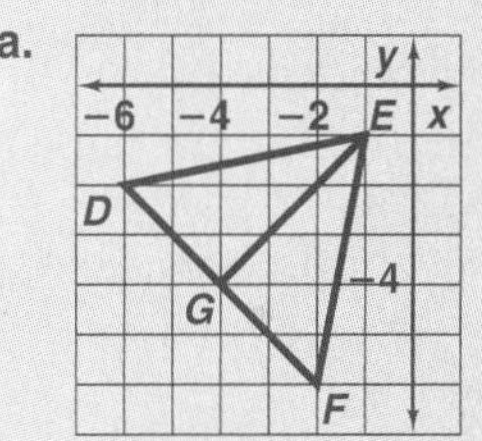

e. $\triangle EGD$ and $\triangle EGF$ share a common leg $\overline{EG}$. Since the hypotenuses are $\cong$, the right $\triangle$s are $\cong$ by HL Thm.

12. 1. $\angle A$ and $\angle C$ are rt. angles. (Given) 2. $\triangle BEA$ and $\triangle BDC$ are rt. $\triangle$s. (Def. of rt. $\triangle$s) 3. B is the midpt. of $\overline{AC}$. (Given) 4. $\overline{AB} \cong \overline{CB}$ (Def. of midpoint) 5. $\overline{EB} \cong \overline{DB}$ (Given) 6. $\triangle BEA \cong \triangle BDC$ (HL Thm.)

13. 1. $\overline{OM}$ and $\overline{ON}$ are radii of $\odot O$. (Given) 2. $\overline{OM} \cong \overline{ON}$ (All radii of a $\odot$ are $\cong$.) 3. $\angle M$ and $\angle N$ are rt. angles. (Given) 4. $\triangle LMO$ and $\triangle LNO$ are rt. $\triangle$s. (Def. of rt. $\triangle$s) 5. $\overline{OL} \cong \overline{OL}$ (Reflexive Prop. of $\cong$) 6. $\triangle LMO \cong \triangle LNO$ (HL Thm.)

CONNECTING TO STUDENTS' WORLD Exercise 15 If you have block scheduling or an extended class period, you may want students to act out this problem in the classroom using tables or desks.

OPEN–ENDED Exercise 16a Students may want to identify real-world triangular-shaped objects with and without line symmetry.

MAKING CONNECTIONS Exercise 17 Modern mechanical clocks can be traced back to the seventeenth century. A mechanical clock must have a source of energy such as a falling weight, a tightly-wound spring, or an electric current. The energy source turns a wheel engaging a system of gears that moves the hands of the clock. An "escapement" regulates the clock so it runs accurately by allowing the teeth of one of the gears to "escape" one by one.

CONSTRUCTIONS Exercises 18–20 Students will need a compass and a straightedge.

Chapter Project **FIND OUT BY OBSERVING** If students cannot find any local structures with exposed frameworks, suggest that they look in library books for pictures of architecture or construction.

14a. The △s are rt. △s with a common hypotenuse and ≅ legs. By HL Thm., the △s are ≅.

b. His estimate was inaccurate. The sun is about 390 times further away from Earth than the moon.

15. Measure the distance from the corner of the room to one corner of the table. The room is a rectangle, so the table forms a rt. △ with the walls. Since the length of the table is the hypotenuse and is the same for each △, if 1 pair of legs are ≅, the △s are ≅ by the HL Thm.

16a. 18.

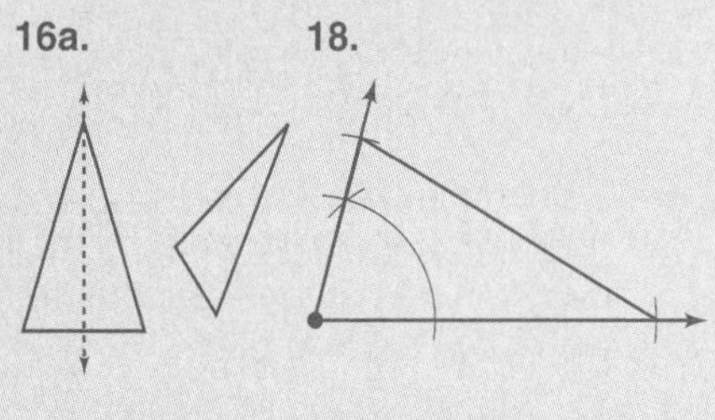

19.

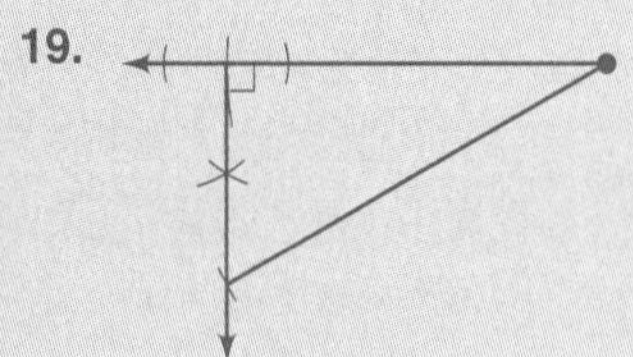

20.

15. *Open-ended* A table has been placed in the corner of a room. What measurements would you make with a tape measure in order to place a matching table in the other corner at exactly the same angle? Explain why your method works. See margin for sample.

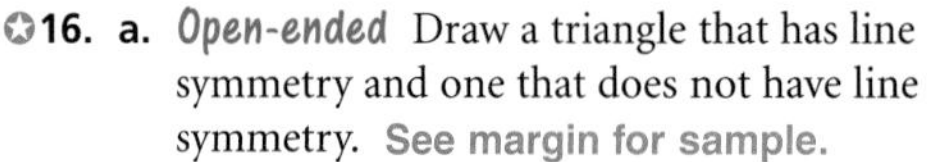

16. a. *Open-ended* Draw a triangle that has line symmetry and one that does not have line symmetry. See margin for sample.

b. *Critical Thinking* Explain why any triangle with line symmetry must be isosceles. See below.

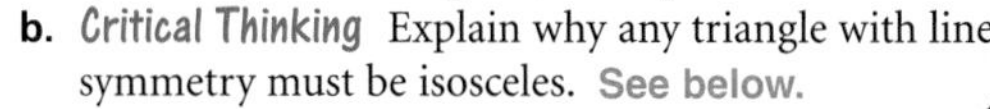

17. *Clock Repair* To repair an antique clock, a 12-toothed wheel has to be made by cutting right triangles out of a regular polygon that has twelve 4-cm sides. The hypotenuse of each triangle is a side of the regular polygon, and the shorter leg is 1 cm long. Explain why the twelve triangles must be congruent. See below.

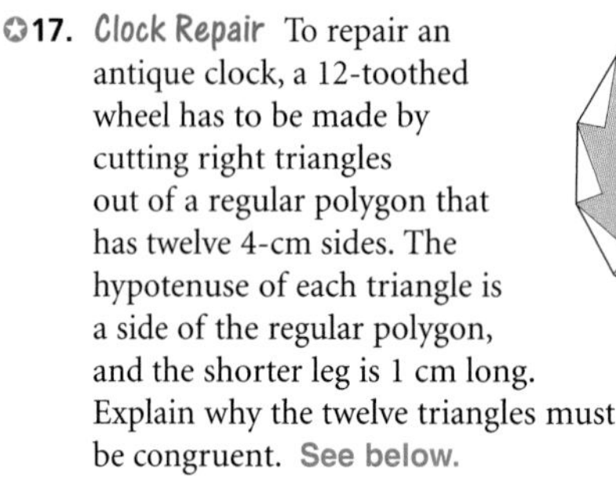

Constructions **Copy the triangle on your paper and construct a triangle congruent to it using the method stated.** 18–20. See margin for samples.

18. by SAS

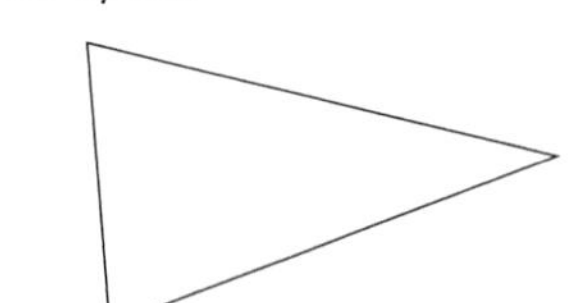

19. by HL

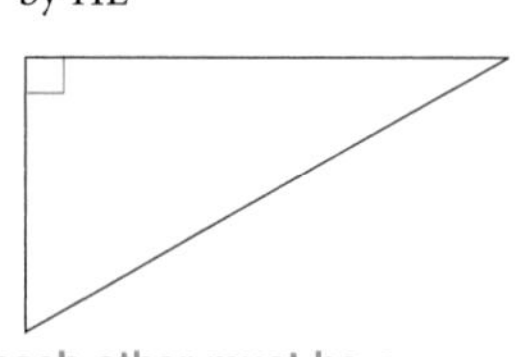

20. by ASA

16b. The sides that are images of each other must be ≅.

17. All sides of a regular polygon are ≅. Since the △s are rt. △s and the shorter legs of all the △s are ≅, by HL Thm., all the △s are ≅.

Chapter Project ***Find Out by Observing***

Visit local bridges, towers, or other structures that have exposed frameworks. Examine these structures for ideas you can use when you design and build a toothpick bridge later in this project. Record your ideas.

Sketch or take pictures of the structures. On the sketches or photos, show where triangles are used for stability. Check students' work.

Exercises MIXED REVIEW

Exercises 21–26 Students review the relationship between pairs of angles formed when two parallel lines are cut by a transversal.

GETTING READY FOR LESSON 8-4 These exercises prepare students to use triangle congruence to prove parts of triangles congruent.

Wrap Up

THE BIG IDEA Ask students to explain why the HL Theorem only applies to right triangles.

RETEACHING ACTIVITY Students determine if triangles are congruent by the HL Theorem. (Reteaching worksheet 8-3)

Exercises CHECKPOINT

In this Checkpoint, your students will assess their own progress in Lessons 8-1 to 8-3.

Exercises 1–6 Students may want to begin by making a list of all the ways they can prove two triangles congruent.

OPEN-ENDED Exercise 7 Ask students if they can draw a pair of right triangles with the given conditions.

Exercises MIXED REVIEW

State the postulate or theorem that justifies each statement.

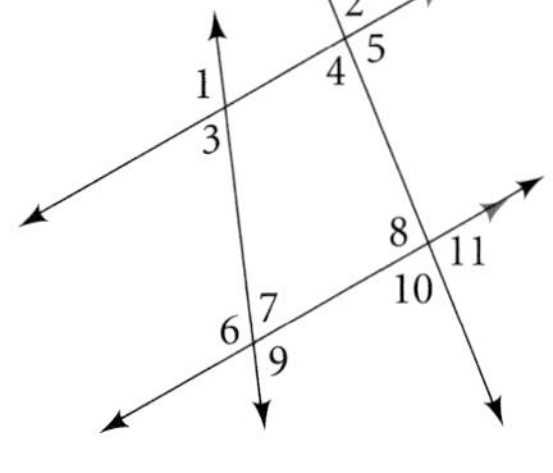

21. $m\angle 1 + m\angle 3 = 180$

22. $\angle 5 \cong \angle 8$

23. $m\angle 4 + m\angle 8 = 180$

24. $\angle 3 \cong \angle 7$

25. $\angle 1 \cong \angle 6$

26. $\angle 5 \cong \angle 11$

21–26. See back of book.

27. *Calculator* A circle has radius 5 m. Two radii form a 35° angle. What is the area of the sector between them to the nearest hundredth? 7.64 m^2

Getting Ready for Lesson 8-4

28. Given that $\triangle TRC \cong \triangle HGV$, list everything you know about the two triangles.
$\angle T \cong \angle H$; $\angle C \cong \angle V$; $\angle R \cong \angle G$;
$\overline{TR} \cong \overline{HG}$; $\overline{RC} \cong \overline{GV}$; $\overline{TC} \cong \overline{HV}$

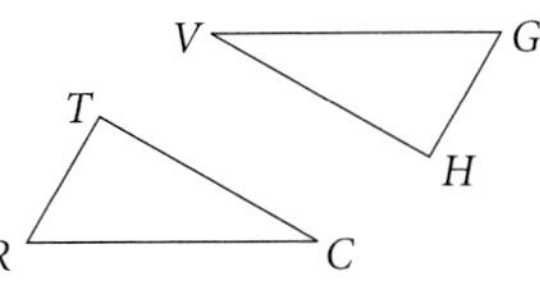

Exercises CHECKPOINT

State the postulate or theorem you can use to prove the triangles congruent. If the triangles *cannot* be proven congruent, write *not possible*.

1. 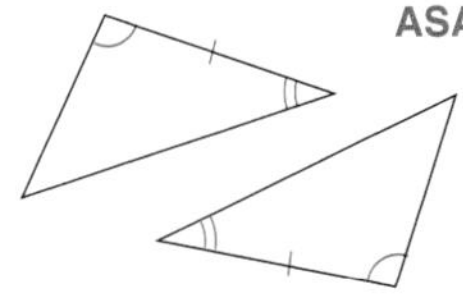 ASA

2. 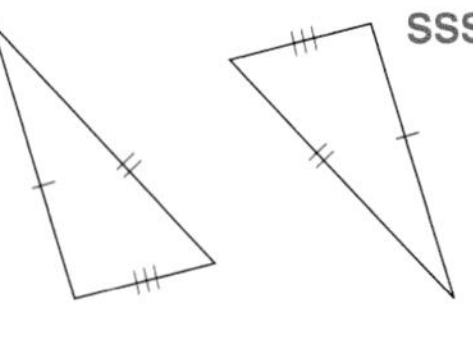 SSS

3. 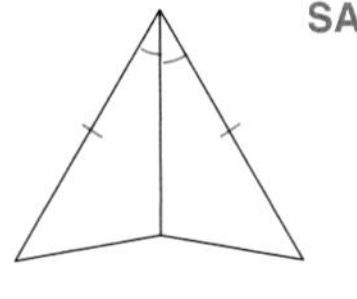 SAS

4. 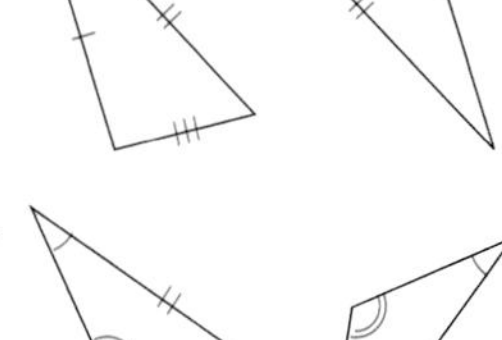 not possible

5. 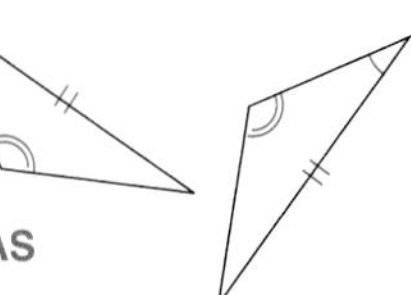 AAS

6. 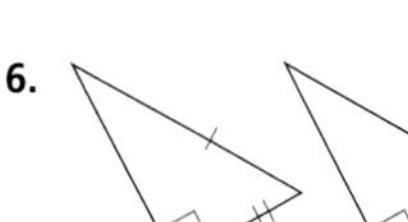 HL

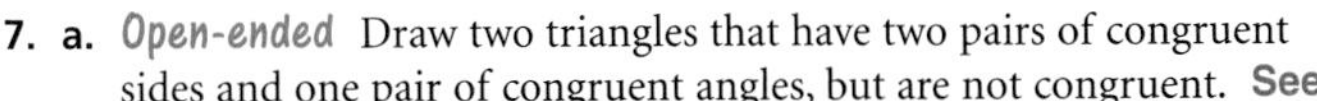

7. a. *Open-ended* Draw two triangles that have two pairs of congruent sides and one pair of congruent angles, but are not congruent. See back of book for sample.

b. Can you draw two noncongruent triangles that have two pairs of congruent angles and one pair of corresponding congruent sides? Explain. See back of book.

8. *Standardized Test Prep* Which congruence statement *cannot* be used to prove two triangles congruent? E

A. AAS **B.** SAS **C.** SSS **D.** ASA **E.** AAA

9. *Writing* Use the HL Theorem as a model to write an HA Theorem. Is the theorem true? **Justify** your answer. See back of book.

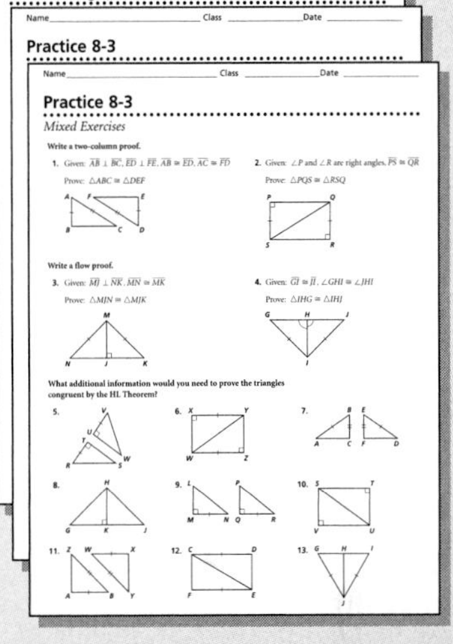

Lesson Quiz

Lesson Quiz is also available in Transparencies.

Give the additional information needed to prove the triangles congruent by the HL Theorem.

1. $\triangle BAT \cong \triangle GEM$
$\angle B$ and $\angle G$ are right angles
$\overline{BA} \cong \overline{GE}$
$\overline{AT} \cong \overline{EM}$

2. $\triangle MNO \cong \triangle PQR$
$\overline{MN} \cong \overline{PQ}$
$\overline{MO} \cong \overline{PR}$
$\angle N$ and $\angle Q$ are right angles

3. $\triangle CDE \cong \triangle CDF$
$\overline{CD} \perp \overline{EF}$
$\overline{CE} \cong \overline{CF}$

4. $\triangle FOR \cong \triangle MIK$
$\angle F$ and $\angle M$ are right angles
$\overline{OR} \cong \overline{IK}$
$\overline{FO} \cong \overline{MI}$ or $\overline{FR} \cong \overline{MK}$

8-4 Teaching Notes

PROBLEM OF THE DAY

Name a polyhedron having the same number of faces as vertices. a tetrahedron

Problem of the Day is also available in Transparencies.

CONNECTING TO PRIOR KNOWLEDGE Draw the following triangles. Ask students: *If △GHI ≅ △JKL by the SSS Postulate, can you say that ∠H ≅ ∠K? ∠I ≅ ∠J?*

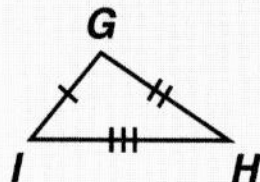

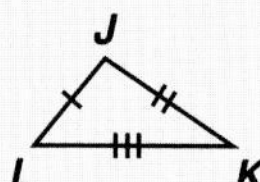

THINK AND DISCUSS

The abbreviation CPCTC is helpful when writing reasons in proofs. Encourage students, however, to state the entire phrase when verbalizing it.

ERROR ALERT! Question 1 Students may not recognize that $\overline{AB} \parallel \overline{DC}$. **Remediation:** Suggest that they extend $\overline{AB}$, $\overline{DC}$, and $\overline{DB}$. This will help them recognize that $\overleftrightarrow{DB}$ is a transversal cutting $\overleftrightarrow{AB}$ and $\overleftrightarrow{DC}$.

Lesson Planning Options

Prerequisite Skills

- Applying the SSS, SAS, and ASA Postulates and the AAS and HL Theorems
- Writing Proofs

Assignment Options for Exercises On Your Own

To provide flexible scheduling, this lesson can be subdivided into parts.

 **Core** 1–8, 10, 12
Extension 15

 **Core** 9, 11, 13, 16–17
Extension 14

Use Mixed Review to maintain skills.

Resources

Student Edition

Skills Handbook, p. 664
Extra Practice, p. 655
Glossary/Study Guide

Teaching Resources

Chapter Support File, Ch. 8
- Practice 8-4 (two worksheets)
- Reteaching 8-4

Classroom Manager 8-4
Glossary, Spanish Resources

 **Transparencies**
87

426

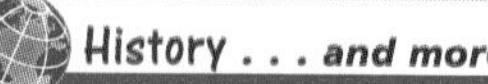

8-4 Using Congruent Triangles in Proofs

What You'll Learn

- Using triangle congruence and CPCTC to prove that parts of two triangles are congruent

...And Why

To see how triangle congruence has been used in the past to measure distances indirectly

THINK AND DISCUSS

Using CPCTC

In the previous lessons you learned to use SSS, SAS, ASA, AAS, and HL to prove that two triangles are congruent. Once you know that triangles are congruent, you can make conclusions about corresponding segments and angles because Corresponding Parts of Congruent Triangles are Congruent. A shorthand way of writing this is **CPCTC.**

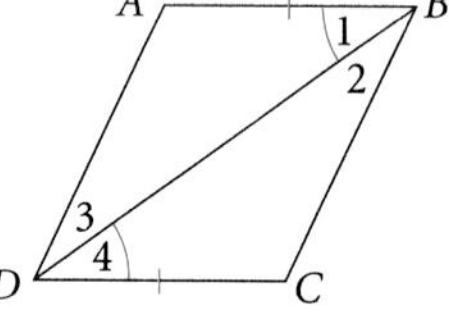

1. a. Suppose you know that △ABD ≅ △CDB by SAS. Which additional pairs of sides and angles are congruent by CPCTC?
   b. *Critical Thinking* What other conclusions can you make about segments in this figure?

a. $\overline{AD} \cong \overline{CB}$, ∠A ≅ ∠C, ∠2 ≅ ∠3 b. $\overline{AB} \parallel \overline{DC}$, $\overline{AD} \parallel \overline{BC}$

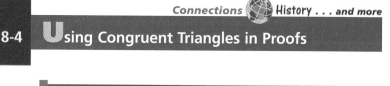

Given: $\overline{AC} \cong \overline{EC}$, $\overline{BC} \cong \overline{DC}$
Prove: ∠A ≅ ∠E

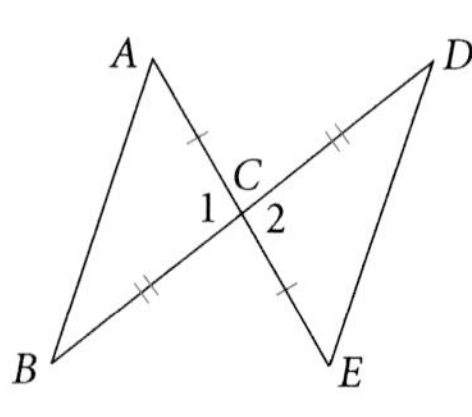

Plan for Proof You can show that ∠A ≅ ∠E if you can show that these angles are corresponding parts of congruent triangles. Prove that △ABC ≅ △EDC and then use CPCTC.

Statements	Reasons
1. $\overline{AC} \cong \overline{EC}$	1. Given
2. $\overline{BC} \cong \overline{DC}$	2. Given
3. ∠1 ≅ ∠2	3. Vertical angles are ≅.
4. △ABC ≅ △EDC	4. SAS Postulate
5. ∠A ≅ ∠E	5. CPCTC

2. a. **Try This** State two relationships that are true for $\overline{AB}$ and $\overline{ED}$ in Example 1. $\overline{AB} \parallel \overline{ED}$, $\overline{AB} \cong \overline{ED}$
   b. **Justify** your answers. If ≅ corres. ∠s, then lines are ∥; CPCTC

Example 1

Emphasize that the intermediate step of this proof is proving $\triangle ABC \cong \triangle EDC$. Once this is proven, you can use CPCTC to prove the angles congruent.

Question 2b Students should not have difficulty with this question if they successfully answered Question 1.

Example 2 **Relating to the Real World** 

ESL Some students may be unfamiliar with the expression "paced off." You may want to demonstrate what it means by pacing off the length of the classroom.

Discuss with students the logical reasoning given in the proof. Begin by discussing why $\angle 1 \cong \angle 2$ and why $\angle 3$ and $\angle 4$ are right angles. Point out that, although $\triangle DEF$ and $\triangle DEG$ are right triangles, they cannot be proven congruent by HL because you do not know $\overline{DF} \cong \overline{DG}$.

KINESTHETIC LEARNING If you have block scheduling or an extended class period, you may want to have students reenact the measurement technique. Students could use congruent triangles to measure indirectly across a football field, part of a parking lot, or a local road. Then they could find the actual measurement and compare the results.

According to legend, one of Napoleon's officers used congruent triangles to estimate the width of a river. The officer stood on the riverbank and lowered the visor of his cap until the farthest thing he could see was the edge of the opposite bank of the river. He then turned and noted the spot on his side of the river that was in line with his eye and the tip of his visor. The officer then paced off the distance to this spot and declared that distance to be the width of the river!

Example 2 **Relating to the Real World**

History Write a proof to show why Napoleon's officer was correct in stating that the distance he paced off equaled the distance across the river.

Given: $\angle EDG \cong \angle EDF$, $\angle DEG$ and $\angle DEF$ are right angles.
Prove: $\overline{EF} \cong \overline{EG}$

Statements	Reasons
1. $\angle EDG \cong \angle EDF$	1. Given
2. $\overline{DE} \cong \overline{DE}$	2. Reflexive Property of $\cong$
3. $\angle DEG$ and $\angle DEF$ are right $\angle$s.	3. Given
4. $\angle DEG \cong \angle DEF$	4. All right angles are $\cong$.
5. $\triangle DEF \cong \triangle DEG$	5. ASA Postulate
6. $\overline{EF} \cong \overline{EG}$	6. CPCTC

PROBLEM SOLVING

Look Back What other angles or sides can be proven congruent in Example 2?
$\angle G \cong \angle F$, $\overline{DG} \cong \overline{DF}$

3. About how wide was the river if the officer stepped off 20 paces and each pace was about $2\frac{1}{2}$ ft? about 50 ft

Additional Examples

FOR EXAMPLE 1

Write a plan for the proof.

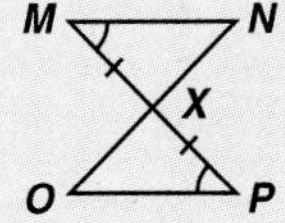

Given: $\angle M \cong \angle P$, X is the midpoint of $\overline{MP}$.
Prove: $\overline{MN} \cong \overline{PO}$. See back of book.

FOR EXAMPLE 2

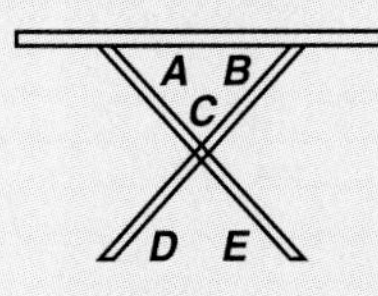

The legs of an ironing board bisect each other. Write a proof to show the board is parallel to the floor by showing that the alternate interior angles are congruent. See back of book.

FOR EXAMPLE 3

Write a paragraph proof.

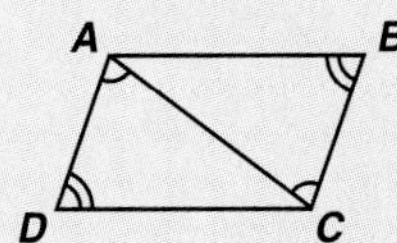

Given: $\angle D \cong \angle B$, $\angle DAC \cong \angle BCA$
Prove: $\overline{AB} \cong \overline{CD}$ See back of book.

Example 3

In Example 3, students draw the bisector of the vertex angle and show that the triangles formed are congruent by the SAS Postulate. In Question 4, students draw the altitude from the vertex angle and show that the two triangles formed are congruent by the HL Theorem. In Exercise 13 students will prove that the bisector of the vertex angle of an isosceles triangle is the perpendicular bisector of the base.

Example 4

Help students understand how the hypothesis and conclusion of the Angle Bisector Theorem are translated into the Given and Prove statements of the proof. Make sure students understand why proving $\overline{PM} \cong \overline{PN}$ implies that P is equidistant from $\overrightarrow{LM}$ and $\overrightarrow{LN}$.

Technology Options

For Exercises 16–17, students may perform the construction using geometry software.

Prentice Hall Technology

Software
- Secondary Math Lab Toolkit™
- Computer Item Generator 8-4

Internet
- See the Prentice Hall site. (http://www.phschool.com)

Part 2

Proving Theorems

You can use congruent triangles to prove many of the theorems you discovered in earlier chapters.

QUICK REVIEW

Isosceles Triangle Theorem
If two sides of a triangle are congruent, then the angles opposite those sides are congruent.

Example 3

Write a paragraph proof of the Isosceles Triangle Theorem.

Begin with isosceles $\triangle XYZ$ with $\overline{XY} \cong \overline{XZ}$. Draw $\overline{XB}$, the bisector of the vertex angle $\angle X$.

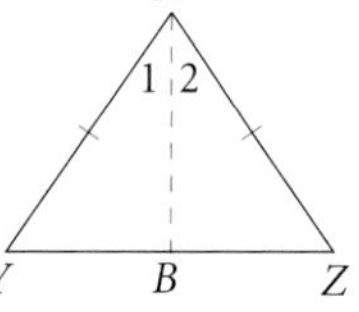

Given: $\overline{XY} \cong \overline{XZ}$, $\overline{XB}$ bisects $\angle YXZ$.
Prove: $\angle Y \cong \angle Z$

Paragraph Proof

By the definition of angle bisector, $\angle 1 \cong \angle 2$. You are given that $\overline{XY} \cong \overline{XZ}$, and by the Reflexive Property of Congruence, $\overline{XB} \cong \overline{XB}$. Thus, $\triangle XYB \cong \triangle XZB$ by the SAS Postulate, and $\angle Y \cong \angle Z$ by CPCTC. ■

4d. By def., $\overline{XA} \perp \overline{YZ}$ and $\triangle XYA$ and $\triangle XZA$ are rt. $\triangle$s. It is given that $\overline{XY} \cong \overline{XZ}$, and by Reflexive Prop. of $\cong$, $\overline{XA} \cong \overline{XA}$. Thus, $\triangle XYA \cong \triangle XZA$ by HL Thm., and $\angle Y \cong \angle Z$ by CPCTC.

4. **Try This** There is more than one way to prove the Isosceles Triangle Theorem. Complete the following steps for a different proof.
   a. Use $\triangle XYZ$ from Example 3 and instead of drawing the bisector of $\angle X$, draw the altitude $\overline{XA}$ from X to $\overline{YZ}$. See margin p. 429.
   b. Write a new *Given* statement. $\overline{XY} \cong \overline{XZ}$, $\overline{XA}$ is altitude of $\triangle XYZ$.
   c. What postulate or theorem can you use to prove $\triangle XYA \cong \triangle XZA$? HL Thm
   d. Write your proof in paragraph form. See left.

Example 4 outlines a proof of the Angle Bisector Theorem.

QUICK REVIEW

Angle Bisector Theorem
If a point is on the bisector of an angle, then it is equidistant from the sides of the angle.

The **distance from a point to a line** is the length of the perpendicular segment from the point to the line.

Example 4

Write a plan for the following proof.

Given: $\overrightarrow{LP}$ bisects $\angle MLN$,
$\overline{PM} \perp \overrightarrow{LM}$,
$\overline{PN} \perp \overrightarrow{LN}$
Prove: $\overline{PM} \cong \overline{PN}$

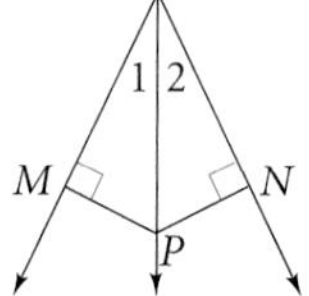

Plan for Proof $\overline{PM}$ and $\overline{PN}$ are corresponding parts of $\triangle LMP$ and $\triangle LNP$. These triangles are congruent by the AAS Theorem because a bisector forms congruent angles, perpendiculars form congruent right angles, and $\overline{LP} \cong \overline{LP}$ by the Reflexive Property of Congruence. ■

5. *Choose* Use the Plan for Proof in Example 4. Write a two-column proof, a paragraph proof, or a flow proof.
Answers may vary. See margin p. 429 for sample.

Exercises ON YOUR OWN

Exercises 1–6 Make sure students state the triangle congruence as part of their explanation.

TACTILE LEARNING Exercise 7 Have students draw the quadrilateral with sides as marked in the figure. Have students justify their answers by measuring $\angle A$ and $\angle C$ with a protractor.

MAKING CONNECTIONS Exercise 8 The city of Ubar, believed to have existed in Southwestern Oman from 2800 B.C. to about 100 A.D., fell into a sinkhole created by the collapse of an underground limestone cavern. Called "Atlantis of the sands" by Lawrence of Arabia, the fabled city was located in 1992 using images from satellites and spacecraft.

CRITICAL THINKING Exercise 8 Ask students if it is possible to find the diameter of the sinkhole using the technique of Napoleon's officers described in Example 2.

Exercises ON YOUR OWN

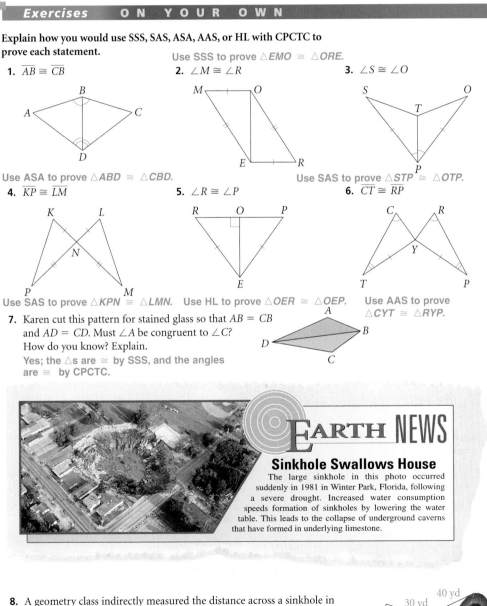

Explain how you would use SSS, SAS, ASA, AAS, or HL with CPCTC to prove each statement.

1. $\overline{AB} \cong \overline{CB}$

Use ASA to prove $\triangle ABD \cong \triangle CBD$.

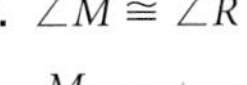

2. $\angle M \cong \angle R$

Use SSS to prove $\triangle EMO \cong \triangle ORE$.

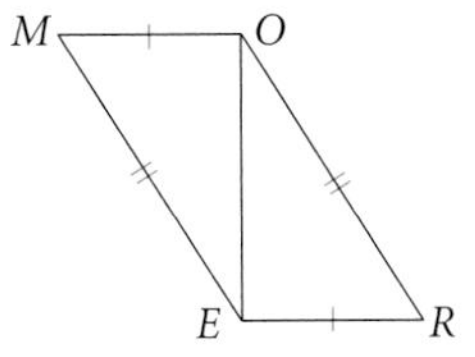

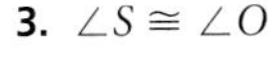

3. $\angle S \cong \angle O$

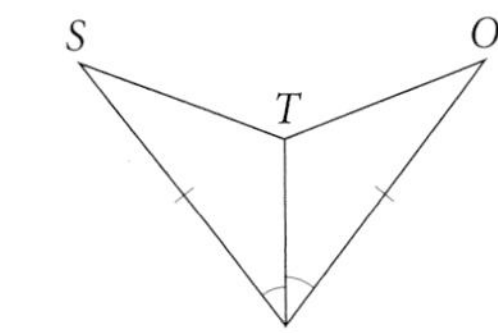

Use SAS to prove $\triangle STP \cong \triangle OTP$.

4. $\overline{KP} \cong \overline{LM}$

Use SAS to prove $\triangle KPN \cong \triangle LMN$.

5. $\angle R \cong \angle P$

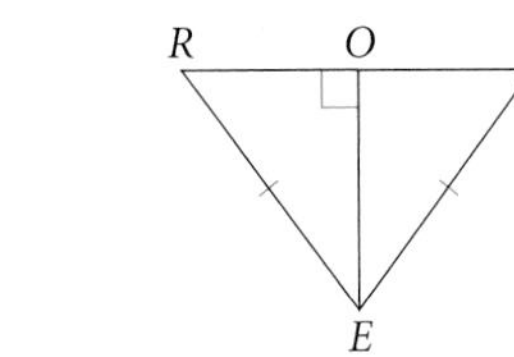

Use HL to prove $\triangle OER \cong \triangle OEP$.

6. $\overline{CT} \cong \overline{RP}$

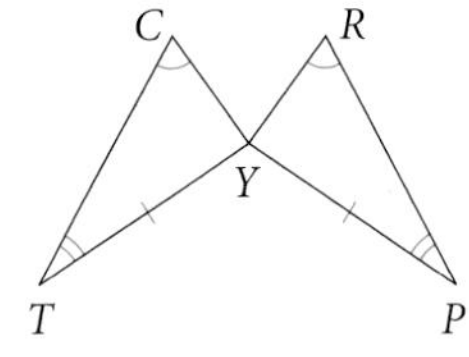

Use AAS to prove $\triangle CYT \cong \triangle RYP$.

7. Karen cut this pattern for stained glass so that $AB = CB$ and $AD = CD$. Must $\angle A$ be congruent to $\angle C$? How do you know? Explain.
Yes; the $\triangle$s are $\cong$ by SSS, and the angles are $\cong$ by CPCTC.

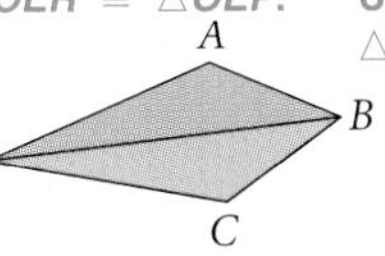

EARTH NEWS

Sinkhole Swallows House

The large sinkhole in this photo occurred suddenly in 1981 in Winter Park, Florida, following a severe drought. Increased water consumption speeds formation of sinkholes by lowering the water table. This leads to the collapse of underground caverns that have formed in underlying limestone.

8. A geometry class indirectly measured the distance across a sinkhole in a nearby field. They measured distances as shown in the diagram. Explain how to use their measurements to find the distance across the sinkhole. The vertical angles are $\cong$, so the $\triangle$s are also $\cong$ by SAS. The distance across the sinkhole is 26.5 yd by CPCTC.

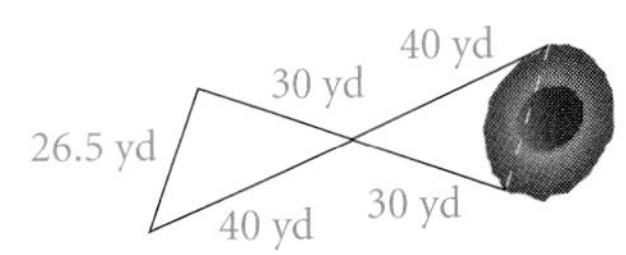

pages 426–428 Think and Discuss

4a.

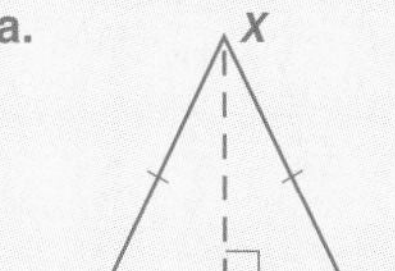

5. $\overrightarrow{LP}$ bisects $\angle MLN$ (Given) 2. $\angle 1 \cong \angle 2$ (Def. of angle bisector) 3. $\overline{PM} \perp \overrightarrow{LM}$ and $\overline{PN} \perp \overrightarrow{LN}$ (Given) 4. $\angle LMP$ and $\angle LNP$ are rt. $\angle$s. (Def. of $\perp$ lines) 5. $\angle LMP \cong \angle LNP$ (All rt. $\angle$s are $\cong$.) 6. $\overline{LP} \cong \overline{LP}$ (Reflexive Prop. of $\cong$) 7. $\triangle LMP \cong \triangle LNP$ (AAS) 8. $\overline{PM} \cong \overline{PN}$ (CPCTC)

ALTERNATIVE ASSESSMENT Exercises 9–10 These exercises can help you assess students' ability to reason logically by their ability to complete and order the two-column proofs. In Exercise 9, students write the reasons for the statements and in Exercise 10, students rearrange the reasons in the correct order.

EXTENSION Exercise 11 After students have completed the flow proof, have them work in groups to copy each of the eight statements and eight reasons on individual pieces of paper. Have them mix them up and then rearrange them to form a two-column proof.

9. Theorem 4-3 states that if two angles of a triangle are congruent, then the sides opposite the angles are congruent.

To prove this theorem, begin with $\triangle ABC$ with $\angle A \cong \angle C$ and draw the bisector of $\angle B$. Supply a reason for each statement in the proof.

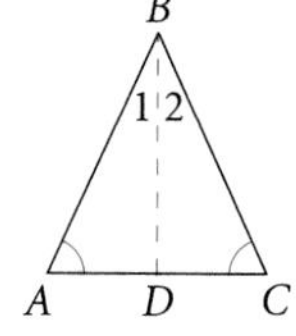

Given: $\angle A \cong \angle C$, $\overline{BD}$ bisects $\angle ABC$.
Prove: $\overline{AB} \cong \overline{CB}$

Statements	Reasons
1. $\angle A \cong \angle C$	a. ? Given
2. $\overline{BD}$ bisects $\angle ABC$.	b. ? Given
3. $\angle 1 \cong \angle 2$	c. ? Def. of angle bisector
4. $\overline{BD} \cong \overline{BD}$	d. ? Reflexive Prop. of $\cong$
5. $\triangle ABD \cong \triangle CBD$	e. ? AAS
6. $\overline{AB} \cong \overline{CB}$	f. ? CPCTC

10. The reasons given in the proof below are correct, but they are in the wrong order. List them in the correct order. d, c, e, b, a

Given: O is the center of the circle.
Prove: $\overline{AB} \cong \overline{CD}$

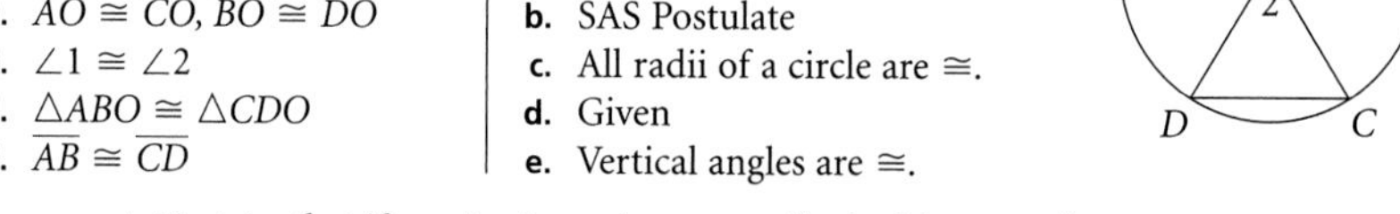

Statements	Reasons
1. O is the center of the circle.	a. CPCTC
2. $\overline{AO} \cong \overline{CO}$, $\overline{BO} \cong \overline{DO}$	b. SAS Postulate
3. $\angle 1 \cong \angle 2$	c. All radii of a circle are $\cong$.
4. $\triangle ABO \cong \triangle CDO$	d. Given
5. $\overline{AB} \cong \overline{CD}$	e. Vertical angles are $\cong$.

11. Theorem 4-12 states that if a point is on the perpendicular bisector of a segment, then it is equidistant from the endpoints of the segment.

Supply the reasons for the following flow proof of the theorem.

Given: $\ell \perp \overline{AB}$, ℓ bisects $\overline{AB}$ at C, P is on ℓ.
Prove: $PA = PB$

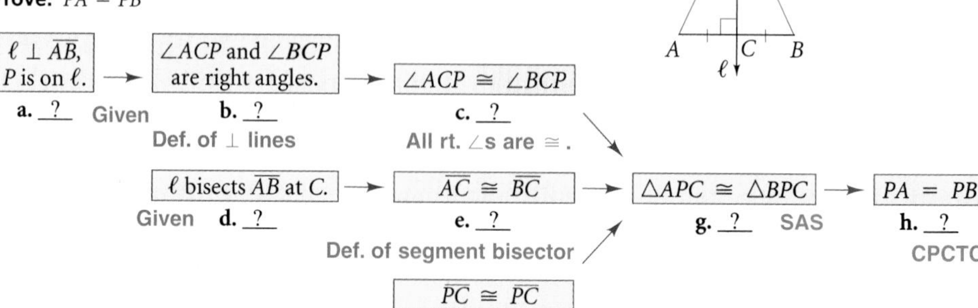

CRITICAL THINKING Exercise 13 Ask students to use the diagram from Exercise 13 and write a plan to prove the following. Then have them discuss the similarities and differences between their plan and the Plan for Proof given in Exercise 13.

Given: Isosceles $\triangle ABC$ with $\overline{BD} \perp \overline{AC}$, $\overline{BD}$ bisects $\overline{AC}$. Prove: $\overline{BA} \cong \overline{BC}$, $\overline{BD}$ bisects $\angle ABC$.

Exercise 14 Make sure students understand that O is the center of the circle.

CONSTRUCTIONS Exercises 16–17 Students use congruent triangles to justify two of the constructions they learned in Lesson 1-6 and 7-3.

12. ***Choose*** Write a two-column proof, a paragraph proof, or a flow proof. **Answers may vary. See margin for sample.**

Given: $\overline{FB} \perp \overline{AD}$, $\overline{GC} \perp \overline{AD}$, $\overline{FB} \cong \overline{GC}$, $\overline{AE} \cong \overline{DE}$
Prove: $\overline{AB} \cong \overline{DC}$

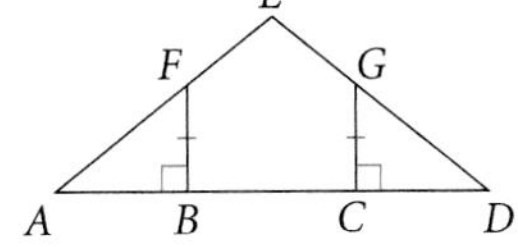

13. Theorem 4-2 states that the bisector of the vertex angle of an isosceles triangle is the perpendicular bisector of the base. **Answers may vary. See margin for sample.**

Use the following Plan for Proof to write a paragraph proof for the theorem.

Given: Isosceles $\triangle ABC$ with $\overline{BA} \cong \overline{BC}$, $\overline{BD}$ bisects $\angle ABC$.
Prove: $\overline{BD} \perp \overline{AC}$, $\overline{BD}$ bisects $\overline{AC}$.

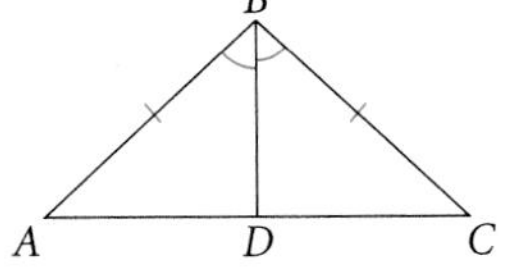

Plan for Proof You can show that $\overline{BD} \perp \overline{AC}$ by showing that $\angle BDA \cong \angle BDC$ and using the fact that congruent supplementary angles are right angles. You can show that $\overline{BD}$ bisects $\overline{AC}$ by showing that $\overline{AD} \cong \overline{CD}$. These angles and segments are corresponding parts of $\triangle ABD$ and $\triangle CBD$. Prove that $\triangle ABD \cong \triangle CBD$.

14. ***Choose*** Write a two-column proof, a paragraph proof, or a flow proof.

Given: $\overline{ZK} \perp \overline{JQ}$ in $\odot O$
Prove: $\overline{JW} \cong \overline{QW}$

Answers may vary. See margin for sample.

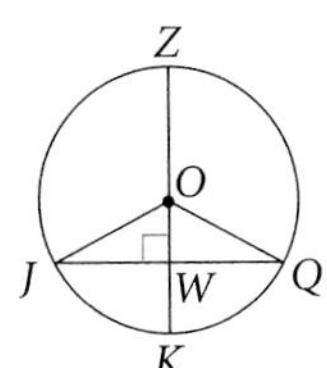

15. a. How can you prove $\triangle BGF \cong \triangle BGD$? **Use SAS on 2 legs and rt. angle.**

b. $BD = 8$ cm. What other segment is 8 cm long? **Justify** your answer. **$\overline{BF}$; CPCTC**

c. How can you prove $\triangle FAB \cong \triangle BCD$? (*Hint:* Use your results from part (b).) **The $\triangle$s are rt. $\triangle$s with $\cong$ hypotenuses and $\cong$ legs. By HL, $\triangle FAB \cong \triangle BCD$.**

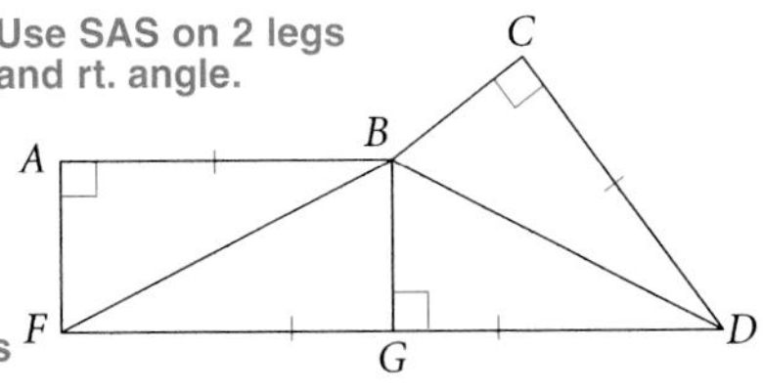

16. ***Constructions*** The construction of the bisector of $\angle A$ is shown below.

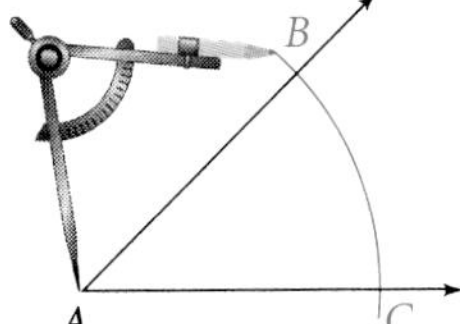

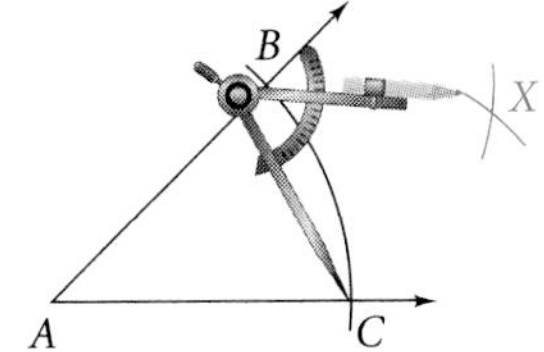

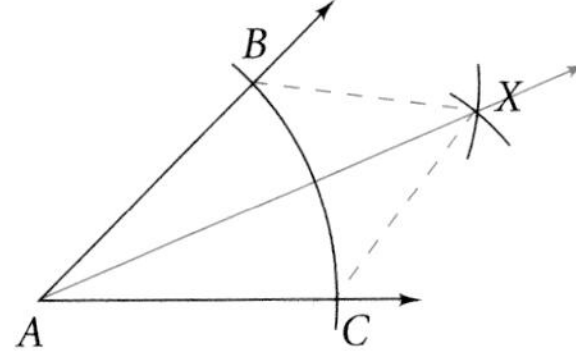

$\overline{AB} \cong \overline{AC}$ because they are radii of the same circle. $\overline{BX} \cong \overline{CX}$ because the same compass setting was used to draw both arcs. Use these facts to prove that $\overrightarrow{AX}$ bisects $\angle BAC$. **$\overline{AX} \cong \overline{AX}$ by Reflexive Prop. of $\cong$. $\triangle ABX \cong \triangle ACX$ by SSS, and $\angle BAX \cong \angle CAX$ by CPCTC. $\overline{AX}$ bisects $\angle BAC$ by def. of angle bisector.**

pages 429–432 On Your Own

12. 1. $\overline{AE} \cong \overline{DE}$ (Given) 2. $\triangle AED$ is isosceles. (Def. of isos. $\triangle$) 3. $\angle A \cong \angle D$ (Base $\angle$s of an isosceles $\triangle$ are $\cong$.) 4. $\overline{FB} \perp \overline{AD}$, $\overline{GC} \perp \overline{AD}$ (Given) 5. $\angle ABF$ and $\angle DCG$ are rt. $\angle$s. (Def. of $\perp$ lines) 6. $\angle ABF \cong \angle DCG$ (All rt. $\angle$s are $\cong$.) 7. $\overline{FB} \cong \overline{GC}$ (Given) 8. $\triangle ABF \cong \triangle DCG$ (AAS) 9. $\overline{AB} \cong \overline{DC}$ (CPCTC)

13. It is given that $\overline{BA} \cong \overline{BC}$ and $\overline{BD}$ bisects $\angle ABC$. $\angle ABD \cong \angle CBD$ by def. of $\angle$ bisector, and $\angle A \cong \angle C$ because base $\angle$s of an isosceles $\triangle$ are $\cong$. Then $\triangle ABD \cong \triangle CBD$ by ASA. $\overline{AD} \cong \overline{CD}$ by CPCTC. Therefore, $\overline{BD}$ bisects $\overline{AC}$ by def. of segment bisector. By the Angle Addition Post., $m\angle ADB + m\angle CDB = 180$. $\angle ADB \cong \angle CDB$ by CPCTC. So, the measure of each angle is $\frac{1}{2}(180) = 90$, and $\angle$s are rt. by def. of rt. $\angle$s. Therefore, $\overline{BD} \perp \overline{AC}$ by def. of $\perp$ lines.

14. 1. $\overline{OJ} \cong \overline{OQ}$ (All radii of a $\odot$ are $\cong$.) 2. $\overline{OW} \cong \overline{OW}$ (Reflexive Prop. of $\cong$) 3. $\overline{ZK} \perp \overline{JQ}$ (Given) 4. $\angle OWJ$ and $\angle OWQ$ are rt. angles. (Def. of $\perp$ lines) 5. $\triangle OWJ$ and $\triangle OWQ$ are rt. $\triangle$s. (Def. of rt. $\triangle$) 6. $\triangle OJW \cong \triangle OQW$ (HL Thm.) 7. $\overline{JW} \cong \overline{QW}$ (CPCTC)

17b. $\overline{CP} \cong \overline{CP}$ by Reflexive Prop. of $\cong$. Then, $\triangle APC \cong \triangle BPC$ by SSS and $\angle APC \cong \angle BPC$ by CPCTC. Therefore, $m\angle APC = m\angle BPC = 90$ by Angle Addition Post., and the $\angle$s are rt. by def. of rt. $\angle$s. Then, $\overline{CP} \perp \overline{AB}$ by def. of $\perp$ lines.

Exercises MIXED REVIEW

Exercises 18–20 Students review transformations.

CONNECTING TO STUDENTS' WORLD Exercise 21 Have students survey each other to find out how many school days a year students miss due to colds. Then have them display the data in a circle graph.

GETTING READY FOR LESSON 8-5 These exercises prepare students to identify congruent overlapping triangles.

Wrap Up

THE BIG IDEA Ask students: *Explain how congruent triangles can be used to measure indirectly.*

RETEACHING ACTIVITY Students use triangle congruence and CPCTC to complete a two-column proof, then write two two-column proofs. (Reteaching worksheet 8-4)

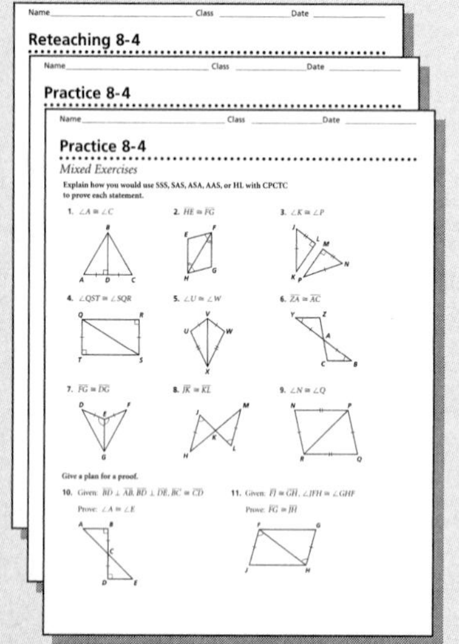

Lesson Quiz

Lesson Quiz is also available in Transparencies.

Explain how you could use SSS, SAS, ASA, AAS, or HL with CPCTC to prove each statement.

1. $\angle PQR \cong \angle TQR$
   See back of book.

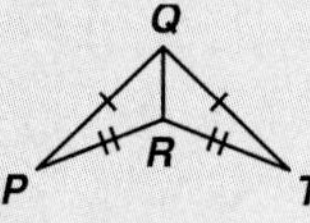

2. $\overline{FG} \cong \overline{FI}$
   See back of book.

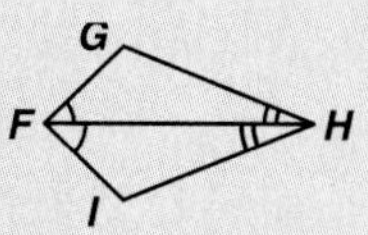

3. Write a proof.
   Given: $\overline{DC} \cong \overline{CE}$ and $\overline{DE}$ is a diameter in $\odot O$.
   Prove: $\angle DOC$ and $\angle COE$ are right angles. See back of book.

17. **Constructions** The construction of a line perpendicular to line ℓ through point P on ℓ is shown here. **a. $\overline{PA} \cong \overline{PB}$; $\overline{AC} \cong \overline{BC}$**
    a. Which segments are congruent by construction?
    b. Prove that $\overleftrightarrow{CP}$ is perpendicular to ℓ. (*Hint:* Copy the diagram and draw $\overline{CA}$ and $\overline{CB}$.) **See margin p. 431.**

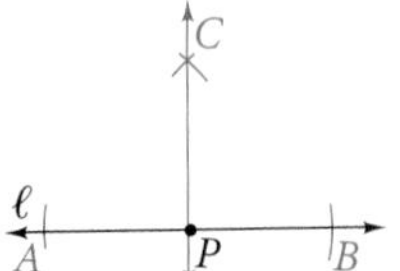

Exercises MIXED REVIEW

Copy each figure and draw its image under the given transformation.

18. reflection in line m

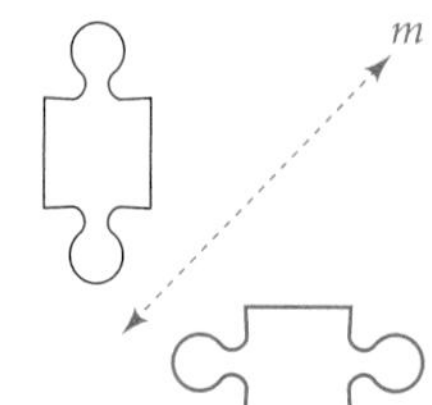

19. 90° counterclockwise rotation about point P

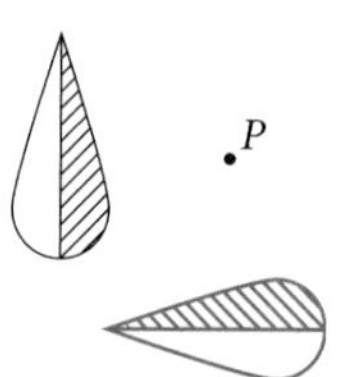

20. a translation of $\langle -2, 4 \rangle$

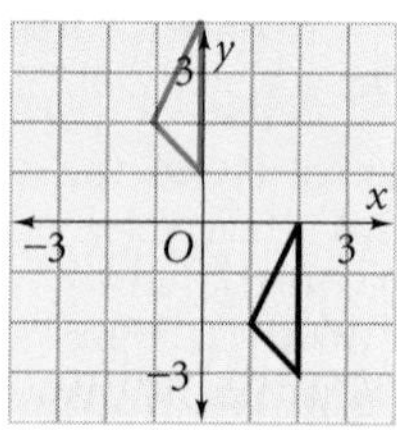

Data Analysis For Exercises 21–23, use the circle graph.

21. What percent of people knew the number of days they take off from work because of colds? **89%**
22. What percent of the people said they take off four or fewer days annually because of colds? **84%**
23. What is the measure of the central angle of the sector for the people who take one or two days off because of colds? **about 79°**

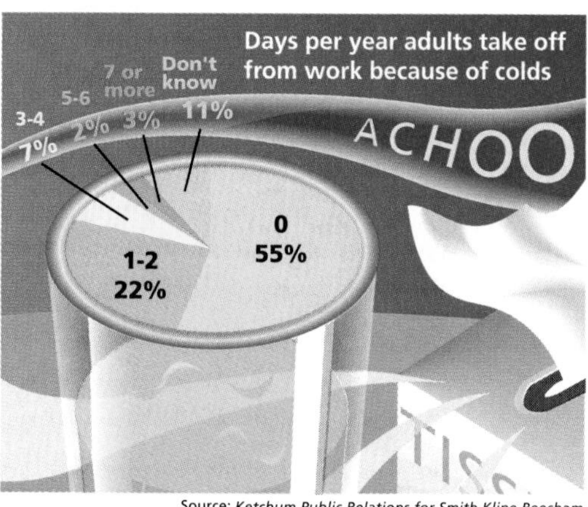

Source: *Ketchum Public Relations for Smith Kline Beecham*

Getting Ready For Lesson 8-5

Copy and label each triangle. Draw its image under a reflection in the red line. State which sides or angles a pair of triangles have in common.

24.

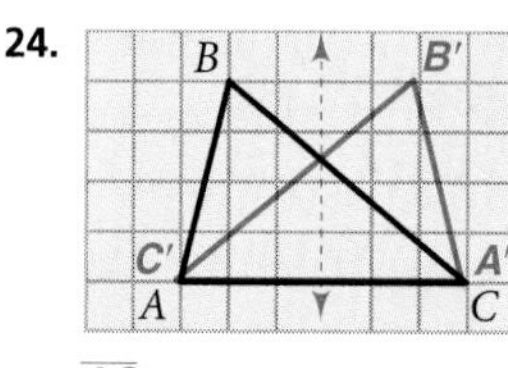

$\overline{AC}$

25.

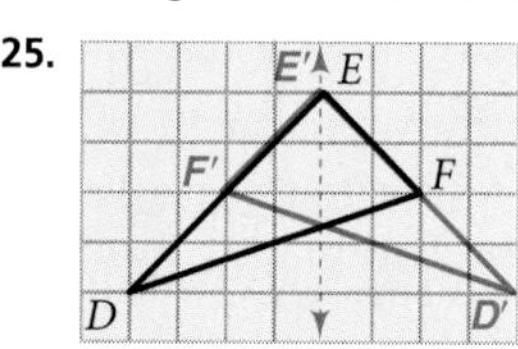

$\angle E$

26.

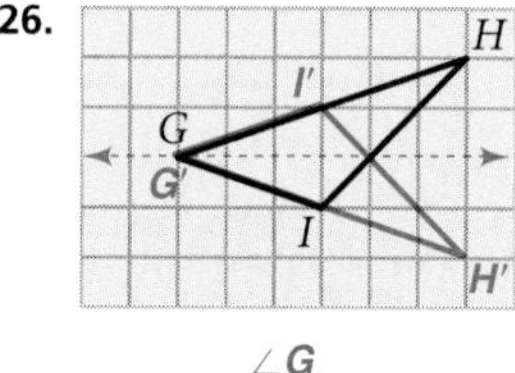

$\angle G$

8-5 Teaching Notes

PROBLEM OF THE DAY

How many noncongruent triangles can you make by joining any three points on a 3-by-3 dot grid? 8

Problem of the Day is also available in Transparencies.

CONNECTING TO PRIOR KNOWLEDGE Draw the figure on the board and have students identify all the triangles. Ask them which triangles appear congruent.

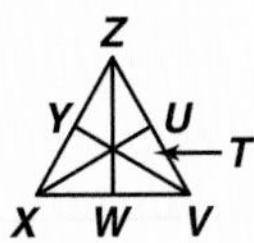

WORK TOGETHER p. 433

ESL Some students may not understand the term overlapping. Use an overhead projector and transparencies with overlays to illustrate its meaning.

Question 1 Some students will see the overlapping triangles $\triangle AFC$ and $\triangle BCF$ but miss $\triangle ABC$ and $\triangle BAF$.

THINK AND DISCUSS

Example 1

VISUAL LEARNING Students can visualize discrete triangles in a complex figure by using tracing paper to redraw overlapping triangles separately.

Connections Engineering . . . and more

What You'll Learn

- Identifying congruent overlapping triangles
- Proving two triangles congruent by first proving two other triangles congruent

...And Why

To be able to visualize overlapping triangles and use pairs of congruent triangles in real-world situations such as engineering

What You'll Need

- tracing paper
- colored pencils or pens

8-5 Using More than One Pair of Congruent Triangles

WORK TOGETHER

Work with a partner. Trace the diagram below and take turns finding pairs of congruent triangles. Use a different colored pencil to outline each pair you find. Then answer the questions below.

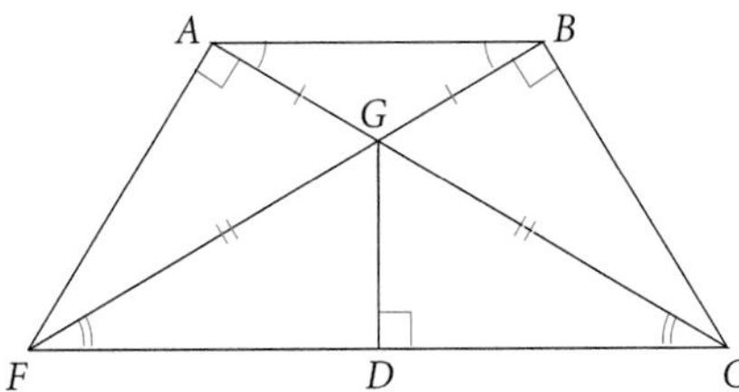

1. Write a congruence statement for each pair of triangles that you colored. State the congruence postulate or theorem you could use to prove the triangles congruent. Compare your results with those of another group. See back of book.
2. a. Name a pair of congruent triangles that overlap.
   b. Identify the common side the triangles share.
   a. Sample: $\triangle ABC$, $\triangle BAF$
   b. For sample in part (a): $\overline{AB}$

THINK AND DISCUSS

Part 1

Using Overlapping Triangles in Proofs

In the Work Together, you identified pairs of overlapping triangles that share a common side. Some overlapping triangles share a common angle. It is helpful to separate and redraw the overlapping triangles.

Example 1

Separate and redraw $\triangle DFG$ and $\triangle EHG$. Identify the common angle.

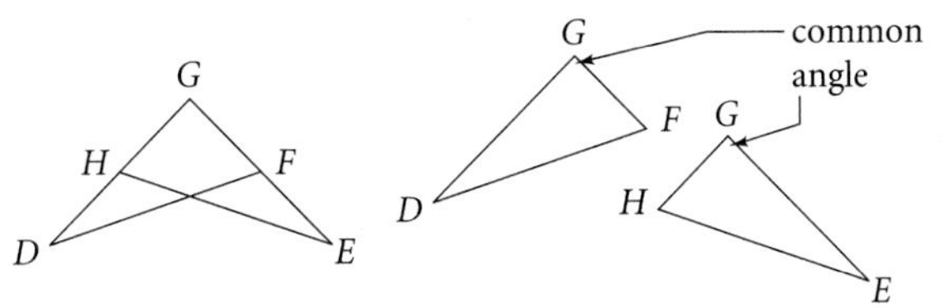

Lesson Planning Options

Prerequisite Skills

- Applying the SSS, SAS, and ASA Postulates and the AAS and HL Theorems
- Writing Proofs

Assignment Options for Exercises On Your Own

To provide flexible scheduling, this lesson can be subdivided into parts.

1 **Core** 1–9, 16
Extension 10

2 **Core** 11–15
Extension 17–18

Use Mixed Review to maintain skills.

Resources

Student Edition

Skills Handbook, p. 664
Extra Practice, p. 655
Glossary/Study Guide

Teaching Resources

Chapter Support File, Ch. 8
- Practice 8-5 (two worksheets)
- Reteaching 8-5

Classroom Manager 8-5
Glossary, Spanish Resources

Transparencies

88, 91, 92

MAKING CONNECTIONS Question 3 The Statue of Liberty is the tallest statue in the United States. Originally named "Liberty Enlightening the World," it was designed and built in France to commemorate the friendship of the two countries. A gift from France, it was received by President Grover Cleveland in 1886.

ERROR ALERT! **Question 3b** Students may think that all triangles sharing a side or an angle are congruent. **Remediation:** Point out that while $\triangle EAC$ and $\triangle DAC$ share a side, they are not congruent.

Example 2

Have students separate the overlapping triangles as shown. Make sure that students accurately label the vertices and mark any sides or angles appearing in both triangles as congruent.

Students may have difficulty writing a proof if they have not first devised a plan. Help them see that planning is essential.

Additional Examples

FOR EXAMPLE 2

Write a two-column proof.

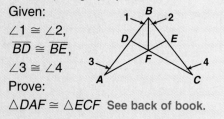

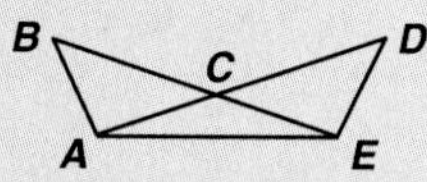

Given: $\overline{BA} \cong \overline{DE}$, $\overline{BE} \cong \overline{DA}$

Prove: $\angle BEA \cong \angle DAE$ See back of book.

FOR EXAMPLE 3

Write a paragraph proof.

Given:

$\angle 1 \cong \angle 2$,

$\overline{BD} \cong \overline{BE}$,

$\angle 3 \cong \angle 4$

Prove:

$\triangle DAF \cong \triangle ECF$ See back of book.

3. *Engineering* The diagram below shows triangles from the scaffolding workers used when they repaired and cleaned the Statue of Liberty.
   a. Identify the common side in $\triangle ADC$ and $\triangle BCD$. $\overline{CD}$
   b. Name another pair of triangles that share a common side. Answers may vary. Sample: $\triangle BCD$ and $\triangle BED$

You can use common angles and common sides to prove overlapping triangles congruent.

Example 2

Given: $\angle ZWX \cong \angle YXW$,
$\angle ZXW \cong \angle YWX$

Prove: $\overline{WZ} \cong \overline{XY}$

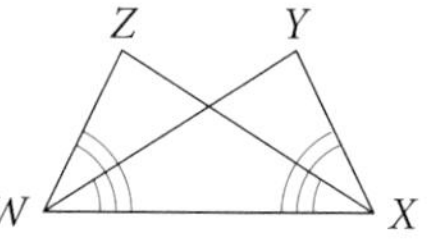

Separate the overlapping triangles. Then write a two-column proof.

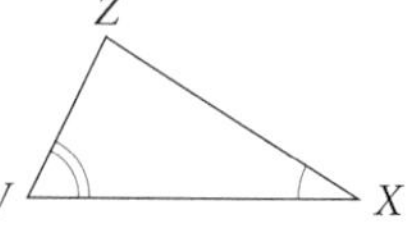

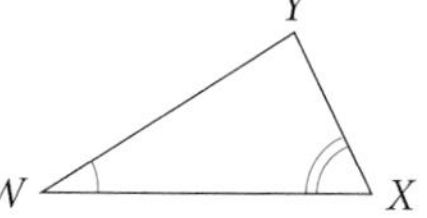

Plan for Proof To use CPCTC to show that $\overline{WZ} \cong \overline{XY}$, you must first prove that $\triangle ZWX \cong \triangle YXW$.

Proof

Statements	Reasons
1. $\angle ZWX \cong \angle YXW$, $\angle ZXW \cong \angle YWX$	1. Given
2. $\overline{WX} \cong \overline{WX}$	2. Reflexive Property of $\cong$
3. $\triangle ZWX \cong \triangle YXW$	3. ASA Postulate
4. $\overline{WZ} \cong \overline{XY}$	4. CPCTC

Example 3

Help students see that they cannot prove $\triangle GED \cong \triangle JEB$ from the information given. However, they can prove that $\triangle AED \cong \triangle CEB$. Proving $\triangle AED \cong \triangle CEB$ allows them to identify other pairs of congruent parts to then prove $\triangle GED \cong \triangle JEB$.

CRITICAL THINKING Ask students what they can say about the relationship between segments *AB* and *DC* and segments *BC* and *AD*. Also ask them what they can conclude about point *E*.

WORK TOGETHER p. 435

Question 4 Before students complete the proof, have them read through the statements and write a plan for the proof. Make sure they understand which pairs of triangles are being used and why.

Part 2

Using Two Pairs of Congruent Triangles

Sometimes you can prove that one pair of triangles is congruent and then use corresponding congruent parts of those triangles to prove that another pair of triangles is congruent.

Example 3

Given: E is the midpoint of $\overline{AC}$ and $\overline{DB}$.
Prove: $\triangle GED \cong \triangle JEB$

There is not enough information about $\triangle GED$ and $\triangle JEB$ to prove that they are congruent. But you can prove that $\triangle AED \cong \triangle CEB$. Then you can use corresponding congruent parts of these triangles to prove that $\triangle GED \cong \triangle JEB$.

Paragraph Proof

Since E is the midpoint of $\overline{AC}$ and $\overline{DB}$, $\overline{AE} \cong \overline{CE}$ and $\overline{DE} \cong \overline{BE}$. $\angle AED \cong \angle CEB$ because vertical angles are congruent. Therefore, $\triangle AED \cong \triangle CEB$ by SAS. $\angle D \cong \angle B$ by CPCTC, and $\angle GED \cong \angle JEB$ because they are vertical angles. Therefore, $\triangle GED \cong \triangle JEB$ by ASA.

WORK TOGETHER

Work with a partner.

4. Copy and complete the two-column proof below using two pairs of congruent triangles. After you prove the first pair of triangles congruent, separate and redraw the second pair of overlapping triangles that you need to use.

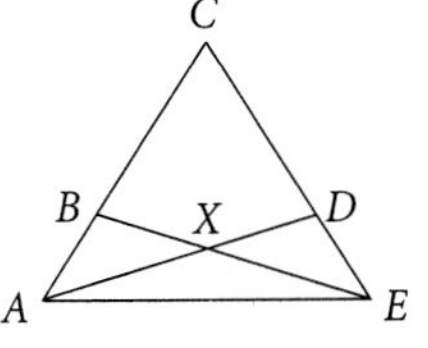

Given: $\overline{CA} \cong \overline{CE}$, $\overline{BA} \cong \overline{DE}$
Prove: $\overline{BX} \cong \overline{DX}$

Statements	Reasons
1. $\overline{CA} \cong \overline{CE}$	a. ? Given
2. $\angle CAE \cong \angle CEA$	b. ? See below.
3. $\overline{AE} \cong \overline{AE}$	c. ? Reflexive Prop. of ≅
4. $\overline{BA} \cong \overline{DE}$	d. ? Given
5. $\triangle BAE \cong \triangle DEA$	e. ? SAS
6. $\angle ABE \cong \angle EDA$	f. ? CPCTC
7. $\angle BXA \cong \angle DXE$	g. ? Vertical ∠s are ≅.
8. $\triangle BXA \cong \triangle DXE$	h. ? AAS
9. $\overline{BX} \cong \overline{DX}$	i. ? CPCTC

b. Base ∠s of an isosceles △ are ≅.

Technology Options

For Exercise 18, students may draw the parallelogram and diagonals using geometry software.

Prentice Hall Technology 

Software
- Secondary Math Lab Toolkit™
- Computer Item Generator 8-5

CD-ROM
- Multimedia Geometry Lab 8

Internet
- See the Prentice Hall site. (http://www.phschool.com)

Exercises ON YOUR OWN

Exercises 1–3 Some students can identify the common side or angle by observation. Some will want to trace the figures separately. Make sure students do not write in the book.

Exercises 4–9 Students should begin by tracing and separating the overlapping triangles. Have them mark the angles and sides that are congruent.

Exercise 10 Students use what they know about special angles formed by parallel lines and transversals to find missing angle measures. Then they use the angle measures to prove that triangles are congruent.

pages 436–438 On Your Own

10a. $m\angle 1 = 56$, $m\angle 2 = 56$, $m\angle 3 = 34$; $m\angle 4 = 90$; $m\angle 5 = 22$; $m\angle 6 = 34$; $m\angle 7 = 34$; $m\angle 8 = 68$; $m\angle 9 = 112$

Exercises ON YOUR OWN

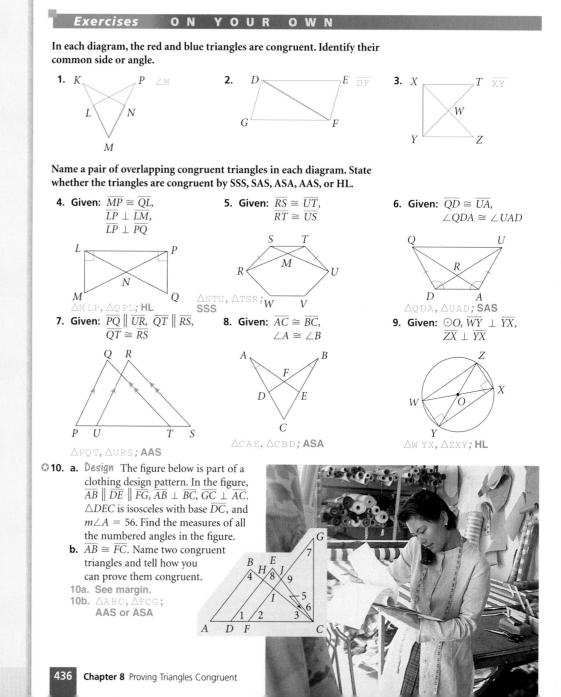

In each diagram, the red and blue triangles are congruent. Identify their common side or angle.

1. 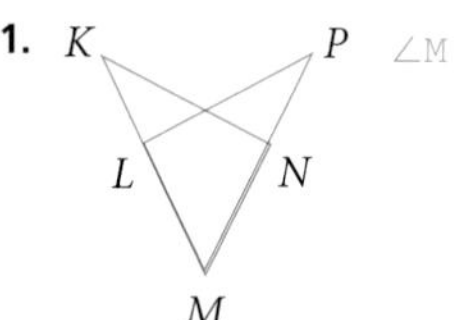
$\angle M$

2. 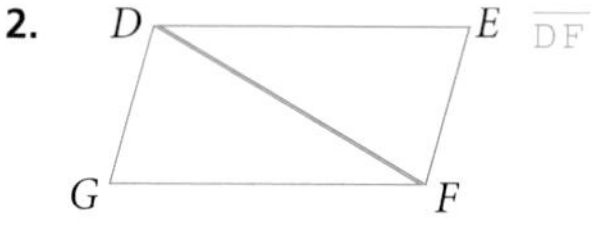
$\overline{DF}$

3. 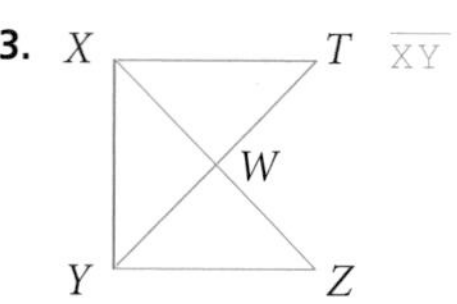
$\overline{XY}$

Name a pair of overlapping congruent triangles in each diagram. State whether the triangles are congruent by SSS, SAS, ASA, AAS, or HL.

4. **Given:** $\overline{MP} \cong \overline{QL}$, $\overline{LP} \perp \overline{LM}$, $\overline{LP} \perp \overline{PQ}$

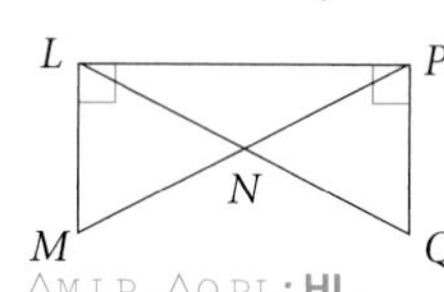

$\triangle MLP$, $\triangle QPL$; **HL**

5. **Given:** $\overline{RS} \cong \overline{UT}$, $\overline{RT} \cong \overline{US}$

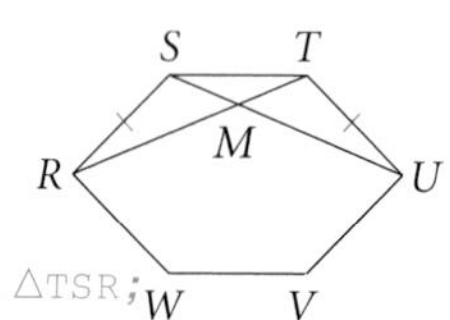
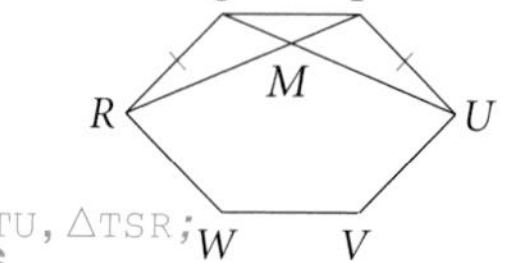

$\triangle STU$, $\triangle TSR$; **SSS**

6. **Given:** $\overline{QD} \cong \overline{UA}$, $\angle QDA \cong \angle UAD$

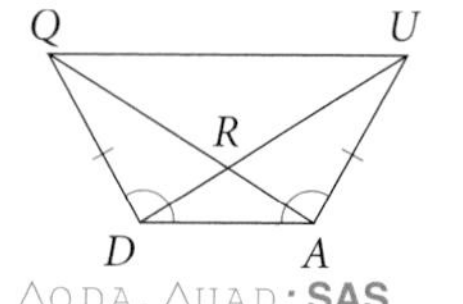

$\triangle QDA$, $\triangle UAD$; **SAS**

7. **Given:** $\overline{PQ} \parallel \overline{UR}$, $\overline{QT} \parallel \overline{RS}$, $\overline{QT} \cong \overline{RS}$

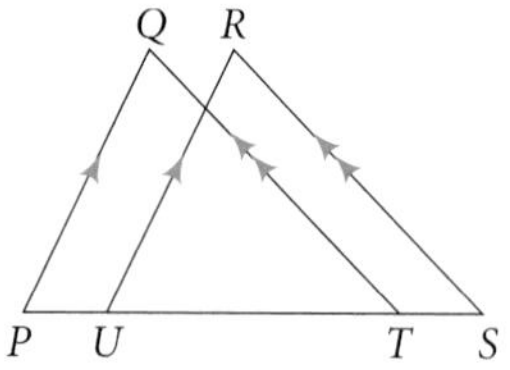

$\triangle PQT$, $\triangle URS$; **AAS**

8. **Given:** $\overline{AC} \cong \overline{BC}$, $\angle A \cong \angle B$

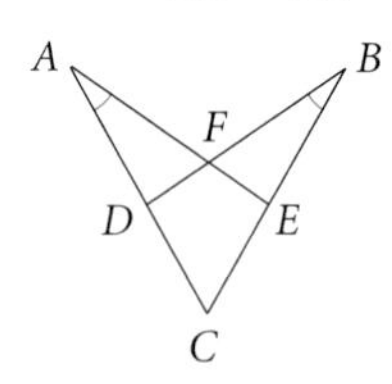

$\triangle CAE$, $\triangle CBD$; **ASA**

9. **Given:** $\odot O$, $\overline{WY} \perp \overline{YX}$, $\overline{ZX} \perp \overline{YX}$

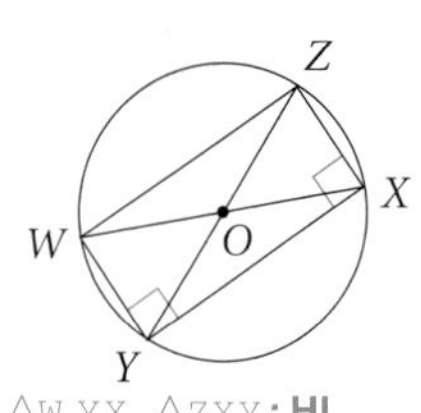

$\triangle WYX$, $\triangle ZXY$; **HL**

10. a. **Design** The figure below is part of a clothing design pattern. In the figure, $\overline{AB} \parallel \overline{DE} \parallel \overline{FG}$, $\overline{AB} \perp \overline{BC}$, $\overline{GC} \perp \overline{AC}$. $\triangle DEC$ is isosceles with base $\overline{DC}$, and $m\angle A = 56$. Find the measures of all the numbered angles in the figure.

b. $\overline{AB} \cong \overline{FC}$. Name two congruent triangles and tell how you can prove them congruent.

10a. See margin.
10b. $\triangle ABC$, $\triangle FCG$; AAS or ASA

ALTERNATIVE ASSESSMENT Exercises 11–12 You can use these exercises to help you assess students' ability to prove two triangles congruent by first proving two other triangles congruent. Have students work in groups and check that everyone can explain the group's plan.

EXTENSION Exercises 13–14 Have students rewrite the completed proofs as paragraph or flow proofs.

STANDARDIZED TEST TIP Exercise 15 Some students will focus on the figure and ignore the Given statement below it. Point out to them that the Given statement should tip them off that they need to use it in combination with the figure to prove two triangles are congruent.

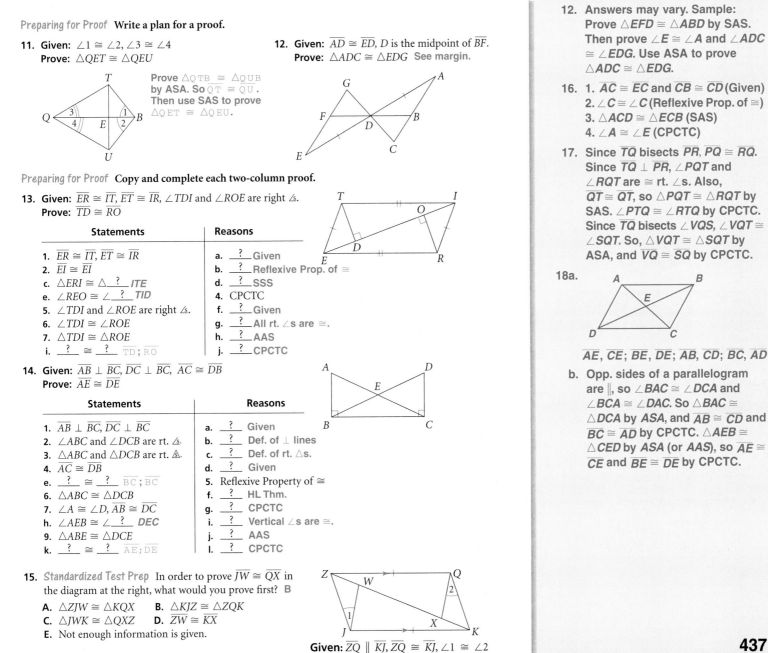

Preparing for Proof Write a plan for a proof.

11. Given: $\angle 1 \cong \angle 2$, $\angle 3 \cong \angle 4$
Prove: $\triangle QET \cong \triangle QEU$

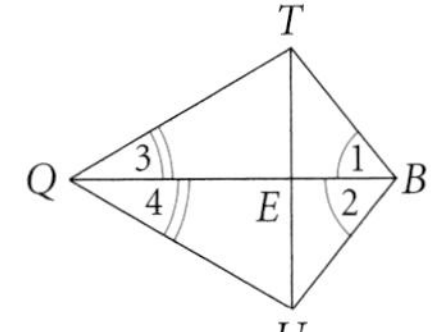

Prove $\triangle QTB \cong \triangle QUB$ by ASA. So $\overline{QT} \cong \overline{QU}$. Then use SAS to prove $\triangle QET \cong \triangle QEU$.

12. Given: $\overline{AD} \cong \overline{ED}$, D is the midpoint of $\overline{BF}$.
Prove: $\triangle ADC \cong \triangle EDG$ See margin.

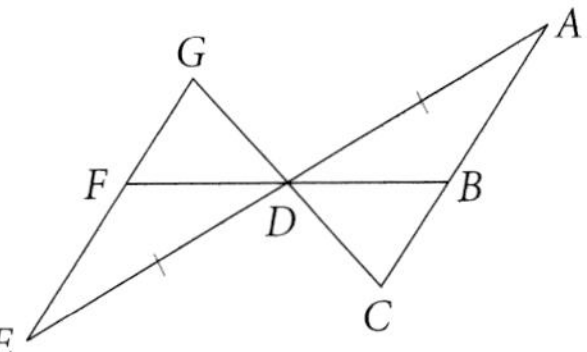

Preparing for Proof Copy and complete each two-column proof.

13. Given: $\overline{ER} \cong \overline{IT}$, $\overline{ET} \cong \overline{IR}$, $\angle TDI$ and $\angle ROE$ are right $\angle$s.
Prove: $\overline{TD} \cong \overline{RO}$

Statements	Reasons
1. $\overline{ER} \cong \overline{IT}$, $\overline{ET} \cong \overline{IR}$	a. ? Given
2. $\overline{EI} \cong \overline{EI}$	b. ? Reflexive Prop. of $\cong$
c. $\triangle ERI \cong \triangle$? ITE	d. ? SSS
e. $\angle REO \cong \angle$? TID	4. CPCTC
5. $\angle TDI$ and $\angle ROE$ are right $\angle$s.	f. ? Given
6. $\angle TDI \cong \angle ROE$	g. ? All rt. $\angle$s are $\cong$.
7. $\triangle TDI \cong \triangle ROE$	h. ? AAS
i. ? $\cong$? TD; RO	j. ? CPCTC

14. Given: $\overline{AB} \perp \overline{BC}$, $\overline{DC} \perp \overline{BC}$, $\overline{AC} \cong \overline{DB}$
Prove: $\overline{AE} \cong \overline{DE}$

Statements	Reasons
1. $\overline{AB} \perp \overline{BC}$, $\overline{DC} \perp \overline{BC}$	a. ? Given
2. $\angle ABC$ and $\angle DCB$ are rt. $\angle$s.	b. ? Def. of $\perp$ lines
3. $\triangle ABC$ and $\triangle DCB$ are rt. $\triangle$s.	c. ? Def. of rt. $\triangle$s.
4. $\overline{AC} \cong \overline{DB}$	d. ? Given
e. ? $\cong$? BC; BC	5. Reflexive Property of $\cong$
6. $\triangle ABC \cong \triangle DCB$	f. ? HL Thm.
7. $\angle A \cong \angle D$, $\overline{AB} \cong \overline{DC}$	g. ? CPCTC
h. $\angle AEB \cong \angle$? DEC	i. ? Vertical $\angle$s are $\cong$.
9. $\triangle ABE \cong \triangle DCE$	j. ? AAS
k. ? $\cong$? AE; DE	l. ? CPCTC

15. Standardized Test Prep In order to prove $\overline{JW} \cong \overline{QX}$ in the diagram at the right, what would you prove first? B

A. $\triangle ZJW \cong \triangle KQX$
B. $\triangle KJZ \cong \triangle ZQK$
C. $\triangle JWK \cong \triangle QXZ$
D. $\overline{ZW} \cong \overline{KX}$
E. Not enough information is given.

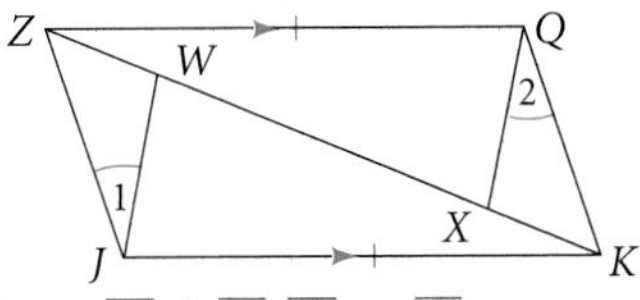

Given: $\overline{ZQ} \parallel \overline{KJ}$, $\overline{ZQ} \cong \overline{KJ}$, $\angle 1 \cong \angle 2$

12. Answers may vary. Sample: Prove $\triangle EFD \cong \triangle ABD$ by SAS. Then prove $\angle E \cong \angle A$ and $\angle ADC \cong \angle EDG$. Use ASA to prove $\triangle ADC \cong \triangle EDG$.

16. 1. $\overline{AC} \cong \overline{EC}$ and $\overline{CB} \cong \overline{CD}$ (Given)
2. $\angle C \cong \angle C$ (Reflexive Prop. of $\cong$)
3. $\triangle ACD \cong \triangle ECB$ (SAS)
4. $\angle A \cong \angle E$ (CPCTC)

17. Since $\overline{TQ}$ bisects $\overline{PR}$, $\overline{PQ} \cong \overline{RQ}$. Since $\overline{TQ} \perp \overline{PR}$, $\angle PQT$ and $\angle RQT$ are $\cong$ rt. $\angle$s. Also, $\overline{QT} \cong \overline{QT}$, so $\triangle PQT \cong \triangle RQT$ by SAS. $\angle PTQ \cong \angle RTQ$ by CPCTC. Since $\overline{TQ}$ bisects $\angle VQS$, $\angle VQT \cong \angle SQT$. So, $\triangle VQT \cong \triangle SQT$ by ASA, and $\overline{VQ} \cong \overline{SQ}$ by CPCTC.

18a. A B E D C

$\overline{AE}, \overline{CE}$; $\overline{BE}, \overline{DE}$; $\overline{AB}, \overline{CD}$; $\overline{BC}, \overline{AD}$

b. Opp. sides of a parallelogram are $\parallel$, so $\angle BAC \cong \angle DCA$ and $\angle BCA \cong \angle DAC$. So $\triangle BAC \cong \triangle DCA$ by ASA, and $\overline{AB} \cong \overline{CD}$ and $\overline{BC} \cong \overline{AD}$ by CPCTC. $\triangle AEB \cong \triangle CED$ by ASA (or AAS), so $\overline{AE} \cong \overline{CE}$ and $\overline{BE} \cong \overline{DE}$ by CPCTC.

OPEN-ENDED Exercise 18 Students use congruent triangles to find that the diagonals of a parallelogram bisect each other.

Chapter Project **FIND OUT BY INVESTIGATING** Have students work in groups keeping a log of the different models they make in their attempt to find one that supports the weight of their geometry book. Have groups compare the successful models and discuss their similarities and differences.

Exercises MIXED REVIEW

COORDINATE GEOMETRY Exercises 19–21 Students review graphing and finding the area and perimeter of a triangle in the coordinate plane.

SELF ASSESSMENT **PORTFOLIO** Share with students the criteria you will use to assess their work in portfolios, as well as how you plan to use the results. Students should understand how the rubrics assess their work, how each piece in the portfolio counts, and how the scores they get in their portfolios will affect their overall evaluation.

Wrap Up

THE BIG IDEA Ask students to draw two right triangles that overlap so that they share a hypotenuse. Ask: *What additional information do you need to prove that they are congruent?*

RETEACHING ACTIVITY Students write a plan for proof and two proofs to prove triangles congruent by first proving two other triangles congruent. (Reteaching worksheet 8-5)

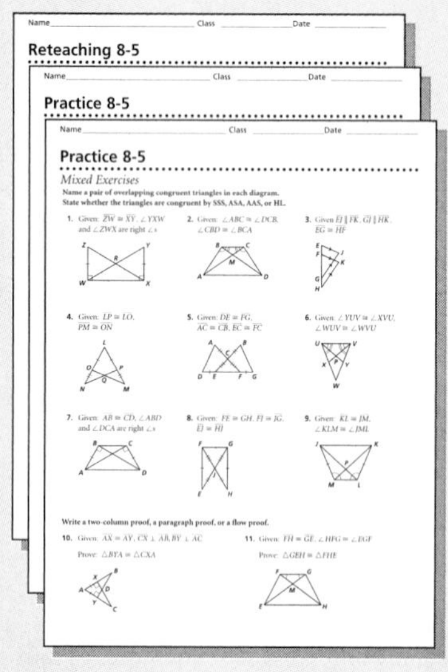

Lesson Quiz

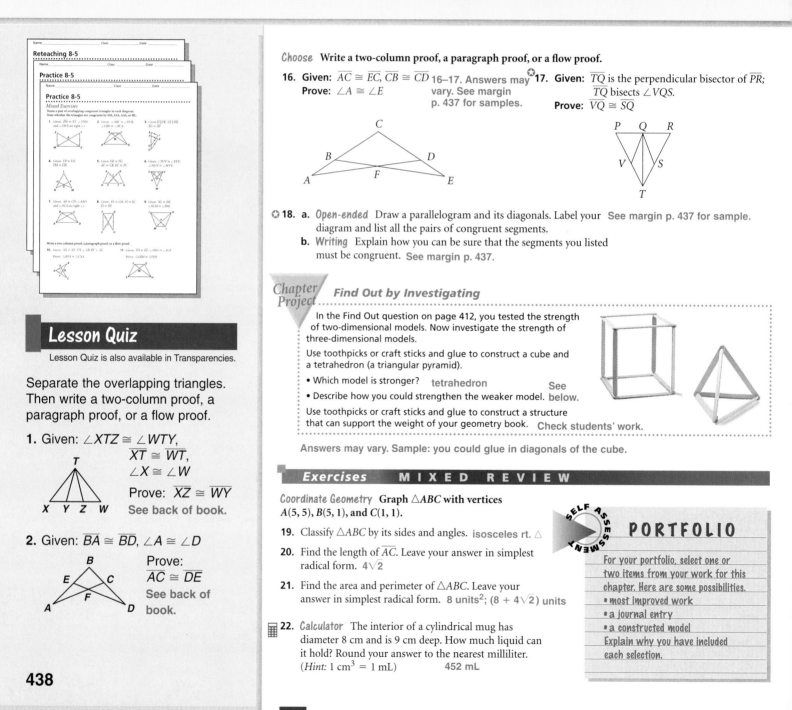

Lesson Quiz is also available in Transparencies.

Separate the overlapping triangles. Then write a two-column proof, a paragraph proof, or a flow proof.

1. Given: $\angle XTZ \cong \angle WTY$, $\overline{XT} \cong \overline{WT}$, $\angle X \cong \angle W$

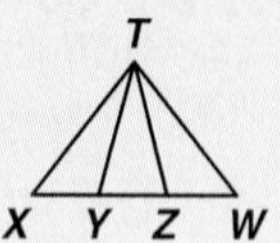

Prove: $\overline{XZ} \cong \overline{WY}$

See back of book.

2. Given: $\overline{BA} \cong \overline{BD}$, $\angle A \cong \angle D$

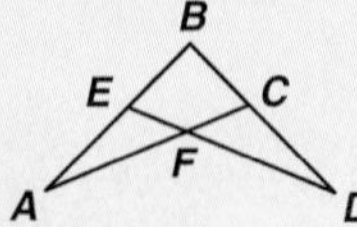

Prove: $\overline{AC} \cong \overline{DE}$

See back of book.

Choose Write a two-column proof, a paragraph proof, or a flow proof.

16. Given: $\overline{AC} \cong \overline{EC}$, $\overline{CB} \cong \overline{CD}$
Prove: $\angle A \cong \angle E$

16–17. Answers may vary. See margin p. 437 for samples.

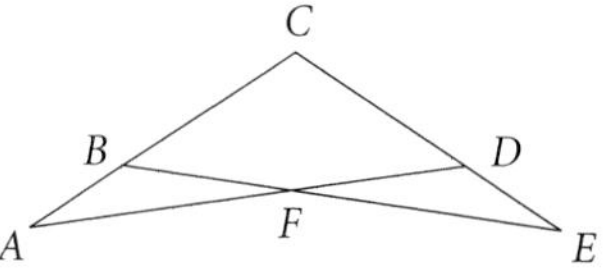

17. Given: $\overline{TQ}$ is the perpendicular bisector of $\overline{PR}$; $\overline{TQ}$ bisects $\angle VQS$.
Prove: $\overline{VQ} \cong \overline{SQ}$

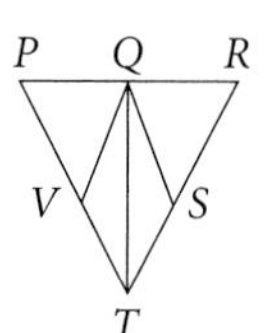

18. a. *Open-ended* Draw a parallelogram and its diagonals. Label your diagram and list all the pairs of congruent segments. See margin p. 437 for sample.
b. *Writing* Explain how you can be sure that the segments you listed must be congruent. See margin p. 437.

Chapter Project: *Find Out by Investigating*

In the Find Out question on page 412, you tested the strength of two-dimensional models. Now investigate the strength of three-dimensional models.

Use toothpicks or craft sticks and glue to construct a cube and a tetrahedron (a triangular pyramid).

- Which model is stronger? tetrahedron
- Describe how you could strengthen the weaker model. See below.

Use toothpicks or craft sticks and glue to construct a structure that can support the weight of your geometry book. Check students' work.

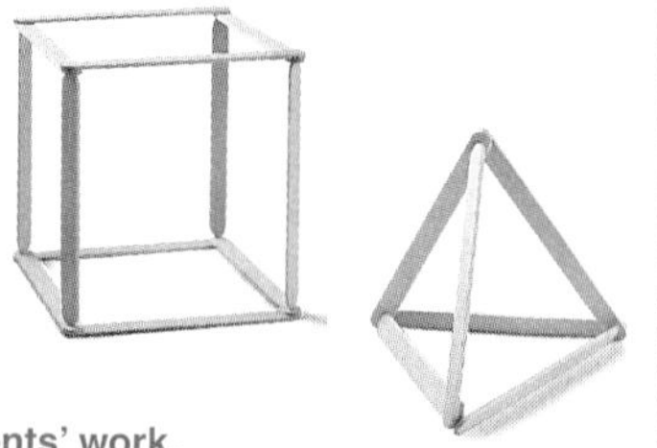

Answers may vary. Sample: you could glue in diagonals of the cube.

Exercises MIXED REVIEW

Coordinate Geometry Graph $\triangle ABC$ with vertices $A(5, 5)$, $B(5, 1)$, and $C(1, 1)$.

19. Classify $\triangle ABC$ by its sides and angles. isosceles rt. △

20. Find the length of $\overline{AC}$. Leave your answer in simplest radical form. $4\sqrt{2}$

21. Find the area and perimeter of $\triangle ABC$. Leave your answer in simplest radical form. 8 units^2; $(8 + 4\sqrt{2})$ units

22. *Calculator* The interior of a cylindrical mug has diameter 8 cm and is 9 cm deep. How much liquid can it hold? Round your answer to the nearest milliliter. (*Hint:* 1 cm^3 = 1 mL) 452 mL

PORTFOLIO

For your portfolio, select one or two items from your work for this chapter. Here are some possibilities.
- most improved work
- a journal entry
- a constructed model

Explain why you have included each selection.

Math ToolboX

Students review solving quadratic equations by using the quadratic formula.

Example 1

ERROR ALERT! Students may think *c* should be 1, not –1. **Remediation:** Help students see that $7x^2 + 6x - 1 = 0$ is not in standard form. It can be written in standard form as $7x^2 + 6x + (-1) = 0$.

Example 2

When simplifying the quadratic formula, it is easy to lose track of negative signs. Encourage students to check that their answers are correct by substituting them into the original equation. If their solutions do not satisfy the equation, they should first check that they used the correct values for *a*, *b*, and *c*, then that they substituted the values correctly, and finally that they performed the computations accurately.

Solve

Some students may recognize that they can solve some of these problems by factoring.

ADDITIONAL PROBLEMS Have students solve the following equations, rounding answers to the nearest hundredth.

1. $3x^2 - 5x - 9 = 0$ **2.** $-x^2 + 4x - 2 = 0$
3. $2x^2 - 8x + 5 = 0$ **4.** $-3x^2 + 5x + 4 = 0$

1. 2.76, −1.09 2. 3.41, 0.59
3. 3.22, 0.78 4. −0.59, 2.26

Math ToolboX Algebra Review

Transparencies
11

Solving Quadratic Equations

After Lesson 8-5

The **standard form of a quadratic equation** is

$$ax^2 + bx + c = 0, a \neq 0.$$

You can solve a quadratic equation by substituting the values for *a*, *b*, and *c* in the **Quadratic Formula.**

$$x = \frac{-b \pm \sqrt{b^2 - 4ac}}{2a}$$

Example 1

Solve $7x^2 + 6x - 1 = 0$. The equation is in standard form.

$a = 7, b = 6, c = -1$

$x = \frac{-6 \pm \sqrt{6^2 - 4(7)(-1)}}{2(7)}$ Substitute in the Quadratic Formula.

$x = \frac{-6 \pm \sqrt{36 + 28}}{14}$ Simplify.

$x = \frac{-6 \pm \sqrt{64}}{14}$

$x = \frac{-6 + 8}{14}$ or $x = \frac{-6 - 8}{14}$

$x = \frac{1}{7}$ or $x = -1$

Sometimes you may need a calculator to approximate solutions.

Example 2

Calculator Solve $-3x^2 - 5x + 1 = 0$.

$a = -3, b = -5, c = 1$

$x = \frac{-(-5) \pm \sqrt{(-5)^2 - 4(-3)(1)}}{2(-3)}$ Substitute in the Quadratic Formula.

$x = \frac{5 \pm \sqrt{25 + 12}}{-6}$ Simplify.

$x = \frac{5 + \sqrt{37}}{-6}$ or $x = \frac{5 - \sqrt{37}}{-6}$

$x \approx -1.85$ or $x \approx 0.18$ Use a calculator.

Solve. Round answers that are not integers to the nearest hundredth.

1. $x^2 + 5x - 14 = 0$ 2, −7
2. $4x^2 - 13x + 3 = 0$ 3, 0.25
3. $2x^2 + 7x + 3 = 0$ −0.5, −3
4. $5x^2 + 2x - 2 = 0$ 0.46, −0.86
5. $6x^2 + 20x = -5$ −0.27, −3.06
6. $1 = 2x^2 - 6x$ 3.16, −0.16
7. $x^2 - 6x = 27$ −3, 9
8. $2x^2 - 10x + 11 = 0$ 1.63, 3.37
9. $8x^2 - 2x - 3 = 0$ −0.5, 0.75

439

Finishing the Chapter Project

PROJECT DAY You may wish to plan a project day during which students share their completed projects. Encourage groups to explain their processes as well as their products.

PROJECT NOTEBOOK Have students review their project work and bring their notebooks up to date.

- Have students review their bridge designs and records of their experiments.
- Ask students to share any insights they found when completing the project, such as how they selected their final bridge design, and what structures or features seemed to work better than others.

SCORING RUBRIC

3 Student's bridge meets all the requirements. Bridge is strong, efficient, and pleasing to the eye. Explanations are clear. Student kept an accurate record of trials and what was learned from each.

2 Student's bridge meets all the requirements. Bridge is relatively strong and efficient. Explanations are complete and contain few errors. Student kept a record of trials with some explanation of what was learned from each.

1 Student's bridge meets some of the requirements. Bridge may lack strength or efficiency. Explanations are complete. Student has some record of trials but may not explain what is learned from each.

0 Major elements are incomplete or missing.

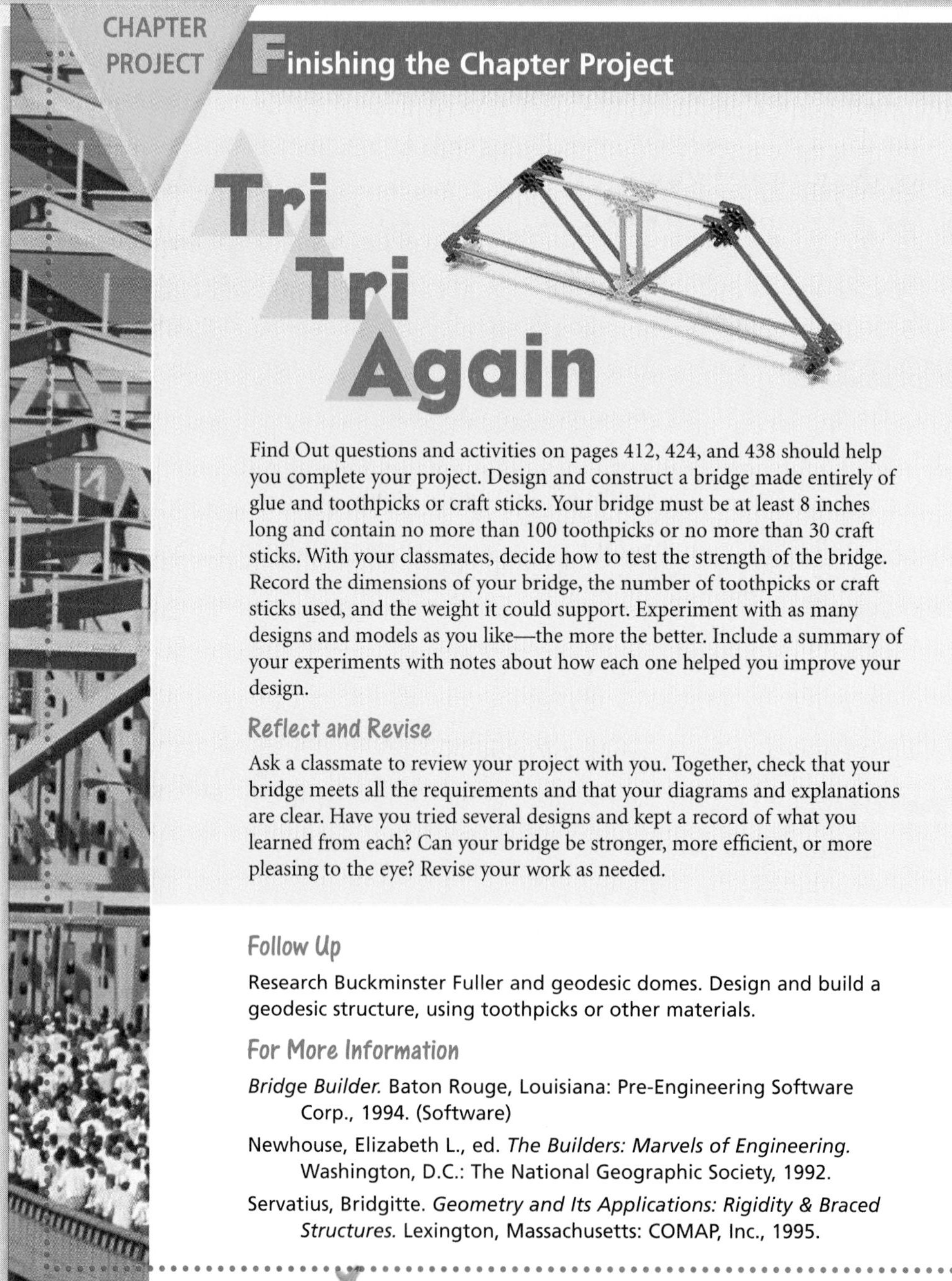

CHAPTER PROJECT

Finishing the Chapter Project

Tri Tri Again

Find Out questions and activities on pages 412, 424, and 438 should help you complete your project. Design and construct a bridge made entirely of glue and toothpicks or craft sticks. Your bridge must be at least 8 inches long and contain no more than 100 toothpicks or no more than 30 craft sticks. With your classmates, decide how to test the strength of the bridge. Record the dimensions of your bridge, the number of toothpicks or craft sticks used, and the weight it could support. Experiment with as many designs and models as you like—the more the better. Include a summary of your experiments with notes about how each one helped you improve your design.

Reflect and Revise

Ask a classmate to review your project with you. Together, check that your bridge meets all the requirements and that your diagrams and explanations are clear. Have you tried several designs and kept a record of what you learned from each? Can your bridge be stronger, more efficient, or more pleasing to the eye? Revise your work as needed.

Follow Up

Research Buckminster Fuller and geodesic domes. Design and build a geodesic structure, using toothpicks or other materials.

For More Information

Bridge Builder. Baton Rouge, Louisiana: Pre-Engineering Software Corp., 1994. (Software)

Newhouse, Elizabeth L., ed. *The Builders: Marvels of Engineering.* Washington, D.C.: The National Geographic Society, 1992.

Servatius, Bridgitte. *Geometry and Its Applications: Rigidity & Braced Structures.* Lexington, Massachusetts: COMAP, Inc., 1995.

Wrap Up

HOW AM I DOING? Have students work in small groups. Ask each group to present a brief explanation of one of the ways to prove triangles congruent. Each presentation must include a visual aid and a sample problem.

KEY TERMS The numbers in parentheses direct students to the pages where the terms are used or defined. Students should be able to (1) write a simple explanation of each term, (2) illustrate the term with a diagram, or (3) show an example that uses the term.

ALTERNATIVE ASSESSMENT **Exercises 1–3** Students identify the congruence and state which theorem or postulate they used. Writing the congruence provides an excellent opportunity for you to assess students' ability to match corresponding parts of congruent triangles.

WRITING Exercise 4 Have students also explain how they determine the order in which the vertices of two triangles are written in a congruence statement.

STANDARDIZED TEST TIP **Exercise 5** Students should recognize that the SAS Postulate requires congruence of two pairs of sides and their included angles. Since the only two sides given are in statements I and II, all but choices A and D can be eliminated. Students should then look for the letters repeated in the segment pairs to determine the required included angles.

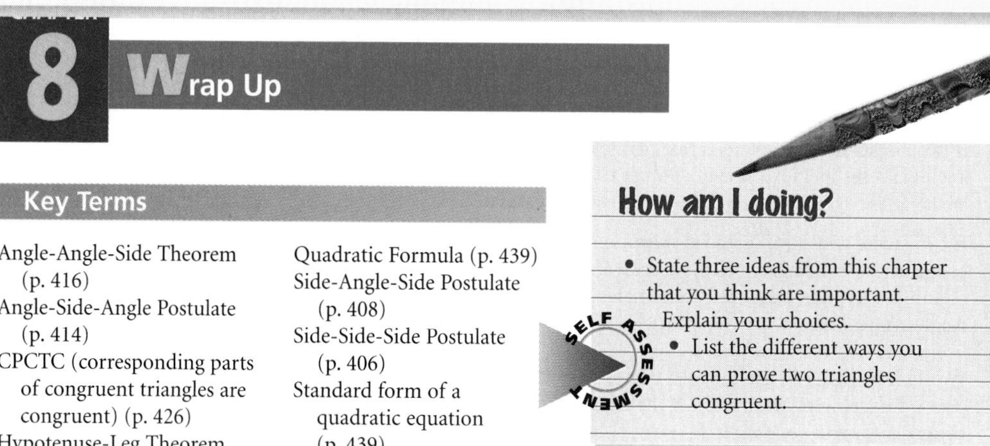

CHAPTER 8 Wrap Up

Key Terms

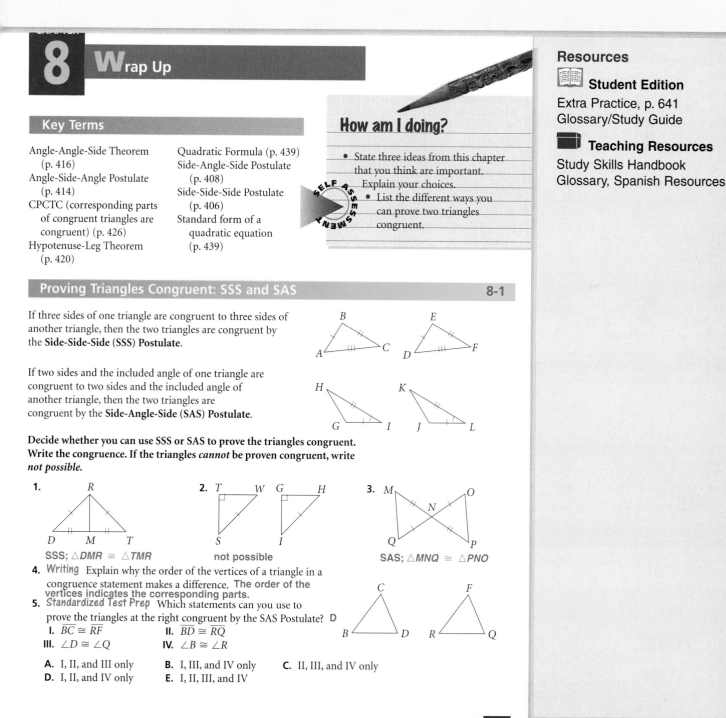

Angle-Angle-Side Theorem (p. 416)
Angle-Side-Angle Postulate (p. 414)
CPCTC (corresponding parts of congruent triangles are congruent) (p. 426)
Hypotenuse-Leg Theorem (p. 420)
Quadratic Formula (p. 439)
Side-Angle-Side Postulate (p. 408)
Side-Side-Side Postulate (p. 406)
Standard form of a quadratic equation (p. 439)

How am I doing?

- State three ideas from this chapter that you think are important. Explain your choices.
- List the different ways you can prove two triangles congruent.

Resources

Student Edition

Extra Practice, p. 641
Glossary/Study Guide

Teaching Resources

Study Skills Handbook
Glossary, Spanish Resources

Proving Triangles Congruent: SSS and SAS — 8-1

If three sides of one triangle are congruent to three sides of another triangle, then the two triangles are congruent by the **Side-Side-Side (SSS) Postulate.**

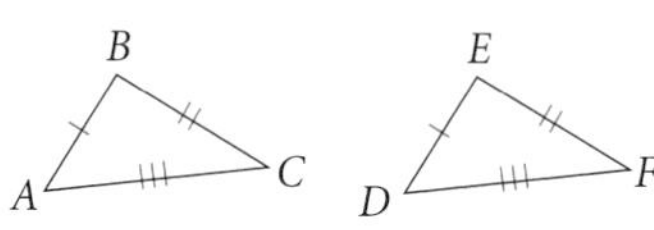

If two sides and the included angle of one triangle are congruent to two sides and the included angle of another triangle, then the two triangles are congruent by the **Side-Angle-Side (SAS) Postulate.**

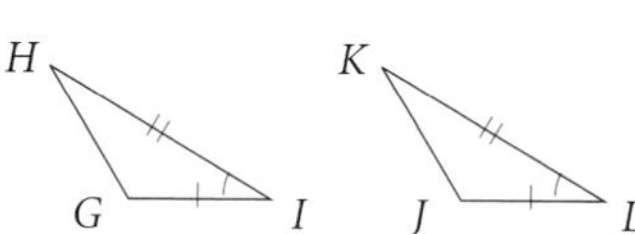

Decide whether you can use SSS or SAS to prove the triangles congruent. Write the congruence. If the triangles *cannot* be proven congruent, write *not possible.*

1. 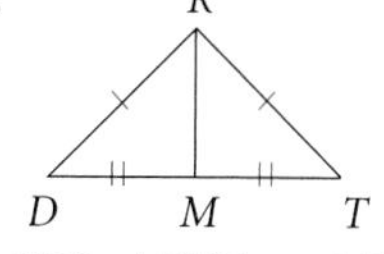

SSS; $\triangle DMR \cong \triangle TMR$

2. 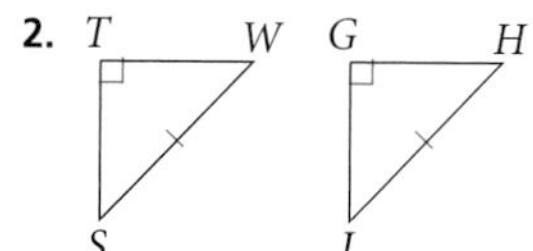

not possible

3. 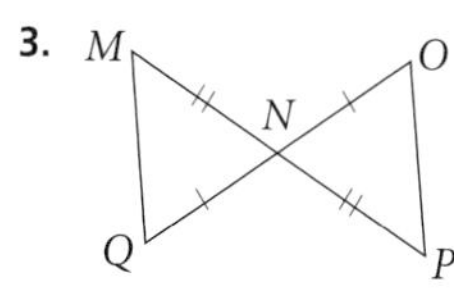

SAS; $\triangle MNQ \cong \triangle PNO$

4. *Writing* Explain why the order of the vertices of a triangle in a congruence statement makes a difference. The order of the vertices indicates the corresponding parts.

5. *Standardized Test Prep* Which statements can you use to prove the triangles at the right congruent by the SAS Postulate? D

   I. $\overline{BC} \cong \overline{RF}$ II. $\overline{BD} \cong \overline{RQ}$
   III. $\angle D \cong \angle Q$ IV. $\angle B \cong \angle R$

   A. I, II, and III only B. I, III, and IV only C. II, III, and IV only
   D. I, II, and IV only E. I, II, III, and IV

CRITICAL THINKING Exercises 6–8 Ask students why any triangle that can be proven congruent by the AAS Theorem can be proven congruent by the ASA Postulate, and vice versa.

Exercises 9–11 Whichever method of proof students choose, encourage them to begin by writing a plan.

OPEN-ENDED Exercise 12 You may want to have students share their responses with the class. As an extra-credit project, students could decorate a bulletin board with drawings or pictures of right triangles found at school.

Wrap Up pages 441–443

9. 1. $\overline{PS} \perp \overline{SQ}$ and $\overline{RQ} \perp \overline{QS}$ (Given) 2. $\angle PSQ$ and $\angle RQS$ are rt. $\angle$s. (Def. of $\perp$ lines) 3. $\triangle PSQ$ and $\triangle RQS$ are rt. $\triangle$s. (Def. of rt. $\triangle$s) 4. $\overline{PQ} \cong \overline{RS}$ (Given) 5. $\overline{QS} \cong \overline{QS}$ (Reflexive Prop. of $\cong$) 6. $\triangle PSQ \cong \triangle RQS$ (HL Thm.)
10. 1. U is the midpt. of $\overline{TV}$. (Given) 2. $\overline{TU} \cong \overline{UV}$ (Def. of midpt.) 3. $\overline{XU} \perp \overline{TV}$ and $\overline{WV} \perp \overline{TV}$ (Given) 4. $\angle XUT$ and $\angle WVU$ are rt. $\angle$s. (Def. of $\perp$ lines) 5. $\triangle TXU$ and $\triangle UWV$ are rt. $\triangle$s. (Def. of rt. $\triangle$s) 6. $\overline{TX} \cong \overline{UW}$ (Given) 7. $\triangle TXU \cong \triangle UWV$ (HL Thm.)
11. 1. $\overline{LN} \perp \overline{KM}$ (Given) 2. $\angle LNK$ and $\angle LNM$ are rt. $\angle$s. (Def. of $\perp$ lines.) 3. $\triangle KLN$ and $\triangle MLN$ are rt. $\triangle$s. (Def. of rt. $\triangle$s.) 4. $\overline{KL} \cong \overline{ML}$ (Given) 5. $\overline{LN} \cong \overline{LN}$ (Reflexive Prop. of $\cong$) 6. $\triangle KLN \cong \triangle MLN$ (HL Thm.)

Proving Triangles Congruent: ASA and AAS — 8-2

If two angles and the included side of one triangle are congruent to two angles and the included side of another triangle, then the two triangles are congruent by the **Angle-Side-Angle (ASA) Postulate.**

If two angles and a nonincluded side of one triangle are congruent to two angles and the corresponding nonincluded side of another triangle, then the two triangles are congruent by the **Angle-Angle-Side (AAS) Theorem.**

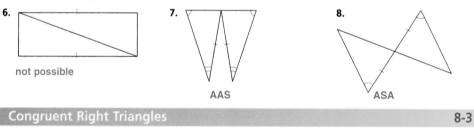

Would it be easier to use the ASA Postulate or the AAS Theorem to prove the triangles congruent? If the triangles *cannot* be proven congruent, write *not possible.*

6.

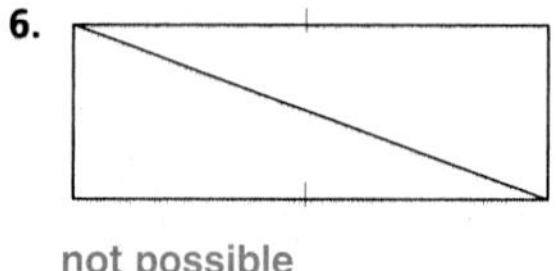

not possible

7. AAS

8.

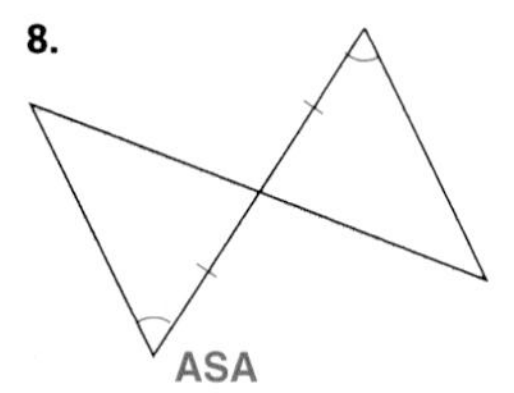

ASA

Congruent Right Triangles — 8-3

If the hypotenuse and a leg of one right triangle are congruent to the hypotenuse and leg of another right triangle, then the triangles are congruent by the **Hypotenuse-Leg (HL) Theorem.**

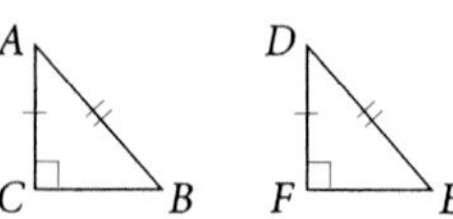

Choose **Write a two-column proof, a paragraph proof, or a flow proof.**

9. Given: $\overline{PS} \perp \overline{SQ}$, $\overline{RQ} \perp \overline{QS}$, $\overline{PQ} \cong \overline{RS}$
Prove: $\triangle PSQ \cong \triangle RQS$

10. Given: $\overline{XU} \perp \overline{TV}$, $\overline{WV} \perp \overline{TV}$, $\overline{TX} \cong \overline{UW}$, U is the midpoint of $\overline{TV}$.
Prove: $\triangle TXU \cong \triangle UWV$

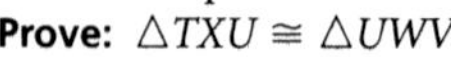

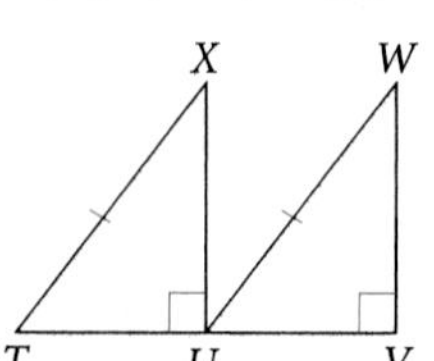

11. Given: $\overline{LN} \perp \overline{KM}$, $\overline{KL} \cong \overline{ML}$
Prove: $\triangle KLN \cong \triangle MLN$

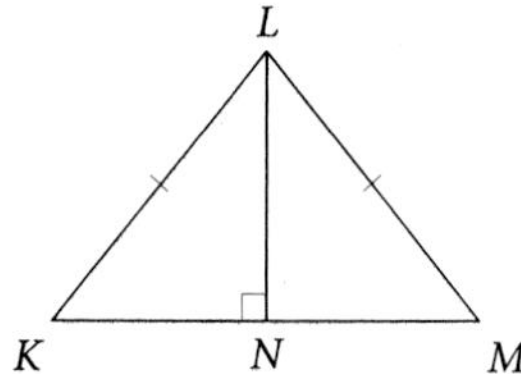

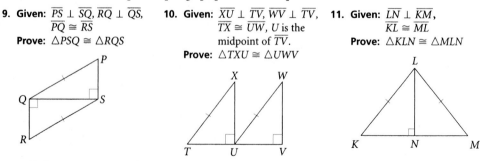

9–11. Answers may vary. See margin for samples.

12. *Open-ended* Find several examples of right triangles in your school, home, or community. Which ones are congruent? What measurements would you make to show that they are congruent? Check students' work.

ALTERNATIVE ASSESSMENT **Exercises 13–15** You can use these exercises to assess students' ability to write proofs. Ask students to write their explanations as paragraph proofs, two-column proofs, or flow proofs.

Exercises 16–18 Remind students that it is helpful to separate and redraw the overlapping triangles.

Remind students that the new mathematical terms in this chapter are defined in the Glossary/Study Guide in the back of the book.

Getting Ready for Chapter 9

Students may work these exercises independently or in small groups. The skills previewed will help prepare students to study the properties of parallelograms.

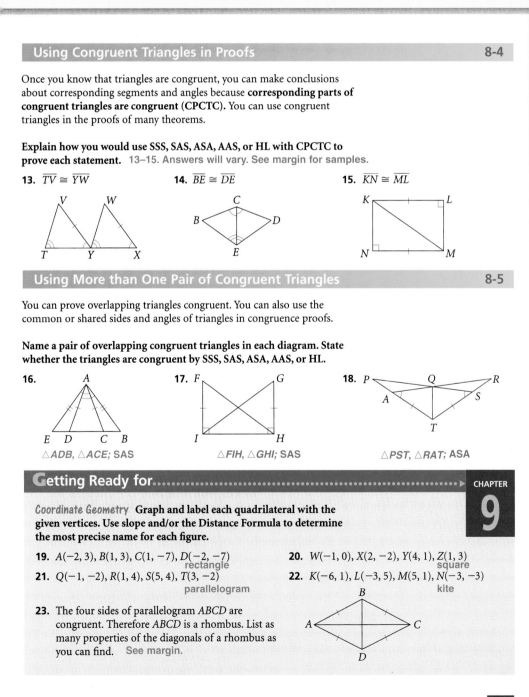

Using Congruent Triangles in Proofs 8-4

Once you know that triangles are congruent, you can make conclusions about corresponding segments and angles because **corresponding parts of congruent triangles are congruent** (CPCTC). You can use congruent triangles in the proofs of many theorems.

Explain how you would use SSS, SAS, ASA, AAS, or HL with CPCTC to prove each statement. 13–15. Answers will vary. See margin for samples.

13. $\overline{TV} \cong \overline{YW}$

14. $\overline{BE} \cong \overline{DE}$

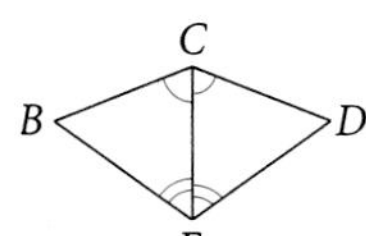

15. $\overline{KN} \cong \overline{ML}$

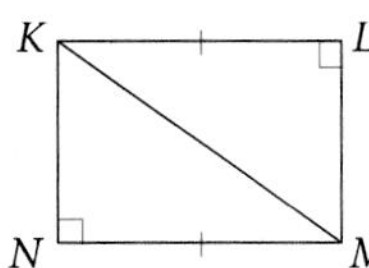

Using More than One Pair of Congruent Triangles 8-5

You can prove overlapping triangles congruent. You can also use the common or shared sides and angles of triangles in congruence proofs.

Name a pair of overlapping congruent triangles in each diagram. State whether the triangles are congruent by SSS, SAS, ASA, AAS, or HL.

16.

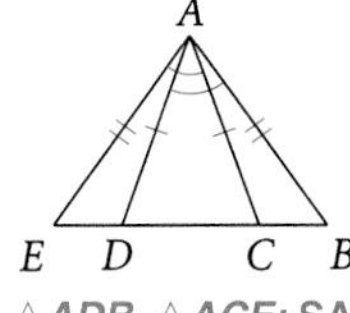

$\triangle ADB, \triangle ACE$; SAS

17.

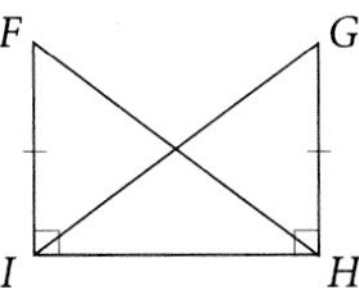

$\triangle FIH, \triangle GHI$; SAS

18.

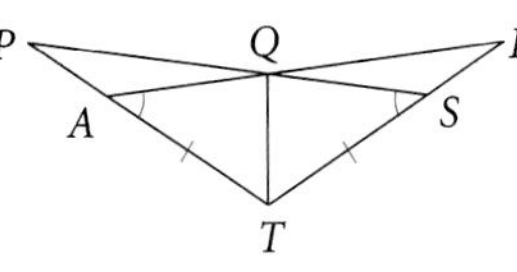

$\triangle PST, \triangle RAT$; ASA

Getting Ready for... CHAPTER 9

Coordinate Geometry **Graph and label each quadrilateral with the given vertices. Use slope and/or the Distance Formula to determine the most precise name for each figure.**

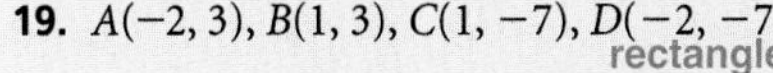

19. $A(-2, 3), B(1, 3), C(1, -7), D(-2, -7)$ rectangle

20. $W(-1, 0), X(2, -2), Y(4, 1), Z(1, 3)$ square

21. $Q(-1, -2), R(1, 4), S(5, 4), T(3, -2)$ parallelogram

22. $K(-6, 1), L(-3, 5), M(5, 1), N(-3, -3)$ kite

23. The four sides of parallelogram *ABCD* are congruent. Therefore *ABCD* is a rhombus. List as many properties of the diagonals of a rhombus as you can find. See margin.

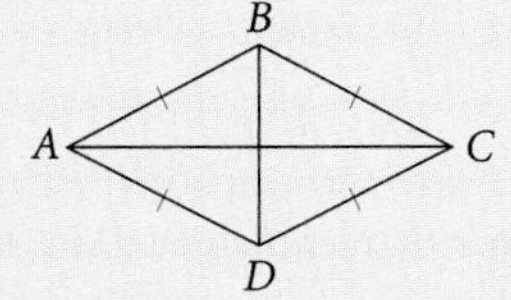

13. Use AAS to show $\triangle TVY \cong \triangle YWX$. $\overline{TV} \cong \overline{YW}$ by CPCTC.

14. Use ASA to show $\triangle BCE \cong \triangle DCE$. $\overline{BE} \cong \overline{DE}$ by CPCTC.

15. Use HL to show $\triangle KLM \cong \triangle MNK$. $\overline{KN} \cong \overline{ML}$ by CPCTC.

23. The diagonals are ⊥ bisectors of each other. Each diagonal is an angle bisector of 2 of the angles of the rhombus. The area of the rhombus is half the product of the lengths of the diagonals.

Assessment

ENHANCED MULTIPLE CHOICE QUESTIONS are more complex than traditional multiple choice questions, which assess only one skill. Enhanced multiple choice questions assess the processes that students use, as well as the end results. The questions are written so that students use more than one strategy to solve the problem. Using multiple strategies is encouraged by the National Council of Teachers of Mathematics (NCTM). **Exercise 8** is an enhanced multiple choice question.

FREE RESPONSE QUESTIONS do not give answer choices. Some exercises have more than one possible answer. Students need to give only one correct response. **Exercises 1–6, and 9–12** are free response questions.

WRITING EXERCISES allow students to describe how they think about and understand the concepts they have learned. **Exercise 7** is a writing exercise.

OPEN-ENDED PROBLEMS allow for more than one solution. Students must construct their own responses instead of choosing from possible answers. The students' responses will help you determine the depth of their understanding and any possible areas of difficulty. **Exercise 13** is an open-ended problem.

Resources

Teaching Resources

Chapter Support File, Ch. 8
- Chapter Assessment, Forms A and B
- Alternative Assessment

Chapter Assessment, Spanish Resources

Teacher's Edition

See also p. 404E for assessment options

Software
Computer Item Generator

Assessment page 444

7. Answers may vary. Sample: 2 equilateral △s with diff. lengths of sides are a counterexample.

9. 1. $\overline{SA} \cong \overline{GA}$ (Radii of the same ⊙ are ≅.) 2. $\overline{ST} \cong \overline{GT}$ (Radii of the same ⊙ are ≅.) 3. $\overline{AT} \cong \overline{AT}$ (Reflexive Prop. of ≅) 4. $\triangle GAT \cong \triangle SAT$ (SSS)

10. $\overline{LN}$ bisects $\angle OLM$. (Given) 2. $\angle OLN \cong \angle MLN$ (Def. of angle bisector) 3. $\overline{LN}$ bisects $\angle ONM$. (Given) 4. $\angle ONL \cong \angle MNL$ (Def. of angle bisector) 5. $\overline{LN} \cong \overline{LN}$ (Reflexive Prop. of ≅) 6. $\triangle OLN \cong \triangle MLN$ (ASA)

8 Assessment

State the postulate or theorem you would use to prove each pair of triangles congruent. If the triangles *cannot* be proven congruent, write *not possible*.

1. 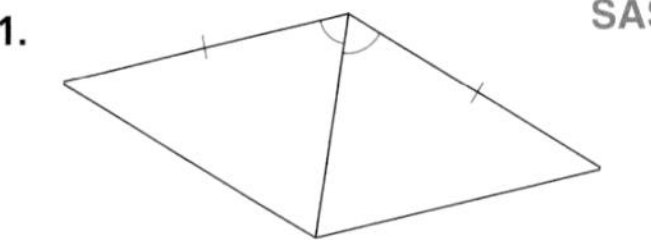 SAS

2. 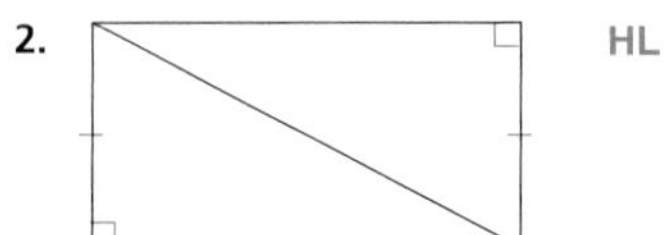 HL

3. 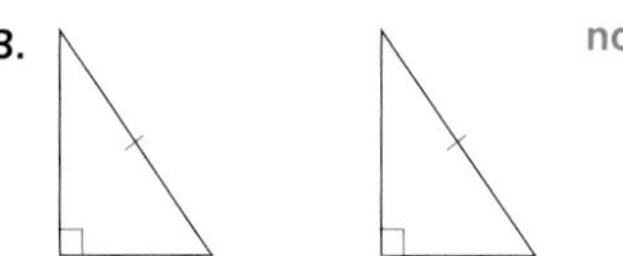 not possible

4. 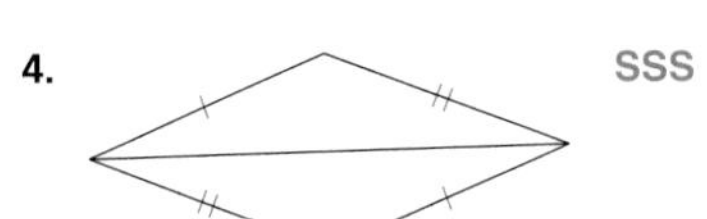 SSS

5. 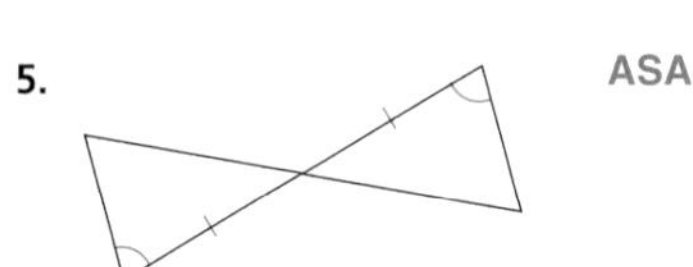 ASA

6. 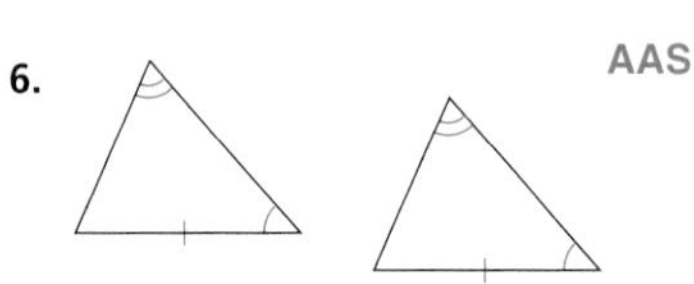 AAS

7. *Writing* Explain why you cannot use AAA to prove two triangles congruent. See margin.

8. *Standardized Test Prep* $\triangle ABC \cong \triangle DEF$. Which of the following are true? C
   I. $\angle A \cong \angle D$ II. $\overline{BC} \cong \overline{DF}$
   III. $\angle C \cong \angle E$ IV. $\overline{DE} \cong \overline{AB}$
   A. I and II B. II and III C. I and IV
   D. III and IV E. I, II, and IV

Write a two-column proof, a paragraph proof, or a flow proof. 9–10. Answers may vary. See margin for samples.

9. Given: ⊙A and ⊙T
   Prove: $\triangle GAT \cong \triangle SAT$

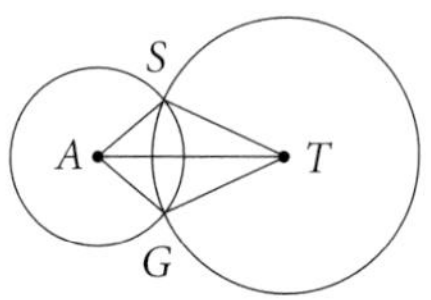

10. Given: $\overline{LN}$ bisects $\angle OLM$ and $\angle ONM$.
    Prove: $\triangle OLN \cong \triangle MLN$

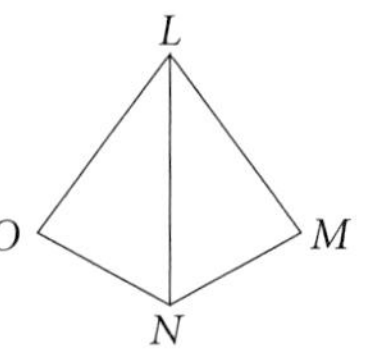

Name a pair of overlapping congruent triangles in each diagram. State whether the triangles are congruent by SSS, SAS, ASA, AAS, or HL.

11. Given: $\overline{CE} \cong \overline{DF}$, $\overline{CF} \cong \overline{DE}$

C D F E

$\triangle CEF, \triangle DFE$; SSS

12. Given: $\overline{RT} \cong \overline{QT}$, $\overline{AT} \cong \overline{ST}$

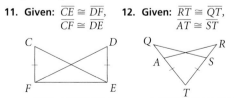

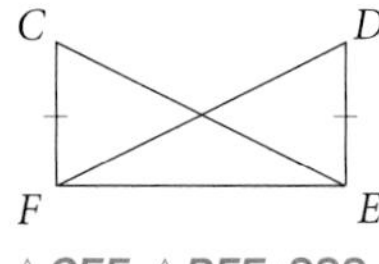

$\triangle QST, \triangle RAT$; SAS

13. *Open-ended* Draw a kite and its diagonals. Which diagonal divides the kite into two congruent triangles? Explain how you know they are congruent. See below.

13. the diagonal that connects the vertices of the ∠s that are not ≅; SSS

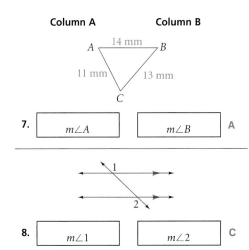

Cumulative Review

Item	Review Topic	Chapter
1	Congruent Figures	2
2, 8	Parallel Lines and Related Angles	7
3	Congruent Triangles	8
4	Volume	6
5	Spherical Geometry	7

Item	Review Topic	Chapter
6	Quadrilaterals	2
7	Triangle Inequalities	4
9	Perspective Drawing	7
10	Logical Reasoning	4
11	Constructing Perpendicular Lines	7

8 Cumulative Review

For Exercises 1–8, choose the correct letter.

1. Quadrilateral $ABCD \cong QRST$. Which segment is congruent to $\overline{TS}$? E

   A. $\overline{AB}$ B. $\overline{BC}$ C. $\overline{BA}$ D. $\overline{CB}$ E. $\overline{DC}$

2. Which condition(s) will allow you to prove that $\ell \parallel m$? E

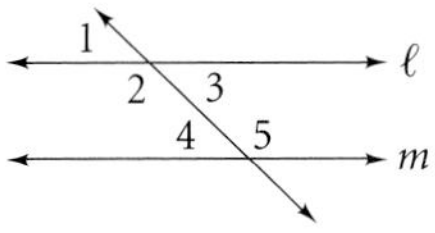

   I. $\angle 1 \cong \angle 4$ II. $\angle 2 \cong \angle 5$

   III. $m\angle 2 + m\angle 4 = 180$ IV. $\angle 3 \cong \angle 4$

   A. I only B. II only

   C. I and II only D. III and IV only

   E. I, II, III, and IV

3. By which postulate or theorem are the triangles congruent? A

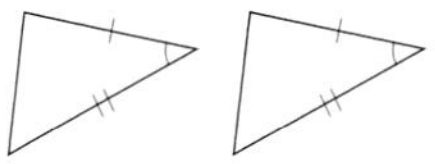

   A. SAS B. SSS C. ASA

   D. AAS E. HL

4. Which solid has the least volume? C

   A.

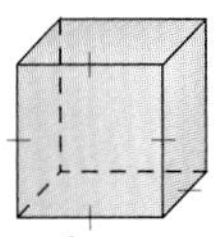

   B.

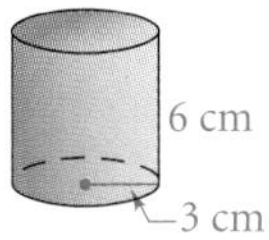

   C.

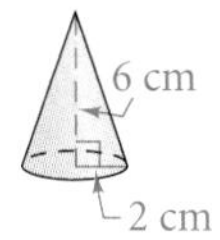

   D.

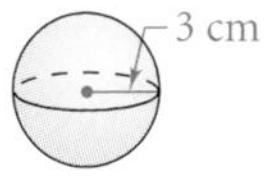

   E. It cannot be determined from the information given.

5. In spherical geometry, how many lines are perpendicular to a line at a given point on the line? B

   A. 0 B. 1 C. 2

   D. 3 E. infinitely many

6. $WXYZ$ is a rectangle. Which segment is longest? C

   A. $\overline{WX}$ B. $\overline{YZ}$ C. $\overline{WY}$ D. $\overline{ZW}$

   E. It cannot be determined from the information given.

Compare the boxed quantity in Column A with the boxed quantity in Column B. Choose the best answer.

A. The quantity in Column A is greater.
B. The quantity in Column B is greater.
C. The two quantities are equal.
D. The relationship cannot be determined on the basis of the information supplied.

	Column A	Column B	

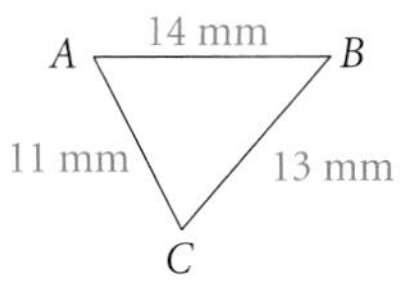

	Column A	Column B	
7.	$m\angle A$	$m\angle B$	A

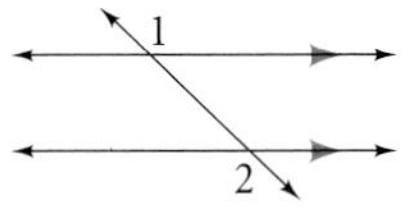

	Column A	Column B	
8.	$m\angle 1$	$m\angle 2$	C

9, 11. See back of book for samples.

Find each answer.

9. *Open-ended* Sketch an object in two-point perspective.

10. Write the contrapositive of the conditional "If the trees have leaves, it is not winter." See below.

11. *Constructions* Draw a line. Construct a line perpendicular to the first line.

10. If it is winter, then the trees do not have leaves.

Resources

Teaching Resources

Chapter Support File, Ch. 8
- Cumulative Review
- Standardized Test Practice

Teacher's Edition

See also p. 404E for assessment options.

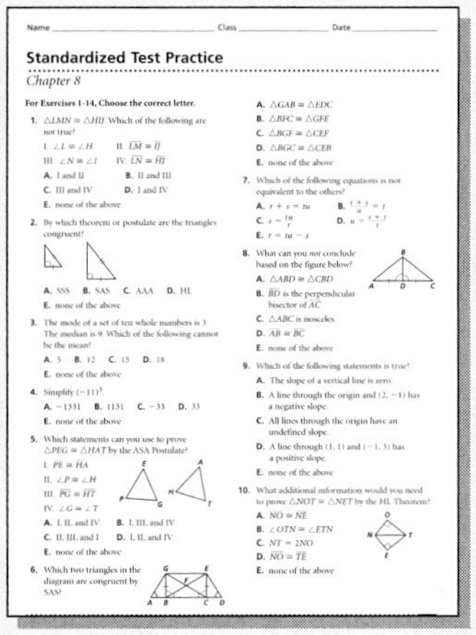
Standardized Test Practice
Chapter 8

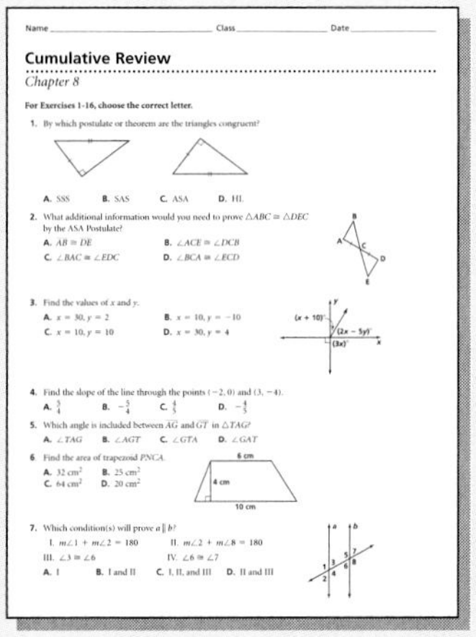
Cumulative Review
Chapter 8

CHAPTER 9 Quadrilaterals

To accommodate flexible scheduling, some lessons are divided into parts. Assignment Options are given in the Lesson Planning Options for each lesson.

9-1 Properties of Parallelograms (pp. 448–453)
Key Term: consecutive angles

9-2 Proving That a Quadrilateral Is a Parallelogram (pp. 454–460)

9-3 Properties of Special Parallelograms (pp. 462–468)
Part 1 Properties of Rhombuses
Part 2 Properties of Rectangles and Parallelograms

9-4 Trapezoids and Kites (pp. 470–476)
Key Term: base angles

9-5 Organizing Coordinate Proofs (pp. 478–482)

9-6 Using Coordinate Geometry in Proofs (pp. 483–487)
Key Term: midsegment of a trapezoid

PACING OPTIONS

This chart suggests pacing only for the core lessons and their parts, and it is provided merely as a possible guide. It will help you determine how much time you have in your schedule to cover other features, such as the Chapter Project, Math Toolboxes, Wrap Up, and Assessment.

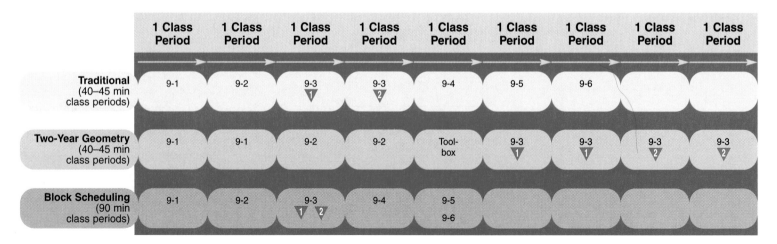

	1 Class Period	1 Class Period	1 Class Period	1 Class Period	1 Class Period	1 Class Period	1 Class Period	1 Class Period	1 Class Period
Traditional (40–45 min class periods)	9-1	9-2	9-3 Part 1	9-3 Part 2	9-4	9-5	9-6		
Two-Year Geometry (40–45 min class periods)	9-1	9-1	9-2	9-2	Toolbox	9-3 Part 1	9-3 Part 1	9-3 Part 2	9-3 Part 2
Block Scheduling (90 min class periods)	9-1	9-2	9-3 Parts 1, 2	9-4	9-5 9-6				

What Students Will Learn and Why

In this chapter, students will build on their knowledge of parallelograms, learned in Chapter 2, by learning properties of parallelograms and finding characteristics of quadrilaterals that indicate they are parallelograms. Then students find properties of rectangles, rhombuses, squares, trapezoids, and kites. Finally, students learn to choose convenient placement of coordinate axes on figures and prove theorems using figures in the coordinate plane. Throughout the chapter, students see how these concepts are used in designing playgrounds, kites, and flags, and solving problems in navigation, construction, and design.

Discussing the Chapter/Building on Experience

The concept map below relates chapter topics to real-world applications. You and your class may wish to add to the map or develop maps of your own. The center oval describes the topic of the chapter. The next level displays topics within the lessons. The outer ovals reflect applications of the content. As you and your class build a concept map, invite students to discuss applications with which they are familiar.

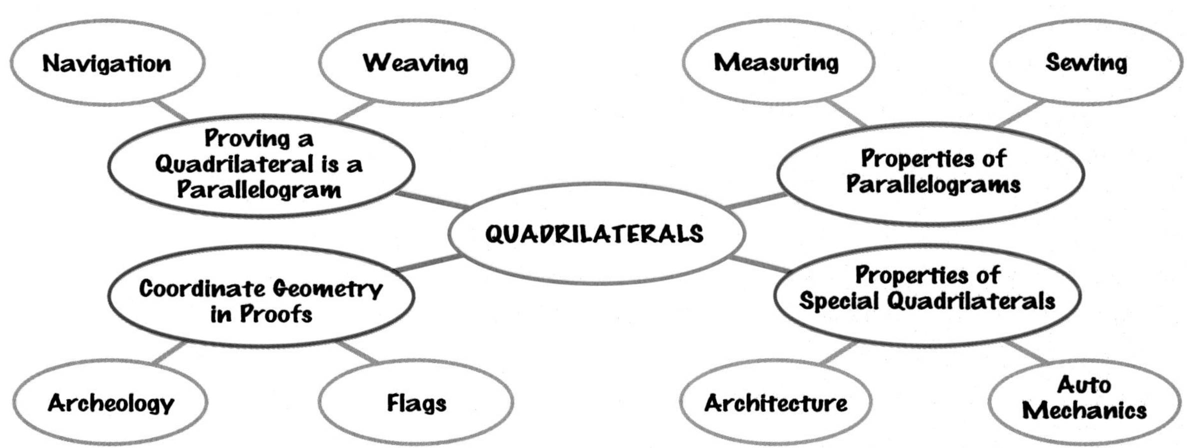

1 Class Period	1 Class Period	1 Class Period	1 Class Period	1 Class Period	1 Class Period	1 Class Period	1 Class Period	1 Class Period	1 Class Period	1 Class Period
Tool-box	9-4	9-4	Tool-box	9-5	9-5	9-6	9-6			

A question is interactive when there is "give and take" between the questioner (teacher or student) and the respondent. In Think and Discuss or when a critical thinking question is asked, it is important to encourage students to explain their answers in detail. Encouraging students to explain their answers promotes active participation and stimulates higher levels of thought. These two elements are essential in developing high-level thinking skills. For example, in Lesson 9-6 students are asked to explain why it is enough to prove just two consecutive sides congruent in order to prove that parallelogram *TWVU* is a rhombus.

Skills Practice

Every lesson provides skill practice with Try This exercises, Exercises On Your Own, and Exercises Mixed Review. The Student Edition includes Checkpoints (pp. 460, 482) and Preparing for Standardized Tests (p. 493). In the Teacher's Edition, the Lesson Planning Options section for each lesson lists Prerequisite Skills students should know for that lesson. At the back of the Student Edition is the Skills Handbook—mini-lessons on math your students may need to review. The Chapter Support File for Chapter 9 in the Teaching Resources box includes two Practice worksheets per lesson, a worksheet for two Checkpoints, and worksheets for Cumulative Review and Standardized Test Preparation.

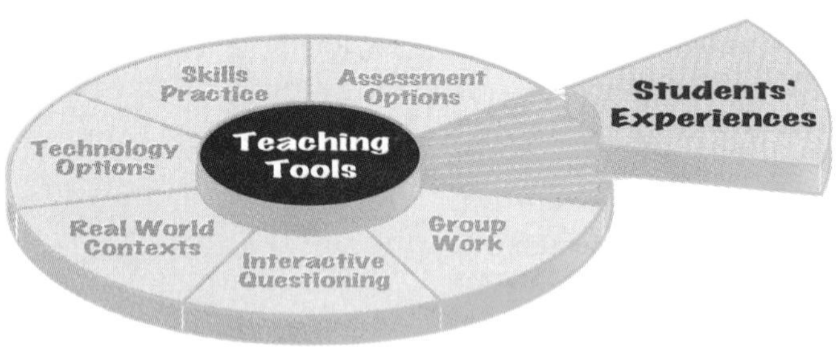

Diverse Learning and Teaching Styles

In your Teacher's Edition, you will find suggestions as to how you can help students complete mathematical tasks in Chapter 9 by reinforcing various learning styles. Here are some examples.

- **Visual learning** draw parallel lines and transversals of varying slopes on lined paper and measure the segment of each transversal cut by the parallel lines (p. 450), copy triangles and mark corresponding angles on the diagram as they are read in the proof (p. 463), draw several trapezoids and identify the legs and base angles (p. 470)
- **Tactile learning** make a parallel ruler using straws and brads (p. 457), prove theorem 9-11 by drawing a rhombus, cutting it along its diagonals and rearranging the resulting triangles to form a rectangle (p. 463), make a cutout of a 10-unit square and trace it in different positions on the coordinate grid (p. 478)
- **Auditory learning** present completed proofs to other students (p. 467)
- **Kinesthetic learning** sketch and discuss geometric patterns on buildings and houses (p. 471)

Alternative Activity for Lesson 9-1

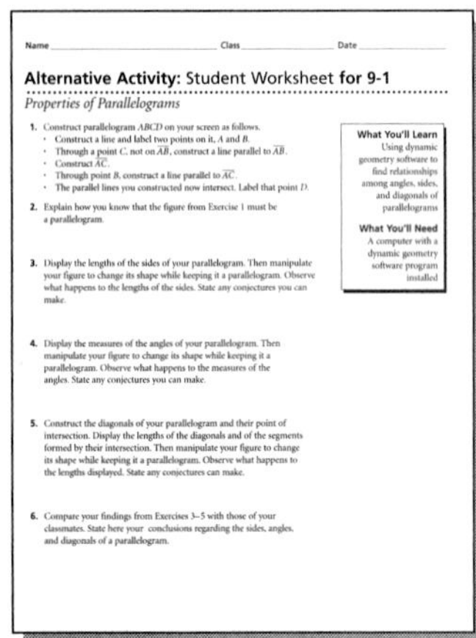
Name ______ Class ______ Date ______

Alternative Activity: Student Worksheet **for 9-1**

Properties of Parallelograms

1. Construct parallelogram *ABCD* on your screen as follows.
   - Construct a line and label two points on it, *A* and *B*.
   - Through a point *C*, not on $\overline{AB}$, construct a line parallel to $\overline{AB}$.
   - Construct $\overline{AC}$.
   - Through point *B*, construct a line parallel to $\overline{AC}$.
   - The parallel lines you constructed now intersect. Label that point *D*.
2. Explain how you know that the figure from Exercise 1 must be a parallelogram.
3. Display the lengths of the sides of your parallelogram. Then manipulate your figure to change its shape while keeping it a parallelogram. Observe what happens to the lengths of the sides. State any conjectures you can make.
4. Display the measures of the angles of your parallelogram. Then manipulate your figure to change its shape while keeping it a parallelogram. Observe what happens to the measures of the angles. State any conjectures you can make.
5. Construct the diagonals of your parallelogram and their point of intersection. Display the lengths of the diagonals and of the segments formed by their intersection. Then manipulate your figure to change its shape while keeping it a parallelogram. Observe what happens to the lengths displayed. State any conjectures can make.
6. Compare your findings from Exercises 3–5 with those of your classmates. State here your conclusions regarding the sides, angles, and diagonals of a parallelogram.

What You'll Learn Using dynamic geometry software to find relationships among angles, sides, and diagonals of parallelograms

What You'll Need A computer with a dynamic geometry software program installed

for use with Theorems 9-1, 9-2, and 9-3, uses geometry software to manipulate parallelograms.

Alternative Activity for Lesson 9-2

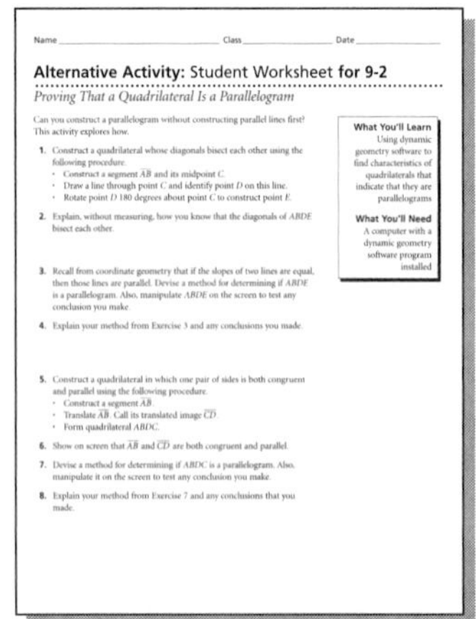
Name ______ Class ______ Date ______

Alternative Activity: Student Worksheet **for 9-2**

Proving That a Quadrilateral Is a Parallelogram

Can you construct a parallelogram without constructing parallel lines first? This activity explores how.

1. Construct a quadrilateral whose diagonals bisect each other using the following procedure.
   - Construct a segment $\overline{AB}$ and its midpoint *C*.
   - Draw a line through point *C* and identify point *D* on this line.
   - Rotate point *D* 180 degrees about point *C* to construct point *E*.
2. Explain, without measuring, how you know that the diagonals of *ABDE* bisect each other.
3. Recall from coordinate geometry that if the slopes of two lines are equal, then those lines are parallel. Devise a method for determining if *ABDE* is a parallelogram. Also, manipulate *ABDE* on the screen to test any conclusion you make.
4. Explain your method from Exercise 3 and any conclusions you made.
5. Construct a quadrilateral in which one pair of sides is both congruent and parallel using the following procedure.
   - Construct a segment $\overline{AB}$.
   - Translate $\overline{AB}$. Call its translated image $\overline{CD}$.
   - Form quadrilateral *ABDC*.
6. Show on screen that $\overline{AB}$ and $\overline{CD}$ are both congruent and parallel.
7. Devise a method for determining if *ABDC* is a parallelogram. Also, manipulate it on the screen to test any conclusion you make.
8. Explain your method from Exercise 7 and any conclusions that you made.

What You'll Learn Using dynamic geometry software to find characteristics of quadrilaterals that indicate that they are parallelograms

What You'll Need A computer with a dynamic geometry software program installed

for use with Theorems 9-5 and 9-6, uses geometry software to manipulate quadrilaterals.

Alternative Activity for Lesson 9-4

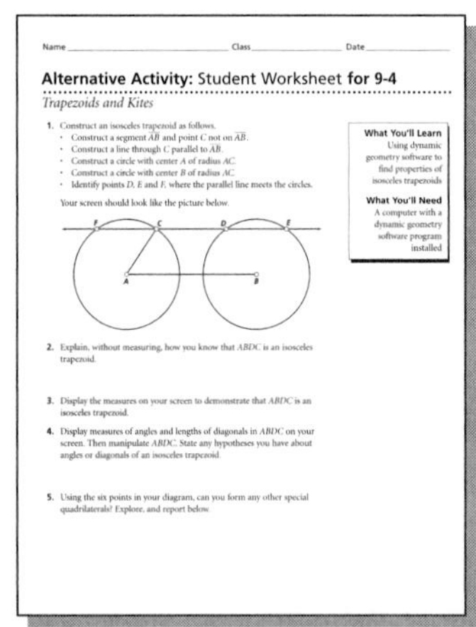
Name ______ Class ______ Date ______

Alternative Activity: Student Worksheet **for 9-4**

Trapezoids and Kites

1. Construct an isosceles trapezoid as follows.
   - Construct a segment $\overline{AB}$ and point *C* not on $\overline{AB}$.
   - Construct a line through *C* parallel to $\overline{AB}$.
   - Construct a circle with center *A* of radius *AC*.
   - Construct a circle with center *B* of radius *AC*.
   - Identify points *D*, *E* and *F*, where the parallel line meets the circles.

   Your screen should look like the picture below.

   F C D E A B

2. Explain, without measuring, how you know that *ABDC* is an isosceles trapezoid.
3. Display the measures on your screen to demonstrate that *ABDC* is an isosceles trapezoid.
4. Display measures of angles and lengths of diagonals in *ABDC* on your screen. Then manipulate *ABDC*. State any hypotheses you have about angles or diagonals of an isosceles trapezoid.
5. Using the six points in your diagram, can you form any other special quadrilaterals? Explore, and report below.

What You'll Learn Using dynamic geometry software to find properties of isosceles trapezoids

What You'll Need A computer with a dynamic geometry software program installed

for use with Theorems 9-16 and 9-17, uses geometry software to construct and manipulate isosceles trapezoids.

Cooperative Learning Tips

When used effectively, cooperative learning can help students develop interpersonal skills, learn to perform specific roles in a group, and learn to carry out specific responsibilities. The components of Chapter 9 provide a range of cooperative learning opportunities.

- In the Student Edition, the ***Work Together*** parts of lessons are specifically designed for cooperative learning activities.
- In the Teacher's Edition, you will find helpful hints for addressing diverse learning styles (see page C for Chapter 9). For every lesson, you will find a ***Reteaching Activity***, which may involve cooperative learning.

Materials and Manipulatives

Opportunities for calculator use—though optional—are integrated throughout the course.

- centimeter graph paper (9-3)
- compass (9-1)
- 11-by-11 peg geoboard (9-2)
- graph paper (9-5, 9-6)
- lined paper (9-4)
- protractor (9-1, 9-3)
- ruler (9-1, 9-3)
- scissors (9-1, 9-3, 9-4)
- straightedge (9-2, 9-4, 9-5, 9-6)

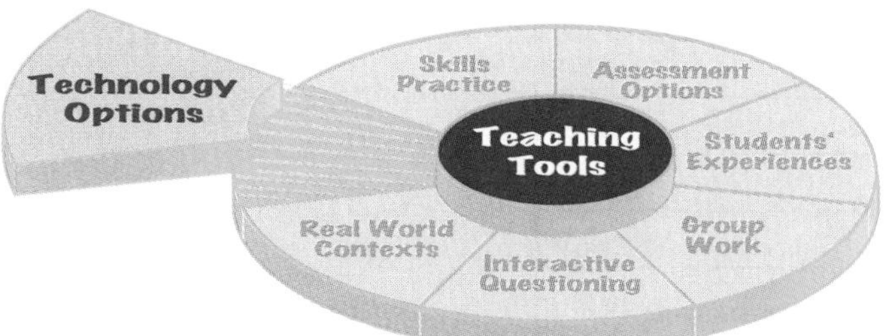

TECHNOLOGY OPTIONS

Technology Tools		Chapter Project	9-1	9-2	9-3	9-4	9-5	9-6
Calculator	Numerous opportunities throughout for students to use scientific calculators.							
Software	Secondary Math Lab Toolkit™		✔	✔	✔	✔	✔	✔
	Integrated Math Lab			✔				✔
	Computer Item Generator		✔	✔	✔	✔	✔	✔
	Student Edition				✔T	✔T	✔	
Video	Video Field Trip	✔						
CD-ROM	Multimedia Geometry Lab		✔		✔	✔		✔
Internet	See the Prentice Hall site. (http://www.phschool.com)							

✔T indicates Math Toolbox.

The Prentice Hall Geometry program offers you a rich variety of technology options. Be assured that all these options are provided as a means of enriching the program and are not essential for the successful completion of the course.

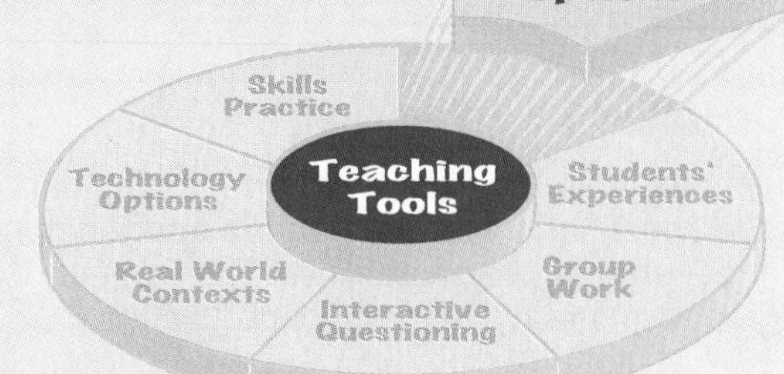

Assessment Options

The Prentice Hall Geometry Program provides you with many options. From these options, you may choose instructional materials and techniques appropriate for your students, or those necessary to meet your district's curriculum requirements. As the chart indicates, the program also supports your teaching efforts by offering you many choices for assessment.

ASSESSMENT OPTIONS

Assessment Support Materials	Chapter Project	9-1	9-2	9-3	9-4	9-5	9-6	Chapter End
Chapter Project	▲■●	▲■		▲■	▲■			▲■
Checkpoints			▲■●			▲■●		
Self-Assessment			▲		▲■		▲■	▲■
Writing Assignment		▲	▲	▲■	▲	▲■	▲■	●
Chapter Assessment								▲■●
Alternative Assessment		■	■	■	■	■	■	●
Cumulative Review								●
Standardized Test Prep			▲■	▲■	▲			▲■●
Computer Item Generator	Can be used to create custom-made practice or assessment at any time.							

▲ = Student Edition ■ = Teacher's Edition ● = Teaching Resources

Checkpoints

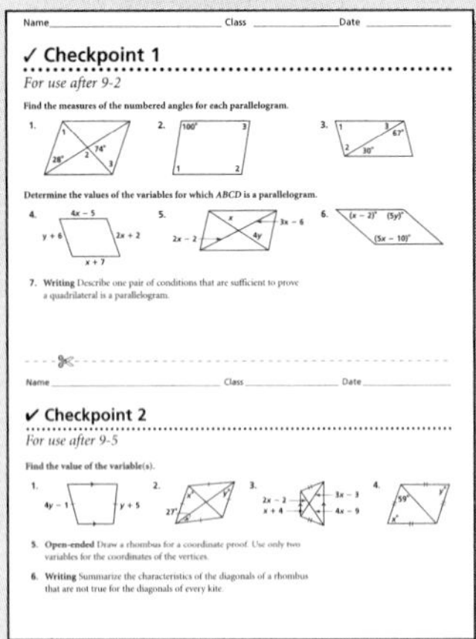

Alternative Assessment

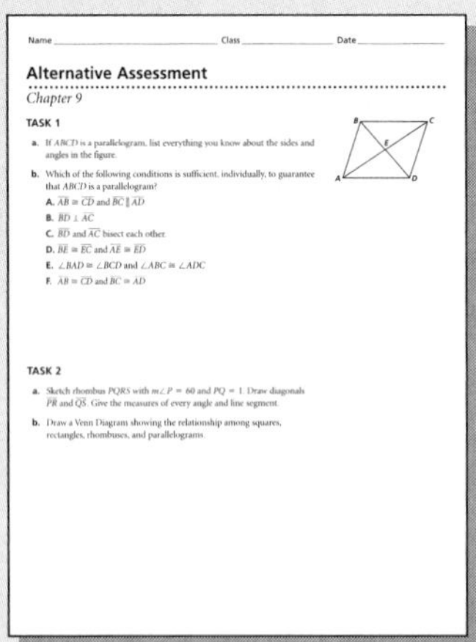

Chapter Assessment

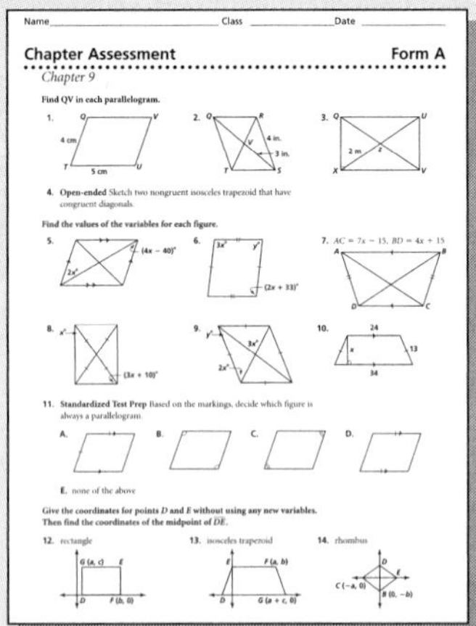

Available in both Form A and Form B

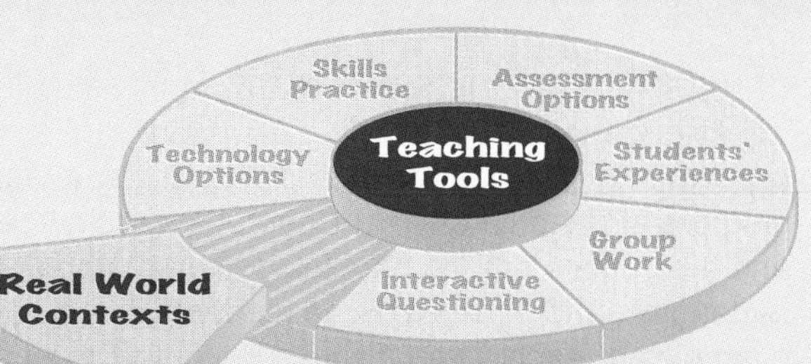

Making the Right Connections

Mathematics is imbedded in nearly every walk of life. The National Council of Teachers of Mathematics (NCTM) encourages educators to recognize these connections and to emphasize them for the purpose of better educating students for success in life and in a global economy. The *Connections* chart below highlights these connections for Chapter 9.

CONNECTIONS

Lesson	Interdisciplinary Connections	Career Prep	Other Real World Connections	Math Integration	NCTM Standards
Chapter Project	Art	Design	Kites		Connections
9-1	Home Economics		Measuring Sewing Building a Kite	Algebra Probability Logical Reasoning	Algebra Communication Problem Solving Reasoning
9-2	Geography Home Economics		Navigation Weaving	Algebra Probability Logical Reasoning Coordinate Geometry	Algebra Communication Problem Solving Reasoning
9-3	Science Social Studies	Carpentry Auto Mechanics	Community Service	Algebra Logical Reasoning	Algebra Communication Problem Solving Reasoning
9-4	Art	Architecture Design	Picture Framing	Algebra Geometry in 3 Dimensions	Algebra Communication Problem Solving
9-5	Science History	Design	Archaeology Egyptian Relief Sculpture	Geometry in 3 Dimensions Coordinate Geometry	Coordinate Geometry Communication Problem Solving Connections
9-6	Art History Science		Flag Mobiles	Coordinate Geometry Logical Reasoning	Coordinate Geometry Communication Reasoning Problem Solving

CHAPTER 9 Quadrilaterals

CONNECTING TO PRIOR LEARNING In this chapter, students will extend their understanding of quadrilaterals by studying properties of parallelograms. Review with students the tree diagram of quadrilaterals in Chapter 2. Discuss the similarities and differences among parallelograms, rhombuses, rectangles, and squares. Have students give real-world examples of each. Then discuss the definitions of kite and trapezoid. Also give real-world examples.

CULTURAL CONNECTIONS Kites have been in use by Asian peoples from time immemorial. Kite-flying as a sport has long been a national pastime of the Koreans, Chinese, Japanese, and Malayans. Kites flying at night over a house were believed to keep evil spirits away.

INTERDISCIPLINARY CONNECTIONS In 1752 Ben Franklin demonstrated the electrical nature of lightning by flying a kite with a metal key hanging from it. Kites have long been used for weather observations. Ask students to research other ways kites have been used in meteorological research and in space exploration.

Technology Options

Prentice Hall Technology

Video
Video Field Trip 9, "Hanging in the Wind," a view from the hang glider's perspective

CHAPTER 9 Quadrilaterals

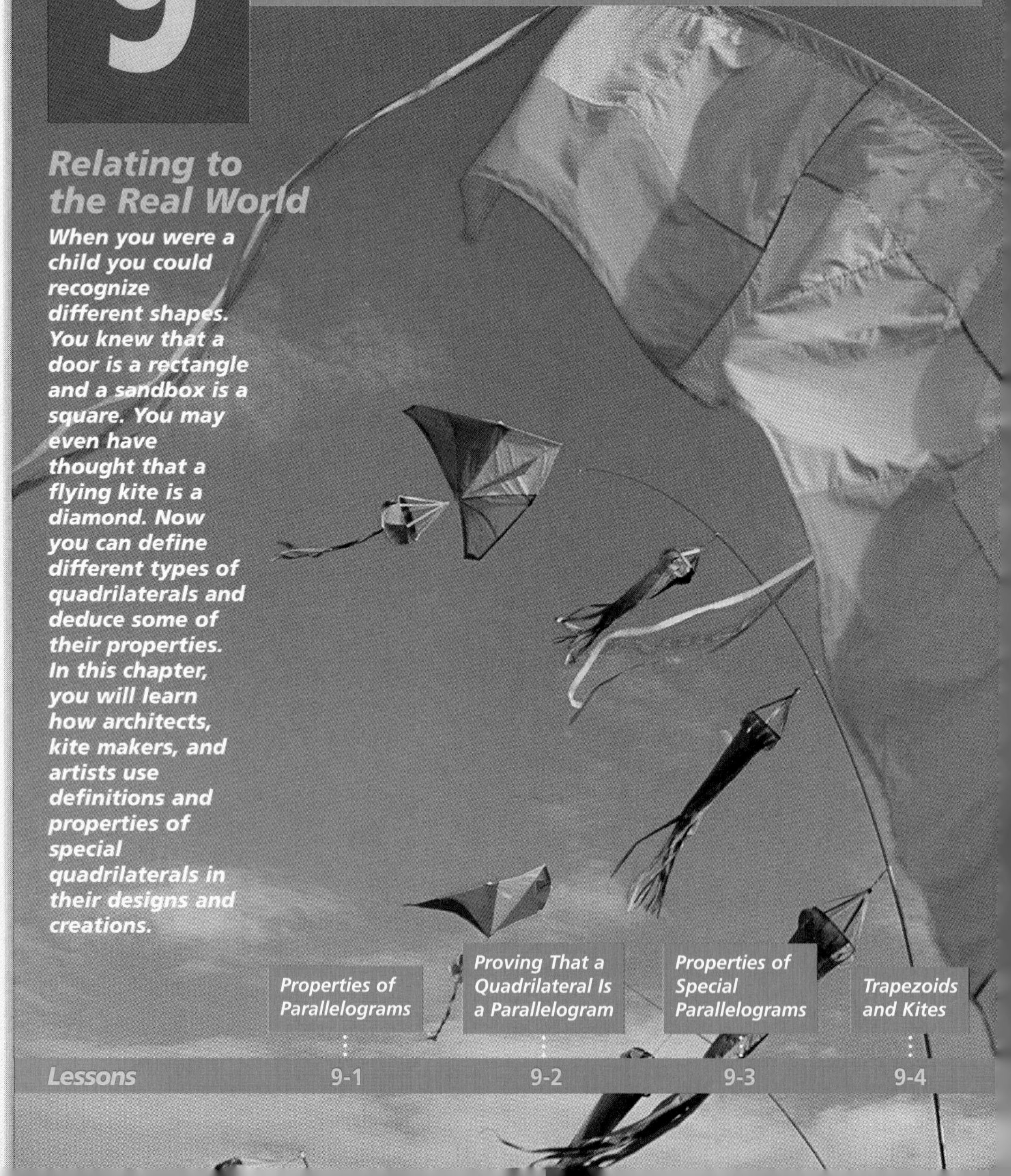

Relating to the Real World

When you were a child you could recognize different shapes. You knew that a door is a rectangle and a sandbox is a square. You may even have thought that a flying kite is a diamond. Now you can define different types of quadrilaterals and deduce some of their properties. In this chapter, you will learn how architects, kite makers, and artists use definitions and properties of special quadrilaterals in their designs and creations.

Lessons	9-1	9-2	9-3	9-4
	Properties of Parallelograms	*Proving That a Quadrilateral Is a Parallelogram*	*Properties of Special Parallelograms*	*Trapezoids and Kites*

ABOUT THE PROJECT Students will make a fully functioning kite using a sheet of paper and two staples. Then they explore how the weight and form of a kite affect its ability to fly. Finally, students will design, build, and fly their own kites.

Launching the Project

PROJECT NOTEBOOK Encourage students to keep all project-related materials in a separate folder or notebook. **See Chapter Project Manager and Scoring Rubric in Chapter Support File.**

- Ask students to share their own experiences with kites. Ask them to describe the shapes and features of kites they have flown. Have them share techniques they used in flying them.

TRACKING THE PROJECT You may wish to have students read Finishing the Chapter Project on page 488 to help them get an overview of the project. Set benchmark deadlines for students to show their work in progress.

CHAPTER PROJECT

GO FLY A KITE

If you think kites are mere child's play, think again. From ancient China to modern times, geometric arrangements of fabric and rods have helped people rescue sailors, vanquish enemies, predict the weather, invent the airplane, study wind power, and, of course, entertain with displays of aerodynamic artistry.

In your project for this chapter, you will turn a sheet of paper and couple of staples into a fully functioning kite. You will explore how weight and form determine whether a kite sinks or soars. Finally you will design, build, and fly your own kite. You will see how geometry can make a kite light and strong—spelling the difference between flight and failure.

To help you complete the project:

- **p. 453** *Find Out by Doing*
- **p. 468** *Find Out by Analyzing*
- **p. 476** *Find Out by Researching*
- **p. 488** *Finishing the Project*

Organizing Coordinate Proofs 9-5

Using Coordinate Geometry in Proofs 9-6

Project Resources

Teaching Resources

Chapter Support File, Ch. 9
- Chapter Project Manager and Scoring Rubric

Transparencies

93

Using the Rubric

Sharing the scoring rubric for the project with your students will alert them to your expectations before they begin work on the project.

As students complete each Find Out question in the chapter, you may wish to have them evaluate their own work or a partner's work based on the scoring rubric. Students should have the opportunity to revise their work after it has been reviewed.

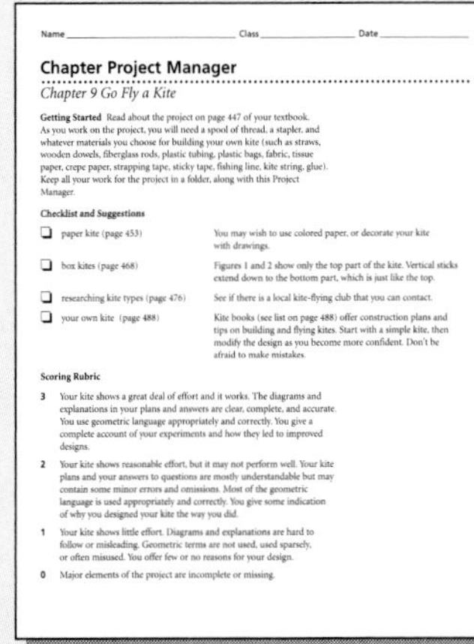

Name ________ Class ________ Date ________

Chapter Project Manager

Chapter 9 Go Fly a Kite

Getting Started Read about the project on page 447 of your textbook. As you work on the project, you will need a spool of thread, a stapler, and whatever materials you choose for building your own kite (such as straws, wooden dowels, fiberglass rods, plastic tubing, plastic bags, fabric, tissue paper, crepe paper, strapping tape, sticky tape, fishing line, kite string, glue). Keep all your work for the project in a folder, along with this Project Manager.

Checklist and Suggestions

❑ paper kite (page 453)	You may wish to use colored paper, or decorate your kite with drawings.
❑ box kites (page 468)	Figures 1 and 2 show only the top part of the kite. Vertical sticks extend down to the bottom part, which is just like the top.
❑ researching kite types (page 476)	See if there is a local kite-flying club that you can contact.
❑ your own kite (page 488)	Kite books (see list on page 488) offer construction plans and tips on building and flying kites. Start with a simple kite, then modify the design as you become more confident. Don't be afraid to make mistakes.

Scoring Rubric

3 Your kite shows a great deal of effort and it works. The diagrams and explanations in your plans and answers are clear, complete, and accurate. You use geometric language appropriately and correctly. You give a complete account of your experiments and how they led to improved designs.

2 Your kite shows reasonable effort, but it may not perform well. Your kite plans and your answers to questions are mostly understandable but may contain some minor errors and omissions. Most of the geometric language is used appropriately and correctly. You give some indication of why you designed your kite the way you did.

1 Your kite shows little effort. Diagrams and explanations are hard to follow or misleading. Geometric terms are not used, used sparsely, or often misused. You offer few or no reasons for your design.

0 Major elements of the project are incomplete or missing.

9-1 Teaching Notes

PROBLEM OF THE DAY

Give the dimensions of at least 5 different, nonsimilar rectangles in which the length, the width, and the length of the diagonals are all integers. Answers may vary. Sample: 3 by 4, 5 by 12, 7 by 24, 16 by 30 , 39 by 80

Problem of the Day is also available in Transparencies.

CONNECTING TO PRIOR KNOWLEDGE Draw the following quadrilaterals. Ask students which appear to be parallelograms and have them find the missing angle measures.

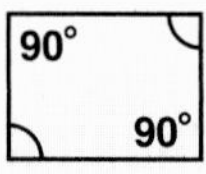

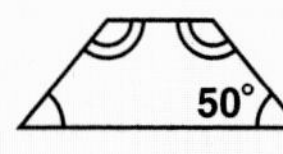

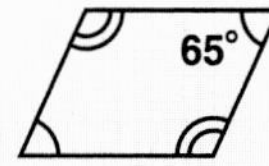

WORK TOGETHER

Begin by reviewing the definition of parallelogram. Make sure that students label the points in order as shown on the diagram so the directions will make sense. Have students label the vertices on the inside of the parallelogram so when they cut it out, the labels remain on the figure.

ALTERNATIVE METHOD To avoid the use of a ruler and a protractor, have students cut out two copies of their parallelograms. Then they can compare sides and angles by rotating the figures and placing them on top of each other.

Lesson Planning Options

Prerequisite Skills

- Understanding definition of a parallelogram
- Using congruent triangles and CPCTC

Assignment Options for Exercises On Your Own

Core 1–30
✪**Extension** 31–33

Use Mixed Review to maintain skills.

Resources

 **Student Edition**

Skills Handbook, pp. 664, 681
Extra Practice, p. 656
Glossary/Study Guide

 **Teaching Resources**

Chapter Support File, Ch. 9
- Practice 9-1 (two worksheets)
- Reteaching 9-1
- Alternative Activity 9-1

Classroom Manager 9-1
Glossary, Spanish Resources

 **Transparencies**
94, 97, 98

9-1 Properties of Parallelograms

What You'll Learn
- Finding relationships among angles, sides, and diagonals of parallelograms

...And Why

To make designs using parallelograms

What You'll Need
- ruler
- protractor
- compass
- scissors

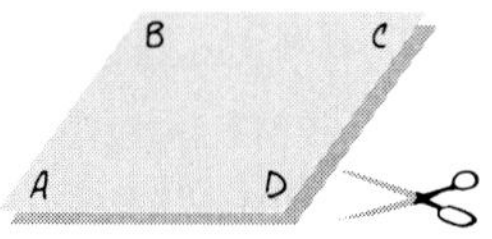

WORK TOGETHER

Work with a partner.

- Draw three noncollinear points to make three vertices of a large parallelogram. Label them *A, B,* and *C*. Draw $\overline{AB}$ and $\overline{BC}$.
- Construct a line parallel to $\overline{BC}$ through *A* and a line parallel to $\overline{AB}$ through *C*. Label their point of intersection *D*.
- Cut out ▱*ABCD*. Use a protractor and ruler to compare the opposite sides and opposite angles of *ABCD*.

1. Make **conjectures** about the relationship between opposite sides and the relationship between opposite angles of a parallelogram. See below.

- Draw $\overline{AC}$ and $\overline{BD}$. Label the point of intersection *E*. Use paper folding or a ruler to compare *AE* to *CE* and *BE* to *DE*.

2. Make a conjecture about the relationship between the diagonals of a parallelogram. The diagonals of a ▱ bisect each other.

1. Opp. sides are ≅ ; opp. angles are ≅ .

THINK AND DISCUSS

The results of the Work Together are the basis of this lesson's theorems.

Theorem 9-1

Opposite sides of a parallelogram are congruent.

If *ABCD* is a parallelogram, then $\overline{AB} \cong \overline{CD}$ and $\overline{BC} \cong \overline{DA}$.

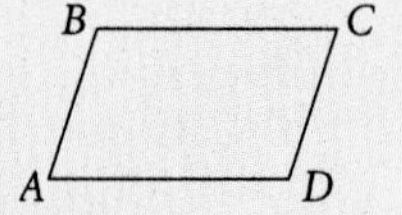

In planning this tessellation, Escher used the fact that opposite sides of a parallelogram are congruent.

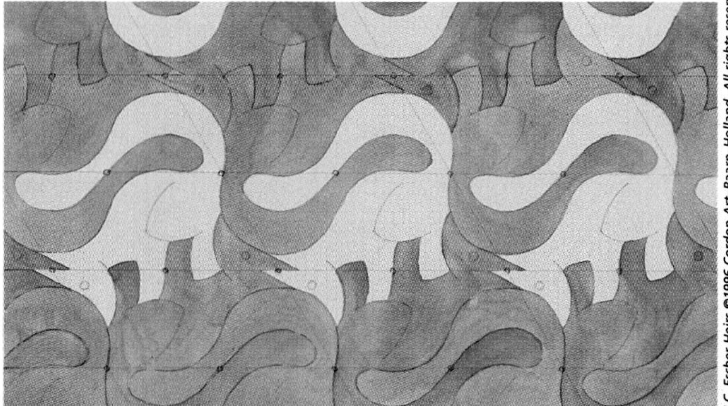

THINK AND DISCUSS

Theorem 9-1 Students may wonder why the opposite sides are named in the opposite direction in the congruence statement. Students will see in the proof for Example 1 that this is because they are corresponding sides of congruent triangles. Writing $\overline{BA} \cong \overline{CD}$ and $\overline{BC} \cong \overline{AD}$ is also correct.

Example 1

Point out that to prove $\overline{AB} \cong \overline{CD}$ and $\overline{BC} \cong \overline{DA}$, you first prove that $\triangle ABC \cong \triangle CDA$ and then use CPCTC.

ERROR ALERT! Some students may have difficulty recognizing that $\angle 1$ and $\angle 4$ are alternate interior angles, as are $\angle 3$ and $\angle 2$.

Remediation: On an overhead, use a different color to draw $\overleftrightarrow{AB}$, $\overleftrightarrow{CD}$, and $\overleftrightarrow{AC}$ on the parallelogram. Students should recognize $\overleftrightarrow{AC}$ as a transversal cutting $\overleftrightarrow{AB}$ and $\overleftrightarrow{CD}$. You could repeat this using $\overleftrightarrow{AD}$, $\overleftrightarrow{BC}$, and $\overleftrightarrow{AC}$ for extra practice.

Question 4 This proof can be done using congruent triangles or using parallel lines and angle sums.

ESL Make sure students understand the meaning of *consecutive angles.* Discuss other contexts, such as sports ("a baseball team won five consecutive games"), in which *consecutive* is used. Point out that it means "one after the other." Also make sure that students understand the difference between consecutive angles and adjacent angles.

Example 1

Use a flow proof to prove Theorem 9-1: Opposite sides of a parallelogram are congruent.

Given: $\square ABCD$
Prove: $\overline{AB} \cong \overline{CD}$, $\overline{BC} \cong \overline{DA}$

Flow Proof

- $ABCD$ is a $\square$. (Given) → $\overline{AB} \parallel \overline{DC}$ (Def. of $\square$) → $\angle 1 \cong \angle 4$ (If $\parallel$ lines, then alt. int. $\angle$s are $\cong$.)
- $ABCD$ is a $\square$. (Given) → $\overline{BC} \parallel \overline{AD}$ (Def. of $\square$) → $\angle 3 \cong \angle 2$ (If $\parallel$ lines, then alt. int. $\angle$s are $\cong$.)
- $\overline{AC} \cong \overline{AC}$ (Reflexive Prop. of $\cong$)
- → $\triangle ABC \cong \triangle CDA$ (ASA) → $\overline{AB} \cong \overline{CD}$, $\overline{BC} \cong \overline{DA}$ (CPCTC)

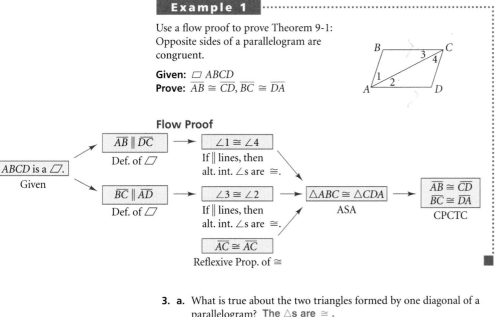

3\. a. What is true about the two triangles formed by one diagonal of a parallelogram? **The $\triangle$s are $\cong$.**
b. **Preparing for Proof** How would you prove your conclusion in part (a)? **Use the proof in Example 1 without the last step.**

Theorem 9-2

Opposite angles of a parallelogram are congruent.
If $ABCD$ is a parallelogram, then $\angle A \cong \angle C$ and $\angle B \cong \angle D$.

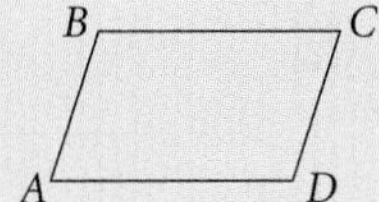

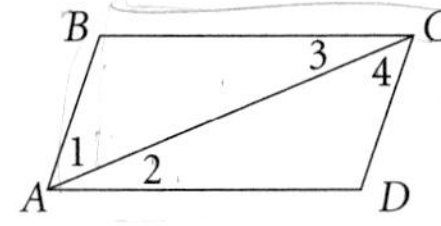

Answers may vary. See back of book for sample.

4\. **Preparing for Proof** Give a plan for proof for Theorem 9-2.

5\. a. **Try This** In $\square ABCD$, $m\angle 1 = 48$ and $m\angle BCD = 70$. Find the measures of $\angle BAD$, $\angle 2$, $\angle 3$, and $\angle 4$. **70; 22; 22; 48**
b. Find the measures of $\angle B$ and $\angle D$. **110; 110**

Angles of a polygon that share a common side are **consecutive angles.** In the figure at the left, $\angle S$ and $\angle T$ are consecutive angles. So are $\angle T$ and $\angle W$.

6\. a. Suppose the measures of two consecutive angles of a parallelogram are x and y. By Theorem 9-2, the other two angles also have measures of x and y. Use algebra and the fact that the sum of the measures of the angles of a quadrilateral is 360 to show that the consecutive angles are supplementary. **See back of book.**
b. **Try This** In $\square RSTW$, $m\angle R = 112$. Find the measure of each angle of the parallelogram.
$m\angle S = 68$; $m\angle T = 112$; $m\angle W = 68$

Additional Examples

FOR EXAMPLE 1

Use a two-column proof to prove Theorem 9-1: Opposite sides of a parallelogram are congruent. **See back of book.**

Discussion: *Which proof of Theorem 9-1 do you prefer? Why?*

FOR EXAMPLE 2

Use a flow proof to prove Theorem 9-3: The diagonals of a parallelogram bisect each other. **See back of book.**

Discussion: *Under what conditions do you think the diagonals of a parallelogram are perpendicular? congruent?*

FOR EXAMPLE 3

You want to divide a blank index card into five equal rows and you do not have a ruler. Explain how to apply Theorem 9-4 to do this using a piece of lined paper and a straightedge. **Answers may vary. Sample: Place a corner of the top of the card on the first line of the paper. Place the bottom of the card on the sixth line. Mark the points where the lines intersect the card. Repeat for the other side of the card. Connect the marks.**

Example 2

TACTILE LEARNING Have students draw a parallelogram and its diagonals. Have them trace each diagonal with a different color, then cut out the four triangles formed. By manipulating the triangles, students can observe that the two pieces of each diagonal are congruent.

ERROR ALERT! Some students may misinterpret Theorem 9-3 to mean that the diagonals are congruent. **Remediation:** Draw a parallelogram with consecutive angles measuring 30° and 150°. Draw the diagonals. It should be clear to students that the diagonals are not congruent.

ALGEBRA Question 7 Students may need to review how to solve a system of linear equations. Refer them to the Math Toolbox on page 370.

VISUAL LEARNING Have students draw three parallel lines on three consecutive lines of a lined sheet of paper. Then have them draw three transversals with different slopes. Using a ruler, have them measure the segments of each transversal cut by the parallel lines. Then have them repeat the activity beginning by drawing parallel lines on the first, second, and fourth lines of the paper. Ask students to summarize their results.

Technology Options

For Exercise 13, students may draw the parallelograms using geometry software. For Exercises 31–33, students may graph the preimage and image of the figure using graphing software.

Prentice Hall Technology

Software
- Secondary Math Lab Toolkit™
- Computer Item Generator 9-1

CD-ROM
- Multimedia Geometry Lab 9

Internet
- See the Prentice Hall site. (http://www.phschool.com)

Theorem 9-3 The diagonals of a parallelogram bisect each other.

Example 2

Use a two-column proof to prove Theorem 9-3.

Given: ▱ $ABCD$
Prove: $\overline{AC}$ and $\overline{BD}$ bisect each other at E.

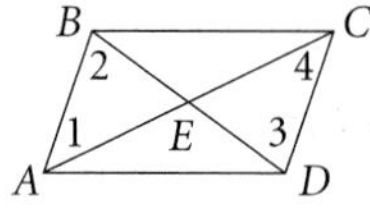

Statements	Reasons
1. $ABCD$ is a parallelogram.	1. Given
2. $\overline{AB} \parallel \overline{DC}$	2. Definition of parallelogram
3. $\angle 1 \cong \angle 4$; $\angle 2 \cong \angle 3$	3. If ∥ lines, then alt. int. ∠s are ≅.
4. $\overline{AB} \cong \overline{CD}$	4. Opposite sides of a parallelogram are ≅.
5. $\triangle ABE \cong \triangle CDE$	5. ASA
6. $\overline{AE} \cong \overline{CE}$; $\overline{BE} \cong \overline{DE}$	6. CPCTC
7. $\overline{AC}$ and $\overline{BD}$ bisect each other at E.	7. Definition of bisect

7. **Algebra** In the figure for Example 2, suppose that $AE = 4x$, $EC = 3y$, $BE = x + 1$, and $ED = y$. Solve the system of linear equations to find the values of x and y. $x = 3$; $y = 4$

In Exercise 28, you will use Theorem 9-1 to prove the following theorem.

Theorem 9-4 If three (or more) parallel lines cut off congruent segments on one transversal, then they cut off congruent segments on every transversal.

If $\overleftrightarrow{AB} \parallel \overleftrightarrow{CD} \parallel \overleftrightarrow{EF}$ and $\overline{AC} \cong \overline{CE}$, then $\overline{BD} \cong \overline{DF}$.

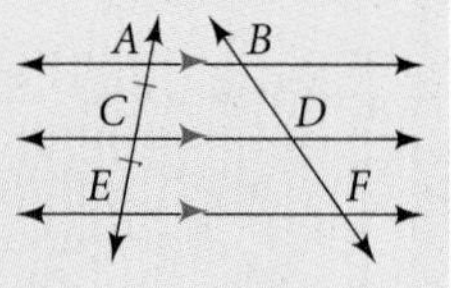

Example 3 Relating to the Real World

Measuring You want to divide a blank card into three equal rows and you do not have a ruler. Apply Theorem 9-4 to do this using a piece of lined paper and a straightedge.

The lines of the paper are parallel and equally spaced. Place a corner of the top edge of the card on the first line of the paper. Place the corner of the bottom edge on the fourth line. Mark the points where the second and third lines intersect the card. The marks will be equally spaced because the edge of the card is a transversal for the equally spaced parallel lines of the paper. Repeat for the other side of the card. Connect the marks.

Example 3 Relating to the Real World 

EXTENSION Have students perform the activity described in the example. Give students different sizes of index cards or cut different-sized rectangles from heavy paper.

CRITICAL THINKING Ask students to explain how the activity described in the example is an application of Theorem 9-4.

Exercises ON YOUR OWN

MAKING CONNECTIONS Exercise 11 Isaac Merrit Singer made the first practical sewing machine with a foot treadle instead of a hand crank in 1851. His first machines sold for $75 each, expensive in those days, leading him to devise installment buying plans. He is credited with creating the first consumer-appliance industry, devising multi-million dollar advertising campaigns, and initiating a system of providing service with sales.

PROBABILITY Exercise 12 Suggest that students draw a parallelogram, label the angles, list all possible combinations of two angles, then check if each angle pair is supplementary.

OPEN-ENDED Exercise 13a Students may want to make two such parallelograms using straws, uncooked spaghetti, toothpicks, or craft sticks.

ALTERNATIVE ASSESSMENT Exercises 14–16 You can use these exercises to help you assess students' understanding of the theorems in this lesson by their ability to apply them in these proofs. Have students work with a partner and allow them to choose the form of proof.

Exercises ON YOUR OWN

Find the measures of the numbered angles for each parallelogram. 4. $m\angle 1 = 95$; $m\angle 2 = 37$; $m\angle 3 = 37$

1. $m\angle 1 = 118$; $m\angle 2 = 62$; $m\angle 3 = 118$

2. 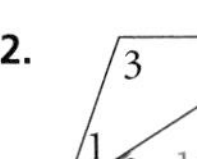 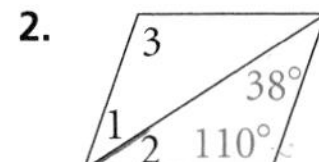

3. 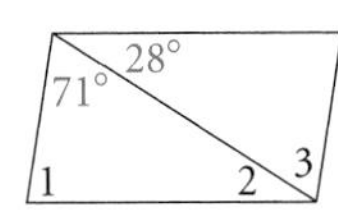

$m\angle 1 = 81$; $m\angle 2 = 28$; $m\angle 3 = 71$

4. 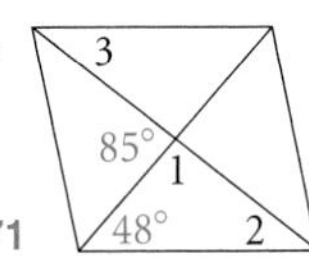

Find the length of $\overline{AP}$ in each parallelogram. 2. $m\angle 1 = 38$; $m\angle 2 = 32$; $m\angle 3 = 110$

5. 32 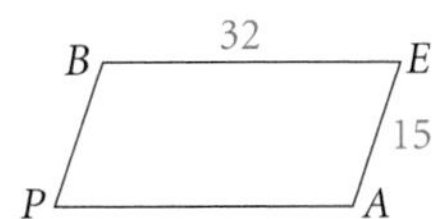

6. $YP = 8$, $TR = 10$ 4

7. $YP = 8$, $TR = 10$ 16

8. $MD = \frac{1}{2}AD$ 21 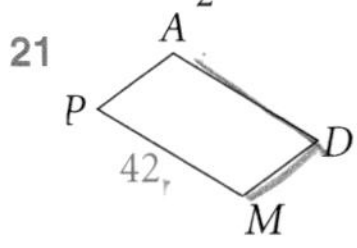

9. The perimeter of parallelogram *RSTW* is 48 cm. If $RS = 17$ cm, find the lengths of the other sides of the parallelogram. $ST = 7$ cm; $TW = 17$ cm; $WR = 7$ cm

10. The perimeter of parallelogram *EFGH* is 48 in. If *EF* is 5 in. less than *EH*, find the lengths of all four sides. $EF = 9.5$ in.; $FG = 14.5$ in.; $GH = 9.5$ in.; $HE = 14.5$ in.

11. *Sewing* Suppose you don't have a ruler. Explain how to space 6 buttons equally on a baby's sweater if you know where the first and last buttons must be placed and you have a large piece of lined paper. See margin.

12. a. *Probability* If two angles of a parallelogram that is not a rectangle are randomly selected, what is the probability that they will be supplementary? $\frac{2}{3}$

b. *Probability* If two angles of a rectangle are randomly selected, what is the probability that they will be supplementary? 1

13. a. *Open-ended* Sketch two parallelograms whose corresponding sides are congruent but whose corresponding angles are not congruent.

b. *Critical Thinking* Is there an SSSS congruence theorem for parallelograms? Explain.

a–b. See margin.

14. Given: ▱ *LENS* and ▱ *NGTH*
Prove: $\angle L \cong \angle T$

14–15. Answers may vary. See margin for samples.

15. Given: ▱ *LENS* and ▱ *NGTH*
Prove: $\overline{LS} \parallel \overline{GT}$

16. Given: ▱ *LENS* and ▱ *NGTH*
Prove: $\angle E$ is supplementary to $\angle T$.

16. Answers may vary. See back of book for sample.

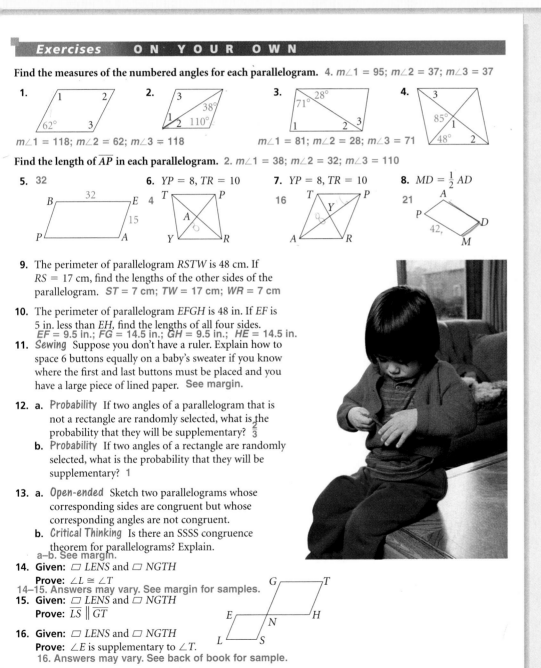

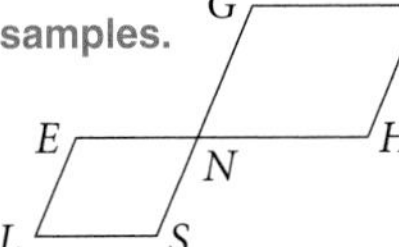

pages 451–453 On Your Own

11. Pick 6 equally spaced lines on the paper. Place the paper so that the 1st button is on the 1st line and the last button is on the 6th line. Draw a line between the first and last buttons. The remaining buttons should be placed where the drawn line crosses the 4 ∥ lines.

13a. Sample:

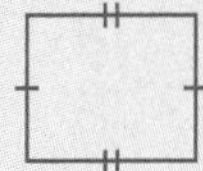 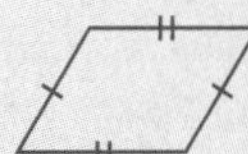

b. No; the pair of ▱s in part (a) is a counterexample.

14. 1. ▱*LENS* (Given) 2. $\angle L \cong \angle ENS$ (Opp. ∠s of a ▱ are ≅.) 3. ▱*NGTH* (Given) 4. $\angle T \cong \angle GNH$ (Opp. ∠s of a ▱ are ≅.) 5. $\angle GNH \cong \angle ENS$ (Vert. ∠s are ≅.) 6. $\angle L \cong \angle T$ (Transitive Prop. of ≅)

15. 1. ▱*LENS* (Given) 2. $\overline{LS} \parallel \overline{EH}$ (Def. of ▱) 3. ▱*NGTH* (Given) 4. $\overline{GT} \parallel \overline{EH}$ (Def. of ▱) 5. $\overline{LS} \parallel \overline{GT}$ (2 lines ∥ to a 3rd line are ∥.)

Exercises 17–24 Ask students to state what theorem or theorems they used in each problem.

LOGICAL REASONING Exercise 27b Remind students that they may have written a plan for this proof in Question 4.

Exercise 28 The proof of Theorem 9-4 involves drawing auxiliary segments $\overline{BG}$ and $\overline{DH}$ and showing $\triangle BGD \cong \triangle DHF$.

CRITICAL THINKING Exercises 29–30 Ask students to make a conjecture about the relationship between *RSTW* and *XYTZ*. (One is a dilation image of the other.)

26a. Rectangles, rhombuses, and squares; a rectangle has 2 lines of symmetry passing through the midpts. of opp. sides. A rhombus has 2 lines of symmetry passing through opp. vertices. A square has both kinds of lines of symmetry.

b. All ▱s have rotational symmetry because opp. sides are ≅, opp. angles are ≅, and the diagonals bisect each other.

27b. Sample:

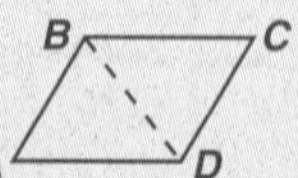

Given: ▱*ABCD*. Prove: $\angle A \cong \angle C$; $\angle B \cong \angle D$. Draw diagonal $\overline{BD}$. 1. ▱*ABCD* (Given) 2. $\overline{AB} \parallel \overline{CD}$ (Def. of ▱) 3. $\angle ABD \cong \angle BDC$ (If $\parallel$ lines, then alt. int. ∠s are ≅.) 4. $\overline{BC} \parallel \overline{DA}$ (Def. of ▱) 5. $\angle ADB \cong \angle CBD$ (If $\parallel$ lines, then alt. int. ∠s are ≅.) 6. $\overline{BD} \cong \overline{BD}$ (Reflexive Prop. of ≅) 7. $\triangle ABD \cong \triangle CDB$ (ASA) 8. $\angle A \cong \angle C$ (CPCTC) Similarly, use diagonal $\overline{AC}$ to prove $\angle B \cong \angle D$.

29. 1. ▱*RSTW* and ▱*XYTZ* (Given) 2. $\angle R \cong \angle T$ (Opp. angles of a ▱ are ≅.) 3. $\angle T \cong \angle X$ (Opp. angles of a ▱ are ≅.) 4. $\angle R \cong \angle X$ (Transitive Prop. of ≅)

30. 1. ▱*RSTW* and ▱*XYTZ* (Given) 2. $\overline{RS} \parallel \overline{TW}$ (Def. of ▱) 3. $\overline{XY} \parallel \overline{TW}$ (Def. of ▱) 4. $\overline{RS} \parallel \overline{XY}$ (2 lines $\parallel$ to a 3rd are $\parallel$.)

Algebra **Find the value of the variable(s) in each parallelogram.**

17.

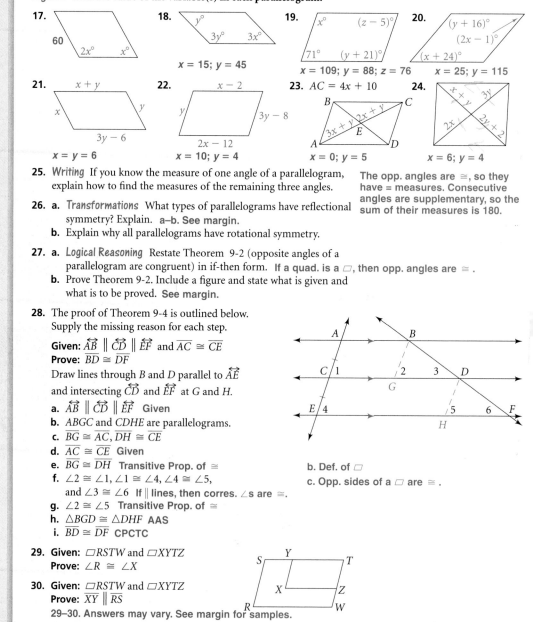

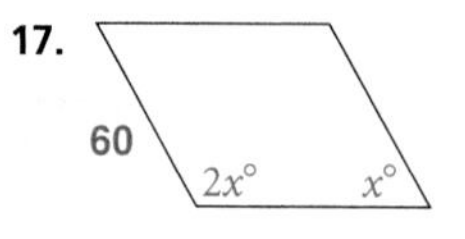

18.

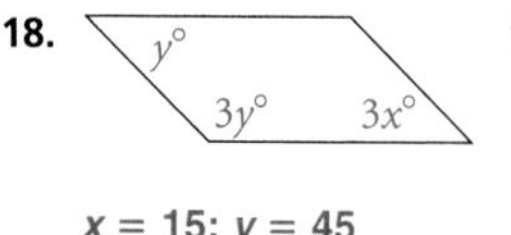

$x = 15$; $y = 45$

19.

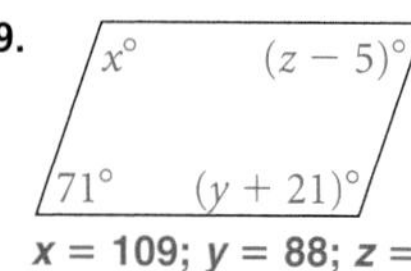

$x = 109$; $y = 88$; $z = 76$

20.

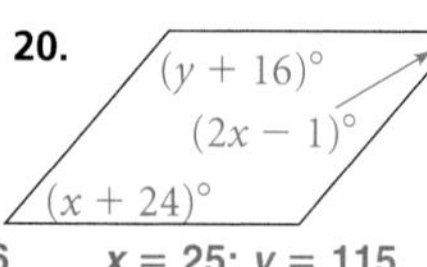

$x = 25$; $y = 115$

21. $x + y$, x, y, $3y - 6$

$x = y = 6$

22.

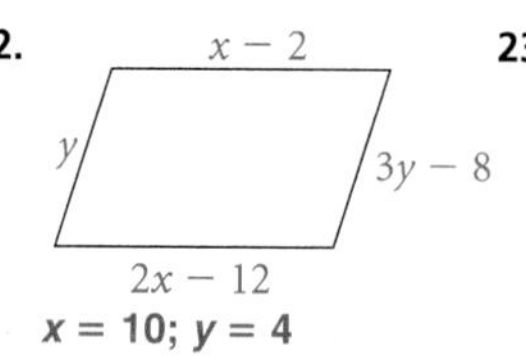

$x = 10$; $y = 4$

23. $AC = 4x + 10$

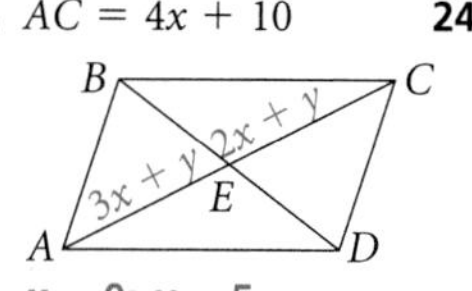

$x = 0$; $y = 5$

24.

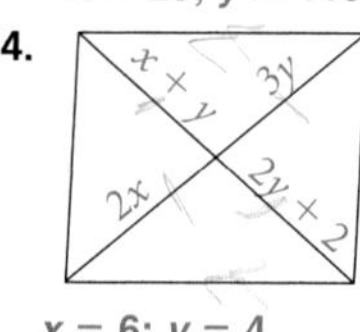

$x = 6$; $y = 4$

25. *Writing* If you know the measure of one angle of a parallelogram, explain how to find the measures of the remaining three angles. **The opp. angles are ≅, so they have = measures. Consecutive angles are supplementary, so the sum of their measures is 180.**

26. a. *Transformations* What types of parallelograms have reflectional symmetry? Explain. **a–b. See margin.**

b. Explain why all parallelograms have rotational symmetry.

27. a. *Logical Reasoning* Restate Theorem 9-2 (opposite angles of a parallelogram are congruent) in if-then form. **If a quad. is a ▱, then opp. angles are ≅.**

b. Prove Theorem 9-2. Include a figure and state what is given and what is to be proved. **See margin.**

28. The proof of Theorem 9-4 is outlined below. Supply the missing reason for each step.

Given: $\overleftrightarrow{AB} \parallel \overleftrightarrow{CD} \parallel \overleftrightarrow{EF}$ and $\overline{AC} \cong \overline{CE}$
Prove: $\overline{BD} \cong \overline{DF}$

Draw lines through *B* and *D* parallel to $\overleftrightarrow{AE}$ and intersecting $\overleftrightarrow{CD}$ and $\overleftrightarrow{EF}$ at *G* and *H*.

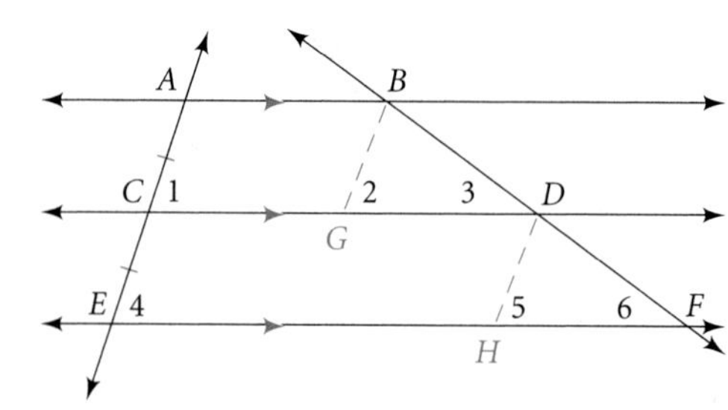

a. $\overleftrightarrow{AB} \parallel \overleftrightarrow{CD} \parallel \overleftrightarrow{EF}$ **Given**
b. *ABGC* and *CDHE* are parallelograms. **b. Def. of ▱**
c. $\overline{BG} \cong \overline{AC}$, $\overline{DH} \cong \overline{CE}$ **c. Opp. sides of a ▱ are ≅.**
d. $\overline{AC} \cong \overline{CE}$ **Given**
e. $\overline{BG} \cong \overline{DH}$ **Transitive Prop. of ≅**
f. $\angle 2 \cong \angle 1$, $\angle 1 \cong \angle 4$, $\angle 4 \cong \angle 5$, and $\angle 3 \cong \angle 6$ **If $\parallel$ lines, then corres. ∠s are ≅.**
g. $\angle 2 \cong \angle 5$ **Transitive Prop. of ≅**
h. $\triangle BGD \cong \triangle DHF$ **AAS**
i. $\overline{BD} \cong \overline{DF}$ **CPCTC**

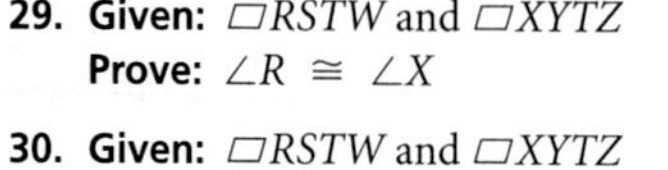

29. Given: ▱*RSTW* and ▱*XYTZ*
Prove: $\angle R \cong \angle X$

30. Given: ▱*RSTW* and ▱*XYTZ*
Prove: $\overline{XY} \parallel \overline{RS}$

29–30. Answers may vary. See margin for samples.

TRANSFORMATIONS Exercises 31–33 Have students copy the diagram onto grid paper and review the methods for reflecting, rotating, and translating the figures in Lessons 3-1 through 3-3.

Chapter Project **FIND OUT BY DOING** To save time, have the supplies (paper, ruler, stapler, thread) ready before students begin this activity. Read the directions aloud with students and make sure they understand each step. You may want to begin by demonstrating the steps. Show students how to use the edge of a ruler to make a crease.

Exercises MIXED REVIEW

Exercises 34–39 Students review angle pairs formed when two lines are cut by a transversal.

GETTING READY FOR LESSON 9-2 These exercises prepare students to prove certain quadrilaterals are parallelograms.

Wrap Up

THE BIG IDEA Ask students: *Describe as many characteristics of a parallelogram as you can.*

RETEACHING ACTIVITY Students prove that opposite angles of a parallelogram are congruent. Then they prove additional relationships between angles and sides of parallelograms. (Reteaching worksheet 9-1)

Transformations **Exercises 31–33 refer to $\triangle ABC$ at the right and its image $\triangle A'B'C'$ under each transformation.**

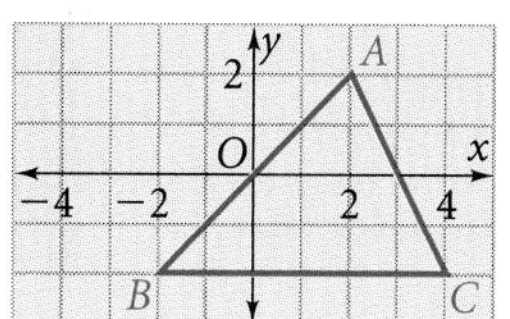

31. Reflect $\triangle ABC$ in $y = -2$. What type of quadrilateral is $ABA'C$? **kite**
32. Rotate $\triangle ABC$ 180° about the origin. What type of quadrilateral is $AC'BC$? **parallelogram**
33. Translate $\triangle ABC$ by $\langle 4, 4 \rangle$. What type of quadrilateral is $A'C'CB$? **trapezoid**

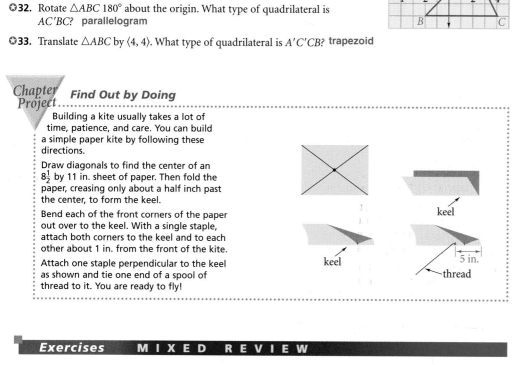

Chapter Project ***Find Out by Doing***

Building a kite usually takes a lot of time, patience, and care. You can build a simple paper kite by following these directions.

Draw diagonals to find the center of an $8\frac{1}{2}$ by 11 in. sheet of paper. Then fold the paper, creasing only about a half inch past the center, to form the keel.

Bend each of the front corners of the paper out over to the keel. With a single staple, attach both corners to the keel and to each other about 1 in. from the front of the kite.

Attach one staple perpendicular to the keel as shown and tie one end of a spool of thread to it. You are ready to fly!

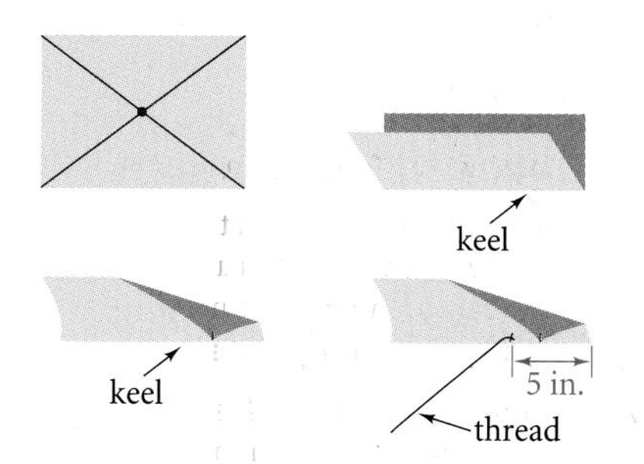

Exercises MIXED REVIEW

Sketch an example of each pair of angles. **34–39. See back of book for samples.**

34. supplementary angles
35. same-side interior angles
36. alternate interior angles
37. complementary angles
38. corresponding angles
39. vertical angles

40. *Coordinate Geometry* A triangle has coordinates $A(3, 0)$, $B(2, 5)$, and $C(-1, 3)$. Find the image of the triangle after a translation right 3 units and down 2 units followed by a reflection in the x-axis. **$A'(6, 2)$; $B'(5, -3)$; $C'(2, -1)$**

Getting Ready for Lesson 9-2

41. a. Find the coordinates of the midpoints of $\overline{AC}$ and $\overline{BD}$. What is the relationship between $\overline{AC}$ and $\overline{BD}$? **See above right.**
    b. Find the slopes of $\overline{BC}$ and $\overline{AD}$. How do they compare? **See above.**
    c. Are $\overline{AB}$ and $\overline{DC}$ parallel? Explain. **See below.**
    d. What type of figure is $ABCD$? **parallelogram**

41c. $\overline{AB} \parallel \overline{DC}$ because they are vertical.

41a. (2.5, 1.5), (2.5, 1.5); $\overline{AC}$ and $\overline{BD}$ bisect each other.

41b. $\frac{1}{3}$; $\frac{1}{3}$; the slopes are =.

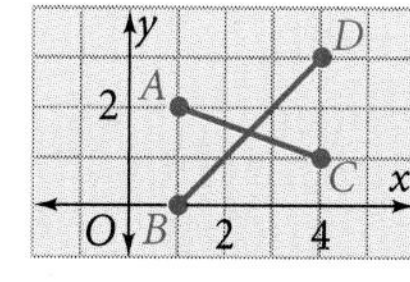

Reteaching 9-1

Practice 9-1

Practice 9-1
Mixed Exercises

Lesson Quiz

Lesson Quiz is also available in Transparencies.

1. Find the missing angle measures.

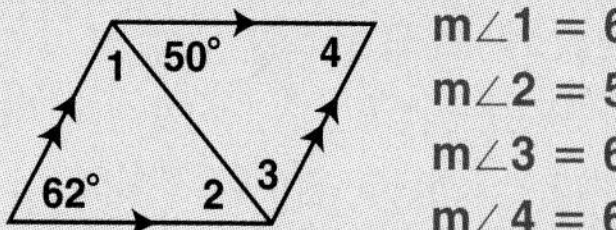

m∠1 = 68, m∠2 = 50, m∠3 = 68, m∠4 = 62

2. The perimeter of a parallelogram *MNOP* is 72 in. If *NO* is 12 in., find the lengths of the other sides. **MN = 24 in., MP = 12 in., OP = 24 in.**

3. Given: *ACDF* and *ABEF* are parallelograms.
   Prove: *BCDE* is a parallelogram. **See back of book.**

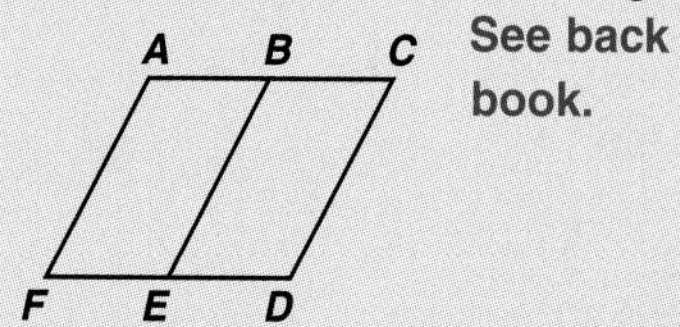

9-2 Teaching Notes

PROBLEM OF THE DAY

The diagram shows a swimming pool with trees at each corner. Show how you can double the size of the pool, keeping it square without cutting down or moving the trees.

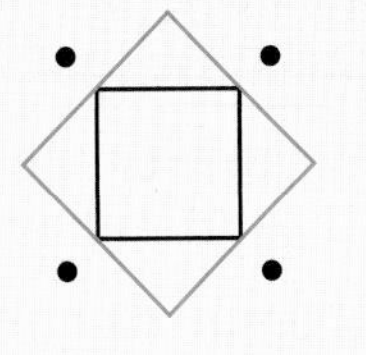

Problem of the Day is also available in Transparencies.

CONNECTING TO PRIOR KNOWLEDGE Have students identify parallelograms in buildings, bridges, artwork, etc. Ask students what they would need to know to prove the figures are parallelograms.

WORK TOGETHER

Students use geoboards to explore ways to determine whether a quadrilateral is a parallelogram. If geoboards are not available, students can use dot paper and a straightedge.

Review with students how to find the slope of a line on a geoboard or on dot paper by finding the ratio $\frac{\text{rise}}{\text{run}}$.

Lesson Planning Options

Prerequisite Skills

- Graphing in the coordinate plane
- Solving systems of linear equations

Assignment Options for Exercises On Your Own

Core 1–30
Extension 31

Use Mixed Review to maintain skills.

Resources

Student Edition

Skills Handbook, pp. 677, 678, 681
Extra Practice, p. 656
Glossary/Study Guide

Teaching Resources

Chapter Support File, Ch. 9
- Practice 9-2(two worksheets)
- Reteaching 9-2
- Alternative Activity 9-2

Classroom Manager 9-2
Glossary, Spanish Resources

Transparencies
94

What You'll Learn

- Finding characteristics of quadrilaterals that indicate that they are parallelograms

...And Why

To solve problems in navigation and sailing

What You'll Need

- 11-by-11 peg geoboard
- straightedge

QUICK REVIEW

slope = $\frac{\text{rise}}{\text{run}}$

Connections Navigation . . . and more

9-2 Proving That a Quadrilateral Is a Parallelogram

WORK TOGETHER

By definition, a quadrilateral is a parallelogram if both pairs of opposite sides are parallel. Work with a partner and a geoboard to explore other ways to determine whether a quadrilateral is a parallelogram.

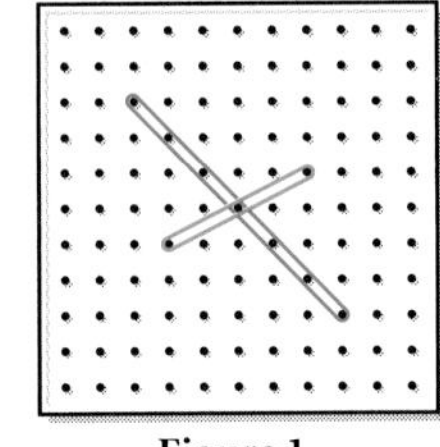

Figure 1 Figure 2

1. The segments in Figure 1 bisect each other. Connect the endpoints to form a quadrilateral. Find the slopes of opposite pairs of sides and determine what type of quadrilateral it is. -4 and $-\frac{2}{5}$; parallelogram

- Make several quadrilaterals by joining the endpoints of pairs of bisecting segments on a geoboard. Classify the quadrilaterals you form.

2. Make a **conjecture** about quadrilaterals whose diagonals bisect each other. If diags. of a quad. bisect each other, the quad. is a ▱.

3. The segments in Figure 2 are congruent and parallel. Connect the endpoints to form a quadrilateral. Find the slopes of all four sides and determine what type of quadrilateral it is. $-\frac{2}{3}$ and $\frac{1}{2}$; parallelogram

- Make several quadrilaterals by joining the endpoints of pairs of congruent and parallel segments on a geoboard. Classify the quadrilaterals you form.

4. Make a **conjecture** about quadrilaterals that have one pair of congruent and parallel sides.
If a quad. has 1 pair of ≅ and ∥ sides, the quad. is a ▱.

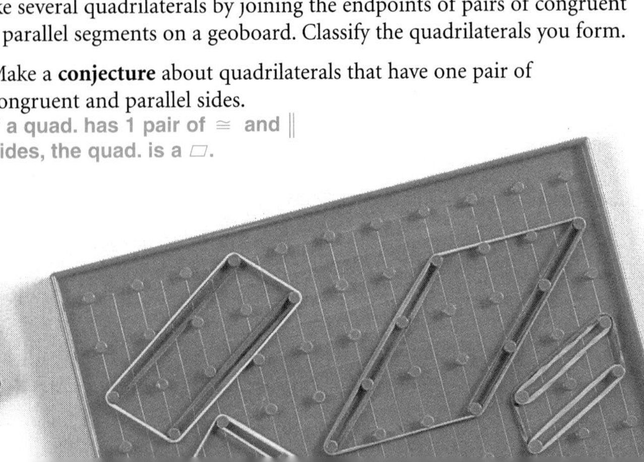

CRITICAL THINKING Ask students if a figure with congruent diagonals is always a parallelogram. Then draw a kite with congruent diagonals as a counterexample.

MENTAL MATH **Question 5** After students find the values of x and y, encourage them to evaluate each expression mentally to check that the two segments of each diagonal are congruent.

THINK AND DISCUSS

Example 1

You may want to start by discussing a plan for the proof: Show $\triangle AEB \cong \triangle CED$ and $\triangle BEC \cong \triangle DEA$. Then use CPCTC to show alternate interior angles are congruent. Then conclude that $\overline{AB} \parallel \overline{CD}$ and $\overline{BC} \parallel \overline{AD}$.

THINK AND DISCUSS

The results you obtained in the Work Together are the basis of Theorem 9-5 and Theorem 9-6.

Theorem 9-5 If the diagonals of a quadrilateral bisect each other, then the quadrilateral is a parallelogram.

Example 1

Use a flow proof to prove Theorem 9-5.

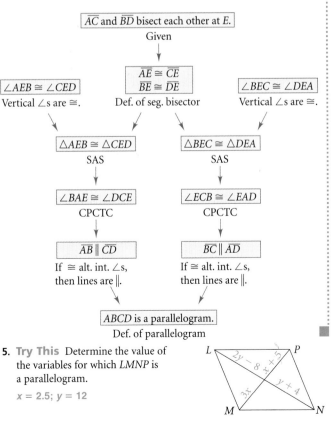

Given: $\overline{AC}$ and $\overline{BD}$ bisect each other at E.
Prove: $ABCD$ is a parallelogram.

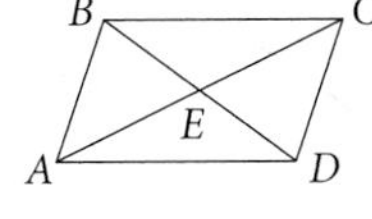

Flow Proof

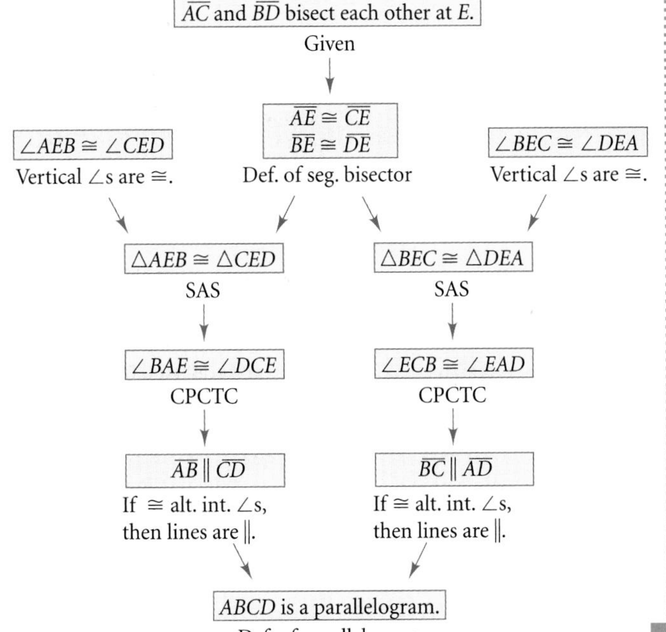

Who? Writing a flow proof is similar to writing a flow chart for a computer program. Ada Byron King, Countess of Lovelace (1815–1852), was the first programmer and the inventor of programming. In 1979, the U.S. Department of Defense named one of its computer languages ADA in her honor.

QUICK REVIEW

A parallelogram is a quadrilateral with both pairs of opposite sides parallel.

5. **Try This** Determine the value of the variables for which $LMNP$ is a parallelogram.
$x = 2.5$; $y = 12$

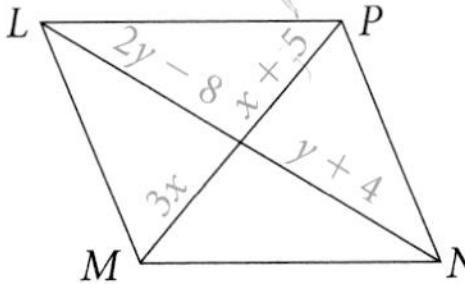

Additional Examples

FOR EXAMPLE 1

Determine the values of the variables for which $QRST$ is a parallelogram.

$x = 3$, $y = 5$

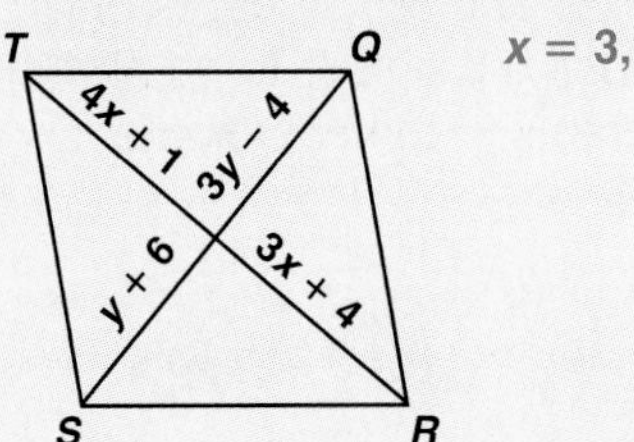

Determine the values of the variables for which $KLMN$ is a parallelogram.

$x = 12$, $y = 9$

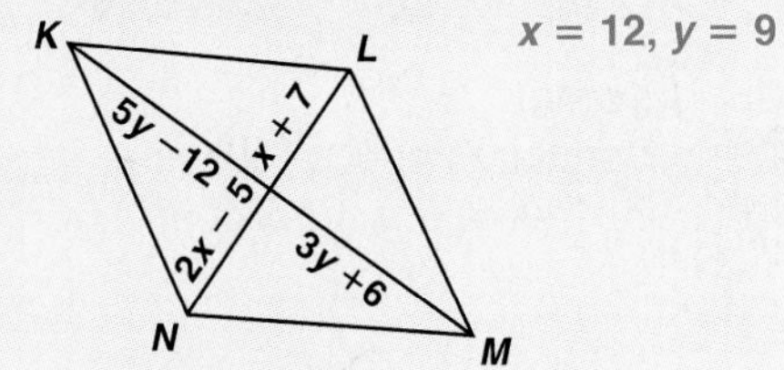

Discussion: *Name two pairs of congruent triangles in each parallelogram.*

FOR EXAMPLE 2

Draw a parallelogram on grid paper with angles 60°, 60°, 120°, and 120°. Describe your steps.

Discussion: *Can two consecutive angles of a parallelogram be 60° each? Explain.*

ERROR ALERT! Question 6a Some students may associate the wrong pair of parallel lines with a pair of alternate interior angles in a parallelogram. **Remediation:** Have students copy the figure and trace over $\overline{BC}$, $\overline{AD}$, and $\overline{BD}$ in one color and $\overline{AB}$, $\overline{CD}$, and $\overline{BD}$ in another color. Students should be able to recognize which sides form each angle.

VISUAL LEARNING Theorem 9-7 Cut out the bottom of a cardboard box. Measure the opposite sides of the box to show they are congruent. Then change the angles between the adjacent edges by pushing the sides to show students that every quadrilateral formed is a parallelogram.

Question 7 To complete this proof, students need to draw only one diagonal and then use congruent triangles and Theorem 9-6.

Question 8b Make sure students recognize that $\angle A$ and $\angle B$, as well as $\angle B$ and $\angle C$, are supplementary *and* same-side interior angles.

Technology Options

For Exercise 23, students may draw the parallelogram using geometry software or a drawing program. For Exercises 25 and 30, students may use a graphing program to graph the parallelograms in the coordinate plane.

Prentice Hall Technology

Software

- Secondary Math Lab Toolkit™
- Integrated Math Lab 39
- Computer Item Generator 9-2

Internet

- See the Prentice Hall site. (http://www.phschool.com)

Theorem 9-6

If one pair of opposite sides of a quadrilateral are both congruent and parallel, then the quadrilateral is a parallelogram.

You can use Theorem 9-5 to show that Theorem 9-6 is true.

6a. $\angle 1 \cong \angle 4$ and $\angle 2 \cong \angle 3$; if $\parallel$ lines, then alt. int. $\angle$s are $\cong$.
b. $\triangle ABE$ and $\triangle CDE$; ASA
d. The diags. of quad. $ABCD$ bisect each other.

6. Given: $\overline{AB} \cong \overline{DC}$; $\overline{AB} \parallel \overline{DC}$

- **a.** Which numbered angles must be congruent? Why?
- **b.** Which triangles must be congruent? Why?
- **c.** Complete: $\overline{AE} \cong$ ■ and $\overline{BE} \cong$ ■. $\overline{CE}$; $\overline{DE}$
- **d.** What follows from part (c)?
- **e.** Why is $ABCD$ a parallelogram? **If the diags. of a quad. bisect each other, the quad. is a ▱.**

Theorems 9-7 and 9-8 provide additional ways to prove that a quadrilateral is a parallelogram.

Theorem 9-7

If both pairs of opposite sides of a quadrilateral are congruent, then the quadrilateral is a parallelogram.

7. *Logical Reasoning* Write a paragraph proof of Theorem 9-7. Use quadrilateral $ABCD$, with $\overline{AB} \cong \overline{CD}$ and $\overline{BC} \cong \overline{DA}$. (*Hint:* Draw diagonal $\overline{BD}$ and use congruent triangles.) **See margin p. 457.**

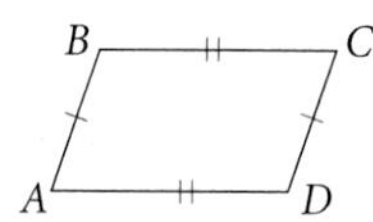

Theorem 9-8

If both pairs of opposite angles of a quadrilateral are congruent, then the quadrilateral is a parallelogram.

You can use the fact that the sum of the measures of the interior angles of a quadrilateral is 360 to show that Theorem 9-8 is true.

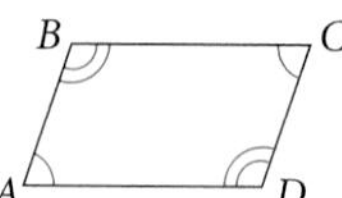

8c. $\angle A$ and $\angle B$ are supplementary; $\angle B$ and $\angle C$ are supplementary.

8. Given: $\angle A \cong \angle C$ and $\angle B \cong \angle D$

- **a.** Let $m\angle A = x$ and $m\angle B = y$. Write an equation expressing the sum of the measures of the angles of quadrilateral $ABCD$ in terms of x and y. **$2x + 2y = 360$**
- **b.** Solve for y in terms of x. **$y = 180 - x$**
- **c.** What is the relationship between $\angle A$ and $\angle B$? between $\angle B$ and $\angle C$? **See left.**
- **d.** What is the relationship between $\overline{AB}$ and $\overline{DC}$? between $\overline{BC}$ and $\overline{AD}$? Explain. **$\overline{AB} \parallel \overline{DC}$, $\overline{BC} \parallel \overline{AD}$; if supplementary same-side interior $\angle$s, then lines are $\parallel$.**
- **e.** Classify quadrilateral $ABCD$. **$ABCD$ is a ▱.**

9. Try This Based on the markings, decide if each figure must be a parallelogram. Justify your answer. **b. No; the quad. could be an isosceles trap.**

9a. Yes; if 1 pair of opp. sides of a quad. are both $\cong$ and $\parallel$, then the quad. is a ▱.

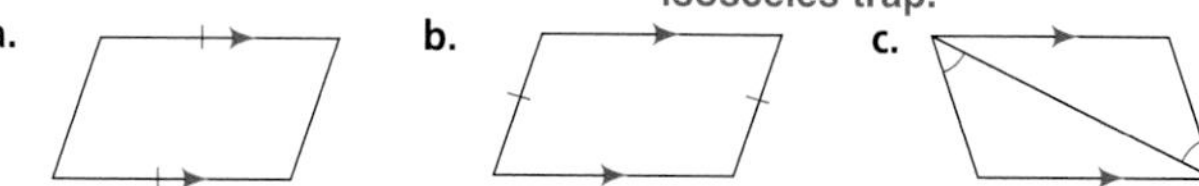

c. Yes; the 2nd pair of sides are $\parallel$ because alt. int. $\angle$s are $\cong$. The quad. is a ▱ by def.

Have students make a list of the five ways to prove two quadrilaterals congruent. It should include the definition of parallelogram and Theorems 9-5 and 9-6. Some students may want to use the results of Question 8 to write a sixth way: If an angle is supplementary to both consecutive angles of a quadrilateral, then the quadrilateral is a parallelogram.

Example 2 Relating to the Real World

TACTILE LEARNING Students can make a parallel ruler using straws and brads. Then have them make their own map on graph paper, labeling a ship's position and its destination. They can make a compass using a protractor. Have them find the angle the ship must travel to reach its destination.

Exercises ON YOUR OWN

Exercises 1–8 Students apply the theorems presented in this lesson to determine whether or not the figures are parallelograms.

Example 2 Relating to the Real World

Navigation A parallel rule is a navigational tool used to plot ship routes on charts. It is made of two rulers connected with congruent crossbars, such that $AB = DC$ and $AD = BC$. You place one ruler on a line connecting the ship's position to its destination point. Then you move the other ruler onto the chart's compass to find the angle of the route. Explain why this instrument works.

Because both the sections of the rulers and the crossbars are congruent, the rulers and crossbars form parallelogram *ABCD*. Since the figure is a parallelogram, the rulers are parallel. Therefore, the angle shown on the chart's compass is congruent to the angle the ship should travel.

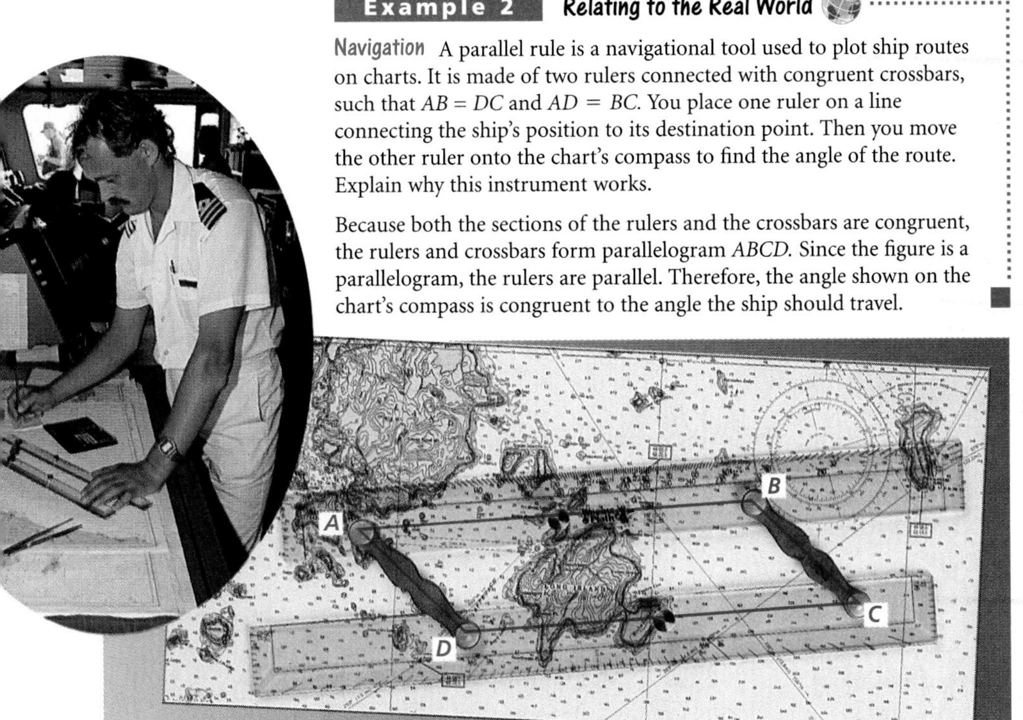

10. Suppose $m\angle B = 60$. Find the measures of the other angles of parallelogram *ABCD* formed by the parallel rule.
$m\angle A = m\angle C = 120$, $m\angle D = 60$

Exercises ON YOUR OWN

Based on the markings, decide if each figure must be a parallelogram. Justify your answer. 1–8. See margin.

1. 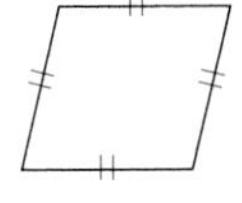
2. 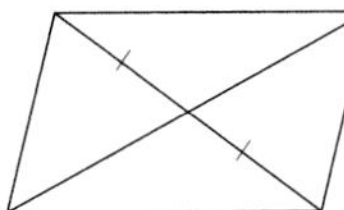
3. 
4. 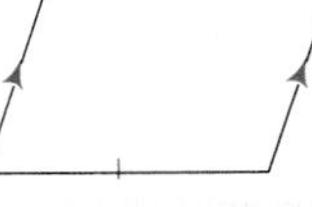
5. 
6. 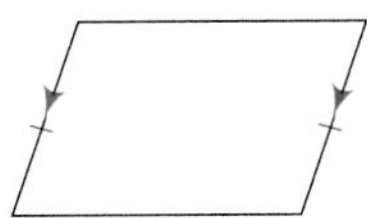
7.  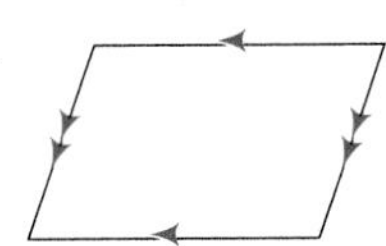 
8. 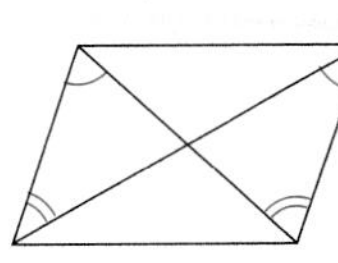

pages 455–457 Think and Discuss

7. Draw diagonal $\overline{BD}$. Since the opp. sides are ≅, $\triangle ABD \cong \triangle CDB$ by SSS. Then $\angle ABD \cong \angle CDB$ by CPCTC. If ≅ alt. int. ∠s, then lines are ∥, so $\overline{AB} \parallel \overline{CD}$. Similarly, $\angle ADB \cong \angle CBD$, and $\overline{BC} \parallel \overline{DA}$. By def., *ABCD* is a ▱.

pages 457–459 On Your Own

1. Yes; if both pairs of opp. sides of a quad. are ≅, the quad. is a ▱.
2. No; the 2nd diagonal may not be bisected by the 1st.
3. Yes; if both pairs of opp. angles of a quad. are ≅, the quad. is a ▱.
4. No; the quad. may be an isosceles trapezoid.
5. Yes; both pairs of opp. sides are ∥ because alt. int. ∠s are ≅. The quad. is a ▱ by def.
6. Yes; if 1 pair of sides of a quad. is both ≅ and ∥, then the quad. is a ▱ by Thm. 9-6.
7. Yes; the quad. is a ▱ by def.
8. No; 1 pair of sides is ∥, but the other pair need not be ∥.

Exercises 9–14 For each exercise, have students copy the figure, label the figure with the given information, and state any theorems they used to justify their answers.

ALGEBRA Exercises 15–17 Make sure that students do not assume the figures are parallel before finding the missing angle measures or side lengths.

ALTERNATIVE ASSESSMENT **Exercises 18–20** After students complete these problems, have them work with a partner to use the properties of parallelograms to create their own algebra problems. Have students exchange problems within their groups and solve them.

STANDARDIZED TEST TIP **Exercise 21** Students will quickly see that A and C are sufficient conditions. In order to see that D and E are also sufficient, students need to recognize that $\angle R$ supplementary to $\angle S$ implies $\overline{RW} \parallel \overline{ST}$.

OPEN-ENDED Exercise 23 Students may want to create these parallelograms using geoboards, straws, or other manipulatives.

458

State whether the information given about quadrilateral *RSTW* is sufficient to determine that it is a parallelogram.

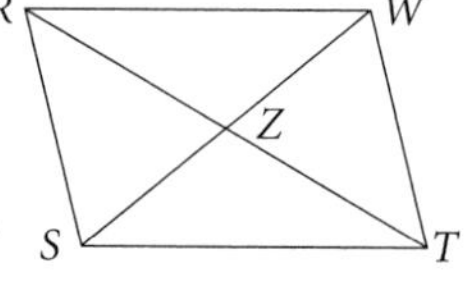

9. $\overline{RS} \parallel \overline{WT}, \overline{RS} \cong \overline{WT}$ yes

10. $\overline{RS} \parallel \overline{WT}, \overline{ST} \cong \overline{RW}$ no

11. $\overline{RS} \cong \overline{WT}, \overline{ST} \cong \overline{RW}$ yes

12. $\angle SRW \cong \angle WTS, \angle RST \cong \angle TWR$ yes

13. $\overline{RZ} \cong \overline{TZ}, \overline{SZ} \cong \overline{WZ}$ yes

14. $\angle TSZ \cong \angle RSZ, \angle TWZ \cong \angle RWZ$ no

Algebra **Find the value of *x*. Then tell whether *ABCD* must be a parallelogram. Explain your answer.**

15.

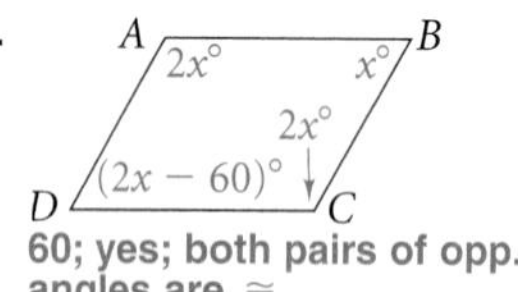

60; yes; both pairs of opp. angles are ≅.

16.

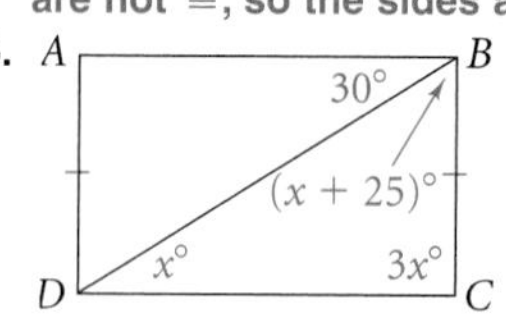

16. 31; no; consecutive $\angle$s are not supplementary and alt. int. $\angle$s are not ≅, so the sides are not parallel.

17.

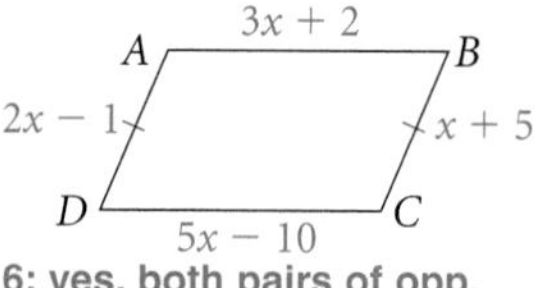

6; yes, both pairs of opp. sides are ≅.

Algebra **Determine the values of the variables for which *ABCD* is a parallelogram.**

18.

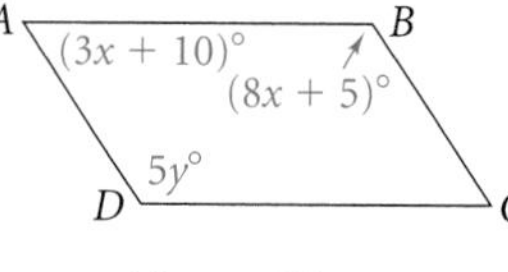

$x = 15; y = 25$

19.

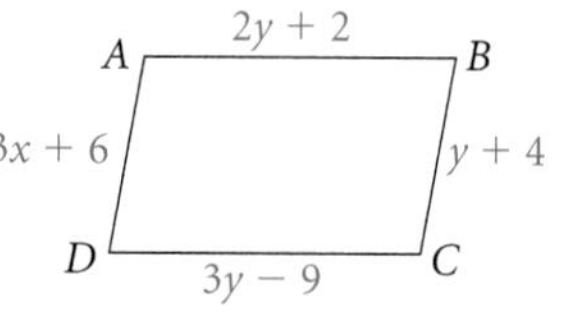

$x = 3; y = 11$

20.

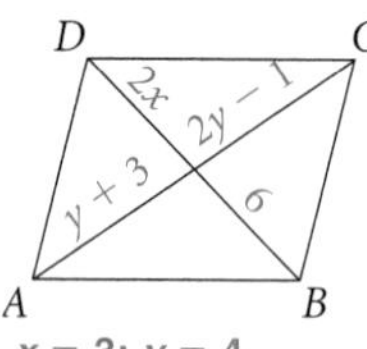

$x = 3; y = 4$

21. *Standardized Test Prep* Which of the following pairs of conditions will *not* be sufficient to prove that quadrilateral *RSTW* is a parallelogram? B

I. $\overline{RS} \parallel \overline{WT}$ **II.** $\overline{RS} \cong \overline{WT}$

III. $\overline{ST} \cong \overline{RW}$ **IV.** $\angle R$ is supplementary to $\angle S$.

A. I and II **B.** I and III **C.** II and III

D. I and IV **E.** III and IV

22. a. *Transformations* Describe the transformation that maps $\overline{AB}$ to $\overline{A'B'}$. $\langle 3, 2 \rangle$

b. Suppose $\overline{C'D'}$ is the image of $\overline{CD}$ under the transformation in part (a). What kind of quadrilateral is $CDD'C'$? Explain. See below.

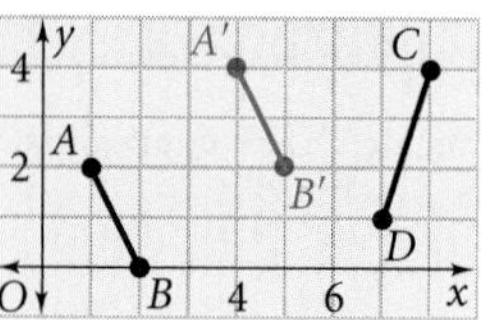

23. *Open-ended* Sketch two noncongruent parallelograms *ABCD* and *EFGH* such that $\overline{AC} \cong \overline{EG}$ and $\overline{BD} \cong \overline{FH}$. See margin p. 459 for sample.

24. *Probability* Two opposite angles of a quadrilateral measure 120. The measures of the other angles are multiples of 10. What is the probability that the quadrilateral is a parallelogram? $\frac{1}{6}$

22b. Parallelogram; at least 1 pair of opp. sides is both ≅ and $\parallel$.

COORDINATE GEOMETRY Exercise 25 Have students copy the grid for each part of the problem.

Exercises 27–29 Have students work in groups to complete the proofs. Then have each group present one of the proofs to the class.

ESL Exercise 31 Help students understand "weaving." Bring in a piece of material in which the vertical and horizontal threads are visible to illustrate the meaning of the term. Help students compare and contrast the uses of weaving in the phrases "fabric weaving," "a car weaving in and out of its lane," and "a spider weaving a web."

DIVERSITY Exercise 31 Have students research the North American Indian art of basket weaving.

---

25. a. *Coordinate Geometry* Find the coordinates of point D so that $ABCD$ is a parallelogram. **(4, 0)**

b. Find the coordinates of point E so that $ABEC$ is a parallelogram. **(6, 6)**

c. Find the coordinates of point F so that $AFBC$ is a parallelogram. **(−2, 4)**

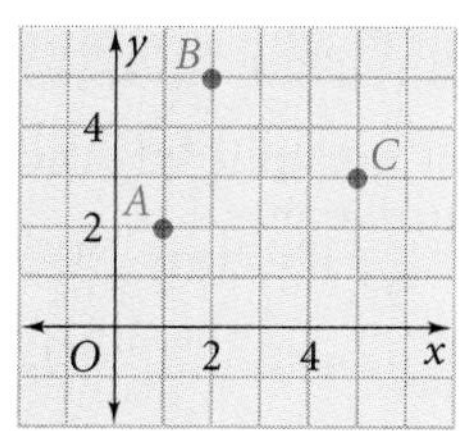

26. *Writing* Which pairs of theorems in Lessons 9-1 and 9-2 can be combined in if-and-only-if statements? Write the statements. **See margin.**

27–28. Answers may vary. See margin for sample.

Choose **Write a paragraph proof, a flow proof, or a two-column proof.**

27. Given: $\triangle TRS \cong \triangle RTW$
Prove: $RSTW$ is a parallelogram.

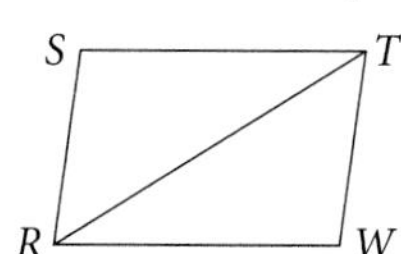

28. Given: $\triangle PKJ \cong \triangle PML$
Prove: $JKLM$ is a parallelogram.

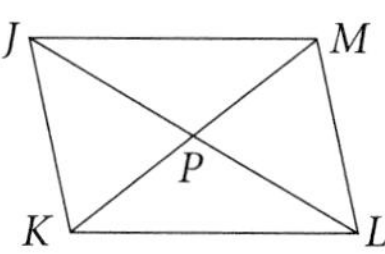

29. Given: Parallelogram $ABCD$;
E is the midpoint of $\overline{BC}$;
F is the midpoint of $\overline{AD}$.

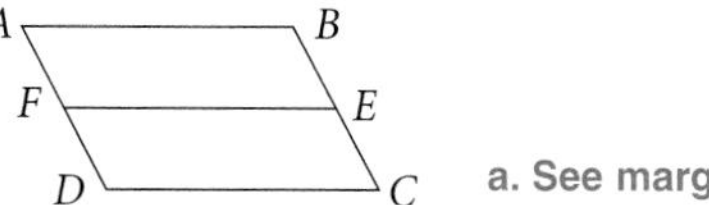

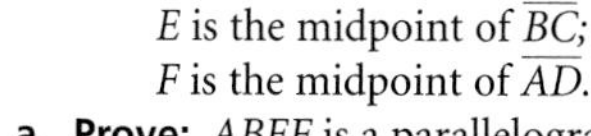

a. Prove: $ABEF$ is a parallelogram. **a. See margin.**

b. What theorem allows you to conclude that $\angle A \cong \angle BEF$? **Opp. angles of a ▱ are ≅.**

c. What theorem allows you to conclude that $\overline{AB} \cong \overline{FE}$? **Opp. sides of a ▱ are ≅.**

30. *Coordinate Geometry* The diagonals of quadrilateral $ABCD$ intersect at $E(-1, 4)$. Two vertices of $ABCD$ are $A(2, 7)$ and $B(-3, 5)$. What must the coordinates of C and D be in order to ensure that $ABCD$ is a parallelogram? **$C(-4, 1)$; $D(1, 3)$**

warp threads
bias
weft threads

31. *Weaving* Fabric is made by weaving threads vertically (the warp) and horizontally (the weft), to form small rectangles. If the fabric is pulled vertically or horizontally, the fabric is rigid; that is, the rectangles keep their shape. **See below.**

a. If the fabric is pulled along its diagonal (the bias), what happens to the weave of the fabric? What figures appear?

b. How does this affect the shape of the fabric? **See below.**

c. *Research* Sail makers have learned techniques to cut sails so that the fabric of the sail will not stretch as the force of the wind hits the sail. Research these techniques and prepare a short report summarizing your findings. **Check students' work.**

a. ∥ threads remain ∥; the small rectangles are replaced with small nonrectangular ▱s.

b. The fabric stretches along one direction of threads and shrinks along the other.

23.

A B E F C D H G

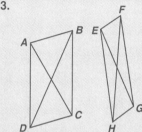

26. Thms. 9-1 and 9-7: A quad. is a ▱ if and only if the opp. sides are ≅. Thms. 9-2 and 9-8: A quad. is a ▱ if and only if the opp. ∠s are ≅. Thms. 9-3 and 9–5: A quad. is a ▱ if and only if the diagonals bisect each other.

27. 1. $\triangle TRS \cong \triangle RTW$ (Given) 2. $\overline{RS} \cong \overline{TW}$; $\overline{ST} \cong \overline{WR}$ (CPCTC) 3. $RSTW$ is a ▱. (If both pairs of opp. sides of a quad. are ≅, then the quad. is a ▱.)

28. 1. $\triangle PKJ \cong \triangle PML$ (Given) 2. $\overline{PK} \cong \overline{PM}$; $\overline{PJ} \cong \overline{PL}$ (CPCTC) 3. $\overline{JL}$ and $\overline{KM}$ bisect each other. (Def. of seg. bisector) 4. $JKLM$ is a ▱. (If the diags. of a quad. bisect each other, then the quad. is a ▱.)

29a. Answers may vary. Sample: 1. E is midpt. of $\overline{BC}$ and F is midpt. of $\overline{AD}$. (Given) 2. $BE = \frac{1}{2}BC$; $AF = \frac{1}{2}AD$ (Def. of midpt.) 3. ▱$ABCD$ (Given) 4. $AD = BC$ (Opp. sides of a ▱ are ≅.) 5. $\frac{1}{2}AD = \frac{1}{2}BC$ (Mult. Prop. of =) 6. $AF = BE$ (Substitution) 7. $\overline{AD} \parallel \overline{BC}$ (Opp. sides of a ▱ are ≅.) 8. $ABEF$ is a ▱. (If 1 pair of opp. sides of a quad. is ≅ and ∥, then the quad. is a ▱.)

Exercises MIXED REVIEW

Exercises 32–35 Students review finding the areas of plane figures.

GETTING READY FOR LESSON 9-3 These exercises prepare students to find properties of special parallelograms.

Wrap Up

THE BIG IDEA Ask students: *If you know that one pair of opposite sides of a quadrilaterals is parallel, what additional information would be sufficient to prove that the quadrilateral is a parallelogram? Give as many answers as possible.*

RETEACHING ACTIVITY Students are given certain characteristics of quadrilaterals to prove that the quadrilaterals are parallelograms. (Reteaching worksheet 9-2)

Exercises CHECKPOINT

In this Checkpoint, your students will assess their own progress in Lessons 9-1 to 9-2.

Exercises 1–6 Students use the properties of parallelograms to find missing angle measures and side lengths.

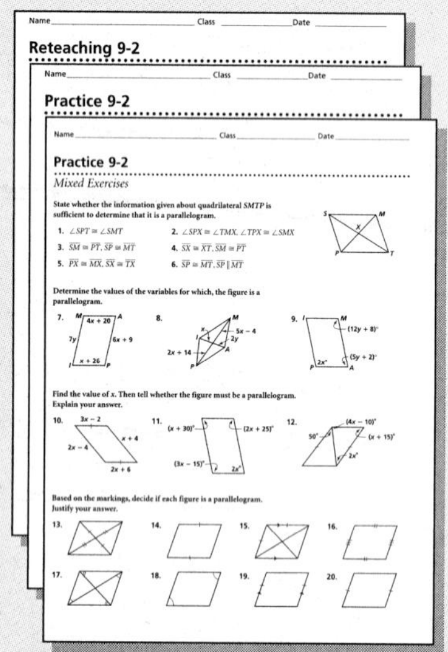
Reteaching 9-2

Practice 9-2

Practice 9-2
Mixed Exercises

Lesson Quiz

Lesson Quiz is also available in Transparencies.

State whether the information given about quadrilateral *EFGH* is sufficient to determine that it is a parallelogram.

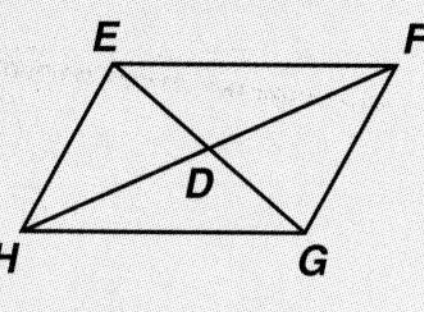

1. $\overline{EF} \parallel \overline{HG}$, $\overline{EH} \parallel \overline{FG}$ **sufficient**
2. $\overline{ED} \cong \overline{DG}$, $\overline{HD} \cong \overline{DF}$ **sufficient**
3. $\angle FEH \cong \angle HGF$, $\angle EHG \cong \angle GFE$ **sufficient**

Determine the values of the variables for which *EFGH* is a parallelogram.

4. $m\angle E = 2x + 20$, $m\angle F = 5y$, $m\angle G = 3x - 25$ **$x = 45$, $y = 14$**

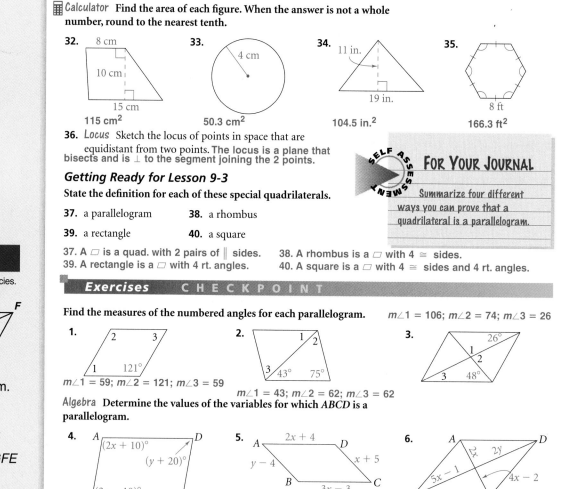

Exercises MIXED REVIEW

Calculator **Find the area of each figure. When the answer is not a whole number, round to the nearest tenth.**

32. 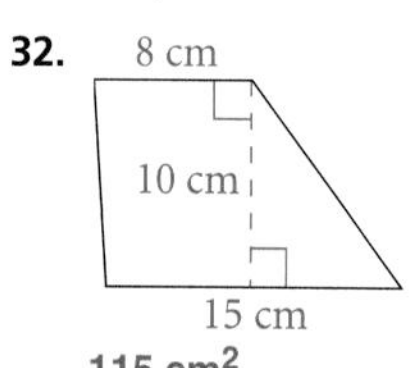

115 cm²

33. 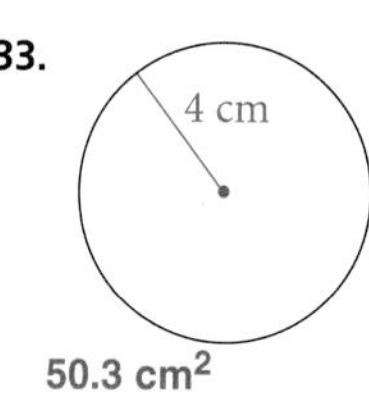

50.3 cm²

34. 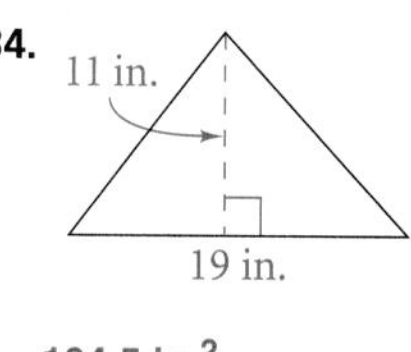

104.5 in.²

35. 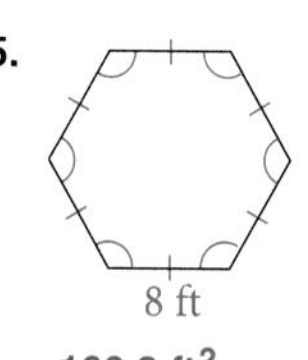

166.3 ft²

36. *Locus* Sketch the locus of points in space that are equidistant from two points. **The locus is a plane that bisects and is ⊥ to the segment joining the 2 points.**

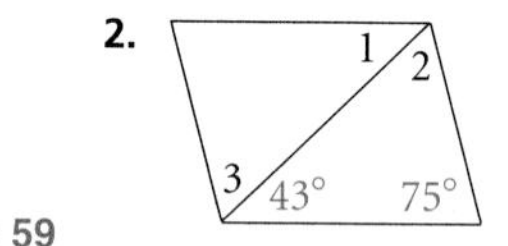

FOR YOUR JOURNAL

Summarize four different ways you can prove that a quadrilateral is a parallelogram.

Getting Ready for Lesson 9-3

State the definition for each of these special quadrilaterals.

37. a parallelogram **38.** a rhombus

39. a rectangle **40.** a square

37. A ▱ is a quad. with 2 pairs of ∥ sides.
38. A rhombus is a ▱ with 4 ≅ sides.
39. A rectangle is a ▱ with 4 rt. angles.
40. A square is a ▱ with 4 ≅ sides and 4 rt. angles.

Exercises CHECKPOINT

Find the measures of the numbered angles for each parallelogram.

1. 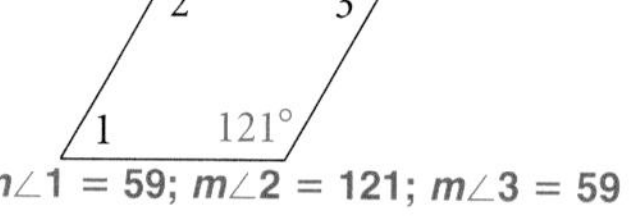

$m\angle 1 = 59$; $m\angle 2 = 121$; $m\angle 3 = 59$

2. 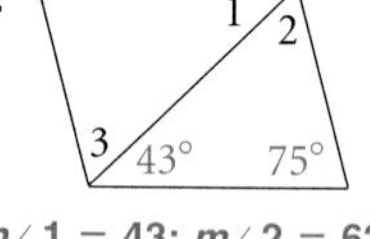

$m\angle 1 = 43$; $m\angle 2 = 62$; $m\angle 3 = 62$

3. 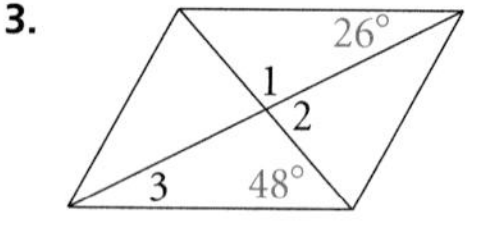

$m\angle 1 = 106$; $m\angle 2 = 74$; $m\angle 3 = 26$

Algebra **Determine the values of the variables for which *ABCD* is a parallelogram.**

4. 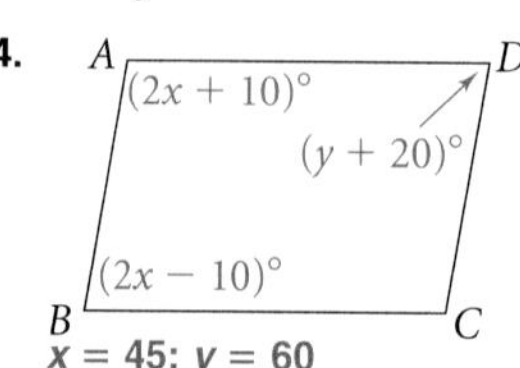

$x = 45$; $y = 60$

5. 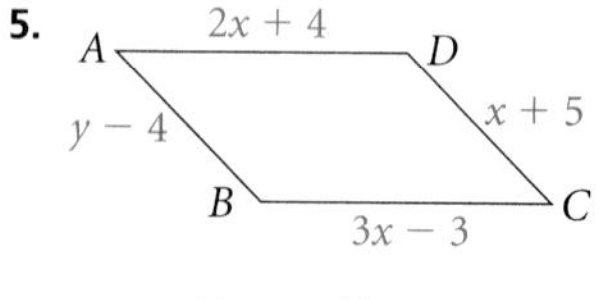

$x = 7$; $y = 16$

6. 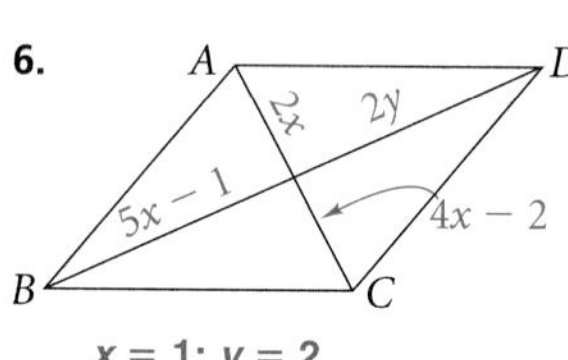

$x = 1$; $y = 2$

7. *Standardized Test Prep* Which is *not* sufficient to prove that a quadrilateral is a parallelogram? **D**

A. The diagonals bisect each other.
B. Both pairs of opposite sides are congruent.
C. Both pairs of opposite angles are congruent.
D. The diagonals are perpendicular.
E. A pair of opposite sides are congruent and parallel.

Math ToolboX

Students explore the properties of the diagonals of rectangles, rhombuses, and squares. These properties will be presented formally in Lesson 9-3.

Using geometry software allows students to construct a parallelogram, to measure segments and angles, and to manipulate the parallelogram making rectangles, rhombuses, and squares.

Investigate

Students should display all the measurements on the screen so they can observe how they change as the shapes of their parallelograms change.

ERROR ALERT! Some students may not understand why the measurements they are asked to make in the Investigate section will help them tell when a parallelogram is a rectangle or a rhombus. **Remediation:** Review the definitions of rectangle (a parallelogram with four right angles) and a rhombus (a parallelogram with four congruent sides).

ADDITIONAL PROBLEMS Have students draw a kite and its diagonals. Then have them investigate the properties of the diagonals. Ask students: *Can the diagonals of a kite be congruent? Can they bisect each other? Can they be perpendicular? Can they bisect the angles of the kite?*

Math ToolboX — Technology

Exploring the Diagonals of Parallelograms

Before Lesson 9-3

Work in pairs or small groups.

Construct
Check students' work.

Use geometry software to construct a parallelogram. First construct segments $\overline{AB}$ and $\overline{BC}$. Construct a line through C parallel to $\overline{AB}$ and a line through A parallel to $\overline{BC}$. Label the point where the two lines intersect as D. Hide the lines and construct $\overline{AD}$ and $\overline{CD}$. Construct the diagonals of parallelogram $ABCD$ and their point of intersection E.

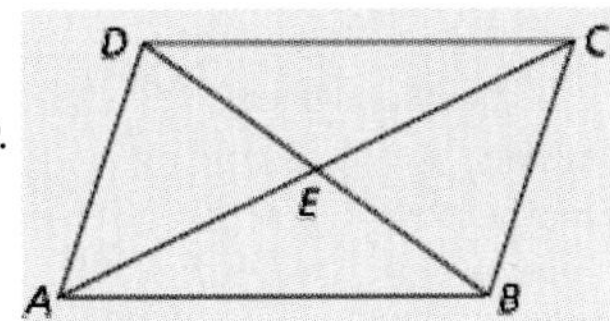

Measure the diagonals of the parallelogram so you can tell when they are congruent. Measure an angle formed by the diagonals so you can tell when the diagonals are perpendicular. Measure the angles formed by the diagonals and the sides of the parallelogram so you can tell when the diagonals bisect the angles of the parallelogram.

Investigate
Answers may vary. Samples are given.

- Measure an angle of the parallelogram so that when you manipulate the figure you can tell when it becomes a rectangle. Make note of any special properties of the diagonals of a rectangle. Manipulate the rectangle to check whether the properties hold. The diagonals are $\cong$.
- Measure two adjacent sides of the parallelogram so you can tell when it is a rhombus. Make note of any special properties of the diagonals of a rhombus. Manipulate the rhombus to check whether the properties hold. The diagonals are perpendicular.

Conjecture
Answers may vary. Samples are given.

- Make as many conjectures as you can about the properties of the diagonals of rectangles and rhombuses. Diags. of a rect. are $\cong$; diags. of a rhombus are $\perp$ bisectors of each other; diags. of a rhombus bisect the $\angle$s of the rhombus.
- Use what you know about squares to make **conjectures** about the diagonals of squares. All the properties of diags. listed above are true for the diags. of squares.

Extend

- Manipulate the diagonals so they are perpendicular. Make a **conjecture** about the type of parallelogram that is determined by perpendicular diagonals. In a ▱, perpendicular diags. determine a rhombus.
- Do the same for congruent diagonals and for diagonals that bisect the angles of the parallelogram. $\cong$ diags. determine a rectangle; diags. that bisect the angles of the ▱ determine a rhombus.

461

9-3 Teaching Notes

PROBLEM OF THE DAY

What is the ratio of the sum of the areas of the two smaller triangles in rectangle *ABCD* to the area of $\triangle DEC$? 1

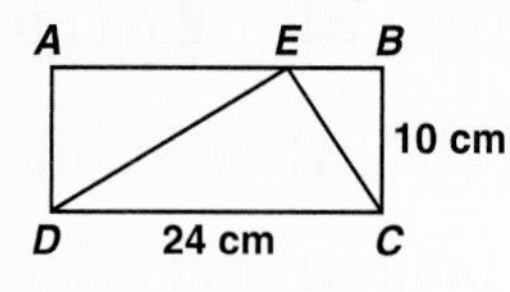

Problem of the Day is also available in Transparencies.

CONNECTING TO PRIOR KNOWLEDGE Copy the Venn diagram from page 93 omitting the labels. Ask students to add the labels: Quadrilaterals, Parallelograms, Rectangles, Squares, Rhombuses, Kites, and Trapezoids. Have them justify the placement of each by giving the definition of the figure.

WORK TOGETHER

Begin by reviewing the definition of each figure. Make sure students accurately draw each on grid paper. You may want to provide a handout with the table shown on page 462.

ERROR ALERT! Some students may check off a property in a category if they can find one example for which it holds. For example, they may check "all sides are ≅" for parallelograms because it is true for some parallelograms. **Remediation:** Make sure students understand that they should check off only properties true for all figures in that category.

Lesson Planning Options

Prerequisite Skills

- Recognizing special quadrilaterals

Assignment Options for Exercises On Your Own

To provide flexible scheduling, this lesson can be subdivided into parts.

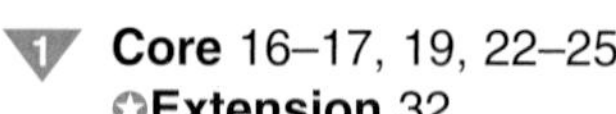

1 **Core** 16–17, 19, 22–25
Extension 32

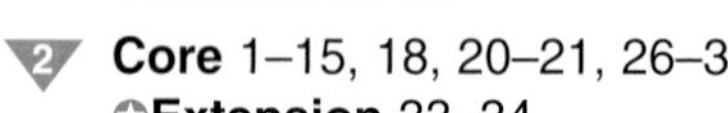

2 **Core** 1–15, 18, 20–21, 26–32
Extension 33–34

Use Mixed Review to maintain skills.

Resources

Student Edition
Skills Handbook, pp. 660, 664, 673
Extra Practice, p. 656
Glossary/Study Guide

Teaching Resources
Chapter Support File, Ch. 9
- Practice 9-3 (two worksheets)
- Reteaching 9-3

Classroom Manager 9-3
Glossary, Spanish Resources

Transparencies
95, 99, 100

Connections

9-3 Properties of Special Parallelograms

What You'll Learn
- Finding properties of rectangles, rhombuses, and squares

...And Why
To help in designing playgrounds and kites

What You'll Need
- centimeter grid paper
- scissors
- protractor
- ruler

WORK TOGETHER

In Lesson 9-1, you explored the properties of parallelograms. Work in a group of three to explore the properties of rhombuses, rectangles, and squares.

- Each member should choose one of these special quadrilaterals and draw a large figure on grid paper.
- Using paper folding or a protractor and ruler, each member should measure and compare the sides, angles, and diagonals of his or her quadrilateral. Then he or she should share the results with the group.
- Use the results to complete a table like the one below. The properties of a parallelogram have been checked off.

Property	Parallelogram	Rhombus	Rectangle	Square
All sides are ≅.		✔		✔
Opposite sides are ≅.	✔	✔	✔	✔
Opposite sides are ∥.	✔	✔	✔	✔
Opposite angles are ≅.	✔	✔	✔	✔
All angles are right ∠s.			✔	✔
Diagonals bisect each other.	✔	✔	✔	✔
Diagonals are ≅.			✔	✔
Diagonals are ⊥.		✔		✔
Each diagonal bisects opposite angles.		✔		✔

THINK AND DISCUSS

Theorem 9-9 Help students see that a diagonal of a rhombus bisects two opposite congruent angles resulting in four congruent angles.

ALTERNATIVE METHOD Question 1 Students can also prove $\triangle ABC \cong \triangle CDA$ by the SAS Postulate. Then $\angle 1 \cong \angle 4$ and $\angle 2 \cong \angle 3$ by CPCTC. Because $\triangle ABC$ and $\triangle CDA$ are isosceles, $\angle 1 \cong \angle 3$ and $\angle 2 \cong \angle 4$. By substitution, $\angle 1 \cong \angle 2$ and $\angle 3 \cong \angle 4$.

Example 1

You may want to begin by discussing a plan for the proof: show $\triangle ABE$ and $\triangle ADE$ are congruent. Then $\angle AEB$ and $\angle AED$ are congruent and supplementary and therefore are right angles.

VISUAL LEARNING Copy *ABCD* and trace $\triangle ABE$ and $\triangle ADE$ in different colors. Mark corresponding sides and angles on the diagram as you read them in the proof.

TACTILE LEARNING Question 3 Have students prove Theorem 9-11 visually. Have them draw a rhombus, draw and label each diagonal d_1 and d_2 with a different color, cut the rhombus along its diagonals, and rearrange the resulting triangles to form a rectangle with base d_1 and height $\frac{d_2}{2}$.

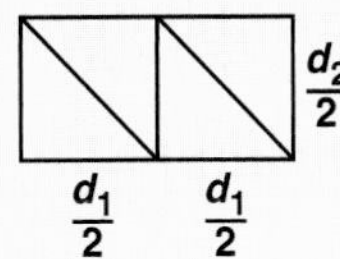

THINK AND DISCUSS

Part 1

Properties of Rhombuses

The properties you discovered in the Work Together are the basis for many of the theorems in this lesson.

Theorem 9-9 Each diagonal of a rhombus bisects two angles of the rhombus.

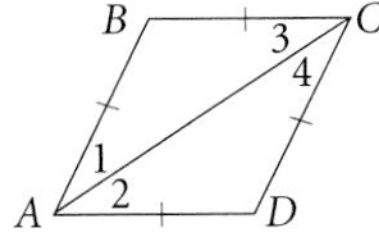

1. Answer the following questions to prove Theorem 9-9.
   a. *ABCD* is a rhombus. Why is $\triangle ABC \cong \triangle ADC$? **SSS or SAS**
   b. What is the relationship between $\angle 1$ and $\angle 2$? between $\angle 3$ and $\angle 4$? Explain. **$\angle 1 \cong \angle 2$; $\angle 3 \cong \angle 4$; CPCTC**
2. **Try This** If $m\angle B = 120$, find the measures of the numbered angles. **30; 30; 30; 30**

Theorem 9-10 The diagonals of a rhombus are perpendicular.

Example 1

Write a paragraph proof of Theorem 9-10.

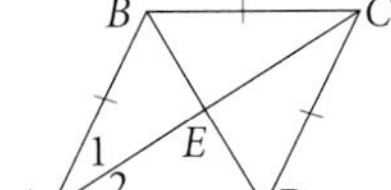

Given: *ABCD* is a rhombus.
Prove: $\overline{AC} \perp \overline{BD}$

Paragraph Proof

By the definition of rhombus, $\overline{AB} \cong \overline{AD}$. Because $\overline{AC}$ is a diagonal of a rhombus, it bisects $\angle BAD$. Therefore $\angle 1 \cong \angle 2$. $\overline{AE} \cong \overline{AE}$ by the Reflexive Property of Congruence. By the SAS Postulate, $\triangle ABE \cong \triangle ADE$. By CPCTC, $\angle AEB \cong \angle AED$. Because $\angle AEB$ and $\angle AED$ are both congruent and supplementary, they are right angles. By the definition of perpendicular, $\overline{AC} \perp \overline{BD}$.

In Chapter 5, you found the area of a rhombus by using the formula for the area of a parallelogram, $A = bh$. Using Theorems 9-9 and 9-10, you can find another formula for the area of a rhombus. You will derive this formula in Exercise 17.

Theorem 9-11 The area of a rhombus is equal to half the product of the lengths of its diagonals.

$$A = \frac{1}{2}d_1d_2$$

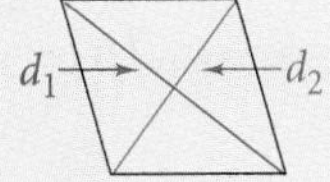

3. **Critical Thinking** Explain why you can use the area formula $A = \frac{1}{2}d_1d_2$ to find the area of a square. **A square is a rhombus.**

Additional Examples

FOR EXAMPLE 1

Write a two-column proof of Theorem 9-10. **See back of book.**

Discussion: *Are the diagonals of a square perpendicular? Explain.*

FOR EXAMPLE 2

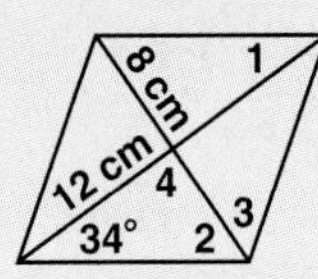

a. Find the measures of the numbered angles of the rhombus. **$m\angle 1 = 34$, $m\angle 2 = 56$, $m\angle 3 = 56$, $m\angle 4 = 90$**

b. Find the area of the rhombus. **192 cm^2**

Discussion: *Explain why the four non-overlapping triangles formed by the diagonals of a rhombus are congruent.*

FOR EXAMPLE 3

Refer to the diagram in Example 3. If the students use two 26-ft long pieces of rope as diagonals, find the possible dimensions of the rectangle they form. **Answers may vary. Sample: 10 ft by 24 ft**

Discussion: *Explain how you can use properties of a parallelogram and a rhombus to stake out a rhombus-shaped garden.*

Example 2

ERROR ALERT! Some students will calculate the area of a rhombus as $\frac{1}{2}d_1 \cdot \frac{1}{2}d_2$, especially when those are the values given on the diagram. **Remediation:** Have students draw rhombuses on grid paper, measuring the diagonals and calculating their areas using $\frac{1}{2}d_1 \cdot d_2$. They can use the squares on the grid paper to estimate the area and check that their answers are reasonable.

Theorem 9-12 Students sometimes think that because the sides of a rhombus are congruent its diagonals must be congruent. Draw or have students draw several counterexamples.

ALTERNATIVE ASSESSMENT **Question 4** You can assess students' understanding of Theorem 9-12 by having them use Question 4 to help them write a two-column proof, a flow proof, or a paragraph proof for the theorem. Have students work in groups where each group presents its proof to the class.

In Theorems 9-13, 9-14, and 9-15, point out that each hypothesis contains two conditions, the first in each being that the figure is a parallelogram.

CRITICAL THINKING Ask students to list all the ways they can prove that a quadrilateral is a rectangle or a rhombus.

Technology Options

For Exercise 10, student may draw the rectangles using geometry software or a drawing program. For Exercise 16, students may use geometry software to draw the quadrilateral using reflections.

Prentice Hall Technology

Software
- Secondary Math Lab Toolkit™
- Computer Item Generator 9-3

CD-ROM
- Multimedia Geometry Lab 9

Internet
- See the Prentice Hall site. (http://www.phschool.com)

Example 2

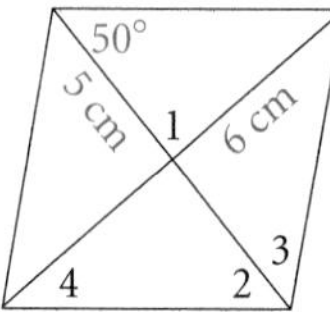

a. Find the measures of the numbered angles in the rhombus.
b. Find the area of the rhombus.

a. $m\angle 1 = 90$ — Diagonals of a rhombus are perpendicular.
$m\angle 2 = 50$ — If ∥ lines, then alt. int. ∠s are ≅.
$m\angle 3 = 50$ — Each diagonal of a rhombus bisects two angles.
$m\angle 4 = 40$ — Acute angles of a right △ are complementary.

b. $d_1 = 2(6) = 12$ — Diagonals of a parallelogram bisect each other.
$d_2 = 2(5) = 10$
$A = \frac{1}{2}d_1d_2$ — Formula for the area of a rhombus
$= \frac{1}{2}(12)(10)$ — Substitute the lengths of the diagonals.
$= 60$ — Simplify.

The area of the rhombus is 60 cm^2.

PROBLEM SOLVING

Look Back Explain how you could use triangles to find the area of the rhombus.

The diagonals divide the rhombus into 4 ≅ △s. Find the area of each △. Then multiply by 4 to get the area of the rhombus.

Part 2

Properties of Rectangles and Parallelograms

In the Work Together on page 462, you probably discovered the following properties of rectangles and parallelograms.

Theorem 9-12 The diagonals of a rectangle are congruent.

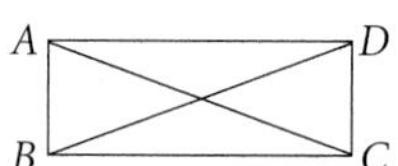

4. Answer the following questions to prove Theorem 9-12.
   a. *ABCD* is a rectangle. What parts of △*ABC* and △*DCB* must be congruent? Explain. See margin p. 465.
   b. Why is △*ABC* ≅ △*DCB*?
   c. Why is $\overline{AC} \cong \overline{BD}$? CPCTC
   b. SAS

The following theorems are suggested by the converses of Theorems 9-9, 9-10, and 9-12. You will write proofs of these theorems in the exercises.

Theorem 9-13 If one diagonal of a parallelogram bisects two angles of the parallelogram, then the parallelogram is a rhombus.

Theorem 9-14 If the diagonals of a parallelogram are perpendicular, then the parallelogram is a rhombus.

Theorem 9-15 If the diagonals of a parallelogram are congruent, then the parallelogram is a rectangle.

5. *Logical Reasoning* Suppose the diagonals of a parallelogram are both perpendicular and congruent. What type of special quadrilateral is it? Explain your reasoning. See margin p. 465.

Example 3 Relating to the Real World 

Refer to the diagram. Discuss how to change the positions of the students to make the play area longer or wider. Make sure students see that the ropes do not need to be perpendicular in order to be the diagonals of a rectangle.

OPEN-ENDED Question 6 This question has more than one answer. Help students see that two consecutive sides of the rectangle and one piece of rope form a right triangle.

DIVERSITY Ask students to share any experiences they have had participating in community service projects. Identify organizations in your area that are looking for volunteers. Help students become aware of the opportunities that exist for students to make meaningful contributions to the community.

Exercises ON YOUR OWN

CRITICAL THINKING Exercises 2–4 Ask students to explain why the figures in Exercises 2 and 3 are rectangles and why the figure in Exercise 4 is a rhombus.

CONNECTING TO STUDENTS' WORLD Exercise 5 Have students investigate the construction of different types of furniture in their homes. Have them sketch different pieces of furniture and describe their geometric properties.

Builders and construction workers use the properties of diagonals to "square off" rectangular foundations and other rectangular constructions.

Example 3 Relating to the Real World 

Community Service Volunteers are helping to build a rectangular play area in a city park. Explain how they can use properties of the diagonals of a parallelogram and a rectangle to stake the vertices of the play area.

The volunteers can use these two theorems to design the play area:

- Theorem 9-5: If the diagonals of a quadrilateral bisect each other, then the quadrilateral is a parallelogram.
- Theorem 9-15: If the diagonals of a parallelogram are congruent, then the parallelogram is a rectangle.

First, cut two pieces of rope of equal length for the diagonals. Then, fold each piece to find the midpoint of each diagonal. Next, position the ropes so that the ropes intersect at the midpoints. Any quadrilateral formed by connecting the endpoints of the two ropes will be a rectangle.

6. *Open-ended* The volunteers use two 20-ft-long pieces of rope as diagonals. Describe possible dimensions of the rectangle they can form. **Answers may vary. Sample: 12 ft by 16 ft**
7. *Critical Thinking* Steven thinks that they can use this same method to stake off a square. Is he right? Explain why or why not. **Yes; if the ropes are ⊥ to each other, the endpoints of the rope determine a square.**

pages 463–465 Think and Discuss

4a. $\overline{AB} \cong \overline{DC}$, opp. sides of ▱ are ≅; $\overline{BC} \cong \overline{BC}$, Reflexive Prop. of ≅; $\angle ABC \cong \angle DCB$, all rt. ∠s are ≅.

5. Square; the diagonals are ⊥, so the ▱ is a rhombus. The diagonals are ≅, so the ▱ is a rectangle. A ▱ that is both a rectangle and a rhombus is a square.

Exercises ON YOUR OWN

For each parallelogram (a) choose the best name and then (b) find the measures of the numbered angles.

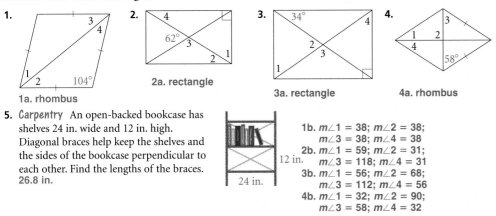

1. 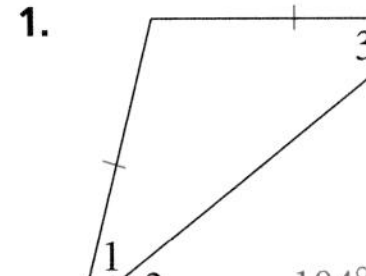

1a. rhombus

2. 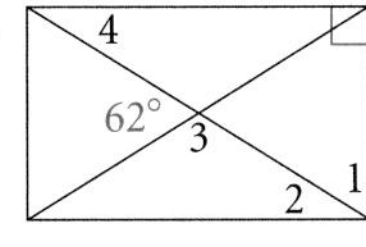

2a. rectangle

3. 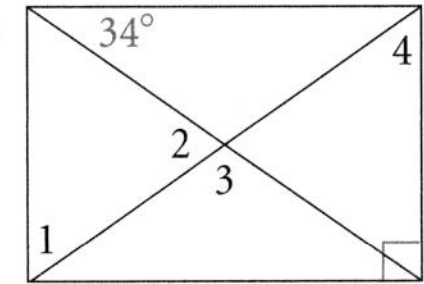

3a. rectangle

4. 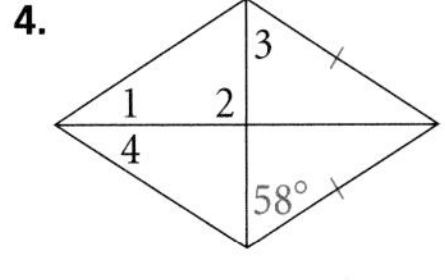

4a. rhombus

5. *Carpentry* An open-backed bookcase has shelves 24 in. wide and 12 in. high. Diagonal braces help keep the shelves and the sides of the bookcase perpendicular to each other. Find the lengths of the braces. **26.8 in.**

1b. $m\angle 1 = 38$; $m\angle 2 = 38$; $m\angle 3 = 38$; $m\angle 4 = 38$
2b. $m\angle 1 = 59$; $m\angle 2 = 31$; $m\angle 3 = 118$; $m\angle 4 = 31$
3b. $m\angle 1 = 56$; $m\angle 2 = 68$; $m\angle 3 = 112$; $m\angle 4 = 56$
4b. $m\angle 1 = 32$; $m\angle 2 = 90$; $m\angle 3 = 58$; $m\angle 4 = 32$

Exercises 6–9 Students use the properties of special parallelograms and the Pythagorean Theorem to find missing side lengths.

OPEN-ENDED Exercise 10 Make sure students understand that the diagonals of one of the rectangles should be congruent to the diagonals of the other.

STANDARDIZED TEST TIP Exercise 11 Suggest students draw *RSTW* and label congruent sides and angles.

TRANSFORMATIONS Exercise 16 Students draw a segment and use reflections to create a rhombus.

Exercise 17 Students prove Theorem 9-11.

pages 465–468 On Your Own

18. Opp. sides of a square are ≅ and ∥; all angles are rt. angles; the 4 sides are ≅; the diagonals are ⊥ bisectors of each other; the diagonals are ≅; each diagonal bisects 2 angles of the square; the area = half the product of the lengths of the diagonals or = the square of the length of each side.
20. Yes; $7^2 + 24^2 = 25^2$, so △*RST* is a rt. △. ∠*S* is a rt. angle, and it follows that ∠*R*, ∠*T*, and ∠*W* are also rt. angles. Therefore, ▱*RSTW* is a rectangle.
21. Yes; $2.5^2 + 6^2 = 6.5^2$, so the diagonals divide the ▱ into 4 rt. △s. Since the diagonals are ⊥, ▱*JKLM* is a rhombus.
26. Yes; since all rt. ∠s are ≅, the opp. angles are ≅, and the quad. is a ▱. A ▱ with all rt. ∠s is a rectangle.
27. Yes; 4 sides are ≅, so the opp. sides are ≅, and the quad. is a ▱. A ▱ with all sides ≅ is a rhombus.
28. Yes; a quad. with 4 ≅ sides is a ▱, and a ▱ with 4 ≅ sides and 4 rt. angles is a square.

466

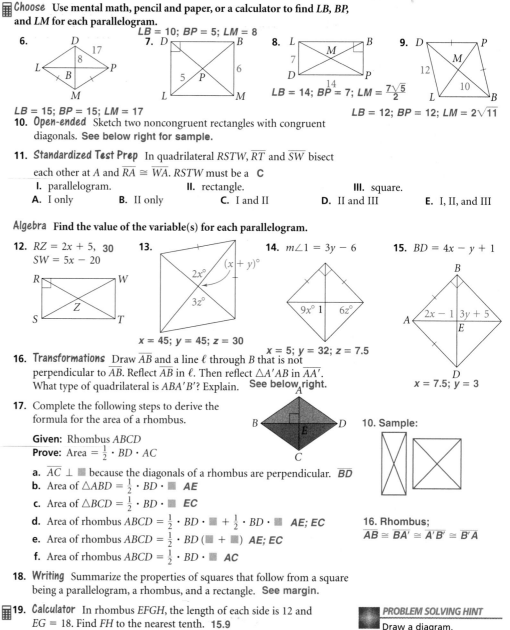

Choose Use mental math, pencil and paper, or a calculator to find *LB*, *BP*, and *LM* for each parallelogram.

6. 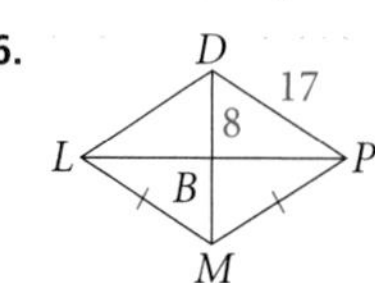

LB = 15; BP = 15; LM = 17

7. 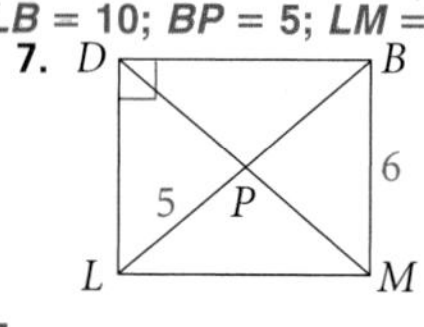

LB = 10; BP = 5; LM = 8

8. 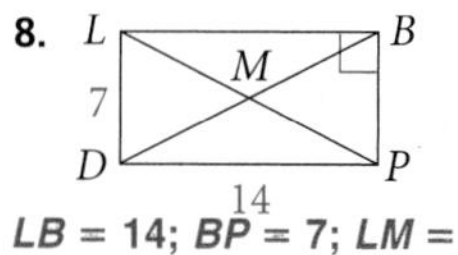

LB = 14; BP = 7; $LM = \frac{7\sqrt{5}}{2}$

9. 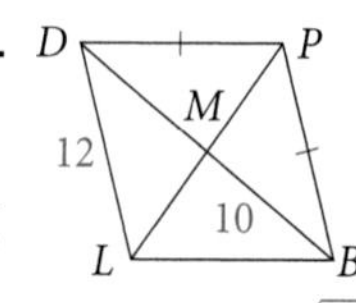

LB = 12; BP = 12; $LM = 2\sqrt{11}$

10. **Open-ended** Sketch two noncongruent rectangles with congruent diagonals. **See below right for sample.**

11. **Standardized Test Prep** In quadrilateral *RSTW*, $\overline{RT}$ and $\overline{SW}$ bisect each other at *A* and $\overline{RA} \cong \overline{WA}$. *RSTW* must be a **C**
    I. parallelogram. II. rectangle. III. square.
    A. I only **B.** II only **C.** I and II **D.** II and III **E.** I, II, and III

Algebra Find the value of the variable(s) for each parallelogram.

12. $RZ = 2x + 5$, $SW = 5x - 20$ **30**

13. **x = 45; y = 45; z = 30**

14. $m\angle 1 = 3y - 6$

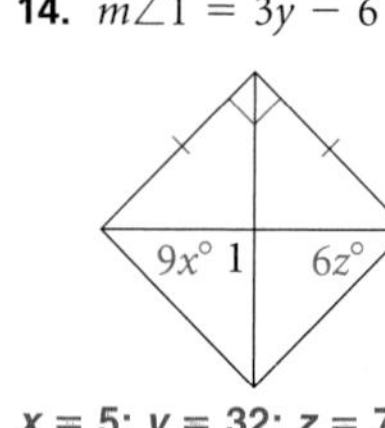

x = 5; y = 32; z = 7.5

15. $BD = 4x - y + 1$

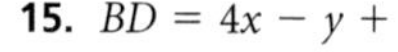
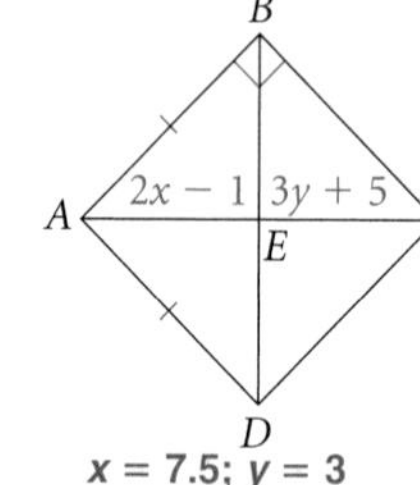

x = 7.5; y = 3

16. **Transformations** Draw $\overline{AB}$ and a line ℓ through *B* that is not perpendicular to $\overline{AB}$. Reflect $\overline{AB}$ in ℓ. Then reflect △*A′AB* in $\overline{AA'}$. What type of quadrilateral is *ABA′B′*? Explain. **See below right.**

17. Complete the following steps to derive the formula for the area of a rhombus.

    Given: Rhombus *ABCD*
    Prove: Area $= \frac{1}{2} \cdot BD \cdot AC$

    a. $\overline{AC} \perp$ ■ because the diagonals of a rhombus are perpendicular. $\overline{BD}$
    b. Area of △*ABD* $= \frac{1}{2} \cdot BD \cdot$ ■ **AE**
    c. Area of △*BCD* $= \frac{1}{2} \cdot BD \cdot$ ■ **EC**
    d. Area of rhombus *ABCD* $= \frac{1}{2} \cdot BD \cdot$ ■ $+ \frac{1}{2} \cdot BD \cdot$ ■ **AE; EC**
    e. Area of rhombus *ABCD* $= \frac{1}{2} \cdot BD\,($■ + ■$)$ **AE; EC**
    f. Area of rhombus *ABCD* $= \frac{1}{2} \cdot BD \cdot$ ■ **AC**

18. **Writing** Summarize the properties of squares that follow from a square being a parallelogram, a rhombus, and a rectangle. **See margin.**

19. **Calculator** In rhombus *EFGH*, the length of each side is 12 and *EG* = 18. Find *FH* to the nearest tenth. **15.9**

10. Sample:

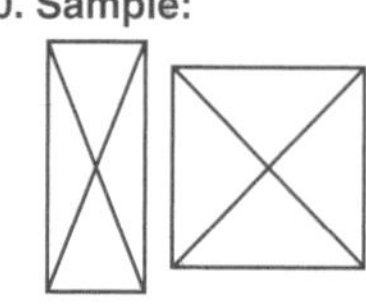

16. Rhombus; $\overline{AB} \cong \overline{BA'} \cong \overline{A'B'} \cong \overline{B'A}$

PROBLEM SOLVING HINT
Draw a diagram.

Exercises 22–25 Students find the lengths of the diagonals in order to find the area of each rhombus.

LOGICAL REASONING Exercises 26–28 Make sure students justify why the definitions imply these quadrilaterals are parallelograms.

AUDITORY LEARNING Exercises 29–31 After students complete these proofs, have them work in pairs, taking turns presenting their proofs to each other.

Exercise 31 This proof is more challenging. Students may want to work in groups to write a plan for the proof. One strategy is to show two consecutive angles are congruent and supplementary.

ESL Exercise 32 Students may not understand the phrase "car jack," which refers to the instrument used to raise one end of a car. The picture shows one type of car jack. Students may confuse "car jack" with "car jacking," which means stealing a car. Relate "car jack" to phrases such as "jack up the price."

20. In ▱$RSTW$, $RS = 7$, $ST = 24$, and $RT = 25$. Is $RSTW$ a rectangle? Explain.
20–21. See margin p. 466.

21. In ▱$JKLM$, $JL = 5$, $KM = 12$, and $JM = 6.5$. Is $JKLM$ a rhombus? Explain.

Find the area of each rhombus.

22.

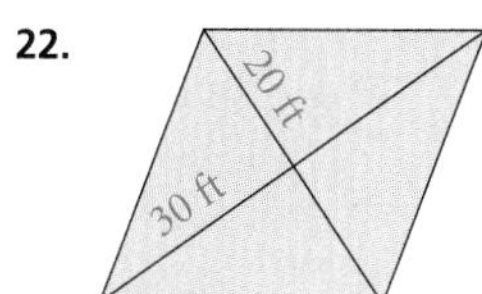

1200 ft²

23.

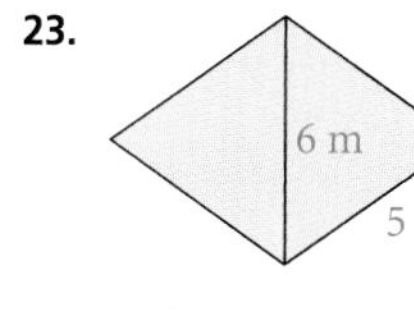

24 m²

24.

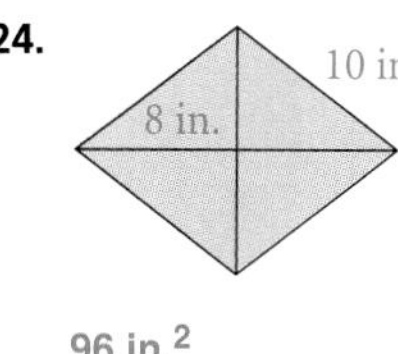

96 in.²

25.

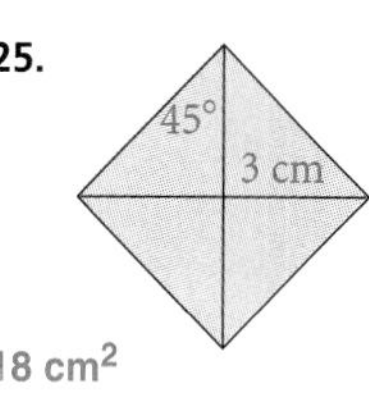

18 cm²

Logical Reasoning **Decide whether each of these is a good definition. Justify your answer.** 26–28. See margin p. 466 for reasoning.

26. A rectangle is a quadrilateral with four right angles. yes

27. A rhombus is a quadrilateral with four congruent sides. yes

28. A square is a quadrilateral with four right angles and four congruent sides. yes

Choose **Write a two-column proof, a paragraph proof, or a flow proof.**

29. Theorem 9-13: If one diagonal of a parallelogram bisects two angles of the parallelogram, then the parallelogram is a rhombus.

Given: ▱$ABCD$; $\overline{AC}$ bisects $\angle BAD$ and $\angle BCD$. 29–31. Answers may vary. See margin for samples.
Prove: $ABCD$ is a rhombus.

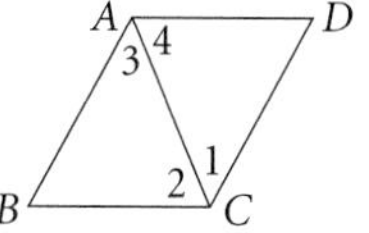

30. Theorem 9-14: If the diagonals of a parallelogram are perpendicular, then the parallelogram is a rhombus.

Given: ▱$ABCD$; $\overline{AC} \perp \overline{BD}$
Prove: $ABCD$ is a rhombus.

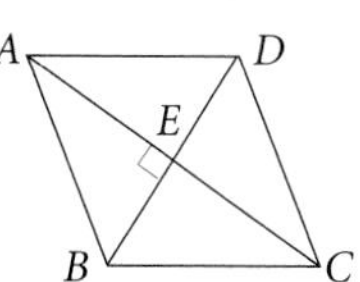

31. Theorem 9-15: If the diagonals of a parallelogram are congruent, then the parallelogram is a rectangle.

Given: ▱$ABCD$; $\overline{AC} \cong \overline{BD}$
Prove: $ABCD$ is a rectangle.

A, D, E, B, C

32. *Auto Repair* A car jack is shaped like a rhombus. As two of the opposite vertices get closer together, the other two opposite vertices get farther apart. The sides of a car jack are 17 cm long. When the horizontal distance between the vertices is 30 cm, what is the vertical distance between the other two vertices? 16 cm

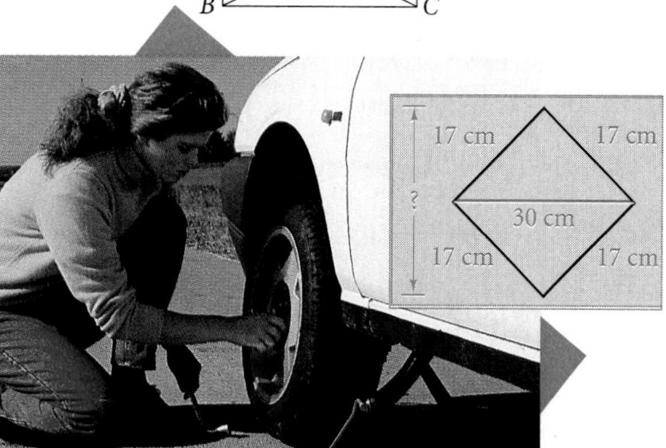

29. 1. $\overline{AC} \cong \overline{AC}$ (Reflexive Prop. of ≅) 2. $\overline{AC}$ bisects $\angle BAD$ and $\angle BCD$. (Given) 3. $\angle 1 \cong \angle 2$; $\angle 3 \cong \angle 4$ (Def. of angle bisector) 4. $\triangle ABC \cong \triangle ADC$ (ASA) 5. $\overline{AB} \cong \overline{DA}$; $\overline{BC} \cong \overline{CD}$ (CPCTC) 6. ▱$ABCD$ (Given) 7. $\overline{AB} \cong \overline{CD}$; $\overline{BC} \cong \overline{DA}$ (Opp. sides of a ▱ are ≅.) 8. $\overline{AB} \cong \overline{BC} \cong \overline{CD} \cong \overline{DA}$ (Transitive Prop. of ≅) 9. $ABCD$ is a rhombus. (Def. of rhombus)

30. 1. ▱$ABCD$ (Given) 2. $\overline{AE} \cong \overline{CE}$; $\overline{BE} \cong \overline{DE}$ (Diags. of a ▱ bisect each other.) 3. $\overline{AC} \perp \overline{BD}$ (Given) 4. $\angle AEB$, $\angle BEC$, $\angle CED$, and $\angle DEA$ are rt. angles. (⊥ lines form 4 rt. angles.) 5. $\angle AEB \cong \angle BEC \cong \angle CED \cong \angle AED$ (All rt. angles are ≅.) 6. $\triangle AEB \cong \triangle CEB \cong \triangle AED \cong \triangle CED$ (SAS) 7. $\overline{AB} \cong \overline{BC} \cong \overline{CD} \cong \overline{DA}$ (CPCTC) 8. $ABCD$ is a rhombus. (Def. of a rhombus)

31. In ▱$ABCD$, $\overline{AB} \cong \overline{DC}$ because opp. sides of a ▱ are ≅. $\overline{AD} \cong \overline{AD}$ by the Reflexive Prop. of ≅. Since $\overline{AC} \cong \overline{BD}$, $\triangle BAD \cong \triangle CDA$ by SSS and $\angle BAD \cong \angle CDA$ by CPCTC. $\angle BAD$ and $\angle CDA$ are consecutive angles of a ▱, so they are supplementary. Therefore, both angles are rt. ∠s and the angles opp. them are rt. ∠s . So ▱$ABCD$ is a rectangle by def.

Exercises 33–34 Make sure students understand that these proofs depend on the quadrilateral's being a parallelogram. Have students show that a quadrilateral with one right angle is not always a rectangle, and a quadrilateral with two consecutive congruent sides is not always a rhombus.

Chapter Project **FIND OUT BY ANALYZING** Make sure students understand *effective area.* If possible, use a box to demonstrate. Also explain to students that a *rhomboid* is a parallelogram with noncongruent adjacent sides.

Exercises MIXED REVIEW

GETTING READY FOR LESSON 9-4 These exercises prepare students to find properties of trapezoids and kites.

Wrap Up

THE BIG IDEA Ask students: *Describe the properties that a rectangle and rhombus have in common. What properties does a rectangle have that a rhombus does not? What properties does a rhombus have that a rectangle does not?*

RETEACHING ACTIVITY Students use the properties of rectangles, rhombuses, and squares to find missing angle measures. (Reteaching worksheet 9-3)

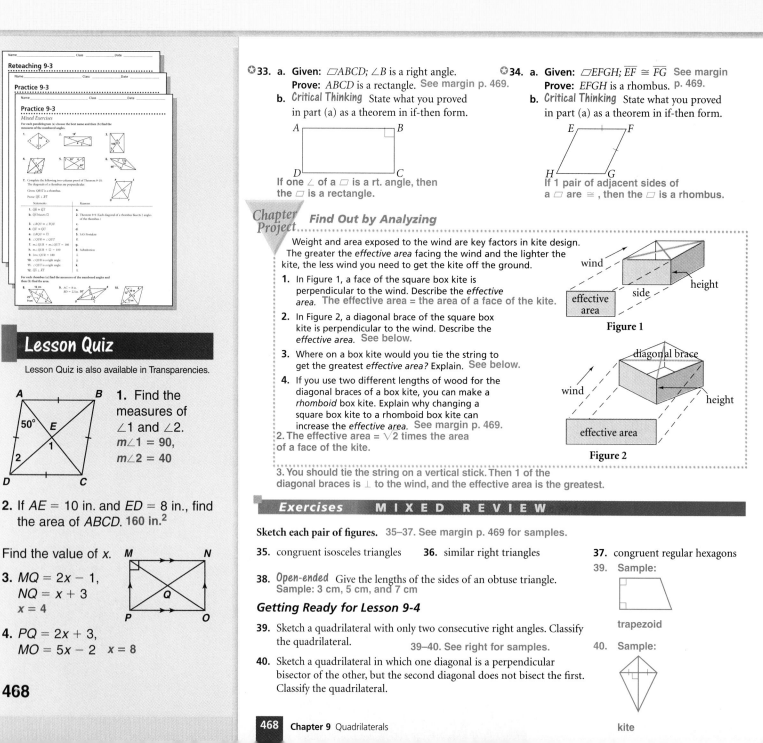

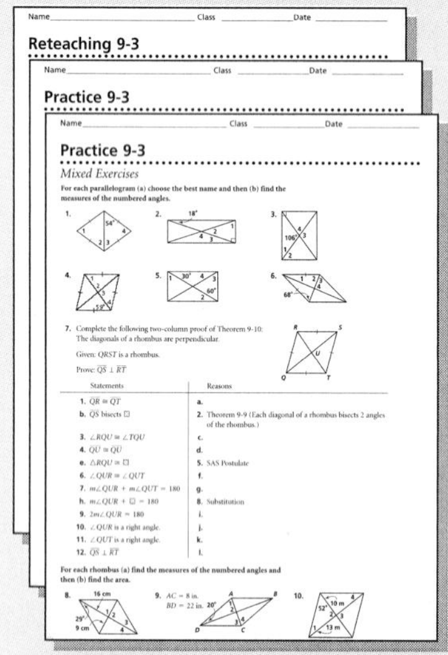

Lesson Quiz

Lesson Quiz is also available in Transparencies.

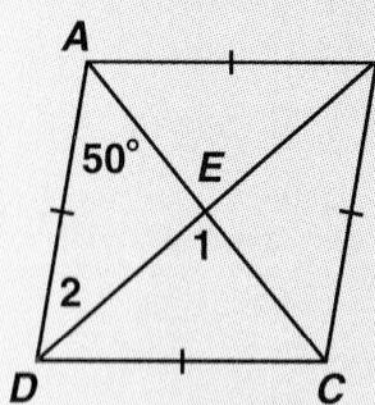

1. Find the measures of $\angle 1$ and $\angle 2$. $m\angle 1 = 90$, $m\angle 2 = 40$
2. If $AE = 10$ in. and $ED = 8$ in., find the area of $ABCD$. 160 in.^{2}

Find the value of *x*.

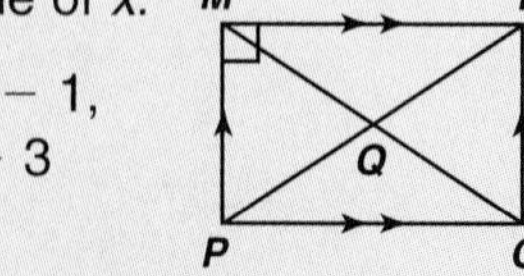

3. $MQ = 2x - 1$, $NQ = x + 3$ $x = 4$
4. $PQ = 2x + 3$, $MO = 5x - 2$ $x = 8$

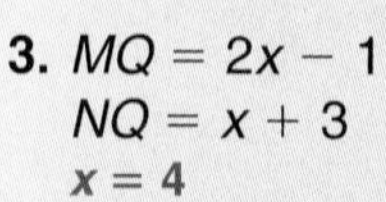

33. a. **Given:** ▱$ABCD$; $\angle B$ is a right angle.
Prove: $ABCD$ is a rectangle. See margin p. 469.
b. **Critical Thinking** State what you proved in part (a) as a theorem in if-then form.

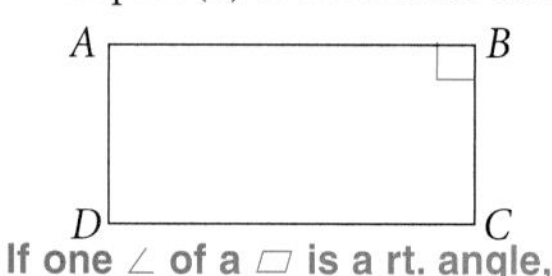

If one ∠ of a ▱ is a rt. angle, then the ▱ is a rectangle.

34. a. **Given:** ▱$EFGH$; $\overline{EF} \cong \overline{FG}$ See margin p. 469.
Prove: $EFGH$ is a rhombus.
b. **Critical Thinking** State what you proved in part (a) as a theorem in if-then form.

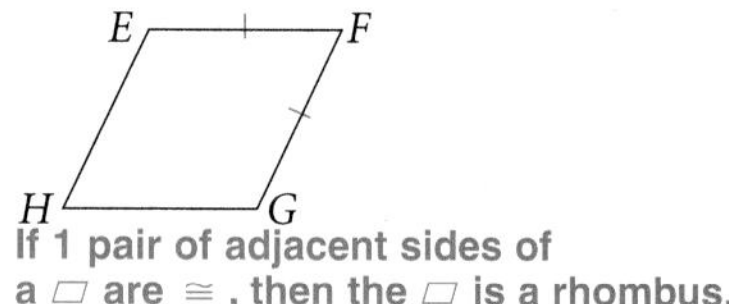

If 1 pair of adjacent sides of a ▱ are ≅, then the ▱ is a rhombus.

Chapter Project: Find Out by Analyzing

Weight and area exposed to the wind are key factors in kite design. The greater the *effective area* facing the wind and the lighter the kite, the less wind you need to get the kite off the ground.

1. In Figure 1, a face of the square box kite is perpendicular to the wind. Describe the *effective area.* The effective area = the area of a face of the kite.
2. In Figure 2, a diagonal brace of the square box kite is perpendicular to the wind. Describe the *effective area.* See below.
3. Where on a box kite would you tie the string to get the greatest *effective area?* Explain. See below.
4. If you use two different lengths of wood for the diagonal braces of a box kite, you can make a *rhomboid* box kite. Explain why changing a square box kite to a rhomboid box kite can increase the *effective area.* See margin p. 469.

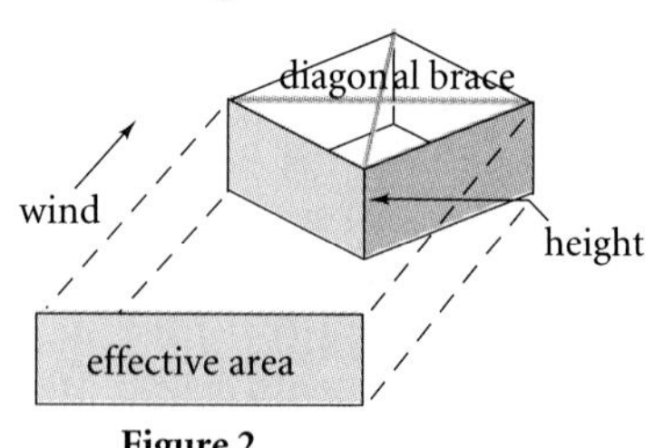

2. The effective area = $\sqrt{2}$ times the area of a face of the kite.

3. You should tie the string on a vertical stick. Then 1 of the diagonal braces is ⊥ to the wind, and the effective area is the greatest.

Exercises MIXED REVIEW

Sketch each pair of figures. 35–37. See margin p. 469 for samples.

35. congruent isosceles triangles
36. similar right triangles
37. congruent regular hexagons
38. **Open-ended** Give the lengths of the sides of an obtuse triangle. Sample: 3 cm, 5 cm, and 7 cm

Getting Ready for Lesson 9-4

39. Sketch a quadrilateral with only two consecutive right angles. Classify the quadrilateral.
40. Sketch a quadrilateral in which one diagonal is a perpendicular bisector of the other, but the second diagonal does not bisect the first. Classify the quadrilateral.

39–40. See right for samples.

39. Sample:

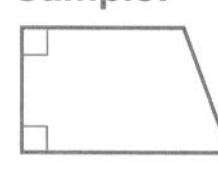

trapezoid

40. Sample:

kite

Math ToolboX

Students connect midpoints of a quadrilateral to form another quadrilateral. Then they manipulate the original quadrilateral and make conjectures about the quadrilateral formed by connecting the midpoints. Students will prove that the quadrilateral is a parallelogram in Lesson 9-5.

The software allows students to manipulate the original quadrilateral while maintaining the vertices of the second quadrilateral at the midpoints.

Conjecture

Suggest that students manipulate *ABCD* so that it is a square, rectangle, rhombus, parallelogram, trapezoid, kite, and a non-convex quadrilateral. Suggest they make a list or a table describing the shapes of *ABCD* and *EFGH*.

ERROR ALERT! Students may not remember the difference between convex and non-convex polygons. **Remediation:** Draw examples of each and have students identify them.

ADDITIONAL PROBLEM Ask students to classify the quadrilaterals formed when connecting the midpoints of the sides of a square, a rhombus, a rectangle, and an isosceles trapezoid.

Math ToolboX — Technology

Exploring Quadrilaterals within Quadrilaterals

Before Lesson 9-4

Work in pairs or small groups.

Construct

Use geometry software to construct a quadrilateral *ABCD*. Construct the midpoint of each side of *ABCD*. Construct segments joining the adjacent midpoints to form quadrilateral *EFGH*. Check students' work.

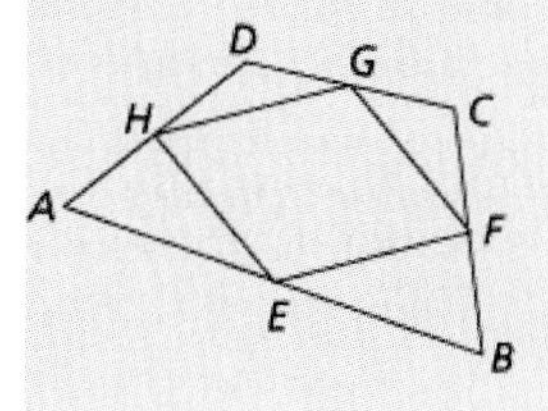

Investigate

Measure the lengths of the sides of *EFGH* and their slopes. Measure the angles of *EFGH*. What kind of quadrilateral does *EFGH* appear to be? parallelogram

Conjecture

Manipulate quadrilateral *ABCD* and make a conjecture about the quadrilateral whose vertices are the midpoints of a quadrilateral. Does your conjecture hold when *ABCD* is convex? Can you manipulate *ABCD* so that your conjecture doesn't hold? The quad. whose vertices are midpts. of another quad. is a ▱; yes; no.

Extend

- Draw the diagonals of *ABCD*. Describe *EFGH* when the diagonals are perpendicular and when they are congruent. rectangle; rhombus
- Construct the midpoints of *EFGH* and use them to construct quadrilateral *IJKL*. Construct the midpoints of *IJKL* and use them to construct quadrilateral *MNOP*. Compare the ratios of the lengths of the sides, perimeters, and areas of *MNOP* and *EFGH*. How are *MNOP* and *EFGH* related? The ratio of lengths of sides and perimeters is $\frac{1}{2}$; the ratio of areas is $\frac{1}{4}$; $MNOP \sim FGHE$.

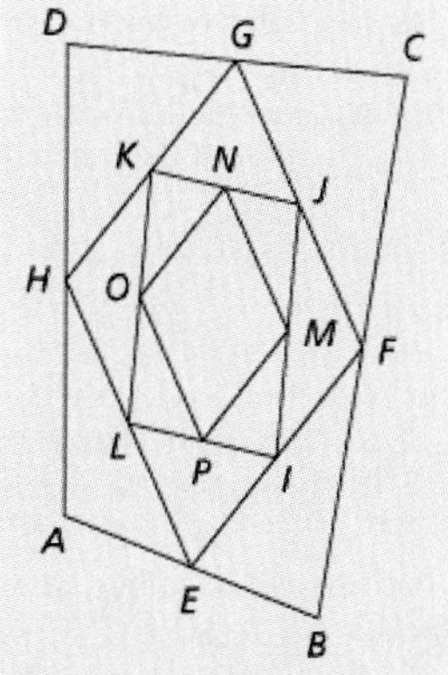

33a. Since *ABCD* is a ▱, opp. ∠s are ≅. So $\angle B \cong \angle D$, therefore ∠*D* is a rt. angle. In a ▱, consecutive ∠s are supplementary. Therefore, ∠*A* and ∠*C* are each supplementary to ∠*B*. The supplement of a rt. angle is a rt. angle, so ∠*A* and ∠*C* are rt. ∠s. Therefore, *ABCD* is a rectangle by def.

34a. 1. ▱*EFGH* (Given) 2. $\overline{EF} \cong \overline{HG}$; $\overline{FG} \cong \overline{HE}$ (Opp. sides of a ▱ are ≅.) 3. $\overline{EF} \cong \overline{FG}$ (Given) 4. $\overline{EF} \cong \overline{HG} \cong \overline{FG} \cong \overline{HE}$ (Transitive Prop. of ≅) 5. *EFGH* is a rhombus. (Def. of rhombus)

Find Out by Analyzing

4. The greatest effective area is proportional to the length of the longer diagonal. If the faces of the kite are unchanged, then 1 diagonal of the rhombus is longer and 1 is shorter than the diagonals of the square.

page 468 Mixed Review

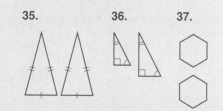

35. 36. 37.

469

9-4 Teaching Notes

PROBLEM OF THE DAY

ABCD is a rectangle. ⊙*C* has radius 10 cm. Find *BD*. *BD* = 10 cm

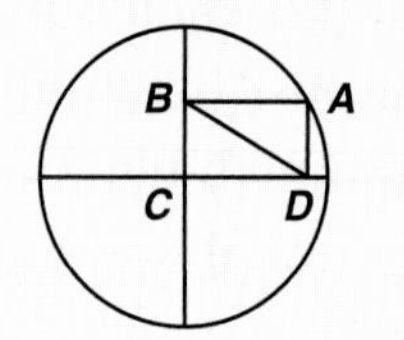

Problem of the Day is also available in Transparencies.

CONNECTING TO PRIOR KNOWLEDGE Draw the following figures. Have students name them and describe how they are alike and how they are different.

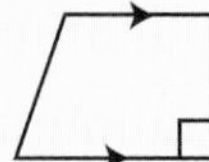
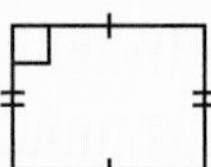
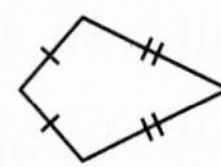

WORK TOGETHER

Students use paper folding and cutting to make an isosceles trapezoid. Help students see that the fold line is a line of symmetry of the isosceles trapezoid. Ask students if the figure has any other symmetries.

THINK AND DISCUSS

VISUAL LEARNING Draw several trapezoids in different orientations and have students identify the legs and base angles.

Lesson Planning Options

Prerequisite Skills

- Recognizing trapezoids and kites
- Using formulas for distance and slope

Assignment Options for Exercises On Your Own

Core 1–19, 22–25

✪**Extension** 20–21, 26–27

Use Mixed Review to maintain skills.

Resources

Student Edition

Skills Handbook, pp. 664, 677
Extra Practice, p. 656
Glossary/Study Guide

Teaching Resources

Chapter Support File, Ch. 9
- Practice 9-4 (two worksheets)
- Reteaching 9-4
- Alternative Activity 9-4

Classroom Manager 9-4
Glossary, Spanish Resources

Transparencies
95

470

Connections  Architecture . . . and more

9-4 Trapezoids and Kites

What You'll Learn
- Finding the properties of trapezoids and kites

...And Why

To solve problems in construction and design

What You'll Need
- lined paper
- scissors
- straightedge

WORK TOGETHER

Work with a partner.

- Choose two lines on a piece of lined paper that are about 2 in. apart. Cut along these lines.
- Make a fold perpendicular to the cut lines so that each of the lines folds onto itself.
- Use a straightedge to draw a nonperpendicular segment from one parallel line to the other. Cut through the folded paper along that segment. Unfold the paper.

1. Classify the figure. isosceles trapezoid
2. a. Describe the relationship between the nonparallel sides of this figure. Nonparallel sides are ≅.
   b. Describe the relationship between the acute angles and the relationship between the obtuse angles. The acute angles are ≅; the obtuse angles are ≅.

THINK AND DISCUSS

QUICK REVIEW

An isosceles trapezoid is a trapezoid whose nonparallel sides are congruent.

In Chapter 5, you learned that the parallel sides of a trapezoid are the bases and the nonparallel sides are the legs. Each pair of angles adjacent to a base of a trapezoid are **base angles** of the trapezoid.

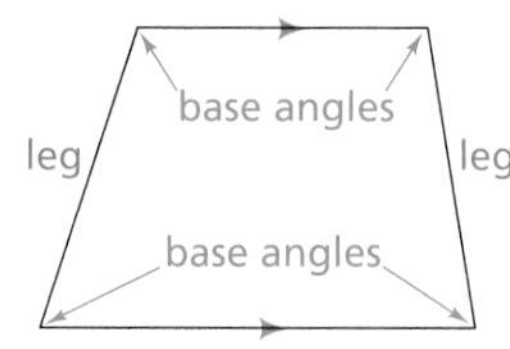

Your results in the Work Together activity are the basis of the following theorem.

Theorem 9-16 Base angles of an isosceles trapezoid are congruent.

3. a. In isosceles trapezoid *ABCD* at the right, what is the relationship between $\angle A$ and $\angle B$? between $\angle D$ and $\angle C$? Explain.
   b. What is the relationship between $\angle A$ and $\angle C$? between $\angle D$ and $\angle B$? Explain. $\angle A$ and $\angle C$ are suppl., and $\angle D$ and $\angle B$ are suppl. because of part (a) and because $\angle B \cong \angle C$.
   c. If $m\angle A = 102$, find $m\angle B$, $m\angle C$, and $m\angle D$.

3a. $\angle A$ and $\angle B$ are supplementary and $\angle C$ and $\angle D$ are supplementary because they are same-side interior $\angle$s formed by ∥ lines and a transversal.

c. $m\angle B = 78$; $m\angle C = 78$; $m\angle D = 102$

Theorem 9-16 Students will prove this theorem in Exercise 24. Intuitively students should find this theorem believable since the base angles of an isosceles triangle are congruent.

ERROR ALERT! **Question 3** Some students may conclude that consecutive angles of an isosceles trapezoid are supplementary. **Remediation:** Help students see that unlike a parallelogram, a base angle of an isosceles trapezoid is supplementary to just one of its consecutive angles.

Example 1 Relating to the Real World 

Copy the diagram onto the board or a transparency. As you review with students the three computational steps, highlight the angle being found on the diagram.

Make sure students understand that because the vertex angles of eight congruent triangles form a straight angle, the sum of their measures is 180, and each vertex angle measures $\frac{180}{8}$.

KINESTHETIC LEARNING Take students outside to sketch geometric patterns on buildings or houses. Have them describe the geometric objects that form the pattern.

Example 2

ALTERNATIVE ASSESSMENT To help you assess students' understanding of the proof of Theorem 9-17, have them write a different proof using $\triangle ABD$ and $\triangle DCA$.

Example 1 Relating to the Real World 

Architecture Part of the window of the World Financial Center in New York City is made from eight congruent isosceles trapezoids that create the illusion of a semicircle. What is the measure of the base angles of these trapezoids?

Each trapezoid is part of an isosceles triangle whose vertex angle is at the center of the circle and whose base angles are the acute base angles of the trapezoid.

The measure of $\angle 1$ is $\frac{180}{8}$, or 22.5.

The measure of each acute base angle is $\frac{180 - 22.5}{2}$, or 78.75.

The measure of each obtuse base angle of the trapezoid is $180 - 78.75$, or 101.25.

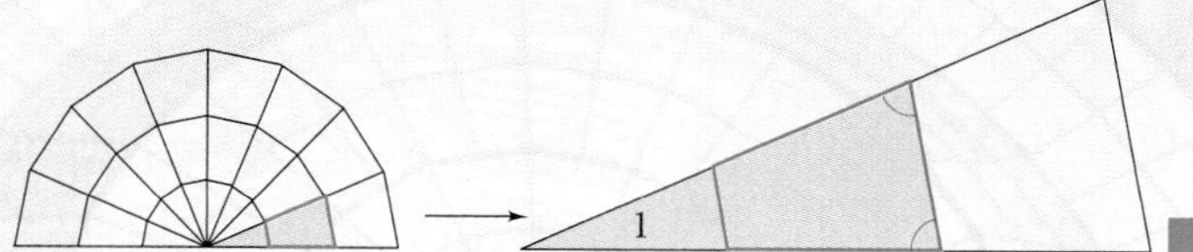

PROBLEM SOLVING HINT

Draw $\triangle ABC$ and $\triangle DCB$ as separate triangles and look for congruent parts.

4. a. *ABCD* is an isosceles trapezoid. How do $\triangle ABC$ and $\triangle DCB$ compare? Explain. **$\triangle ABC \cong \triangle DCB$; SAS**
   b. What must be true of the diagonals of isosceles trapezoid *ABCD*? Explain. **The diagonals are $\cong$; CPCTC.**

A D B C

Theorem 9-17 The diagonals of an isosceles trapezoid are congruent.

Example 2

Write a paragraph proof of Theorem 9-17.

Given: Isosceles trapezoid *ABCD* with $\overline{AB} \cong \overline{DC}$

Prove: $\overline{AC} \cong \overline{DB}$

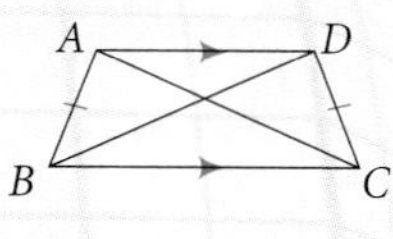

Paragraph Proof

It is given that $\overline{AB} \cong \overline{DC}$. Because the base angles of an isosceles trapezoid are congruent, $\angle ABC \cong \angle DCB$. By the Reflexive Property of Congruence, $\overline{BC} \cong \overline{BC}$. Then by the SAS Postulate, $\triangle ABC \cong \triangle DCB$. Therefore $\overline{AC} \cong \overline{DB}$ by CPCTC.

Additional Examples

FOR EXAMPLE 1

Part of a spider's web is shown. Each trapezoid is isosceles. Find the measures of the base angles of *KLMN*. **$m\angle M = m\angle N = 72$, $m\angle L = m\angle K = 108$**

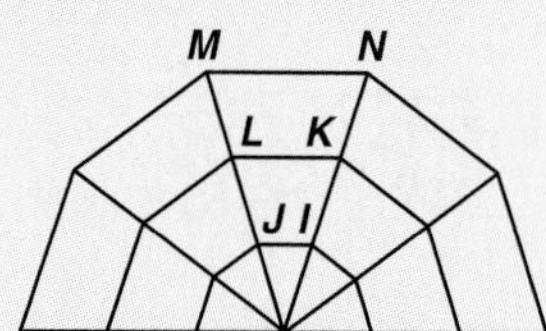

Discussion: *How are trapezoids KLMN and IJLK related?*

FOR EXAMPLE 2

Write a flow proof for Theorem 9-17. **See back of book.**

Discussion: *Describe another way to prove this theorem by using a different set of triangles.*

FOR EXAMPLE 3

Refer to the diagram in Example 3. If $LF = 10$ cm, $LA = 10$ cm, and $FG = 22$ cm, find the height of isosceles trapezoid *FLAG*. **8 cm**

Discussion: *Explain how to find the area of trapezoid FLAG.*

Example 3

Help students understand why $\triangle FLM \cong \triangle GAB$ by the AAS Theorem and why $FM = BG = 5$.

Question 5 Review the formula for the area of a trapezoid $A = \frac{1}{2}(b_1 + b_2)h$.

Question 6d Students should conclude that $\overline{OC} \perp \overline{BD}$. If students do not reach this conclusion, check that they calculated the slopes correctly and recognize that the products of the slopes is -1.

Theorem 9-18 Point out to students that the diagonals of a kite and a rhombus are both perpendicular. Therefore, knowing a quadrilateral has perpendicular diagonals is not a sufficient condition to conclude it is a kite, because it may be a rhombus.

In the Look Back question, help students see that T is equidistant from S and W and therefore must lie on the perpendicular bisector of $\overline{SW}$.

In the proof of Theorem 9-18, students justify why $\triangle STZ \cong \triangle WTZ$. By CPCTC, $\overline{SZ} \cong \overline{SW}$. Help students see that the diagonal of a kite whose endpoints are shared by noncongruent sides is always bisected by the other diagonal.

Technology Options

For Exercise 11, have students construct a kite using geometry software and measure its angles. Then have them investigate the relationships between consecutive angles and opposite angles as they manipulate the kite.

Prentice Hall Technology

Software
- Secondary Math Lab Toolkit™
- Computer Item Generator 9-4

CD-ROM
- Multimedia Geometry Lab 9

Internet
- See the Prentice Hall site. (http://www.phschool.com)

472

You can use the lengths of the sides of an isosceles trapezoid to find the height of the trapezoid.

Example 3

Find the height of isosceles trapezoid *FLAG*.

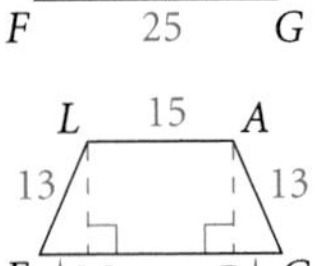

Draw altitudes $\overline{LM}$ and $\overline{AB}$, creating rectangle *MLAB*, with $MB = 15$. $\triangle FLM \cong \triangle GAB$ by AAS.

By CPCTC, $\overline{FM} \cong \overline{GB}$.
$FM = (25 - 15) \div 2 = 5$.

Use the Pythagorean Theorem to solve for *LM*.

$$5^2 + (LM)^2 = 13^2$$
$$25 + (LM)^2 = 169$$
$$(LM)^2 = 144$$
$$LM = 12$$

The height of isosceles trapezoid *FLAG* is 12 cm.

5. What is the area of trapezoid *FLAG*? **240 cm²**

Another special quadrilateral that is not a parallelogram is a kite.

6. a. **Coordinate Geometry** Find the lengths of the sides of *OBCD*. **See below.**
   b. Classify *OBCD*. **kite**
   c. Find the slopes of $\overline{OC}$ and $\overline{BD}$. **1; –1**
   d. What is the relationship between $\overline{OC}$ and $\overline{BD}$? $\overline{OC} \perp \overline{BD}$

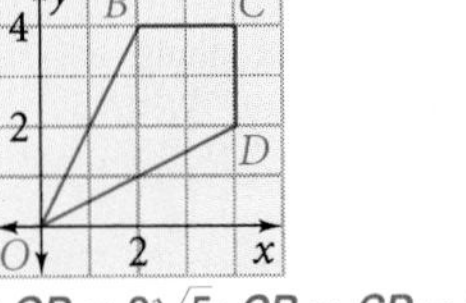

6a. $OB = OD = 2\sqrt{5}$; $CB = CD = 2$

Theorem 9-18 The diagonals of a kite are perpendicular.

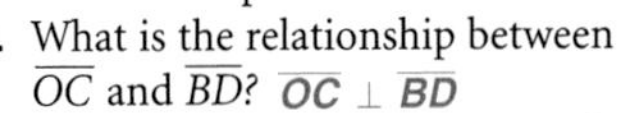

7. Answer the following questions to prove Theorem 9-18.

   Given: Kite *RSTW* with $\overline{RS} \cong \overline{RW}$ and $\overline{ST} \cong \overline{WT}$
   Prove: $\overline{RT} \perp \overline{SW}$

   a. What triangle is congruent to $\triangle RST$? Justify your answer. **$\triangle RWT$; SSS**
   b. Why is $\angle 1 \cong \angle 2$? **CPCTC**
   c. Why is $\triangle STZ \cong \triangle WTZ$? **SAS**
   d. Why is $\angle 3 \cong \angle 4$? **CPCTC**
   e. Why are $\angle 3$ and $\angle 4$ right angles? **See below.**
   f. Why is $\overline{RT} \perp \overline{SW}$? **Def. of ⊥ lines**

T, 1, 2, 3, 4, S, Z, W, R

8. **Try This** If $RS = 15$, $ST = 13$, and $SW = 24$, find *RT*. (*Hint:* Use Pythagorean triples.) **14**

7e. If 2 ∠s are ≅ and supplementary, then they are rt. ∠s.

PROBLEM SOLVING

Look Back Explain why Theorem 9-18 could easily be a corollary of Theorem 4-13: Converse of Perpendicular Bisector Theorem.

Since 2 pairs of adjacent sides are ≅, 2 vertices are equidistant from the end-points of a diagonal. So, those vertices are on the ⊥ bisector of the diagonal.

Questions 9–11 Have students work in groups. You may want to provide students with the following diagram and have them fill in the names of the quadrilaterals.

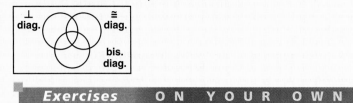

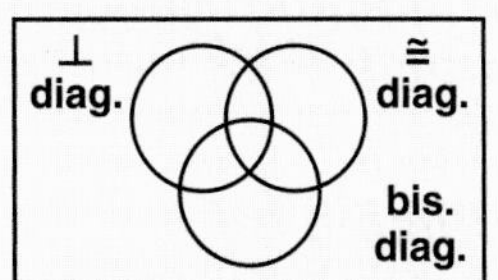

Exercises ON YOUR OWN

Exercises 1–5 Students use the properties of trapezoids and kites to find missing angle measures and segment lengths. Ask students to state the theorem(s) they apply to solve each problem.

Exercise 6 Students can use algebra or Guess and Test to find the side lengths.

Exercise 8 Make sure students correctly identify the isosceles triangles, the vertex angle, and the quadrilateral shown between the dark stripes.

The following statements are suggested by the converses of the theorems in this lesson. Draw figures to show that the statements are false.

9. A quadrilateral with perpendicular diagonals is a kite or a rhombus.

10. A quadrilateral with congruent diagonals is an isosceles trapezoid or a rectangle.

11. A quadrilateral with diagonals that are congruent and perpendicular is a square.

9–11. See margin for samples.

Exercises ON YOUR OWN

Find the measures of $\angle 1$ and $\angle 2$.

1. 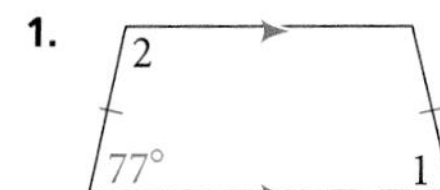

$m\angle 1 = 77$; $m\angle 2 = 103$

2. 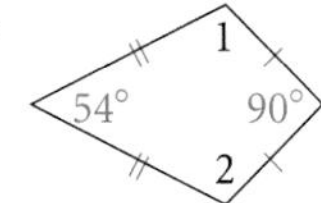

$m\angle 1 = 108$; $m\angle 2 = 108$

3. 22°, 1, 2

$m\angle 1 = 90$; $m\angle 2 = 68$

4. 111°, 1, 2

$m\angle 1 = 69$; $m\angle 2 = 69$

5. Find UI, IT, and UT, if $AS = 16$.

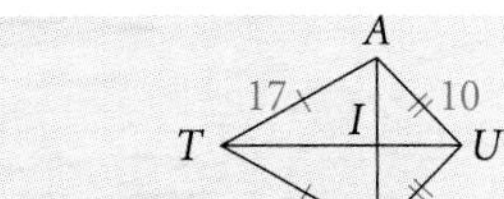

$UI = 6$; $IT = 15$; $UT = 21$

6. **a.** Find the height of an isosceles trapezoid with bases 30 cm and 70 cm long and legs 29 cm long. 21 cm

b. Find the area of the trapezoid. 1050 cm^2

7. The perimeter of a kite is 66 cm. The length of one of its sides is 3 cm less than twice the length of another. Find the length of each side of the kite.
12 cm, 12 cm, 21 cm, 21 cm

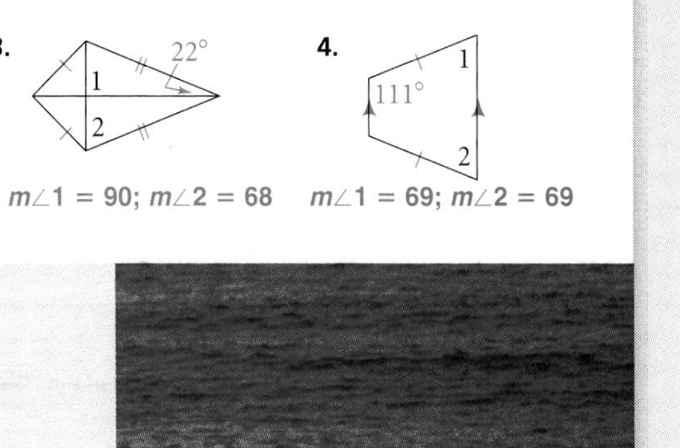

8. *Design* To make a beach umbrella, Taheisha cut eight panels from material with parallel stripes. The panels were congruent isosceles triangles with a vertex angle of 40° as shown at the right.

a. Classify each yellow quadrilateral. isos. trap.

b. Find the measures of the interior angles of each yellow quadrilateral.
70, 110, 110, 70

pages 470–473 Think and Discuss

9. 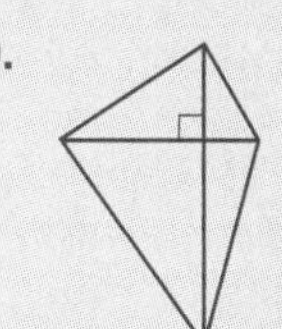

10. 

11. 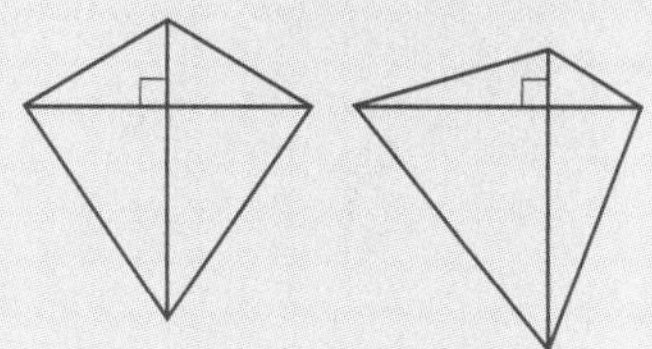

473

Exercise 9 Suggest students trace the quadrilateral that is outlined and label the measures of the interior angles on the figure.

Exercise 10a Students may want to trace the kite they sketch and cut it out in order to use paper folding and rotation to find symmetries.

CRITICAL THINKING Exercise 11 Have students discuss their responses in groups and revise their answers if necessary.

OPEN-ENDED Exercise 17 Students may want to create these triangles using toothpicks as diagonals and string as the sides of the kite.

Exercise 18b Students will need to expand $(12 - x)^2$ to solve this problem.

Exercise 19 Make sure that students understand the directions.

pages 473–476 On Your Own

11a. No; If one pair of consecutive $\angle$s is supplementary, then another pair must be also because a pair of opp. $\angle$s of a kite is $\cong$. Therefore, the opp. sides are $\parallel$, which means the figure is a ▱ and cannot be a kite.

b. Yes; if 2 $\cong$ angles are rt. angles, they are supplementary. The other 2 angles are also supplementary.

17.

19. $\overline{AA'} \cong \overline{AA''}$ and $\overline{BA'} \cong \overline{BA''}$, so it is a kite (unless $x = 60$, in which case the 4 sides are $\cong$ and it is a rhombus).

9. a. *Construction* At the right, a quadrilateral formed by the beams of the bridge is outlined. Classify the quadrilateral. Explain your reasoning. See below right.
   b. Find the measures of the other interior angles of the figure. 112; 68; 68

10. a. *Transformations* Sketch a kite and describe its symmetries. reflectional symmetry
    b. *Critical Thinking* A classmate claims that the longer diagonal of a kite is a line of symmetry for the kite. Is he correct? Explain. See below right.

11. a. *Critical Thinking* Can two consecutive angles of a kite be supplementary? Explain.
    b. Can two opposite angles of a kite be supplementary? Explain. a–b. See margin.

12. *Standardized Test Prep* In quadrilateral *DEAL*, $\angle D$ is supplementary to $\angle E$. Quadrilateral *DEAL* could be a __?__. C

I. trapezoid	II. kite	III. rhombus
A. I only	B. III only	C. I or III
D. II or III	E. I, II, or III	

9a. Isosceles trapezoid; all the large rt. $\triangle$s appear to be $\cong$.
10b. No; the line of symmetry of a kite is the diagonal between the noncongruent angles.

Algebra **Find the value of the variable(s).**

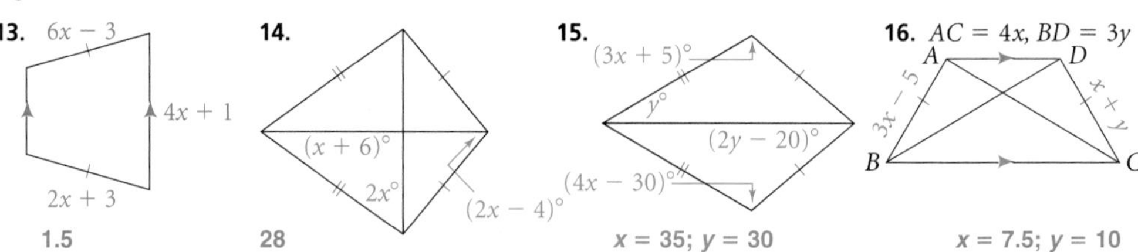

13. 1.5 14. 28 15. $x = 35$; $y = 30$ 16. $x = 7.5$; $y = 10$

17. *Open-ended* Sketch two kites that are not congruent, but such that the diagonals of one are congruent to the diagonals of the other. See margin for sample.

18. a. *Calculator* If $SW = 8$, find RT to the nearest tenth. 13.6
    b. If $RT = 12$, find SW to the nearest tenth. (*Hint:* Let $TZ = x$, $RZ = 12 - x$, and $SZ = y$. Write two equations and then solve.) 10.0

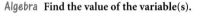

19. *Transformations* Draw $\overline{AB}$. Rotate $\overline{AB}$ $x°$ about B, where $0 < x < 90$. Reflect $\triangle ABA'$ in $\overline{AB}$, labeling the image of A' as A''. What type of quadrilateral is $AA'BA''$? Explain. See margin.

20. a. *Geometry in 3 Dimensions* If a plane parallel to the base intersects a square pyramid, what shape is the cross section? square
    b. If the plane is not parallel to the base, what shapes can the cross section have? isosceles trapezoid, kite, triangle, pentagon, or a scalene quad.

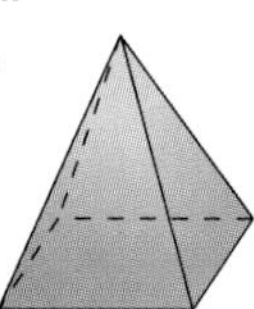

OPEN-ENDED Exercise 21 Have students compare their kites. They should discover that there are infinitely many possible kites that can be drawn.

ESL Exercise 21 Have students translate the cartoon into their native languages and create a bulletin board display of the different translations.

EXTENSION Exercise 23 A trapezoid is sometimes defined as a quadrilateral with one pair of parallel sides. Have students compare this to the definition they learned in Chapter 2 and describe how this definition changes the quadrilateral tree diagram in Chapter 2.

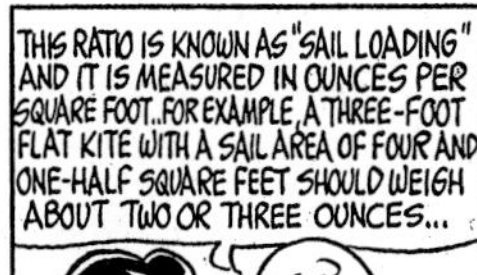

21. *Open-ended* Charlie Brown is talking to Lucy about a "three-foot flat kite with a sail area of four and one-half square feet." Draw a kite with two 3-ft diagonals that has an area of $4\frac{1}{2}$ ft^2. Show the lengths of the segments of both diagonals. **See margin for sample.**

22. *Critical Thinking* If *KLMN* is an isosceles trapezoid, is it possible for $\overline{KM}$ to bisect $\angle LMN$ and $\angle LKN$? Explain. **No; if $\overline{KM}$ bisects $\angle LMN$ and $\angle LKN$, then $\triangle LMK \cong \triangle NMK$. Then 2 pairs of adj. sides are $\cong$ and *KLMN* is a kite or a rhombus, which is impossible.**

23. *Writing* A *kite* is sometimes defined as a quadrilateral with two pairs of congruent adjacent sides. Compare this to the definition on page 91. Are parallelograms, trapezoids, rhombuses, rectangles, or squares special kinds of kites according to the changed definition? Explain. **Rhombuses and squares would be kites.**

24. Complete the following two-column proof of Theorem 9-16: The base angles of an isosceles trapezoid are congruent.

Given: *ABCD* is an isosceles trapezoid with $\overline{AB} \cong \overline{DC}$.
Prove: $\angle B \cong \angle C$ and $\angle BAD \cong \angle D$
Begin by drawing $\overline{AE} \parallel \overline{DC}$.

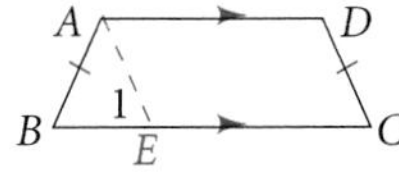

Statements	Reasons
1. *ABCD* is an isosceles trapezoid; $\overline{AB} \cong \overline{DC}$.	1. Given
a. ■ $\parallel \overline{EC}$ **$\overline{AD}$**	2. Definition of trapezoid
3. *AECD* is a ▱.	b. ? **Def. of ▱**
4. $\angle C \cong \angle 1$	c. ? **If $\parallel$ lines, then corres. $\angle$s are $\cong$.**
d. $\overline{DC} \cong$ ■ **$\overline{AE}$**	5. Opposite sides of a ▱ are $\cong$.
6. $\overline{AE} \cong \overline{AB}$	e. ? Property of $\cong$ **Transitive**
7. $\angle B \cong \angle 1$	f. ? **Base $\angle$s of an isos. $\triangle$ are $\cong$.**
8. $\angle B \cong \angle C$	g. ? **Transitive Prop. of $\cong$**
9. $\angle B$ and $\angle BAD$ are supplements; $\angle C$ and $\angle ADC$ are supplements.	h. ? **If $\parallel$ lines, then same-side interior $\angle$s are supplementary.**
10. $\angle BAD \cong \angle CDA$	i. Supplements of $\cong$ $\angle$s are ? . **congruent**

25. a. *Picture Framing* Describe the shape of the four pieces of wood that are joined to form the picture frame at the right. **isosceles trapezoids**

b. Find the angle measures of each piece of wood. **45, 135, 135, 45**

21.

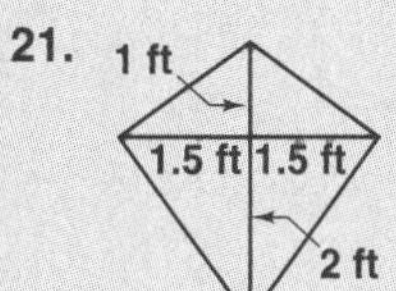

Exercises 26–27 Have each student work with a partner to complete the proofs.

FIND OUT BY RESEARCHING Check with your school library or local library to see if they have the books listed on page 488. If not, see if it is possible for them to borrow the books from another library, or ask for a list of references for books they have on making kites.

Exercises MIXED REVIEW

JOURNAL You may also want students to describe the properties of kites.

PROBABILITY Exercises 28–30 Students find the geometric probability of a dart's landing in a certain area of a dart board.

GETTING READY FOR LESSON 9-5 These exercises prepare students to organize coordinate proofs.

Wrap Up

THE BIG IDEA Ask students: *How are a kite and a rhombus similar? different? How are a trapezoid and a rectangle similar? different?*

RETEACHING ACTIVITY Students use properties of trapezoids to find missing measurements. (Reteaching worksheet 9-4)

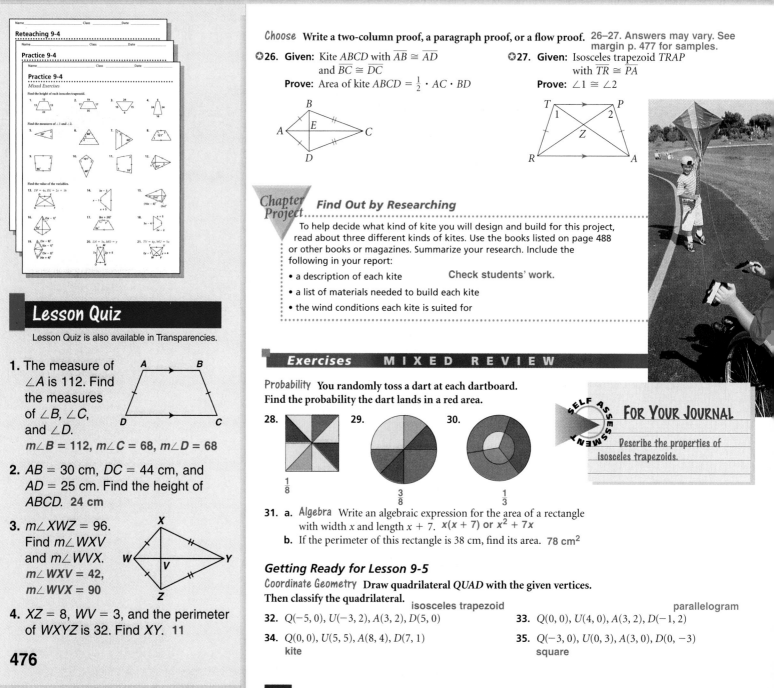

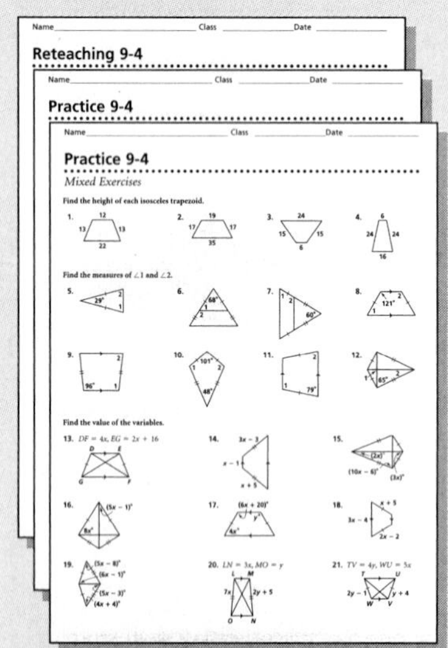

Lesson Quiz

Lesson Quiz is also available in Transparencies.

1. The measure of $\angle A$ is 112. Find the measures of $\angle B$, $\angle C$, and $\angle D$. $m\angle B = 112$, $m\angle C = 68$, $m\angle D = 68$

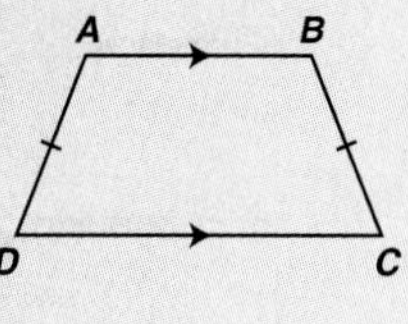

2. $AB = 30$ cm, $DC = 44$ cm, and $AD = 25$ cm. Find the height of $ABCD$. 24 cm

3. $m\angle XWZ = 96$. Find $m\angle WXV$ and $m\angle WVX$. $m\angle WXV = 42$, $m\angle WVX = 90$

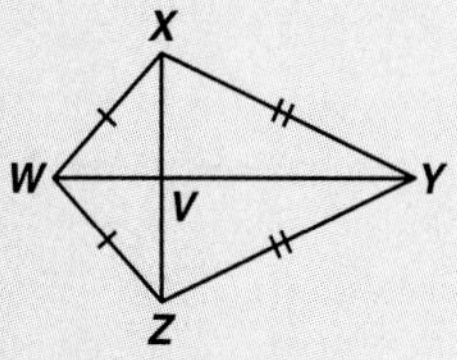

4. $XZ = 8$, $WV = 3$, and the perimeter of $WXYZ$ is 32. Find XY. 11

Choose **Write a two-column proof, a paragraph proof, or a flow proof.** 26–27. Answers may vary. See margin p. 477 for samples.

26. **Given:** Kite $ABCD$ with $\overline{AB} \cong \overline{AD}$ and $\overline{BC} \cong \overline{DC}$
Prove: Area of kite $ABCD = \frac{1}{2} \cdot AC \cdot BD$

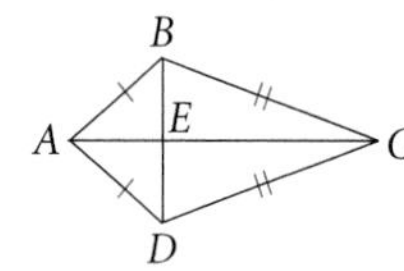

27. **Given:** Isosceles trapezoid $TRAP$ with $\overline{TR} \cong \overline{PA}$
Prove: $\angle 1 \cong \angle 2$

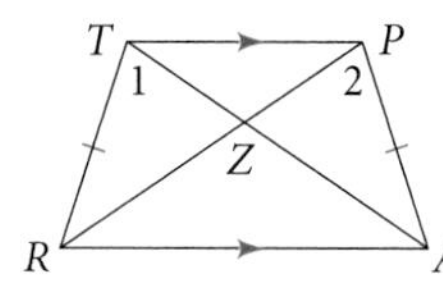

Chapter Project: Find Out by Researching

To help decide what kind of kite you will design and build for this project, read about three different kinds of kites. Use the books listed on page 488 or other books or magazines. Summarize your research. Include the following in your report: Check students' work.

- a description of each kite
- a list of materials needed to build each kite
- the wind conditions each kite is suited for

Exercises MIXED REVIEW

Probability **You randomly toss a dart at each dartboard. Find the probability the dart lands in a red area.**

28. 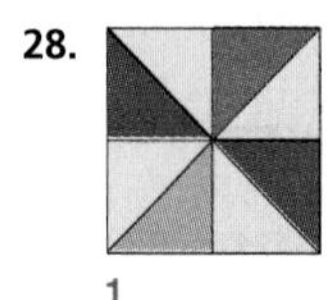 $\frac{1}{8}$

29. 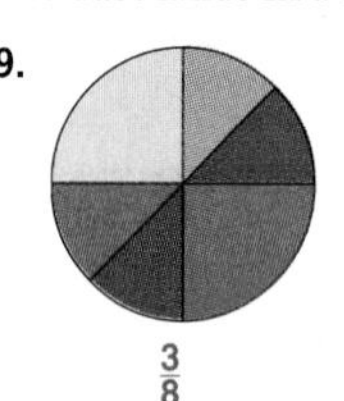 $\frac{3}{8}$

30. 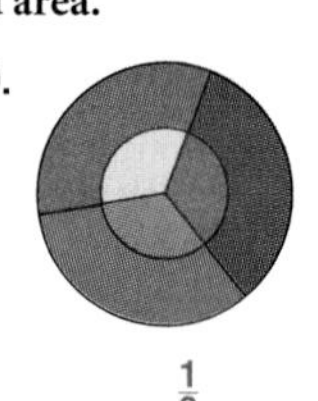 $\frac{1}{3}$

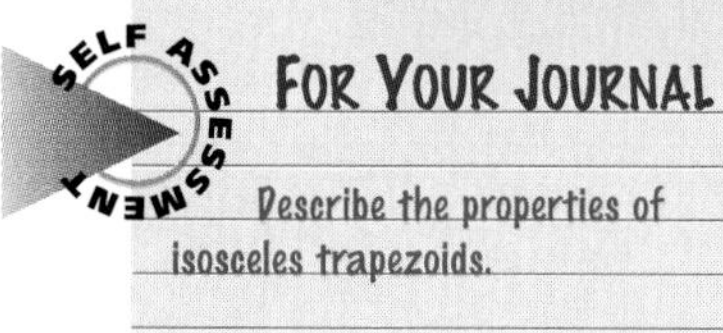

FOR YOUR JOURNAL
Describe the properties of isosceles trapezoids.

31. a. Algebra Write an algebraic expression for the area of a rectangle with width x and length $x + 7$. $x(x + 7)$ or $x^2 + 7x$
b. If the perimeter of this rectangle is 38 cm, find its area. 78 cm^2

Getting Ready for Lesson 9-5

Coordinate Geometry **Draw quadrilateral $QUAD$ with the given vertices. Then classify the quadrilateral.**

32. $Q(-5, 0)$, $U(-3, 2)$, $A(3, 2)$, $D(5, 0)$ isosceles trapezoid

33. $Q(0, 0)$, $U(4, 0)$, $A(3, 2)$, $D(-1, 2)$ parallelogram

34. $Q(0, 0)$, $U(5, 5)$, $A(8, 4)$, $D(7, 1)$ kite

35. $Q(-3, 0)$, $U(0, 3)$, $A(3, 0)$, $D(0, -3)$ square

Math ToolboX

Students review the definition of *rational expression.* Then they practice simplifying, multiplying, and dividing them.

Review with students why the variable has restrictions and how to find the restrictions in each of the three examples.

Example 1

ERROR ALERT! Some students may try to cancel out part of sums. For example, they might try to cancel out the *x*'s or divide the 6 by 2. **Remediation:** Remind students that to simplify fractions, they can cancel out only common *factors* in the numerator and denominator.

Example 2

Point out that it is easier to factor the terms in the numerator and denominator and divide by common factors before multiplying.

Example 3

Make sure students remember how to find the reciprocal of a non-zero whole number.

ALTERNATIVE ASSESSMENT Have students work in groups. Assign each group five problems from each section to solve. Make sure that all problems are assigned. Then have each member of all groups present one of the problems to the class.

Math ToolboX — Algebra Review

Rational Expressions

After Lesson 9-4

A **rational expression** is an expression that can be written in the form $\frac{\text{polynomial}}{\text{polynomial}}$, where a variable is in the denominator. A rational expression is in simplest form if the numerator and denominator have no common factors except 1.

To multiply rational expressions $\frac{a}{b}$ and $\frac{c}{d}$, where b and $d \neq 0$, multiply the numerators and multiply the denominators. Then write the product in simplest form.

$$\frac{a}{b} \cdot \frac{c}{d} = \frac{ac}{bd}$$

To divide $\frac{a}{b}$ by $\frac{c}{d}$, where b, c, and $d \neq 0$, multiply by the reciprocal of $\frac{c}{d}$.

$$\frac{a}{b} \div \frac{c}{d} = \frac{a}{b} \cdot \frac{c}{d}$$

Example 1

Simplify $\frac{3x-6}{x-2}$.

$$\frac{3x-6}{x-2} = \frac{3(x-2)}{x-2}$$

$$= 3, x \neq 2$$

Example 2

Multiply $\frac{3x}{x-1} \cdot \frac{2x-2}{9x^2}$.

$$\frac{3x}{x-1} \cdot \frac{2x-2}{9x^2} = \frac{3x(2)(x-1)}{(x-1)(3x)(3x)}$$

$$= \frac{2}{3x}, x \neq 0 \text{ or } 1$$

Example 3

Divide $\frac{4x^5}{3}$ by $16x^7$.

$$\frac{4x^5}{3} \div 16x^7 = \frac{4x^5}{3} \cdot \frac{1}{16x^7}$$

$$= \frac{1}{12x^2}, x \neq 0$$

Simplify each expression.

1. $\frac{4x+12}{x+3}$ — $4, x \neq -3$
2. $\frac{6c^3}{3c^4}$ — $\frac{2}{c}, c \neq 0$
3. $\frac{3x-9}{3x+9}$ — $\frac{x-3}{x+3}, x \neq -3$
4. $\frac{2a^6}{16a}$ — $\frac{a^5}{8}, a \neq 0$
5. $\frac{28w+12}{4}$ — $7w+3$
6. $\frac{m+7}{m^2-49}$ — $\frac{1}{m-7}, m \neq -7 \text{ or } 7$
7. $\frac{5t^2}{25t^3}$ — $\frac{1}{5t}, t \neq 0$
8. $\frac{6x^2+6x}{4x^2+4x}$ — $\frac{3}{2}, x \neq -1 \text{ or } 0$
9. $\frac{4x^3-12x^2}{x-3}$ — $4x^2, x \neq 3$
10. $\frac{3s^2+s}{s^3}$ — $\frac{3s+1}{s^2}, s \neq 0$
11. $\frac{v^2+2v+1}{v+1}$ — $v+1, v \neq -1$
12. $\frac{8r^7}{56r^2}$ — $\frac{r^5}{7}, r \neq 0$

Find each product or quotient.

13. $\frac{3r^2}{4} \cdot \frac{20}{5r^3}$ — $\frac{3}{r}, r \neq 0$
14. $\frac{x-1}{x+2} \div (2x-2)$
15. $\frac{3c+6}{5} \cdot \frac{25c}{c+2}$
16. $\frac{4}{w^2} \div \frac{16}{w}$ — $\frac{1}{4w}, w \neq 0$
17. $20x^2 \div \frac{4x}{3}$ — $15x, x \neq 0$
18. $\frac{3x^2+x}{2x} \cdot \frac{4x^2}{3x+1}$
19. $\frac{9a^5}{2a} \div \frac{12a^3}{4}$ — $\frac{3a}{2}, a \neq 0$
20. $\frac{x+2}{x-7} \div \frac{x}{x-7}$
21. $\frac{t+3}{t-2} \cdot \frac{t^2-4}{5t+15}$
22. $\frac{x^4-x^3}{x-1} \cdot \frac{2}{x^2}$
23. $\frac{a-5}{a+5} \div (2a-10)$
24. $\frac{4r^2}{r^5} \cdot \frac{r^2}{2}$ — $\frac{2}{r}, r \neq 0$
25. $9y^4 \div \frac{3y}{y+1}$
26. $\frac{9w^3-w}{2w-1} \cdot \frac{1-2w}{w}$
27. $\frac{6c+2}{c^2+1} \div \frac{2}{c-1}$
28. $\frac{4m+2}{m-3} \cdot \frac{3-m}{4m^2-1}$

14. $\frac{1}{2x+4}, x \neq -2 \text{ or } 1$ 15. $15c, c \neq -2$ 18. $2x^2, x \neq -\frac{1}{3} \text{ or } 0$ 20. $\frac{x+2}{x}, x \neq 0 \text{ or } 7$
21. $\frac{t+2}{5}, t \neq -3 \text{ or } 2$ 22. $2x, x \neq 0 \text{ or } 1$ 23. $\frac{1}{2a+10}, a \neq -5 \text{ or } 5$ 25. $3y^4+3y^3, y \neq -1 \text{ or } 0$
26. $1-9w^2, w \neq 0 \text{ or } \frac{1}{2}$ 27. $\frac{3c^2-2c-1}{c^2+1}, c \neq 1$ 28. $\frac{2}{1-2m}, m \neq -\frac{1}{2}, \frac{1}{2}, \text{ or } 3$

Transparencies
11

26. 1. kite *ABCD* (Given) 2. $\overline{AC} \perp \overline{BD}$ (Diagonals of a kite are ⊥.) 3. Area of $\triangle ABC = \frac{1}{2} \cdot AC \cdot BE$ $(A = \frac{1}{2}bh)$ 4. Area of $\triangle CDA = \frac{1}{2} \cdot AC \cdot DE$ $(A = \frac{1}{2}bh)$ 5. Area of $ABCD$ = Area of $\triangle ABC$ + Area of $\triangle CDA$ (Area of a figure = the sum of areas of its nonoverlapping parts.) 6. Area of $ABCD = \frac{1}{2} \cdot AC \cdot (BE + DE)$ (Distributive Prop.) 7. Area of $ABCD = \frac{1}{2} \cdot AC \cdot BD$ (Segment Addition Post.)
27. Answers may vary. Sample: 1. Isosceles trapezoid *TRAP* (Given) 2. $\overline{TA} \cong \overline{PR}$ (Diagonals of an isos. trap. are ≅.) 3. $\overline{TR} \cong \overline{PA}$ (Given) 4. $\overline{RA} \cong \overline{RA}$ (Reflexive Prop. of ≅) 5. $\triangle TRA \cong \triangle PAR$ (SSS) 6. $\angle 1 \cong \angle 2$ (CPCTC)

9-5 Teaching Notes

PROBLEM OF THE DAY

Eight identical tables shaped as isosceles trapezoids fit together to make an octagonal table with a hole. Find the measures of the interior angles of the trapezoids.
112.5, 112.5, 67.5, 67.5

Problem of the Day is also available in Transparencies.

CONNECTING TO PRIOR KNOWLEDGE Have students graph each set of coordinates, connect the vertices, and classify the figure.

a. $A(-2, 2)$, $B(-5, 6)$, $C(-2, 6)$, $D(1, 2)$

b. $X(3, 4)$, $Y(5, -2)$, $Z(-5, -2)$, $W(-3, 4)$

WORK TOGETHER

Before students begin, review the formulas for slope and midpoint. Check that students correctly identify the slopes of vertical and horizontal lines.

TACTILE LEARNING Suggest that students make a cutout of a 10-unit square and trace it in different positions on the coordinate grid. Also suggest that students place each vertex of the square on an intersection of grid lines so the coordinates will be integers.

Lesson Planning Options

Prerequisite Skills

- Graphing in the coordinate plane
- Finding slopes and midpoints

Assignment Options for Exercises On Your Own

Core 1–20, 22–23, 25
✪Extension 21, 24, 26

Use Mixed Review to maintain skills.

Resources

Student Edition
Skills Handbook, pp. 674, 678
Extra Practice, p. 656
Glossary/Study Guide

Teaching Resources
Chapter Support File, Ch. 9
- Practice 9-5 (two worksheets)
- Reteaching 9-5

Classroom Manager 9-5
Glossary, Spanish Resources

Transparencies
5, 96, 101, 102

What You'll Learn
- Choosing convenient placement of coordinate axes on figures

...And Why
To use coordinate proofs to solve design problems

What You'll Need
- graph paper
- straightedge

Connections  Archaeology . . . and more

9-5 Organizing Coordinate Proofs

WORK TOGETHER

Work with a small group.

- Use graph paper to draw a number of coordinate planes with x- and y-coordinates from -12 to 12. On each, draw one or more squares with sides 10 units long. Draw the squares in different positions, with sides on one or both axes, parallel to the axes, or not parallel to either axis. Use more than one quadrant. Label each square $ABCD$.
- On each square, record the slope of each side, the slope of each diagonal, and the coordinates of the midpoints of the diagonals.
- Discuss which type of squares made your calculations easiest. **Generalize** your conclusions and explain your reasons.

THINK AND DISCUSS

In the Work Together, you saw that the position of a figure has an effect on how easy the figure is to work with. In coordinate proofs, it is generally easiest to use the origin as the center for the figure or to place a vertex at the origin and at least one side of the figure on an axis.

Example 1

Use the properties of each figure to find the missing coordinates.

a. rectangle $KLMN$

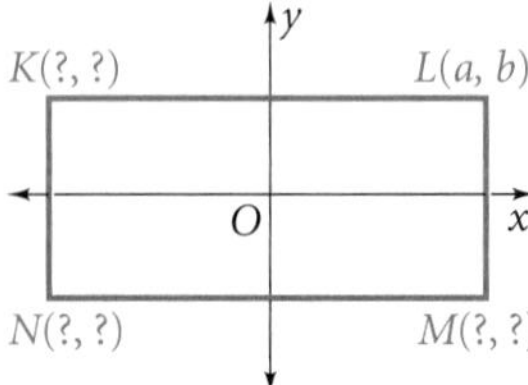

The x- and y-axes are horizontal and vertical lines of symmetry. The coordinates are $K(-a, b)$, $M(a, -b)$, and $N(-a, -b)$.

b. ▱$OPQR$

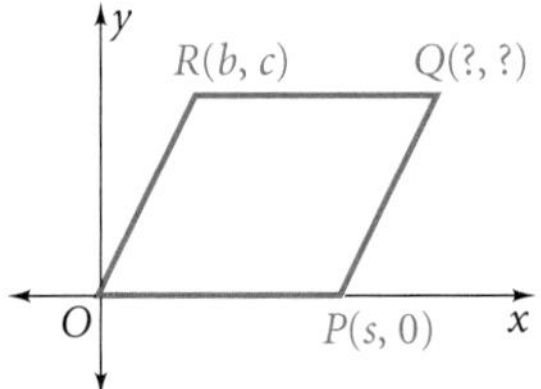

To go from point P to point Q keeping $OP = RQ$, go right b units and up c units. Point Q has coordinates $Q(s + b, c)$.

1. **Try This** When you place two sides of a figure on the coordinate axes, what are you assuming about the figure? **The 2 sides are ⊥.**

THINK AND DISCUSS

Relate coordinate proofs to other styles of proofs students have used. Explain to students that in a coordinate proof, the figure is placed in the coordinate plane and algebraic arguments are used.

Example 1

In Part a, explain to students that, starting from the origin, point L is a units to the right and b units up. Since point M has the same horizontal distance and direction from the origin and the same vertical distance but opposite direction, it has coordinates $(a, -b)$. Have students give a similar explanation for the coordinates of points K and N.

Example 2 Relating to the Real World 

The Math Toolbox on page 461 provides a way to use technology to investigate this property of quadrilaterals.

Make sure students see that because the coordinates of the quadrilateral were picked randomly, the results are true for all types of convex quadrilaterals.

Help students see that by picking the coordinates as multiples of 2, they avoid getting fractional values for the midpoints.

CONNECTING TO STUDENTS' WORLD Have students create designs for T-shirts using only quadrilaterals. Have them describe how they made them, using geometric terms to describe the shapes, angles, and lines.

It is often convenient to use coordinates that are multiples of 2 so that when you find midpoints you will not need to use fractions.

Example 2 Relating to the Real World 

Design The assignment in art class is to create a T-shirt design by drawing any quadrilateral, connecting its midpoints to form another quadrilateral, and coloring the regions. Elena claims that everyone's inner quadrilateral will be a parallelogram. Is she correct? Explain.

Draw a quadrilateral on a coordinate plane. Locate one vertex at the origin and one side on the x-axis. Since you are finding midpoints, use coordinates that are multiples of 2. Find the coordinates of the midpoints T, W, V, and U, and the slopes of the sides of $TWVU$.

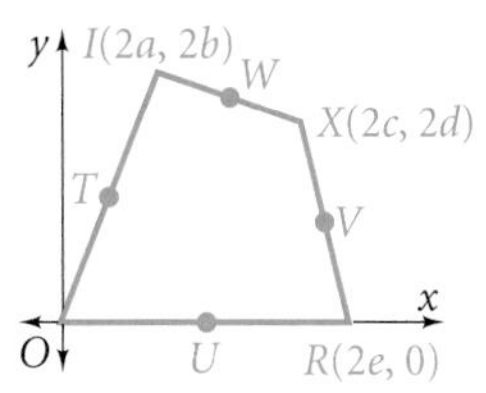

$T = \text{midpoint of } \overline{OI} = \left(\frac{2a+0}{2}, \frac{2b+0}{2}\right) = (a, b)$

$W = \text{midpoint of } \overline{IX} = \left(\frac{2a+2c}{2}, \frac{2b+2d}{2}\right) = (a+c, b+d)$

$V = \text{midpoint of } \overline{XR} = \left(\frac{2c+2e}{2}, \frac{2d+0}{2}\right) = (c+e, d)$

$U = \text{midpoint of } \overline{OR} = \left(\frac{0+2e}{2}, \frac{0+0}{2}\right) = (e, 0)$

slope of $\overline{TW} = \frac{b-(b+d)}{a-(a+c)} = \frac{d}{c}$

slope of $\overline{VU} = \frac{d-0}{(c+e)-e} = \frac{d}{c}$ The slopes are equal, so the lines are parallel.

slope of $\overline{WV} = \frac{(b+d)-d}{(a+c)-(c+e)} = \frac{b}{a-e}$

slope of $\overline{TU} = \frac{b-0}{a-e} = \frac{b}{a-e}$ The slopes are equal, so the lines are parallel.

Since both pairs of opposite sides of $TWVU$ are parallel, $TWVU$ is a parallelogram and Elena is correct!

PROBLEM SOLVING

Look Back Explain how you could prove that Elena is correct without using coordinate geometry.
See back of book.

2. **Try This** Use a different method to show that $TWVU$ is a parallelogram by finding the midpoints of the diagonals.
Midpoint of $\overline{TV} = \left(\frac{a+c+e}{2}, \frac{b+d}{2}\right)$ = midpoint of $\overline{UW}$. So, the diagonals bisect each other and $TWVU$ is a ▱.

Additional Examples

FOR EXAMPLE 1

Use the properties of each figure to find the missing coordinates.

a. square $ABCD$ 

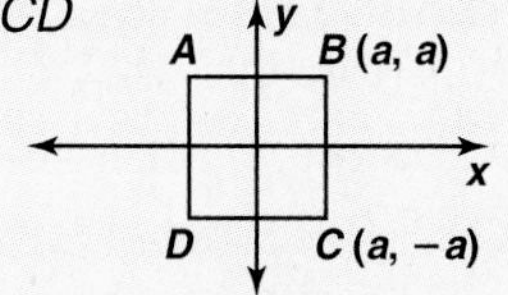

$A(-a, a)$, $D(-a, -a)$

b. rectangle $WXYZ$ $W(0, t)$, $Y(s, 0)$

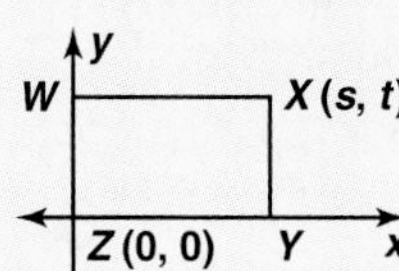

Discussion: *What properties of squares and rectangles did you use?*

FOR EXAMPLE 2

Use a coordinate plane to show the diagonals of a square are perpendicular. See back of book.

Discussion: *Describe a different method to show the diagonals of a square are perpendicular.*

Exercises ON YOUR OWN

ERROR ALERT! **Exercises 1–6** Some student may transpose the *x*- and *y*-coordinates. **Remediation:** Have students check their results by using numbers for the variables and checking the coordinates make sense.

ALTERNATIVE ASSESSMENT **Exercise 6** The following activity will help you assess students' understanding of the best placement of a figure in the coordinate plane. Have students work in groups. Ask them to draw an isosceles trapezoid in three different positions on a coordinate grid and to label the vertices using as few variables as possible. Then have them explain which is the most convenient position and why.

OPEN-ENDED **Exercise 13** It is sufficient for students to find the slope of four sides and the lengths of two consecutive sides.

Exercise 14 Because no directions were given as to where to place the square in the coordinate plane, there are many possible answers to this question. Students may want to compare their answers and discuss which placement of the square is most convenient.

ERROR ALERT! **Exercise 15** Students may experience difficulty drawing the square because its sides are not vertical or horizontal. **Remediation.** Suggest that students draw the diagonals first, then use a ruler to connect the endpoints of the diagonals.

Technology Options

For Exercises 21 and 22, students may graph the lines using geometry software.

Prentice Hall Technology

Software

- Secondary Math Lab Toolkit™
- Computer Item Generator 9-5

Internet

- See the Prentice Hall site. (http://www.phschool.com)

Exercises ON YOUR OWN

Give coordinates for points *W* and *Z* without using any new variables.

1. rectangle $W(0, h)$; $Z(b, 0)$

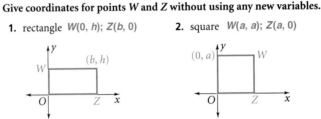

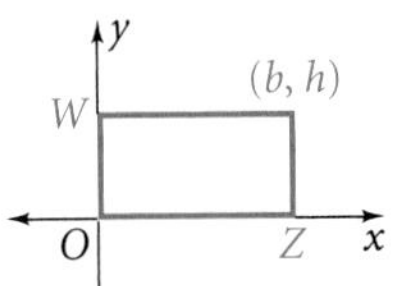

2. square $W(a, a)$; $Z(a, 0)$

3. square $W(-b, b)$; $Z(-b, -b)$

4. parallelogram $W(0, b)$; $Z(a, 0)$

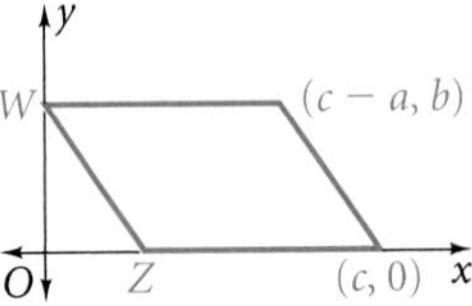

5. rhombus $W(-r, 0)$; $Z(0, -t)$

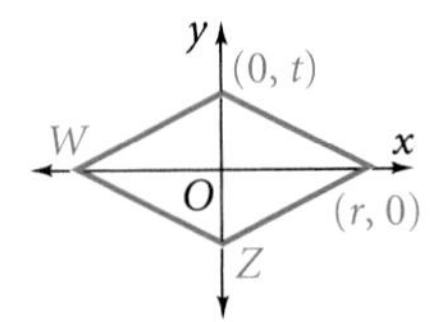

6. isosceles trapezoid

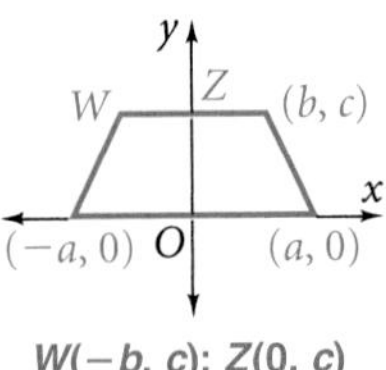

$W(-b, c)$; $Z(0, c)$

Find the coordinates of the midpoint of $\overline{WZ}$ and find *WZ* in the exercise named.

7. Exercise 1 $\left(\frac{b}{2}, \frac{h}{2}\right)$, $\sqrt{b^2 + h^2}$

8. Exercise 2 $\left(a, \frac{a}{2}\right)$, a

9. Exercise 3 $(-b, 0)$, $2b$

10. Exercise 4 $\left(\frac{a}{2}, \frac{b}{2}\right)$, $\sqrt{a^2 + b^2}$

11. Exercise 5 $\left(-\frac{r}{2}, -\frac{t}{2}\right)$, $\sqrt{r^2 + t^2}$

12. Exercise 6 $\left(-\frac{b}{2}, c\right)$, b

13. a. *Open-ended* Choose values for *r* and *t* in Exercise 5. Find the slope and length of each side. Sample: $r = 3$, $t = 2$; slopes are $\frac{2}{3}$ and $-\frac{2}{3}$; all lengths are $\sqrt{13}$.

b. Does the figure satisfy the definition of a rhombus? Explain. Yes; the opp. sides have the same slope, so they are ∥. The 4 sides are ≅ .

14. Draw a square with sides 2*a* units long on the coordinate plane. Give coordinates for each vertex. Answers may vary. See right for sample.

14. $(-a, a)$ y (a, a) O x $(-a, -a)$ $(a, -a)$

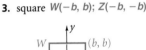

15. a. Draw a square centered at the origin whose diagonals of length 2*b* units lie on the *x*- and *y*-axes. See back of book.

b. Give the coordinates of the vertices of the square. $(-b, 0)$, $(0, b)$, $(b, 0)$, $(0, -b)$

c. Compute the length of a side of the square. $b\sqrt{2}$

d. Find the slopes of two adjacent sides of the square. 1 and −1

e. Do the slopes show that the sides are perpendicular? Explain. Yes, because the product of the slopes is −1.

16. a. Draw an isosceles triangle with base length 2*b* units and height 2*c*, placing one vertex on the origin. a–b. See back of book.

b. Draw an isosceles triangle with base length 2*b* units and height 2*c*, placing the base on the *x*-axis and the line of symmetry on the *y*-axis.

c. Find the lengths of the legs of the triangle in part (a). $\sqrt{b^2 + 4c^2}$

d. Find the lengths of the legs of the triangle in part (b). $\sqrt{b^2 + 4c^2}$

e. How do the results of parts (c) and (d) compare? Explain. The lengths are =; the △ in (b) is ≅ to the △ in (a).

Exercise 17 Suggest students copy the figure and draw two vertical lines to make a rectangle and two triangles. This may help students see that the x-coordinate of P is $c - a$.

GEOMETRY IN 3 DIMENSIONS Exercise 20 Have students work in groups. Provide models of the coordinate axes to help students visualize the solids.

TRANSFORMATIONS Exercises 23–24 Suggest students do these exercises using geometry software or paper folding.

WRITING Exercise 25b Ask students to support their explanation with a diagram.

MAKING CONNECTIONS Exercise 26 Until the 1990s, most underwater archaeology was done in the Mediterranean Sea. With improved scuba equipment and mapping methods, divers have discovered wrecks of Spanish Armada ships off the coast of Ireland, Viking and Renaissance ships near Northern Europe, a Portuguese merchant ship off the coast of Kenya, and many other significant underwater archeological treasures.

Give the coordinates for point *P* without using any new variables.

17. isosceles trapezoid $(c - a, b)$

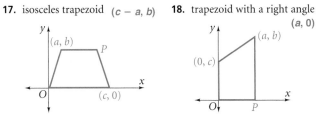

18. trapezoid with a right angle $(a, 0)$

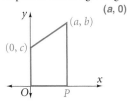

19. kite $(-b, 0)$

20. *Geometry in 3 Dimensions* Choose coordinates (x, y, z) for the vertices of a rectangular prism whose dimensions are a, b, and c. Use the origin as one of the vertices. Sample: (0, 0, 0), (0, 0, c), (0, b, 0), (a, 0, 0), (0, b, c), (a, 0, c), (a, b, 0), (a, b, c)

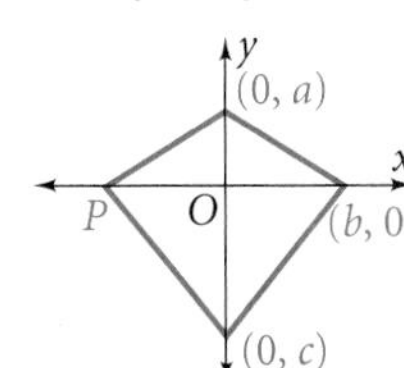

21. *Geometry in 3 Dimensions* A cube has edges $2a$ units long.

a. Choose coordinates for the vertices, using the origin as one vertex.

b. Choose coordinates for the vertices, using the origin as the center of the cube and making each of the cube's faces parallel to two of the three axes. a–b. See margin.

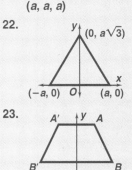

22. Draw a model for an equilateral triangle with sides $2a$ units long. Give coordinates of the vertices without introducing new variables. See margin for sample.

23. *Transformations* In Quadrant I draw $\overline{AB}$ that is not parallel to either axis. Let $\overline{A'B'}$ be its reflection over the y-axis. What type of quadrilateral is $BAA'B'$? Explain. See margin.

TECHNOLOGY HINT

You could do Exercises 23 and 24 with geometry software.

24. *Transformations* In Quadrant I draw $\overline{AB}$ that is parallel to the y-axis. Let $\overline{A'B'}$ be its reflection over the y-axis. What type of quadrilateral is $BAA'B'$? Explain. See margin.

25a. The diagonals of a rhombus are ⊥.

25. a. What property of a rhombus makes it convenient to place its diagonals on the x- and y-axes? See above right.

b. *Writing* Suppose a parallelogram is not a rhombus. Explain why it is inconvenient to place opposite vertices on the y-axis. See margin.

26. *Archaeology* Divers searching a shipwreck sometimes use gridded-plastic sheets to establish a coordinate system on the ocean floor. They record the coordinates of points where artifacts are found. Assume that divers search a square area and can go no farther than b units from their starting points. Draw a model for the area one diver can search. Assign coordinates to the vertices without using any new variables. Answers may vary. See back of book for sample.

21a. (0, 0, 0), (0, 0, $2a$), (0, $2a$, 0), ($2a$, 0, 0), (0, $2a$, $2a$), ($2a$, 0, $2a$), ($2a$, $2a$, 0), ($2a$, $2a$, $2a$)

b. ($-a$, $-a$, $-a$), ($-a$, $-a$, a) ($-a$, a, $-a$), (a, $-a$, $-a$), ($-a$, a, a), (a, $-a$, a), (a, a, $-a$), (a, a, a)

22.

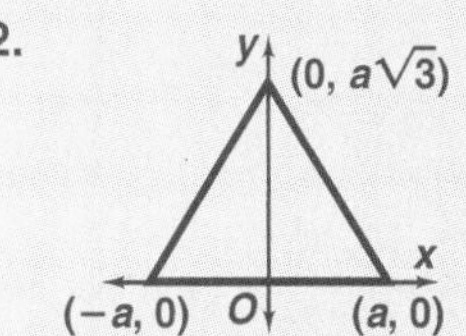

23.

Isosceles trapezoid; the y-axis is the ⊥ bisector of $\overline{AA'}$ and $\overline{BB'}$. In a plane, 2 lines ⊥ to a 3rd line are ∥, so $\overline{AA'} \parallel \overline{BB'}$. Also, $AB = A'B'$.

24.

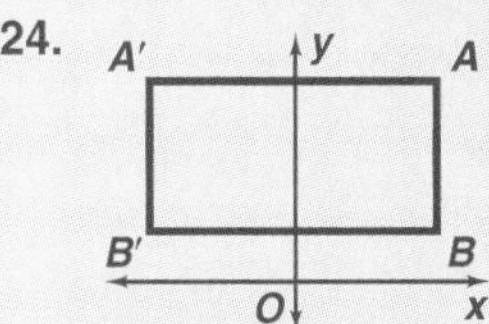

Rectangle; the y-axis is the ⊥ bisector of $\overline{AA'}$ and $\overline{BB'}$. In a plane, 2 lines ⊥ to a 3rd line are ∥, so $\overline{AA'} \parallel \overline{BB'}$. Also, 2 lines ∥ to a 3rd line are ∥, so $\overline{AB} \parallel \overline{A'B'}$ and $\overline{AB} \perp \overline{AA'}$.

25b. The diagonals of a ▱ that is not a rhombus are not ⊥.

Exercises MIXED REVIEW

GETTING READY FOR LESSON 9-6 These exercises prepare students to use coordinate geometry in proofs.

Wrap Up

THE BIG IDEA Ask students: *What is the most convenient way to draw and label a square on a coordinate grid? a parallelogram?*

RETEACHING ACTIVITY Students find coordinates of figures on the coordinate plane. Then they prove statements about quadrilaterals using coordinate proofs. (Reteaching worksheet 9-5)

Exercises CHECKPOINT

In this Checkpoint, your students will assess their own progress in Lessons 9-3 to 9-5.

A Point in Time

ESL Students may be confused by the term "relief sculpture." It may help to think of a "relief sculpture" as a carving that "releases" a work from its background.

You may wish to have students investigate the various types of relief sculpture such as *bas-relief*, *high relief*, and *intaglio*, the tools used by relief-sculptors, and Mayan, Southeast Asian, and Roman relief sculpture.

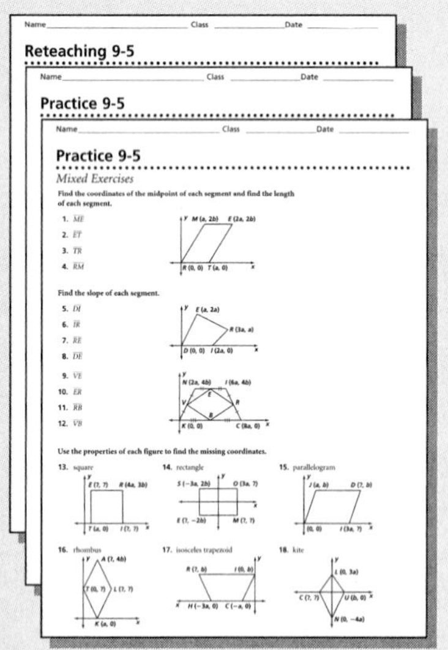

Reteaching 9-5

Practice 9-5

Practice 9-5

Mixed Exercises

Lesson Quiz

Lesson Quiz is also available in Transparencies.

Draw each figure in the coordinate plane and give the coordinates of each vertex.

1. a square with sides *d* units long **Answers may vary. Sample:**

   (0, *d*) (*d*, *d*) (0, 0) (*d*, 0) *x* *y*

2. an isosceles trapezoid **Answers may vary. Sample:**

   (*a*, *b*) (*s* – *a*, *b*) (0, 0) (*s*, 0) *x* *y*

3. a rectangle with its diagonals intersecting at the origin **See back of book.**

Exercises MIXED REVIEW

Find the area of each figure.

27. an equilateral triangle with altitude $6\sqrt{3}$ in. **$36\sqrt{3}$ in.^{2}**

28. a square with diagonals $5\sqrt{2}$ ft **25 ft^2**

29. How much cardboard do you need to make a box 4 ft by 5 ft by 2 ft? **76 ft^2**

Getting Ready for Lesson 9-6

30. a. **Coordinate Geometry** Graph the rhombus with vertices $A(2, 2)$, $B(7, 2)$, $C(4, -2)$, $D(-1, -2)$.
    b. Connect the midpoints of consecutive sides to form a quadrilateral. What do you notice about the figure formed? **The figure is a rectangle.**

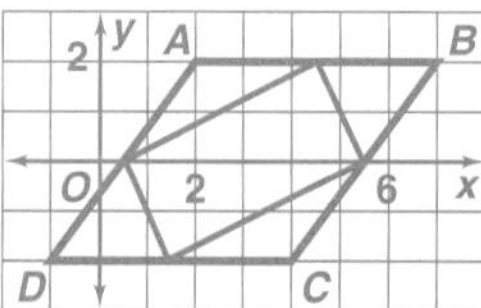

Exercises CHECKPOINT

Find the value of the variable(s).

1. $y°$ $x°$ $78°$

   $x = 51$; $y = 51$

2. **3**

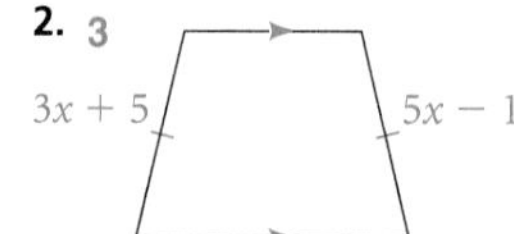

3.

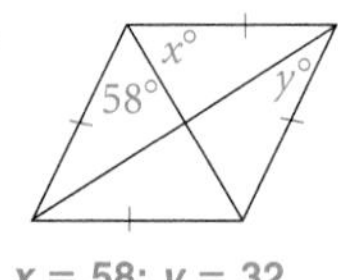

$x = 58$; $y = 32$

4.

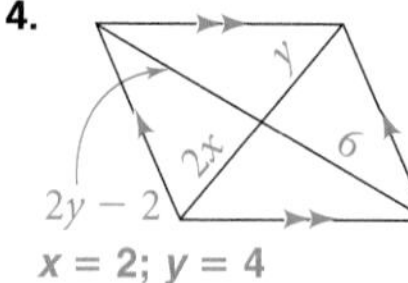

$x = 2$; $y = 4$

5. **Writing** Summarize the characteristics of the diagonals of a rhombus that are not true for the diagonals of every parallelogram.

   The diagonals of a rhombus are ⊥; each diagonal bisects 2 opp. angles of the rhombus.

A Point in Time

500 B.C. 0 500 A.D. 1000 A.D. 1500 A.D. 2000 A.D.

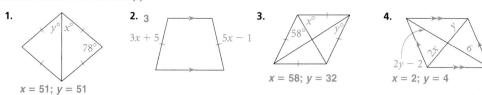

Egyptian Relief Sculpture

Many walls in ancient Egypt were decorated with relief sculptures. The relief sculpture in the photo was created in the year **255 B.C.** First the artist sketched the scene on papyrus overlaid with a grid. Next the wall was marked with a grid the size of the intended sculpture. To draw each line, a tightly stretched string that had been dipped in red ochre was plucked, like a guitar string.

Using the grid squares as guides, the artist transferred the drawing to the wall. Then a relief sculptor cut the background away, leaving the scene slightly raised. Finally an artist painted the scene.

9-6 Teaching Notes

PROBLEM OF THE DAY

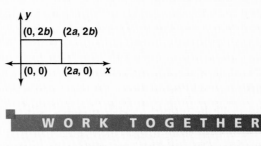

An artist has fourteen cubes, each with an edge of 1 m. She forms a sculpture on the ground and paints the exposed surface. How many square meters does she paint? 33

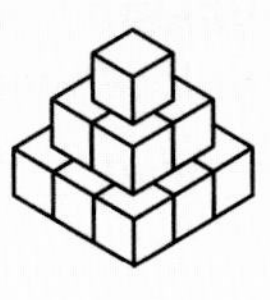

Problem of the Day is also available in Transparencies.

CONNECTING TO PRIOR KNOWLEDGE

Draw the following rectangle on a coordinate grid and have students find the slopes and the midpoints of the sides.

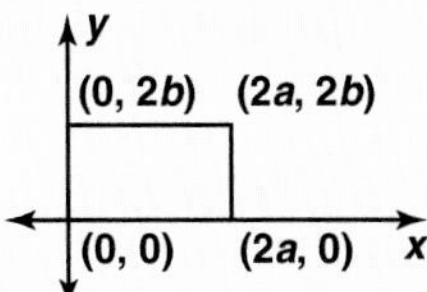

WORK TOGETHER

VISUAL LEARNING Suggest that partners draw different trapezoids. At least one partner should draw a trapezoid that is not isosceles. Make sure students understand that they are to find numerical coordinates for *M* and *N*.

Connections — Flags . . . and more

9-6 Using Coordinate Geometry in Proofs

What You'll Learn

- Proving theorems using figures in the coordinate plane

...And Why

To use coordinate geometry to design flags

What You'll Need

- graph paper
- straightedge

WORK TOGETHER

Work with a partner. Each of you should make your own figures.

- On graph paper, draw a trapezoid with one vertex at the origin and one base on the positive *x*-axis. Find the coordinates of each vertex.
- Find the coordinates of the midpoints *M* and *N* of the two nonparallel sides. Draw $\overline{MN}$.
- Find the slopes of $\overline{MN}$ and both bases of the trapezoid. Compare the slopes to find a relationship between $\overline{MN}$ and the bases.
- Compare the length of $\overline{MN}$ and the sum of the lengths of the bases.
- Compare your results with your partner. Make **conjectures** about the relationships between $\overline{MN}$ and the bases of a trapezoid.

THINK AND DISCUSS

The segment that joins the midpoints of the nonparallel sides of a trapezoid is the **midsegment of the trapezoid.** Your conjectures in the Work Together lead to the following theorem about the midsegment of a trapezoid.

Theorem 9-19 The midsegment of a trapezoid is (1) parallel to the bases and (2) half as long as the sum of the lengths of the bases.

Your main tools in coordinate geometry proofs are the formulas for slope, midpoint, and distance. Use these tools to prove Theorem 9-19 by answering the following questions.

y, R(2b, 2c), A(2d, 2c), M, N, x, T, P(2a, 0)

Given: $\overline{MN}$ is the midsegment of trapezoid *TRAP*.

Prove: $\overline{MN} \parallel \overline{TP}$, $\overline{MN} \parallel \overline{RA}$, and $MN = \frac{1}{2}(TP + RA)$.

1. Find the coordinates of midpoints *M* and *N*. $M(b, c)$; $N(a + d, c)$
2. a. Find the slopes of the bases of the trapezoid. 0
   b. Find the slope of $\overline{MN}$. 0
   c. Compare the slopes. The slopes are =.
3. a. Find the sum of the lengths of the bases. $2a + 2d - 2b$
   b. Find the length of $\overline{MN}$. $a + d - b$
   c. Compare the lengths.
   The midsegment is half the sum of the lengths of the bases.

Lesson Planning Options

Prerequisite Skills

- Graphing in the coordinate plane
- Finding distance, slope, and midpoints

Assignment Options for Exercises On Your Own

Core 1–8, 12
Extension 9–11

Use Mixed Review to maintain skills.

Resources

Student Edition

Skills Handbook, pp. 674, 678
Extra Practice, p. 656
Glossary/Study Guide

Teaching Resources

Chapter Support File, Ch. 9
- Practice 9-6 (two worksheets)
- Reteaching 9-6

Classroom Manager 9-6
Glossary, Spanish Resources

Transparencies

5, 96

THINK AND DISCUSS

Students should be familiar with midsegments of triangles. Have them compare the properties of midsegments of triangles and midsegments of trapezoids.

CRITICAL THINKING Refer to trapezoid *RAPT* on page 483. Ask students: *If $\overline{TR}$ and $\overline{PA}$ were extended to form $\triangle TQP$, what could you say about $\overline{RQ}$ and $\overline{AQ}$?*

Example **Relating to the Real World** 

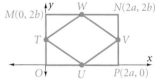

Discuss with students the placement of *MNPO*. Point out that placing two sides on the axes makes identifying the coordinates simpler by making use of as many zeros as possible. Also point out that by using only the first quadrant, all the non-zero coordinates are positive.

DIVERSITY Have students bring in flags from their native countries and discuss the meaning or symbolism of each.

CRITICAL THINKING Question 4 Ask students if it would be enough to prove two consecutive sides congruent if they did not know *TWVU* was a parallelogram.

MAKING CONNECTIONS The study of flag design, history, symbolism, etiquette, terminology, and development is known as vexillology (from the Latin *vexillum*, meaning "flag").

Additional Examples

FOR EXAMPLE

Use coordinate geometry to prove that the quadrilateral formed by connecting the midpoints of the sides of a rhombus is a square.

E (0, 2b), H(−2a, 0), F(2a, 0), G(0, −2b), M, J, L, K

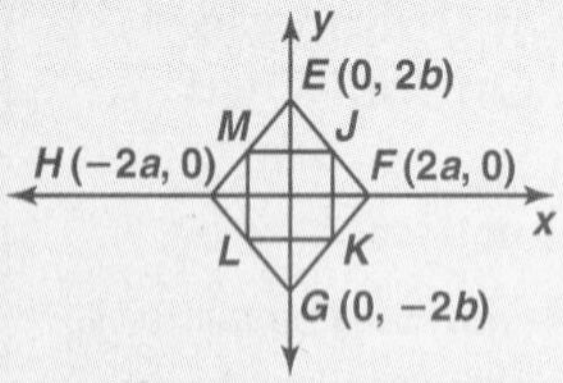

Let *EFGH* be a rhombus. Choose convenient axes and coordinates, as shown. Let *J, K, L,* and *M* be the midpoints of the sides: *J(a, b), K(a, −b), L(−a, −b),* and *M(−a, b)*. Show $\angle MJK$ is a right angle.

Slope of $\overline{MJ} = 0$

Slope of $\overline{JK}$ is undefined.

$\overline{MJ}$ is horizontal and $\overline{JK}$ is vertical, thus they are perpendicular and *JKLM* is a square.

Discussion: *Explain why it is enough to prove just one angle is a right angle in order to prove that the quadrilateral formed by connecting the midpoints of a rhombus is a square.*

Example **Relating to the Real World**

Flags The flag at the left is constructed by connecting the midpoints of the sides of a rectangle. Use coordinate geometry to prove that the quadrilateral formed by connecting the midpoints of the sides of a rectangle is a rhombus.

Let *MNPO* be a rectangle. Choose convenient axes and coordinates, as shown in the figure at the right. Let *T, W, V,* and *U* be the midpoints of the sides of the rectangle.

M(0, 2b), W, N(2a, 2b), T, V, O, U, P(2a, 0)

Use the Midpoint Formula to find the coordinates of the midpoints:

$T(0, b)$ $W(a, 2b)$ $V(2a, b)$ $U(a, 0)$

From Lesson 9-5, you know that *TWVU* is a parallelogram. To prove that *TWVU* is a rhombus, show that consecutive sides are congruent.

$TW = \sqrt{(a-0)^2 + (2b-b)^2} = \sqrt{a^2 + b^2}$

$WV = \sqrt{(2a-a)^2 + (b-2b)^2} = \sqrt{a^2 + b^2}$

$TW = WV$, so parallelogram *TWVU* is a rhombus.

4. **Critical Thinking** In the Example, explain why it is enough to prove just two consecutive sides congruent in order to prove that parallelogram *TWVU* is a rhombus. **Opp. sides of a ▱ are ≅. Use the Transitive Prop. of ≅ to prove all sides ≅.**
5. **Try This** In the Example, use another method to prove that parallelogram *TWVU* is a rhombus. **See back of book.**

Exercises ON YOUR OWN

WRITING Exercise 1 Students' answers may vary. Make sure they give reasons for their choices.

ALTERNATIVE ASSESSMENT Exercises 2–5 You can use these exercises to help you assess students' understanding of coordinate proof. Have students work with a partner. Check that students use the midpoint and distance formulas correctly.

Exercise 5 Students may prove the sides of *DEFG* are congruent or that opposite sides are parallel and two consecutive sides are congruent.

Exercise 7 Students may prove that *KLMN* has four right angles or that opposite sides are parallel and one angle is a right angle.

OPEN-ENDED Exercise 8 Suggest that students look back at some of the proofs from Chapter 8 where they used congruent triangles.

Exercises ON YOUR OWN

1. **Writing** The midpoints of $\overline{OR}$ and $\overline{ST}$ are W and Z, respectively. Which of the following figures would you prefer to use to find the coordinates of the midpoint of $\overline{WZ}$? Explain your choice. Answers may vary. Sample: C; you need to divide the coordinates by 2 twice to find the midpoint of $\overline{WZ}$.

A. 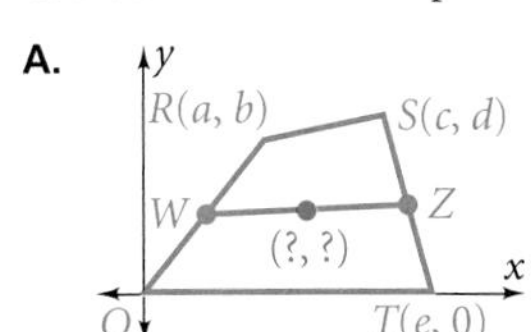

B. 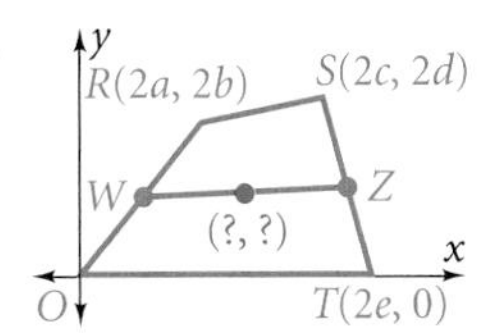

C. 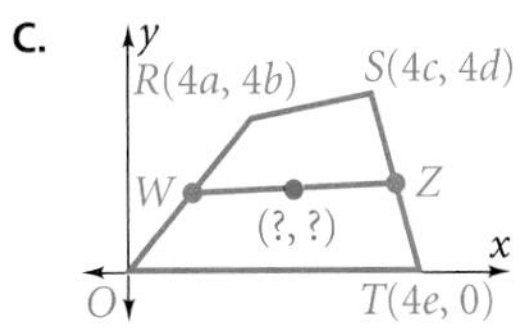

Complete the coordinates for each figure. Then use coordinate geometry to prove the statement. 2–3, 5. See margin p. 486.

2. The diagonals of a parallelogram bisect each other (Theorem 9-3).

   Given: Parallelogram *ABCD*
   Prove: $\overline{AC}$ bisects $\overline{BD}$, and $\overline{BD}$ bisects $\overline{AC}$.

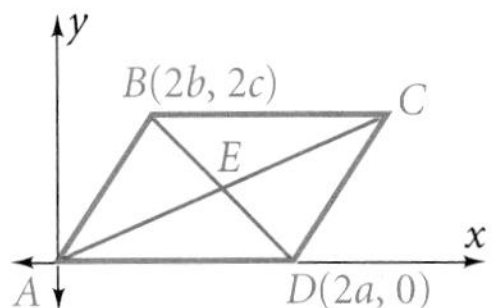

3. The diagonals of an isosceles trapezoid are congruent (Theorem 9-17).

   Given: Trapezoid *EFGH*, $\overline{FE} \cong \overline{GH}$
   Prove: $\overline{EG} \cong \overline{HF}$

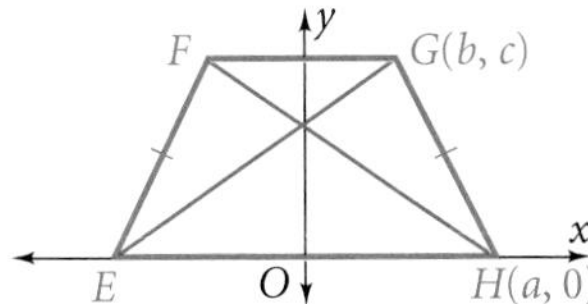

4. The midpoint of the hypotenuse of a right triangle is equidistant from the vertices.

   Given: $\angle MON$ is a right angle, P is the midpoint of $\overline{MN}$.
   Prove: $MP = PN = OP$

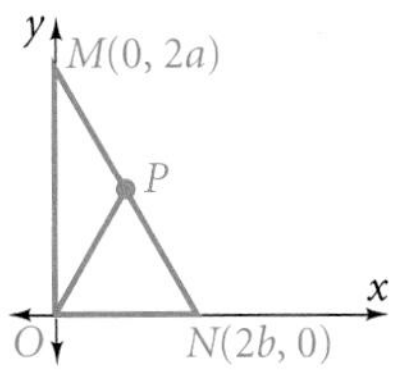

$P(b, a)$; $MP = PN = OP = \sqrt{a^2 + b^2}$

5. The segments joining the midpoints of consecutive sides of an isosceles trapezoid form a rhombus.

   Given: Trapezoid *TRAP* with $\overline{TR} \cong \overline{AP}$, D, E, F, and G are midpoints of the indicated sides.
   Prove: *DEFG* is a rhombus.

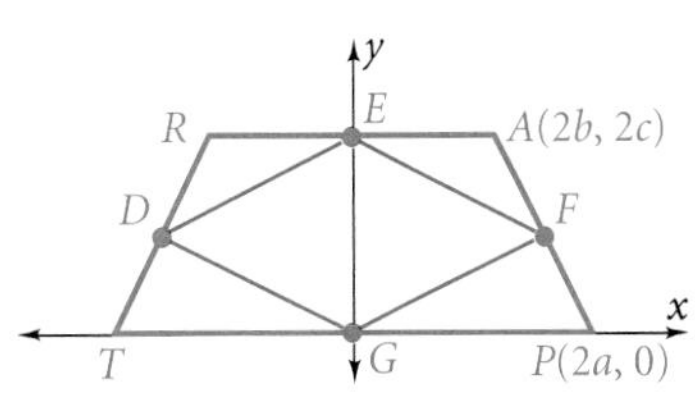

6. Compare your coordinate proof of Theorem 9-3 in Exercise 2 with the two-column proof on page 450. Which proof do you think is easier to understand? Explain. Check students' work.

Prentice Hall Technology

Software
- Secondary Math Lab Toolkit™
- Integrated Math Lab 40
- Computer Item Generator 9-6

CD-ROM
- Multimedia Geometry Lab 9

Internet
- See the Prentice Hall site. (http://www.phschool.com)

ESL Exercise 9 Some students may not know what a "mobile" is. If possible, bring one in for students to see. Using the picture, ask students to name it in their native languages.

RESEARCH Exercise 9 Students should be able to find this information in an encyclopedia or physics textbook.

EXTENSION Exercise 9 If you have block scheduling or an extended class period, have students cut out a nonregular quadrilateral from a piece of lightweight cardboard. Have students try to balance the quadrilateral on the tip of a sharpened pencil.

Exercise 11 Students prove Theorem 4-18 from Lesson 4-8: The lines that contain the altitudes of a triangle are concurrent.

pages 485–487 On Your Own

2. $A(0, 0)$, $C(2a + 2b, 2c)$, $E(a + b, c)$; use the Midpoint Formula to find the midpts. of $\overline{AC}$, $(a + b, c)$, and $\overline{BD}$, $(a + b, c)$. Since the midpts. are the same, the diagonals bisect each other.
3. $E(-a, 0)$, $F(-b, c)$; use the Distance Formula to find the lengths of $\overline{EG}$, $\sqrt{(b + a)^2 + c^2}$, and of $\overline{HF}$, $\sqrt{(a + b)^2 + (-c)^2}$. The lengths are $=$, so the diagonals are $\cong$.
5. $T(-2a, 0)$, $R(-2b, 2c)$, $D(-a - b, c)$, $E(0, 2c)$, $F(a + b, c)$, $G(0, 0)$; $DE = EF = FG = GD = \sqrt{(a + b)^2 + c^2}$
7. $K(-b, a + c)$, $L(b, a + c)$, $M(b, c)$, $N(-b, c)$; slope of $\overline{KL}$ and slope of $\overline{MN}$ are 0. Slope of $\overline{LM}$ and slope of $\overline{NK}$ are undef. Lines with 0 slope and with undef. slope are $\perp$ to each other. Therefore, $KLMN$ is a rectangle.
8. The Triangle Midsegment Thm.—The segment connecting the midpts. of 2 sides of the triangle is $\parallel$ to the 3rd side and is half its length; you can use the Midpoint Formula and the Distance Formula to prove the statement directly.

486

7. Use coordinate geometry to prove that the midpoints of the sides of a kite determine a rectangle.

Given: Kite $DEFG$, $DE = EF$, $DG = GF$, K, L, M, and N are midpoints of the indicated sides.
Prove: $KLMN$ is a rectangle. See margin.

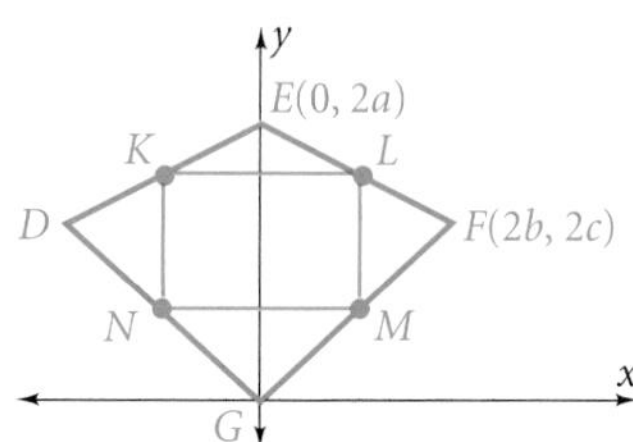

8. *Open-ended* Give an example of a statement that you think is easier to prove with coordinate geometry than with a two-column proof. Explain your choice. See margin for sample.

Alexander Calder

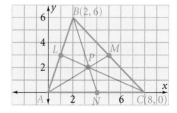

Alexander Calder (1898–1976) was an American sculptor who is considered the founder of modern kinetic art. Kinetic art, which is art that involves motion, is perhaps best seen in Calder's mobiles. His mobiles consist of a series of carefully balanced metal shapes hanging from wires. Calder's early mobiles are motorized. In his later ones, however, the shapes float gracefully and move in different directions with currents of air.

Calder was inspired to make mobiles by watching circus performers. His initial attempts at kinetic art were motorized circus figures made of wire and wood.

9. *Research* For a mobile to be in balance, the artist must suspend the mobile from its center of gravity. The center of gravity, or *centroid,* is the point around which the weight of an object is evenly distributed. Choose an object from Calder's mobile. Research how you would find the center of gravity of the object. Check students' work.

10. The centroid of a triangle is the point where the medians meet. The centroid is $\frac{2}{3}$ of the distance from each vertex to the midpoint of the opposite side. Complete the following steps to find the centroid of the triangle at the right.

a. Find the coordinates of points L, M, and N, the midpoints of the sides of the triangle. $L(1, 3)$, $M(5, 3)$, $N(4, 0)$
b. Find the equations of lines $\overleftrightarrow{AM}$, $\overleftrightarrow{BN}$, and $\overleftrightarrow{CL}$. See below.
c. Find the coordinates of point P, the of intersection of lines $\overleftrightarrow{AM}$ and $\overleftrightarrow{BN}$. $P\left(\frac{10}{3}, 2\right)$
d. **Verify** that point P is the intersection of lines $\overleftrightarrow{AM}$ and $\overleftrightarrow{CL}$. $2 = -\frac{3}{7} \cdot \frac{10}{3} + \frac{24}{7}$ ✓

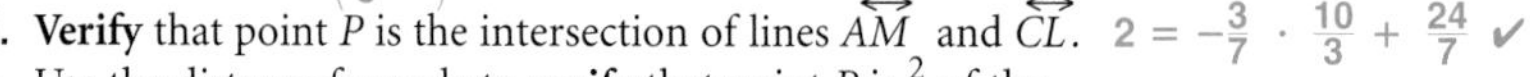

e. Use the distance formula to **verify** that point P is $\frac{2}{3}$ of the distance from each vertex to the midpoint of the opposite side. Check students' work.

b. $\overleftrightarrow{AM} : y = \frac{3}{5}x$; $\overleftrightarrow{BN} : y = -3x + 12$; $\overleftrightarrow{CL} : y = -\frac{3}{7}x + \frac{24}{7}$

Exercises MIXED REVIEW

CONNECTING TO STUDENTS' WORLD Exercise 13 Have students write a survey question with 4–6 possible responses. Have them survey at least 25 people. Then have them calculate the percent that chose each response and display their results in a bar graph.

SELF ASSESSMENT PORTFOLIO Share with students the criteria you will use to assess their work in portfolios, as well as how you plan to use the results. Students should understand how the rubrics assess their work, how each piece in the portfolio counts, and how the scores they get in their portfolios will affect their overall evaluation.

Wrap Up

THE BIG IDEA Ask students: *Describe the algebraic properties you use when writing a coordinate proof.*

RETEACHING ACTIVITY Students prove theorems using coordinate geometry. (Reteaching worksheet 9-6)

11. Given $\triangle ABC$ with altitudes p, q, and r, complete the following to show that p, q, and r intersect in a point. (This point is called the *orthocenter* of the triangle.) b, d, f, g. See back of book.

a. The slope of $\overline{BC}$ is $\frac{c}{-b}$. What is the slope of line p? $\frac{b}{c}$

b. Show that the equation of line p is $y = \frac{b}{c}(x - a)$.

c. What is the equation of line q? $x = 0$

d. Show that lines p and q intersect at $(0, \frac{-ab}{c})$.

e. The slope of $\overline{AC}$ is $\frac{c}{-a}$. What is the slope of line r? $\frac{a}{c}$

f. Show that the equation of line r is $y = \frac{a}{c}(x - b)$.

g. Show that lines r and q intersect at $(0, \frac{-ab}{c})$.

h. Give the coordinates of the orthocenter of $\triangle ABC$. $\left(0, -\frac{ab}{c}\right)$

12. *RSTW* is a rhombus. Give the coordinates of *S* and *T*. In part (c) give the coordinates in terms of *a* and *c*, without introducing any new variables.

a. $S(3, 4)$; $T(8, 4)$

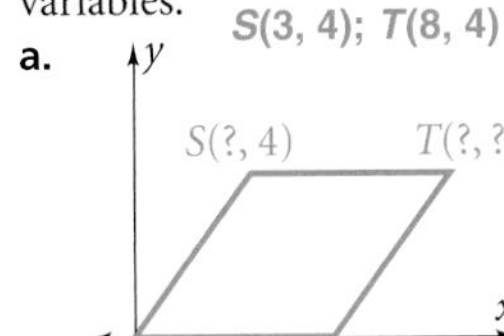

b. $S(5, 12)$; $T(18, 12)$

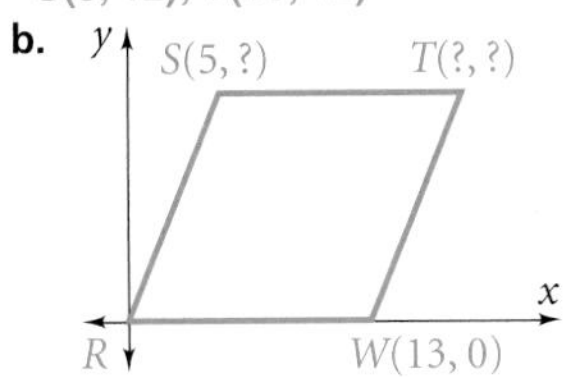

c. $S(a, \sqrt{c^2 - a^2})$; $T(a + c, \sqrt{c^2 - a^2})$

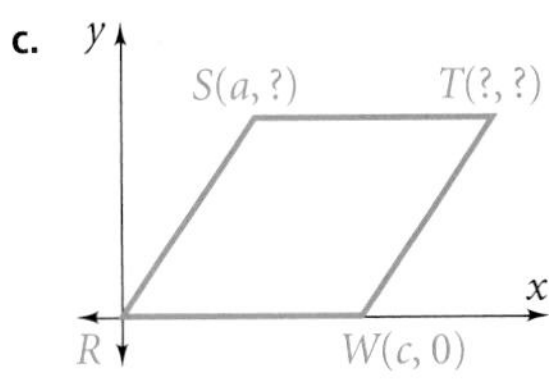

d. Use your figure in part (c) for a coordinate proof that the diagonals of a rhombus are perpendicular.
The slope of $\overline{SW}$ is $\frac{\sqrt{c^2 - a^2}}{a - c}$. The slope of $\overline{TR}$ is $\frac{\sqrt{c^2 - a^2}}{a + c}$ and $\frac{\sqrt{c^2 - a^2}}{a + c} \cdot \frac{\sqrt{c^2 - a^2}}{a - c} = -1$, so the lines are $\perp$.

Exercises MIXED REVIEW

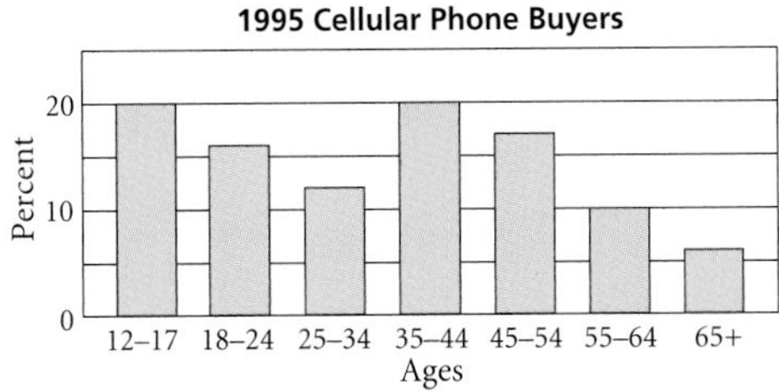

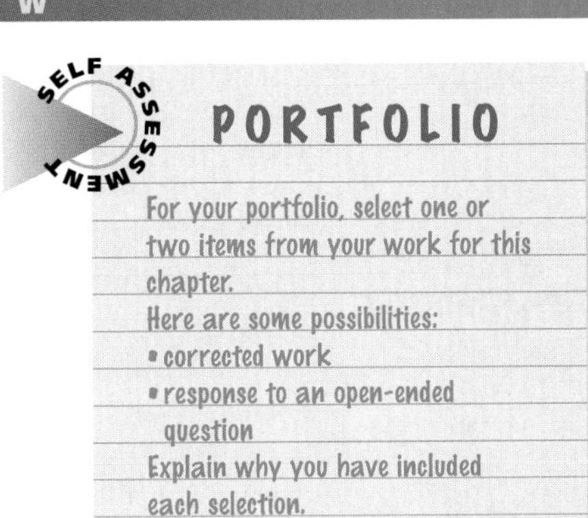

13. *Data Analysis* What percent of cellular phone buyers were younger than 25? 36%

14. *Writing* Describe two ways to find what percent of cellular phone buyers were younger than 65. Use both methods. Are the answers the same? Explain. See back of book.

15. *Critical Thinking* Explain why the total of all cellular phone buyers is greater than 100%.
The percent figure in each category is rounded to the nearest integer.

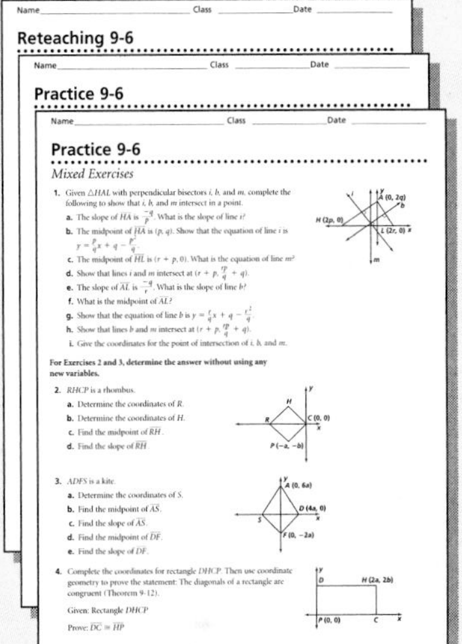
Reteaching 9-6
Practice 9-6
Practice 9-6
Mixed Exercises

Lesson Quiz

Lesson Quiz is also available in Transparencies.

Find the coordinates of the remaining vertices for each figure. Then use coordinate geometry to prove the statement. See back of book.

1. Given: Rectangle *CDEF*
Prove: $\overline{CE} \cong \overline{DF}$

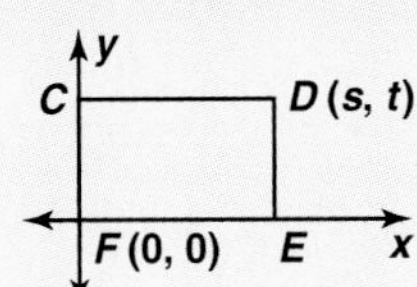

2. Given: Parallelogram *MNOP*
Prove: $\overline{NO} \cong \overline{MP}$, $\overline{NM} \cong \overline{OP}$

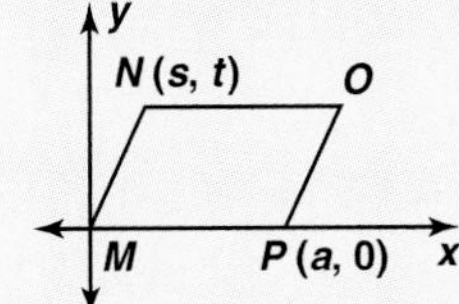

Finishing The Chapter Project

PROJECT DAY You may wish to plan a project day during which students share their completed projects. Encourage groups to explain their processes as well as their products.

PROJECT NOTEBOOK Have students review their project work and bring their notebooks up to date.

- Have students review their kite designs. Ask them to share the different designs and models they tried and how each model or design performed.
- Ask students to share any insights they had when designing their kites, such as what made their kites perform better and what did not work.

SCORING RUBRIC

3 Student designs, constructs, and flies a kite. Student accurately uses geometric terms to describe it. There was experimentation. Student thoroughly describes how the kite performed and suggests how to improve it.

2 Student designs, constructs, and flies a kite. Student uses some geometric terms to describe it. There was some experimentation. Student describes how the kite performed but may not suggest how to improve it.

1 Student designs and constructs a kite, but may not successfully fly it. Student uses few geometric terms to describe the kite or may use them incorrectly. There is little evidence of experimentation.

0 Major elements are incomplete or missing.

Finishing the Chapter Project

Find Out activities on pages 453, 468, and 476 should help you complete your project. Design and construct a kite and then fly it. Include complete plans for building the kite, specifying the size, shape, and material for each piece. Use geometric terms in your plans. Experiment with different designs and models. Describe how your model performs and what you would do to improve it.

Reflect and Revise

Ask a classmate to review your project with you. Together, check that the diagrams and explanations are clear, complete, and accurate. Have you tried several designs and kept a record of what you learned from each? Could your kite be stronger, more efficient, or more pleasing to the eye? Revise your work as needed.

Follow Up

Research the history of kites. Try to find examples of each use mentioned on page 447. You might make an illustrated time line to show special events like Benjamin Franklin's discovery about lightning and electricity and Samuel Cody's man-lifting kite.

For More Information

Baker, Rhoda, and Miles Denyer. *Flying Kites.* Edison, New Jersey: Chartwell Books, 1995.

Eden, Maxwell. *Kiteworks: Explorations in Kite Building & Flying.* New York: Sterling Publishing Co., 1989.

Kremer, Ron. *From Crystals to Kites.* Palo Alto, California: Dale Seymour Publications, 1995.

Morgan, Paul and Helene. *The Ultimate Kite Book.* New York: Simon & Schuster, 1992.

Wrap Up

HOW AM I DOING? Have students work in small groups. Ask each group to present the properties of a different quadrilateral. Each presentation must include a visual aid and a sample problem.

KEY TERMS The numbers in parentheses direct students to the pages where the terms are used or defined. Students should be able to (1) write a simple explanation of each term, (2) illustrate the term with a diagram, or (3) show an example that uses the term.

ERROR ALERT! **Exercises 1–4** Some students may not realize that the opposite sides of the figures are parallel because they are not marked with arrows. **Remediation:** Point out that the directions say that the figures are parallelograms.

STANDARDIZED TEST TIP **Exercise 5** Remind students not to classify the quadrilaterals by appearance but to use the properties of parallelograms along with the side and angle markings.

9 Wrap Up

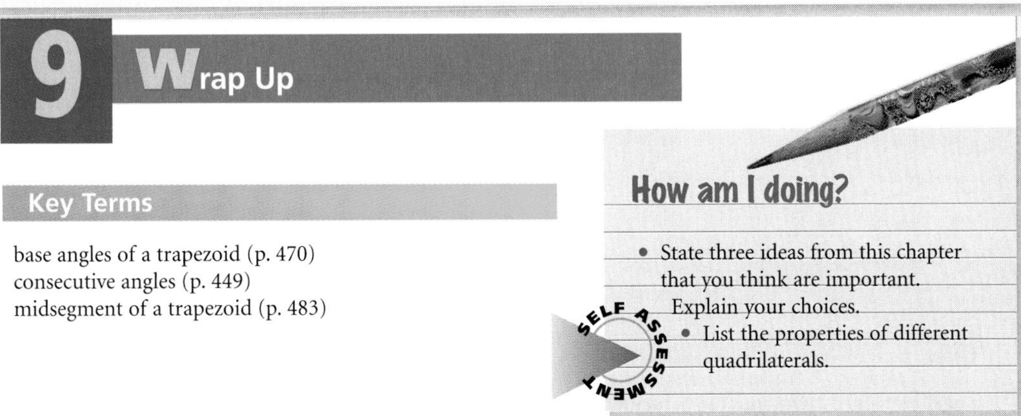

Key Terms

base angles of a trapezoid (p. 470)
consecutive angles (p. 449)
midsegment of a trapezoid (p. 483)

How am I doing?

- State three ideas from this chapter that you think are important. Explain your choices.
- List the properties of different quadrilaterals.

Resources

Student Edition
Extra Practice, p. 642
Glossary/Study Guide

Teaching Resources
Study Skills Handbook
Glossary, Spanish Resources

Properties of Parallelograms 9-1

Opposite sides and opposite angles of a parallelogram are congruent. The diagonals of a parallelogram bisect each other.

If three or more parallel lines cut off congruent segments on one transversal, then they cut off congruent segments on every transversal.

Find the measures of the numbered angles for each parallelogram.

1. 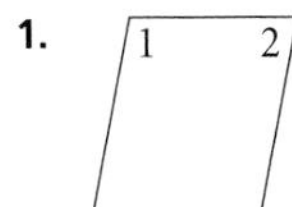

$m\angle 1 = 101$; $m\angle 2 = 79$; $m\angle 3 = 101$

2. 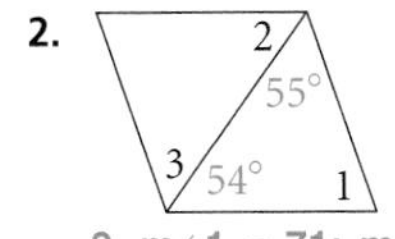

2. $m\angle 1 = 71$; $m\angle 2 = 54$; $m\angle 3 = 55$

3. 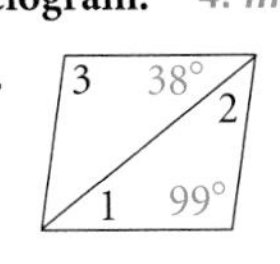

3. $m\angle 1 = 38$; $m\angle 2 = 43$; $m\angle 3 = 99$

4. 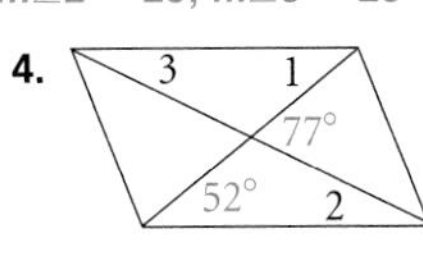

4. $m\angle 1 = 52$; $m\angle 2 = 25$; $m\angle 3 = 25$

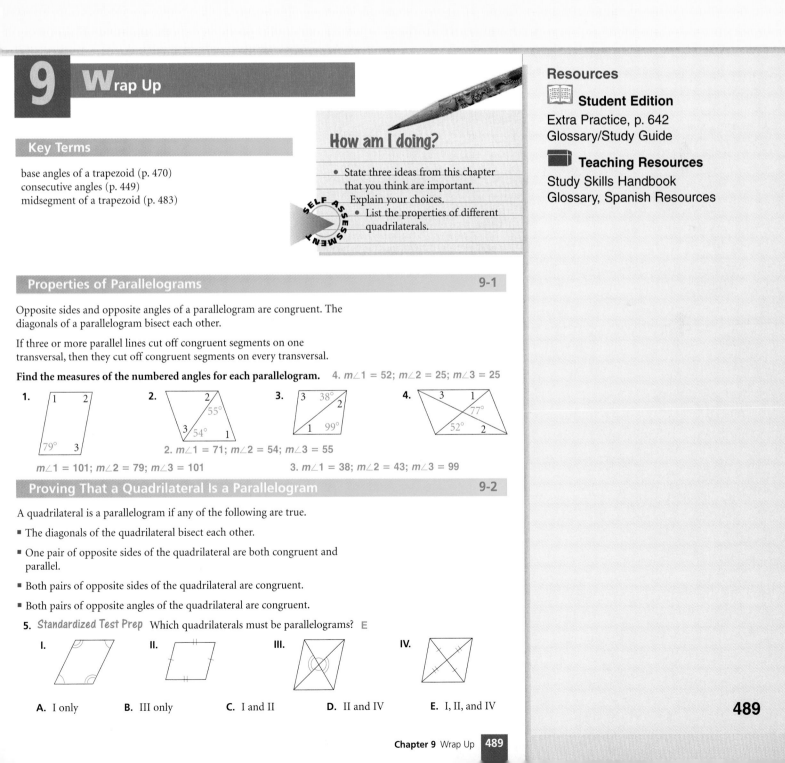

Proving That a Quadrilateral Is a Parallelogram 9-2

A quadrilateral is a parallelogram if any of the following are true.

- The diagonals of the quadrilateral bisect each other.
- One pair of opposite sides of the quadrilateral are both congruent and parallel.
- Both pairs of opposite sides of the quadrilateral are congruent.
- Both pairs of opposite angles of the quadrilateral are congruent.

5. *Standardized Test Prep* Which quadrilaterals must be parallelograms? E

I. 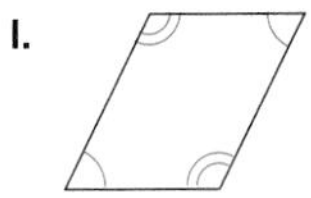

II. 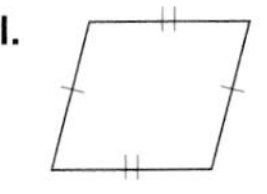

III. 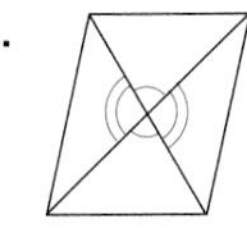 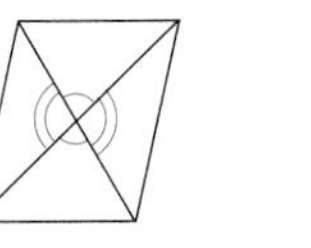

IV. 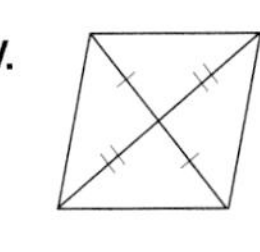

A. I only **B.** III only **C.** I and II **D.** II and IV **E.** I, II, and IV

ALGEBRA Exercises 6–8 Students can solve each system of equations simultaneously or by using substitution.

WRITING Exercise 17 Have students include a diagram along with the explanation.

Wrap Up pages 489–491

17. Pick 6 equally spaced lines on the lined paper. Place 1 corner of index card on the 1st line and the next corner on the 6th line. Mark the pts. where the remaining 4 lines intersect the edge of the index card. Repeat on the opp. edge of the index card. Then connect the marked pts. with ∥ lines.

Algebra **Determine the values of the variables for which *ABCD* is a parallelogram.**

6.

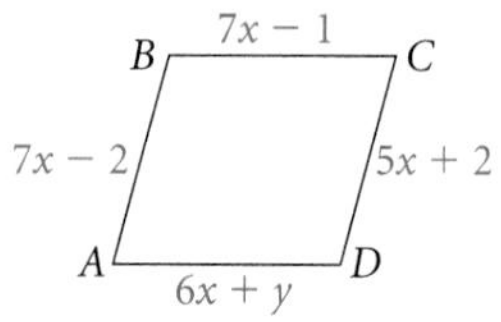

$x = 2$; $y = 1$

7.

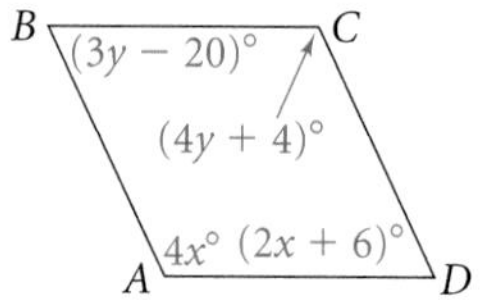

$x = 29$; $y = 28$

8.

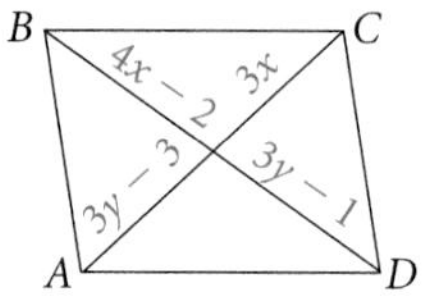

$x = 4$; $y = 5$

Properties of Special Parallelograms, Trapezoids, and Kites 9-3, 9-4

The diagonals of a rhombus are perpendicular. Each diagonal of a rhombus bisects two angles of the rhombus. The area of a rhombus is half the product of the lengths of its diagonals, $A = \frac{1}{2}d_1d_2$.

The diagonals of a rectangle are congruent.

If one diagonal of a parallelogram bisects two angles of the parallelogram, it is a rhombus. If the diagonals of a parallelogram are perpendicular, it is a rhombus. If the diagonals of a parallelogram are congruent, it is a rectangle.

The nonparallel sides of a trapezoid are the legs. Each pair of angles adjacent to a base of a trapezoid are **base angles** of the trapezoid.

Base angles of an isosceles trapezoid are congruent. The diagonals of an isosceles trapezoid are congruent.

The diagonals of a kite are perpendicular.

Find the measures of the numbered angles for each quadrilateral.

9.

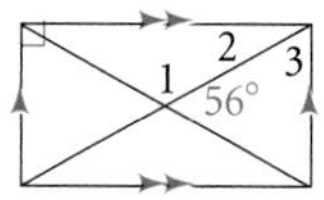

10.

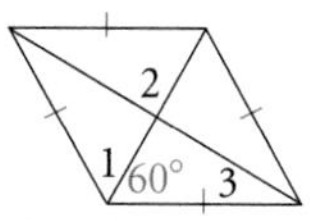

11.

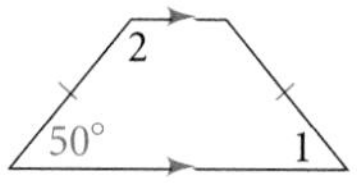

12.

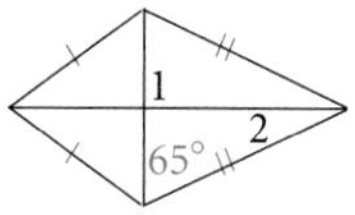

$m\angle1 = 124$; $m\angle2 = 28$; $m\angle3 = 62$

$m\angle1 = 50$; $m\angle2 = 130$

10. $m\angle1 = 60$; $m\angle2 = 90$; $m\angle3 = 30$

$m\angle1 = 90$; $m\angle2 = 25$

Find *AC* for each quadrilateral.

13.

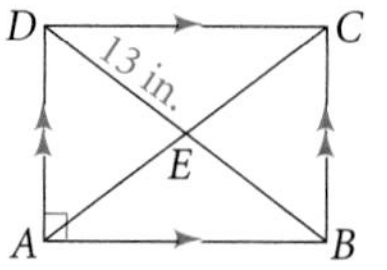

26 in.

14.

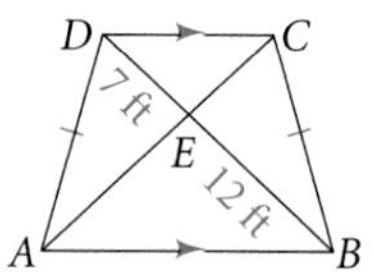

19 ft

15.

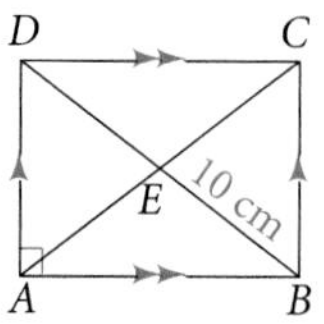

20 cm

16. A rhombus has sides that are 10 ft long and a diagonal that is 16 ft long. Find its area. 96 ft^2

17. **Writing** Explain how you could use a piece of lined paper to draw four lines on a blank index card that divide it into five equal sections. See margin.

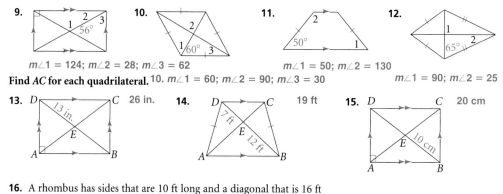

ALTERNATIVE ASSESSMENT **Exercises 18–21** Have students work in groups. Ask them to draw a rectangle, rhombus, square, and parallelogram in different positions in the coordinate plane from those shown. Then have them label the vertices of each figure using as few variables as possible.

Exercises 22–23 Have students work in groups to write these proofs. Then have the groups present their proofs to the class.

Remind students that the new mathematical terms in this chapter are defined in the Glossary/Study Guide in the back of the book.

Getting Ready For Chapter 10

Students may work these exercises independently or in small groups. The skills previewed will help prepare students to study similar triangles.

Organizing Coordinate Proofs 9-5

In coordinate proofs, it is usually easiest to use the origin as the center for the figure or to place a vertex at the origin and at least one side of the figure on an axis.

Give the coordinates of point *P* without using any new variables.

18. rectangle

(a, b)

19. rhombus

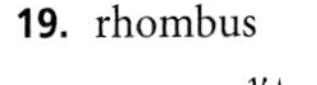

$(-a, 0)$

20. square

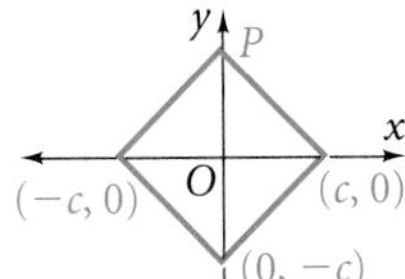

$(0, c)$

21. parallelogram

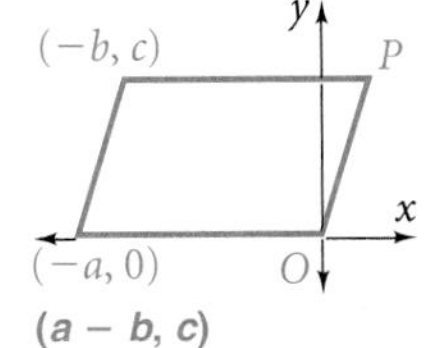

$(a - b, c)$

Using Coordinate Geometry in Proofs 9-6

The segment that joins the midpoints of the nonparallel sides of a trapezoid is the **midsegment of the trapezoid**. It is parallel to the bases and half as long as the sum of the lengths of the bases.

The formulas for slope, midpoint, and distance are used in coordinate proofs.

Choose coordinates for each figure. Then use coordinate geometry to prove the statement. 22–24. See margin.

22. The diagonals of a rectangle are congruent.
Given: Rectangle *ABCD*
Prove: $\overline{AC} \cong \overline{BD}$

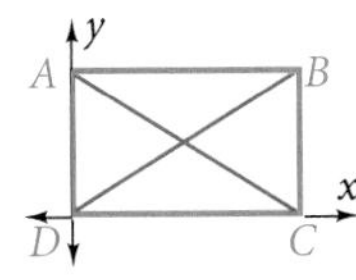

23. The diagonals of a square are perpendicular.
Given: Square *FGHI*
Prove: $\overline{FH} \perp \overline{GI}$

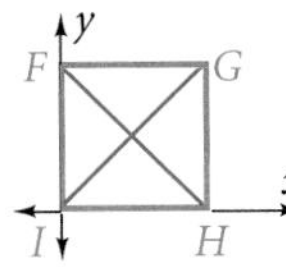

24. *Open-ended* Show two different ways to draw an isosceles triangle for a coordinate proof.

Getting Ready for... CHAPTER 10

25–30. Answers may vary. Samples are given.

Write a fraction equivalent to the given fraction.

25. $\frac{4}{5}$ $\frac{8}{10}$ **26.** $\frac{9}{4}$ $\frac{27}{12}$ **27.** $\frac{6}{8}$ $\frac{3}{4}$ **28.** $\frac{1}{10}$ $\frac{2}{20}$ **29.** $\frac{4}{7}$ $\frac{16}{28}$ **30.** $\frac{3}{8}$ $\frac{6}{16}$

Solve each proportion.

31. $\frac{3}{4} = \frac{x}{8}$ 6 **32.** $\frac{2}{x} = \frac{8}{24}$ 6 **33.** $\frac{x}{9} = \frac{1}{3}$ 3 **34.** $\frac{10}{25} = \frac{2}{x}$ 5

22. Sample: $A(0, a)$, $B(b, a)$, $C(b, 0)$, $D(0, 0)$; $AC = \sqrt{a^2 + b^2}$, $BD = \sqrt{a^2 + b^2}$, so $AC = BD$, and $\overline{AC} \cong \overline{BD}$.

23. Sample: $F(0, a)$, $G(a, a)$, $H(a, 0)$, $I(0, 0)$. The slope of $\overline{FH}$ is -1. The slope of $\overline{GI}$ is 1. Since the product of the slopes is -1, $\overline{FH} \perp \overline{GI}$.

24. Sample:

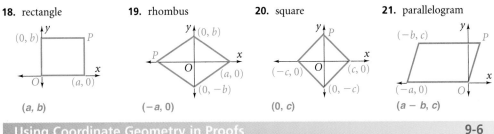

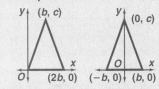

Assessment

ENHANCED MULTIPLE CHOICE QUESTIONS are more complex than traditional multiple choice questions, which assess only one skill. Enhanced multiple choice questions assess the processes that students use, as well as the end results. The questions are written so that students use more than one strategy to solve the problem. Using multiple strategies is encouraged by the National Council of Teachers of Mathematics (NCTM). **Exercise 8** is an enhanced multiple choice question.

FREE RESPONSE QUESTIONS do not give answer choices. Some exercises have more than one possible answer. Students need to give only one correct response. **Exercises 1–2, 4–7, and 10–17** are free response questions.

WRITING EXERCISES allow students to describe how they think about and understand the concepts they have learned. **Exercise 9** is a writing exercise.

OPEN-ENDED PROBLEMS allow for more than one solution. Students must construct their own responses instead of choosing from possible answers. The students' responses will help you determine the depth of their understanding and any possible areas of difficulty. **Exercise 3** is an open-ended problem.

Resources

 **Teaching Resources**

Chapter Support File, Ch. 9
- Chapter Assessment, Forms A and B
- Alternative Assessment

Chapter Assessment, Spanish Resources

 **Teacher's Edition**

See also p. 446E for assessment options

 **Software**
- Computer Item Generator

Assessment page 492

3.

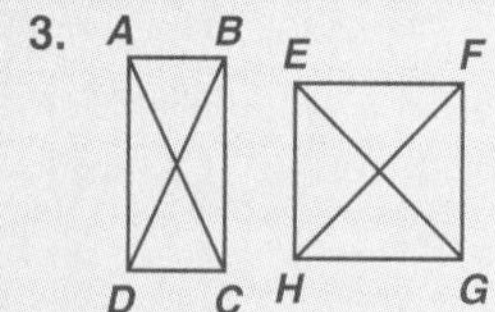

Preparing for Standardized Tests page 493

10.

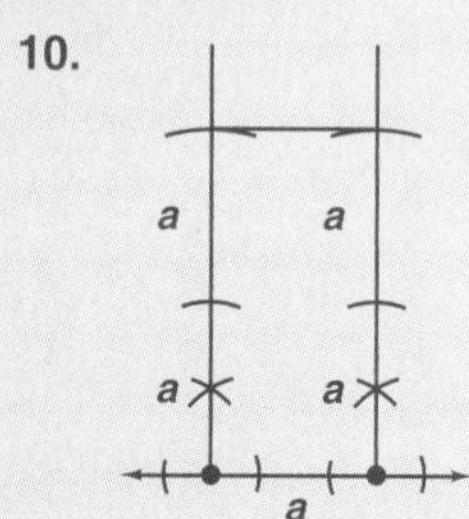

9 Assessment

Find *AN* in each parallelogram.

1. **6 in.**

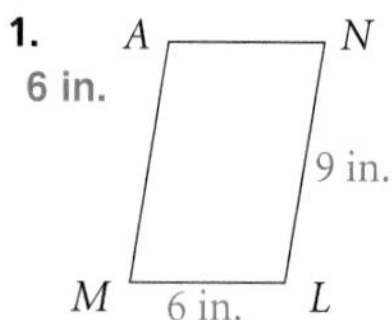

2. **9 cm**

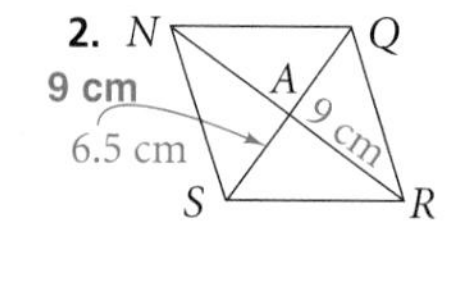

3. *Open-ended* Sketch two noncongruent parallelograms *ABCD* and *EFGH* such that $\overline{AC} \cong \overline{BD} \cong \overline{EG} \cong \overline{FH}$. **See margin for sample.**

Algebra **Find the values of the variables for each parallelogram.**

4.

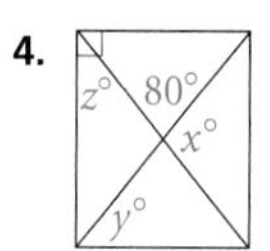

$x = 100$; $y = 50$; $z = 40$

5.

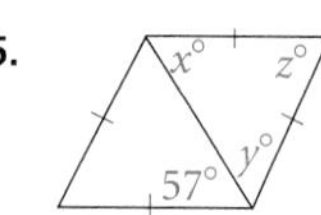

$x = 57$; $y = 57$; $z = 66$

6.

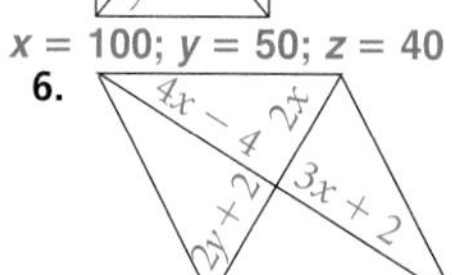

$x = 6$; $y = 5$

7.

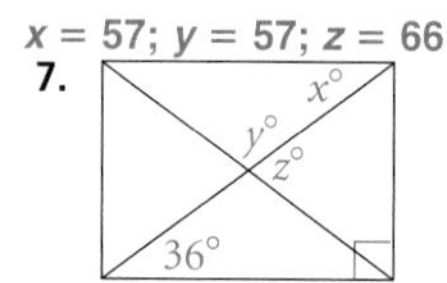

$x = 36$; $y = 108$; $z = 72$

8. *Standardized Test Prep* What is sufficient to prove that *ABCD* is a parallelogram? **E**

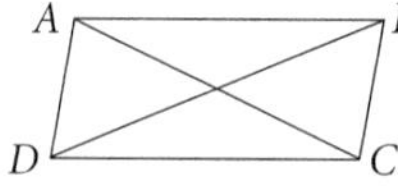

I. $\overline{AC}$ bisects $\overline{BD}$.
II. $\overline{AB} \cong \overline{DC}$; $\overline{AB} \parallel \overline{DC}$
III. $\overline{AB} \cong \overline{DC}$; $\overline{BC} \cong \overline{AD}$
IV. $\angle DAB \cong \angle BCD$ and $\angle ABC \cong \angle CDA$

A. I and III B. II and IV C. II and III
D. I and IV E. II, III, and IV

9. *Writing* Explain why a square cannot be a kite. **Answers may vary. Sample: A square is a rhombus. So it has 4 ≅ sides. A kite has no opp. sides ≅.**

Find the measures of ∠1 and ∠2.

10.

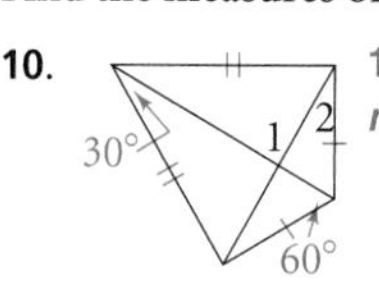

10. $m\angle 1 = 90$; $m\angle 2 = 30$

11.

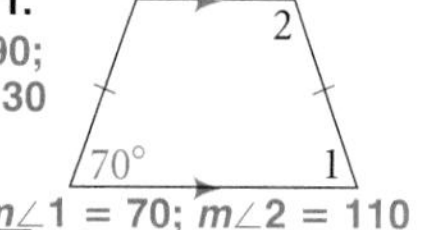

$m\angle 1 = 70$; $m\angle 2 = 110$

12. *Transformations* Draw $\overline{AB}$ with midpoint *M*. Rotate $\overline{AB}$ $x°$ about *M*, where $0 < x < 180$. What type of quadrilateral is $AA'BB'$? Explain. **Rectangle; the diagonals are ≅ and bisect each other.**

Find the area of each rhombus. If the answer is not an integer, round to the nearest tenth.

13.

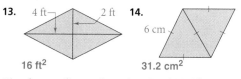

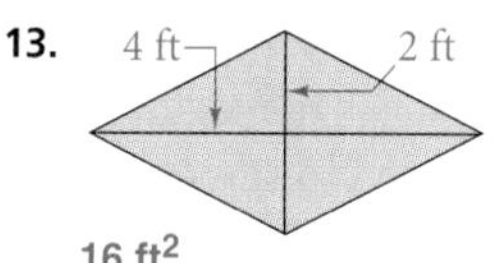

16 ft²

14. 6 cm **31.2 cm²**

Give the coordinates for points *S* and *T* without using any new variables. Then find the coordinates of the midpoint of $\overline{ST}$.

15. T (a, b) O S (a, −b)

$S(-a, -b)$, $T(-a, b)$; $(-a, 0)$

16.

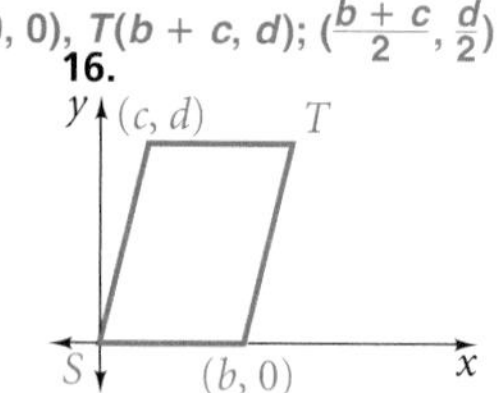

$S(0, 0)$, $T(b + c, d)$; $(\frac{b+c}{2}, \frac{d}{2})$

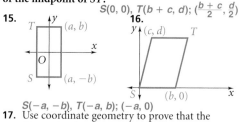

17. Use coordinate geometry to prove that the diagonals of a square are congruent.

Given: *ABCD* is a square with vertices $A(0, 0)$, $B(a, 0)$, $C(a, a)$, and $D(0, a)$.
Prove: $AC = BD$

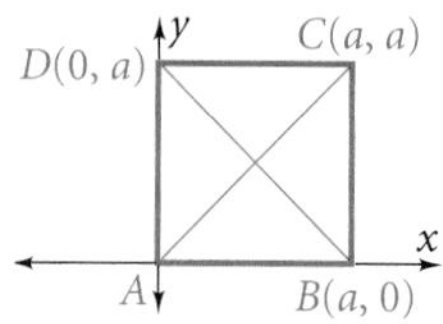

$AC = a\sqrt{2}$; $BD = a\sqrt{2}$. So $AC = BD$.

Preparing For Standardized Tests

Standardized tests, such as those administered for state assessment, the SAT, or the ACT, include regular math questions, quantitative comparison questions, open-ended problems, and free response questions (which the SAT calls *grid-ins*).

MULTIPLE CHOICE QUESTIONS are followed by five answer choices, one of which is correct. **Exercises 1–6** are multiple choice questions.

QUANTITATIVE COMPARISON QUESTIONS ask students to compare two quantities. **Exercises 7 and 8** are quantitative comparison questions.

FREE RESPONSE QUESTIONS do not give answer choices. Students must provide one correct answer on their own. **Exercises 9 and 10** are free response questions.

OPEN-ENDED PROBLEMS allow for more than one solution. Students must construct their own responses instead of choosing a single answer. The responses students give will help you determine the depth of their understanding and what difficulties, if any, they are experiencing. **Exercise 11** is an open-ended problem.

STANDARDIZED TEST TIP **Exercise 5** Students can save time by adding −4 to the *x*-coordinates and −1 to the *y*-coordinates of *A, B,* and *C* to find the image of $\triangle ABC$ instead of using a coordinate grid.

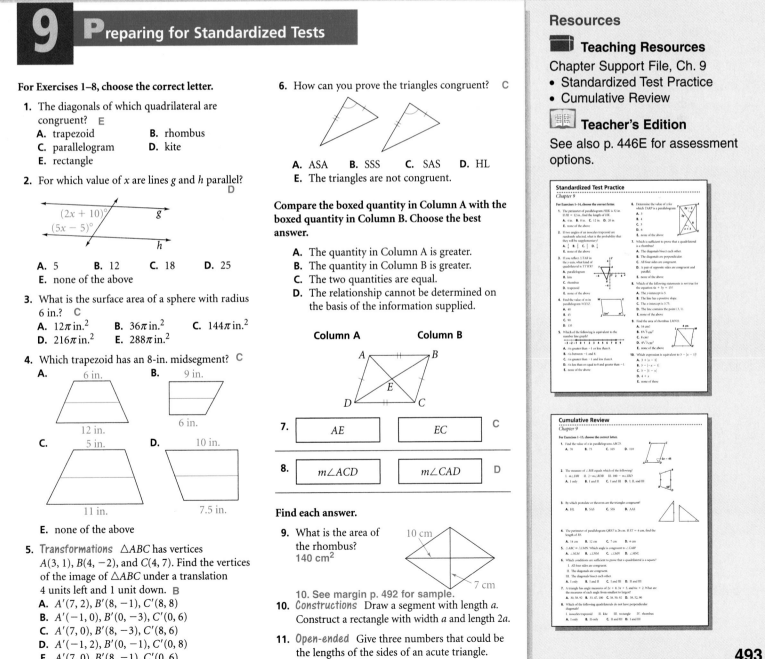

9 Preparing for Standardized Tests

For Exercises 1–8, choose the correct letter.

1. The diagonals of which quadrilateral are congruent? E
   - **A.** trapezoid
   - **B.** rhombus
   - **C.** parallelogram
   - **D.** kite
   - **E.** rectangle

2. For which value of x are lines g and h parallel? D

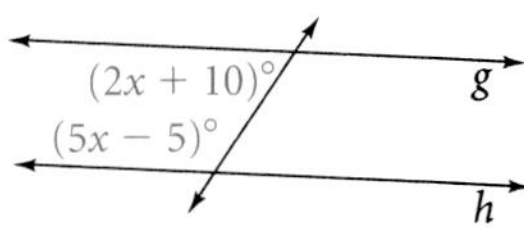

   - **A.** 5
   - **B.** 12
   - **C.** 18
   - **D.** 25
   - **E.** none of the above

3. What is the surface area of a sphere with radius 6 in.? C
   - **A.** 12π in.^{2}
   - **B.** 36π in.^{2}
   - **C.** 144π in.^{2}
   - **D.** 216π in.^{2}
   - **E.** 288π in.^{2}

4. Which trapezoid has an 8-in. midsegment? C

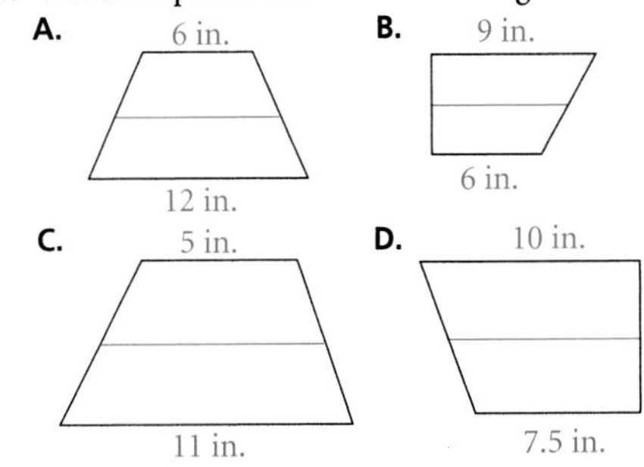

   - **E.** none of the above

5. ***Transformations*** $\triangle ABC$ has vertices $A(3, 1)$, $B(4, -2)$, and $C(4, 7)$. Find the vertices of the image of $\triangle ABC$ under a translation 4 units left and 1 unit down. B
   - **A.** $A'(7, 2), B'(8, -1), C'(8, 8)$
   - **B.** $A'(-1, 0), B'(0, -3), C'(0, 6)$
   - **C.** $A'(7, 0), B'(8, -3), C'(8, 6)$
   - **D.** $A'(-1, 2), B'(0, -1), C'(0, 8)$
   - **E.** $A'(7, 0), B'(8, -1), C'(0, 6)$

6. How can you prove the triangles congruent? C

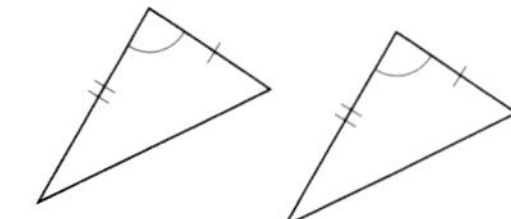

   - **A.** ASA
   - **B.** SSS
   - **C.** SAS
   - **D.** HL
   - **E.** The triangles are not congruent.

Compare the boxed quantity in Column A with the boxed quantity in Column B. Choose the best answer.

- **A.** The quantity in Column A is greater.
- **B.** The quantity in Column B is greater.
- **C.** The two quantities are equal.
- **D.** The relationship cannot be determined on the basis of the information supplied.

	Column A	Column B	
7.	AE	EC	C
8.	$m\angle ACD$	$m\angle CAD$	D

Find each answer.

9. What is the area of the rhombus? 140 cm^2

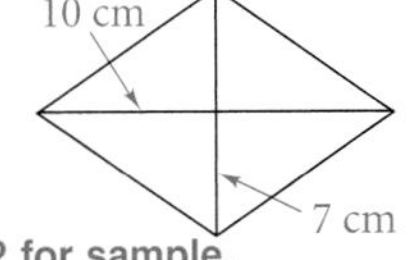

10. ***Constructions*** Draw a segment with length a. Construct a rectangle with width a and length $2a$. 10. See margin p. 492 for sample.

11. ***Open-ended*** Give three numbers that could be the lengths of the sides of an acute triangle. Sample: 5, 6, 7

Resources

Teaching Resources

Chapter Support File, Ch. 9

- Standardized Test Practice
- Cumulative Review

Teacher's Edition

See also p. 446E for assessment options.

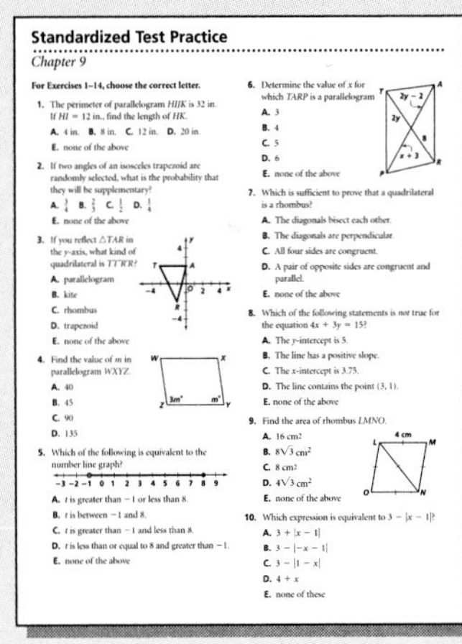

Standardized Test Practice

Chapter 9

For Exercises 1–14, choose the correct letter.

1. The perimeter of parallelogram $HIJK$ is 32 in. If HI = 12 in., find the length of HK.
   A. 4 in. B. 8 in. C. 12 in. D. 20 in.
   E. none of the above
2. If two angles of an isosceles trapezoid are randomly selected, what is the probability that they will be supplementary?
   A. [illegible] B. [illegible] C. [illegible] D. [illegible]
   E. none of the above
3. If you reflect $\triangle TAR$ in the y-axis, what kind of quadrilateral is $TT'R'R$?
   A. parallelogram
   B. kite
   C. rhombus
   D. trapezoid
   E. none of the above
4. Find the value of m in parallelogram $WXYZ$.
   A. 40
   B. 45
   C. 90
   D. 135
5. Which of the following is equivalent to the number line graph?
   A. t is greater than −1 or less than 8.
   B. t is between −1 and 8.
   C. t is greater than −1 and less than 8.
   D. t is less than or equal to 8 and greater than −1.
   E. none of the above
6. Determine the value of x for which $TARP$ is a parallelogram.
   A. 3
   B. 4
   C. 5
   D. 6
   E. none of the above
7. Which is sufficient to prove that a quadrilateral is a rhombus?
   A. The diagonals bisect each other.
   B. The diagonals are perpendicular.
   C. All four sides are congruent.
   D. A pair of opposite sides are congruent and parallel.
   E. none of the above
8. Which of the following statements is *not* true for the equation $4x + 3y = 15$?
   A. The y-intercept is 5.
   B. The line has a positive slope.
   C. The x-intercept is 3.75.
   D. The line contains the point (3, 1).
   E. none of the above
9. Find the area of rhombus $LMNO$.
   A. 16 cm^2
   B. $8\sqrt{3}$ cm^2
   C. 8 cm^2
   D. $4\sqrt{3}$ cm^2
   E. none of the above
10. Which expression is equivalent to $3 - |x - 1|$?
   A. $3 + |x - 1|$
   B. $3 - |-x - 1|$
   C. $3 - |1 - x|$
   D. $4 + x$
   E. none of these

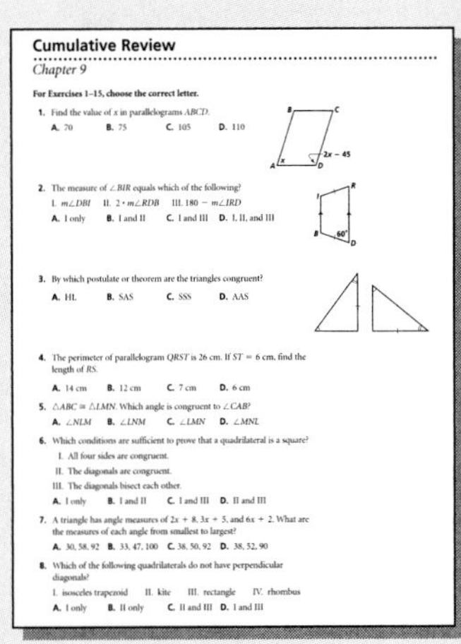

Cumulative Review

Chapter 9

For Exercises 1–15, choose the correct letter.

1. Find the value of x in parallelograms $ABCD$.
   A. 70 B. 75 C. 105 D. 110
2. The measure of $\angle BIR$ equals which of the following?
   I. $m\angle DBI$ II. $2 \cdot m\angle RDB$ III. $180 - m\angle IRD$
   A. I only B. I and II C. I and III D. I, II, and III
3. By which postulate or theorem are the triangles congruent?
   A. HL B. SAS C. SSS D. AAS
4. The perimeter of parallelogram $QRST$ is 26 cm. If ST = 6 cm, find the length of RS.
   A. 14 cm B. 12 cm C. 7 cm D. 6 cm
5. $\triangle ABC \cong \triangle LMN$. Which angle is congruent to $\angle CAB$?
   A. $\angle NLM$ B. $\angle LNM$ C. $\angle LMN$ D. $\angle MNL$
6. Which conditions are sufficient to prove that a quadrilateral is a square?
   I. All four sides are congruent.
   II. The diagonals are congruent.
   III. The diagonals bisect each other.
   A. I only B. I and II C. I and III D. II and III
7. A triangle has angle measures of $2x + 8$, $3x + 5$, and $6x + 2$. What are the measures of each angle from smallest to largest?
   A. 30, 58, 92 B. 33, 47, 100 C. 38, 50, 92 D. 38, 52, 90
8. Which of the following quadrilaterals do not have perpendicular diagonals?
   I. isosceles trapezoid II. kite III. rectangle IV. rhombus
   A. I only B. II only C. II and III D. I and III

CHAPTER 10 Similarity

To accommodate flexible scheduling, some lessons are divided into parts. Assignment Options are given in the Lesson Planning Options for each lesson.

10-1 Ratio, Proportion, and Similarity (pp. 496–502)

Part 1 Ratio and Proportion in Similar Figures

Part 2 Using Proportions

Key Terms: Cross-Product Property, extended proportion, Golden Ratio, Golden Rectangle, proportion, scale, scale drawing

10-2 Proving Triangles Similar: AA, SAS, and SSS (pp. 504–510)

Part 1 Using the AA Similarity Postulate

Part 2 Using the SAS and SSS Similarity Theorems

Key Terms: Angle-Angle Similarity Postulate (AA~), indirect measurement , Side-Angle-Side Similarity Theorem (SAS~), Side-Side-Side Similarity Theorem (SSS~)

10-3 Similarity in Right Triangles (pp. 511–516)

Key Term: geometric mean

10-4 Proportions and Similar Triangles (pp. 517–523)

Part 1 Using the Side-Splitter Theorem

Part 2 Using the Triangle-Angle-Bisector Theorem

10-5 Perimeters and Areas of Similar Figures (pp. 524–529)

10-6 Areas and Volumes of Similar Solids (pp. 531–535)

Key Term: similar solids, similarity ratio

PACING OPTIONS

This chart suggests pacing only for the core lessons and their parts, and it is provided merely as a possible guide. It will help you determine how much time you have in your schedule to cover other features, such as the Chapter Project, Math Toolboxes, Wrap Up, and Assessment.

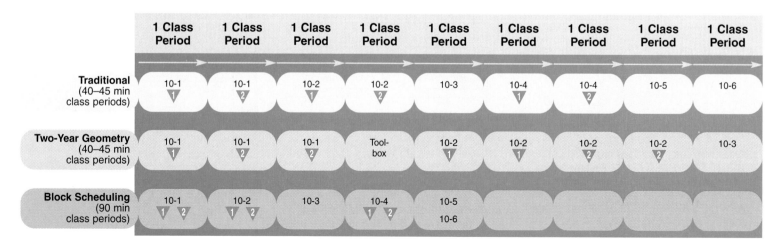

	1 Class Period	1 Class Period	1 Class Period	1 Class Period	1 Class Period	1 Class Period	1 Class Period	1 Class Period	1 Class Period
Traditional (40–45 min class periods)	10-1 Part 1	10-1 Part 2	10-2 Part 1	10-2 Part 2	10-3	10-4 Part 1	10-4 Part 2	10-5	10-6
Two-Year Geometry (40–45 min class periods)	10-1 Part 1	10-1 Part 2	10-1 Part 2	Tool-box	10-2 Part 1	10-2 Part 1	10-2 Part 2	10-2 Part 2	10-3
Block Scheduling (90 min class periods)	10-1 Parts 1, 2	10-2 Parts 1, 2	10-3	10-4 Parts 1, 2	10-5, 10-6				

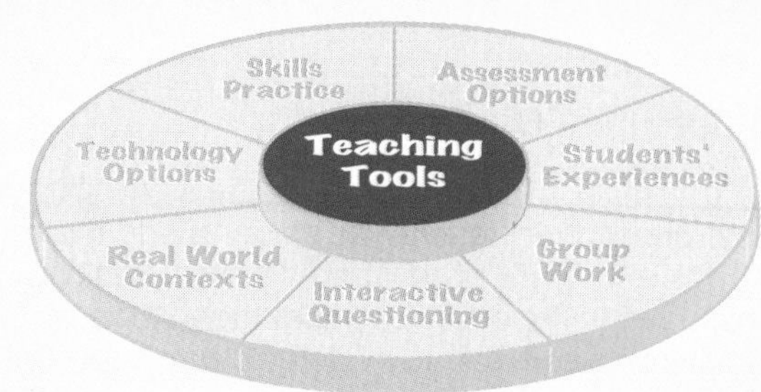

What Students Will Learn and Why

In this chapter, students will build on their knowledge of similarity, learned in Chapter 2, by learning how to use ratio and proportion with similar polygons. They also learn how to prove two triangles similar using the AA~ Postulate, and the SAS~ and SSS~ Theorems. Students apply these concepts to find distances using indirect measurement. Then students study similarity in right triangles and proportional relationships in triangles. Finally, they learn relationships among the similarity ratio, perimeter, and area of similar figures and among the similarity ratio, surface area, and volume of similar solids. The concepts presented in this chapter have uses in photography, architecture, and design.

Discussing the Chapter/Building on Experience

The concept map below relates chapter topics to real-world applications. You and your class may wish to add to the map or develop maps of your own. The center oval describes the topic of the chapter. The next level displays topics within the lessons. The outer ovals reflect applications of the content. As you and your class build a concept map, invite students to discuss applications with which they are familiar.

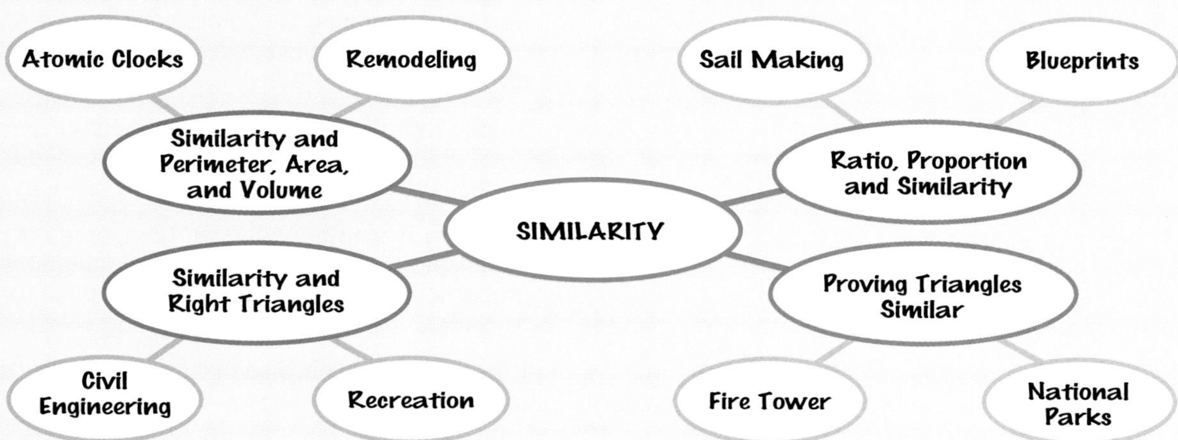

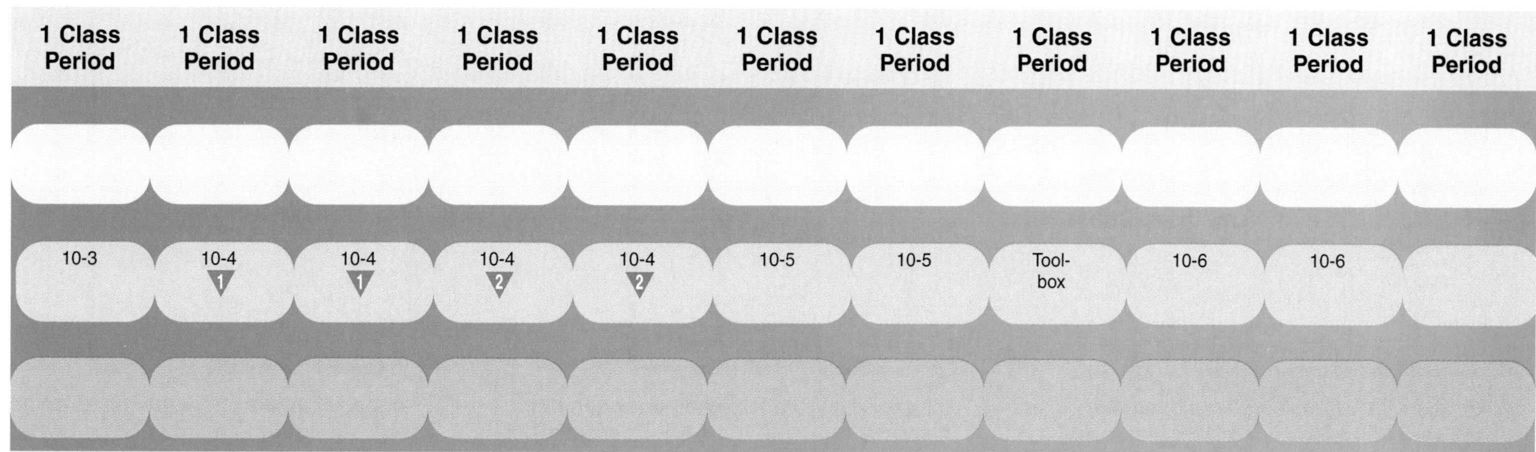

1 Class Period	1 Class Period	1 Class Period	1 Class Period	1 Class Period	1 Class Period	1 Class Period	1 Class Period	1 Class Period	1 Class Period	1 Class Period
10-3	10-4 ▼1	10-4 ▼1	10-4 ▼2	10-4 ▼2	10-5	10-5	Tool-box	10-6	10-6	

Skills Practice
Assessment Options
Technology Options
Teaching Tools
Students' Experiences
Real World Contexts
Group Work
Interactive Questioning

Interactive Questioning Tips

A question is interactive when there is "give and take" between the questioner (teacher or student) and the respondent. In Think and Discuss or when a critical thinking question is asked, it is important to encourage students to support their answers with facts. Ask "How do you know this?" to encourage logical reasoning. For example, in Lesson 10-1, Question 5, students are asked to explain why a particular solution *cannot* be the length of a Golden Rectangle.

Skills Practice

Every lesson provides skill practice with Try This exercises, Exercises On Your Own, and Exercises Mixed Review. The Student Edition includes Checkpoints (pp. 510, 529) and Cumulative Review (p. 541). In the Teacher's Edition, the Lesson Planning Options section for each lesson lists Prerequisite Skills students should know for that lesson. At the back of the Student Edition is the Skills Handbook—mini-lessons on math your students may need to review. The Chapter Support File for Chapter 10 in the Teaching Resources box includes two Practice worksheets per lesson, a worksheet for two Checkpoints, and worksheets for Cumulative Review and Standardized Test Preparation.

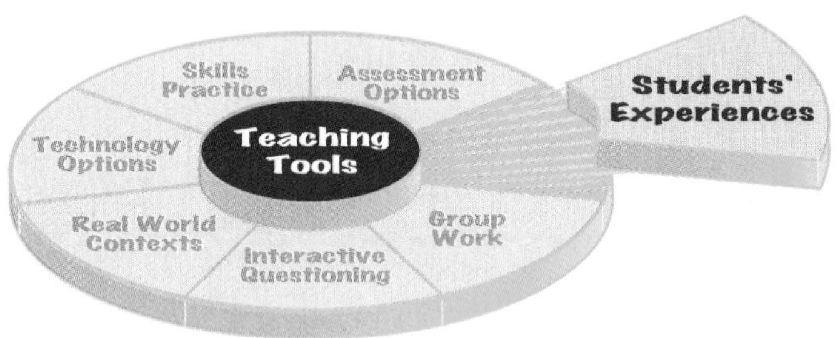

Diverse Learning and Teaching Styles

In your Teacher's Edition, you will find suggestions as to how you can help students complete mathematical tasks in Chapter 10 by reinforcing various learning styles. Here are some examples.

- **Visual learning** identify corresponding parts of figures by tracing and rotating the figures to the same position (p. 500), use color coding to indicate pairs of congruent angles in a given triangle (p. 511)
- **Tactile learning** use geoboards to create similar rectangles (p. 524), use models of pairs of similar solids to measure corresponding dimensions (p. 532)
- **Auditory learning** understand properties of proportions by describing how the properties are related to the original proportion (p. 497), practice naming corresponding sides (p. 505)
- **Kinesthetic learning** identify which objects shaped like rectangles found outside are Golden Rectangles (p. 498)

Alternative Activity for Lesson 10-1

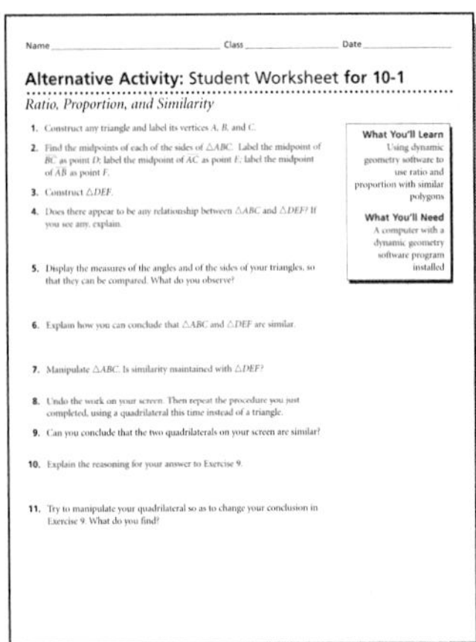

Name ________ Class ________ Date ________

Alternative Activity: Student Worksheet for 10-1

Ratio, Proportion, and Similarity

1. Construct any triangle and label its vertices A, B, and C.
2. Find the midpoints of each of the sides of $\triangle ABC$. Label the midpoint of $\overline{BC}$ as point D; label the midpoint of $\overline{AC}$ as point E; label the midpoint of $\overline{AB}$ as point F.
3. Construct $\triangle DEF$.
4. Does there appear to be any relationship between $\triangle ABC$ and $\triangle DEF$? If you see any, explain.
5. Display the measures of the angles and of the sides of your triangles, so that they can be compared. What do you observe?
6. Explain how you can conclude that $\triangle ABC$ and $\triangle DEF$ are similar.
7. Manipulate $\triangle ABC$. Is similarity maintained with $\triangle DEF$?
8. Undo the work on your screen. Then repeat the procedure you just completed, using a quadrilateral this time instead of a triangle.
9. Can you conclude that the two quadrilaterals on your screen are similar?
10. Explain the reasoning for your answer to Exercise 9.
11. Try to manipulate your quadrilateral so as to change your conclusion in Exercise 9. What do you find?

What You'll Learn Using dynamic geometry software to use ratio and proportion with similar polygons

What You'll Need A computer with a dynamic geometry software program installed

for use with Example 1, uses geometry software to explore similar triangles.

Alternative Activity for Lesson 10-2

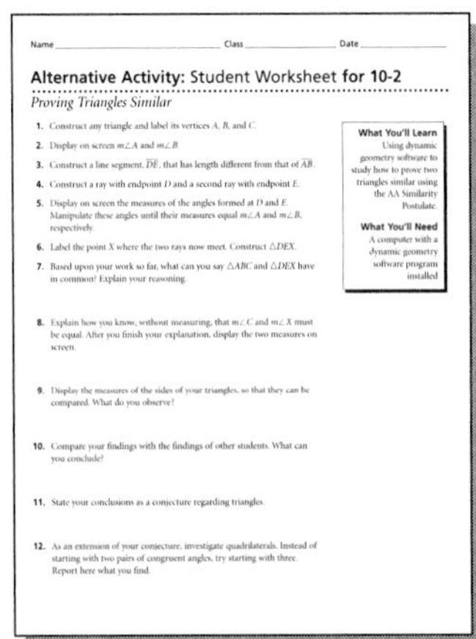

Name ________ Class ________ Date ________

Alternative Activity: Student Worksheet for 10-2

Proving Triangles Similar

1. Construct any triangle and label its vertices A, B, and C.
2. Display on screen $m\angle A$ and $m\angle B$.
3. Construct a line segment, $\overline{DE}$, that has length different from that of $\overline{AB}$.
4. Construct a ray with endpoint D and a second ray with endpoint E.
5. Display on screen the measures of the angles formed at D and E. Manipulate these angles until their measures equal $m\angle A$ and $m\angle B$, respectively.
6. Label the point X where the two rays now meet. Construct $\triangle DEX$.
7. Based upon your work so far, what can you say $\triangle ABC$ and $\triangle DEX$ have in common? Explain your reasoning.
8. Explain how you know, without measuring, that $m\angle C$ and $m\angle X$ must be equal. After you finish your explanation, display the two measures on screen.
9. Display the measures of the sides of your triangles, so that they can be compared. What do you observe?
10. Compare your findings with the findings of other students. What can you conclude?
11. State your conclusions as a conjecture regarding triangles.
12. As an extension of your conjecture, investigate quadrilaterals. Instead of starting with two pairs of congruent angles, try starting with three. Report here what you find.

What You'll Learn Using dynamic geometry software to study how to prove two triangles similar using the AA Similarity Postulate.

What You'll Need A computer with a dynamic geometry software program installed

for use with Work Together, uses geometry software to explore the AA Similarity Postulate.

Alternative Activity for Lesson 10-5

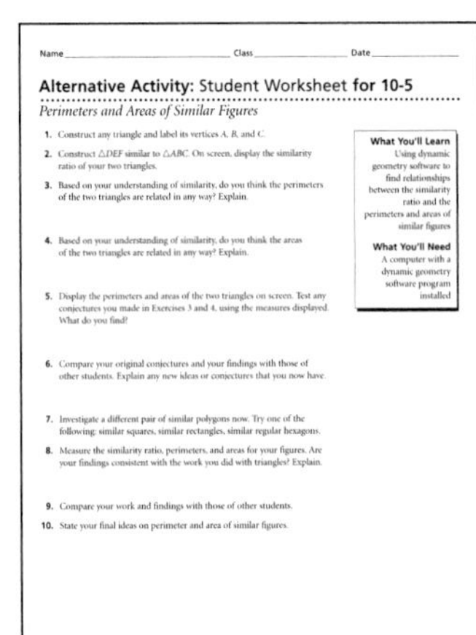

Name ________ Class ________ Date ________

Alternative Activity: Student Worksheet for 10-5

Perimeters and Areas of Similar Figures

1. Construct any triangle and label its vertices A, B, and C.
2. Construct $\triangle DEF$ similar to $\triangle ABC$. On screen, display the similarity ratio of your two triangles.
3. Based on your understanding of similarity, do you think the perimeters of the two triangles are related in any way? Explain.
4. Based on your understanding of similarity, do you think the areas of the two triangles are related in any way? Explain.
5. Display the perimeters and areas of the two triangles on screen. Test any conjectures you made in Exercises 3 and 4, using the measures displayed. What do you find?
6. Compare your original conjectures and your findings with those of other students. Explain any new ideas or conjectures that you now have.
7. Investigate a different pair of similar polygons now. Try one of the following: similar squares, similar rectangles, similar regular hexagons.
8. Measure the similarity ratio, perimeters, and areas for your figures. Are your findings consistent with the work you did with triangles? Explain.
9. Compare your work and findings with those of other students.
10. State your final ideas on perimeter and area of similar figures.

What You'll Learn Using dynamic geometry software to find relationships between the similarity ratio and the perimeters and areas of similar figures

What You'll Need A computer with a dynamic geometry software program installed

for use with Work Together, uses geometry software to explore area and perimeter of similar polygons.

Skills Practice
Assessment Options
Technology Options
Teaching Tools
Students' Experiences
Real World Contexts
Interactive Questioning
Group Work

Cooperative Learning Tips

When used effectively, cooperative learning can help students develop interpersonal skills, learn to perform specific roles in a group, and learn to carry out specific responsibilities. The components of Chapter 10 provide a range of cooperative learning opportunities.

- In the Student Edition, the ***Work Together*** parts of lessons are specifically designed for cooperative learning activities.
- In the Teacher's Edition, you will find helpful hints for addressing diverse learning styles (see page C for Chapter 10). For every lesson, you will find a ***Reteaching Activity***, which may involve cooperative learning.

Materials and Manipulatives

Opportunities for calculator use—though optional—are integrated throughout the course.

- calculator (10-1, 10-2, 10-5, 10-6)
- compass (10-1)
- geometry software (10-4)
- graph paper (10-1, 10-5)
- isometric dot paper (10-6)
- metric ruler (10-2)
- protractor (10-2)
- ruler (10-1)
- scissors (10-3)
- straightedge (10-1, 10-3)

Technology Options
Skills Practice
Assessment Options
Teaching Tools
Students' Experiences
Real World Contexts
Interactive Questioning
Group Work

TECHNOLOGY OPTIONS

Technology Tools		Chapter Project	10-1	10-2	10-3	10-4	10-5	10-6
Calculator	Numerous opportunities throughout for students to use scientific calculators.							
Software	Secondary Math Lab Toolkit™		✔	✔	✔	✔	✔	✔
	Integrated Math Lab				✔	✔		
	Computer Item Generator		✔	✔	✔	✔	✔	✔
	Student Edition					✔		✔T
Video	Video Field Trip	✔						
CD-ROM	Multimedia Geometry Lab		✔	✔			✔	✔
Internet	See the Prentice Hall site. (http://www.phschool.com)							

✔T indicates Math Toolbox.

The Prentice Hall Geometry program offers you a rich variety of technology options. Be assured that all these options are provided as a means of enriching the program and are not essential for the successful completion of the course.

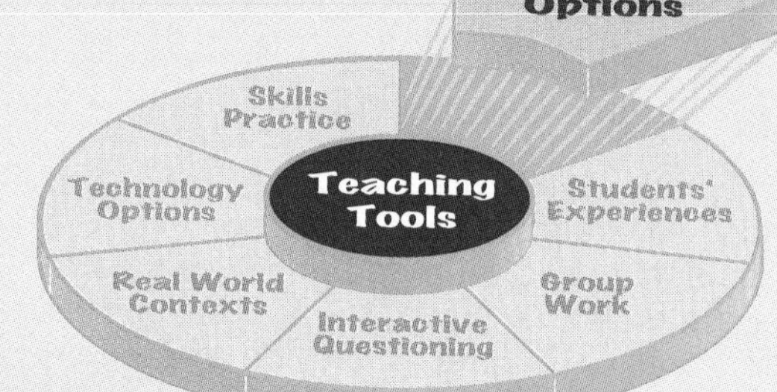

Assessment Options

The Prentice Hall Geometry Program provides you with many options. From these options, you may choose instructional materials and techniques appropriate for your students, or those necessary to meet your district's curriculum requirements. As the chart indicates, the program also supports your teaching efforts by offering you many choices for assessment.

ASSESSMENT OPTIONS

Assessment Support Materials	Chapter Project	10-1	10-2	10-3	10-4	10-5	10-6	Chapter End
Chapter Project	▲ ■ ●	▲ ■		▲ ■	▲ ■	▲ ■	▲ ■	▲ ■
Checkpoints			▲ ■ ●			▲ ■ ●		
Self-Assessment			▲ ■			▲ ■	▲ ■	▲ ■
Writing Assignment		▲	▲ ■	▲	▲	▲ ■	▲ ■	▲ ■ ●
Chapter Assessment								▲ ■ ●
Alternative Assessment		■	■	■	■	■	■	■ ●
Cumulative Review								▲ ■ ●
Standardized Test Prep		▲ ■	▲ ■	▲ ■	▲	▲	▲ ■	▲ ■ ●
Computer Item Generator	Can be used to create custom-made practice or assessment at any time.							

▲ = Student Edition ■ = Teacher's Edition ● = Teaching Resources

Checkpoints

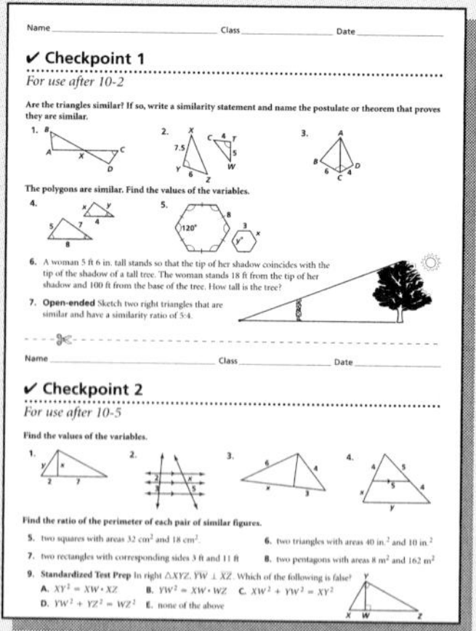

Alternative Assessment

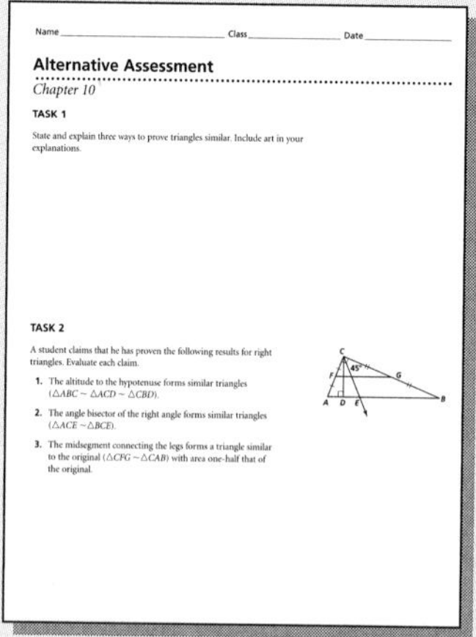

Chapter Assessment

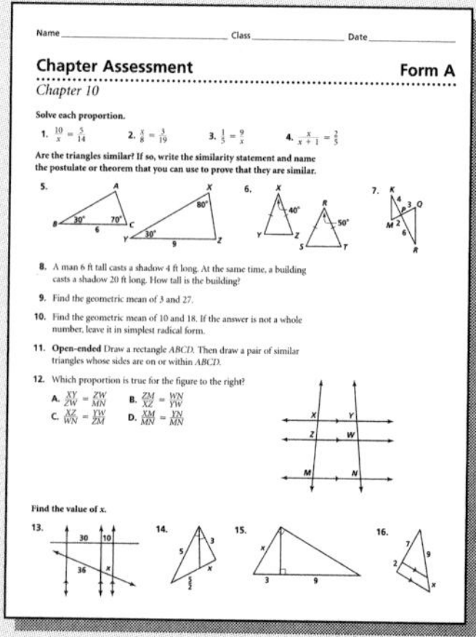

Available in both Form A and Form B

Making the Right Connections

Mathematics is imbedded in nearly every walk of life. The National Council of Teachers of Mathematics (NCTM) encourages educators to recognize these connections and to emphasize them for the purpose of better educating students for success in life and in a global economy. The ***Connections*** chart below highlights these connections for Chapter 10.

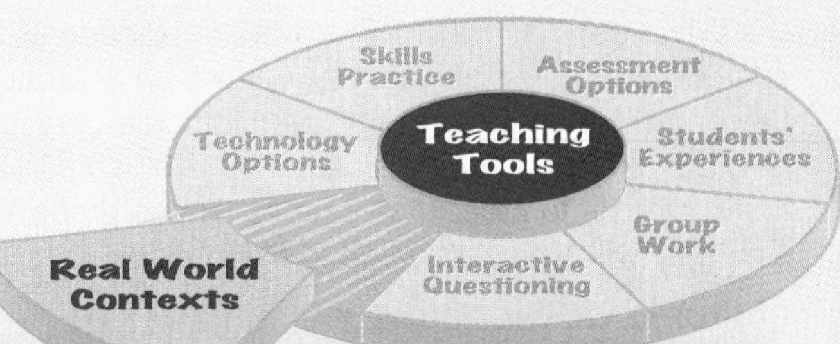

CONNECTIONS

Lesson	Interdisciplinary Connections	Career Prep	Other Real World Connections	Math Integration	NCTM Standards
Chapter Project	Environmental Science	Research Computer Design	Nature Photographs Scale Models	Fractal Geometry	Algebra
10-1	History Art Geography	Architecture	Basketball Blueprints Leonardo DaVinci Leaning Tower of Pisa Money	Algebra Coordinate Geometry Data Analysis	Algebra Communication Connections Problem Solving
10-2	History	Architecture	National Parks Fire Tower Indirect Measurement	Algebra	Algebra Reasoning Communication Connections
10-3		Civil Engineering	Recreation Koch Snowflake Dental Services	Algebra Coordinate Geometry Data Analysis	Algebra Reasoning Communication Connections
10-4	Geography	Surveying	Sail Making Lakes Streets	Algebra Logical Reasoning Geometry in 3 Dimensions Transformational Geometry	Reasoning Communication Connections Problem Solving
10-5		Surveying	Community Service Remodeling School Enrollment	Algebra Data Analysis Transformational Geometry	Reasoning Communication Connections Problem Solving
10-6	Literature	Carpentry Package Design	Russian Dolls Paperweights Atomic Clocks Packaging	Coordinate Geometry Algebra	Reasoning Communication Connections Problem Solving

CHAPTER 10 Similarity

CONNECTING TO PRIOR LEARNING Ask students if they have ever seen a movie or a TV show in which a famous place was blown up, set on fire, or destroyed in some other way. Discuss how computers use properties of similar figures to generate scale models to create the scenes. Those properties of similarity will be investigated in this chapter.

CULTURAL CONNECTIONS The simplest fractal is called the Cantor bar, named after a nineteenth century German mathematician Georg Cantor. Have students construct a Cantor bar as follows: divide a line segment into three parts, then remove the middle part. Repeat this procedure on the remaining two parts, then on the remaining four parts, and so on.

INTERDISCIPLINARY CONNECTIONS Fractal geometry has implications in physics, biology, geography, statistics, and art. Discuss with students the work of Benoit B. Mandlebrot, a French mathematician, who observed fractals in the fluctuations of the stock market, the distribution of galaxies, and the English shoreline.

Technology Options

Prentice Hall Technology

Video
Video Field Trip 10, "Fractally Speaking," an interview with Benoit Mandlebrot, one of the discoverers of the fractal world

CHAPTER 10 Similarity

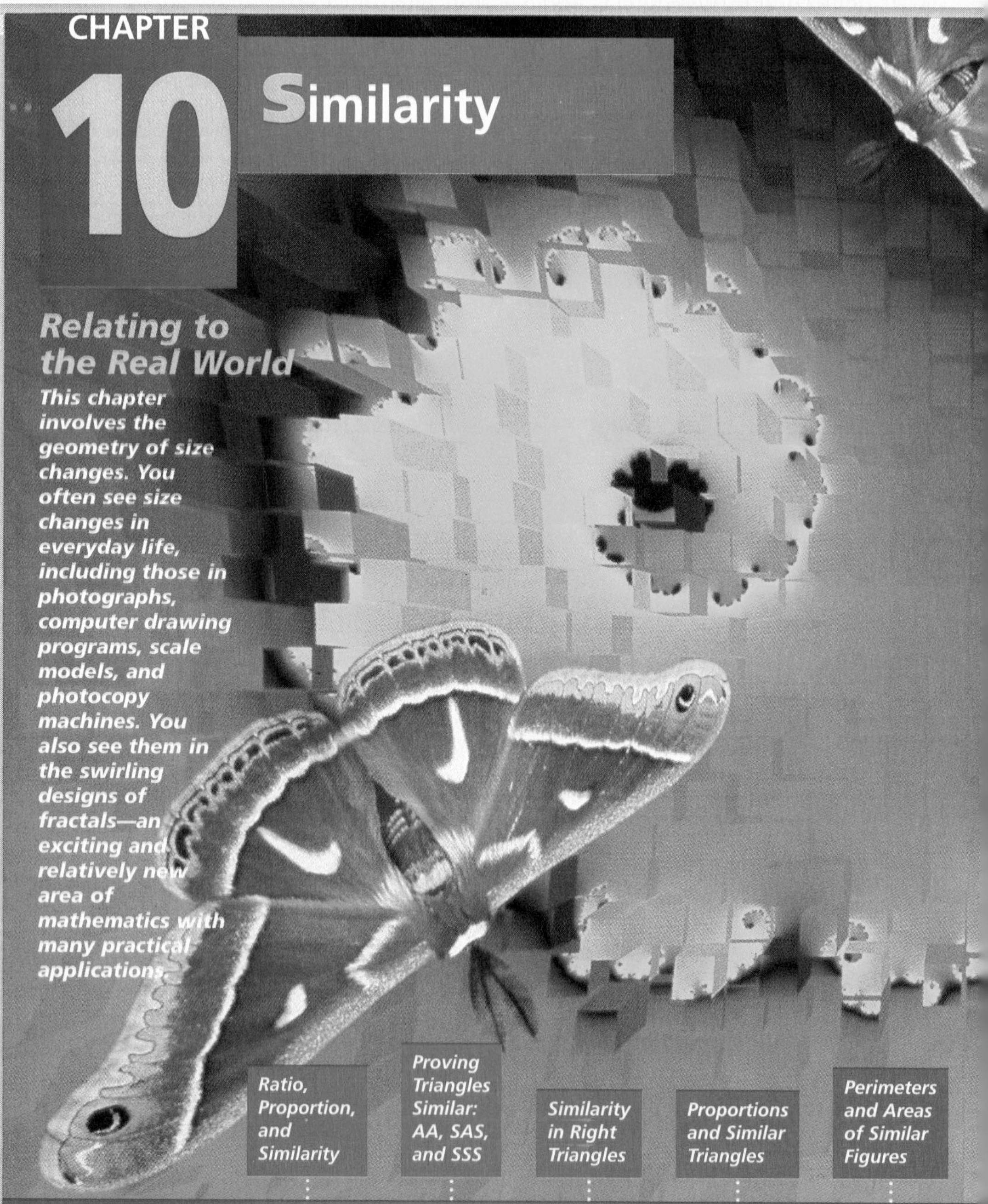

Relating to the Real World

This chapter involves the geometry of size changes. You often see size changes in everyday life, including those in photographs, computer drawing programs, scale models, and photocopy machines. You also see them in the swirling designs of fractals—an exciting and relatively new area of mathematics with many practical applications.

ABOUT THE PROJECT Students investigate fractal designs. In completing the Find Out questions, students learn how to do an iterative process and investigate the properties of the side lengths, areas, and similarity of fractals. Then students create fractal trees or fractals of their own design.

Launching the Project

PROJECT NOTEBOOK Encourage students to keep all project-related materials in a separate folder or notebook. **See Chapter Project Manager and Scoring Rubric in Chapter Support File.**

- Ask students to describe any patterns they may have seen on a fern, a pineapple, or a pinecone.
- Ask students to give examples of objects found in nature, other than those described on pages 494–495, that have repeating patterns.

TRACKING THE PROJECT You may wish to have students read Finishing the Chapter Project on page 536 to help them get an overview of the project. Set benchmark deadlines for students to show their work in progress.

CHAPTER PROJECT

Fractals FOREVER

Nature is full of shapes that are not straight lines, smooth curves, or flat surfaces. Just look at a cloud bank or the bark on a tree. Many shapes contain patterns that repeat themselves on different scales—a head of cauliflower, a fern frond, and details of a coastline, to name but a few. Fractal geometry, developed in the last 20 years, is the study of these irregular, *self-similar* shapes, called *fractals.*

In your project for this chapter, you will create fractals. You will learn how to do an iterative process—one in which steps are repeated in a regular cycle. Finally, you will investigate properties of fractals, including some surprising facts about length and area.

To help you complete the project:

- **p. 502** *Find Out by Doing*
- **p. 516** *Find Out by Analyzing*
- **p. 523** *Find Out by Doing*
- **p. 529** *Find Out by Thinking*
- **p. 536** *Finishing the Project*

Areas and Volumes of Similar Solids

10-6

Project Resources

Teaching Resources

Chapter Support File, Ch. 10
- Chapter Project Manager and Scoring Rubric

Transparencies
103

Using the Rubric

Sharing the scoring rubric for the project with your students will alert them to your expectations before they begin work on the project.

As students complete each Find Out question in the chapter, you may wish to have them evaluate their own work or a partner's work based on the scoring rubric. Students should have the opportunity to revise their work after it has been reviewed.

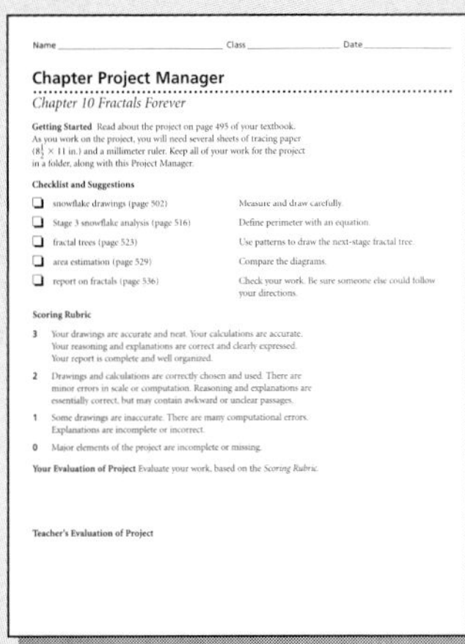

Name ______________ Class ________ Date ________

Chapter Project Manager

Chapter 10 Fractals Forever

Getting Started Read about the project on page 495 of your textbook. As you work on the project, you will need several sheets of tracing paper ($8\frac{1}{2} \times 11$ in.) and a millimeter ruler. Keep all of your work for the project in a folder, along with this Project Manager.

Checklist and Suggestions

- ❑ snowflake drawings (page 502) — Measure and draw carefully.
- ❑ Stage 3 snowflake analysis (page 516) — Define perimeter with an equation.
- ❑ fractal trees (page 523) — Use patterns to draw the next-stage fractal tree.
- ❑ area estimation (page 529) — Compare the diagrams.
- ❑ report on fractals (page 536) — Check your work. Be sure someone else could follow your directions.

Scoring Rubric

3 Your drawings are accurate and neat. Your calculations are accurate. Your reasoning and explanations are correct and clearly expressed. Your report is complete and well organized.

2 Drawings and calculations are correctly chosen and used. There are minor errors in scale or computation. Reasoning and explanations are essentially correct, but may contain awkward or unclear passages.

1 Some drawings are inaccurate. There are many computational errors. Explanations are incomplete or incorrect.

0 Major elements of the project are incomplete or missing.

Your Evaluation of Project Evaluate your work, based on the *Scoring Rubric.*

Teacher's Evaluation of Project

10-1 Teaching Notes

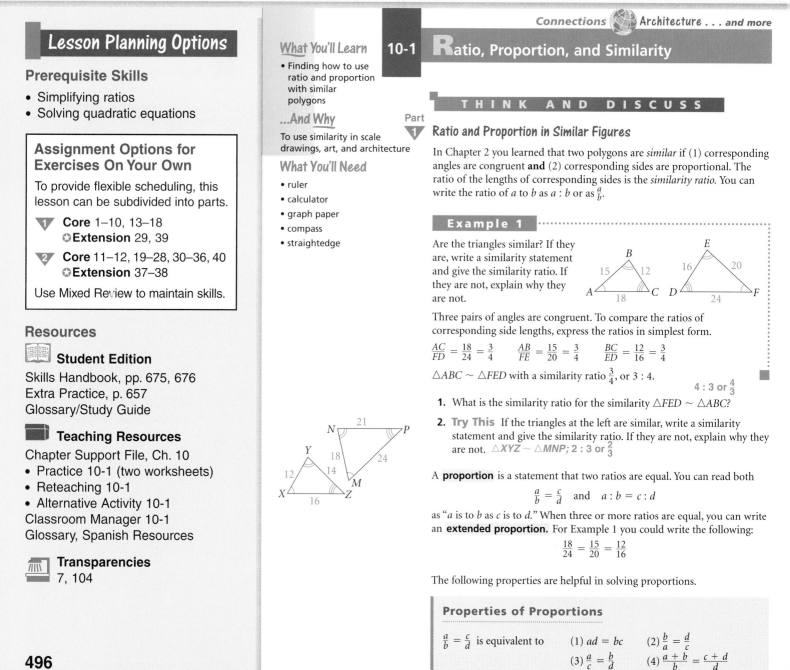

PROBLEM OF THE DAY

Find the area of the enclosed figure.

8.5 sq units

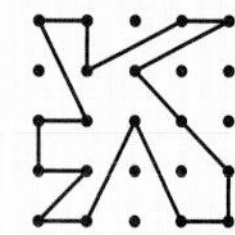

Problem of the Day is also available in Transparencies.

CONNECTING TO PRIOR KNOWLEDGE Ask students if the following pairs of ratios are equivalent.

$\frac{12}{32}, \frac{3}{8}$ $\frac{2}{4}, \frac{8}{4}$ $\frac{20}{32}, \frac{35}{56}$

THINK AND DISCUSS

ESL Discuss with the use of the word *similar* in English compared to its use in mathematics. Point out that you may say "these two sweaters are similar" because they have the same color or pattern, not because they have same shape and their corresponding "dimensions" are proportional.

Example 1

Make sure students understand that the similarity ratio is dependent on the order of the similarity statement. $\triangle ABC \sim \triangle FED$ with similarity ratio $\frac{3}{4}$, but $\triangle FED \sim \triangle ABC$ with similarity ratio $\frac{4}{3}$.

Lesson Planning Options

Prerequisite Skills

- Simplifying ratios
- Solving quadratic equations

Assignment Options for Exercises On Your Own

To provide flexible scheduling, this lesson can be subdivided into parts.

1 **Core** 1–10, 13–18
Extension 29, 39

2 **Core** 11–12, 19–28, 30–36, 40
Extension 37–38

Use Mixed Review to maintain skills.

Resources

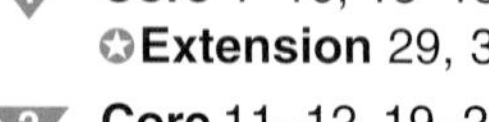

Student Edition

Skills Handbook, pp. 675, 676
Extra Practice, p. 657
Glossary/Study Guide

Teaching Resources

Chapter Support File, Ch. 10
- Practice 10-1 (two worksheets)
- Reteaching 10-1
- Alternative Activity 10-1

Classroom Manager 10-1
Glossary, Spanish Resources

Transparencies
7, 104

Connections Architecture . . . and more

10-1 Ratio, Proportion, and Similarity

What You'll Learn

- Finding how to use ratio and proportion with similar polygons

...And Why

To use similarity in scale drawings, art, and architecture

What You'll Need

- ruler
- calculator
- graph paper
- compass
- straightedge

THINK AND DISCUSS

Part 1

Ratio and Proportion in Similar Figures

In Chapter 2 you learned that two polygons are *similar* if (1) corresponding angles are congruent **and** (2) corresponding sides are proportional. The ratio of the lengths of corresponding sides is the *similarity ratio.* You can write the ratio of a to b as $a : b$ or as $\frac{a}{b}$.

Example 1

Are the triangles similar? If they are, write a similarity statement and give the similarity ratio. If they are not, explain why they are not.

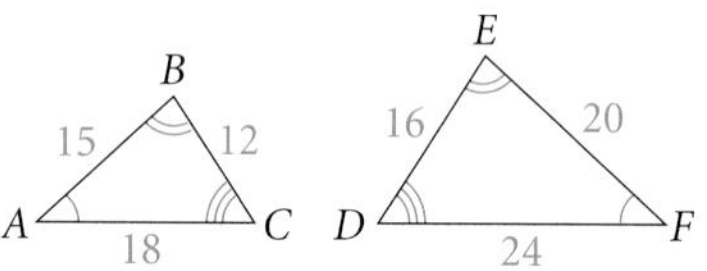

Three pairs of angles are congruent. To compare the ratios of corresponding side lengths, express the ratios in simplest form.

$\frac{AC}{FD} = \frac{18}{24} = \frac{3}{4}$ $\frac{AB}{FE} = \frac{15}{20} = \frac{3}{4}$ $\frac{BC}{ED} = \frac{12}{16} = \frac{3}{4}$

$\triangle ABC \sim \triangle FED$ with a similarity ratio $\frac{3}{4}$, or 3 : 4.

1. What is the similarity ratio for the similarity $\triangle FED \sim \triangle ABC$? 4 : 3 or $\frac{4}{3}$
2. **Try This** If the triangles at the left are similar, write a similarity statement and give the similarity ratio. If they are not, explain why they are not. $\triangle XYZ \sim \triangle MNP$; 2 : 3 or $\frac{2}{3}$

N 21 P 18 24 M; Y 12 14 X 16 Z

A **proportion** is a statement that two ratios are equal. You can read both

$$\frac{a}{b} = \frac{c}{d} \quad \text{and} \quad a : b = c : d$$

as "a is to b as c is to d." When three or more ratios are equal, you can write an **extended proportion.** For Example 1 you could write the following:

$$\frac{18}{24} = \frac{15}{20} = \frac{12}{16}$$

The following properties are helpful in solving proportions.

Properties of Proportions

$\frac{a}{b} = \frac{c}{d}$ is equivalent to (1) $ad = bc$ (2) $\frac{b}{a} = \frac{d}{c}$ (3) $\frac{a}{c} = \frac{b}{d}$ (4) $\frac{a+b}{b} = \frac{c+d}{d}$

To help students understand the properties of proportions, give values for *a, b, c,* and *d* such that $\frac{a}{b} = \frac{c}{d}$ and have them substitute to check that the four properties are true.

AUDITORY LEARNING Students will better understand the properties of proportions if they describe how the properties are related to the original proportion. For example, the first property can be stated as "the product of the extremes is equal to the product of the means." The third property can be stated as "the ratio of the numerators of the proportion is equal to the ratio of the denominators of the proportion."

CRITICAL THINKING **Question 3** Have students justify the remaining three properties of proportions.

Example 2 **Relating to the Real World** 

Make sure students understand that a scale given with an equal sign, such as 1 in. = 16 ft, can be rewritten as $\frac{1}{16}$.

ERROR ALERT! Students may have difficulty setting up and solving proportions with complex fractions. **Remediation:** Show students how the proportions in Example 2 were set up and how the Cross-Product Property was used to simplify the equations. Then have students work in groups to answer Question 4, which involves similar proportions.

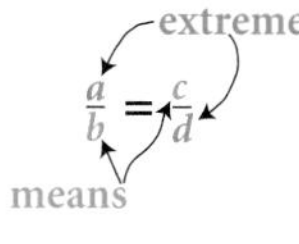
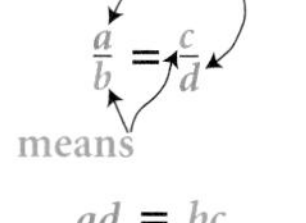

$ad = bc$

The first property is called the **Cross-Product Property.** It can be stated as "The product of the extremes is equal to the product of the means."

3. To eliminate the denominators in $\frac{a}{b} = \frac{c}{d}$, by what would you multiply both sides of the equation? What would be the result? Use your answers to **justify** the Cross-Product Property. *bd; ad = bc;* the product of the extremes, *a* and *d*, = the product of the means, *b* and *c*.

Part 2

Using Proportions

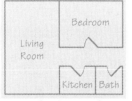

Who? As a 21-year-old architecture student, Maya Ying Lin won the design competition for the Vietnam War Memorial. She also designed the Civil Rights Memorial in Montgomery, Alabama.

A similarity ratio always compares dimensions in the same unit, such as meters. In a **scale drawing,** the **scale** compares each length in the drawing to the actual length being represented. The scale in a scale drawing can be in different units. A scale might be written as 1 in. to 100 mi, 1 in. = 12 ft, or 1 mm : 1 m.

Example 2 **Relating to the Real World** 

Architecture What are the actual dimensions of the bedroom?

Use a ruler to find that the bedroom is $\frac{7}{8}$ in. by $\frac{5}{8}$ in. on the scale drawing.

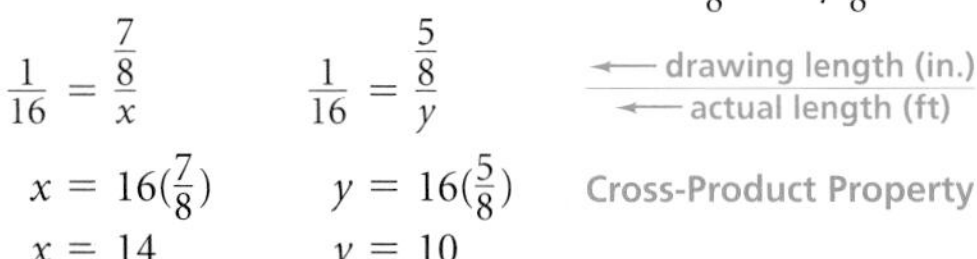

Scale 1 in. = 16 ft

$\frac{1}{16} = \frac{\frac{7}{8}}{x}$	$\frac{1}{16} = \frac{\frac{5}{8}}{y}$	← drawing length (in.) / ← actual length (ft)
$x = 16(\frac{7}{8})$	$y = 16(\frac{5}{8})$	Cross-Product Property
$x = 14$	$y = 10$	

The actual bedroom is 14 ft by 10 ft.

4. a. **Try This** What are the dimensions of the actual living room? 12 ft by 20 ft
   b. What is the area of the actual living room? 240 ft^2

Additional Examples

FOR EXAMPLE 1

Are the triangles similar? If they are, write a similarity statement and give the similarity ratio. If they are not, explain.

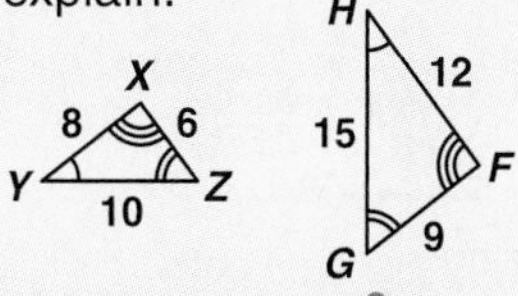

$\triangle YZX \sim \triangle HGF; \frac{2}{3}$

Discussion: *Sarah claims that $\triangle YZX \sim \triangle HGF$. Jerry claims that $\triangle ZXY \sim \triangle GFH$. Who is correct? Explain.*

FOR EXAMPLE 2

Refer to the diagram in Example 2. What are the actual dimensions of the kitchen? the bathroom? 8 ft by 8 ft; 8 ft by 6 ft

Discussion: *What is the ratio of the area of the kitchen in the scale drawing to the area of the actual kitchen?*

Make sure students understand that *DFEA* is a square with side length 1. You may also want to explain why $EB = x - 1$ and review how to solve $x^2 - x = 1$.

Question 6 Help students understand that the ratio of the length to the width of any Golden Rectangle ≈ 1.618 : 1.

EXTENSION Have students research other real-world examples of Golden Rectangles in architecture and in art. For an example of its use in modern art, see the paintings of Piet Mondrian.

MAKING CONNECTIONS Have students find the ratio of pairs of consecutive terms in the Fibonacci Sequence 1, 1, 2, 3, 5, 8, 13, . . . Have them approximate each ratio to the nearest thousandth. They should discover that the ratios get closer and closer to the Golden Ratio.

Technology Options

For Exercise 29, students may use geometry software to graph the triangles. For Exercise 37, students may use drawing software to draw the rectangles.

Prentice Hall Technology

Software
- Secondary Math Lab Toolkit™
- Computer Item Generator 10-1

CD-ROM
- Multimedia Geometry Lab 10

Internet
- See the Prentice Hall site. (http://www.phschool.com)

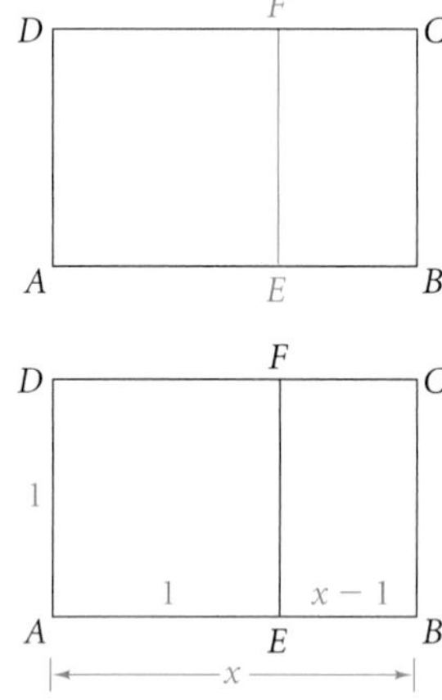

A **Golden Rectangle** is a rectangle that can be divided into a square and a rectangle that is similar to the original rectangle. The ratio of the length of a Golden Rectangle to the width is called the **Golden Ratio.** To find the Golden Ratio, you can find the length x of a Golden Rectangle whose width is 1.

$ABCD \sim BCFE$	Definition of Golden Rectangle
$\frac{AB}{BC} = \frac{BC}{CF}$	Corresponding sides of ~ polygons are proportional.
$\frac{x}{1} = \frac{1}{x - 1}$	Substitution
$x^2 - x = 1$	Cross-Product Property
$x^2 - x - 1 = 0$	Subtract 1 from each side.

Using the Quadratic Formula to solve this equation, you get $x = \frac{1 \pm \sqrt{5}}{2}$.

5. **Critical Thinking** Why does the answer $x = \frac{1 - \sqrt{5}}{2}$ not apply to this problem? The ratio cannot be negative.

6. a. **Calculator** Find the value of x to the nearest thousandth. 1.618
   b. What is the length of a Golden Rectangle whose width is 3 cm?
   c. What is the width of a Golden Rectangle whose length is 5 cm?
   b. 4.854 cm c. 3.090 cm

The Golden Rectangle is considered pleasing to the human eye and has appeared in architecture and art since ancient times. It has intrigued artists including Leonardo da Vinci (1452–1519), who illustrated *The Divine Proportion,* a book about the Golden Rectangle. The Golden Rectangle also occurs frequently in nature and in the proportions of the human body.

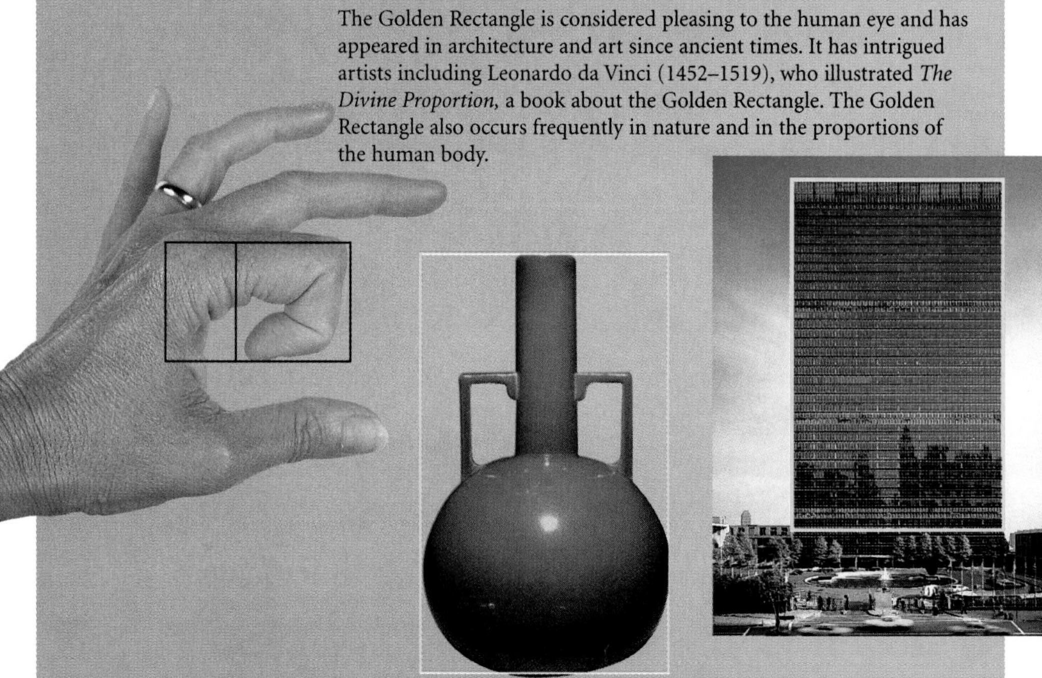

WORK TOGETHER

Student use a compass and a straightedge to construct a Golden Rectangle. Students may need to review Lesson 7-3 to construct a line perpendicular to a point on a line.

Exercises ON YOUR OWN

Exercises 1–10 Students can use the properties of proportions to justify their answers or they may choose values for a and b such that $\frac{a}{b} = \frac{3}{4}$ and substitute into each equation.

ALTERNATIVE ASSESSMENT **Exercises 11 and 12** You can use these exercises to help you assess students' ability to use ratio and proportions in similar triangles. Have students work in pairs and encourage them to draw diagrams and write the proportions they use to solve the problems. This will help you better diagnose where students' errors are occurring.

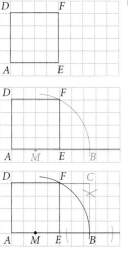

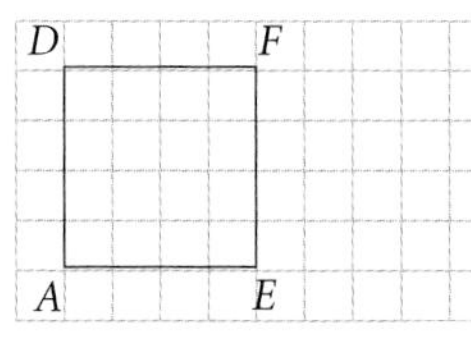

WORK TOGETHER

Work with a partner to draw a Golden Rectangle using graph paper, a compass, and a straightedge.

- On graph paper draw a square $AEFD$ with an even number of units on each side.
- Find the midpoint M of $\overline{AE}$.
- With radius MF draw an arc that intersects $\overrightarrow{AE}$ at point B.
- Construct the perpendicular to $\overleftrightarrow{AB}$ at point B.
- Let point C be the intersection of this perpendicular and $\overrightarrow{DF}$.
- Draw the rectangle $ABCD$.

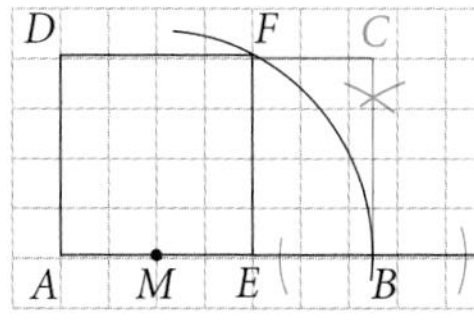

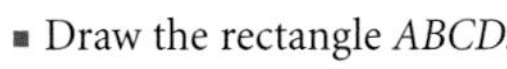

a–c. Answers may vary. Samples are given.

7. a. Use ME, EF, and the Pythagorean Theorem to find MF. $2\sqrt{5}$
   b. Use MF to find EB. $2\sqrt{5} - 2$
   c. What are the dimensions of rectangle $ABCD$? $2 + 2\sqrt{5}$; 4
   d. **Verify** that $ABCD$ is a Golden Rectangle. $\frac{AB}{BC} = \frac{1 + \sqrt{5}}{2}$ ✓

Exercises ON YOUR OWN

Algebra **If $\frac{a}{b} = \frac{3}{4}$, which of the following must be true? Explain why.**

1. $4a = 3b$ T
2. $3a = 4b$ F
3. $\frac{a}{3} = \frac{b}{4}$ T
4. $\frac{4}{3} = \frac{b}{a}$ T
5. $\frac{4}{b} = \frac{3}{a}$ T
6. $ab = 3(4)$ F
7. $\frac{a+b}{b} = \frac{3+4}{4}$ T
8. $\frac{a+b}{a} = \frac{7}{3}$ T
9. $\frac{a+3}{3} = \frac{b+4}{4}$ T
10. $\frac{a}{b} = \frac{6}{8} = \frac{0.75}{1}$ T

11. **Models** The Leaning Tower of Pisa in Italy is about 180 ft tall. A souvenir paperweight of the Leaning Tower is 6 in. tall. What is the similarity ratio of the paperweight to the real tower? 1 : 360

12. Suppose the designer of the pyramid at the right wanted the base to be a 675-m square. The sides of the base of the pyramid that was built measure 0.675 m. What is the similarity ratio of the pyramid that was built to the one the designer had planned? 1 : 1000

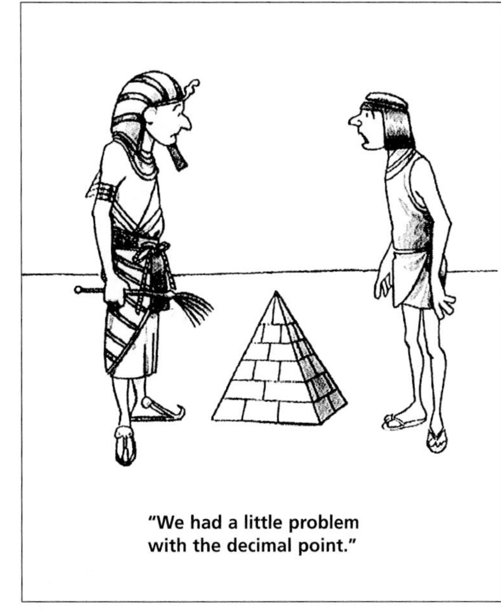

"We had a little problem with the decimal point."

VISUAL LEARNING Exercises 14–18 Students may have difficulty identifying corresponding parts of figures. It may help some students to trace one of the figures in each pair and rotate or reflect it so that the figures are in the same position.

Exercises 23 and 24 Check that students accurately use the distributive property.

KINESTHETIC LEARNING Exercise 28 If you have block scheduling or an extended class period, take students outside to measure rectangles, such as a seat on a playground swing, a football field, a soccer field, the door to the school, or the school steps, to determine which are Golden Rectangles.

CONNECTING TO STUDENTS' WORLD Exercise 30 Provide students with copies of a map of your state. Have them locate the distance between your city or town and other locations familiar to them in the state.

Are the polygons similar? If they are, write a similarity statement and give the similarity ratio. If they are not, explain.

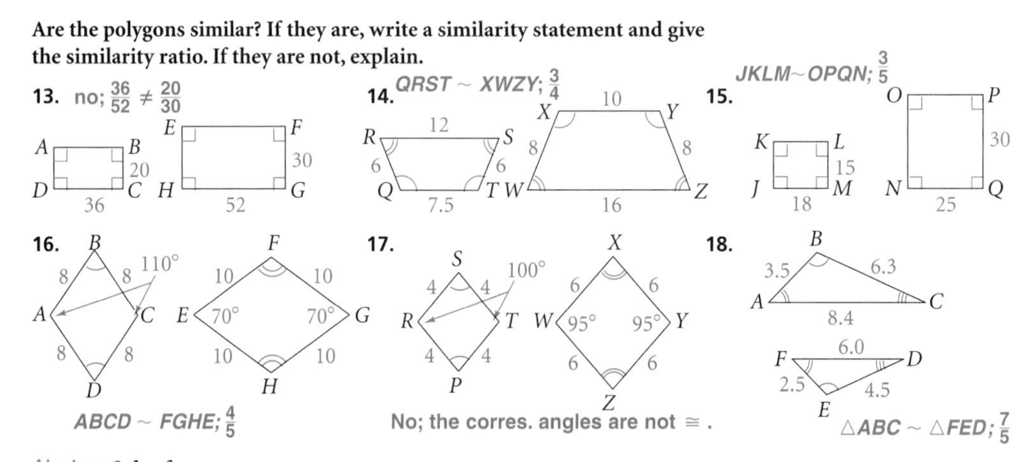

Algebra **Solve for *x*.**

19. $\frac{x}{10} = \frac{15}{25}$ **6**

20. $\frac{9}{24} = \frac{12}{x}$ **32**

21. $\frac{11}{14} = \frac{x}{21}$ **16.5**

22. $\frac{5}{x} = \frac{8}{11}$ $6\frac{7}{8}$

23. $\frac{x+3}{3} = \frac{10+4}{4}$ **7.5**

24. $\frac{x+7}{7} = \frac{15}{5}$ **14**

25. $\frac{4}{x} = \frac{x}{9}$ **−6 or 6**

26. $\frac{x}{2} = \frac{50}{x}$ **−10 or 10**

27. Mental Math A postcard is 6 in. by 4 in. A commercial printing shop will enlarge it to any size up to 3 ft on the longer dimension. What are the dimensions of the largest possible enlargement for this postcard? **3 ft by 2 ft**

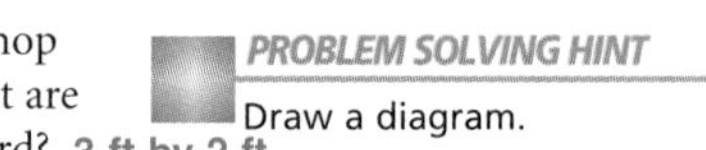

PROBLEM SOLVING HINT

Draw a diagram.

28. Open-ended Measure the dimensions of the fronts of several boxes in your home, such as cereal boxes and laundry detergent boxes. Which box is closest to the shape of a Golden Rectangle? **Check students' work.**

29. Coordinate Geometry $\triangle ABC$ with vertices $A(2, 3)$, $B(2, 6)$, and $C(4, 6)$ is similar to $\triangle QRS$ with vertices $Q(6, 9)$, $R(6, 24)$, and S. Give two possibilities for the coordinates of vertex S. **(−4, 24), (16, 24)**

30. Geography A map of Louisiana is drawn to the scale 1 in. = 40 mi. On the map, the distance from Lake Charles to Baton Rouge is about $3\frac{1}{4}$ in. About how far apart are the two cities? **130 mi**

500

DIVERSITY Exercise 35 If possible, bring in or have students bring in currency from other countries. You may want to assign each group a country and have them research the currency from that country and its value in U.S. dollars.

TRANSFORMATIONS Exercise 39 This exercise helps students see the connections between dilations and similarity.

STANDARDIZED TEST TIP Exercise 40 Help students see that they can solve this problem by comparing the ratio of two adjacent sides in each rectangle with the ratio of adjacent sides of *ABCD*.

The polygons are similar. Find the values of the variables.

31. 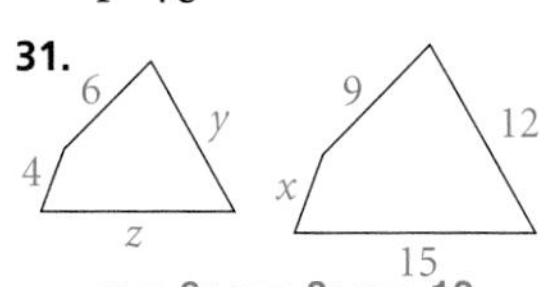

$x = 6$; $y = 8$; $z = 10$

32. 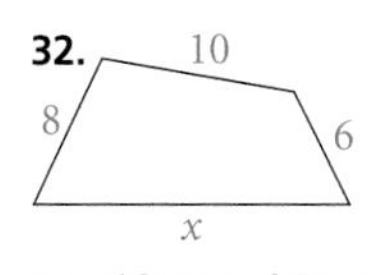

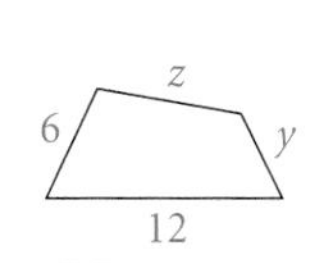

$x = 16$; $y = 4.5$; $z = 7.5$

33. 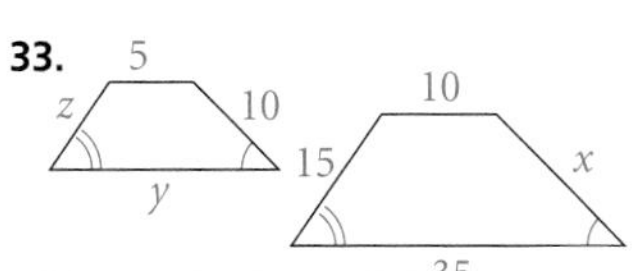

$x = 20$; $y = 17.5$; $z = 7.5$

34. *Calculator* The switch plate for a standard electric light switch is in the shape of a Golden Rectangle. The longer side of a standard switch plate is about 114 mm. What is the length of the shorter side? Round your answer to the nearest millimeter. **70 mm**

35. *Money* From 1861 to 1928 the dollar bill measured $7\frac{7}{16}$ in. by $3\frac{1}{8}$ in. The dimensions of the current dollar bill are shown at the right. Are the two dollar bills similar rectangles? Explain. **See below.**

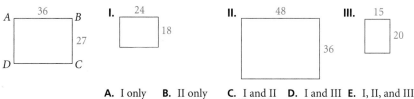

$6\frac{1}{8}$ in.

$2\frac{5}{8}$ in.

36. *Geography* Students on the campus of the University of Minnesota in Minneapolis built a model globe 42 ft in diameter on a scale of 1 : 1,000,000. About how tall would Mount Everest be on the model? (Mount Everest is about 29,000 ft tall.) **0.029 ft or 0.348 in.**

37. *Data Collection* On a single sheet of white paper, draw rectangles with the following dimensions: 3 in. by 3 in., 3 in. by 4 in., 3 in. by 5 in., and 3 in. by 6 in. Show the sheet to ten different people and ask them to select their first and second choices for most pleasing rectangles. Combine your findings with those of your classmates. Describe how your results do or do not confirm that the Golden Rectangle is the most pleasing rectangle. **Check students' work.**

38. a. *Sports* A basketball court is 84 ft by 50 ft. Choose a scale and draw a scale drawing of a basketball court. **a–b. Check students' work.**
b. *Writing* Explain how you chose the scale for your drawing.

39. a. *Transformations* Draw *JKLM* with vertices $J(-2, -2)$, $K(6, -2)$, $L(6, 4)$, and $M(-2, 4)$. Then draw its image $J'K'L'M'$ under the dilation with center $O(0, 0)$ and scale factor $\frac{1}{2}$. **See margin.**
b. How are *JKLM* and $J'K'L'M'$ related? Explain. **$JKLM \sim J'K'L'M'$ with similarity ratio 2:1**
c. Is $J'K'L'M'$ an enlargement or reduction of *JKLM*? **reduction**

40. *Standardized Test Prep* Which rectangles are similar to rectangle *ABCD*? **E**

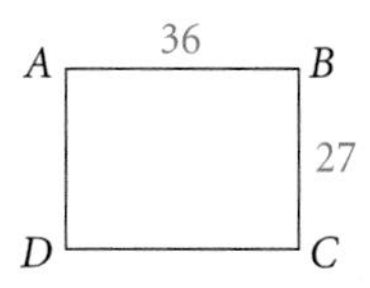

I. 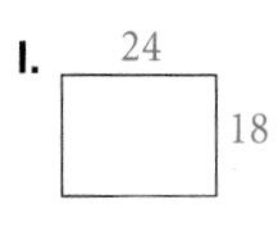

II. 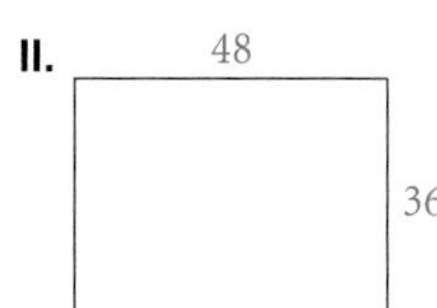

III. 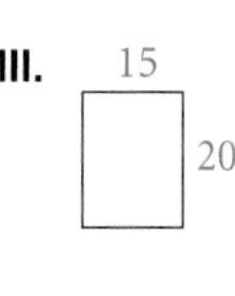

A. I only **B.** II only **C.** I and II **D.** I and III **E.** I, II, and III

35. No; the ratios of the corres. sides are not =; $\frac{17}{14} \neq \frac{25}{21}$.

pages 499–502 On Your Own

39a.

M, y, L, M′, 3, L′, 1, O, 2, 4, x, J′, K′, J, K

page 502 Mixed Review

42. 

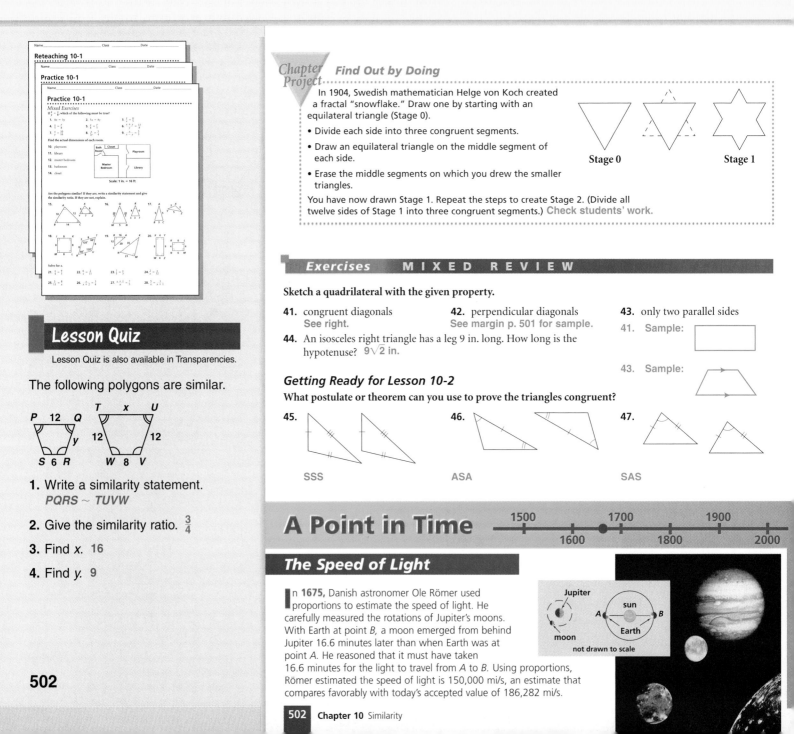

Chapter Project FIND OUT BY DOING Suggest students draw the triangle with side length divisible by 9 so the measurements will not be difficult. Have them start in the center of a sheet of paper so there will be room for the added triangles.

Exercises MIXED REVIEW

GETTING READY FOR LESSON 10-2 Students prove triangles congruent to prepare them to prove triangles similar.

Wrap Up

THE BIG IDEA Ask students to write a proportion, then to rewrite it in four equivalent ways.

RETEACHING ACTIVITY Students decide if polygons are similar or not. If similar, they write similarity statements. (Reteaching worksheet 10-1)

A Point in Time

If you have block scheduling or an extended class period you may wish to have students investigate these topics:

- fields of astronomy such as radar astronomy, ultraviolet astronomy, X-ray astronomy, and optical astronomy
- other contributions to astronomy by Ole Römer such as the invention of the astronomical transit circle
- how today's accepted value for the speed of light was derived

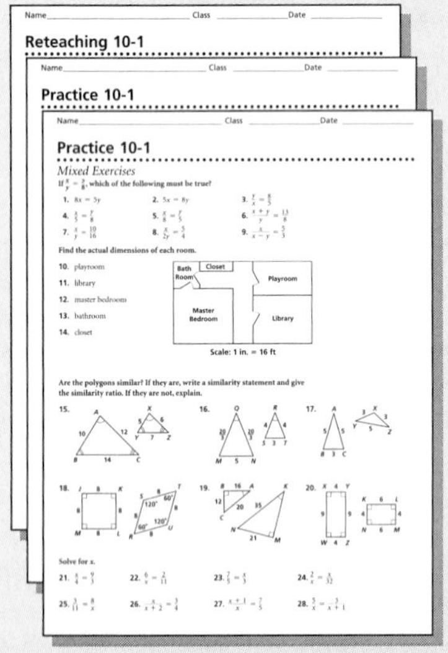

Lesson Quiz

Lesson Quiz is also available in Transparencies.

The following polygons are similar.

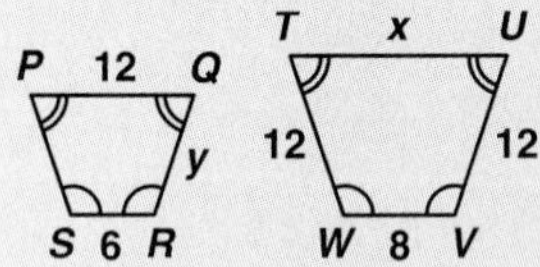

1. Write a similarity statement. *PQRS* ~ *TUVW*
2. Give the similarity ratio. $\frac{3}{4}$
3. Find *x*. 16
4. Find *y*. 9

Chapter Project — Find Out by Doing

In 1904, Swedish mathematician Helge von Koch created a fractal "snowflake." Draw one by starting with an equilateral triangle (Stage 0).

- Divide each side into three congruent segments.
- Draw an equilateral triangle on the middle segment of each side.
- Erase the middle segments on which you drew the smaller triangles.

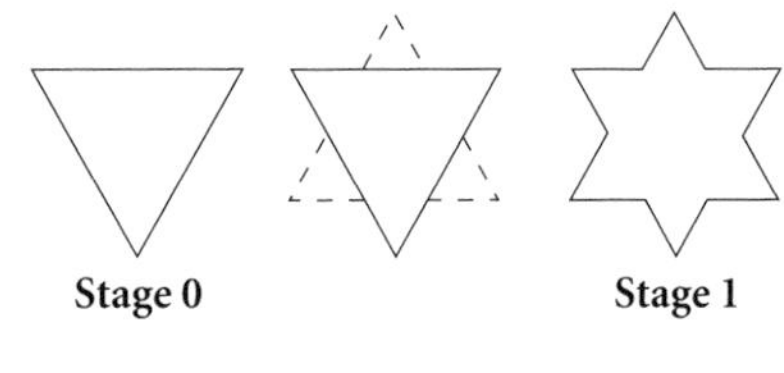

You have now drawn Stage 1. Repeat the steps to create Stage 2. (Divide all twelve sides of Stage 1 into three congruent segments.) Check students' work.

Exercises MIXED REVIEW

Sketch a quadrilateral with the given property.

41. congruent diagonals
See right.

42. perpendicular diagonals
See margin p. 501 for sample.

43. only two parallel sides

41. Sample:

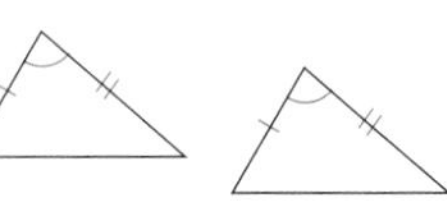

43. Sample:

44. An isosceles right triangle has a leg 9 in. long. How long is the hypotenuse? $9\sqrt{2}$ in.

Getting Ready for Lesson 10-2

What postulate or theorem can you use to prove the triangles congruent?

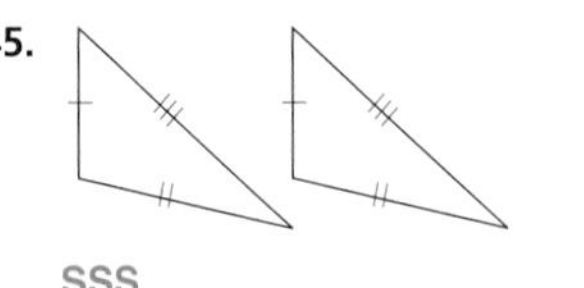

45. SSS

46. ASA

47. SAS

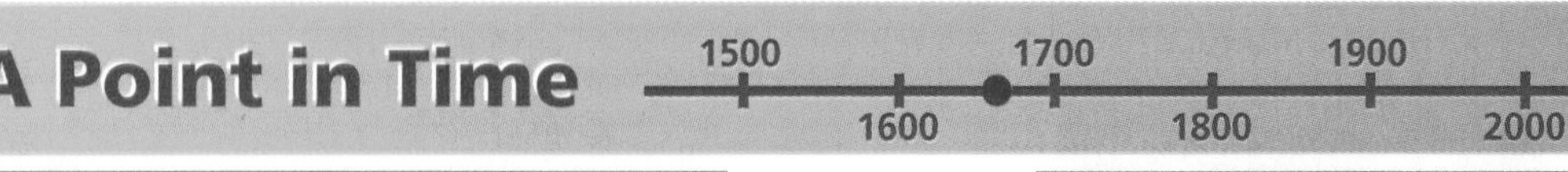

A Point in Time

The Speed of Light

In **1675,** Danish astronomer Ole Römer used proportions to estimate the speed of light. He carefully measured the rotations of Jupiter's moons. With Earth at point *B*, a moon emerged from behind Jupiter 16.6 minutes later than when Earth was at point *A*. He reasoned that it must have taken 16.6 minutes for the light to travel from *A* to *B*. Using proportions, Römer estimated the speed of light is 150,000 mi/s, an estimate that compares favorably with today's accepted value of 186,282 mi/s.

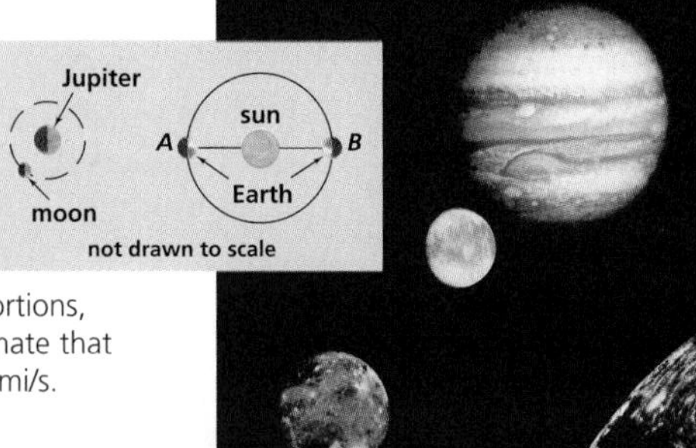

Math ToolboX

Students review how to solve problems using direct variation.

Have students experiment with different values of k and ask them how x and y are related when $k > 0$ and when $k < 0$. Students will use direct variation to solve problems in Lessons 10-5 and 10-6.

Example

Help students see that k represents Juan's hourly wage and the equation $e = 5.75w$ can be used to find Juan's earnings for any number of hours worked.

ERROR ALERT! Exercises 1–4 Students may have difficulty writing the direct variation and may interchange the positions of the variables. **Remediation:** Help students see the relationship between $y = kx$ and "y varies directly as x."

ALTERNATIVE ASSESSMENT Have students work in groups to write and solve three direct variation problems. Then have the groups exchange their problems with those of other groups and solve.

Math ToolboX: Algebra Review

Transparencies
5

Direct Variation

Before Lesson 10-2

The perimeter p of an equilateral triangle depends on its side length s. The table shows perimeters for various side lengths. An equation that describes this relationship is $p = 3s$. This type of relationship is called a direct variation.

s	1	2	5	10
p	3	6	15	30

A **direct variation** is a relationship that can be described by an equation in the form $y = kx$, where $k \neq 0$. In the equation, k is called the **constant of variation.** You say that "y varies directly as x."

Example

Retail Sales Juan worked 16 hours last week at a department store and earned $92.00.

a. Assuming that his earnings e vary directly as the number of hours w he works, write an equation that relates these two variables.
b. How much will Juan earn if he works 12.5 hours in a week?

a.
$e = kw$ — Write a direct variation equation.
$92 = k(16)$ — Substitute for e and w.
$k = 5.75$ — Solve for k.

The equation $e = 5.75w$ describes this direct variation.

b.
$e = 5.75w$ — Use the equation from part (a).
$= 5.75(12.5)$ — Substitute 12.5 for w.
$= 71.875$ — Simplify.

Juan will earn $71.88 for working 12.5 hours.

Solve each problem.

1. *Taxes* The sales tax t on a purchase varies directly as the cost c of the items purchased. Write an equation relating these two variables if the sales tax rate is 6.5%. $t = 0.065c$
2. The circumference C of a circle varies directly as its diameter d. Write an equation that relates these two variables. $C = \pi d$
3. *Consumer Issues* Tandrell spends $16.48 for 12.3 gallons of gasoline.
   a. Write an equation that relates the total amount t spent on gasoline to the number of gallons purchased n. $t = 1.34n$
   b. How many gallons can Tandrell buy for $20.00? 14.9 gal
4. *Astronomy* An object that weighs 6 lb on Earth weighs 1 lb on the moon. If the weight w of an object on the moon varies directly as its weight on Earth e, write an equation relating these variables. $w = \frac{1}{6}e$

10-2 Teaching Notes

PROBLEM OF THE DAY

A cake has three circular tiers, each 4 in. high. The tiers have diameters of 30 in., 24 in., and 18 in. What is the surface area to be covered by frosting if there is no frosting between layers? 513π in.$^2 \approx 1611.6$ in.^{2}

Problem of the Day is also available in Transparencies.

CONNECTING TO PRIOR KNOWLEDGE Ask students to explain how to use the SSS Postulate, the SAS Postulate, the ASA Postulate, and the AAS Theorem to prove two triangles congruent.

WORK TOGETHER

Suggest that students begin by drawing two segments $\overline{AB}$ and $\overline{A'B'}$ of different lengths, then make A and A' the vertices of the 50° angle and B and B' the vertices of the 60° angles.

THINK AND DISCUSS

Angle-Angle Similarity Postulate Make sure students understand that this postulate is true for triangles but is not true for other polygons.

Lesson Planning Options

Prerequisite Skills

- Applying congruence postulates and theorems

Assignment Options for Exercises On Your Own

To provide flexible scheduling, this lesson can be subdivided into parts.

Core 11–19, 27–28
Extension 26

Core 1–10, 20–25, 29–30
Extension 31

Use Mixed Review to maintain skills.

Resources

Student Edition

Skills Handbook, pp. 660, 664
Extra Practice, p. 657
Glossary/Study Guide

Teaching Resources

Chapter Support File, Ch. 10
- Practice 10-2 (two worksheets)
- Reteaching 10-2
- Alternative Activity 10-2

Classroom Manager 10-2
Glossary, Spanish Resources

Transparencies
104, 107

Connections Geysers . . . and more

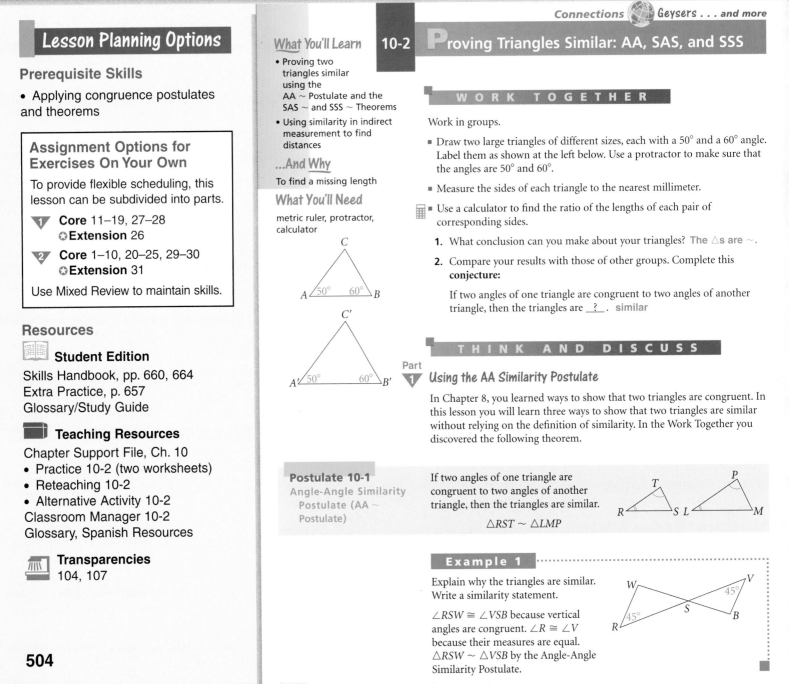

10-2 Proving Triangles Similar: AA, SAS, and SSS

What You'll Learn

- Proving two triangles similar using the AA ~ Postulate and the SAS ~ and SSS ~ Theorems
- Using similarity in indirect measurement to find distances

...And Why

To find a missing length

What You'll Need

metric ruler, protractor, calculator

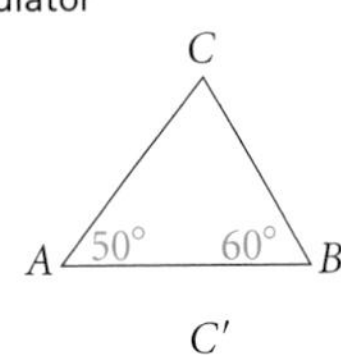

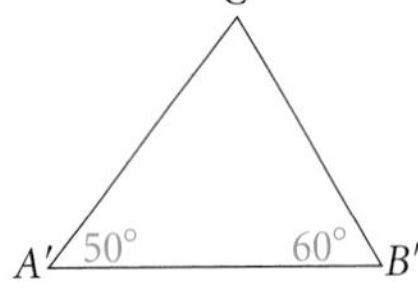

WORK TOGETHER

Work in groups.

- Draw two large triangles of different sizes, each with a 50° and a 60° angle. Label them as shown at the left below. Use a protractor to make sure that the angles are 50° and 60°.
- Measure the sides of each triangle to the nearest millimeter.
-  Use a calculator to find the ratio of the lengths of each pair of corresponding sides.

1. What conclusion can you make about your triangles? The $\triangle$s are ~.
2. Compare your results with those of other groups. Complete this **conjecture:**

   If two angles of one triangle are congruent to two angles of another triangle, then the triangles are __?__. similar

THINK AND DISCUSS

Part 1 **Using the AA Similarity Postulate**

In Chapter 8, you learned ways to show that two triangles are congruent. In this lesson you will learn three ways to show that two triangles are similar without relying on the definition of similarity. In the Work Together you discovered the following theorem.

Postulate 10-1 Angle-Angle Similarity Postulate (AA ~ Postulate)

If two angles of one triangle are congruent to two angles of another triangle, then the triangles are similar.

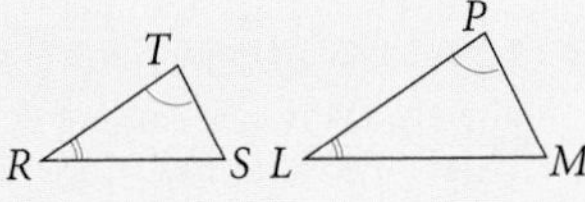

$\triangle RST \sim \triangle LMP$

Example 1

Explain why the triangles are similar. Write a similarity statement.

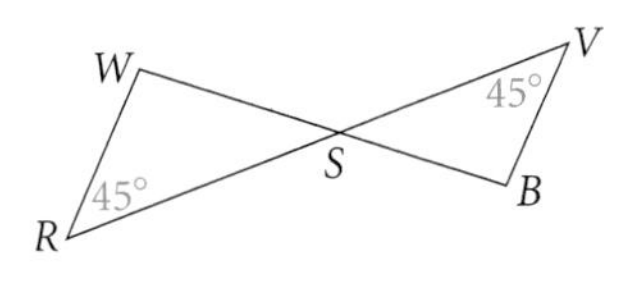

$\angle RSW \cong \angle VSB$ because vertical angles are congruent. $\angle R \cong \angle V$ because their measures are equal. $\triangle RSW \sim \triangle VSB$ by the Angle-Angle Similarity Postulate.

Example 1

AUDITORY LEARNING Have students practice naming the corresponding sides. Check that they do not name $\overline{VS}$ as the side corresponding to $\overline{WS}$.

Example 2 **Relating to the Real World** 

ESL Students may be unfamiliar with the term "geyser." Explain that a geyser is a flow of hot water or steam that emerges naturally from the ground into the air, sometimes to a great height and for a considerable amount of time. The word "geyser" means to "gush forth" and comes from Iceland where there are about 30 active geysers. There are about 200 geysers located in Yellowstone National Park.

CONNECTING TO STUDENTS' WORLD If you have block scheduling or an extended class period, bring in mirrors and take students outside to measure the height of a school building, goal post, or tree.

Question 3 Suggest that students draw a diagram similar to that in Example 2. Then have them model the steps used to solve Example 2.

You can use similar triangles and measurements to compute distances that are difficult to measure directly. These methods are called **indirect measurement.** One method uses the fact that light reflects off a mirror at the same angle at which it hits the mirror.

Example 2 **Relating to the Real World**

Geysers Ramon places a mirror on the ground 45 ft from the base of a geyser. He walks backward until he can see the top of the geyser in the middle of the mirror. At that point, Ramon's eyes are 6 ft above the ground and he is 7.5 ft from the mirror. Use similar triangles to find the height of the geyser.

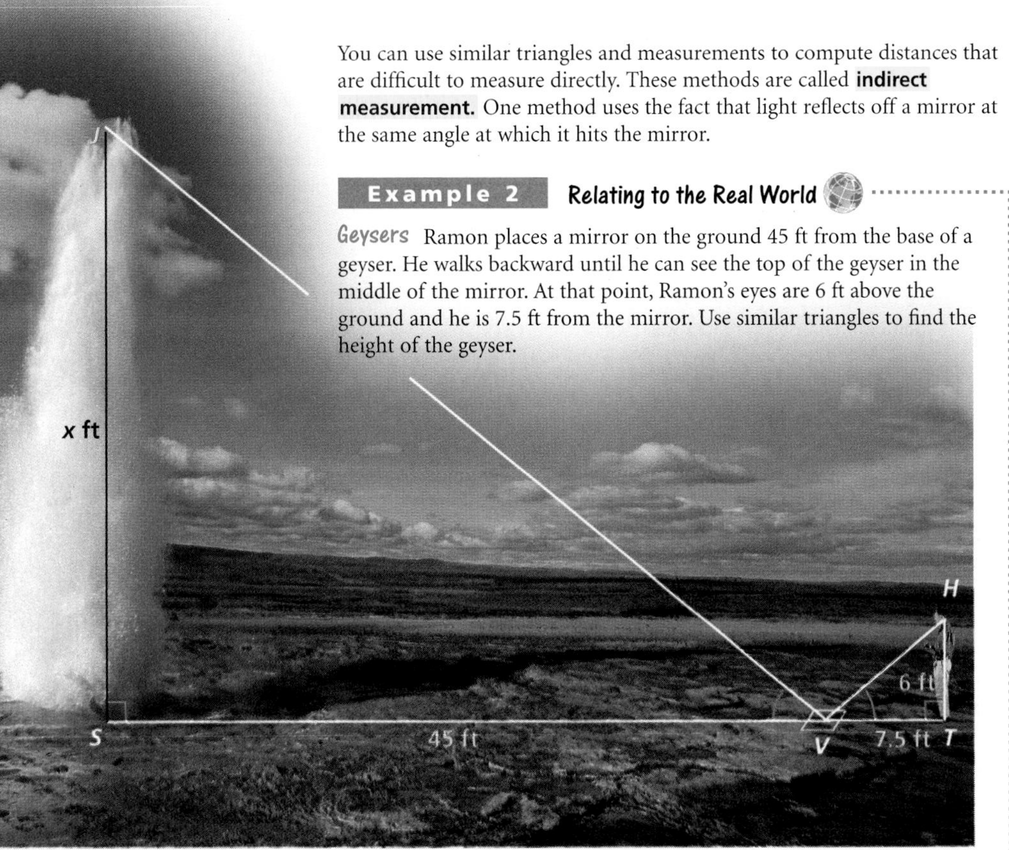

$\triangle HTV \sim \triangle JSV$	AA ~ Postulate
$\frac{HT}{JS} = \frac{TV}{SV}$	Corr. sides of ~ triangles are proportional.
$\frac{6}{x} = \frac{7.5}{45}$	Substitute.
$270 = 7.5x$	Cross-Product Property
$36 = x$	Divide each side by 7.5.

The geyser is 36 ft high.

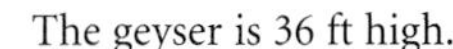

3. **Try This** To find the height of a fire tower, Latisha places a mirror on the ground 40 ft from the base of the tower. Latisha's eyes are $5\frac{1}{2}$ ft above the ground. When Latisha stands 4 ft from the mirror, she can see the top of the tower. How tall is the fire tower? **55 ft**

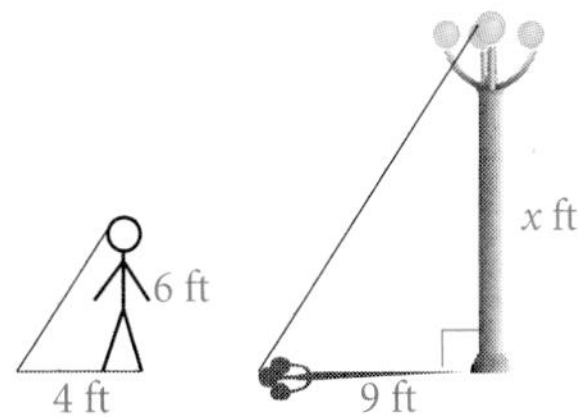

4. A lamppost casts a 9-ft shadow at the same time a person 6 ft tall casts a 4-ft shadow. Use similar triangles to find the height of the lamppost. **13.5 ft**

Additional Examples

FOR EXAMPLE 1

Explain why the triangles are similar. Write a similarity statement.

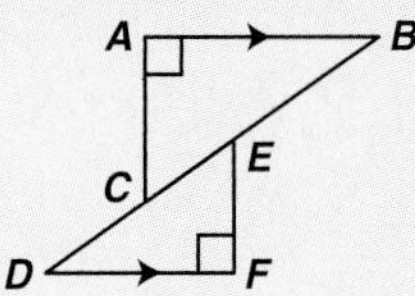

If two ∥ lines are cut by a transversal, then alt. int. ∠s are ≅. Therefore, ∠ABD ≅ ∠BDF. ∠BAC ≅ ∠DFE because right ∠s are ≅. Therefore, △CAB ~ △EFD by the AA ~ Postulate.

FOR EXAMPLE 2

Luis places a mirror on the ground 30 ft from the base of a tree. When he stands 5 ft from the mirror, he can see the top of the tree reflected in the mirror. If his eyes are 6 ft above the ground, how tall is the tree? **36 ft**

FOR EXAMPLE 3

Explain why the triangles are similar. Write a similarity statement. Find *NO*.

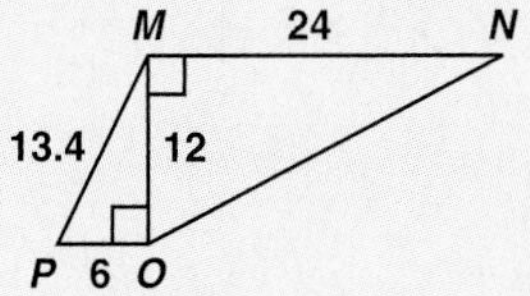

∠POM ≅ ∠NMO because right ∠s are ≅. $\frac{PO}{MO} = \frac{6}{12} = \frac{1}{2}$ and $\frac{MO}{MN} = \frac{12}{24} = \frac{1}{2}$. Therefore, △MOP ~ △NMO by the SAS~ Postulate. *NO* = 26.8

SAS Similarity Theorem Make sure students understand that the angle must be included between the sides that are proportional.

Point out that the proof of the SAS Similarity Theorem uses the SAS Congruence Theorem and the proof of the SSS Similarity Theorem uses the SSS Congruence Theorem.

Make sure students understand that if a triangle is similar to another triangle, then any triangle congruent to it is also similar to the other triangle.

Technology Options

For Exercise 10, student may construct the triangles using construction tools in geometry software.

Prentice Hall Technology

Software
- Secondary Math Lab Toolkit™
- Computer Item Generator 10-2

CD-ROM
- Multimedia Geometry Lab 10

Internet
- See the Prentice Hall site. (http://www.phschool.com)

506

Part 2

Using the SAS and SSS Similarity Theorems

The following two theorems follow from the AA Similarity Postulate.

Theorem 10-1
Side-Angle-Side Similarity Theorem (SAS ~ Theorem)

If an angle of one triangle is congruent to an angle of a second triangle, and the sides including the two angles are proportional, then the triangles are similar.

Given: $\angle A \cong \angle Q, \frac{AB}{QR} = \frac{AC}{QS}$
Prove: $\triangle ABC \sim \triangle QRS$

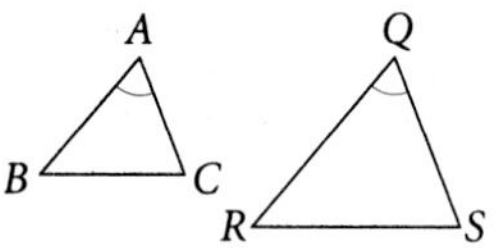

Outline of Proof of Theorem 10-1:

- Choose X on $\overline{QR}$ so that $AB = QX$. Draw $\overline{XY} \parallel \overline{RS}$. Use the AA ~ Postulate to show that $\triangle QXY \sim \triangle QRS$ and thus $\frac{QX}{QR} = \frac{QY}{QS}$.
- Combine this proportion with the given proportion and the fact that $AB = QX$ to show that $AC = QY$.
- Prove that $\triangle ABC \cong \triangle QXY$ and $\triangle ABC \sim \triangle QRS$.

Theorem 10-2
Side-Side-Side Similarity Theorem (SSS ~ Theorem)

If the corresponding sides of two triangles are proportional, then the triangles are similar.

Given: $\frac{AB}{QR} = \frac{BC}{RS} = \frac{AC}{QS}$
Prove: $\triangle ABC \sim \triangle QRS$

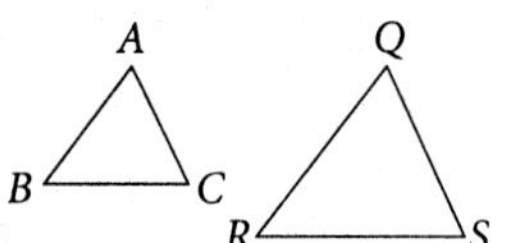

Outline of Proof of Theorem 10-2:

- Draw $\overline{XY}$ as in the proof for Theorem 10-1. Show that $\triangle QXY \sim \triangle QRS$ and thus $\frac{QX}{QR} = \frac{XY}{RS} = \frac{QY}{QS}$.
- Combine this proportion with the given proportion and the fact that $AB = QX$ to show that $BC = XY$ and $AC = QY$. Show that $\triangle ABC \cong \triangle QXY$ and $\triangle ABC \sim \triangle QRS$.

5. What postulate or theorem proves the pairs of triangles similar?

a.

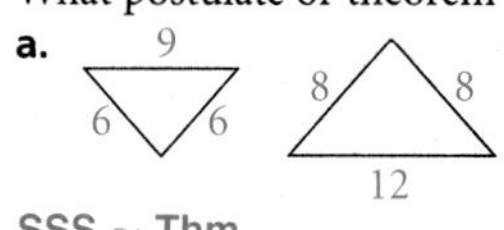

SSS ~ Thm.

b.

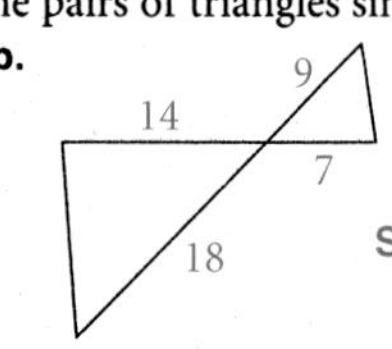

SAS ~ Thm.

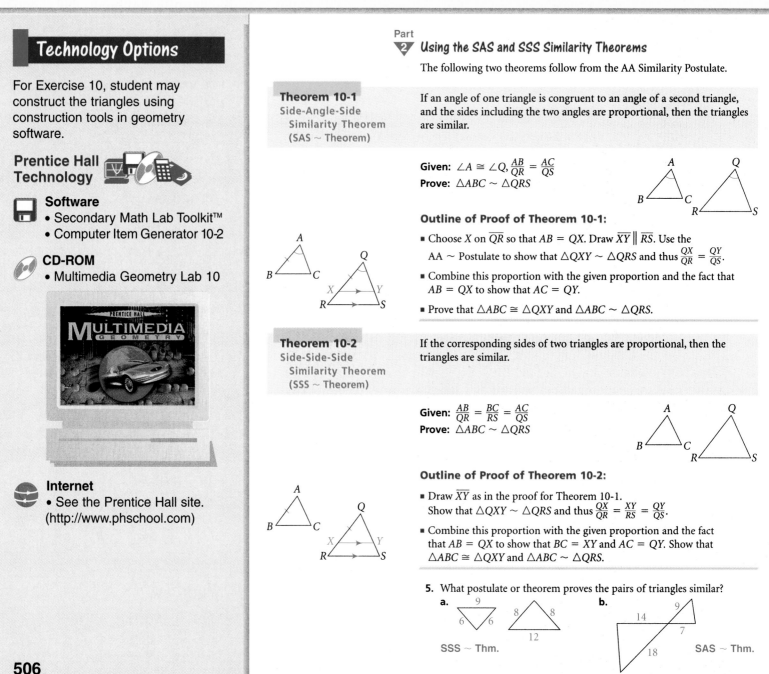

Example 3

ERROR ALERT! Students may have difficulty identifying the corresponding parts. **Remediation:** Help them see that since 12 is less than 16 and 18 is less than 24, the side with length 12 corresponds to the side with length 18 and the side with length 16 corresponds to the side with length 24.

EXTENSION Have students research how a pantograph is used to make similar figures.

Exercises ON YOUR OWN

Exercises 1–9 Check that students name the theorems and postulates correctly using the symbol ~ or the word "similarity."

Exercise 10 Completing the Work Together on page 504 will prepare students for the construction.

Example 3

Write a similarity statement and explain why the triangles are similar. Then find the length of $\overline{DE}$.

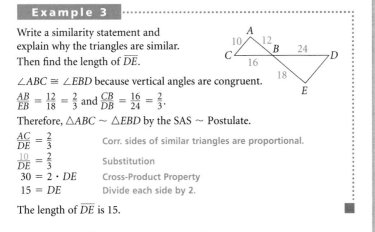

$\angle ABC \cong \angle EBD$ because vertical angles are congruent.

$\frac{AB}{EB} = \frac{12}{18} = \frac{2}{3}$ and $\frac{CB}{DB} = \frac{16}{24} = \frac{2}{3}$.

Therefore, $\triangle ABC \sim \triangle EBD$ by the SAS ~ Postulate.

$\frac{AC}{DE} = \frac{2}{3}$	Corr. sides of similar triangles are proportional.
$\frac{10}{DE} = \frac{2}{3}$	Substitution
$30 = 2 \cdot DE$	Cross-Product Property
$15 = DE$	Divide each side by 2.

The length of $\overline{DE}$ is 15.

6. Find $m\angle E$ if $m\angle C = 49$ and $m\angle ABC = 39$. 92

Exercises ON YOUR OWN

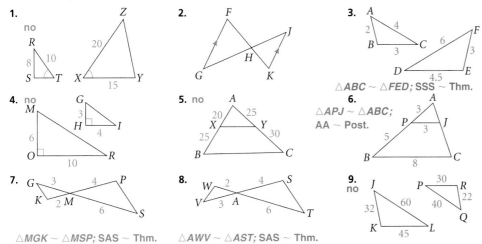

Can you prove the triangles similar? If so, write the similarity statement and name the postulate or theorem you used. $\triangle HFG \sim \triangle HKJ$; Alt. Interior Angles Thm. and AA ~ Post.

1. no

2.

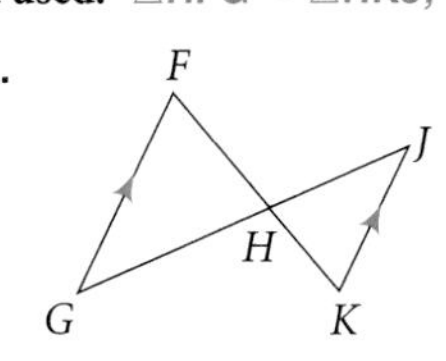

3.

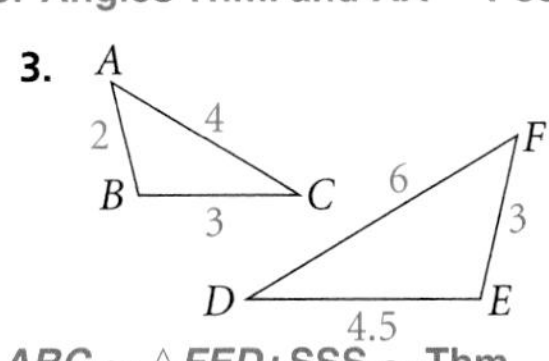

$\triangle ABC \sim \triangle FED$; SSS ~ Thm.

4. no

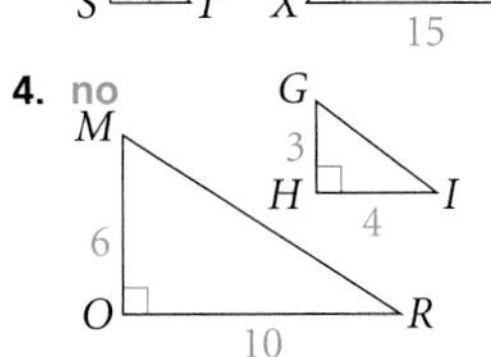

5. no

6. $\triangle APJ \sim \triangle ABC$; AA ~ Post.

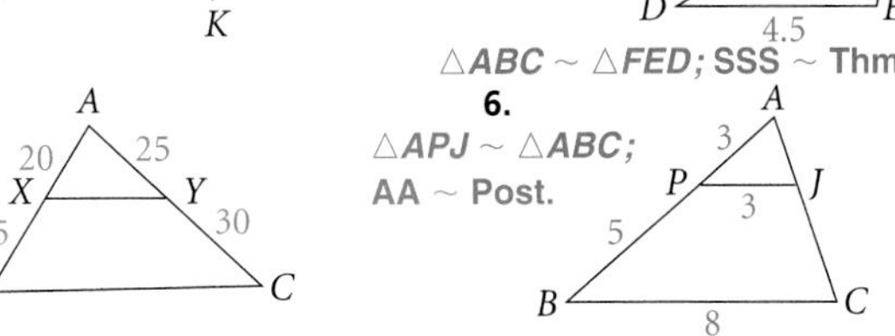

7.

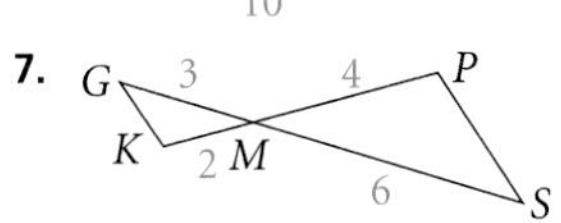

$\triangle MGK \sim \triangle MSP$; SAS ~ Thm.

8.

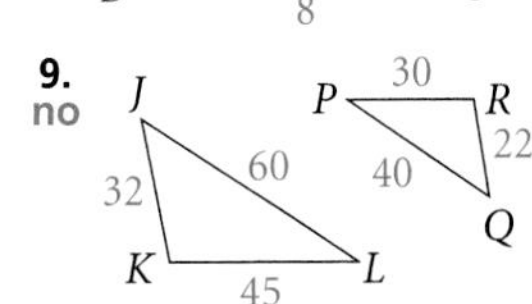

$\triangle AWV \sim \triangle AST$; SAS ~ Thm.

9. no

10. *Constructions* Draw any $\triangle ABC$. Use a straightedge and a compass to construct $\triangle RST$ so that $\triangle ABC \sim \triangle RST$ with similarity ratio 1 : 3. See margin for sample.

pages 507–509 On Your Own

10.

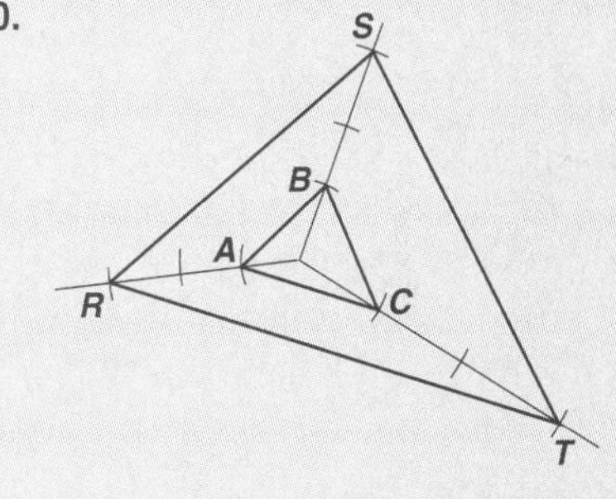

STANDARDIZED TEST TIP Exercise 11 Help students see that the triangles are isosceles.

CRITICAL THINKING Exercise 12 Have students name a theorem or postulate or draw a counterexample to support their answers.

ERROR ALERT! Exercises 16–18 Students may have difficulty identifying the lengths of corresponding sides because the sides of one triangle are contained in the sides of another. **Remediation:** Have students redraw the triangles separately and label the appropriate side lengths.

ALTERNATIVE ASSESSMENT Exercises 20–23 You can use these exercises to help you assess students' ability to use similar triangles to find missing lengths. Have students work in small groups and name the theorem or postulate they used to prove the triangles similar and the proportion they solved to find *x*.

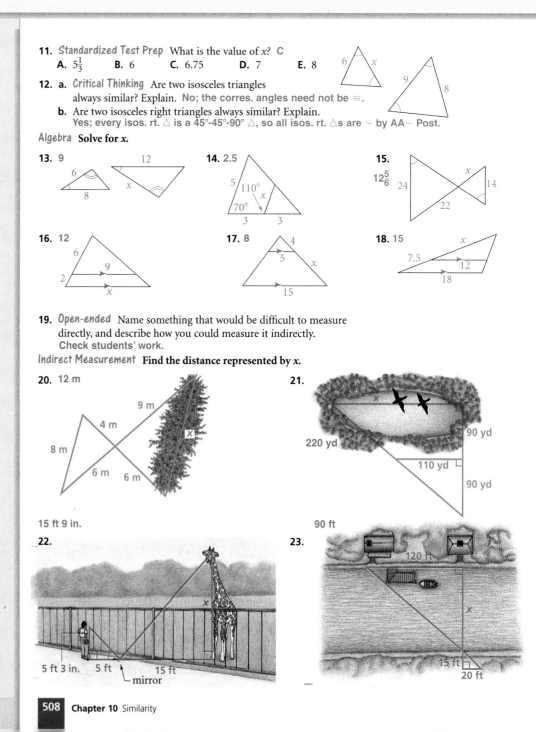

11. *Standardized Test Prep* What is the value of *x*? C

  A. $5\frac{1}{3}$ B. 6 C. 6.75 D. 7 E. 8

12. a. *Critical Thinking* Are two isosceles triangles always similar? Explain. No; the corres. angles need not be ≅.

  b. Are two isosceles right triangles always similar? Explain. Yes; every isos. rt. △ is a 45°-45°-90° △, so all isos. rt. △s are ~ by AA~ Post.

Algebra **Solve for *x*.**

13. 9

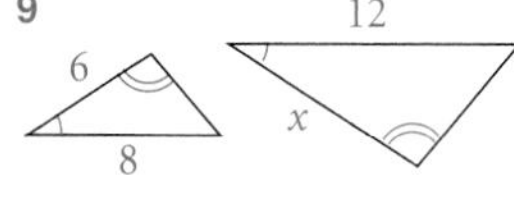

14. 2.5

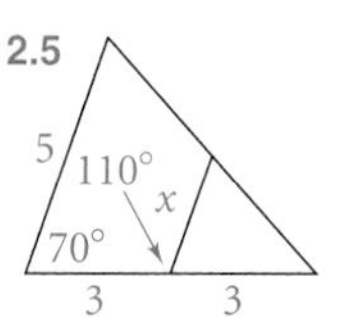

15. $12\frac{5}{6}$

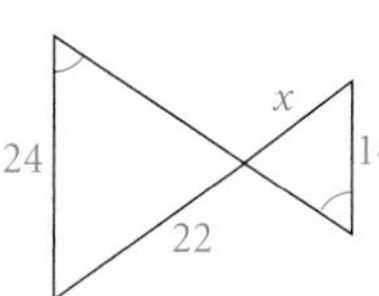

16. 12

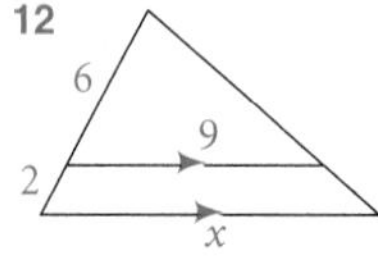

17. 8

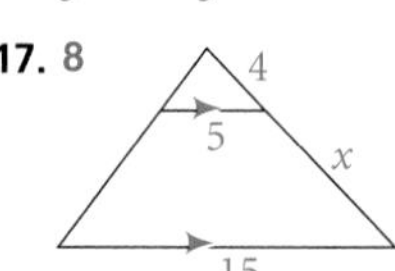

18. 15

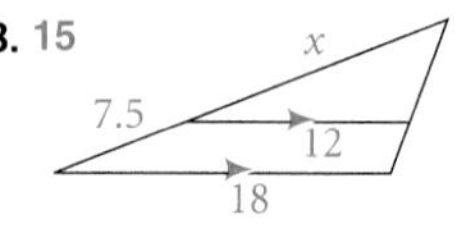

19. *Open-ended* Name something that would be difficult to measure directly, and describe how you could measure it indirectly. Check students' work.

Indirect Measurement **Find the distance represented by *x*.**

20. 12 m

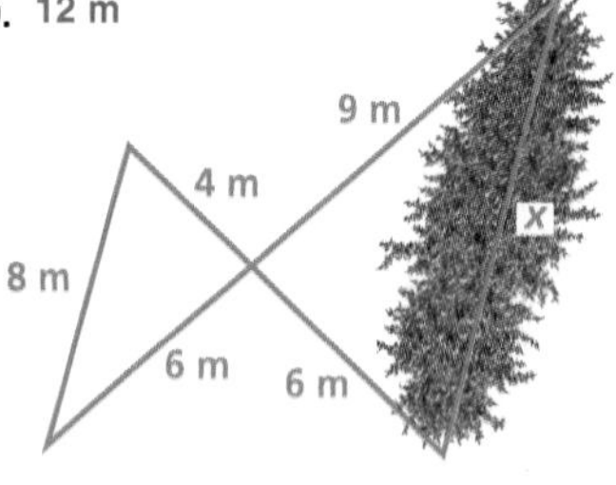

21.

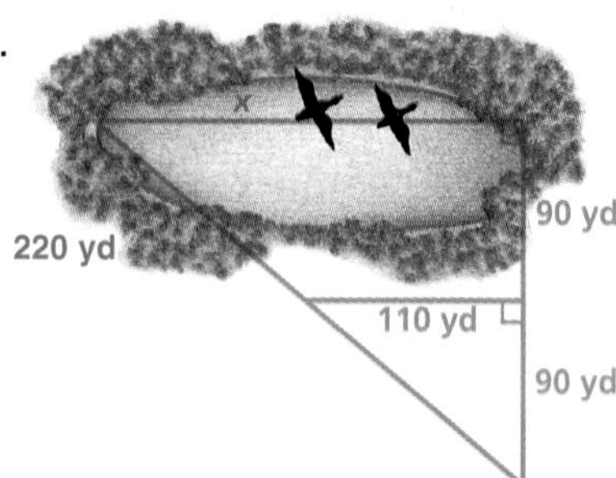

15 ft 9 in.

22.

90 ft

23.

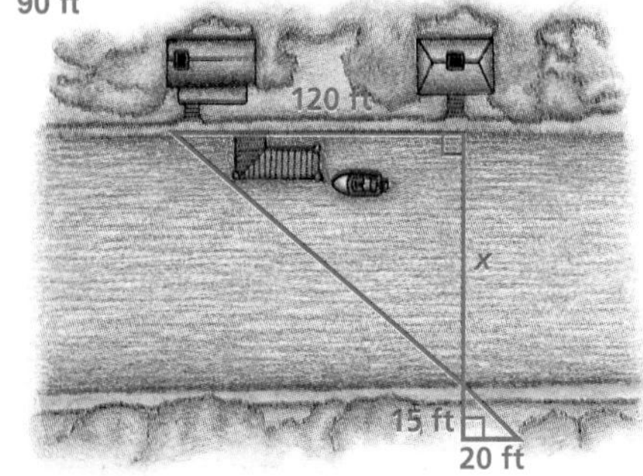

Exercise 26 Students may want to copy the diagram twice and trace a different pair of similar triangles on each.

WRITING Exercise 27 Have students research and write about the responsibilities of city or town planners, paying special attention to their role in investigating the environmental consequences of proposed buildings or industries.

Exercise 28 Have students find their heights in meters and compare them to Hannalore's height.

Exercises 29–30 You may want to assign these exercises as a group or partner activity.

Exercise 31 Students will study the areas and perimeters of similar figures in Lesson 10-5.

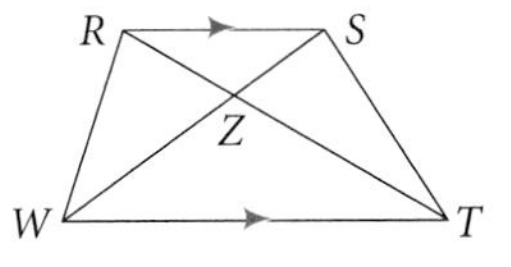

24. **a.** Classify $RSTW$. **Trapezoid**

b. Must any of the triangles shown be similar? Explain.
$\triangle RSZ \sim \triangle TWZ$ by AA~ Post.

25. **Mental Math** A yardstick casts a 1-ft shadow at the same time that a nearby tree casts a 15-ft shadow. How tall is the tree? **45 ft**

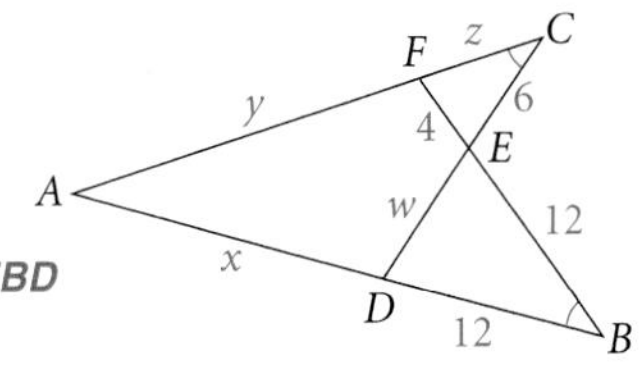

26. **a.** Write similarity statements involving two different pairs of similar triangles for the figure shown at the right. **$\triangle ABF \sim \triangle ACD$, $\triangle ECF \sim \triangle EBD$**

b. **Algebra** Find the missing lengths.
$w = 8$; $x = 16.8$; $y = 19.2$; $z = 6$

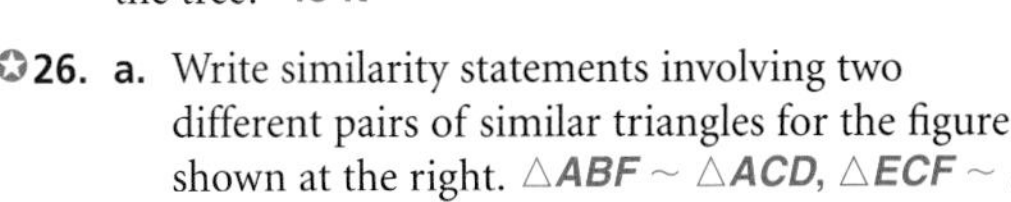

Skyscraper? *Nein!*

Hannalore Krause of Frankfurt, Germany, stopped the development of what was to be the tallest skyscraper in Europe because she wanted her apartment to get its fair amount of sunlight. To halt the construction she used a German law that specifies that every homeowner is entitled to sunlight.

Krause was offered 1.6 million dollars to drop her lawsuit, but she refused. The skyscraper, which would have cost about 400 million dollars, was to be built on a site that was only 60 m from Krause's apartment. Scheduled to be 265 m tall, it would have been slightly less than three-fourths the height of the Empire State Building.

Use the magazine article to answer Exercises 27 and 28.

27. **Writing** Explain how Hannalore Krause can use indirect measurement to estimate the length of the shadow of the building at a particular time of day.

27. Hannalore Krause can measure her shadow and use ~ △s to find the length of the shadow of the proposed building.

28. Suppose Hannalore is 1.75 m tall. When her shadow is 1 m long, about how long would the shadow of the proposed building be? **151 m**

Choose **Write a paragraph proof, a two-column proof, or a flow proof.** **29–30. Answers may vary. See margin for samples.**

29. **Given:** $\overline{BC} \parallel \overline{DF}$
Prove: $\triangle BYC \sim \triangle DYF$

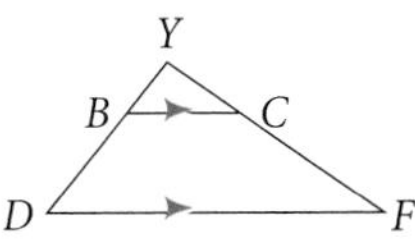

30. **Given:** $RT \cdot TQ = MT \cdot TS$
Prove: $\triangle RTM \sim \triangle STQ$

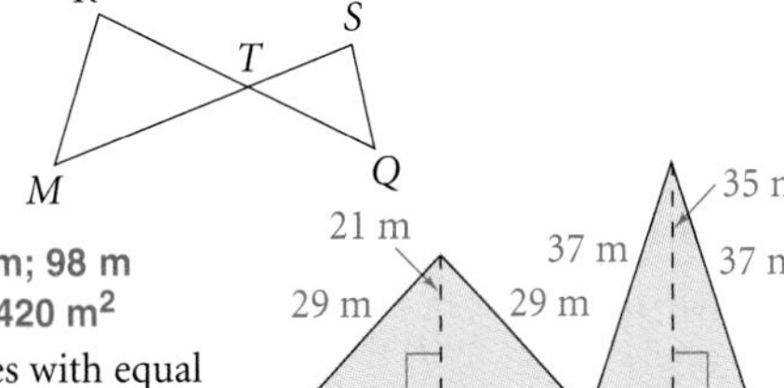

31. **a.** Find the perimeters of the triangles at the right. **98 m; 98 m**

b. Find the areas of the triangles at the right. **420 m^2; 420 m^2**

c. **Critical Thinking** Can you conclude that two triangles with equal perimeters and equal areas are similar? Explain.
No; corres. sides need not be proportional.

29. 1. $\overline{BC} \parallel \overline{DF}$ (Given) 2. $\angle YBC \cong \angle YDF$ (If $\parallel$ lines, then corres. $\angle$s are $\cong$.) 3. $\angle DYF \cong \angle DYF$ (Reflexive Prop. of $\cong$) 4. $\triangle BYC \sim \triangle DYF$ (AA~ Post.)

30. 1. $RT \cdot TQ = MT \cdot TS$ (Given) 2. $\frac{MT}{TQ} = \frac{RT}{TS}$ (Prop. of Proportions) 3. $\angle RTM \cong \angle STQ$ (Vert. $\angle$s are $\cong$.) 4. $\triangle RTM \sim \triangle STQ$ (SAS~ Thm.)

page 510 Mixed Review

34.

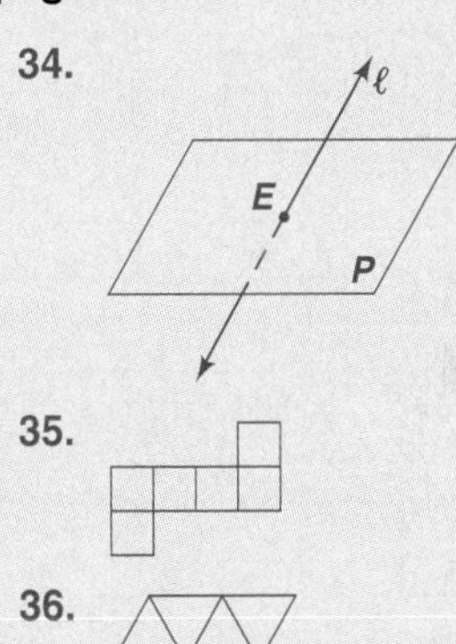

35.

36.

Checkpoint page 510

7.

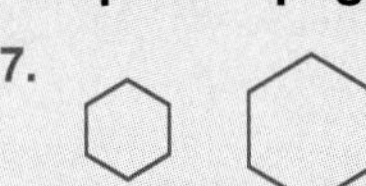

Exercises MIXED REVIEW

JOURNAL Students may want to begin by drawing an example of two such similar triangles. Help them use geometric vocabulary to describe what their diagrams indicate.

GETTING READY FOR LESSON 10-3 These exercises prepare students to find the geometric mean.

Wrap Up

THE BIG IDEA Ask students: *Explain the ways that you can prove two triangles similar.*

RETEACHING ACTIVITY Students decide whether or not two triangles are similar, justifying their answers with theorems and postulates. Then they write similarity statements. (Reteaching worksheet 10-2)

Exercises CHECKPOINT

In this Checkpoint, your students will assess their own progress in Lessons 10-1 to 10-2.

Exercise 3 Students may want to choose side lengths for the congruent sides to show the ratio of the sides are equal.

OPEN-ENDED Exercise 7 Students may want to use graph paper to sketch their figures. Encourage students to give several examples using different shapes.

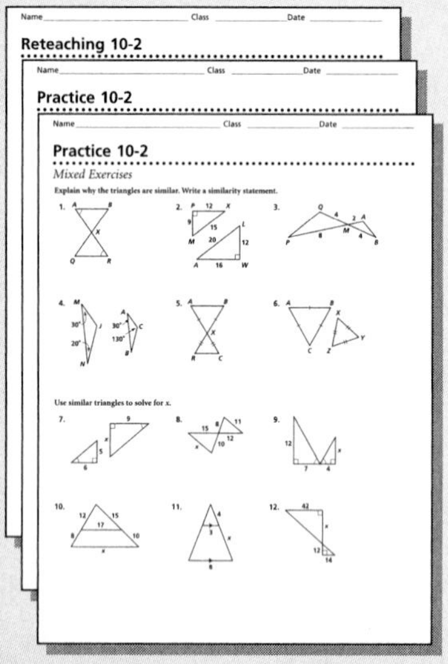

Lesson Quiz

Lesson Quiz is also available in Transparencies.

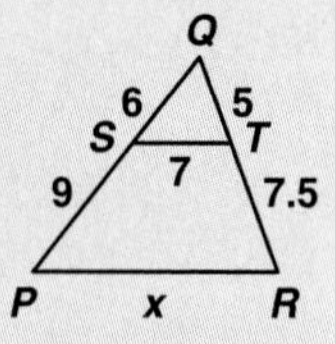

1. State the postulate or theorem you can use to prove the triangles are similar. SAS Similarity Postulate
2. Write a similarity statement. $\triangle QST \sim \triangle QPR$
3. Find *x*. 17.5

510

Exercises MIXED REVIEW

Sketch each figure.

32. a regular hexagon Sample: 

33. opposite rays $\overrightarrow{RS}$ and $\overrightarrow{RB}$ Sample: 

34. line ℓ intersecting plane *P* at point *E* See margin p. 509 for sample.

Draw a net for each space figure. 35–36. See margin p. 509 for samples.

35. a cube 36. a pyramid with a triangular base

FOR YOUR JOURNAL

Write a brief paragraph explaining why two isosceles triangles with congruent vertex angles are always similar.

Getting Ready for Lesson 10-3

Solve each proportion. Leave your answers in simplest radical form.

37. $\frac{4}{x} = \frac{x}{5}$ $\pm 2\sqrt{5}$ 38. $\frac{3}{m} = \frac{m}{8}$ $\pm 2\sqrt{6}$ 39. $\frac{w}{2} = \frac{20}{w}$ $\pm 2\sqrt{10}$ 40. $\frac{a}{6} = \frac{27}{a}$ $\pm 9\sqrt{2}$

Exercises CHECKPOINT

Are the triangles similar? If so, write the similarity statement and name the postulate or theorem that proves they are similar.

1. 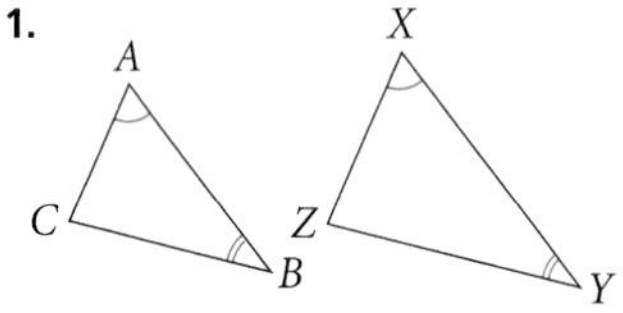

$\triangle ABC \sim \triangle XYZ$; AA~ Post.

2. 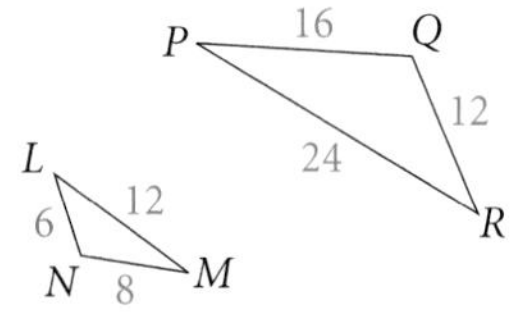

$\triangle LMN \sim \triangle RPQ$; SSS~ Thm.

3. 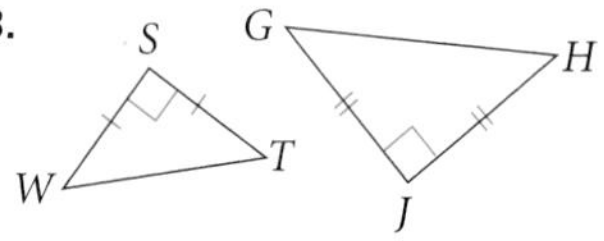

$\triangle WST \sim \triangle GJH$; SAS~ Thm.

The polygons are similar. Find the values of the variables.

4. 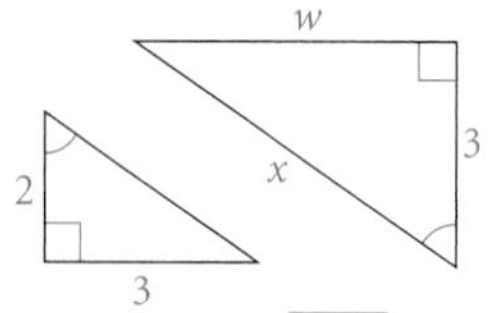

$w = 4.5$; $x = \sqrt{29.25}$

5. 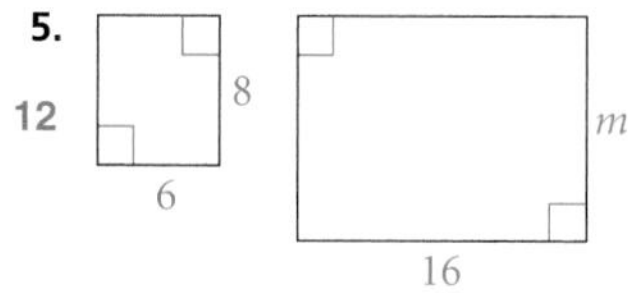

6. Do you remember the movie in which a giant made of marshmallow roams the streets of New York City? Suppose that a man 6 ft 3 in. tall stands so that the tip of his shadow coincides with the tip of the giant's shadow. The man is 4 ft from the tip of the shadows and 24 ft from the marshmallow giant. How tall is the giant? 43 ft 9 in.

7. *Open-ended* Sketch two figures that are similar and have a similarity ratio of 2 : 3. See margin p. 509 for sample.

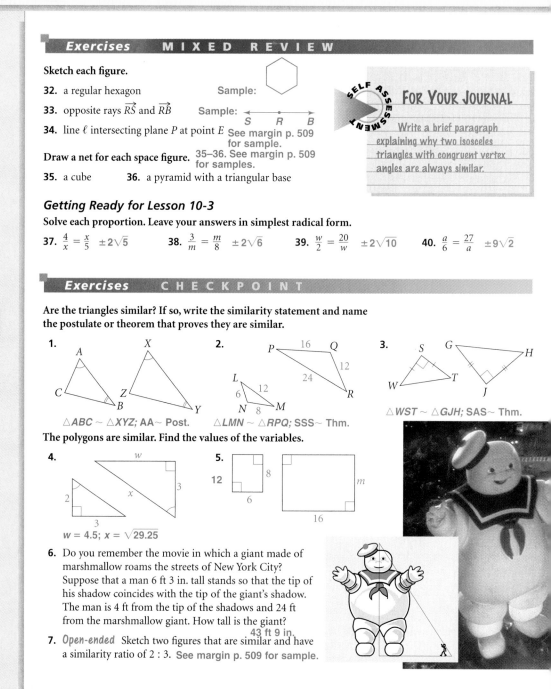

10-3 Teaching Notes

PROBLEM OF THE DAY

How many different ways can four unit squares be shaded in a 4-unit by 4-unit grid so that there shall never be more than one shaded square in any row or column? (Rotations and reflections do not count as different arrangements.) 7

Problem of the Day is also available in Transparencies.

CONNECTING TO PRIOR KNOWLEDGE Have students draw several right triangles and then draw the altitude to the hypotenuse of each triangle. Ask them to make a conjecture about the triangles formed.

WORK TOGETHER

Make sure that students draw the altitude to the hypotenuse, and not the median to the hypotenuse.

Question 4 Help students see that since all of the smaller triangles are similar to the larger triangle, they are similar to each other.

THINK AND DISCUSS

VISUAL LEARNING Copy $\triangle ABC$ three times and use color coding to indicate two pairs of congruent angles in $\triangle ABC$ and $\triangle ACD$ on the first copy, two pairs of congruent angles in $\triangle ABC$ and $\triangle CBD$ on the second copy, and two pairs of congruent angles in $\triangle ACD$ and $\triangle CBD$ on the third copy.

Connections — Recreation . . . and more

10-3 Similarity in Right Triangles

What You'll Learn

- Finding relationships among the lengths of the sides of a right triangle and the altitude to the hypotenuse

...And Why

To find distances by indirect measurement

What You'll Need

- straightedge
- scissors

WORK TOGETHER

Work with a partner.

- Draw one diagonal of a rectangular sheet of paper. Cut the paper on the diagonal to make two congruent right triangles.
- In one of the triangles, use paper folding to locate the altitude to the hypotenuse. Cut the triangle along the altitude to make two smaller right triangles.
- Label the angles of the three triangles as shown.

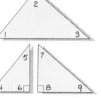

1. Compare the angles of the three triangles by placing the triangles on top of one another. Which angles have the same measure as $\angle 1$? $\angle 4$, $\angle 7$
2. Which angles have the same measure as $\angle 2$? $\angle 6$, $\angle 8$
3. Which angles have the same measure as $\angle 3$? $\angle 5$, $\angle 9$
4. Based on your results, what is true about the three triangles? The $\triangle$s are $\sim$.
5. Use the diagram at the left to complete the similarity statement. $\triangle RST \sim \triangle$■ $\sim \triangle$■ *RWS; SWT*

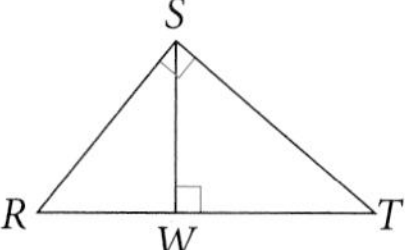

THINK AND DISCUSS

Your findings in the Work Together suggest the following theorem.

Theorem 10-3

The altitude to the hypotenuse of a right triangle divides the triangle into two triangles that are similar to the original triangle and to each other.

Given: Right $\triangle ABC$, $\overline{CD}$ is the altitude to the hypotenuse.
Prove: $\triangle ABC \sim \triangle ACD \sim \triangle CBD$

Proof of Theorem 10-3

Both smaller triangles are similar to $\triangle ABC$ by the AA Similarity Postulate because they each share an acute angle with $\triangle ABC$ and all three triangles are right triangles. Since both smaller triangles are similar to $\triangle ABC$, their corresponding angles are congruent. Thus they are similar to each other.

Lesson Planning Options

Prerequisite Skills

- Simplifying radicals
- Using quadratic formula

Assignment Options for Exercises On Your Own

Core 1–28, 32–35
Extension 29–31

Use Mixed Review to maintain skills.

Resources

Student Edition

Skills Handbook, pp. 674, 675, 676
Extra Practice, p. 657
Glossary/Study Guide

Teaching Resources

Chapter Support File, Ch. 10
- Practice 10-3 (two worksheets)
- Reteaching 10-3

Classroom Manager 10-3
Glossary, Spanish Resources

Transparencies
105, 108

MAKING CONNECTIONS Just as the arithmetic mean has applications in geometry, the geometric mean has applications in algebra. Have students research these applications and present their findings to the class. Also have students research the harmonic mean and its applications in algebra and music.

Example 1

Help students understand that the proportion can also be written $\frac{18}{x} = \frac{x}{4}$. Also check that students understand how $\sqrt{72}$ was simplified to $6\sqrt{2}$.

ERROR ALERT! Corollaries 1 and 2 Some students may not understand the meaning of "the lengths of the segments of the hypotenuse" and "the segment of the hypotenuse that is adjacent to that leg." **Remediation:** Copy $\triangle ABC$ and label the segments of the hypotenuse and the legs adjacent to the segments.

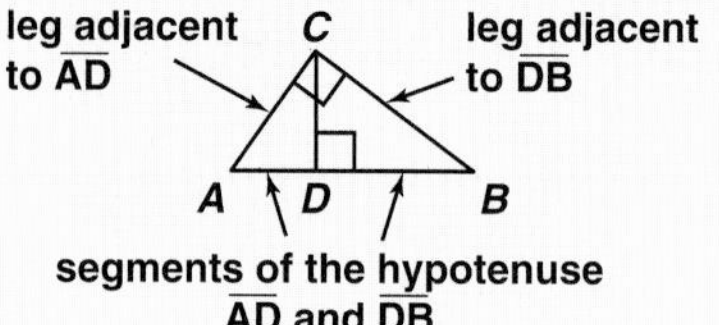

Additional Examples

FOR EXAMPLE 1

Find the geometric mean of 6 and 20. Leave your answer in simplest radical form. $2\sqrt{30}$

FOR EXAMPLE 2

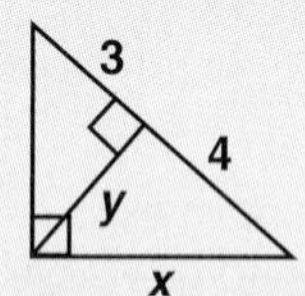

Solve for x and y.
$2\sqrt{7}$; $2\sqrt{3}$

FOR EXAMPLE 3

A road from Taj's house and a road from Sonya's house meet at their school at a right angle. The public pool is 2 mi east of the school and 4 mi north of Sonya's house.

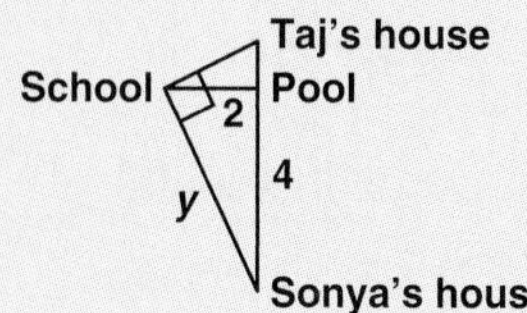

a. What is the distance from Taj's house to the pool? 1 mi

b. What is the distance from Sonya's house to school? $2\sqrt{5}$ mi

QUICK REVIEW

In the proportion
$\frac{a}{b} = \frac{c}{d}$,
b and c are the means.

Proportions in which the means are equal occur frequently in geometry. For any two positive numbers a and b, the **geometric mean** of a and b is the positive number x such that $\frac{a}{x} = \frac{x}{b}$.

Example 1

Algebra Find the geometric mean of 4 and 18.

$\frac{4}{x} = \frac{x}{18}$	Write a proportion.
$x^2 = 72$	Use the Cross-Product Property
$x = \sqrt{72}$	Find the positive square root.
$x = 6\sqrt{2}$	Write in simplest radical form.

PROBLEM SOLVING

Look Back Give an alternate definition of geometric mean that does not involve a proportion.

For any 2 pos. numbers a and b, the geometric mean of a and b is $\sqrt{ab}$.

6. a. Try This Find the geometric mean of 15 and 20. Leave your answer in simplest radical form. $10\sqrt{3}$

b. Calculator Find the answer to part (a) rounded to the nearest tenth. 17.3

Two important corollaries of Theorem 10-3 involve the geometric mean.

Corollary 1

The length of the altitude to the hypotenuse of a right triangle is the geometric mean of the lengths of the segments of the hypotenuse.

Proof of Corollary 1

Given: Right $\triangle ABC$,
$\overline{CD}$ is the altitude to the hypotenuse.

Prove: $\frac{AD}{CD} = \frac{CD}{DB}$

By Theorem 10-3, $\triangle CDB \sim \triangle ADC$. Since corresponding sides of similar triangles are proportional, $\frac{AD}{CD} = \frac{CD}{DB}$.

Corollary 2

The altitude to the hypotenuse of a right triangle intersects it so that the length of each leg is the geometric mean of the length of its adjacent segment of the hypotenuse and the length of the entire hypotenuse.

Proof of Corollary 2

Given: Right $\triangle ABC$,
$\overline{CD}$ is the altitude to the hypotenuse.

Prove: $\frac{AB}{AC} = \frac{AC}{AD}$, $\frac{AB}{CB} = \frac{CB}{DB}$

By Theorem 10-3, $\triangle ABC \sim \triangle ACD$. Their corresponding sides are proportional, so $\frac{AB}{AC} = \frac{AC}{AD}$. Similarly, $\triangle ABC \sim \triangle CBD$ and $\frac{AB}{CB} = \frac{CB}{DB}$.

Example 2

Discuss with students how to determine which theorem or corollary to apply to find a missing value. Since x is a leg, use Corollary 2, which gives the relationship between the legs and the segments of the hypotenuse. Since y is the altitude, use Corollary 1, which gives the relationship between the altitude and the segments of the hypotenuse.

Example 3 Relating to the Real World 

Check that students understand that $AB = 500$ because 300, 400, and 500 are a Pythagorean triple, that $\overline{CD}$ is the altitude to $\overline{AB}$ because "walks straight across" means the shortest distance which is perpendicular to the ocean, and that the proportion $\frac{AD}{AC} = \frac{AC}{AB}$ applies Corollary 2.

Question 8 Students can use the results of Example 3 to find $DB = AB - AD = 320$.

Example 2

Solve for x and y.

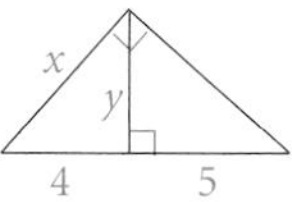

Use Corollary 2 to solve for x.

$$\frac{4+5}{x} = \frac{x}{4}$$
$$x^2 = 36$$
$$x = 6$$

Use Corollary 1 to solve for y.

$$\frac{4}{y} = \frac{y}{5}$$
$$y^2 = 20$$
$$y = 2\sqrt{5}$$

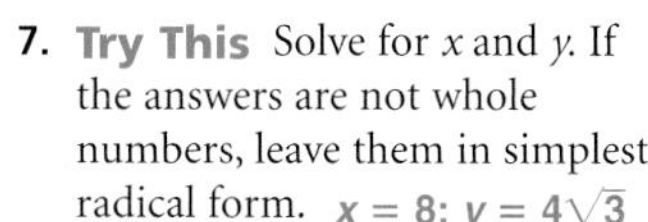

7. **Try This** Solve for x and y. If the answers are not whole numbers, leave them in simplest radical form. $x = 8$; $y = 4\sqrt{3}$

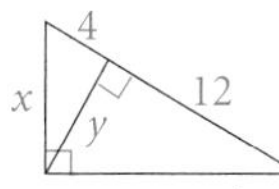

You can use the Corollaries to Theorem 10-3 to find distances.

Example 3 Relating to the Real World 

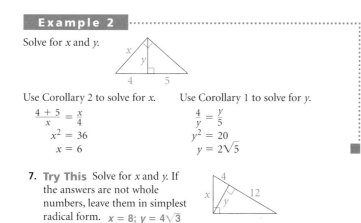

Recreation At the parking lot of a State Park, the 300-m path to the snack bar and the 400-m path to the boat rental shop meet at a right angle. Marla walks straight from the parking lot to the ocean. How far is Marla from the snack bar?

$\overline{CD}$, the perpendicular segment from point C to $\overline{AB}$, is the shortest path to the ocean. $\triangle ABC$ is a right triangle. Using Pythagorean triples, $AB = 500$. To find AD, apply Corollary 2.

$\frac{AD}{AC} = \frac{AC}{AB}$	Corollary 2
$\frac{AD}{300} = \frac{300}{500}$	Substitute.
$500(AD) = 90{,}000$	Cross-Product Property
$AD = 180$	Divide each side by 500.

Marla is 180 m from the snack bar.

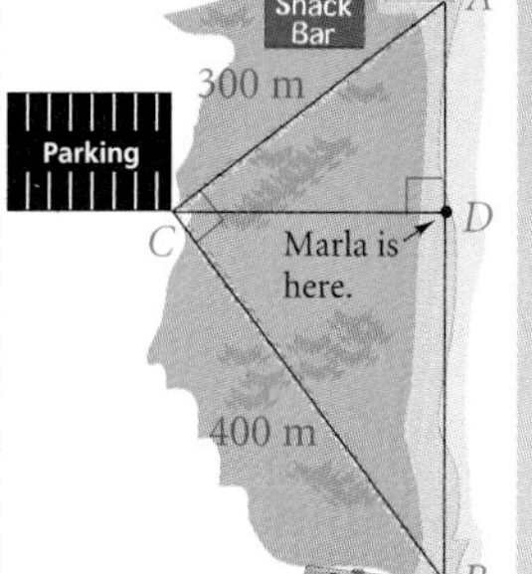

8. How far did Marla walk from the parking lot to the ocean? 240 m

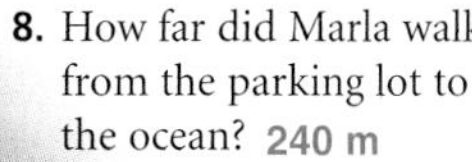

Technology Options

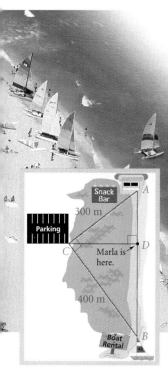

For Exercise 21, students may use graphing software to graph the triangles. For Exercises 20 and 35, students may use a drawing program to draw the triangles.

Prentice Hall Technology 

 **Software**
- Secondary Math Lab Toolkit™
- Integrated Math Lab 41
- Computer Item Generator 10-3

 **Internet**
- See the Prentice Hall site. (http://www.phschool.com)

Exercises ON YOUR OWN

ALTERNATIVE ASSESSMENT Have students work with a partner to choose 5 problems that represent the key topics of the lesson. Have them write the problem, the concept, and the solution for each.

ALGEBRA Exercises 8–15 Ask students to justify their answers by naming the property they apply.

ALGEBRA Exercises 16–19 Have students write the proportion they use to find *x*. Check especially Exercises 17–19 where students have to subtract or add to find one of the terms for the proportion.

Exercise 20 Students may want to draw sketches for part a, then adjust their sketches after finding *h* for part b.

Exercise 23 Students use the Pythagorean Theorem to find the length of the highway from Blare to Albany and Corollary 2 to find the distance from Blare to the proposed service station.

pages 514–516 On Your Own

20b.

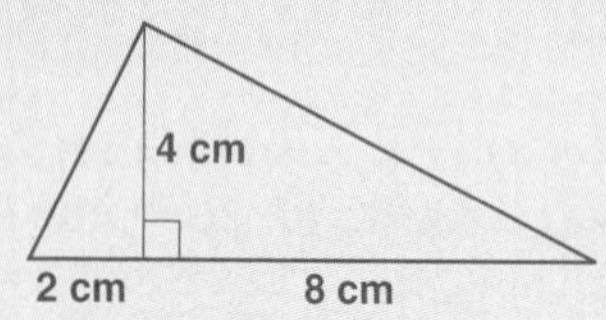

c. Draw a 10 cm segment. At a pt. 2 cm from 1 endpt. draw a ⊥ segment 4 cm long. Draw segments connecting the other endpt. of the 4 cm segment with the endpts. of the 10 cm segment.

Exercises ON YOUR OWN

1. Complete: $\triangle JKL \sim \triangle$ ■ $\sim \triangle$ ■ JNK; KNL

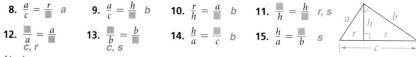

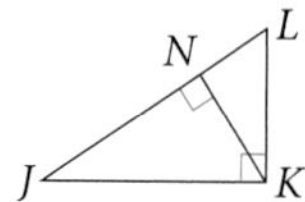

Algebra **Find the geometric mean of each pair of numbers. If an answer is not a whole number, leave it in simplest radical form.**

2. 4 and 9 6
3. 4 and 10 $2\sqrt{10}$
4. 4 and 12 $4\sqrt{3}$
5. 3 and 48 12
6. 5 and 125 25
7. 11 and 1331 121

Algebra **Refer to the figure to complete each proportion.**

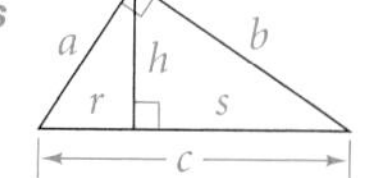

8. $\frac{a}{c} = \frac{r}{■}$ a
9. $\frac{a}{c} = \frac{h}{■}$ b
10. $\frac{r}{h} = \frac{a}{■}$ b
11. $\frac{■}{h} = \frac{h}{■}$ r, s
12. $\frac{■}{a} = \frac{a}{■}$ c, r
13. $\frac{■}{b} = \frac{b}{■}$ c, s
14. $\frac{h}{a} = \frac{■}{c}$ b
15. $\frac{h}{a} = \frac{■}{b}$ s

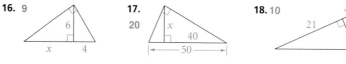

Algebra **Solve for *x*. If an answer is not a whole number, leave it in simplest radical form.**

16. 9

17. 20

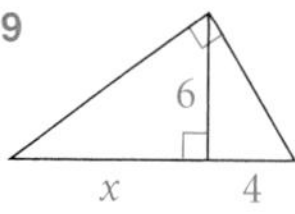

18. 10

19. $6\sqrt{3}$

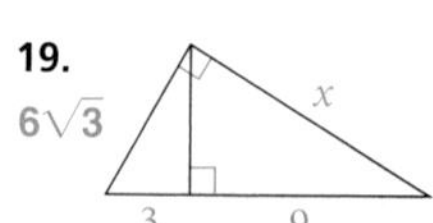

20. a. The altitude to the hypotenuse of a right triangle divides the hypotenuse into segments 2 cm and 8 cm long. Find the length *h* of the altitude. 4 cm b–c. See margin.
    b. Drawing Use the value you found for *h* in part (a), along with the lengths 2 cm and 8 cm, to draw the right triangle accurately.
    c. Writing Explain how you drew the triangle in part (b).

21. Coordinate Geometry $\overline{CD}$ is the altitude to the hypotenuse of right $\triangle ABC$. The coordinates of *A*, *D*, and *B* are (4, 2), (4, 6), and (4, 15), respectively. Find all possible coordinates of point *C*. (−2, 6), (10, 6)

22. Algebra The altitude to the hypotenuse of a right triangle divides the hypotenuse into segments whose lengths are in the ratio 1 : 2. The length of the altitude is 8. How long is the hypotenuse? $12\sqrt{2}$

23. Civil Engineering Study the plan at the right. A service station will be built on the interstate highway and a road will connect it with Cray. How far from Blare should the service station be located so that the proposed road will be perpendicular to the interstate? How long will the new road be? 18 mi; 24 mi

STANDARDIZED TEST TIP **Exercise 28** One strategy for solving this problem is to apply Corollary 1 relating the altitude to the segments of the hypotenuse.

Exercise 31 Students will need to use the quadratic formula.

Exercise 32 Another proof of the Pythagorean Theorem is presented.

Exercise 33 Students should begin by making a sketch. They can find the hypotenuse by remembering the proportions of a 30°-60°-90° triangle. The altitude is the side opposite the 60° angle in a right triangle with hypotenuse of length 10.

Exercise 34 Students may want to begin by testing the validity of the corollary in right triangles with side lengths 3, 4, and 5 or 5, 12, and 13.

Algebra Find the values of the variables. If an answer is not a whole number, leave it in simplest radical form.

24. 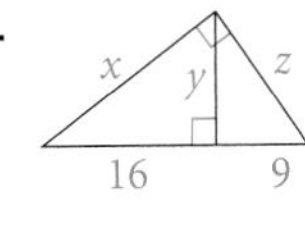

$x = 20;\ y = 12;\ z = 15$

25. 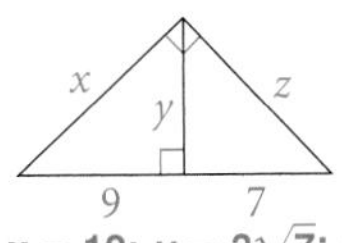

$x = 12;\ y = 3\sqrt{7};\ z = 4\sqrt{7}$

26. 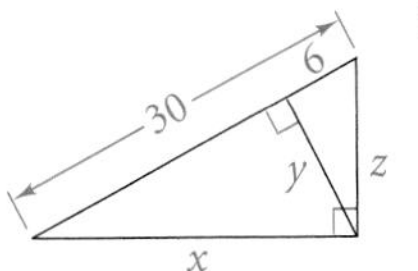

$x = 12\sqrt{5};\ y = 12;\ z = 6\sqrt{5}$

27. 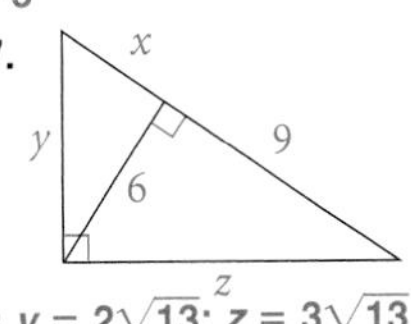

$x = 4;\ y = 2\sqrt{13};\ z = 3\sqrt{13}$

28. Standardized Test Prep The length of the altitude to the hypotenuse of a right triangle is 8. The length of the hypotenuse is 16. What is the length of one of the segments into which the altitude divides the hypotenuse? A

A. 8 B. $8\sqrt{2}$ C. 4 D. $4\sqrt{2}$ E. cannot be determined

Algebra Find the value of x. If an answer is not a whole number, leave it in simplest radical form.

PROBLEM SOLVING HINT
Use the Quadratic Formula. (See page 439.)

29. 3 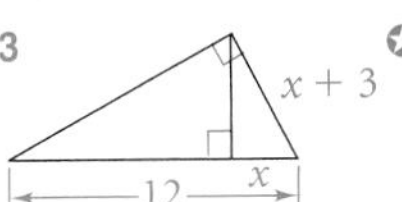

30. 4 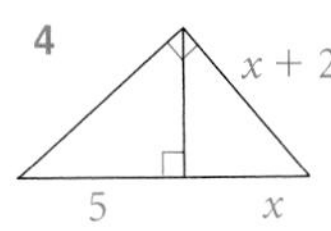

31. 4.5 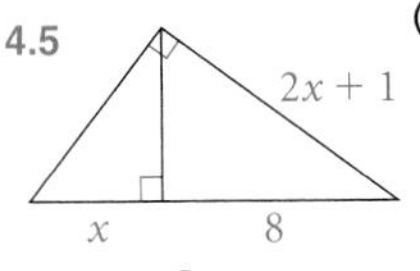

32. Pythagorean Theorem You can use Corollary 2 of Theorem 10-3 to prove the Pythagorean Theorem. Complete the following proof.

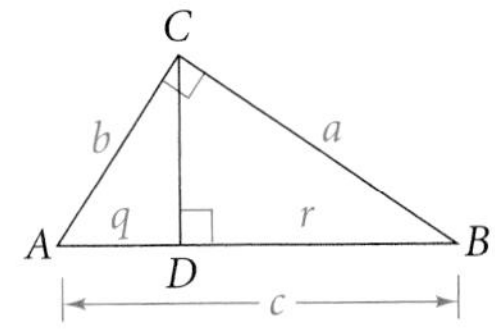

Given: Right $\triangle ABC$ with altitude $\overline{CD}$
Prove: $c^2 = a^2 + b^2$

Statements	Reasons
1. Right $\triangle ABC$ with altitude $\overline{CD}$	a. ? Given
2. $\frac{c}{a} = \frac{a}{r}, \frac{c}{b} = \frac{b}{q}$	b. ? See margin.
c. ■ $= a^2$, ■ $= b^2$ cr; cq	d. ? Cross-Product Prop.
3. $cr + cq = a^2 + b^2$	e. ? Addition Prop. of =
4. $c(r + q) = a^2 + b^2$	f. ? Distributive Prop.
5. $r + q = c$	g. ? Segment Addition Post.
6. $c^2 = a^2 + b^2$	h. ? Substitution

33. The length of the shorter leg of a 30°-60°-90° triangle is 10 cm. What is the length of the altitude to the hypotenuse? $5\sqrt{3}$ cm

34. a. Lauren thinks she has found a new corollary: The product of the lengths of the two legs of a right triangle is equal to the product of the lengths of the hypotenuse and the altitude from the right angle. Draw a figure for this corollary and write the *Given* and *To Prove*. a–b. See also margin.

b. Critical Thinking Is Lauren's corollary true? Explain. It is true.

35. Open-ended Draw a right triangle so that the altitude from the right angle to the hypotenuse bisects the hypotenuse.

35. Sample:

32b. The altitude of the hypotenuse of a rt. △ intersects it so that the length of each leg is the geometric mean of the length of its adjacent segment of the hypotenuse and the length of the entire hypotenuse.

34a. Given: Right $\triangle ABC$ with altitude $\overline{CD}$; Prove: $BC \cdot CA = AB \cdot CD$

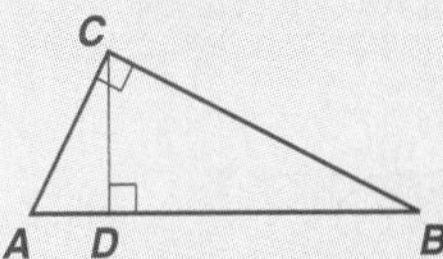

b. Answers may vary. Sample: Yes; each product = twice the area of the △.

page 516 Mixed Review

38. The number of people getting dental exams is increasing while the number of extractions is declining. As the total number of patients receiving dental services is increasing, the ratio of exams to extractions is increasing sharply.

39.

Chapter Project **FIND OUT BY ANALYZING** Students discover a pattern in the perimeters of Koch snowflakes. Have students work in groups to complete the questions.

Exercises MIXED REVIEW

ESL Exercises 36–38 Some students may be unfamiliar with the word "extraction." Explain that it means the removal of a tooth.

GETTING READY FOR LESSON 10-4 These exercises prepare students to apply the Side-Splitter Theorem.

Wrap Up

THE BIG IDEA Ask students to explain in their own words the relationships between the lengths of sides of a right triangle and the altitude to the hypotenuse.

RETEACHING ACTIVITY Students use the relationships between the lengths of the sides of a right triangle and the altitude to the hypotenuse to find missing lengths. (Reteaching worksheet 10-3)

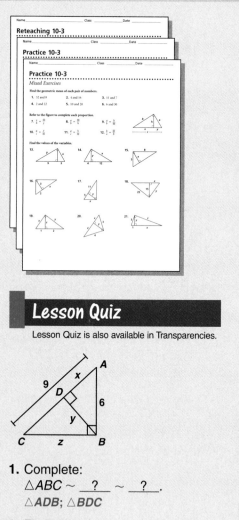

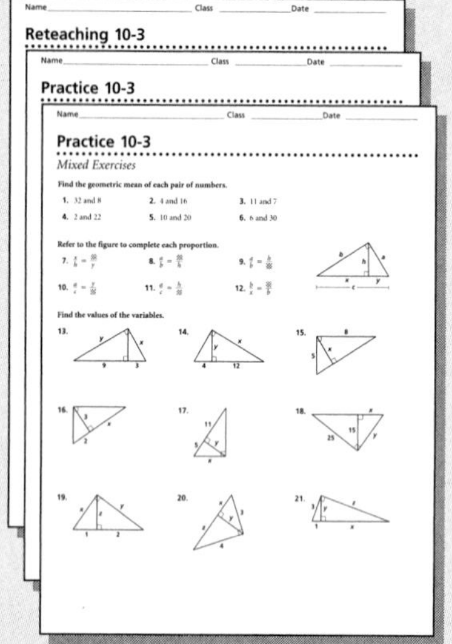

Lesson Quiz

Lesson Quiz is also available in Transparencies.

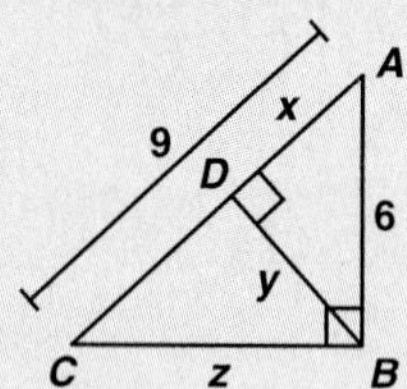

1. Complete: $\triangle ABC \sim$ __?__ $\sim$ __?__.
   $\triangle ADB$; $\triangle BDC$
2. Find x. 4
3. Find y. $2\sqrt{5}$
4. Find z. $3\sqrt{5}$

Chapter Project Find Out by Analyzing

Use the Stage 3 Koch snowflake shown here and the earlier stages you made in the Find Out question on page 502.

- At each stage, is the snowflake equilateral? yes
- Suppose each side of the original triangle is one unit. Complete the table to find the perimeter of each stage.

Stage	Number of sides	Length of a side	Perimeter
0	3	1	3
1	■ 12	$\frac{1}{3}$	■ 4
2	48	■ $\frac{1}{9}$	■ $5\frac{1}{3}$
3	■ 192	■ $\frac{1}{27}$	■ $7\frac{1}{9}$

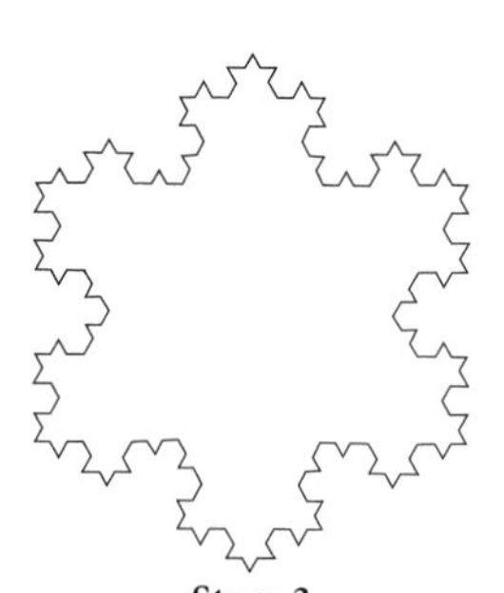
Stage 3

- Patterns Can you **predict** the perimeter at Stage 4? mult. by $\frac{4}{3}$; $9\frac{13}{27}$
- Inductive Reasoning Will there be a stage with a perimeter greater than 100 units? Explain. The perimeter exceeds 100 at Stage 13.

Exercises MIXED REVIEW

Data Analysis Use the graph showing the percent of people in the United States who received dental services.

Percent of U.S. Population Receiving Dental Services

Percent: 0, 20, 40, 60, 80, 100

Dental Exam: '59 27; '69 41; '79 58; '89 89

Extraction: '59 34; '69 28; '79 23; '89 19

36. In which year did more people have an extraction than a dental exam? 1959
37. Between which years did the percent of the population having a dental exam increase the most? 1979–1989
38. Critical Thinking Compare the ratio of dental exams to extractions for each year. What trend do you see in dental services? See margin p. 515.
39. Draw a rectangular prism in two-point perspective.
    See margin p. 515 for sample.

Getting Ready for Lesson 10-4

Find the length of the midsegment of each trapezoid or triangle.

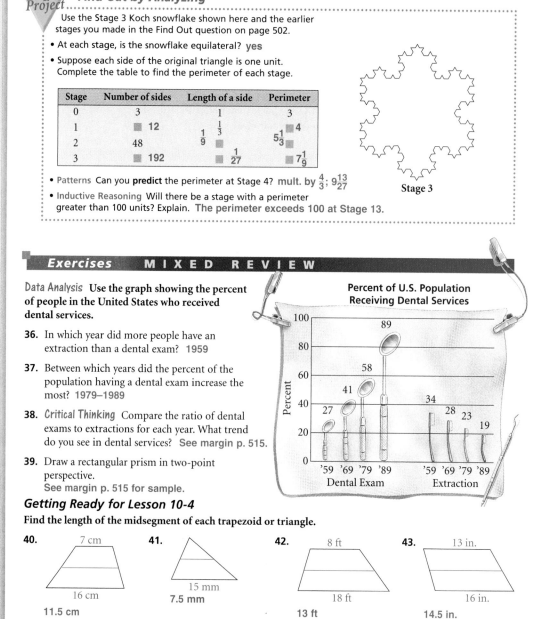

40. 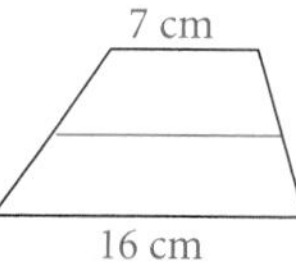

11.5 cm

41. 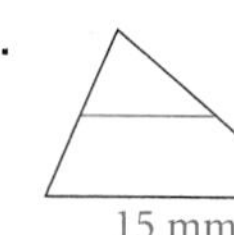

7.5 mm

42. 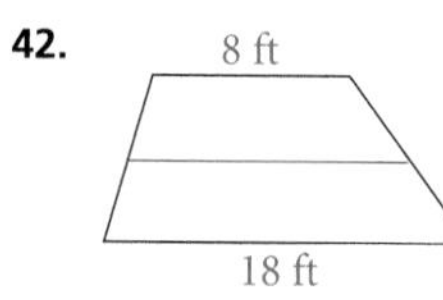

13 ft

43. 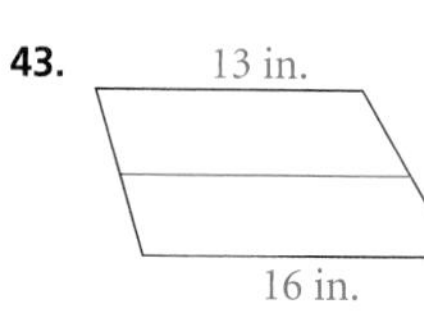

14.5 in.

10-4 Teaching Notes

PROBLEM OF THE DAY

A ball of yarn can be knit into one mitten. If the diameter of the ball is doubled, how many mittens can be knit? 8

Problem of the Day is also available in Transparencies.

CONNECTING TO PRIOR KNOWLEDGE Draw the following triangle and ask students to explain which pairs of angles are congruent.

WORK TOGETHER p. 517

Question 1 Students should discover that the equivalency of the ratios does not depend on the shape of the triangle or the distance between the parallel lines.

THINK AND DISCUSS p. 517

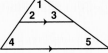

VISUAL LEARNING Copy the diagram and the proportion. Color code the segment name in the proportion and the segment in the diagram to help students visualize the relationship.

Connections Sail Making . . . and more

10-4 Proportions and Similar Triangles

What You'll Learn

- Investigating proportional relationships in triangles

...And Why

To find lengths of material needed to make a sail and to determine distances on a city map

What You'll Need

- geometry software

WORK TOGETHER

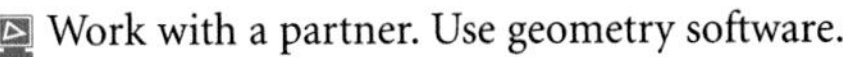

Work with a partner. Use geometry software.

- Construct $\triangle ABC$ and a point D on $\overline{AB}$.
- Construct a line through D parallel to $\overline{AC}$.
- Construct the intersection E of the parallel line with $\overline{BC}$.
- Measure $\overline{BD}$, $\overline{DA}$, $\overline{BE}$, and $\overline{EC}$.
- Calculate the ratios $\frac{BD}{DA}$ and $\frac{BE}{EC}$.

1. *Patterns* Compare the ratios $\frac{BD}{DA}$ and $\frac{BE}{EC}$ as you move the parallel line $\overleftrightarrow{DE}$ and as you change the shape of the triangle. $\frac{BD}{DA} = \frac{BE}{EC}$

THINK AND DISCUSS

Part 1

Using the Side-Splitter Theorem

In the Work Together you discovered the following relationship.

Theorem 10-4
Side-Splitter Theorem

If a line is parallel to one side of a triangle and intersects the other two sides, then it divides those sides proportionally.

Proof of Theorem 10-4

Given: $\triangle QXY$ with $\overleftrightarrow{RS} \parallel \overleftrightarrow{XY}$

Prove: $\frac{XR}{RQ} = \frac{YS}{SQ}$

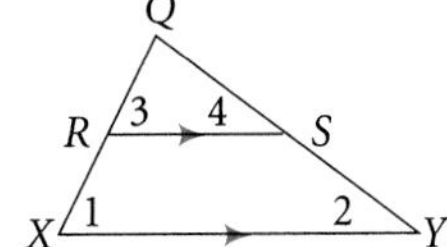

Statements	Reasons
1. $\overleftrightarrow{RS} \parallel \overleftrightarrow{XY}$	1. Given
2. $\angle 1 \cong \angle 3$, $\angle 2 \cong \angle 4$	2. If $\parallel$ lines, then corr. $\angle$s are $\cong$.
3. $\triangle QXY \sim \triangle QRS$	3. AA $\sim$ Postulate
4. $\frac{XQ}{RQ} = \frac{YQ}{SQ}$	4. Corresponding sides of $\sim$ triangles are proportional.
5. $XQ = XR + RQ$, $YQ = YS + SQ$	5. Segment Addition Postulate
6. $\frac{XR + RQ}{RQ} = \frac{YS + SQ}{SQ}$	6. Substitution
7. $\frac{XR}{RQ} = \frac{YS}{SQ}$	7. A Property of Proportions

Lesson Planning Options

Prerequisite Skills

- Using geometry software to construct triangles, parallel lines, and angle bisectors

Assignment Options for Exercises On Your Own

To provide flexible scheduling, this lesson can be subdivided into parts.

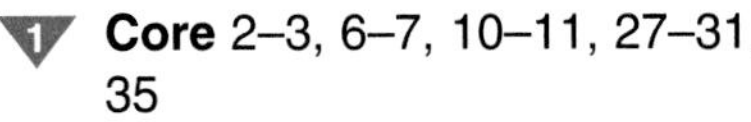

1 **Core** 2–3, 6–7, 10–11, 27–31, 35
Extension 24

2 **Core** 1, 4–5, 8–9, 12–23, 25–26, 34
Extension 32–33

Use Mixed Review to maintain skills.

Resources

Student Edition

Skills Handbook, pp. 660, 664
Extra Practice, p. 657
Glossary/Study Guide

Teaching Resources

Chapter Support File, Ch. 10
- Practice 10-4 (two worksheets)
- Reteaching 10-4

Classroom Manager 10-4
Glossary, Spanish Resources

Transparencies

105, 109

Corollary to Theorem 10-4 Help students understand that the parallel lines divide the transversals into proportional segments, not congruent segments.

Example 1 **Relating to the Real World** 

Make sure students understand that the pieces of the sail are cut and sewn so the bases of the pieces are parallel.

ESL To help students understand the phrases "sail maker," "chalk outline," and "cutting floor," have them use the appropriate dictionary to learn how to express them in their native languages.

DIVERSITY Have students who have sailed in a sailboat share their experiences with the class.

CRITICAL THINKING Ask students how they could use the Side-Splitter Theorem to find y.

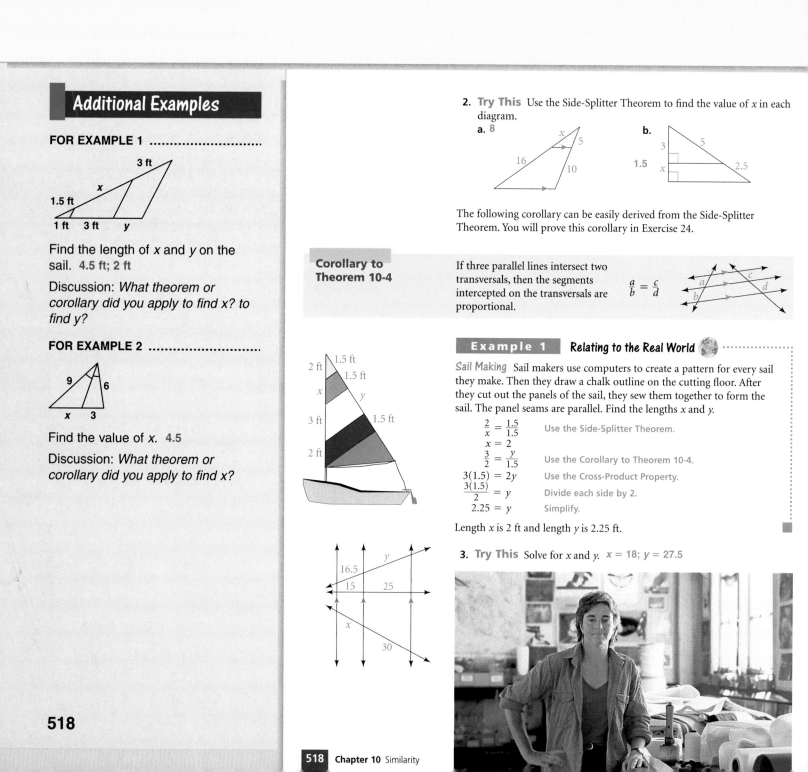

Additional Examples

FOR EXAMPLE 1

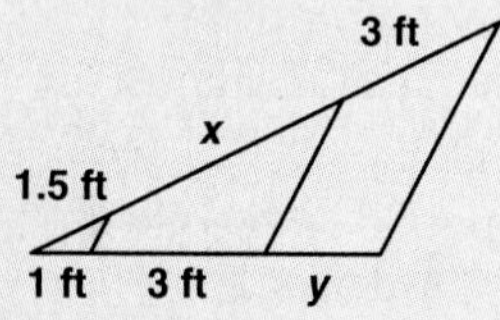

Find the length of x and y on the sail. 4.5 ft; 2 ft

Discussion: *What theorem or corollary did you apply to find x? to find y?*

FOR EXAMPLE 2

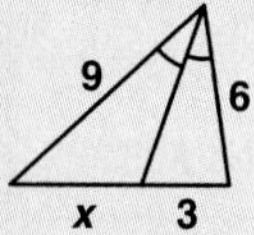

Find the value of x. 4.5

Discussion: *What theorem or corollary did you apply to find x?*

2. **Try This** Use the Side-Splitter Theorem to find the value of x in each diagram.

a. 8

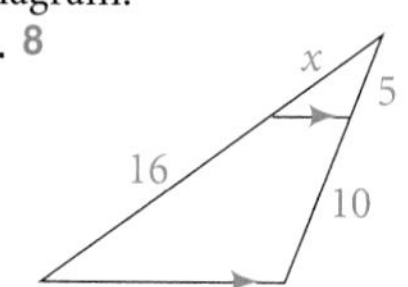

b. 1.5

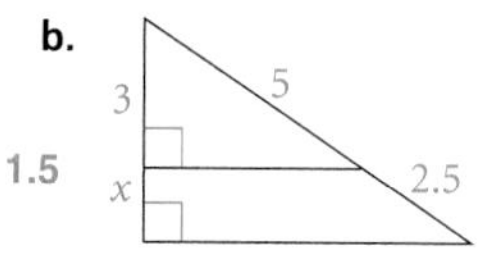

The following corollary can be easily derived from the Side-Splitter Theorem. You will prove this corollary in Exercise 24.

Corollary to Theorem 10-4

If three parallel lines intersect two transversals, then the segments intercepted on the transversals are proportional. $\frac{a}{b} = \frac{c}{d}$

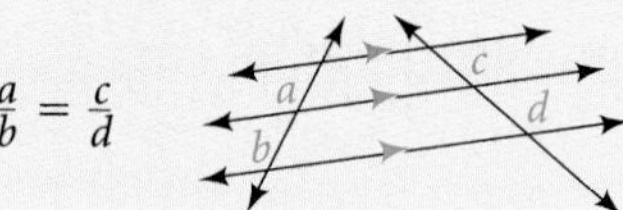

Example 1 **Relating to the Real World** 

Sail Making Sail makers use computers to create a pattern for every sail they make. Then they draw a chalk outline on the cutting floor. After they cut out the panels of the sail, they sew them together to form the sail. The panel seams are parallel. Find the lengths x and y.

2 ft, 1.5 ft, 1.5 ft, x, y, 3 ft, 1.5 ft, 2 ft

$\frac{2}{x} = \frac{1.5}{1.5}$ Use the Side-Splitter Theorem.

$x = 2$

$\frac{3}{2} = \frac{y}{1.5}$ Use the Corollary to Theorem 10-4.

$3(1.5) = 2y$ Use the Cross-Product Property.

$\frac{3(1.5)}{2} = y$ Divide each side by 2.

$2.25 = y$ Simplify.

Length x is 2 ft and length y is 2.25 ft.

3. **Try This** Solve for x and y. $x = 18$; $y = 27.5$

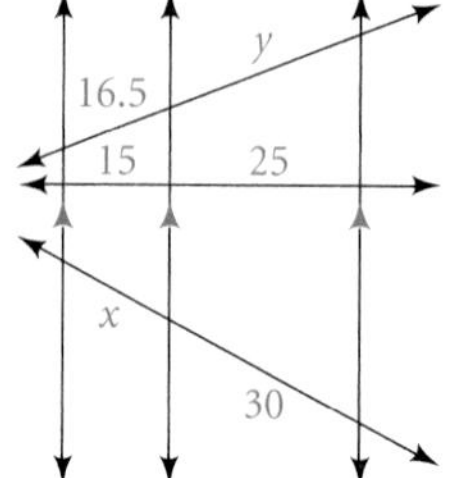

WORK TOGETHER p. 519

Check that students construct point D correctly so that when they manipulate the triangle in Question 4, D remains the point of intersection of the angle bisector and $\overline{CB}$.

THINK AND DISCUSS p. 519

Explain to students that in the proof of the Triangle-Angle-Bisector Theorem, $\overleftrightarrow{BE}$ must be drawn in order to apply the Side-Splitter Theorem.

Example 2

ERROR ALERT! Some students may confuse the Triangle-Angle-Bisector Theorem with Corollary 2 of Theorem 10-3 and write $\frac{PR}{PS} = \frac{PS}{PQ}$. **Remediation:** Reinforce that Theorem 10-3 and its corollaries apply to right triangles, and that the Triangle-Angle-Bisector Theorem states that the two segments formed by the angle bisector are proportional to the other two sides of the triangle.

Part 2

WORK TOGETHER

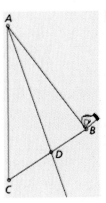

Work with a partner. Use geometry software.

- Construct $\triangle ABC$ and the bisector of $\angle A$. Label point D, the intersection of the bisector and $\overline{CB}$.
- Measure $\overline{BD}$, $\overline{BA}$, $\overline{CD}$, and $\overline{CA}$.
- Calculate the ratios $\frac{CD}{DB}$ and $\frac{CA}{BA}$.

4. *Patterns* Compare the ratios as you change the triangle. $\frac{CD}{DB} = \frac{CA}{BA}$

Using the Triangle-Angle-Bisector Theorem

In the Work Together you discovered the following relationship.

Theorem 10-5
Triangle-Angle-Bisector Theorem

If a ray bisects an angle of a triangle, then it divides the opposite side into two segments that are proportional to the other two sides of the triangle.

Given: $\triangle ABC$, $\overrightarrow{AD}$ bisects $\angle CAB$.

Prove: $\frac{CD}{DB} = \frac{CA}{BA}$

Draw $\overleftrightarrow{BE} \parallel \overline{DA}$.

Extend $\overline{CA}$ to meet $\overleftrightarrow{BE}$ at point F.

By the Side-Splitter Theorem, $\frac{CD}{DB} = \frac{CA}{AF}$. By the Corresponding Angles Theorem, $\angle 3 \cong \angle 1$. Since $\overrightarrow{AD}$ bisects $\angle CAB$, $\angle 1 \cong \angle 2$. By the Alternate Interior Angles Theorem, $\angle 2 \cong \angle 4$. Using the Transitive Property of Congruence, you know that $\angle 3 \cong \angle 4$. By the Converse of the Isosceles Triangle Theorem, $AF = AB$. Substituting BA for AF, $\frac{CD}{DB} = \frac{CA}{BA}$.

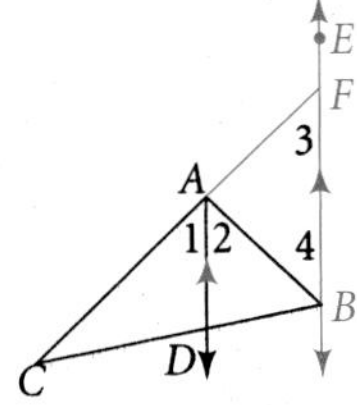

Example 2

Find the value of x.

$\frac{PS}{SR} = \frac{PQ}{RQ}$ Use the Triangle-Angle-Bisector Theorem.

$\frac{x}{6} = \frac{8}{5}$ Substitute.

$x = \frac{6 \cdot 8}{5} = 9.6$

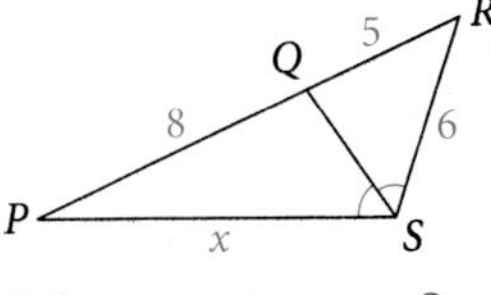

5. Use the diagram in Example 2 and the properties of proportions to write four equivalent proportions.

5. Answers may vary. Sample: $\frac{PS}{PQ} = \frac{SR}{RQ}$, $\frac{SR}{PS} = \frac{RQ}{PQ}$, $\frac{PQ}{PS} = \frac{RQ}{SR}$, $\frac{PS + SR}{SR} = \frac{PQ + RQ}{RQ}$

Technology Options

For Exercise 32, students may draw the dilations using geometry software. For Exercise 33, students may draw and measure the triangles using geometry software.

Prentice Hall Technology

Software
- Secondary Math Lab Toolkit™
- Integrated Math Lab 42
- Computer Item Generator 10-4

Internet
- See the Prentice Hall site. (http://www.phschool.com)

Exercises ON YOUR OWN

ALTERNATIVE ASSESSMENT **Exercises 9–16** You can use these exercises to help you assess students' ability to apply the theorems and corollary presented in this lesson. After students have completed the exercises, have them share their answers with a partner, then discuss and correct any errors they find.

DIVERSITY **Exercise 17** Have students research the history of transportation and road construction. Students may be surprised to learn that certain countries still have few paved roads. Another interesting statistic students may want to research is the number of automobiles compared to population in different countries.

Exercises ON YOUR OWN

Use the figure at the right to complete each proportion.

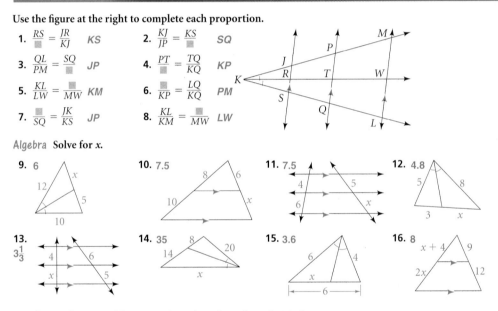

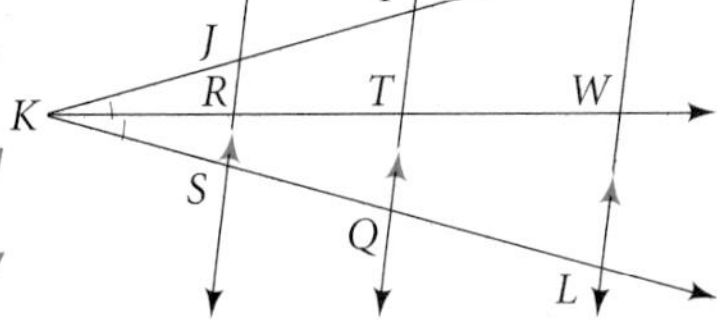

1. $\frac{RS}{\blacksquare} = \frac{JR}{KJ}$ KS
2. $\frac{KJ}{JP} = \frac{KS}{\blacksquare}$ SQ
3. $\frac{QL}{PM} = \frac{SQ}{\blacksquare}$ JP
4. $\frac{PT}{\blacksquare} = \frac{TQ}{KQ}$ KP
5. $\frac{KL}{LW} = \frac{\blacksquare}{MW}$ KM
6. $\frac{\blacksquare}{KP} = \frac{LQ}{KQ}$ PM
7. $\frac{\blacksquare}{SQ} = \frac{JK}{KS}$ JP
8. $\frac{KL}{KM} = \frac{\blacksquare}{MW}$ LW

Algebra **Solve for x.**

9. 6

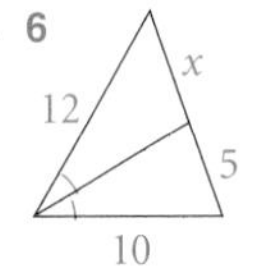

10. 7.5
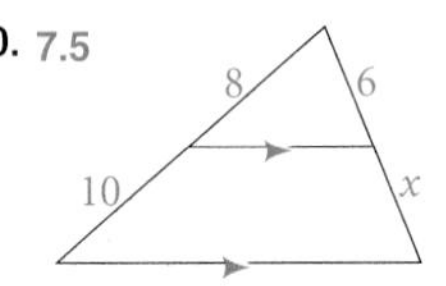

11. 7.5

12. 4.8
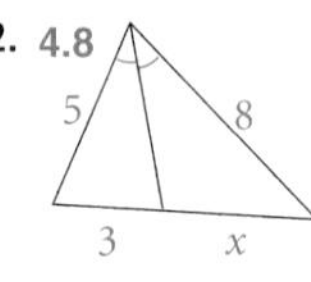

13. $3\frac{1}{3}$

14. 35
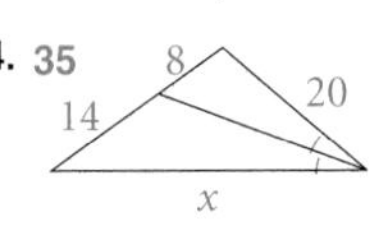

15. 3.6
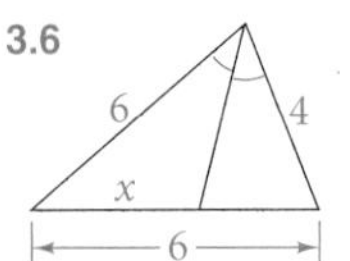

16. 8
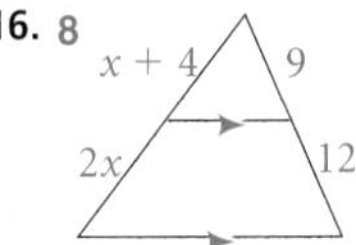

17. Geography In Washington, D.C., 17th, 18th, 19th, and 20th Streets are parallel streets that intersect Pennsylvania Avenue and I Street.
    a. How long (to the nearest foot) is Pennsylvania Avenue between 19th Street and 18th Street? 559 ft
    b. How long (to the nearest foot) is Pennsylvania Avenue between 18th Street and 17th Street? 671 ft

The United States Capitol viewed from Pennsylvania Avenue

Exercise 18 Students should apply the Pythagorean Theorem to find the hypotenuse is 13, then label the segments of the hypotenuse x and $13 - x$.

ALGEBRA Exercises 20–22 Make sure students apply the Distributive Property correctly, especially when multiplying a binomial by a binomial.

CRITICAL THINKING Exercise 23 Students discover that if a bisector of an angle of a triangle also bisects the opposite side, the triangle must be isosceles.

Exercise 24 Students answer parts a–c to prove the Corollary to the Side-Splitter Theorem. You may want to have students rewrite the steps as a paragraph proof.

18. The legs of a right triangle are 5 cm and 12 cm long. Find the lengths, to the nearest tenth, of the segments into which the bisector of the right angle divides the hypotenuse. **3.8 cm, 9.2 cm**

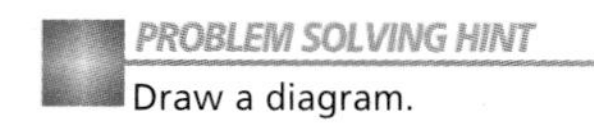

PROBLEM SOLVING HINT
Draw a diagram.

19. *Standardized Test Prep* In a triangle, the bisector of an angle divides the opposite side into two segments with lengths 6 cm and 9 cm. Which of the following can be the lengths of the other two sides of the triangle? **D**

I. 4 cm and 6 cm **II.** 20 cm and 30 cm **III.** 12 cm and 18 cm

A. I only **B.** II only **C.** I and II **D.** II and III **E.** I, II, and III

Algebra **Solve for *x*.**

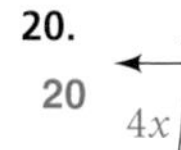

20. **20**

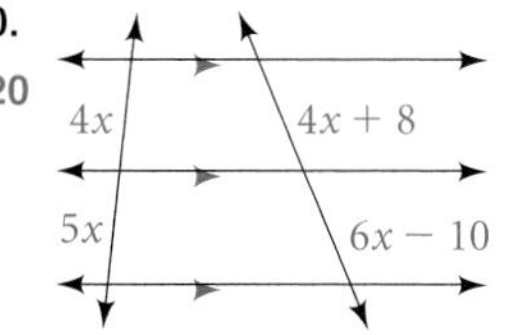

21. **2.5**

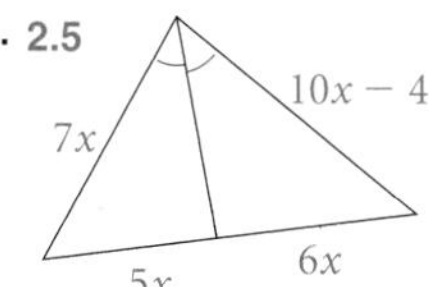

22. **9**

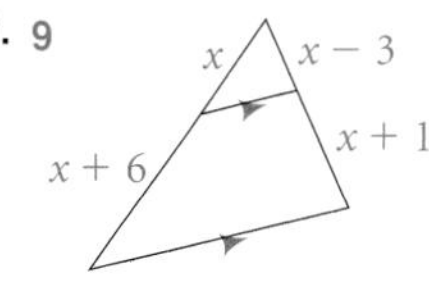

23. *Critical Thinking* Sharell draws $\triangle ABC$. She finds that the bisector of $\angle C$ bisects the opposite side.

a. Sketch $\triangle ABC$ and the bisector. **See margin for sample.**

b. What type of triangle is $\triangle ABC$? Explain your reasoning. **b. Isosceles; use the Triangle-Angle-Bisector Thm.**

24. Answer the following questions to prove the Corollary to the Side-Splitter Theorem.

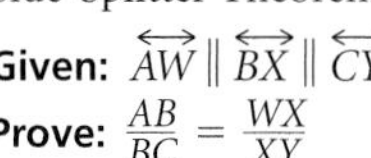

Given: $\overleftrightarrow{AW} \parallel \overleftrightarrow{BX} \parallel \overleftrightarrow{CY}$

Prove: $\frac{AB}{BC} = \frac{WX}{XY}$

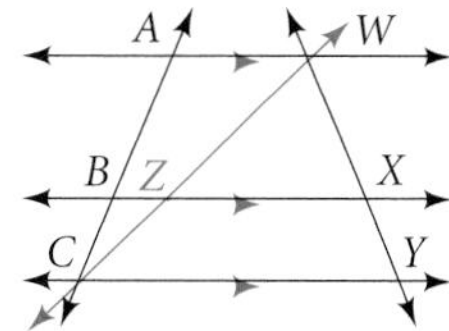

Begin by drawing $\overleftrightarrow{WC}$, intersecting $\overline{BX}$ at point Z.

a. Apply the Side-Splitter Theorem to $\triangle ACW$: $\frac{■}{■} = \frac{WZ}{ZC}$. ***AB; BC***

b. Apply the Side-Splitter Theorem to $\triangle CWY$: $\frac{WZ}{ZC} = \frac{■}{■}$. ***WX; XY***

c. Substitute to prove the corollary. $\frac{AB}{BC} = \frac{WX}{XY}$

25. An angle bisector of a triangle divides the opposite side of the triangle into segments 5 cm and 3 cm long. One side of the triangle is 7.5 cm long. Find all possible lengths for the third side of the triangle. **4.5 cm; 12.5 cm**

26. *Surveying* The perimeter of the triangular lot at the right is 50 m. The surveyor's tape bisects an angle. Find lengths x and y. (*Hint:* You can use a system of linear equations. See Skills Handbook page 667.)
$x = 18$; $y = 12$

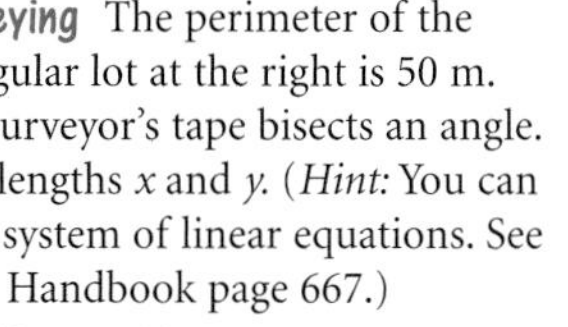

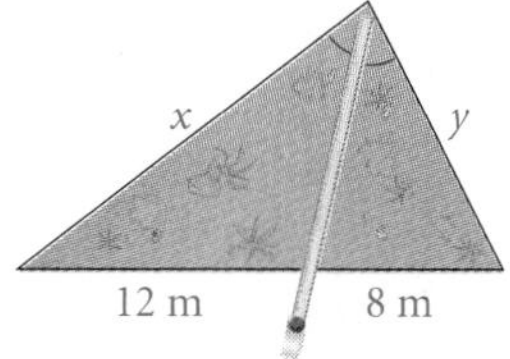

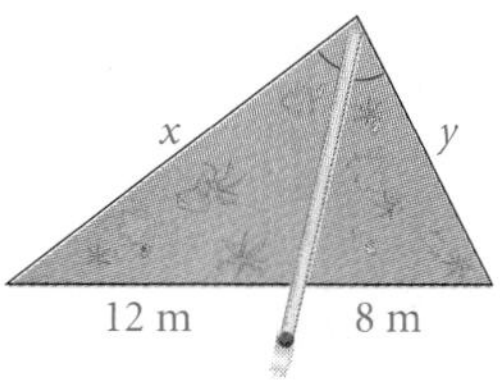

pages 520–523 On Your Own

23a.

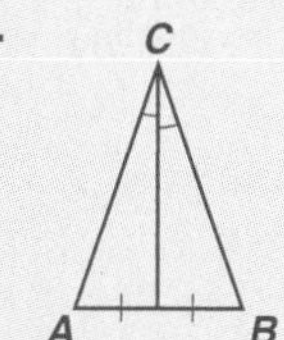

LOGICAL REASONING Exercise 27a Have students read their statements to a partner to make sure that they are clear.

TECHNOLOGY Exercise 32 Students may want to use construction tools in geometry software to construct the triangles. Ask students to explain how their answers are related to the scale factors of the dilations in parts a and b.

GEOMETRY IN 3 DIMENSIONS Exercise 33 Students should use the answer from part a to solve part b, and the answers from parts a and b to solve part c.

Chapter Project **FIND OUT BY DOING** Before students draw the fractal tree, discuss with them the three properties of fractals. Use the diagrams on page 502 and 516 to illustrate the property of self-similarity.

27a. **If a line that intersects 2 sides of a $\triangle$ divides them proportionally, then the line is $\parallel$ to the 3rd side.**

b. **Answers may vary. Sample:**

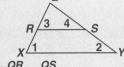

Given: $\frac{QR}{RX} = \frac{QS}{SY}$

Prove: $\overline{RS} \parallel \overline{XY}$

Plan for Proof: To prove that $\overline{RS} \parallel \overline{XY}$, show that $\angle 3 \cong \angle 1$. To prove that $\angle 3 \cong \angle 1$, prove that $\triangle QRS \sim \triangle QXY$ by the SAS $\sim$ Thm.

35. **Measure AC, CE and BD. Using the Side-Splitter Thm., $\frac{AC}{CE} = \frac{AB}{BD}$. Then, $AB = \frac{BD \cdot AC}{CE}$.**

27. a. *Logical Reasoning* Write the converse of the Side-Splitter Theorem.

b. Draw a diagram, state the *Given* and *To Prove* for the converse, and write a Plan for Proof. **a–b. See margin.**

Determine whether the red segments are parallel. Explain each answer. You can use the result of Exercise 27.

28.

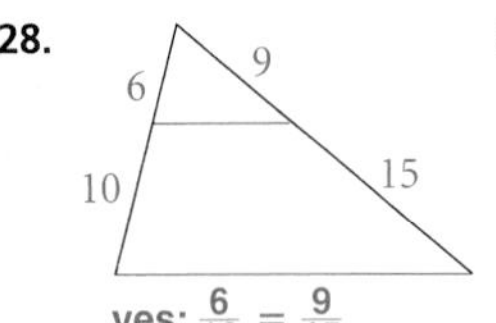

yes; $\frac{6}{10} = \frac{9}{15}$

29.

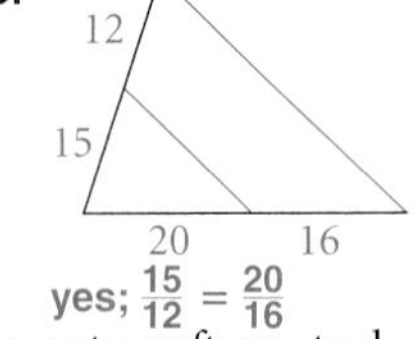

yes; $\frac{15}{12} = \frac{20}{16}$

30.

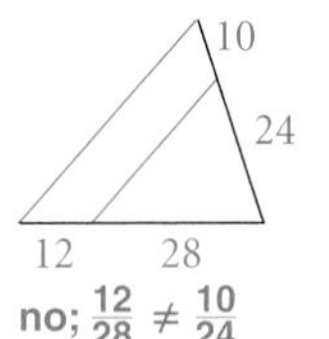

no; $\frac{12}{28} \neq \frac{10}{24}$

31.

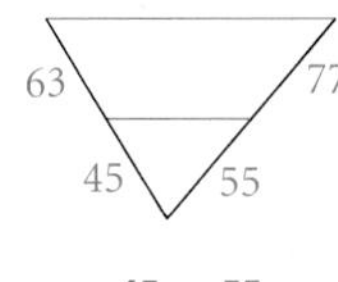

yes; $\frac{45}{63} = \frac{55}{77}$

32. *Technology* Claire used geometry software to draw the red triangle. She dilated it with center (0, 0) and scale factor $\frac{3}{2}$ to get the blue triangle. Then she dilated the blue triangle with center (0, 0) and scale factor $\frac{1}{3}$ to get the green triangle.

a. What is the scale factor of the dilation of the red triangle to the green one? $\frac{1}{2}$

b. The scale factor of the dilation of the green triangle to the red one is 2. What is the scale factor of the dilation of the green triangle to the blue one? **3**

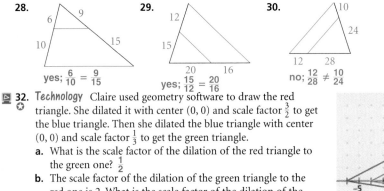

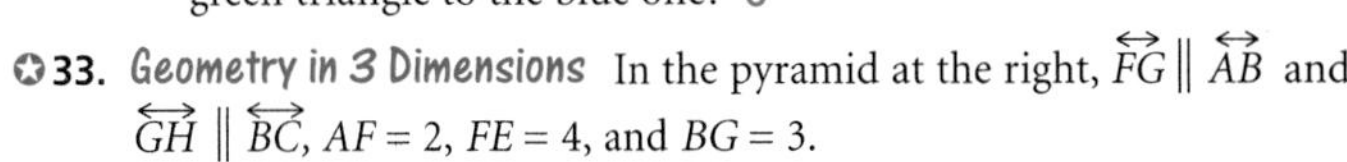

33. *Geometry in 3 Dimensions* In the pyramid at the right, $\overleftrightarrow{FG} \parallel \overleftrightarrow{AB}$ and $\overleftrightarrow{GH} \parallel \overleftrightarrow{BC}$, $AF = 2$, $FE = 4$, and $BG = 3$.

a. Find GE. **6**

b. If $EH = 5$, find HC. **2.5**

c. If $FG = 3$, find the perimeter of $\triangle ABE$. **19.5**

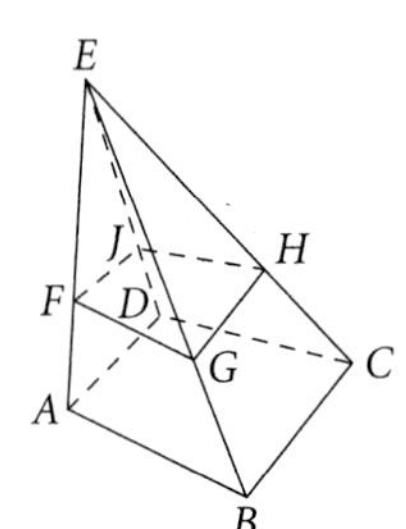

34. The legs of a right triangle are 6 cm and 8 cm long. The bisector of the right angle divides the hypotenuse into two segments. **a. Check students' work.**

a. Draw a sketch of the right triangle with its angle bisector.

b. Find the lengths of these segments to the nearest tenth. **4.3 cm, 5.7 cm**

35. *Writing* Describe how you could use the figure at the right to find the length of the oil spill indirectly. What measurements and calculations would you use? **Answers may vary. See margin for sample.**

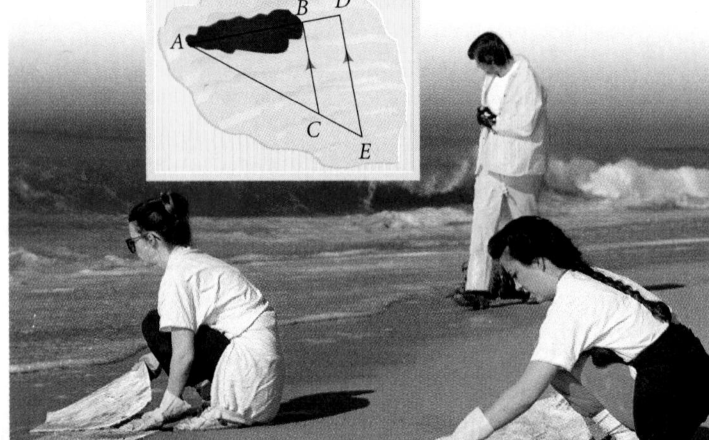

Exercises MIXED REVIEW

TRANSFORMATIONS Exercises 36–39 Have students graph the preimage and the image of each transformation.

GETTING READY FOR LESSON 10-5 These exercises prepare students to find the perimeters and areas of similar polygons.

Wrap Up

THE BIG IDEA Have students write a paragraph summarizing the proportional relationships in triangles. Have them illustrate each theorem with a carefully labeled and color-coded diagram.

RETEACHING ACTIVITY Students use proportional relationships in triangles to find missing lengths. (Reteaching worksheet 10-4)

Chapter Project — *Find Out by Doing*

Fractals have three important properties:

- You can form them by repeating steps in a process called *iteration.*
- You can continue until the steps become too small to draw. Even then the steps could continue in your mind—there are an infinite number of iterations.
- At each stage, a portion of the figure is a reduced copy of the entire figure at the previous stage. This property is called *self-similarity.*

The diagrams below show Stages 0, 1, and 2 for a fractal tree. Make larger copies of these stages and draw the next stage.

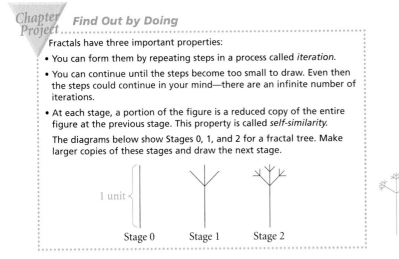

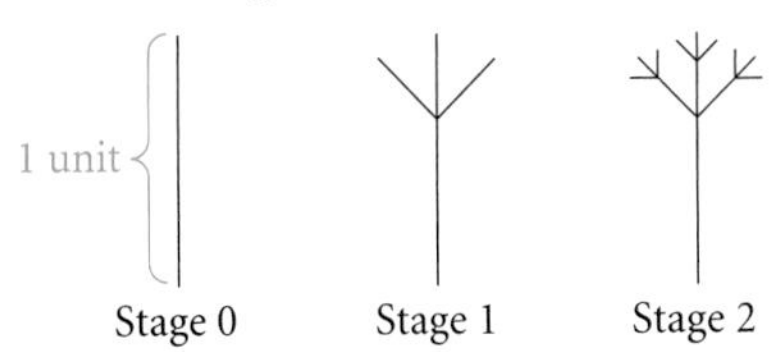

Exercises MIXED REVIEW

Transformations $\triangle ABC$ **has vertices** $A(3, -1)$, $B(0, -8)$, **and** $C(-2, 4)$. **Find the coordinates of the vertices of its image under each transformation.**

36. $A'(3, 1)$, $B'(0, 8)$, $C'(-2, -4)$
37. $A'(1, 3)$, $B'(8, 0)$, $C'(-4, -2)$

36. reflection in the x-axis

37. rotation 90° counterclockwise about the origin

38. translation 4 units right and 6 units up
$A'(7, 5)$, $B'(4, -2)$, $C'(2, 10)$

39. reflection in the line $y = -x$
$A'(1, -3)$, $B'(8, 0)$, $C'(-4, 2)$

40. On Museum Wharf in Boston, Massachusetts, there is a sandwich shop shaped like a giant milk bottle. It is 40 ft tall and has a circumference of 58 ft at its base. What is the approximate circumference of a similar bottle with a height of 24 cm? 34.8 cm

Getting Ready for Lesson 10-5

Find the area and perimeter of each figure.

41. 49 in.^{2}; 28 in.

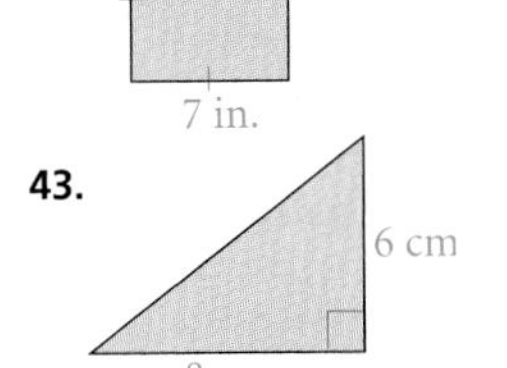

42. 32 m^2, 24 m

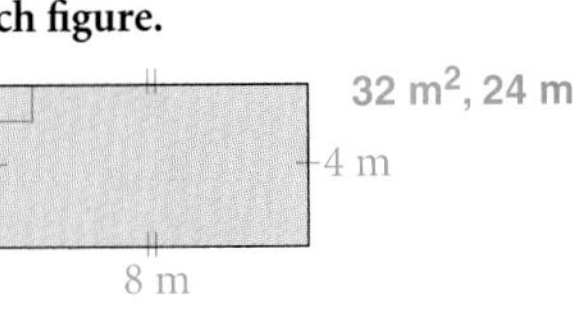

43.

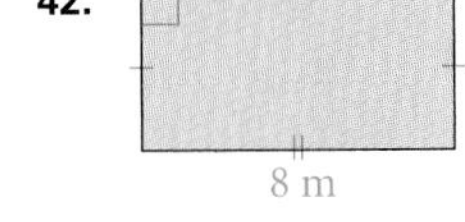

24 cm^2; 24 cm

44.

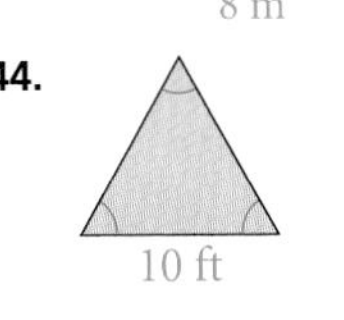

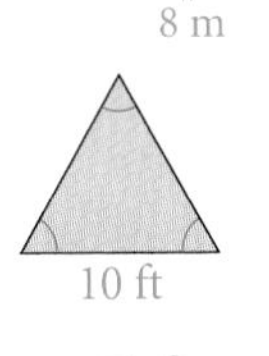

$25\sqrt{3}$ ft^2; 30 ft

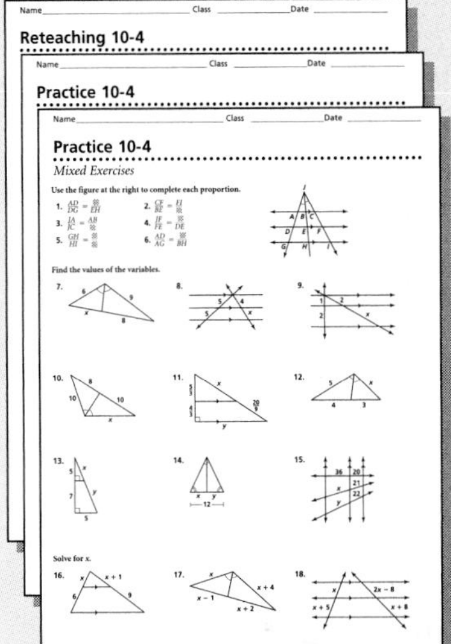

Lesson Quiz

Lesson Quiz is also available in Transparencies.

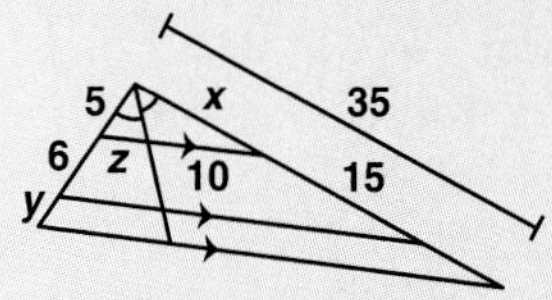

1. Find x. 12.5
2. Find y. 3
3. Find z. 4

10-5 Teaching Notes

PROBLEM OF THE DAY

The images show the front and side views of an object. What would a three-dimensional view of the object look like?

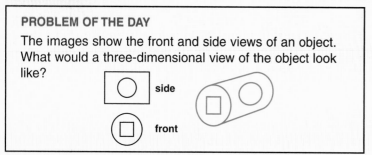

side

front

Problem of the Day is also available in Transparencies.

CONNECTING TO PRIOR KNOWLEDGE Draw a triangle, rectangle, and trapezoid, labeling the base(s) and height of each. Have students find the areas.

WORK TOGETHER

If students use centimeter graph paper, the largest scale factor they can choose is 5. Provide graph paper with smaller squares to accommodate similar figures with large scale factors.

TACTILE LEARNING Students can use geoboards to create the similar rectangles. Because geoboards have fewer "squares" than graph paper, you may want to have students start with a 2-unit by 3-unit rectangle and restrict the choice of scale factors.

Question 3 Students may need to simplify ratios in order to recognize the relationship between the ratios of the perimeters and the ratios of the areas.

Lesson Planning Options

Prerequisite Skills

- Finding the areas of polygons

Assignment Options for Exercises On Your Own

Core 1–7, 9–21, 23
✪**Extension** 8, 22

Use Mixed Review to maintain skills.

Resources

Student Edition

Skills Handbook, p. 662, 673
Extra Practice, p. 657
Glossary/Study Guide

Teaching Resources

Chapter Support File, Ch. 10
- Practice 10-5 (two worksheets)
- Reteaching 10-5
- Alternative Activity 10-5

Classroom Manager 10-5
Glossary, Spanish Resources

Transparencies
18, 19, 106, 110

10-5 Perimeters and Areas of Similar Figures

What You'll Learn
- Finding the relationships between the similarity ratio and the perimeters and areas of similar figures

...And Why

To determine the perimeter or area of a figure when you know the perimeter or area of a similar figure

What You'll Need
- graph paper
- calculator

WORK TOGETHER

Work with a partner to investigate perimeters and areas of similar rectangles.

In the corner of a sheet of graph paper, draw a 3 unit-by-4 unit rectangle as shown at the right.

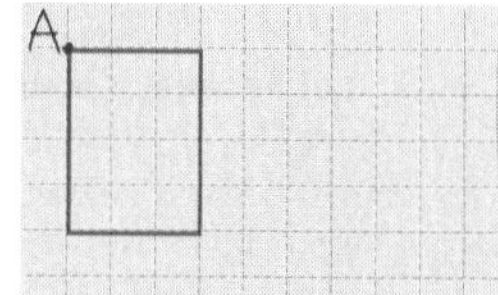

Choose three scale factors from the set {2, 3, 4, . . . , 10}. Using the three scale factors and point A as the center, draw three dilations of the rectangle. Label them Rectangles I, II, and III.

Centimeter Grid Paper

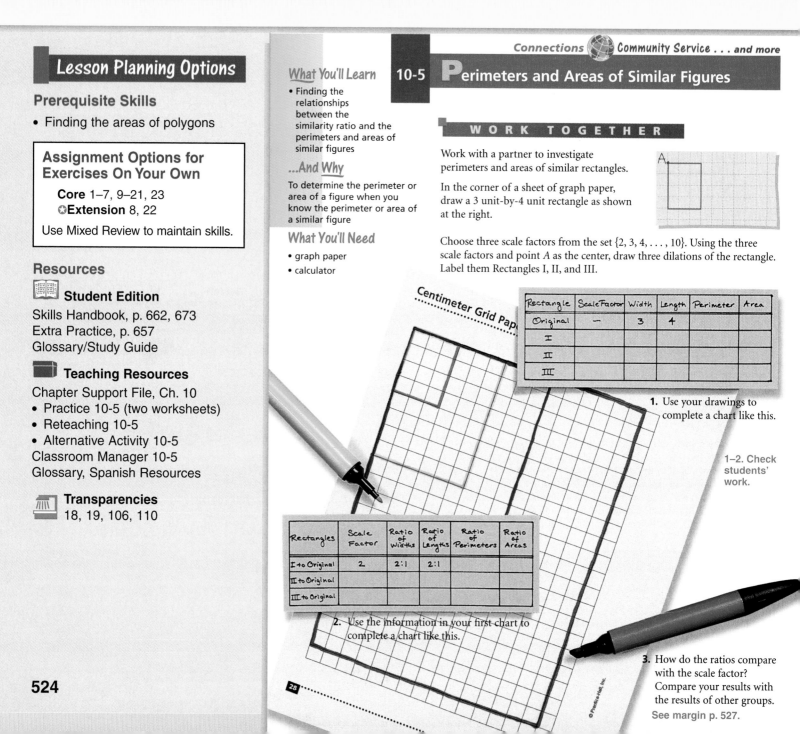

Rectangle	Scale Factor	Width	Length	Perimeter	Area
Original	—	3	4		
I					
II					
III					

1. Use your drawings to complete a chart like this.

1–2. Check students' work.

Rectangles	Scale Factor	Ratio of Widths	Ratio of Lengths	Ratio of Perimeters	Ratio of Areas
I to Original	2	2:1	2:1		
II to Original					
III to Original					

2. Use the information in your first chart to complete a chart like this.

3. How do the ratios compare with the scale factor? Compare your results with the results of other groups. See margin p. 527.

THINK AND DISCUSS

Help students see how the Distributive Property is applied to simplify the ratio of the perimeters of similar rectangles and how the Associative Property is used to simplify the ratio of the areas of similar rectangles.

Questions 5 and 6 Suggest that students begin by copying the diagrams and labeling the remaining sides with appropriate variables. You may need to review with students the area formulas of a triangle and a trapezoid.

CRITICAL THINKING Theorem 10-6 Ask students if the converse of the theorem is true: If the area of two similar figures have a ratio of $a : b$, then they are similar and have a similarity ratio of $\sqrt{a} : \sqrt{b}$.

ERROR ALERT! Some students might confuse the ratio of perimeters of similar figures with the ratio of areas of similar figures. **Remediation:** Point out that since perimeter is a linear measurement, the ratio of the perimeters is the same as the similarity ratio. Since area is measured in square units, the ratio of the areas is the square of the similarity ratio.

Example 1

You may want to solve $\frac{4}{25} = \frac{27.5}{A}$ in two steps to help students see how the calculator steps were derived.

$4A = (25)(27.5)$

$A = \frac{(25)(27.5)}{4}$

THINK AND DISCUSS

Rectangle I is similar to Rectangle II with a similarity ratio of $1 : k$. You can use algebra to simplify the ratio of their perimeters and the ratio of their areas.

$$\frac{\text{Perimeter of Rect. I}}{\text{Perimeter of Rect. II}} = \frac{2l + 2w}{2(kl) + 2(kw)} = \frac{\cancel{2l + 2w}\,1}{k(\cancel{2l + 2w})} = \frac{1}{k}$$

$$\frac{\text{Area of Rect. I}}{\text{Area of Rect. II}} = \frac{lw}{(kl)(kw)} = \frac{\cancel{lw}\,1}{(k^2)(\cancel{lw})} = \frac{1}{k^2}$$

4. How do these algebraic results compare with the results you obtained in the Work Together? **The results agree.**

5. **Try This** Triangle I is similar to Triangle II with a similarity ratio of 1 : 2. Find each ratio.

 a. $\frac{\text{Perimeter of Triangle I}}{\text{Perimeter of Triangle II}}$ $\frac{1}{2}$ b. $\frac{\text{Area of Triangle I}}{\text{Area of Triangle II}}$ $\frac{1}{4}$

6. **Try This** Trapezoid I is similar to Trapezoid II with a similarity ratio of 2 : 3. Find each ratio.

 a. $\frac{\text{Perimeter of Trapezoid I}}{\text{Perimeter of Trapezoid II}}$ $\frac{2}{3}$ b. $\frac{\text{Area of Trapezoid I}}{\text{Area of Trapezoid II}}$ $\frac{4}{9}$

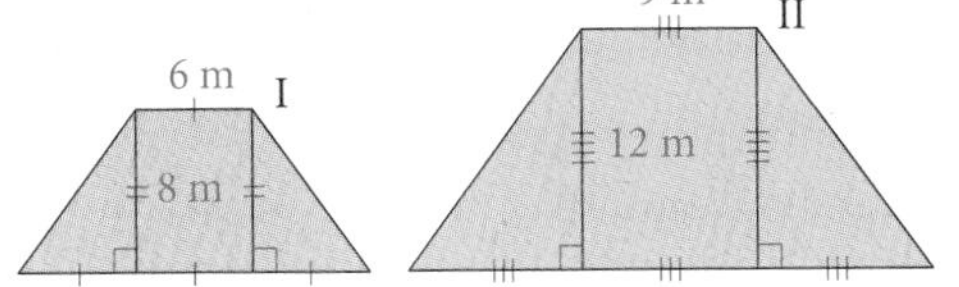

7. Any two circles are similar. If the radii of two circles are r and kr, find the ratios of their circumferences and their areas. $\frac{1}{k}, \frac{1}{k^2}$

The results you obtained above for rectangles, triangles, trapezoids, and circles are generalized for all similar figures in the following theorem.

Theorem 10-6
Perimeters and Areas of Similar Figures

If the similarity ratio of two similar figures is $a : b$, then (1) the ratio of their perimeters is $a : b$, and (2) the ratio of their areas is $a^2 : b^2$.

Example 1

Calculator The area of the smaller regular pentagon is about 27.5 cm^2. Find the area A of the larger regular pentagon.

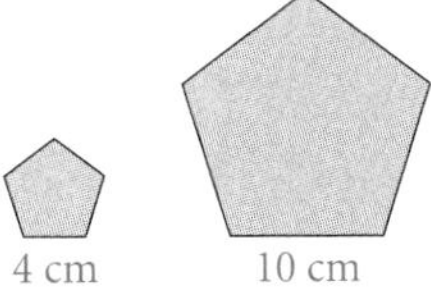

Any two regular pentagons are similar. The ratio of the lengths of the corresponding sides is $\frac{4}{10}$, or $\frac{2}{5}$. The ratio of the area is $\frac{2^2}{5^2}$, or $\frac{4}{25}$.

$\frac{4}{25} = \frac{27.5}{A}$

$A \approx 25$ ⊠ 27.5 ÷ 4 = 171.875

The area of the larger pentagon is about 172 cm^2.

8. **Try This** What is the area of a regular pentagon with sides 16 cm long? Round your answer to the nearest square centimeter. **440 cm^2**

Additional Examples

FOR EXAMPLE 1

The area of a regular hexagon with side length 3 cm is 23.4 cm^2. Find the area of a regular hexagon with side length 5 cm. **65 cm^2**

Discussion: *Explain another way to find the area of a regular hexagon with side length 5 cm.*

FOR EXAMPLE 2

Madeline used 144 tiles to tile a rectangular kitchen floor. If each dimension of the kitchen were doubled, how many tiles would Madeline need to cover the floor? **576 tiles**

FOR EXAMPLE 3

The areas of two similar rectangles are 48 in.^{2} and 75 in.^{2} What is the ratio of their perimeters? **4 : 5**

Example 2 Relating to the Real World 

It is assumed that the number of bushels of corn harvested varies directly with the area of the plot of land.

Explain to students that the lengths of the plots are ℓ and 2.5ℓ for some $\ell > 0$, not 1 and 2.5. Likewise, the widths of the plots are w and $2.5w$ for some $w > 0$.

DIVERSITY Some students, especially those in rural areas, may be surprised to learn that some people living in cities cannot plant gardens because they do not have enough land around the apartment or house they live in. However, these people can often lease space in a community garden in which to grow their own vegetables and flowers.

Example 3

ERROR ALERT! Students may simplify $\frac{a^2}{b^2} = \frac{25}{49}$ by dividing the numerators and denominators by two instead of taking the square roots of the numerators and denominators.

Remediation: Review the meaning of an exponent and have students practice solving equations such as $a^2 = 25$ and $b^2 = 49$.

EXTENSION Have students work in groups to answer the following question: *By what amount would the side lengths of a regular n-gon be multiplied to produce a similar figure whose area is twice the area of the original figure? three times the area?*

Technology Options

For Exercise 13, students may use geometry software to draw the triangles. For Exercise 17, students may use geometry software to graph the quadrilateral and find the image under the dilation.

Prentice Hall Technology

Software
- Secondary Math Lab Toolkit™
- Computer Item Generator 10-5

CD-ROM
- Multimedia Geometry Lab 10

Internet
- See the Prentice Hall site. (http://www.phschool.com)

Example 2 Relating to the Real World 

Community Service During the summer, a group of high school students used a plot of town land to grow 13 bushels of vegetables, which they gave to shelters for the homeless. Their project was so successful that next summer the town will let them use a larger, similar plot of land where each dimension is two and a half times the dimension of the original plot. How much can they expect to grow?

The ratio of the dimensions is 2.5 : 1, so the ratio of the areas of the two plots is $(2.5)^2 : 1^2$, or 6.25 : 1. With 6.25 times as much land they can expect to raise 6.25 times as much, or about 81 bushels. ■

9. Try This The similarity ratio of the dimensions of two similar pieces of window glass is 3 : 5. If the smaller piece costs \$2.50, what should be the cost of the larger piece? \$6.95

When you know the ratio of the areas of two similar figures, you can work backward to find the ratio of their perimeters.

Example 3

The areas of two similar triangles are 50 cm^2 and 98 cm^2. What is the ratio of their perimeters?

First find the similarity ratio $a : b$.

$\frac{a^2}{b^2} = \frac{50}{98}$ The ratio of the areas is $a^2 : b^2$.

$\frac{a^2}{b^2} = \frac{25}{49}$ Simplify $\frac{50}{98}$.

$\frac{a}{b} = \frac{5}{7}$ Find the square root of each side.

The ratio of the perimeters equals the similarity ratio 5 : 7. ■

10. Try This The areas of two similar rectangles are 1875 ft^2 and 135 ft^2. Find the ratio of their perimeters. $5\sqrt{5} : 3$

Exercises ON YOUR OWN

Exercises 1–3 Check that students write the ratio of the first figure to the second one, even when the first figure is larger than the second one.

DATA ANALYSIS Exercise 8a Ask students to draw a more appropriate pictograph.

RESEARCH Exercise 8b *USA Today* is a good source of pictographs.

TRANSFORMATIONS Exercise 10 Have students calculate the area by finding the similarity ratio and setting up a proportion. Then have them check their answer by copying the diagram, drawing $\overline{W'S'}$, and finding the area of each quadrilateral as the sum of the areas of two triangles.

Exercise 11 Make sure students read this problem carefully. The area of the smaller square, not the side length, is 4. Remind students to pay close attention to the units given.

Exercises ON YOUR OWN

For each pair of similar figures, give the ratio of the perimeters and the ratio of the areas of the first figure to the second one.

1. $\frac{1}{2}; \frac{1}{4}$

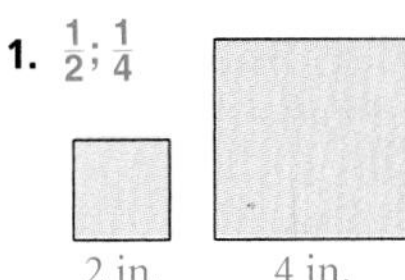

2. $\frac{4}{3}; \frac{16}{9}$

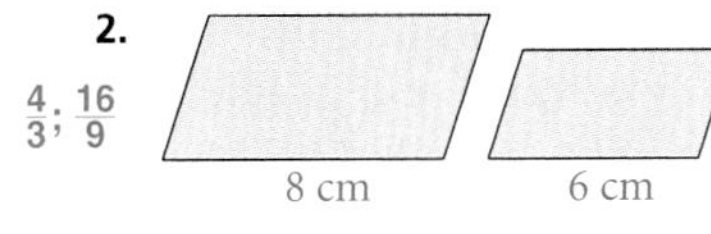

3. $\frac{2}{3}; \frac{4}{9}$

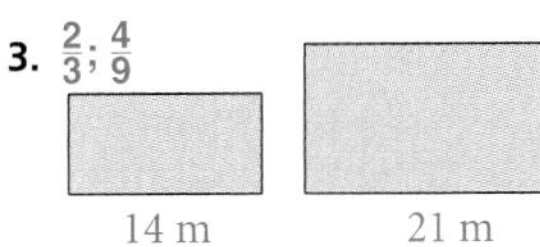

What is the similarity ratio of each pair of similar figures?

4. two circles with areas 2π cm^2 and 200π cm^2 $\frac{1}{10}$
5. two regular octagons with areas 4 ft^2 and 16 ft^2 $\frac{1}{2}$
6. two triangles with areas 80 m^2 and 20 m^2 2
7. two trapezoids with areas 49 cm^2 and 9 cm^2 $\frac{7}{3}$

8a. The similarity ratio is 1 : 2, so the ratio of the areas is 1 : 4.

8. a. *Data Analysis* A reporter used the pictograph at the right to show that the number of houses with more than two televisions has doubled in the past few years. Why is such a pictograph misleading?
   b. *Research* Find examples in magazines or newspapers in which areas of similar figures give misleading information. Check students' work.

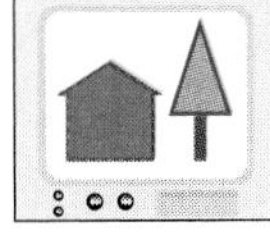

9. *Remodeling* It costs the Johnsons $216 to have a 9 ft-by-12 ft wooden floor refinished. At that rate, how much would it cost them to have a 12 ft-by-16 ft wooden floor refinished? $384
10. *Transformations* $R'S'T'W'$ is the image of $RSTW$ under a dilation with center (1, 1). How do the areas of $RSTW$ and $R'S'T'W'$ compare? Explain. The ratio of the areas is 1 : 9; the scale factor is 3.
11. *Drawing* Draw a square with an area of 4 in.^{2}. Draw a second square with an area that is four times as large. What is the ratio of their perimeters? 2 : 1
12. The area of a regular decagon is 50 cm^2. What is the area of a regular decagon with sides four times the length of the smaller decagon? 800 cm^2
13. In $\triangle RST$, $RS = 20$ m, $ST = 25$ m, and $RT = 40$ m.
    a. *Open-ended* Choose a convenient scale. Then use a compass and a metric ruler to draw $\triangle R'S'T' \sim \triangle RST$.
    b. *Constructions* Construct an altitude of $\triangle R'S'T'$ and measure its length. Find the area of $\triangle R'S'T'$. a–c. See margin.
    c. *Estimation* Estimate the area of $\triangle RST$.
14. The area of the smaller triangle shown at the right is 24 cm^2. Solve for x and y. $x = 4\sqrt{2}$ cm; $y = 6\sqrt{2}$ cm

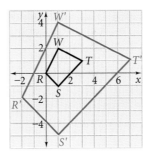

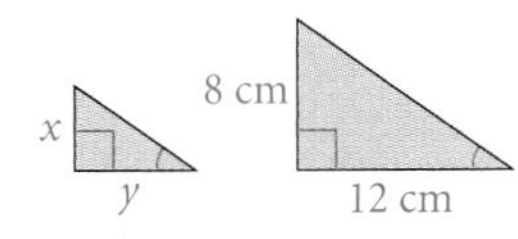

page 524 Work Together

3. The ratios of lengths, widths, and perimeters = the scale factor; the ratio of areas = the square of the scale factor.

pages 527–529 On Your Own

13a. Answers may vary. Sample: Use 1 : 1000 scale.

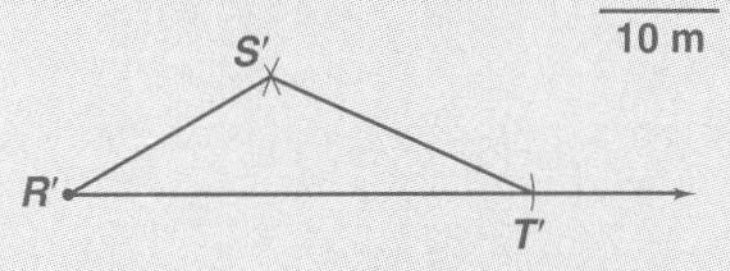

b. Answers may vary. For sample in part (a): 10 mm; 200 mm^2

c. Estimates may vary slightly. Sample: 200 m^2

ALTERNATIVE ASSESSMENT Exercises 16–17 You can use these exercises to assess students' understanding of the relationships between the similarity ratio and the perimeters and areas of similar figures. Have students work with a partner and allow them to use geometry software.

ESL Exercises 18–20 These exercises may be helpful in evaluating ESL students' understanding of the lesson content because they rely on visual cues.

Chapter Project **FIND OUT BY THINKING** Help students see that the third diagram shows a figure with area 2 square units, twice the area of a Koch snowflake at stage 0. The fourth diagram shows that the area of a Stage 2 Koch snowflake is less than 2 square units.

16a. The lengths of the sides of the 2nd polygon are k times the lengths of the sides of the 1st polygon.

17a.

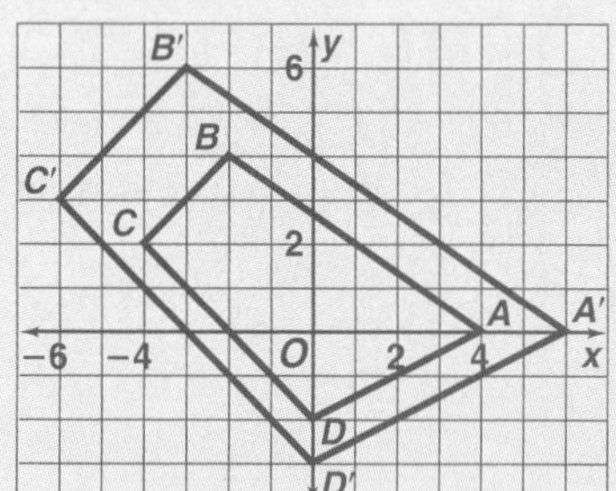

21a.

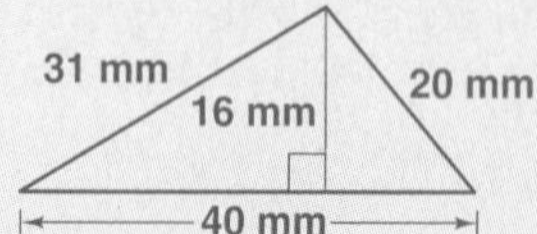

b. For sample in part (a): 91 mm; 320 mm^2

c. 455 yd; 8000 yd^2

23. Answers may vary. Sample: The proposed playground is more than adequate. The number of students is approximately double the earlier number. The area of the proposed playground is 4 times as large as the area of the orig. playground.

15. The areas of two similar rectangles are 27 in.^{2} and 48 in.^{2}. The longer side of the larger rectangle is 16 in. long. What is the length of the longer side of the smaller rectangle? **12 in.**

16. a. *Transformations* If a dilation with scale factor k maps a polygon onto a second polygon, what is the relationship between the lengths of the corresponding sides of the polygons? **See margin.**
    b. Complete: A dilation with scale factor k maps any polygon to a similar polygon whose area is ■ times as large. **k^2**

17. a. *Transformations* Graph $ABCD$ with vertices $A(4, 0)$, $B(-2, 4)$, $C(-4, 2)$, and $D(0, -2)$. Then graph its image $A'B'C'D'$ under the dilation with center (0, 0) and scale factor $\frac{3}{2}$. **See margin.**
    b. The area of $ABCD$ is 22 square units. What is the area of $A'B'C'D'$? **49.5 units^2**

Find the ratio of the perimeters and the ratio of the areas of the blue figure to the red one.

18. **$\frac{5}{2}$; $\frac{25}{4}$**

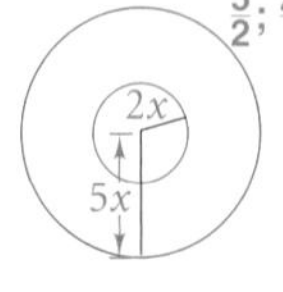

19. **$\frac{8}{3}$; $\frac{64}{9}$**

20. **$\frac{3}{2}$; $\frac{9}{4}$**

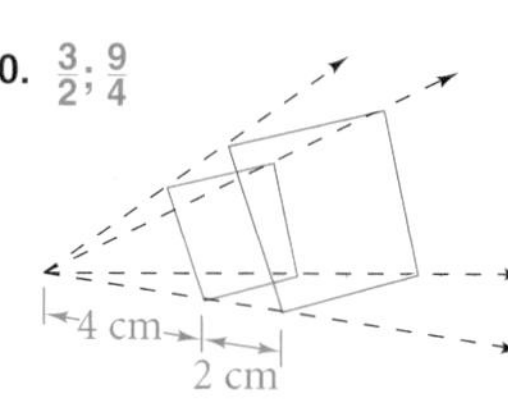

21a–c. See margin for samples.

21. a. *Surveying* A surveyor measured one side and two angles of a field as shown in the diagram. Use a ruler and a protractor to draw a similar triangle.
    b. Measure the sides and an altitude of your triangle and find its perimeter and area.
    c. *Estimation* Estimate the perimeter and area of the field.

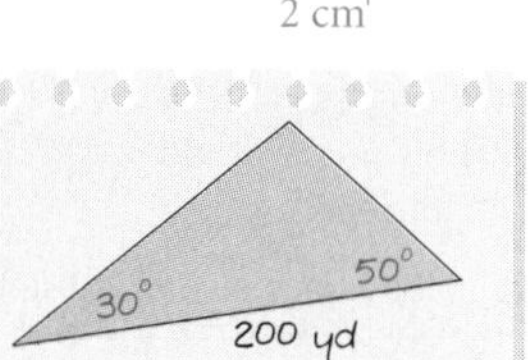

22b. $54\sqrt{3}$ cm^2; $\frac{27\sqrt{3}}{2}$ cm^2; $96\sqrt{3}$ cm^2

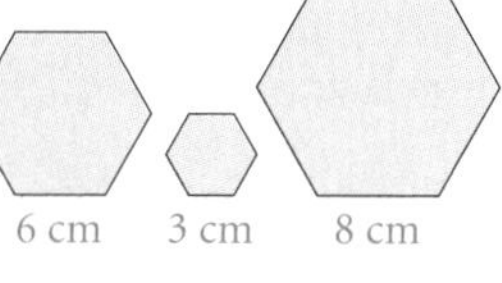

22. a. Find the area of a regular hexagon with sides 2 cm long. Leave your answer in simplest radical form. **$6\sqrt{3}$ cm^2**
    b. Use your answer to part (a) and the ratio of the areas of similar polygons to find the areas of these regular hexagons. **See above.**

23. *Writing* The enrollment at an elementary school is going to increase from 200 students to 395 students. The local parents' group is planning to increase the playground area from 100 ft by 200 ft to a larger area that is 200 ft by 400 ft. What would you tell the parents' group when they ask your opinion about whether the new playground area will be large enough? **See margin.**

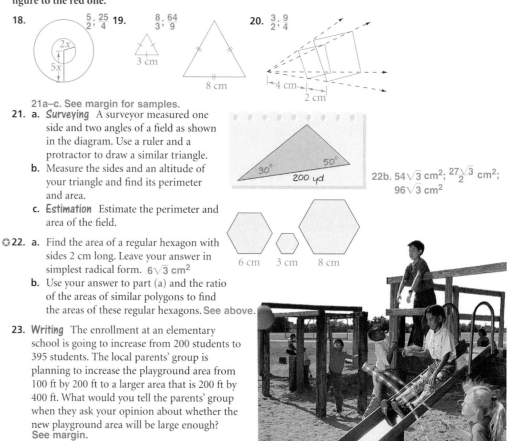

Exercises MIXED REVIEW

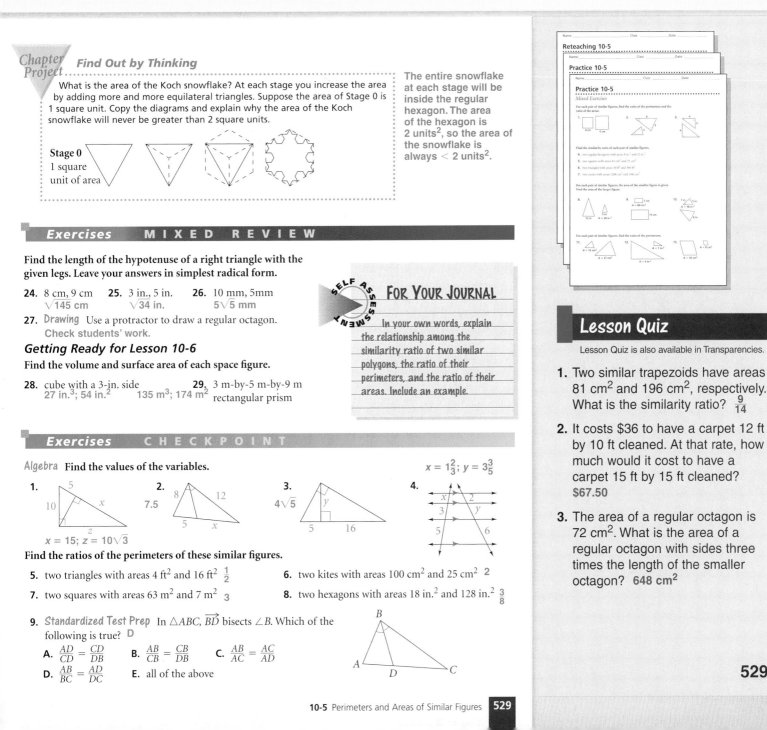

JOURNAL Have students share their journal entries with a partner. Partners should critique the entries for clarity, accuracy, and thoroughness. Then allow students to revise their entries.

GETTING READY FOR LESSON 10-6 These exercises prepare students to find the relationship between the similarity ratio and the ratio of areas and volumes of similar solids.

Wrap Up

THE BIG IDEA Ask students to write a word problem which can be solved by using the ratio of areas or perimeters.

RETEACHING ACTIVITY Students find the ratio of perimeters and areas of similar figures. (Reteaching worksheet 10-5)

Exercises CHECKPOINT

In this Checkpoint, your students will assess their own progress in Lessons 10-3 to 10-5.

ALGEBRA Exercises 1–4 Have students explain how they found their answers by stating the theorem, postulate, or corollary they applied.

Exercises 5–8 Remind students that they can simplify the ratios of the areas before taking the square roots of the numerators and denominators.

Chapter Project — *Find Out by Thinking*

What is the area of the Koch snowflake? At each stage you increase the area by adding more and more equilateral triangles. Suppose the area of Stage 0 is 1 square unit. Copy the diagrams and explain why the area of the Koch snowflake will never be greater than 2 square units.

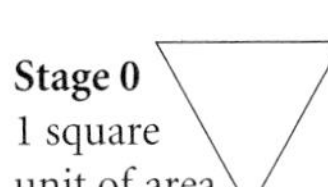

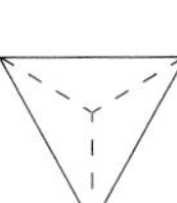

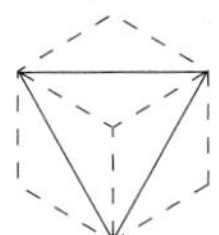

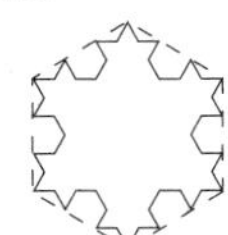

The entire snowflake at each stage will be inside the regular hexagon. The area of the hexagon is 2 units^2, so the area of the snowflake is always $<$ 2 units^2.

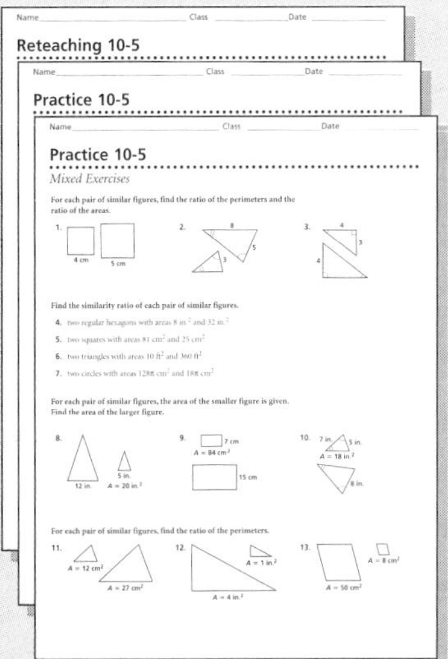

Exercises MIXED REVIEW

Find the length of the hypotenuse of a right triangle with the given legs. Leave your answers in simplest radical form.

24. 8 cm, 9 cm $\sqrt{145}$ cm **25.** 3 in., 5 in. $\sqrt{34}$ in. **26.** 10 mm, 5mm $5\sqrt{5}$ mm

27. *Drawing* Use a protractor to draw a regular octagon. Check students' work.

Getting Ready for Lesson 10-6

Find the volume and surface area of each space figure.

28. cube with a 3-in. side 27 in.^{3}; 54 in.^{2} **29.** 3 m-by-5 m-by-9 m rectangular prism 135 m^3; 174 m^2

For Your Journal

In your own words, explain the relationship among the similarity ratio of two similar polygons, the ratio of their perimeters, and the ratio of their areas. Include an example.

Exercises CHECKPOINT

Algebra **Find the values of the variables.**

1.

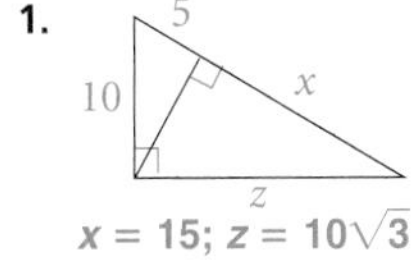

$x = 15$; $z = 10\sqrt{3}$

2. 7.5

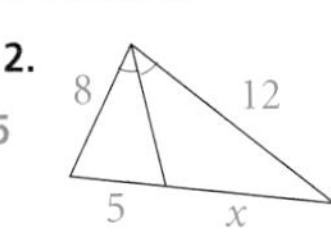

3. $4\sqrt{5}$

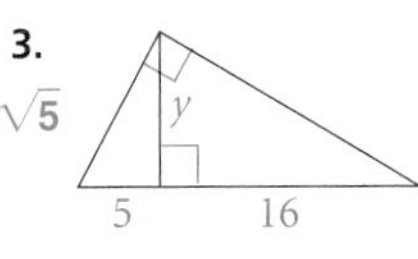

4. $x = 1\frac{2}{3}$; $y = 3\frac{3}{5}$

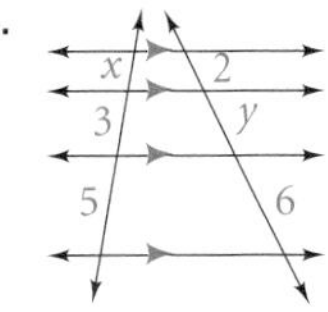

Find the ratios of the perimeters of these similar figures.

5. two triangles with areas 4 ft^2 and 16 ft^2 $\frac{1}{2}$

6. two kites with areas 100 cm^2 and 25 cm^2 2

7. two squares with areas 63 m^2 and 7 m^2 3

8. two hexagons with areas 18 in.^{2} and 128 in.^{2} $\frac{3}{8}$

9. *Standardized Test Prep* In $\triangle ABC$, $\overrightarrow{BD}$ bisects $\angle B$. Which of the following is true? D

A. $\frac{AD}{CD} = \frac{CD}{DB}$ **B.** $\frac{AB}{CB} = \frac{CB}{DB}$ **C.** $\frac{AB}{AC} = \frac{AC}{AD}$

D. $\frac{AB}{BC} = \frac{AD}{DC}$ **E.** all of the above

Lesson Quiz

Lesson Quiz is also available in Transparencies.

1. Two similar trapezoids have areas 81 cm^2 and 196 cm^2, respectively. What is the similarity ratio? $\frac{9}{14}$
2. It costs \$36 to have a carpet 12 ft by 10 ft cleaned. At that rate, how much would it cost to have a carpet 15 ft by 15 ft cleaned? \$67.50
3. The area of a regular octagon is 72 cm^2. What is the area of a regular octagon with sides three times the length of the smaller octagon? 648 cm^2

Math ToolboX

Students use spreadsheets to explore the surface areas and volumes of similar rectangular prisms. The relationships among the similarity ratio, areas, and volumes of similar solids will be presented formally in Lesson 10-6.

Students enter formulas into the spreadsheet so that when given the lengths widths, and heights of similar rectangular prisms, the program will calculate the surface areas, volumes, similarity ratio, ratio of the surface areas, and ratio of the volumes.

ERROR ALERT! Some students may have difficulty entering the data, especially the formulas, into the correct rows and columns. **Remediation:** Pair students who have more experience using spreadsheets with those with less experience.

Extend

For similar right cylinders, students will need to change columns B, C, and D to be π, radius, and height, then adjust the formulas for surface area and volume. For similar square pyramids, students will need to change columns B, C, and D to base length, height, and slant height, then adjust the formulas for surface area and volume.

ADDITIONAL PROBLEM Have students set up a spreadsheet to investigate the ratios of the surface areas and volumes of similar right cones.

Math Toolbox page 530

Conjecture

The ratio of the surface areas of similar solids is the square of the ratio of their linear dimensions; the ratio of the volumes of similar solids is the cube of the ratio of their linear dimensions.

Math ToolboX — Technology

Exploring Similar Solids

With Lesson 10-6

Work in pairs or small groups.

Input
Check students' work.

To explore surface areas and volumes of similar rectangular prisms, set up a spreadsheet like the one below. You choose numbers for the length, width, height, and similarity ratio. All other numbers will be calculated by formulas.

	A	B	C	D	E	F	G	H	I
1					Surface		Similarity		
2		Length	Width	Height	Area	Volume	Ratio (II : I)	Ratio of	Ratio of
3	Rectangular Prism I	6	4	23	508	552	2	Surface	Volumes
4								Areas (II : I)	(II : I)
5	Similar Prism II	12	8	46	2032	4416		4	8

In cell E3 enter the formula = 2 * (B3 * C3 + B3 * D3 + C3 * D3), which will calculate the sum of the areas of the six faces of Prism I. In cell F3 enter the formula = B3 * C3 * D3, which will calculate the volume of Prism I.

In cells B5, C5, and D5 enter the formulas = G3 * B3, = G3 * C3, and = G3 * D3, respectively, which will calculate the dimensions of similar Prism II. Copy the formulas from E3 and F3 into E5 and F5 to calculate the surface area and volume of Prism II.

In cell H5 enter the formula = E5/E3 and in cell I5 enter the formula = F5/F3 to calculate the ratios of the surface areas and volumes.

Investigate
Check students' work.

In row 3, enter numbers for the length, width, height, and similarity ratio. Change those numbers to investigate how the ratios of the surface areas and volumes are related to the similarity ratio.

Conjecture
See margin.

Make conjectures about the relationships you have discovered.

Extend
Check students' work.

- Set up a spreadsheet to investigate the ratios of the surface areas and volumes of similar right cylinders. Do the same for similar square pyramids.

10-6 Teaching Notes

PROBLEM OF THE DAY

A circular track is 5 m wide. It takes a horse, traveling his fastest, π more seconds to travel the outer edge than the inner edge. How fast can the horse travel? 10 m/sec

Problem of the Day is also available in Transparencies.

CONNECTING TO PRIOR KNOWLEDGE Draw a rectangular prism, labeling the length, width, and height, and a right cylinder, labeling the radius and height. Have students find the surface area and volume of each.

WORK TOGETHER

ALTERNATIVE METHOD Instead of drawing the rectangular prisms on isometric dot paper, have students construct them using wooden, plastic, or sugar cubes.

THINK AND DISCUSS

Emphasize that similar solids have the same shape and proportional size, which means that corresponding dimensions are proportional. List the solids students have studied: prism, pyramid, cone, cylinder, and sphere. Ask them to describe the conditions necessary for two of each type of solid to be similar.

Connections Literature . . . and more

10-6 Areas and Volumes of Similar Solids

What You'll Learn

- Finding the relationships between the similarity ratio and the ratios of the areas and volumes of similar solids

...And Why

To determine the area or volume of a solid when you know the area or volume of a similar solid

What You'll Need

- isometric dot paper
- calculator

WORK TOGETHER

Work with a group.

- Draw a 2-by-3-by-2 rectangular prism on isometric dot paper.
- Choose a value of k from the set {2, 3, 4, 5} and draw a $2k$-by-$3k$-by-$2k$ rectangular prism and call it Prism I. Choose two other values of k and draw Prisms II and III.
- Find the surface area and volume of each prism. Compare the original prism to each of the three prisms. Organize your data in a table like this.

	Value of k	Ratio of Corresponding Edges	Ratio of Surface Areas	Ratio of Volumes
Original to I	■	■ : ■	■ : ■	■ : ■
Original to II	■	■ : ■	■ : ■	■ : ■
Original to III	■	■ : ■	■ : ■	■ : ■

1. a. If the corresponding dimensions of two rectangular prisms are in the ratio $1 : k$, what will be the ratio of their surface areas? $1 : k^2$
   b. What will be the ratio of their volumes? $1 : k^3$
2. a. If the corresponding dimensions of two rectangular prisms are in the ratio $a : b$, what will be the ratio of their surface areas? $a^2 : b^2$
   b. What will be the ratio of their volumes? $a^3 : b^3$

THINK AND DISCUSS

These nested Russian dolls are similar solids. **Similar solids** have the same shape and all their corresponding dimensions are proportional.

Lesson Planning Options

Prerequisite Skills

- Finding the volumes and surface areas of solids

Assignment Options for Exercises On Your Own

Core 1–17

✪**Extension** 18–19

Use Mixed Review to maintain skills.

Resources

Student Edition

Skills Handbook, pp. 662, 673
Extra Practice, p. 657
Glossary/Study Guide

Teaching Resources

Chapter Support File, Ch. 10
- Practice 10-6 (two worksheets)
- Reteaching 10-6

Classroom Manager 10-6
Glossary, Spanish Resources

Transparencies
11, 18, 106

Question 3 You may want to review with students that all circles are similar and that all spheres are similar.

Theorem 10-7 Help students understand that this theorem applies to all similar solids, not just similar rectangular prisms, which they investigated in the Work Together.

Some students may be surprised to learn that the relationship between the similarity ratio and the area of similar polygons is the same as the relationship between the similarity ratio and the surface areas of similar solids. Point out that area and surface area are both measured in square units.

Example 1

Point out to students that the ratios of the radii to the heights of similar cylinders are equal.

ERROR ALERT! Some students may confuse the ratio of the areas of cylinders with the similarity ratio and cube the ratio of the areas to find the ratio of the volumes. **Remediation:** Reinforce that the ratios of the areas of similar cylinders is the square of the similarity ratio, and the ratio of the volumes of similar cylinders is the cube of the similarity ratio.

TACTILE LEARNING Have students use models of pairs of similar solids to measure corresponding dimensions. Have them find the similarity ratio, then compute and compare the surface areas and volumes of each pair.

Additional Examples

FOR EXAMPLE 1

The surface areas of two similar cylinders are 80 π m^2 and 180 π m^2. The volume of the larger cylinder is 324 π m^3. Find the volume of the smaller cylinder. **96 π m^3**

FOR EXAMPLE 2

A cylindrical can holds 16 ounces of water. How many gallons of water does a similarly-shaped can hold if its radius and height are four times the radius and height of the smaller can? (1 gal = 128 oz) **8 gal**

3. **Critical Thinking** Which of the following *must* be similar solids?
   a. two spheres **yes** b. two cones **no** c. two cubes **yes**
4. Can a right triangular prism be similar to an oblique triangular prism? Explain why or why not. **No; the corres. edges are not proportional.**
5. Can a triangular pyramid be similar to a square pyramid? Explain why or why not. **No; a square pyramid does not have the same shape as a triangular pyramid.**

The ratio of corresponding dimensions of two similar solids is the **similarity ratio.** In the Work Together, you discovered that the ratio of the surface areas of similar solids equals the square of their similarity ratio, and the ratio of their volumes equals the cube of their similarity ratio. The ratios you have investigated for similar rectangular prisms apply to *all* similar solids.

Theorem 10-7
Areas and Volumes of Similar Solids

If the similarity ratio of two similar solids is $a : b$, then (1) the ratio of their corresponding areas is $a^2 : b^2$, and (2) the ratio of their volumes is $a^3 : b^3$.

Example 1

The lateral areas of two similar cylinders are 196π in.^{2} and 324π in.^{2}. The volume of the smaller cylinder is 686π in.^{3}. Find the volume of the larger cylinder.

First find the similarity ratio $a : b$.

$\frac{a^2}{b^2} = \frac{196\pi}{324\pi}$	The ratio of the surface areas is $a^2 : b^2$.
$\frac{a^2}{b^2} = \frac{49}{81}$	Divide the numerator and denominator by the common factor 4π.
$\frac{a}{b} = \frac{7}{9}$	Find the square root of each side.
$\frac{V_1}{V_2} = \frac{7^3}{9^3}$	The ratio of the volumes is $a^3 : b^3$.
$\frac{686\pi}{V_2} = \frac{343}{729}$	Substitute 686π for V_1.
$343V_2 = 686\pi \cdot 729$	Cross-Product Property
$V_2 = 1458\pi$	Divide both sides by 343.

The volume of the larger cylinder is 1458π in.^{3}.

6. **Try This** The surface areas of two similar solids are 160 m^2 and 250 m^2. The volume of the larger one is 250 m^3. What is the volume of the smaller one? **128 m^3**

Example 2 **Relating to the Real World** 

ESL Make sure students understand what a "paperweight" is. It would be helpful to show an example of a paperweight and how one is used.

ESTIMATION Encourage students to estimate the solution first as a way to check that the answer is reasonable. The weight of the larger paperweight is about 30 times the weight of the smaller paperweight, which weighs 0.15 lb. So, the weight of the larger paperweight is about 4.5 lb.

Exercises ON YOUR OWN

CONNECTING TO STUDENTS' WORLD Exercises 1–3 Have students bring in packaging from commercial products that are similar, such as different-sized bottles of the same brand of salad dressing.

STANDARDIZED TEST TIP Exercise 5 A common error is for students to assume that the area of the smaller solid is 16. Make sure students understand that knowing the ratio of surface areas is not enough information to determine the surface area (or volume) of either solid.

The weights of objects made of the same material are proportional to their volumes.

Example 2 **Relating to the Real World**

Paperweights A marble paperweight shaped like a pyramid weighs 0.15 lb. How much does a similarly-shaped paperweight weigh if each dimension is three times as large?

The similarity ratio is 1 : 3, so the ratio of the volumes is $1^3 : 3^3$, or 1 : 27.

$\frac{1}{27} = \frac{0.15}{x}$ Let x = weight of the larger paperweight.

$x = 27\,(0.15)$ Cross-Product Property

$x = 4.05$

The larger marble paperweight weighs about 4 lb.

7. **Try This** There are 750 toothpicks in a regular-size box. If a jumbo box is made by doubling all the dimensions of the regular box, how many toothpicks will the jumbo box hold? 6000 toothpicks

8. **Try This** A regular pentagonal prism with base edges 9 cm long is enlarged to a similar prism with base edges 36 cm long. By what factor is its volume increased? 64

Exercises ON YOUR OWN

Are the solids similar? Explain.

1\. 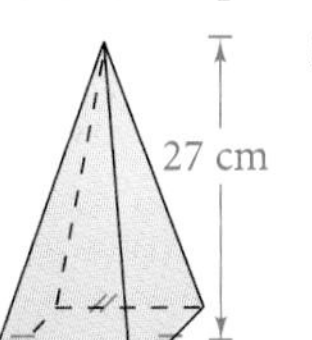

no; $\frac{18}{27} \neq \frac{9}{12}$

2\. yes; $\frac{18}{12} = \frac{30}{20}$

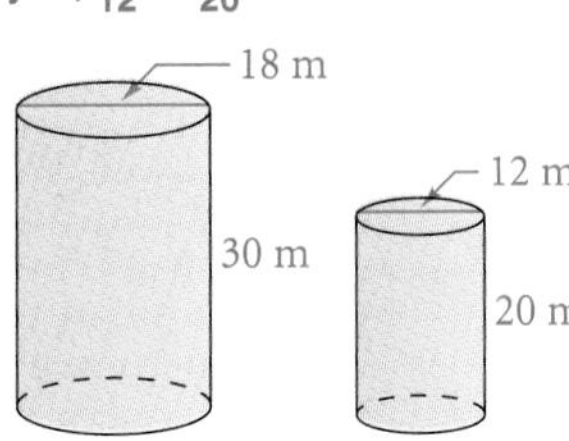

3\. yes; $\frac{4}{6} = \frac{6}{9} = \frac{8}{12}$

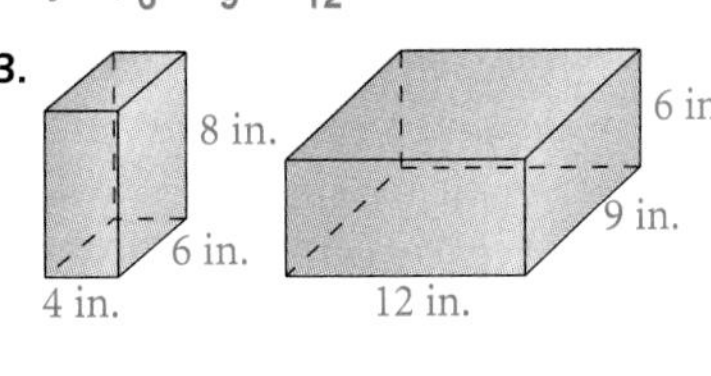

4. Two similar prisms have heights 4 cm and 10 cm.
   a. What is the similarity ratio? 2 : 5
   b. What is the ratio of the surface areas? 4 : 25
   c. What is the ratio of the volumes? 8 : 125

5. *Standardized Test Prep* The ratio of the surface areas of two similar solids is 16 : 49. What is the volume of the smaller one? E

   A. 4 **B.** 7 **C.** 64 **D.** 343 **E.** cannot be determined

Technology Options

Prentice Hall Technology 

Software
- Secondary Math Lab Toolkit™
- Computer Item Generator 10-6

CD-ROM
- Multimedia Geometry Lab 10

Internet
- See the Prentice Hall site. (http://www.phschool.com)

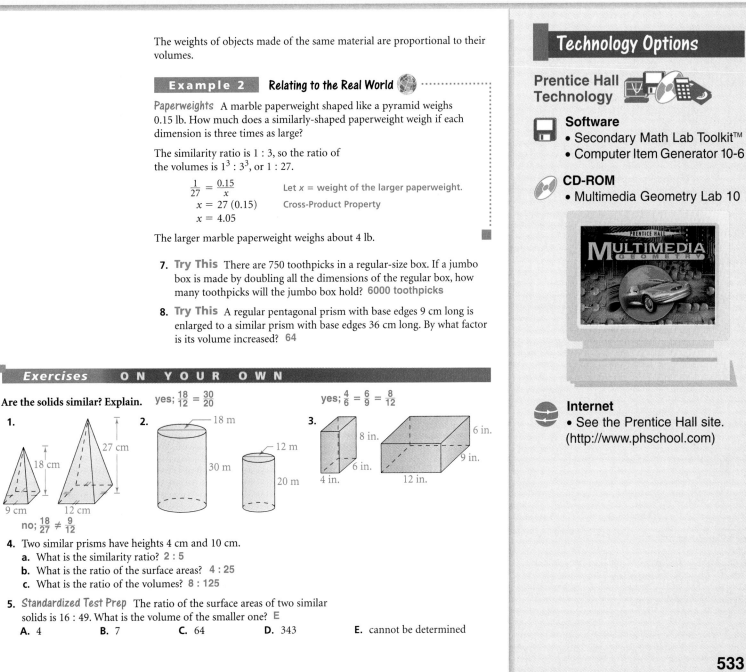

ERROR ALERT! Exercise 6 Because of the positions of the solids in the diagram, some students may choose the 80-m side and the 45-m side as corresponding sides and conclude that the rectangular prisms cannot be similar. **Remediation:** Point out that since the 80-m side and the 60-m side appear to be the longest sides, students should try them as corresponding sides.

ALTERNATIVE ASSESSMENT Exercises 14–17 These exercises can help you assess students' ability to apply Theorem 10-7 to solve real-world problems. Have students work in groups. Have them write one or two sentences explaining how they solved each problem.

MAKING CONNECTIONS Exercise 15 An atomic clock is based on the changes in the energy states of atoms. It is highly accurate because it is not affected by external conditions, such as air pressure and magnetic fields. The most accurate atomic clock is located at the National Institute of Standards and Technology in Boulder, Colorado. It is accurate to one- 10 billionths of a second per day. Watches and clocks are now being made that tell time by picking up radio signals from this atomic clock.

EXTENSION Exercise 15 Have students research how an atomic clock works.

pages 533–535 On Your Own

15. Answers may vary. Sample: No; if the dimensions of the box are $\frac{1}{10}$ of the orig. dimensions, then the new clock's weight should be $\frac{1}{1000}$ of the orig. weight.

19d. Paul Bunyan's weight is 1000 times the weight of an average person, but his bones can only support 600 times the weight of an average person.

page 535 Mixed Review

20.

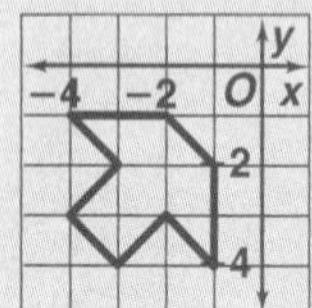

21.

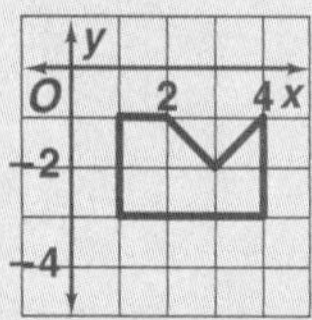

6. Is there a value of x for which the rectangular solids at the right are similar? Explain. See right.

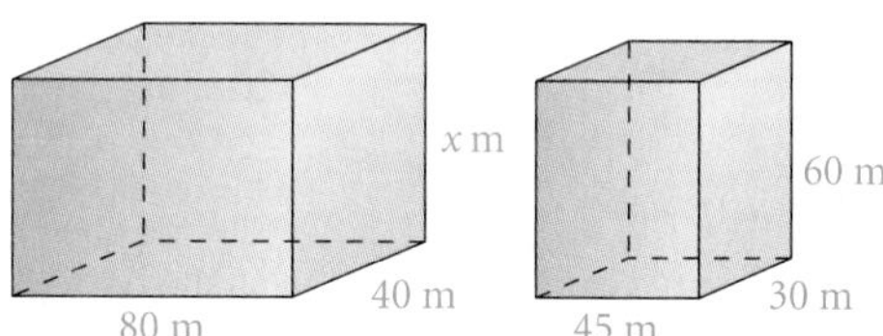

7. The volumes of two spheres are 729 in.^{3} and 81 in.^{3}. Find the ratio of their radii. $\sqrt[3]{9} : 1$ or $3 : \sqrt[3]{3}$

8. A carpenter is making a copy of an antique blanket chest that has the shape of a rectangular solid. The length, width, and height of the copy will be 4 in. greater than the original dimensions. Will the chests be similar? Explain. See right.

6. 60; solve for x: $\frac{80}{60} = \frac{40}{30} = \frac{x}{45}$.

8. No; unless the chest is a cube, the increase in the lengths of the sides is not proportional.

9. *Estimation* The volume of a spherical balloon with radius 3.1 cm is about 125 cm^3. Estimate the volume of a similar balloon with radius 6 cm. about 1000 cm^3

Copy and complete the table for two similar solids.

	Similarity Ratio	Ratio of Surface Areas	Ratio of Volumes
10.	1 : 2	1 ■ : ■ 4	1 ■ : ■ 8
11.	3 : 5	9 ■ : ■ 25	27 ■ : ■ 125
12.	7 ■ : ■ 9	49 : 81	343 ■ : ■ 729
13.	5 ■ : ■ 8	25 ■ : ■ 64	125 : 512

14. A clown's face on a balloon is 4 in. high when the balloon holds 108 in.^{3} of air. How much air must the balloon hold for the face to be 8 in. high? 864 in.^{3}

15. *Critical Thinking* A company recently announced that it had developed the technology to reduce the size of *atomic clocks,* which are used in electronic devices that transmit data. The company claims that the smaller clock will be $\frac{1}{10}$ the size of existing atomic clocks and $\frac{1}{100}$ the weight. Do these ratios make sense? Explain. See margin.

16. *Packaging* A cylinder 4 in. in diameter and 6 in. high holds 1 lb of oatmeal. To the nearest ounce, how much oatmeal will a similar 10-in. high cylinder hold? 74 oz

17. *Estimation* A teapot 4 in. tall and 4 in. in diameter holds about 1 quart of tea. About how many quarts would this teapot-shaped building hold?
Answers may vary. Sample: about 27,000 qt

LITERATURE Exercises 18 Some students may not be familiar with *Gulliver's Travels*. You may want to give a synopsis of the story or ask students who have read the book to give a synopsis.

RESEARCH Exercise 19 Have students research Robert Pershing Wadlow, the tallest man in medical history. Standing at 8 ft 11.1 in., he needed to wear braces on his legs to support his 439 pounds.

Exercises MIXED REVIEW

COORDINATE GEOMETRY Exercises 20 and 21 Have students review the methods taught in Chapter 3 for finding images of rotations and reflections.

SELF ASSESSMENT **PORTFOLIO** Share with students the criteria you will use to assess their work in portfolios, as well as how you plan to use the results. Students should understand how the rubrics assess their work, how each piece in the portfolio counts, and how the scores they get in their portfolios will affect their overall evaluation.

Wrap Up

THE BIG IDEA Ask students to compare and contrast the ratios of areas and perimeters of similar plane figures to the ratios of surface areas and volumes of similar solids.

RETEACHING ACTIVITY Students find the similarity ratios, the ratios of surface areas, and the ratios of volumes of similar solids. (Reteaching worksheet 10-6)

18. **Literature** In *Gulliver's Travels* by Jonathan Swift, Gulliver first traveled to Lilliput. The average height of a Lilliputian was one twelfth Gulliver's height.

a. How many Lilliputian coats could be made from the material in Gulliver's coat? (*Hint:* Use the ratio of surface areas.) **144 coats**

b. How many Lilliputian meals would be needed to make a meal for Gulliver? (*Hint:* Use the ratio of volumes.) **1728 meals**

c. **Research** Visit your local library and read about Gulliver's voyage to Brobdingnag in *Gulliver's Travels*. Describe the size of the people and objects in this land. Use ratios of areas and volumes to describe Gulliver's life there. **Check students' work.**

19. Giants such as King Kong, Godzilla, and Paul Bunyan cannot exist because their bone structure could not support them. The legendary Paul Bunyan is ten times as tall as the average human.

a. The strength of bones is proportional to the area of their cross-section. How many times stronger than the average person's bones would Paul Bunyan's bones be? **100 times**

b. Weights of objects made of the same material are proportional to their volumes. How many times the average person's weight would Paul Bunyan's weight be? **1000 times**

c. Human leg bones can support about 6 times the average person's weight. How many times the average person's weight could Paul Bunyan's legs support? **600 times**

d. Use your answers to parts (b) and (c) to explain why Paul Bunyan's legs could not support his weight. **See margin p. 534.**

e. **Writing** Explain why massive animals such as elephants have such thick legs. **The increase in the diameter of the legs must be greater than the average increase in other dimensions.**

Exercises MIXED REVIEW

Coordinate Geometry **Draw the image of each figure for the given transformation.** **20–21. See margin p. 534.**

20. 90° rotation clockwise about the origin

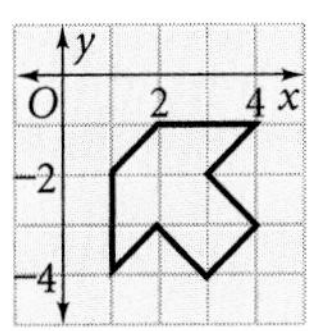

21. reflection in the line $y = x$

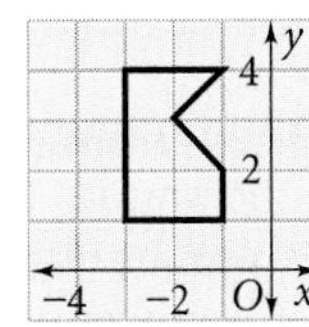

22. What is the area of a 30°-60°-90° triangle with a shorter leg that is 4 cm long? Leave your answer in simplest radical form. **$8\sqrt{3}$ cm²**

SELF ASSESSMENT **PORTFOLIO**

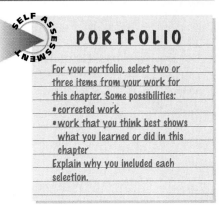

For your portfolio, select two or three items from your work for this chapter. Some possibilities:
- corrected work
- work that you think best shows what you learned or did in this chapter

Explain why you included each selection.

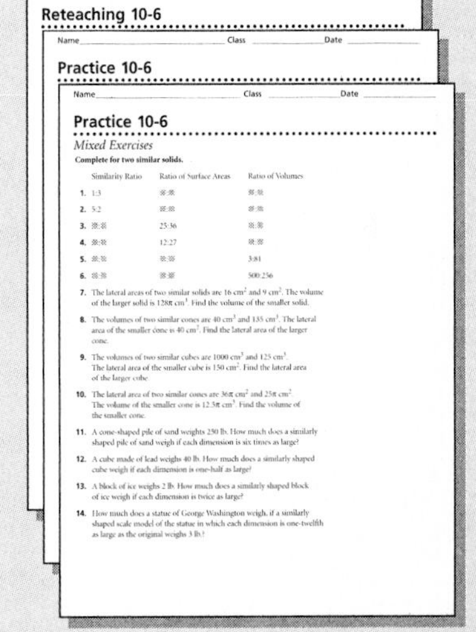

Name ______ Class ______ Date ______

Reteaching 10-6

Name ______ Class ______ Date ______

Practice 10-6

Name ______ Class ______ Date ______

Practice 10-6

Mixed Exercises

Complete for two similar solids.

	Similarity Ratio	Ratio of Surface Areas	Ratio of Volumes
1.	1:3	■:■	■:■
2.	5:2	■:■	■:■
3.	■:■	25:36	■:■
4.	■:■	12:27	■:■
5.	■:■	■:■	3:81
6.	■:■	■:■	500:256

7. The lateral areas of two similar solids are 16 cm² and 9 cm². The volume of the larger solid is 128π cm³. Find the volume of the smaller solid.

8. The volumes of two similar cones are 40 cm³ and 135 cm³. The lateral area of the smaller cone is 40 cm². Find the lateral area of the larger cone.

9. The volumes of two similar cubes are 1000 cm³ and 125 cm³. The lateral area of the smaller cube is 150 cm². Find the lateral area of the larger cube.

10. The lateral area of two similar cones are 36π cm² and 25π cm². The volume of the smaller cone is 12.5π cm³. Find the volume of the smaller cone.

11. A cone-shaped pile of sand weights 250 lb. How much does a similarly shaped pile of sand weigh if each dimension is six times as large?

12. A cube made of lead weighs 40 lb. How much does a similarly shaped cube weigh if each dimension is one-half as large?

13. A block of ice weighs 2 lb. How much does a similarly shaped block of ice weigh if each dimension is twice as large?

14. How much does a statue of George Washington weigh, if a similarly shaped scale model of the statue in which each dimension is one-twelfth as large as the original weighs 3 lb.?

Lesson Quiz

Lesson Quiz is also available in Transparencies.

For Exercises 1–3, two similar prisms have widths 6 in. and 9 in.

1. What is the similarity ratio? $\frac{2}{3}$

2. What is the ratio of the surface areas? $\frac{4}{9}$

3. What is the ratio of the volumes? $\frac{8}{27}$

4. The volume of a sphere is about 268 cm³. Estimate the volume of a sphere with a radius two times that of the smaller sphere. **about 2144 cm³**

Finishing the Chapter Project

PROJECT DAY You may wish to plan a project day on which students share their completed projects. Encourage groups to explain their processes as well as their products.

PROJECT NOTEBOOK Have students review their project work and bring their notebooks up to date.

- Have students review their fractal designs and their directions for creating them.
- Ask groups to share any insights they found when completing the project, such as the properties of side lengths or areas of fractals.

SCORING RUBRIC

3 Student correctly answers the Find Out questions and provides photos that illustrate properties of fractals. Student's design is accurate and directions are clear and use geometric terms correctly.

2 Student answers the Find Out questions with minor errors and provides photos that illustrate properties of fractals. Student's design is accurate and directions are clear enough to be followed and use some geometric terms.

1 Student answers the Find Out questions with major errors. Photos do not clearly illustrate properties of fractals. Student's design is inaccurate and directions are unclear.

0 Major elements are incomplete or missing.

CHAPTER PROJECT

Finishing the Chapter Project

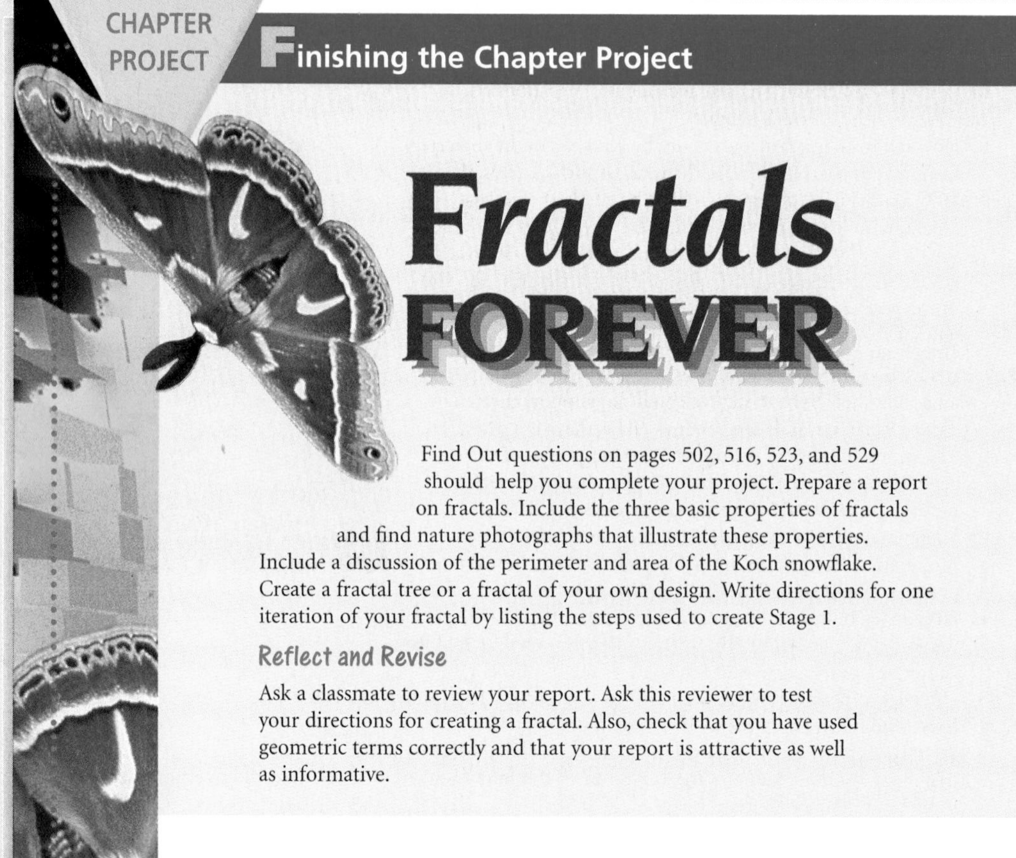

Fractals FOREVER

Find Out questions on pages 502, 516, 523, and 529 should help you complete your project. Prepare a report on fractals. Include the three basic properties of fractals and find nature photographs that illustrate these properties. Include a discussion of the perimeter and area of the Koch snowflake. Create a fractal tree or a fractal of your own design. Write directions for one iteration of your fractal by listing the steps used to create Stage 1.

Reflect and Revise

Ask a classmate to review your report. Ask this reviewer to test your directions for creating a fractal. Also, check that you have used geometric terms correctly and that your report is attractive as well as informative.

Follow Up

In studying the Koch snowflake, you noticed that the total perimeter increases beyond any fixed number (it is infinite), while the area remains less than some fixed number (it is finite). Find or create another fractal with this property and include it in your report.

For More Information

Coes, III, Loring. "Building Fractal Models with Manipulatives." *Mathematics Teacher* (November 1993): 646–651.

Peitgen, Heinz-Otto, et al. *Fractals for the Classroom: Strategic Activities Volume One.* New York: Springer-Verlag, 1991.

Peterson, Ivers. *The Mathematical Tourist.* New York: W.H. Freeman, 1988.

Wrap Up

HOW AM I DOING? Have students work in six groups. Ask each group to make a short presentation explaining the key concepts from one of the lessons in the chapter. Each presentation must include a visual aid and a sample problem.

KEY TERMS The numbers in parentheses direct students to the pages where the terms are used or defined. Students should be able to (1) write a simple explanation of each term, (2) illustrate the term with a diagram, or (3) show an example that uses the term.

ERROR ALERT! **Exercises 1–3** Some students may incorrectly identify corresponding sides based on the positions of the figures. **Remediation:** Have students trace the figures separately on small pieces of paper and rotate them so they are in the same position. Also remind students, that the longest sides correspond to each other and the shortest sides correspond to each other.

10 Wrap Up

Key Terms

Angle-Angle Similarity Postulate (AA~) (p. 504)
constant of variation (p. 503)
Cross-Product Property (p. 497)
direct variation (p. 503)
extended proportion (p. 496)
geometric mean (p. 512)
Golden Ratio (p. 498)
Golden Rectangle (p. 498)
indirect measurement (p. 505)
proportion (p. 496)
scale (p. 497)
scale drawing (p. 497)
Side-Angle-Side Similarity Theorem (SAS~) (p. 506)
Side-Side-Side Similarity Theorem (SSS~) (p. 506)
similar solids (p. 531)
similarity ratio (p. 532)

How am I doing?

- State three ideas from this chapter that you think are important. Explain your choices.
- Describe the properties of similar figures.

Resources

Student Edition
Extra Practice, p. 643
Glossary/Study Guide

Teaching Resources
Study Skills Handbook
Glossary, Spanish Resources

Ratio, Proportion, and Similarity — 10-1

A **proportion** is a statement that two ratios are equal.

$\frac{a}{b} = \frac{c}{d}$ is equivalent to:

(1) $ad = bc$ (2) $\frac{b}{a} = \frac{d}{c}$ (3) $\frac{a}{c} = \frac{b}{d}$ (4) $\frac{a+b}{b} = \frac{c+d}{d}$

In a **scale drawing,** the **scale** compares each length in the drawing to the actual length being represented.

A **Golden Rectangle** is a rectangle that can be divided into a square and a rectangle that is similar to the original rectangle. The lengths of the adjacent sides of a Golden Rectangle are in a ratio called the **Golden Ratio,** which is $1 : \frac{1+\sqrt{5}}{2}$.

The polygons below are similar. Find the values of the variables.

1. 4

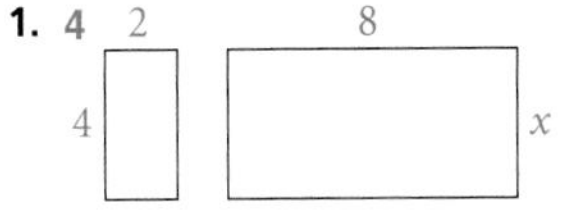

2. 9

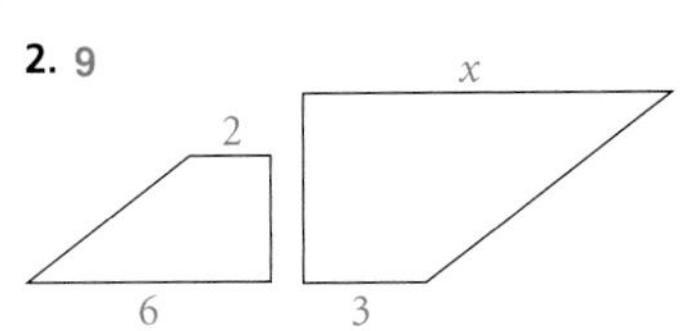

3. $x = 12$; $y = 15$

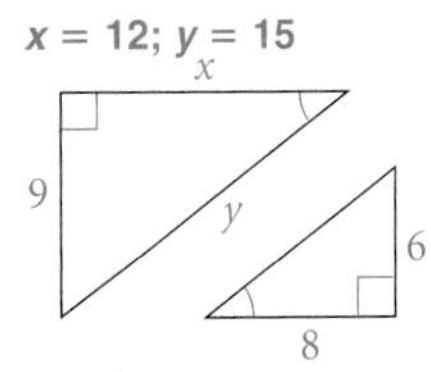

Proving Triangles Similar: AA, SAS, and SSS — 10-2

If two angles of one triangle are congruent to two angles of another triangle, then the two triangles are similar by the **Angle-Angle Similarity Postulate (AA~).** If an angle of one triangle is congruent to an angle of a second triangle, and the sides including the two angles are proportional, then the triangles are similar by the **Side-Angle-Side Similarity Theorem (SAS~).**

STANDARDIZED TEST TIP **Exercise 7** Remind students that right triangles have congruent right angles, so they need only one other pair of congruent angles to use the AA ~ Postulate.

ALTERNATIVE ASSESSMENT **Exercise 10** To assess students' understanding of the relationships between the sides of a right triangle, the altitude to the hypotenuse, and the segments of the hypotenuse, have students work in groups to write an indirect measurement problem requiring the use of these relationships in the solution.

WRITING **Exercise 11** Students may need to review Lesson 4-4 for the definition of *midsegment of a triangle.*

538

If the corresponding sides of two triangles are proportional, then the triangles are similar by the **Side-Side-Side Similarity Theorem (SSS~).**

Are the triangles similar? If so, write the similarity statement and name the postulate or theorem that proves they are similar.

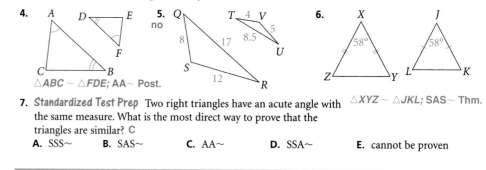

4.

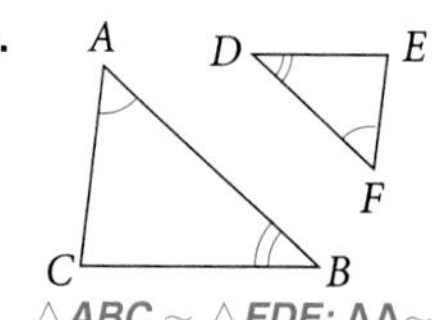

$\triangle ABC \sim \triangle FDE$; AA~ Post.

5. no

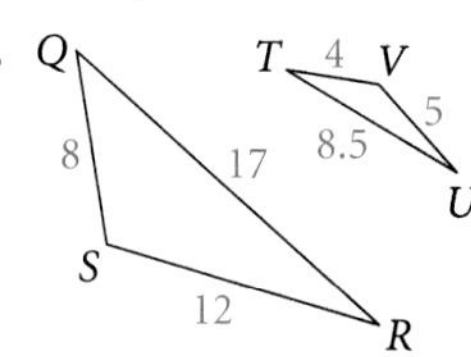

6.

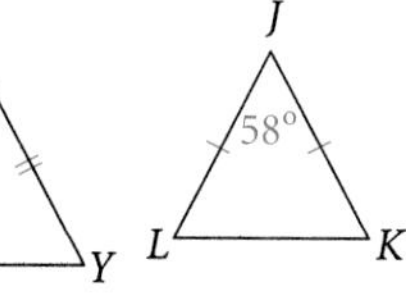

$\triangle XYZ \sim \triangle JKL$; SAS~ Thm.

7. *Standardized Test Prep* Two right triangles have an acute angle with the same measure. What is the most direct way to prove that the triangles are similar? C

A. SSS~ **B.** SAS~ **C.** AA~ **D.** SSA~ **E.** cannot be proven

Similarity in Right Triangles 10-3

The **geometric mean** of two positive numbers a and b is the positive number x such that $\frac{a}{x} = \frac{x}{b}$.

When the altitude is drawn to the hypotenuse of a right triangle:

- the two triangles formed are similar to the original triangle and to each other;
- the length of the altitude is the geometric mean of the lengths of the segments of the hypotenuse; and
- the length of each leg is the geometric mean of the lengths of the hypotenuse and the segment of the hypotenuse that is adjacent to that leg.

Find the values of the variables. When an answer is not a whole number, leave it in simplest radical form.

8.

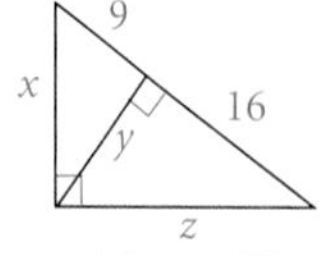

$x = 15$; $y = 12$; $z = 20$

9.

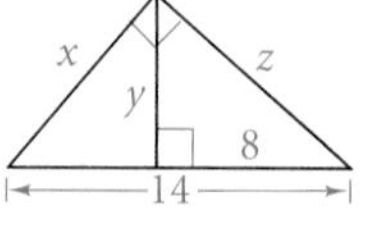

$x = 2\sqrt{21}$; $y = 4\sqrt{3}$; $z = 4\sqrt{7}$

10.

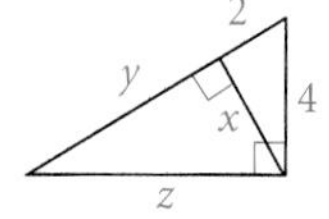

$x = 2\sqrt{3}$; $y = 6$; $z = 4\sqrt{3}$

Proportions and Similar Triangles 10-4

If a line is parallel to one side of a triangle and intersects the other two sides, then it divides those sides proportionally. If three parallel lines intersect two transversals, then the segments intercepted on the transversals are proportional. The bisector of an angle of a triangle divides the opposite side into two segments that are proportional to the sides of the triangle.

11. *Writing* Explain why a line that intersects the legs of a trapezoid and is parallel to the bases divides the legs proportionally.

11. Answers may vary. Sample: The legs of the trapezoid are transversals intersected by 3 ∥ lines, so they are divided proportionally.

Remind students that the new mathematical terms in this chapter are defined in the Glossary/Study Guide in the back of the book.

Getting Ready for Chapter 11

Students may work these exercises independently or in small groups. The skills previewed will help prepare students to study right triangle trigonometry.

Find the value of x.

12. 7.5

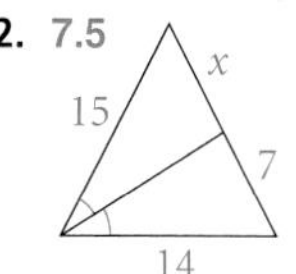

13. 5.5

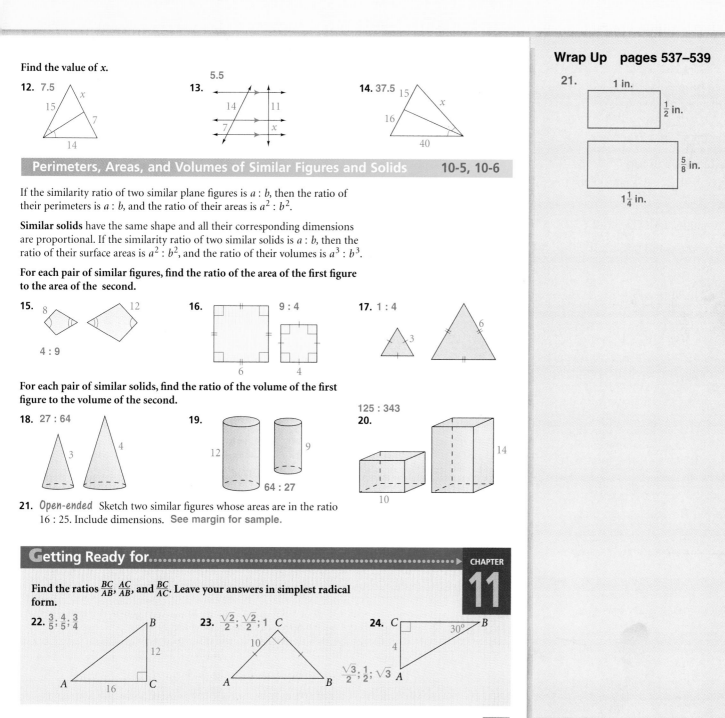

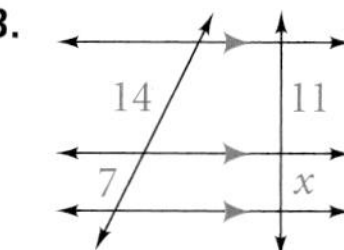

14. 37.5

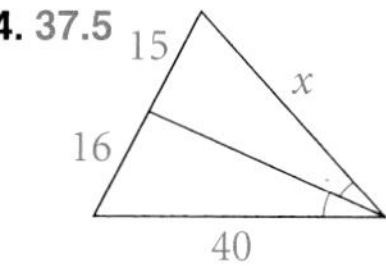

Perimeters, Areas, and Volumes of Similar Figures and Solids — 10-5, 10-6

If the similarity ratio of two similar plane figures is $a : b$, then the ratio of their perimeters is $a : b$, and the ratio of their areas is $a^2 : b^2$.

Similar solids have the same shape and all their corresponding dimensions are proportional. If the similarity ratio of two similar solids is $a : b$, then the ratio of their surface areas is $a^2 : b^2$, and the ratio of their volumes is $a^3 : b^3$.

For each pair of similar figures, find the ratio of the area of the first figure to the area of the second.

15.

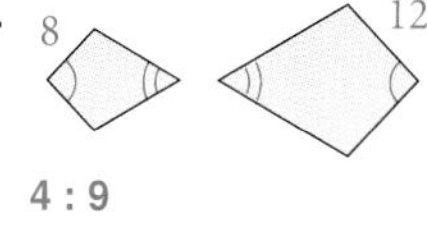

4 : 9

16. 9 : 4

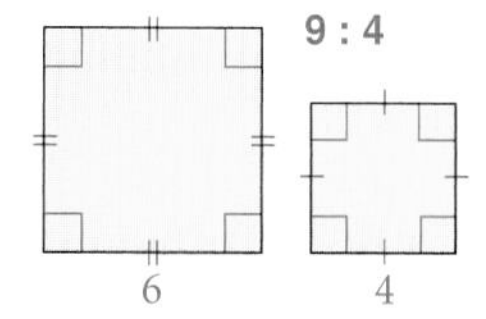

17. 1 : 4

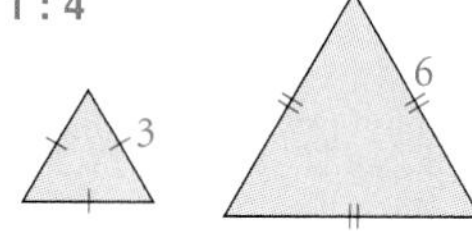

For each pair of similar solids, find the ratio of the volume of the first figure to the volume of the second.

18. 27 : 64

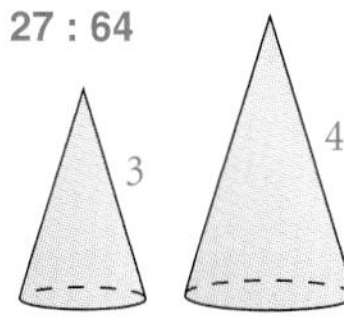

19.

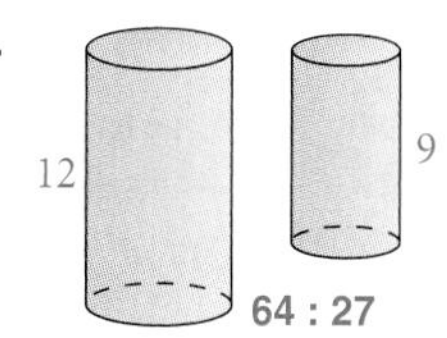

64 : 27

20. 125 : 343

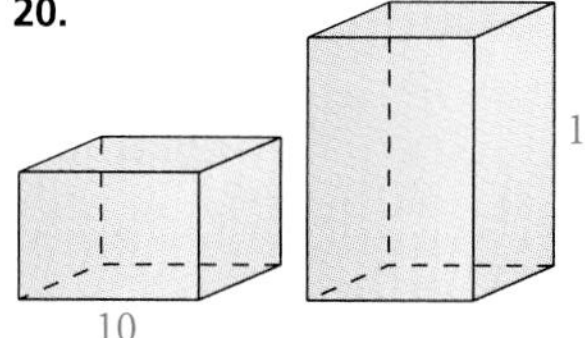

21. *Open-ended* Sketch two similar figures whose areas are in the ratio 16 : 25. Include dimensions. See margin for sample.

Getting Ready for... CHAPTER 11

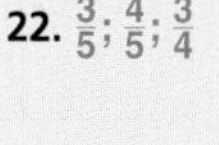

Find the ratios $\frac{BC}{AB}$, $\frac{AC}{AB}$, and $\frac{BC}{AC}$. Leave your answers in simplest radical form.

22. $\frac{3}{5}; \frac{4}{5}; \frac{3}{4}$

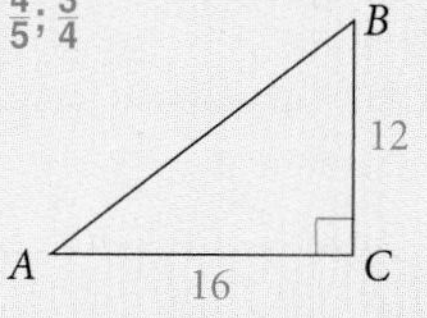

23. $\frac{\sqrt{2}}{2}; \frac{\sqrt{2}}{2}; 1$

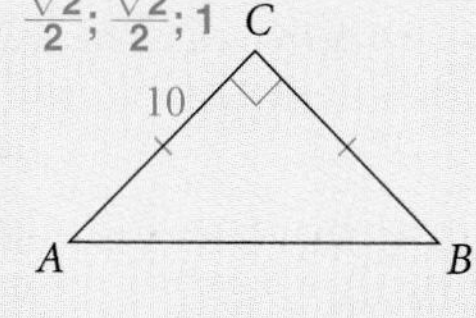

24. $\frac{\sqrt{3}}{2}; \frac{1}{2}; \sqrt{3}$

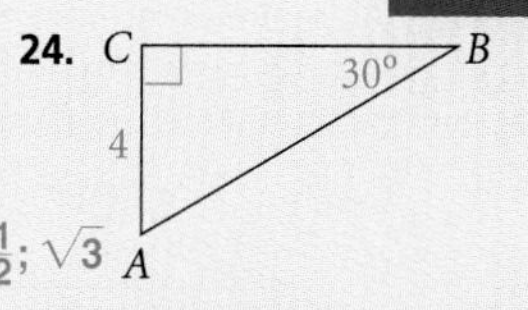

Wrap Up pages 537–539

21.

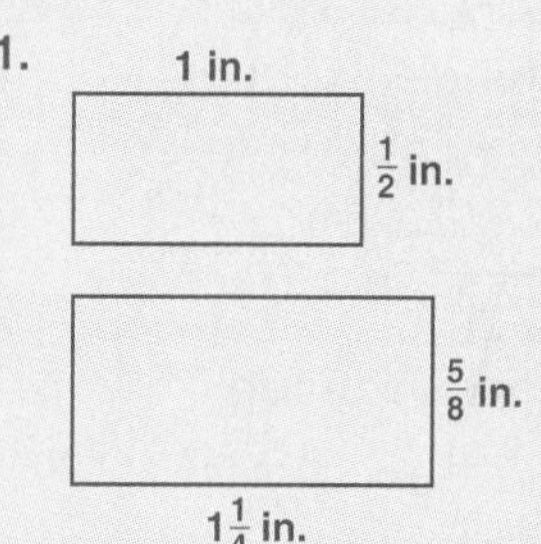

Assessment

ENHANCED MULTIPLE CHOICE QUESTIONS are more complex than traditional multiple choice questions, which assess only one skill. Enhanced multiple choice questions assess the processes that students use, as well as the end results. The questions are written so that students use more than one strategy to solve the problem. Using multiple strategies is encouraged by the National Council of Teachers of Mathematics (NCTM). **Exercise 10** is an enhanced multiple choice question.

FREE RESPONSE QUESTIONS do not give answer choices. Some exercises have more than one possible answer. Students need to give only one correct response. **Exercises 1–9, 12–15, and 17–19** are free response questions.

WRITING EXERCISES allow students to describe how they think about and understand the concepts they have learned. **Exercise 16** is a writing exercise.

OPEN-ENDED PROBLEMS allow for more than one solution. Students must construct their own responses instead of choosing from possible answers. The students' responses will help you determine the depth of their understanding and any possible areas of difficulty. **Exercise 11** is an open-ended problem.

Resources

Teaching Resources

Chapter Support File, Ch. 10
- Cumulative Review
- Standardized Test Practice

Teacher's Edition

See also p. 494E for assessment options

Software
Computer Item Generator

Assessment page 540

11. 4 : 3

16. Height of a tree; stretch out your arm with the thumb pointing up. Walk away from the tree until the top of the tree lines up with the top of the thumb and the base of the tree lines up with the base of the thumb. Measure the distance to the tree, the length of your arm, and the length of your thumb. Solve the proportion.

Cumulative Review page 541

9. A median of a △ is a segment whose endpoints are a vertex and the midpoint of the side opp. the vertex. An altitude of a △ is a ⊥ segment from a vertex to a line containing the side opp. the vertex.

11.

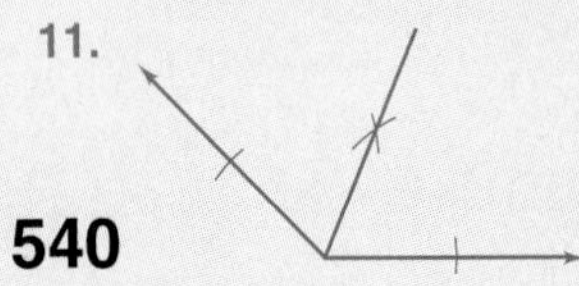

10 Assessment

Solve each proportion.

1. $\frac{4}{5} = \frac{x}{20}$ 16
2. $\frac{6}{x} = \frac{10}{7}$ 4.2
3. $\frac{x}{3} = \frac{8}{12}$ 2

Are the triangles similar? If so, write the similarity statement and name the postulate or theorem that you can use to prove they are similar.

4. △PRQ ~ △TWV; SSS~

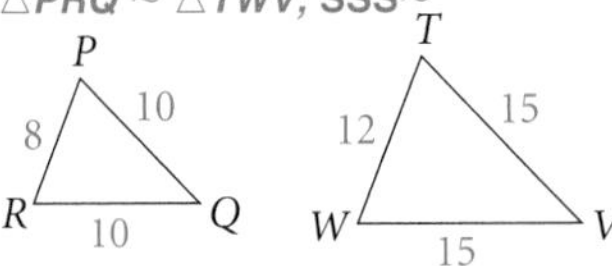

5. no

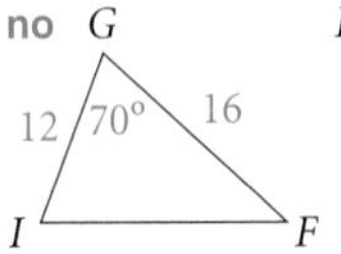

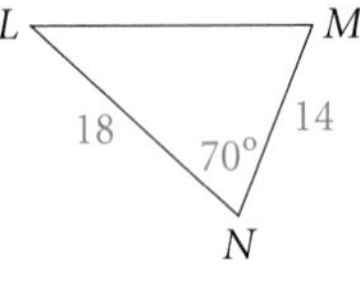

6. A meter stick is held perpendicular to the ground. It casts a shadow 1.5 m long. At the same time, a telephone pole casts a shadow that is 9 m long. How tall is the telephone pole? 6 m

Find the geometric mean of each pair of numbers. If the answer is not a whole number, leave it in simplest radical form.

7. 10, 15 $5\sqrt{6}$
8. 4, 9 6
9. 6, 12 $6\sqrt{2}$

10. *Standardized Test Prep* Which proportion is true for the triangle below? A

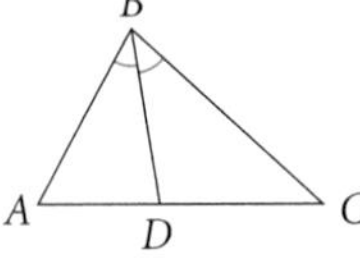

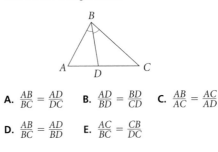

A. $\frac{AB}{BC} = \frac{AD}{DC}$ B. $\frac{AD}{BD} = \frac{BD}{CD}$ C. $\frac{AB}{AC} = \frac{AC}{AD}$

D. $\frac{AB}{BC} = \frac{AD}{BD}$ E. $\frac{AC}{BC} = \frac{CB}{DC}$

11. *Open-ended* Draw an isosceles triangle △ABC. Then draw a triangle △DEF so that △ABC ~ △DEF. State the similarity ratio of △ABC to △DEF. See margin for sample.

Find the value of x.

12. $16\frac{2}{3}$

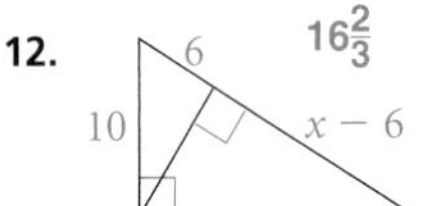

13. 10

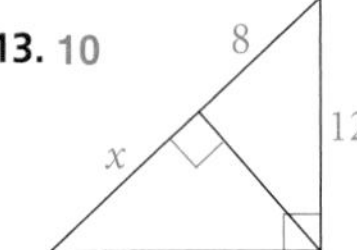

14. 10

12
6
x
20

15. $5\frac{5}{11}$

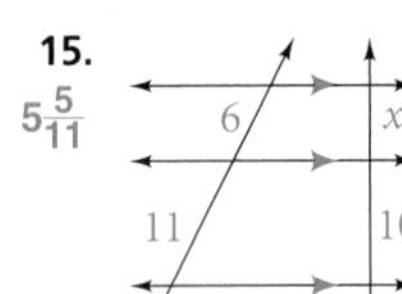

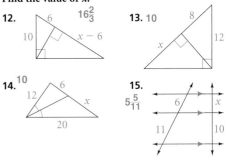

16. *Writing* Describe an object whose height or length would be difficult to measure directly. Then describe a method for measuring the object that involves using similar triangles. See margin for sample.

For each pair of similar figures, find the ratio of the area of the first figure to the area of the second.

17. 49 : 64

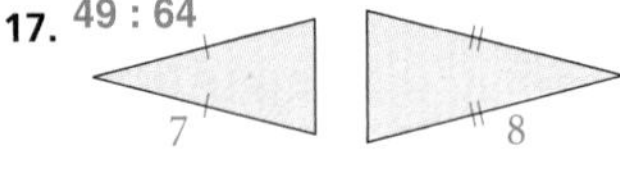

18. 9 : 4

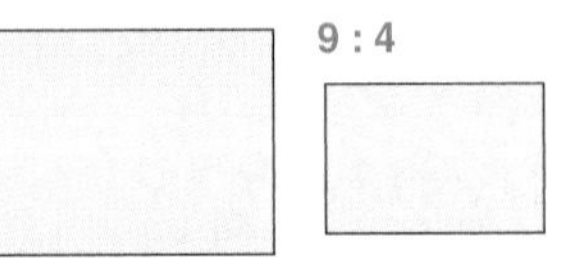

19. The two solids are similar. Find the ratio of the volume of the first figure to the volume of the second. 64 : 125

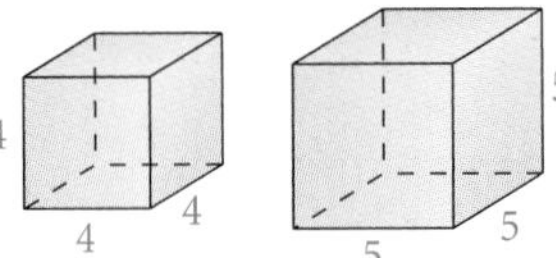

Cumulative Review

Item	Review Topic	Chapter
1	Symmetry	3
2	Volumes of Similar Solids	10
3	Surface Area	6
4	Proving Triangles Congruent	8
5	Special Quadrilaterals	2

Item	Review Topic	Chapter
6, 7	Similarity in Right Triangles	10
8	Properties of Parallelogram	9
9	Triangles	3
10	Area	5
11	Basic Constructions	1

10 Cumulative Review

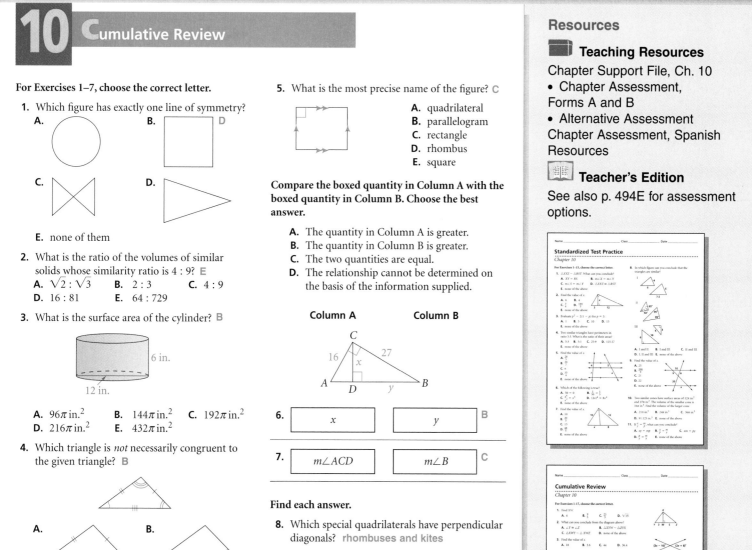

For Exercises 1–7, choose the correct letter.

1. Which figure has exactly one line of symmetry? D

A. 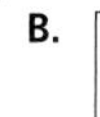

B. 

C.  

D. 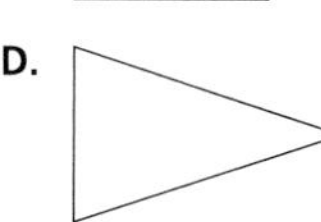

E. none of them

2. What is the ratio of the volumes of similar solids whose similarity ratio is 4 : 9? E
   A. $\sqrt{2} : \sqrt{3}$ B. 2 : 3 C. 4 : 9
   D. 16 : 81 E. 64 : 729

3. What is the surface area of the cylinder? B

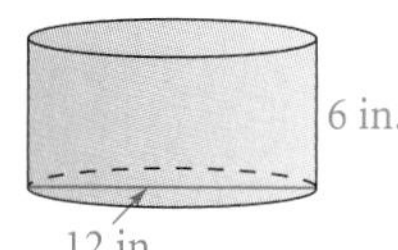

   A. $96\pi\,\text{in.}^2$ B. $144\pi\,\text{in.}^2$ C. $192\pi\,\text{in.}^2$
   D. $216\pi\,\text{in.}^2$ E. $432\pi\,\text{in.}^2$

4. Which triangle is *not* necessarily congruent to the given triangle? B

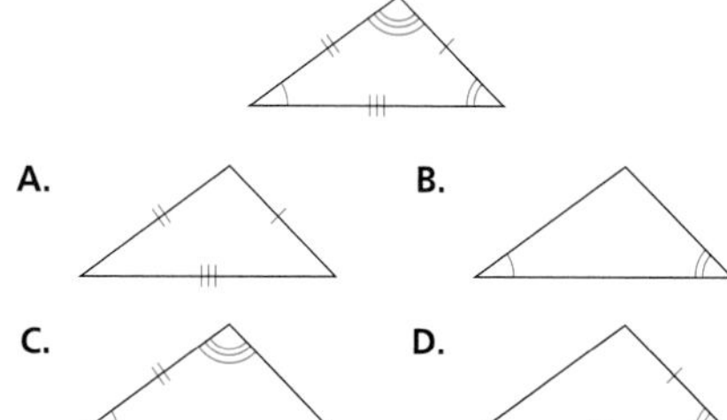

   E. All of the triangles are congruent.

5. What is the most precise name of the figure? C

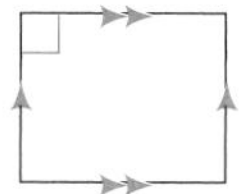

   A. quadrilateral
   B. parallelogram
   C. rectangle
   D. rhombus
   E. square

Compare the boxed quantity in Column A with the boxed quantity in Column B. Choose the best answer.

   A. The quantity in Column A is greater.
   B. The quantity in Column B is greater.
   C. The two quantities are equal.
   D. The relationship cannot be determined on the basis of the information supplied.

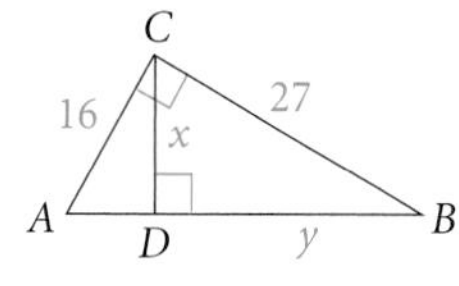

	Column A	Column B	
6.	x	y	B
7.	$m\angle ACD$	$m\angle B$	C

Find each answer.

8. Which special quadrilaterals have perpendicular diagonals? rhombuses and kites

9. Writing Explain the difference between a median and an altitude of a triangle.
   See margin p. 540.

10. How many nonoverlapping circles with 1-in. radius can you fit on a 4-in. square? Find the area of the square not covered by circles.
    4; $(16 - 4\pi)\,\text{in.}^2$

11. Constructions Draw an angle of about 150°. Construct its angle bisector.
    See margin p. 540 for sample.

Resources

Teaching Resources

Chapter Support File, Ch. 10
- Chapter Assessment, Forms A and B
- Alternative Assessment

Chapter Assessment, Spanish Resources

Teacher's Edition

See also p. 494E for assessment options.

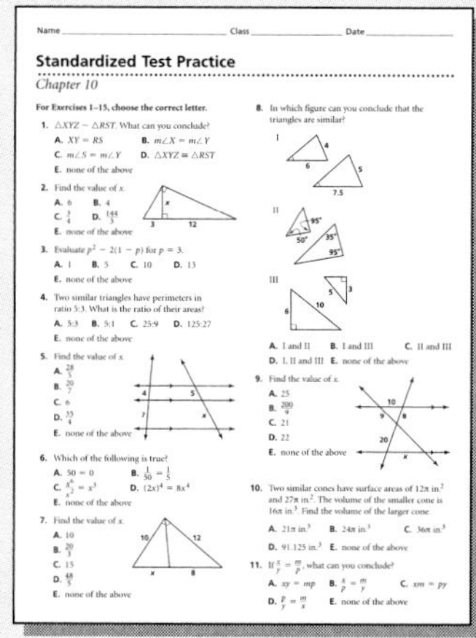

Standardized Test Practice
Chapter 10

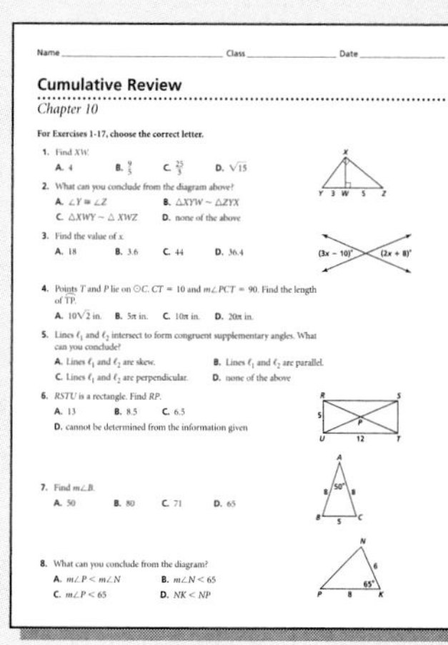

Cumulative Review
Chapter 10

CHAPTER 11 Right Triangle Trigonometry

To accommodate flexible scheduling, some lessons are divided into parts. Assignment Options are given in the Lesson Planning Options for each lesson.

PACING OPTIONS

This chart suggests pacing only for the core lessons and their parts, and it is provided merely as a possible guide. It will help you determine how much time you have in your schedule to cover other features, such as the Chapter Project, Math Toolboxes, Wrap Up, and Assessment.

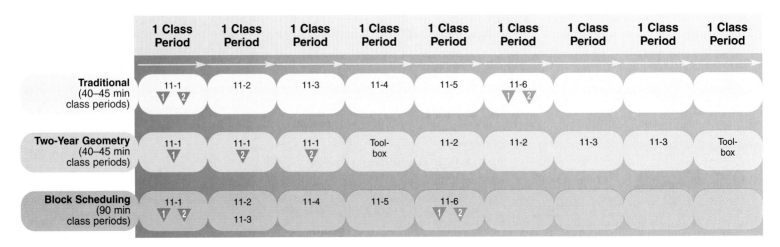

	1 Class Period	1 Class Period	1 Class Period	1 Class Period	1 Class Period	1 Class Period	1 Class Period	1 Class Period	1 Class Period
Traditional (40–45 min class periods)	11-1 1 2	11-2	11-3	11-4	11-5	11-6 1 2			
Two-Year Geometry (40–45 min class periods)	11-1 1	11-1 2	11-1 2	Tool-box	11-2	11-2	11-3	11-3	Tool-box
Block Scheduling (90 min class periods)	11-1 1 2	11-2 11-3	11-4	11-5	11-6 1 2				

What Students Will Learn and Why

In this chapter, students will build on their knowledge of right triangles, learned in Chapter 5, by learning to calculate tangent ratios, sine ratios, and cosine ratios of right triangles. They learn to use these ratios to determine unknown measures in right triangles. Students then apply these skills by using angles of elevation and depression and trigonometric ratios to solve problems. They also learn how to describe vectors using ordered pair notation, how to describe the magnitude and direction of vectors, and how to solve problems that involve vector addition. Finally, students use trigonometry to find the area of regular polygons and acute triangles. Trigonometry is used by engineers, astronomers, surveyors, and others to measure distance indirectly. Vectors are used to model real-world situations involving velocity and to find the speed and direction of an object that has two forces acting on it.

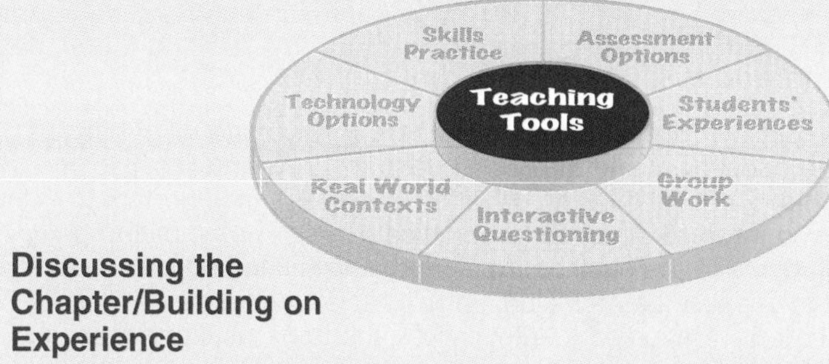

Discussing the Chapter/Building on Experience

The concept map below relates chapter topics to real-world applications. You and your class may wish to add to the map or develop maps of your own. The center oval describes the topic of the chapter. The next level displays topics within the lessons. The outer ovals reflect applications of the content. As you and your class build a concept map, invite students to discuss applications with which they are familiar.

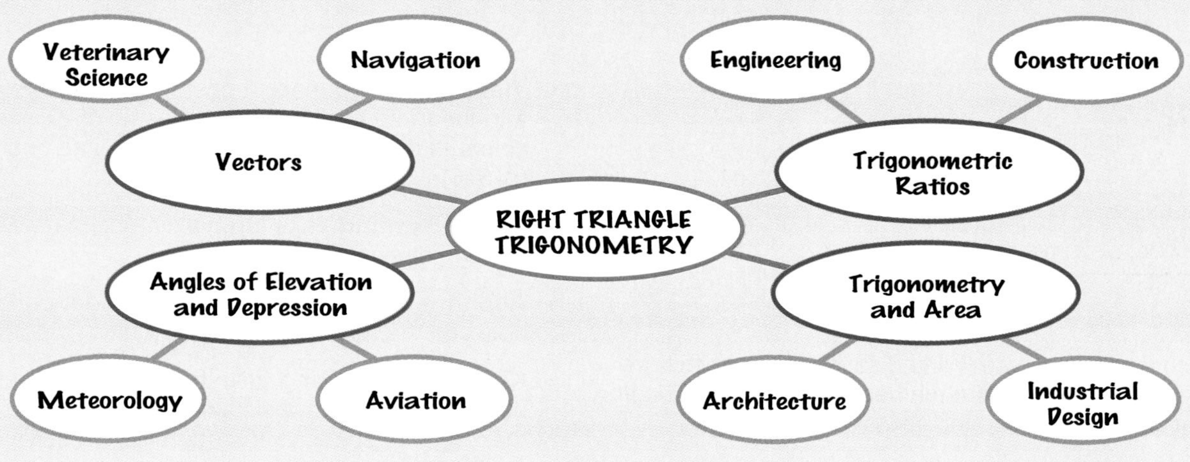

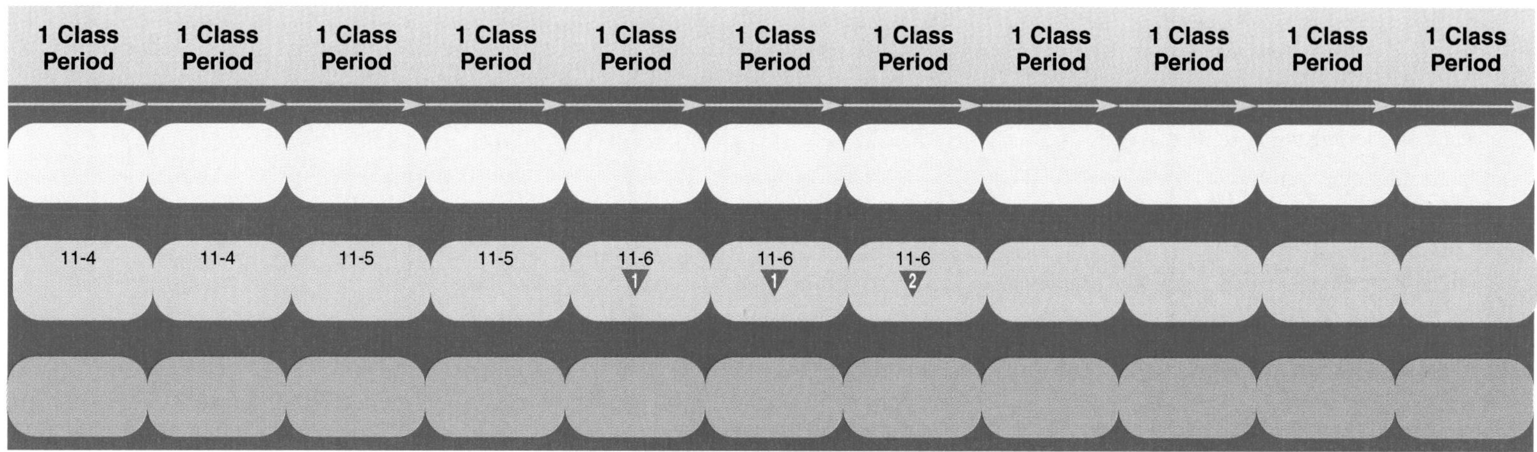

1 Class Period	1 Class Period	1 Class Period	1 Class Period	1 Class Period	1 Class Period	1 Class Period	1 Class Period	1 Class Period	1 Class Period	1 Class Period
11-4	11-4	11-5	11-5	11-6 ▽1	11-6 ▽1	11-6 ▽2				

Skills Practice

Assessment Options

Technology Options

Teaching Tools

Students' Experiences

Real World Contexts

Group Work

Interactive Questioning

Interactive Questioning Tips

A question is interactive when there is "give and take" between the questioner and the respondent. In Think and Discuss or when a critical thinking question is asked, it is important to encourage all students to participate. It can be helpful to bring students to the chalkboard so they can illustrate their answers and support their thinking. For example, in Lesson 11-5, students are asked to explain why the term resultant, meaning the sum of two vectors, makes sense.

Skills Practice

Every lesson provides skills practice with Try This exercises, Exercises On Your Own, and Exercises Mixed Review. The Student Edition includes Checkpoints (pp. 561, 572) and Preparing for Standardized Tests (p. 583). In the Teacher's Edition, the Lesson Planning Options section for each lesson lists Prerequisite Skills students should know for that lesson. At the back of the Student Edition is the Skills Handbook—mini-lessons on math your students may need to review. The Chapter Support File for Chapter 11 in the Teaching Resources box includes two Practice worksheets per lesson, a worksheet for two Checkpoints, and worksheets for Cumulative Review and Standardized Test Preparation.

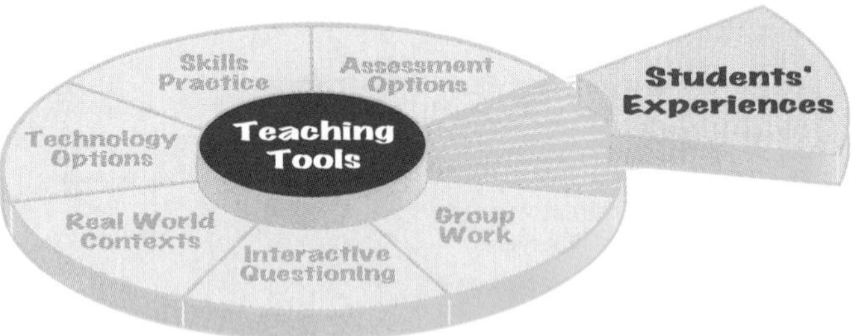

Diverse Learning and Teaching Styles

In your Teacher's Edition, you will find suggestions as to how you can help students complete mathematical tasks in Chapter 11 by reinforcing various learning styles. Here are some examples.

- **Visual learning** make a poster that displays a right triangle and the three trigonometric ratios (p. 552), use different colors to indicate angles of elevation and depression (p. 556)
- **Tactile learning** take turns moving a marble by blowing through straws (p. 570)
- **Auditory learning** use a mnemonic device to differentiate between the three trigonometric ratios (p. 552)
- **Kinesthetic learning** use the method in Example 2 to go outside and measure distances indirectly (p. 545), measure the length of shadows to determine the sun's elevation (p. 560)

Alternative Activity for Lesson 11-1

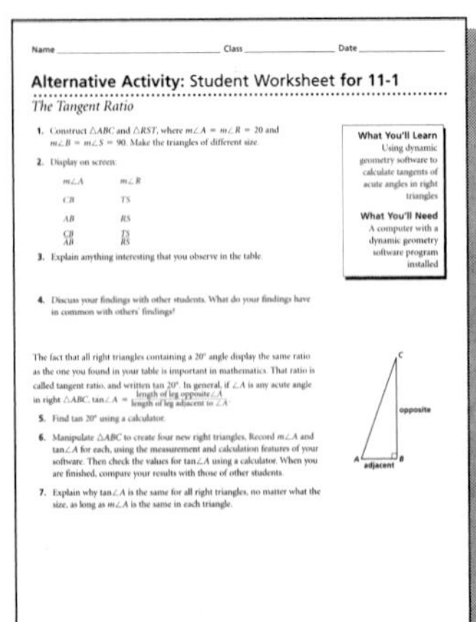

Name ______ Class ______ Date ______

Alternative Activity: Student Worksheet for 11-1

The Tangent Ratio

1. Construct $\triangle ABC$ and $\triangle RST$, where $m\angle A = m\angle R = 20$ and $m\angle B = m\angle S = 90$. Make the triangles of different size.
2. Display on screen:

$m\angle A$	$m\angle R$
CB	TS
AB	RS
$\frac{CB}{AB}$	$\frac{TS}{RS}$

3. Explain anything interesting that you observe in the table.
4. Discuss your findings with other students. What do your findings have in common with others' findings?

What You'll Learn
Using dynamic geometry software to calculate tangents of acute angles in right triangles

What You'll Need
A computer with a dynamic geometry software program installed

The fact that all right triangles containing a 20° angle display the same ratio as the one you found in your table is important in mathematics. That ratio is called tangent ratio, and written tan 20°. In general, if $\angle A$ is any acute angle in right $\triangle ABC$, $\tan \angle A = \frac{\text{length of leg opposite } \angle A}{\text{length of leg adjacent to } \angle A}$.

5. Find tan 20° using a calculator.
6. Manipulate $\triangle ABC$ to create four new right triangles. Record $m\angle A$ and $\tan\angle A$ for each, using the measurement and calculation features of your software. Then check the values for $\tan\angle A$ using a calculator. When you are finished, compare your results with those of other students.
7. Explain why $\tan\angle A$ is the same for all right triangles, no matter what the size, as long as $m\angle A$ is the same in each triangle.

for use with Work Together and Example 1, uses geometry software to explore ratios of sides in similar right triangles.

Alternative Activity for Lesson 11-2

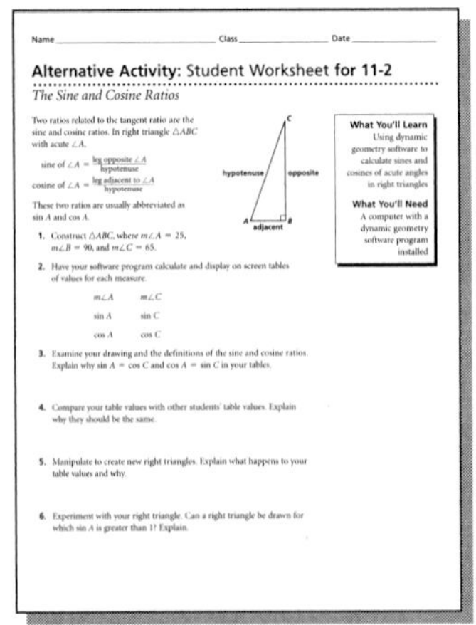

Name ______ Class ______ Date ______

Alternative Activity: Student Worksheet for 11-2

The Sine and Cosine Ratios

Two ratios related to the tangent ratio are the sine and cosine ratios. In right triangle $\triangle ABC$ with acute $\angle A$,

sine of $\angle A = \frac{\text{leg opposite } \angle A}{\text{hypotenuse}}$

cosine of $\angle A = \frac{\text{leg adjacent to } \angle A}{\text{hypotenuse}}$

These two ratios are usually abbreviated as sin A and cos A.

What You'll Learn
Using dynamic geometry software to calculate sines and cosines of acute angles in right triangles

What You'll Need
A computer with a dynamic geometry software program installed

1. Construct $\triangle ABC$, where $m\angle A = 25$, $m\angle B = 90$, and $m\angle C = 65$.
2. Have your software program calculate and display on screen tables of values for each measure.

$m\angle A$	$m\angle C$
sin A	sin C
cos A	cos C

3. Examine your drawing and the definitions of the sine and cosine ratios. Explain why $\sin A = \cos C$ and $\cos A = \sin C$ in your tables.
4. Compare your table values with other students' table values. Explain why they should be the same.
5. Manipulate to create new right triangles. Explain what happens to your table values and why.
6. Experiment with your right triangle. Can a right triangle be drawn for which sin A is greater than 1? Explain.

for use with Example 1, uses geometry software to investigate sine and cosine ratios in right triangles.

Alternative Activity for Lesson 11-6

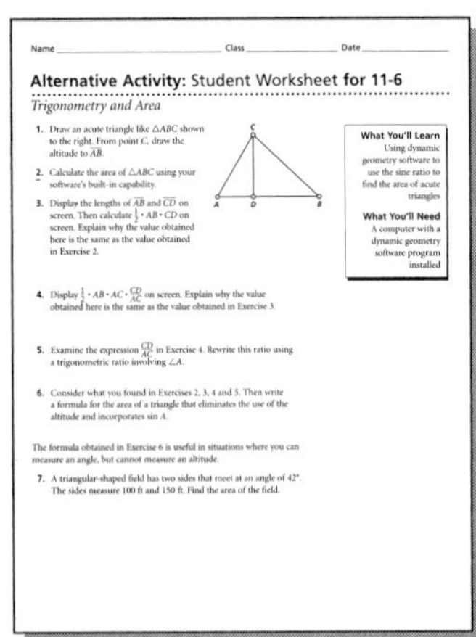

Name ______ Class ______ Date ______

Alternative Activity: Student Worksheet for 11-6

Trigonometry and Area

1. Draw an acute triangle like $\triangle ABC$ shown to the right. From point C, draw the altitude to $\overline{AB}$.
2. Calculate the area of $\triangle ABC$ using your software's built-in capability.
3. Display the lengths of $\overline{AB}$ and $\overline{CD}$ on screen. Then calculate $\frac{1}{2} \cdot AB \cdot CD$ on screen. Explain why the value obtained here is the same as the value obtained in Exercise 2.

What You'll Learn
Using dynamic geometry software to use the sine ratio to find the area of acute triangles

What You'll Need
A computer with a dynamic geometry software program installed

4. Display $\frac{1}{2} \cdot AB \cdot AC \cdot \frac{CD}{AC}$ on screen. Explain why the value obtained here is the same as the value obtained in Exercise 3.
5. Examine the expression $\frac{CD}{AC}$ in Exercise 4. Rewrite this ratio using a trigonometric ratio involving $\angle A$.
6. Consider what you found in Exercises 2, 3, 4 and 5. Then write a formula for the area of a triangle that eliminates the use of the altitude and incorporates sin A.

The formula obtained in Exercise 6 is useful in situations where you can measure an angle, but cannot measure an altitude.

7. A triangular-shaped field has two sides that meet at an angle of 42°. The sides measure 100 ft and 150 ft. Find the area of the field.

for use with Example 3, uses geometry software to study formulas for the area of a triangle.

Skills Practice
Assessment Options
Teaching Tools
Technology Options
Students' Experiences
Real World Contexts
Interactive Questioning
Group Work

Cooperative Learning Tips

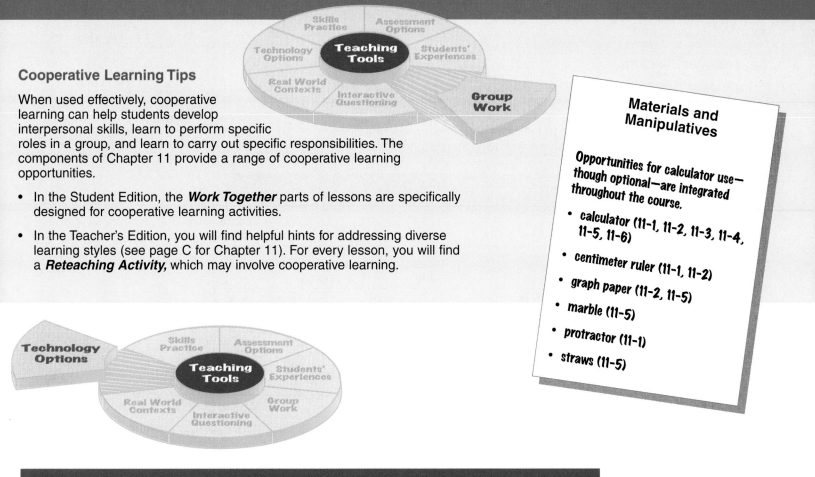

When used effectively, cooperative learning can help students develop interpersonal skills, learn to perform specific roles in a group, and learn to carry out specific responsibilities. The components of Chapter 11 provide a range of cooperative learning opportunities.

- In the Student Edition, the ***Work Together*** parts of lessons are specifically designed for cooperative learning activities.
- In the Teacher's Edition, you will find helpful hints for addressing diverse learning styles (see page C for Chapter 11). For every lesson, you will find a ***Reteaching Activity,*** which may involve cooperative learning.

Materials and Manipulatives

Opportunities for calculator use—though optional—are integrated throughout the course.

- calculator (11-1, 11-2, 11-3, 11-4, 11-5, 11-6)
- centimeter ruler (11-1, 11-2)
- graph paper (11-2, 11-5)
- marble (11-5)
- protractor (11-1)
- straws (11-5)

Technology Options
Skills Practice
Assessment Options
Teaching Tools
Students' Experiences
Real World Contexts
Group Work
Interactive Questioning

TECHNOLOGY OPTIONS

Technology Tools		Chapter Project	11-1	11-2	11-3	11-4	11-5	11-6
Calculator		Numerous opportunities throughout for students to use scientific calculators.						
Software	Secondary Math Lab Toolkit™		✔	✔	✔	✔	✔	✔
	Integrated Math Lab		✔	✔				
	Computer Item Generator		✔	✔	✔	✔	✔	✔
	Student Edition			✔T				
Video	Video Field Trip	✔						
CD-ROM	Multimedia Geometry Lab		✔	✔			✔	✔
Internet		See the Prentice Hall site. (http://www.phschool.com)						

✔T indicates Math Toolbox.

The Prentice Hall Geometry program offers you a rich variety of technology options. Be assured that all these options are provided as a means of enriching the program and are not essential for the successful completion of the course.

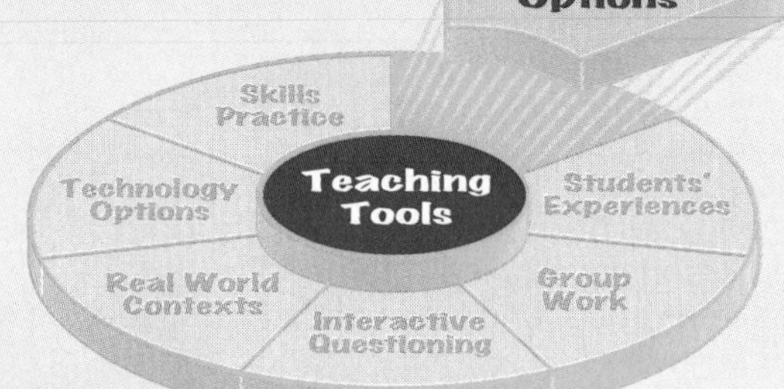

Assessment Options

The Prentice Hall Geometry Program provides you with many options. From these options, you may choose instructional materials and techniques appropriate for your students, or those necessary to meet your district's curriculum requirements. As the chart indicates, the program also supports your teaching efforts by offering you many choices for assessment.

ASSESSMENT OPTIONS

Assessment Support Materials	Chapter Project	11-1	11-2	11-3	11-4	11-5	11-6	Chapter End
Chapter Project	▲■●	▲■			▲■		▲■	▲■
Checkpoints				▲■●		▲■●		
Self-Assessment		▲■			▲■		▲■	▲■
Writing Assignment		▲■	▲	▲	▲■	▲	▲■	▲■●
Chapter Assessment								▲■●
Alternative Assessment		■	■	■	■	■	■	▲■●
Cumulative Review								●
Standardized Test Prep			▲■	▲■				▲■●
Computer Item Generator	Can be used to create custom-made practice or assessment at any time.							

▲ = Student Edition ■ = Teacher's Edition ● = Teaching Resources

Checkpoints

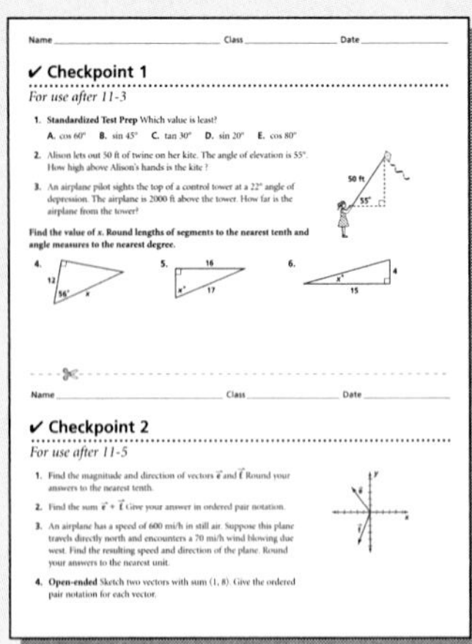
Checkpoint 1
For use after 11-3

Checkpoint 2
For use after 11-5

Alternative Assessment

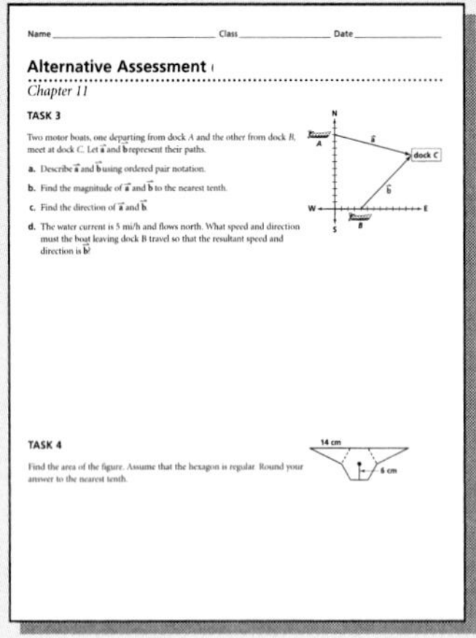
Alternative Assessment
Chapter 11

Chapter Assessment

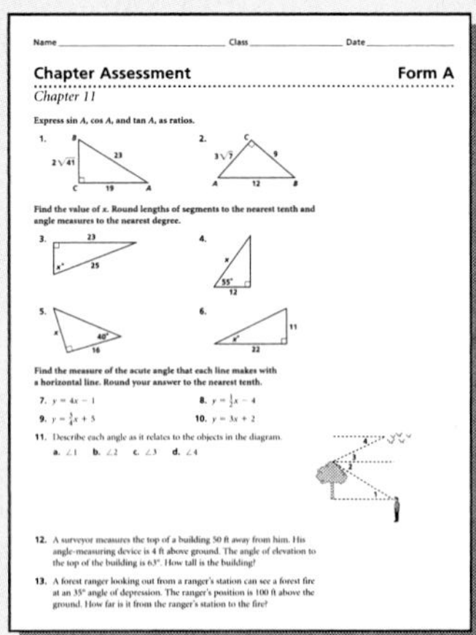
Chapter Assessment Form A
Chapter 11

Available in both Form A and Form B

Making the Right Connections

Mathematics is imbedded in nearly every walk of life. The National Council of Teachers of Mathematics (NCTM) encourages educators to recognize these connections and to emphasize them for the purpose of better educating students for success in life and in a global economy. The ***Connections*** chart below highlights these connections for Chapter 11.

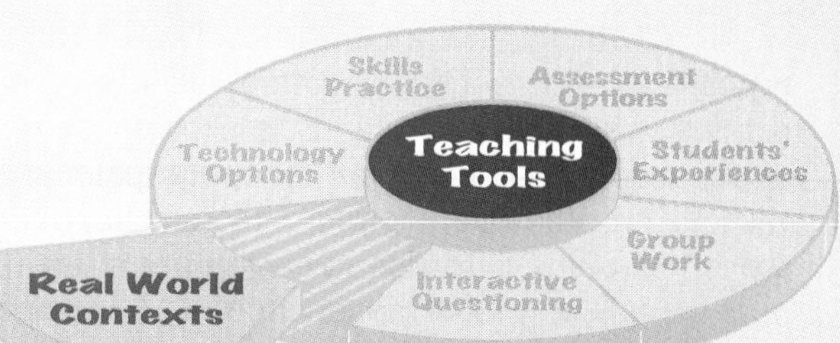

CONNECTIONS

Lesson	Interdisciplinary Connections	Career Prep	Other Real World Connections	Math Integration	NCTM Standards
Chapter Project	Physics Astronomy		Navigation Measuring Heights Stars	Algebra	Communication Connections Problem Solving
11-1	History Language Arts	Engineering Construction	Suspension Bridges Backpacking Pyramids Katoomba Scenic Railway	Algebra Coordinate Geometry	Algebra Connections Communication Problem Solving
11-2	Astronomy History	Farming	Escalators Agriculture Orbits of Planets Sports	Algebra	Algebra Connections Communication Problem Solving
11-3	Meteorology	Surveying Aviation Engineering	Navigation Blimp Flag Pole	Algebra Coordinate Geometry Data Analysis	Coordinate Geometry Connections Communication Problem Solving
11-4	Science	Aviation Veterinary Science	Air Travel Golden Retrievers Homing Pigeons Honeybees European Eel	Algebra Coordinate Geometry	Coordinate Geometry Connections Communication Problem Solving
11-5	Physics Meteorology	Aviation	Navigation Boat Travel Air Travel Hurricanes	Coordinate Geometry Probability Geometry in 3 Dimensions	Coordinate Geometry Connections Communication Problem Solving
11-6	History	Architecture Surveying Industrial Design	Castle del Monte Land Plots Measuring Devices	Geometry in 3 Dimensions	Connections Communication Problem Solving

CHAPTER 11 Right Triangle Trigonometry

CONNECTING TO PRIOR LEARNING Draw three noncongruent right triangles. Label the lengths of the legs on one, the lengths of the shorter leg and the hypotenuse on the second, and the lengths of the longer leg and hypotenuse on the third. Discuss how the Pythagorean Theorem can be used to find the length of the third side of each triangle. Then draw a fourth right triangle and label the length of one side and the measure of one angle. Discuss that, in this chapter, students will learn how to find the lengths of the other two sides from this information.

CULTURAL CONNECTIONS In ancient Egypt, every year after the Nile River overflowed its banks and washed out farm boundaries, the Egyptians fixed new boundaries by surveying. Surveying is the technique of measuring angles and triangles to determine the position of points or boundaries. A surveyor maps boundaries with an instrument called a transit.

INTERDISCIPLINARY CONNECTIONS Distances of the stars can be determined from trigonometric parallax. If the position of a nearby star is measured from two points on opposite sides of the Earth's orbit, a small angular displacement is

Technology Options

Prentice Hall Technology

Video

Video Field Trip 11, "Playing with Numbers," a look at how teachers apply trigonometry in the world of amusement parks

CHAPTER 11 Right Triangle Trigonometry

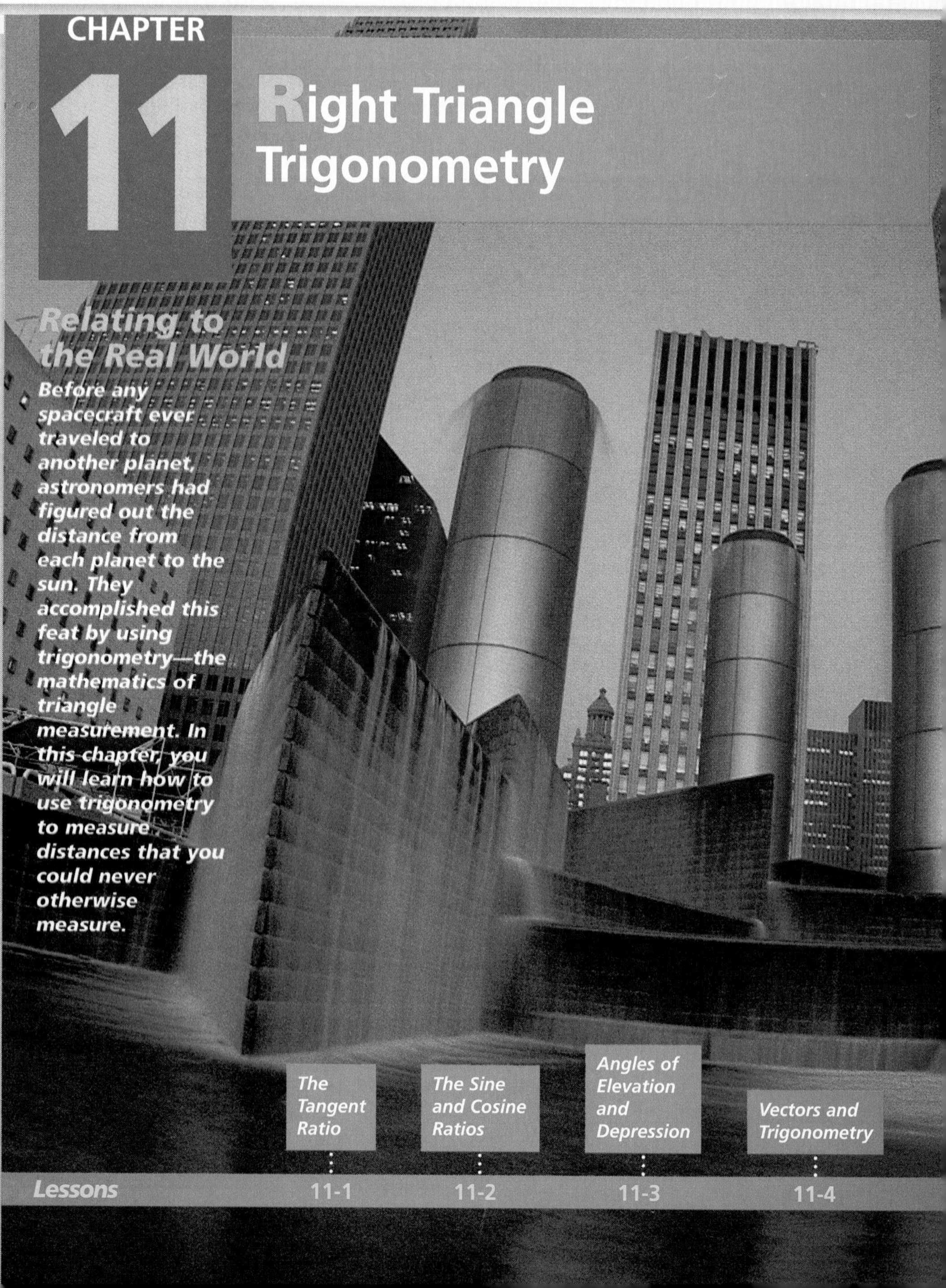

Relating to the Real World

Before any spacecraft ever traveled to another planet, astronomers had figured out the distance from each planet to the sun. They accomplished this feat by using trigonometry—the mathematics of triangle measurement. In this chapter, you will learn how to use trigonometry to measure distances that you could never otherwise measure.

seen. Using the Earth's orbit as the base line, the distance of the star can be found from the angular size of the parallax. Interested students might like to make a presentation on finding star distances.

ABOUT THE PROJECT Students construct clinometers and use them to measure the heights of objects in the school yard. Then students use their clinometers to measure the angle of elevation of the star Polaris.

Launching the Project

PROJECT NOTEBOOK Encourage students to keep all project-related materials in a separate folder or notebook. **See Chapter Project Manager and Scoring Rubric in Chapter Support File.**

- Ask students to give some examples of distances that must have been measured indirectly, such as the distance from Earth to Mercury and the distance to the center of the earth.
- Ask students to describe some fields in which indirect measurement is used. Examples might be surveying, astronomy, and navigation.

TRACKING THE PROJECT You may wish to have students read Finishing the Chapter Project on page 578 to help them get an overview of the project. Set benchmark deadlines for students to show their work in progress.

CHAPTER PROJECT

MEASURE FOR MEASURE

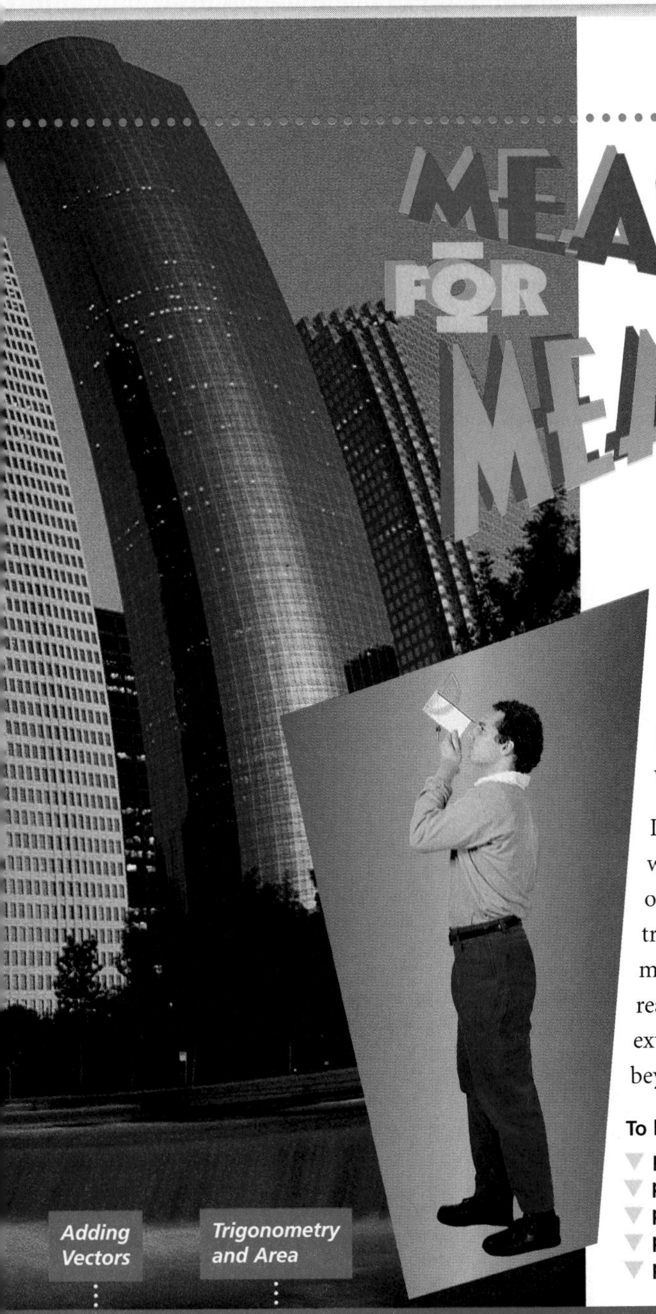

How do we know how far away the sun is without laying a tape measure across millions of miles? How do we know the mass of an electron when we can't even see one? Since ancient times, people have found ways to measure indirectly what they could not measure directly.

In your project for this chapter, you will construct an instrument similar to ones used by ancient astronomers and travelers. You will use your device to measure heights you cannot easily reach. You will see how mathematics can extend your power to measure things far beyond your physical grasp.

To help you complete the project:

Adding Vectors — 11-5

Trigonometry and Area — 11-6

Project Resources

Teaching Resources

Chapter Support File, Ch. 11
- Chapter Project Manager and Scoring Rubric

Transparencies

111

Using the Rubric

Sharing the scoring rubric for the project with your students will alert them to your expectations before they begin work on the project.

As students complete each Find Out question in the chapter, you may wish to have them evaluate their own work or a partner's work based on the scoring rubric. Students should have the opportunity to revise their work after it has been reviewed.

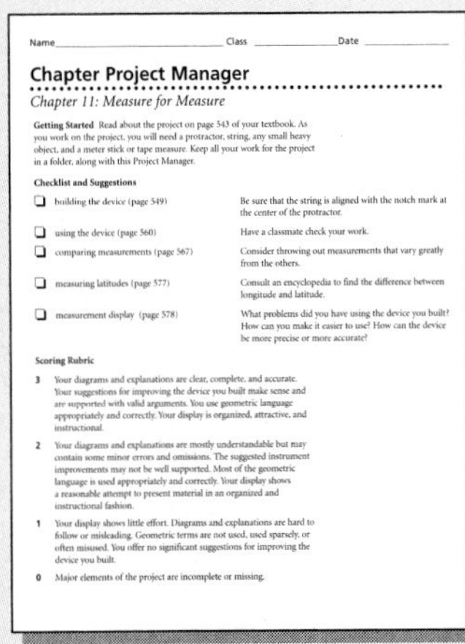

Name________ Class ________ Date ________

Chapter Project Manager

Chapter 11: Measure for Measure

Getting Started Read about the project on page 543 of your textbook. As you work on the project, you will need a protractor, string, any small heavy object, and a meter stick or tape measure. Keep all your work for the project in a folder, along with this Project Manager.

Checklist and Suggestions

❑ building the device (page 549)	Be sure that the string is aligned with the notch mark at the center of the protractor.
❑ using the device (page 560)	Have a classmate check your work.
❑ comparing measurements (page 567)	Consider throwing out measurements that vary greatly from the others.
❑ measuring latitudes (page 577)	Consult an encyclopedia to find the difference between longitude and latitude.
❑ measurement display (page 578)	What problems did you have using the device you built? How can you make it easier to use? How can the device be more precise or more accurate?

Scoring Rubric

3 Your diagrams and explanations are clear, complete, and accurate. Your suggestions for improving the device you built make sense and are supported with valid arguments. You use geometric language appropriately and correctly. Your display is organized, attractive, and instructional.

2 Your diagrams and explanations are mostly understandable but may contain some minor errors and omissions. The suggested instrument improvements may not be well supported. Most of the geometric language is used appropriately and correctly. Your display shows a reasonable attempt to present material in an organized and instructional fashion.

1 Your display shows little effort. Diagrams and explanations are hard to follow or misleading. Geometric terms are not used, used sparsely, or often misused. You offer no significant suggestions for improving the device you built.

0 Major elements of the project are incomplete or missing.

11-1 Teaching Notes

PROBLEM OF THE DAY

Find the area of the polygon.

3 square units

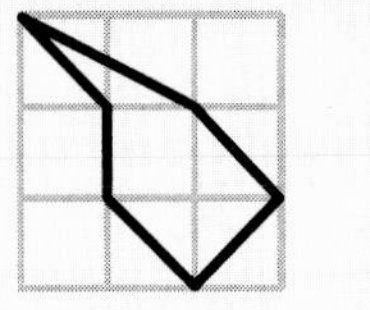

Problem of the Day is also available in Transparencies.

CONNECTING TO PRIOR KNOWLEDGE Draw two similar triangles and label the vertices. Have students use corresponding sides to write as many proportions as possible.

WORK TOGETHER

ERROR ALERT! Some students will confuse the leg opposite an angle with the leg adjacent to an angle. **Remediation:** Draw several right triangles in different positions. Have students practice naming the legs opposite and adjacent to each acute angle.

THINK AND DISCUSS

Help students see that because the tangent ratio is defined for the acute angles of a right triangle, the tangent ratio can be found for all angles between 0° and 90°. In more advanced courses, students may learn how to find the tangent ratio for angles with measures greater than 90°.

Lesson Planning Options

Prerequisite Skills

- Understanding of ratios
- Graphing lines in the coordinate plane

Assignment Options for Exercises On Your Own

To provide flexible scheduling, this lesson can be subdivided into parts.

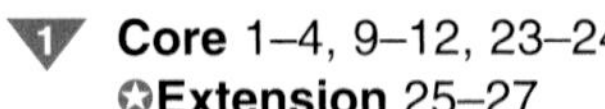

1. **Core** 1–4, 9–12, 23–24
   Extension 25–27

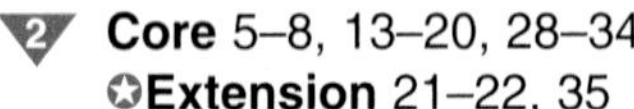

2. **Core** 5–8, 13–20, 28–34
   Extension 21–22, 35

Use Mixed Review to maintain skills.

Resources

Student Edition

Skills Handbook, p. 660
Extra Practice, p. 658
Glossary/Study Guide

Teaching Resources

Chapter Support File, Ch. 11
- Practice 11-1 (two worksheets)
- Reteaching 11-1
- Alternative Activity 11-1

Classroom Manager 11-1
Glossary, Spanish Resources

Transparencies
5, 11, 112, 115

544

What You'll Learn

- Calculating tangents of acute angles in right triangles
- Using tangents to determine side lengths in triangles

...And Why

To calculate distances that cannot be measured directly

What You'll Need

- protractor
- centimeter ruler
- calculator

1. Answers may vary slightly: 10°: 0.18, 20°: 0.36, 30°: 0.58, 40°: 0.84, 50°: 1.19, 60°: 1.73, 70°: 2.75, 80°: 5.67
2. The ratio is the same for all rt. △s with the given angle.

When? The word *trigonometry* was first used in a publication in 1595 by German clergyman and mathematician Bartholomaus Pitiscus (1561–1613).

Connections 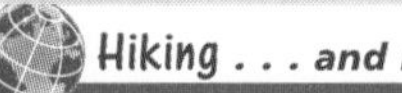 Hiking . . . and more

11-1 The Tangent Ratio

WORK TOGETHER

- Work in small groups. Your teacher will assign each group a different angle measure from the set $\{10°, 20°, \ldots, 80°\}$.
- Have each member of your group draw a right triangle containing the assigned angle. Make the triangles different sizes. Label your triangle $\triangle PAW$, where $\angle P$ is the assigned angle.
- Use a ruler to measure and label the lengths of the legs of $\triangle PAW$ to the nearest millimeter.

1. *Calculator* Use a calculator to compute the ratio $\frac{\text{leg opposite } \angle P}{\text{leg adjacent to } \angle P}$. Round your answer to two decimal places. See left.
2. Compare the results of Question 1 within your group. Make a **conjecture** based on your comparison. See left.
3. Compare your results with those of other groups. What do you notice? For each given angle, the ratio does not depend on the size of the △.

THINK AND DISCUSS

Part 1

Using the Tangent Ratio

The word *trigonometry* comes from the Greek words meaning "triangle measurement." In the Work Together, you made a discovery about a ratio of the lengths of sides of a right triangle. This ratio is called the tangent ratio.

tangent of $\angle A = \frac{\text{leg opposite } \angle A}{\text{leg adjacent to } \angle A}$

This equation can be abbreviated:

$$\tan A = \frac{\text{opposite}}{\text{adjacent}}$$

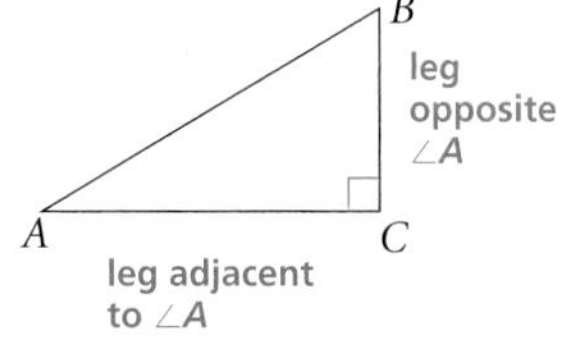

Example 1

Write the tangent ratios for $\angle U$ and $\angle T$.

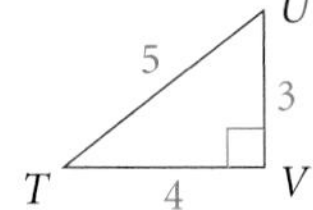

$$\tan U = \frac{\text{opposite}}{\text{adjacent}} = \frac{TV}{UV} = \frac{4}{3}$$

$$\tan T = \frac{\text{opposite}}{\text{adjacent}} = \frac{UV}{TV} = \frac{3}{4}$$

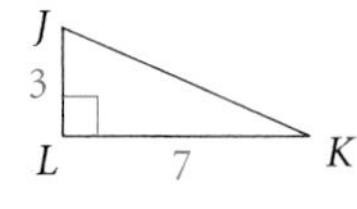

4. a. **Try This** Write the tangent ratios for $\angle K$ and $\angle J$. $\frac{3}{7}; \frac{7}{3}$
   b. How is $\tan K$ related to $\tan J$? $\tan K$ is the reciprocal of $\tan J$.

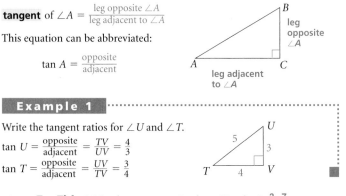

Example 1

Point out to students that one of the tangent ratios is greater than 1 and the other is less than 1. Ask students if this is always true of the acute angles of a right triangle.

Question 4 Ask students to describe the relationship between $\angle J$ and $\angle K$. Students should observe that the tangent ratios of complementary angles are reciprocals.

ALTERNATIVE ASSESSMENT To assess students' understanding of why tangent ratios for congruent angles are equal, ask them to use $\triangle TOW$ and $\triangle T'O'W'$ to explain why $\tan W = \tan W'$.

Example 2 Relating to the Real World 

ESL Students may be confused by this meaning of the term "compass" thinking that it refers to the instrument they use for constructions. If possible, bring in a directional compass and demonstrate how to take readings from it.

Make sure students understand how $\tan 86° = \frac{x}{50}$ was derived and why $x = 50(\tan 86°)$.

Help students check that their calculators are in degree mode before they use the tan key. Also show students how to use the table of trigonometric functions on page 674.

KINESTHETIC LEARNING If you have block scheduling or an extended class period, take students outside to measure distances indirectly using the method described in Example 2.

You discovered in the Work Together that the tangent ratio for a given acute angle does not depend on the size of the triangle. Why is this true? Consider the two right triangles shown below.

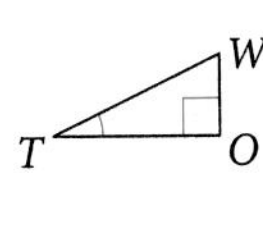

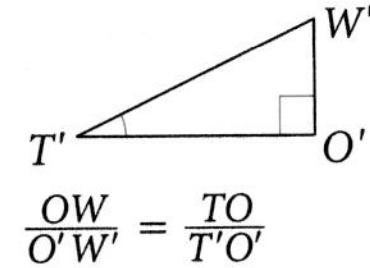

By the AA Similarity Postulate, the two triangles are similar.

$\frac{OW}{O'W'} = \frac{TO}{T'O'}$ Because the triangles are similar, these corresponding sides are in proportion.

$\frac{OW}{TO} = \frac{O'W'}{T'O'}$ Applying a property of proportions yields the tangent ratios for $\angle T$ and $\angle T'$.

You can use the tangent ratio to measure distances that would be difficult to measure directly.

Example 2 Relating to the Real World 

Hiking You are hiking in the Rocky Mountains. You come to a canyon and follow these steps to estimate its width.

Step 1: Point your compass at an object on the opposite edge of the canyon and note the reading.

Step 2: Turn 90° and walk off a distance in a straight line along the edge of the canyon.

Step 3: Turn and point the compass at the object again, taking another reading.

50 ft 1 86° not to scale

Using your readings in Steps 1 and 3, you find that $m\angle 1 = 86$. The distance you walked in Step 2 was 50 ft. What is the width of the canyon?

$\tan 86° = \frac{x}{50}$ Use the tangent ratio.

$x = 50(\tan 86°)$ Solve for x.

50 [×] 86 [TAN] [=] 715.03331

The canyon is about 700 ft wide.

GRAPHING CALCULATOR HINT

The keystrokes for a scientific calculator are shown at the right. On a graphing calculator, enter 50 [×] [TAN] 86 [ENTER].

Additional Examples

FOR EXAMPLE 1

Refer to the triangle in Example 1. If $UV = 5$ and $VT = 12$, find the tangent ratios for $\angle U$ and $\angle V$.

$\tan U = \frac{12}{5}$; $\tan T = \frac{5}{12}$

Discussion: *If $UV = 6$ and $UT = 10$, explain how to find the tangent ratios for $\angle U$ and $\angle V$.*

FOR EXAMPLE 2

Find the value of g to the nearest tenth.

11.8

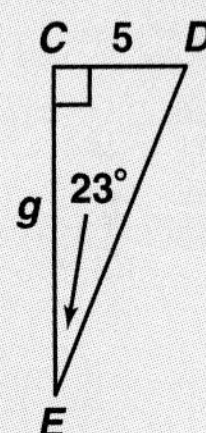

FOR EXAMPLE 3

Find the measure to the nearest degree of the acute angles that the line $y = 2x - 4$ makes with a horizontal line. 63°

Discussion: *Describe a line for which the measure of the acute angle that the line makes with a horizontal line is 90. Describe a line for which the measure of the acute angle that the line makes with a horizontal line is 0.*

Question 5 In part b, make sure students correctly set up the equation with *w* in the denominator. You might want to review how to solve such equations. In part c, students may write different equations depending on which angle they use.

Explain to students that given an acute angle, they can use the tan function to find the tangent ratio. Given the tangent ratio, they can use the $\tan^{-1}$ function to find the angle. Then help students locate the $\tan^{-1}$ key on their calculator and give several problems for them to solve using it.

CRITICAL THINKING Question 7 Students should discover that the tangent of a 45° angle is 1.

Example 3

Make sure students understand how $\angle A$ is formed. The choice of the horizontal line is arbitrary. Copy the diagram and draw several other right triangles using different horizontal lines. Show that $\tan A = \frac{\text{rise}}{\text{run}} = 3$.

EXTENSION Have students choose three acute angles whose sum is 180°. Ask them to show that $\tan A + \tan B + \tan C = \tan A \cdot \tan B \cdot \tan C$. Have them repeat the problem with three different angle measures satisfying the above conditions.

Technology Options

For Exercise 25, students may make the table and graph using graphing software or graphing calculators.

Prentice Hall Technology 

Software
- Secondary Math Lab Toolkit™
- Integrated Math Lab 43
- Computer Item Generator 11-1

CD-ROM
- Multimedia Geometry Lab 11

Internet
- See the Prentice Hall site. (http://www.phschool.com)

546

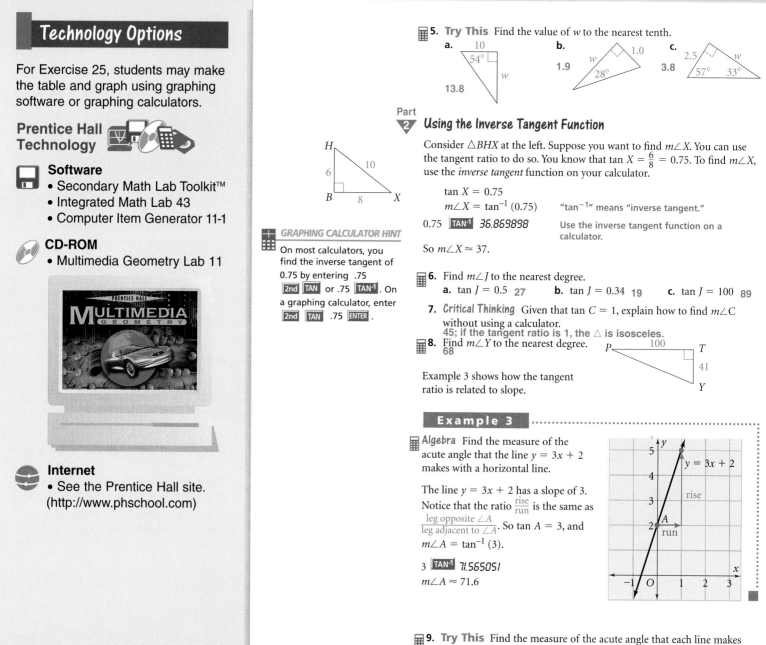

5. Try This Find the value of *w* to the nearest tenth.

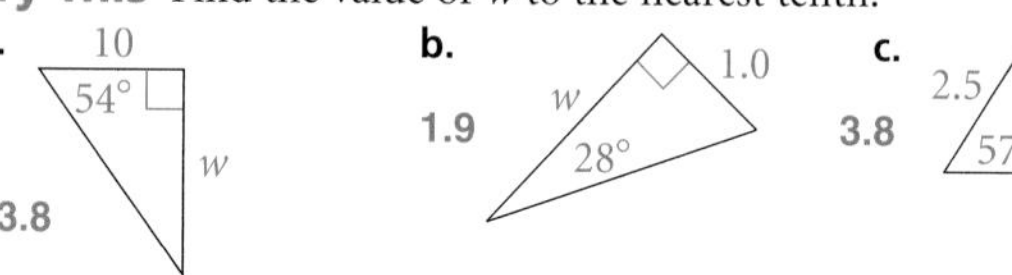

a. 13.8 b. 1.9 c. 3.8

Part 2

Using the Inverse Tangent Function

Consider $\triangle BHX$ at the left. Suppose you want to find $m\angle X$. You can use the tangent ratio to do so. You know that $\tan X = \frac{6}{8} = 0.75$. To find $m\angle X$, use the *inverse tangent* function on your calculator.

H, B, X; 6, 8, 10

$\tan X = 0.75$

$m\angle X = \tan^{-1}(0.75)$ "$\tan^{-1}$" means "inverse tangent."

0.75 TAN⁻¹ 36.869898 Use the inverse tangent function on a calculator.

So $m\angle X \approx 37$.

GRAPHING CALCULATOR HINT

On most calculators, you find the inverse tangent of 0.75 by entering .75 2nd TAN or .75 TAN⁻¹. On a graphing calculator, enter 2nd TAN .75 ENTER.

6. Find $m\angle J$ to the nearest degree.

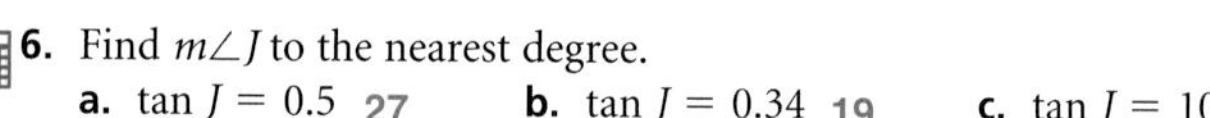

a. $\tan J = 0.5$ **27** b. $\tan J = 0.34$ **19** c. $\tan J = 100$ **89**

7. Critical Thinking Given that $\tan C = 1$, explain how to find $m\angle C$ without using a calculator.
45; if the tangent ratio is 1, the △ is isosceles.

8. Find $m\angle Y$ to the nearest degree. **68**

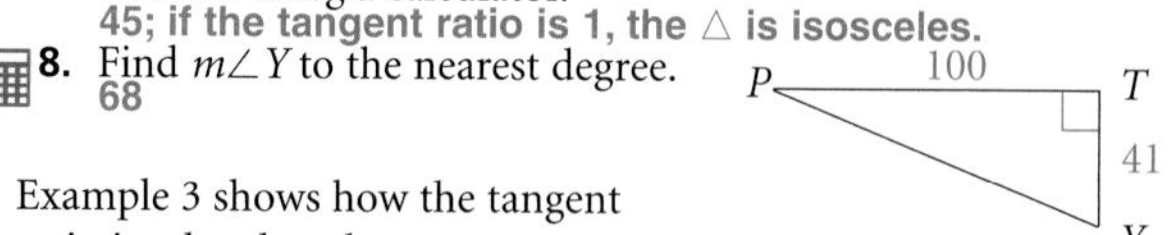

Example 3 shows how the tangent ratio is related to slope.

Example 3

Algebra Find the measure of the acute angle that the line $y = 3x + 2$ makes with a horizontal line.

The line $y = 3x + 2$ has a slope of 3. Notice that the ratio $\frac{\text{rise}}{\text{run}}$ is the same as $\frac{\text{leg opposite } \angle A}{\text{leg adjacent to } \angle A}$. So $\tan A = 3$, and $m\angle A = \tan^{-1}(3)$.

3 TAN⁻¹ 71.565051

$m\angle A \approx 71.6$

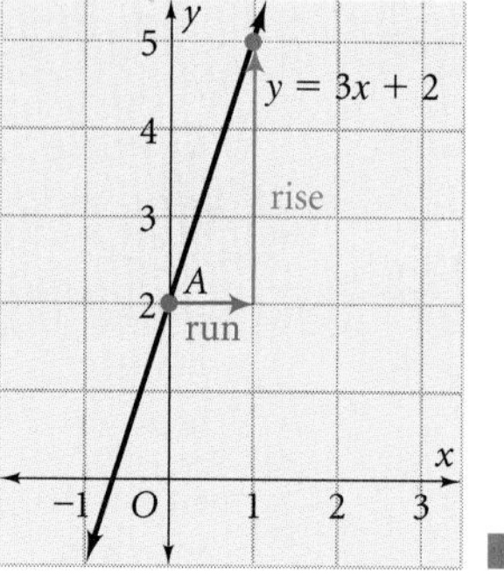

9. Try This Find the measure of the acute angle that each line makes with a horizontal line. Round your answer to the nearest tenth.

a. $y = \frac{1}{2}x + 6$ **26.6** b. $y = 6x - 1$ **80.5**

Exercises ON YOUR OWN

ERROR ALERT! Exercise 1–4 Some students may be confused by the right angle's being in different positions. **Remediation:** It may help some students to draw arrows from the vertices to the opposite sides. They may also want to highlight the hypotenuse so they do not confuse it with a leg.

Exercises 9–20 Ask students to write the equation they use to find the missing value. This will help you determine if students are having difficulty setting up the equation or solving it.

MAKING CONNECTIONS Exercise 21 The Katoomba Scenic Railway is 1020 feet long. Railway cars are attached to two steel cables 22 mm in diameter which are pulled by a 220-hp electric winding machine. The ride takes 1 min 40 sec. The railway carries about 420,000 passengers a year.

Exercises ON YOUR OWN

Express tan A and tan B as ratios.

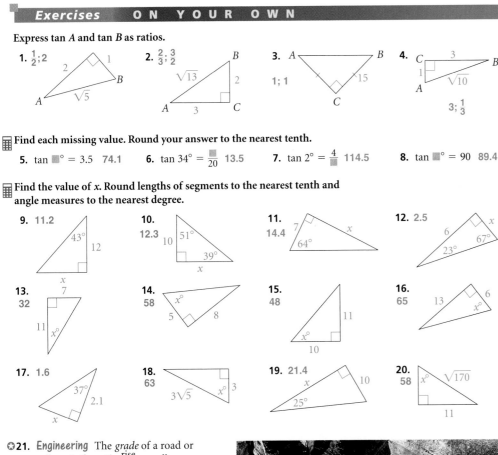

1. $\frac{1}{2}$; 2

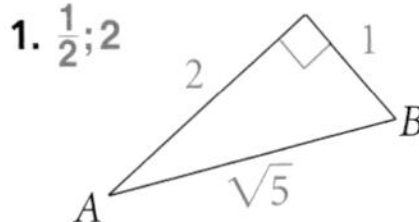

2. $\frac{2}{3}$; $\frac{3}{2}$

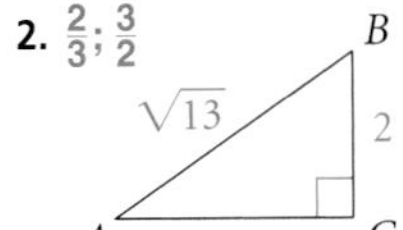

3. 1; 1

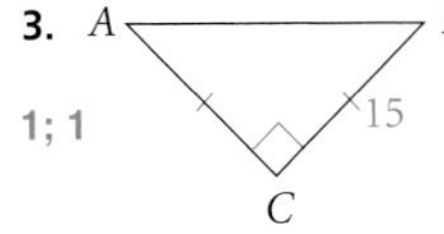

4. 3; $\frac{1}{3}$

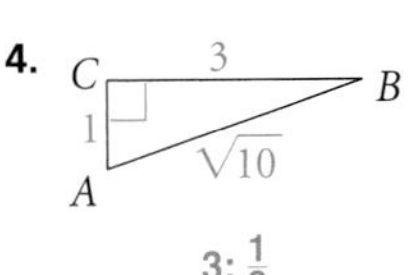

Find each missing value. Round your answer to the nearest tenth.

5. $\tan ■° = 3.5$ 74.1
6. $\tan 34° = \frac{■}{20}$ 13.5
7. $\tan 2° = \frac{4}{■}$ 114.5
8. $\tan ■° = 90$ 89.4

Find the value of x. Round lengths of segments to the nearest tenth and angle measures to the nearest degree.

9. 11.2

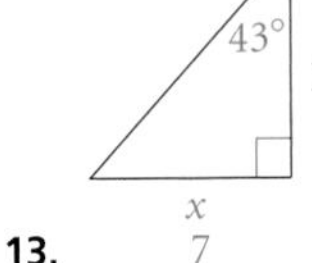

10. 12.3

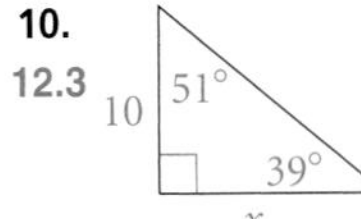

11. 14.4

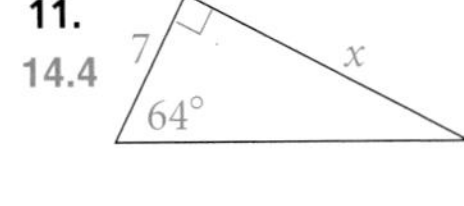

12. 2.5

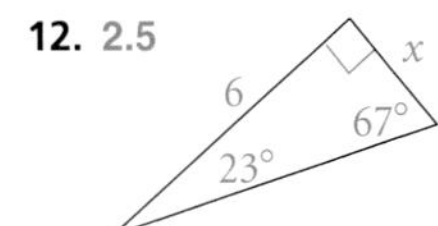

13. 32

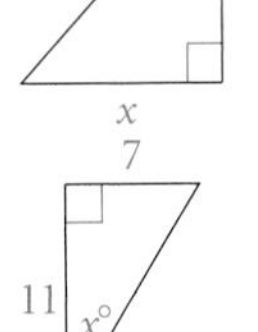

14. 58

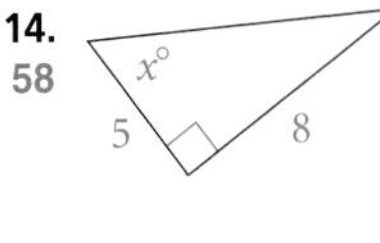

15. 48

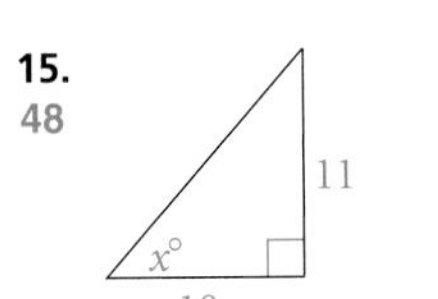

16. 65

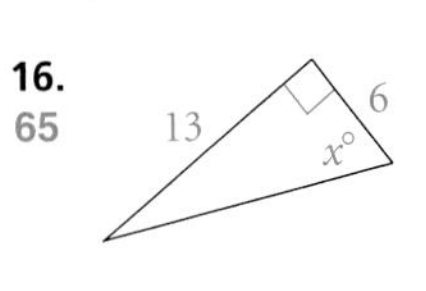

17. 1.6

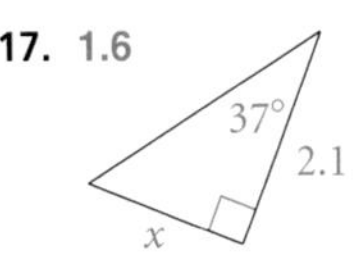

18. 63

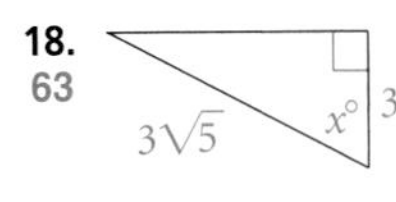

19. 21.4

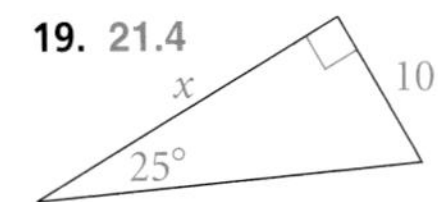

20. 58

x°, √170, 11

21. **Engineering** The *grade* of a road or railway is the ratio $\frac{\text{rise}}{\text{run}}$, usually expressed as a percent. For example, a railway with a grade of 5% rises 5 ft for every 100 ft of horizontal distance. The world's steepest railway is the Katoomba Scenic Railway in the Blue Mountains of Australia. It has a grade of 122%. At what angle does this railway go up? about 51°

22. The lengths of the diagonals of a rhombus are 2 in. and 5 in. Find the measures of the angles of the rhombus to the nearest degree. 44° and 136°

pages 547–549 On Your Own

25a.

x	tan $x°$
5	0.1
10	0.2
15	0.3
20	0.4
25	0.5
30	0.6
35	0.7
40	0.8
45	1

x	tan $x°$
50	1.2
55	1.4
60	1.7
65	2.1
70	2.7
75	3.7
80	5.7
85	11.4

b.

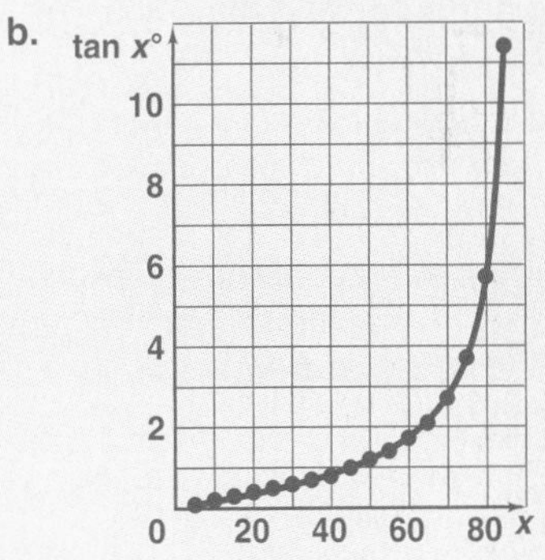

Exercise 23 Make sure students understand how the right triangle shown on the diagram is formed and how to find the length of its base.

WRITING Exercise 24 Suggest that students make a chart showing the tangent ratios for the special right triangles. They can add the sine and cosine ratios to the chart after the next lesson.

Exercise 26 Students should not assume that the two triangles shown are right triangles but, using the SAS Congruence Postulate, can easily deduce it.

OPEN-ENDED Exercise 35 You may want to share with students the following method for calculating Pythagorean triples: For any positive numbers x and y with $x > y$, the three numbers $x^2 - y^2$, $2xy$, and $x^2 + y^2$ form a Pythagorean triple.

Chapter Project **FIND OUT BY BUILDING** In this activity, students follow the directions to make a clinometer. You may want to make one ahead of time for the class to use as a model. Have students work in groups with all students making their own clinometers.

Find Out by Building

$\angle 1$ and $\angle 2$ are complementary, and $\angle 2$ and $\angle 3$ are complementary, so $m\angle 1 = m\angle 3$.

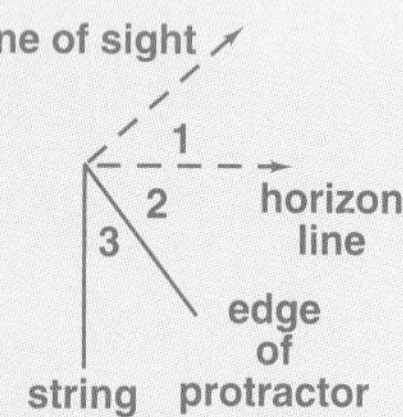

page 549 Mixed Review

36a. If a quadrilateral has ≅ diagonals, then the quadrilateral is a ▱.

37a. If a flag is a United States flag, then it contains the colors red, white, and blue.

38a. If diagonals of a quadrilateral are ⊥ bisectors of each other, then the quadrilateral is a rhombus.

39a. If you live on an island, then you live in Hawaii.

41a–b.

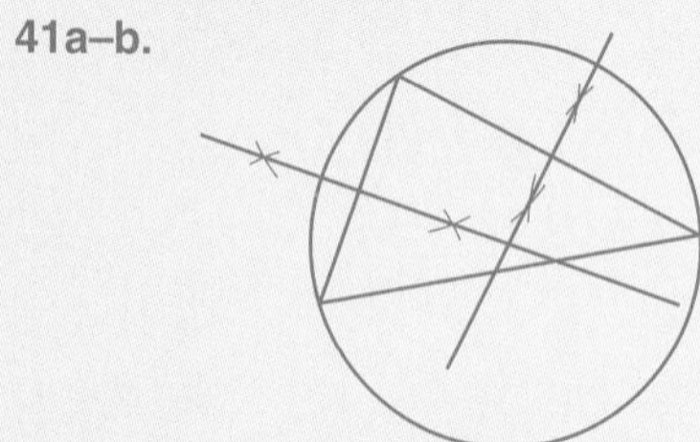

548

23. Pyramids All but two of the pyramids built by the ancient Egyptians have faces inclined at 52° angles. (The remaining two have faces inclined at $43\frac{1}{2}$°.) Suppose an archaeologist discovers the ruins of a pyramid. Most of the pyramid has eroded, but she is able to determine that the length of a side of the square base is 82 m. How tall was the pyramid, assuming its faces were inclined at 52°? Round your answer to the nearest meter. 52 m

52°

82 m

24. Writing Explain why $\tan 60° = \sqrt{3}$. Include a diagram with your explanation. For any length of the short leg s, the length of the leg opposite the 60° angle is $s\sqrt{3}$. So $\tan 60° = \frac{s\sqrt{3}}{s} = \sqrt{3}$.

25. a. Coordinate Geometry Use a calculator to complete the table of values at the right. Give your answers to the nearest tenth.

x	$\tan x°$
5	■
10	■
⋮	⋮
85	■

b. Plot the points $(x, \tan x°)$ on the coordinate plane. Connect them with a smooth curve. a–b. See margin p. 547.

c. What happens to the tangent ratio as the measure of the angle approaches 0? as it approaches 90? See below.

d. Use the graph to estimate each value. Estimates may vary slightly. Samples are given.

$\tan$ ■° = 7 82 $\qquad \tan 68° =$ ■ 2.5 $\qquad \tan$ ■° = 3.5 74

c. The ratio approaches 0; the ratio increases rapidly.

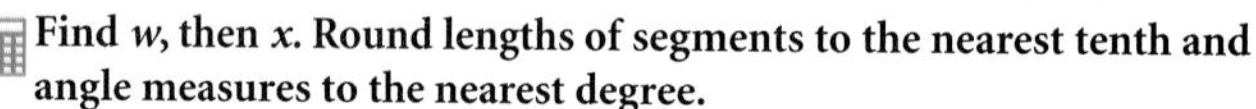

Find w, then x. Round lengths of segments to the nearest tenth and angle measures to the nearest degree.

26.

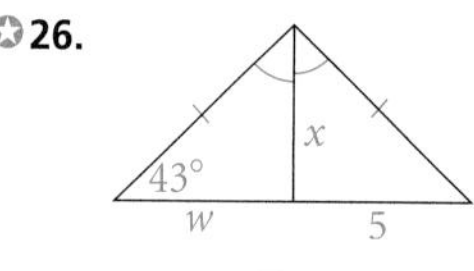

$w = 5$; $x = 4.7$

27.

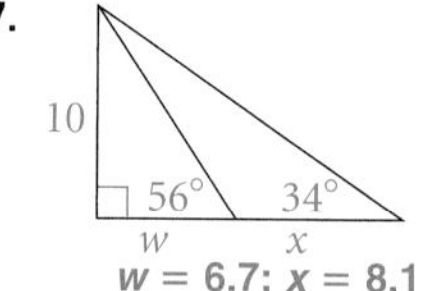

$w = 6.7$; $x = 8.1$

28.

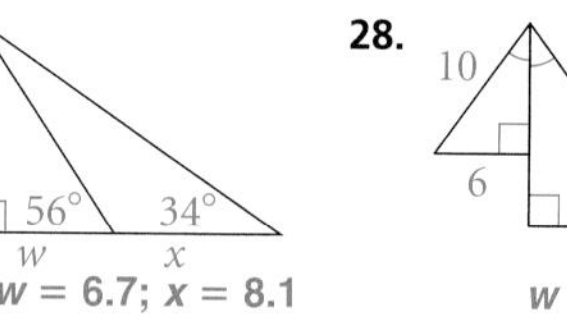

$w = 15$; $x = 53$

29.

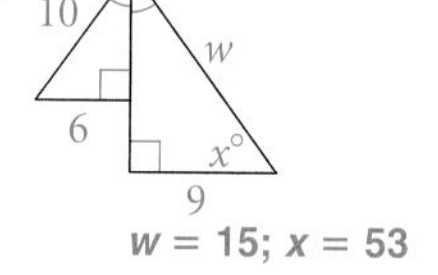

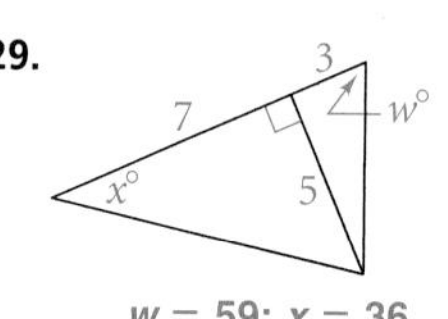

$w = 59$; $x = 36$

Algebra **Find the measure of the acute angle that each line makes with a horizontal line. Round your answer to the nearest tenth.**

30. $y = 5x - 7$ 78.7 **31.** $y = \frac{4}{3}x - 1$ 53.1 **32.** $3x - 4y = 8$ 36.9 **33.** $-2x + 3y = 6$ 33.7

34. Construction The roadway of a suspension bridge is supported by cables, as shown. The cables extend from the roadway to a point on the tower 50 ft above the roadway. The cables are set at 10-ft intervals along the roadway. Find the angles from the roadway to the top of the tower for the six cables nearest the tower. Round your answers to the nearest tenth.
78.7°, 68.2°, 59.0°, 51.3°, 45°, 39.8°

35. Open-ended Select a Pythagorean triple other than a multiple of 3, 4, 5. Find the measures of the acute angles of the right triangle associated with your Pythagorean triple. Round each measure to the nearest tenth.
Sample: 5, 12, 13 triple; 22.6 and 67.4

Exercises MIXED REVIEW

Exercises 36–39 Students review writing converses of statements and evaluating their truth values.

JOURNAL Suggest that students include diagrams with their explanations. You also might ask if their explanations are dependent on the angle's measuring 60.

GETTING READY FOR LESSON 11-2 These exercises prepare students to calculate sines and cosines of acute angles.

Wrap Up

THE BIG IDEA Ask students: *Describe a right triangle in which the tangent ratios of its two acute angles are equal.*

RETEACHING ACTIVITY Students calculate the measure of the acute angles that lines make with the *x*-axis. (Reteaching worksheet 11-1)

Chapter Project — *Find Out by Building*

Use the diagram at the right to build a *clinometer*, an angle-measuring device similar to instruments used by navigators for hundreds of years. You will need a protractor, string, tape, a piece of heavy cardboard, a small weight, and a straw.

To use the clinometer, look through the straw at the object you want to measure (the top of a building, for example). Have someone else read the angle marked by the hanging string.

- Why is the angle measure indicated by the string on the protractor the same as $m\angle 1$? (*Hint:* The string is always perpendicular to the horizon.) See margin p. 548.

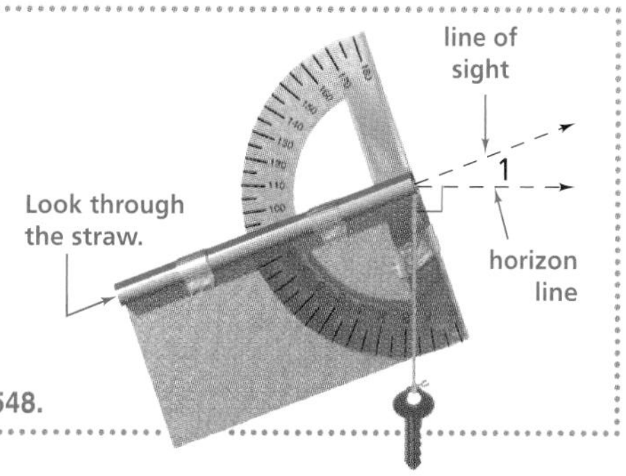

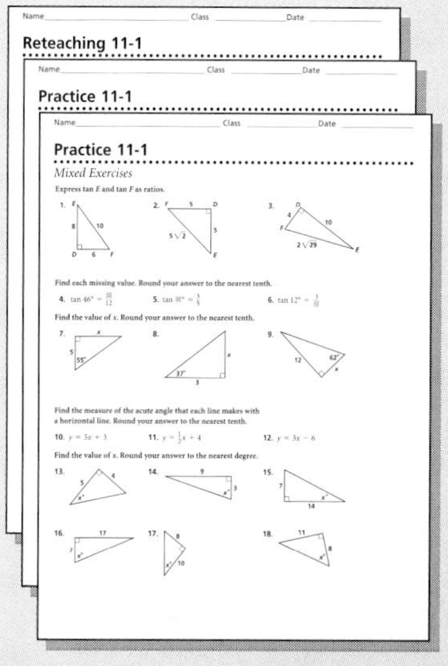

Exercises MIXED REVIEW

In Exercises 36–39: (a) Write the converse of each conditional. (b) Determine the truth value of the statement and its converse. 36a–39a. See margin p. 548.

36. If a quadrilateral is a parallelogram, then the quadrilateral has congruent diagonals. b. false; false
37. If a flag contains the colors red, white, and blue, then the flag is a United States flag. b. false; true
38. If a quadrilateral is a rhombus, then its diagonals are perpendicular bisectors of one another. b. true; true
39. If you live in Hawaii, then you live on an island. b. true; false

FOR YOUR JOURNAL

Two different right triangles each have an angle that measures 60. Explain why tan 60° is the same for both of these triangles.

40. *Locus* Sketch the locus of points in a plane that are equidistant from the diagonals of a kite. See right.

41. a. *Constructions* Draw a triangle. Then construct the perpendicular bisectors of two of its sides. a–b. See margin p. 548 for sample.
    b. Draw the circle that circumscribes the triangle. (*Hint:* The intersection of the perpendicular bisectors is its center.)

40.

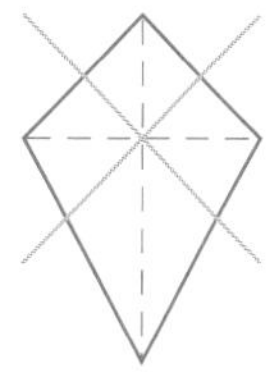

Getting Ready for Lesson 11-2

For each triangle, find the ratios $\frac{\text{leg opposite } \angle B}{\text{hypotenuse}}$ and $\frac{\text{leg adjacent to } \angle B}{\text{hypotenuse}}$.

42.

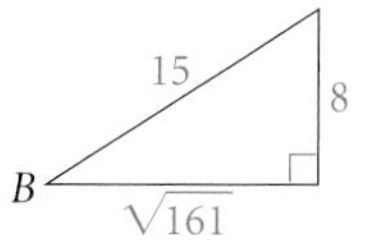

$\frac{8}{15}$; $\frac{\sqrt{161}}{15}$

43.

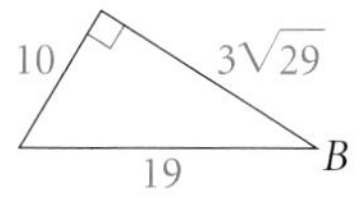

$\frac{10}{19}$; $\frac{3\sqrt{29}}{19}$

44.

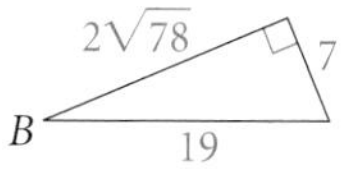

$\frac{7}{19}$; $\frac{2\sqrt{78}}{19}$

45.

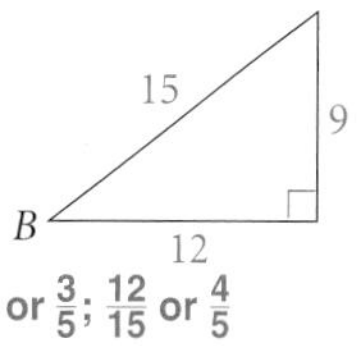

$\frac{9}{15}$ or $\frac{3}{5}$; $\frac{12}{15}$ or $\frac{4}{5}$

Lesson Quiz

Lesson Quiz is also available in Transparencies.

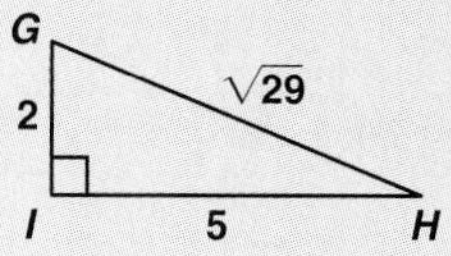

1. Write the tangent ratio for $\angle G$. $\frac{5}{2}$
2. Write the tangent ratio for $\angle H$. $\frac{2}{5}$

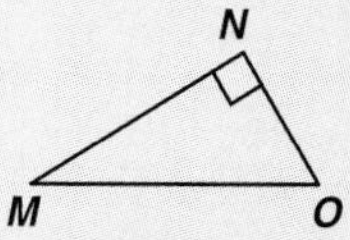

3. If $MN = 8$ and $m\angle M = 36$, find NO to the nearest tenth. 5.8
4. If $MO = \sqrt{65}$ and $NO = 4$, find $m\angle M$ to the nearest degree. 30

Math ToolboX

Students construct a triangle and calculate the sine of one of its acute angles. Then they manipulate the triangle and observe how this affects the sine. In the Extend, students repeat the investigation calculating the cosine and tangent ratios.

Using geometry software allows students to calculate the sine of an angle in many triangles without having to draw each triangle individually and measure the sides.

Check that students construct the figures correctly. When moving point D, $\overleftrightarrow{ED}$ should remain perpendicular to $\overrightarrow{AB}$. When moving point C, it should remain on $\overrightarrow{AE}$.

Conjecture

ERROR ALERT! Students may have trouble reading the table of trigonometric functions. **Remediation:** Explain what is represented by each column, row, and intersection of a row and column. Then have students practice finding different values in the table.

ADDITIONAL PROBLEM Have students make a table that shows $m\angle A$ and the ratios $\frac{\text{leg opposite } \angle A}{\text{hypotenuse}}$, $\frac{\text{leg adjacent to } \angle A}{\text{hypotenuse}}$, and $\frac{\text{leg opposite } \angle A}{\text{leg adjacent to } \angle A}$. Include values of 10, 20, 30, ..., 80 for $m\angle A$. Ask them to describe any relationships they observe among the ratios.

Materials and Manipulatives

- Geometry software

Transparencies
11

Math Toolbox page 550

Investigate

$m\angle A$	$\frac{DE}{AE}$
10	0.17
20	0.34
30	0.5
40	0.64
50	0.77
60	0.87
70	0.94
80	0.98

Extend

$m\angle A$	$\frac{DA}{AE}$
10	0.98
20	0.94
30	0.87
40	0.77
50	0.64
60	0.5
70	0.34
80	0.17

$m\angle A$	$\frac{DE}{DA}$
10	0.18
20	0.36
30	0.58
40	0.84
50	1.19
60	1.73
70	2.75
80	5.67

Math ToolboX — Technology

Exploring Trigonometric Ratios

Before Lesson 11-2

Work in pairs or small groups.

Construct

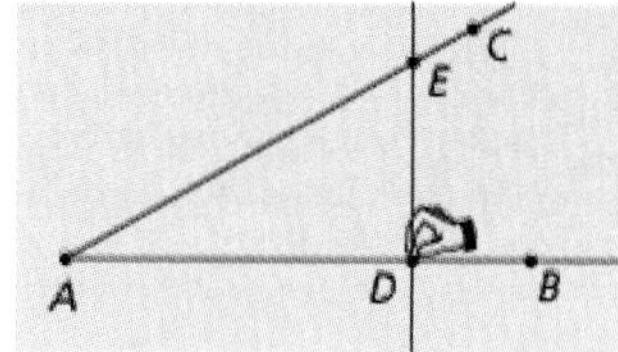

Use geometry software to construct $\overrightarrow{AB}$ and $\overrightarrow{AC}$ so that $\angle A$ is acute. Through a point D on $\overrightarrow{AB}$ construct a line perpendicular to $\overrightarrow{AB}$ that intersects $\overrightarrow{AC}$ in point E. Moving point D enlarges or reduces $\triangle ADE$. Moving point C changes the size of $\angle A$. **Check students' work.**

Investigate

hypotenuse
leg opposite ∠A
leg adjacent to ∠A

- Measure $\angle A$ and then find the lengths of the sides of the triangle. Calculate the ratio $\frac{\text{length of leg opposite } \angle A}{\text{length of hypotenuse}}$, which is $\frac{DE}{AE}$. **Check students' work.**
- Move point D to change the size of the right triangle without changing the size of $\angle A$. Does the ratio change as the size of the triangle changes? **no**
- Move point C to change the size of $\angle A$. How does the ratio change as the size of $\angle A$ changes? What value does the ratio approach as $m\angle A$ approaches 0? as $m\angle A$ approaches 90? **As $m\angle A$ increases, so does the ratio; 0; 1.**
- Make a table that shows $m\angle A$ and the ratio $\frac{\text{length of leg opposite } \angle A}{\text{length of hypotenuse}}$. In your table, include values of 10, 20, 30, . . . , 80 for $m\angle A$. **See margin for table.**

Conjecture

Compare your table with the table of trigonometric ratios on page 674. Do your values for $\frac{\text{length of leg opposite } \angle A}{\text{length of hypotenuse}}$ match the values in one of the columns of the table? What is the name of this ratio in the table?
The values match those in the sine column; sine.

Extend

- Repeat the investigation for the ratio $\frac{\text{length of leg adjacent to } \angle A}{\text{length of hypotenuse}}$, which is $\frac{DA}{EA}$.
- Repeat the investigation for the ratio $\frac{\text{length of leg opposite } \angle A}{\text{length of leg adjacent to } \angle A}$, which is $\frac{ED}{DA}$.
- **The smaller the measure of the angle, the closer DA is to AE; the values are between 0 and 1.**
- **The greater the measure of the angle, the greater is the ratio; the values are positive and can be arbitrarily large.**

See margin for tables.

11-2 Teaching Notes

PROBLEM OF THE DAY

A rectangle with integral side lengths has an area numerically equivalent to three times its perimeter. What are its possible dimensions? **7 by 42, 8 by 24, 9 by 18, 10 by 15, or 12 by 12**

Problem of the Day is also available in Transparencies.

CONNECTING TO PRIOR KNOWLEDGE Draw several right triangles. For each acute angle, have students find the ratios of the following lengths.

$\frac{\text{leg opposite the angle}}{\text{hypotenuse}}$ and $\frac{\text{leg adjacent the angle}}{\text{hypotenuse}}$

THINK AND DISCUSS

Example 1

Discuss with students each step taken to find the cosine and sine of the angles in parts a–d: writing the definition, identifying the legs, and substituting side lengths.

Make sure students understand why their observations in Question 1 can be expressed as $\sin x° = \cos (90 - x)°$ by having them substitute several values for x, noticing the angles are complements and the ratios are equal.

CRITICAL THINKING Questions 2–3 Ask students to summarize what they learned about the sine and cosine ratios of the special right triangles.

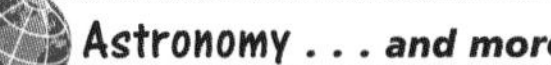

11-2 The Sine and Cosine Ratios

What You'll Learn

- Calculating sines and cosines of acute angles in right triangles
- Using sine and cosine to determine unknown measures in right triangles

...And Why

To understand how the ratios were used to calculate the sizes of orbits of planets

What You'll Need

- centimeter ruler
- graph paper
- calculator

THINK AND DISCUSS

The tangent ratio, as you've seen, involves both legs of a right triangle. The sine and cosine ratios involve one leg and the hypotenuse.

sine of $\angle A = \frac{\text{leg opposite } \angle A}{\text{hypotenuse}}$

cosine of $\angle A = \frac{\text{leg adjacent to } \angle A}{\text{hypotenuse}}$

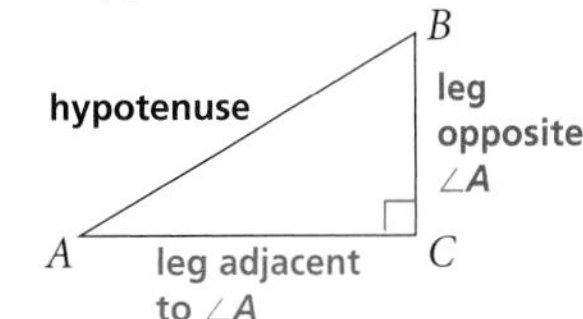

These equations can be abbreviated:

$$\sin A = \frac{\text{opposite}}{\text{hypotenuse}}$$

$$\cos A = \frac{\text{adjacent}}{\text{hypotenuse}}$$

Example 1

Refer to $\triangle GRT$ at the right. Find each ratio.

a. $\sin T$ **b.** $\cos T$
c. $\sin G$ **d.** $\cos G$

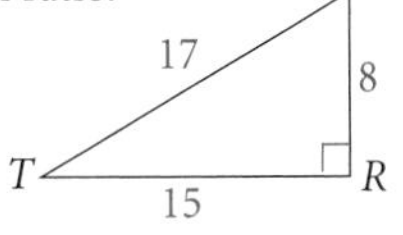

a. $\sin T = \frac{\text{opposite}}{\text{hypotenuse}} = \frac{8}{17}$ **b.** $\cos T = \frac{\text{adjacent}}{\text{hypotenuse}} = \frac{15}{17}$

c. $\sin G = \frac{\text{opposite}}{\text{hypotenuse}} = \frac{15}{17}$ **d.** $\cos G = \frac{\text{adjacent}}{\text{hypotenuse}} = \frac{8}{17}$

1a. The leg adjacent to $\angle G$ is opposite $\angle T$.

1. a. Explain why $\sin T = \cos G = \frac{8}{17}$. **See left.**

b. The word *cosine* is derived from the words *co*mplement's *sine*. Which angle in $\triangle GRT$ is the complement of $\angle T$? of $\angle G$? **$\angle G$; $\angle T$**

c. Explain why the derivation of the word *cosine* makes sense. **The cosine of an angle is the sine of the complementary angle.**

Another way of describing the pattern in Question 1 is to say that $\sin x° = \cos (90 - x)°$ for values of x between 0 and 90. This type of equation is called an **identity** because it is always true for the allowed values of the variable. You will discover other identities in the exercises.

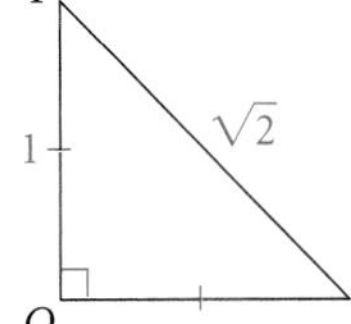

2. Refer to $\triangle PQR$ at the left. Find each ratio.

a. $\sin P$ $\frac{\sqrt{2}}{2}$ **b.** $\cos P$ $\frac{\sqrt{2}}{2}$
c. $\sin R$ $\frac{\sqrt{2}}{2}$ **d.** $\cos R$ $\frac{\sqrt{2}}{2}$

3. Refer to $\triangle TSN$ at the right. Find each ratio.

a. $\sin S$ $\frac{\sqrt{3}}{2}$ **b.** $\cos S$ $\frac{1}{2}$
c. $\sin T$ $\frac{1}{2}$ **d.** $\cos T$ $\frac{\sqrt{3}}{2}$

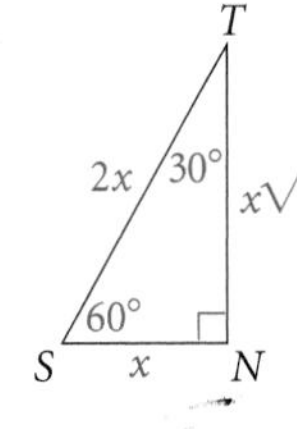

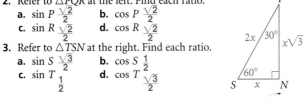

Lesson Planning Options

Prerequisite Skills

- Understanding of ratios

Assignment Options for Exercises On Your Own

Core 1–16, 20–23
✪Extension 17–19

Use Mixed Review to maintain skills.

Resources

Student Edition

Skills Handbook, p. 660
Extra Practice, p. 658
Glossary/Study Guide

Teaching Resources

Chapter Support File, Ch. 11
- Practice 11-2 (two worksheets)
- Reteaching 11-2
- Alternative Activity 11-2

Classroom Manager 11-2
Glossary, Spanish Resources

Transparencies
5, 11, 112, 116

AUDITORY LEARNING Some students will confuse the definitions of the three trigonometric ratios. Suggest the mnemonic device **SOHCAHTOA**, or **S**ome **O**ld **H**orse **C**aught **A** **H**orse **T**aking **O**ats **A**way for: **S**ine equals **O**pposite over **H**ypotenuse; **C**osine equals **A**djacent over **H**ypotenuse; **T**angent equals **O**pposite over **A**djacent.

VISUAL LEARNING Have students make a poster which displays a right triangle and the three trigonometric ratios.

Example 2 **Relating to the Real World** 

Make sure students understand the diagram. Begin by asking them to identify the two planets and to describe what each side of the triangle represents. Then have them identify which side of the triangle is the hypotenuse and which leg is opposite ∠1.

Students may want to calculate how many miles Mercury is from the sun by multiplying 0.38 by 93 million miles.

CRITICAL THINKING Ask students to describe two ways to find the distance from Earth to Mercury.

ERROR ALERT! **Question 5b and c** Some students will have difficulty solving equations with x in the denominator.
Remediation: Review techniques for solving, such as cross multiplying, multiplying by the LCD, or taking the reciprocal of both sides.

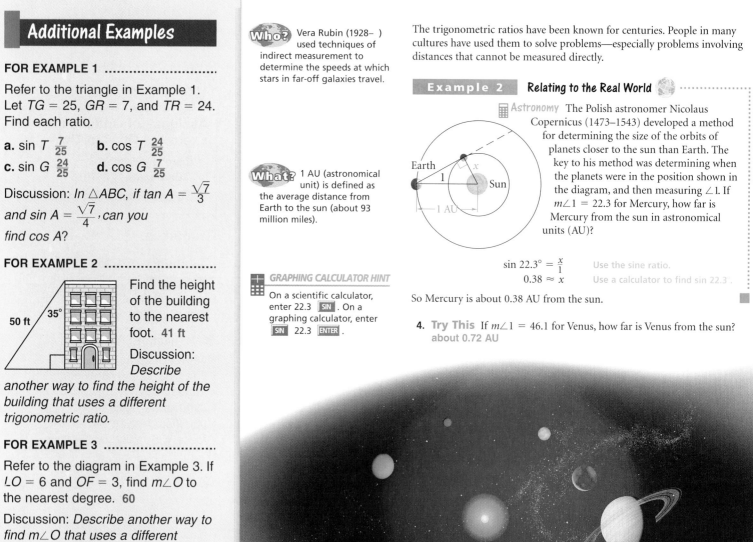

Additional Examples

FOR EXAMPLE 1

Refer to the triangle in Example 1. Let $TG = 25$, $GR = 7$, and $TR = 24$. Find each ratio.

a. $\sin T$ $\frac{7}{25}$ **b.** $\cos T$ $\frac{24}{25}$
c. $\sin G$ $\frac{24}{25}$ **d.** $\cos G$ $\frac{7}{25}$

Discussion: *In △ABC, if* $\tan A = \frac{\sqrt{7}}{3}$ *and* $\sin A = \frac{\sqrt{7}}{4}$, *can you find cos A?*

FOR EXAMPLE 2

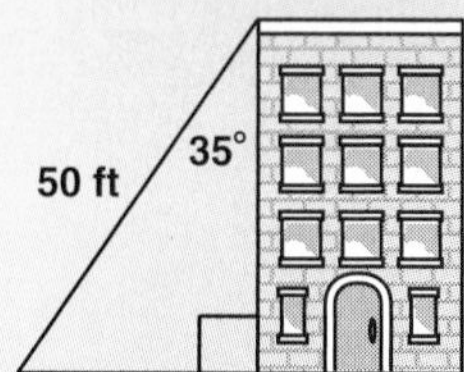

Find the height of the building to the nearest foot. 41 ft

Discussion: *Describe another way to find the height of the building that uses a different trigonometric ratio.*

FOR EXAMPLE 3

Refer to the diagram in Example 3. If $LO = 6$ and $OF = 3$, find $m\angle O$ to the nearest degree. 60

Discussion: *Describe another way to find m∠O that uses a different trigonometric ratio.*

Who? Vera Rubin (1928–) used techniques of indirect measurement to determine the speeds at which stars in far-off galaxies travel.

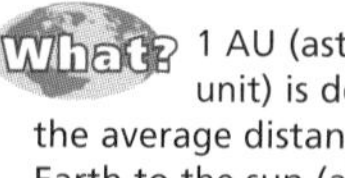

What? 1 AU (astronomical unit) is defined as the average distance from Earth to the sun (about 93 million miles).

GRAPHING CALCULATOR HINT

On a scientific calculator, enter 22.3 SIN. On a graphing calculator, enter SIN 22.3 ENTER.

The trigonometric ratios have been known for centuries. People in many cultures have used them to solve problems—especially problems involving distances that cannot be measured directly.

Example 2 **Relating to the Real World** 

Astronomy The Polish astronomer Nicolaus Copernicus (1473–1543) developed a method for determining the size of the orbits of planets closer to the sun than Earth. The key to his method was determining when the planets were in the position shown in the diagram, and then measuring ∠1. If $m\angle 1 = 22.3$ for Mercury, how far is Mercury from the sun in astronomical units (AU)?

Earth, 1, x, Sun, 1 AU

$\sin 22.3° = \frac{x}{1}$ Use the sine ratio.
$0.38 \approx x$ Use a calculator to find sin 22.3°.

So Mercury is about 0.38 AU from the sun.

4. **Try This** If $m\angle 1 = 46.1$ for Venus, how far is Venus from the sun? about 0.72 AU

Example 3

Check that students know where the $\cos^{-1}$ and $\sin^{-1}$ keys are on their calculators. If their calculators do not have parentheses, they should use the following keystrokes: 5 [÷] 8 [=] [COS⁻¹].

WORK TOGETHER

Question 7 Some students may have difficulty visualizing each triangle. You may want to provide a handout for students with four copies of the figure. On each copy they can outline a different triangle.

ALGEBRA Questions 8 and 9 Suggest that students make 10-degree increments on the *x*- and *y*-axes.

TRANSFORMATIONS Question 10 Ask students to describe any symmetries the curves or parts of the curves have.

5. Find the value of *x* to the nearest tenth.

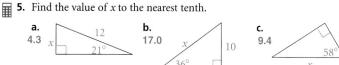

a. 4.3 b. 17.0 c. 9.4

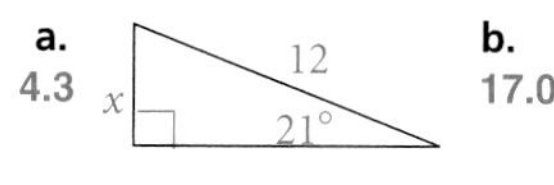

x
10
36°

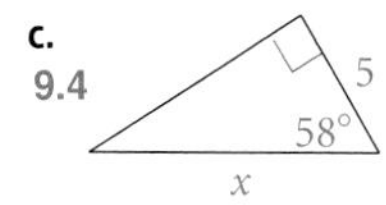

When you know the lengths of a leg and the hypotenuse of a right triangle, you can use inverse sine or inverse cosine functions on a calculator to find the measures of the acute angles.

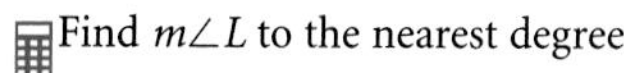

Example 3

Find $m\angle L$ to the nearest degree.

$\cos L = \frac{2.5}{4.0}$ Use the cosine ratio.

$= \frac{5}{8}$ Simplify the right side.

$m\angle L = \cos^{-1}\left(\frac{5}{8}\right)$ Use inverse cosine.

[(] 5 [÷] 8 [)] [COS⁻¹] 51.317813

So $m\angle L \approx 51$.

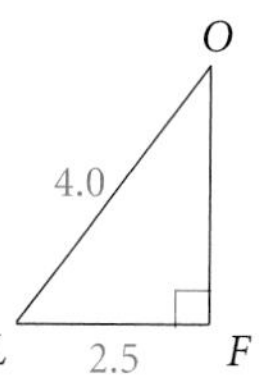

6. **Try This** Find the value of *x*. Round your answer to the nearest degree.

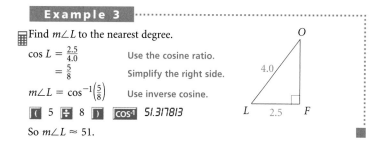

a. 41 b. 68 c. 59

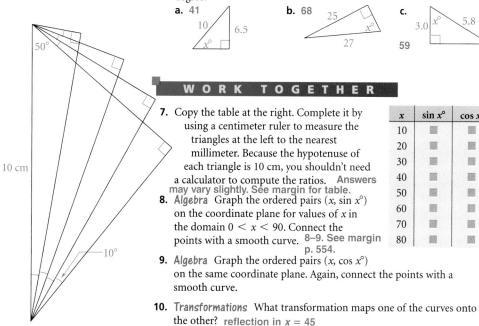

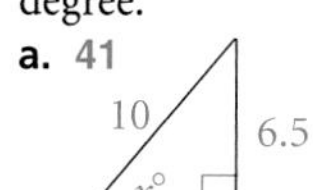

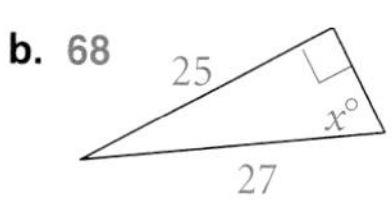

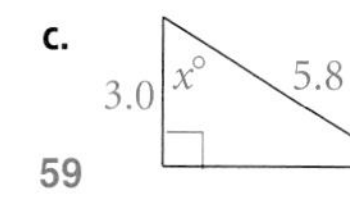

50°

10 cm

10°

WORK TOGETHER

7. Copy the table at the right. Complete it by using a centimeter ruler to measure the triangles at the left to the nearest millimeter. Because the hypotenuse of each triangle is 10 cm, you shouldn't need a calculator to compute the ratios. Answers may vary slightly. See margin for table.

x	$\sin x°$	$\cos x°$
10	■	■
20	■	■
30	■	■
40	■	■
50	■	■
60	■	■
70	■	■
80	■	■

8. **Algebra** Graph the ordered pairs $(x, \sin x°)$ on the coordinate plane for values of *x* in the domain $0 < x < 90$. Connect the points with a smooth curve. 8–9. See margin p. 554.

9. **Algebra** Graph the ordered pairs $(x, \cos x°)$ on the same coordinate plane. Again, connect the points with a smooth curve.

10. **Transformations** What transformation maps one of the curves onto the other? reflection in $x = 45$

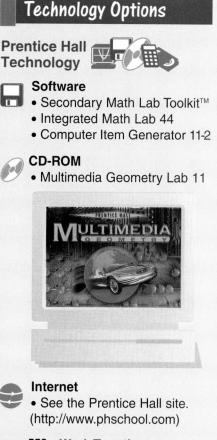

Technology Options

Prentice Hall Technology

Software
- Secondary Math Lab Toolkit™
- Integrated Math Lab 44
- Computer Item Generator 11-2

CD-ROM
- Multimedia Geometry Lab 11

Internet
- See the Prentice Hall site. (http://www.phschool.com)

page 553 Work Together

7.

x	$\sin x°$	$\cos x°$
10	0.17	0.98
20	0.34	0.94
30	0.50	0.87
40	0.64	0.77
50	0.77	0.64
60	0.87	0.50
70	0.94	0.34
80	0.98	0.17

Exercises ON YOUR OWN

WRITING Exercise 5 Students may want to support their explanations with examples. Suggest they draw a right triangle with one acute angle measure and one side length labeled and show how to find the missing angle measure and side lengths.

ALTERNATIVE ASSESSMENT Exercises 6–14 Use the following activity to help you assess students' ability to apply the trigonometric ratios. Choose one of the triangles from these exercises. Have students find the missing angle measure and side lengths in two different ways, if possible.

STANDARDIZED TEST TIP Exercise 15 Students are less likely to confuse the legs if they first draw a right triangle and label the vertices *A*, *B*, and *C*. Since the side opposite vertex B is $\overline{AC}$, the hypotenuse, the only possible answer choices have $\overline{AC}$ in the denominator.

ESL Exercise 16 Make sure students understand what it means for "the roof to overhang the edge of the silo by 1 ft." If possible, use physical models of a cylinder and a cone to illustrate.

CONNECTING TO STUDENTS' WORLD Exercise 16 Have students make a model of the silo. Then have them approximate the radius and the slant height of the conical roof. Using this information, have them approximate the slope of the roof.

8–9.

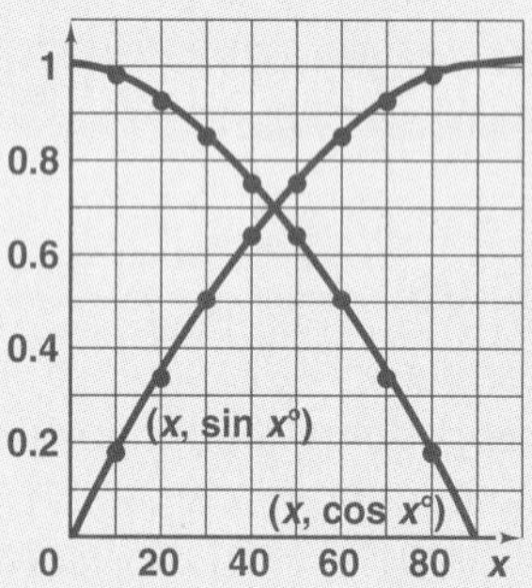

pages 554–555 On Your Own

5. Yes; the other acute angle is the complement of the 1st. You can use the sine, cosine, and tangent ratios to find the length of the other sides.

17. $\sin A \div \cos A$

$= \frac{\text{opposite}}{\text{hypotenuse}} \div \frac{\text{adjacent}}{\text{hypotenuse}}$

$= \frac{\text{opposite}}{\text{adjacent}} = \tan A$

for any $\angle A$ $0 < m\angle A < 90$

18. For any value of *x* between 0 and 90: $(\sin x°)^2 + (\cos x°)^2 =$

$\left(\frac{\text{opposite}}{\text{hypotenuse}}\right)^2 + \left(\frac{\text{adjacent}}{\text{hypotenuse}}\right)^2 =$

$\frac{(\text{opposite})^2 + (\text{adjacent})^2}{(\text{hypotenuse})^2} =$

(by the Pythagorean Theorem)

$\frac{(\text{hypotenuse})^2}{(\text{hypotenuse})^2} = 1$

Exercises ON YOUR OWN

Express sin *M* and cos *M* as ratios.

1. $\frac{7}{25}, \frac{24}{25}$

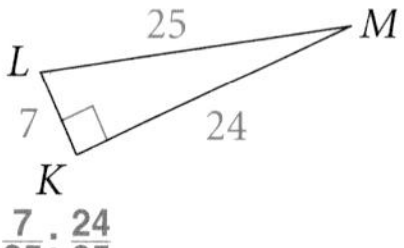

2. $\frac{4\sqrt{2}}{9}, \frac{7}{9}$

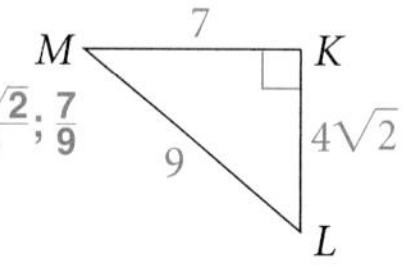

3. $\frac{1}{2}, \frac{\sqrt{3}}{2}$

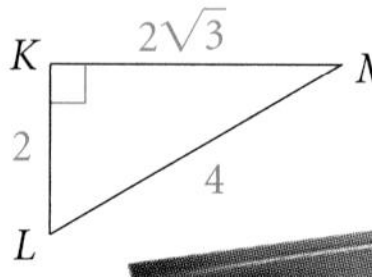

4. *Escalators* The world's longest escalator is in the subway system of St. Petersburg, Russia. The escalator has a vertical rise of 195 ft 9.5 in. and rises at an angle of 10.4°. How long is the escalator? Round your answer to the nearest foot. 1085 ft

5. *Writing* Leona Halfmoon said that if she had a diagram that showed the measure of one acute angle and the length of one side of a right triangle, she could find the measure of the other acute angle and the lengths of the other sides. Is she right? Explain. See margin.

Find the value of *x*. Round lengths of segments to the nearest tenth and angle measures to the nearest degree.

6. 11.5

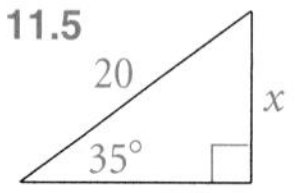

7. 8.3

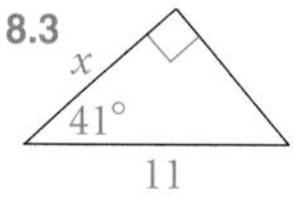

8. 17.9

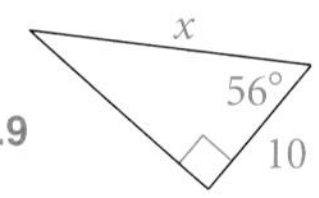

9. 21

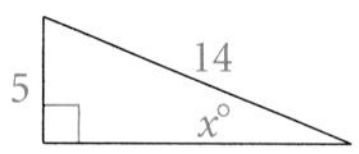

10. 51

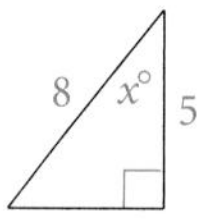

11. 46

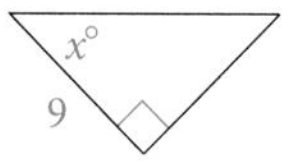

12. 66

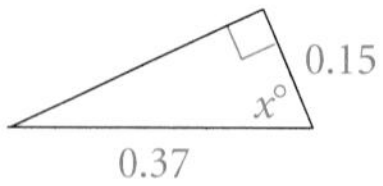

13. 106.5

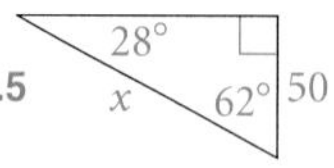

14. 3.4

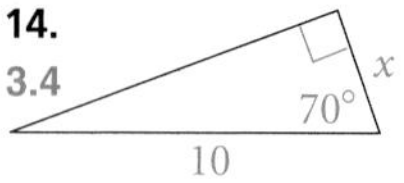

15. *Standardized Test Prep* In $\triangle ABC$, $m\angle B = 90$. Find sin *C*. D

A. $\frac{BC}{AC}$ B. $\frac{BC}{AB}$ C. $\frac{AB}{BC}$ D. $\frac{AB}{AC}$ E. $\frac{AC}{AB}$

16. *Agriculture* Jane is planning to build a new grain silo with a radius of 15 ft. She reads that the recommended slope of the roof is 22°. She wants the roof to overhang the edge of the silo by 1 ft. What should the slant height of the roof be? Give your answer in feet and inches. about 17 ft 3 in.

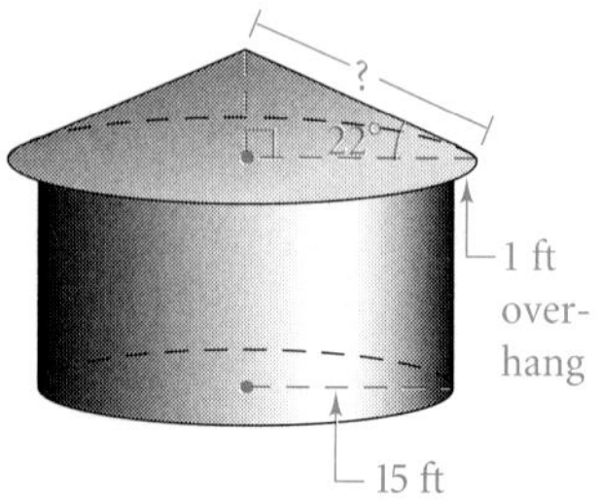

17. *Critical Thinking* Use what you know about trigonometric ratios to show that the following equations is an identity. See margin.

$$\tan A = \sin A \div \cos A$$

EXTENSION Exercise 18 Have students use the definitions of sine and cosine and the Pythagorean Theorem to prove their conjectures are true.

Exercises MIXED REVIEW

Exercise 28 Students are given the circumferences of two spheres and asked to find the ratio of their volumes. Point out that the simplified ratio of the volumes does not contain π.

GETTING READY FOR LESSON 11-3 These exercises prepare students to identify and use angles of elevation and depression to solve problems.

Wrap Up

THE BIG IDEA Ask students: *Explain how you decide which trigonometric ratio to use to solve a problem.*

RETEACHING ACTIVITY Students use sine and cosine to determine unknown measures in right triangles. (Reteaching worksheet 11-2)

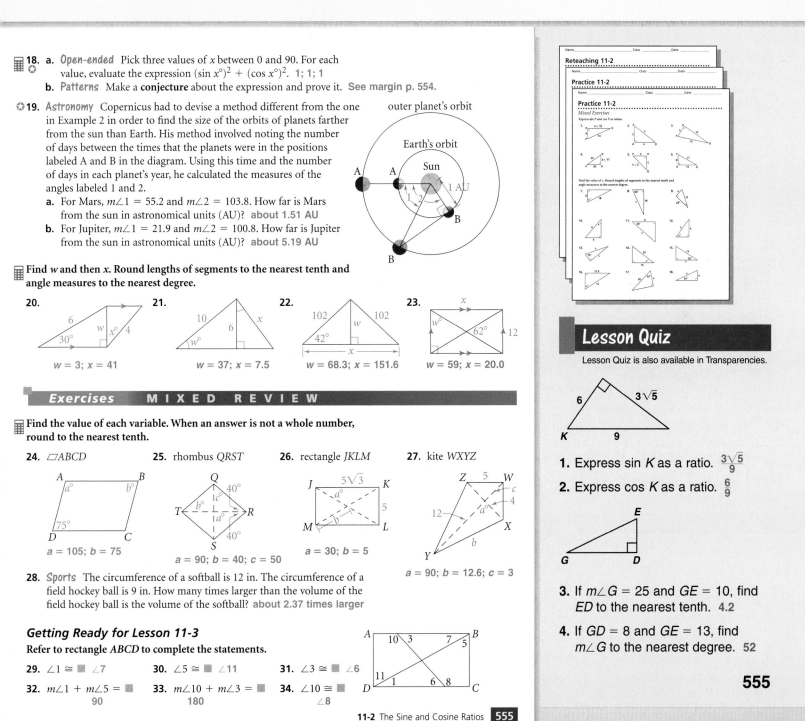

18. a. *Open-ended* Pick three values of x between 0 and 90. For each value, evaluate the expression $(\sin x°)^2 + (\cos x°)^2$. 1; 1; 1

b. *Patterns* Make a **conjecture** about the expression and prove it. See margin p. 554.

19. *Astronomy* Copernicus had to devise a method different from the one in Example 2 in order to find the size of the orbits of planets farther from the sun than Earth. His method involved noting the number of days between the times that the planets were in the positions labeled A and B in the diagram. Using this time and the number of days in each planet's year, he calculated the measures of the angles labeled 1 and 2.

a. For Mars, $m\angle 1 = 55.2$ and $m\angle 2 = 103.8$. How far is Mars from the sun in astronomical units (AU)? about 1.51 AU

b. For Jupiter, $m\angle 1 = 21.9$ and $m\angle 2 = 100.8$. How far is Jupiter from the sun in astronomical units (AU)? about 5.19 AU

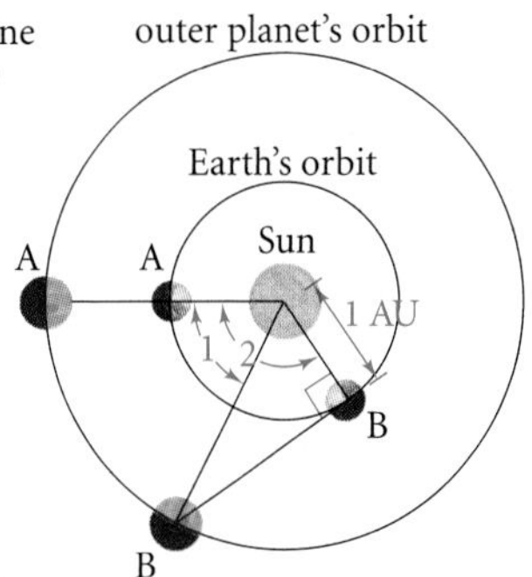

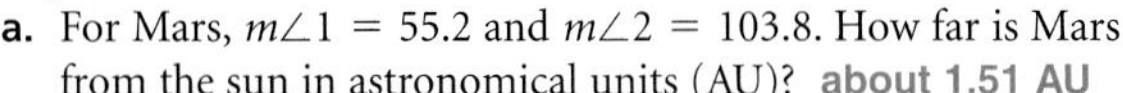

Find w and then x. Round lengths of segments to the nearest tenth and angle measures to the nearest degree.

20.

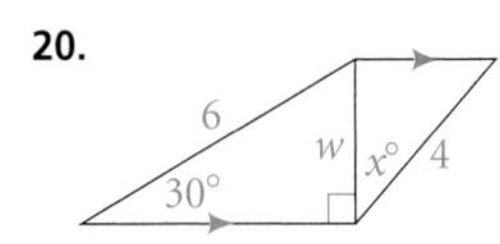

$w = 3$; $x = 41$

21.

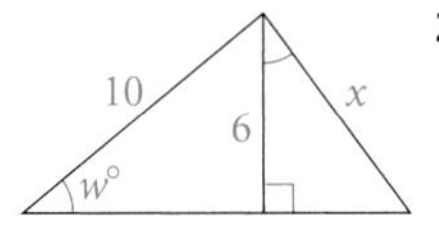

$w = 37$; $x = 7.5$

22.

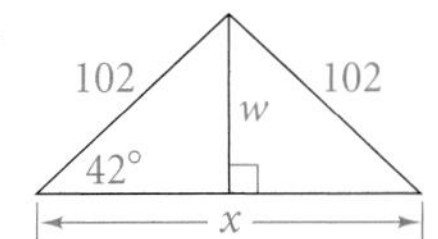

$w = 68.3$; $x = 151.6$

23.

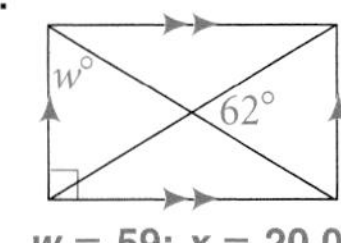

$w = 59$; $x = 20.0$

Exercises MIXED REVIEW

Find the value of each variable. When an answer is not a whole number, round to the nearest tenth.

24. ▱$ABCD$

$a = 105$; $b = 75$

25. rhombus $QRST$

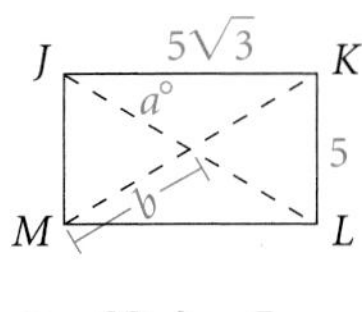

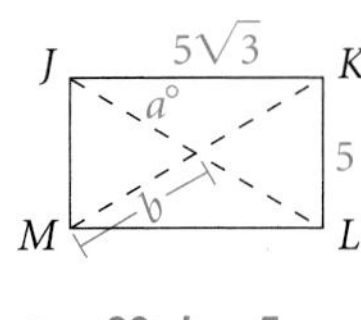

$a = 90$; $b = 40$; $c = 50$

26. rectangle $JKLM$

$a = 30$; $b = 5$

27. kite $WXYZ$

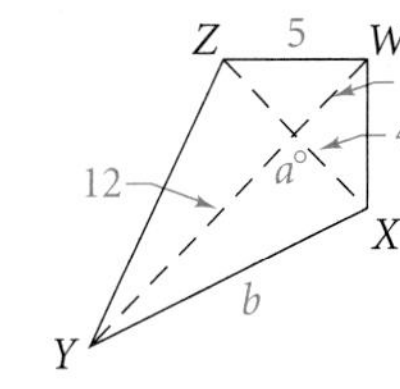

$a = 90$; $b = 12.6$; $c = 3$

28. *Sports* The circumference of a softball is 12 in. The circumference of a field hockey ball is 9 in. How many times larger than the volume of the field hockey ball is the volume of the softball? about 2.37 times larger

Getting Ready for Lesson 11-3

Refer to rectangle $ABCD$ to complete the statements.

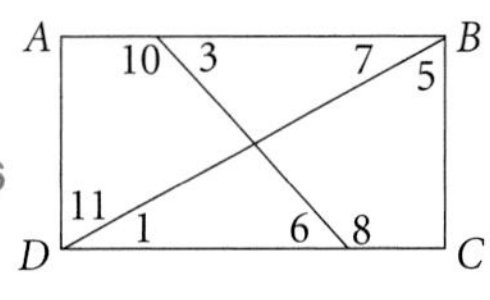

29. $\angle 1 \cong$ ■ $\angle 7$

30. $\angle 5 \cong$ ■ $\angle 11$

31. $\angle 3 \cong$ ■ $\angle 6$

32. $m\angle 1 + m\angle 5 =$ ■ 90

33. $m\angle 10 + m\angle 3 =$ ■ 180

34. $\angle 10 \cong$ ■ $\angle 8$

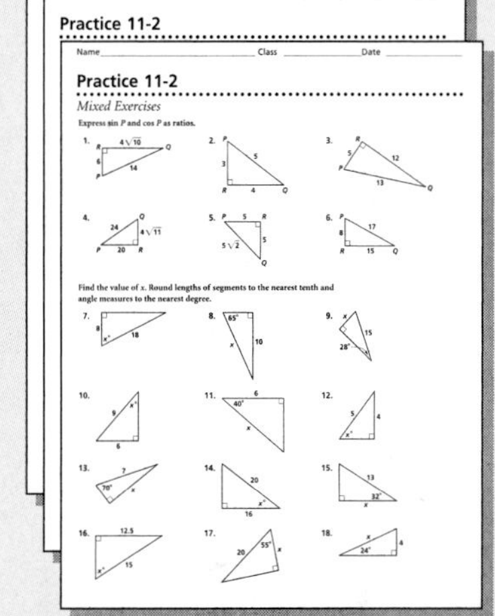

Lesson Quiz

Lesson Quiz is also available in Transparencies.

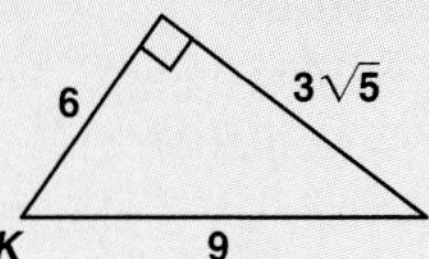

1. Express $\sin K$ as a ratio. $\frac{3\sqrt{5}}{9}$
2. Express $\cos K$ as a ratio. $\frac{6}{9}$

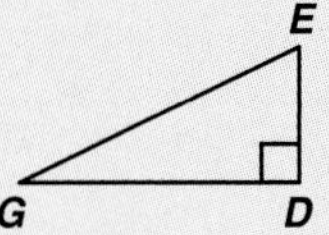

3. If $m\angle G = 25$ and $GE = 10$, find ED to the nearest tenth. 4.2
4. If $GD = 8$ and $GE = 13$, find $m\angle G$ to the nearest degree. 52

11-3 Teaching Notes

PROBLEM OF THE DAY

Can you move two lines of the "house" to make it face the other direction?

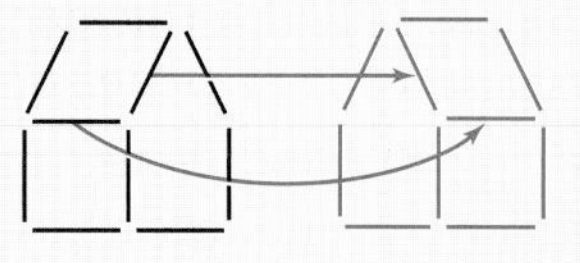

Problem of the Day is also available in Transparencies.

CONNECTING TO PRIOR KNOWLEDGE Draw two parallel lines cut by a transversal. Label the angles formed with the numbers 1–8. Then ask students to identify congruent angles. Have them justify their answers.

THINK AND DISCUSS

ESL Relate the meaning of *angle of depression* to depressions in terrain or the Great Depression. Relate the meaning of and *angle of elevation* to an elevator or land elevation.

VISUAL LEARNING Use different colors to indicate angles of elevation and angles of depression.

ERROR ALERT! Some students will label the angle of elevation or depression as the angle made with a vertical line instead of a horizontal line. **Remediation:** Draw several examples of objects at two different heights and have students practice drawing the angles of elevation and depression.

Lesson Planning Options

Prerequisite Skills

- Using trigonometric ratios

Assignment Options for Exercises On Your Own

Core 1–9, 12–14
✪**Extension** 10–11

Use Mixed Review to maintain skills.

Resources

Student Edition

Skills Handbook, p. 660
Extra Practice, p. 658
Glossary/Study Guide

Teaching Resources

Chapter Support File, Ch. 11
- Practice 11-3 (two worksheets)
- Reteaching 11-3

Classroom Manager 11-3
Glossary, Spanish Resources

Transparencies
113

What You'll Learn

- Identifying angles of elevation and depression
- Using angles of elevation and depression and trigonometric ratios to solve problems

...And Why

To calculate distances indirectly in a variety of real-world settings

What You'll Need

- calculator

1. The horizontal lines are ∥, so alt. interior ∠s are ≅.

Choose the letter of the correct answer.

City A is 5 miles due south of City B. City C is 10 miles due west of City B.

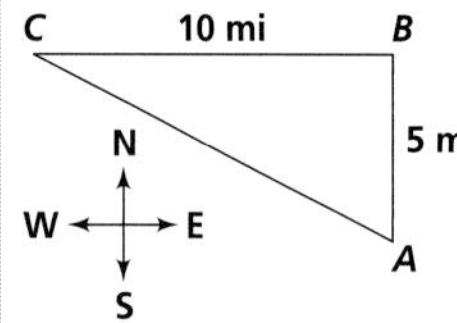

To the nearest mile, what is the straight-line distance from City A to City C?

A 9 mi
B 10 mi
C 11 mi
D 15 mi

$\sqrt{53.28}$ is between which pair of consecutive integers?

A 5 and 6
B 7 and 8
C 8 and 9
D 27 and 28

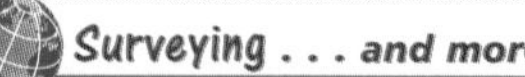

11-3 Angles of Elevation and Depression

THINK AND DISCUSS

Suppose a person in a hot-air balloon sees a person at an angle 38° *below* a horizontal line. This angle is an **angle of depression.** At the same time, the person on the ground sees the hot-air balloon at an angle 38° *above* a horizontal line. This angle is an **angle of elevation.**

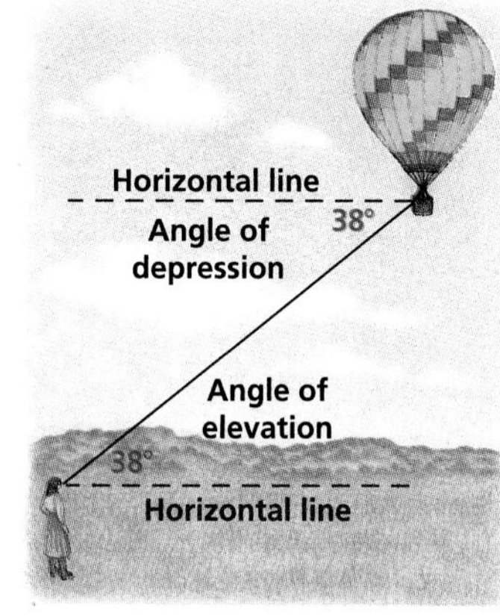

1. Refer to the diagram. What property of parallel lines ensures that the angle of elevation is congruent to the angle of depression? See left.

Example 1

Describe each angle as it relates to the objects in the diagram.

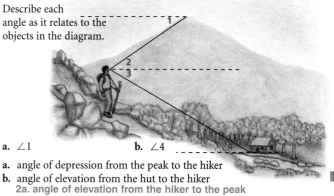

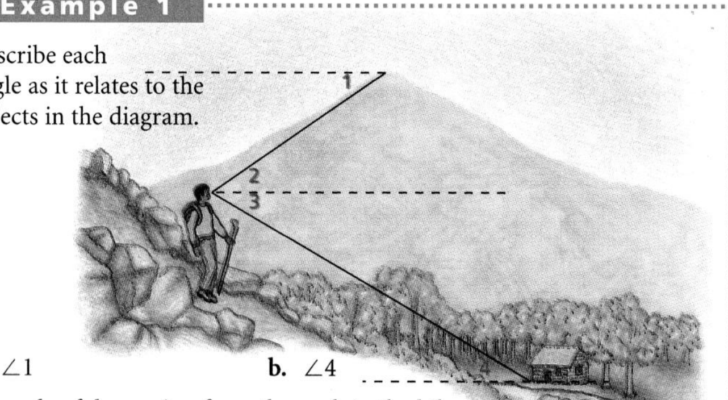

a. ∠1   b. ∠4

a. angle of depression from the peak to the hiker
b. angle of elevation from the hut to the hiker

2a. angle of elevation from the hiker to the peak

2. **Try This** Describe each angle as it relates to the diagram in Example 1.
   a. ∠2   b. ∠3

2b. angle of depression from the hiker to the hut

Surveyors use two main instruments to measure angles of elevation and depression. They are the *transit* and the *theodolite.* On both instruments, the surveyor sets the horizon line perpendicular to the direction of gravity. Using gravity to find the horizon line ensures accurate measures even on sloping surfaces.

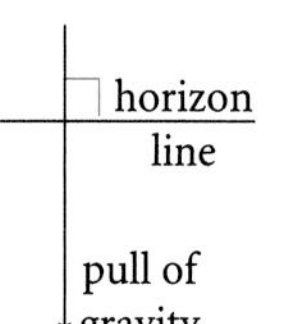

Example 1

Make sure that students understand the need to state from where and to where (i.e., "from the peak to the hiker" or "from the hut to the hiker") when describing an angle of elevation or depression.

MAKING CONNECTIONS One of the tools surveyors use to measure distance is an electronic distance measurement device (EDM). An electromagnetic impulse is transmitted from one point to another, from where it is reflected back to the original point. The time the signal travels and the known speed of the impulse are used to calculate the distance between points.

Example 2 Relating to the Real World

MAKING CONNECTIONS Delicate Arch is one of 90 arches that have been discovered in the park. These giant stone arches are carved from the red sandstone of the Colorado plateau by the erosive forces of frost, wind, and rain. The red sandstone dates to the Jurassic Period, the age of dinosaurs.

Question 3 Discuss with students the most convenient ratio to use in solving this problem. Then ask students to describe alternative methods.

Example 2 Relating to the Real World

Surveying To find the height of Delicate Arch in Arches National Park in Utah, a surveyor places a theodolite at the same level as the bottom of the arch. From there, she measures the angle of elevation to the top of the arch. She then uses a steel tape to measure the distance from her location to the spot directly under the arch. The results of her survey are shown in the diagram. How tall is Delicate Arch?

not to scale

x ft, 48°, 36 ft, 5 ft

$\tan 48^\circ = \frac{x}{36}$ Use the tangent ratio.

$x = 36(\tan 48^\circ)$ Solve for x.

36 × 48 TAN = 39.982051 Use a calculator.

So $x \approx 40$. To find the height of the arch, add the height of the theodolite. $40 + 5 = 45$, so Delicate Arch is about 45 feet tall.

3. **Try This** A surveyor uses a theodolite to measure the angle of elevation to the top of a cliff. He then uses an electronic distance measurement device to measure the distance from the theodolite to the top of the cliff. His measurements are shown in the diagram. How tall is the cliff? Round your answer to the nearest foot. about 234 ft

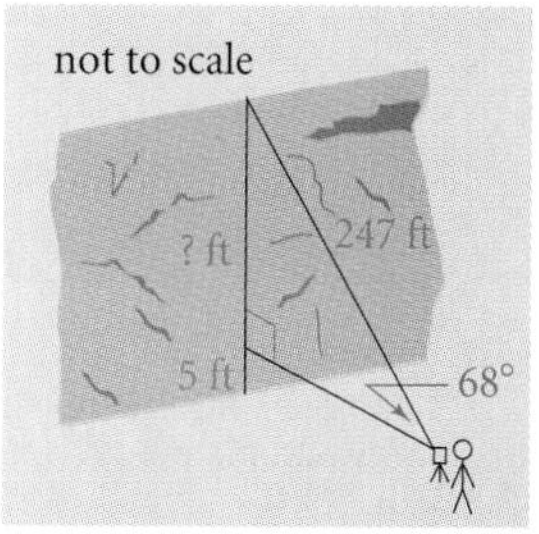

not to scale

? ft, 247 ft, 5 ft, 68°

Additional Examples

FOR EXAMPLE 1

Describe ∠1 and ∠2 as they relate to the objects in the diagram.

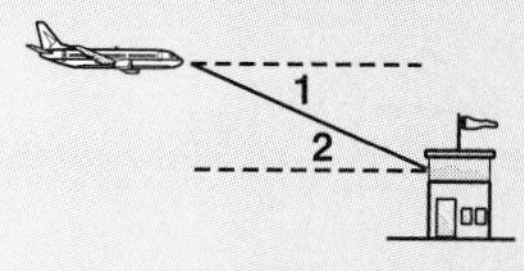

∠1 is the angle of depression from the plane to the tower; ∠2 is the angle of elevation from the tower to the plane.

Discussion: *How are ∠1 and ∠2 related? Explain.*

FOR EXAMPLE 2

Refer to the diagram above. The angle of depression from the plane to the tower is 25° and the plane is 1000 ft above the tower. What is the horizontal distance from the plane to the tower? **≈ 2145 ft**

Discussion: *Describe another way you could solve this problem.*

FOR EXAMPLE 3

Refer to the diagram above. The angle of depression is 15° and the horizontal distance from the plane to the tower is 5,200 ft. How high above the tower is the plane? **≈ 1393 ft**

Example 3 Relating to the Real World 

Help students understand that the distance from the airplane to the airport is different from the *horizontal* distance from the airplane to the airport. Ask students which distance is greater and why.

Explain to students that the airport's having an altitude of 1007 ft does not mean it is 1007 ft above ground. The airport is 1107 ft above sea level. Also make sure that students understand why the plane is 1707 ft above the airport, not 2714 ft.

Exercises ON YOUR OWN

Exercises 1 and 2 Students should state whether each angle is an angle of elevation or an angle of depression, and from what object to what object.

DIVERSITY Exercise 3 This is a good opportunity to discuss disabilities with students. Students may be surprised to learn that while some people are born with disabilities caused by cerebral palsy, spina bifida, and Down's syndrome, about three-fourths of the disabled Americans today are so because of accidents, diseases, and war.

Technology Options

For Exercise 13, students may use a drawing program to draw the diagrams and a word-processing program to write their problems.

Prentice Hall Technology 

Software
- Secondary Math Lab Toolkit™
- Computer Item Generator 11-3

Internet
- See the Prentice Hall site. (http://www.phschool.com)

558

Example 3 Relating to the Real World 

Aviation If you live near an airport, you have probably noticed that airplanes follow certain paths as they prepare for landing. These paths are called *approaches*. The approach to runway 17 of the Ponca City Municipal Airport in Oklahoma calls for the pilot to begin a 3° descent starting from an altitude of 2714 ft. How many miles from the runway is an airplane at the beginning of this approach?

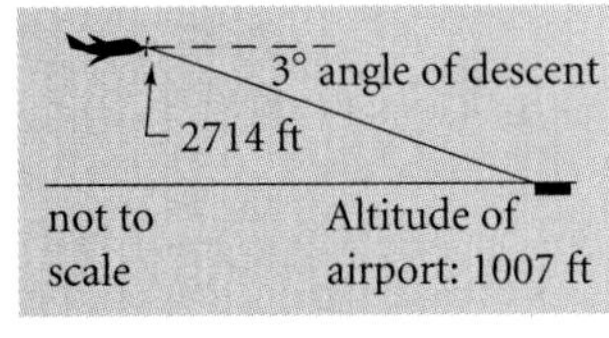

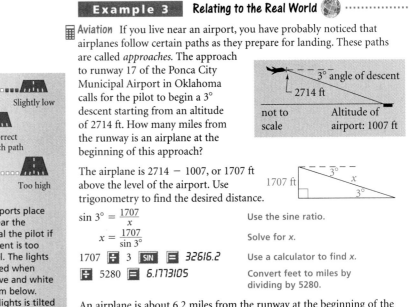

The airplane is 2714 − 1007, or 1707 ft above the level of the airport. Use trigonometry to find the desired distance.

$\sin 3^\circ = \frac{1707}{x}$ Use the sine ratio.

$x = \frac{1707}{\sin 3^\circ}$ Solve for x.

1707 ÷ 3 SIN = 32616.2 Use a calculator to find x.

÷ 5280 = 6.1773105 Convert feet to miles by dividing by 5280.

An airplane is about 6.2 miles from the runway at the beginning of the approach to runway 17 at Ponca City.

Too low · Slightly low · On correct approach path · Slightly high · Too high

How? Most airports place lights near the runway that signal the pilot if the angle of descent is too great or too small. The lights shown here are red when viewed from above and white when viewed from below. Each of the four lights is tilted at a different angle.

Exercises ON YOUR OWN

Describe each angle as it relates to the objects in the diagram. 1–2. See margin p. 559.

1. a. ∠1
   b. ∠2
   c. ∠3
   d. ∠4

2. a. ∠1
   b. ∠2
   c. ∠3
   d. ∠4

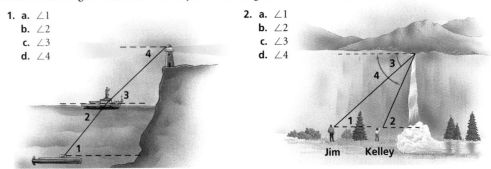

3. **Engineering** The Americans with Disabilities Act states that wheelchair ramps can have a slope no greater than $\frac{1}{12}$. Find the maximum angle of elevation of a ramp with this slope. Round your answer to the nearest tenth. **4.8°**

ERROR ALERT! Exercise 4 Students may have difficulty if they try to find the height of the building directly. **Remediation:** Help students see that the height of the smaller building equals the height of the taller building minus the height of the right triangle shown.

Exercises 4–5 Discuss with students that the phrase "not to scale" shown in the diagram means that the lengths and heights of objects are not proportional.

Exercise 7 Make sure students understand that the distance of 1503 m is the length of the hypotenuse of the triangle created by the meteorologist, the weather balloon, and the point on the ground directly below the weather balloon.

Exercise 8 Make sure students understand how to label the "angle of elevation of the sun" in their diagrams.

Exercise 9 Help students draw a diagram for this problem or have them work on it in groups. Make sure students understand that they are to find the horizontal distance from the blimp to the stadium.

Solve each problem. Round your answer to the nearest unit unless instructed otherwise.

4. Two office buildings are 51 m apart. The height of the taller building is 207 m. The angle of depression from the top of the taller building to the top of the shorter building is 15°. Find the height of the shorter building. **193 m**

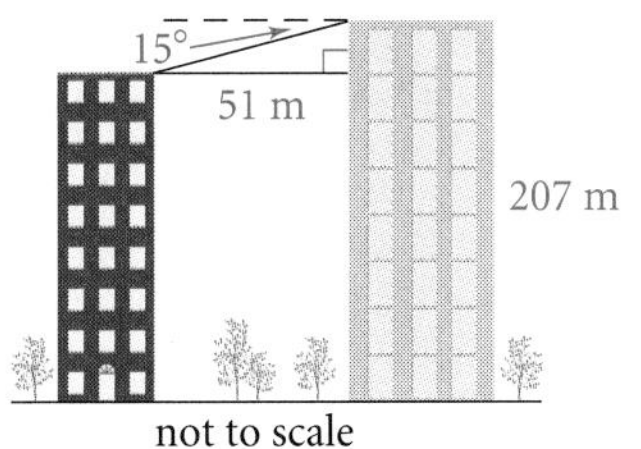

5. A surveyor is 980 ft from the base of the world's tallest fountain at Fountain Hills, Arizona. The angle of elevation to the top of the column of water is 29.7°. His angle measuring device is at the same level as the base of the fountain. Find the height of the column of water to the nearest 10 ft. **560 ft**

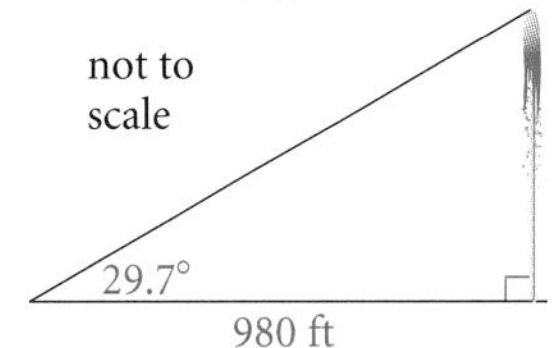

6. On the observation platform in the crown of the Statue of Liberty, Miguel is approximately 250 ft above ground. He sights a ship in New York harbor and measures the angle of depression as 18°. Find the distance from the ship to the base of the statue. **769 ft**

PROBLEM SOLVING HINT

Draw a diagram using the given information. Then decide which trigonometric ratio you can use to solve the problem.

7. A meteorologist measures the angle of elevation of a weather balloon as 41°. A radio signal from the balloon indicates that it is 1503 m from her location. How high is the weather balloon above the ground? **986 m**

8. The world's tallest unsupported flagpole is a 282-ft-tall steel pole in Surrey, British Columbia. The shortest shadow cast by the pole during the year is 137 ft long. What is the angle of elevation of the sun when the shortest shadow is cast? **64°**

9. A blimp is flying to cover a football game. The pilot sights the stadium at a 7° angle of depression. The blimp is flying at an altitude of 400 m. How many kilometers is the blimp from the point 400 m above the stadium? Round your answer to the nearest tenth. **3.3 km**

pages 558–560 On Your Own

1a. angle of elevation from the submarine to the boat
b. angle of depression from the boat to the submarine
c. angle of elevation from the boat to the lighthouse
d. angle of depression from the lighthouse to the boat
2a. angle of elevation from Jim to the waterfall
b. angle of elevation from Kelley to the waterfall
c. angle of depression from the waterfall to Jim
d. angle of depression from the waterfall to Kelley

KINESTHETIC LEARNING Exercise 10 If possible, take students outside right before noon. Drive a stick upright into the ground in full sun. At noon have students measure the length of the stick's shadow and the height of the stick that is above ground. Then have them calculate the elevation of the sun.

CRITICAL THINKING Exercise 11 You may also want to ask students how they could find the height of the tower.

ESL Exercise 11 Explain to students what "guy wires" are and why and how they are used.

ALTERNATIVE ASSESSMENT Exercise 13 Have students create their own problems using trigonometric ratios. Have them write each problem on an index card and the worked out solution on the back. Use them as a review or testing.

STANDARDIZED TEST TIP Exercise 14 Students may want to let $m\angle Y = 60$ and $m\angle Z = 30$. This satisfies $m\angle Y > m\angle Z$ and students can use the side lengths 1, $\sqrt{3}$, and 2 to calculate the trigonometric ratios quickly.

Chapter Project **FIND OUT BY MEASURING** Before assigning this activity, decide whether you want all students to measure the height of the same object. Also, tell students that each solution should be accompanied by a diagram showing the distances and angle they measured.

10a. Measure the length of the stick. Then measure the length of the shortest shadow. The ratio of the length of the stick to the length of the shadow is the tangent ratio of the angle of elevation of the sun at noon.

11. The ground is one leg of a rt. △ and the wire is the hypotenuse. Measure the distance from the ground end of the wire to the base of the tower. Then divide this length by the cosine ratio of the angle formed by the wire and the ground.

page 561 Mixed Review

18.

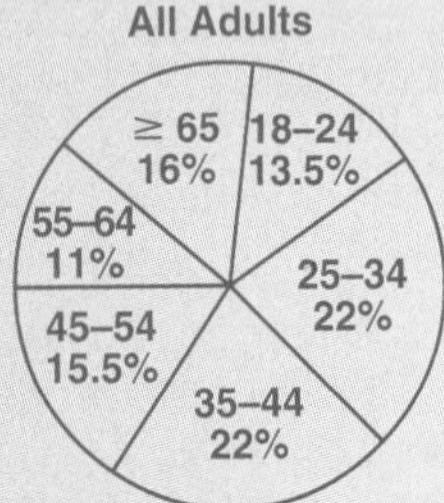

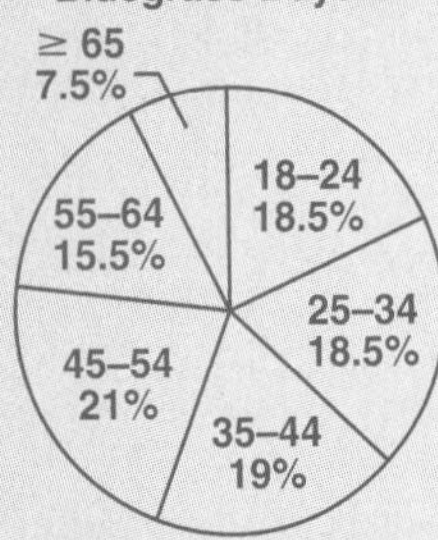

19b. 55–64; 55–64 year olds have a higher share of bluegrass sales than their share of population.

560

See margin.

✪10. a. *Navigation* A simple method for finding a north-south line is shown in the diagram. How could you use this method to also find the angle of elevation of the sun at noon?

b. *Research* For locations in the continental United States, the relationship between the latitude ℓ and angle of elevation a of the sun at noon on the first day of summer is $a = 90° - \ell + 23\frac{1}{2}°$. Find the latitude of your town and determine the angle of elevation of the sun on the first day of summer. Check students' work.

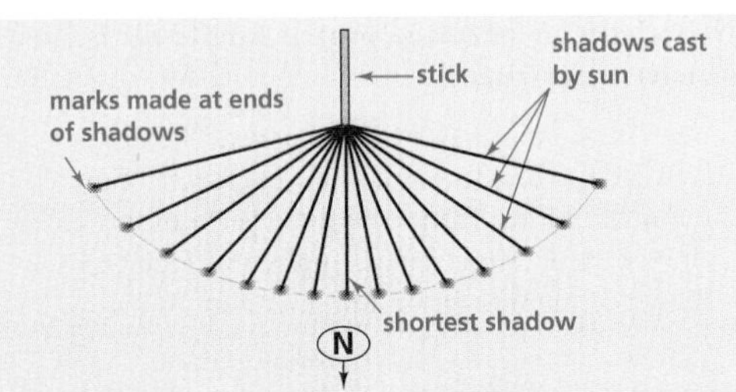

Put a stick in the ground before noon and mark the end of its shadow every 15 minutes. When the shadows begin to lengthen, stop marking the shadows. The mark closest to the stick is directly north of the stick.

✪11. *Critical Thinking* A television tower is located on a flat plot of land. The tower is supported by several guy wires. Explain how you could find the length of any of these wires. Assume that you are able to measure distances along the ground as well as angles formed by wires and the ground. See margin.

12. *Meteorology* One method that meteorologists use to find the height of a layer of clouds above the ground is to shine a bright spotlight directly up onto the cloud layer and measure the angle of elevation from a known distance away. Find the height of the cloud layer in the diagram to the nearest 10 m. 1080 m

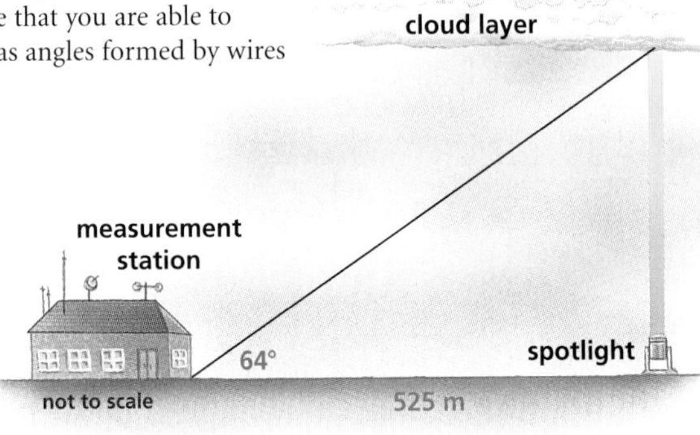

13. a. *Open-ended* Draw and label a diagram that shows a real-world example of an angle of elevation and an angle of depression.

b. *Writing* Write a word problem that uses the angle of depression from your diagram. Include a detailed solution to your problem.

a–b. Answers may vary. See back of book for sample.

14. *Standardized Test Prep* In the diagram, $m\angle Y > m\angle Z$. Which statement is *not* true? E

A. $\sin Y > \cos Y$ B. $\cos Y < \cos Z$ C. $\tan Y > \sin Y$
D. $\tan Z > \cos Y$ E. $\cos Z > \sin Y$

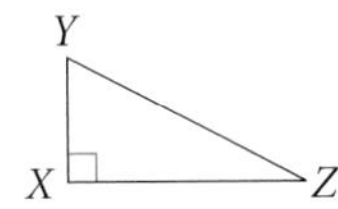

Chapter Project ***Find Out by Measuring***

Use your clinometer to measure the angle of elevation to an object such as the roof of your school or the top of a flagpole. Then determine how far away you are from the object that you measured. Use what you've learned about trigonometry to find the height of the object. Be sure to add your own height to the height you come up with!

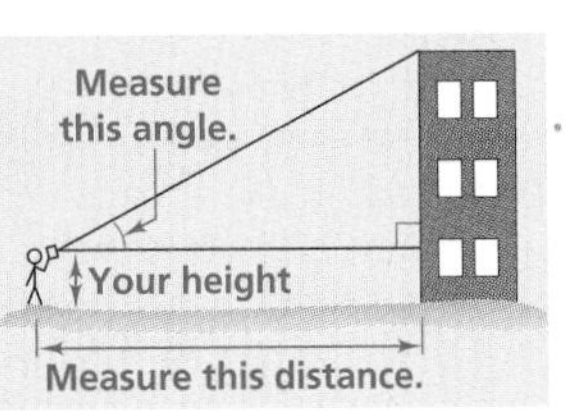

Check students' work.

Exercises MIXED REVIEW

Exercises 15–19 Make sure students understand what the two bars represent on the graph and why the grey bar can be shorter than the blue bar.

GETTING READY FOR LESSON 11-4 These exercises prepare students to find the magnitude and direction of vectors.

Wrap Up

THE BIG IDEA Ask students: *Describe how you decide if an angle in a diagram is an angle of depression or an angle of elevation.*

RETEACHING ACTIVITY Students use angles of elevation and depression and trigonometric ratios to solve problems. (Reteaching worksheet 11-3)

Exercises CHECKPOINT

In this Checkpoint, your students will assess their own progress in Lessons 11-1 to 11-3.

STANDARDIZED TEST TIP **Exercise 1** Students can solve this problem without doing any calculations by using the fact that sine and cosine are always less than one for an acute angle and that the tangent of an angle 45° or greater is greater than one.

Exercises MIXED REVIEW

Data Analysis **Refer to the graph to answer the questions.** 15–18. Answers may vary slightly.

15. What percent of adults are 18–24 years old? about 13.5%

16. What percent of bluegrass purchases did adults 18–24 make? about 18.5%

17. Which age group contains the least number of people? 55–64

18. Create two circle graphs using the data from the double bar graph. See margin p. 560.

19. a. Which age group buys more bluegrass: 35–44-year-olds or 55–64-year-olds? 35–44

b. Which of these two age groups likes bluegrass more? Explain. 55–64; see margin p. 560 for explanation.

20. Coordinate Geometry Find the equation of the line that passes through (3, 7) and is parallel to the line $y = \frac{3}{2}x - 5$. $y = \frac{3}{2}x + \frac{5}{2}$

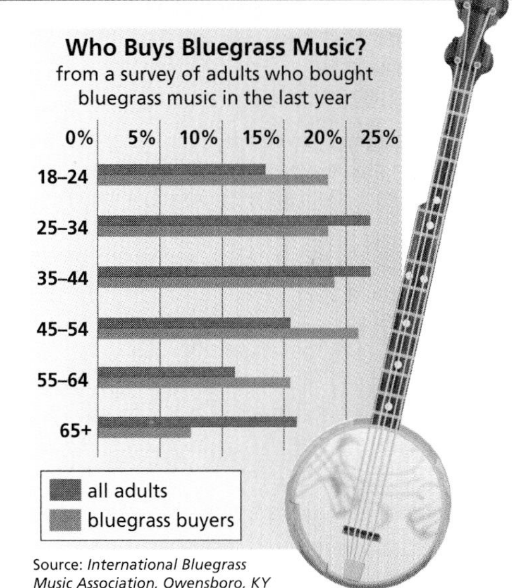

Source: *International Bluegrass Music Association, Owensboro, KY*

Getting Ready for Lesson 11-4

Transformations **Find the image of each point under a translation with the given translation vector.**

21. (2, 7); ⟨1, −9⟩ (3, −2)

22. (−3, 0); ⟨6, −1⟩ (3, −1)

23. (4, −7); ⟨5, 0⟩ (9, −7)

24. (−5, 12); ⟨−8, −11⟩ (−13, 1)

Exercises CHECKPOINT

1. Standardized Test Prep Which value is greatest? C

A. sin 30° **B.** cos 45° **C.** tan 60°
D. sin 10° **E.** cos 70°

2. Architecture The Leaning Tower of Pisa leans about 5.5° from vertical. How far from the base of the tower will an object dropped from the tower land? about 17 ft

3. A captain of a sailboat sights the top of a lighthouse at a 17° angle of elevation. A navigation chart shows the height of the lighthouse to be 120 m. How far is the sailboat from the lighthouse? about 393 m

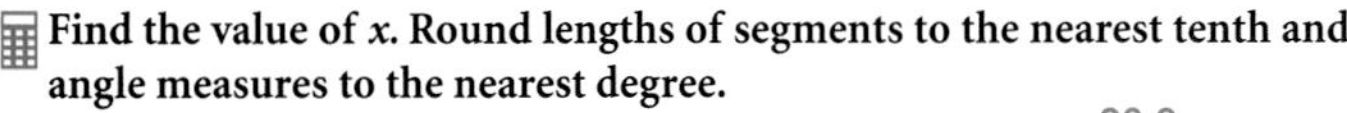

Find the value of *x*. Round lengths of segments to the nearest tenth and angle measures to the nearest degree.

4. 15.0

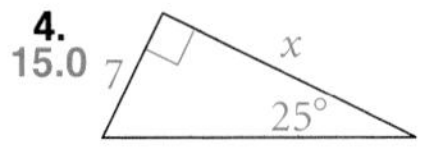

5. 61

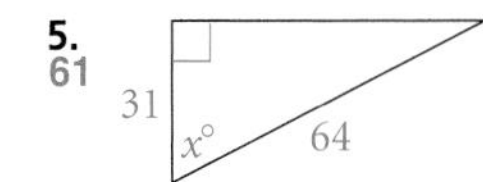

6. 20.8

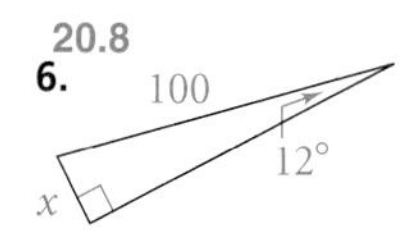

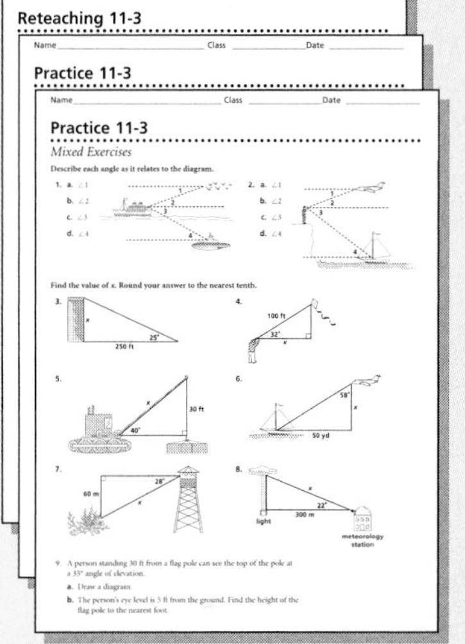

Lesson Quiz

Lesson Quiz is also available in Transparencies.

1. Describe ∠1 and ∠2 as they relate to the objects in the diagram.

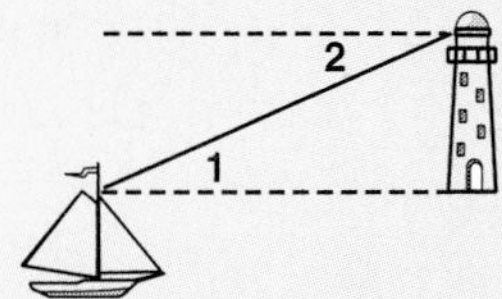

∠1 is the angle of elevation from the boat to the lighthouse beacon; ∠2 is the angle of depression from the lighthouse beacon to the boat.

2. Refer to the diagram above. The captain of the boat knows that the lighthouse on the coast is 100 m tall. If she measures the angle of elevation to be 2°, how far is the boat from the coast? ≈ 2864 m

Math ToolboX

Students review how to transform literal equations by solving for one variable in terms of the other.

Example 1

Explain to students that it must be stated that $r \neq 0$ because division by zero is not defined.

Example 2

ERROR ALERT! A common error made by students is dividing $2\pi rh$ and A by $2\pi r$ first, then subtracting $2\pi r^2$. **Remediation:** Review the steps for solving an equation: Add or subtract first, then multiply or divide. Use a simpler example like solving $y = 2x + 1$ for x to show that the steps are not interchangeable.

ALTERNATIVE ASSESSMENT Have students work in five groups. Assign each group three of the problems to solve. Then have them present their worked-out solutions to the class.

Transparencies 15, 16

Math ToolboX — Algebra Review

Literal Equations

Before Lesson 11-4

A **literal equation** is an equation involving two or more variables. Formulas are special types of literal equations. You solve for one variable in terms of the others when you transform a literal equation.

Example 1

The formula for the volume of a cylinder is $V = \pi r^2 h$. Find a formula for the height in terms of the radius and volume.

$$V = \pi r^2 h$$

$$\frac{V}{\pi r^2} = \frac{\pi r^2 h}{\pi r^2} \quad \leftarrow \text{Divide each side by } \pi r^2,\ r \neq 0.$$

$$\frac{V}{\pi r^2} = h \quad \leftarrow \text{Simplify.}$$

The formula for the height is $h = \frac{V}{\pi r^2}$.

Example 2

The formula for the surface area of a cylinder is $A = 2\pi rh + 2\pi r^2$. Solve for h.

$$A = 2\pi rh + 2\pi r^2$$

$$A - 2\pi r^2 = 2\pi rh + 2\pi r^2 - 2\pi r^2 \quad \leftarrow \text{Subtract } 2\pi r^2 \text{ from each side.}$$

$$A - 2\pi r^2 = 2\pi rh \quad \leftarrow \text{Simplify.}$$

$$\frac{A - 2\pi r^2}{2\pi r} = \frac{2\pi rh}{2\pi r} \quad \leftarrow \text{Divide each side by } 2\pi r,\ r \neq 0.$$

$$\frac{A - 2\pi r^2}{2\pi r} = h \quad \leftarrow \text{Simplify.}$$

The formula for the height is $h = \frac{A - 2\pi r^2}{2\pi r}$.

Solve each equation for the variable in red.

1. $P = 2w + 2\ell$ $w = \frac{P - 2\ell}{2}$
2. $\tan A = \frac{y}{x}$ $x = \frac{y}{\tan A}$
3. $A = \frac{1}{2}bh$ $b = \frac{2A}{h}$
4. $C = 2\pi r$ $r = \frac{C}{2\pi}$
5. $A = \frac{1}{2}(b_1 + b_2)h$ See below.
6. $V = \ell wh$ $h = \frac{V}{\ell w}$
7. $A = \frac{1}{2}ap$ $a = \frac{2A}{p}$
8. $m\angle C + m\angle D = 180$ See below.
9. $A = \pi r^2$ $r = \sqrt{\frac{A}{\pi}}$
10. $S = 180(n - 2)$ $n = \frac{S + 360}{180}$
11. $V = \frac{1}{3}\ell wh$ $w = \frac{3V}{\ell h}$
12. $a^2 + b^2 = c^2$ $b = \sqrt{c^2 - a^2}$
13. $\cos A = \frac{b}{c}$ $b = c \cos A$
14. $V = \frac{1}{3}\pi r^2 h$ $r = \sqrt{\frac{3V}{\pi h}}$
15. $S = \pi r^2 + \pi r\ell$ $\ell = \frac{S - \pi r^2}{\pi r}$

5. $b_2 = \frac{2A}{h} - b_1$ 8. $m\angle C = 180 - m\angle D$

11-4 Teaching Notes

PROBLEM OF THE DAY

Let π be the ratio of the height h of a tin can to the diameter of the top of the can. What are the dimensions of the label? *h* by *h*

Problem of the Day is also available in Transparencies.

CONNECTING TO PRIOR KNOWLEDGE Draw a triangle in the coordinate plane and its image under a translation. Have students give the vector that describes the translation. Repeat this using several different triangles.

THINK AND DISCUSS

Help students see that both the vectors used to describe translations and the real-world examples shown have magnitude and direction.

Point out that magnitude is not distance only. For example, magnitude can be weight, speed, or acceleration.

Question 2 Draw the following diagram and discuss the abbreviations. Also discuss the angles formed by the lines.

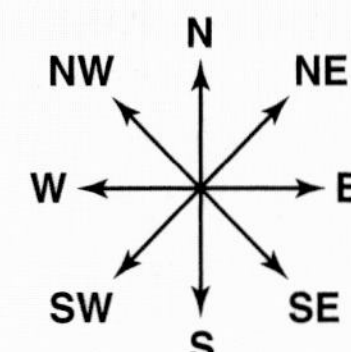

Connections Air Travel . . . and more

11-4 Vectors and Trigonometry

What You'll Learn

- Describing vectors using ordered pair notation
- Describing the magnitude and direction of vectors

...And Why

To model real-world situations such as those involving velocity

What You'll Need

- calculator

THINK AND DISCUSS

A **vector** is any quantity that has *magnitude* (size) and *direction.* In Chapter 3, you used vectors to describe translations. In this lesson you will explore some other applications of vectors. Here are a few.

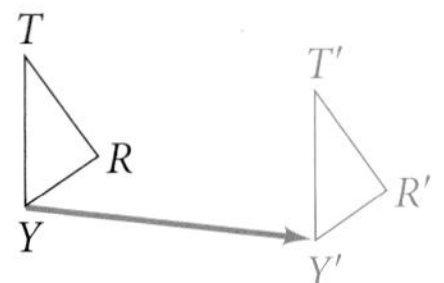

This vector describes the translation $\triangle TRY \to \triangle T'R'Y'$.

Magnitude: 25 mi/h
Direction: Straight up

Magnitude: 1.62 m/s^2
Direction: Toward center of the moon

Magnitude: 34 yd
Direction: Straight through the uprights

1. *Critical Thinking* Does the sentence contain enough information to describe a vector? Explain. No; the description gives the direction but no magnitude.
   a. A car heads northwest.
   b. A hiker walks south at 5 miles per hour. See left.
   c. The wind blows at 45 kilometers per hour. No; the description gives magnitude but no direction.

1b. Yes; the description includes magnitude and direction.

2. Two sisters, Altheia and Chenice, drive from point *A* to point *B*. In describing their trip, Altheia says, "We ended up 71 miles northwest of where we started." Chenice says, "We ended up 50 miles west and 50 miles north of where we started." Explain why both sisters' descriptions of their trip are accurate. Both descriptions allow you to find the pt. where the trip ended.

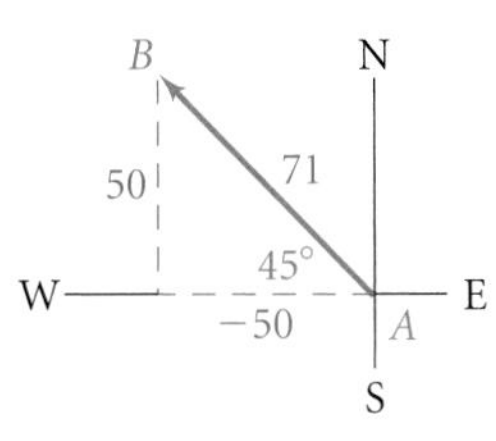

Question 2 suggests two different ways that you can describe a vector.

- *Use its size and direction.* The magnitude of $\overrightarrow{AB}$ is 71 (about $50\sqrt{2}$), and its direction is northwest (or 45° north of west).
- *Use its horizontal and vertical change.* The ordered pair notation $\langle -50, 50 \rangle$ describes $\overrightarrow{AB}$, where -50 represents the horizontal change from *A* to *B*, and 50 represents the vertical change.

Lesson Planning Options

Prerequisite Skills

- Finding trigonometric ratios

Assignment Options for Exercises On Your Own

Core 1–14, 17–23
Extension 15–16, 24–26

Use Mixed Review to maintain skills.

Resources

Student Edition

Skills Handbook, p. 674
Extra Practice, p. 658
Glossary/Study Guide

Teaching Resources

Chapter Support File, Ch. 11
- Practice 11-4 (two worksheets)
- Reteaching 11-4
- Alternative Activity 11-4

Classroom Manager 11-4
Glossary, Spanish Resources

Transparencies
5, 113

Point out the symbol used to indicate a vector. Make sure students differentiate it from the symbol used to indicate a ray.

Remind students that in ordered pair notation, a negative sign is used to indicate a horizontal change to the left or a vertical change down.

Example 1

VISUAL LEARNING Help students understand that the *x*-coordinate is positive and the *y*-coordinate is negative because the direction from the origin to point *L* is right and down.

ERROR ALERT! Some students will have difficulty knowing if an arrow signifies a vector or a ray. **Remediation:** Help students understand that a vector is a directed line segment with a beginning (initial point) and end (terminal point). The arrow indicates which point is the initial point and which is the terminal point. Assure students that the context of the problem will clarify whether the arrow is a vector or a ray.

ESL Some students may have difficulty understanding the difference between "south of east" and "east of south." It may be helpful to display a poster with diagrams illustrating the difference. Also include diagrams illustrating "east of north" and "north of east."

Example 2 **Relating to the Real World**

Discuss with students why the lengths of the legs of the right triangle are 40 and 25.

Additional Examples

FOR EXAMPLE 1

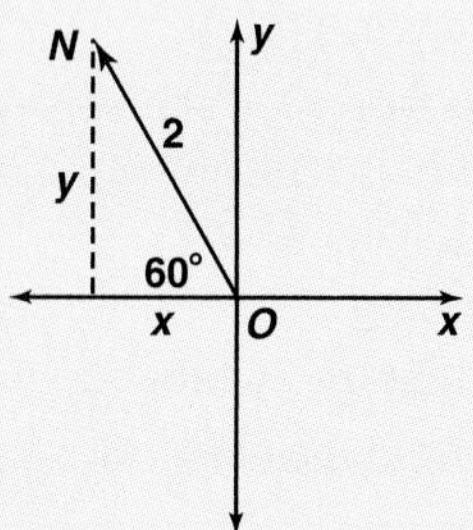

Describe $\overrightarrow{ON}$ by using ordered pair notation. Give the coordinates to the nearest tenth. ⟨−1, 1.7⟩

Discussion: *Explain how you determine if the x- and y-coordinates are positive or negative.*

FOR EXAMPLE 2

A tour bus driver drove to a point 20 mi east and 32 mi south of the point at which he started. Find the distance from the starting point and the direction traveled.

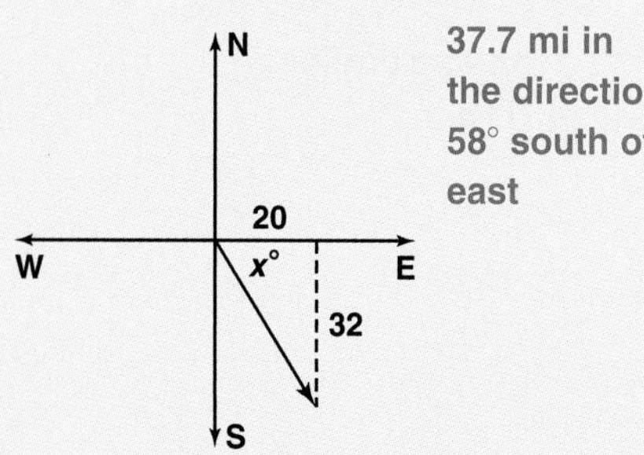

37.7 mi in the direction 58° south of east

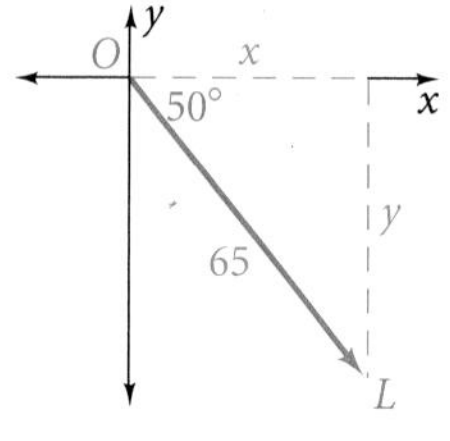

QUICK REVIEW

In the diagram, *I* is the *initial point* of $\overrightarrow{IT}$ and *T* is its *terminal point.*

Example 1

Coordinate Geometry Describe $\overrightarrow{OL}$ by using ordered pair notation. Give the coordinates to the nearest tenth.

Use the sine and cosine ratios to find the values of *x* and *y*.

$\cos 50° = \frac{x}{65}$	$\sin 50° = \frac{y}{65}$	Use sine and cosine.
$x = 65(\cos 50°)$	$y = 65(\sin 50°)$	Solve for the variable.
≈ 41.8	≈ 49.8	Use a calculator.

The *y*-coordinate of the ordered pair is negative since *L* is in the fourth quadrant. So $\overrightarrow{OL} = \langle 41.8, -49.8\rangle$.

In many applications of vectors, the direction of the vector is described in relation to north, south, east, and west. Here are a few examples.

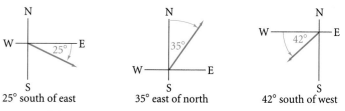

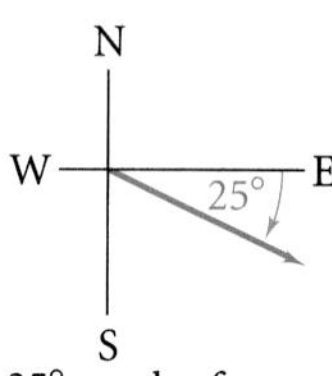

25° south of east

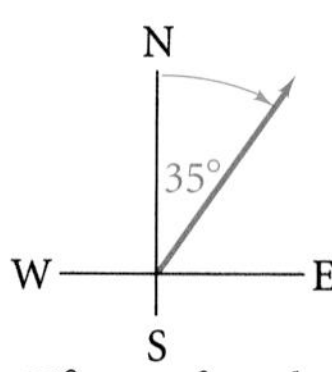

35° east of north

N, W, E, 42°, S — 42° south of west

3. **Try This** Sketch a vector that has a direction of 30° west of north. See margin p. 566 for sample.

Example 2 **Relating to the Real World** 

Air Travel A helicopter lands at a point 40 km west and 25 km south of the point at which it took off. Find the distance that the helicopter flew and the direction of its flight.

N, W, −40, x°, E, −25, c, S

Start by drawing a diagram of the vector. To find the distance flown *c*, use the Pythagorean Theorem.

$40^2 + 25^2 = c^2$	Substitute 40 and 25 for the lengths of the legs.
$2225 = c^2$	Simplify the left side.
$c \approx 47$	Take the square root.

To find the direction of the helicopter's flight, find the angle that the vector makes with west.

$\tan x° = \frac{25}{40}$	Use the tangent ratio.
(25 ÷ 40) TAN⁻¹ 32.005383	Use a calculator.

The helicopter flew about 47 km at 32° south of west.

4. **Try This** A small plane lands at a point 246 mi east and 76 mi north of the point at which it took off. Find the distance that the plane flew and the direction of its flight. about 257 mi; 17° north of east

Exercises ON YOUR OWN

Exercises 1–4 Suggest that students draw triangles like those shown in Example 1, labeling the legs x and y. Check that they remember to indicate direction with a negative sign, if appropriate, in their ordered pairs.

Exercises 5–8 Make sure students understand their answers should be phrases like "50° north of east."

DIVERSITY Exercise 9 The Greeks were responsible for originating our modern Olympics. The Olympic games originated in ancient Greece in 776 B.C., if not earlier, as a way of saluting their gods. In addition to the sports festival, there were music and oratory competitions and theatrical performances. The Olympics were abolished in the early Christian era (A.D. 386) because of their explicitly pagan overtones. They were revived in 1896.

Exercises ON YOUR OWN

Coordinate Geometry **Describe each vector by using ordered pair notation. Give the coordinates to the nearest unit.**

1. **2.**

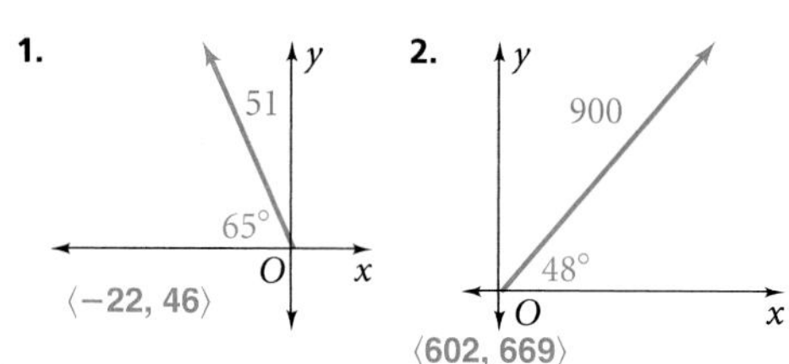

⟨−22, 46⟩ ⟨602, 669⟩

3.

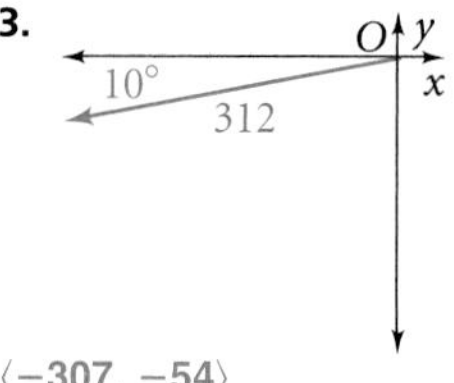

⟨−307, −54⟩

4.

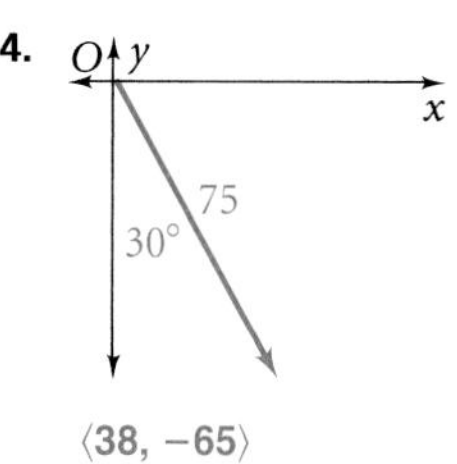

⟨38, −65⟩

Describe the direction of each vector.

5.

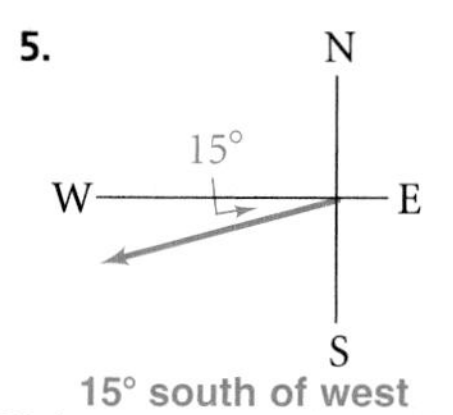

15° south of west

6.

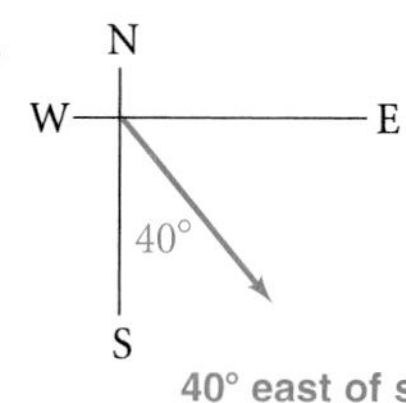

40° east of south

7.

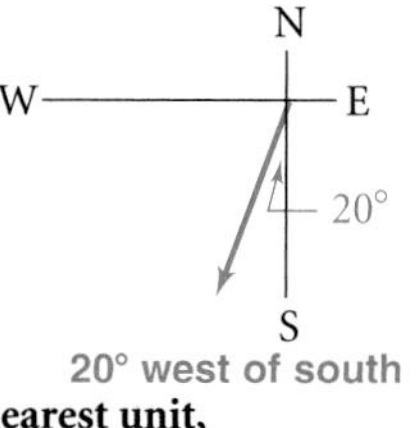

20° west of south

8.

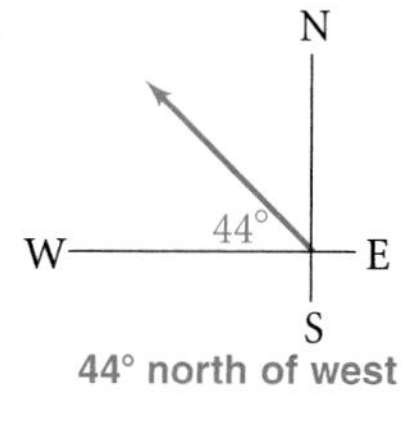

44° north of west

Biology **Solve each problem. Round your answers to the nearest unit, unless otherwise directed.**

9. Homing pigeons are capable of returning to their home upon release. Homing pigeons carried news of Olympic victories to various cities in ancient Greece. Suppose one such pigeon took off from Athens and landed in Sparta, which is 73 mi west and 64 mi south of Athens. Find the distance and direction of its flight. about 97 mi; 41° south of west

10. Honeybees describe vectors through movement. A bee that discovers a new source of pollen flies back to the hive and does a "dance" for the other bees. The movements of this dance tell other bees how to get to the pollen. Suppose a bee describes a source of pollen 1000 ft away and 60° counterclockwise from the direction of the sun. Draw a diagram of this vector. Include labels for the sun, the hive, and the pollen. See margin p. 566.

11. During its adult life, a European eel travels from the Belgian coast to breeding grounds in the Sargasso Sea. This part of the Atlantic Ocean is about 2300 mi south and 4800 mi west of Belgium. Find the distance and direction of the eel's journey. Round the distance to the nearest 100 mi. 5300 mi at 26° south of west

12. The owners of a golden retriever named Ginger took her from her home to a location 17 mi north and 29 miles east. There, they somehow lost her. Ginger, however, managed to find her way home after 3 days. Find the distance and direction of her journey home (assuming she took the shortest route). 34 mi at 30° south of west

Technology Options

For Exercises 9–12, students can use a graphing program or a drawing program to draw the diagrams.

Prentice Hall Technology

Software
- Secondary Math Lab Toolkit™
- Computer Item Generator 11-4

Internet
- See the Prentice Hall site. (http://www.phschool.com)

WRITING Exercise 13 Ask students to explain how the cartoon illustrates the similarities and differences between $\overrightarrow{AB}$ and $\overrightarrow{BA}$.

ALTERNATIVE ASSESSMENT Exercise 14 This exercise can help you assess students' understanding of direction. Ask them to support their answer with a diagram and another example.

Exercise 15 Students may need to review the terms *dilation* and *scale factor* which can be found in Lesson 3-7 or the glossary.

CRITICAL THINKING Exercises 17–19 If a sentence does not contain enough information, ask students to rewrite it so it does.

PATTERNS Exercises 24 and 25 Have students compare their definitions and revise them, if necessary.

pages 563–564 Think and Discuss

3.

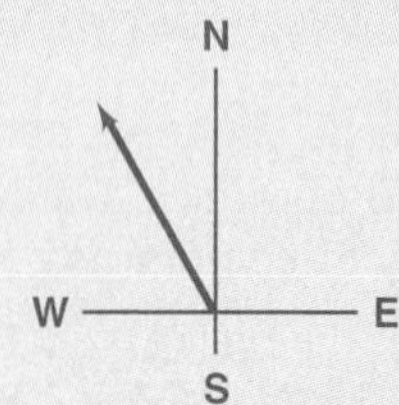

pages 565–567 On Your Own

10.

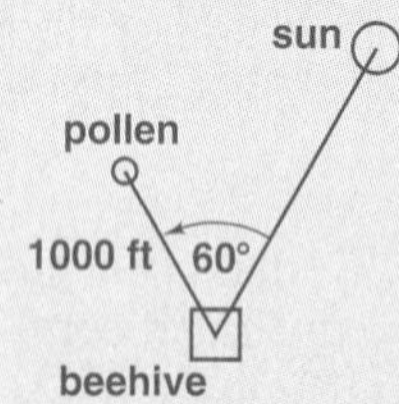

14. Yes; since 35° and 55° are complementary angles, both statements describe the same direction.

15. The directions of both vectors are the same. The ratio of the magnitude of the image to the magnitude of the orig. vector is k.

13. **Writing** How are the vectors $\overrightarrow{AB}$ and $\overrightarrow{BA}$ alike? How are they different? Vectors AB and BA have the same magnitude but opp. directions.

14. **Critical Thinking** Valerie described the direction of a vector as 35° south of east. Pablo described it as 55° east of south. Could the two be describing the same vector? Explain. See margin.

15. **Transformational Geometry** Point A' is the image of A under a dilation with scale factor k and center O. How are the direction and magnitude of $\overrightarrow{OA}$ related to the direction and magnitude of $\overrightarrow{OA'}$? See margin.

16. **Open-ended** Name four other vectors with the same magnitude as $\langle -7, -24 \rangle$. Sample: $\langle 7, 24 \rangle$, $\langle 24, -7 \rangle$, $\langle 20, 15 \rangle$, $\langle -15, -20 \rangle$

POINT A

POINT B

"Well, lemme think. ... You've stumped me, son. Most folks only wanna know how to go the other way."

Critical Thinking Does each sentence contain enough information to describe a vector? Explain your answer.

17. The angle of elevation of a baseball hit by Frank Thomas is 35°. No; the description gives the direction but no magnitude.

18. A rocket is launched upward with an initial thrust of 400,000 lb. Yes; the description includes magnitude and direction.

19. A cheetah runs at 71 miles per hour. No; the description gives magnitude but no direction.

21. about 54 mi/h; 22° north of east

23. about 0.22 in./h; 32° north of east

Find the magnitude and direction of each vector.

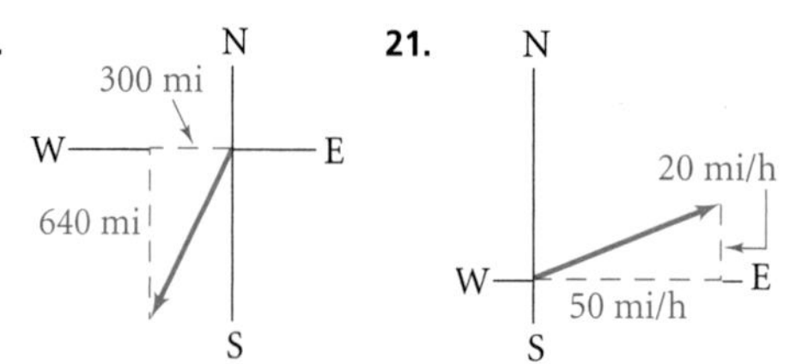

20. about 707 mi; 25° west of south

21. See above.

22. (N, 1000 km, W, E, 4700 km, S) about 4800 km; 12° north of west

23. (N, 0.12 in./h, W, E, 0.19 in./h, S) See above.

24. **Patterns** Use the diagrams below to write a definition of *equal vectors*.

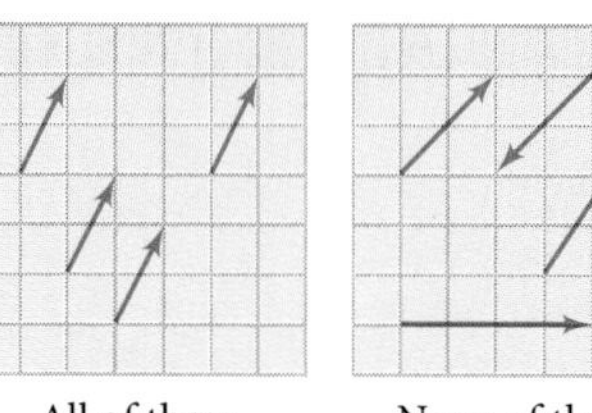

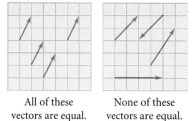

All of these vectors are equal. None of these vectors are equal.

25. **Patterns** Use the diagrams below to write a definition of *parallel vectors*.

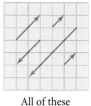

All of these vectors are parallel. None of these vectors are parallel.

24. Vectors are = if they have = magnitudes and the same direction.

25. Vectors are ∥ if they have the same or opp. directions.

Chapter Project **FIND OUT BY COMPARING** Have students measure different objects from the ones in Lesson 11-3. It may be easier to let one group measure at a time. This will allow you to keep a better eye on what is going on and it will avoid the confusion of students getting in each other's way.

Exercises MIXED REVIEW

SELF ASSESSMENT JOURNAL Check that students' diagrams and tables include how to describe vectors using ordered pair notation and how to describe the magnitude and direction of vectors.

GETTING READY FOR LESSON 11-5 These exercises prepare students to add vectors.

Wrap Up

THE BIG IDEA Ask students: *Explain the difference between a vector, a line segment, and a ray.*

RETEACHING ACTIVITY Students describe vectors using ordered pair notation. (Reteaching worksheet 11-4)

26. **Air Travel** A plane takes off on a runway in the direction 10° east of south. When it reaches 5000 ft, it turns right 45°. It cruises at this altitude for 60 mi. It then turns left 160°, descends, and lands. Match each velocity vector with the appropriate portion of the flight.

A. The plane ascends.
B. The plane cruises.
C. The plane descends.

I. C

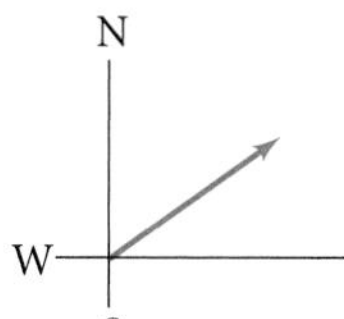

II. B

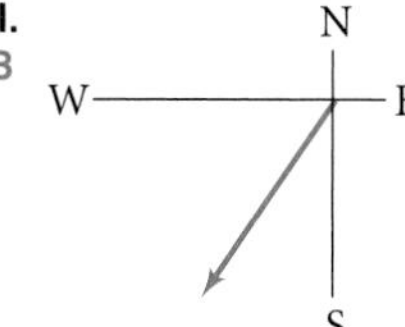

III. A

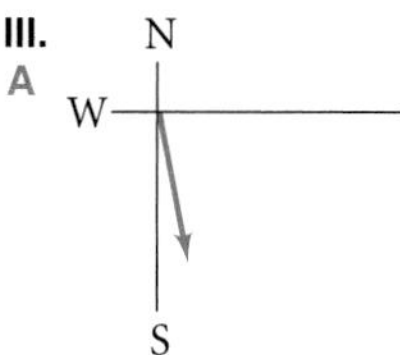

Chapter Project *Find Out by Comparing*

Repeat the activity on page 560, but this time work in groups to estimate the height of a single object on your school grounds. Have each person in your group measure the angle of elevation from a different distance. Then compare results within the group. Write a brief report explaining the variations in your estimates of the object's height. Decide as a group on a single estimate of the object's height. Check students' work.

27. Neither; you need information about at least 1 acute angle or at least 1 other side.

Exercises MIXED REVIEW

Is each pair of triangles *congruent, similar,* or *neither*? Justify your answers. 27. See above.

27.

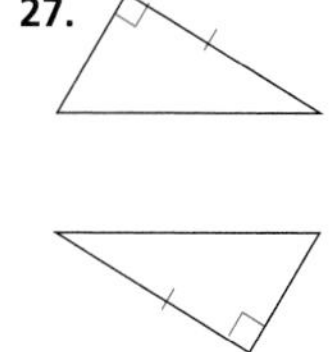

28.

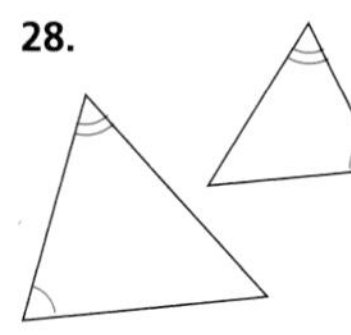

similar; AA~

29.

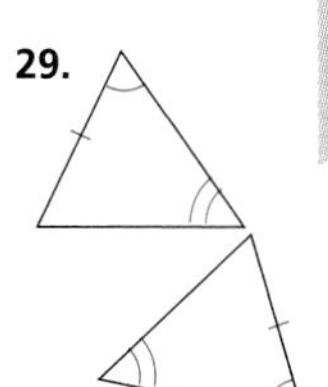

congruent; AAS

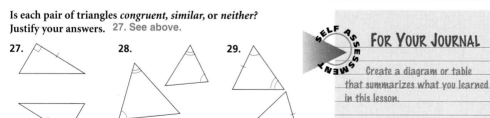

FOR YOUR JOURNAL

Create a diagram or table that summarizes what you learned in this lesson.

30. **Sports** A cylindrical hockey puck is 1 in. high and 3 in. in diameter. What is its volume? Round your answer to the nearest tenth. about 7.1 in.^{3}

31. A circle has radius 7 m. Two radii form a 100° angle. What is the length of the minor arc? Round your answer to the nearest tenth. 12.2 m

Getting Ready for Lesson 11-5

32. a. Find A', the image of $A(4, 3)$ under the translation $\langle 2, 5\rangle$. $A'(6, 8)$
b. Find A'', the image of A' under the translation $\langle -5, 6\rangle$. $A''(1, 14)$
c. What single translation maps A to A''? $\langle -3, 11\rangle$

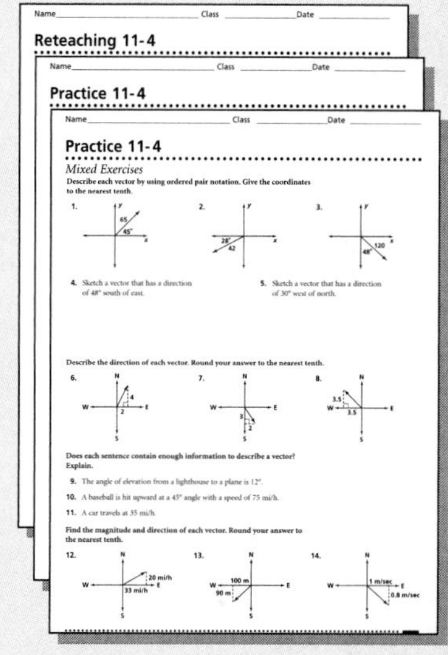

Reteaching 11-4

Practice 11-4

Practice 11-4

Mixed Exercises

Describe each vector by using ordered pair notation. Give the coordinates to the nearest tenth.

Describe the direction of each vector. Round your answer to the nearest tenth.

Does each sentence contain enough information to describe a vector? Explain.

Find the magnitude and direction of each vector. Round your answer to the nearest tenth.

Lesson Quiz

Lesson Quiz is also available in Transparencies.

1. Find the magnitude and direction of the vector. Round to the nearest whole unit. 43 mi/h in the direction of 55° north of east

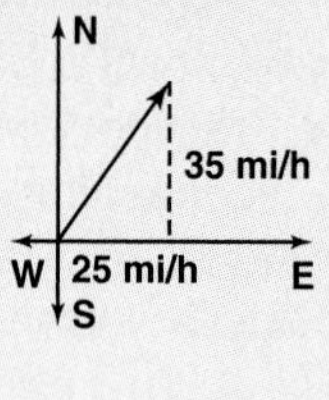

2. Describe the vector using ordered pair notation. Give the coordinates to the nearest unit. $\langle -65, 55\rangle$

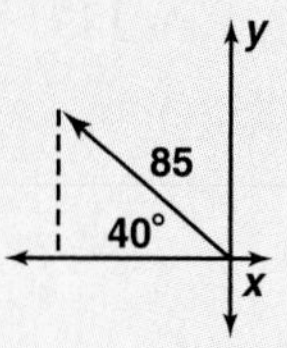

11-5 Teaching Notes

PROBLEM OF THE DAY

If the net shown is folded to form a cube, what is the largest sum of numbers on the three faces meeting at a corner? 14

	1		
6	2	4	5
	3		

Problem of the Day is also available in Transparencies.

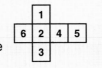

CONNECTING TO PRIOR KNOWLEDGE Draw a triangle with vertices $A(1, 2)$, $B(6, 1)$, and $C(3, 5)$. Then have students find its image under the translation $\langle -2, -3\rangle$ followed by the translation $\langle -1, 5\rangle$. Ask them to give one translation vector that would produce the same image.

THINK AND DISCUSS

Make sure students understand that $\vec{u}$, $\vec{v}$, and $\vec{w}$ represent vectors in ordered pair notation and do not represent lengths.

Example 1

Review with students their definitions of equal vectors from Exercise 24 of Lesson 11-4. Then point out that the head-to-tail method is possible because $\vec{c}$ is "equal" to its image under a translation.

Lesson Planning Options

Prerequisite Skills

- Describing vectors

Assignment Options for Exercises On Your Own

Core 1–16, 20
✪Extension 17–19

Use Mixed Review to maintain skills.

Resources

 **Student Edition**

Skills Handbook, pp. 660, 674
Extra Practice, p. 658
Glossary/Study Guide

 **Teaching Resources**

Chapter Support File, Ch. 11
- Practice 11-5 (two worksheets)
- Reteaching 11-5

Classroom Manager 11-5
Glossary, Spanish Resources

 **Transparencies**

5, 114, 117, 118

568

Connections  Navigation . . . and more

11-5 Adding Vectors

What You'll Learn

- Solving problems that involve vector addition

...And Why

To find the speed and direction of an object that has two forces acting on it

What You'll Need

- graph paper
- a marble
- three straws
- calculator

1. Answers may vary. Sample: The trip from Houston to Memphis is the result of the trip from Houston to New Orleans followed by the trip from New Orleans to Memphis.

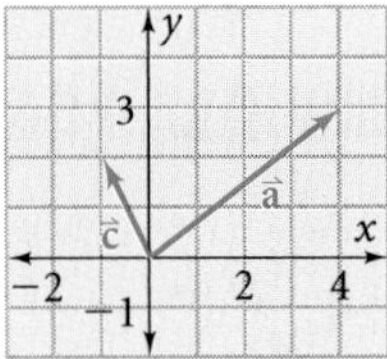

THINK AND DISCUSS

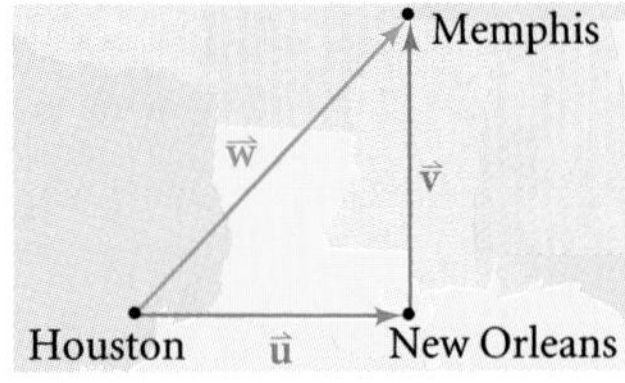

Until now, you've named vectors by using the initial point and terminal point ($\overrightarrow{AB}$, for example). You can also name vectors by using a single lowercase letter, such as $\vec{u}$.

The map shows vectors representing a flight from Houston to Memphis with a stopover in New Orleans. The vector from Houston to Memphis is called the *sum* of the other two vectors. You write this as $\vec{u} + \vec{v} = \vec{w}$.

1. *Critical Thinking* The sum of two vectors is called a **resultant.** Use the example of the trip from Houston to Memphis to explain why this name makes sense. See left.

Example 1

Coordinate Geometry Refer to the diagram at the left. Find $\vec{e}$, the sum of $\vec{a}$ and $\vec{c}$.

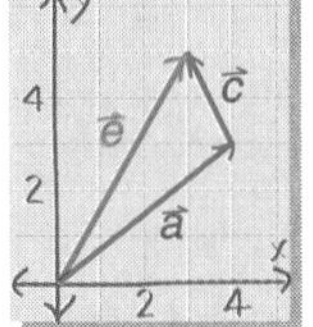

Draw $\vec{a}$ with its initial point at the origin. Then draw $\vec{c}$ so that its initial point is the terminal point of $\vec{a}$. Finally, draw a vector from the initial point of $\vec{a}$ to the terminal point of $\vec{c}$. This vector is $\vec{e}$, the resultant.

The method of adding vectors shown in Example 1 is called the *head-to-tail method.* (Do you see why?) You can describe the head-to-tail method mathematically by using ordered pair notation.

$\vec{a} + \vec{c} = \langle 4, 3\rangle + \langle -1, 2\rangle$ — Express $\vec{a}$ and $\vec{c}$ in ordered pair notation.
$= \langle 4 + (-1), 3 + 2\rangle$ — Add the x- and y-coordinates.
$= \langle 3, 5\rangle$ — Simplify.

A look back at the diagram confirms that $\langle 3, 5\rangle$ is indeed the resultant.

Adding Vectors

For $\vec{a} = \langle x_1, y_1\rangle$ and $\vec{c} = \langle x_2, y_2\rangle$, $\vec{a} + \vec{c} = \langle x_1 + x_2, y_1 + y_2\rangle$.

Example: For $\vec{a} = \langle -3, 2\rangle$ and $\vec{c} = \langle 1, 5\rangle$, $\vec{a} + \vec{c} = \langle -2, 7\rangle$.

ERROR ALERT! Some students may think connecting the two terminal points in the diagram on the left is equivalent to the head-to-tail method. **Remediation:** Show that a vector connecting the terminal points in the diagram would have a different length and direction than $\vec{\mathbf{e}}$.

Point out that it is best to place the initial point at the origin when representing vectors in the coordinate plane. Then the sum of the vectors will be indicated by the coordinates of the terminal point of the resultant.

ERROR ALERT! Some students may think that either diagonal of the parallelogram is the vector sum. **Remediation:** Point out that the resultant is drawn from the initial point of the first vector to the terminal point of the second vector.

Example 2 Relating to the Real World 

CONNECTING TO STUDENTS' WORLD Have students share their experiences of paddling a boat or swimming with and against a current.

ESL Some students may not know what a "ferry" is and what it means to "shuttle people." If possible, give the meaning of ferry in their native languages. Explain and/or demonstrate that shuttling people means moving them a relatively short distance.

The diagram at the right shows that you can add vectors in any order. That is, $\vec{\mathbf{u}} + \vec{\mathbf{v}} = \vec{\mathbf{v}} + \vec{\mathbf{u}}$. Notice also that the four vectors shown in red form a quadrilateral. This quadrilateral is a parallelogram because its opposite sides are congruent. The result $\vec{\mathbf{w}}$ is a diagonal of this parallelogram. This characteristic of vector addition is called the *parallelogram rule.*

Vector sums can show the result of actions that take place one after the other, such as a trip from Houston to Memphis by way of New Orleans. Vector sums can also show the result of two forces that act at the same time on an object. An example of this is the two forces that act on a boat—the forces of its engine and the current. As shown in the diagram, the force of the current combines with the force of the engine to give the boat its velocity.

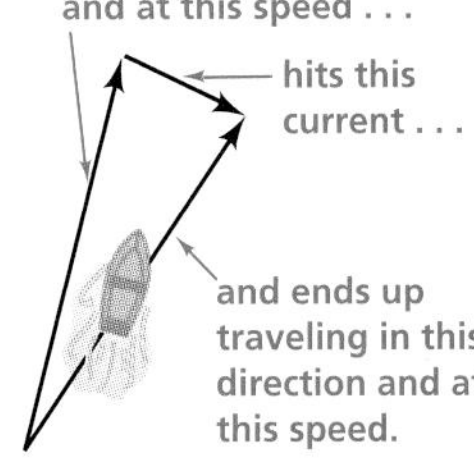

Example 2  Relating to the Real World 

Navigation A ferry shuttles people from one side of a river to the other. The speed of the ferry in still water is 25 mi/h, and the river flows directly south at 7 mi/h. Suppose the ferry heads directly west. What are the ferry's resulting speed and direction?

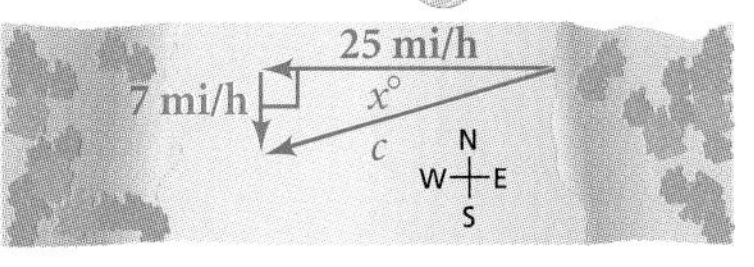

The diagram shows the sum of the two vectors. To find the ferry's speed, use the Pythagorean Theorem to find the length of the resultant.

$c^2 = 25^2 + 7^2$ The lengths of the legs are 25 and 7.

$c^2 = 674$ Simplify.

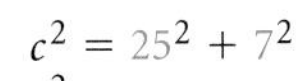

$c \approx 25.96151$ Use a calculator to take the square root.

To find the ferry's direction, use trigonometry.

$\tan x° = \frac{7}{25}$ Use the tangent ratio.

$x = \tan^{-1}\left(\frac{7}{25}\right)$

$x \approx 15.642246$ Use a calculator.

The ferry's speed is about 26 mi/h, and its direction is about 16° south of west.

2. Try This Use the diagram to find the angle at which the ferry must head upriver in order to travel directly across the river.

7 mi/h, 25 mi/h, x°

about 16° north of west

Additional Examples

FOR EXAMPLE 1

Use the head-to-tail method to find $\vec{\mathbf{w}}$, the sum of $\vec{\mathbf{u}}$ and $\vec{\mathbf{v}}$.

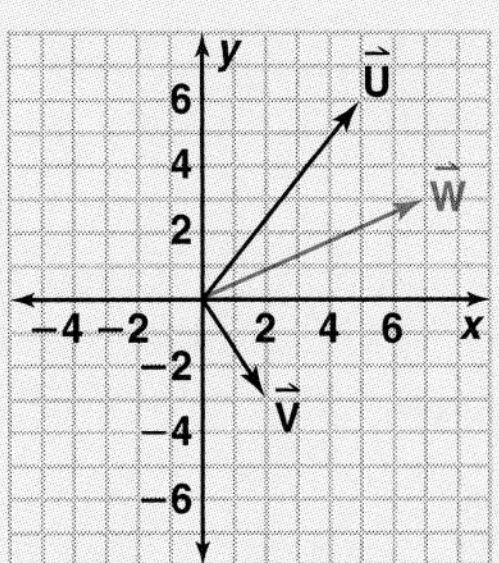

Discussion: *Describe another way to use the head-to-tail method to find* $\vec{\mathbf{w}}$.

FOR EXAMPLE 2

You are paddling a canoe east on a river at a speed of 5 mi/h. The river flows south at 4 mi/h. What is the resulting speed and direction of your canoe? Round to the nearest tenth, if necessary. 6.4 mi/h in the direction of 38.7° south of east

Discussion: *How could you determine the direction in which you should head in order to travel directly east?*

WORK TOGETHER

TACTILE LEARNING Allow students enough time for this activity so that each student in the group has an opportunity to be both a straw blower and an observer.

DIVERSITY Be conscious of any disabled students in your class who may have difficulty blowing through the straw or positioning themselves level with the paper and straw. Make sure that there is a task they can perform such as catching the marble or drawing the vector, so they can actively participate in the activity.

EXTENSION Equip students with a stopwatch so they can keep track of the time it takes for the marble to roll off the paper. Then have them measure the length of the vector in mm and calculate the speed of the marble in mm/sec.

Exercises ON YOUR OWN

ALTERNATIVE ASSESSMENT **Exercises 1–8** Have students copy each diagram and draw the resultant using the head-to-tail method or the parallelogram rule. Then have them write each vector in ordered pair notation and use the rule for adding vectors to find the sum. Students can then compare their answers and make corrections as necessary.

Technology Options

For Exercises 17–18, students may use a graphing program or a drawing program to draw the diagrams.

Prentice Hall Technology 

Software
- Secondary Math Lab Toolkit™
- Computer Item Generator 11-5

CD-ROM
- Multimedia Geometry Lab 11

Internet
- See the Prentice Hall site. (http://www.phschool.com)

570

WORK TOGETHER

Work in groups of at least three. Draw a set of axes on a piece of graph paper, as shown in the photo. Place a marble at the origin. Have two members of your group aim straws along the x- and y-axes. When the third member of the group gives a signal, blow through the straws at the marble. Stop the marble before it rolls off the paper, and mark its stopping point.

3. Draw a vector from the origin to the stopping point. Then draw the vectors that represent the two forces on the marble. Which of the forces has the greater magnitude?

3–4. See back of book.

4. Come up with a way to tell who in your group can exert the most force on the marble. Explain why your method works.

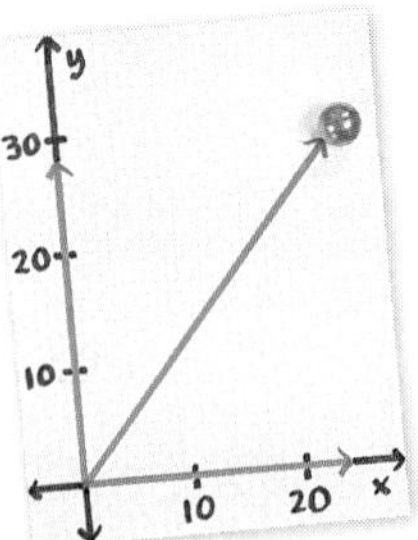

Exercises ON YOUR OWN

Coordinate Geometry **Find the sum of each pair of vectors. Give your answers in ordered pair notation.**

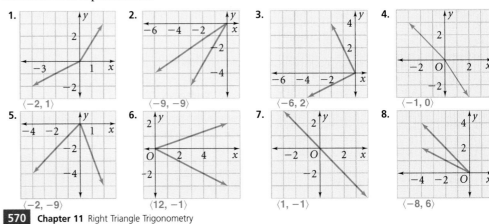

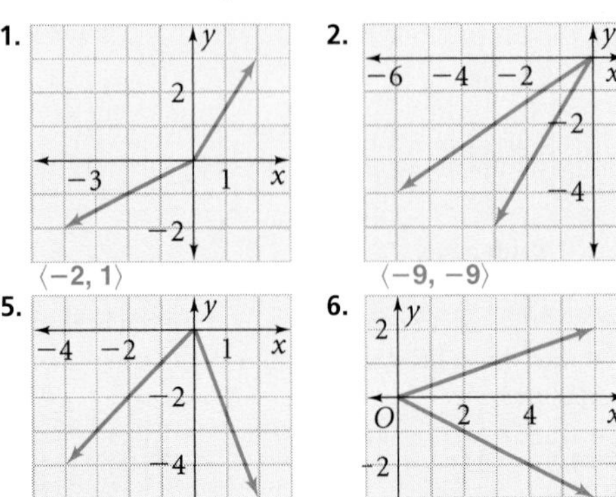

1. ⟨−2, 1⟩
2. ⟨−9, −9⟩
5. ⟨−2, −9⟩
6. ⟨12, −1⟩

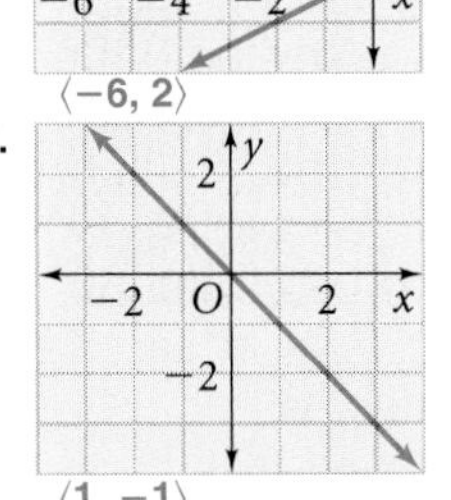

3. ⟨−6, 2⟩
7. ⟨1, −1⟩

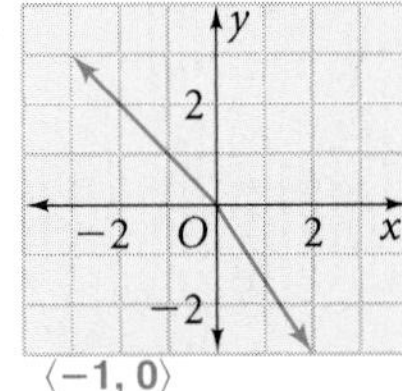

4. ⟨−1, 0⟩

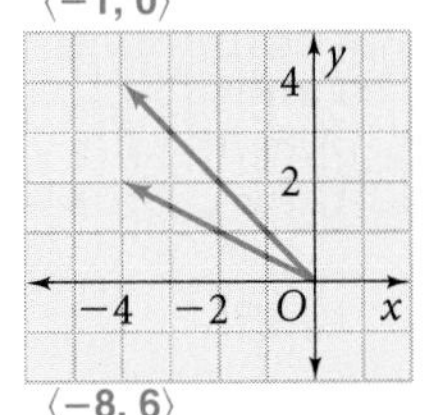

8. ⟨−8, 6⟩

Exercises 13–16 Remind students that the length of the hypotenuse of a 30°-60°-90° triangle is twice the length of the shortest leg and the length of the longer leg is $\sqrt{3}$ times the shorter leg.

Exercise 17a Suggest students use a scale of 1 cm = 1 km on their graph. Point out that 10° west of north is the same as 80° north of west.

EXTENSION Have students research how to find the dot product of two vectors. Have them give the rule and several examples. Ask them how the dot product can be used to determine if two vectors are perpendicular.

9. a. **Probability** Find the probability that the sum of any two of the vectors at the right has a greater magnitude than the third. $\frac{2}{3}$
   b. **Open-ended** Draw three vectors of your own. Then use your diagram to find the answer to part (a). See back of book for sample.

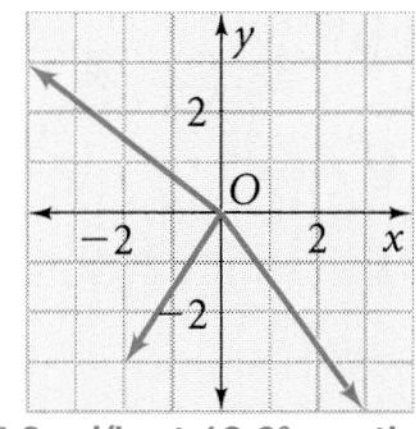

10. **Boat Travel** The speed of a powerboat in still water is 35 mi/h. This powerboat heads directly west across the Trinity River at a point at which it flows directly south at 8 mi/h. What are the resulting speed and direction of the boat? Round your answers to the nearest tenth. 35.9 mi/h at 12.9° south of west

11. **Navigation** A fishing trawler leaves its home port and travels 150 mi directly east. It then changes course and travels 40 mi due north.
   a. In what direction should the trawler head to return to its home port? 15° south of west
   b. How long will the return trip take if the trawler averages 23 mi/h? about 6.7 h or 6 h 40 min

12. a. Find the sum $\vec{a} + \vec{c}$, where $\vec{a} = \langle 45, -60 \rangle$ and $\vec{c} = \langle -45, 60 \rangle$. $\langle 0, 0 \rangle$
   b. **Writing** What does your answer to part (a) tell you about $\vec{a}$ and $\vec{c}$? $\vec{a}$ and $\vec{c}$ have opposite directions and = magnitude.

In Exercises 13–16: (a) Copy the diagram and then draw a parallelogram that has the given vectors as adjacent sides. (b) Find the magnitude and direction of the resultant. 13a–16a. See margin.

13.

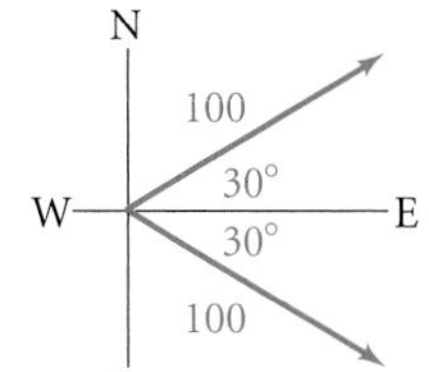

b. about 173 due east

14.

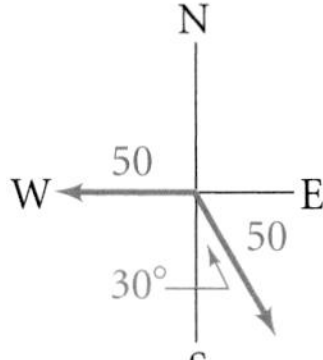

b. 50 at 30° west of south

15.

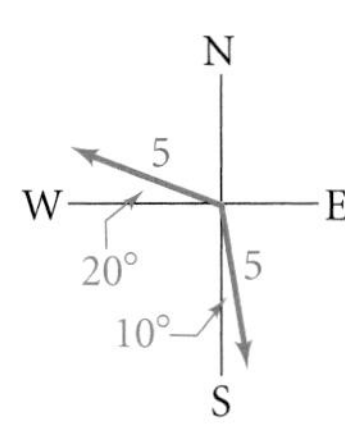

b. 5 at 40° south of west

16.

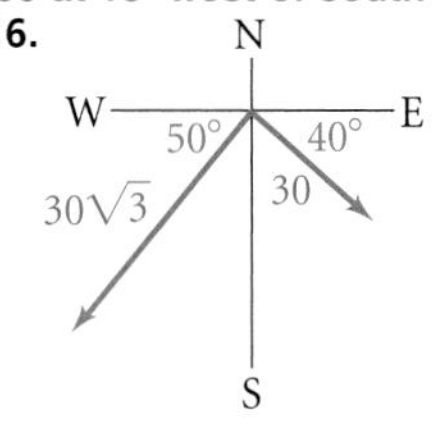

b. 60 at 10° west of south

17. A Red Cross helicopter takes off and flies 75 km at 20° south of west. There, it drops off some relief supplies. It then flies 125 km at 10° west of north to pick up three medics. a–b. See back of book.
   a. Make an accurate head-to-tail drawing of the two vectors described.
   b. Draw the resultant and measure it to find the helicopter's distance from its point of origin and the direction it should head to get back.

18. **Air Travel** The cruising speed of a Boeing 767 in still air is 530 mi/h. Suppose that a 767 cruising directly east encounters a 80 mi/h wind blowing 40° south of west.
   a. Sketch the vectors for the velocity of the plane and the wind. See margin.
   b. Express both vectors from part (a) in ordered pair notation. $\langle 530, 0 \rangle$, $\langle -61.3, -51.4 \rangle$
   c. Find the sum of the vectors from part (b). $\langle 468.7, -51.4 \rangle$
   d. Find the magnitude and direction of the vector from part (c). about 471.5 mi/h at 6.3° south of east

19. **Geometry in 3 Dimensions** A bear leaves home and ambles 10 km straight south. She then turns and walks another 10 km straight west. After a short rest, she turns and wanders straight north another 10 km, ending up at the point at which she started. What color is the bear? (*Hint:* Figure out where on Earth she is.) white

13a.

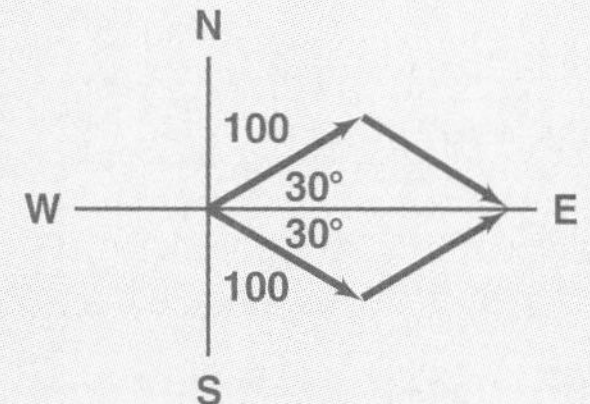

14a.

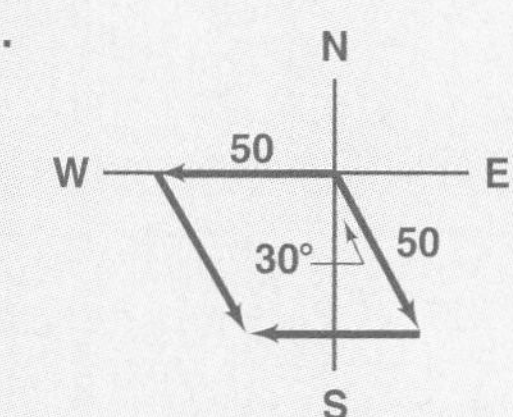

15a.

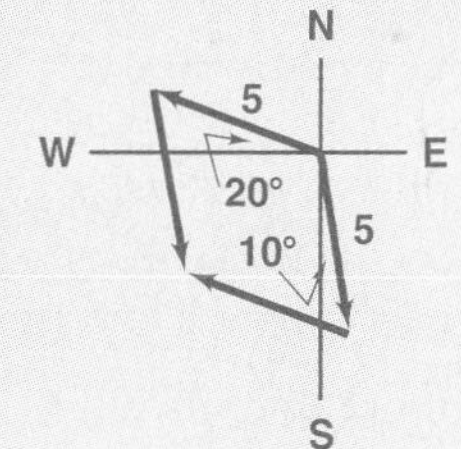

16a.

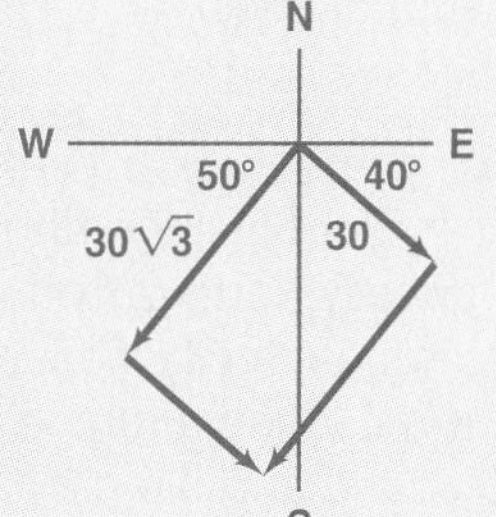

18a.

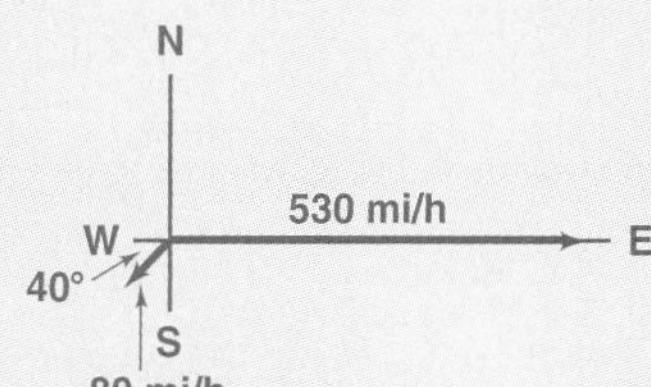

Exercises MIXED REVIEW

Exercises 23 and 24 Students will need to calculate the heights before they can find the areas.

GETTING READY FOR LESSON 11-6 These exercises prepare students to use trigonometry to find the areas of regular polygons.

Wrap Up

THE BIG IDEA Ask students to describe three ways to find the sum of two vectors.

RETEACHING ACTIVITY Students solve problems that involve vector addition. (Reteaching worksheet 11-5)

Exercises CHECKPOINT

In this Checkpoint, your students will assess their own progress in Lessons 11-4 to 11-5.

Exercise 2 Suggest that students copy the diagram and draw the vector sum as a way to check their answers.

Exercise 3 Check that students do not confuse the direction "east of south" with "south of east."

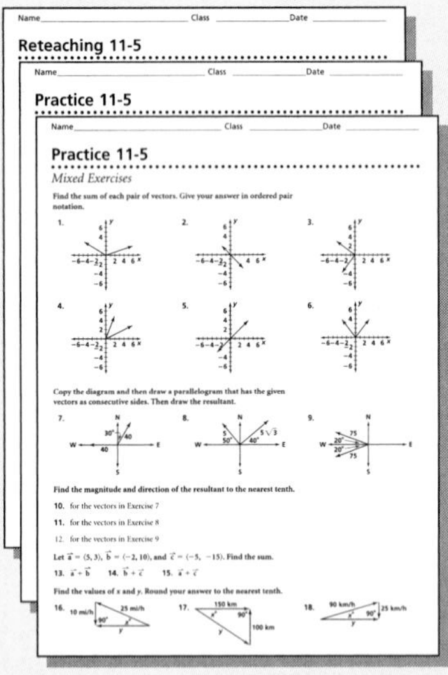

Lesson Quiz

Lesson Quiz is also available in Transparencies.

1. Find the sum of vectors ⟨3, 5⟩ and ⟨−2, 1⟩. Draw a diagram to support your answer. ⟨1, 6⟩; See back of book.
2. The cruising speed of an airplane is 400 mi/h. Suppose the airplane cruising directly north encounters a wind blowing directly west at 30 mi/h. What is the airplane's resulting speed and direction? ≈ 401 mi/h in the direction 4° west of north

572

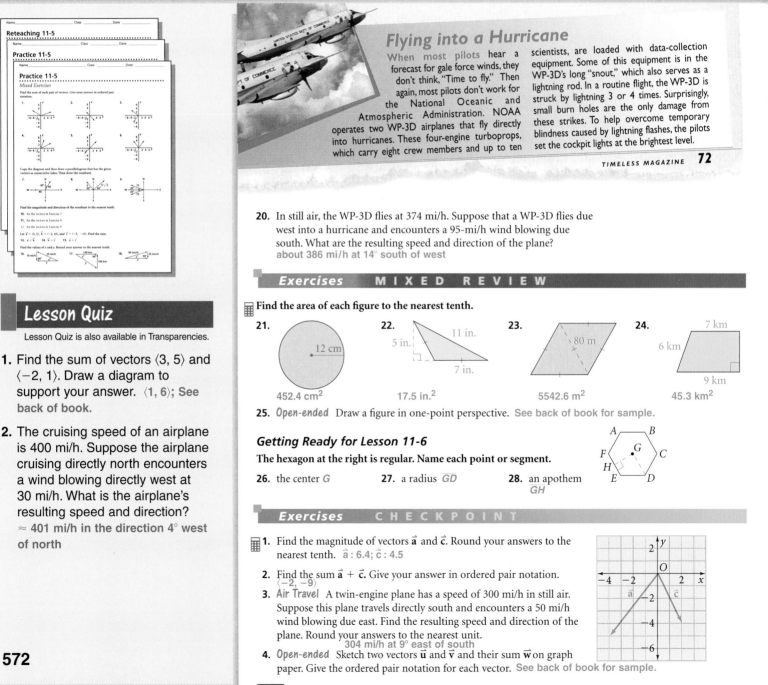

Flying into a Hurricane

When most pilots hear a forecast for gale force winds, they don't think, "Time to fly." Then again, most pilots don't work for the National Oceanic and Atmospheric Administration. NOAA operates two WP-3D airplanes that fly directly into hurricanes. These four-engine turboprops, which carry eight crew members and up to ten scientists, are loaded with data-collection equipment. Some of this equipment is in the WP-3D's long "snout," which also serves as a lightning rod. In a routine flight, the WP-3D is struck by lightning 3 or 4 times. Surprisingly, small burn holes are the only damage from these strikes. To help overcome temporary blindness caused by lightning flashes, the pilots set the cockpit lights at the brightest level.

TIMELESS MAGAZINE 72

20. In still air, the WP-3D flies at 374 mi/h. Suppose that a WP-3D flies due west into a hurricane and encounters a 95-mi/h wind blowing due south. What are the resulting speed and direction of the plane? about 386 mi/h at 14° south of west

Exercises MIXED REVIEW

Find the area of each figure to the nearest tenth.

21. (circle, radius 12 cm) 452.4 cm^2
22. (triangle, 5 in., 11 in., 7 in.) 17.5 in.^{2}
23. (rhombus, 80 m) 5542.6 m^2
24. (trapezoid, 7 km, 6 km, 9 km) 45.3 km^2

25. *Open-ended* Draw a figure in one-point perspective. See back of book for sample.

Getting Ready for Lesson 11-6

The hexagon at the right is regular. Name each point or segment.

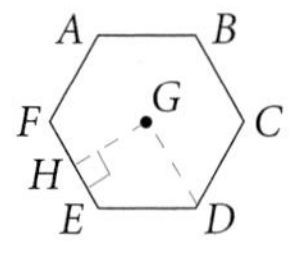

26. the center G
27. a radius $\overline{GD}$
28. an apothem $\overline{GH}$

Exercises CHECKPOINT

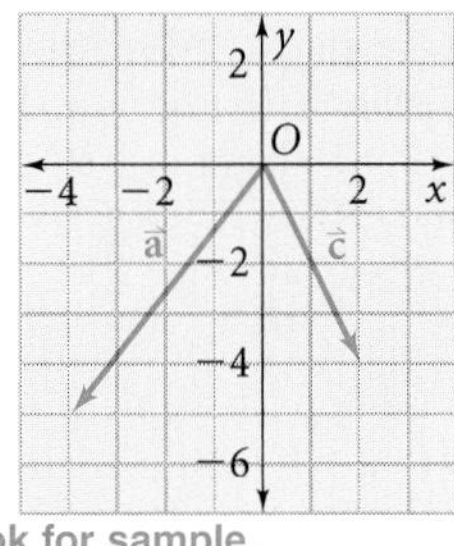

1. Find the magnitude of vectors $\vec{a}$ and $\vec{c}$. Round your answers to the nearest tenth. $\vec{a}$: 6.4; $\vec{c}$: 4.5
2. Find the sum $\vec{a} + \vec{c}$. Give your answer in ordered pair notation. ⟨−2, −9⟩
3. Air Travel A twin-engine plane has a speed of 300 mi/h in still air. Suppose this plane travels directly south and encounters a 50 mi/h wind blowing due east. Find the resulting speed and direction of the plane. Round your answers to the nearest unit. 304 mi/h at 9° east of south
4. *Open-ended* Sketch two vectors $\vec{u}$ and $\vec{v}$ and their sum $\vec{w}$ on graph paper. Give the ordered pair notation for each vector. See back of book for sample.

11-6 Teaching Notes

PROBLEM OF THE DAY

Draw a continuous line which has no more than six straight parts and passes through all sixteen points.

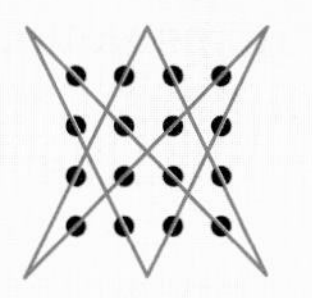

Problem of the Day is also available in Transparencies.

CONNECTING TO PRIOR KNOWLEDGE Draw a regular hexagon on the board. Label the apothem 5 cm and the radius 5.6 cm and have students calculate the area.

THINK AND DISCUSS

VISUAL LEARNING Copy the diagram and the definitions onto a poster and display it for the class.

Example 1

Help students see that $\triangle XCY \cong \triangle ZCY$ by the HL Theorem. Therefore, $m\angle XCY = m\angle ZCY$ (or $m\angle XCY = \frac{1}{2}m\angle XCZ$) and $XY = ZY$ (or $XY = \frac{1}{2}XZ$).

Make sure students understand the keystrokes used to evaluate the expression and do not insert parentheses around "80 ÷ 36."

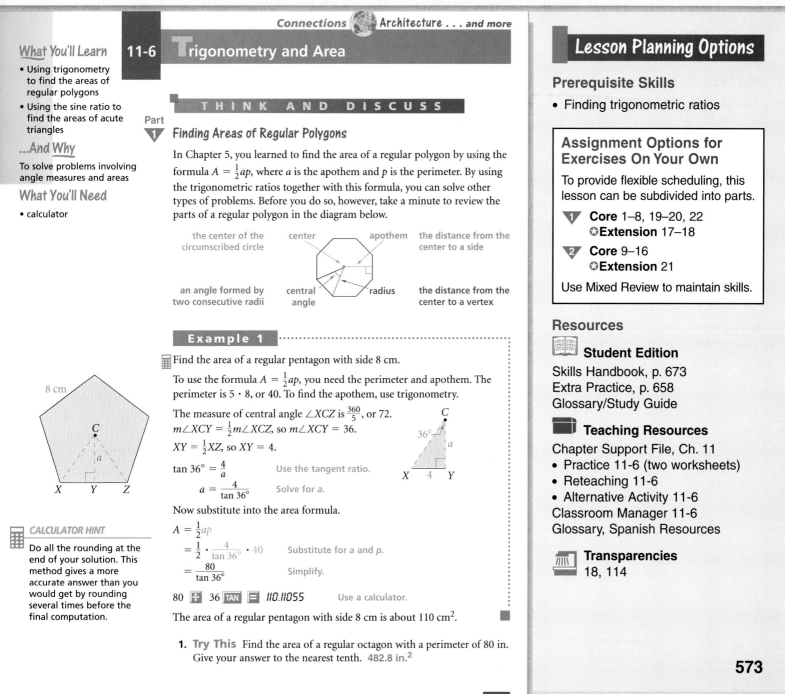

Connections Architecture . . . and more

11-6 Trigonometry and Area

What You'll Learn

- Using trigonometry to find the areas of regular polygons
- Using the sine ratio to find the areas of acute triangles

...And Why

To solve problems involving angle measures and areas

What You'll Need

- calculator

THINK AND DISCUSS

Part 1

Finding Areas of Regular Polygons

In Chapter 5, you learned to find the area of a regular polygon by using the formula $A = \frac{1}{2}ap$, where a is the apothem and p is the perimeter. By using the trigonometric ratios together with this formula, you can solve other types of problems. Before you do so, however, take a minute to review the parts of a regular polygon in the diagram below.

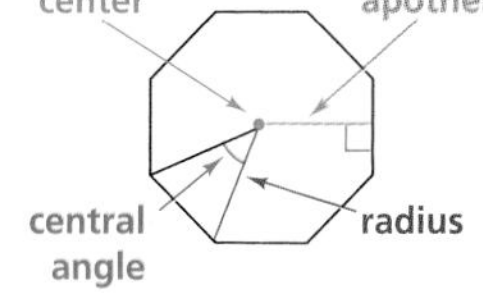

Example 1

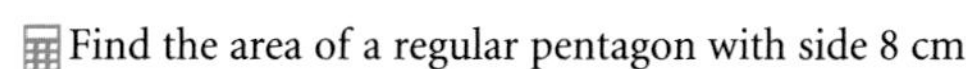

Find the area of a regular pentagon with side 8 cm.

To use the formula $A = \frac{1}{2}ap$, you need the perimeter and apothem. The perimeter is $5 \cdot 8$, or 40. To find the apothem, use trigonometry.

The measure of central angle $\angle XCZ$ is $\frac{360}{5}$, or 72.

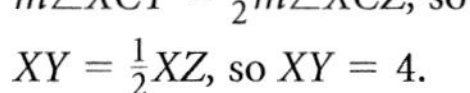

$m\angle XCY = \frac{1}{2}m\angle XCZ$, so $m\angle XCY = 36$.

$XY = \frac{1}{2}XZ$, so $XY = 4$.

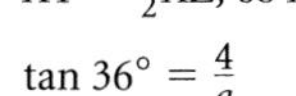

$\tan 36° = \frac{4}{a}$ Use the tangent ratio.

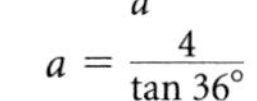

$a = \frac{4}{\tan 36°}$ Solve for a.

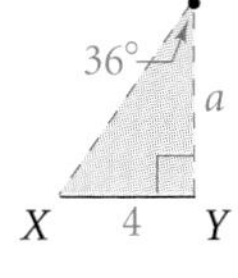

Now substitute into the area formula.

$A = \frac{1}{2}ap$

$= \frac{1}{2} \cdot \frac{4}{\tan 36°} \cdot 40$ Substitute for a and p.

$= \frac{80}{\tan 36°}$ Simplify.

80 ÷ 36 TAN = 110.11055 Use a calculator.

The area of a regular pentagon with side 8 cm is about 110 cm^2.

8 cm, C, a, X, Y, Z

CALCULATOR HINT

Do all the rounding at the end of your solution. This method gives a more accurate answer than you would get by rounding several times before the final computation.

1. **Try This** Find the area of a regular octagon with a perimeter of 80 in. Give your answer to the nearest tenth. 482.8 in.^{2}

Lesson Planning Options

Prerequisite Skills

- Finding trigonometric ratios

Assignment Options for Exercises On Your Own

To provide flexible scheduling, this lesson can be subdivided into parts.

1 **Core** 1–8, 19–20, 22
Extension 17–18

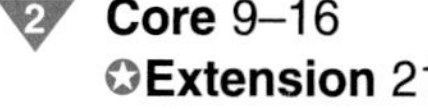

2 **Core** 9–16
Extension 21

Use Mixed Review to maintain skills.

Resources

Student Edition

Skills Handbook, p. 673
Extra Practice, p. 658
Glossary/Study Guide

Teaching Resources

Chapter Support File, Ch. 11

- Practice 11-6 (two worksheets)
- Reteaching 11-6
- Alternative Activity 11-6

Classroom Manager 11-6
Glossary, Spanish Resources

Transparencies

18, 114

Example 2 Relating to the Real World 

Review with students that eight congruent central angles are formed by the radii of the octagon and that their sum is 360°. Therefore, the measure of one of the central angles is $\frac{360}{8}$.

Make sure that students understand why the length of the side is $2x$ and how the step $8 \cdot 2x$ becomes $16 \cdot 16(\sin 22.5°)$.

ERROR ALERT! Because this problem requires many steps, some students will have difficulty determining what information needs to be found and organizing the information in a useful way. **Remediation:** Work through each step of the problem with students. Point out that in order to use the area formula, they need to find the apothem and the perimeter. To find the perimeter, they need to know the side length. It may help to draw a box around the solution to each part.

Question 2 Review with students the term *horizontal cross section.*

Additional Examples

FOR EXAMPLE 1

Find the area of a regular octagon with side length 12 cm to the nearest tenth. 695.3 cm^2

FOR EXAMPLE 2

The floor of a gazebo is a regular pentagon. Its radius is 8 ft. Find the area of the floor to the nearest whole number. 152 ft^2

FOR EXAMPLE 3

A landscaper designs a triangular garden. Two edges of the garden have lengths 12 ft and 10 ft. The angle between the edges is 54°. Find the area of the garden to the nearest whole number. 49 ft^2

The Castel del Monte, situated on a hill in southern Italy, contains many regular octagons. It was built in the 1200s as a hunting residence for Frederick II, the king of Sicily.

Example 2 Relating to the Real World 

Architecture The radius of the castle's inner courtyard is 16 m. Find the area of the courtyard.

Use trigonometry to find the apothem and the perimeter. The measure of the central angle of an octagon is $\frac{360}{8}$, or 45. So $m\angle C = \frac{1}{2}(45) = 22.5$.

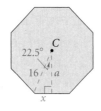

$\cos 22.5° = \frac{a}{16}$ $\quad$ $a = 16(\cos 22.5°)$

$\sin 22.5° = \frac{x}{16}$ $\quad$ $x = 16(\sin 22.5°)$

Now use x to find the perimeter p.

$p = 8 \cdot \text{length of side}$

$= 8 \cdot 2x$ — The length of each side is $2x$.

$= 16 \cdot 16(\sin 22.5°)$ — Simplify and substitute for x.

$= 256(\sin 22.5°)$ — Simplify.

Finally, substitute into the area formula, $A = \frac{1}{2}ap$.

$A = \frac{1}{2} \cdot 16(\cos 22.5°) \cdot 256(\sin 22.5°)$ — Substitute for a and p.

$= 2048(\cos 22.5°)(\sin 22.5°)$ — Simplify.

$= 724.07734$ — Use a calculator.

The area of the courtyard of the Castel del Monte is about 724 m^2.

2. **Try This** All of the eight small towers around the castle are also regular octagons. The radius of each is 7.3 m. Find the area of a horizontal cross section of each tower to the nearest square meter. 151 m^2

The examples and exercises in this lesson will be restricted to triangles in which the included angle is acute. However, you may want to tell students that there is a method for finding the sine ratio of an obtuse angle so the area formula applies to all triangles.

Example 3 Relating to the Real World 

KINESTHETIC LEARNING If you have block scheduling or an extended class period, take students outside. Have them work in groups of five. Have three students be vertices of a triangle. Use twine to make the sides. Have the other two students measure two of the sides with a tape measure and the included angle with a compass. Then have the groups calculate the area of the triangle they formed.

Exercises ON YOUR OWN

ALTERNATIVE ASSESSMENT **Exercises 1–8** Have students work in pairs. Assign half of the pairs the odd problems and the other half the even problems. After the pairs complete their solutions, have odds and evens exchange and correct each other's solutions. Any errors should be discussed jointly by the two pairs until an solution is agreed upon.

Part 2

Finding the Area of a Triangle Given SAS

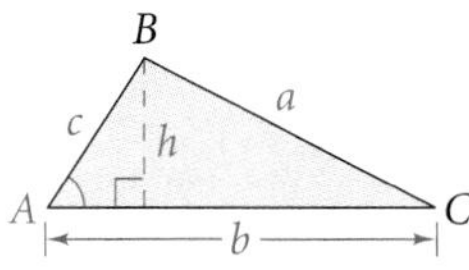

Suppose you want to find the area of $\triangle ABC$, but you know only the lengths b and c, and $m\angle A$. To use the formula Area $= \frac{1}{2}bh$, you need to know the height. You can find the height by using trigonometry.

$\sin A = \frac{h}{c}$ Use the sine ratio.

$h = c(\sin A)$ Solve for h.

Now substitute for h in the formula Area $= \frac{1}{2}bh$.

Area $= \frac{1}{2}bc(\sin A)$

Theorem 11-1
Area of a Triangle Given SAS

The area of a triangle is one half the product of the lengths of two sides and the sine of the included angle.

Area of triangle $= \frac{1}{2}$ · side length · side length · sine of included angle

The proof of this theorem for the case in which the given angle is obtuse requires a more complete definition of sine. You will study this definition in later math courses.

Example 3 Relating to the Real World 

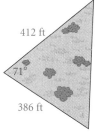

Surveying When surveyed, two adjacent sides of a triangular plot of land measured 412 ft and 386 ft. The angle between the sides was 71°. Find the area of the plot.

Area $= \frac{1}{2}$ · side length · side length · sine of included angle

$= \frac{1}{2} \cdot 412 \cdot 386 \cdot \sin 71°$ Substitute the given information.

$= 75183.855$ Use a calculator.

$\approx 75{,}200 \text{ ft}^2$

3. **Try This** Two adjacent sides of a triangular building plot measure 120 ft and 85 ft. The angle between them measures 85°. Find the area of the land. Round your answer to the nearest square foot. 5081 ft^2

Exercises ON YOUR OWN

Find the area of each polygon. Give your answers to the nearest tenth.

1. equilateral triangle with apothem 4 in. 83.1 in.^2
2. regular octagon with apothem 6 cm 119.3 cm^2
3. regular hexagon with radius 10 ft 259.8 ft^2
4. regular dodecagon with apothem 10 ft 321.5 ft^2
5. regular decagon with radius 4 in. 47.0 in.^2
6. regular pentagon with apothem 7 cm 178.0 cm^2
7. regular 15-gon with side length 12 yd 2540.5 yd^2
8. regular decagon with perimeter 80 cm 492.4 cm^2

Technology Options

For Exercise 26, students may use construction software to construct the parallel lines.

Prentice Hall Technology 

Software
- Secondary Math Lab Toolkit™
- Computer Item Generator 11-6

CD-ROM
- Multimedia Geometry Lab 11

Internet
- See the Prentice Hall site. (http://www.phschool.com)

ESL Exercise 17 Some students may think a "hexagonal nut" is a type of edible nut like a peanut or a walnut. Help them understand that a "hexagonal nut" is a small block of metal that is used in conjunction with a bolt to fasten something. If possible, bring some nuts and bolts to class to illustrate.

Exercise 18 Steps a–f help students derive a formula for the area of a regular *n*-gon.

CONNECTING TO STUDENTS' WORLD Exercise 20 Have students investigate the shapes and dimensions of other street signs and calculate their areas.

Exercise 21 Make sure students understand how to solve for one of the legs of a triangle given the area formula.

WRITING Exercise 22 Suggest that students draw a regular polygon and describe why the statement is true for that polygon. Then they can generalize their explanation to other polygons.

Chapter Project **FIND OUT BY RESEARCHING** Allow students several days to complete this activity. Make sure students understand where to find the star Polaris.

pages 575–577 On Your Own

18a. The segments connecting C with the vertices of the polygon form $n \cong$ angles. The sum of the measures of these angles is 360, so the measure of each angle is $\frac{360}{n}$. The apothem is the angle bisector for each of these angles, so $m\angle C = \frac{1}{2}\left(\frac{360}{n}\right) = \frac{180}{n}$.

f. The area of a regular polygon with apothem 1 approaches π as the number of sides increases.

21. 320 ft

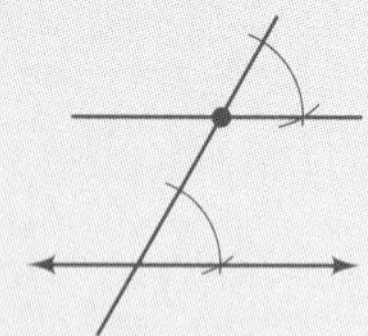

22. Each apothem is the altitude of an isosceles △, so it is also the angle bisector and the median.

page 577 Mixed Review

26.

576

Find the area of each triangle. Give your answers to the nearest tenth.

9. 27.7 m²

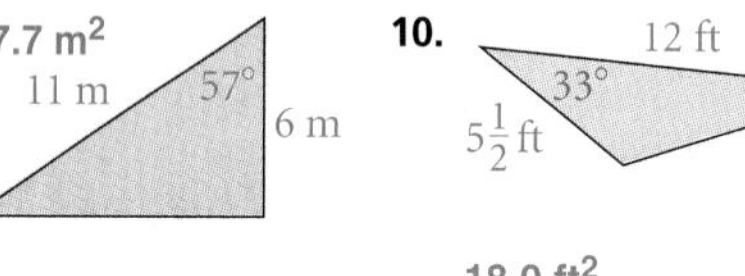

10. 18.0 ft²

11. 7554.0 m²

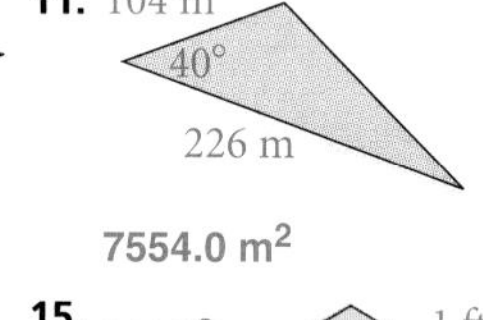

12. 50.9 cm²

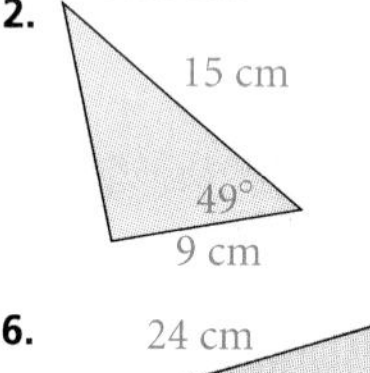

13. 311.3 km²

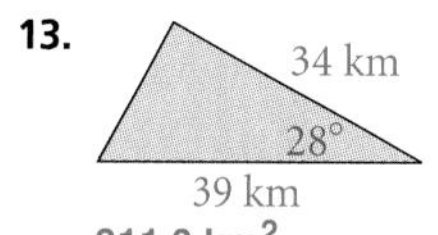

14. 151.4 mm²

15. 0.7 ft²

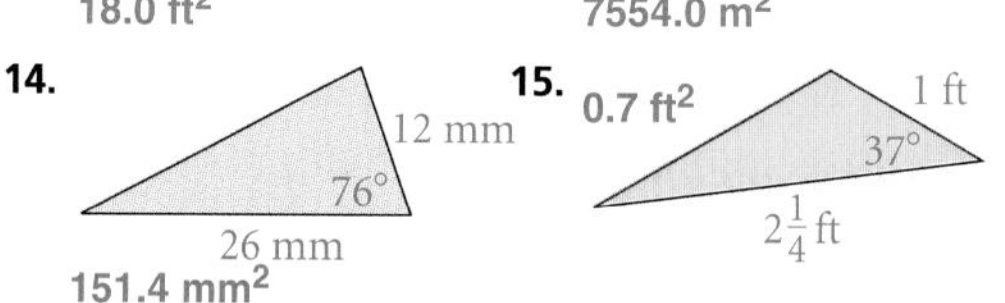

16. 82.7 cm²

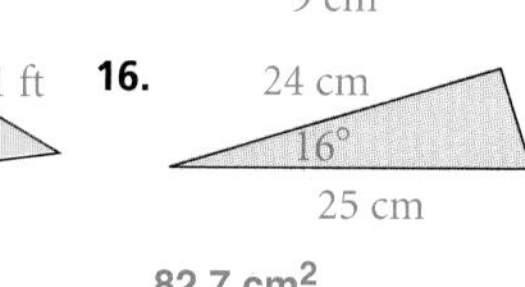

17. *Industrial Design* Refer to the diagram of the hexagonal nut. Round each answer to the nearest unit.
  a. Find the area of the circular space in the nut. 50 mm²
  b. Find the area of the hexagon minus the area of the circle. 116 mm²
  c. *Geometry in 3 Dimensions* Find the volume of the nut. 232 mm³

4 mm
8 mm
2 mm

18. Suppose a circle is inscribed in a regular *n*-gon with center C and apothem 1, as shown in the diagram.
  a. Explain why $m\angle C = \frac{1}{2}\left(\frac{360}{n}\right) = \frac{180}{n}$. See margin.
  b. Explain why $s = \tan C$. b–d. See right.
  c. Explain why the perimeter of the *n*-gon is $2n(\tan C)$.
  d. Explain why the area of the *n*-gon is $n\left(\tan \frac{180}{n}\right)$.
  e. *Open-ended* Pick a value for n between 0 and 10. Use a calculator to find the area of the *n*-gon. Then find the area of regular polygons with $10n$ sides and $100n$ sides. Sample: $n = 9$: 3.276; 3.143; 3.142
  f. What do you notice about your answers to part (e)? Explain. See margin.

C
1
s

18b. s is the leg opp. $\angle C$, so $\tan C = \frac{s}{1} = s$.
c. The length of each side is $2s$. So the perimeter is $n \cdot 2s = 2n(\tan C)$.
d. The area of a regular *n*-gon is $\frac{1}{2}ap = n(\tan \frac{180}{n})$.

19. *Architecture* The Pentagon, in Arlington, Virginia, is one of the world's largest office buildings. It is a regular pentagon, and the length of each of its sides is 921 ft. Find the amount of space covered by the Pentagon. Round your answer to the nearest thousand square feet. 1,459,000 ft²

20. The standard length of a side of a stop sign is 1 ft $\frac{1}{4}$ in. Find the area of this stop sign to the nearest tenth of a square foot. 5.0 ft²

21. *Surveying* A surveyor wants to mark off a triangular parcel with an area of 1 acre. One boundary of the triangle extends 300 ft along a straight road. A second boundary extends at an angle of 65° from one end of this boundary. Draw a triangle to represent the piece of land and determine the length of the second boundary line to the nearest foot. (1 acre = 43,560 ft²) See margin.

22. *Writing* Explain why each apothem of a regular polygon bisects a central angle and a side of the polygon. See margin.

Exercises MIXED REVIEW

PORTFOLIO Share with students the criteria you will use to assess their work in portfolios, as well as how you plan to use the results. Students should understand how the rubrics assess their work, how each piece in the portfolio counts, and how the scores they get in their portfolios will affect their overall evaluation.

Wrap Up

THE BIG IDEA Ask students to explain how to find the area of a regular decagon if the perimeter is 80 cm.

RETEACHING ACTIVITY Students use trigonometry to find the areas of regular polygons. (Reteaching worksheet 11-6)

Geometry at Work

To become a surveyor requires a background in mathematics and the ability to work with computers. Job opportunities are available in construction planning and in urban and regional planning.

Encourage students to investigate these topics:

- geodetic, hydrographic, and plane surveying
- the use of aerial photography, the NAVSTAR Global Positioning System (GPS), and electronic distance measurement equipment (EDM)
- basic surveying methods such as trilateration

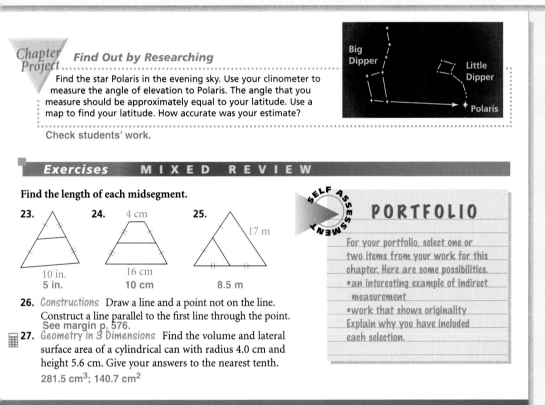

Chapter Project *Find Out by Researching*

Find the star Polaris in the evening sky. Use your clinometer to measure the angle of elevation to Polaris. The angle that you measure should be approximately equal to your latitude. Use a map to find your latitude. How accurate was your estimate?

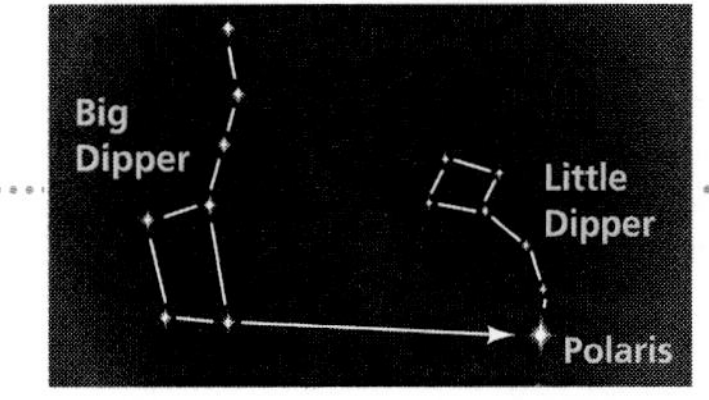

Check students' work.

Exercises MIXED REVIEW

Find the length of each midsegment.

23. 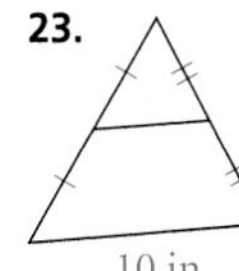

5 in.

24. 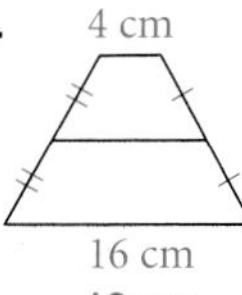

10 cm

25. 17 m
8.5 m

26. *Constructions* Draw a line and a point not on the line. Construct a line parallel to the first line through the point. See margin p. 576.

27. *Geometry in 3 Dimensions* Find the volume and lateral surface area of a cylindrical can with radius 4.0 cm and height 5.6 cm. Give your answers to the nearest tenth.
281.5 cm^3; 140.7 cm^2

For your portfolio, select one or two items from your work for this chapter. Here are some possibilities.
- an interesting example of indirect measurement
- work that shows originality

Explain why you have included each selection.

Geometry at Work

Surveyor

Surveyors calculate the locations, shapes, and areas of plots of land. A survey begins with a benchmark—a reference point whose latitude, longitude, and elevation are known. The surveyor uses a device called a *transit* to measure the angles of the plot of land and the distances of key points from the benchmark. Using trigonometry, the surveyor finds the latitude, longitude, and elevation of each key point in the survey. These points are located on a map and an accurate sketch of the plot is drawn. Finally, the area is calculated. One method involves dividing the plot into triangles and measuring the lengths of two sides and the included angle of each. The formula $A = \frac{1}{2}ab(\sin C)$ gives the area of each triangle. The area of the entire plot is the sum of the areas of the triangles.

Mini Project: On a flat area outside your school, place four objects to mark the vertices of an irregular quadrilateral. Calculate the area of the quadrilateral. Explain your method, and tell how you measured the sides and angles of the figure.

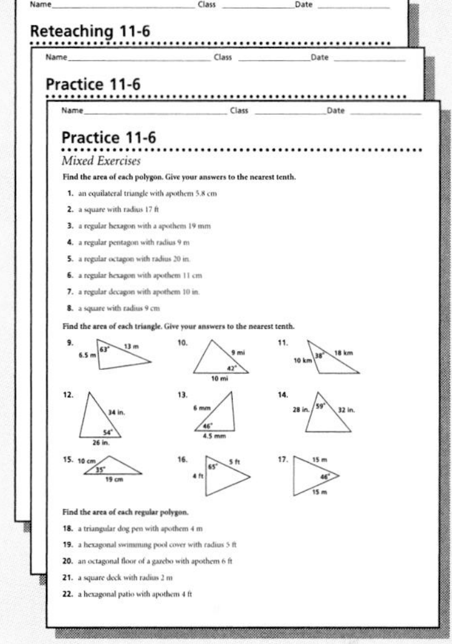

Name ______ Class ______ Date ______

Reteaching 11-6

Name ______ Class ______ Date ______

Practice 11-6

Name ______ Class ______ Date ______

Practice 11-6

Mixed Exercises

Find the area of each polygon. Give your answers to the nearest tenth.

1. an equilateral triangle with apothem 5.8 cm
2. a square with radius 17 ft
3. a regular hexagon with a apothem 19 mm
4. a regular pentagon with radius 9 m
5. a regular octagon with radius 20 in.
6. a regular hexagon with apothem 11 cm
7. a regular decagon with apothem 10 in.
8. a square with radius 9 cm

Find the area of each triangle. Give your answers to the nearest tenth.

9. 6.5 m, 13 m, 63°
10. 9 mi, 10 mi, 42°
11. 10 km, 18 km, 38°
12. 34 in., 26 in., 54°
13. 6 mm, 4.5 mm, 46°
14. 28 in., 32 in., 59°
15. 10 cm, 19 cm, 35°
16. 4 ft, 5 ft, 65°
17. 15 m, 15 m, 46°

Find the area of each regular polygon.

18. a triangular dog pen with apothem 4 m
19. a hexagonal swimming pool cover with radius 5 ft
20. an octagonal floor of a gazebo with apothem 6 ft
21. a square deck with radius 2 m
22. a hexagonal patio with apothem 4 ft

Lesson Quiz

Lesson Quiz is also available in Transparencies.

Give each answer to the nearest tenth.

1. Find the area of a regular pentagon with apothem 6 cm. 130.8 cm^2
2. Find the area of a regular decagon with radius 3 m. 26.5 m^2
3. Two sides of a triangle measure 7 in. and 12 in. The angle between the two sides is 35°. Find the area of the triangle. 24.1 $in.^2$
4. Two sides of a triangle measure 50 ft and 70 ft. The angle between the two sides is 58°. Find the area of the triangle. 1484.1 ft^2

Finishing The Chapter Project

PROJECT DAY You may wish to plan a project day during which students share their completed projects. Encourage groups to explain their processes as well as their products.

PROJECT NOTEBOOK Have students review their project work and bring their notebooks up to date.

- Have students present their displays. Ask each student to explain one measurement.
- Ask students to share any insights they found when completing the project, such as how the clinometer is used to find an angle of elevation.

SCORING RUBRIC

3 Student's display is complete. It includes a clinometer and suggestions to improve it. All measurements, calculations, diagrams, and explanations are accurate and presented in an organized manner.

2 Student's display is complete. It includes a clinometer and suggestions to improve it. The measurements, calculations, diagrams, and explanations contain minor errors but are presented in an organized manner.

1 Student's display is complete. It includes a clinometer and suggestions to improve it. The measurements, calculations, diagrams, and explanations contain errors or are not presented in an organized manner.

0 Major elements are incomplete or missing.

Finishing the Chapter Project

Find Out questions and activities on pages 549, 560, 567, and 577 should help you complete your project. Create a display on indirect measurement. Include the device you built and suggestions for improving it. Also include all measurements, calculations, diagrams, and explanations from the Find Out activities in this chapter, plus some additional measurements.

Reflect and Revise

Ask a classmate to review your project with you. Together, check that the diagrams and explanations are clear, complete, and accurate. Have you explained why your suggestions for changing the device you built will improve it? Have you made measurements in addition to those called for in the Find Out activities? Revise your work as needed.

Follow Up

Research various navigation devices, including ones invented long ago, such as the sextant or the astrolabe, and modern ones, such as GPS (Global Positioning Satellites). Explain how each navigation device works.

For More Information

Bishop, Owen. *Yardsticks of the Universe.* New York: Peter Bedrick Books, 1982.

Boyer, Carl B., and Uta C. Merzbach, rev. editor. *A History of Mathematics.* New York: John Wiley & Sons, 1991.

Murdoch, John E. *Album of Science: Antiquity and the Middle Ages.* New York: Charles Scribner's Sons, 1984.

Wrap Up

HOW AM I DOING? Have students work in small groups. Ask each group to make a short presentation explaining how to use one of the trigonometric ratios to solve problems. Each presentation should include a visual aid and two worked-out examples.

KEY TERMS The numbers in parentheses direct students to the pages where the terms are used or defined. Students should be able to (1) write a simple explanation of each term, (2) illustrate the term with a diagram, or (3) show an example that uses the term.

Exercises 1–4 Students should leave their answers as ratios.

Exercises 5–8 Ask students to write the equation they used to solve each problem. This will help you assess where students are having difficulty in setting up the equations or in solving them.

11 Wrap Up

Key Terms

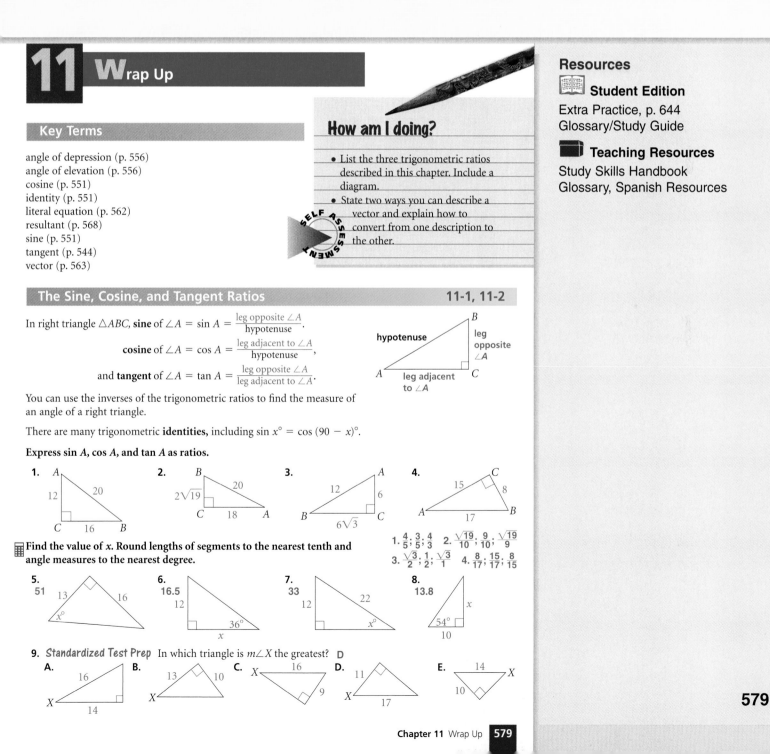

angle of depression (p. 556)
angle of elevation (p. 556)
cosine (p. 551)
identity (p. 551)
literal equation (p. 562)
resultant (p. 568)
sine (p. 551)
tangent (p. 544)
vector (p. 563)

How am I doing?

- List the three trigonometric ratios described in this chapter. Include a diagram.
- State two ways you can describe a vector and explain how to convert from one description to the other.

The Sine, Cosine, and Tangent Ratios — 11-1, 11-2

In right triangle $\triangle ABC$, **sine** of $\angle A = \sin A = \frac{\text{leg opposite } \angle A}{\text{hypotenuse}}$.

cosine of $\angle A = \cos A = \frac{\text{leg adjacent to } \angle A}{\text{hypotenuse}}$,

and **tangent** of $\angle A = \tan A = \frac{\text{leg opposite } \angle A}{\text{leg adjacent to } \angle A}$.

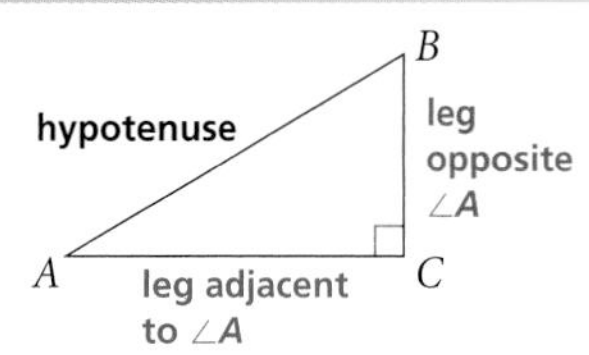

You can use the inverses of the trigonometric ratios to find the measure of an angle of a right triangle.

There are many trigonometric **identities,** including $\sin x° = \cos (90 - x)°$.

Express sin *A*, cos *A*, and tan *A* as ratios.

1. 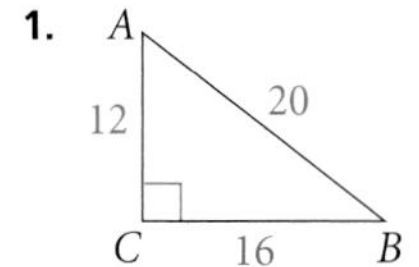

2. B, $2\sqrt{19}$, 20, C, 18, A

3. 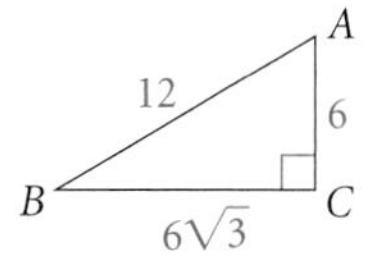

4. 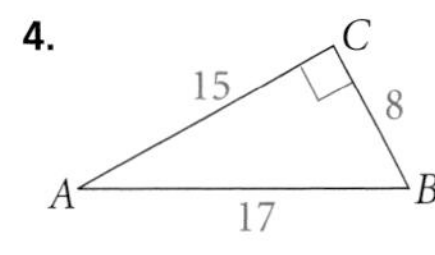

1. $\frac{4}{5}; \frac{3}{5}; \frac{4}{3}$ 2. $\frac{\sqrt{19}}{10}; \frac{9}{10}; \frac{\sqrt{19}}{9}$
3. $\frac{\sqrt{3}}{2}; \frac{1}{2}; \frac{\sqrt{3}}{1}$ 4. $\frac{8}{17}; \frac{15}{17}; \frac{8}{15}$

Find the value of *x*. Round lengths of segments to the nearest tenth and angle measures to the nearest degree.

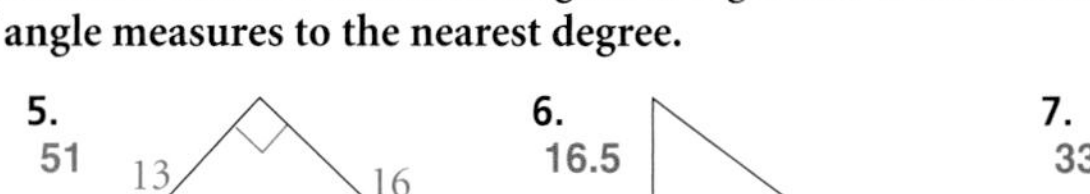

5. 51
6. 16.5
7. 33
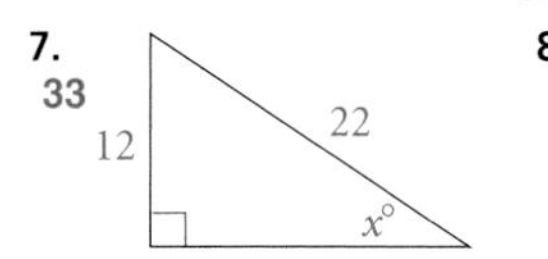

8. 13.8
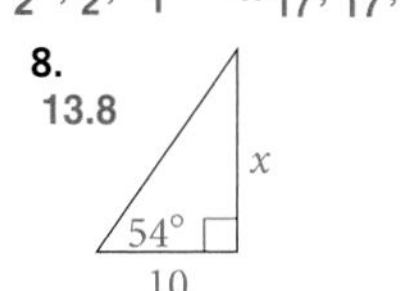

9. *Standardized Test Prep* In which triangle is $m\angle X$ the greatest? D

A. 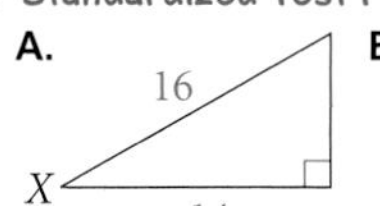

B. 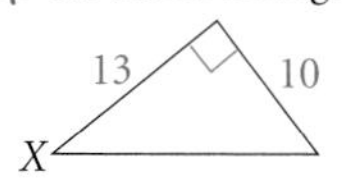

C. 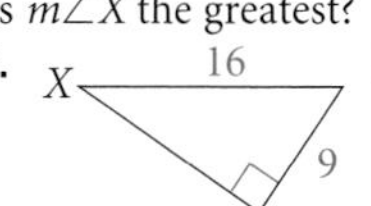

D. 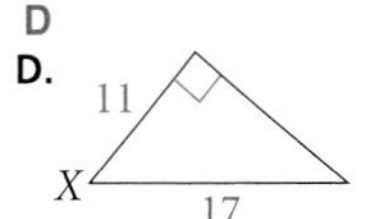

E. 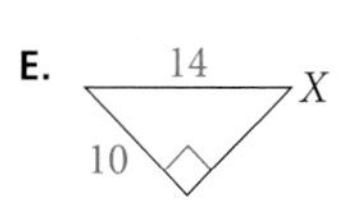

Resources

Student Edition

Extra Practice, p. 644
Glossary/Study Guide

Teaching Resources

Study Skills Handbook
Glossary, Spanish Resources

ERROR ALERT! Exercise 10 Some students may not convert miles to feet. **Remediation:** Remind students that units in the numerator and denominator of the ratio must be equal.

Exercise 11 You may want to ask students to include their diagrams with their solutions to help you assess whether they are having difficulty interpreting the word problem.

WRITING Exercise 12 Ask students to describe how an angle of elevation or an angle of depression is measured. Make sure that they describe measuring it from the horizontal and not the vertical line.

ALTERNATIVE ASSESSMENT Exercises 13–20 Have students work in pairs, each student creating a problem similar to Exercises 13–16 and a problem similar to Exercises 17–20. Have them solve their problems on a separate piece of paper. Then have pairs exchange the problems, solve them, and compare answers.

OPEN-ENDED Exercise 21 Ask students to include diagrams to support their answers.

580

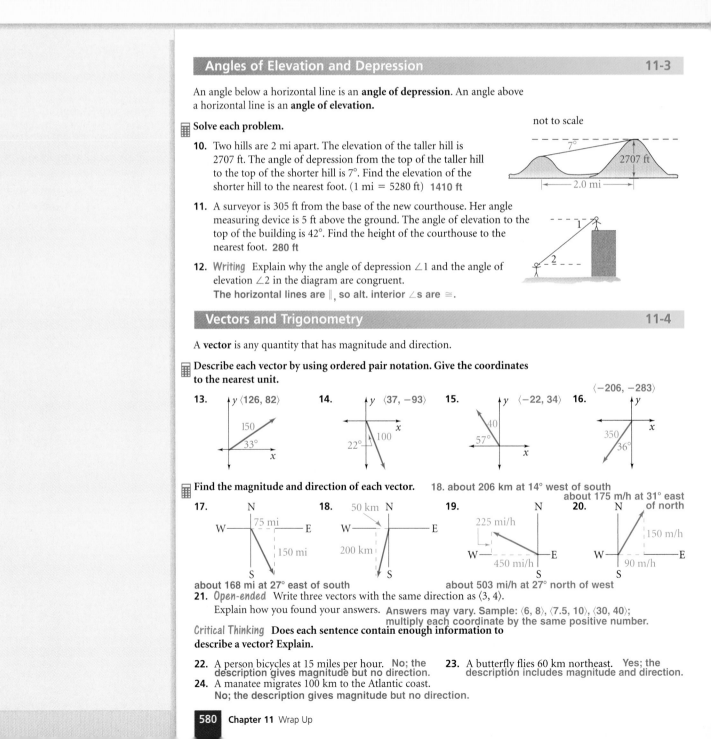

Angles of Elevation and Depression 11-3

An angle below a horizontal line is an **angle of depression.** An angle above a horizontal line is an **angle of elevation.**

Solve each problem.

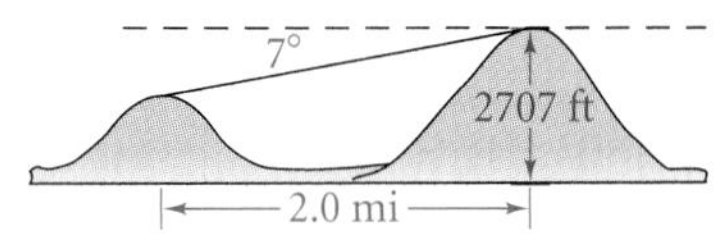

10. Two hills are 2 mi apart. The elevation of the taller hill is 2707 ft. The angle of depression from the top of the taller hill to the top of the shorter hill is 7°. Find the elevation of the shorter hill to the nearest foot. (1 mi = 5280 ft) **1410 ft**

11. A surveyor is 305 ft from the base of the new courthouse. Her angle measuring device is 5 ft above the ground. The angle of elevation to the top of the building is 42°. Find the height of the courthouse to the nearest foot. **280 ft**

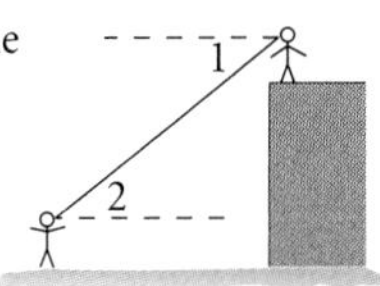

12. *Writing* Explain why the angle of depression ∠1 and the angle of elevation ∠2 in the diagram are congruent.
The horizontal lines are ∥, so alt. interior ∠s are ≅.

Vectors and Trigonometry 11-4

A **vector** is any quantity that has magnitude and direction.

Describe each vector by using ordered pair notation. Give the coordinates to the nearest unit.

13. **⟨126, 82⟩**
150, 33°

14. **⟨37, −93⟩**

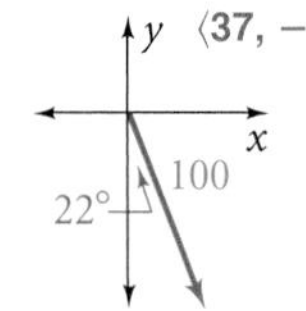

15. **⟨−22, 34⟩**

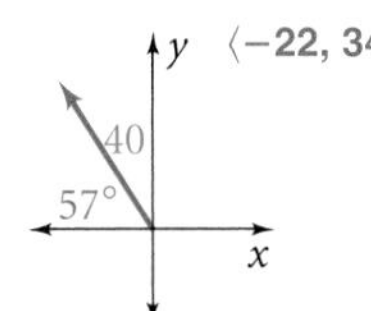

16. **⟨−206, −283⟩**

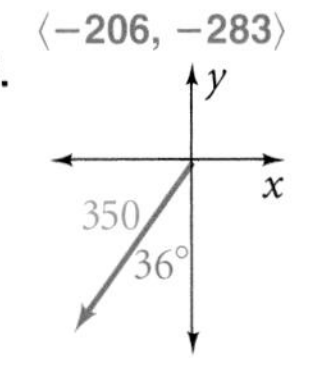

Find the magnitude and direction of each vector.

17.

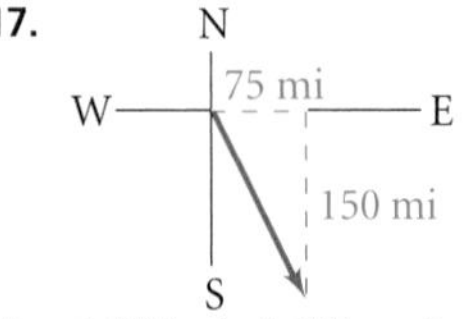

about 168 mi at 27° east of south

18. **about 206 km at 14° west of south**

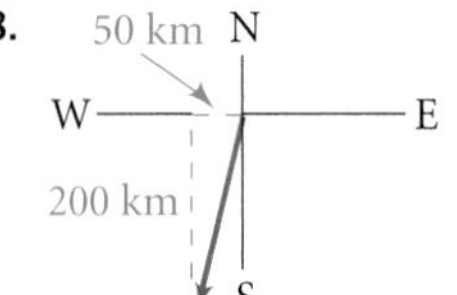

19.

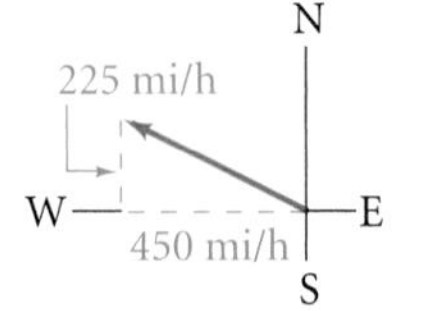

about 503 mi/h at 27° north of west

20. **about 175 m/h at 31° east of north**

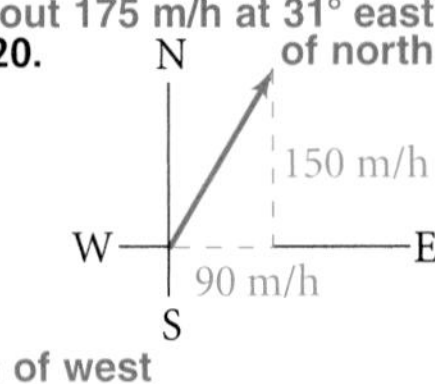

21. *Open-ended* Write three vectors with the same direction as ⟨3, 4⟩. Explain how you found your answers. **Answers may vary. Sample: ⟨6, 8⟩, ⟨7.5, 10⟩, ⟨30, 40⟩; multiply each coordinate by the same positive number.**

Critical Thinking **Does each sentence contain enough information to describe a vector? Explain.**

22. A person bicycles at 15 miles per hour. **No; the description gives magnitude but no direction.**

23. A butterfly flies 60 km northeast. **Yes; the description includes magnitude and direction.**

24. A manatee migrates 100 km to the Atlantic coast. **No; the description gives magnitude but no direction.**

Exercises 25–28 Suggest that student solve these problems in more than one way.

Exercises 30–35 Check that students express their answers with the appropriate units.

Remind students that the new mathematical terms in this chapter are defined in the Glossary/Study Guide in the back of the book.

Getting Ready for Chapter 12

Students may work these exercises independently or in small groups. The skills previewed will help prepare students to study chords, secants, and tangents of circles.

Adding Vectors 11-5

The sum of two vectors is a **resultant**. You can add vectors by using the head-to-tail method or by using ordered pair notation. Vector sums can show the result of actions that take place one after the other or the result of two forces that act at the same time on an object.

Coordinate Geometry **Find the sum of each pair of vectors. Give your answers in ordered pair notation.**

25. 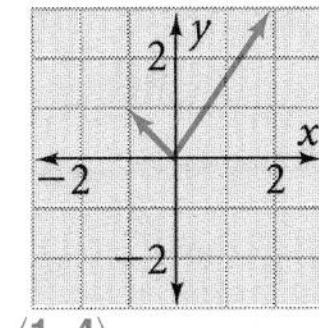
⟨1, 4⟩

26. 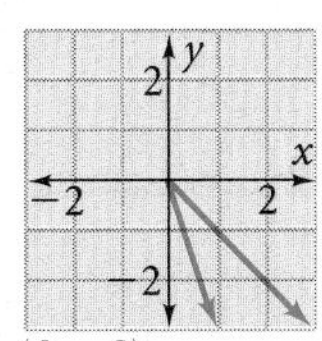
⟨4, −6⟩

27. 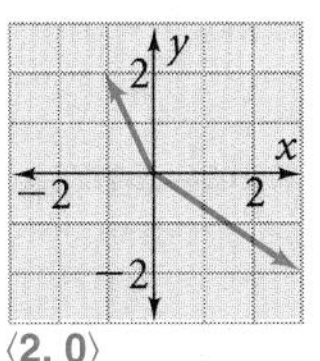
⟨2, 0⟩

28. 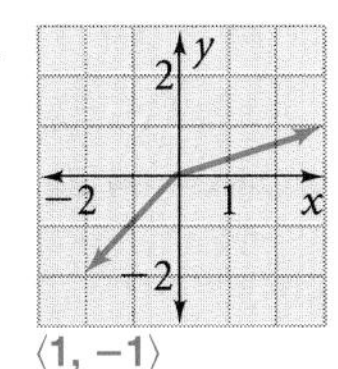
⟨1, −1⟩

29. A whale-watching tour leaves port and travels 60 mi directly north. The tour then travels 5 mi due east.

a. In what direction should the boat head to return to port? 5° west of south

b. How long will the return trip take if the boat averages 20 mi/h? about 3 h

Trigonometry and Area 11-6

You can use trigonometry to find the area of regular polygons. You can also use trigonometry to find the area of a triangle when you know the lengths of two sides and the measure of the included angle.

Area of triangle $= \frac{1}{2} \cdot$ side length $\cdot$ side length $\cdot$ sine of included angle

Find the area of each polygon. Round your answers to the nearest tenth.

30. regular decagon with radius 5 ft 73.5 ft^2

31. regular pentagon with apothem 8 cm 232.5 cm^2

32. 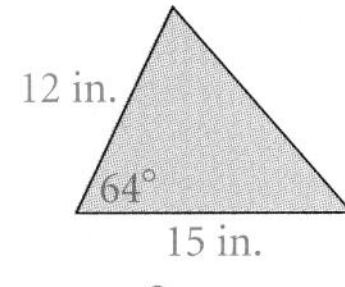

80.9 in.^{2}

33. 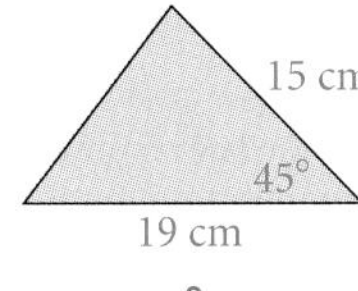

100.8 cm^2

34. 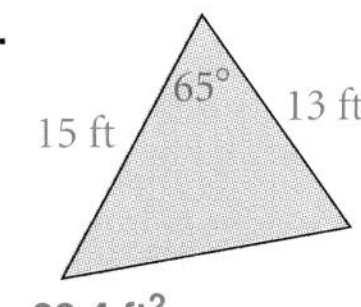

88.4 ft^2

35. 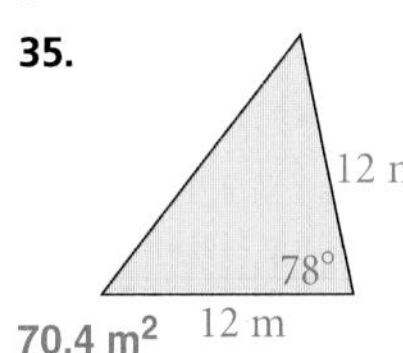

70.4 m^2

Getting Ready for.......... CHAPTER 12

36. *Open-ended* Draw a circle. Then draw two central angles, one twice the measure of the other. See margin for sample.

Find the area and circumference of a circle with the given radius or diameter. Leave your answer in terms of π.

37. $r = 5$ in. 25π in.^{2}; 10π in.

38. $d = 8$ cm 16π cm^2; 8π cm

39. $r = 11$ m 121π m^2; 22π m

40. $d = 4$ ft 4π ft^2; 4π ft

Wrap Up pages 579–581

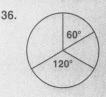

36. 60° 120°

Assessment

ENHANCED MULTIPLE CHOICE QUESTIONS are more complex than traditional multiple choice questions, which assess only one skill. Enhanced multiple choice questions assess the processes that students use, as well as the end results. The questions are written so that students use more than one strategy to solve the problem. Using multiple strategies is encouraged by the National Council of Teachers of Mathematics (NCTM). There are no enhanced multiple choice questions on this assessment.

FREE RESPONSE QUESTIONS do not give answer choices. Some exercises have more than one possible answer. Students need to give only one correct response. **Exercises 1–12, 14–18, and 20–24** are free response questions.

WRITING EXERCISES allow students to describe how they think about and understand the concepts they have learned. **Exercise 13** is a writing exercise.

OPEN-ENDED PROBLEMS allow for more than one solution. Students must construct their own responses instead of choosing from possible answers. The students' responses will help you determine the depth of their understanding and any possible areas of difficulty. **Exercise 19** is an open-ended problem.

Resources

Teaching Resources

Chapter Support File, Ch. 11

- Chapter Assessment, Forms A and B
- Alternative Assessment

Chapter Assessment, Spanish Resources

Teacher's Edition

See also p. 542E for assessment options

Software

Computer Item Generator

Assessment page 582

13. The acute ∠s of a rt. △ are complementary, so, in rt. △*ABC*, if $m\angle A = x$, $m\angle B = 90 - x$. So $\sin x° = \frac{BC}{AB} = \cos (90 - x)°$.

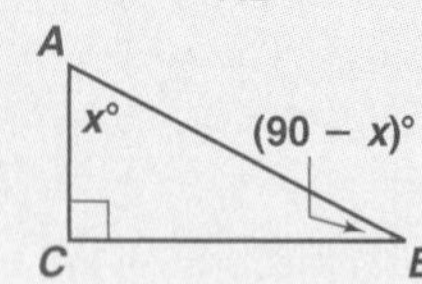

19.

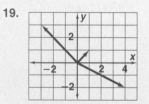

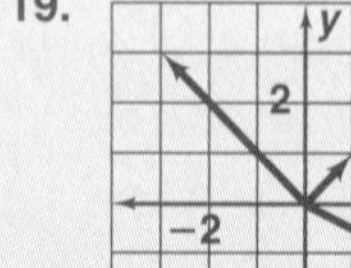

11 Assessment

Express sin *B*, cos *B*, and tan *B* as ratios.

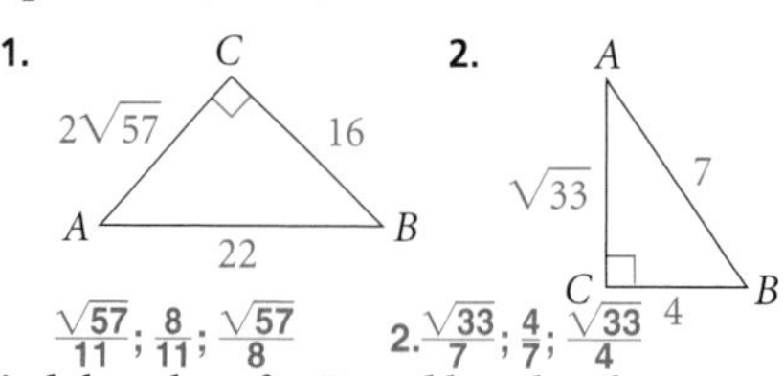

1. $\frac{\sqrt{57}}{11}; \frac{8}{11}; \frac{\sqrt{57}}{8}$

2. $\frac{\sqrt{33}}{7}; \frac{4}{7}; \frac{\sqrt{33}}{4}$

Find the value of *x*. Round lengths of segments to the nearest tenth and angle measures to the nearest degree.

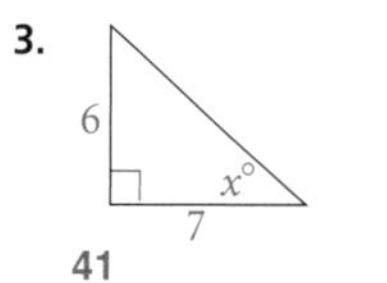

3. 41

4. 18.7

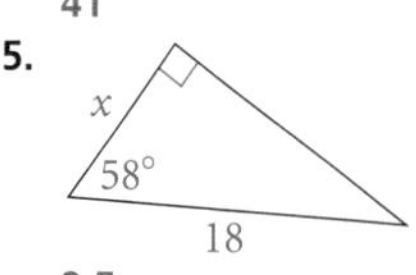

5. 9.5

6. 28

Algebra **Find the measure of the acute angle that each line makes with a horizontal line. Round your answer to the nearest tenth.**

7. $y = 3x - 2$ 71.6
8. $y = x + 1$ 45
9. $y = \frac{1}{2}x + 5$ 26.6
10. $x - 2y = 6$ 26.6

Solve each problem.

11. A surveyor measuring the tallest tree in a park stands 100 ft from it. His angle-measuring device is 5 ft above the ground. The angle of elevation to the top of the tree is 48°. How tall is the tree? about 116 ft

12. A hot-air balloon is competing in a race. After 20 min, the balloon is at an altitude of 300 m. The pilot can still see the starting point at a 25° angle of depression. How many meters is the balloon from the starting point on the ground? about 710 m

13. ***Writing*** Explain why $\sin x° = \cos (90 - x)°$. Include a diagram with your explanation. See margin.

Describe each vector using ordered pair notation. Round the coordinates to the nearest unit.

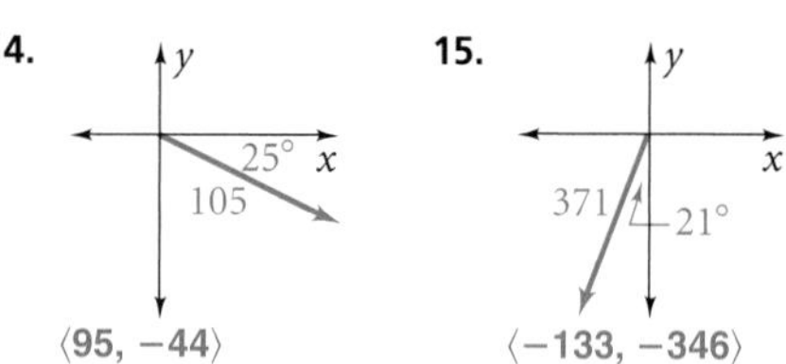

14. ⟨95, –44⟩

15. ⟨–133, –346⟩

16. A family went on vacation to a beach 120 mi east and 30 mi south of their home. Find the distance and the direction the beach is from their home. about 124 mi at 14° south of east

Find the sum of each pair of vectors. Give your answers in ordered pair notation.

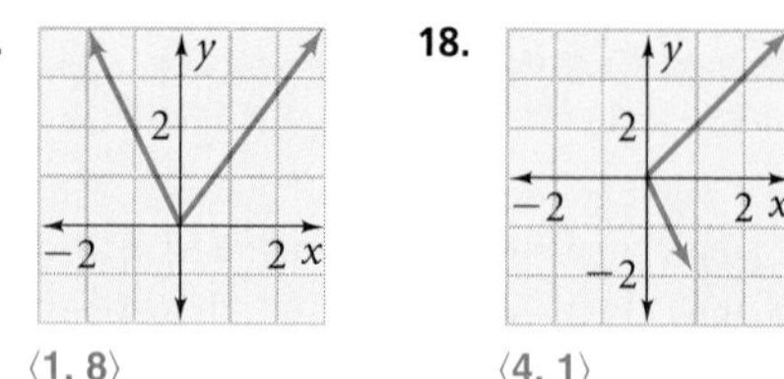

17. ⟨1, 8⟩

18. ⟨4, 1⟩

19. ***Open-ended*** Draw two vectors with different directions on a coordinate grid. Then draw their resultant and describe the sum using ordered pair notation. See margin for sample.

Find the area of each polygon. Round your answer to the nearest tenth.

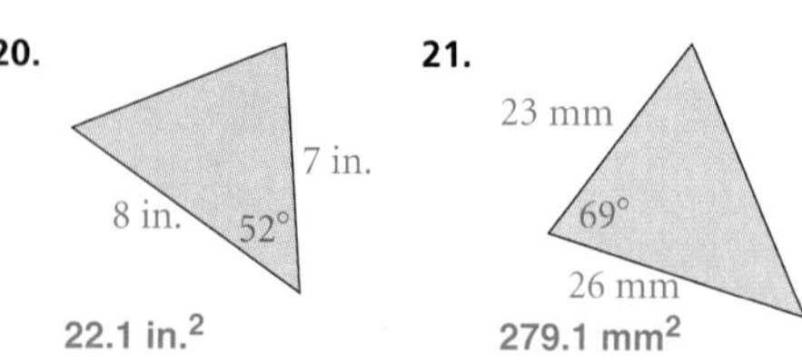

20. 22.1 in.^{2}

21. 279.1 mm^2

22. a regular hexagon with apothem 5 ft 86.6 ft^2
23. a regular pentagon with radius 3 cm 21.4 cm^2
24. a regular decagon with perimeter 90 in. 623.2 in.^{2}

Preparing for Standardized Tests

Standardized tests, such as those administered for state assessment, the SAT, or the ACT, include regular math questions, quantitative comparison questions, open-ended problems, and free response questions (which the SAT calls *grid-ins*).

MULTIPLE CHOICE QUESTIONS are followed by five answer choices, one of which is correct. **Exercises 1–7** are multiple choice questions.

QUANTITATIVE COMPARISON QUESTIONS ask students to compare two quantities. **Exercises 8 and 9** are quantitative comparison questions.

FREE RESPONSE QUESTIONS do not give answer choices. Students must provide one correct answer on their own. **Exercises 10 and 12** are free response questions.

OPEN-ENDED PROBLEMS allow for more than one solution. Students must construct their own responses instead of choosing a single answer. The responses students give will help you determine the depth of their understanding and what difficulties, if any, they are experiencing. **Exercise 11** is an open-ended problem.

STANDARDIZED TEST TIP **Exercise 3** Students can use the Pythagorean Theorem to find the length of the hypotenuse but it is not necessary. Help students observe that because the hypotenuse is the longest side, all the answer choices are less than 1 except tan *A*.

11 Preparing for Standardized Tests

For Exercises 1–9, choose the correct letter.

1. In which transformation is the image *not* necessarily congruent to the preimage? D
   - **A.** rotation **B.** reflection
   - **C.** translation **D.** dilation
   - **E.** glide translation

2. Which quadrilaterals have congruent diagonals? A
   - **I.** square **II.** trapezoid
   - **III.** parallelogram **IV.** kite

   - **A.** I only **B.** III only
   - **C.** I and II only **D.** III and IV only
   - **E.** I, II, and IV only

3. Which is greatest in the triangle below? C

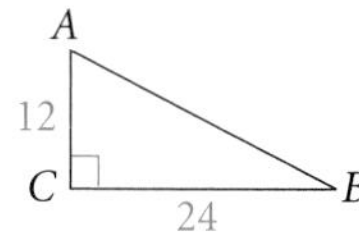

   - **A.** sin *A* **B.** cos *A* **C.** tan *A*
   - **D.** sin *B* **E.** cos *B*

4. What is the surface area of a rectangular prism with length 9 cm, width 8 cm, and height 10 cm? D
   - **A.** 27 cm^2 **B.** 240 cm^2 **C.** 242 cm^2
   - **D.** 484 cm^2 **E.** 720 cm^2

5. For what value of *x* will the two triangles be similar? A

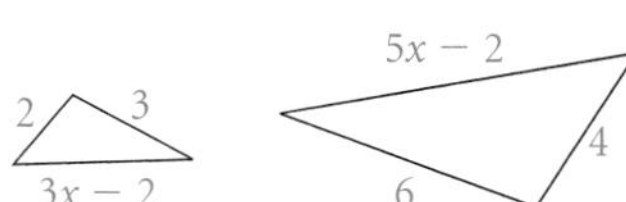

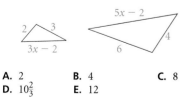

   - **A.** 2 **B.** 4 **C.** 8
   - **D.** $10\frac{2}{3}$ **E.** 12

6. Which information *cannot* be used to prove two triangles congruent? E
   - **A.** SSS **B.** SAS **C.** ASA
   - **D.** AAS **E.** AAA

7. What is the locus of points in a plane a given distance from a given line? E
   - **A.** a line **B.** a circle **C.** a cylinder
   - **D.** a ray **E.** two parallel lines

Compare the boxed quantity in Column A with the boxed quantity in Column B. Choose the best answer.

- **A.** The quantity in Column A is greater.
- **B.** The quantity in Column B is greater.
- **C.** The two quantities are equal.
- **D.** The relationship cannot be determined on the basis of the information supplied.

	Column A	Column B	
8.	 sin 30°	cos 30°	B
9.	the magnitude of $\vec{c} + \vec{a}$	the magnitude of $\vec{a} + \vec{c}$	C

Find each answer.
10–12. See margin for samples.

10. **Aviation** Pilots often refer to the angle of an object outside the plane in terms of a clock face. Thus, an object at 12 o'clock is straight ahead, an object at 3 o'clock is 90° to the right, and so on.
    - **a.** Suppose that two pilots flying in the same direction spot the same object. One reports it at 1 o'clock, the other at 2 o'clock. Draw a diagram showing the possible locations of the two planes and the object.
    - **b.** Suppose that at the same time one pilot sights the object, she sights the other plane at 9 o'clock. Draw a diagram of the positions of the planes and the object.

11. **Open-ended** Draw a triangle. Measure two sides and the angle between them. Then find the area of the triangle.

12. **Constructions** Construct a square with side length *a*.

Resources

Teaching Resources

Chapter Support File, Ch. 11
- Standardized Test Practice
- Cumulative Review

Teacher's Edition

See also p. 542E for assessment options.

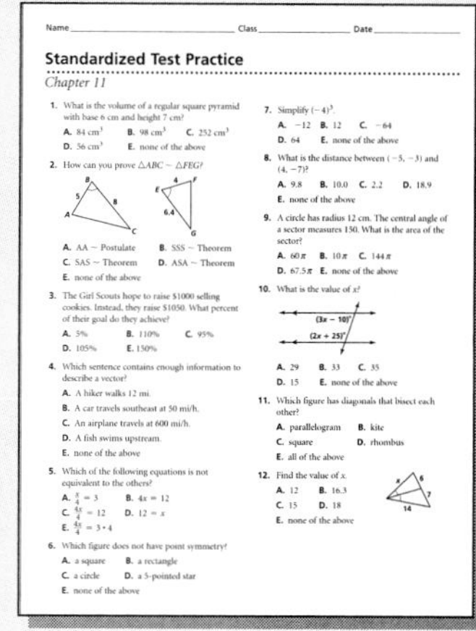

Standardized Test Practice
Chapter 11

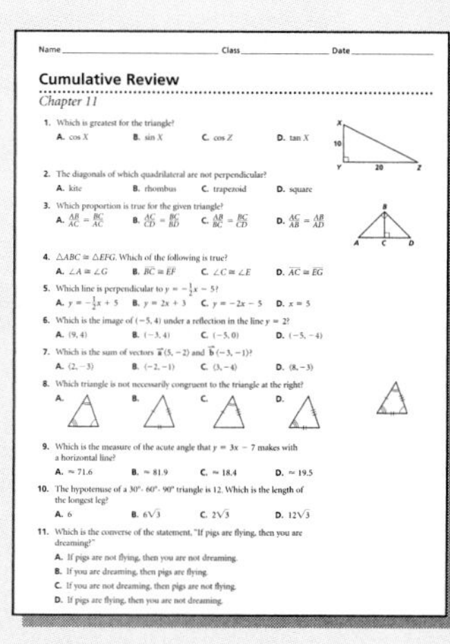

Cumulative Review
Chapter 11

CHAPTER 12 Chords, Secants, and Tangents

To accommodate flexible scheduling, some lessons are divided into parts. Assignment Options are given in the Lesson Planning Options for each lesson.

12-1 Circles in the Coordinate Plane (pp. 586–591)

Part 1 Writing the Equation of a Circle
Part 2 Using the Equation of a Circle

Key Term: standard form of an equation of a circle

12-2 Properties of Tangents (pp. 593–599)

Part 1 Tangents to Circles
Part 2 Circumscribing Circles

Key Terms: circumscribed about, inscribed in, point of tangency, tangent to a circle

12-3 Properties of Chords and Arcs (pp. 600–606)

Part 1 Congruent Arcs and Chords
Part 2 Chords Equidistant from the Center of a Circle

Key Term: chord

12-4 Inscribed Angles (pp. 607–613)

Part 1 Measuring Inscribed Angles
Part 2 Angles Formed by Tangents and Chords

Key Terms: circumscribed about, inscribed in, inscribed angle, intercepted arc

12-5 Angles Formed by Chords, Secants, and Tangents (pp. 614–619)

Key Term: secant

12-6 Circles and Lengths of Segments (pp. 621–626)

PACING OPTIONS

This chart suggests pacing only for the core lessons and their parts, and it is provided merely as a possible guide. It will help you determine how much time you have in your schedule to cover other features, such as the Chapter Project, Math Toolboxes, Wrap Up, and Assessment.

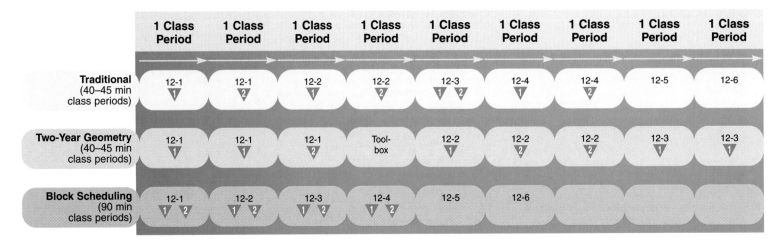

	1 Class Period	1 Class Period	1 Class Period	1 Class Period	1 Class Period	1 Class Period	1 Class Period	1 Class Period	1 Class Period
Traditional (40–45 min class periods)	12-1 Part 1	12-1 Part 2	12-2 Part 1	12-2 Part 2	12-3 Parts 1, 2	12-4 Part 1	12-4 Part 2	12-5	12-6
Two-Year Geometry (40–45 min class periods)	12-1 Part 1	12-1 Part 1	12-1 Part 2	Tool-box	12-2 Part 1	12-2 Part 2	12-2 Part 2	12-3 Part 1	12-3 Part 1
Block Scheduling (90 min class periods)	12-1 Parts 1, 2	12-2 Parts 1, 2	12-3 Parts 1, 2	12-4 Parts 1, 2	12-5	12-6			

What Students Will Learn and Why

In this chapter, students will use their knowledge of congruent triangles and similar triangles, learned in Chapters 8 and 10, to discover characteristics of circles. Students learn how to write the equation of a circle and how to use the equation of a circle to solve real-world problems. Students learn properties of tangents, chords, and arcs. Then they find the measure of inscribed angles, the arcs they intercept, and angles formed by chords, secants, and tangents. Finally, students learn to find the lengths of segments associated with circles. The principles students learn in this chapter have applications in photography, architecture, and communications.

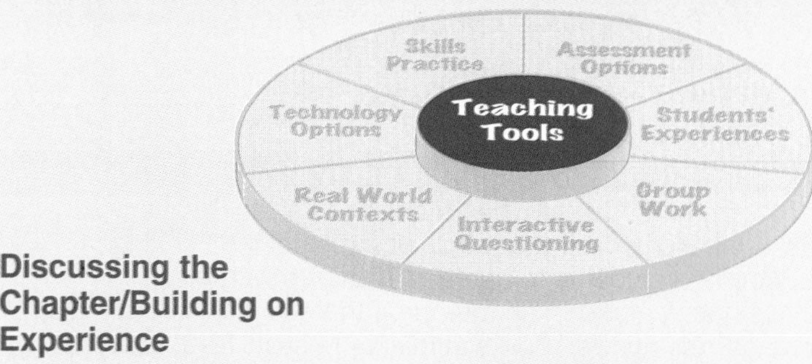

Discussing the Chapter/Building on Experience

The concept map below relates chapter topics to real-world applications. You and your class may wish to add to the map or develop maps of your own. The center oval describes the topic of the chapter. The next level displays topics within the lessons. The outer ovals reflect applications of the content. As you and your class build a concept map, invite students to discuss applications with which they are familiar.

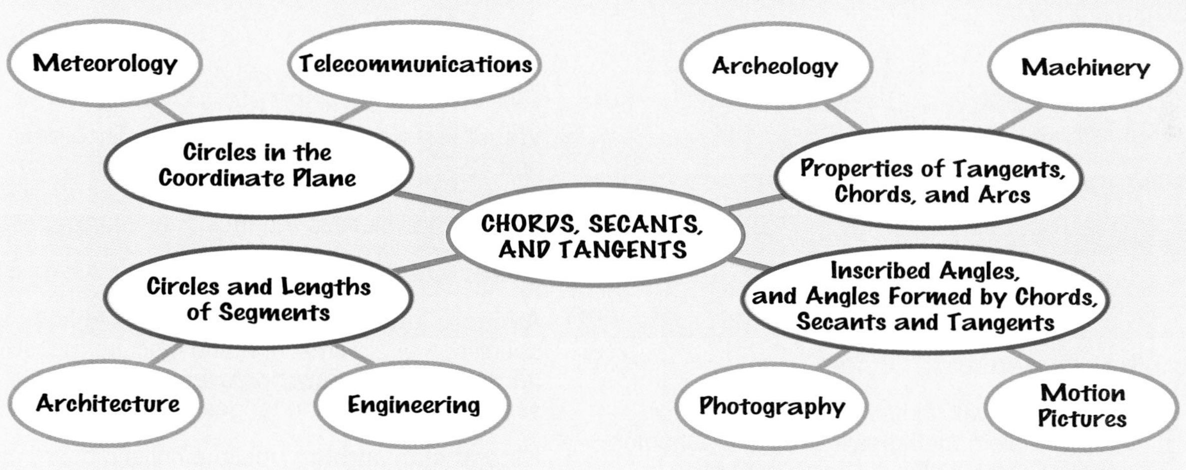

1 Class Period	1 Class Period	1 Class Period	1 Class Period	1 Class Period	1 Class Period	1 Class Period	1 Class Period	1 Class Period	1 Class Period	1 Class Period
12-3 ▽2	12-4 ▽1	12-4 ▽1	12-4 ▽2	12-4 ▽2	12-5	12-5	Tool-box	12-6	12-6	

Interactive Questioning Tips

A question is interactive when there is "give and take" between the questioner (teacher or student) and the respondent. In Think and Discuss or when a critical thinking question is asked, it is important to get all of the students thinking. Encourage students to agree or disagree with their classmates, and remind them that there is often more than one correct answer. For example, in Lesson 12-6, Example 2, students are asked to explain why a segment perpendicular to a chord is contained in a diameter of the circle.

Skills Practice

Every lesson provides skill practice with Try This exercises, Exercises On Your Own, and Exercises Mixed Review. The Student Edition includes Checkpoints (pp. 606, 619) and Cumulative Review (p. 632). In the Teacher's Edition, the Lesson Planning Options section for each lesson lists Prerequisite Skills students should know for that lesson. At the back of the Student Edition is the Skills Handbook—mini-lessons on math your students may need to review. The Chapter Support File for Chapter 12 in the Teaching Resources box includes two Practice worksheets per lesson, a worksheet for two Checkpoints, and worksheets for Cumulative Review and Standardized Test Preparation.

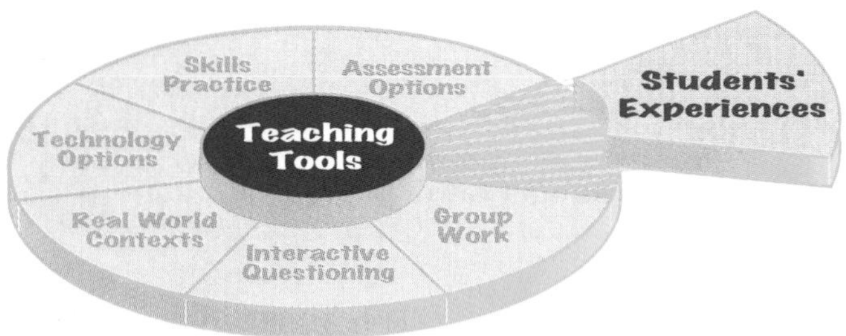

Diverse Learning and Teaching Styles

In your Teacher's Edition, you will find suggestions as to how you can help students complete mathematical tasks in Chapter 12 by reinforcing various learning styles. Here are some examples.

- **Visual learning** draw diagrams for Theorems 12-5, 12-6, and 12-7 (p. 601), construct a circle and chords (p. 609), shade the interior angles formed by chords, secants, and tangents to visualize the arcs they intercept (615)
- **Tactile learning** experiment with MIRA™ (p. 600)
- **Auditory learning** learn verbal cues to help remember the definitions of circumscribe and inscribe (p. 596), practice naming segments or chords, secant segments, exterior secant segments, and tangent segments (p. 621)
- **Kinesthetic learning** make a bulletin board display showing many colorful circles and their equations (p. 590)

Alternative Activity for Lesson 12-1

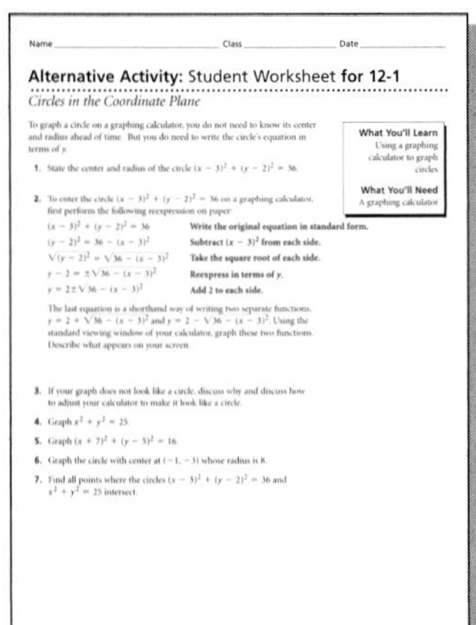

Name ______ Class ______ Date ______

Alternative Activity: Student Worksheet **for 12-1**

Circles in the Coordinate Plane

To graph a circle on a graphing calculator, you do not need to know its center and radius ahead of time. But you do need to write the circle's equation in terms of y.

What You'll Learn Using a graphing calculator to graph circles

What You'll Need A graphing calculator

1. State the center and radius of the circle $(x - 3)^2 + (y - 2)^2 = 36$.
2. To enter the circle $(x - 3)^2 + (y - 2)^2 = 36$ on a graphing calculator, first perform the following reexpression on paper:

   $(x - 3)^2 + (y - 2)^2 = 36$ **Write the original equation in standard form.**
   $(y - 2)^2 = 36 - (x - 3)^2$ **Subtract $(x - 3)^2$ from each side.**
   $\sqrt{(y - 2)^2} = \sqrt{36 - (x - 3)^2}$ **Take the square root of each side.**
   $y - 2 = \pm\sqrt{36 - (x - 3)^2}$ **Reexpress in terms of y.**
   $y = 2 \pm \sqrt{36 - (x - 3)^2}$ **Add 2 to each side.**

   The last equation is a shorthand way of writing two separate functions, $y = 2 + \sqrt{36 - (x - 3)^2}$ and $y = 2 - \sqrt{36 - (x - 3)^2}$. Using the standard viewing window of your calculator, graph these two functions. Describe what appears on your screen.
3. If your graph does not look like a circle, discuss why and discuss how to adjust your calculator to make it look like a circle.
4. Graph $x^2 + y^2 = 25$.
5. Graph $(x + 7)^2 + (y - 5)^2 = 16$.
6. Graph the circle with center at $(-1, -3)$ whose radius is 8.
7. Find all points where the circles $(x - 3)^2 + (y - 2)^2 = 36$ and $x^2 + y^2 = 25$ intersect.

for use with Think and Discuss, uses a graphing calculator to graph circles.

Alternative Activity for Lesson 12-4

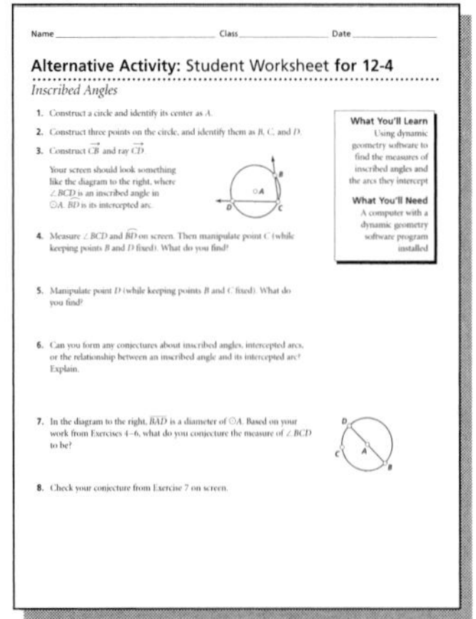

Name ______ Class ______ Date ______

Alternative Activity: Student Worksheet **for 12-4**

Inscribed Angles

What You'll Learn Using dynamic geometry software to find the measures of inscribed angles and the arcs they intercept

What You'll Need A computer with a dynamic geometry software program installed

1. Construct a circle and identify its center as A.
2. Construct three points on the circle, and identify them as B, C, and D.
3. Construct $\overline{CB}$ and ray $\overrightarrow{CD}$.

   Your screen should look something like the diagram to the right, where $\angle BCD$ is an inscribed angle in $\odot A$. $\widehat{BD}$ is its intercepted arc.
4. Measure $\angle BCD$ and $\widehat{BD}$ on screen. Then manipulate point C (while keeping points B and D fixed). What do you find?
5. Manipulate point D (while keeping points B and C fixed). What do you find?
6. Can you form any conjectures about inscribed angles, intercepted arcs, or the relationship between an inscribed angle and its intercepted arc? Explain.
7. In the diagram to the right, $\overline{BAD}$ is a diameter of $\odot A$. Based on your work from Exercises 4–6, what do you conjecture the measure of $\angle BCD$ to be?
8. Check your conjecture from Exercise 7 on screen.

for use with Work Together, uses geometry software to explore properties of inscribed angles and their intersected arcs.

Alternative Activity for Lesson 12-5

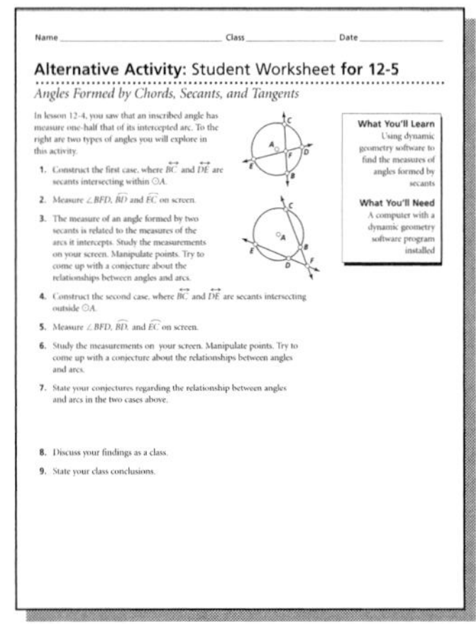

Name ______ Class ______ Date ______

Alternative Activity: Student Worksheet **for 12-5**

Angles Formed by Chords, Secants, and Tangents

In lesson 12-4, you saw that an inscribed angle has measure one-half that of its intercepted arc. To the right are two types of angles you will explore in this activity.

What You'll Learn Using dynamic geometry software to find the measures of angles formed by secants

What You'll Need A computer with a dynamic geometry software program installed

1. Construct the first case, where $\overleftrightarrow{BC}$ and $\overleftrightarrow{DE}$ are secants intersecting within $\odot A$.
2. Measure $\angle BFD$, $\widehat{BD}$ and $\widehat{EC}$ on screen.
3. The measure of an angle formed by two secants is related to the measures of the arcs it intercepts. Study the measurements on your screen. Manipulate points. Try to come up with a conjecture about the relationships between angles and arcs.
4. Construct the second case, where $\overleftrightarrow{BC}$ and $\overleftrightarrow{DE}$ are secants intersecting outside $\odot A$.
5. Measure $\angle BFD$, $\widehat{BD}$, and $\widehat{EC}$ on screen.
6. Study the measurements on your screen. Manipulate points. Try to come up with a conjecture about the relationships between angles and arcs.
7. State your conjectures regarding the relationship between angles and arcs in the two cases above.
8. Discuss your findings as a class.
9. State your class conclusions.

for use with Work Together, uses geometry software to explore properties of secants and their intercepted arcs.

Cooperative Learning Tips

When used effectively, cooperative learning can help students develop interpersonal skills, learn to perform specific roles in a group, and learn to carry out specific responsibilities. The components of Chapter 12 provide a range of cooperative learning opportunities.

- In the Student Edition, the Work Together parts of lessons are specifically designed for cooperative learning activities.
- In the Teacher's Edition, you will find helpful hints for addressing diverse learning styles (see page C for Chapter 12). For every lesson, you will find a Reteaching Activity, which may involve cooperative learning.

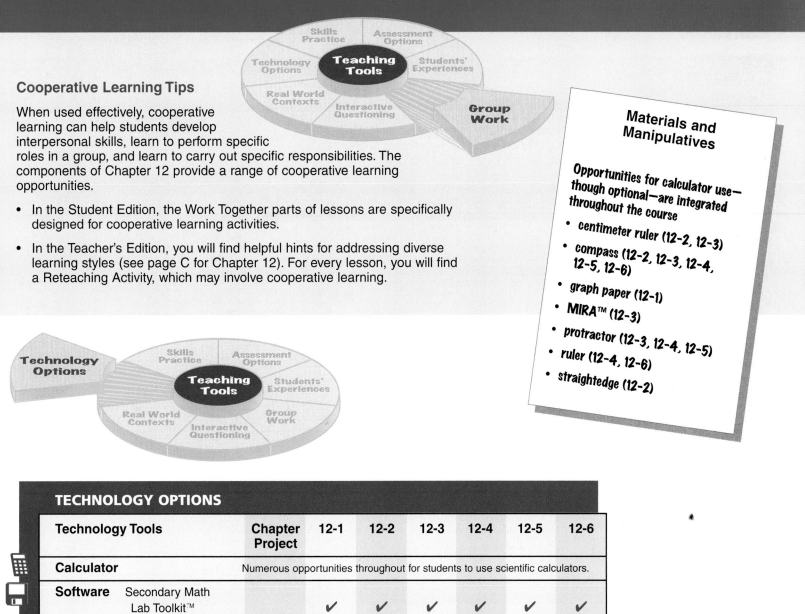

Materials and Manipulatives

Opportunities for calculator use—though optional—are integrated throughout the course

- centimeter ruler (12-2, 12-3)
- compass (12-2, 12-3, 12-4, 12-5, 12-6)
- graph paper (12-1)
- MIRA™ (12-3)
- protractor (12-3, 12-4, 12-5)
- ruler (12-4, 12-6)
- straightedge (12-2)

TECHNOLOGY OPTIONS

Technology Tools		Chapter Project	12-1	12-2	12-3	12-4	12-5	12-6
Calculator		Numerous opportunities throughout for students to use scientific calculators.						
Software	Secondary Math Lab Toolkit™		✔	✔	✔	✔	✔	✔
	Integrated Math Lab				✔		✔	
	Computer Item Generator		✔	✔	✔	✔	✔	✔
	Student Edition				✔	✔		✔T
Video	Video Field Trip	✔						
CD-ROM	Multimedia Geometry Lab		✔	✔	✔	✔		
Internet		See the Prentice Hall site. (http://www.phschool.com)						

✔T indicates Math Toolbox.

The Prentice Hall Geometry program offers you a rich variety of technology options. Be assured that all these options are provided as a means of enriching the program and are not essential for the successful completion of the course.

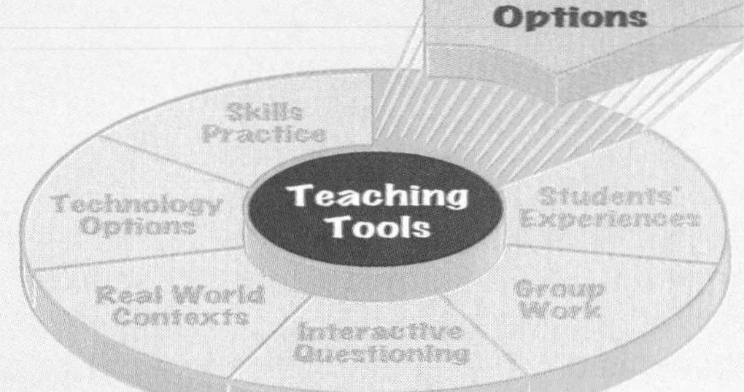

Assessment Options

The Prentice Hall Geometry Program provides you with many options. From these options, you may choose instructional materials and techniques appropriate for your students, or those necessary to meet your district's curriculum requirements. As the chart indicates, the program also supports your teaching efforts by offering you many choices for assessment.

ASSESSMENT OPTIONS

Assessment Support Materials	Chapter Project	12-1	12-2	12-3	12-4	12-5	12-6	Chapter End
Chapter Project	▲■●	▲■		▲■		▲■		▲■
Checkpoints				▲■●		▲■●		
Self-Assessment			▲■		▲■	▲■	▲■	▲■
Writing Assignment		▲■	▲■	▲	▲■	▲■	▲■	▲■●
Chapter Assessment								▲■●
Alternative Assessment		■	■	■	■	■	■	▲■●
Cumulative Review								▲■●
Standardized Test Prep			▲■			▲■	▲	▲■●
Computer Item Generator	Can be used to create custom-made practice or assessment at any time.							

▲ = Student Edition ■ = Teacher's Edition ● = Teaching Resources

Checkpoints

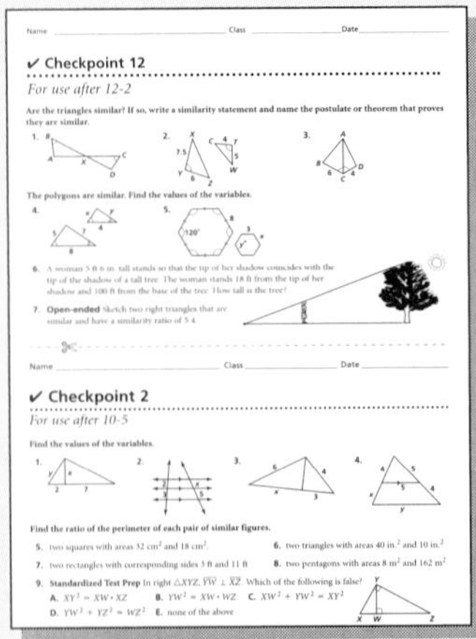

Alternative Assessment

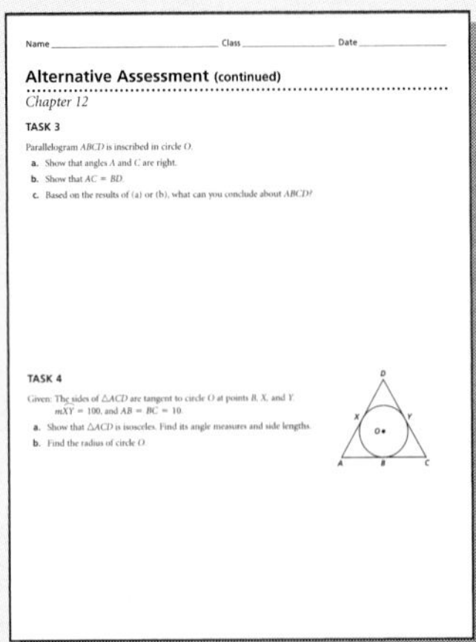

Chapter Assessment

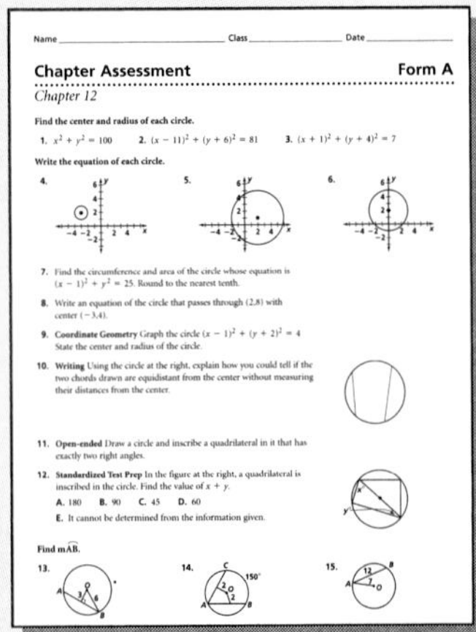

Available in both Form A and Form B

Making the Right Connections

Mathematics is imbedded in nearly every walk of life. The National Council of Teachers of Mathematics (NCTM) encourages educators to recognize these connections and to emphasize them for the purpose of better educating students for success in life and in a global economy. The ***Connections*** chart below highlights these connections for Chapter 12.

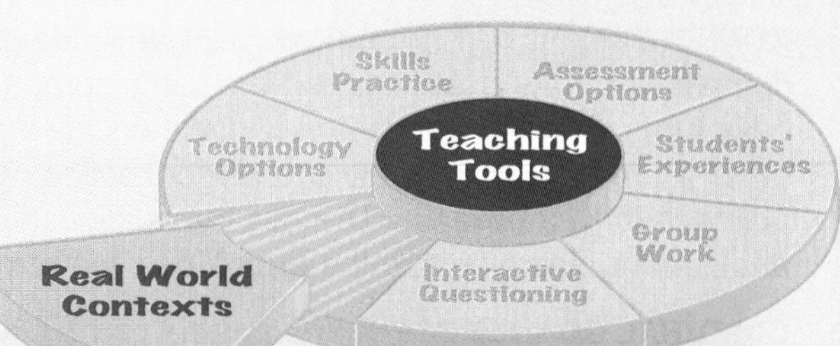

CONNECTIONS

Lesson	Interdisciplinary Connections	Career Prep	Other Real World Connections	Math Integration	NCTM Standards
Chapter Project	Art History	Design	Jewelry Stone Carvings Clothing Islamic Art	Coordinate Geometry	Connections Communication Problem Solving
12-1	Meteorology History	Engineering Telecommunications	Cellular Telephones Earth Weather	Algebra Geometry in 3 Dimensions Coordinate Geometry	Communication Connections Coordinate Geometry Problem Solving
12-2	Astronomy	Machinery Construction Design	Air Conditioning Eclipse Clocks	Coordinate Geometry Algebra	Communication Connections Reasoning Problem Solving
12-3	Art	Archeology Transportation	Compact Disc Transporting Milk	Coordinate Geometry Logical Reasoning	Communication Connections Reasoning Problem Solving
12-4		Photography	Technology Motion Pictures	Logical Reasoning	Communication Connections Reasoning Problem Solving
12-5	History Astronomy	Photography	Space Travel Surveys	Algebra Logical Reasoning	Communication Connections Reasoning Problem Solving
12-6	Astronomy	Architecture Engineering Aerospace Engineering	Space Exploration Wankel Engine	Logical Reasoning	Communication Connections Reasoning Problem Solving

CHAPTER 12 Chords, Secants, and Tangents

CONNECTING TO PRIOR LEARNING Have students use a compass to draw a circle. Using the same compass setting, have them mark six points on the circle equidistant from each other. Then have them draw chords connecting consecutive points to form a hexagon. Discuss the relationship between an angle of the hexagon and the arc of the circle it intercepts.

CULTURAL CONNECTIONS The symbol of the Olympic Games is five entwined circles, each ring representing a continent. Students might research the history of the Olympic rings and present a visual/verbal report on the meaning and the significance of the symbol.

INTERDISCIPLINARY CONNECTIONS While artists use circles to create patterns and designs, astronomers and physicists also study circles, particularly circular motion. Ancient scholars believed that the planets traveled in perfect circular motion about the Earth. Have students research how this theory was eventually proven false.

ABOUT THE PROJECT Students explore techniques used for centuries to produce circular art. They then apply the techniques to create their own designs.

Technology Options

Prentice Hall Technology

Video
Video Field Trip 12, "A Touch of Glass," a visit to a glass blowing factory

CHAPTER 12 Chords, Secants, and Tangents

Relating to the Real World

Geometric figures drawn in circles and drawn about circles have many interesting characteristics. You will rely on your knowledge of congruent triangles and similar triangles as you discover some of these characteristics. The principles you will study in this chapter have applications in photography, architecture, and communications.

Lessons	12-1	12-2	12-3	12-4
	Circles in the Coordinate Plane	*Properties of Tangents*	*Properties of Chords and Arcs*	*Inscribed Angles*

Launching the Project

PROJECT NOTEBOOK Encourage students to keep all project-related materials in a separate folder or notebook. **See Chapter Project Manager and Scoring Rubric in Chapter Support File.**

- Ask students to describe designs, emblems, or logos they have seen that use circles. Students should be familiar with the Olympic rings or emblems on different automobiles made from circles and arcs.
- Have students list other real-world examples of objects that are made of intertwined circles, such as chains, necklaces, and key rings.

TRACKING THE PROJECT You may wish to have students read Finishing the Chapter Project on page 627 to help them get an overview of the project. Set benchmark deadlines for students to show their work in progress.

CHAPTER PROJECT

GO FOR A SPIN

For centuries, artists have used the simple elegance of the circle in their designs. Some have crafted intertwining patterns that like the circle itself have no beginning and no end. Some have disturbed the symmetry of the circle to create optical illlusions.

In your chapter project, you will explore some of the techniques used through the ages to produce circular art such as the painting at the left by Alma Thomas. You will then apply your discoveries to create a dizzying design. You will see why some artists find that "going in circles" may be the best way to reach their objective.

To help you complete the project:

- **p. 591** *Find Out by Doing*
- **p. 605** *Find Out by Exploring*
- **p. 618** *Find Out by Constructing*
- **p. 627** *Finishing the Project*

Project Resources

Teaching Resources

Chapter Support File, Ch. 12
- Chapter Project Manager and Scoring Rubric

Transparencies
119

Using the Rubric

Sharing the scoring rubric for the project with your students will alert them to your expectations before they begin work on the project.

As students complete each Find Out question in the chapter, you may wish to have them evaluate their own work or a partner's work based on the scoring rubric. Students should have the opportunity to revise their work after it has been reviewed.

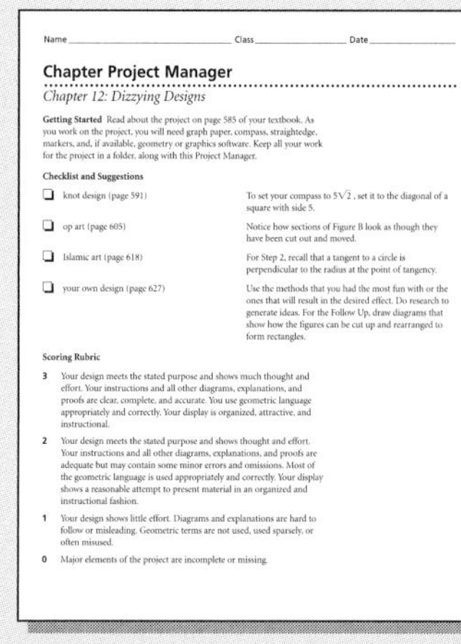

Name ______ Class ______ Date ______

Chapter Project Manager

Chapter 12: Dizzying Designs

Getting Started Read about the project on page 585 of your textbook. As you work on the project, you will need graph paper, compass, straightedge, markers, and, if available, geometry or graphics software. Keep all your work for the project in a folder, along with this Project Manager.

Checklist and Suggestions

☐ knot design (page 591)	To set your compass to $5\sqrt{2}$, set it to the diagonal of a square with side 5.
☐ op art (page 605)	Notice how sections of Figure B look as though they have been cut out and moved.
☐ Islamic art (page 618)	For Step 2, recall that a tangent to a circle is perpendicular to the radius at the point of tangency.
☐ your own design (page 627)	Use the methods that you had the most fun with or the ones that will result in the desired effect. Do research to generate ideas. For the Follow Up, draw diagrams that show how the figures can be cut up and rearranged to form rectangles.

Scoring Rubric

3 Your design meets the stated purpose and shows much thought and effort. Your instructions and all other diagrams, explanations, and proofs are clear, complete, and accurate. You use geometric language appropriately and correctly. Your display is organized, attractive, and instructional.

2 Your design meets the stated purpose and shows thought and effort. Your instructions and all other diagrams, explanations, and proofs are adequate but may contain some minor errors and omissions. Most of the geometric language is used appropriately and correctly. Your display shows a reasonable attempt to present material in an organized and instructional fashion.

1 Your design shows little effort. Diagrams and explanations are hard to follow or misleading. Geometric terms are not used, used sparsely, or often misused.

0 Major elements of the project are incomplete or missing.

12-1 Teaching Notes

PROBLEM OF THE DAY

In two moves, moving one circle each time, can you place these circles in a circle?

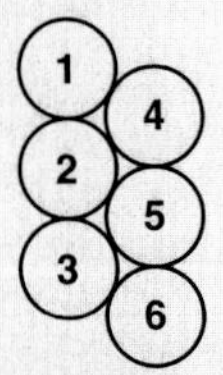

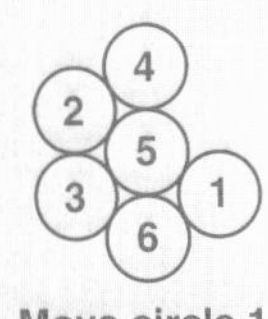

Move circle 1.

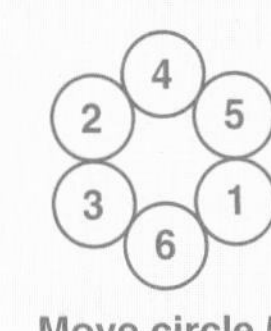

Move circle 5.

Problem of the Day is also available in Transparencies.

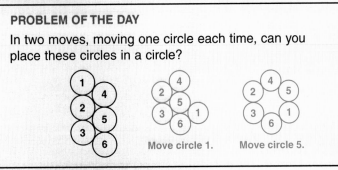

CONNECTING TO PRIOR KNOWLEDGE On a coordinate grid, draw a circle. Label the coordinates of the center and a point on the circle. Have students find the length of the radius.

WORK TOGETHER

ALTERNATIVE METHOD Questions 3 and 4 Have students solve $x^2 + y^2 = 25$ for y ($y = \sqrt{25 - x^2}$ or $y = -\sqrt{25 - x^2}$). Then have them use the table feature on graphing calculators to determine points that satisfy the equation. Students can also use the graphing calculator to graph the points.

THINK AND DISCUSS

Theorem 12-1 Help students understand that x and y are variables and h, k, and r are constants.

Lesson Planning Options

Prerequisite Skills

- Using the distance formula

Assignment Options for Exercises On Your Own

To provide flexible scheduling, this lesson can be subdivided into parts.

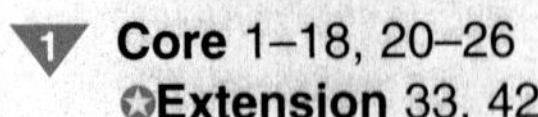

1 **Core** 1–18, 20–26
Extension 33, 42

2 **Core** 19, 27–32, 34–39
Extension 40–41, 43

Use Mixed Review to maintain skills.

Resources

Student Edition

Skills Handbook, pp. 673, 674
Extra Practice, p. 659
Glossary/Study Guide

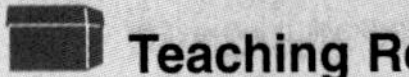

Teaching Resources

Chapter Support File, Ch. 12
- Practice 12-1 (two worksheets)
- Reteaching 12-1
- Alternative Activity 12-1

Classroom Manager 12-1
Glossary, Spanish Resources

Transparencies
5, 12, 120, 123

Connections  Communications . . . and more

12-1 Circles in the Coordinate Plane

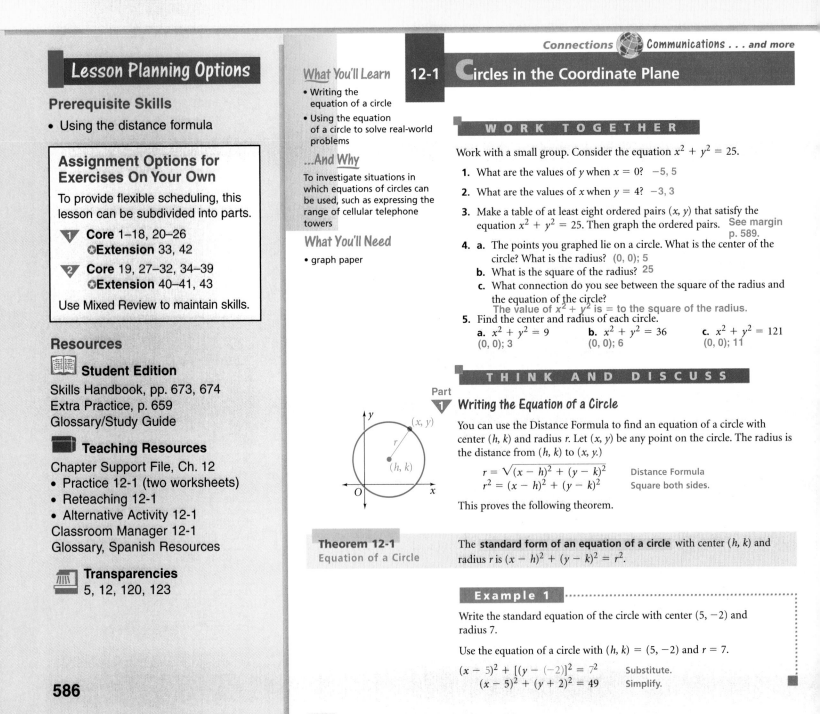

What You'll Learn
- Writing the equation of a circle
- Using the equation of a circle to solve real-world problems

...And Why

To investigate situations in which equations of circles can be used, such as expressing the range of cellular telephone towers

What You'll Need
- graph paper

WORK TOGETHER

Work with a small group. Consider the equation $x^2 + y^2 = 25$.

1. What are the values of y when $x = 0$? $-5, 5$
2. What are the values of x when $y = 4$? $-3, 3$
3. Make a table of at least eight ordered pairs (x, y) that satisfy the equation $x^2 + y^2 = 25$. Then graph the ordered pairs. See margin p. 589.
4. a. The points you graphed lie on a circle. What is the center of the circle? What is the radius? (0, 0); 5
   b. What is the square of the radius? 25
   c. What connection do you see between the square of the radius and the equation of the circle?
   The value of $x^2 + y^2$ is = to the square of the radius.
5. Find the center and radius of each circle.
   a. $x^2 + y^2 = 9$ (0, 0); 3
   b. $x^2 + y^2 = 36$ (0, 0); 6
   c. $x^2 + y^2 = 121$ (0, 0); 11

THINK AND DISCUSS

Part 1

Writing the Equation of a Circle

You can use the Distance Formula to find an equation of a circle with center (h, k) and radius r. Let (x, y) be any point on the circle. The radius is the distance from (h, k) to (x, y).

$r = \sqrt{(x - h)^2 + (y - k)^2}$ Distance Formula

$r^2 = (x - h)^2 + (y - k)^2$ Square both sides.

This proves the following theorem.

Theorem 12-1
Equation of a Circle

The **standard form of an equation of a circle** with center (h, k) and radius r is $(x - h)^2 + (y - k)^2 = r^2$.

Example 1

Write the standard equation of the circle with center $(5, -2)$ and radius 7.

Use the equation of a circle with $(h, k) = (5, -2)$ and $r = 7$.

$(x - 5)^2 + [(y - (-2)]^2 = 7^2$ Substitute.

$(x - 5)^2 + (y + 2)^2 = 49$ Simplify.

Example 1

ERROR ALERT! Some students may have trouble substituting negative values into the equation. **Remediation:** Remind students that subtracting a negative number is the same as adding its opposite.

EXTENSION Some graphing software allows students to graph circles. Give students opportunity to use the software throughout the lesson to check graphs and equations.

ERROR ALERT! **Question 7** Some students will use the wrong signs for the coordinates of the center. **Remediation:** Remind students that the equation of a circle in standard form has minus signs. Help them see that $(x-7)^2+(y+2)^2=64$ is equivalent to $(x-7)^2+[y-(-2)]^2=64$.

CRITICAL THINKING Question 8 Ask students if the following are equations of circles. If an equation describes a circle, have them find the center and radius.

a. $x^2+y^2=144$ **b.** $x^2-y^2=9$ **c.** $y^2+x^2=49$

Example 2 Relating to the Real World 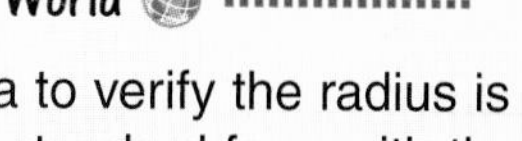

Have students use the distance formula to verify the radius is 10. Point out that the equation is left in standard form with the binomials not expanded.

TRANSFORMATIONS Question 10 Help students see that the translation vector describing the translation of $\odot A$ to $\odot B$ is the same translation vector describing the translation of point A to point B.

6a. $(x-3)^2+(y-5)^2=36$
b. $(x+2)^2+(y+1)^2=2$
7a. (7, −2); 8
b. (2, 3); 10

9. $\odot B$: $(x-16)^2+(y-10)^2=100$; $\odot O$: $x^2+y^2=144$

6. **Try This** Write the equation of each circle.
   a. center (3, 5); $r=6$ b. center (−2, −1); $r=\sqrt{2}$
7. **Try This** Find the center and radius of each circle.
   a. $(x-7)^2+(y+2)^2=64$ b. $(x-2)^2+(y-3)^2=100$
8. What is the standard form of the equation of a circle with center at the origin and radius r? $x^2+y^2=r^2$

Part 

Using the Equation of a Circle

You can use equations of circles to model real-world situations.

 Relating to the Real World 

Communications When you make a call from a cellular phone, a tower receives the call. In the graph, the center of each circle is the location of a cellular telephone tower. The equation of a circle can describe the receiving and transmitting range of a tower. Find the equation that describes the position and the range of Tower A.

The center of $\odot A$ is (4, 20), and the radius is 10. Use the equation of a circle with $(h, k) = (4, 20)$ and $r = 10$.

$(x-4)^2+(y-20)^2=10^2$ Substitute.
$(x-4)^2+(y-20)^2=100$ Simplify.

9. Find the equation of the positions and ranges of the other two towers. **See above left.**
10. *Transformations* $\odot B$ is a translation of $\odot A$. Use ordered pair notation to describe the translation vector. $\langle 12, -10\rangle$

Additional Examples

FOR EXAMPLE 1

Write the standard equation of the circle with center (3, −4) and radius 6. $(x-3)^2+(y+4)^2=36$

FOR EXAMPLE 2

In the graph, the center of each circle is the location of a broadcasting tower for a radio station. Find the equation that describes the position and range of tower F.

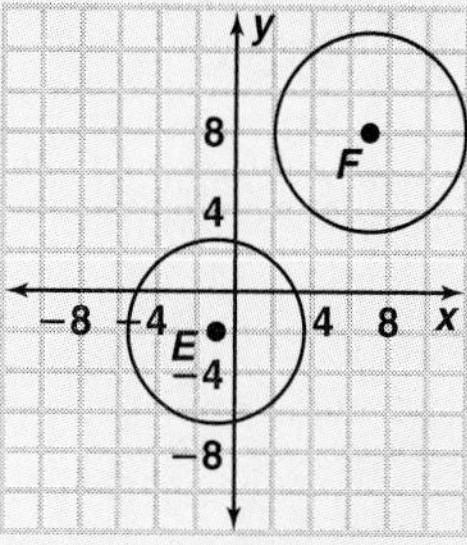

$(x-7)^2+(y-8)^2=25$

Discussion: *Describe the transformation that takes $\odot F$ onto $\odot E$.*

FOR EXAMPLE 3

Write an equation of a circle with center (1, 2) that passes through the point (3, −4). $(x-1)^2+(y-2)^2=40$

Discussion: *Describe the center and the radius of a circle that is entirely in the second quadrant.*

Example 3

Make sure students understand why $(h, k) = (1, -3)$ and not $(4, 2)$.

VISUAL LEARNING Question 11 Discuss with students that a circle separates a plane into the interior of the circle, the exterior of the circle, and the circle itself. You may want to have students practice graphing $x^2 + y^2 < 1$, $x^2 + y^2 = 1$, $x^2 + y^2 > 1$, $x^2 + y^2 \leq 1$, and $x^2 + y^2 \geq 1$.

Question 12 To solve this problem, students must realize that the center of the circle is the midpoint of the diameter.

Exercises ON YOUR OWN

Exercises 1–6 Check that students use the proper signs and remember to square the radii in the equations.

ALTERNATIVE ASSESSMENT Exercises 7–10 Have students work in pairs. Have them write on index cards five equations or inequalities similar to those in these exercises. Then have them draw the graphs on different index cards. After shuffling the cards, have students exchange them with another pair and match each equation or inequality with the appropriate graph.

Technology Options

For Exercises 15–18 and Exercise 41, students may use graphing software or a graphing calculator to graph the circles.

Prentice Hall Technology

Software
- Secondary Math Lab Toolkit™
- Computer Item Generator 12-1

CD-ROM
- Multimedia Geometry Lab 12

Internet
- See the Prentice Hall site. (http://www.phschool.com)

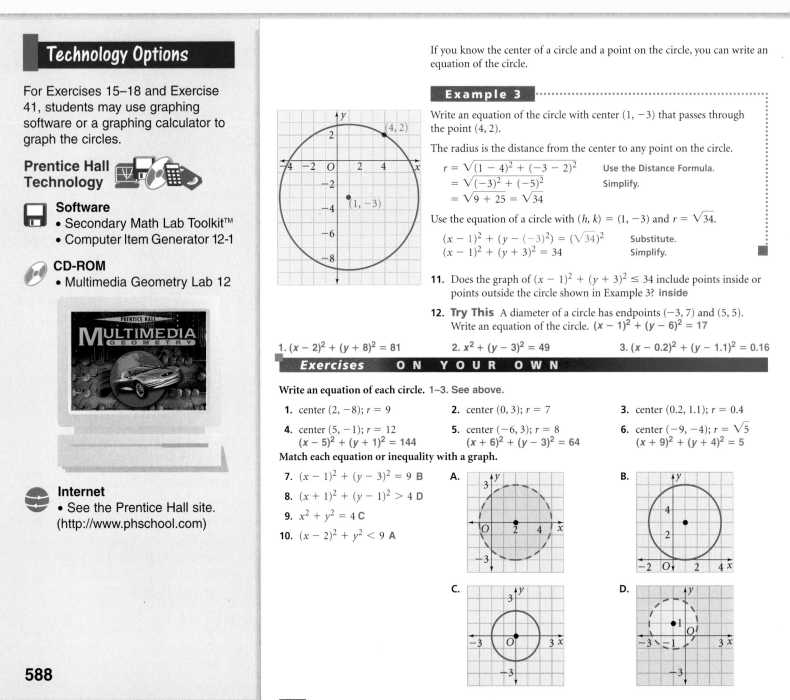

If you know the center of a circle and a point on the circle, you can write an equation of the circle.

Example 3

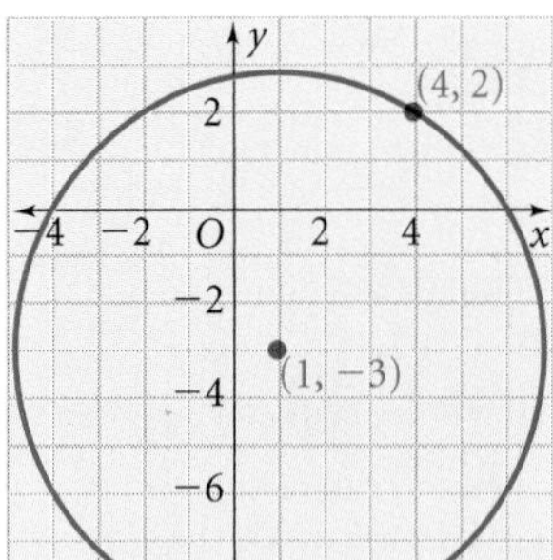

Write an equation of the circle with center $(1, -3)$ that passes through the point $(4, 2)$.

The radius is the distance from the center to any point on the circle.

$$r = \sqrt{(1-4)^2 + (-3-2)^2} \quad \text{Use the Distance Formula.}$$
$$= \sqrt{(-3)^2 + (-5)^2} \quad \text{Simplify.}$$
$$= \sqrt{9 + 25} = \sqrt{34}$$

Use the equation of a circle with $(h, k) = (1, -3)$ and $r = \sqrt{34}$.

$$(x-1)^2 + (y-(-3)^2) = (\sqrt{34})^2 \quad \text{Substitute.}$$
$$(x-1)^2 + (y+3)^2 = 34 \quad \text{Simplify.}$$

11. Does the graph of $(x-1)^2 + (y+3)^2 \leq 34$ include points inside or points outside the circle shown in Example 3? **inside**

12. **Try This** A diameter of a circle has endpoints $(-3, 7)$ and $(5, 5)$. Write an equation of the circle. $(x-1)^2 + (y-6)^2 = 17$

1. $(x-2)^2 + (y+8)^2 = 81$ **2.** $x^2 + (y-3)^2 = 49$ **3.** $(x-0.2)^2 + (y-1.1)^2 = 0.16$

Exercises ON YOUR OWN

Write an equation of each circle. 1–3. See above.

1. center $(2, -8)$; $r = 9$
2. center $(0, 3)$; $r = 7$
3. center $(0.2, 1.1)$; $r = 0.4$
4. center $(5, -1)$; $r = 12$ $(x-5)^2 + (y+1)^2 = 144$
5. center $(-6, 3)$; $r = 8$ $(x+6)^2 + (y-3)^2 = 64$
6. center $(-9, -4)$; $r = \sqrt{5}$ $(x+9)^2 + (y+4)^2 = 5$

Match each equation or inequality with a graph.

7. $(x-1)^2 + (y-3)^2 = 9$ **B**
8. $(x+1)^2 + (y-1)^2 > 4$ **D**
9. $x^2 + y^2 = 4$ **C**
10. $(x-2)^2 + y^2 < 9$ **A**

A.
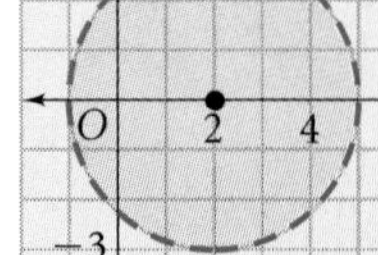

B.
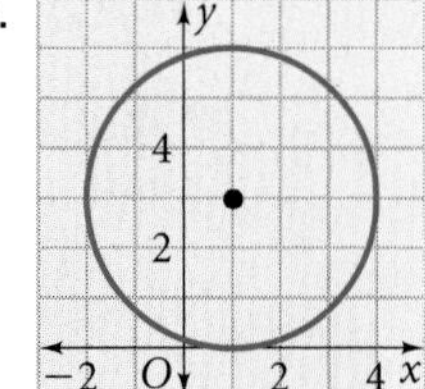

C.
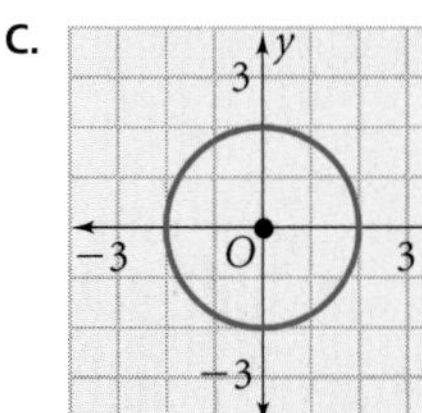

D.
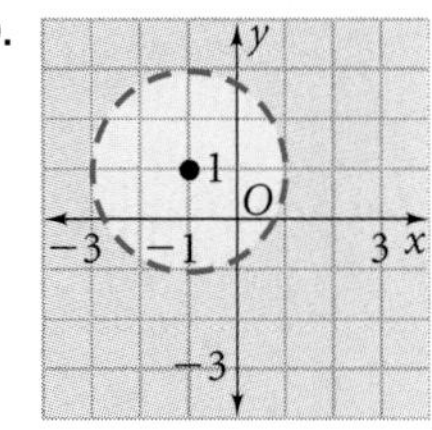

Exercises 11–14 Check that students have the proper signs for the coordinates of the center and that they take the square root to find the radius.

WRITING Exercise 19c Ask students to support their answers with several examples.

ESL Exercise 20 Explain to students that an "anemometer" is an instrument used to measure wind speed.

DIVERSITY Exercise 20 Take this opportunity to discuss weather patterns in parts of the United States, or in different parts of the world. Discuss, for example, that in December it may be snowing in some parts of the world and sunny and hot in others.

Exercises 21–26 Help students see that the most convenient point on the circle to pick to find the length of the radius is a point on the horizontal or vertical diameter.

Find the center and the radius of each circle.

11. $(x + 7)^2 + (y - 5)^2 = 16$ (−7, 5); 4

12. $(x - 3)^2 + (y + 8)^2 = 100$ (3, −8); 10

13. $(x - 0.3)^2 + y^2 = 0.04$ (0.3, 0); 0.2

14. $(x + 5)^2 + (y + 2)^2 = 48$ (−5, −2); $4\sqrt{3}$

Graph each circle. Label its center and state its radius. 15–17. See margin for graph. 18. See margin p. 590 for graph.

15. $x^2 + y^2 = 36$ 6

16. $x^2 + (y - 4)^2 = 16$ 4

17. $(x + 2)^2 + y^2 = 9$ 3

18. $(x + 4)^2 + (y - 1)^2 = 25$ 5

19. a. *Transformations* The circle with equation $(x + 5)^2 + (y - 3)^2 = 64$ is a translation image of $x^2 + y^2 = 64$. Use ordered pair notation to describe the translation vector. ⟨−5, 3⟩
    b. *Transformations* The circle $x^2 + y^2 = 64$ is the dilation image of $x^2 + y^2 = 1$. What is the center and scale factor of the dilation? (0, 0); 8
    c. *Writing* Write *true* or *false*. Every circle in the coordinate plane is a transformation image of $x^2 + y^2 = 1$. Explain. See margin.

20. a. *Weather* Consider a point on the edge of a cup of an anemometer. Describe the locus of points that this point passes through as the cup spins in the wind. circle
    b. *Locus* Suppose the distance from the center of the anemometer to a point on the edge of a cup is 6 in. Write an equation for the locus of points you described in part (a). Use the center of the anemometer as the origin. $x^2 + y^2 = 36$

The speed at which the cups of an anemometer spin indicates the speed of the wind.

Write an equation of each circle. See below.

21.

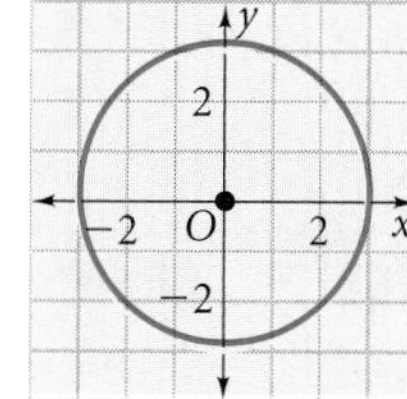

22. $x^2 + (y - 3)^2 = 4$

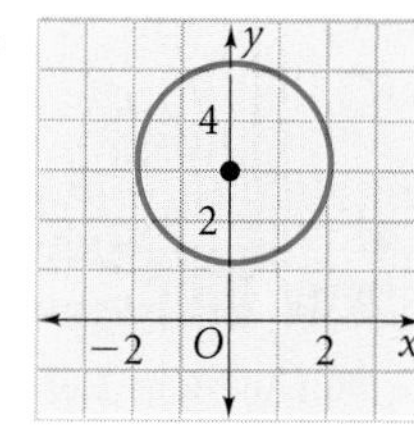

23. $(x - 2)^2 + (y - 2)^2 = 16$

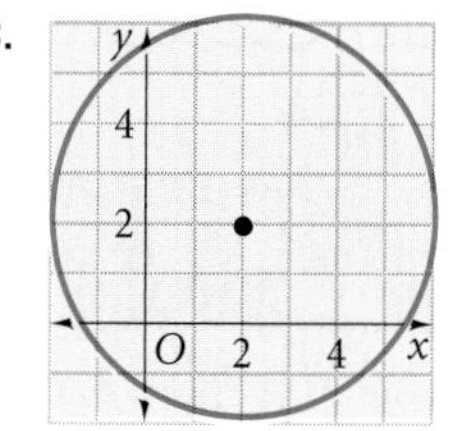

24.

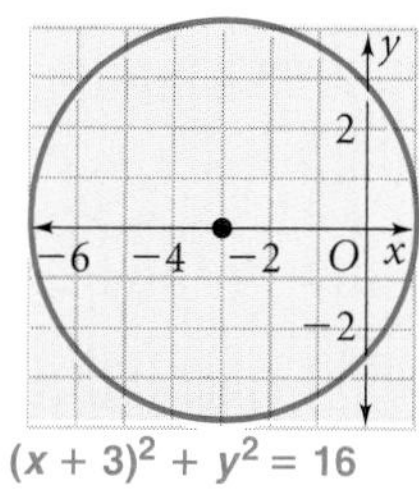

$(x + 3)^2 + y^2 = 16$

25.

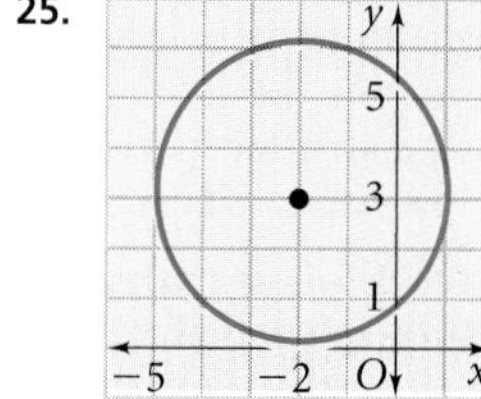

$(x + 2)^2 + (y - 3)^2 = 9$

26.

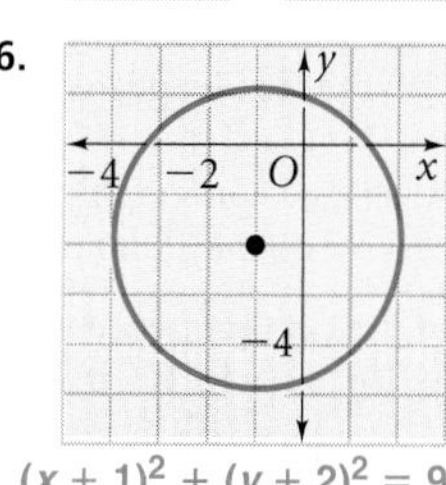

$(x + 1)^2 + (y + 2)^2 = 9$

21. $x^2 + y^2 = 9$

page 586 Work Together

3.

x	y
0	5
5	0
−5	0
0	−5
3	4
−4	3
−3	−4
4	−3

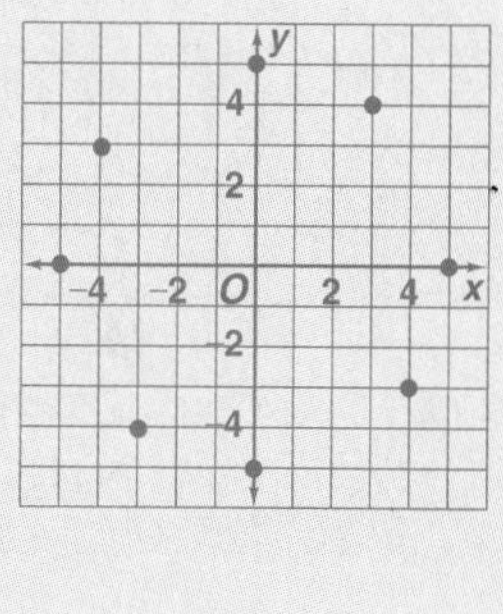

pages 588–591 On Your Own

15. 6

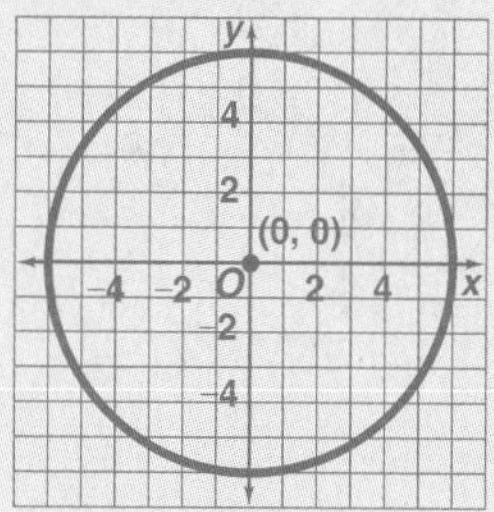

16. 4

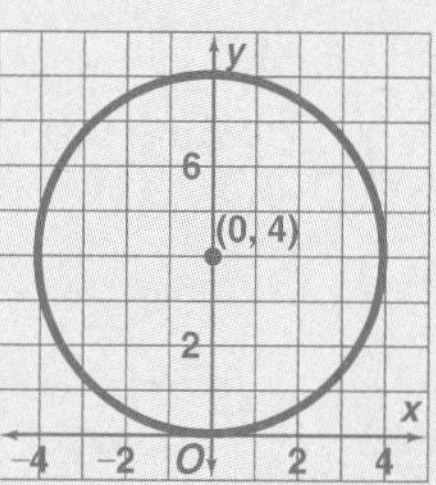

17. 3

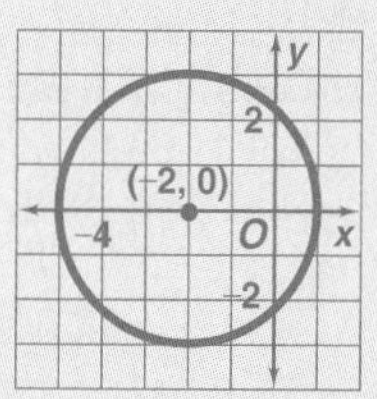

Exercises 27–30 Check that students substitute the correct ordered pair into the standard form.

CRITICAL THINKING Exercise 31 Ask students to explain why the radius of the image is 10.

Exercise 33b Review with students the formula for finding arc length.

Exercises 34–39 Have students review how they answered Question 12 before beginning these exercises.

KINESTHETIC LEARNING Exercise 41 Students may want to decorate their designs and display them on a bulletin board.

GEOMETRY IN 3 DIMENSIONS Exercise 43b Review with students the distance formula for points in three dimensions: $d = \sqrt{(x - x_1)^2 + (y - y_1)^2 + (z - z_1)^2}$.

18. 5

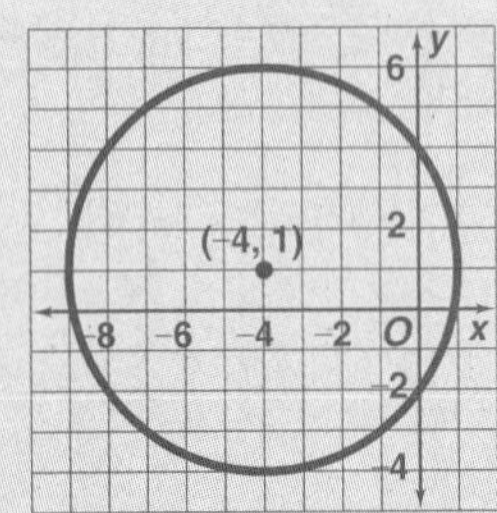

19c. True; a transformation consisting of a translation and a dilation can move the center of the ⊙ to any pt. and make the ⊙ any size.

41.

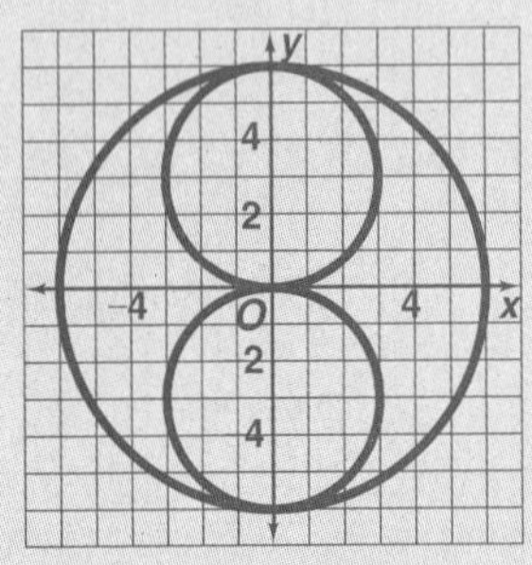

$x^2 + y^2 = 36$; $x^2 + (y - 3)^2 = 9$; $x^2 + (y + 3)^2 = 9$

page 591 Mixed Review

45. $\angle AEB \cong \angle DEC$ because vertical $\angle$s are $\cong$. Then $\triangle ABE \cong \triangle DCE$ by AAS, and $\overline{BE} \cong \overline{CE}$, $\overline{AE} \cong \overline{DE}$ by CPCTC. $\overline{AC} \cong \overline{DB}$ by the Segment Addition Post. $\overline{BC} \cong \overline{BC}$ by Reflexive Prop. of $\cong$. Then $\triangle ABC \cong \triangle DCB$ by SSS.

31. $(x - 3)^2 + (y + 5)^2 = 100$
32b. No; the variables are not squared.

Write an equation of the circle with the given center passing through the given point.

27. center $(-2, 6)$; through $(-2, 10)$ $(x + 2)^2 + (y - 6)^2 = 16$
28. center $(1, 2)$; through $(0, 6)$ $(x - 1)^2 + (y - 2)^2 = 17$
29. center $(7, -2)$; through $(1, -6)$ $(x - 7)^2 + (y + 2)^2 = 52$
30. center $(-10, -5)$; through $(-5, 5)$ $(x + 10)^2 + (y + 5)^2 = 125$
31. *Transformations* The graph of $x^2 + y^2 = 100$ is translated so that its center is $(3, -5)$. What is the equation of the image? See above.
32. *Critical Thinking* Determine whether each equation is an equation of a circle. If it is not, explain why. a. yes
   a. $(x - 1)^2 + (y + 2)^2 = 9$
   b. $x + y = 9$ See above.
   c. $x + (y - 3)^2 = 9$ No; x is not squared.
   d. $x^2 + (y - 1)^2 = 9$ yes

33a–c. See below.

33. a. Write the equation of the equator with the center of Earth as the origin. The equator's radius is about 3960 mi long.
   b. Find the length of a 1° arc on the equator to the nearest tenth.
   c. At the equator, a 1° arc in latitude is 60 nautical miles long. How many miles are in a nautical mile? Round to the nearest tenth.
   d. *History* Columbus planned his trip to the east by going west. He thought each 1° arc was 45 miles long. He estimated that the trip would take 21 days. Use your answer to part (b) to find a better estimate. about 32 days

33a. $x^2 + y^2 = 15{,}681{,}600$ b. 69.1 mi c. 1.2 mi

Write an equation of a circle with diameter $\overline{AB}$. 34–36. See below right.

34. $A(0, 0)$, and $B(8, 6)$
35. $A(3, 0)$, and $B(7, 6)$
36. $A(1, 1)$, and $B(5, 5)$
37. $A(-1, 0)$, and $B(-5, -3)$ $(x + 3)^2 + (y + 1.5)^2 = 6.25$
38. $A(-3, 1)$, and $B(0, 9)$ $(x + 1.5)^2 + (y - 5)^2 = 18.25$
39. $A(-2, 3)$, and $B(6, -7)$ $(x - 2)^2 + (y + 2)^2 = 41$

PEANUTS® by Charles M. Schulz

MAKES YOU WISH YOU KNEW HOW TO HANDLE A COMPASS, DOESN'T IT?

40. Snoopy can't draw a square with a compass. But he could construct a square and use it to find the length $5\sqrt{2}$ in. Then he could draw a circle with that length as the radius. Explain how. The diagonals of the square have length $5\sqrt{2}$ in.

41. *Open-ended* On graph paper, make a design that includes at least three circles. Write the equations of your circles. See margin for sample.

42. Find the circumference and the area of the circle whose equation is $(x - 9)^2 + (y - 3)^2 = 64$. Leave your answers in terms of π. 16π units; 64π units^2

34. $(x - 4)^2 + (y - 3)^2 = 25$
35. $(x - 5)^2 + (y - 3)^2 = 13$
36. $(x - 3)^2 + (y - 3)^2 = 8$

Chapter Project FIND OUT BY DOING Some students may need help drawing circles with radii $5\sqrt{2}$ and $4\sqrt{2}$. Remind them that these are the diameters of squares with sides 5 and 4, respectively.

Exercises MIXED REVIEW

Exercises 44–45 Have students trace $\triangle ABC$ and $\triangle DCB$ separately.

GETTING READY FOR LESSON 12-2 These exercises prepare students to study properties of tangents of circles.

Wrap Up

THE BIG IDEA Ask students to describe the steps they would take to find an equation of a circle with center $(-2, -5)$ passing through $(1, 3)$.

RETEACHING ACTIVITY Students find the equations of circles whose centers and radii are given. (Reteaching worksheet 12-1)

43. *Geometry in 3 Dimensions* The equation of a sphere is similar to the equation of a circle. The equation of a sphere with center (h, j, k) and radius r is $(x - h)^2 + (y - j)^2 + (z - k)^2 = r^2$.

a. $M(-1, 3, 2)$ is the center of a sphere passing through $T(0, 5, 1)$. What is the radius of the sphere? $\sqrt{6}$

b. Write an equation of the sphere. $(x + 1)^2 + (y - 3)^2 + (z - 2)^2 = 6$

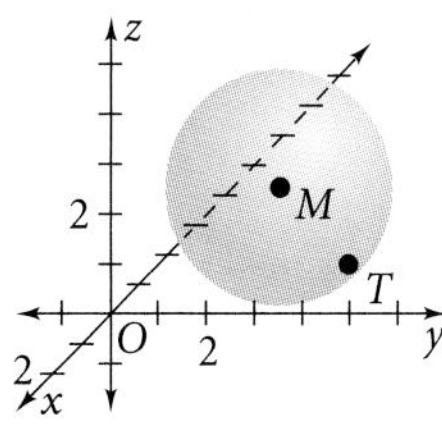

Chapter Project *Find Out by Doing*

For many centuries, artists throughout the world have used ropelike patterns called *knots* on jewelry, clothing, stone carvings, and other items. You can create a knot design using graph paper and a compass. Use a pencil because you will need to erase portions of your drawing.

- Mark the origin at the center of a sheet of graph paper, but do not draw any axes. Draw four circles with centers (0, 5), (5, 0), (0, −5), and (−5, 0) and with radius $5\sqrt{2}$. Using the same centers draw four circles with radius $4\sqrt{2}$.
- Connect the four centers to form a square. (shown in red)
- Draw segments through the intersections of the smaller and larger circles. (shown in green)
- Erase arcs to make bands that appear to weave in and out. Color your design. Check students' work.

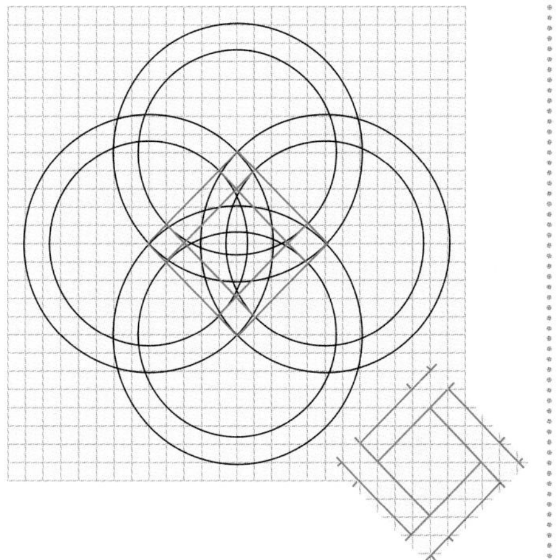

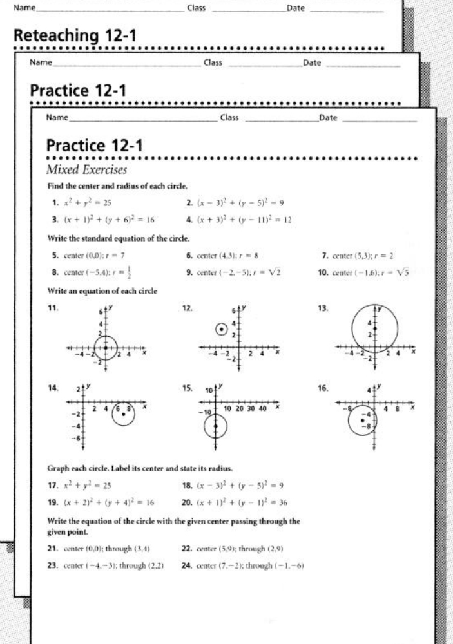

Name ______ Class ______ Date ______

Reteaching 12-1

Name ______ Class ______ Date ______

Practice 12-1

Name ______ Class ______ Date ______

Practice 12-1

Mixed Exercises

Find the center and radius of each circle.

1. $x^2 + y^2 = 25$
2. $(x - 3)^2 + (y - 5)^2 = 9$
3. $(x + 1)^2 + (y + 6)^2 = 16$
4. $(x + 3)^2 + (y - 11)^2 = 12$

Write the standard equation of the circle.

5. center (0,0); $r = 7$
6. center (4,3); $r = 8$
7. center (5,3); $r = 2$
8. center (−5,4); $r = \frac{1}{2}$
9. center (−2,−5); $r = \sqrt{2}$
10. center (−1,6); $r = \sqrt{5}$

Write an equation of each circle

11. 12. 13. 14. 15. 16.

Graph each circle. Label its center and state its radius.

17. $x^2 + y^2 = 25$
18. $(x - 3)^2 + (y - 5)^2 = 9$
19. $(x + 2)^2 + (y + 4)^2 = 16$
20. $(x + 1)^2 + (y - 1)^2 = 36$

Write the equation of the circle with the given center passing through the given point.

21. center (0,0); through (3,4)
22. center (5,9); through (2,9)
23. center (−4,−3); through (2,2)
24. center (7,−2); through (−1,−6)

Exercises MIXED REVIEW

Use the given information. Explain how to prove $\triangle ABC \cong \triangle DCB$.

44. Given: $\angle BCA \cong \angle CBD$, $\overline{BD} \cong \overline{CA}$ $\overline{BC} \cong \overline{BC}$; use SAS Post.

45. Given: $\angle ABE \cong \angle DCE$, $\overline{AB} \cong \overline{DC}$ See margin p. 590.

B C E A D

46. A cube has surface area 96 in.^{2}. What is the surface area of a cube with sides twice as long? 384 in.^{2}

47. The volume of a cube is 64 in.^{3}. What is the volume of a cube with sides twice as long? 512 in.^{3}

Getting Ready for Lesson 12-2

Find the complement and supplement of each angle.

48. 48° 42°; 132°

49. 73° 17°; 107°

50. 21° 69°; 159°

51. 87° 3°; 93°

Lesson Quiz

Lesson Quiz is also available in Transparencies.

1. Write an equation of the circle with center (3, −6) and radius 8. $(x - 3)^2 + (y + 6)^2 = 64$

2. Find the center and radius of the circle given by the equation $(x - 4)^2 + (y + 9)^2 = 121$. center (4, −9), $r = 11$

3. Write an equation of the circle with center (5, −2) and passing through (0, 4). $(x - 5)^2 + (y + 2)^2 = 61$

4. A diameter of a circle has endpoints (−2, 5) and (4, 7). Write an equation of the circle. $(x - 1)^2 + (y - 6)^2 = 10$

Math ToolboX

Students learn how to describe the location of a point using polar coordinates and how to graph points with polar coordinates.

Help students see how finding polar coordinates is similar to finding the magnitude and direction of a vector which they learned in Lesson 11-4.

Example 1

ERROR ALERT! Some students may measure angles in the clockwise direction. **Remediation:** Help students understand that in the polar coordinate system angles are measured in the counterclockwise direction starting from the polar axis.

Example 2

Help students understand that the radius of each circle in the diagram increases by 1 unit.

ADDITIONAL PROBLEMS

1. Graph $S(2, 60^\circ)$. Find the polar coordinates of a point T such that $m\angle SOT = 90$. **Answers may vary. Sample: (3, 150°)**

2. Graph $Q(3, 210^\circ)$. Find the polar coordinates of a point R such that $m\angle QOR = 180$. **Answers may vary. Sample: (5, 30°)**

Transparencies
12, 123

Math ToolboX — Algebra

Polar Coordinates

Extends Lesson 12-1

The polar-coordinate system locates a point using its distance from the origin, or **pole,** and the measure of a central angle formed by the polar axis and a ray from the pole through the point. The coordinates of A are $(2, 60^\circ)$ because A is 2 units from the pole O and the measure of the angle formed by the polar axis and $\overrightarrow{OA}$ is 60.

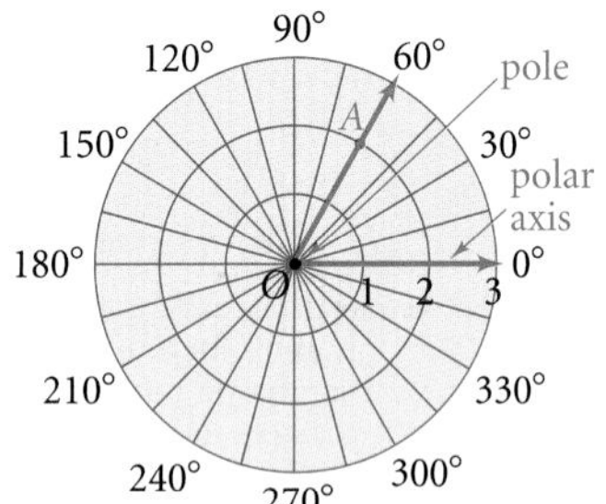

Example 1

What are the polar coordinates of P, Q, R, and S?

The coordinates of P are $(3, 90^\circ)$.

The coordinates of Q are $(2, 210^\circ)$.

The coordinates of R are $(4, 45^\circ)$.

The coordinates of S are $(3.5, 285^\circ)$.

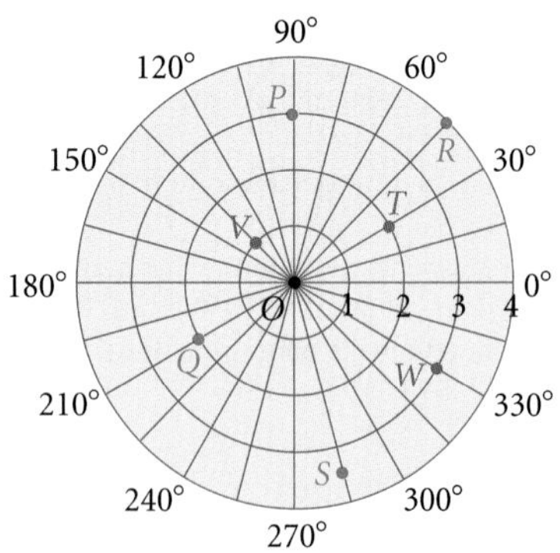

Example 2

Graph the points $T(2, 30^\circ)$, $V(1, 135^\circ)$, and $W(3, 330^\circ)$.

Find the polar coordinates of each point.

1. A **(3, 120°)** **2.** B **(2, 75°)** **3.** C **(5, 315°)**

4. D **(4, 285°)** **5.** E **(2, 240°)** **6.** F **(3, 330°)**

Graph each point.

7. $G(5, 180^\circ)$ **8.** $H(4, 60^\circ)$

9. $I(3, 45^\circ)$ **10.** $J(1, 225^\circ)$

11. $K(3.5, 150^\circ)$ **12.** $L(5, 270^\circ)$

13. Explain how you can use the polar coordinates of X and Y to find the measure of $\angle XOY$.
Read the measures of the central ∠s for points X and Y from the graph, and subtract the measures.

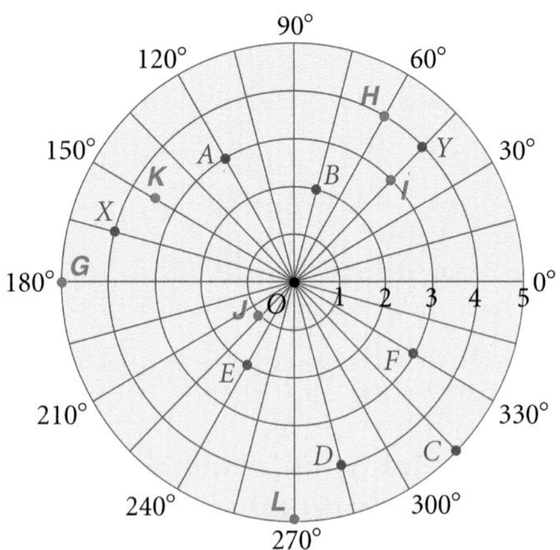

592

12-2 Teaching Notes

PROBLEM OF THE DAY

How can you place 21 marbles in four boxes so that each box contains an odd number of marbles? Answers may vary. Sample given.

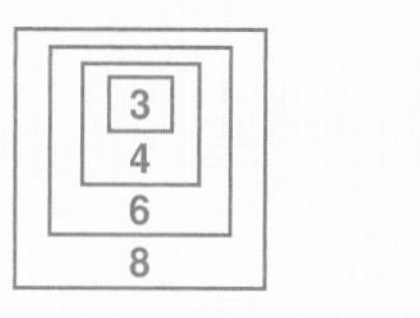

Problem of the Day is also available in Transparencies.

CONNECTING TO PRIOR KNOWLEDGE Draw several different right triangles on the board. Label the lengths of two sides of each and have students find the length of the third side.

WORK TOGETHER p. 593

Check that students do not draw a segment that intersects a circle at one point rather than drawing a line that touches a circle at one point.

THINK AND DISCUSS p. 593

MAKING CONNECTIONS The term *tangent* comes from the Latin verb *tangere* which means "to touch."

ESL Students may be confused by using *tangent* in a new way. Try to use the phrases "tangent of an angle" and "tangent to a circle" to help reinforce the difference.

Connections Machine Shops . . . *and more*

12-2 Properties of Tangents

What You'll Learn

- Finding the relationship between a radius and a tangent, and between two tangents drawn from the same point
- Circumscribing a circle

...And Why

To use tangents to circles in real-world situations, such as working in a machine shop

What You'll Need

- compass
- straightedge
- centimeter ruler

WORK TOGETHER

Work in a group.

- Use a compass to draw a circle. Label the center O.
- Use a straightedge to draw a line that intersects the circle in only one point. Label the point B.
- Draw $\overline{OB}$.

1. What seems to be true about the angle formed by the radius and the line that you drew? Compare results within your group. The radius and the line form a rt. angle.

THINK AND DISCUSS

Part 1

Tangents to Circles

In Chapter 11, you studied *the tangent of an angle in a right triangle.* Now you will study properties of *a tangent to a circle.*

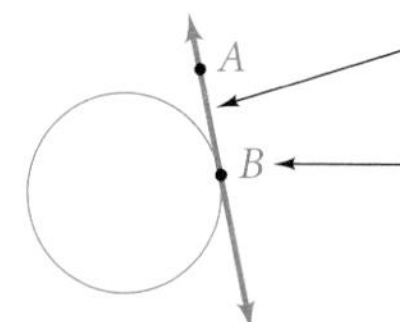

A **tangent to a circle** is a line in the plane of the circle that intersects the circle in exactly one point.

The point where a circle and a tangent intersect is the **point of tangency.**

$\overrightarrow{BA}$ is a tangent ray and $\overline{BA}$ is a tangent segment. The word *tangent* may refer to a tangent line, a tangent ray, or a tangent segment.

Your observation in the Work Together suggests the following theorem.

Theorem 12-2

If a line is tangent to a circle, then it is perpendicular to the radius drawn to the point of tangency.

If $\overleftrightarrow{AB}$ is tangent to $\odot O$ at P, then $\overleftrightarrow{AB} \perp \overline{OP}$.

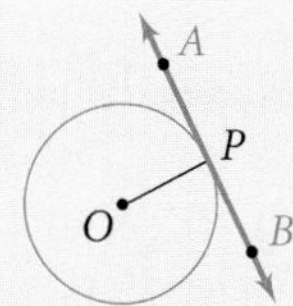

2. How many lines can you draw that are tangent to a circle at a given point on the circle? 1

Lesson Planning Options

Prerequisite Skills

- Using the Pythagorean Theorem
- Expanding binomials

Assignment Options for Exercises On Your Own

To provide flexible scheduling, this lesson can be subdivided into parts.

1 **Core** 1–12, 17, 22–23
Extension 13, 25

2 **Core** 14–16, 18–19
Extension 20, 21, 24

Use Mixed Review to maintain skills.

Resources

Student Edition

Skills Handbook, p. 664
Extra Practice, p. 659
Glossary/Study Guide

Teaching Resources

Chapter Support File, Ch. 12
- Practice 12-2 (two worksheets)
- Reteaching 12-2

Classroom Manager 12-2
Glossary, Spanish Resources

Transparencies

120

Read through the proof of Theorem 12-2 with students. Make sure students understand why assuming $\overline{OP}$ is not perpendicular to n makes it possible to draw a segment $\overline{OL}$ that is perpendicular. Also make sure students understand why they can pick a point K such that $\overline{LK} \cong \overline{LP}$.

Example 1

Check that students understand why $SQ = r + 4$. Also review with students how to expand a binomial.

Example 2 Relating to the Real World 

ERROR ALERT! Some students will think $\angle EAD$ is a right angle and $\overline{ED}$ is the hypotenuse of $\triangle AED$. **Remediation:** Label all four right angles of $EBCD$ and remind students that the supplement of a right angle is a right angle.

Additional Examples

FOR EXAMPLE 1

Refer to the diagram in Example 1. $\overline{PQ}$ is tangent to $\odot S$ at P. If $PQ = 8$ and $TQ = 5$, find the length of the radius of $\odot S$. 3.9

FOR EXAMPLE 2

Find the distance between the centers of the pulleys. ≈ 20.4 in.

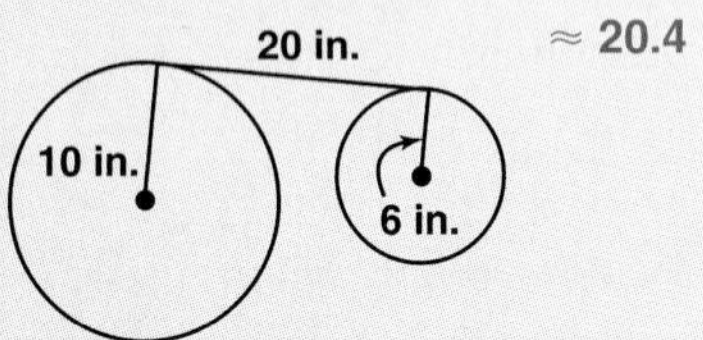

Discussion: *Explain how you can solve this problem in a different way.*

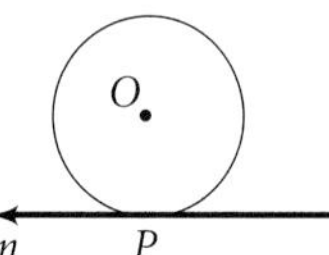

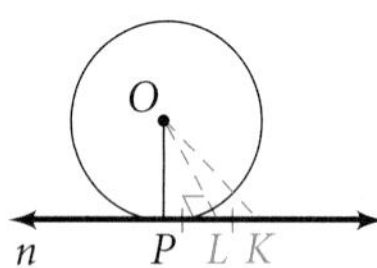

Indirect Proof of Theorem 12-2

Given: n is tangent to $\odot O$ at P.

Prove: $n \perp \overline{OP}$

Step 1: Assume that n is not perpendicular to $\overline{OP}$.

Step 2: If n is not perpendicular to $\overline{OP}$, some other segment $\overline{OL}$ must be perpendicular to n. Also there is a point K on n such that $\overline{LK} \cong \overline{LP}$. $\angle OLK \cong \angle OLP$ because perpendicular lines form congruent adjacent angles. $\overline{OL} \cong \overline{OL}$. So, $\triangle KLO \cong \triangle PLO$ by SAS. By CPCTC, $\overline{OK} \cong \overline{OP}$, which means K and P are both on $\odot O$ by the definition of a circle. For two points on n to also be on $\odot O$ contradicts the given fact that n is tangent to $\odot O$ at P. So the assumption that n is not perpendicular to $\overline{OP}$ must be false.

Step 3: Therefore, $n \perp \overline{OP}$ must be true.

Who? Alma Thomas (1891–1978) used geometric designs in many of her paintings. In *A Joyful Scene of Spring* (p. 585), Thomas used wedges of color to represent the many circular gardens planted throughout Washington, D.C.

You can use the Pythagorean Theorem to solve problems involving tangents.

Example 1

$\overline{PQ}$ is tangent to $\odot S$ at P. Find the length of a radius of $\odot S$.

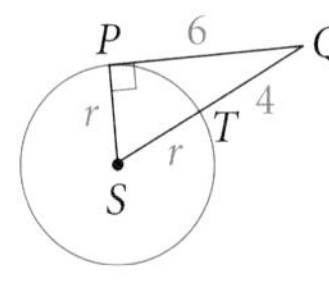

Since $\overline{PQ}$ is tangent to $\odot S$ at P, $\triangle PQS$ is a right triangle with hypotenuse $\overline{SQ}$. $\overline{PS}$ and $\overline{ST}$ are radii of $\odot S$.

$PS^2 + PQ^2 = SQ^2$	Pythagorean Theorem
$r^2 + 6^2 = (r + 4)^2$	$PS = ST = r$; $ST + TQ = SQ$
$r^2 + 36 = r^2 + 8r + 16$	Simplify.
$20 = 8r$	Subtract r^2 and 16 from each side.
$r = 2.5$	Divide each side by 8.

Tangents are formed by belts and ropes that pass over pulleys and wheels.

Example 2 Relating to the Real World

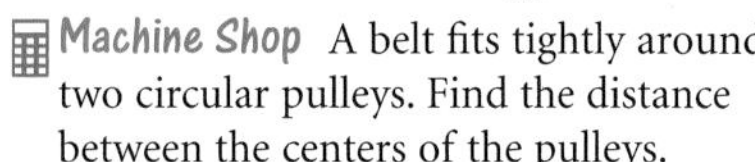

Machine Shop A belt fits tightly around two circular pulleys. Find the distance between the centers of the pulleys.

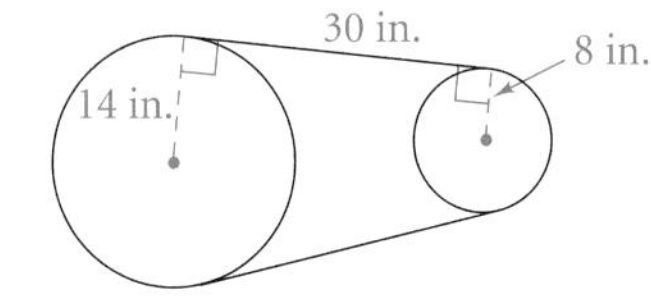

Question 3 Make sure students can justify that $\overline{BE} \parallel \overline{CD}$ because $\overline{BE}$ and $\overline{CD}$ are perpendicular to the same segment.

ALTERNATIVE ASSESSMENT To assess students' understanding of indirect proof, have students work in groups to write an indirect proof of Theorem 12-3. Then have them compare their proofs with those of other groups.

WORK TOGETHER p. 595

ALTERNATIVE METHOD Have students draw two intersecting lines on a sheet of paper. Then have them use a compass to draw a circle on another sheet of paper that is small enough to fit between the lines. Have them cut out the circle and place it between the lines so it is tangent to both lines, mark the points of tangency, and measure the distances from the point of intersection to the points of tangency.

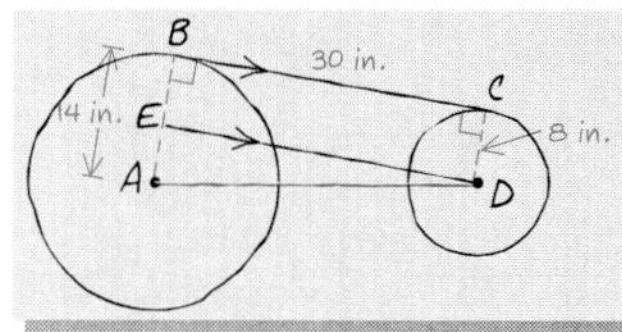

Label the diagram. Draw a segment parallel to $\overline{CB}$ from D to $\overline{AB}$. Label the intersection E.

$EBCD$ is a rectangle. $\triangle AED$ is a right triangle with $ED = 30$ in. and $AE = 14 - 8 = 6$ in.

Use the Pythagorean Theorem to find the distance between the centers, AD.

$AE^2 + ED^2 = AD^2$	Pythagorean Theorem
$6^2 + 30^2 = AD^2$	Substitute.
$936 = AD^2$	Simplify.
$30.594117 = AD$	Use a calculator.

The distance between the centers is about 30.6 in.

PROBLEM SOLVING

Look Back Explain how you could solve the problem in Example 2 by drawing a line from *C* rather than from *D*.

Draw a segment ∥ to $\overline{AD}$ from *C* to $\overline{AB}$. Label the intersection *E*. $AE = 8$ because opp. sides of a ▱ are ≅. Then $EB = 6$. Use the Pythagorean Thm. to find the hypotenuse of $\triangle EBC$.

3–4. See margin p. 596.

3. Explain why $EBCD$ in Example 2 is a rectangle.

4. Explain why $\triangle AED$ in Example 2 is a right triangle.

5. **Try This** In the diagram at the right, $\overline{PQ}$ is tangent to $\odot O$ at P. Find the radius of $\odot O$. 8 in.

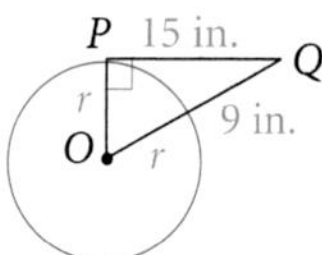

The converse of Theorem 12-2 is also true. You can use the Converse of Theorem 12-2 to determine if a segment is tangent to a circle. You can also use the converse to construct a tangent to a circle.

Theorem 12-3
Converse of Theorem 12-2

If a line in the same plane as a circle is perpendicular to a radius at its endpoint on the circle, then the line is tangent to the circle.

If $\overleftrightarrow{AB} \perp \overline{OP}$ at P, then $\overleftrightarrow{AB}$ is tangent to $\odot O$.

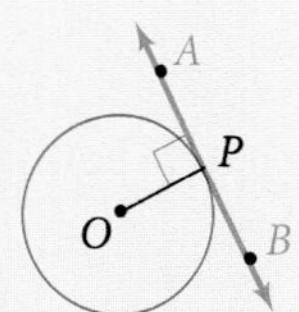

6. In the diagram at the right, is $\overline{LM}$ tangent to $\odot N$ at L? Explain.

Yes; $7^2 + 24^2 = 25^2$, so $\triangle NLM$ is a rt. △ and ∠L is a rt. angle.

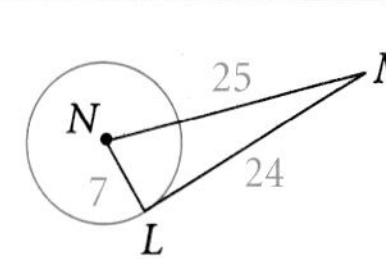

Part 2

WORK TOGETHER

TECHNOLOGY HINT

The Work Together could be done using geometry software.

Have each member of your group construct a circle and select a point outside the circle. From the point, draw two tangent segments to the circle.

7. a. Measure the tangent segments. What do you notice? Compare results within your group. The segments have = lengths.

b. Write a **conjecture** based on your results. 2 segments with a common endpt. outside a ⊙ and tangent to that ⊙ are ≅.

Technology Options

For Exercises 9 and 23, students may draw circles using graphing software or graphing calculators.

Prentice Hall Technology

Software
- Secondary Math Lab Toolkit™
- Computer Item Generator 12-2

CD-ROM
- Multimedia Geometry Lab 12

Internet
- See the Prentice Hall site. (http://www.phschool.com)

THINK AND DISCUSS

p. 596

ESL AUDITORY LEARNING Some students may confuse the terms *circumscribe* and *inscribe*. It may help students to remember that a figure that is circumscribed goes "around" another figure and a figure that is inscribed is "in" another figure.

TECHNOLOGY Theorem 12-4 If you have block scheduling or an extended period, give examples of Theorem 12-4 using geometry software.

Example 3

Make sure students understand that $\overline{AB}$, $\overline{BC}$, and $\overline{AC}$ are tangent to the circle.

CRITICAL THINKING Have students copy the diagram and draw radii $\overline{DO}$, $\overline{FO}$, and $\overline{EO}$. Then ask them to classify the three quadrilaterals formed.

pages 593–595 Think and Discuss

3. Answers may vary. Sample: The radii are ∥ because, in a plane, 2 lines ⊥ to a 3rd line are ∥. Then *EBCD* is a ▱ with 2 rt. angles. So it is a rectangle.
4. ∠*AED* is supplementary to right angle ∠*BED*, so it is also a right angle. So ∠*AED* is a right △.

pages 596–599 On Your Own

9a.

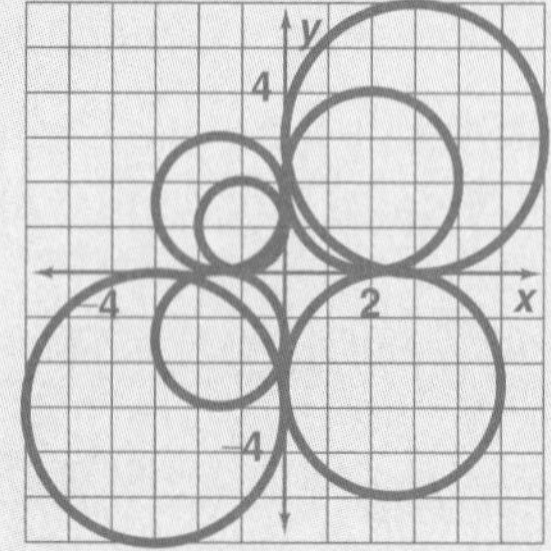

10. 1. $\overline{BA}$ and $\overline{BC}$ are tangent to ⊙*O* at *A* and *C*, respectively. (Given) 2. $\overline{BA} \perp \overline{OA}$, $\overline{BC} \perp \overline{OC}$ (A line tangent to a ⊙ is ⊥ to the radius drawn to the pt. of tangency.) 3. △*OAB* and △*OCB* are rt. △s. (Def. of rt. △) 4. $\overline{OA} \cong \overline{OC}$ (All radii of a ⊙ are ≅.) 5. $\overline{OB} \cong \overline{OB}$ (Reflexive Prop. of ≅) 6. △*OAB* ≅ △*OCB* (HL Thm.) 7. $\overline{BA} \cong \overline{BC}$ (CPCTC)

12a.

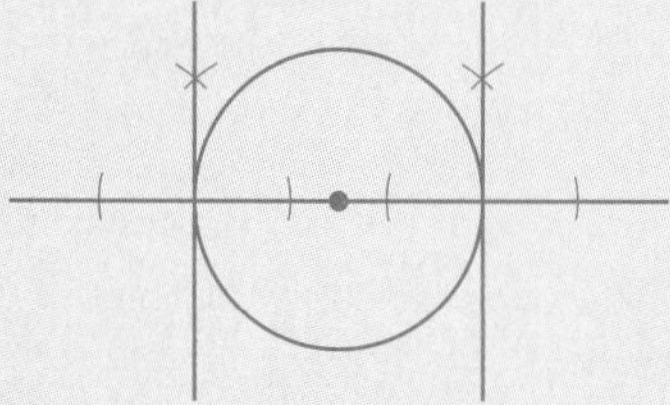

THINK AND DISCUSS

Circumscribing Circles

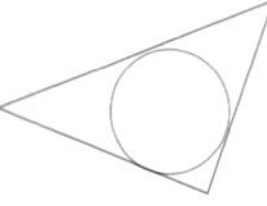

In the figure at the left, the sides of the triangle are tangent to the circle. The triangle is **circumscribed about** the circle. The circle is **inscribed in** the triangle.

Theorem 12-4 allows you to investigate figures that circumscribe a circle. You will prove this theorem in Exercise 10.

Theorem 12-4

Two segments tangent to a circle from a point outside the circle are congruent.

If $\overline{AB}$ and $\overline{CB}$ are tangent to ⊙*O* at *A* and *C*, respectively, then $\overline{AB} \cong \overline{CB}$.

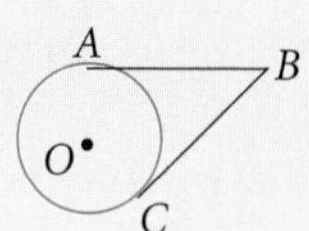

Example 3

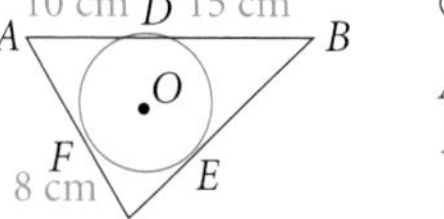

⊙*O* is inscribed in △*ABC*. Find the perimeter of △*ABC*.

$AD = AF = 10$ cm
$BD = BE = 15$ cm
$CF = CE = 8$ cm

Two segments tangent to a circle from a point outside the circle are congruent.

$AD + AF + BD + BE + CF + CE =$ the perimeter
$10 + 10 + 15 + 15 + 8 + 8 = 66$
The perimeter is 66 cm.

8. a. **Try This** ⊙*O* is inscribed in △*PQR*. Copy the diagram and label each length you know based on Theorem 12-4.
   b. △*PQR* has a perimeter 88 cm. Find *QY*. 12 cm

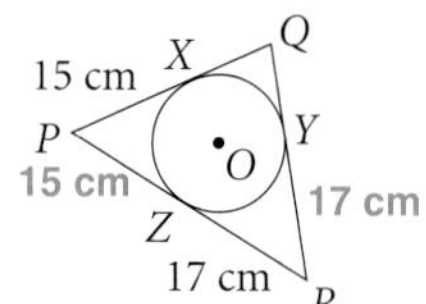

Exercises ON YOUR OWN

Assume that lines that appear to be tangent are tangent. *O* is the center of each circle. Find the value of *x*.

1. 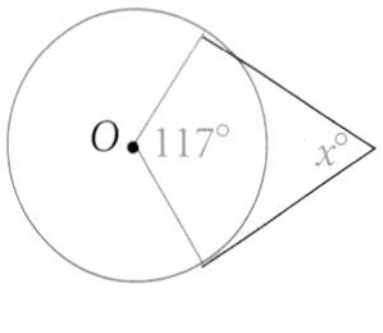 O 117° x° — 63

2. 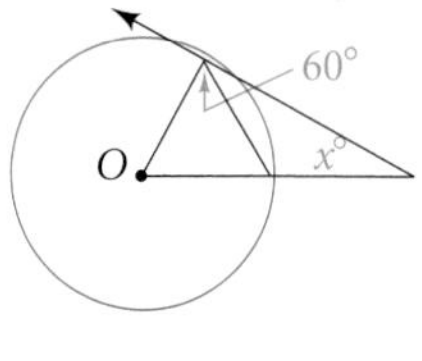 60° O x° — 30

3. 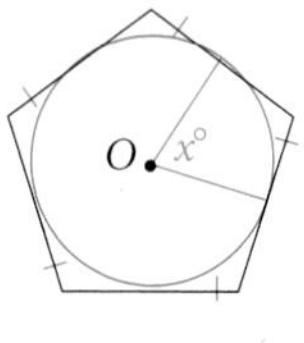 O x° — 72

4. 52

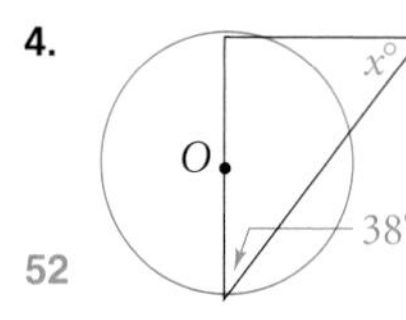

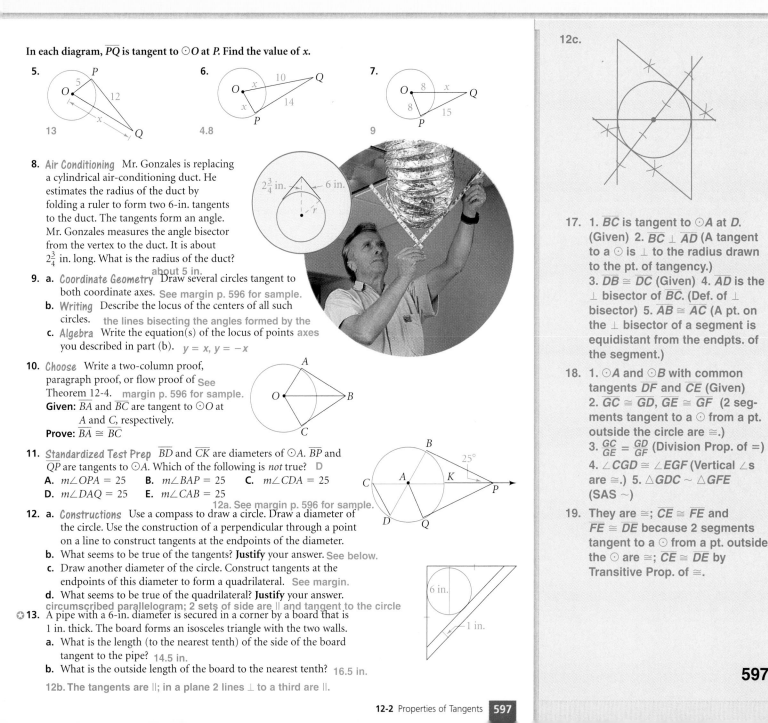

Exercises ON YOUR OWN

Exercises 1–4 Remind students that the sum of the measures of the angles of a quadrilateral is 360 and the sum of the measures of the angles of a pentagon is 540.

ERROR ALERT! **Exercises 5–7** Some students may think that the tangent is the hypotenuse. **Remediation:** Have students copy the triangles and insert a right angle symbol at the vertex where the tangent and radius meet.

COORDINATE GEOMETRY Exercise 9a Make sure that students draw circles in all four quadrants.

WRITING Exercise 9b Students may need to review Lesson 4-7 to describe a locus of points.

STANDARDIZED TEST TIP **Exercise 11** Suggest that students try to eliminate as many answers as possible before trying to find each measure.

In each diagram, $\overline{PQ}$ is tangent to $\odot O$ at P. Find the value of x.

5. 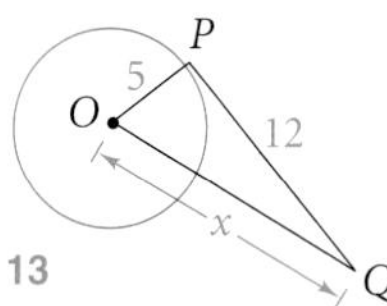

13

6. 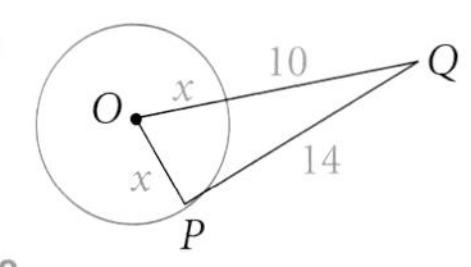

4.8

7. 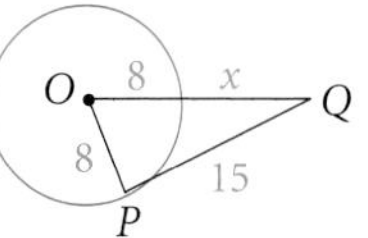

9

8. Air Conditioning Mr. Gonzales is replacing a cylindrical air-conditioning duct. He estimates the radius of the duct by folding a ruler to form two 6-in. tangents to the duct. The tangents form an angle. Mr. Gonzales measures the angle bisector from the vertex to the duct. It is about $2\frac{3}{4}$ in. long. What is the radius of the duct? about 5 in.

$2\frac{3}{4}$ in. 6 in. r

9. a. Coordinate Geometry Draw several circles tangent to both coordinate axes. See margin p. 596 for sample.

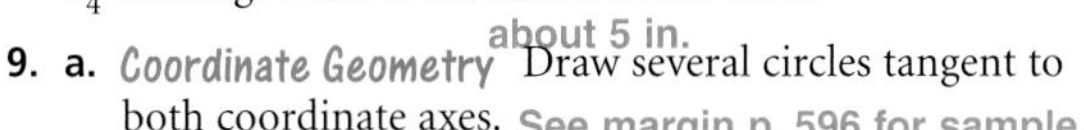

b. Writing Describe the locus of the centers of all such circles. the lines bisecting the angles formed by the axes

c. Algebra Write the equation(s) of the locus of points you described in part (b). $y = x, y = -x$

10. Choose Write a two-column proof, paragraph proof, or flow proof of Theorem 12-4. See margin p. 596 for sample.

Given: $\overline{BA}$ and $\overline{BC}$ are tangent to $\odot O$ at A and C, respectively.

Prove: $BA \cong BC$

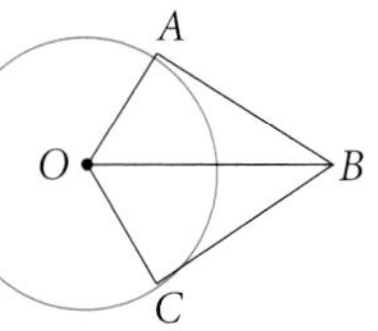

11. Standardized Test Prep $\overline{BD}$ and $\overline{CK}$ are diameters of $\odot A$. $\overline{BP}$ and $\overline{QP}$ are tangents to $\odot A$. Which of the following is *not* true? D

A. $m\angle OPA = 25$ **B.** $m\angle BAP = 25$ **C.** $m\angle CDA = 25$

D. $m\angle DAQ = 25$ **E.** $m\angle CAB = 25$

B 25° C A K P D Q

12. a. Constructions Use a compass to draw a circle. Draw a diameter of the circle. Use the construction of a perpendicular through a point on a line to construct tangents at the endpoints of the diameter. 12a. See margin p. 596 for sample.

b. What seems to be true of the tangents? **Justify** your answer. See below.

c. Draw another diameter of the circle. Construct tangents at the endpoints of this diameter to form a quadrilateral. See margin.

d. What seems to be true of the quadrilateral? **Justify** your answer. circumscribed parallelogram; 2 sets of side are ∥ and tangent to the circle

13. A pipe with a 6-in. diameter is secured in a corner by a board that is 1 in. thick. The board forms an isosceles triangle with the two walls.

a. What is the length (to the nearest tenth) of the side of the board tangent to the pipe? 14.5 in.

b. What is the outside length of the board to the nearest tenth? 16.5 in.

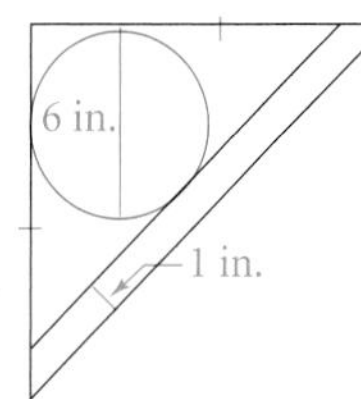

12b. The tangents are ∥; in a plane 2 lines ⊥ to a third are ∥.

12c.

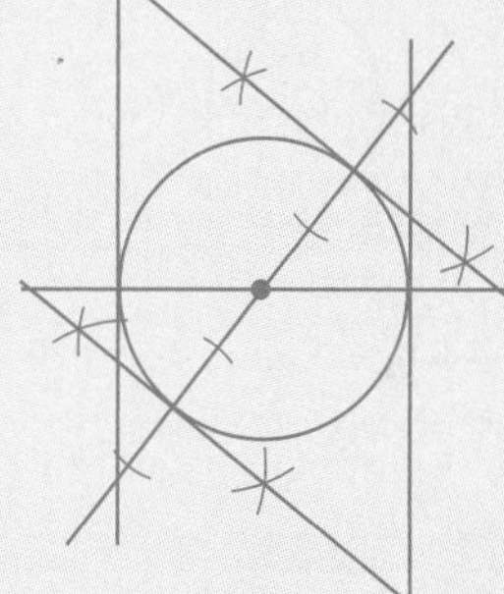

17. 1. $\overline{BC}$ is tangent to $\odot A$ at D. (Given) 2. $\overline{BC} \perp \overline{AD}$ (A tangent to a ⊙ is ⊥ to the radius drawn to the pt. of tangency.) 3. $\overline{DB} \cong \overline{DC}$ (Given) 4. $\overline{AD}$ is the ⊥ bisector of $\overline{BC}$. (Def. of ⊥ bisector) 5. $\overline{AB} \cong \overline{AC}$ (A pt. on the ⊥ bisector of a segment is equidistant from the endpts. of the segment.)

18. 1. $\odot A$ and $\odot B$ with common tangents $\overline{DF}$ and $\overline{CE}$ (Given) 2. $\overline{GC} \cong \overline{GD}$, $\overline{GE} \cong \overline{GF}$ (2 segments tangent to a ⊙ from a pt. outside the circle are ≅.) 3. $\frac{GC}{GE} = \frac{GD}{GF}$ (Division Prop. of =) 4. $\angle CGD \cong \angle EGF$ (Vertical ∠s are ≅.) 5. $\triangle GDC \sim \triangle GFE$ (SAS ~)

19. They are ≅; $\overline{CE} \cong \overline{FE}$ and $\overline{FE} \cong \overline{DE}$ because 2 segments tangent to a ⊙ from a pt. outside the ⊙ are ≅; $\overline{CE} \cong \overline{DE}$ by Transitive Prop. of ≅.

Exercises 17–18 Have students work with partners or in small groups. Suggest they begin by writing a plan for each proof. Make sure students do not assume anything about the segments from the appearance of the diagrams.

MAKING CONNECTIONS Exercise 21 The maximum duration of an eclipse of the sun is 7 min, 31 sec and there can be at most five solar eclipses per year.

CONNECTING TO STUDENTS' WORLD Exercise 21 Have students research other facts about a solar or lunar eclipse and share them with the class.

EXTENSION Exercise 21 Challenge students to draw a pair of circles for which there is exactly one common tangent, exactly two common tangents, exactly three common tangents, and exactly four common tangents.

20a.

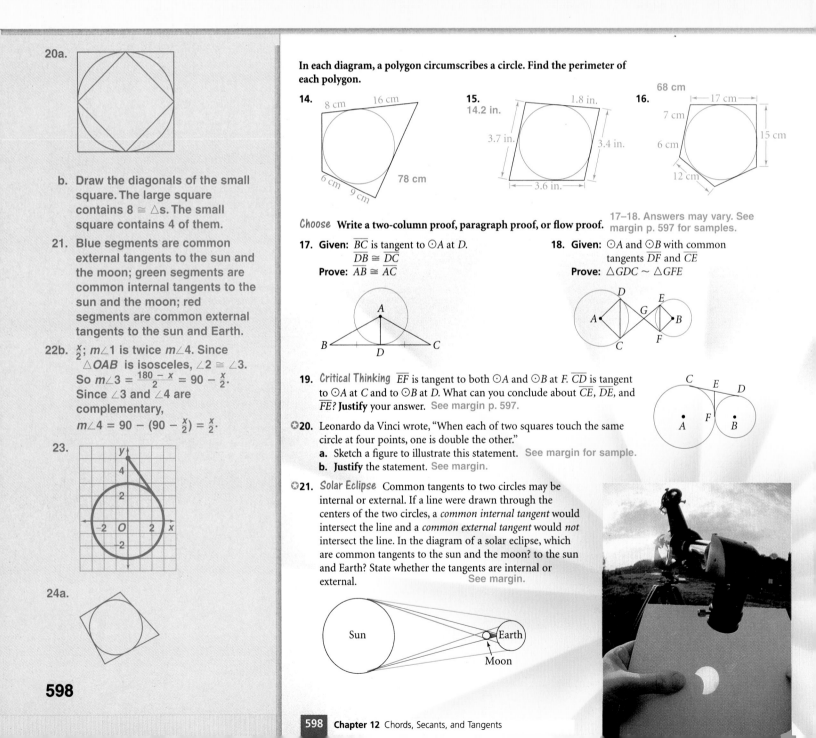

b. Draw the diagonals of the small square. The large square contains 8 ≅ △s. The small square contains 4 of them.

21. Blue segments are common external tangents to the sun and the moon; green segments are common internal tangents to the sun and the moon; red segments are common external tangents to the sun and Earth.

22b. $\frac{x}{2}$; $m\angle 1$ is twice $m\angle 4$. Since $\triangle OAB$ is isosceles, $\angle 2 \cong \angle 3$. So $m\angle 3 = \frac{180 - x}{2} = 90 - \frac{x}{2}$. Since $\angle 3$ and $\angle 4$ are complementary, $m\angle 4 = 90 - (90 - \frac{x}{2}) = \frac{x}{2}$.

23.

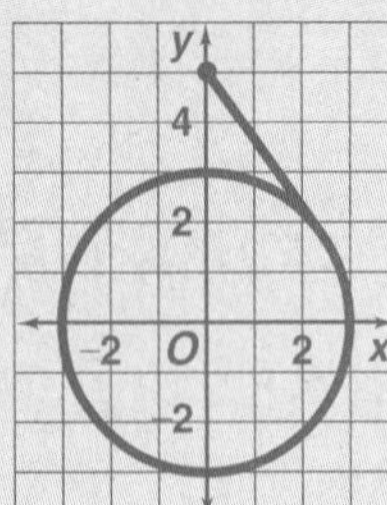

24a.

In each diagram, a polygon circumscribes a circle. Find the perimeter of each polygon.

14. 78 cm

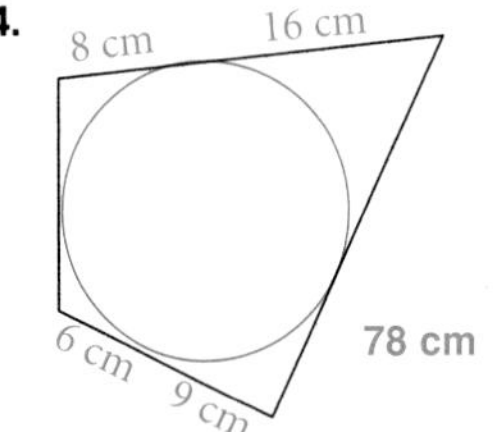

15. 14.2 in.

1.8 in.
3.7 in.
3.4 in.
3.6 in.

16. 68 cm

17 cm
7 cm
15 cm
6 cm
12 cm

Choose **Write a two-column proof, paragraph proof, or flow proof.** 17–18. Answers may vary. See margin p. 597 for samples.

17. Given: $\overline{BC}$ is tangent to $\odot A$ at D.
$\overline{DB} \cong \overline{DC}$
Prove: $\overline{AB} \cong \overline{AC}$

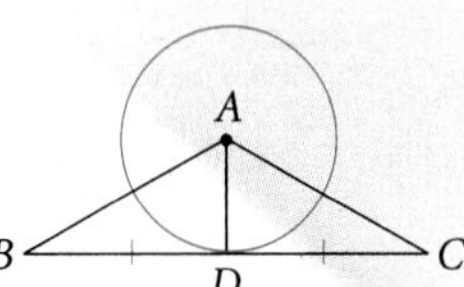

18. Given: $\odot A$ and $\odot B$ with common tangents $\overline{DF}$ and $\overline{CE}$
Prove: $\triangle GDC \sim \triangle GFE$

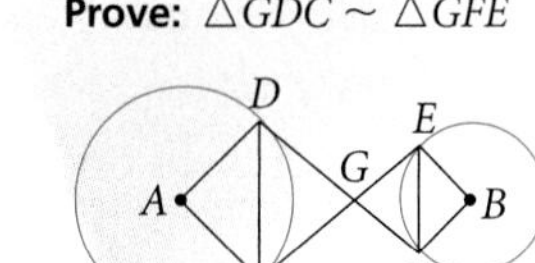

19. *Critical Thinking* $\overline{EF}$ is tangent to both $\odot A$ and $\odot B$ at F. $\overline{CD}$ is tangent to $\odot A$ at C and to $\odot B$ at D. What can you conclude about $\overline{CE}$, $\overline{DE}$, and $\overline{FE}$? **Justify** your answer. See margin p. 597.

C
E
D
F
A
B

20. Leonardo da Vinci wrote, "When each of two squares touch the same circle at four points, one is double the other."

a. Sketch a figure to illustrate this statement. See margin for sample.

b. **Justify** the statement. See margin.

21. *Solar Eclipse* Common tangents to two circles may be internal or external. If a line were drawn through the centers of the two circles, a *common internal tangent* would intersect the line and a *common external tangent* would *not* intersect the line. In the diagram of a solar eclipse, which are common tangents to the sun and the moon? to the sun and Earth? State whether the tangents are internal or external. See margin.

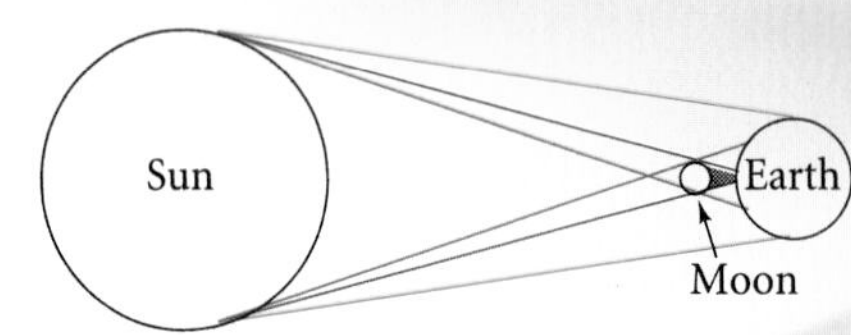

OPEN-ENDED Exercise 24a Students sometimes have difficulty drawing circumscribed figures. Make sure that each side of their quadrilaterals intersects the circle only once.

CRITICAL THINKING Exercise 24b Ask students to prove their conjectures using Theorem 12-4.

Exercises MIXED REVIEW

Exercises 26–28 You may want students to give their answers as both ratios and decimals in order to assess whether they are using their calculators or the tables correctly.

JOURNAL You may want to provide students with an example such as the edge of a bicycle tire and the floor.

GETTING READY FOR LESSON 12-3 These exercises prepare students to find the lengths of chords of circles.

Wrap Up

THE BIG IDEA Ask students to define a *tangent to a circle* and give two of its properties.

RETEACHING ACTIVITY Students use the relationship between a radius and a tangent and between two tangents drawn from the same point to solve problems. (Reteaching worksheet 12-2)

---

22. a. $\overline{AC}$ is tangent to $\odot O$ at A and $m\angle 1 = 70$. Find $m\angle 4$. 35

b. Let $m\angle 1 = x$. Find $m\angle 4$ in terms of x. What is the relationship between $\angle 1$ and $\angle 4$? Explain. See margin p. 598.

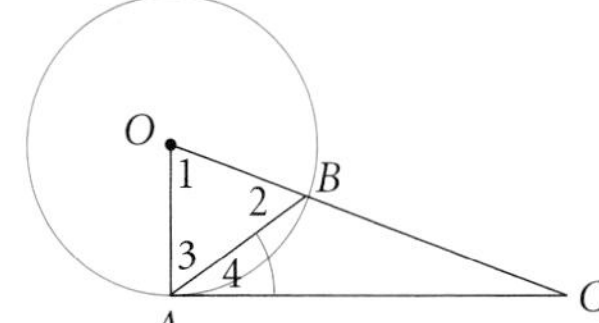

23. *Coordinate Geometry* Graph the equation $x^2 + y^2 = 9$. Then draw a segment from (0, 5) tangent to the circle. Find the length of the segment. See margin p. 598 for diagram; 4

24. a. *Open-ended* Draw a quadrilateral circumscribed about a circle. See margin p. 598 for sample.

b. *Patterns* Compare the sums of the lengths of the opposite sides. Repeat the experiment with another circle and quadrilateral. Make a **conjecture** based on your observations. See below.

25. *Clock Making* Mr. Franklin is building a case for a clock. The case will be in the shape of a regular hexagon. The diameter of the circular face is 10 in. Find the inside perimeter of the clock case. about 34.6 in.

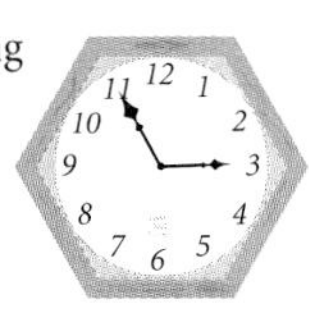

24b. The sums of lengths of opp. sides are =.

Exercises MIXED REVIEW

Find sin *A* and cos *A*. Leave your answers in simplest radical form. 26. $\frac{\sqrt{5}}{5}; \frac{2\sqrt{5}}{5}$

26.

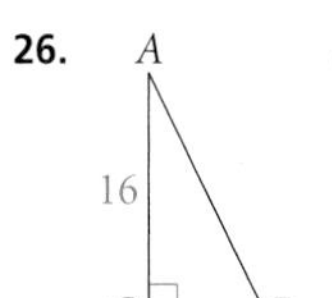

27.

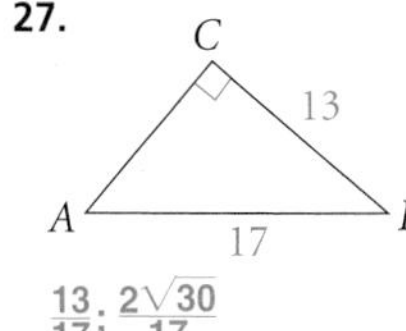

$\frac{13}{17}; \frac{2\sqrt{30}}{17}$

28.

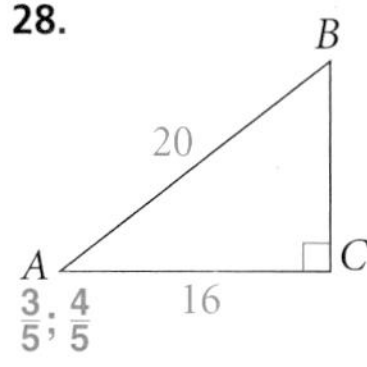

$\frac{3}{5}; \frac{4}{5}$

29. a. Sketch a quadrilateral whose diagonals are congruent and bisect each other. What kind of quadrilateral did you sketch? rectangle

b. *Coordinate Geometry* Decide where you would place coordinate axes on the quadrilateral if you were using it in a coordinate proof. Sketch your axes. Answers may vary. Sample: See right.

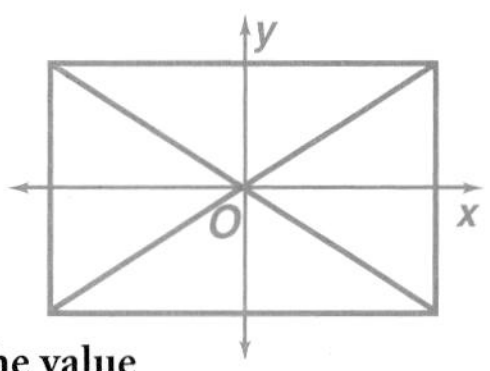

Getting Ready for Lesson 12-3

Choose **Use mental math, paper and pencil, or a calculator. Find the value of *x*. If your answer is not an integer, round to the nearest tenth.**

30. 5

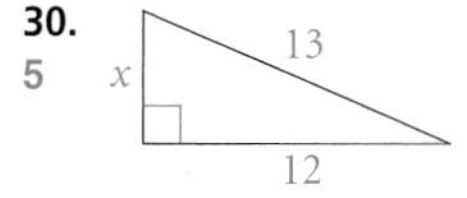

31. 8.1

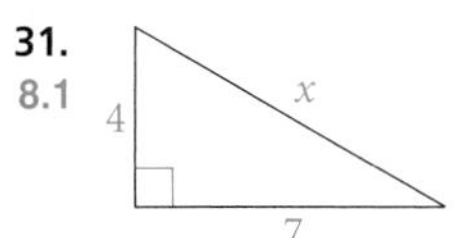

32. 7.2

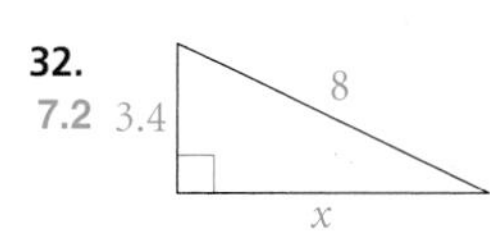

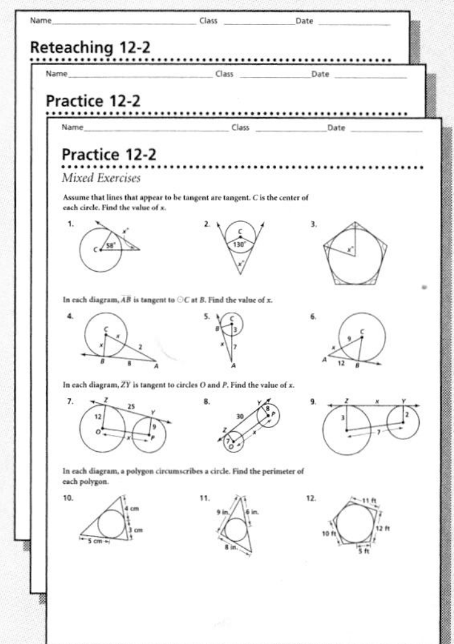

Lesson Quiz

Lesson Quiz is also available in Transparencies.

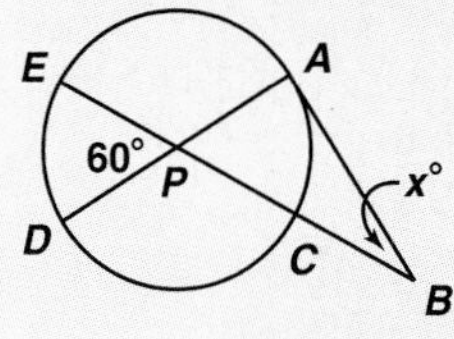

1. $\overline{AB}$ is tangent to $\odot P$. $\overline{EC}$ and $\overline{AD}$ are diameters. Find the value of x. 30

2. If $AP = 5$ and $AB = 10$, find CB. 6.2

12-3 Teaching Notes

PROBLEM OF THE DAY

If the ratio of the lengths of the edges of a right rectangular prism is 1:2:3 and the total surface area is 352 cm^2, find the volume. 384 cm^3

Problem of the Day is also available in Transparencies.

CONNECTING TO PRIOR KNOWLEDGE Draw a circle and label four points on it. Have students name all the major and minor arcs.

WORK TOGETHER

TACTILE LEARNING Make sure students understand how to use MIRA™. Allow students time to experiment with it before beginning this activity.

ALTERNATIVE METHOD If MIRA™ is not available, students can use paper folding to reflect $\widehat{AB}$. Make sure students fold the circle onto itself though its center. Similarly, students can use paper folding to construct a perpendicular to $\overline{GH}$.

Lesson Planning Options

Prerequisite Skills

- Finding the measures of arcs
- Using the Pythagorean Theorem

Assignment Options for Exercises On Your Own

To provide flexible scheduling, this lesson can be subdivided into parts.

1 **Core** 9, 14–19, 21, 23–24, 26
✪**Extension** 20, 27

2 **Core** 1–8, 10–13, 22
✪**Extension** 25

Use Mixed Review to maintain skills.

Resources

Student Edition

Skills Handbook, pp. 660, 664
Extra Practice, p. 659
Glossary/Study Guide

Teaching Resources

Chapter Support File, Ch. 12
- Practice 12-3 (two worksheets)
- Reteaching 12-3

Classroom Manager 12-3
Glossary, Spanish Resources

Transparencies
12, 121

What You'll Learn
- Finding the lengths of chords and measures of arcs of a circle
- Locating the center of a circle using chords

...And Why

To find the radius of a circle in real-life situations such as archaeology

What You'll Need

compass, MIRA™, protractor, centimeter ruler

TECHNOLOGY HINT

The Work Together could be done using geometry software.

QUICK REVIEW

The measure of a minor arc is the measure of its corresponding central angle. The measure of a major arc is 360 minus the measure of its related minor arc.

QUICK REVIEW

Congruent arcs have the same measure and are in the same circle or in congruent circles.

5. Yes; a diameter is a segment with endpts. on the ⊙.

Connections Archaeology . . . and more

12-3 Properties of Chords and Arcs

WORK TOGETHER

Have each member of your group use a compass to draw a large circle. Label its center *O*. Create $\widehat{AB}$ by labeling two points *A* and *B* on your circle.

- Construct an arc congruent to $\widehat{AB}$ by placing a MIRA on ⊙*O* and moving it until the circle maps on itself and you see the images of *A* and *B*. Label the images *A′* and *B′*. Draw radii $\overline{OA}$, $\overline{OB}$, $\overline{OA'}$, and $\overline{OB'}$.

1. a. Use a protractor to measure $\angle AOB$ and $\angle A'OB'$. Compare results. The measures are =.
   b. Write a **conjecture** about the central angles of congruent arcs. Central angles of ≅ arcs are ≅.

- Draw $\overline{AB}$ and $\overline{A'B'}$.

2. a. Measure $\overline{AB}$ and $\overline{A'B'}$. Compare results within your group. AB and $A'B'$ are =.
   b. Write a **conjecture** about the segments joining the endpoints of congruent arcs. Segments joining the endpts. of ≅ arcs are ≅.

- Use a compass to draw another circle. Label its center *M*. Label two points *G* and *H* on your circle. Draw $\overline{GH}$. While keeping an edge of the MIRA on point *M*, construct a diameter perpendicular to $\overline{GH}$ by moving the MIRA until the image of *G* maps onto *H*. Draw the MIRA line. Label its intersection with $\overline{GH}$ as *F* and label its intersection with the circle as *J* so that *F* is between *J* and *M*.

3. Measure $\overline{GF}$ and $\overline{HF}$. What do you notice? Compare results. $GF = FH$
4. Find $m\widehat{GJ}$ and $m\widehat{HJ}$. What do you notice? Compare results. $m\widehat{GJ} = m\widehat{HJ}$

THINK AND DISCUSS

Part 1

Congruent Arcs and Chords

In the Work Together, you created segments with endpoints on a circle. These segments are **chords** of the circle. The diagram shows arc $\widehat{PQ}$ and its related chord $\overline{PQ}$.

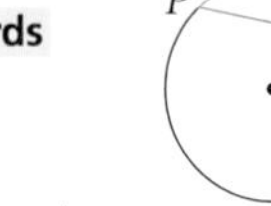

5. Is a diameter a chord? Explain why or why not.
6. Is a radius a chord? Explain why or why not. No; 1 endpt. of a radius is not on the ⊙.

THINK AND DISCUSS

Review with students why congruent arcs must be in the same circle or in congruent circles. Also point out that a chord is related to the *minor arc* it intercepts.

VISUAL LEARNING Students will benefit from drawing diagrams for Theorems 12-5, 12-6, and 12-7. Suggest they draw and label different parts of the circles with different colors.

LOGICAL REASONING Question 7 Point out that students can use Theorem 12-5 to justify Theorem 12-6.

Example 1

ERROR ALERT! Some students may think that $\overline{TC}$ and $\overline{TE}$ are radii of the circle so $\overline{TC} \cong \overline{TE}$. **Remediation:** Review the definition of radius and emphasize that one endpoint must be the *center* of the circle.

CRITICAL THINKING Ask students how they could use $\sin^{-1}$ or $\cos^{-1}$ to find $m\angle A$.

Your observations in the Work Together suggest the following theorems. You will prove Theorem 12-7 in Exercise 18.

Theorem 12-5 In the same circle or in congruent circles, (1) congruent central angles have congruent arcs; and (2) congruent arcs have congruent central angles.

Theorem 12-6 In the same circle or in congruent circles, (1) congruent chords have congruent arcs; and (2) congruent arcs have congruent chords.

Theorem 12-7 A diameter that is perpendicular to a chord bisects the chord and its arc.

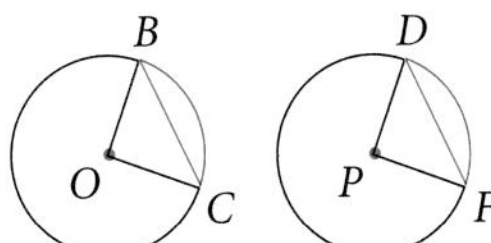

7. **Logical Reasoning** In the diagram at the left, $\odot O \cong \odot P$.
   a. Given that $\overline{BC} \cong \overline{DF}$, **justify** Theorem 12-6, part (1), by explaining why $\widehat{BC} \cong \widehat{DF}$.
   b. Given that $\widehat{BC} \cong \widehat{DF}$, **justify** Theorem 12-6, part (2), by explaining why $\overline{BC} \cong \overline{DF}$. **a–b. See margin p. 603.**

A segment that contains the center of a circle is part of a diameter. So, you may use Theorem 12-7 for a segment that is part of a diameter and is perpendicular to a chord.

QUICK REVIEW

The distance from a point to a line is the length of the perpendicular segment from the point to the line.

Example 1

Chord $\overline{CE}$ is 24 in. long and 5 in. from the center of $\odot A$.

a. Find the radius of $\odot A$.
b. Find $m\widehat{CE}$.

a. Copy the diagram and draw radius $\overline{AC}$ as shown at the left.

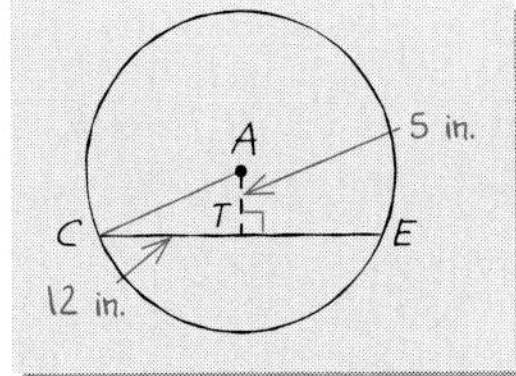

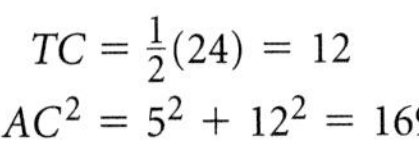

$TC = \frac{1}{2}(24) = 12$ — The diameter ⊥ to a chord bisects the chord.

$AC^2 = 5^2 + 12^2 = 169$ — Use the Pythagorean Theorem.

$AC = 13$ in.

b. Extend $\overline{AT}$ to intersect the circle at D as shown below.

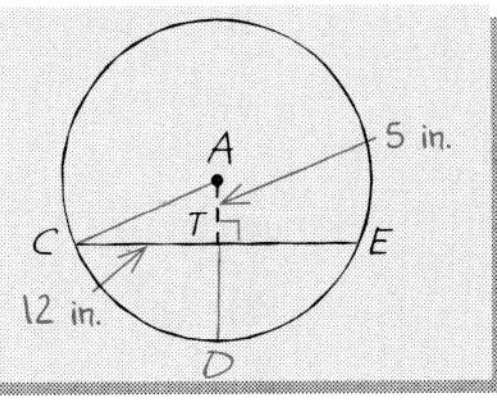

$\frac{1}{2}m\widehat{CE} = m\widehat{CD}$ — A diameter ⊥ to a chord bisects the chord and its arc.

$m\widehat{CE} = 2m\widehat{CD}$

$m\widehat{CD} = m\angle CAT$ — The measure of a minor arc = the measure of its central angle.

$m\widehat{CE} = 2m\angle CAT$ — Substitution

$\tan \angle CAT = \frac{12}{5} = 2.4$ — $\tan \angle A = \frac{\text{opp.}}{\text{adj.}} = \frac{CT}{AT}$

$m\angle CAT \approx$ 67.380135 — Use a calculator to find $\tan^{-1}$ (2.4).

$m\widehat{CE} \approx$ 2 ⊠ 67.380135

$m\widehat{CE} \approx 134.8$

Additional Examples

FOR EXAMPLE 1

Refer to the diagram in Example 1. Let chord $\overline{CE}$ be 30 in. long and 6 in. from the center of $\odot A$.

a. Find the radius of $\odot A$. **≈ 16.2 in.**

b. Find $m\widehat{CE}$. **≈ 136.4**

FOR EXAMPLE 2

Trace the bottom of a can. Use the method described in Example 2 to find the center of the can. **Answers may vary. Sample:**

FOR EXAMPLE 3

Refer to the diagram in Example 3. If $AO = 13$ in. and $EO = 5$ in., find CD. Explain your reasoning. **$AE = 12$ in. by the Pythagorean Theorem. Because a diameter (or part of a diameter) that is perpendicular to a chord bisects it, $AB = 2AE = 24$. Because chords that are equidistant from the center of the same circle are congruent, $CD = AB = 24$ in.**

Question 8 Have students model the steps given in Example 1 to find the radius and arc measure.

AUDITORY LEARNING Have students work in pairs. Have partners take turns reading their justifications aloud. Reading their justifications aloud will help students assess whether their reasoning is clear and organized.

Example 2 **Relating to the Real World** 

CONNECTING TO STUDENTS' WORLD Have students bring in a jar or other circular object. Have them trace part of it, then construct the center of the circle.

Theorem 12-9 Give several examples of pairs of congruent chords including pairs that are parallel to each other and pairs that are not.

Technology Options

For Exercise 17, students may use geometry software to draw the diagram. For Exercise 26, students may use graphing software or graphing calculators to graph the line and circle.

Prentice Hall Technology 

Software
- Secondary Math Lab Toolkit™
- Integrated Math Lab 45
- Computer Item Generator 12-3

Internet
- See the Prentice Hall site. (http://www.phschool.com)

602

8. a. **Try This** Find the radius of $\odot C$ to the nearest tenth. 13.0

b. Find $m\widehat{AB}$ to the nearest tenth. 115.1

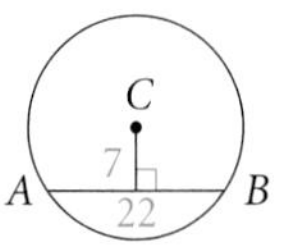

You can use the following theorem to reconstruct a circle from an arc.

Theorem 12-8 The perpendicular bisector of a chord contains the center of the circle.

9. *Logical Reasoning* Use the Converse of the Perpendicular Bisector Theorem (Theorem 4-13 on page 219) to **justify** Theorem 12-8. See margin p. 603.

Example 2 **Relating to the Real World** 

Archaeology An archaeologist found pieces of a jar. She wants to find the radius of the rim of the jar to help guide her as she reassembles the pieces. How can she find the center and radius of the rim?

First, she should carefully trace a piece of the rim. Then she should draw two chords and construct the perpendicular bisector of each chord. Since each perpendicular bisector contains the center of the circle, the point where they intersect must be the center. (Two lines intersect in exactly one point.) After finding the center, she can measure the radius.

Part 2

Chords Equidistant from the Center of a Circle

The following theorem shows the relationship between two congruent chords and their distances from the center of a circle.

Theorem 12-9 In the same circle or in congruent circles, (1) chords equidistant from the center are congruent; and (2) congruent chords are equidistant from the center.

Example 3

Although this proof has nine statements, students should not have difficulty following the reasoning. Challenge students to rewrite the proof by drawing $\overline{OB}$ and $\overline{OD}$ and showing $\triangle BOE \cong \triangle DOF$.

Exercises ON YOUR OWN

ALTERNATIVE ASSESSMENT Have students choose five exercises, excluding proofs, that cover all the concepts in this lesson. Have them write each exercise, the concepts needed to answer it, and a detailed answer.

Exercises 1–8 You may want to point out to students that in some figures they will need to draw auxiliary lines. They will apply the important fact that all radii of a circle are congruent.

Example 3

Prove Theorem 12-9, part (1).

Given: $\odot O$, $\overline{OE} \perp \overline{AB}$, $\overline{OF} \perp \overline{CD}$, $\overline{OE} \cong \overline{OF}$

Prove: $\overline{AB} \cong \overline{CD}$

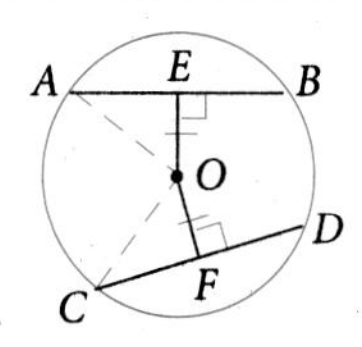

Begin by drawing $\overline{OA}$ and $\overline{OC}$.

Statements	Reasons
1. $\overline{OA} \cong \overline{OC}$	1. All radii of a circle are $\cong$.
2. $\overline{OE} \cong \overline{OF}$	2. Given
3. $\overline{OE} \perp \overline{AB}$, $\overline{OF} \perp \overline{CD}$	3. Given
4. $\angle AEO$ and $\angle CFO$ are right angles.	4. Definition of right angles
5. $\triangle AEO \cong \triangle CFO$	5. HL Theorem
6. $AE = CF$	6. CPCTC
7. $AE = \frac{1}{2}AB$, $CF = \frac{1}{2}CD$	7. A diameter $\perp$ to a chord bisects the chord.
8. $\frac{1}{2}AB = \frac{1}{2}CD$	8. Substitution
9. $AB = CD$, or $\overline{AB} \cong \overline{CD}$	9. Multiplication Property of Equality

Exercises ON YOUR OWN

Calculator **Find the value of *x*. If your answer is not an integer, round it to the nearest tenth.**

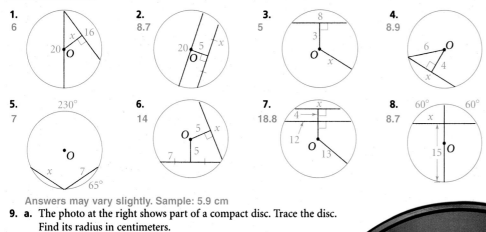

1. 6

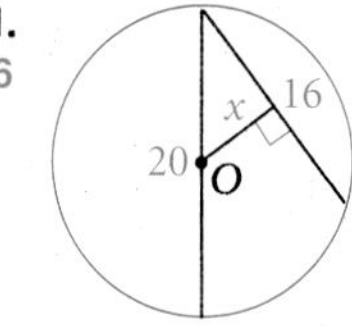

2. 8.7

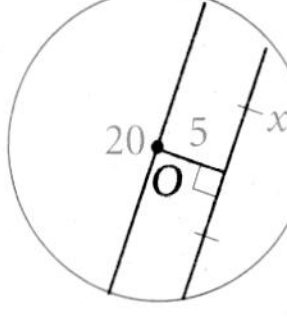

3. 5

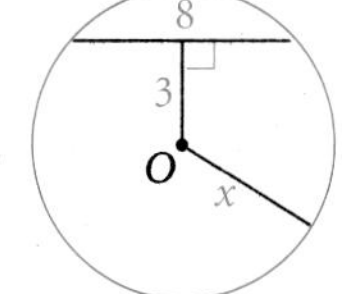

4. 8.9

6
O
4
x

5. 7

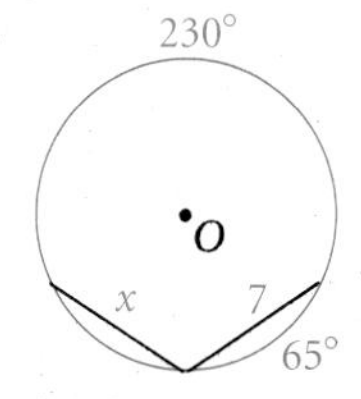

6. 14

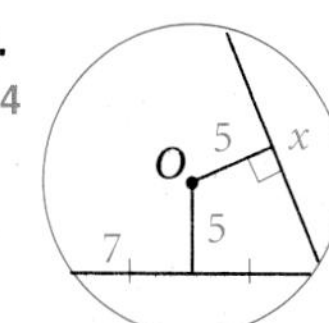

7. 18.8

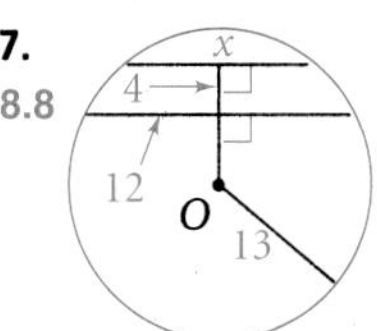

8. 8.7

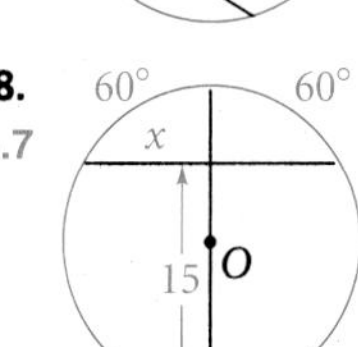

Answers may vary slightly. Sample: 5.9 cm

9. a. The photo at the right shows part of a compact disc. Trace the disc. Find its radius in centimeters.

b. Writing Explain how you found the radius of the compact disc.

Answers may vary. Sample: Draw 2 nonparallel chords. Construct the $\perp$ bisector of each chord. The intersection of the $\perp$ bisectors is the center of the $\odot$. Measure the radius.

pages 600–603 Think and Discuss

7a. $\overline{OB} \cong \overline{PD}$ and $\overline{OC} \cong \overline{PF}$ because radii of $\cong$ $\odot$s are $\cong$. $\triangle OBC \cong \triangle PDF$ by the SSS Post. Then $m\angle BOC = m\angle DPF$ by CPCTC. But $m\widehat{BC} = m\angle BOC$ and $m\widehat{DF} = m\angle DPF$ so by substitution, $m\widehat{BC} = m\widehat{DF}$, or $\widehat{BC} \cong \widehat{DF}$.

b. $m\widehat{BC} = m\angle O$ and $m\widehat{DF} = m\angle P$. Since $\widehat{BC} \cong \widehat{DF}$, it follows that $\angle O \cong \angle P$. $\triangle OBC \cong \triangle PDF$ by SAS. Then $\overline{BC} \cong \overline{DF}$ by CPCTC.

9. The center of a $\odot$ is equidistant from the endpts. of any chord. By the Converse of the Perpendicular Bisector Thm., the center must lie on the $\perp$ bisector of the chord.

ESL Exercises 10–13 To reinforce the vocabulary from this chapter, have students take turns with a partner stating the theorem they used to solve each problem.

Exercises 11–12 Students can avoid extra work if they recognize the triangles are 45°-45°-90° and 30°-60°-90° triangles, respectively.

ERROR ALERT! **Exercise 14** Some students may not understand that the radii of a sphere and of a circle on the sphere be different. **Remediation:** Cut an orange through the center and again in a different parallel plane. Show that the circular cross section through the center is larger than the other circular cross section.

Exercise 19 If you had students do this exercise already in class, make sure that they use different objects for their homework.

Exercise 20 You may want to have students solve this problem in small groups. One approach is to find the area of the shaded region shown in the diagram below:

$\frac{1}{2}\pi(29.5)^2$ – [area of triangle + 2(area of sectors)].

The volume of the milk equals the area times 470.

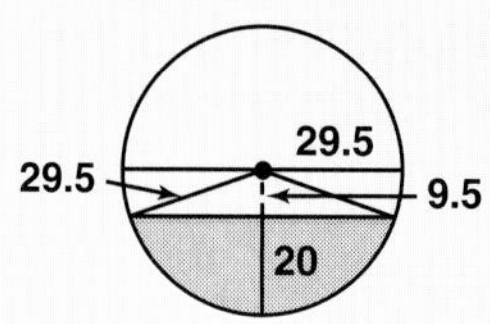

pages 603–605 On Your Own

21. 1. $\overline{CE} \perp \overline{BD}$ (Given) 2. $\overline{BF} \cong \overline{FD}$ (A diameter ⊥ to a chord bisects the chord.) 3. $\overline{CE}$ is the ⊥ bisector of $\overline{BD}$. (Def. of ⊥ bisector) 4. $\overline{BC} \cong \overline{DC}$ (A point on the ⊥ bisector of a segment is equidistant from the endpts. of the segment.) 5. $\widehat{BC} \cong \widehat{DC}$ (≅ chords have ≅ arcs.)
22. 1. $\widehat{BC} \cong \widehat{DE}$ (Given) 2. $\overline{BC} \cong \overline{DE}$ (≅ arcs have ≅ chords.) 3. $\overline{AF} \perp \overline{BC}, \overline{AG} \perp \overline{DE}$ (Given) 4. $\overline{AF} \cong \overline{AG}$ (≅ chords are equidistant from the center.) 5. $\angle AFG \cong \angle AGF$ (Base ∠s of an isos. △ are ≅.)

604

Find $m\widehat{AB}$.

10. 108

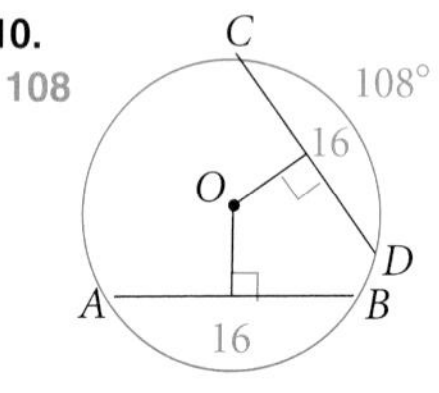

11. 90

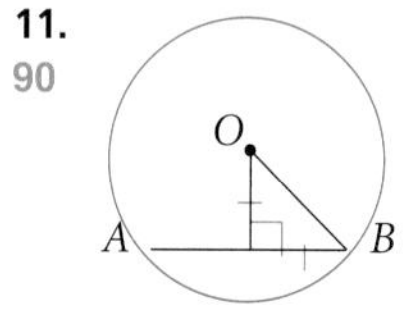

12. 120

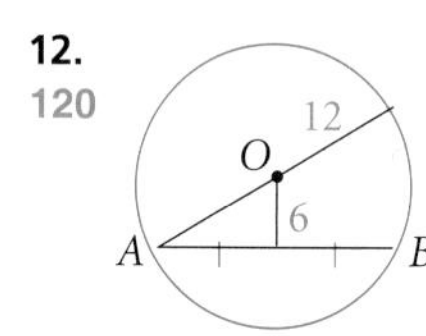

13. about 123.9

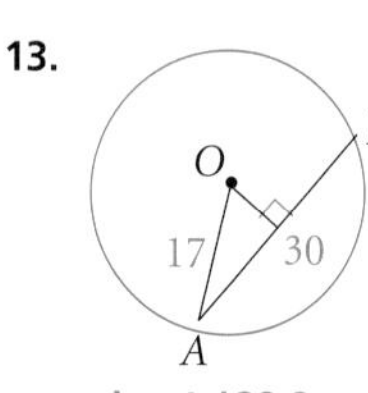

14. *Geometry in 3 Dimensions* Sphere O with radius 13 cm is intersected by a plane 5 cm from its center forming ⊙A. Find the radius of ⊙A. 12 cm

15. A plane intersects a sphere that has radius 10 in. forming ⊙B with radius 8 in. How far is the plane from the center of the sphere? 6 in.

16. A plane intersects a sphere 12 in. from the sphere's center forming ⊙C with radius 18 in. What is the radius of the sphere? Round to the nearest tenth. 21.6 in.

17. Two concentric circles have radii of 4 cm and 8 cm. A segment tangent to the smaller circle is a chord of the larger circle. What is the length of the segment? $8\sqrt{3}$ cm

PROBLEM SOLVING HINT
Draw a diagram.

18. Supply the reasons for each statement in this proof of Theorem 12-7.

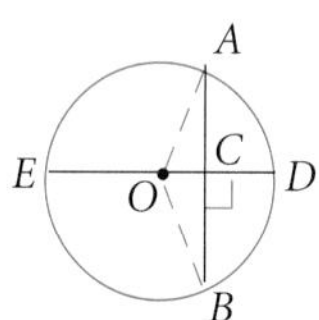

Given: ⊙O with diameter $\overline{ED} \perp \overline{AB}$ at C
Prove: $\overline{AC} \cong \overline{BC}$ and $\widehat{AD} \cong \widehat{BD}$

Begin by drawing $\overline{OA}$ and $\overline{OB}$.

Statements	Reasons
1. $\overline{OA} \cong \overline{OB}$	a. ? All radii of a ⊙ are ≅.
2. $\overline{ED} \perp \overline{AB}$	b. ? Given
3. $\angle ACO$ and $\angle BCO$ are right angles.	c. ? Def of ⊥ lines
4. $\overline{OC} \cong \overline{OC}$ Reflexive Prop. of ≅	d. ?
5. $\triangle AOC \cong \triangle BOC$ HL	e. ?
6. $\overline{AC} \cong \overline{BC}$ CPCTC	f. ?
7. $\angle AOC \cong \angle BOC$ CPCTC	g. ?
8. $\widehat{AD} \cong \widehat{BD}$	h. ?

h. ≅ central angles have ≅ arcs.

19. *Constructions* Use a circular object such as a can or a saucer to draw a circle. Construct the center of the circle. Check students' work.

20. *Transporting Milk* The diameter of the base of a cylindrical milk tank is 59 in. The height of the tank is 470 in. A delivery person estimates that the depth of the milk in the tank is 20 in. Find the number of gallons of milk in the tank to the nearest gallon. (231 in.^{3} = 1 gal) 1661 gal

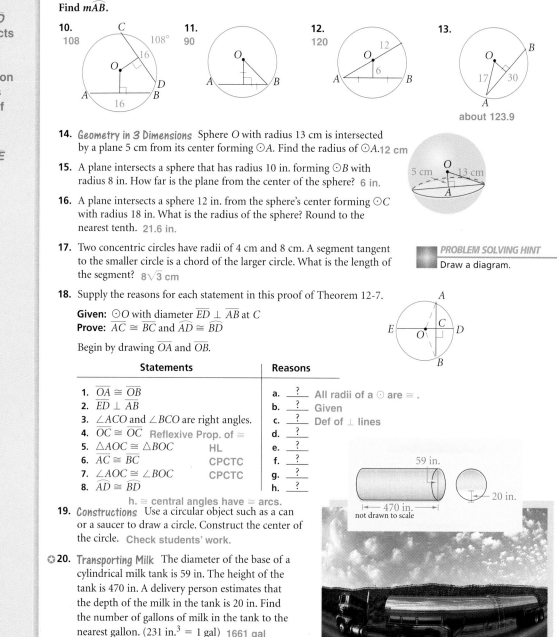

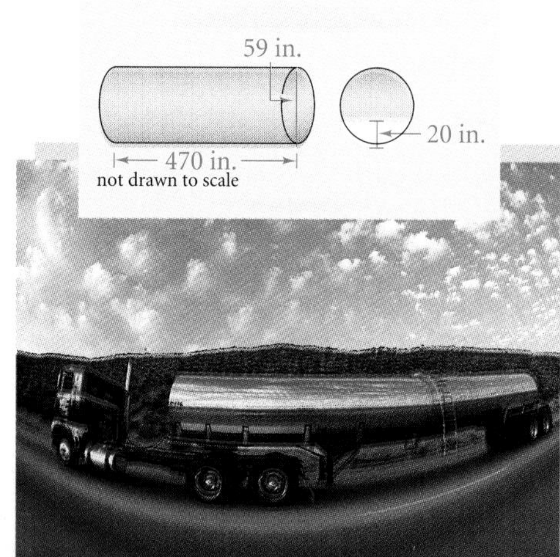

Exercises 21–22 Make sure students copy the figure as well as copy the "given" and "prove" statements so they can mark congruent segments and angles.

OPEN-ENDED Exercise 23d In part a, students restate Theorems 12-7 and 12-8 in terms of the given circle. Have students use this model for part d.

Exercise 24 Students apply the Pythagorean Theorem.

Chapter Project **FIND OUT BY EXPLORING** Students may want to use drawing software to create their own op art. Display students' work on a bulletin board and ask them to explain how they created their designs.

Choose **Write a two-column proof, paragraph proof, or flow proof.**

21. Given: $\odot A$ with $\overline{CE} \perp \overline{BD}$
Prove: $\widehat{BC} \cong \widehat{DC}$

21–22. Answers may vary. See margin p. 604 for samples.

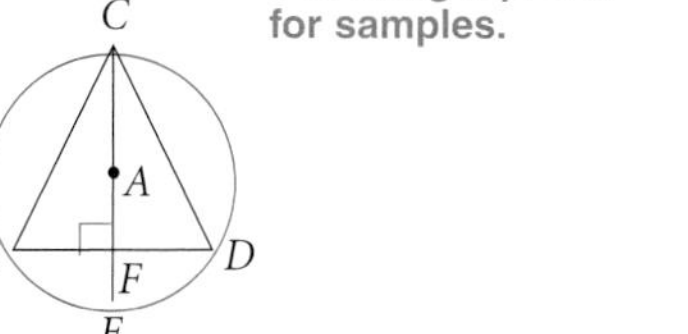

22. Given: $\odot A$ with $\widehat{BC} \cong \widehat{DE}$, $\overline{AF} \perp \overline{BC}$, $\overline{AG} \perp \overline{DE}$
Prove: $\angle AFG \cong \angle AGF$

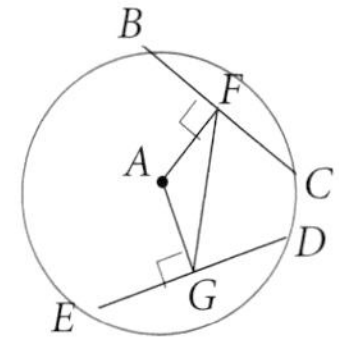

23. a. Use the diagram at the right. Complete each statement. Given that $\overline{AB}$ is a diameter of the circle and $\overline{AB} \perp \overline{CD}$, then ■ ≅ ■, and ■ ≅ ■. $\overline{EC}$; $\overline{ED}$; $\widehat{BC}$; $\widehat{BD}$

b. Given that $\overline{AB}$ is the perpendicular bisector of $\overline{CD}$, then $\overline{AB}$ contains the __?__ . center of the ⊙

c. Which theorems are illustrated in parts (a) and (b)? See margin.

d. *Open-ended* Draw a figure or figures to illustrate the other theorems presented in this lesson. See margin.

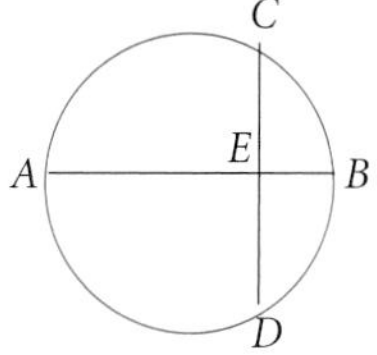

24. $\odot A$ and $\odot B$ are congruent. $AB = 8$ in. $\overline{CD}$ is a chord of both circles. $CD = 6$ in. How long is a radius? 5 in.

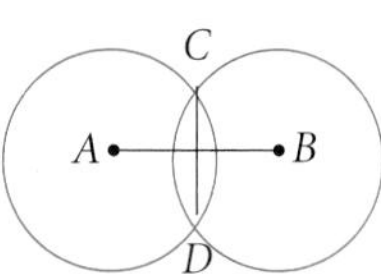

25. *Writing* Explain why the phrase "in the same circle or in congruent circles" is essential to Theorems 12-5, 12-6, and 12-9. See margin.

26. *Coordinate Geometry* Find the length of the chord of the circle $x^2 + y^2 = 25$ that is determined by the line $x = 3$. 8

27. a. *Critical Thinking* The diameter of a circle is 20 cm. Two chords in the circle are 6 cm and 16 cm. In how many ways can you draw the chords so that they are parallel to the same diameter? (*Hint:* Draw a diagram.) 2

b. What are the possible distances between the chords to the nearest tenth of a centimeter? 3.5 cm and 15.5 cm

Chapter Project ***Find Out by Exploring***

Stare at these circular patterns for a few seconds. Notice how they seem to pulsate. In contrast to the ancient art form you explored in the Find Out activity on page 591, op art is a twentieth-century phenomenon. See margin.

- Use geometric terms to describe how Figures A and B are related.
- Create your own op art by transforming a *target* design like Figure A. Use geometric terms to describe your design. Check students' work.

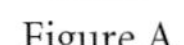

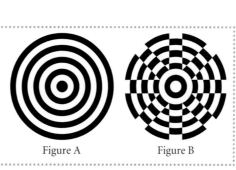

Figure A Figure B

23c. A diameter ⊥ to a chord bisects the chord and its arc; the ⊥ bisector of a chord contains the center of the ⊙.

d. Sample: Theorem 12-5

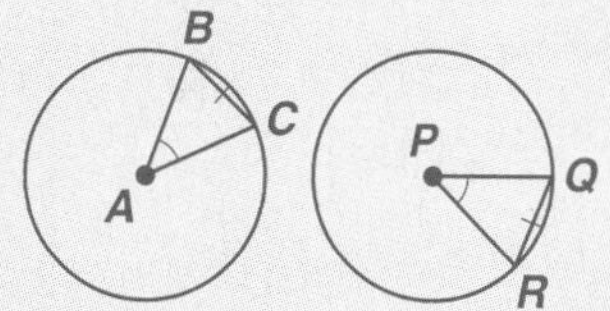

25. The thms. are not true for angles, chords, or arcs that are in noncongruent ⊙s.

Find Out By Exploring

Both figures are made from 9 circles with the same center. In Figure A, the smallest circle and alternate rings are black. In Figure B, vertical and horizontal tangents to the smallest circle are drawn. Then tangents at 45° angles to the first ones are drawn. Alternating sections of the 6 outer rings are black as well as the smallest ring.

Checkpoint page 606

10a.

Exercises MIXED REVIEW

Exercises 28–33 Ask students to justify their reasoning by writing an equation or inequality.

GETTING READY FOR LESSON 12-4 Students review how to find measures of arcs formed by central angles. These exercises prepare students to find measures of arcs formed by inscribed angles.

Wrap Up

THE BIG IDEA Ask students to summarize what they learned about chords and their associated arcs in this lesson.

RETEACHING ACTIVITY Students find the lengths of chords and measures of arcs of a circle. (Reteaching worksheet 12-3)

Exercises CHECKPOINT

In this Checkpoint, your students will assess their own progress in Lessons 12-1 to 12-3.

Exercises 1–3 Make sure students find the length of the radius, not the diameter.

Exercises 4–6 Check that students do not think an inscribed circle bisects a tangent at the point of tangency.

OPEN-ENDED Exercise 10 If students use a right triangle, one of the quadrilaterals will be a square and the other two will be kites.

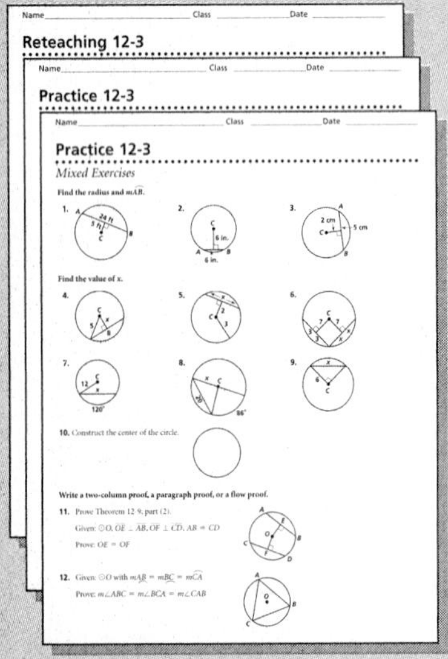

Lesson Quiz

Lesson Quiz is also available in Transparencies.

For Exercises 1–2, if your answer is not an integer, round to the nearest tenth.

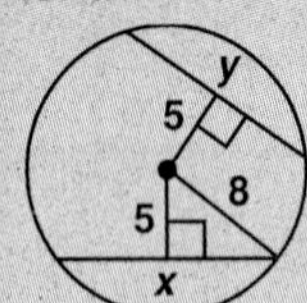

1. Find the value of x. 12.5
2. Find the value of y. 12.5
3. Use a circular object such as a can to draw a circle. Construct the center of the circle. Answers may vary. Sample: See back of book.

606

Exercises MIXED REVIEW

Determine whether a triangle with the given side lengths is acute, right, or obtuse.

28. 4, 4, 4 acute
29. 3, 5, 6 obtuse
30. 6, 8, 10 right
31. 2, 3, 4 obtuse
32. $7, \sqrt{63}, 10$ acute
33. $5, 8, \sqrt{70}$ acute
34. You want to find out how tall a tree in a park is. Your shadow length is $\frac{3}{4}$ of your height. The tree's shadow is 57 ft long. How tall is the tree? 76 ft

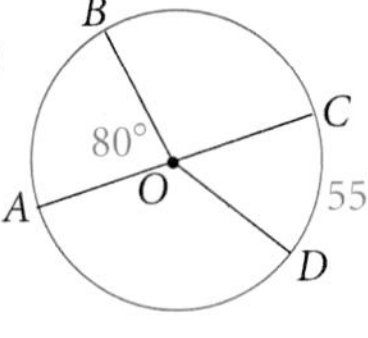

Getting Ready for Lesson 12-4

Find the measure of each arc in ⊙O.

35. $\widehat{AB}$ 80
36. $\widehat{BC}$ 100
37. $\widehat{AD}$ 125

Exercises CHECKPOINT

Coordinate Geometry **The points are endpoints of the diameter of a circle. Write the equation of the circle.**

1. (3, 1) and (0, 0) $(x - 1.5)^2 + (y - 0.5)^2 = 2.5$
2. (−2, 5) and (9, −3) $(x - 3.5)^2 + (y - 1)^2 = 46.25$
3. (−4, −8) and (1, 0) $(x + 1.5)^2 + (y + 4)^2 = 22.25$

In each diagram, the polygon circumscribes a circle. Find the perimeter of the polygon.

4. 76 cm

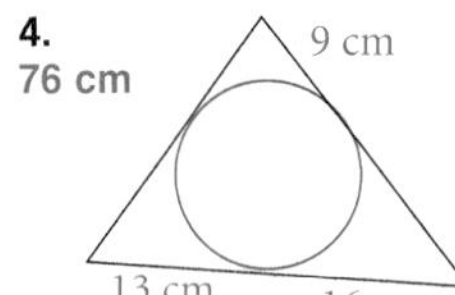

5. 48 in.

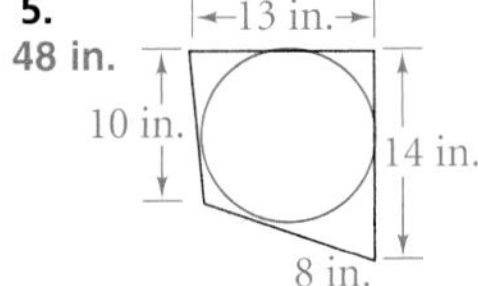

6. 51 m

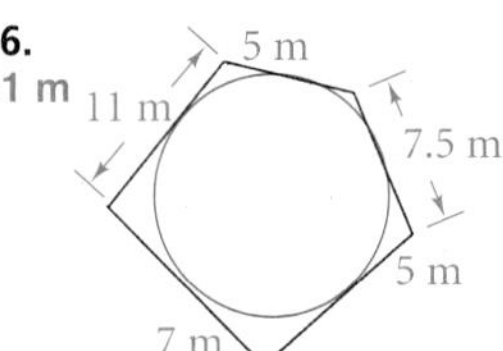

Find the value of *x*.

7. 24

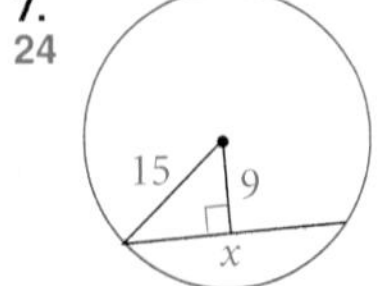

8. 5

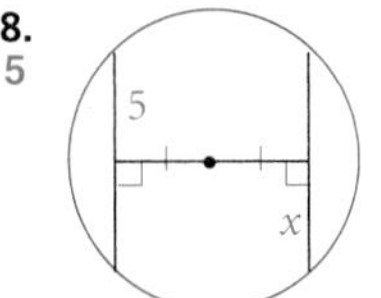

9. 8

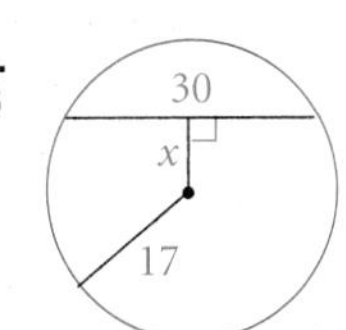

10. a. ***Open-ended*** Draw a triangle circumscribed about a circle. Then draw the radii to each tangent. See margin p. 605 for sample.
    b. How many convex quadrilaterals are in the figure you drew in part (a)? 3
    c. What is the name of these special quadrilaterals? **Justify** your answer. Kites; the sides inside the ⊙ are ≅ because they are radii of the same ⊙; the sides outside the ⊙ are ≅ because they are tangent segments to a ⊙ drawn from a pt. outside the ⊙.

TECHNOLOGY HINT

This exercise could be done using geometry software.

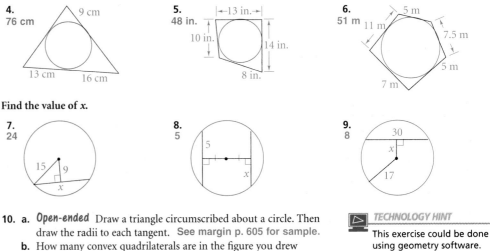

12-4 Teaching Notes

PROBLEM OF THE DAY

Draw three paths staying within the boundary so that X goes to Y, Z goes to W, and U goes to V. The paths may not cross. Answers may vary. Sample given.

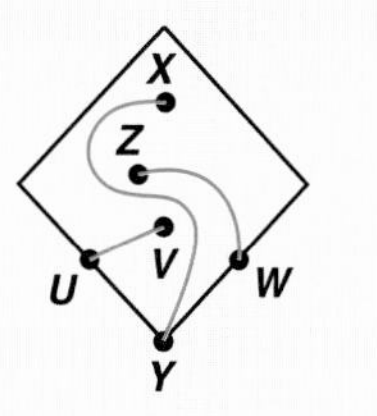

Problem of the Day is also available in Transparencies.

CONNECTING TO PRIOR KNOWLEDGE Draw a circle and several central angles. Label the angle measures and have students give the measures of the intercepted arcs.

WORK TOGETHER

Question 1 Some students may be surprised that ∠1, ∠2, and ∠3 are congruent because their sides are different lengths. Reinforce the concept that the measure of an angle does not depend on the lengths of the sides.

THINK AND DISCUSS

ERROR ALERT! Some students may have difficulty identifying arcs intercepted by inscribed angles, especially when several chords are shown in the diagram. **Remediation:** Have students use colored pencils or markers to trace intercepted arcs from one endpoint to the other.

12-4 Inscribed Angles

What You'll Learn

- Finding the measure of inscribed angles and the arcs they intercept

...And Why

To use the relationships between inscribed angles and arcs in real-world situations, such as motion pictures

What You'll Need

compass, protractor, ruler

WORK TOGETHER

Have each member of your group draw two large circles. Label the centers X and Y. Draw the following diagrams on the circles.

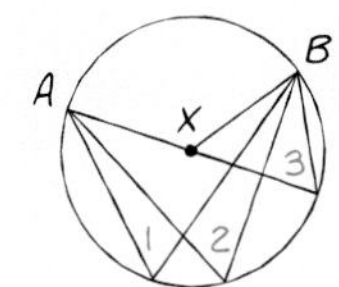

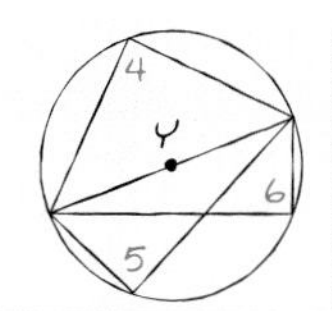

1. a. *Patterns* In ⊙X, use a protractor to measure $\angle AXB$ and each numbered angle. Determine $m\overset{\frown}{AB}$. Record your results and look for patterns. Compare results within your group. b. $m\overset{\frown}{AB} = 2m\angle 1$
   b. Write a **conjecture** about the relationship between $m\angle 1$ and $m\overset{\frown}{AB}$.
   c. Write a **conjecture** about the measures of ∠1, ∠2, and ∠3.

1a. Answers may vary. The results should reflect $m\angle 1 = m\angle 2 = m\angle 3$; $m\overset{\frown}{AB} = 2m\angle 1$

1c. $m\angle 1 = m\angle 2 = m\angle 3$

TECHNOLOGY HINT

The Work Together could be done using geometry software.

2. a. *Patterns* Use a protractor to measure the numbered angles in ⊙Y. Record your results and look for patterns. Compare your results.
   b. Write a **conjecture** about an angle whose vertex is on a circle and whose sides intersect the endpoints of a diameter of the circle.
   2a. Answers may vary. The results should reflect $m\angle 4 = m\angle 5 = m\angle 6 = 90$. b. See margin p. 610.

THINK AND DISCUSS

Part

Measuring Inscribed Angles

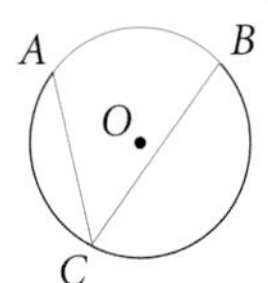

At the left, the vertex of $\angle C$ is on ⊙O, and the sides of $\angle C$ are chords of the circle. $\angle C$ is an **inscribed angle.** $\overset{\frown}{AB}$ is the **intercepted arc** of $\angle C$.

A polygon is **inscribed in** a circle if all its vertices lie on the circle. $\triangle DEF$ is inscribed in ⊙Q. ⊙Q is **circumscribed about** $\triangle DEF$.

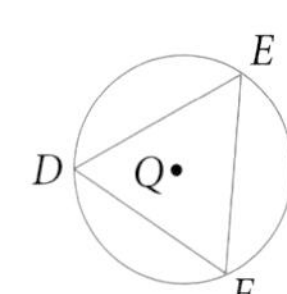

3. In the diagram at the left, which arc does $\angle A$ intercept? $\overset{\frown}{BCD}$
4. Which angle intercepts $\overset{\frown}{DAB}$? $\angle C$
5. Is quadrilateral $ABCD$ inscribed in the circle or is the circle inscribed in $ABCD$? $ABCD$ is inscribed in the ⊙.
6. a. Which angles appear to intercept major arcs? $\angle B$, $\angle C$
   b. What kind of angles do these appear to be? obtuse

Lesson Planning Options

Prerequisite Skills

- Finding the measures of central angles and intercepted arcs

Assignment Options for Exercises On Your Own

To provide flexible scheduling, this lesson can be subdivided into parts.

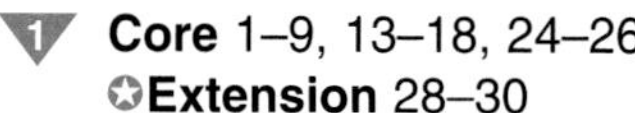

1 **Core** 1–9, 13–18, 24–26
✪**Extension** 28–30

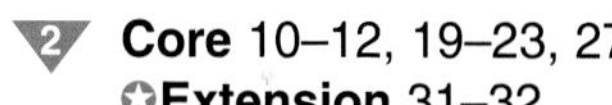

2 **Core** 10–12, 19–23, 27
✪**Extension** 31–32

Use Mixed Review to maintain skills.

Resources

Student Edition

Skills Handbook, p. 664
Extra Practice, p. 659
Glossary/Study Guide

Teaching Resources

Chapter Support File, Ch. 12
- Practice 12-4 (two worksheets)
- Reteaching 12-4
- Alternative Activity 12-4

Classroom Manager 12-4
Glossary, Spanish Resources

Transparencies

121, 124

ERROR ALERT! **Theorem 12-10** Some students may confuse "The measure of an inscribed angle is half the measure of its intercepted arc" with "The measure of an intercepted arc is half the measure of its inscribed angle." **Remediation:** Have students estimate the angle measures and arc measures as a way to check that their answers are reasonable.

Example 1

ESTIMATION Begin by having students estimate the values of *a* and *b*. Explain that $\overset{\frown}{PT}$ appears to be more than one fourth of the circle and $\angle PRS$ appears to be less than 90°.

Additional Examples

FOR EXAMPLE 1

Refer to the diagram in Example 1. If $m\angle PQT = 70$ and $m\overset{\frown}{TS} = 25$, find the values of *a* and *b*. **a = 140, b = 82.5**

FOR EXAMPLE 2

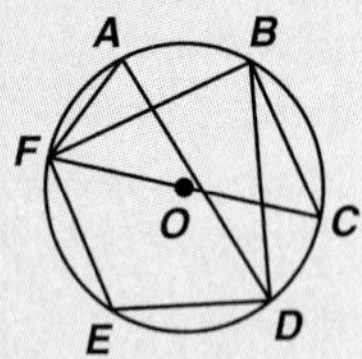

a. Name a pair of congruent inscribed angles. **Sample: $\angle FAD$ and $\angle FBD$**

b. Name a right angle. **$\angle FBC$**

c. Name a pair of supplementary angles. **Samples: $\angle FED$ and $\angle FBD$, $\angle EFB$ and $\angle EDB$**

FOR EXAMPLE 3

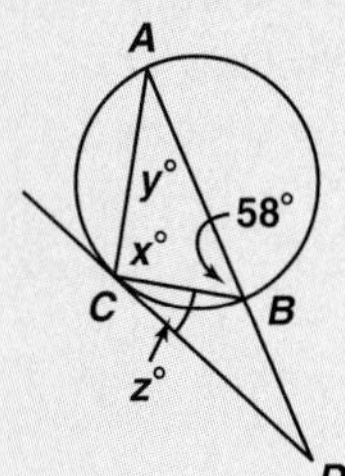

Find the values of *x*, *y*, and *z* if $\overline{AB}$ is a diameter.
x = 90, y = 32, z = 32

Your observations in the Work Together suggest the following theorem.

Theorem 12-10
Inscribed Angle Theorem

The measure of an inscribed angle is half the measure of its intercepted arc.

$m\angle B = \frac{1}{2}m\overset{\frown}{AC}$

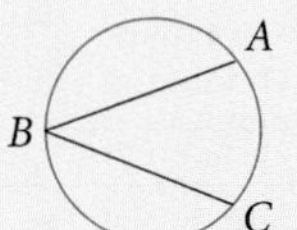

There are three cases of this theorem to consider.

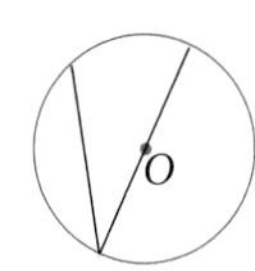

Case I: The center is on a side of the angle.

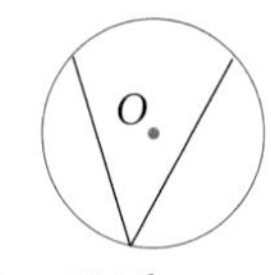

Case II: The center is inside the angle.

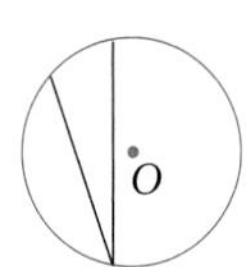

Case III: The center is outside the angle.

Case I is proved below. You will prove Case II in Exercise 13.

Proof of Theorem 12-10, Case I

Given: $\odot O$ with inscribed $\angle ABC$ and diameter $\overline{BC}$

Prove: $m\angle ABC = \frac{1}{2}m\overset{\frown}{AC}$

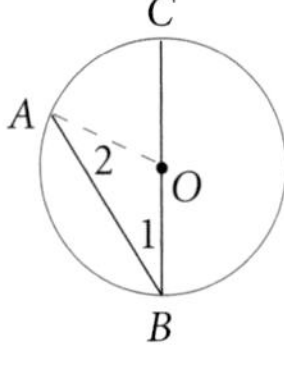

Draw radius $\overline{OA}$. By the Exterior Angle Theorem, $m\angle 1 + m\angle 2 = m\angle AOC$. Since $OA = OB$, $\triangle AOB$ is isosceles and $m\angle 1 = m\angle 2$. Therefore, by substitution, $2(m\angle 1) = m\angle AOC$, or $m\angle 1 = \frac{1}{2}m\angle AOC$. Since $m\angle AOC = m\overset{\frown}{AC}$, $m\angle 1 = \frac{1}{2}m\overset{\frown}{AC}$ by substitution.

Example 1

Find the values of *a* and *b* in the diagram at the right.

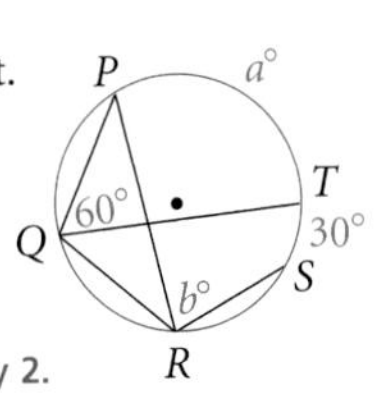

Use the Inscribed Angle Theorem.

$m\angle PQT = \frac{1}{2}m\overset{\frown}{PT}$	
$60 = \frac{1}{2}a$	Substitution
$a = 120$	Multiply each side by 2.
$m\angle PRS = \frac{1}{2}m\overset{\frown}{PS}$	Inscribed Angle Theorem
$m\angle PRS = \frac{1}{2}(m\overset{\frown}{PT} + m\overset{\frown}{TS})$	Arc Addition Postulate
$b = \frac{1}{2}(120 + 30)$	Substitution
$b = \frac{1}{2}(150) = 75$	Simplify.

7. **Try This** Find $m\angle PQR$ if $m\overset{\frown}{PTR} = 230$. **115**

CRITICAL THINKING Corollary 2 Ask students how they can use this corollary to draw a right triangle without using a protractor.

Example 2

VISUAL LEARNING If you have block scheduling or an extended class period, have students construct a circle and chords similar to the one shown. Then have them move point *E* and observe the effect on the chords, arcs, and angles.

EXTENSION Have students find the center of a circle by constructing two right triangles inscribed in a circle and finding the intersection of their hypotenuses. Have students explain why this method works.

In the Work Together, you investigated the first two of the following three corollaries that follow from the Inscribed Angle Theorem. You will justify the corollaries in Exercises 14, 20, and 21.

Corollary 1	Two inscribed angles that intercept the same arc are congruent.
Corollary 2	An angle inscribed in a semicircle is a right angle.
Corollary 3	The opposite angles of a quadrilateral inscribed in a circle are supplementary.

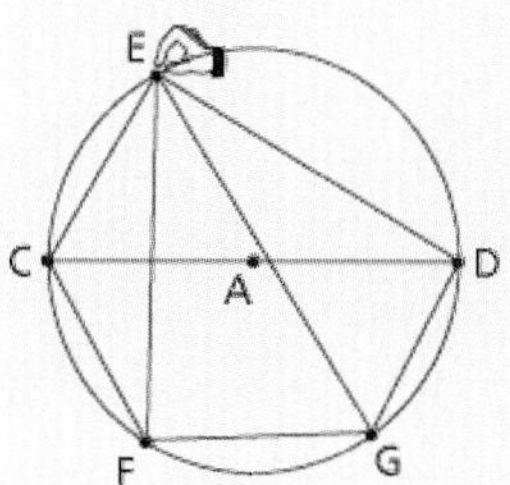

Example 2

Technology Dolores constructed $\odot A$ and the chords shown with geometry software.

a. As Dolores moves *E* on $\overset{\frown}{CED}$ between *C* and *D*, which pairs of inscribed angles will remain congruent to each other?
b. Which inscribed angle will remain a right angle?
c. Which pairs of inscribed angles will remain supplementary in quadrilateral *EFGD?*

a. $\angle CFE \cong \angle CDE$ — Corollary 1
$\angle ECD \cong \angle EGD$

b. $\angle CED$ is a right angle. — Corollary 2

c. $\angle DEF$ and $\angle FGD$ are supplementary. — Corollary 3
$\angle EFG$ and $\angle GDE$ are supplementary.

8. **Try This** Find the value of each variable.

a. $v = 84$; $w = 42$; $x = 36$; $y = 108$; $z = 42$

96° v° w° x° y° z° 72°

b.

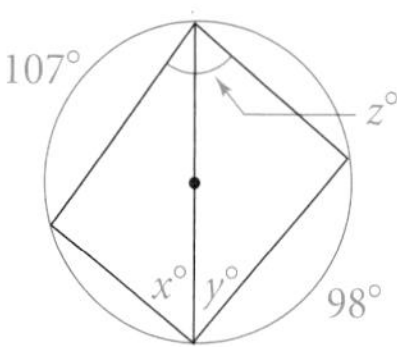

$x = 53.5$; $y = 41$; $z = 85.5$

Technology Options

For Exercise 22c, students may draw the diagram using drawing software. For Exercise 29, students may draw several examples of trapezoids inscribed in circles using drawing software. For Exercises 31–32, student may use construction tools in geometry software to do the constructions.

Prentice Hall Technology

Software
- Secondary Math Lab Toolkit™
- Computer Item Generator 12-4

CD-ROM
- Multimedia Geometry Lab 12

Internet
- See the Prentice Hall site. (http://www.phschool.com)

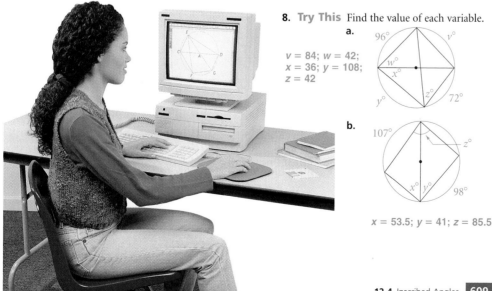

Theorem 12-11 Emphasize that $\angle C$ is formed by a chord and a tangent, not by two tangents, and that the vertex of $\angle C$ is on the circle, not in the exterior.

Example 3

In order to find x and y, students must recognize that $\overline{QL}$ is a diameter. Help students see that $\angle KJL$ and $\angle Q$ intercept the same arc. Therefore, $m\angle Q = \frac{1}{2}m\widehat{JL} = z$.

Exercises ON YOUR OWN

Exercises 1–4 Students may not recognize that the polygons in Exercises 2 and 4 are neither inscribed nor circumscribed. Remind them that each side of a polygon circumscribed about a circle must touch the circle at only one point and that a polygon inscribed in a circle must touch the circle at each vertex.

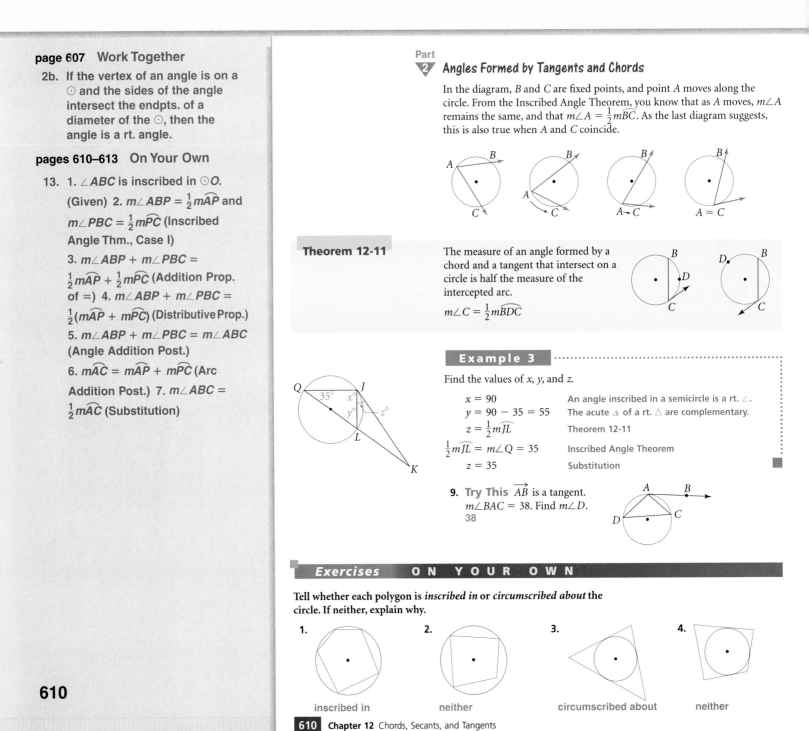

page 607 Work Together

2b. **If the vertex of an angle is on a ⊙ and the sides of the angle intersect the endpts. of a diameter of the ⊙, then the angle is a rt. angle.**

pages 610–613 On Your Own

13. **1. $\angle ABC$ is inscribed in ⊙O. (Given) 2. $m\angle ABP = \frac{1}{2}m\widehat{AP}$ and $m\angle PBC = \frac{1}{2}m\widehat{PC}$ (Inscribed Angle Thm., Case I) 3. $m\angle ABP + m\angle PBC = \frac{1}{2}m\widehat{AP} + \frac{1}{2}m\widehat{PC}$ (Addition Prop. of =) 4. $m\angle ABP + m\angle PBC = \frac{1}{2}(m\widehat{AP} + m\widehat{PC})$ (Distributive Prop.) 5. $m\angle ABP + m\angle PBC = m\angle ABC$ (Angle Addition Post.) 6. $m\widehat{AC} = m\widehat{AP} + m\widehat{PC}$ (Arc Addition Post.) 7. $m\angle ABC = \frac{1}{2}m\widehat{AC}$ (Substitution)**

Part 2

Angles Formed by Tangents and Chords

In the diagram, B and C are fixed points, and point A moves along the circle. From the Inscribed Angle Theorem, you know that as A moves, $m\angle A$ remains the same, and that $m\angle A = \frac{1}{2}m\widehat{BC}$. As the last diagram suggests, this is also true when A and C coincide.

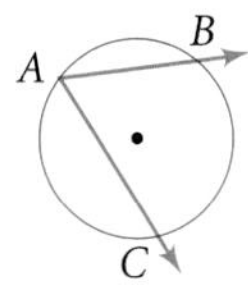

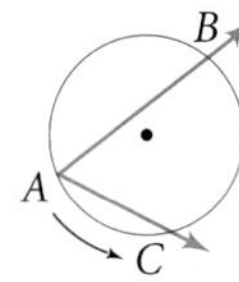

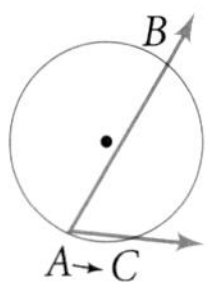

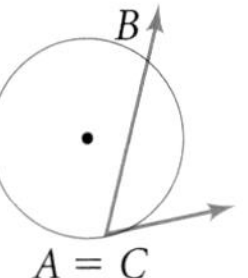

Theorem 12-11

The measure of an angle formed by a chord and a tangent that intersect on a circle is half the measure of the intercepted arc.

$m\angle C = \frac{1}{2}m\widehat{BDC}$

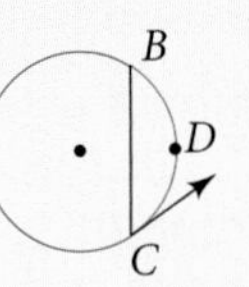

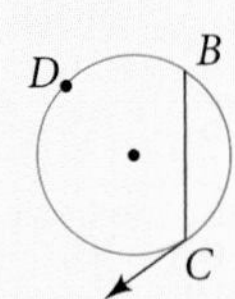

Example 3

Find the values of x, y, and z.

$x = 90$	An angle inscribed in a semicircle is a rt. ∠.
$y = 90 - 35 = 55$	The acute ∠s of a rt. △ are complementary.
$z = \frac{1}{2}m\widehat{JL}$	Theorem 12-11
$\frac{1}{2}m\widehat{JL} = m\angle Q = 35$	Inscribed Angle Theorem
$z = 35$	Substitution

9. **Try This** $\overrightarrow{AB}$ is a tangent. $m\angle BAC = 38$. Find $m\angle D$. 38

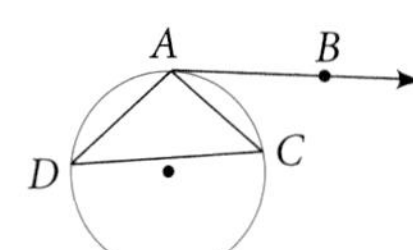

Exercises ON YOUR OWN

Tell whether each polygon is *inscribed in* or *circumscribed about* the circle. If neither, explain why.

1. 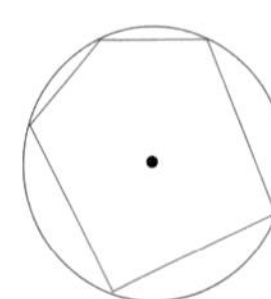
inscribed in

2. 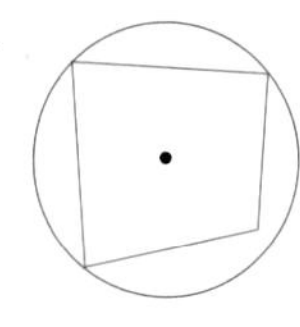
neither

3. 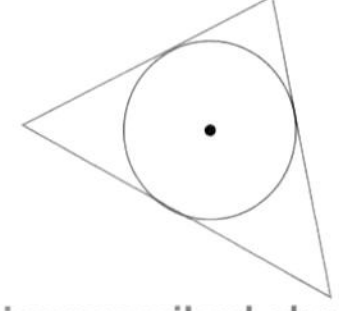
circumscribed about

4. 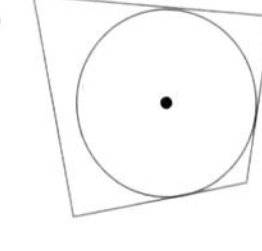
neither

ERROR ALERT! Exercises 5–12 Some students may confuse inscribed angles with central angles and think that the measure of an inscribed angle equals the measure of its intercepted arc. **Remediation:** Draw a central angle and an inscribed angle that intercept the same arc and show that the central angle is twice the measure of the inscribed angle.

ESL Exercises 13–16 Some students may understand the logical reasoning of a proof but may have trouble expressing their thoughts using the proper vocabulary and grammar. Have students work with a partner or in a small group to write the proofs. Each member should read each proof and agree that the reasoning is well-organized, accurate, and clear.

Exercise 17 Make sure students draw several examples so they can see that the parallelogram can be a square, but must be a rectangle.

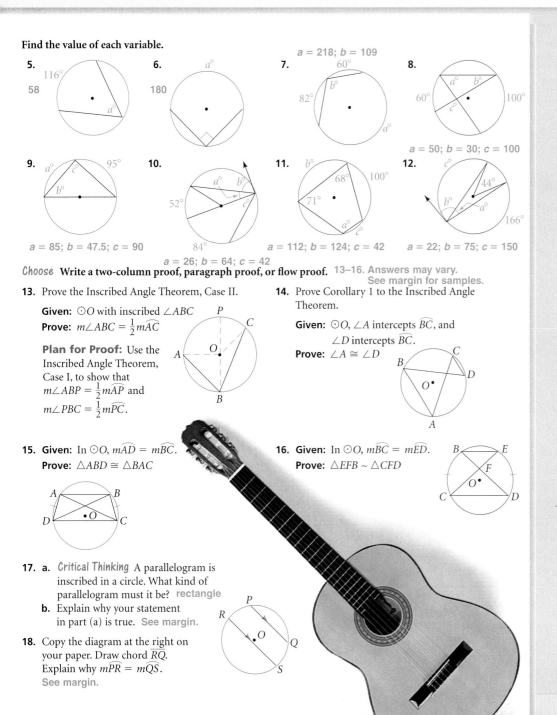

Find the value of each variable.

5. 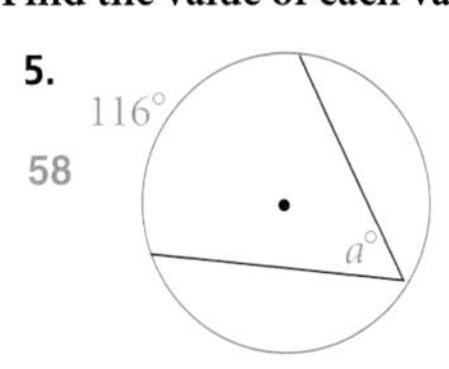

58

6. 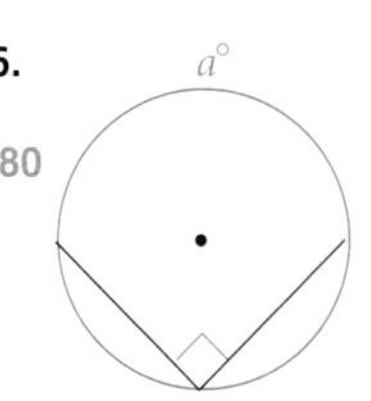

180

7. a = 218; b = 109
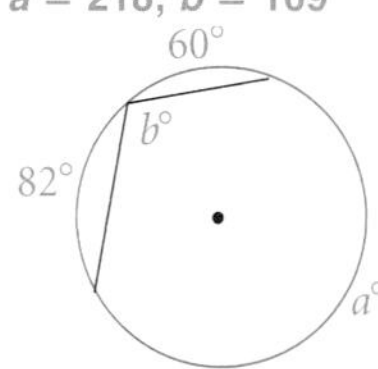

8. 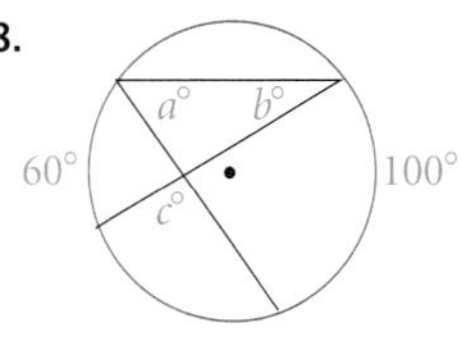

a = 50; b = 30; c = 100

9. 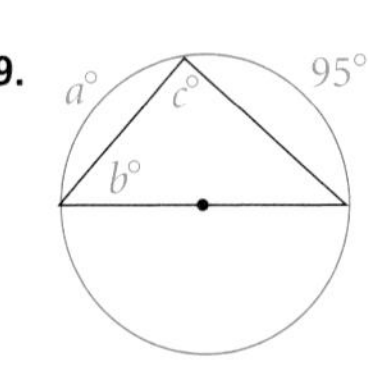

a = 85; b = 47.5; c = 90

10. 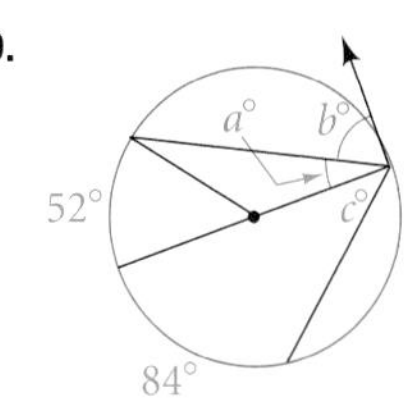

a = 26; b = 64; c = 42

11. 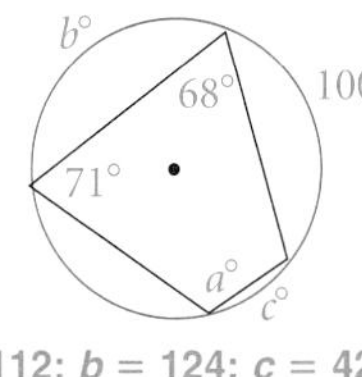

a = 112; b = 124; c = 42

12. 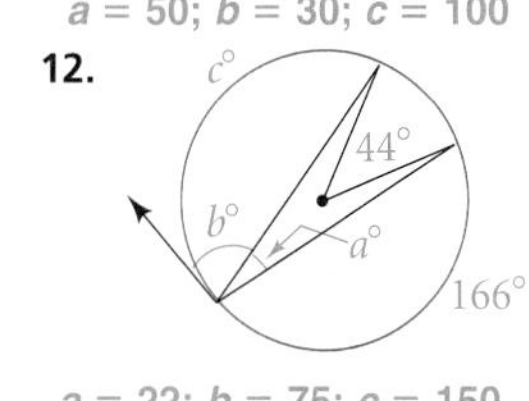

a = 22; b = 75; c = 150

Choose **Write a two-column proof, paragraph proof, or flow proof.** 13–16. Answers may vary. See margin for samples.

13. Prove the Inscribed Angle Theorem, Case II.

Given: $\odot O$ with inscribed $\angle ABC$

Prove: $m\angle ABC = \frac{1}{2}m\widehat{AC}$

Plan for Proof: Use the Inscribed Angle Theorem, Case I, to show that $m\angle ABP = \frac{1}{2}m\widehat{AP}$ and $m\angle PBC = \frac{1}{2}m\widehat{PC}$.

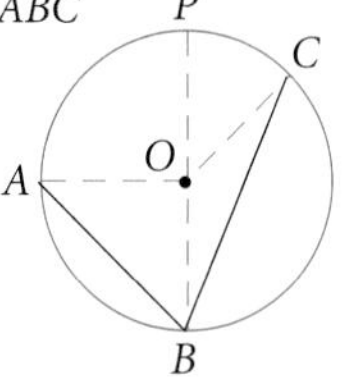

14. Prove Corollary 1 to the Inscribed Angle Theorem.

Given: $\odot O$, $\angle A$ intercepts $\widehat{BC}$, and $\angle D$ intercepts $\widehat{BC}$.

Prove: $\angle A \cong \angle D$

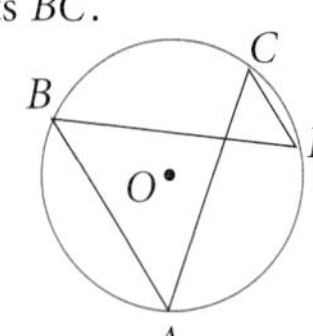

15. Given: In $\odot O$, $m\widehat{AD} = m\widehat{BC}$.

Prove: $\triangle ABD \cong \triangle BAC$

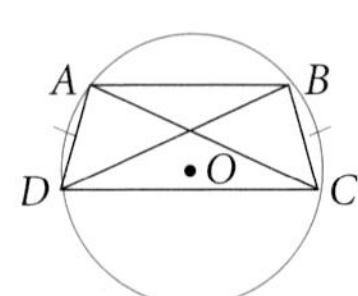

16. Given: In $\odot O$, $m\widehat{BC} = m\widehat{ED}$.

Prove: $\triangle EFB \sim \triangle CFD$

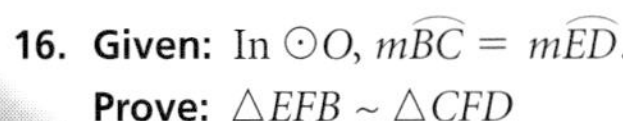
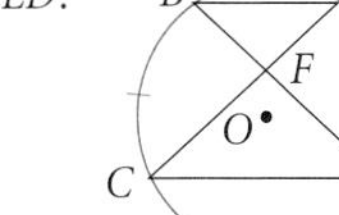
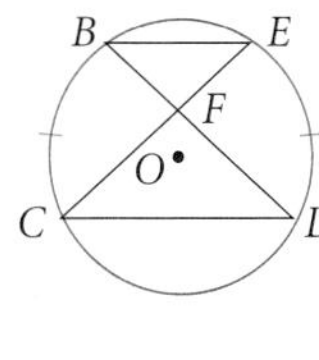
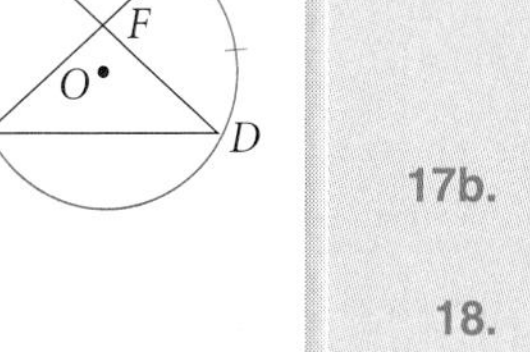

17. a. *Critical Thinking* A parallelogram is inscribed in a circle. What kind of parallelogram must it be? rectangle

b. Explain why your statement in part (a) is true. See margin.

18. Copy the diagram at the right on your paper. Draw chord $\overline{RQ}$. Explain why $m\widehat{PR} = m\widehat{QS}$. See margin.

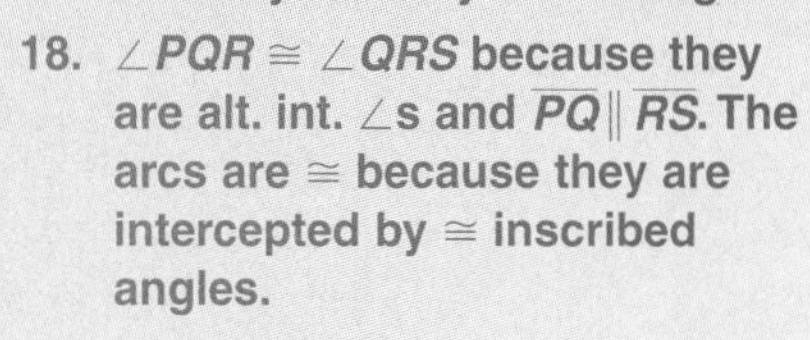

14. 1. $\angle A$ intercepts $\widehat{BC}$. (Given) 2. $m\angle A = \frac{1}{2}m\widehat{BC}$ (Measure of an inscribed $\angle$ is half the measure of its intercepted arc.) 3. $\angle D$ intercepts $\widehat{BC}$. (Given) 4. $m\angle D = \frac{1}{2}m\widehat{BC}$ (Measure of an inscribed $\angle$ is half the measure of its intercepted arc.) 5. $m\angle A = m\angle D$, or $\angle A \cong \angle D$ (Substitution)

15. 1. $m\widehat{AD} = m\widehat{BC}$ (Given) 2. $m\angle ABD = \frac{1}{2}m\widehat{AD}$ and $m\angle BAC = \frac{1}{2}m\widehat{BC}$ (Measure of an inscribed $\angle$ is half the measure of its intercepted arc.) 3. $m\angle BAC = m\angle ABD$ (Substitution) 4. $\overline{AD} \cong \overline{BC}$ ($\cong$ arcs have $\cong$ chords.) 5. $\angle ACB \cong \angle BDA$ (2 inscribed angles that intercept the same arc are $\cong$.) 6. $\triangle ABD \cong \triangle BAC$ (AAS)

16. 1. $m\widehat{BC} = m\widehat{ED}$ (Given) 2. $\angle BEC \cong \angle EBD$ (2 inscribed angles that intercept $\cong$ arcs are $\cong$.) 3. $\angle BFE \cong \angle CFD$ (Vertical $\angle$s are $\cong$.) 4. $\triangle EFB \sim \triangle CFD$ (AA~)

17b. Opp. angles are $\cong$ and supplementary. So they are rt. angles.

18. $\angle PQR \cong \angle QRS$ because they are alt. int. $\angle$s and $\overline{PQ} \parallel \overline{RS}$. The arcs are $\cong$ because they are intercepted by $\cong$ inscribed angles.

TACTILE LEARNING Exercise 19 Students may want to first perform the construction and then describe the steps used.

LOGICAL REASONING Exercises 20–21 In these exercises, students justify Corollaries 2 and 3.

CRITICAL THINKING Exercise 22 Students show that the converse of Corollary 3 is true.

ALTERNATIVE ASSESSMENT Exercises 24–27 These exercises can be used to help you assess students' ability to apply the theorems and corollaries presented in this lesson. Assign one problem to each group and have them present their solutions to the class.

Exercise 28 Help students understand that the angles drawn indicate the camera's field of vision.

Exercise 31 Students may not know how to draw the star. Have them draw five points unequally spaced on a circle, then connect the appropriate points to form a star.

CRITICAL THINKING Exercise 32c Review the meaning of *geometric mean.*

20. $m\widehat{BDC} = 180$ and $m\angle A = \frac{1}{2}m\widehat{BDC}$. So $m\angle A = 90$ and $\angle A$ is a rt. angle.

21b. $m\widehat{DAB} + m\widehat{BCD} = 360$. $m\angle A = \frac{1}{2}m\widehat{BCD}$ and $m\angle C = \frac{1}{2}m\widehat{DAB}$, so $m\angle A + m\angle C = \frac{1}{2} \cdot 360 = 180$. $\angle A$ and $\angle C$ are supplementary.

23. $\angle ACB$ is inscribed in a semicircle so it is a rt. angle. Then $\overleftrightarrow{BC}$ is $\perp$ to radius $\overline{AC}$ and passes through its endpt. on the ⊙. Therefore, $\overleftrightarrow{BC}$ is tangent to ⊙A.

28a. The angles captured by each camera are ≅.

b. No; the cameras capture the scene from diff. locations.

30. Construct the ⊥ bisector to the hypotenuse to find the center of the ⊙. Use half the length of the hypotenuse as a radius to construct the ⊙.

32a. Sample:

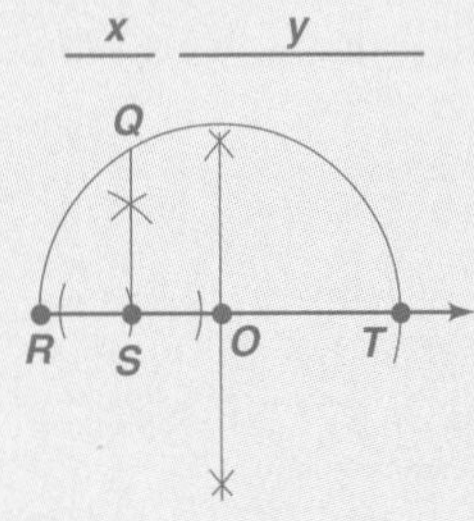

612

19. *Constructions* Explain how you would construct the tangent to a circle at any point on the circle. Draw the diameter through the given pt. Construct the line ⊥ to the diameter through this pt.

20. *Logical Reasoning* In the diagram at the right, $\angle A$ is inscribed in a semicircle. Write a justification of Corollary 2 of the Inscribed Angle Theorem. See margin.

A B O C D

21. In the diagram at the right, quadrilateral $ABCD$ is inscribed in ⊙O.
 a. Find the sum of the measures of the arcs intercepted by $\angle A$ and $\angle C$. 360
 b. *Logical Reasoning* Explain why Corollary 3 to the Inscribed Angle Theorem must be true. See margin.

A B O D C

22. *Critical Thinking* Decide whether the following statements are true or false. Give a counterexample for each false statement.
 a. If two angles inscribed in a circle are congruent, then they intercept the same arc. False; the inscribed angles can intercept congruent arcs.
 b. If a right angle is an inscribed angle, then it is inscribed in a semicircle. true
 c. A circle can always be circumscribed about a quadrilateral whose opposite angles are supplementary. true

23. *Constructions* The diagrams below show the construction of a tangent to a circle from a point outside the circle. Explain why $\overleftrightarrow{BC}$ must be tangent to ⊙A. (*Hint:* Copy the third diagram and draw $\overline{AC}$.) See margin.

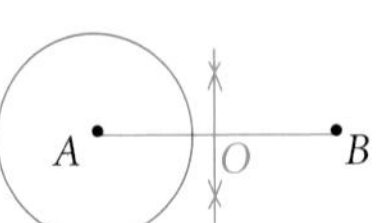

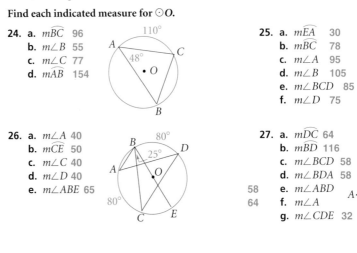

Given: ⊙A and point B
Construct the midpoint of $\overline{AB}$. Label the point O.

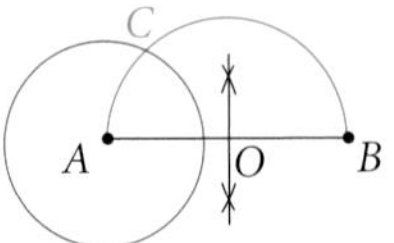

Construct a semicircle with radius OA and center O. Label its intersection with ⊙A as C.

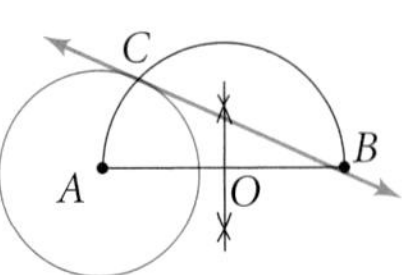

Draw $\overleftrightarrow{BC}$.

Find each indicated measure for ⊙O.

24. a. $m\widehat{BC}$ 96
 b. $m\angle B$ 55
 c. $m\angle C$ 77
 d. $m\widehat{AB}$ 154

110° A C 48° O B

25. a. $m\widehat{EA}$ 30
 b. $m\widehat{BC}$ 78
 c. $m\angle A$ 95
 d. $m\angle B$ 105
 e. $m\angle BCD$ 85
 f. $m\angle D$ 75

A 72° E B O 51° D C 112°

26. a. $m\angle A$ 40
 b. $m\widehat{CE}$ 50
 c. $m\angle C$ 40
 d. $m\angle D$ 40
 e. $m\angle ABE$ 65

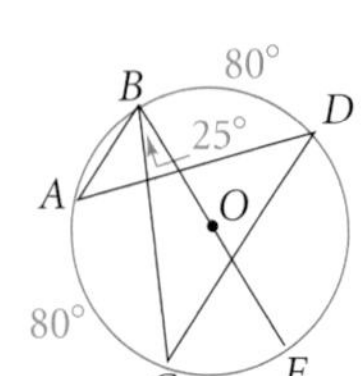

27. a. $m\widehat{DC}$ 64
 b. $m\widehat{BD}$ 116
 c. $m\angle BCD$ 58
 d. $m\angle BDA$ 58
 e. $m\angle ABD$ 58
 f. $m\angle A$ 64
 g. $m\angle CDE$ 32

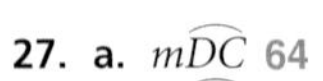

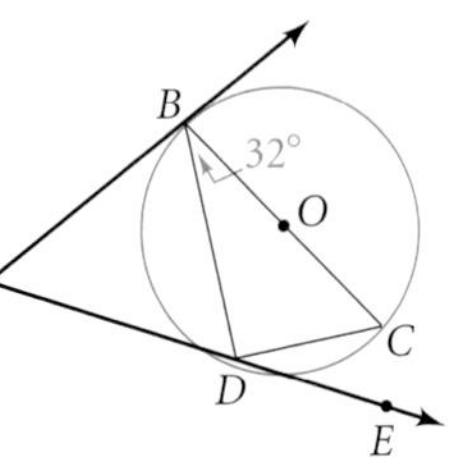

Exercises MIXED REVIEW

Exercises 33–34 Students review finding the lengths of midsegments of trapezoids.

JOURNAL Have students include both inscribed and central angles in their descriptions.

GETTING READY FOR LESSON 12-5 These exercises prepare students to find arcs formed by intersecting chords.

Wrap Up

THE BIG IDEA Ask students to summarize the theorems and corollaries in this lesson.

RETEACHING ACTIVITY Students find the measure of inscribed angles and the arcs they intercept. (Reteaching worksheet 12-4)

28. a. **Motion Pictures** A director wants to capture the same scene on film from three different viewpoints. Explain why the cameras in the positions shown will record the same scene.
    b. **Critical Thinking** Will the scenes look the same when they are shown? Explain.
    a–b. See margin p. 612.

Scene
Camera 1
Camera 2
Camera 3

29. a. **Patterns** Sketch a trapezoid inscribed in a circle. Repeat several times using different circles. Check students' work.
    b. Make a **conjecture** about the kind of trapezoid that can be inscribed in a circle. See below.

30. **Writing** Explain how to construct a circle circumscribed about a right triangle. See margin p. 612.

31. **Mental Math** Draw a circle and inscribe an irregular five-pointed star. Find the sum of the measures of the five inscribed angles. 180

32. a. **Constructions** Draw two segments. Label their lengths x and y. Construct the geometric mean of x and y by following these steps. See margin p. 612 for sample.
    Step 1: On a line, construct $\overline{RS}$ with length x and $\overline{ST}$ with length y such that S is between R and T.
    Step 2: Bisect $\overline{RT}$. Label the midpoint O. Use the length RO to construct a semicircle with diameter $\overline{RT}$.
    Step 3: Construct the perpendicular to $\overline{RT}$ at S. Label the point of intersection of the perpendicular with the semicircle as Q.
    b. What kind of triangle is $\triangle RQT$? rt. triangle
    c. **Critical Thinking** Why is QS the geometric mean of x and y? Since $\overline{QS}$ is the altitude to the hypotenuse of a rt. △, QS is the geometric mean of RS and ST.

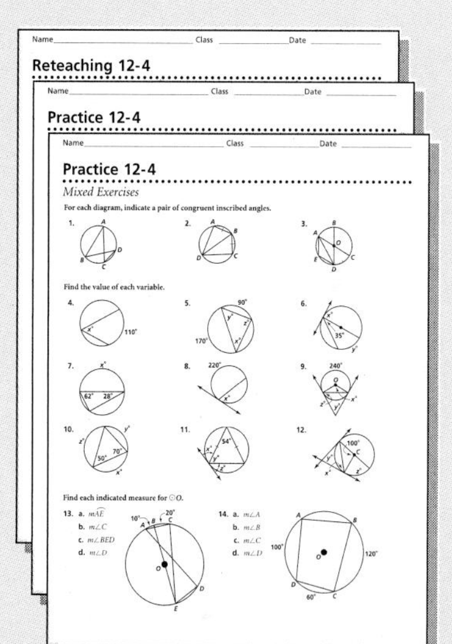

Lesson Quiz

Lesson Quiz is also available in Transparencies.

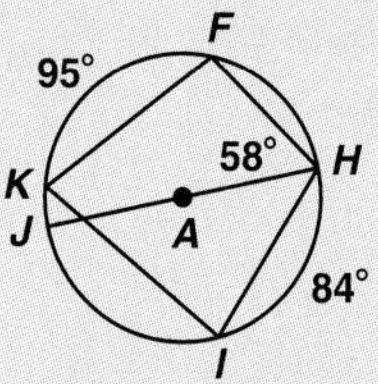

Find each measure for ⊙A.

1. $m\widehat{KJ}$ 21
2. $m\widehat{JI}$ 96
3. $m\angle JHI$ 48
4. $m\angle KFH$ 100.5

Exercises MIXED REVIEW

Find the length of the midsegment of a trapezoid with the given bases.

33. $b_1 = 3$ cm, $b_2 = 7$ cm 5 cm
34. $b_1 = 8$ in., $b_2 = 13$ in. 10.5 in.
35. What is the measure of an interior angle of a regular pentagon? 108

FOR YOUR JOURNAL

Describe the relationships between arcs and angles on a circle.

Getting Ready for Lesson 12-5

***O* is the center of each circle. Find the measure of $\widehat{AB}$.**

36. 110

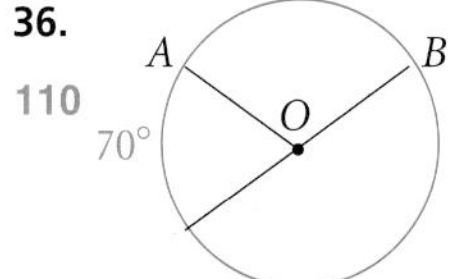

37. 130

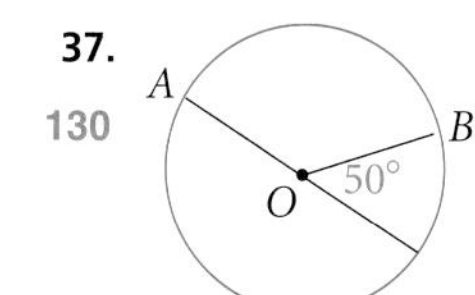

38. 90

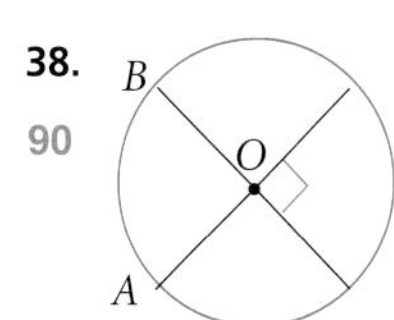

29b. If a trapezoid is inscribed in a ⊙, then it is an isosceles trapezoid.

12-5 Teaching Notes

PROBLEM OF THE DAY

If you folded the pattern into a cube, how many semicircles would have diameters that coincide? two

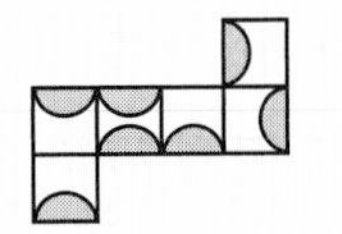

Problem of the Day is also available in Transparencies.

CONNECTING TO PRIOR KNOWLEDGE Have students draw a circle, an inscribed angle, and a central angle that intercept the same arc. Have students explain how the measures of the angles can be calculated knowing the measure of the arc.

WORK TOGETHER

Encourage students to draw the circles and segments with a sharp pencil or fine-point pen so that the points where the segments intersect the circle are clear.

Question 1 Review the directions with students. Make sure they understand that they need to draw and measure central angles to find x and y.

THINK AND DISCUSS

Question 4 Help students see that a secant segment must have at least one endpoint in the exterior of a circle.

Lesson Planning Options

Prerequisite Skills

- Finding the measures of central angles and their intercepted arcs

Assignment Options for Exercises On Your Own

Core 1–14, 16–17
Extension 15, 18

Use Mixed Review to maintain skills.

Resources

Student Edition

Skills Handbook, pp. 664, 670
Extra Practice, p. 659
Glossary/Study Guide

Teaching Resources

Chapter Support File, Ch. 12
- Practice 12-5 (two worksheets)
- Reteaching 12-5
- Alternative Activity 12-5

Classroom Manager 12-5
Glossary, Spanish Resources

Transparencies

12, 122, 125

614

Connections Photography . . . and more

12-5 Angles Formed by Chords, Secants, and Tangents

What You'll Learn

- Finding the measures of angles formed by chords, secants, and tangents

...And Why

To use measures of angles in real-world applications such as photography

What You'll Need

- protractor
- compass

TECHNOLOGY HINT

The Work Together could be done using geometry software.

WORK TOGETHER

- Have each member of your group draw four circles. Label the centers M, N, P, and Q. Draw segments intersecting inside and outside the circles as shown below.

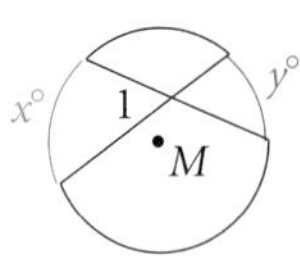

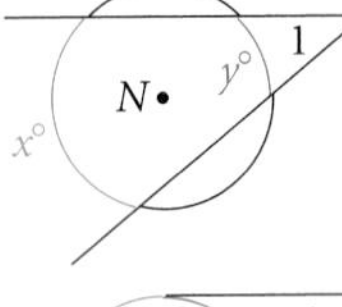

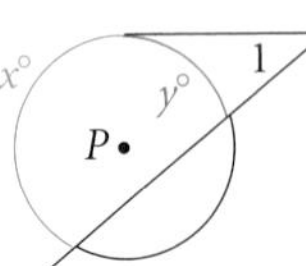

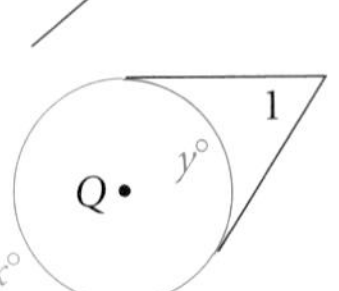

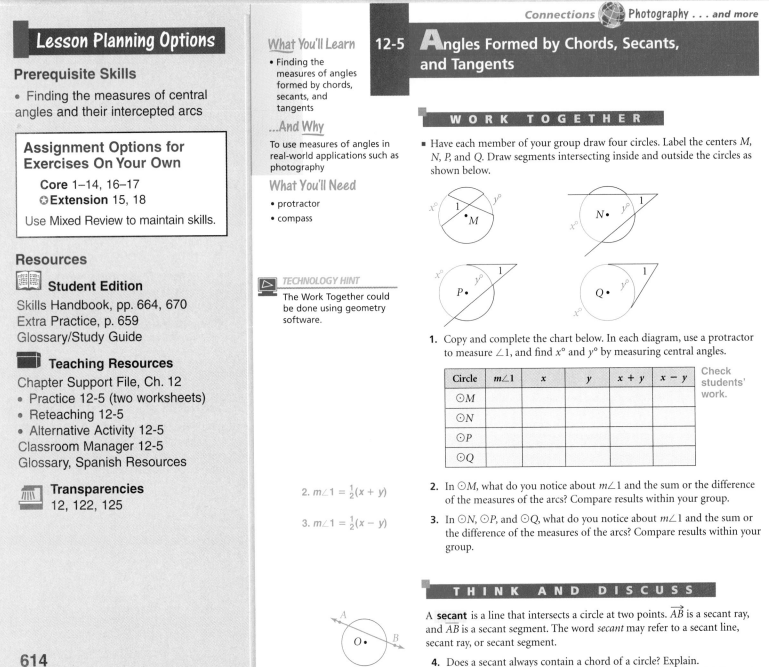

1. Copy and complete the chart below. In each diagram, use a protractor to measure $\angle 1$, and find $x°$ and $y°$ by measuring central angles.

Circle	$m\angle 1$	x	y	$x + y$	$x - y$
$\odot M$					
$\odot N$					
$\odot P$					
$\odot Q$					

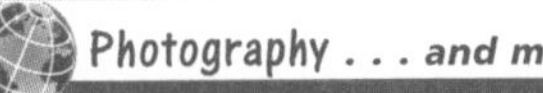

Check students' work.

2. In $\odot M$, what do you notice about $m\angle 1$ and the sum or the difference of the measures of the arcs? Compare results within your group.

2. $m\angle 1 = \frac{1}{2}(x + y)$

3. In $\odot N$, $\odot P$, and $\odot Q$, what do you notice about $m\angle 1$ and the sum or the difference of the measures of the arcs? Compare results within your group.

3. $m\angle 1 = \frac{1}{2}(x - y)$

THINK AND DISCUSS

A **secant** is a line that intersects a circle at two points. $\overrightarrow{AB}$ is a secant ray, and $\overline{AB}$ is a secant segment. The word *secant* may refer to a secant line, secant ray, or secant segment.

4. Does a secant always contain a chord of a circle? Explain. Yes; the segment connecting the pts. where the secant intersects the ⊙ is a chord.

VISUAL LEARNING Some students may want to shade the interior of the angles formed by chords, secants, and tangents as a way to visualize the arcs they intercept.

ERROR ALERT! Theorems 12-12 and 12-13 Some students may be confused when to add and when to subtract. **Remediation:** Draw a circle and segments as shown below. Measure ∠1 and ∠2 and show that the angle whose vertex is in the interior is larger (therefore, add) than the angle whose vertex is in the exterior of the circle (therefore, subtract).

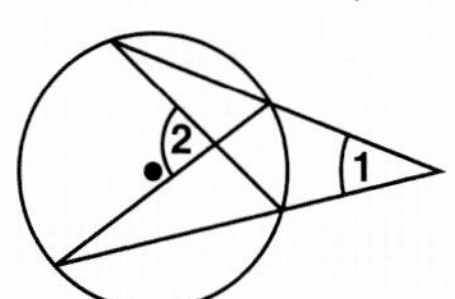

AUDITORY LEARNING It may help students to repeat the phrase "interior add, exterior subtract" several times to help them remember the difference between Theorem 12-12 and Theorem 12-13.

Students are asked to write a plan for the proof of Theorem 12-13 as it applies to two secants in Exercise 14.

The proof of Theorem 12-12 uses the Exterior Angle Theorem. You may want to review the theorem by drawing several triangles and having students identify exterior angles and then write their measures as sums of measures of interior angles.

The diagrams below show arcs intercepted by chords, secants, and tangents.

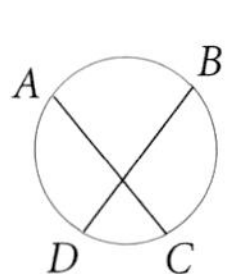

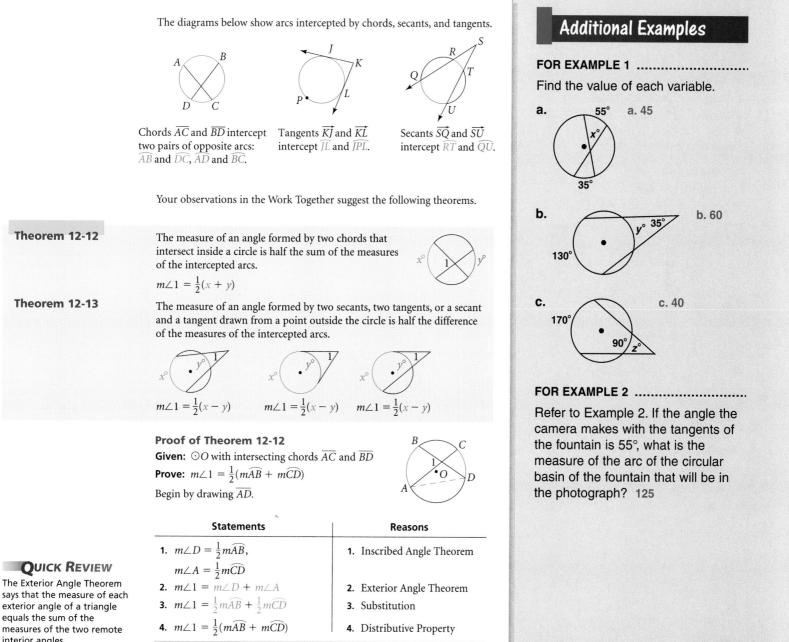

Chords $\overline{AC}$ and $\overline{BD}$ intercept two pairs of opposite arcs: $\widehat{AB}$ and $\widehat{DC}$, $\widehat{AD}$ and $\widehat{BC}$.

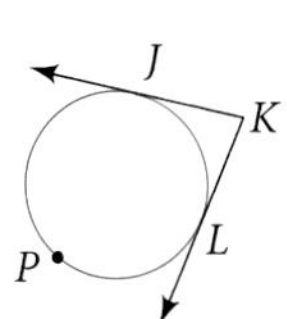

Tangents $\overrightarrow{KJ}$ and $\overrightarrow{KL}$ intercept $\widehat{JL}$ and $\widehat{JPL}$.

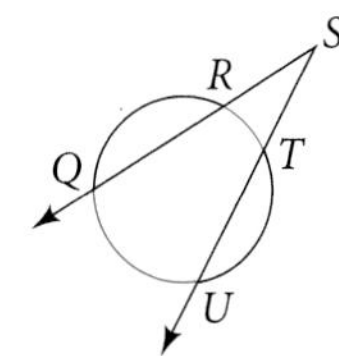

Secants $\overrightarrow{SQ}$ and $\overrightarrow{SU}$ intercept $\widehat{RT}$ and $\widehat{QU}$.

Your observations in the Work Together suggest the following theorems.

Theorem 12-12

The measure of an angle formed by two chords that intersect inside a circle is half the sum of the measures of the intercepted arcs.

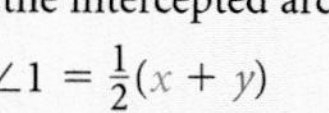

$m\angle 1 = \frac{1}{2}(x + y)$

Theorem 12-13

The measure of an angle formed by two secants, two tangents, or a secant and a tangent drawn from a point outside the circle is half the difference of the measures of the intercepted arcs.

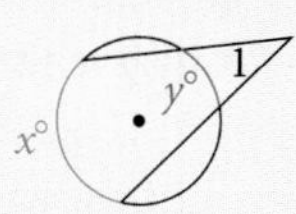

$m\angle 1 = \frac{1}{2}(x - y)$

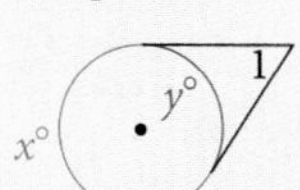

$m\angle 1 = \frac{1}{2}(x - y)$

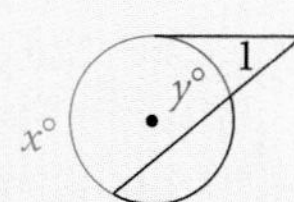

$m\angle 1 = \frac{1}{2}(x - y)$

Proof of Theorem 12-12

Given: $\odot O$ with intersecting chords $\overline{AC}$ and $\overline{BD}$

Prove: $m\angle 1 = \frac{1}{2}(m\widehat{AB} + m\widehat{CD})$

Begin by drawing $\overline{AD}$.

Statements	Reasons
1. $m\angle D = \frac{1}{2}m\widehat{AB}$, $m\angle A = \frac{1}{2}m\widehat{CD}$	**1.** Inscribed Angle Theorem
2. $m\angle 1 = m\angle D + m\angle A$	**2.** Exterior Angle Theorem
3. $m\angle 1 = \frac{1}{2}m\widehat{AB} + \frac{1}{2}m\widehat{CD}$	**3.** Substitution
4. $m\angle 1 = \frac{1}{2}(m\widehat{AB} + m\widehat{CD})$	**4.** Distributive Property

QUICK REVIEW

The Exterior Angle Theorem says that the measure of each exterior angle of a triangle equals the sum of the measures of the two remote interior angles.

Additional Examples

FOR EXAMPLE 1

Find the value of each variable.

a.

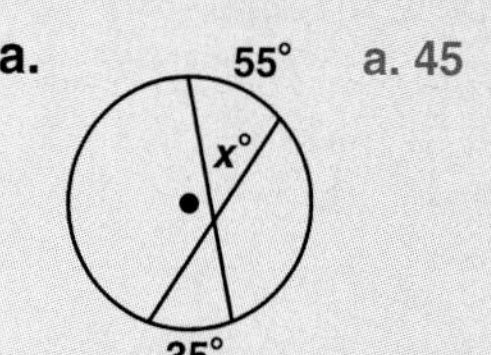

a. 45

b.

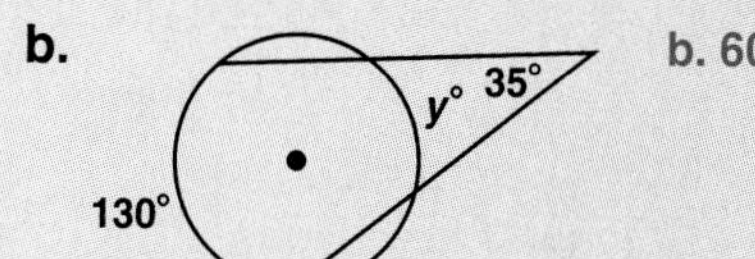

b. 60

c.

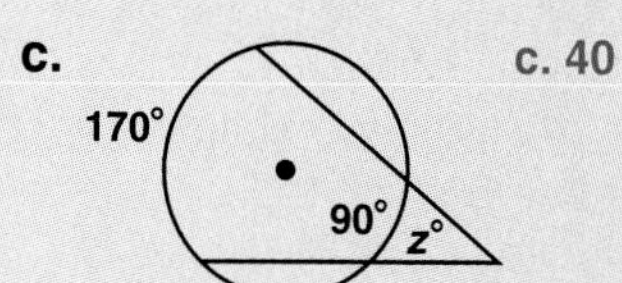

c. 40

FOR EXAMPLE 2

Refer to Example 2. If the angle the camera makes with the tangents of the fountain is 55°, what is the measure of the arc of the circular basin of the fountain that will be in the photograph? 125

Example 1

ERROR ALERT! In part a, some students may think that $x = 46$. **Remediation:** Point out that the chords do not intersect in the center of the circle, so the angles formed are not central angles.

ALTERNATIVE ASSESSMENT **Question 5** Have students work in groups to make up problems like those in parts a–c. Have them write each problem on an index card with the solution on the back. Then have them exchange cards with another group and check each other's answers. Save the cards to use in a "math bee" or another review game.

Example 2 Relating to the Real World  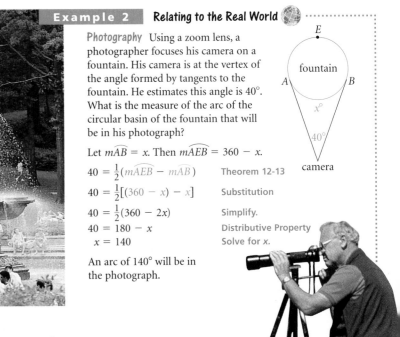

Some students may think that there is not enough information given to solve this problem. Help them see that only one piece of information is missing; once you know $m\widehat{AB}$, you can find $m\widehat{AEB}$.

ESL Make sure students understand the words *fountain* and *basin.* Ask students to share examples of decorative fountains they have seen.

CONNECTING TO STUDENTS' WORLD Have students research the viewing angles of cameras. Have them bring in manuals for cameras they or their parents own, gather information from newspaper advertisements, or visit a store that sells cameras.

Technology Options

For Exercise 10, students may use a drawing program of geometry software to create a figure using tangents and secants. Then they can use the software to find the measures of the angles.

Prentice Hall Technology 

Software
- Secondary Math Lab Toolkit™
- Integrated Math Lab 46
- Computer Item Generator 12-5

Internet
- See the Prentice Hall site. (http://www.phschool.com)

616

Example 1

Find the value of each variable.

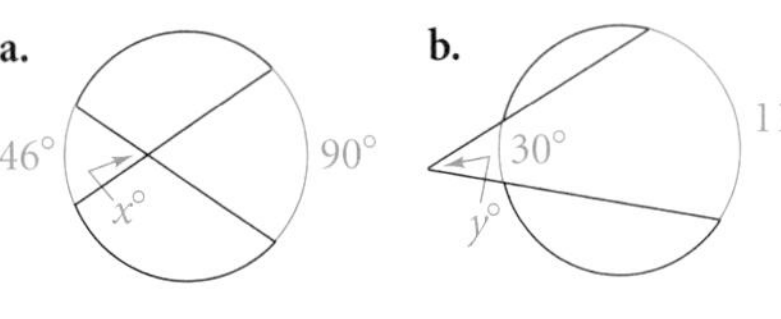

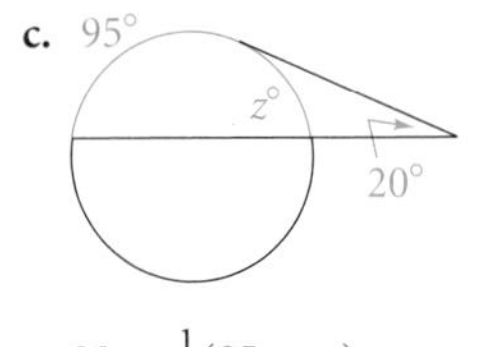

a. $x = \frac{1}{2}(46 + 90)$
$x = 68$

b. $y = \frac{1}{2}(110 - 30)$
$y = 40$

c. $20 = \frac{1}{2}(95 - z)$
$40 = 95 - z$
$z = 55$

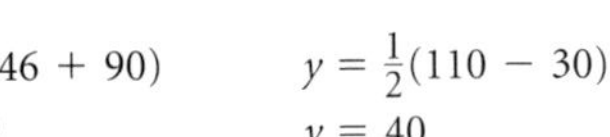

5. Try This Find the value of each variable.

a. **25** b. **32** c. **64**

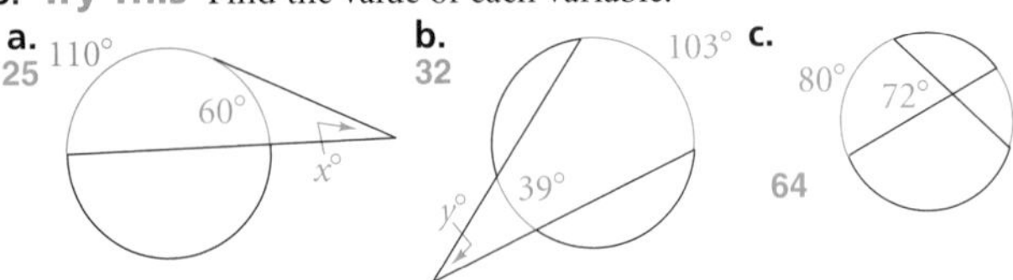

You can find the measures of arcs of a circle intercepted by tangents if you know the measure of the angle formed by the tangents.

Example 2 Relating to the Real World

Photography Using a zoom lens, a photographer focuses his camera on a fountain. His camera is at the vertex of the angle formed by tangents to the fountain. He estimates this angle is 40°. What is the measure of the arc of the circular basin of the fountain that will be in his photograph?

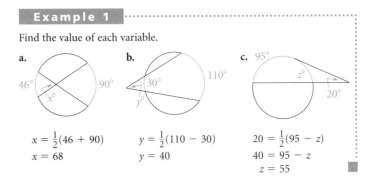

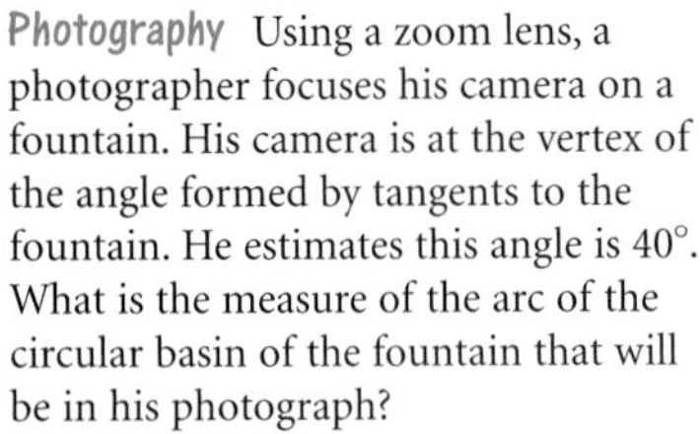

Let $m\widehat{AB} = x$. Then $m\widehat{AEB} = 360 - x$.

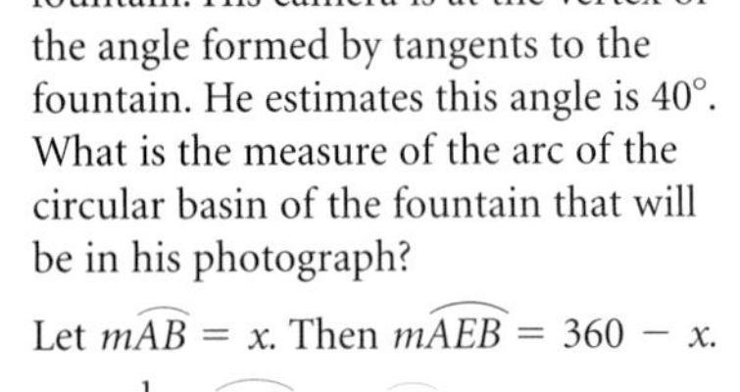

$40 = \frac{1}{2}(m\widehat{AEB} - m\widehat{AB})$ Theorem 12-13

$40 = \frac{1}{2}[(360 - x) - x]$ Substitution

$40 = \frac{1}{2}(360 - 2x)$ Simplify.

$40 = 180 - x$ Distributive Property

$x = 140$ Solve for x.

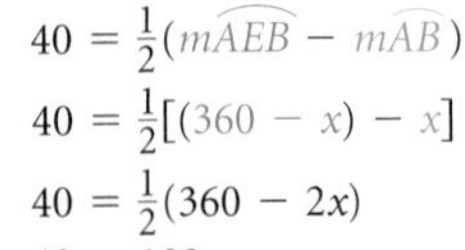

An arc of 140° will be in the photograph.

Exercises ON YOUR OWN

Exercises 1–8 Ask students to write the equation they solved as well as the answer to each problem. This will help you determine if their errors are in setting up the equations or in solving them.

DIVERSITY Exercise 9 Have students research space travel and space research done in other countries, and cooperative space explorations among countries. Also have students research the contributions of women in these areas. Have students share what they learn with the class.

Exercise 9a This exercise is similar to Example 2. Have students copy the diagram in Exercise 9, label the arcs, then model the solution steps in Example 2.

OPEN-ENDED Exercise 10 Encourage students to be creative in drawing a design made from tangents and secants.

STANDARDIZED TEST TIP Exercise 11 Some students may not see the significance of the phrase "the center of ⊙*O* is inside ∠*ABC*" and ignore it. Emphasize that standardized test questions are usually written concisely. The statement would likely not be given unless it was significant.

WRITING Exercise 12 Have students draw several different examples to test their conjectures, making sure that in at least one of their drawings neither chord is a diameter.

7. Step away; as she steps away, the measure of the angle between the tangents decreases and the measure of the arc increases.

6. In Example 2, what is $m\overset{\frown}{AEB}$? 220
7. *Critical Thinking* To capture a greater arc of the circular basin in the photo, should the photographer step closer to or farther away from the fountain? Explain.
8. What should the angle at the camera be in order to photograph a 70° arc of the basin? 110°

Exercises ON YOUR OWN

Assume that lines that appear tangent are tangent. Find the value of each variable.

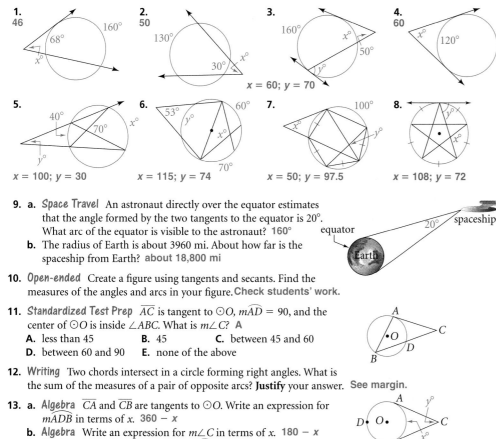

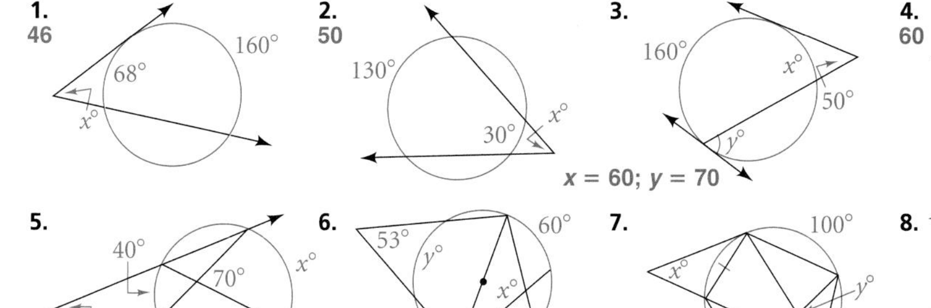

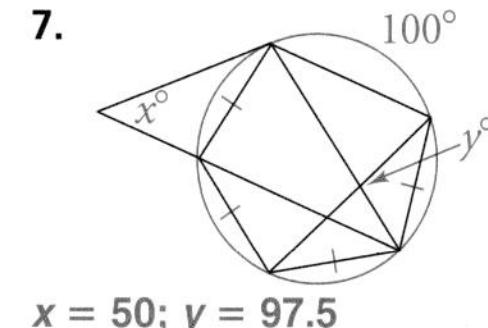

9. a. *Space Travel* An astronaut directly over the equator estimates that the angle formed by the two tangents to the equator is 20°. What arc of the equator is visible to the astronaut? 160°
   b. The radius of Earth is about 3960 mi. About how far is the spaceship from Earth? about 18,800 mi

equator
Earth
20°
spaceship

10. *Open-ended* Create a figure using tangents and secants. Find the measures of the angles and arcs in your figure. Check students' work.
11. *Standardized Test Prep* $\overline{AC}$ is tangent to ⊙*O*, $m\overset{\frown}{AD} = 90$, and the center of ⊙*O* is inside ∠*ABC*. What is *m*∠*C*? A
    A. less than 45 **B.** 45 **C.** between 45 and 60
    D. between 60 and 90 **E.** none of the above

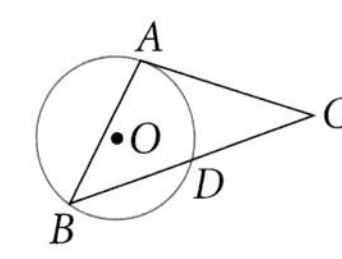

12. *Writing* Two chords intersect in a circle forming right angles. What is the sum of the measures of a pair of opposite arcs? **Justify** your answer. See margin.

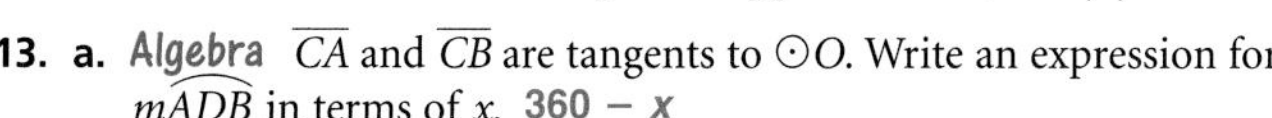

13. a. *Algebra* $\overline{CA}$ and $\overline{CB}$ are tangents to ⊙*O*. Write an expression for $m\overset{\frown}{ADB}$ in terms of *x*. 360 − *x*
    b. *Algebra* Write an expression for *m*∠*C* in terms of *x*. 180 − *x*
    c. *Algebra* Write an expression for $m\overset{\frown}{AB}$ in terms of *y*. 180 − *y*

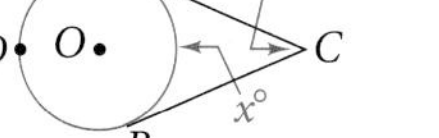

pages 617–618 On Your Own

12. The sum of the measures of the opp. arcs is 180; the measure of an ∠ formed by 2 chords inside a ⊙ is half the sum of the measures of the intercepted arcs.

Exercise 14 Students may need help recognizing that $\angle ABE$ is an exterior angle of $\triangle EBC$.

Exercise 15 Explain to students that, in this problem, *A* and *B* are fixed points, whereas *X*, *Y*, and *Z* are "variable" points.

Chapter Project **FIND OUT BY CONSTRUCTING** Help students see how they can use diameters of a circle to draw a square and the diagonals of a square to draw a circle. Students may want to use construction tools in geometry software to create this or other designs.

Exercises MIXED REVIEW

DIVERSITY Exercises 19–21 Be aware that students' definitions of family will differ. Be especially conscious of students who may live in nontraditional family settings.

14. Since they are inscribed $\angle$s, $m\angle ABE = \frac{1}{2}m\widehat{AE}$ and $m\angle BED = \frac{1}{2}m\widehat{BD}$. Apply the Exterior Angle Thm. to $\triangle BCE$ to prove that $m\angle C = \frac{1}{2}(m\widehat{AE} - m\widehat{BD})$.

15b. The ship is in safe waters if the measure of the angle is ≤ 30.

Checkpoint page 619

5. A secant extends outside the $\odot$, a chord does not.

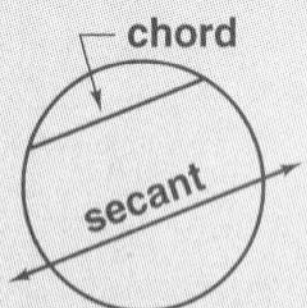

14. Write a Plan for Proof for Theorem 12-13 as it applies to two secants drawn from a point outside a circle. Answers may vary. See margin for samples.

Given: $\odot O$ with secants $\overline{CA}$ and $\overline{CE}$ intersecting at *C*.

Prove: $m\angle ACE = \frac{1}{2}(m\widehat{AE} - m\widehat{BD})$

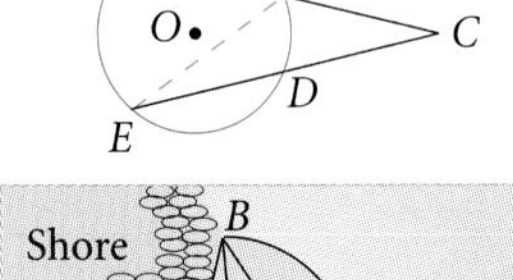

15. *Critical Thinking* A navigational map shows that the waters near lighthouses *A* and *B* are dangerous. The unsafe area is within $\widehat{AXB}$, a 300° arc. $m\angle X = 30$; $30 < m\angle Y < 180$; $0 < m\angle Z < 30$

a. *X* represents locations of a ship on $\odot O$. *Y* represents locations of a ship inside $\odot O$. *Z* represents locations of a ship outside $\odot O$. What is the measure of $\angle X$? What is the possible range of measures of $\angle Y$? of $\angle Z$?

b. Using the angle a ship makes with the lighthouses, how can a ship's navigator be sure the ship is in safe waters? See margin.

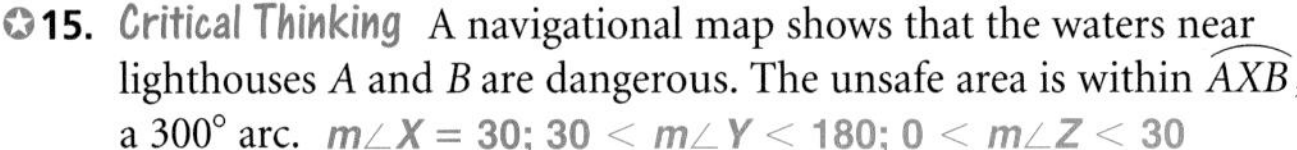

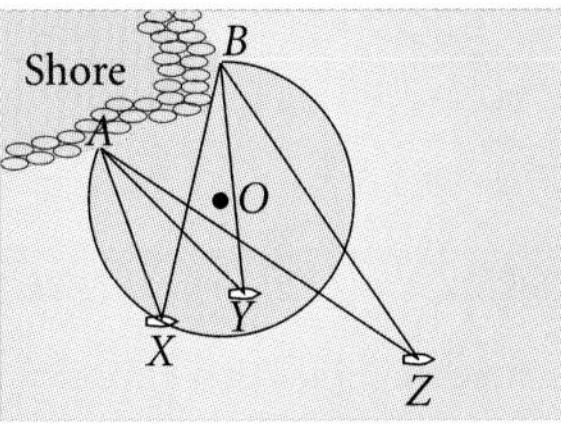

Find the value of each variable.

16.

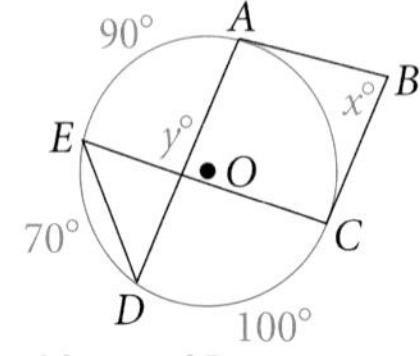

$x = 80$; $y = 95$

17.

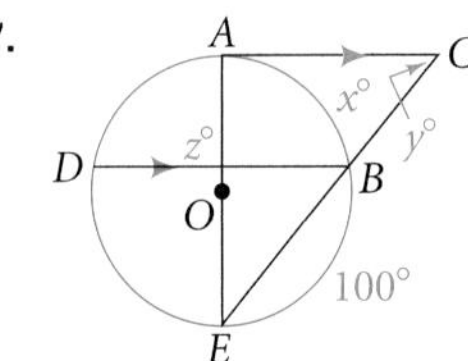

$x = 80$; $y = 50$; $z = 90$

18. The angles of a quadrilateral measure 85, 76, 94, and 105. A circle is inscribed in the quadrilateral. What are the measures of the arcs between each two consecutive points of tangency? 95; 104; 86; 75

Chapter Project *Find Out by Constructing*

Follow the steps below to create a pattern commonly found in 14th-century Islamic art and furniture. Check students' work.

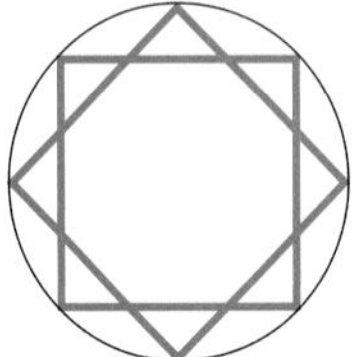

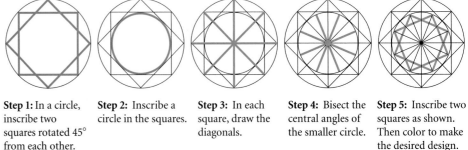

Step 1: In a circle, inscribe two squares rotated 45° from each other.

Step 2: Inscribe a circle in the squares.

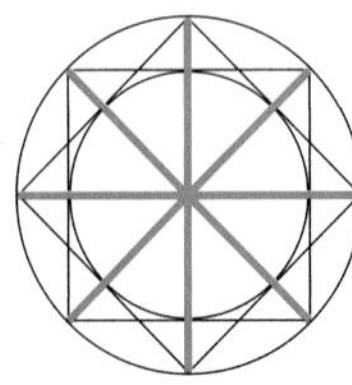

Step 3: In each square, draw the diagonals.

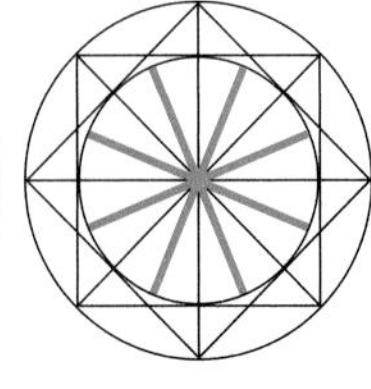

Step 4: Bisect the central angles of the smaller circle.

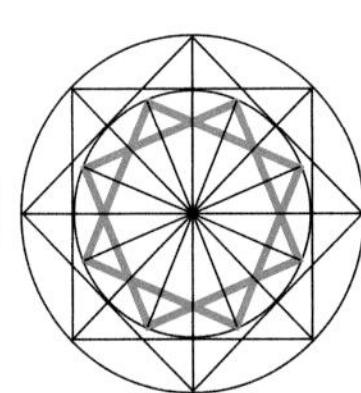

Step 5: Inscribe two squares as shown. Then color to make the desired design.

JOURNAL Have students share their journal entries with a partner. Have them critique one another's entries for thoroughness, accuracy, clarity, and organization.

GETTING READY FOR LESSON 12-6 These exercises prepare students to prove relationships about lengths of segments of chords, secants, and tangents.

Wrap Up

THE BIG IDEA Ask students to explain the difference between finding the measure of an angle formed by a chord and a tangent and the measure of an angle formed by two tangents.

RETEACHING ACTIVITY Students find the measures of angles formed by chords, secants, and tangents. (Reteaching worksheet 12-5)

Exercises CHECKPOINT

In this Checkpoint, your students will assess their own progress in Lessons 12-4 to 12-5.

WRITING Exercise 5 Check that students show a secant can be a ray, a line, or a segment.

Exercises MIXED REVIEW

Data Analysis Use the graph showing the number of living siblings, including step-siblings and half-siblings, adults of different ages have.

Number of Living Siblings

Age: 18–24, 45–64, 25–44, 65+

0%, 10%, 20%, 30%, 40%, 50%

none, one, two or three, four or more

Source: *American Demographics*

19. About what percent of 45–64-year-olds have four or more siblings? 35%

20. About what percent of 25–44-year-olds have two or more siblings? 80%

21. Which age group is least likely to have only one sibling? 25–44

Getting Ready for Lesson 12-6

Each pair of figures is similar. Complete each statement.

22. 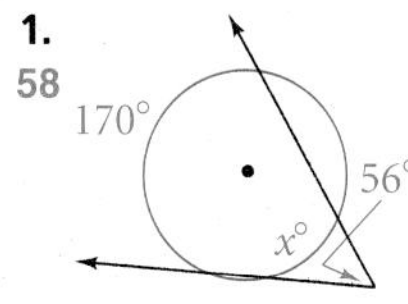

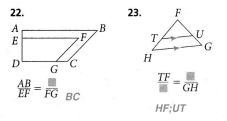

$\frac{AB}{EF} = \frac{■}{FG}$ BC

23. 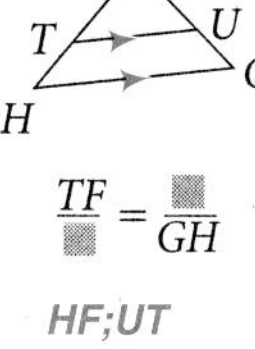

$\frac{TF}{■} = \frac{■}{GH}$

HF; UT

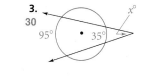

FOR YOUR JOURNAL

Summarize what you have learned in this lesson. Draw a diagram showing the angles formed by chords, secants, and tangents. Explain how to find the measure of each angle.

Exercises CHECKPOINT

Assume that lines that appear tangent are tangent. Find the value of each variable.

1. 58 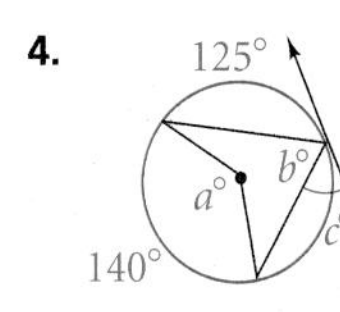

2. (100°, 60°, 84°, $a°$, $b°$, $c°$, $d°$)

3. 30 (95°, 35°, $x°$)

4. (125°, 140°, $a°$, $b°$, $c°$)

$a = 30$; $b = 42$; $c = 80$; $d = 116$

$a = 140$; $b = 70$; $c = 47.5$

5. *Writing* Explain the difference between a chord and a secant. Include a diagram. See margin p. 618.

6. *Standardized Test Prep* In the circle at the right, which measure is greatest? D

A. $m\angle C$ B. $m\angle EBD$ C. $m\angle ABE$

D. $m\widehat{BF}$ E. $m\angle BDF$

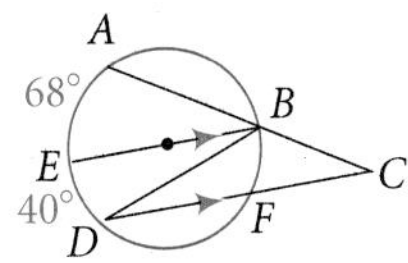

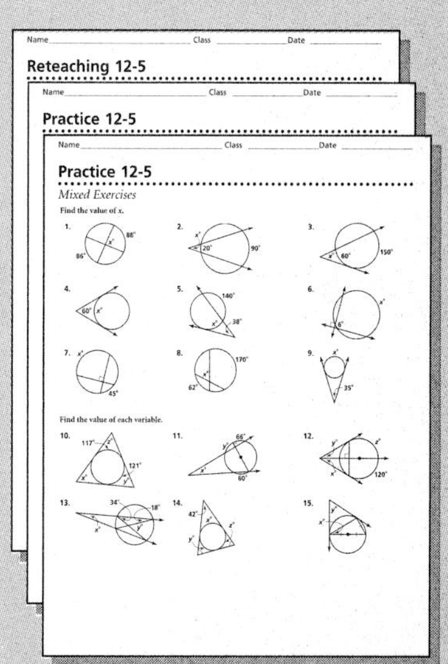

Lesson Quiz

Lesson Quiz is also available in Transparencies.

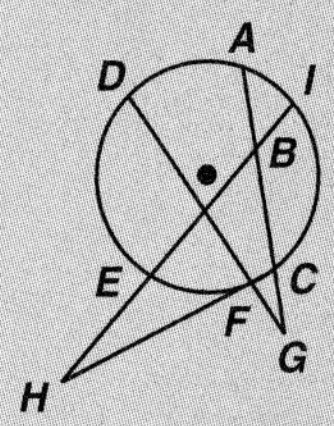

C is a point of tangency.

1. If $m\widehat{AI} = 60$ and $m\widehat{EC} = 100$, find $m\angle ABI$. 80

2. If $m\angle G = 30$ and $m\widehat{AD} = 90$, find $m\widehat{FC}$. 30

3. If $m\widehat{ECI} = 170$ and $m\widehat{EC} = 50$, find $m\angle IHC$. 35

Math ToolboX

Students explore the relationship between chord segments and the relationship between secant segments and external secant segments. These relationships will be presented formally in Lesson 12-6.

Using the geometry software allows students to manipulate their constructions so they can observe that the relationship between the segments does not depend on which segments they drew.

ERROR ALERT! Some students may measure the wrong segments or calculate the wrong products and, thus, reach the wrong conclusions. **Remediation:** Have students compare their results with those of other pairs or groups. Have them discuss any discrepancies.

ADDITIONAL PROBLEM Have students take turns drawing circles similar to those on page 620. Ask them to label the measurements of three of the four segments. Then have their partners or other group members find the length of the fourth segment.

Math ToolboX Technology

Exploring Chords and Secants

Before Lesson 12-6

Work in pairs or small groups.

Construct

Construct a circle with center A and two chords $\overline{BC}$ and $\overline{DE}$ that intersect each other at F. **Check students' work.**

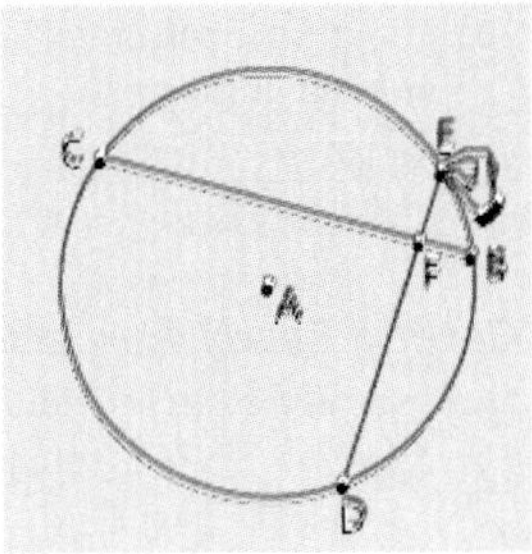

Investigate

Measure the segments $\overline{BF}$, $\overline{FC}$, $\overline{EF}$, and $\overline{FD}$. Use the calculator program of your software to find the products $BF \cdot FC$ and $EF \cdot FD$. Manipulate your construction and observe the products. What do you discover?
The 2 products are =.

Conjecture

Make a conjecture about the products of the lengths of the segments formed by the intersection of two chords in a circle.
The products of the lengths of segments formed by the intersection of 2 chords in a ⊙ are =.

Construct

Construct another circle and two secants that intersect in a point outside the circle. Label your construction as shown in the diagram.
Check students' work.

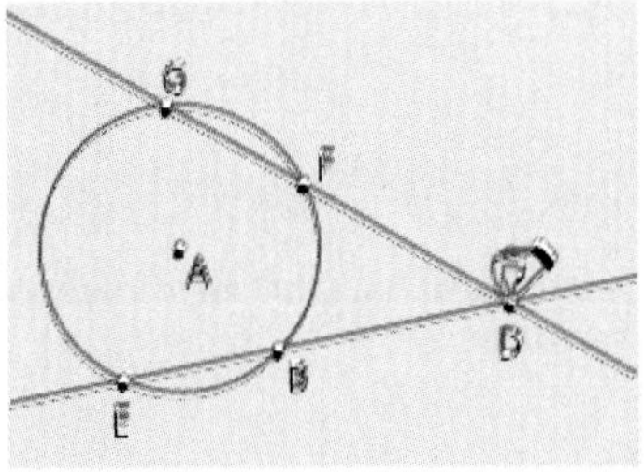

Investigate

Measure the segments $\overline{DG}$, $\overline{DF}$, $\overline{DE}$, and $\overline{DB}$. Calculate the products $DG \cdot DF$ and $DE \cdot DB$. Manipulate your construction and observe the products. What do you discover? **The 2 products are =.**

Conjecture

Make a **conjecture** about the products of the lengths of the segments formed by the intersection of two secants. **When 2 secants, such as $\overleftrightarrow{GF}$ and $\overleftrightarrow{EB}$ above, intersect at a point D outside the circle, $DG \cdot DF = DE \cdot DB$.**

Extend

Manipulate your construction so that secant $\overleftrightarrow{DG}$ becomes a tangent. What happens to the products you calculated? Can you explain how this special case is related to the case of two secants? **The product of the lengths of the segments formed by the secant is = to the square of the length of the tangent segment. When $\overleftrightarrow{DF}$ becomes tangent, pts. F and G coincide. So $DF \cdot DG = DF^2 = DG^2$.**

PROBLEM OF THE DAY

A circular sheet of paper of radius 12 cm is cut into three equal sectors. Each sector is then formed into a cone with no overlap. What is the height of each cone? $8\sqrt{2}$

Problem of the Day is also available in Transparencies.

CONNECTING TO PRIOR KNOWLEDGE Copy the triangles onto the board and ask students to explain why they are similar and then to write three proportions relating to the sides of the triangles.

WORK TOGETHER

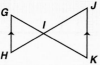

Question 2 Some students may have trouble measuring the length *t* because they have difficulty determining the exact point of tangency. Recommend that students use sharp pencils or fine-tipped pens to draw the circles and tangents. Advise them to draw large circles.

THINK AND DISCUSS

AUDITORY LEARNING Copy the three diagrams. Label the points where the segments intersect the circle or each other and have students practice naming segments of chords, secant segments, exterior secant segments and tangent segments.

Connections Architecture . . . and more

12-6 Circles and Lengths of Segments

What You'll Learn
- Finding the lengths of segments associated with circles

...And Why

To use the lengths of segments associated with circles in real-world applications such as architecture

What You'll Need
- ruler
- compass

WORK TOGETHER

Have members of your group draw two large circles. Draw and label segments as shown. Note that segment *t* is tangent to ⊙*Q*.

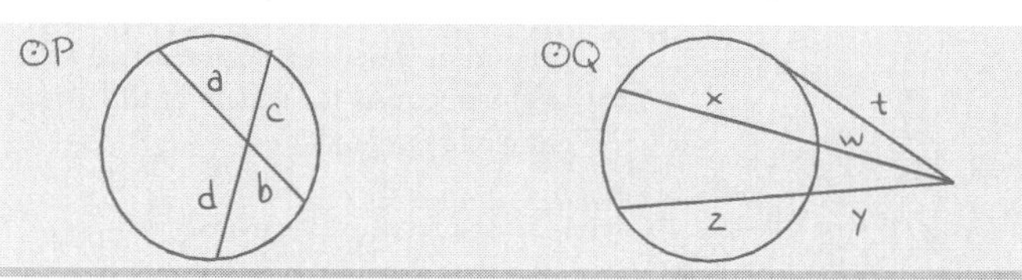

1. In ⊙*P*, measure lengths *a*, *b*, *c*, and *d*. Then find $a \cdot b$ and $c \cdot d$. What do you notice? Compare results within your group. $ab = cd$

TECHNOLOGY HINT

The Work Together could be done using geometry software.

2. **a.** In ⊙*Q*, measure lengths *w*, *x*, *y*, and *z*. Then find $(w + x)w$ and $(y + z)y$. What do you notice? Compare results within your group.
   b. Measure length *t*. Find t^2. What do you notice about t^2 and $(w + x)w$ and $(y + z)y$? Compare results within your group.
   a. $(w + x)w = (y + z)y$ b. t^2 is = to each product.

THINK AND DISCUSS

In the Work Together, you measured segments associated with circles. The diagram below will give you the vocabulary you need to refer to these segments.

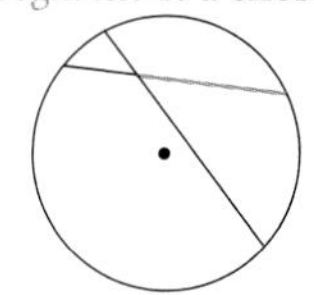

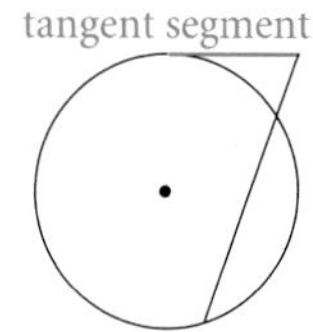

tangent segment

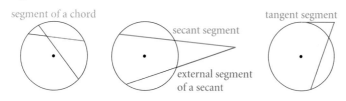

Your observations in the Work Together suggest the following theorems.

Theorem 12-14

If two chords intersect inside a circle, then the product of the lengths of the segments of one chord equals the product of the lengths of the segments of the other chord.

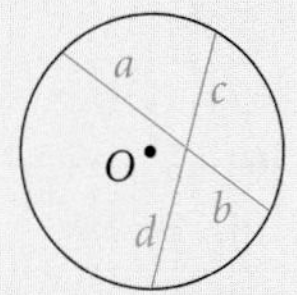

$$a \cdot b = c \cdot d$$

Lesson Planning Options

Prerequisite Skills
- Proving triangles similar

Assignment Options for Exercises On Your Own

Core 1–14, 16, 18–20
✪**Extension** 15, 17, 21

Use Mixed Review to maintain skills.

Resources

Student Edition

Skills Handbook, p. 664
Extra Practice, p. 659
Glossary/Study Guide

Teaching Resources

Chapter Support File, Ch. 12
- Practice 12-6 (two worksheets)
- Reteaching 12-6

Classroom Manager 12-6
Glossary, Spanish Resources

Transparencies
5, 11, 12, 122, 126

ESL Some students may have difficulty understanding the statements of Theorems 12-14, 12-15, and 12-16. Copy the diagrams onto a transparency and highlight each segment as you read through the theorems. Have students practice using the diagrams and the equations to state the theorems in their own words.

Example 1

ERROR ALERT! Some students may apply Theorem 12-14 to secant and tangent segments writing $8 \cdot 5 = y \cdot 4$ in part b, and $16 \cdot 8 = z^2$ in part c . **Remediation:** Display diagrams of the three theorems along with their equations. It may help students to write the theorem and the equation for each problem.

EXTENSION The *power of a point* in the exterior of a circle is the product of the lengths of a secant segment and its external secant segment for any secant drawn from that point. Have students draw several secant segments from the same point and calculate the power of the point for each of the segments. Students should discover that the products are the same.

Question 3 Have students begin by identifying the lengths of the segments of the chords, the secant segment, the external secant segment, and the tangent segment.

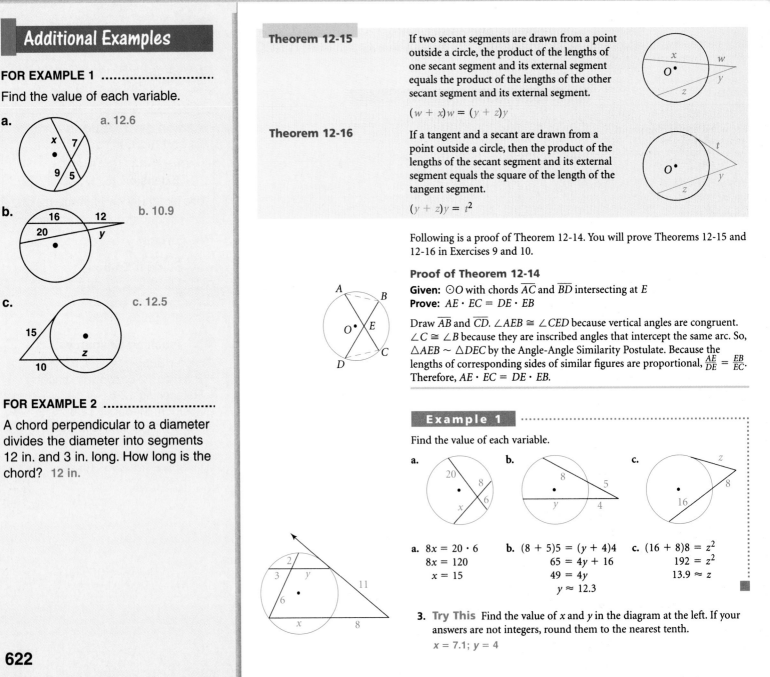

Additional Examples

FOR EXAMPLE 1

Find the value of each variable.

a.

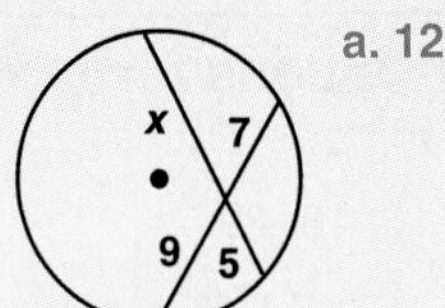

a. 12.6

b.

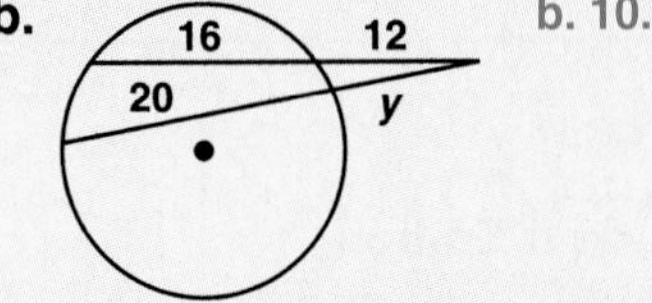

b. 10.9

c.

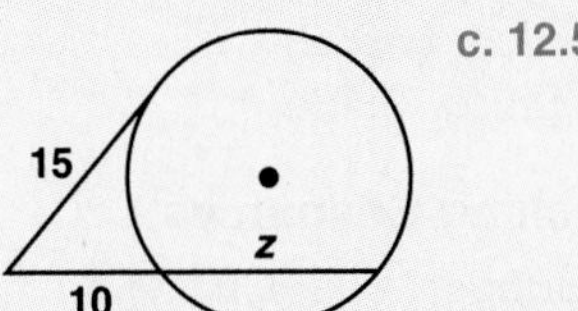

c. 12.5

FOR EXAMPLE 2

A chord perpendicular to a diameter divides the diameter into segments 12 in. and 3 in. long. How long is the chord? 12 in.

622

Theorem 12-15 If two secant segments are drawn from a point outside a circle, the product of the lengths of one secant segment and its external segment equals the product of the lengths of the other secant segment and its external segment.

$(w + x)w = (y + z)y$

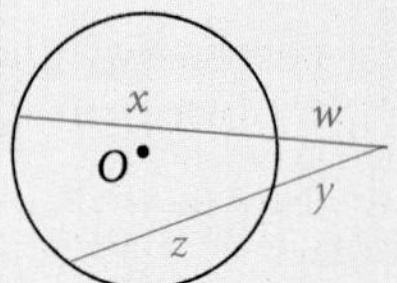

Theorem 12-16 If a tangent and a secant are drawn from a point outside a circle, then the product of the lengths of the secant segment and its external segment equals the square of the length of the tangent segment.

$(y + z)y = t^2$

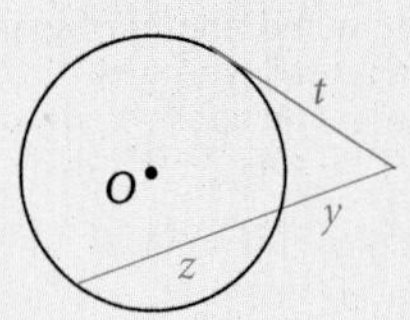

Following is a proof of Theorem 12-14. You will prove Theorems 12-15 and 12-16 in Exercises 9 and 10.

Proof of Theorem 12-14

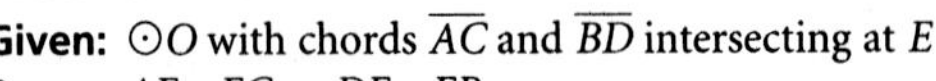

Given: ⊙O with chords $\overline{AC}$ and $\overline{BD}$ intersecting at E

Prove: $AE \cdot EC = DE \cdot EB$

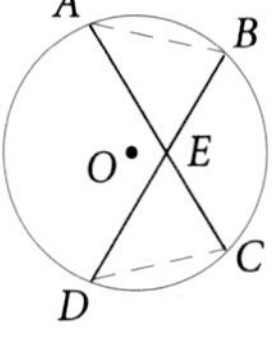

Draw $\overline{AB}$ and $\overline{CD}$. $\angle AEB \cong \angle CED$ because vertical angles are congruent. $\angle C \cong \angle B$ because they are inscribed angles that intercept the same arc. So, $\triangle AEB \sim \triangle DEC$ by the Angle-Angle Similarity Postulate. Because the lengths of corresponding sides of similar figures are proportional, $\frac{AE}{DE} = \frac{EB}{EC}$. Therefore, $AE \cdot EC = DE \cdot EB$.

Example 1

Find the value of each variable.

a.

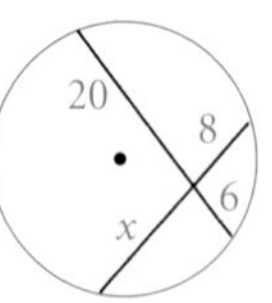

b.

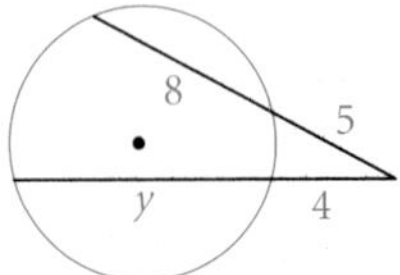

c.

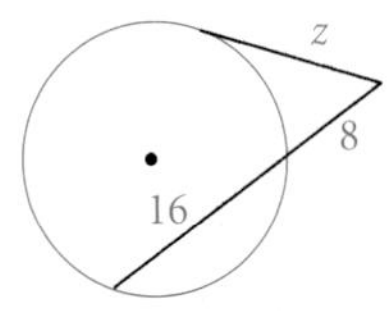

a. $8x = 20 \cdot 6$
$8x = 120$
$x = 15$

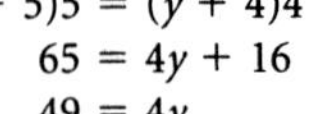

b. $(8 + 5)5 = (y + 4)4$
$65 = 4y + 16$
$49 = 4y$
$y \approx 12.3$

c. $(16 + 8)8 = z^2$
$192 = z^2$
$13.9 \approx z$

3. Try This Find the value of x and y in the diagram at the left. If your answers are not integers, round them to the nearest tenth.
$x = 7.1$; $y = 4$

Example 2 Relating to the Real World 

Make sure students understand why 70 was added to 321.4 to find the diameter. Also make sure students see that the radius is half the diameter, not half of *x*.

DIVERSITY The history of bridges may fascinate some students. Have students research the longest bridge, the oldest bridge, or the fastest bridge ever built. Have them highlight the contributions made by bridge builders in India, Turkey, Japan, England, France, and Canada.

KINESTHETIC LEARNING If you have block scheduling or an extended class period, take students to the gymnasium. Use a circle on the basketball court. Have one student stand outside the circle holding two pieces of string. Have two other students stand on the circle, each holding an end of one of the pieces of string. Then have other students measure the lengths of the tangent segments and secant segments formed by the string. Have students calculate the appropriate products and discuss whether their results support Theorem 12-5 or Theorem 12-6. Have the students standing on the circle move to different positions and repeat the activity.

Exercises ON YOUR OWN

ALTERNATIVE ASSESSMENT **Exercises 1–6** You can use these exercises to assess students' understanding of Theorems 12-14, 12-15, and 12-16 by their ability to find the missing lengths. Have students work in groups of three and take turns recording the solutions to the problems.

You can use the theorems in the lesson to solve real-world problems.

Example 2 Relating to the Real World 

Architecture The arch of a pedestrian bridge that crosses the San Antonio River is an arc of a circle. Find the radius of the circle.

The 300-ft chord is bisected by the perpendicular from the midpoint of the arch. Draw a sketch showing the chords of a circle. Then find the value of the unknown segment of the diameter.

$$70x = 150 \cdot 150$$
$$70x = 22{,}500$$
$$x \approx 321.4$$
$$\text{diameter} \approx 70 + 321.4 = 391.4 \text{ ft}$$
$$\text{radius} \approx 195.7 \text{ ft}$$

The radius is about 196 ft.

4. **Critical Thinking** Explain why the chord that contains the 70-ft segment is a diameter of the circle.
The $\perp$ bisector of a chord contains the center of the $\odot$.

Technology Options

For Exercise 21c, students may perform the constructions using construction tools in geometry software.

Prentice Hall Technology 

Software
- Secondary Math Lab Toolkit™
- Computer Item Generator 12-6

Internet
- See the Prentice Hall site. (http://www.phschool.com)

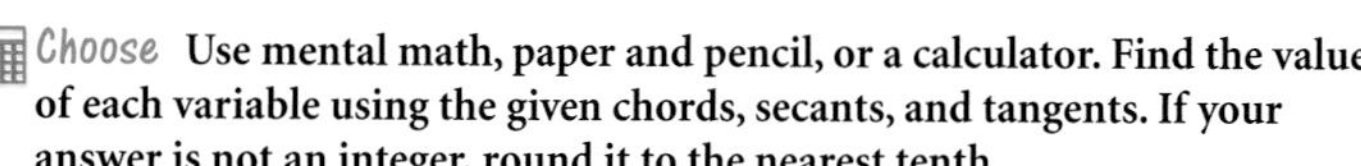

Exercises ON YOUR OWN

Choose **Use mental math, paper and pencil, or a calculator. Find the value of each variable using the given chords, secants, and tangents. If your answer is not an integer, round it to the nearest tenth.**

1. 11.5
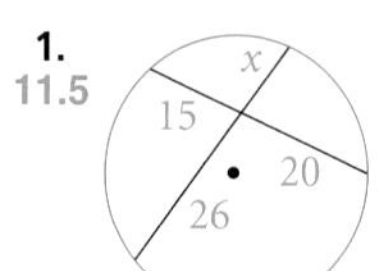
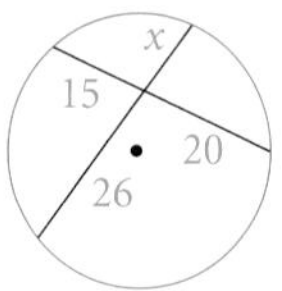

2. 13.8
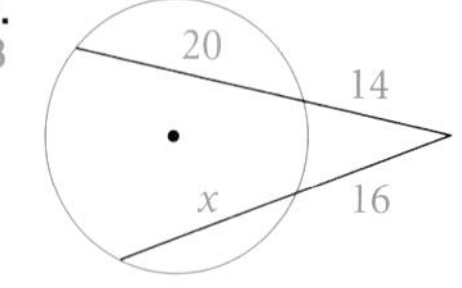

3. 7.8
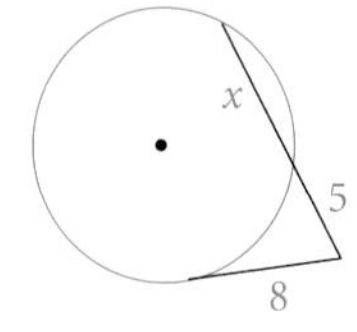

4. 3.5
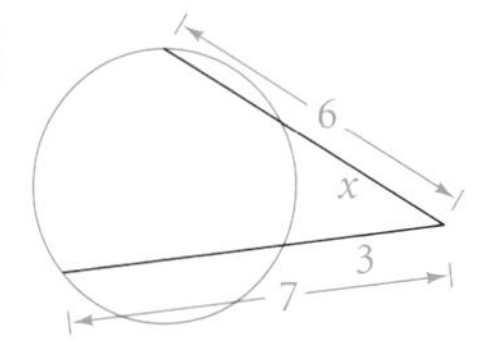

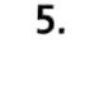

5.
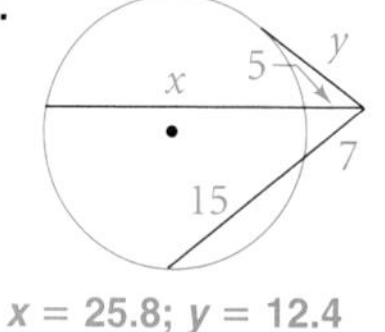

$x = 25.8$; $y = 12.4$

6.
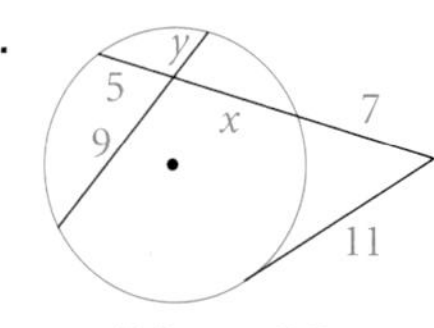

$x = 5.3$; $y = 2.9$

Exercise 7 Help students see that this problem is similar to Example 2 and have them model the solution steps.

Exercise 8 Have students compare their methods of solving this problem. This exercise provides a good opportunity to review problem-solving strategies.

Exercise 12 Students must recognize that a diameter perpendicular to a chord bisects the chord in order to solve this problem.

ERROR ALERT! **Exercise 13** Some students may think that there is not enough information to solve this problem. **Remediation:** Suggest students copy the diagram and draw the chords. Then hint that they should use the Pythagorean Theorem and Theorem 12-7.

Exercise 15 Make sure students correctly label the distance from the space craft to Jupiter on their diagrams.

pages 623–625 On Your Own

9. 1. $\overline{AC}$ and $\overline{BC}$ are secants of $\odot O$. (Given) 2. $\angle CAE \cong \angle CBD$ (2 inscribed $\angle$s that intercept the same arc are $\cong$.) 3. $\angle ACE \cong \angle DCB$ (Reflexive Prop. of $\cong$) 4. $\triangle AEC \sim \triangle BDC$ (AA$\sim$) 5. $\frac{EC}{DC} = \frac{AC}{BC}$ (In similar figures, corres. sides are proportional.) 6. $BC \cdot EC = AC \cdot DC$ (Prop. of Proportions)

10. 1. $\overline{AC}$ is a tangent and $\overline{BC}$ is a secant of $\odot O$. (Given) 2. $m\angle ABC = \frac{1}{2}m\widehat{AD}$ (The measure of an inscribed $\angle$ is half the measure of its intercepted arc.) 3. $m\angle DAC = \frac{1}{2}m\widehat{AD}$ (The measure of an $\angle$ formed by a chord and a tangent that intersect on a $\odot$ is half the measure of the intercepted arc.) 4. $m\angle ABC = m\angle DAC$ (Transitive Prop. of =) 5. $\angle ACB \cong \angle DCA$ (Reflexive Prop. of $\cong$) 6. $\triangle BAC \sim \triangle ADC$ (AA$\sim$) 7. $\frac{AC}{DC} = \frac{BC}{AC}$ (In similar figures, corres. sides are proportional.) 8. $BC \cdot DC = AC^2$ (Prop. of Proportions)

7. *Geology* This natural arch, in Arches National Park, Utah, is an arc of a circle. Find the diameter of the circle. about 271 ft

30 ft
170 ft

8. Two chords of a circle intersect. The segments of the first chord are 16 cm and 18 cm long. The lengths of the segments of the second chord are in the ratio 2 : 1. Find the lengths of the segments of the second chord. 24 cm and 12 cm

Choose **Write a two-column proof, paragraph proof, or flow proof.** 9–10. Answers may vary. See margin for samples.

9. Prove Theorem 12-15.

Given: $\odot O$ with secants $\overline{AC}$ and $\overline{BC}$ (Chords $\overline{AE}$ and $\overline{BD}$ are drawn for you.)
Prove: $BC \cdot EC = AC \cdot DC$

Plan for Proof: In order to use the properties of proportions, prove $\triangle AEC \sim \triangle BDC$.

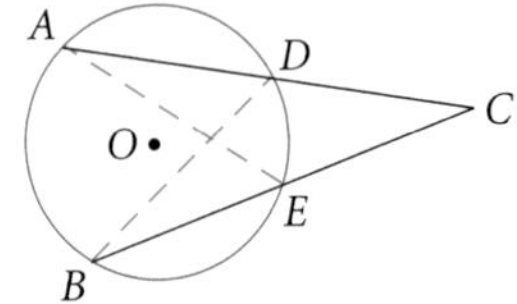

10. Prove Theorem 12-16.

Given: $\odot O$ with tangent $\overline{AC}$ and secant $\overline{BC}$ (Chords $\overline{AB}$ and $\overline{AD}$ are drawn for you.)
Prove: $BC \cdot DC = AC^2$

Plan for Proof: In order to use the properties of proportions, prove $\triangle BAC \sim \triangle ADC$.

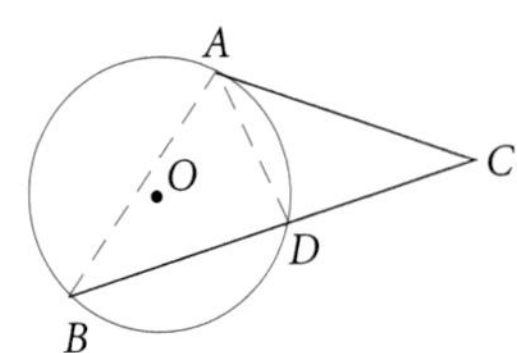

Find the diameter of $\odot O$ given the chords, secants, and tangents. Round your answer to the nearest tenth.

11. 26.7

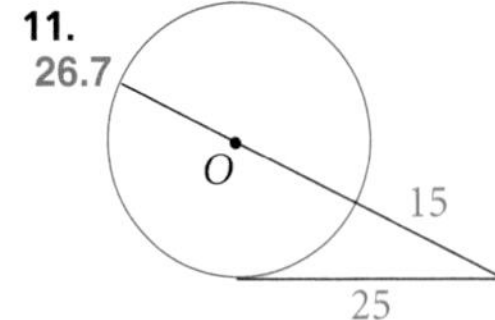

12. 16.7

8
6
O

13. 14.1

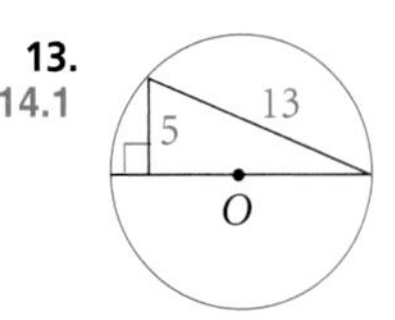

14. *Standardized Test Prep* $\overline{AB}$ is tangent to $\odot O$ at A. $\overline{AB} \perp \overline{EB}$. $AB = BF$. $BC = 1$ and $CE = 7$. Find AF. C

A. 2 B. $3\frac{1}{2}$ C. 4
D. $4\frac{1}{3}$ E. none of the above

15. *Space Exploration* The line of sight from an object above a planet to the horizon of the planet is a tangent line. The *Galileo* orbiter is a spacecraft that circles 133,300 mi above Jupiter. Jupiter's diameter is 88,700 mi. What is the distance from the *Galileo* orbiter to Jupiter's horizon? Round your answer to the nearest hundred miles. 172,000 mi

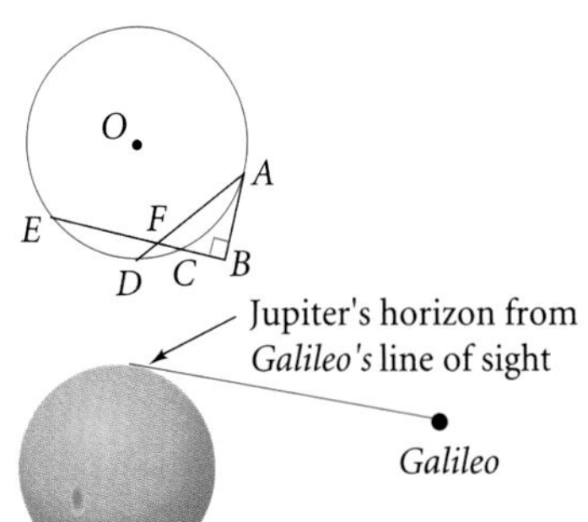

WRITING Exercise 16 You may want to ask students to write the correct equation.

OPEN-ENDED Exercise 17 Suggest that students choose points near the center of the circle and points near the boundary of the circle.

RESEARCH Exercise 21 You may want to ask students to research which car companies have experimented with using Wankel engines, what the advantages and disadvantages of a Wankel engine are, who invented the Wankel engine, and when it was invented.

Exercise 22 Suggest that students draw a diagram.

16. *Writing* To find the value of x, a student wrote the equation $(7.5)6 = x^2$. What error did the student make? **See margin.**

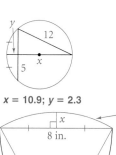

17. a. *Open-ended* Draw a circle. Place a point inside the circle. Draw a chord through the point. Measure the segments of the chord that you drew. Find the product of the lengths.
    b. Choose three other points. Find the product of the lengths of the segments of a chord through each of these points. **a–b. Check students' work.**
    c. *Patterns* Use your answers to parts (a) and (b) to make a **conjecture.** What point inside a circle has the greatest product of the lengths of segments of chords?

17c. The center has the greatest product of the lengths of the segments of chords passing through it.

Find the value of x and y using the given chords, secants, and tangents. If your answer is not an integer, round to the nearest tenth.

18. 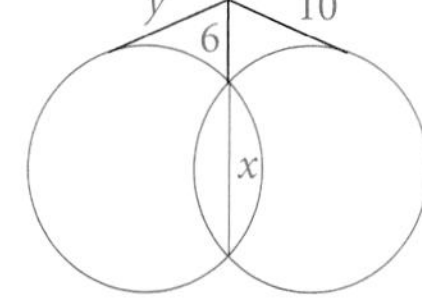

$x = 10.7$; $y = 10$

19. 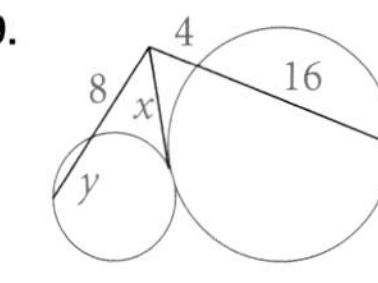

$x = 8.9$; $y = 2$

20. $x = 10.9$; $y = 2.3$

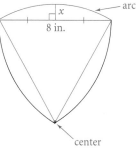

21. a. *Engineering* The basis of a design of a rotor for a Wankel engine is an equilateral triangle. Each side of the triangle is a chord of an arc of a circle. The center of each circle is a vertex of the triangle. In the diagram at the right, each side of the equilateral triangle is 8 in. long. Find the value of x to the nearest tenth. **1.1 in.**
    b. *Research* Rotary engines are used in some snowmobiles. Find other uses of rotary engines. **Check students' work.**
    c. *Constructions* Construct an equilateral triangle. Then construct the arcs to draw a rotor. **See below right.**

22. *Calculator* The diameter of a circle is 24 cm. A chord perpendicular to the diameter is 5 cm from the center of the circle. What is the length of the chord? Round your answer to the nearest tenth. **21.8 cm**

23. Following is a proof of the Pythagorean Theorem that uses a theorem presented in this lesson. Supply the missing reasons.

Given: $\odot O$ with tangent $\overline{PQ}$

Prove: $a^2 + b^2 = c^2$

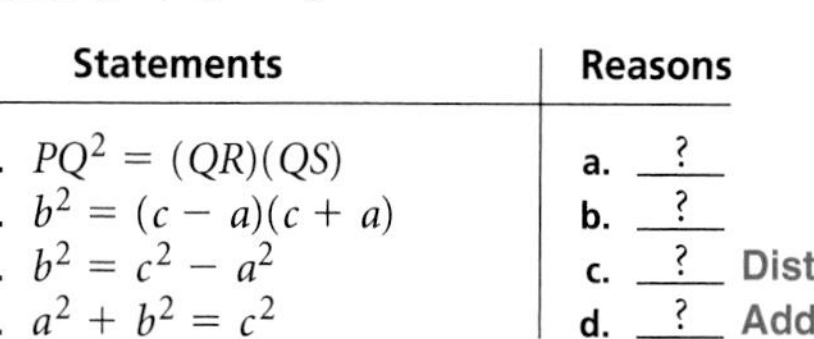

Statements	Reasons
1. $PQ^2 = (QR)(QS)$	a. ?
2. $b^2 = (c - a)(c + a)$	b. ?
3. $b^2 = c^2 - a^2$	c. ? **Distributive Prop.**
4. $a^2 + b^2 = c^2$	d. ? **Addition Prop. of =**

a. See margin. **b. Substitution**

21c.

16. The student should have used the length of the whole secant, 13.5, instead of the length of the internal segment, 7.5.

23a. If a tangent and a secant are drawn from a pt. outside a $\odot$, then the product of the lengths of the secant segment and its external segment = the square of the length of the tangent segment.

Exercises MIXED REVIEW

PORTFOLIO Share with students the criteria you will use to assess their work in portfolios, as well as how you plan to use the results. Students should understand how the rubrics assess their work, how each piece in the portfolio counts, and how the scores they get in their portfolios will affect their overall evaluation.

Wrap Up

THE BIG IDEA Ask students to summarize how to find the lengths of chord segments, secant segments, and tangent segments.

RETEACHING ACTIVITY Students find the lengths of segments associated with circles. (Reteaching worksheet 12-6)

Geometry at Work

For further information about aerospace engineering, have students contact NASA, the U.S. Department of Defense, or space centers such as the Johnson Space Center in Texas or the Marshall Space Flight Center in Alabama. Encourage students to investigate these topics:

- the training necessary to become an aerospace engineer
- systems engineering and operations research, and their role in the manufacture of aerospace equipment
- the history and development of the aerospace industry and artificial satellites

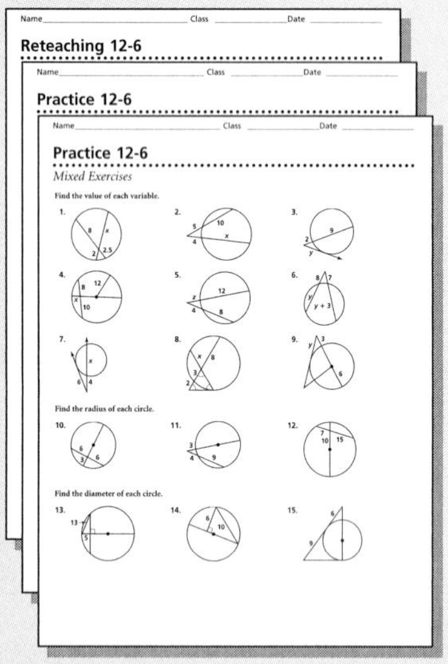
Reteaching 12-6

Practice 12-6

Practice 12-6

Mixed Exercises

Find the value of each variable.

Find the radius of each circle.

Find the diameter of each circle.

Lesson Quiz

Lesson Quiz is also available in Transparencies.

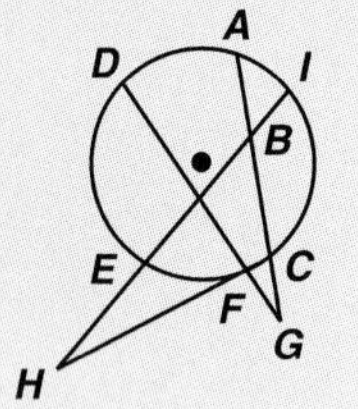

C is a point of tangency.

1. If $AB = 10$, $BC = 8$, and $IB = 5$, find BE. **16**
2. If $HI = 24$ and $EI = 16$, find HC. **13.9**
3. If $DF = 12$, $FG = 8$, and $CG = 6$, find AG. **20.7**

Exercises MIXED REVIEW

Find the value of *x* to the nearest tenth.

24.

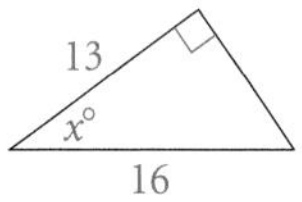

35.7

25.

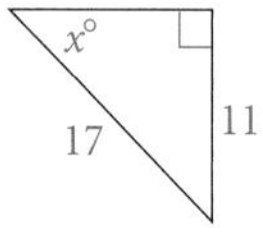

40.3

26. a. *Calculator* A ball has circumference 60 cm. What is its radius? Round your answer to the nearest millimeter. **9.5 cm or 95 mm**

b. What is the length of an edge of the smallest box that could contain this ball? **19.1 cm**

PORTFOLIO

For your portfolio, select one or two items from your work for this chapter. Here are some possibilities:
- corrected work
- a journal entry
- results from a Work Together activity

Explain why you have included each selection.

Geometry at Work

Aerospace Engineer

Aerospace engineers design and build all types of spacecraft, from the low-orbit space shuttle to interplanetary probes. Much of today's aerospace work involves communications satellites that relay TV, telephone, computer, and other signals to receivers around the world. The portion of Earth's surface that can communicate with a satellite increases as the height of the orbit increases.

The figure shows a satellite 12,000 miles above Earth, which has a radius of about 3960 miles. $\overset{\frown}{AB}$ is the arc of Earth that is in the range of the satellite. You can find $m\overset{\frown}{AB}$ by finding $m\angle AEB$, which is twice $m\angle AES$.

cosine of $\angle AES = \frac{AE}{SE} = \frac{3960}{3960 + 12{,}000} \approx 0.2481$

$m\angle AES \approx \cos^{-1}(0.2481) \approx 75.63$

$m\overset{\frown}{AB} = m\angle AEB \approx 2 \cdot 75.63 \approx 151.3$

The arc of Earth in the range of the satellite is about 151.3°.

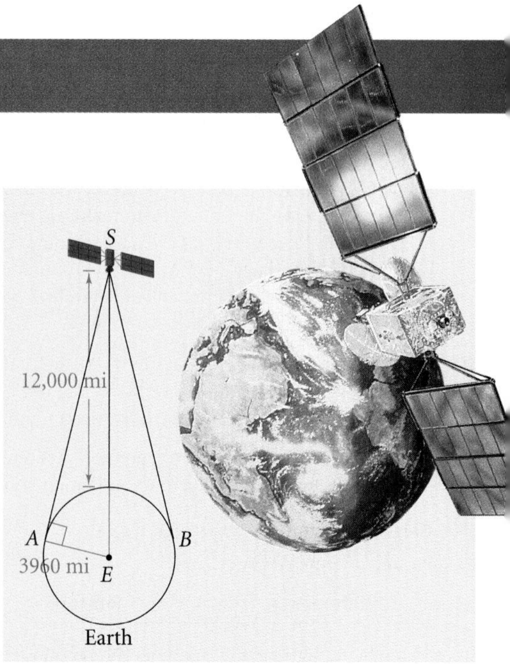

Mini Project: A geosynchronous orbit is used by communications satellites. Research geosynchronous orbits. Find the height of a geosynchronous orbit and find the arc of Earth that is in the range of a satellite in a geosynchronous orbit.

Finishing the Chapter Project

PROJECT DAY You may wish to plan a project day on which students share their completed projects. Encourage groups to explain their processes as well as their products.

PROJECT NOTEBOOK Have students review their project work and bring their notebooks up to date.

- Have students review both their designs and their instructions to draw them.
- Ask groups to share the techniques they used to create their designs, any experimentations with other designs, and how they made improvements in their designs.

SCORING RUBRIC

3 Student's design shows creativity and has a clearly defined purpose. Student's instructions are clear and easy to follow. Student accurately explains the geometric concepts incorporated in the design.

2 Student's design shows some creativity and has a stated purpose. Student's instructions are clear enough to follow. Student explains with only minor errors the geometric concepts incorporated in the design.

1 Student's design shows little creativity and its purpose is unclear. Student's instructions lack organization and are hard to follow. Student explains the geometric concepts incorporated in the design, but with major errors.

0 Major elements are incomplete or missing.

Finishing the Chapter Project

CHAPTER PROJECT

GO FOR A SPIN

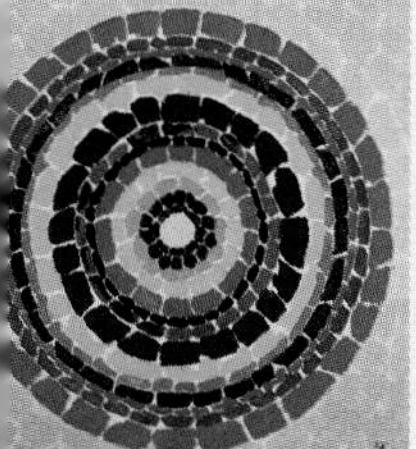

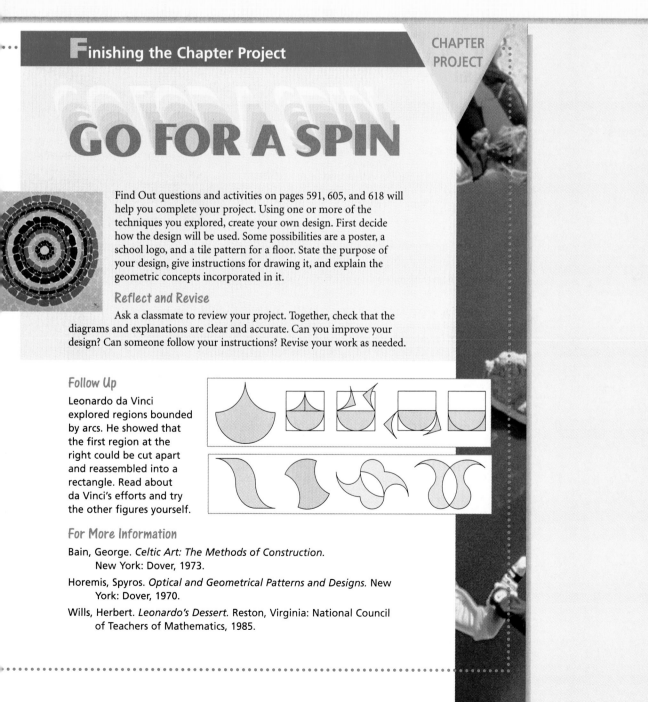

Find Out questions and activities on pages 591, 605, and 618 will help you complete your project. Using one or more of the techniques you explored, create your own design. First decide how the design will be used. Some possibilities are a poster, a school logo, and a tile pattern for a floor. State the purpose of your design, give instructions for drawing it, and explain the geometric concepts incorporated in it.

Reflect and Revise

Ask a classmate to review your project. Together, check that the diagrams and explanations are clear and accurate. Can you improve your design? Can someone follow your instructions? Revise your work as needed.

Follow Up

Leonardo da Vinci explored regions bounded by arcs. He showed that the first region at the right could be cut apart and reassembled into a rectangle. Read about da Vinci's efforts and try the other figures yourself.

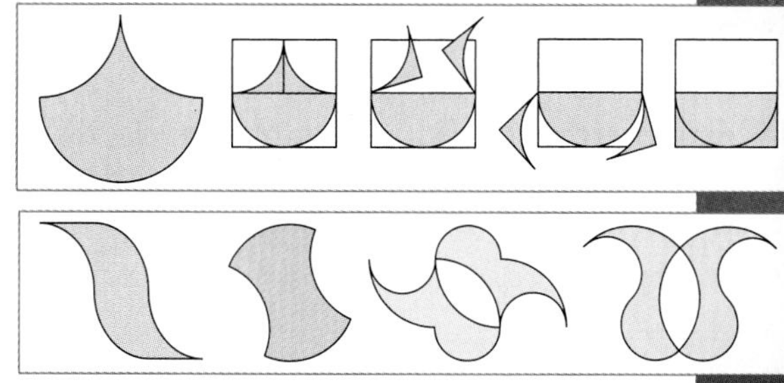

For More Information

Bain, George. *Celtic Art: The Methods of Construction.* New York: Dover, 1973.

Horemis, Spyros. *Optical and Geometrical Patterns and Designs.* New York: Dover, 1970.

Wills, Herbert. *Leonardo's Dessert.* Reston, Virginia: National Council of Teachers of Mathematics, 1985.

Wrap Up

HOW AM I DOING? Divide the class into six groups with each group reviewing a different lesson. Ask each group to make a short presentation explaining the key ideas of the lesson. Each presentation must include a visual aid and a sample problem.

KEY TERMS The numbers in parentheses direct students to the pages where the terms are used or defined. Students should be able to (1) write a simple explanation of each term, (2) illustrate the term with a diagram, or (3) show an example that uses the term.

STANDARDIZED TEST TIP **Exercise 7** Students can save valuable time by realizing that they do not need to graph any circles, but need only consider the radii.

Resources

Student Edition
Extra Practice, p. 645
Glossary/Study Guide

Teaching Resources
Study Skills Handbook
Glossary, Spanish Resources

12 Wrap Up

Key Terms

How am I doing?

- State three ideas from this chapter that you think are important. Explain your choices.
- Describe the properties of different segments of a circle.

Circles in the Coordinate Plane — 12-1

The **standard form of an equation of a circle** with center (h, k) and radius r is $(x - h)^2 + (y - k)^2 = r^2$.

If you know the center and a point on a circle, you can find an equation of the circle. Find the radius by using the Distance Formula to find the distance from the center to the given point. Then substitute the coordinates of the center for (h, k) and the radius for r in the standard form of the equation of a circle.

Find an equation of a circle with the given center and radius.

1. center $= (2, 5)$; $r = 3$ — $(x - 2)^2 + (y - 5)^2 = 9$
2. center $= (-3, 1)$; $r = \sqrt{5}$ — $(x + 3)^2 + (y - 1)^2 = 5$
3. center $= (9, -4)$; $r = 3.5$ — $(x - 9)^2 + (y + 4)^2 = 12.25$

Find an equation of the circle with the given center passing through the given point.

4. center $(0, 1)$, through $(4, 9)$ — $x^2 + (y - 1)^2 = 80$
5. center $(-2, 3)$, through $(4, -4)$ — $(x + 2)^2 + (y - 3)^2 = 85$
6. center $(10, 7)$, through $(-8, -5)$ — $(x - 10)^2 + (y - 7)^2 = 468$
7. *Standardized Test Prep* Which circle has the least area? E

   A. $(x - 1)^2 + (y - 3)^2 = 4$ B. $(x + 2)^2 + y^2 = 7$ C. $x^2 + (y - 5)^2 = 9$
   D. $x^2 + y^2 = 10$ E. $(x + 3)^2 + (y + 2)^2 = 3$

Properties of Tangents — 12-2

A **tangent to a circle** is a line, ray, or segment in the plane of the circle that intersects the circle in exactly one point, the **point of tangency**.

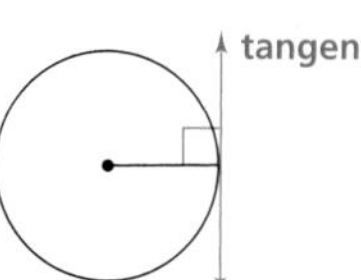

If a line is tangent to a circle, then the line is perpendicular to the radius drawn to the point of tangency. If a line is perpendicular to a radius at its endpoint on the circle, then the line is tangent to the circle.

Two segments tangent to a circle from a point outside the circle are congruent.

ERROR ALERT! **Exercises 8-10** Some students may think that the point of tangency bisects the side of the polygons. **Remediation.** Help students see that two tangents *drawn from the same point outside the circle* are congruent.

Each polygon circumscribes a circle. Find the perimeter of the polygon.

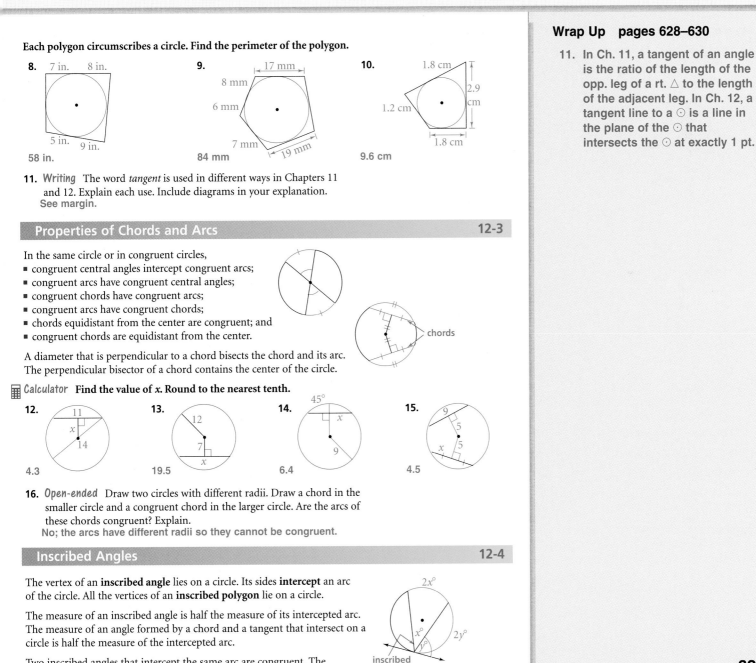

8. 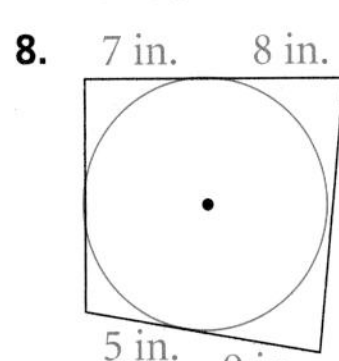

58 in.

9. 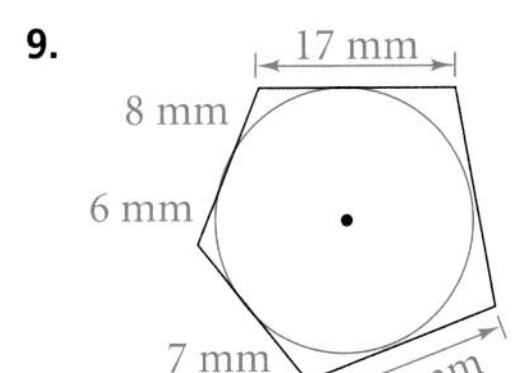

84 mm

10. 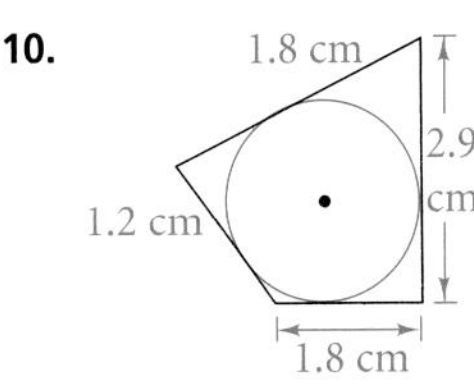

9.6 cm

11. *Writing* The word *tangent* is used in different ways in Chapters 11 and 12. Explain each use. Include diagrams in your explanation.
See margin.

Properties of Chords and Arcs 12-3

In the same circle or in congruent circles,
- congruent central angles intercept congruent arcs;
- congruent arcs have congruent central angles;
- congruent chords have congruent arcs;
- congruent arcs have congruent chords;
- chords equidistant from the center are congruent; and
- congruent chords are equidistant from the center.

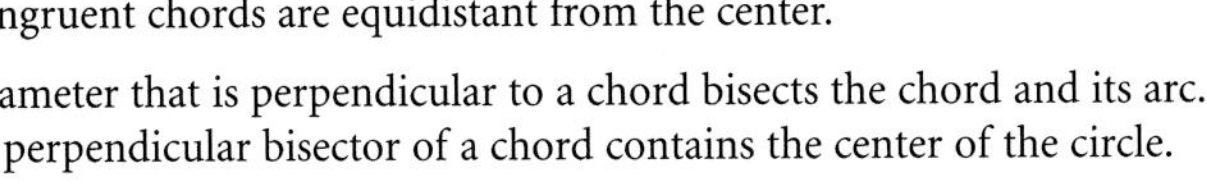

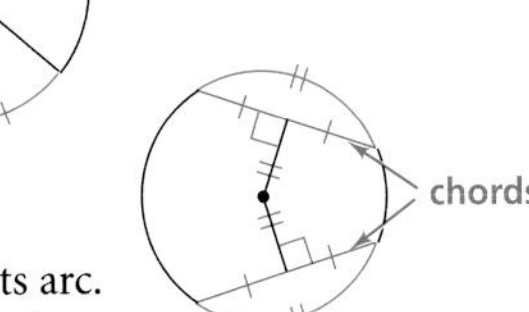

A diameter that is perpendicular to a chord bisects the chord and its arc. The perpendicular bisector of a chord contains the center of the circle.

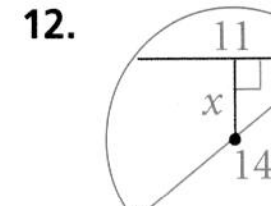 *Calculator* **Find the value of x. Round to the nearest tenth.**

12. 

4.3

13. 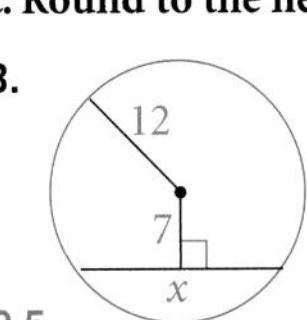

19.5

14. 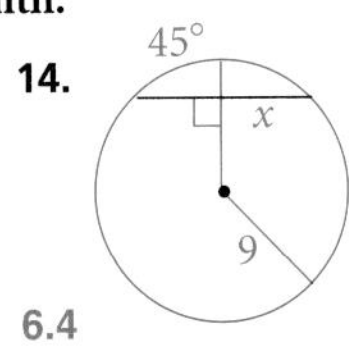

6.4

15. 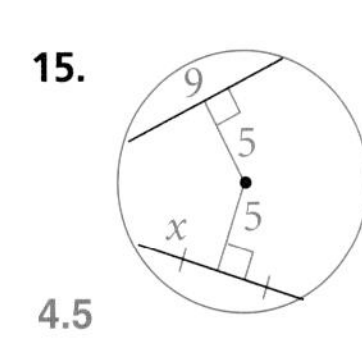

4.5

16. *Open-ended* Draw two circles with different radii. Draw a chord in the smaller circle and a congruent chord in the larger circle. Are the arcs of these chords congruent? Explain.
No; the arcs have different radii so they cannot be congruent.

Inscribed Angles 12-4

The vertex of an **inscribed angle** lies on a circle. Its sides **intercept** an arc of the circle. All the vertices of an **inscribed polygon** lie on a circle.

The measure of an inscribed angle is half the measure of its intercepted arc. The measure of an angle formed by a chord and a tangent that intersect on a circle is half the measure of the intercepted arc.

Two inscribed angles that intercept the same arc are congruent. The opposite angles of a quadrilateral inscribed in a circle are supplementary.

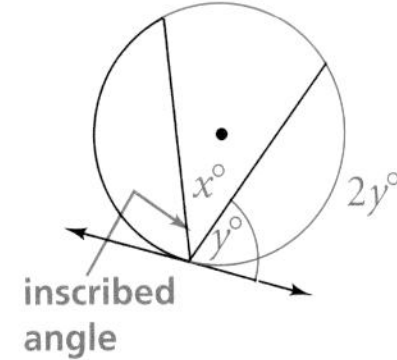

Wrap Up pages 628–630

11. In Ch. 11, a tangent of an angle is the ratio of the length of the opp. leg of a rt. △ to the length of the adjacent leg. In Ch. 12, a tangent line to a ⊙ is a line in the plane of the ⊙ that intersects the ⊙ at exactly 1 pt.

ALTERNATIVE ASSESSMENT **Exercises 17–28** Have students work in groups. Assign each group one problem from each section to solve. Then have them create and solve three problems that incorporate the concepts from each lesson.

Remind students that the new mathematical terms in this chapter are defined in the Glossary/Study Guide in the back of the book.

Assessment page 631

8a–b.

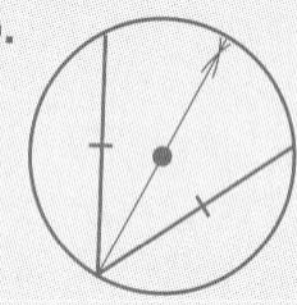

b. The center lies on the angle bisector.

11.

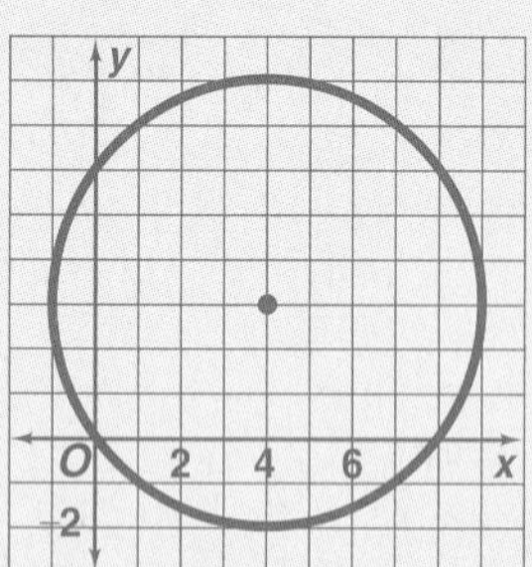

21. A rhombus inscribed in a ⊙ is a square. Opp. ∠s of a quad. inscr. in a ⊙ are suppl. (Corollary 3). Opp ∠s of a rhombus are ≅. So all the ∠s must be right ∠s. All the sides of a rhombus are ≅, so the rhombus must be a square.

Assume that lines that appear tangent are tangent. Find the value of each variable. 18. $a = 118$; $b = 49$; $c = 144$; $d = 98$

$a = 90$; $b = 90$; $c = 70$; $d = 65$

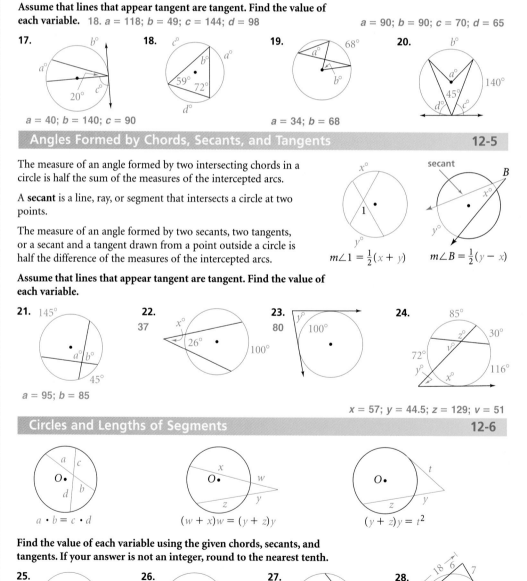

17.

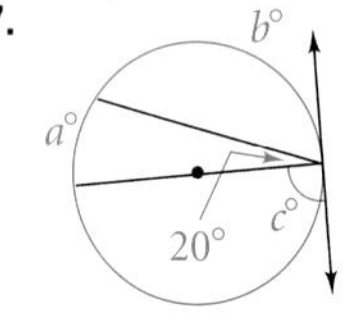

$a = 40$; $b = 140$; $c = 90$

18.

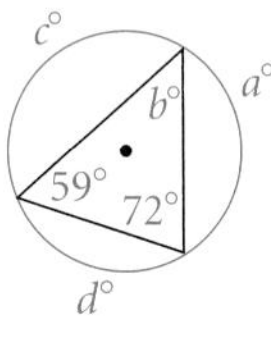

19.

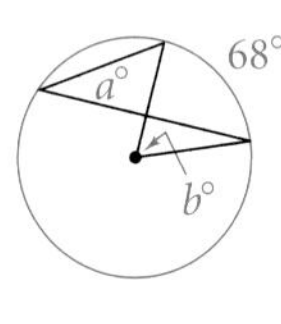

$a = 34$; $b = 68$

20.

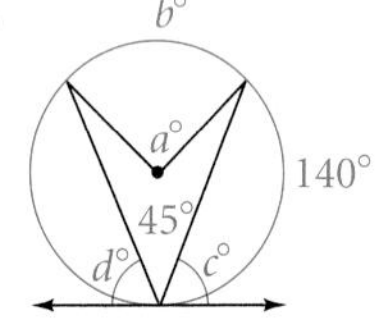

Angles Formed by Chords, Secants, and Tangents 12-5

The measure of an angle formed by two intersecting chords in a circle is half the sum of the measures of the intercepted arcs.

A **secant** is a line, ray, or segment that intersects a circle at two points.

The measure of an angle formed by two secants, two tangents, or a secant and a tangent drawn from a point outside a circle is half the difference of the measures of the intercepted arcs.

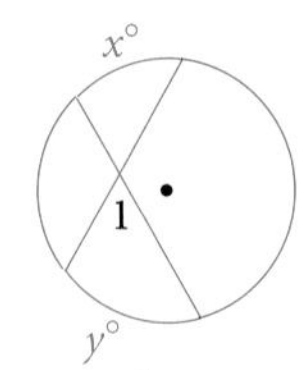

$m\angle 1 = \frac{1}{2}(x + y)$

secant B x° y°

$m\angle B = \frac{1}{2}(y - x)$

Assume that lines that appear tangent are tangent. Find the value of each variable.

21.

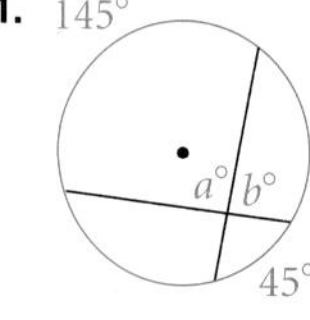

$a = 95$; $b = 85$

22. 37

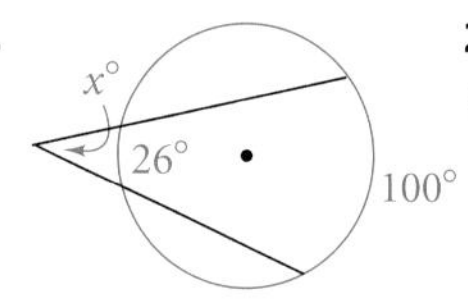

23. 80

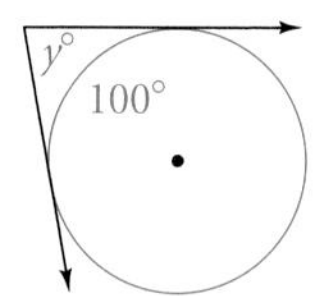

24.

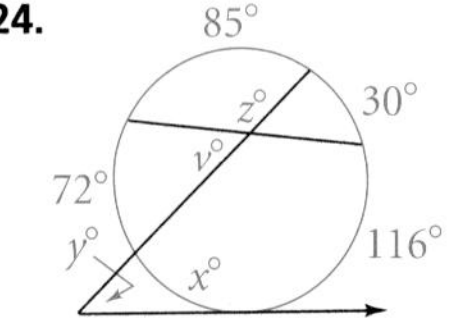

$x = 57$; $y = 44.5$; $z = 129$; $v = 51$

Circles and Lengths of Segments 12-6

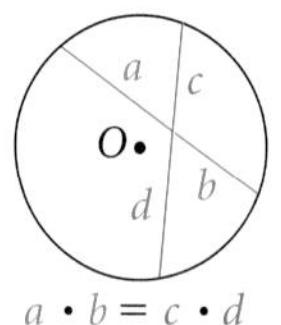

$a \cdot b = c \cdot d$

$(w + x)w = (y + z)y$

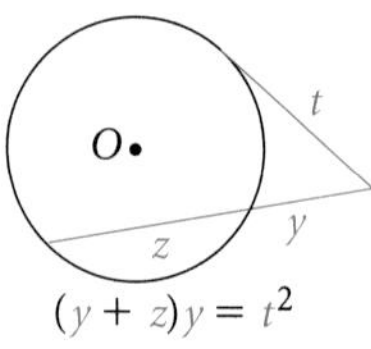

$(y + z)y = t^2$

Find the value of each variable using the given chords, secants, and tangents. If your answer is not an integer, round to the nearest tenth.

25. 9.5

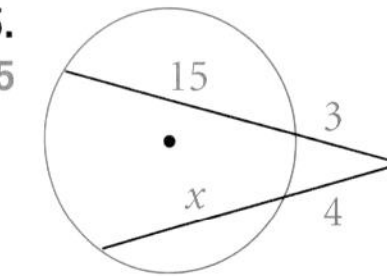

26. 4

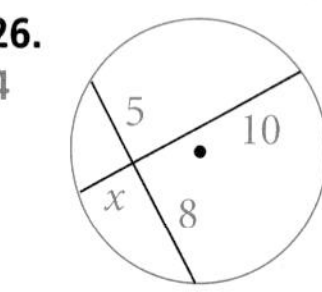

27. 17.1

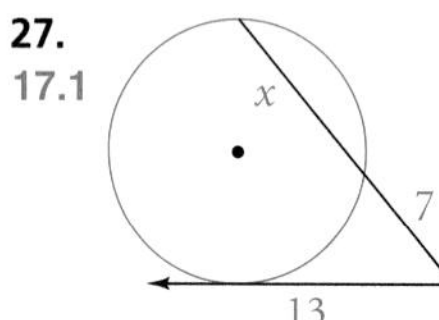

28. 8.4

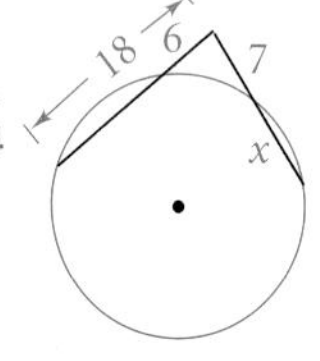

Assessment

ENHANCED MULTIPLE CHOICE QUESTIONS are more complex than traditional multiple choice questions, which assess only one skill. Enhanced multiple choice questions assess the processes that students use, as well as the end results. The questions are written so that students use more than one strategy to solve the problem. Using multiple strategies is encouraged by the National Council of Teachers of Mathematics (NCTM). **Exercise 14** is an enhanced multiple choice question.

FREE RESPONSE QUESTIONS do not give answer choices. Some exercises have more than one possible answer. Students need to give only one correct response. **Exercises 1–7, 9–13, and 15–20** are free response questions.

WRITING EXERCISES allow students to describe how they think about and understand the concepts they have learned. **Exercise 21** is a writing exercise.

OPEN-ENDED PROBLEMS allow for more than one solution. Students must construct their own responses instead of choosing from possible answers. The students' responses will help you determine the depth of their understanding and any possible areas of difficulty. **Exercise 8** is an open-ended problem.

12 Assessment

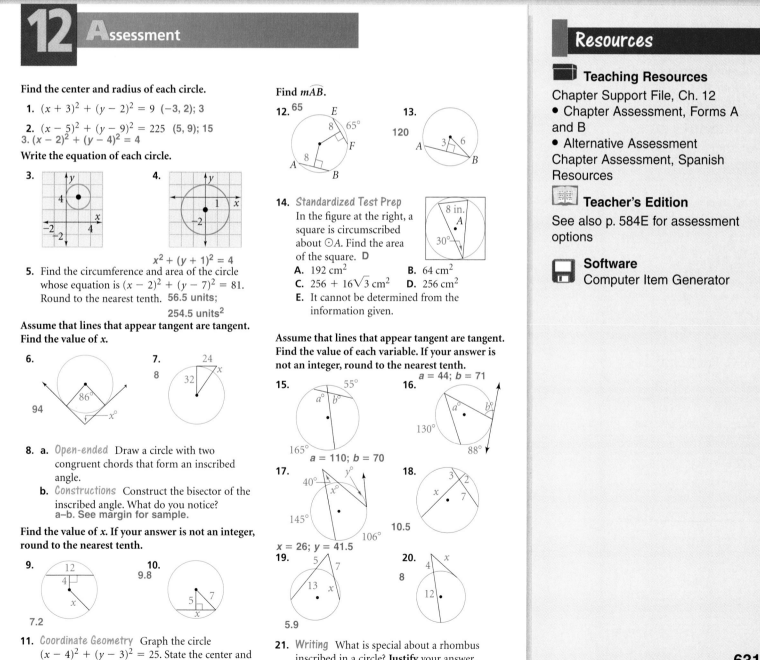

Find the center and radius of each circle.

1. $(x + 3)^2 + (y - 2)^2 = 9$ $(-3, 2); 3$
2. $(x - 5)^2 + (y - 9)^2 = 225$ $(5, 9); 15$

3. $(x - 2)^2 + (y - 4)^2 = 4$

Write the equation of each circle.

3.

4. 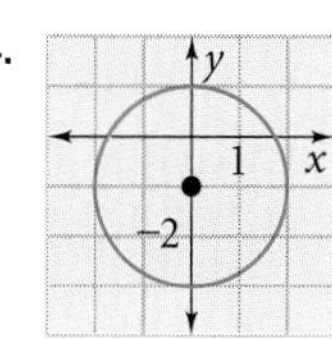

$x^2 + (y + 1)^2 = 4$

5. Find the circumference and area of the circle whose equation is $(x - 2)^2 + (y - 7)^2 = 81$. Round to the nearest tenth. 56.5 units; 254.5 units^2

Assume that lines that appear tangent are tangent. Find the value of *x*.

6. 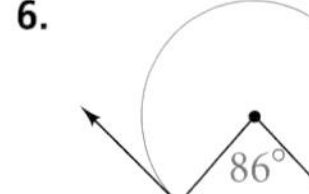 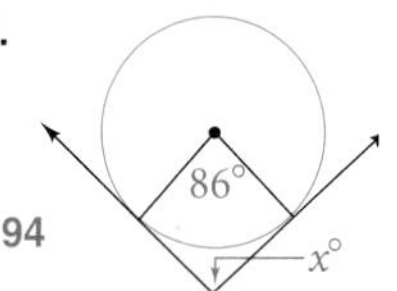 94

7. 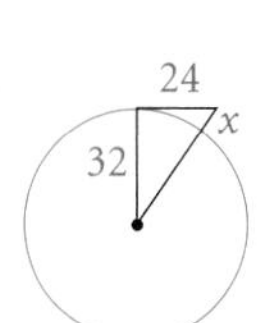 8

8. a. *Open-ended* Draw a circle with two congruent chords that form an inscribed angle.
   b. *Constructions* Construct the bisector of the inscribed angle. What do you notice?
   a–b. See margin for sample.

Find the value of *x*. If your answer is not an integer, round to the nearest tenth.

9. 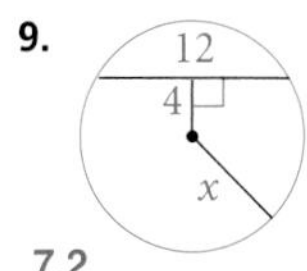 7.2

10. 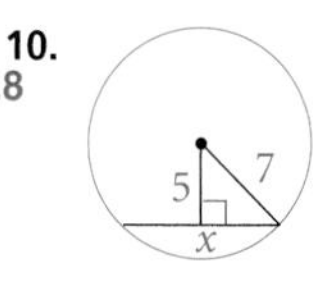 9.8

11. *Coordinate Geometry* Graph the circle $(x - 4)^2 + (y - 3)^2 = 25$. State the center and the radius of the circle.
    See margin for graph; (4, 3); 5.

Find $m\widehat{AB}$.

12. 65 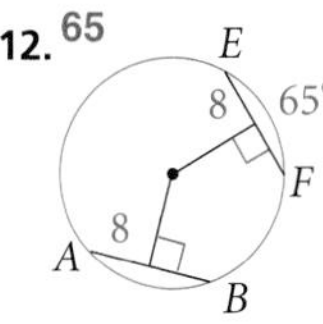

13. 120 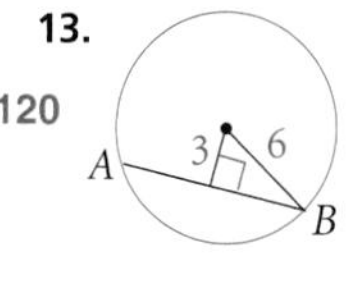

14. *Standardized Test Prep* In the figure at the right, a square is circumscribed about $\odot A$. Find the area of the square. D

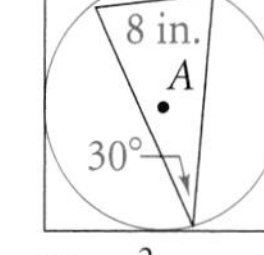

A. 192 cm^2 B. 64 cm^2
C. $256 + 16\sqrt{3} \text{ cm}^2$ D. 256 cm^2
E. It cannot be determined from the information given.

Assume that lines that appear tangent are tangent. Find the value of each variable. If your answer is not an integer, round to the nearest tenth.

15. 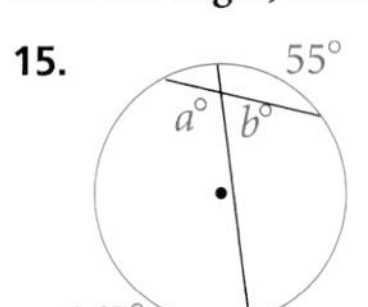 $a = 110$; $b = 70$

16. 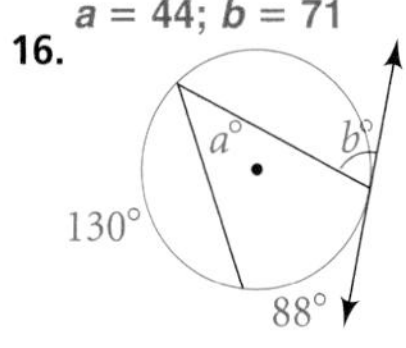 $a = 44$; $b = 71$

17. 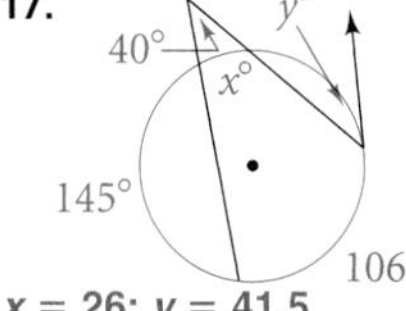 $x = 26$; $y = 41.5$

18. 10.5

19. 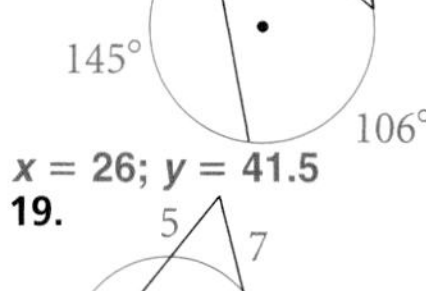 5.9

20. 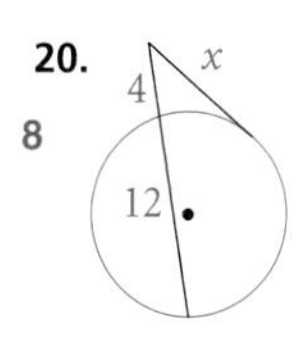 8

21. *Writing* What is special about a rhombus inscribed in a circle? **Justify** your answer.
    See margin.

Resources

Teaching Resources

Chapter Support File, Ch. 12
- Chapter Assessment, Forms A and B
- Alternative Assessment

Chapter Assessment, Spanish Resources

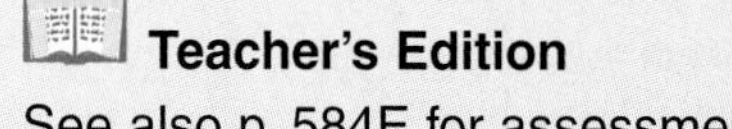

Teacher's Edition

See also p. 584E for assessment options

Software
Computer Item Generator

Cumulative Review

Item	Review Topic	Chapter
1	Triangles	2
2, 15	Coordinate Plane	1
3	Proving Triangles Congruent	8
3	Parallel Lines	7
4, 21	Area	5
5	Volume	6
6	Using Logical Reasoning	4
7	Transformations	3
8	Perpendicular Lines	2
9, 17	Quadrilaterals	9

Item	Review Topic	Chapter
10, 13	Circles	12
11	Medians of Triangles	4
12	Vectors	11
14	Proportions	10
16	Symmetry	3
17, 19	Constructions	1
18	Proofs	9
19	Areas of Similar Figures	10
20	Using Similar Triangles	10
21	Right Triangle Trigonometry	11

Resources

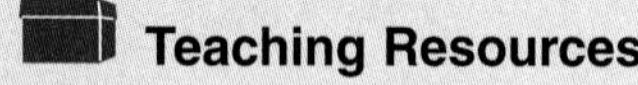

Teaching Resources

Chapter Support File, Ch. 12
- Cumulative Review
- Standardized Test Practice

Teacher's Edition

See also p. 584E for assessment options

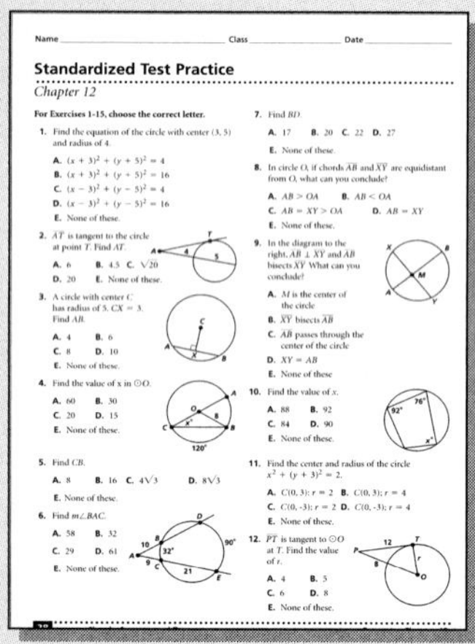

Standardized Test Practice
Chapter 12

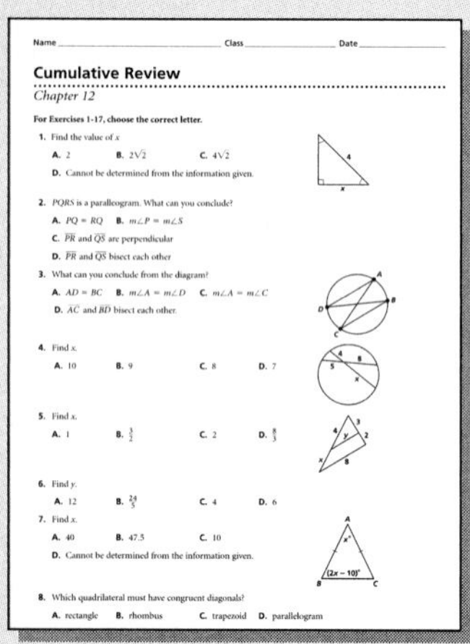

Cumulative Review
Chapter 12

12 Cumulative Review

For Exercises 1–15, choose the correct letter.

1. What is the best description of the triangle below? E

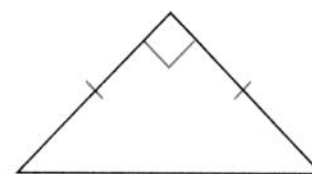

A. acute scalene B. right
C. equilateral D. obtuse scalene
E. isosceles right

2. What are the coordinates of the midpoint of $\overline{QS}$ with endpoints $Q(-2, -5)$ and $S(3, -8)$? B
A. $(-2.5, 6.5)$ B. $(0.5, -6.5)$ C. $(0.5, 1.5)$
D. $(-2.5, 1.5)$ E. $(-3.5, -5.5)$

3. Which theorem or postulate can you *not* use to prove $\triangle ABC \cong \triangle CDA$? A

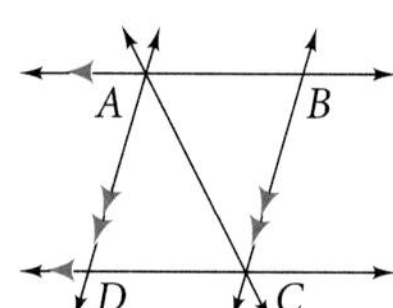

A. HL B. ASA C. AAS
D. SAS E. SSS

4. What is the area of an isosceles right triangle with hypotenuse length $5\sqrt{2}$ in.? B
A. 5 in.^{2} B. 12.5 in.^{2} C. 25 in.^{2}
D. $25\sqrt{2}$ in.^{2} E. $(10 + 5\sqrt{2})$ in.^{2}

5. What is the volume of the figure? E

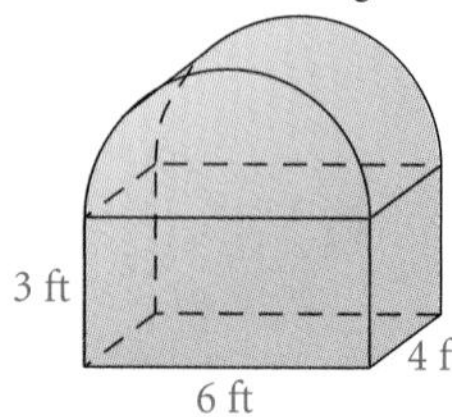

A. 288 ft^3 B. 72 ft^3 C. 72π ft^3
D. $(13 + 72\pi)$ ft^3 E. $(72 + 18\pi)$ ft^3

6. Which of the following statements can be derived from the biconditional statement "The day is long if and only if it is summer"? E
A. If the day is long, then it is summer.
B. If it is summer, then the day is long.
C. If the day is not long, then it is not summer.
D. If it is not summer, then the day is not long.
E. all of the above

7. Which is a reflection of the figure in the x-axis? B

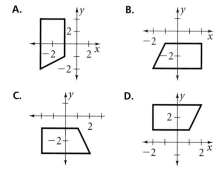

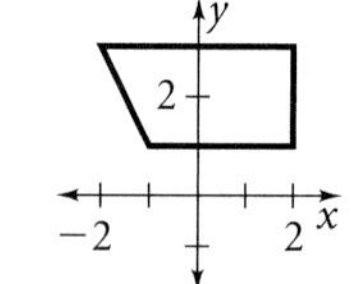

A.

B.

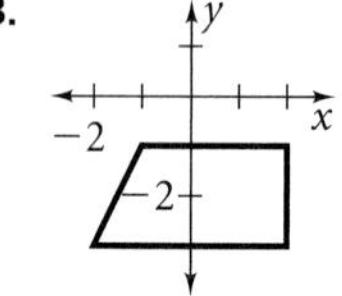

C.

D.

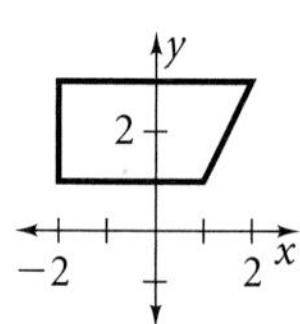

E. none of the above

8. Which line(s) is(are) perpendicular to the line $y = 4x - 1$? D
I. $y = 4x + 7$ II. $y = \frac{1}{4}x + 3$
III. $y = -\frac{1}{4}x - 5$ IV. $x + 4y = 16$
A. I only B. II only C. I and II
D. III and IV E. I, II, III, and IV

9. Which statement is true for both a rhombus and a kite? D
A. Opposite angles are congruent.
B. The diagonals are congruent.
C. Opposite sides are congruent.
D. The diagonals are perpendicular.
E. Opposite sides are parallel.

10. What is the value of x to the nearest tenth?
C

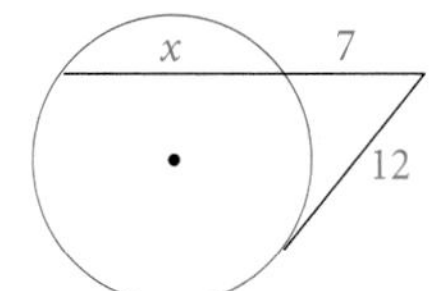

A. 5 B. 9 C. 13.6 D. 15 E. 20.6

11. Which triangle is drawn with its medians? B

A. 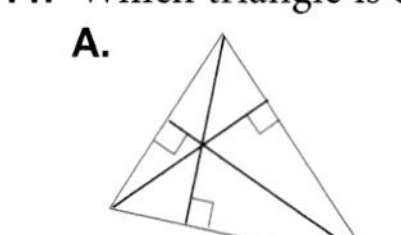

B. 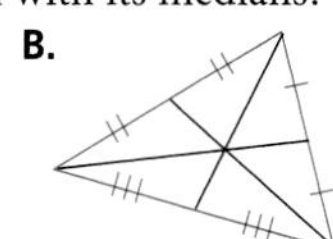

C. 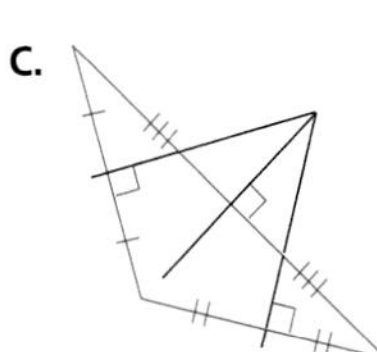

D. 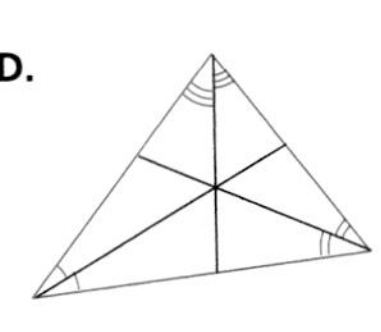

E. none of the above

Compare the boxed quantity in Column A with the one in Column B. Choose the best answer.

A. The quantity in Column A is greater.
B. The quantity in Column B is greater.
C. The two quantities are equal.
D. The relationship cannot be determined on the basis of the information supplied.

	Column A	Column B	
12.	the magnitude of $\langle 5, 1\rangle$	the magnitude of $\langle -4, 2\rangle$	A
13.	the measure of an inscribed angle of a circle that intercepts a 78° arc	the measure of a central angle of a circle that intercepts a 78° arc	B

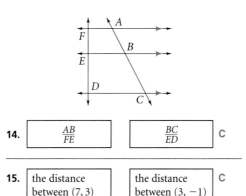

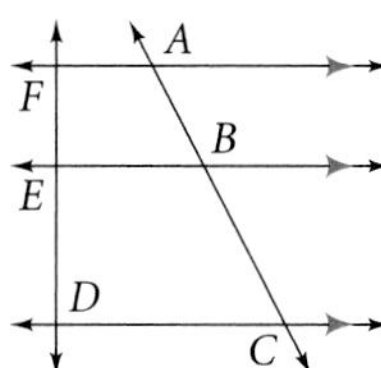

14.	$\frac{AB}{FE}$	$\frac{BC}{ED}$	C
15.	the distance between (7, 3) and (10, −2)	the distance between (3, −1) and (0, 4)	C

Find each answer. 16–17. See margin for samples.

16. **Open-ended** Sketch a figure with two lines of symmetry.

17. **Constructions** Draw a segment. Construct a kite whose diagonals are congruent to the segment you drew.

18. **Writing** What information is provided by a flow proof that is not in a two-column proof? See margin.

19. **Constructions** Copy the trapezoid. Construct a trapezoid similar to it whose perimeter is twice that of the original figure. What is the ratio of the area of the smaller figure to the area of the larger figure?

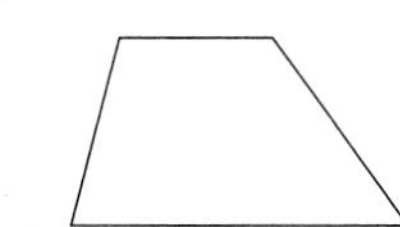

See margin for diagram; 1:4.

20. You are 5 ft 6 in. tall. When your shadow is 6 ft long, the shadow of a sculpture is 30 ft long. How tall is the sculpture? 27 ft 6 in.

21. A diagonal of a rectangular field makes a 70° angle with the side of the field that is 100 ft long. What is the area of the rectangle? 27,475 ft^2

Cumulative Review pp. 632–633

16. 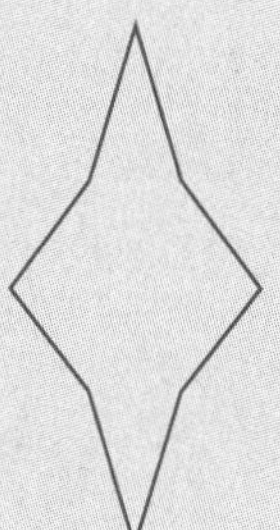

17. 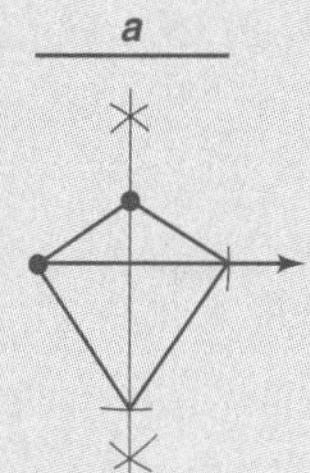

18. Answers may vary. Sample: A flow proof clearly shows the structure of the proof. That is, it shows how the given statements lead to other statements and, finally, to the statement to be proved.

19. 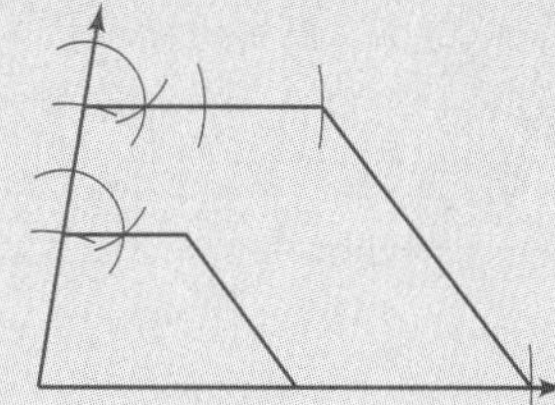

CHAPTER 1

1-1(1)a. 1, −1, −3, −5, −7

b. 1, 3, 6, 10, 15, 21

c. 1, 3, 6, 10, 15, 21; it is the same sequence as in part (b).

d. The number of dots is $n(n + 1)$, or $n^2 + n$, made up of an equal number of dots of each color. For each color, there are $\frac{n^2 + n}{2}$ dots. The numbers represented by these dots are also referred to as triangular numbers because they form triangular arrays with the same number of dots on each side. (See Exercise 32 on page 8.)

e.

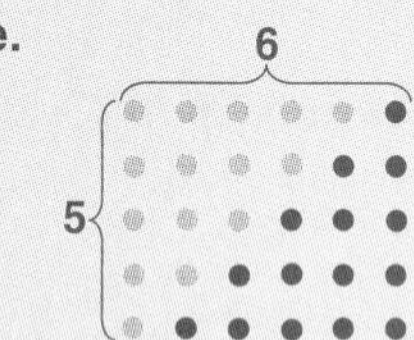

1-1(2) Answers may vary. Sample: When you add consecutive numbers beginning with 1, the pattern of the sums is 1, 3, 6, 10, 15, . . . which is the same as the pattern in Exercise 1-1 parts (b) and (c). The sum of the whole numbers from 1 to n is $\frac{n^2 + n}{2}$.

1-2a. six lines: $\overleftrightarrow{AB}$, $\overleftrightarrow{AC}$, $\overleftrightarrow{AD}$, $\overleftrightarrow{BC}$, $\overleftrightarrow{BD}$, $\overleftrightarrow{CD}$

b. ten lines: $\overleftrightarrow{AB}$, $\overleftrightarrow{AC}$, $\overleftrightarrow{AD}$, $\overleftrightarrow{AE}$, $\overleftrightarrow{BC}$, $\overleftrightarrow{BD}$, $\overleftrightarrow{BE}$, $\overleftrightarrow{CD}$, $\overleftrightarrow{CE}$, $\overleftrightarrow{DE}$

c. four planes: *ABC, ABD, ACD, BCD*

d. ten planes: *ABC, ABD, ABE, ACD, ACE, ADE, BCD, BCE, BDE, CDE*

1-3a. Answers may vary. Sample: $\overleftrightarrow{SP}$, $\overleftrightarrow{SR}$, and $\overleftrightarrow{SV}$; any 3 of $\overleftrightarrow{VP}$, $\overleftrightarrow{VQ}$, $\overleftrightarrow{VR}$, $\overleftrightarrow{VS}$

b. $\overleftrightarrow{PQ}$ and $\overleftrightarrow{PS}$

c. $\overleftrightarrow{QR}$

d. yes; no; yes; Possible explanation:

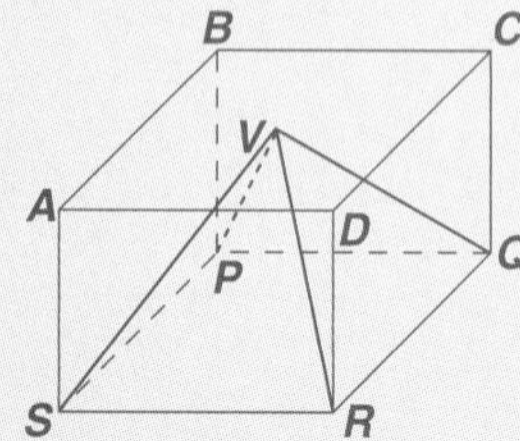

Suppose the pyramid is inside a box as shown, with point V lying in plane *ABCD*. Then $\overleftrightarrow{AD} \parallel \overleftrightarrow{SR}$ and $\overleftrightarrow{AB}$ is skew to $\overleftrightarrow{SR}$. Since plane *ABCD* $\parallel$ plane *QRSP* and $\overleftrightarrow{SR}$ lies in plane *QRSP*, no line lying in plane *ABCD* can intersect $\overleftrightarrow{SR}$.

1-4 First, draw a diagram for reference. If $DC = 16$, then $ED = 8$, $CB = 32$, $FD = 4$, and $GF = 2$. Then $DB = DC + CB = 16 + 32 = 48$. So, $DH = 24$. Thus, $GH = GF + FD + DH = 2 + 4 + 24 = 30$.

1-5a. $\overleftrightarrow{CD}$ is the perpendicular bisector of $\overline{AB}$, since $m\angle AEC = 90$ and $AE = EB$.

b. $AF = BF$. If you mark a point F on $\overleftrightarrow{CB}$ and draw $\overline{AF}$ and $\overline{BF}$, these segments coincide when you fold the paper along the line $\overleftrightarrow{CD}$.

1-6a. always

b. never

1-7(1) $m\angle ABC + m\angle CBF = 180$, so $(4x + y) + (2x + 2y) = 180$ and $m\angle CBF + m\angle FBD = 180$, so $(2x + 2y) + (2x + 6y) = 180$. Solve the two simultaneous equations to find that $y = 10$ and $x = 25$. Then $m\angle ABD = m\angle FBC = 70$.

Challenge Problems

CHAPTER 1

1-1(1) In the sequence 2, 4, 6, 8, 10, . . . , the difference between consecutive terms is 2.

sequence	2	4	6	8	10 . . .
differences	2	2	2	2 . . .	

a. Write the first five terms of the sequence that starts with 1, and for which the difference between consecutive terms is −2.

b. Write the first six terms of the sequence that starts with 1, and for which the difference between consecutive terms is first 2, and then 3, 4, 5, and 6.

c. Evaluate $\frac{n^2 + n}{2}$ for $n = 1, 2, 3, 4, 5$, and 6. Compare the sequence you get with your answer for part (b).

d. Examine the diagram below and explain how it illustrates a value of $\frac{n^2 + n}{2}$.

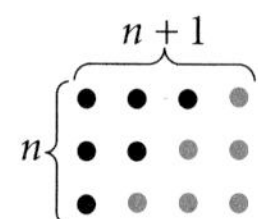

e. Draw a similar diagram to represent $\frac{n^2 + n}{2}$ for $n = 5$.

1-1(2) When he was in the third grade, German mathematician Karl Gauss (1777–1855) added the numbers from 1 to 100 in ten seconds. Use patterns to find a quick way to find such sums.

1-2 Consider points *A*, *B*, *C*, *D*, and *E*. No three of them are collinear and no four of them are coplanar.

a. Name as many lines as possible that contain two of the points *A*, *B*, *C*, and *D*.

b. Name as many lines as possible that contain two of the points *A*, *B*, *C*, *D*, and *E*.

c. Name as many planes as possible that contain three of the points *A*, *B*, *C*, and *D*.

d. Name as many planes as possible that contain three of the points *A*, *B*, *C*, *D*, and *E*.

1-3 The figure below is a pyramid.

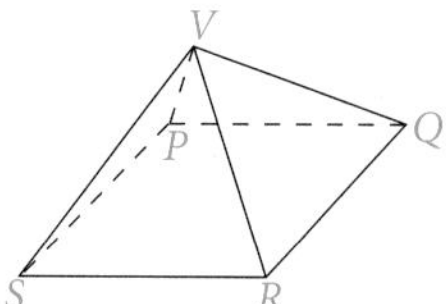

a. Name three lines that intersect at one point.

b. Name two lines that are skew to $\overleftrightarrow{VR}$.

c. What line is parallel to $\overleftrightarrow{PS}$?

d. Consider a plane through *V* that is parallel to plane *PQRS*. Can a line in that plane be parallel to $\overleftrightarrow{SR}$? Intersect $\overleftrightarrow{SR}$? Be skew to $\overleftrightarrow{SR}$? Explain your answers.

1-4 *C* is the midpoint of $\overline{AB}$, *D* is the midpoint of $\overline{AC}$, *E* is the midpoint of $\overline{AD}$, *F* is the midpoint of $\overline{ED}$, *G* is the midpoint of $\overline{EF}$, and *H* is the midpoint of $\overline{DB}$. If $DC = 16$, find *GH*.

1-5 Draw and label two points *A* and *B* anywhere on a sheet of paper. Then fold the paper so the two points coincide (lie on top of each other). Label the fold line $\overleftrightarrow{CD}$. Draw $\overline{AB}$. Label the intersection of $\overline{AB}$ and $\overleftrightarrow{CD}$ point *E*.

a. Describe the relationship between $\overline{AB}$ and the fold $\overleftrightarrow{CD}$. Support your conclusion by giving the measures of angles and lengths of segments.

b. For any point *F* on the fold line, describe the relationship between *AF* and *BF*. Explain.

1-6 Draw a large square on graph paper. Also draw a large rectangle that is not a square. Construct the bisectors of the angles of each figure. Complete the following statements with *always*, *sometimes*, or *never*.

a. The bisectors of the angles of a square __?__ contain the diagonals.

b. The bisectors of the angles of a rectangle that is not a square __?__ contain the diagonals.

1-7(2) Because $\angle 1$ and $\angle 2$ are complementary, $m\angle 1 + m\angle 2 = 90$. Because $\angle 3$ and $\angle 4$ are complementary, $m\angle 3 + m\angle 4 = 90$. So $m\angle 1 + m\angle 2 = m\angle 3 + m\angle 4$. But, $m\angle 1 = m\angle 3$. Subtract equations to get $m\angle 2 = m\angle 4$. Therefore, $\angle 2 \cong \angle 4$.

1-8 Sample answer:

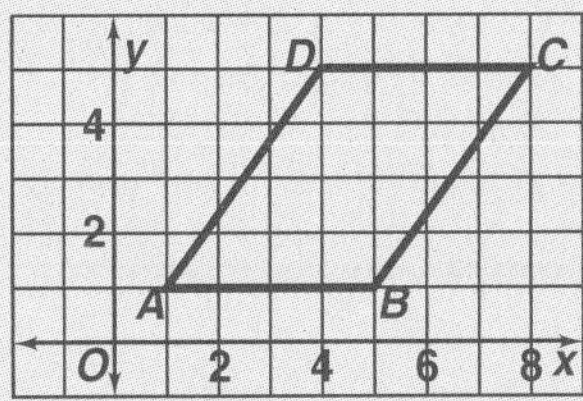

a. $BC = \sqrt{3^2 + 4^2} = 5$; $AC = \sqrt{3^2 + 4^2} = 5$; $\overline{BC} \cong \overline{AD}$

b. If one pair of opposite sides of a quadrilateral is congruent and parallel, the other pair of opposite sides is congruent.

c. The midpoint of $\overline{AC} = \left(\frac{1+8}{2}, \frac{1+5}{2}\right) = \left(\frac{9}{2}, 3\right)$. The midpoint of $\overline{BD} = \left(\frac{5+4}{2}, \frac{1+5}{2}\right) = \left(\frac{9}{2}, 3\right)$. Both diagonals have the same midpoint.

d. If one pair of opposite sides of a quadrilateral is congruent and parallel, the diagonals of the quadrilateral bisect each other.

e. $EF = AB$

f. If one pair of opposite sides of a quadrilateral is congruent and parallel, the segment joining the midpoints of the second pair of sides is congruent to the first pair of sides.

CHAPTER 2

2-1 $5x - 25 = 3x - 1$. Solving, $x = 12$. Then $m\angle BCD = 35$ and $m\angle DBF = 90 + 35 = 125$.

2-2(1)

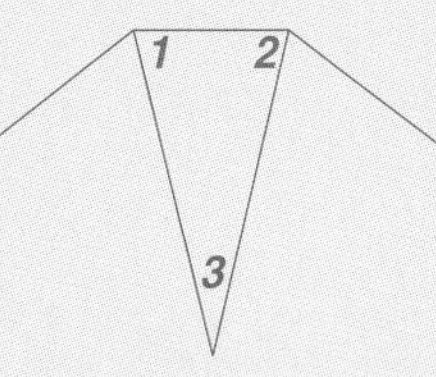

The measure of each interior angle $= \frac{(10 - 2)180}{10} = 144$.
$m\angle 1 = m\angle 2 = 72$ and $m\angle 3 = 180 - 72 - 72 = 36$.

2-2(2)a.

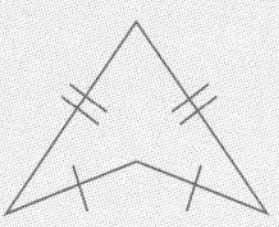

b. not possible

c.

d. not possible

2-3a. $AC = \sqrt{(7 - 9)^2 + (11 - 1)^2} = \sqrt{104}$
$BD = \sqrt{(13 - 3)^2 + (7 - 5)^2} = \sqrt{104}$

b. Solutions may vary. Sample: The slope of $\overline{AC}$ is $\frac{11 - 1}{7 - 9} = -5$ and its midpoint is $\left(\frac{7+9}{2}, \frac{11+1}{2}\right) = (8, 6)$. The slope of $\overline{BD}$ is $\frac{7 - 5}{13 - 3} = \frac{1}{5}$ and its midpoint is $\left(\frac{3+13}{2}, \frac{5+7}{2}\right) = (8, 6)$. Since the product of the slopes of the diagonals is -1, the diagonals are perpendicular. Since the diagonals have the same midpoint, they bisect each other.

1-7(1) In the figure below, find $m\angle ABD$.

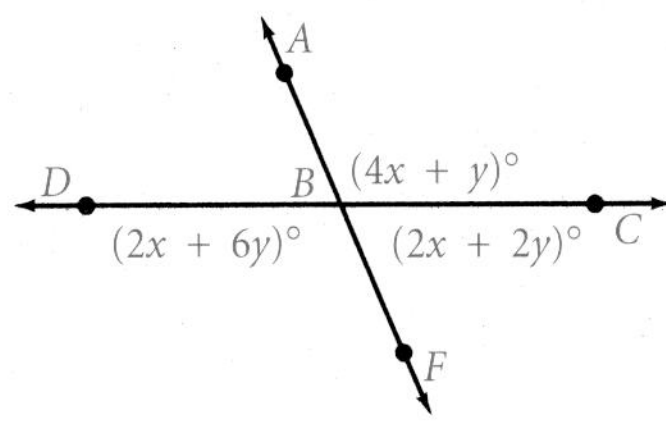

1-7(2) Write a convincing argument to show that complements of congruent angles are congruent.

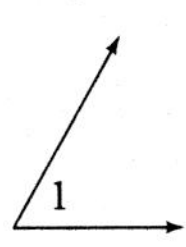

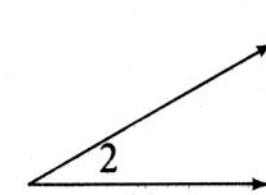

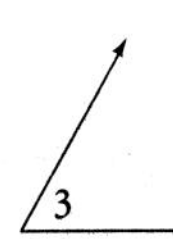

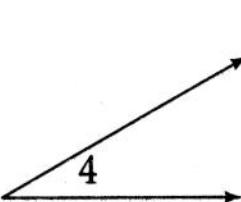

Given: $\angle 1$ and $\angle 2$ are complementary.
$\angle 3$ and $\angle 4$ are complementary.
$\angle 1 \cong \angle 3$
Prove: $\angle 2 \cong \angle 4$

1-8 *Open-ended* In a coordinate plane, draw any $\overline{AB}$. Draw another segment that is both congruent and parallel to $\overline{AB}$. Label the new segment $\overline{CD}$ in such a way that $ABCD$ is a quadrilateral.

a. Find BC and AD. What do you notice?
b. Write a conjecture that generalizes the result you found in part (a).
c. Find the midpoint of $\overline{AC}$ and the midpoint of $\overline{BD}$. What do you notice?
d. Write a conjecture that generalizes the result you found in part (c).
e. Find the midpoint E of $\overline{AD}$ and the midpoint F of $\overline{BC}$. Find EF and AB. What do you notice?
f. Write a conjecture that generalizes the result you found in part (e).

CHAPTER 2

2-1 In this figure, $\overline{CD} \perp \overline{AB}$ and $\overline{CD}$ bisects $\angle ACB$. Find $m\angle DBF$.

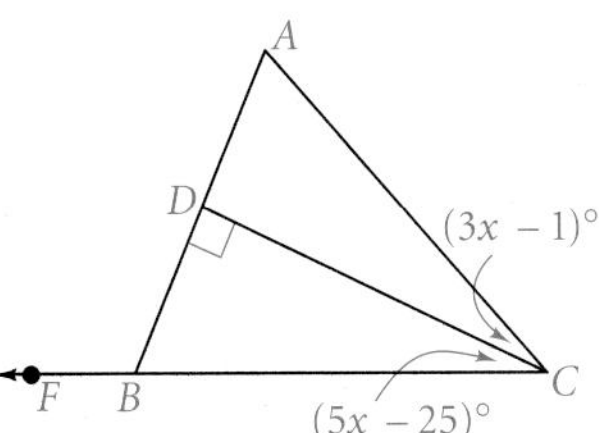

2-2(1) Two rays bisect two consecutive angles of a regular decagon and intersect in the decagon's interior. Find the measure of the acute angles formed by the intersecting rays.

2-2(2) Draw, if possible, the following figures.

a. a concave quadrilateral with two pairs of congruent adjacent sides
b. a concave quadrilateral with two pairs of congruent opposite sides
c. a concave quadrilateral with three congruent sides
d. a concave quadrilateral with four congruent sides

2-3 Figure $ABCD$ is a square.

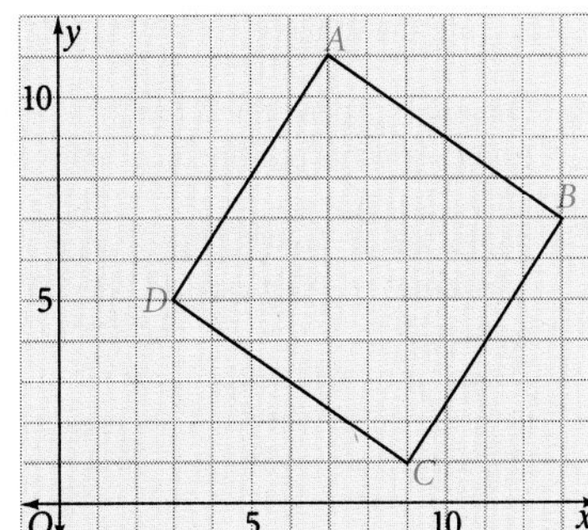

a. Show that the diagonals are congruent.
b. Show that the diagonals are perpendicular bisectors of each other.

2-4a. Solutions may vary. Sample: Yes, $\overline{PR}$ bisects $\overline{QS}$ since the vertical segment $\overline{PR}$ intersects the horizontal segment $\overline{QS}$ at $(2, -3)$, and $(2, -3)$ is the midpoint of $\overline{QS}$. No, $\overline{QS}$ does not bisect $\overline{PR}$, since the midpoint of $\overline{PR}$ is $(2, \frac{1}{2})$, not $(2, -3)$.

b. $PQ = PS = \sqrt{73}$
$QR = SR = \sqrt{10}$
The perimeter is
$2\sqrt{73} + 2\sqrt{10} \approx 23.4$.

2-5a. Answers may vary. Samples:
$m\widehat{BD} = m\widehat{FE} = 70$
$m\widehat{AB} = m\widehat{FG} = 110$
$m\widehat{GFE} = m\widehat{ABD} = 180$

b. $m\angle GOF = m\widehat{FG} = 110$, so $x + x + 110 = 180$ and $x = 35$.

2-6

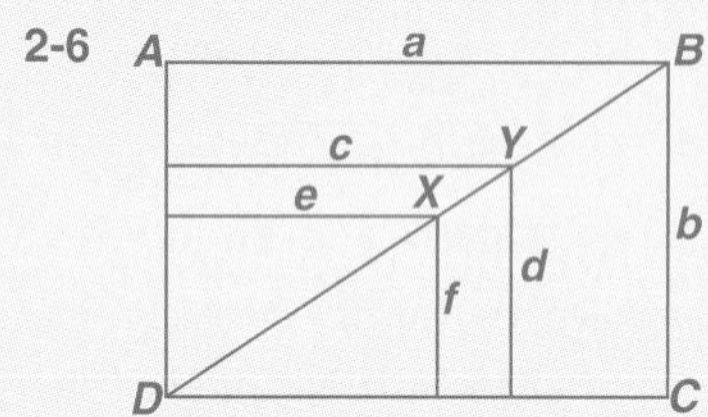

Rectangles and measurements may vary, but the ratios $\frac{a}{b}, \frac{c}{d}$, and $\frac{e}{f}$ should be equal. The rectangles are similar because corresponding angles are congruent and corresponding sides are proportional.

2-7(1) 6, 6, 8, 10

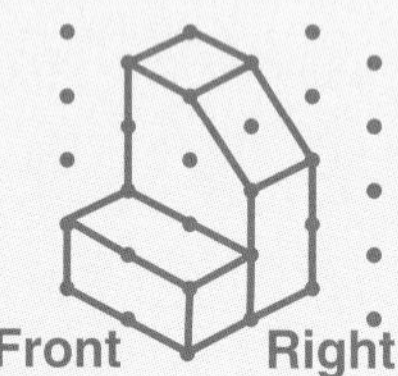

CHAPTER 3

3-1(1) a. $(4, 2)$

b. $(-2, -4)$

c. $(-4, -2)$

d. $(2, 4)$

e. A and A'''' are the same point.

3-1(2) a. The midpoint of $\overline{CD} = \left(\frac{a+b}{2}, \frac{b+a}{2}\right)$. Since the x- and y-coordinates are equal, the midpoint lies on $y = x$.

b. The slope of $\overleftrightarrow{CD} = \frac{a-b}{b-a} = -1$. The slope of $y = x$ is 1. The product of the slopes is -1 so $\overleftrightarrow{CD}$ is perpendicular to the line $y = x$.

3-2a. The vertices of $\triangle A'B'C'$ are $A'(2, 7)$, $B'(0, 1)$, and $C'(6, -1)$.

b. The midpoint of $\overline{AB}$ is $(-3, 2)$; its image under the translation is $(1, 4)$. The midpoint of $\overline{A'B'}$ is $\left(\frac{2}{2}, \frac{8}{2}\right) = (1, 4)$. The midpoint of $\overline{BC}$ is $(-1, -2)$; its image under the translation is $(3, 0)$. The midpoint of $\overline{B'C'}$ is $\left(\frac{6}{2}, \frac{0}{2}\right) = (3, 0)$.

The midpoint of $\overline{AC}$ is $\left(\frac{0}{2}, \frac{2}{2}\right) = (0, 1)$; its image under the translation is $(4, 3)$. The midpoint of $\overline{A'C'}$ is $\left(\frac{8}{2}, \frac{6}{2}\right) = (4, 3)$. In each case, the image of the midpoint is the midpoint of the image.

3-3

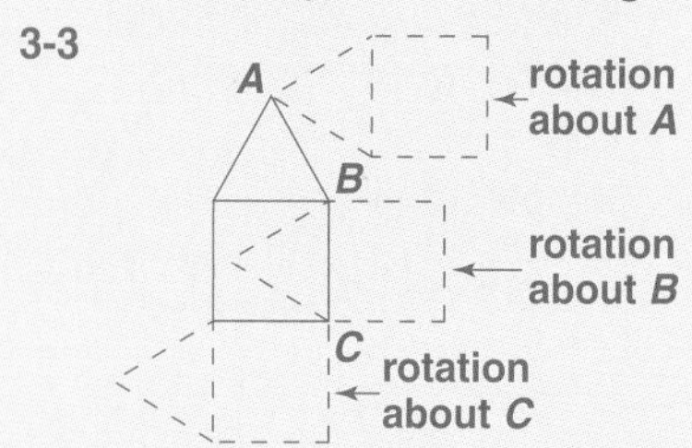

2-4 *PQRS* is a kite.

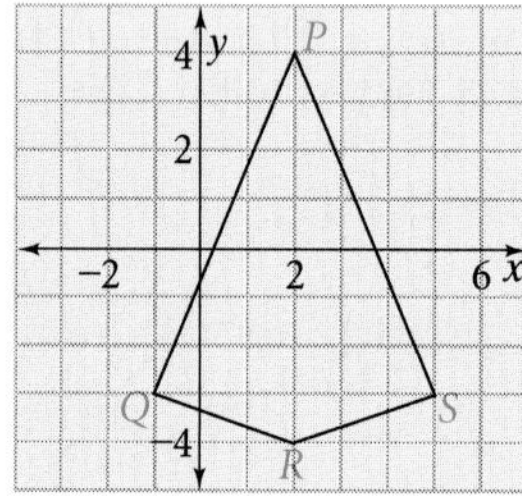

a. Does $\overline{PR}$ bisect $\overline{QS}$? Does $\overline{QS}$ bisect $\overline{PR}$? Explain your answers.
b. Find the perimeter of *PQRS*.

2-5 The two circles shown are concentric because they lie in the same plane and have the same center, *O*.

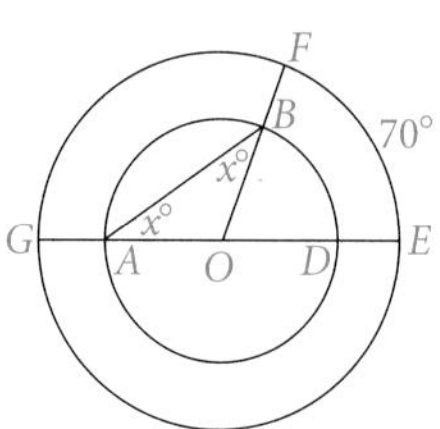

a. Name two arcs that have the same measure.
b. Find the value of *x*.

2-6 On graph paper, draw a rectangle *ABCD* using segments of horizontal and vertical grid lines. Draw the diagonal $\overline{BD}$ and pick any two points *X* and *Y* on $\overline{BD}$. Using segments of horizontal and vertical grid lines, draw rectangles that have $\overline{DX}$ and $\overline{DY}$ as diagonals. Determine whether the three rectangles you have drawn are similar. Use measurements and ratios to support your answer.

2-7(1) How many cubes are needed to build each figure in Excercises 1 through 4 on page 112?

2-7(2) Create an isometric drawing for the orthographic drawing below.

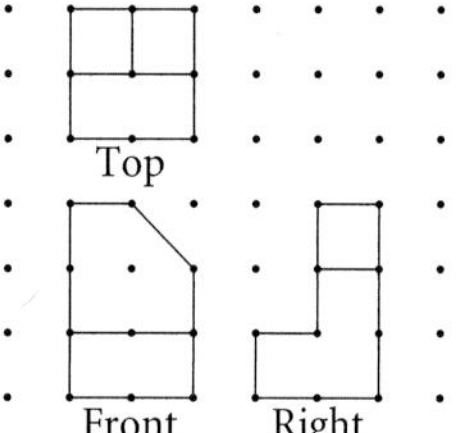

CHAPTER 3

3-1(1)

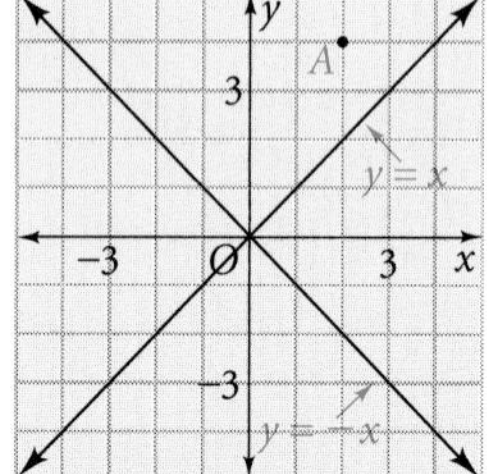

a. Find the coordinates of A', the reflection of A over the line $y = x$.
b. Find the coordinates of A'', the reflection of A' over the line $y = -x$.
c. Find the coordinates of A''', the reflection of A'' over the line $y = x$.
d. Find the coordinates of A'''', the reflection of A''' over the line $y = -x$.
e. How are A and A'''' related?

3-1(2) Show that the point $D(b, a)$ is the reflection image of point $C(a, b)$ over the line $y = x$ by showing that
a. the midpoint of $\overline{CD}$ is on the line $y = x$, and
b. $\overleftrightarrow{CD}$ is perpendicular to the line $y = x$.

3-4a.

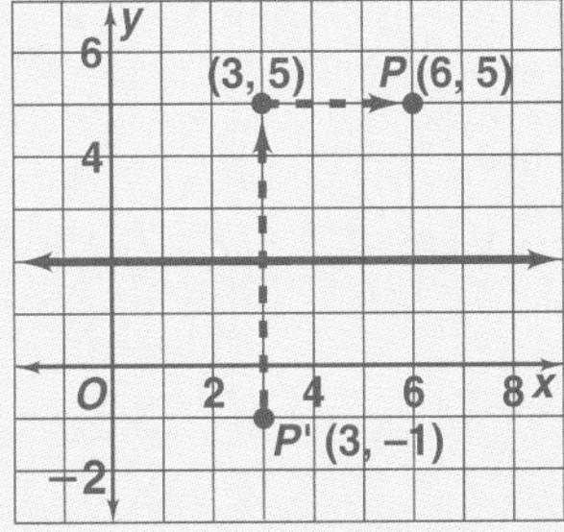

(3, −1) is the image of a point reflected in $y = 2$, so it is the image of (3, 5). (3, 5) is the image of point P under the translation ⟨−3, 0⟩, so P is (6, 5).

b.

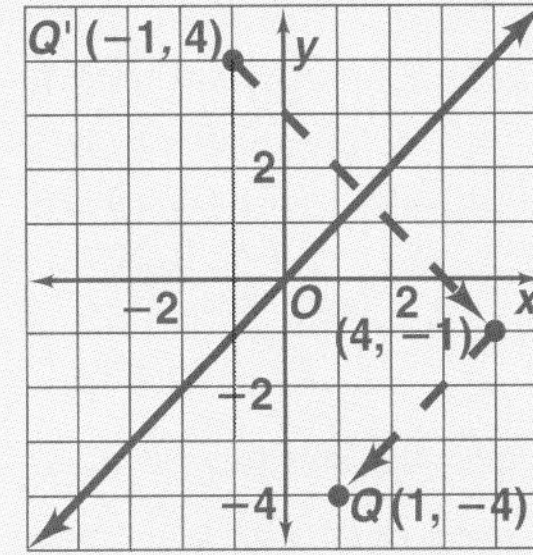

(−1, 4) is the reflection image of a point in the line $y = x$, so it is the image of (4, −1). (4, −1) is the image of point Q under the translation ⟨3, 3⟩, so Q is (1, −4).

3-5 Samples of the possible symmetries are given. The first figure has rotational symmetry. The second has line symmetry.

a.

b.

3-6(1)

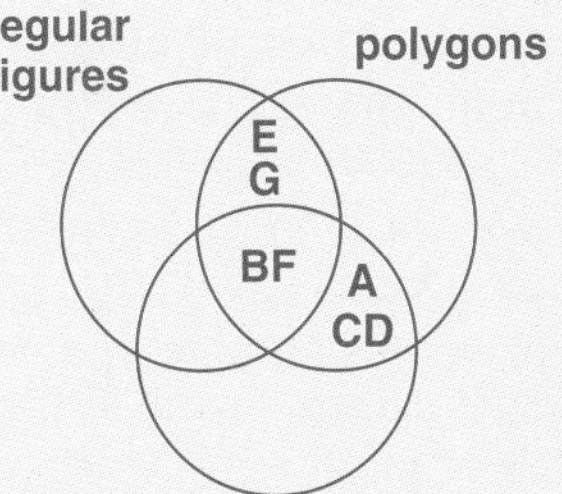

3-6(2) Sample answer:

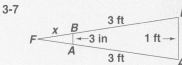

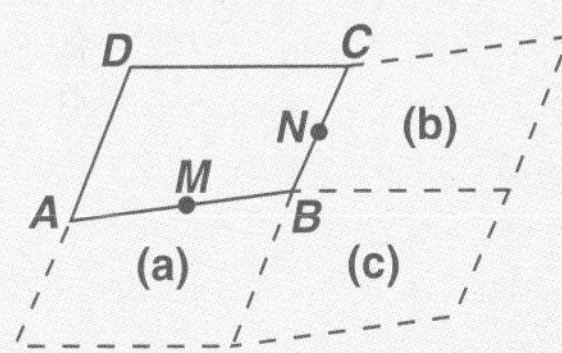

d. Quadrilateral $ABCD$ tessellates. The sum of the measures of the angles of a quadrilateral is 360. Copies of the quadrilateral can be arranged so that the four angles have the same vertex. So the quadrilateral fills the plane, leaving no gaps.

3-7

F, x, B, 3 ft, B', 3 in, 1 ft, A, 3 ft, A'

The scale factor of the dilation is $\frac{12 \text{ in.}}{3 \text{ in.}} = 4$. So $\frac{x + 3}{x} = 4$. Solving, $x = 1$. Each vertex is 1 ft from the light.

3-2 a. $A(-2, 5)$, $B(-4, -1)$, and $C(2, -3)$ are the vertices of $\triangle ABC$. Find the coordinates of the vertices of $\triangle A'B'C'$, the image of $\triangle ABC$ under the translation ⟨4, 2⟩.

b. Show that the images of the midpoints of the sides of $\triangle ABC$ are the midpoints of $\triangle A'B'C'$.

3-3 Copy the figure below. Then draw the image of the figure under a rotation of 90° about A, about B, and about C.

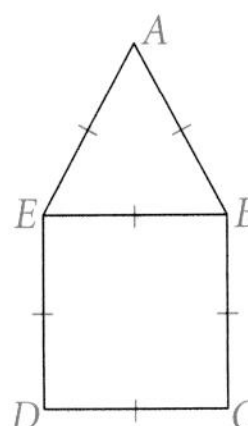

3-4 a. $P'(3, -1)$ is the image of P under the glide reflection ⟨−3, 0⟩ and $y = 2$. Find the coordinates of P.

b. $Q'(-1, 4)$ is the image of Q under the glide reflection ⟨3, 3⟩ and $y = x$. Find the coordinates of Q.

3-5 For each three-dimensional object below, draw two-dimensional figures that could be cut out and folded to form the object. For each object, try to draw figures that have rotational symmetry and figures that have 1, 2, or 4 lines of symmetry.

a.

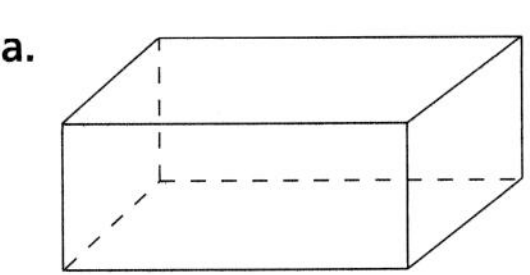

b.

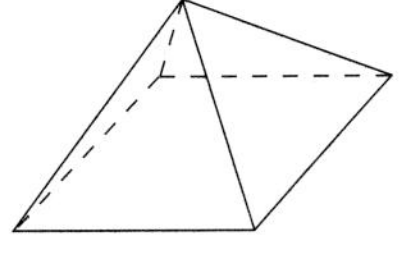

3-6(1) Copy the Venn diagram below. Then write each letter A through G in the correct region of the Venn diagram.

A. scalene triangle **B.** equilateral triangle
C. isosceles trapezoid **D.** parallelogram
E. regular pentagon **F.** regular hexagon
G. regular octagon

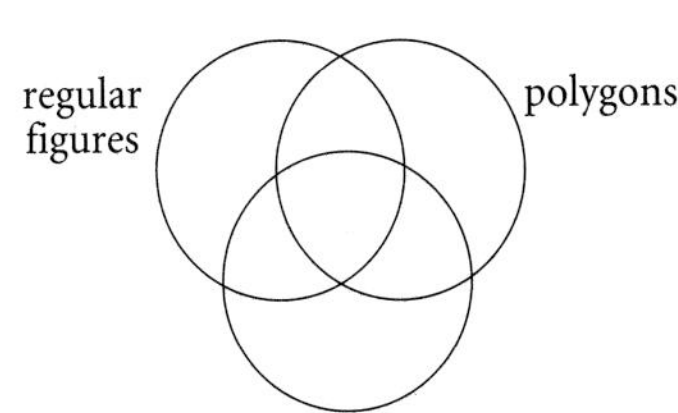

3-6(2) *Open-ended* On graph paper, draw a quadrilateral and label it $ABCD$. Locate M, the midpoint of $\overline{AB}$, and N, the midpoint of $\overline{BC}$.

a. Draw the image of $ABCD$ under a 180° rotation about M.

b. Draw the image of $ABCD$ under a 180° rotation about N.

c. Draw the image of $ABCD$ under the translation that maps D to B.

d. Make a conjecture about whether your quadrilateral tessellates, using the pattern in parts (a)–(c). Justify your answer.

3-7 A flashlight projects an image of rectangle $ABCD$ on a wall so that each vertex of $ABCD$ is 3 ft away from the corresponding vertex of $A'B'C'D'$. The length of $\overline{AB}$ is 3 in. and the length of $\overline{A'B'}$ is 1 ft. How far from each vertex of $ABCD$ is the light?

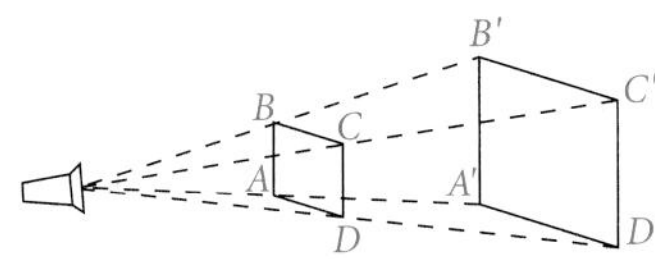

CHAPTER 4

4-1 Answers may vary. Samples:

a. A point is the midpoint of a segment if and only if it divides the segment into two congruent segments.

b. An angle is acute if and only if its measure is between 0 and 90.

c. A figure is a rectangle if and only if it is a parallelogram with four right angles.

d. A figure is an isosceles triangle if and only if it is a triangle with at least two congruent sides.

4-2

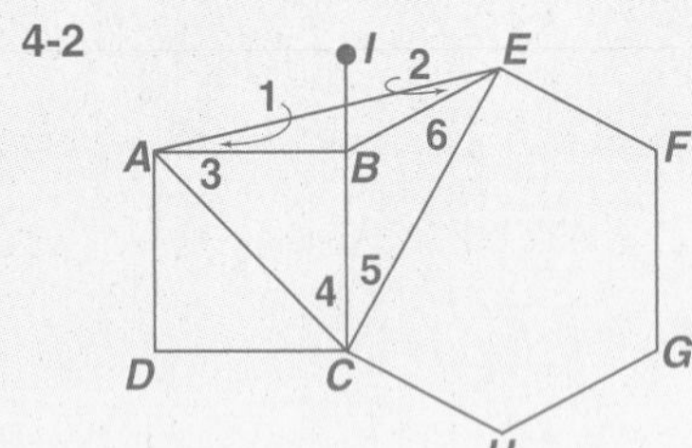

a. Extend $\overline{CB}$ to point I as shown. Then $\angle IBE$ is an exterior angle of the regular hexagon. $m\angle IBE = \frac{360}{6} = 60$ and $m\angle ABI = 90$, so $m\angle ABE = 60 + 90 = 150$. $\triangle ABE$ is isosceles and the sum of the base angles is $180 - 150 = 30$. Then $m\angle 1 = m\angle 2 = 15$.

b. $\triangle ABC$ is an isosceles right triangle, so $m\angle 3 = 45$. $m\angle EAC = 15 + 45 = 60$. Since $\triangle EBC$ is isosceles, $m\angle 5 = m\angle 6$. So $2m\angle 6 = m\angle IBE = 60$. Dividing, $m\angle 6 = 30$. So $m\angle AEC = 15 + 30 = 45$ and $m\angle ACE = 180 - 60 - 45 = 75$.

4-3a. Since $\angle CDB \cong \angle CBD$, $DC = CB = 8$. Since $\angle ADB \cong \angle ABD$, so $AD = AB = 6.5$. $DC \neq AB$ and $DA \neq CB$. Therefore $ABCD$ is a kite because it is a quadrilateral with two pairs of adjacent sides congruent and no pairs of opposite sides congruent.

b. By the angle addition postulate, $m\angle ADC = m\angle ADB + m\angle BDC$ and $m\angle ABC = m\angle ABD + m\angle DBC$. By substitution, $m\angle ADC = 60 + 65$ and $m\angle ABC = 60 + 65$. So $m\angle ADC = m\angle ABC$ by the transitive property of equality.

4-4a. The translation from A to B is $\langle -2, -4\rangle$; applying that to $B(-6, -2)$ gives $C(-8, -6)$. The translation from A to D is $\langle 5, -3\rangle$; applying that to $D(1, -1)$ gives $E(6, -4)$.

b. $BD = 5\sqrt{2}$ and $CE = 10\sqrt{2}$. So $BD = \frac{1}{2}CE$.

c. The slope of $\overrightarrow{BD} = \frac{-2-(-1)}{-6-1} = \frac{1}{7}$; the slope of $\overleftrightarrow{CE} = \frac{-6-(-4)}{-8-6} = \frac{1}{7}$; they are parallel.

4-5 Step 1: Assume that $\overline{XB} \perp \overline{AC}$.

Step 2: If $\overline{XB} \perp \overline{AC}$, then $\angle AXB \cong \angle CXB$. $\angle ABX \cong \angle CBX$ since their measures are equal and $BX = BX$ by reflexivity. So $\triangle ABX \cong \triangle CBX$ by ASA. Then $AB = BC$ by CPCTC and $\triangle ABC$ is isosceles. This contradicts the given statement that $\triangle ABC$ is scalene. So the assumption that $\overline{XB} \perp \overline{AC}$ is false.

Step 3: Therefore $\overline{XB}$ is not perpendicular to $\overline{AC}$.

4-6(1)a. $m\angle 1 + m\angle 2 = 180$ so $(6x + 4) + (7x - 6) = 180$. Then $x = 14$. So $m\angle 1 = 6(14) + 4 = 88$, and $m\angle 2 = 7(14) - 6 = 92$.

CHAPTER 4

4-1 Write the definition of each term as a biconditional statement.

a. midpoint
b. acute angle
c. rectangle
d. isosceles triangle

4-2 *ABCD* is a square and *CBEFGH* is a regular hexagon.

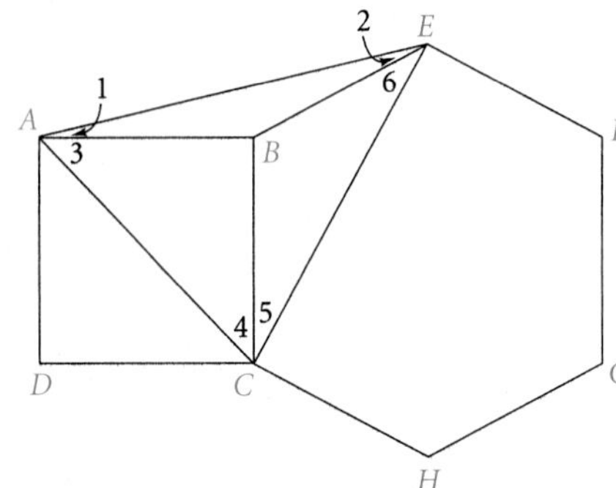

a. Find the measure of each angle in $\triangle ABE$.
b. Find the measure of each angle in $\triangle ACE$.

4-3 **a.** Write a paragraph proof for the following.

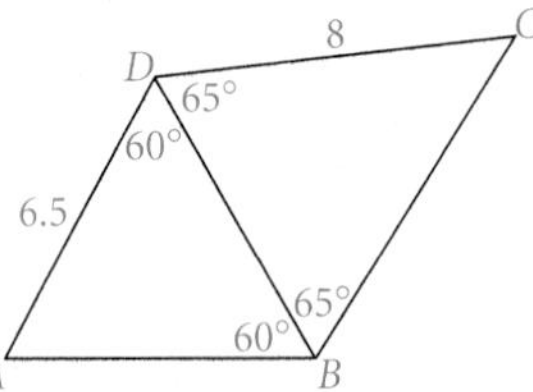

Given: $m\angle ABD = 60$, $m\angle ADB = 60$, $m\angle CBD = 65$, $m\angle CDB = 65$, $AD = 6.5$, $DC = 8$

Prove: *ABCD* is a kite.

b. Use the figure and the given from part (a) to prove that $\angle ADC \cong \angle ABC$.

4-4 In the diagram below, B is the midpoint of $\overline{AC}$ and D is the midpoint of $\overline{AE}$.

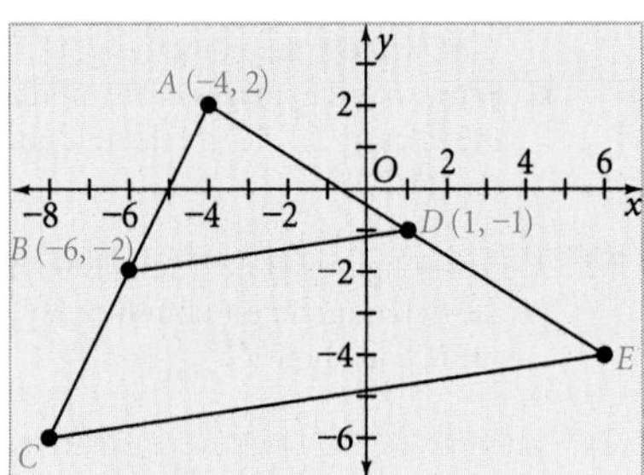

a. Find the coordinates of points C and E.
b. Show that $BD = \frac{1}{2}CE$.
c. Show that $\overleftrightarrow{BD} \parallel \overleftrightarrow{CE}$.

4-5 Write a convincing argument that uses indirect reasoning.

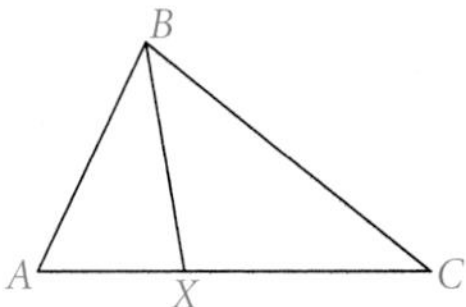

Given: $\triangle ABC$ is scalene, $m\angle ABX = 36$, and $m\angle CBX = 36$.

Prove: $\overline{XB}$ is *not* perpendicular to $\overline{AC}$.

4-6(1)

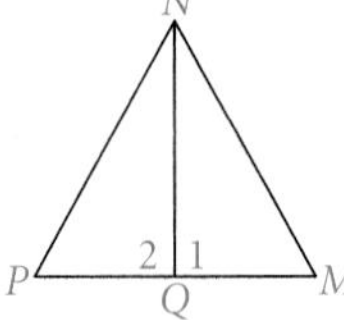

In this diagram, $MQ = QP$, $m\angle 1 = 6x + 4$, and $m\angle 2 = 7x - 6$.

a. Find the measures of $\angle 1$ and $\angle 2$.
b. Which is shorter, $\overline{NM}$ or $\overline{PN}$? Explain. (*Hint:* See Exercise 25 on page 217.)
c. Which is smaller, $\angle M$ or $\angle P$? Explain.

b. $m\angle 1 < m\angle 2$, $\overline{PQ} \approx \overline{MQ}$, and $\overline{NQ} \cong \overline{NQ}$, so by the Hinge Theorem (Exercise 25 on page 217) $\overline{MN}$ is shorter than $\overline{PN}$.

c. The smaller angle is $\angle P$ because in $\triangle MNP$ it is opposite the shorter side $\overline{MN}$.

4-6(2)

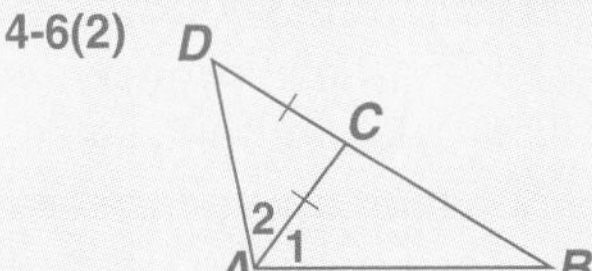

Extend $\overleftrightarrow{BC}$ to point D so that $DC = AC$. Draw $\overline{DA}$, as shown. $m\angle DAB = m\angle 1 + m\angle 2$, so $m\angle DAB > m\angle 2$. By the Isosceles Triangle Theorem, $m\angle D = m\angle 2$. By substitution, $m\angle DAB > m\angle D$. Then in $\triangle ABD$, $DB > AB$ by Theorem 4-11. We know that $DB = DC + CB$ so by substitution, $DC + CB > AB$. Since $DC = AC$, $AC + CB > AB$.

4-7a. The slope of $\overline{AB}$ is $-\frac{1}{2}$ and its midpoint is (4, 3). The perpendicular bisector of $\overline{AB}$ has slope 2 and contains (4, 3). Substituting in $y = mx + b$ produces $b = -5$. An equation is $y = 2x - 5$.

b. Sample answer: The point $C(5, 5)$ is on $y = 2x - 5$. $CA = \sqrt{10}$ and $CB = \sqrt{10}$. So $CA = CB$ and $\triangle ABC$ is an isosceles triangle.

4-8a. Construct the perpendicular bisectors of two sides of the triangle. Their point of intersection is equidistant from the vertices of the triangle. Using the point of intersection as the center, draw a circle that contains the vertices.

b. Students start with their own triangles, so diagrams will vary. To check students' work, be sure the center of each circle is the intersection of the perpendicular bisectors of two sides of the triangle.

c. The center of the circle is inside the triangle for acute triangles, on the triangle (at the midpoint of the hypotenuse) for right triangles, and outside the triangle for obtuse triangles.

CHAPTER 5

5-1a. Area $= \frac{2a}{5b} \cdot \frac{3b}{8} = \frac{3a}{20}$

b. Side $= \frac{5n}{2}$, Area $= \frac{25n^2}{4}$

c. Area $= (3m - 4n)^2 = 9m^2 - 24mn + 16n^2$

5-2 $P = 100$, so $DC + BC = 50$. Area $= 12(DC) = 18(CB)$, so $DC = \frac{3}{2}(CB)$. Then $\frac{3}{2}(CB) + CB = 50$ and $CB = 20$. Area $= 360$ units^2

5-3 Let $AB = AC = x$. Then $BC = 36 - 2x$ and $PC = 18 - x$. In $\triangle APC$, $12^2 + (18 - x)^2 = x^2$ so $x = 13$ and $AB = 13$ cm.

5-4a. If the altitude is 1 unit, then half the base is $\frac{1}{\sqrt{3}}$ and area $= 1 \cdot \frac{1}{\sqrt{3}} = \frac{1}{\sqrt{3}} = \frac{\sqrt{3}}{3}$.

b. If the length of a side of an equilateral triangle is s, then half its base is $\frac{s}{2}$ and its altitude is $\frac{s\sqrt{3}}{2}$. $A = \frac{s}{2} \cdot \frac{s\sqrt{3}}{2} = \frac{s^2\sqrt{3}}{4}$

c. $A = \frac{s^2\sqrt{3}}{4} = \frac{(6x)^2\sqrt{3}}{4} = 9x^2\sqrt{3}$ units^2

5-5 See back of book.

4-6(2) Prove Theorem 4-9: The sum of the lengths of any two sides of a triangle is greater than the length of the third side.

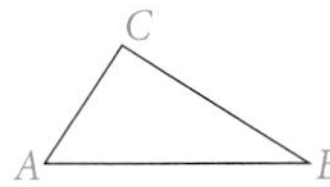

Given: $\triangle ABC$
Prove: $AC + CB > AB$

(*Hint:* Extend $\overrightarrow{BC}$ to point D so that $DC = AC$. Draw $\overline{DA}$ and use Theorem 4-11 with $\triangle ABD$.)

4-7 **a.** For the points $A(2, 4)$ and $B(6, 2)$, find an equation for the perpendicular bisector of $\overline{AB}$.

b. Select a point C on the perpendicular bisector of $\overline{AB}$ (except for the midpoint of $\overline{AB}$). What is the relation between CB and CA? What kind of triangle is $\triangle ABC$? Justify your answer.

4-8 A circle is circumscribed about a triangle if the vertices of the triangle are on the circle.

a. Explain how you can use the Perpendicular Bisector Construction to circumscribe a circle about a triangle.

b. Draw an acute triangle, an obtuse triangle, and a right triangle. Circumscribe a circle about each triangle.

c. Are the centers of the circles you constructed in part (b) inside, on, or outside the triangles?

CHAPTER 5

5-1 Find the area of each figure.

a. a rectangle with sides $\frac{2a}{5b}$ units and $\frac{3b}{8}$ units

b. a square with perimeter $10n$ units

c. a square with side $(3m - 4n)$ units

5-2 The perimeter of parallelogram $ABCD$ is 100 units. Find the area of the parallelogram.

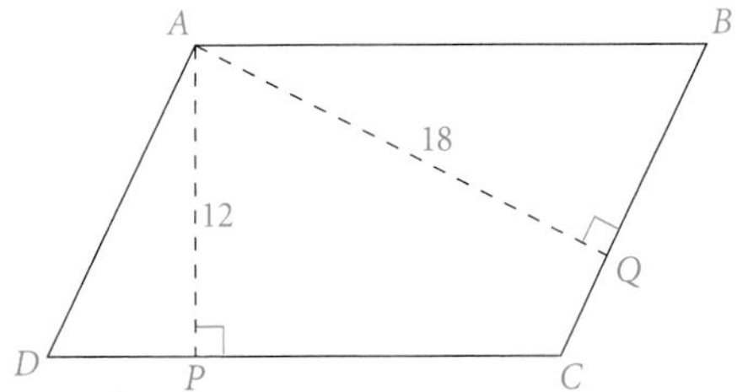

5-3 The perimeter of $\triangle ABC$ is 36 cm. $AB = AC$, $\overline{AP}$ bisects $\angle BAC$, and $AP = 12$ cm. Find AB.

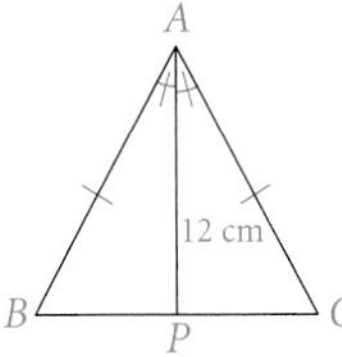

5-4 **a.** Find the area of an equilateral triangle with altitude 1 unit.

b. Use the relationships among the lengths of the sides in a 30°-60°-90° triangle to find a formula for the area of an equilateral triangle in terms of the length of a side. Explain each step.

c. Use your formula to find the area of an equilateral triangle with side $6x$ units.

5-5 In trapezoid $ABCD$, $\overline{AB} \parallel \overline{DC}$. Find the area of $ABCD$.

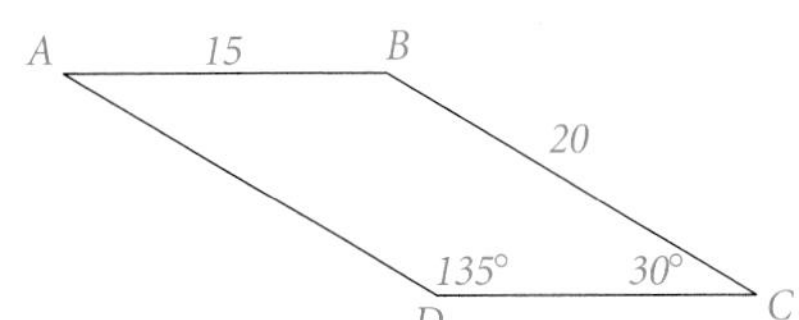

5-6a. The length of a side of each square is $\sqrt{10}$ cm. For the triangle,
$A = \frac{s^2\sqrt{3}}{4} = \frac{(\sqrt{10})^2\sqrt{3}}{4} = \frac{5\sqrt{3}}{2}$ cm^2.

b. For the triangles, $A = \frac{s^2\sqrt{3}}{4} = 10$. So, $s^2 = \frac{40}{\sqrt{3}} = \frac{40\sqrt{3}}{3}$ cm^2, which is the area of the square.

5-7 The lengths of the two arcs equal the circumference of a circle with radius 30 yd. Perimeter of the outside of the track $= 2(100) + 2\pi(30) = 200 + 60\pi \approx 388.5$ yd.

5-8 Let $PQ = 2$. Since $\triangle POQ$ is an isosceles right triangle, $OQ = \sqrt{2}$. Since OQ is a radius of the circle, $AB = 2\sqrt{2}$. The area of the large square is $(2\sqrt{2})^2 = 8$, of the circle is $\pi(\sqrt{2})^2 = 2\pi$, and of the small square is $2^2 = 4$. The blue area $= 8 - 2\pi \approx 1.7$. The red area $= 2\pi - 4 \approx 2.3$. The blue area is smaller.

CHAPTER 6

6-1 The square at the top (which will be opposite the 3) can be labeled with 11, 13, or 7. If the top square is 11, then the bottom square (which will be opposite the 2) must be 13 and there are two ways to label the 5 and 7. If the top square is 13, the bottom square must be 11 and there are two ways to label the 5 and 7. If the top square is 7, then the bottom square can be 11 or 13; there are two ways to label the remaining numbers for each choice. There are 8 ways to label the number cube.

6-2a. There are no cubes painted on 4 faces. The 8 corner cubes are painted on 3 faces. The 12 middle cubes on the edges are painted on 2 faces. The 6 cubes in the middle of the faces are painted on 1 face. The 1 cube in the middle of the large cube has no painted faces.

b. There are $(27)(6) = 162$ faces on the small cubes. Each of the 6 faces of the large cube has 9 small cubes with a painted face, so there are $(9)(6) = 54$ painted faces. There are $162 - 54 = 108$ unpainted faces. Each small cube is 4 in. on a side, so the area of a face is 16 in.^{2}. The total unpainted surface area is $(108)(16) = 1728$ in.^{2}.

6-3 The area of the disk is 100π and the area of the blue sector is 64π, so the area of the sector cut away is 36π. The measure of the angle of the cutaway sector is $\frac{36\pi}{100\pi}(360°) \approx 129.6°$.

6-4(1) Let e represent the edge of the cube. $e^3 = 2M$ and $6e^2 = 3M$. Multiplying the first equation by 3 and the second by 2 gives $3e^3 = 6M$ and $12e^2 = 6M$, so $3e^3 = 12e^2$ and $e = 4$. The edge of the cube is 4 units.

6-4(2) For cylinder A, if r is the radius and h is the height, the volume is $\pi r^2 h$. For cylinder B, the radius is $2r$ and the height is $\frac{h}{2}$, so the volume is $\pi(2r^2)\frac{h}{2} = 2\pi r^2 h$. The volume of cylinder B is twice the volume of cylinder A.

6-4(3) The lateral area of both cylinders is 8.5(11) in.^{2}. The circumference of the first cylinder is 11, so the radius is $\frac{11}{2\pi}$ and the volume is $\pi\left(\frac{11}{2\pi}\right)^2(8.5) \approx 81.8$ in.^{3}. The circumference of the second cylinder is 8.5, so the radius is $\frac{8.5}{2\pi}$ and the volume is

5-6 **a.** Find the area of the triangle if the area of each square is 10 cm^2.

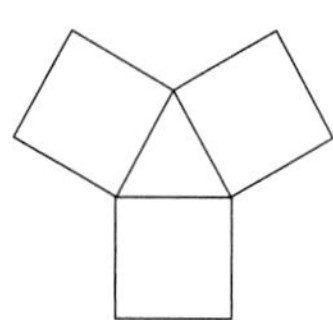

b. Find the area of the square if each triangle is equilateral with area 10 cm^2.

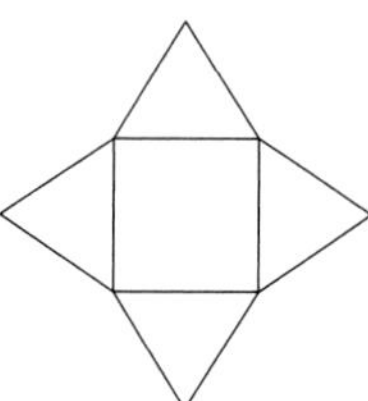

5-7 An athletic field is a rectangle, 100 yards by 40 yards, with a semicircle at each of the short sides. A running track 10 yards wide surrounds the field. Find the perimeter of the outside of the running track to the nearest tenth of a yard.

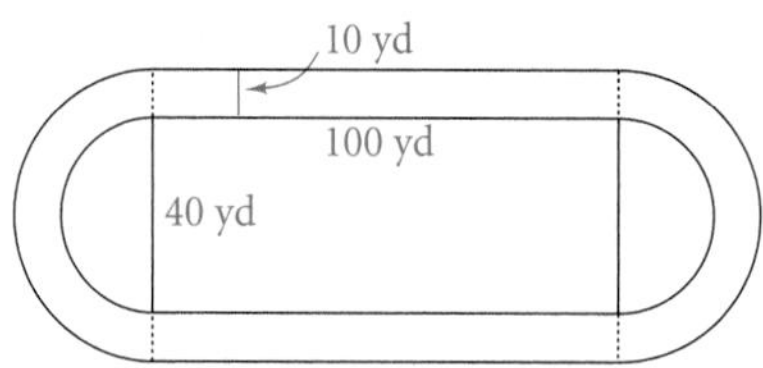

5-8 Circle O is inscribed in square $ABCD$ and square $PQRS$ is inscribed in circle O. Which is smaller, the blue area or the red area? Explain your answer.

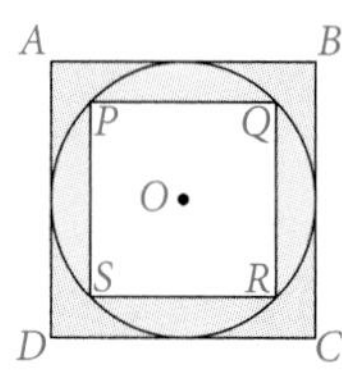

CHAPTER 6

6-1 Here is a net for a number cube. In how many ways can the unlabeled squares be labeled with 5, 7, 11, and 13, so that the sum of the numbers on opposite faces of the cube is a two-digit number? Explain your answer.

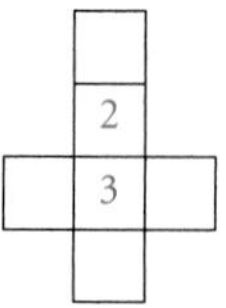

6-2 Each edge of the large cube is 12 inches. The cube is painted on the outside, and then it is cut into 27 smaller cubes.

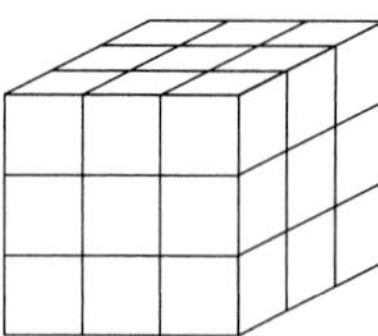

a. How many of the smaller cubes are painted on 4, 3, 2, 1, and 0 faces?
b. What is the total surface area that is unpainted?

6-3 A disk has radius 10 cm. A sector is cut out of the disk, and the radii are taped together without overlapping to form a cone.

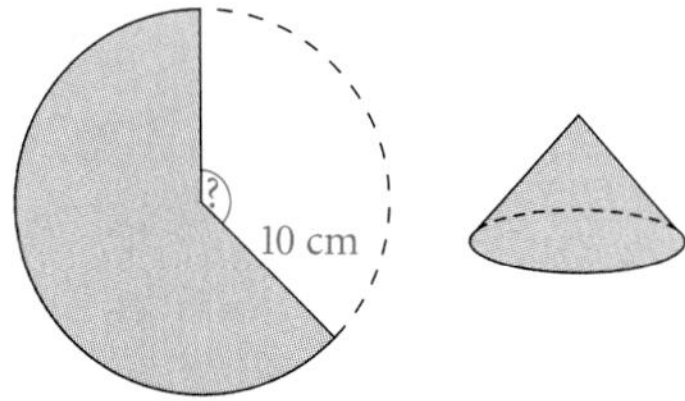

If the lateral area of the cone is 64π cm^2, find the central angle of the sector that was removed.

$\pi\left(\frac{8.5}{2\pi}\right)^2(11) \approx 63.2$ in.^{3}. The first cylinder has the greater volume.

6-5a. The circumference of the base of the cone is $\frac{3}{4}$ of the circumference of the disk $= \frac{3}{4}(2\pi)(10) = 15\pi \approx 47.1$ cm.

b. For the base of the cone, $C = 2\pi r = 15\pi$, so $r = 7.5$ cm. Then $A = \pi r^2 = \pi(7.5)^2 = 56.25\pi \approx 176.7$ cm^2.

c. The slant height, 10, is the hypotenuse of a right triangle with the radius, 7.5, as one leg and the height, h, of the cone as the other leg. So, $h = \sqrt{10^2 - 7.5^2} = \sqrt{43.75}$.

Then the volume is $\frac{1}{3}Bh = \frac{1}{3}(56.25\pi)(\sqrt{43.75}) \approx 389.6$ cm^3.

6-6a.

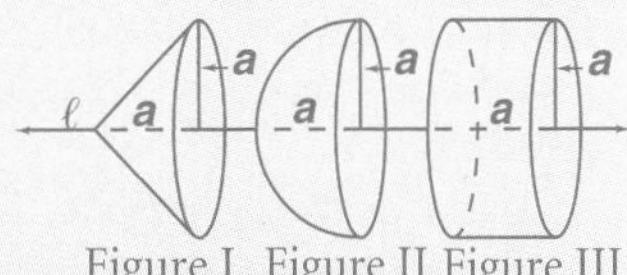

Figure I Figure II Figure III

The three-dimensional figures, from left to right, are a cone, a hemisphere, and a cylinder.

b. The volume of the cone is $\frac{1}{3}Bh = \frac{1}{3}(\pi a^2)(a) = \frac{1}{3}\pi a^3$.
The volume of the hemisphere is $\frac{1}{2}\left(\frac{4}{3}\right)\pi a^3 = \frac{2}{3}\pi a^3$.

The volume of the cylinder is $Bh = (\pi a^2)a = \pi a^3$.

The volume of the hemisphere is twice the volume of the cone. The volume of the cylinder is three times the volume of the cone.

6-7 If r is the radius of the base of the cone, then the diameter is $2r$. The height of the cone is also $2r$. The volume of the cone is $V = \frac{1}{3}(\pi r^2)h = \frac{1}{3}(\pi r^2)(2r) = \frac{2}{3}\pi r^3$. The volume of the hemisphere is $V = \frac{1}{2}\left(\frac{4}{3}\right)\pi r^3 = \frac{2}{3}\pi r^3$. There is the same amount of ice cream inside the cone as there is on top of it.

6-8 The gray area is $\pi(7)^2 - \pi(5)^2 = 24\pi$. The sum of the blue and red areas is $\pi(5)^2 - \pi(1)^2 = 24\pi$. The two probabilities are equal.

CHAPTER 7

7-1a. never; Since the lines lie in parallel planes that never intersect, the lines never intersect.

b. sometimes; Lines m and n can be the intersection of a plane P with planes M and N. Then m and n are coplanar because they are both in plane P.

c. sometimes; Lines m and n never intersect and if they are coplanar as in part (b), then they are parallel.

d. sometimes; Lines m and n never intersect and if they are not coplanar as in part (b), then they are skew.

7-2(1)a. $\angle A$ and $\angle D$ are supplementary by the Same-Side Interior Angles Theorem, so $2(3x - 13) + (3x + 17) = 180$ and $x = 21$. Then $m\angle C = 180 - m\angle B$ so $m\angle C = 180 - 5(x - 1) = 80$.

b. $m\angle D = 3x + 17 = 3(21) + 17 = 80$, so $\angle D \cong \angle C$ and $ABCD$ is an isosceles trapezoid.

6-4(1) A cube has a volume of $2M$ cubic units and a total surface area of $3M$ square units. Find the length of the edge of the cube.

6-4(2) The radius of cylinder B is twice the radius of cylinder A. The height of cylinder B is half the height of cylinder A. Compare their volumes.

6-4(3) A cylinder is formed by joining the shorter edges of a piece of paper 8.5 in. by 11 in. Another cylinder is formed by joining the longer edges of the same size paper. Do the two cylinders have the same lateral area? The same volume? Explain your answers.

6-5 A disk has radius 10 cm. A 90° sector is cut away, and a cone is formed.

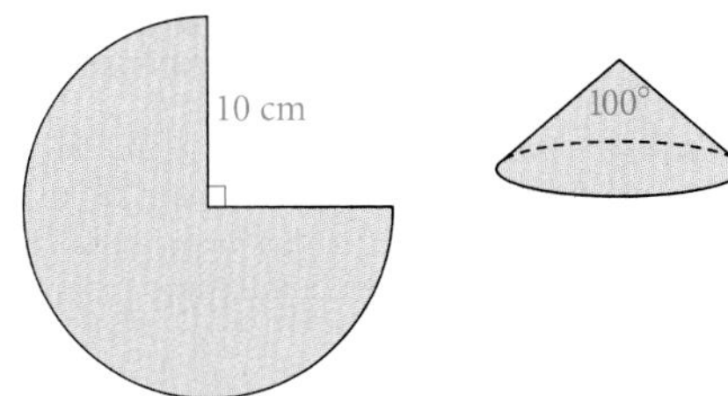

a. What is the circumference of the base of the cone?
b. What is the area of the base of the cone?
c. What is the volume of the cone? (*Hint:* Use the slant height and the radius of the base to find the height.)

6-6

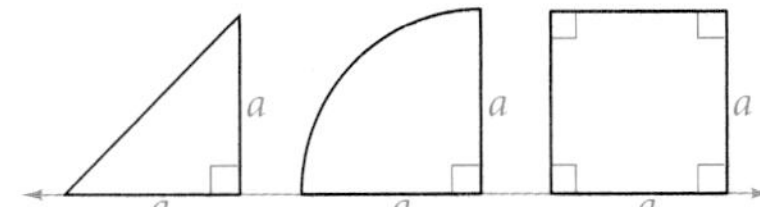

a. Sketch the space figures formed by rotating each of the above figures 360° about line ℓ. (*Hint:* The first figure is a cone.)
b. Compare the volumes of the three space figures.

6-7 The height of a cone for serving ice cream is the same as its diameter. The cone is filled with ice cream, and a hemisphere of ice cream covers the top of the cone. Compare the amount of ice cream inside the cone with the amount on top of it. Justify your answer.

6-8 A target has a central circle and three concentric rings. The diameters of the circles are 2, 6, 10, and 14.

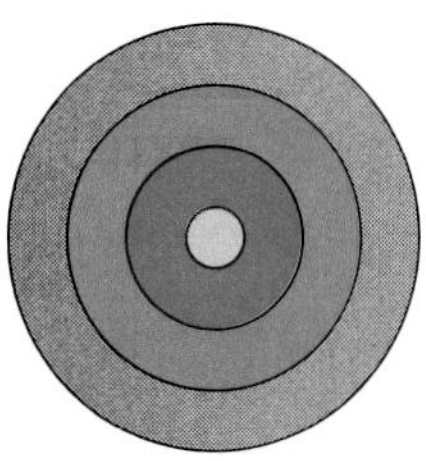

Compare the probability of landing in the gray region with the probability of landing in *either* the blue or red region.

CHAPTER 7

7-1 Line m is in plane M and line n is in plane N. Planes M and N are parallel. Complete the following statements with *sometimes, always,* or *never.* Justify each answer.
a. Lines m and n __?__ intersect.
b. Lines m and n are __?__ coplanar.
c. Lines m and n are __?__ parallel.
d. Lines m and n are __?__ skew.

7-2(1)

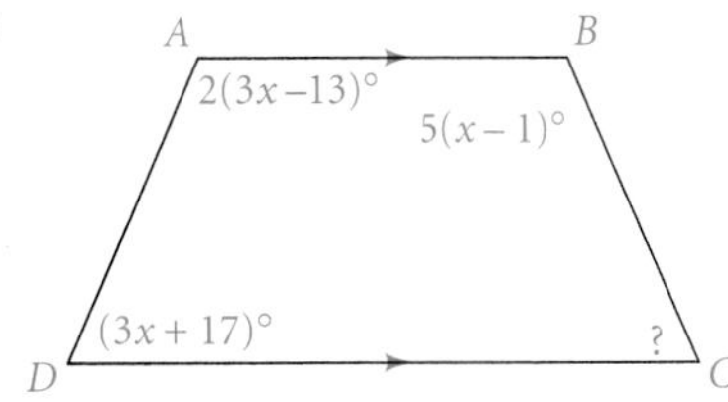

a. If $\overleftrightarrow{AB} \parallel \overleftrightarrow{DC}$, find $m\angle C$.
b. What kind of figure is $ABCD$? Justify your answer.

7-2(2) Sample proof: Since $\ell \perp n$, $\angle 2$ is a right angle. $\angle 2$ and $\angle 8$ are alternate interior angles formed by the parallel lines ℓ and m. So $\angle 2 \cong \angle 8$ and $\angle 8$ is a right angle. Therefore $m \perp n$ because they intersect to form right angles.

7-3 Sample answer: Construct the perpendicular bisectors of $\overline{AB}$ and $\overline{CD}$. Set the compass for the length $\frac{1}{2}AB$, place the compass point at the midpoint of $\overline{CD}$ and draw arcs that intersect the perpendicular bisector. Label the intersections E and F. Draw $\overline{EC}$, $\overline{ED}$, $\overline{FC}$, and $\overline{FD}$. The four small triangles are congruent by SAS so $\overline{EC} \cong \overline{ED} \cong \overline{FC} \cong \overline{FD}$ and $CEDF$ is a rhombus. The quadrilateral is a nonsquare rhombus.

7-4a.

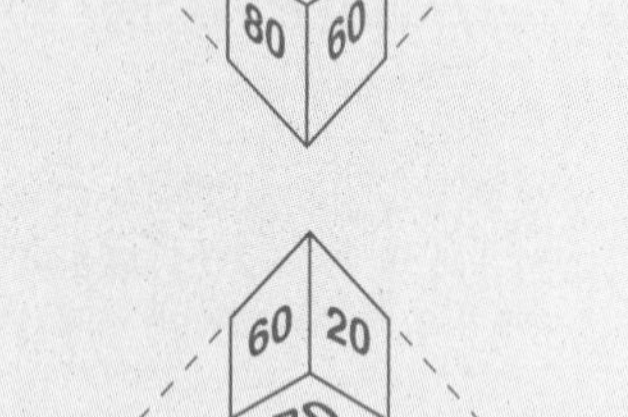

b.

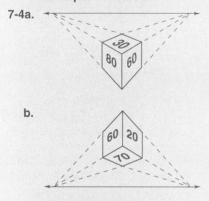

7-5(1) $C = 24{,}900 = 2\pi r$, so $r = \frac{24{,}900}{2\pi} \approx 3963$. $\triangle AOB$ is equilateral so $AB \approx 3963$ miles. $m\widehat{AB} = \frac{60}{360}(24{,}900) \approx 4150$. The tunnel is about 187 miles shorter.

7-5(2) Step 1: Assume that $\ell \nparallel m$.
Step 2: Since ℓ and m are two coplanar lines that are not parallel, they intersect at some point P. P is not on n because P is on lines that are parallel to n. So ℓ and n are two lines through P that are parallel to n. This contradicts Euclid's Parallel Postulate that through a point not on a line there is only one line parallel to the given line.
Step 3: Therefore the assumption in Step 1 is false and $\ell \parallel m$.

CHAPTER 8

8-1 Sample answers:

a. Given: $\overline{RS}$ is a median of $\triangle PQS$, and $\overline{PQ}$ is the base of isosceles $\triangle PQS$.

Prove: $\triangle PRS \cong \triangle QRS$

Proof: Since $\overline{PQ}$ is the base of isosceles $\triangle PQS$, $\overline{PS} \cong \overline{QS}$. Since $\overline{RS}$ is a median of $\triangle PQS$, R is the midpoint of $\overline{PQ}$ and $\overline{PR} \cong \overline{QR}$. $\overline{RS} \cong \overline{RS}$ by the Reflexive Property of $\cong$. So $\triangle PRS \cong \triangle QRS$ by SSS.

b. Given: $\overline{RS}$ is the bisector of $\angle PSQ$, and $\angle PSQ$ is the vertex angle of isosceles $\triangle PSQ$.

Prove: $\triangle PRS \cong \triangle QRS$

Proof: Since $\overline{RS}$ is the bisector of $\angle PSQ$, $\angle PSR \cong \angle QSR$. Since $\angle PSQ$ is the vertex angle of isosceles $\triangle PSQ$, $\overline{PS} \cong \overline{QS}$. $\overline{RS} \cong \overline{RS}$ by the Reflexive Property of $\cong$. So $\triangle PRS \cong \triangle QRS$ by SAS.

7-2(2) Prove: In a plane, if one of two parallel lines is perpendicular to a third line, the other is also.

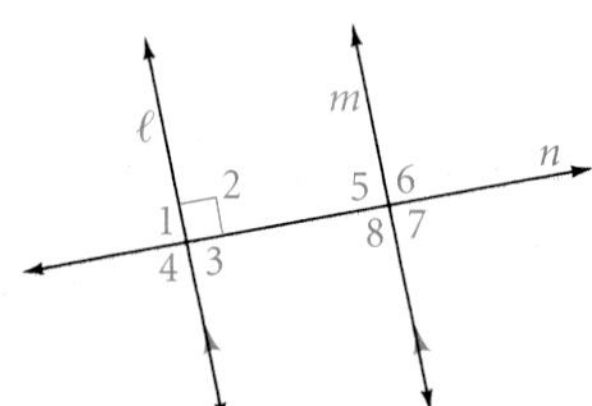

Given: $\ell \parallel m$, $\ell \perp n$
Prove: $m \perp n$

7-3 Draw two noncongruent segments $\overline{AB}$ and $\overline{CD}$. Construct a quadrilateral whose diagonals are congruent to $\overline{AB}$ and $\overline{CD}$ and whose diagonals are perpendicular bisectors of each other. What kind of quadrilateral do you think you have constructed? Justify your answer.

7-4 A small cube is centered inside a larger cube. The sum of the numbers on opposite faces of the small cube is 100.

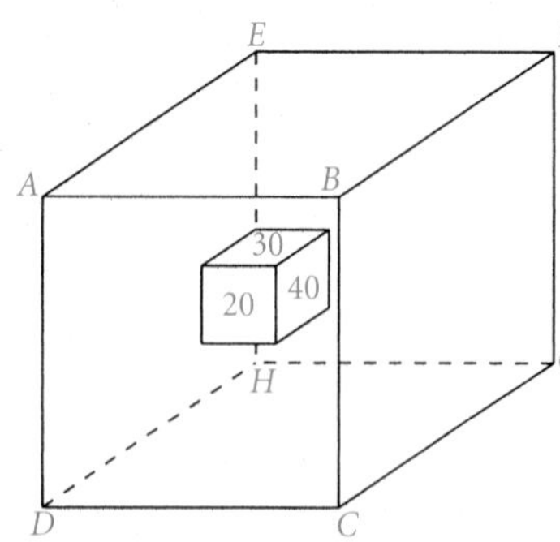

a. Make a two-point perspective drawing of the small cube as viewed from point E. Be sure to label the faces of the cube that are visible from that point.

b. Repeat part (a), using point D as the point of view.

7-5(1) Point O is the center of Earth and $m\angle AOB = 60$.

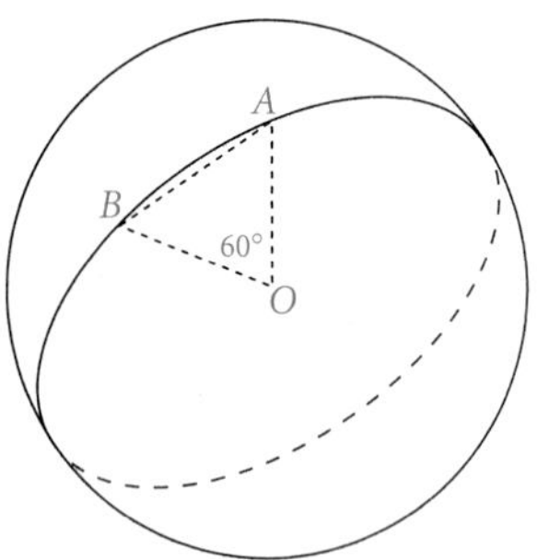

Suppose a straight tunnel is constructed from A to B. How much shorter is the tunnel than the distance from A to B along a great circle? (The circumference of Earth is about 24,900 mi.)

7-5(2) Use Euclid's Parallel Postulate and the definition of parallel lines (page 18) to write an indirect proof of this theorem: In a plane, two lines parallel to a third line are parallel to each other.

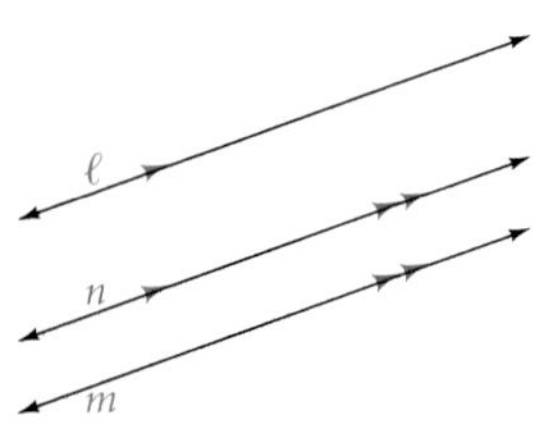

Given: $\ell \parallel n$, $m \parallel n$
Prove: $\ell \parallel m$

CHAPTER 8

8-1

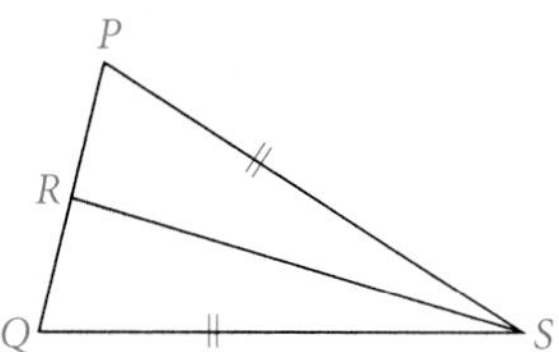

8-2 Sample answer:

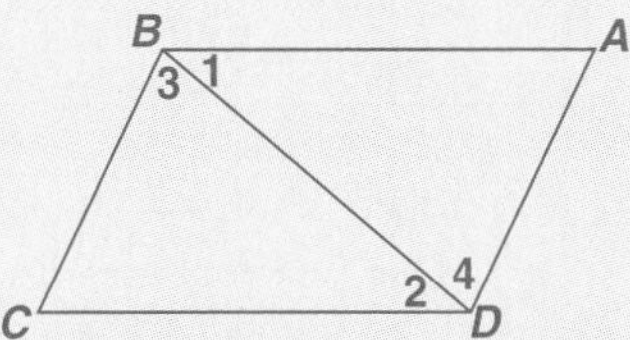

Given: *ABCD* is a parallelogram.
Prove: $\triangle ABD \cong \triangle CDB$
Proof: Since *ABCD* is a parallelogram, $\overleftrightarrow{AB} \parallel \overleftrightarrow{CD}$ and $\overleftrightarrow{BC} \parallel \overleftrightarrow{AD}$. $\angle 3 \cong \angle 4$ and $\angle 1 \cong \angle 2$ because they are alternate interior angles formed by parallel lines. $\overline{BD} \cong \overline{BD}$ by the Reflexive Property of $\cong$. So $\triangle ABD \cong \triangle CDB$ by ASA.

8-3 Sample answer—Given: $\overline{MQ}$ is the altitude to the base of isosceles $\triangle MNP$.
Prove: $\triangle PMQ \cong \triangle NMQ$
Proof: Since $\overline{NP}$ is the base of isosceles $\triangle MNP$, $\overline{MN} \cong \overline{MP}$. Since $\overline{MQ}$ is an altitude, $\angle MQN$ and $\angle MQP$ are right angles and $\triangle MQN$ and $\triangle MQP$ are right triangles. $\overline{MQ} \cong \overline{MQ}$ by the Reflexive Property of $\cong$. So $\triangle PMQ \cong \triangle NMQ$ by the HL Theorem.

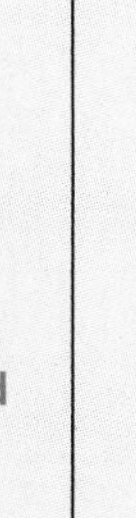

8-4(1) Sample answer:

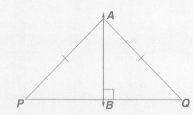

$\overleftrightarrow{AB}$ is drawn perpendicular to $\overline{PQ}$, so $\angle PBA$ and $\angle QBA$ are right angles and $\triangle PBA$ and $\triangle QBA$ are right triangles. $\overline{AB} \cong \overline{AB}$ by the Reflexive Property of $\cong$, and it is given that $\overline{AP} \cong \overline{AQ}$. So $\triangle PBA \cong \triangle QBA$ by the HL Theorem. $\overline{PB} \cong \overline{QB}$ by CPCTC, so *B* is the midpoint of $\overline{PQ}$ and $\overleftrightarrow{AB}$ is the perpendicular bisector of $\overline{PQ}$.

8-4(2) Since $\overline{PB} \perp \overrightarrow{AB}$ and $\overline{PC} \perp \overrightarrow{AC}$, $\triangle ABP$ and $\triangle ACP$ are right triangles. $\overline{AP} \cong \overline{AP}$ by the Reflexive Property of $\cong$ and it is given that $PB = PC$, so $\triangle ABP \cong \triangle ACP$ by the HL Theorem. $\angle BAP \cong \angle CAP$ by CPCTC and $\overrightarrow{AB}$ bisects $\angle BAC$ by the defintion of angle bisector.

8-5 Sample answer:

a.

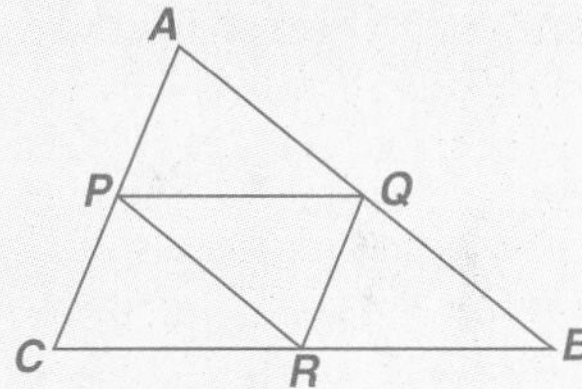

b. Given: $\overline{PQ}$, $\overline{QR}$, and $\overline{RP}$ are midsegments of $\triangle ABC$.
Prove: $\triangle AQP \cong \triangle QBR \cong \triangle PRC \cong \triangle RPQ$
Proof: Since $\overline{RP}$ is a midsegment, *R* is the midpoint of $\overline{BC}$ and $\overline{BR} \cong \overline{CR}$. Since $\overline{PQ}$ is a midsegment it is half the length of $\overline{BC}$. So $\overline{PQ} \cong \overline{BR} \cong \overline{CR}$.
Similarly, $\overline{PR} \cong \overline{AQ} \cong \overline{BQ}$ and $\overline{QR} \cong \overline{AP} \cong \overline{CP}$. So $\triangle AQP \cong \triangle QBR \cong \triangle PRC \cong \triangle RPQ$ by SSS.

CHAPTER 9

9-1(1) and 9-1(2) See back of book.

a. Prove that if $\overline{RS}$ is the median to the base of isosceles $\triangle PQS$, then $\triangle PRS \cong \triangle QRS$. As part of your proof, state what is given and what is to be proved.

b. Prove that if $\overline{RS}$ bisects the vertex angle of isosceles $\triangle PQS$, then $\triangle PRS \cong \triangle QRS$. Again, state what is given and what is to be proved.

8-2 Prove this statement: If $\overline{BD}$ is a diagonal of parallelogram *ABCD*, then $\overline{BD}$ divides the parallelogram into two congruent triangles. Be sure your proof contains a diagram, a statement of what is given, and a statement of what is to be proved.

8-3

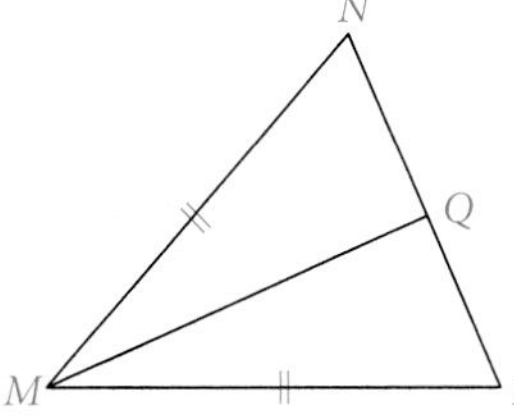

Prove that if $\overline{MQ}$ is the altitude to the base of isosceles $\triangle MNP$, then $\triangle PMQ \cong \triangle NMQ$. As part of your proof, state what is given and what is to be proved.

8-4(1) Prove Theorem 4-13: If a point is equidistant from the endpoints of a segment, then it is on the perpendicular bisector of the segment.

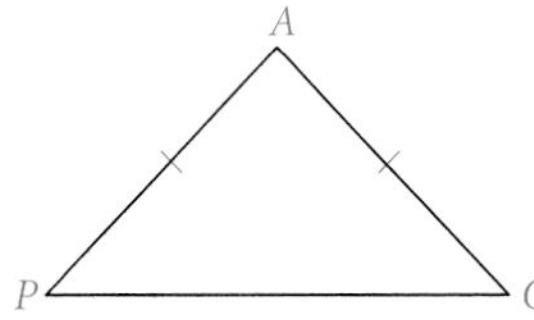

Given: $AP = AQ$
To prove that *A* is on the perpendicular bisector of $\overline{PQ}$, draw the line through *A* that is perpendicular to $\overline{PQ}$ and label the intersection *B*. Complete the proof by showing that $\overleftrightarrow{AB}$ is the perpendicular bisector of $\overline{PQ}$.

8-4(2) Prove Theorem 4-15: If a point in the interior of an angle is equidistant from the sides of the angle, then it is on the angle bisector.

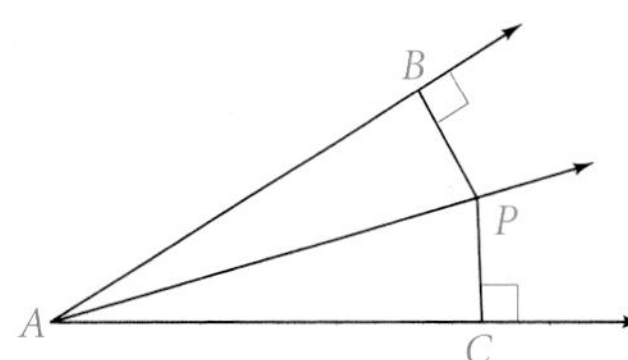

Given: $\overline{PB} \perp \overrightarrow{AB}$, $\overline{PC} \perp \overrightarrow{AC}$, $PB = PC$
Prove: $\overrightarrow{AP}$ bisects $\angle BAC$

8-5 **a.** Draw a triangle and its three midsegments.
b. Prove that the four small triangles in your drawing are congruent. State what is given and what is to be proved using the letters in your drawing.

CHAPTER 9

9-1(1)a. Prove that if two sides and the included angle of one parallelogram are congruent to the corresponding parts of another parallelogram, then the parallelograms are congruent. (*Hint:* Prove that all the corresponding parts of the parallelograms are congruent.)
b. Is there a theorem similar to SAS for trapezoids? Explain.

9-1(2)

Given: $\square ABCD$, and $\overline{AC}$ bisects $\angle A$.
Prove: $\overline{AC}$ bisects $\angle C$.

9-2 By construction, $\overline{AB} \cong \overline{CD}$ and $\overline{AC} \cong \overline{BD}$. Then $ABDC$ is a parallelogram because both pairs of opposite sides are congruent. M is the midpoint of $\overline{BC}$ because the diagonals of a parallelogram bisect each other, and $\overline{AM}$ is a median by the definition of median.

9-3a. Suppose the radius of circle O is 1. Then the area of circle O is $\pi(1)^2 \approx 3.14$. $BE = 2$, so $BC = 2$. $m\angle CBE$ is 60, so $\triangle BCE$ is equilateral. That means $CE = 2$. The altitude from B in $\triangle BCE$ is $\sqrt{3}$, so $BD = 2\sqrt{3}$. Thus the area of $BCDE$ is $\frac{1}{2}d_1d_2 = \frac{1}{2}(2)(2\sqrt{3}) = 2\sqrt{3} \approx 3.46$. The area of the rhombus is greater than the area of the circle.

b. $\dfrac{\text{Area of circle}}{\text{Area of rhombus}} = \dfrac{\pi}{2\sqrt{3}}$ or $\dfrac{\pi\sqrt{3}}{6}$

9-4. Sample answer:

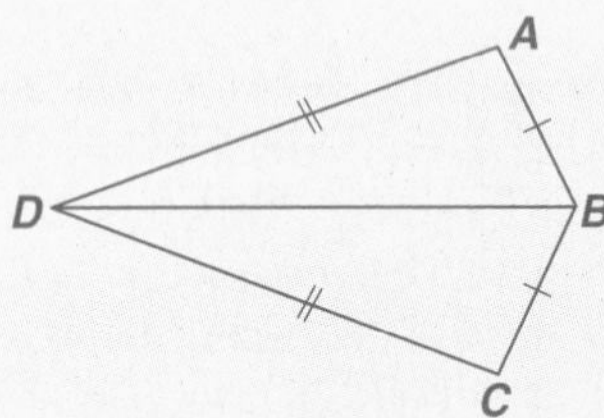

Given: Kite $ABCD$ with $\overline{AB} \cong \overline{BC}$ and $\overline{CD} \cong \overline{DA}$

Prove: $\angle A \cong \angle C$

Proof: Draw diagonal $\overline{DB}$. Since $\overline{DB} \cong \overline{DB}$ by the Reflexive Property of $\cong$ and it is given that $\overline{AB} \cong \overline{BC}$ and $\overline{CD} \cong \overline{DA}$, $\triangle ABD \cong \triangle CBD$ by SSS. $\angle A \cong \angle C$ by CPCTC.

9-4(2) It is a rhombus

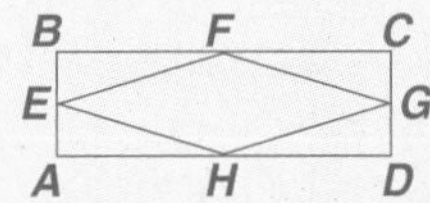

Given: $ABCD$ is a rectangle, and E, F, G, and H, are midpoints.

Prove: $EFGH$ is a rhombus.

Plan: By Thm. 9-12, the diagonals of the rectangle are congruent. By Thm 4-8, the sides of $EFGH$ are parallel to and half the length of the diagonals of the rectangle. So, the sides of $EFGH$ are congruent and opposite sides are parallel.

9-5a.

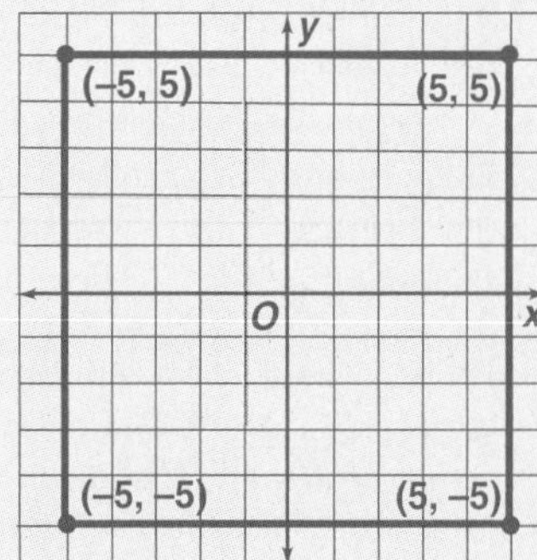

b.

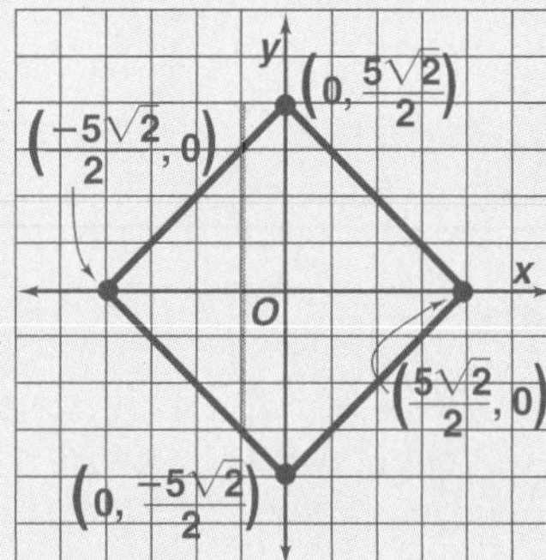

9-2 In this figure, point D is constructed by drawing an arc with center C and radius AB and an arc with center B and radius AC. Prove that $\overline{AM}$ is a median of $\triangle ABC$.

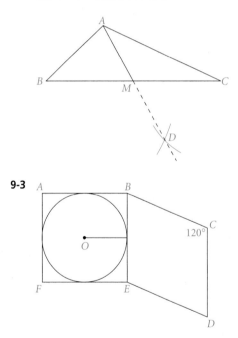

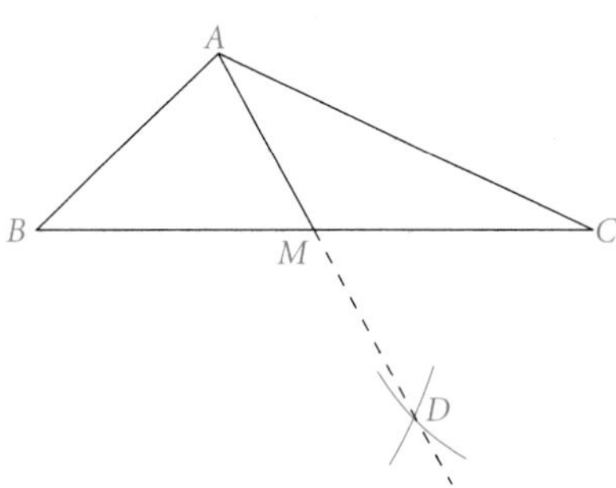

9-3 A B 120° C O F E D

Circle O is inscribed in square $ABEF$. $BCDE$ is a rhombus, and $m\angle C = 120$.

a. Which is greater, the area of circle O or the area of rhombus $BCDE$?

b. Find the exact value for the ratio of the area of the circle to the area of the rhombus. Explain your answer.

9-4(1) Prove that the angles formed by the noncongruent sides of a kite are congruent. (*Hint:* Draw a diagonal of the kite.)

9-4(2) Join the midpoints of consecutive sides of a rectangle. Make a conjecture about the quadrilateral formed, and prove the conjecture.

9-5 Suppose each quadrilateral described below is placed on a coordinate grid so that the diagonals intersect at the origin. Find the coordinates of the vertices of each quadrilateral.

a. A square has horizontal and vertical sides, and the length of each side is 10 units.

b. A square has horizontal and vertical diagonals, and the length of each side is 5 units.

c. The sides of a rectangle are in the ratio 2 : 3. The length of a shorter side is n and it is horizontal.

9-6 a. The endpoints of $\overline{AB}$ are $A(-1, 5)$ and $B(8, 26)$. Find the coordinates of the points on $\overline{AB}$ that divide $\overline{AB}$ into three congruent segments.

b. If the endpoints of $\overline{XY}$ are (a, b) and (p, q), find the coordinates of the points on $\overline{XY}$ that divide $\overline{XY}$ into three congruent segments.

CHAPTER 10

10-1 a. In the Fibonacci Sequence, each term after the first two is the sum of the two preceding terms. Find the next seven terms of the Fibonacci Sequence 1, 1, 2, 3, 5, 8, 13, . . .

b. The first four ratios of each term to its preceding term are shown below.

$\frac{1}{1} = 1$ $\qquad \frac{2}{1} = 2$

$\frac{3}{2} = 1.5$ $\qquad \frac{5}{3} = 1.6667$

Calculate the next nine ratios. When necessary, round to the nearest ten thousandth.

c. Express the Golden Ratio, $\frac{1 + \sqrt{5}}{2}$, in decimal form rounded to the nearest ten thousandth. What do you notice?

10-2 A triangle has vertices $A(-1, 3)$, $B(2, 5)$, and $C(1, -2)$. $\triangle A'B'C'$ is the image of $\triangle ABC$ under the dilation with center $(0, 0)$ and scale factor 3. Find the coordinates of A', B', and C' and use them to prove that $\triangle ABC \sim \triangle A'B'C'$.

c. If the length is ℓ then $\frac{n}{\ell} = \frac{2}{3}$ and $\ell = \frac{3n}{2}$.

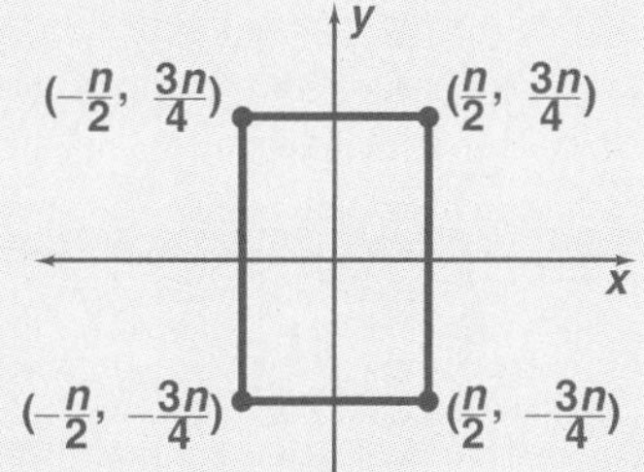

9-6a. The translation from (−1, 5) to (8, 26) is ⟨9, 21⟩, so one third of that translation is ⟨3, 7⟩. Applying that translation to (−1, 5), the result is (−1 + 3, 5 + 7) = (2, 12). Applying it again, the result is (2 + 3, 12 + 7) = (5, 19). To check: a third application results in (5 + 3, 19 + 7) = (8, 26), which is point *B*.

b. The translation from (*m*, *n*) to (*p*, *q*) is ⟨*p* − *m*, *q* − *n*⟩. One point is $\left(m + \frac{p - m}{3}, n + \frac{q - n}{3}\right)$ or $\left(\frac{2m + p}{3}, \frac{2n + q}{3}\right)$.

The other point is $\left(\frac{2m + p}{3} + \frac{p - m}{3}, \frac{2n + q}{3} + \frac{q - n}{3}\right)$ or $\left(\frac{m + 2p}{3}, \frac{n + 2q}{3}\right)$.

CHAPTER 10

10-1a. The next 7 terms are 21, 34, 55, 89, 144, 233, and 377.

b. $\frac{8}{5} = 1.6$ $\quad \frac{13}{8} \approx 1.625$

$\frac{21}{13} \approx 1.6154$ $\quad \frac{34}{21} \approx 1.6190$

$\frac{55}{34} \approx 1.6176$ $\quad \frac{89}{55} \approx 1.6182$

$\frac{144}{89} \approx 1.6180$ $\quad \frac{233}{144} \approx 1.6181$

$\frac{377}{233} \approx 1.6180$

c. $\frac{1 + \sqrt{5}}{2} \approx 1.6180$

The ratio of consecutive terms in the Fibonacci sequence approaches the Golden Ratio.

10-2 In △*ABC*, $AB = \sqrt{13}$, $BC = 5\sqrt{2}$, and $AC = \sqrt{29}$. For △*A′B′C′*, the three vertices are *A′*(−3, 9), *B′*(6, 15), and *C′*(3, −6). $A'B' = 3\sqrt{13}$, $B'C' = 15\sqrt{2}$, and $A'C' = 3\sqrt{29}$. The ratio of each pair of corresponding sides is 1 : 3, so the sides are proportional and △*ABC* ~ △*A′B′C′* by the SSS~ Theorem.

10-3(1)a.

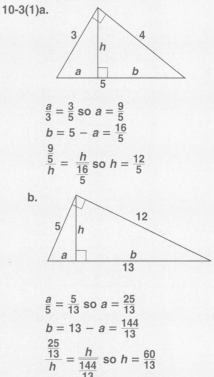

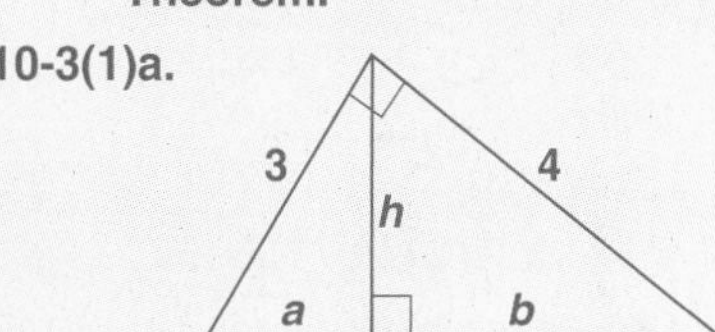

$\frac{a}{3} = \frac{3}{5}$ so $a = \frac{9}{5}$

$b = 5 - a = \frac{16}{5}$

$\frac{\frac{9}{5}}{h} = \frac{h}{\frac{16}{5}}$ so $h = \frac{12}{5}$

b.

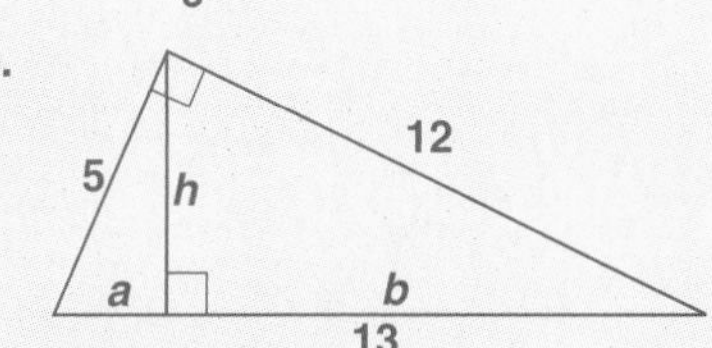

$\frac{a}{5} = \frac{5}{13}$ so $a = \frac{25}{13}$

$b = 13 - a = \frac{144}{13}$

$\frac{\frac{25}{13}}{h} = \frac{h}{\frac{144}{13}}$ so $h = \frac{60}{13}$

10-3(1)c. through 11-3 See back of book.

10-3(1) Each Pythagorean triple listed below represents the lengths of the sides of a right triangle. For each triangle, find the length of the altitude to the hypotenuse.

a. 3, 4, 5
b. 5, 12, 13
c. 8, 15, 17

10-3(2) Britt says that the product of the lengths of the legs of a right triangle equals the product of the lengths of the hypotenuse and the altitude drawn to the hypotenuse. Is she right? Explain.

10-4 **a.** Write a definition for a midsegment of a parallelogram.
b. Prove that a midsegment of a parallelogram is parallel to two sides of the parallelogram.
c. Prove that a midsegment of a parallelogram bisects the diagonals of the parallelogram.

10-5 Complete each statement with *sometimes, always,* or *never.* Justify your answers.
a. Two similar rectangles with the same perimeter are __?__ congruent.
b. Two rectangles with the same area are __?__ similar.
c. Two regular hexagons are __?__ similar.
d. A pentagon and a hexagon are __?__ similar.
e. Similar triangles __?__ have the same area.
f. A trapezoid is __?__ similar to a parallelogram.

10-6 Two right square pyramids, pyramid *A* and pyramid *B*, are similar. For pyramid *A*, each edge of the base is 12 cm. For pyramid *B*, each edge of the base is 3 cm and the volume is 6 cm^3.
a. Find the volume of pyramid *A*.
b. Find the ratio of the surface area of pyramid *A* to the surface area of pyramid *B*.
c. Find the surface area of each pyramid.

CHAPTER 11

11-1 Use the given information to find $m\angle A$. Round to the nearest whole number.
a. $\tan 2A = 9.5144$
b. $\tan \frac{A}{3} = 0.4663$
c. $(\tan 5A)^2 = 0.3333$
d. $\frac{\tan A}{1 + \tan A} = 0.5437$

11-2

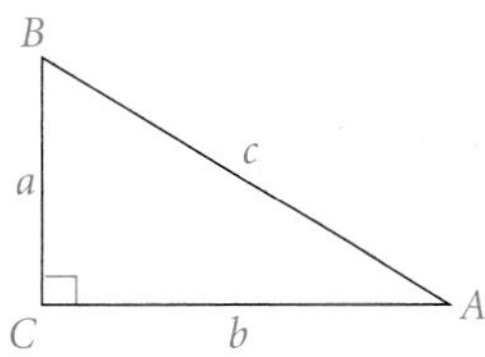

Prove that the value of each expression is 1.
a. $(\sin A)^2 + (\cos A)^2$
b. $(\sin B)^2 + (\cos B)^2$
c. $\frac{1}{(\cos A)^2} - (\tan A)^2$

11-3

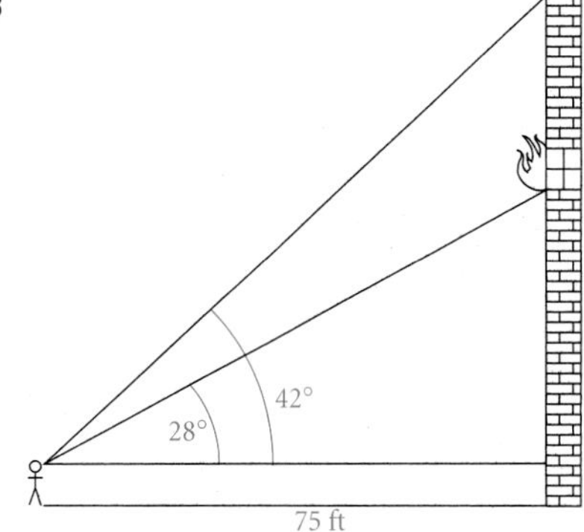

A firefighter spots a fire in the window of a building at an angle of elevation of 28°. The angle of elevation to the top of the building is 42°. The firefighter is 75 ft from the building and her eyes are 5 ft above the ground. Will a 30-ft rope ladder lowered from the top of the building reach the window? Explain your reasoning.

11-4(1)a.

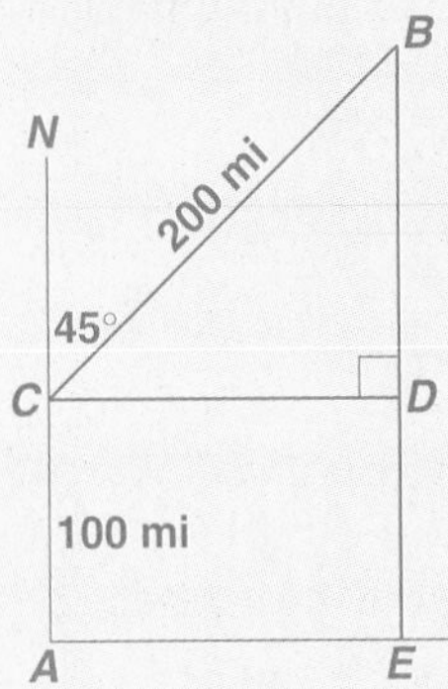

$\triangle BCD$ is an isosceles right triangle with hypotenuse 200, so $BD = CD = \frac{200}{\sqrt{2}} =$ $100\sqrt{2} \approx 141.4$. The plane traveled $100 + 141.4 = 241.4$ miles north, and 141.4 miles east.

b.

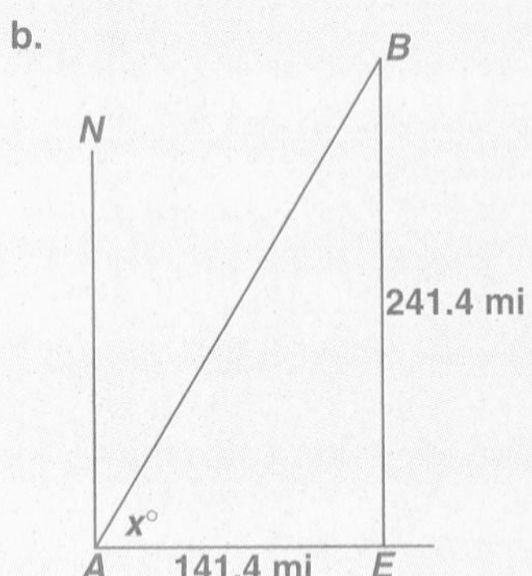

$AB = \sqrt{241.4^2 + 141.4^2} \approx$ 280 mi

$\tan x° = \frac{242.4}{141.4} \approx 1.7072$

$x° = \tan^{-1}(1.7072) \approx 60°$

The magnitude of $\overrightarrow{AB'}$ is about 280 miles and its direction is about 30° east of north.

11-4(2)

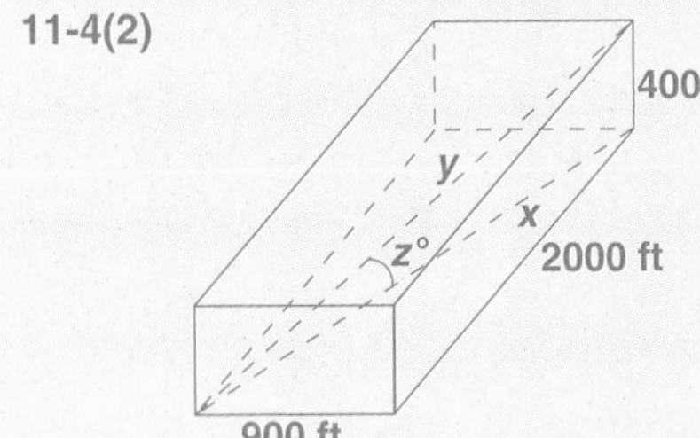

$x = \sqrt{900^2 + 2000^2} \approx 2193.17$

$y = \sqrt{x^2 + 400^2} \approx 2229$

$z = \tan^{-1}\left(\frac{400}{x}\right) \approx 10$

the magnitude of the vector is about 2229 ft and the angle of elevation of the balloon is about 10°.

11-5a. Addition of vectors is commutative because addition of real numbers is commutative. Proof: $\langle x_1, y_1\rangle + \langle x_2, y_2\rangle =$ $\langle x_1 + x_2, y_1 + y_2\rangle =$ $\langle x_2 + x_1, y_2 + y_1\rangle =$ $\langle x_2, y_2\rangle + \langle x_1, y_1\rangle$ Similarly, addition of vectors is associative because addition of real numbers is associative. Since addition of vectors is commutative and associative, the sum of the three flight vectors, taken in any order, must be the same. The helicopter always lands at the same place.

b. Since addition of vectors is commutative, when the order of the first two flights is switched, the second flight ends at the same place as the second flight of the first trip.

11-6

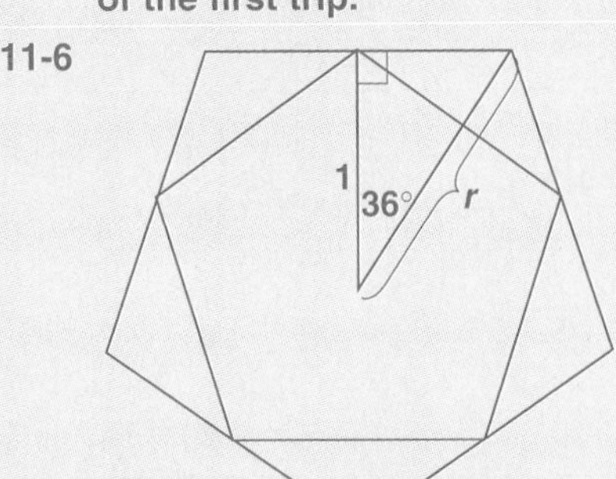

11-4(1) A plane took off from airport A, flew north for 100 miles, then 45° east of north for 200 miles, and landed at airport B.

a. How far north did the plane travel? How far east did it travel?

b. Find the magnitude and direction of the vector that describes a direct flight from A to B.

11-4(2) A hot air balloon traveled 2000 ft north and 900 ft east, and it rose 400 ft. This trip can be described with the vector $\langle 2000, 900, 400\rangle$. What is the magnitude of the vector? What is the angle of elevation of the balloon from its starting point?

11-5 A helicopter starts at (0, 0) and makes three flights represented by the vectors $\langle 10, 10\rangle$, $\langle 5, -4\rangle$, and $\langle -3, 5\rangle$, in that order.

a. If the same flights were made in a different order, could the helicopter end the trip at a different place? Justify your answer.

b. If the same flights were made in a different order, could the second flight end at the same place as the second flight of the original trip? Justify your answer.

11-6 Segments are drawn between the midpoints of consecutive sides of a regular pentagon to form another regular pentagon. Find, to the nearest hundredth, the ratio of the area of the smaller pentagon to the area of the larger pentagon.

CHAPTER 12

12-1 **a.** On a graph, shade the intersection of the graphs of these inequalities.

$$(x - 3)^2 + (y - 5)^2 \leq 64$$
$$(x - 3)^2 + (y - 5)^2 \geq 25$$
$$y \geq \tfrac{2}{3}x + 3$$

b. Find the area of the overlapping region graphed in part (a).

c. Add $y \leq 5$ to the list of inequalities in part (a). Shade the intersection of the graphs of all four inequalities. Find its area.

12-2(1) $\overline{PR}$ is tangent to circle O at R, $OP = 17$ cm, and $RP = 15$ cm.

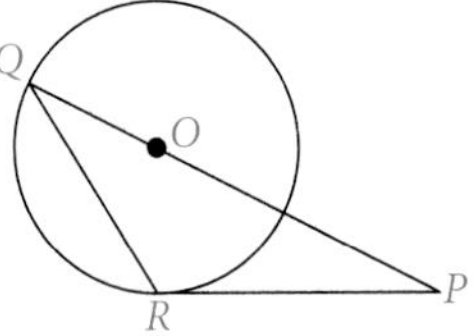

Find the area of $\triangle QPR$ to the nearest tenth of a square centimeter.

12-2(2) Write an indirect proof of Theorem 12-3: If a line in the same plane as a circle is perpendicular to a radius at its endpoint on the circle, then the line is tangent to the circle.

Given: $\odot O$, $\overline{OP} \perp \overleftrightarrow{PQ}$
Prove: $\overleftrightarrow{PQ}$ is tangent to $\odot O$.
(*Hint:* The diagram illustrates the assumption that $\overleftrightarrow{PQ}$ intersects the circle in a second point, Q.)

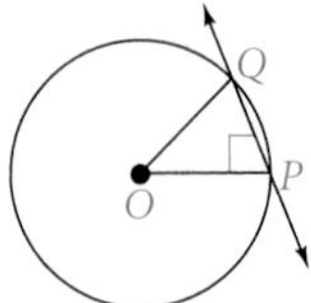

12-3 If two circles are concentric and a chord of the larger circle is tangent to the smaller circle, prove that the point of tangency is the midpoint of the chord.

12-4(1) Prove that a trapezoid inscribed in a circle must be isosceles.

12-4(2) Bisect the angles of a quadrilateral inscribed in a circle. Join consecutive intersections of the bisectors with the circle. Repeat with various shapes of inscribed quadrilaterals. Make a conjecture about the quadrilateral formed by joining the vertices.

Let the radius of the small pentagon be 1 unit and the radius of the large pentagon be r. Then $\cos 36^\circ = \frac{1}{r}$. The ratio of the areas equals the ratio of the squares of the radii.

$\frac{1^2}{r^2} = \left(\frac{1}{r}\right)^2 = (\cos 36^\circ)^2 \approx 0.65$

CHAPTER 12

12-1a.

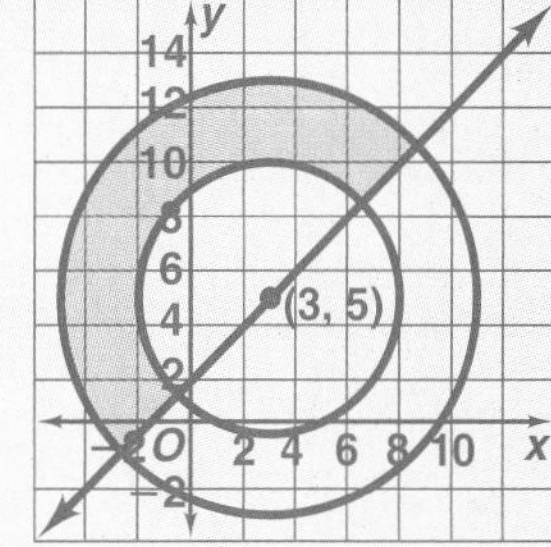

b. The area of the shaded region is the area of a semicircle of radius 8 minus the area of a semicircle of radius 5.

$A = \frac{1}{2}\pi 8^2 - \frac{1}{2}\pi 5^2 = \frac{39}{2}\pi \approx$ 61.3 units^2

c.

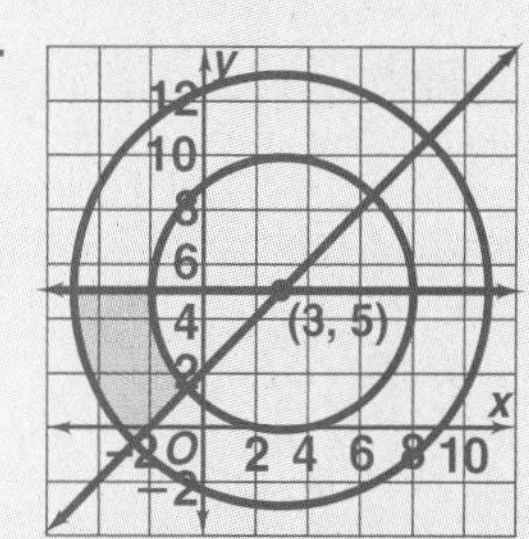

The circles have the same center, (3, 5), and the two lines go through the center of the circle. The lines form an acute central angle whose tangent is $\frac{2}{3}$, so the measure of the angle is $\tan^{-1}\left(\frac{2}{3}\right) \approx 33.69^\circ$. The circles have radii of 8 and 5, so the area of the ring is $64\pi - 25\pi = 39\pi$. The area of the shaded region is $\frac{33.69}{360}(39\pi) \approx$ 11.5 units^2.

12-2(1)

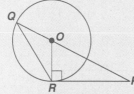

$\triangle POR$ is an 8-15-17 right triangle, so $OR = 8$, $QO = 8$, and $QP = 8 + 17 = 25$. If h is the altitude of $\triangle QPR$, then $h = 15 \sin P$. In $\triangle ORP$, $\sin P = \frac{8}{17}$. So the area of $\triangle QPR = \frac{1}{2}(QP)(h) = \frac{1}{2}(25)(15)\left(\frac{8}{17}\right) \approx 88.2$ cm^2.

12-2(2) Assume $\overline{OP}$ is not tangent to $\odot O$ at P. Then $\overrightarrow{PQ}$ intersects $\odot O$ at some other point Q. $OQ = OP$ since they are both radii. By the Isosceles Triangle Theorem, $m\angle OQP = m\angle OPQ$. Since $\overline{OP} \perp \overrightarrow{PQ}$, $m\angle OPQ = 90 = m\angle OQP$. This contradicts the fact that there cannot be two right angles in one triangle. So the assumption that $\overline{OP}$ is *not* tangent to $\odot O$ at P is false. Therefore, $\overline{OP}$ is tangent to $\odot O$ at P.

12-3 through 12-6 See back of book.

12-4(3) Prove Theorem 12-11: The measure of an angle formed by a chord and a tangent that intersect on a circle is half the measure of the intercepted arc.

The proof of this theorem can be divided into three cases.

Case 1. The center of the circle is on the chord.

Case 2. The center of the circle is in the interior of the angle.

Case 3. The center of the circle is in the exterior of the angle.

a. Prove Case 1.

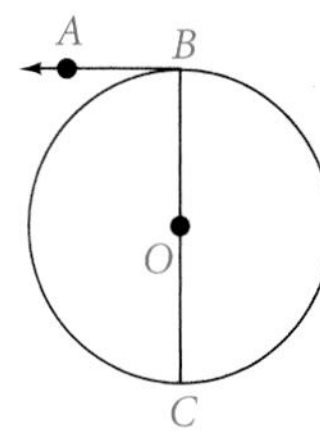

Given: $\overleftrightarrow{AB}$ tangent to $\odot O$ at B and O is on $\overline{BC}$.
Prove: $m\angle ABC = \frac{1}{2}m\widehat{BDC}$

b. Prove Case 2.

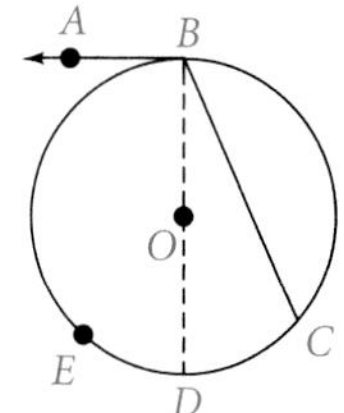

Given: $\overleftrightarrow{AB}$ is tangent to $\odot O$ at B and O is in the interior of $\angle ABC$.
Prove: $m\angle ABC = \frac{1}{2}m\widehat{BDC}$
Plan for Proof: Use the result of Case 1, $m\angle DBC = \frac{1}{2}m\widehat{DC}$, and $m\widehat{BDC} = m\widehat{BED} + m\widehat{DC}$.

c. Prove Case 3.

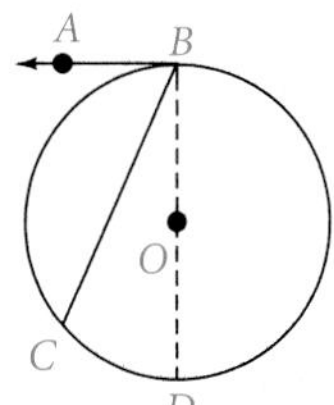

Given: $\overleftrightarrow{AB}$ is tangent to $\odot O$ at B and O is in the exterior of $\angle ABC$.
Prove: $m\angle ABC = \frac{1}{2}m\widehat{BC}$
Plan for Proof: Similar to Case 2, but use $m\widehat{BC} = m\widehat{BCD} - m\widehat{DC}$.

12-5 If an equilateral triangle is inscribed in a circle, prove that the tangents to the circle at the vertices form an equilateral triangle.

12-6 The radius of each circle is 5 cm and $\triangle PQR$ is equilateral.

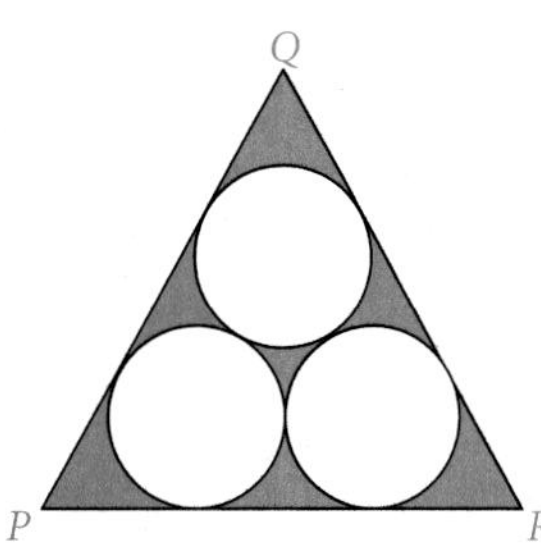

a. Find the perimeter of $\triangle PQR$.
b. Find the area of the red region.

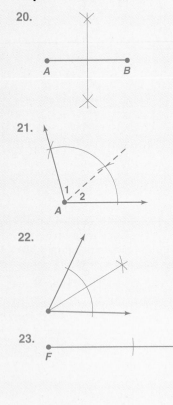

20.

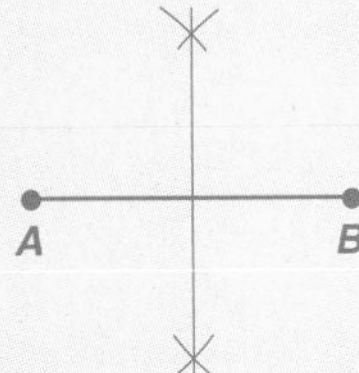

21.

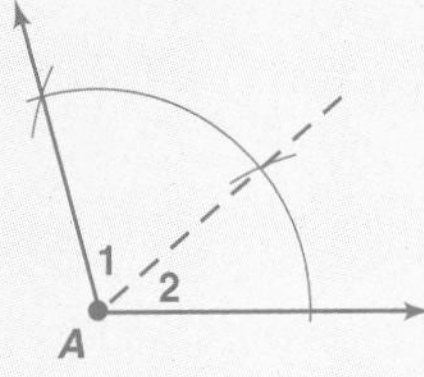

22.

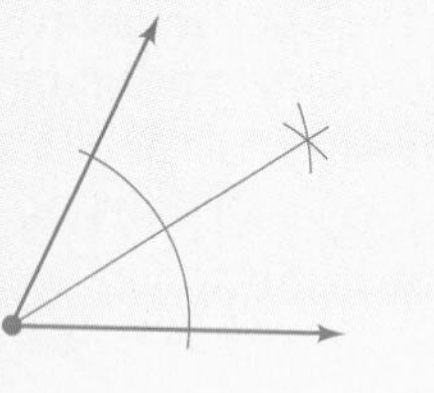

23. F G

CHAPTER 1

Extra Practice

Find the next two terms in each sequence. ■ Lesson 1-1

1. 12, 17, 22, 27, 32, . . . 37, 42
2. 1, 1.1, 1.11, 1.111, 1.1111, . . . 1.111 11, 1.111 111
3. 5000, 1000, 200, 40, . . . 8, $\frac{8}{5}$
4. 1, 12, 123, 1234, . . . 12,345, 123,456
5. 3, 0.3, 0.03, 0.003, . . . 0.0003, 0.000 03
6. 1, 4, 9, 16, 25, . . . 36, 49

Write *true* or *false*. ■ Lessons 1-2 and 1-3

D A F E C B

7. *A*, *D*, *F* are coplanar. true
8. $\overleftrightarrow{AC}$ and $\overleftrightarrow{FE}$ are coplanar. false
9. *A*, *B*, *E* are collinear. false
10. *D*, *A*, *B*, *E* are coplanar. true
11. $\overleftrightarrow{FC} \parallel \overleftrightarrow{EF}$ false
12. plane *ABC* $\parallel$ plane *FDE* true
13. $\overleftrightarrow{BC}$ and $\overleftrightarrow{DF}$ are skew lines. true
14. $\overleftrightarrow{AD}$ and $\overleftrightarrow{EB}$ are skew lines. false

Use the figure at the right for Exercises 15–19. ■ Lessons 1-4 and 1-5

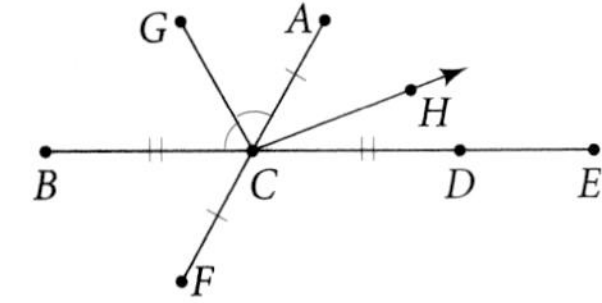

15. If $BC = 12$ and $CE = 15$, then $BE = $ ■. 27
16. ■ is the angle bisector of ■. $\overline{CG}$; $\angle ACB$
17. $BC = 3x + 2$ and $CD = 5x - 10$. Solve for *x*. 6
18. $m\angle BCG = 60$, $m\angle GCA = $ ■, $m\angle BCA = $ ■ 60; 120
19. $m\angle ACD = 60$ and $m\angle DCH = 20$. Find $m\angle HCA$. 40

Draw a diagram larger than the given one. Then do the construction. ■ Lesson 1-6

A B

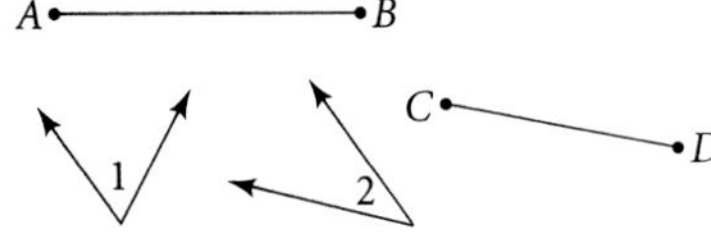

20. Construct the perpendicular bisector of $\overline{AB}$.
21. Construct $\angle A$ so that $m\angle A = m\angle 1 + m\angle 2$.
22. Construct the angle bisector of $\angle 1$.
23. Construct $\overline{FG}$ so that $FG = AB + CD$.

20–23. See margin.

Algebra **Find the value of *x*.** ■ Lesson 1-7

24. 24

$(3x - 14)°$ $(2x + 10)°$

25. 15

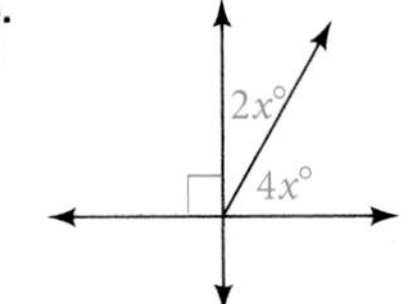

26. 25

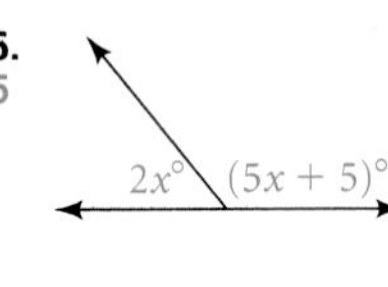

In Exercises 27–32: (a) Find the distance between the points to the nearest tenth. (b) Find the coordinates of the midpoint of the segment with the given endpoints. ■ Lesson 1-8

27. $A(2, 1)$, $B(3, 0)$ a. 1.4 b. (2.5, 0.5)
28. $R(5, 2)$, $S(-2, 4)$ a. 7.3 b. (1.5, 3)
29. $Q(-7, -4)$, $T(6, 10)$ a. 19.1 b. (−0.5, 3)
30. $C(-8, -1)$, $D(-5, -11)$ a. 10.4 b. (−6.5, −6)
31. $J(0, -5)$, $N(3, 4)$ a. 9.5 b. (1.5, −0.5)
32. $Y(-2, 8)$, $Z(3, -5)$ a. 13.9 b. (0.5, 1.5)

Chapter 2 Extra Practice

25.

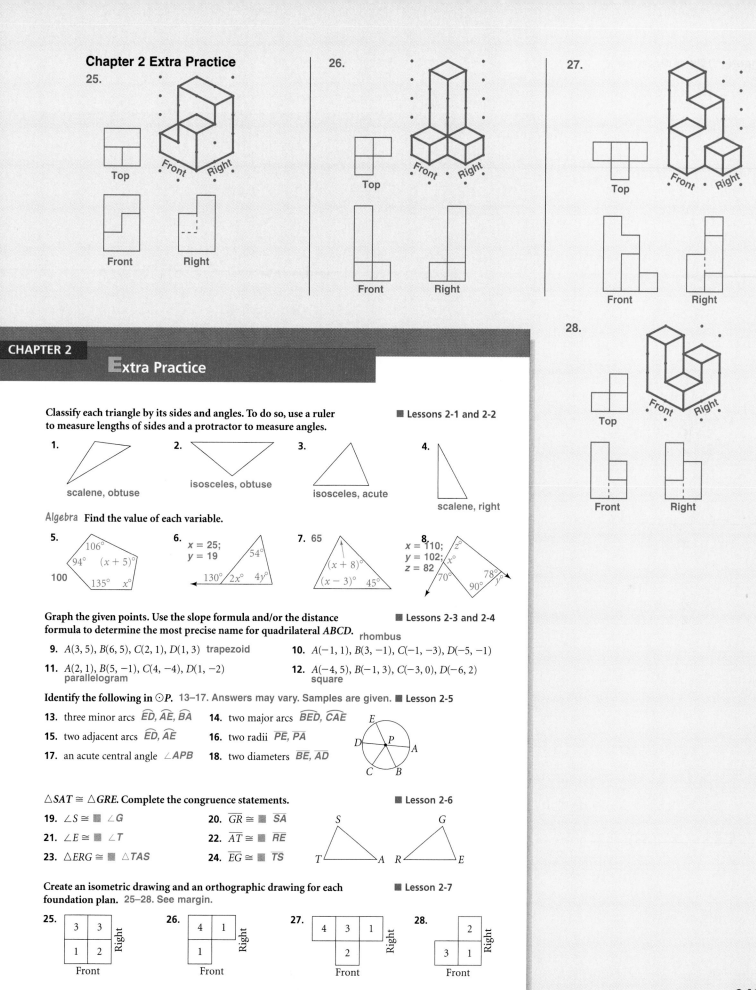

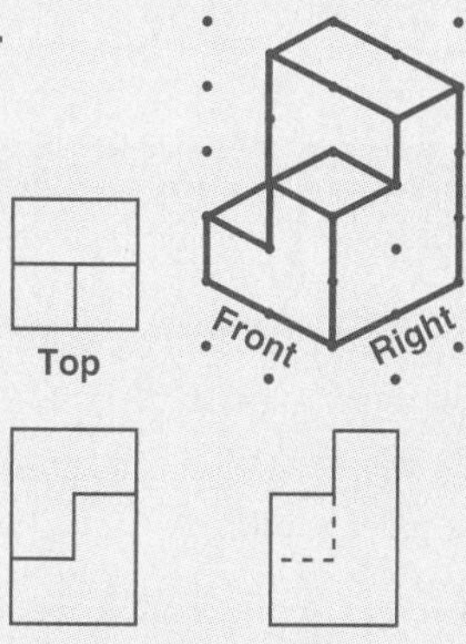

Front Right

26.

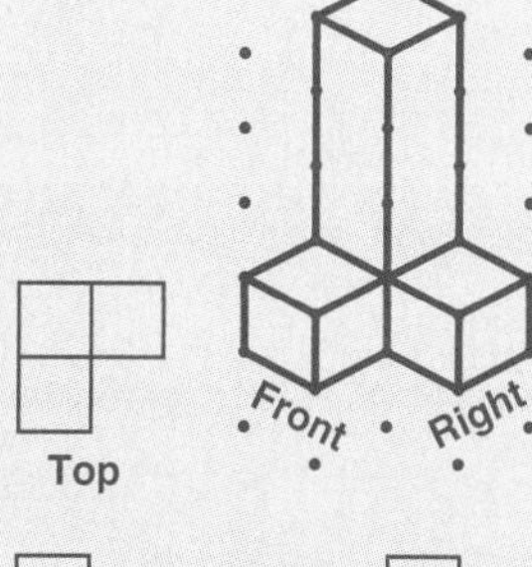

Top

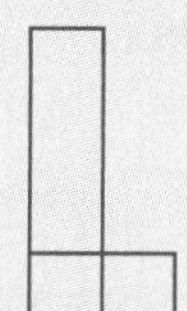

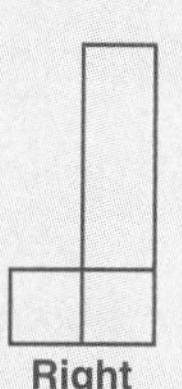

Front Right

27.

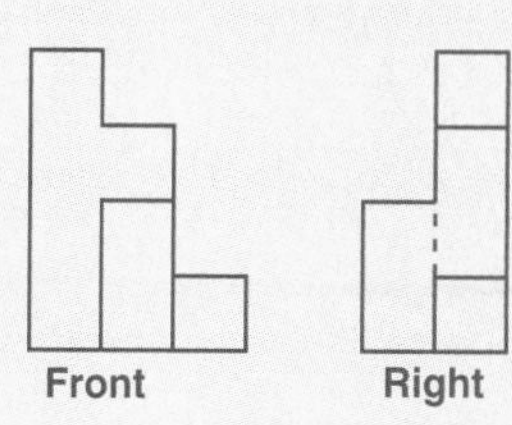

Top Front Right

28.

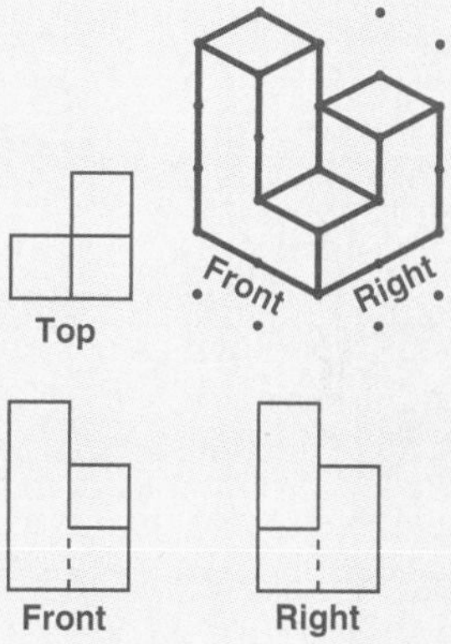

Top Front Right

CHAPTER 2

Extra Practice

Classify each triangle by its sides and angles. To do so, use a ruler to measure lengths of sides and a protractor to measure angles. ■ Lessons 2-1 and 2-2

1. 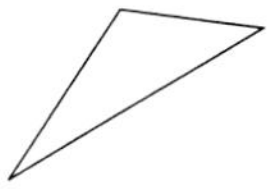 scalene, obtuse
2. isosceles, obtuse
3. isosceles, acute
4. scalene, right

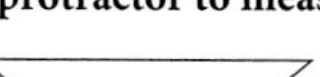

Algebra Find the value of each variable.

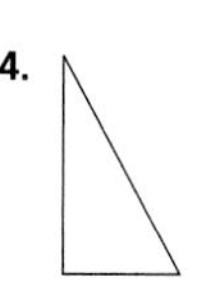

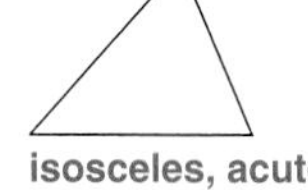

5. 100

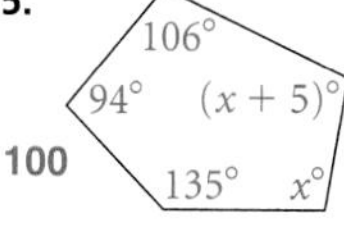

6. $x = 25$; $y = 19$

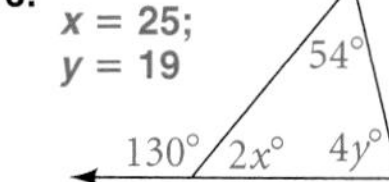

7. 65

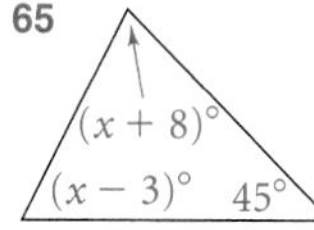

8. $x = 110$; $y = 102$; $z = 82$

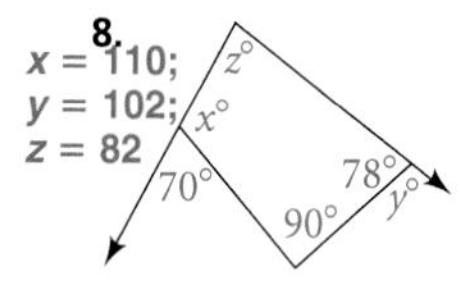

Graph the given points. Use the slope formula and/or the distance formula to determine the most precise name for quadrilateral $ABCD$. ■ Lessons 2-3 and 2-4

9. $A(3, 5)$, $B(6, 5)$, $C(2, 1)$, $D(1, 3)$ trapezoid
10. $A(-1, 1)$, $B(3, -1)$, $C(-1, -3)$, $D(-5, -1)$ rhombus
11. $A(2, 1)$, $B(5, -1)$, $C(4, -4)$, $D(1, -2)$ parallelogram
12. $A(-4, 5)$, $B(-1, 3)$, $C(-3, 0)$, $D(-6, 2)$ square

Identify the following in $\odot P$. 13–17. Answers may vary. Samples are given. ■ Lesson 2-5

13. three minor arcs $\widehat{ED}, \widehat{AE}, \widehat{BA}$
14. two major arcs $\widehat{BED}, \widehat{CAE}$
15. two adjacent arcs $\widehat{ED}, \widehat{AE}$
16. two radii $\overline{PE}, \overline{PA}$
17. an acute central angle $\angle APB$
18. two diameters $\overline{BE}, \overline{AD}$

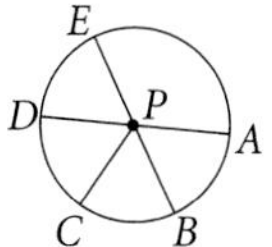

$\triangle SAT \cong \triangle GRE$. Complete the congruence statements. ■ Lesson 2-6

19. $\angle S \cong$ ■ $\angle G$
20. $\overline{GR} \cong$ ■ $\overline{SA}$
21. $\angle E \cong$ ■ $\angle T$
22. $\overline{AT} \cong$ ■ $\overline{RE}$
23. $\triangle ERG \cong$ ■ $\triangle TAS$
24. $\overline{EG} \cong$ ■ $\overline{TS}$

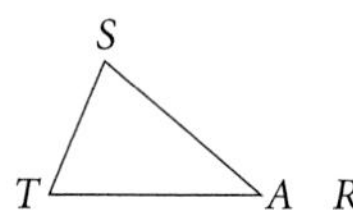

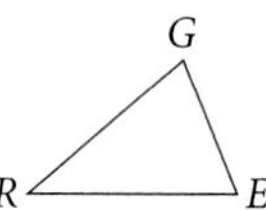

Create an isometric drawing and an orthographic drawing for each foundation plan. 25–28. See margin. ■ Lesson 2-7

25.

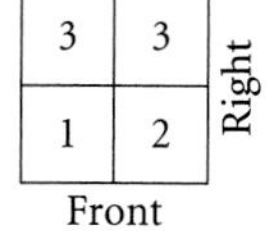

26.

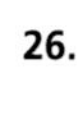

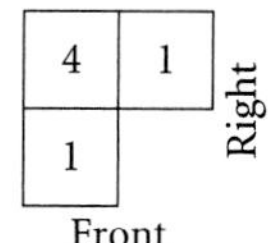

27.

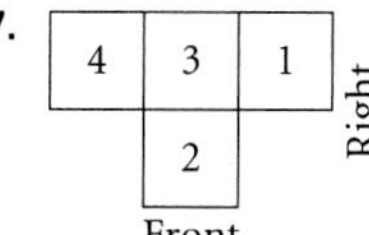

28.

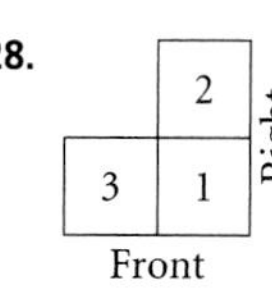

Chapter 3 Extra Practice

1.

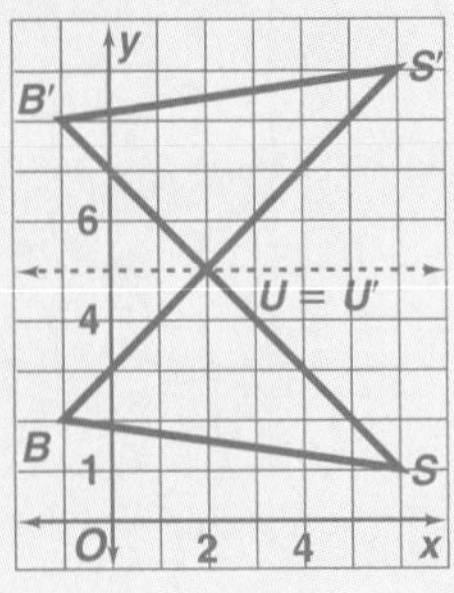

2.

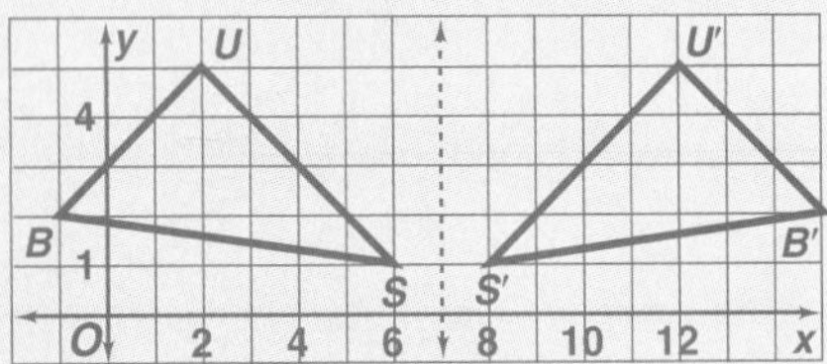

3.

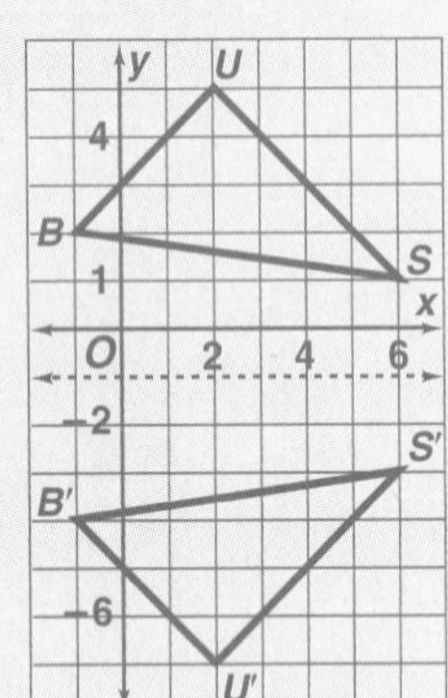

4.

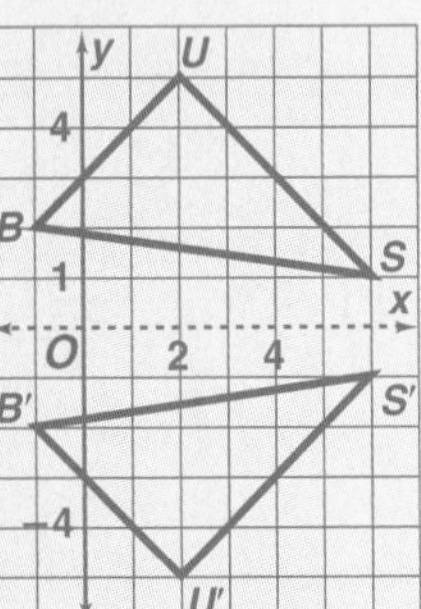

5.

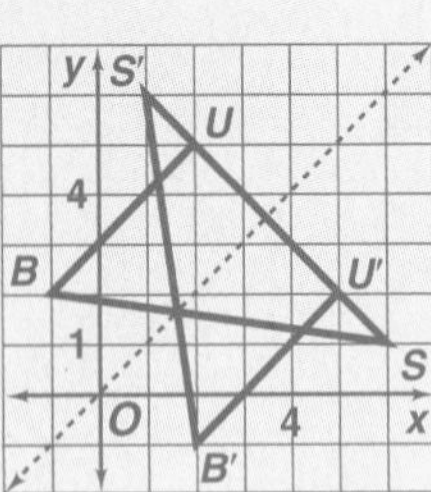

6.

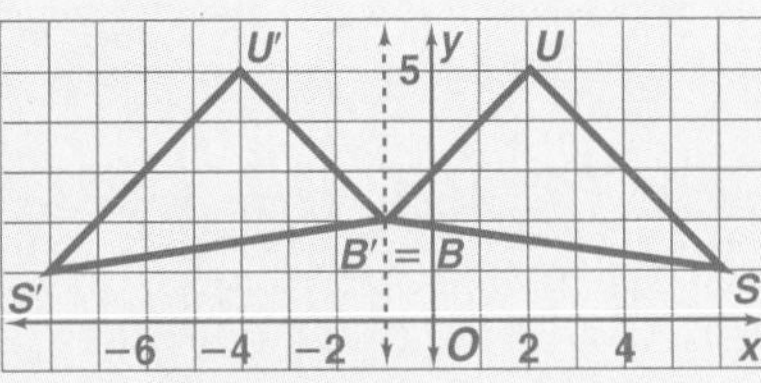

7.

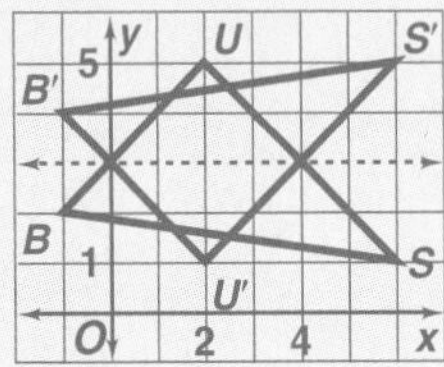

8.

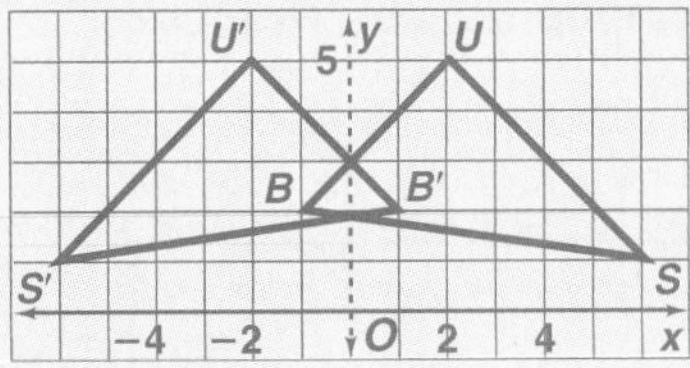

23a. line, rotational, point b. yes

24a. line b. yes

25a. line b. yes

26a. line, point b. yes

CHAPTER 3

Extra Practice

Lesson 3-1

Coordinate Geometry **Given points $S(6, 1)$, $U(2, 5)$, and $B(-1, 2)$, draw $\triangle SUB$ and its reflection image in the given line.** 1–8. See margin.

1. $y = 5$
2. $x = 7$
3. $y = -1$
4. the x-axis
5. $y = x$
6. $x = -1$
7. $y = 3$
8. the y-axis

Lesson 3-2

In Exercises 9–14, refer to the figure at the right.

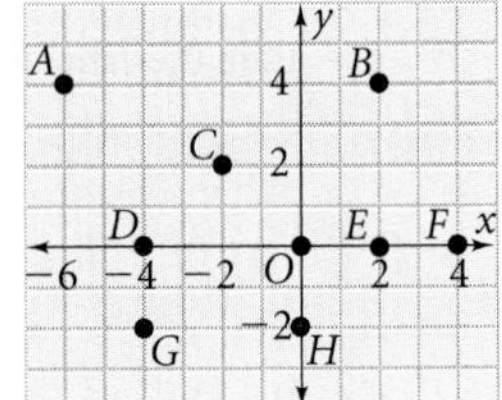

9. What is the image of C under the translation $\langle 4, -2\rangle$? E
10. What vector describes the translation $F \longrightarrow B$? $\langle -2, 4\rangle$
11. What is the image of H under the translation $\langle -2, 4\rangle$? C
12. What vector describes the translation $D \longrightarrow H$? $\langle 4, -2\rangle$
13. What is the image of C under the translation $\langle -2, -4\rangle$? G
14. What vector describes the translation $B \longrightarrow A$? $\langle -8, 0\rangle$

Lesson 3-3

Copy each figure and point P. Rotate the figure the given number of degrees about P. Label the vertices of the image.

15. $60°$

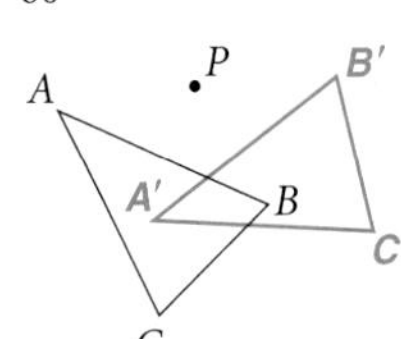

16. $90°$

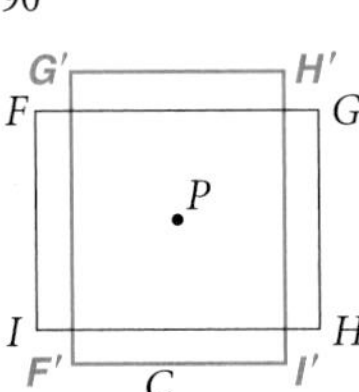

17. $180°$

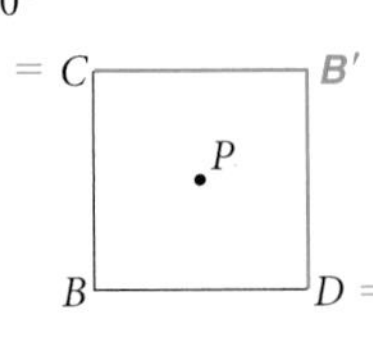

18. $45°$

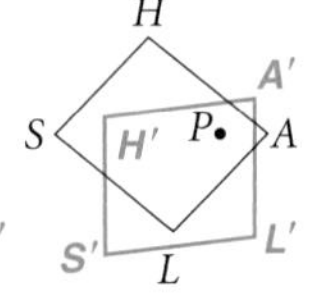

Lessons 3-4 and 3-7

The blue figure is the image of the black figure. State whether the mapping is a reflection, rotation, translation, glide reflection, or dilation.

19.

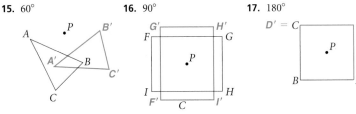

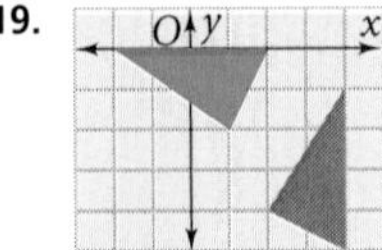

rotation

20.

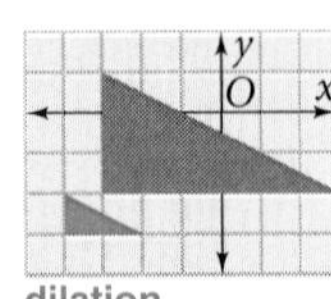

dilation

21.

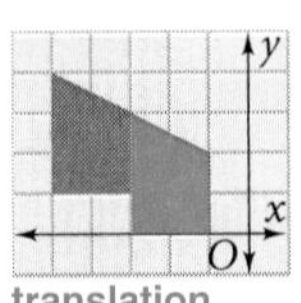

translation

22.

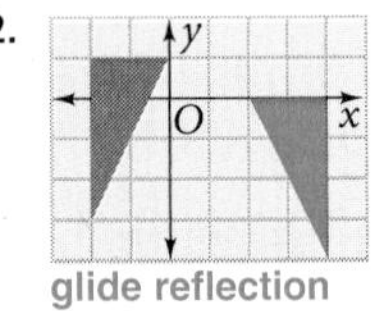

glide reflection

Lessons 3-5 and 3-6

In Exercises 23–26: (a) State what kind of symmetry each figure has. (b) State whether each figure tessellates. 23–26. See margin.

23.

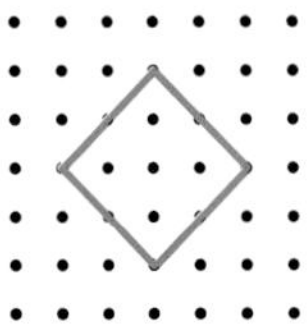

24.

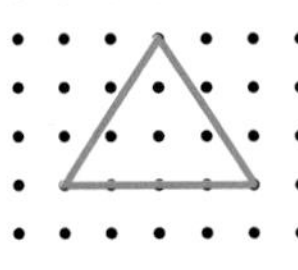

25.

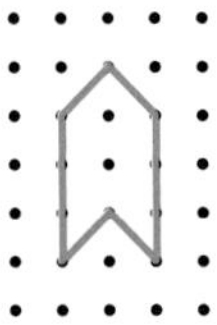

26.

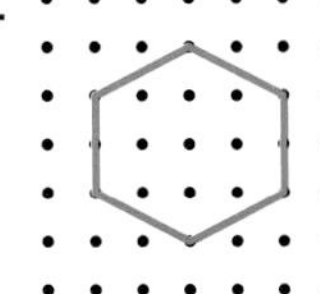

Chapter 4 Extra Practice

1. If 2 angles are ≅, then they are vert.; if 2 angles are not vert., then they are not ≅; if 2 angles are not ≅, then they are not vert.
2. If the side lengths of figures are proportional, then they are similar; if figures are not similar, then their side lengths are not proportional; if the side lengths of figures are not proportional, then they are not similar.
3. If a car has no doors, then it is blue; if a car is not blue, then it has doors; if a car has doors, then it is not blue.

8. 1. ▱$BGKM$ (Given) 2. $m\angle B + m\angle G + m\angle K + m\angle M = 360$ (Sum of the measures of the int. ∠s of an n-gon = $(n - 2)180$.) 3. $m\angle B = m\angle G = m\angle K = m\angle M$ (Given) 4. $4(m\angle B) = 360$ (Substitution) 5. $m\angle B = 90$ (Division Prop. of =) 6. $m\angle G = m\angle K = m\angle M = 90$ (Substitution) 7. ∠B, ∠G, ∠K, and ∠M are rt. angles. (Def. of rt. angle) 8. ▱$BGKM$ is a rectangle (Def. of rectangle)

16.

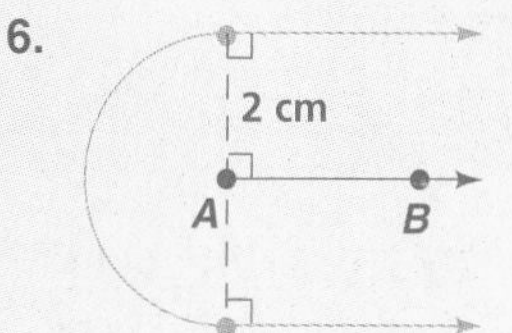

17.

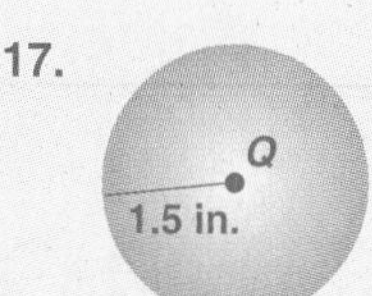

18.

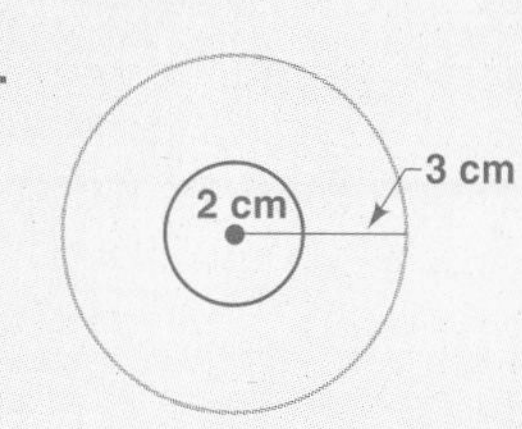

CHAPTER 4

Extra Practice

For each statement, write the converse, the inverse, and the contrapositive. 1–3. See margin. ■ Lesson 4-1

1. If two angles are vertical angles, then they are congruent.
2. If figures are similar, then their side lengths are proportional.
3. If a car is blue, then it has no doors.

Find the value of each variable. ■ Lessons 4-2 and 4-4

4. 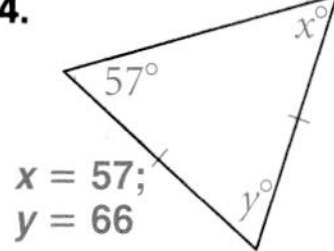

$x = 57$; $y = 66$

5. 10

6. 7

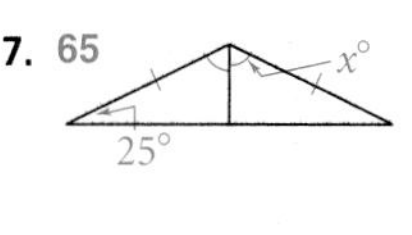

7. 65

8. Rewrite this paragraph proof as a two-column proof. ■ Lesson 4-3
Given: ▱$BGKM$, $m\angle B = m\angle G = m\angle K = m\angle M$
Prove: ▱$BGKM$ is a rectangle. See margin.

By the Polygon Interior Angle-Sum Thm., $m\angle B + m\angle G + m\angle K + m\angle M = 360$. We are given that $m\angle B = m\angle G = m\angle K = m\angle M$, so by Substitution, $4(m\angle B) = 360$. Dividing each side by 4 yields $m\angle B = 90$. By Substitution, $m\angle G = m\angle K = m\angle M = 90$. So ∠$B$, ∠$G$, ∠$K$, and ∠$M$ are rt. angles. ▱$BGKM$ is a rectangle by definition.

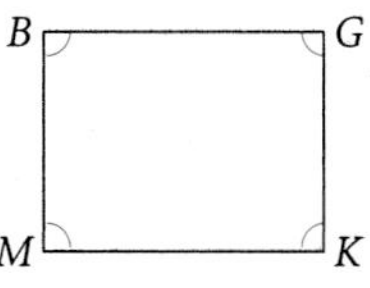

Write the first step of an indirect proof of each statement. ■ Lesson 4-5

9. △ABC is a right triangle. Assume △ABC is not a rt. △.
10. Points J, K, and L are collinear. Assume pts. J, K, and L are not collinear.
11. Lines ℓ and m are parallel. Assume lines ℓ and m are not ∥.

List the sides of each triangle in order from shortest to longest. ■ Lesson 4-6

12. 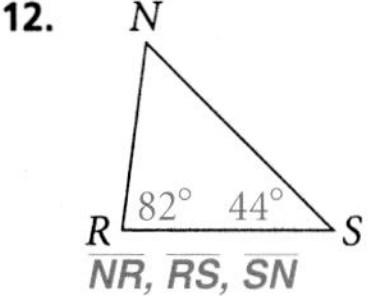

$\overline{NR}$, $\overline{RS}$, $\overline{SN}$

13. 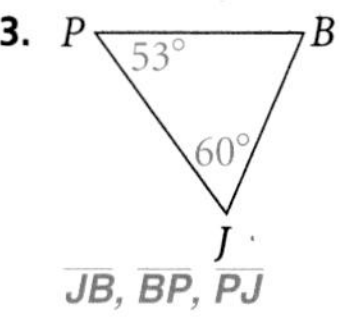

$\overline{JB}$, $\overline{BP}$, $\overline{PJ}$

14. 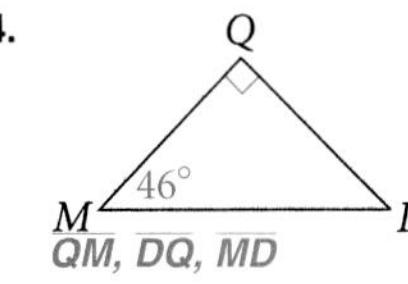

$\overline{QM}$, $\overline{DQ}$, $\overline{MD}$

15. 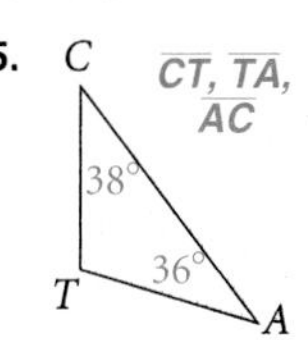

$\overline{CT}$, $\overline{TA}$, $\overline{AC}$

Sketch and label each locus. 16–18. See margin. ■ Lesson 4-7

16. all points in a plane 2 cm from $\overrightarrow{AB}$
17. all points in space 1.5 in. from point Q
18. all points in a plane 3 cm from a circle with radius 2 cm

Is $\overline{AB}$ an angle bisector, altitude, median, or perpendicular bisector? ■ Lesson 4-8

19. altitude
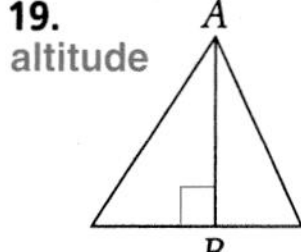

20. 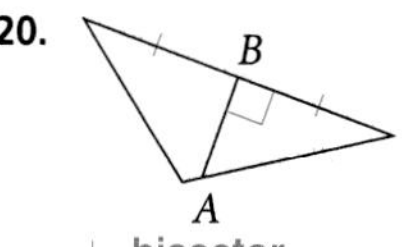

⊥ bisector

21. 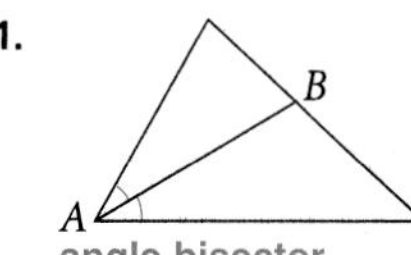

angle bisector

22. 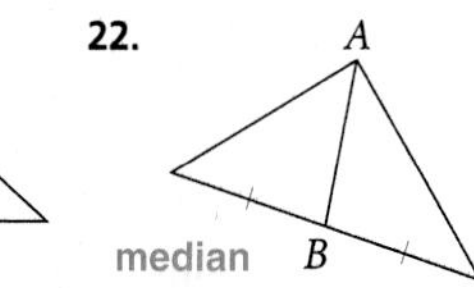

median

Extra Practice

Find the perimeter and area of each figure. ■ Lessons 5-1 and 5-2

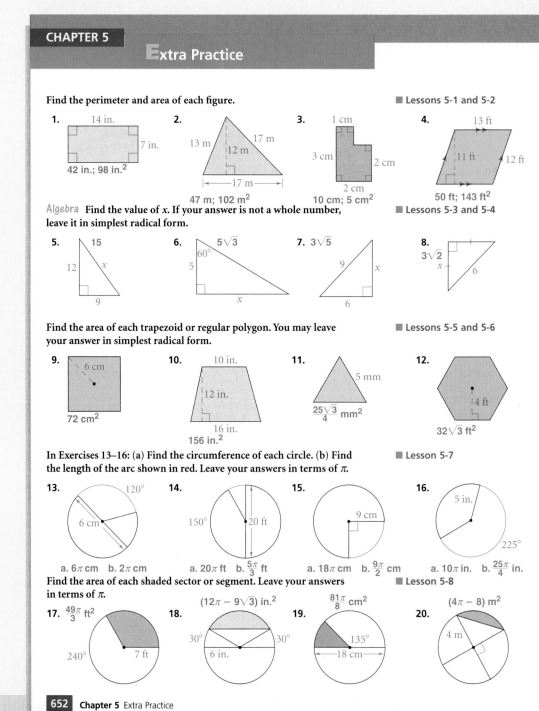

1. 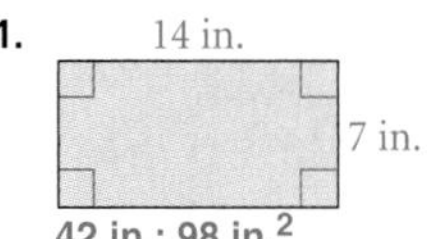

42 in.; 98 in.^{2}

2. 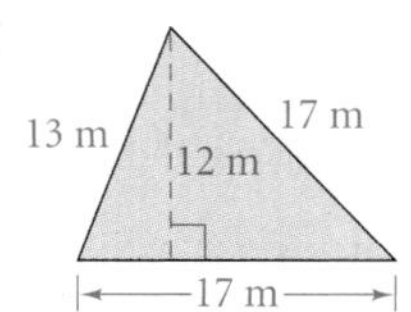

47 m; 102 m^2

3. 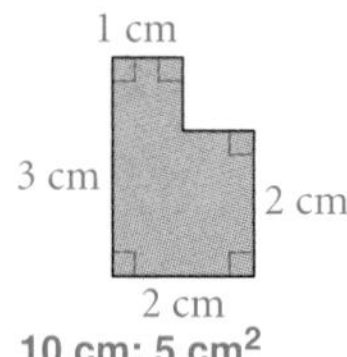

10 cm; 5 cm^2

4. 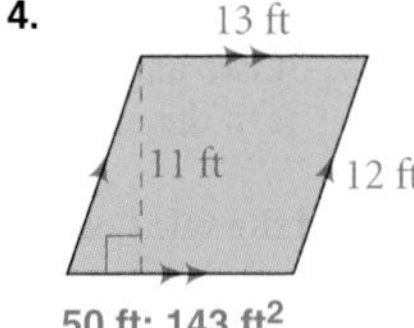

50 ft; 143 ft^2

Algebra **Find the value of x. If your answer is not a whole number, leave it in simplest radical form.** ■ Lessons 5-3 and 5-4

5. **15**
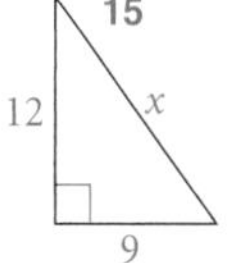

6. **$5\sqrt{3}$**
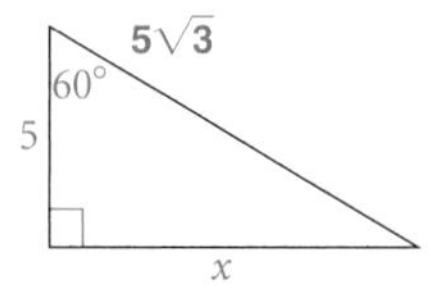

7. **$3\sqrt{5}$**
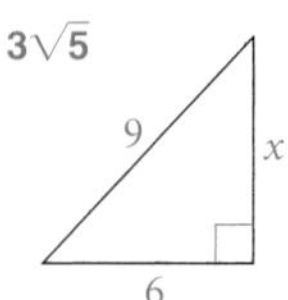

8. **$3\sqrt{2}$**
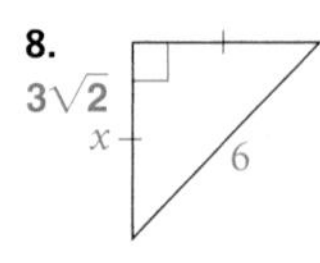

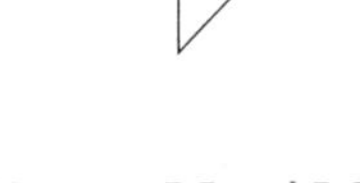

Find the area of each trapezoid or regular polygon. You may leave your answer in simplest radical form. ■ Lessons 5-5 and 5-6

9. 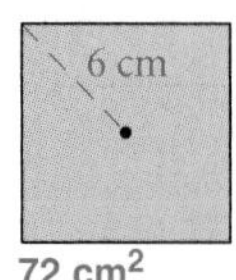

72 cm^2

10. 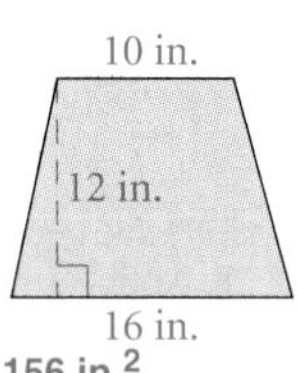

156 in.^{2}

11. 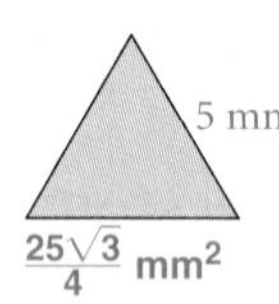

$\frac{25\sqrt{3}}{4}$ mm^2

12. 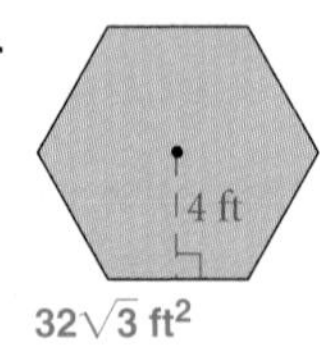

$32\sqrt{3}$ ft^2

In Exercises 13–16: (a) Find the circumference of each circle. (b) Find the length of the arc shown in red. Leave your answers in terms of π. ■ Lesson 5-7

13. 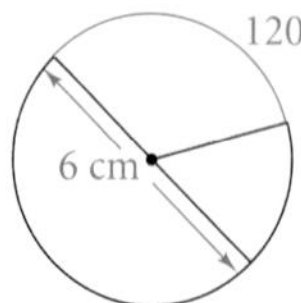

a. 6π cm b. 2π cm

14. 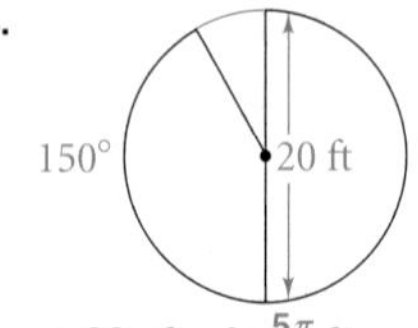

a. 20π ft b. $\frac{5\pi}{3}$ ft

15. 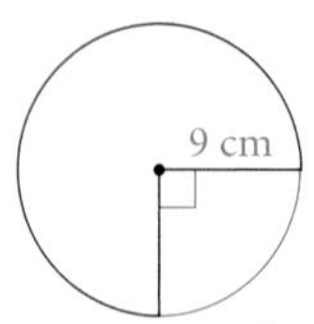

a. 18π cm b. $\frac{9\pi}{2}$ cm

16. 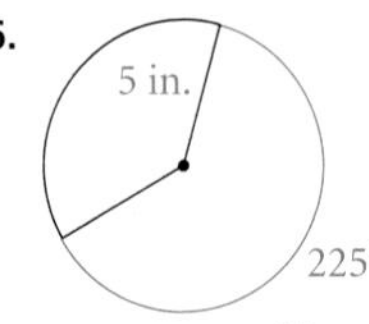

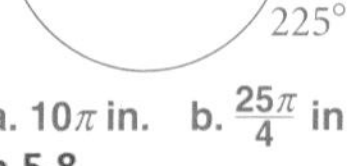

a. 10π in. b. $\frac{25\pi}{4}$ in.

Find the area of each shaded sector or segment. Leave your answers in terms of π. ■ Lesson 5-8

17. **$\frac{49\pi}{3}$ ft^2**

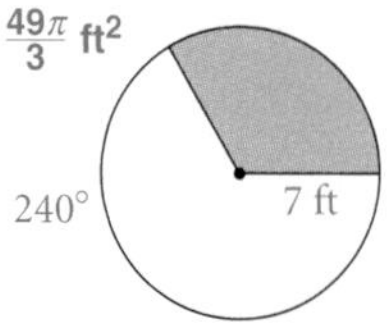

240° 7 ft

18. **$(12\pi - 9\sqrt{3})$ in.^{2}**
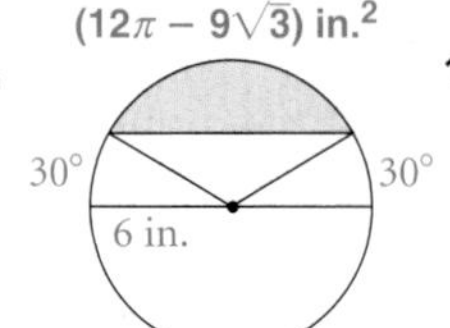

19. **$\frac{81\pi}{8}$ cm^2**
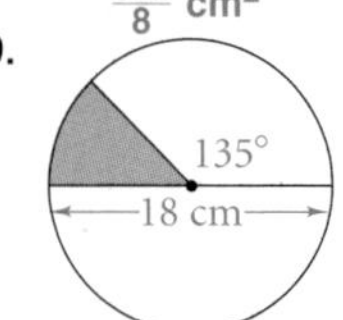

20. **$(4\pi - 8)$ m^2**
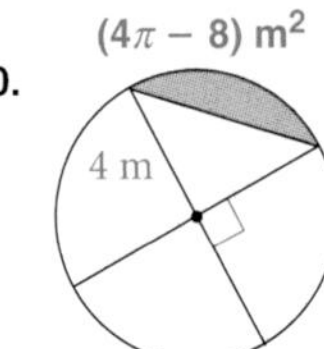

Chapter 6 Extra Practice

13. $\frac{500\pi}{3}$ cm^3; 100π cm^2

14. $\frac{256\pi}{3}$ in.^{3}; 64π in.^{2}

15. $\frac{4\pi}{3}$ ft^3; 4π ft^2

16. $\frac{\pi}{6}$ in.^{3}; π in.^{2}

17. $\frac{243\pi}{2}$ m^3; 81π m^2

CHAPTER 6

Extra Practice

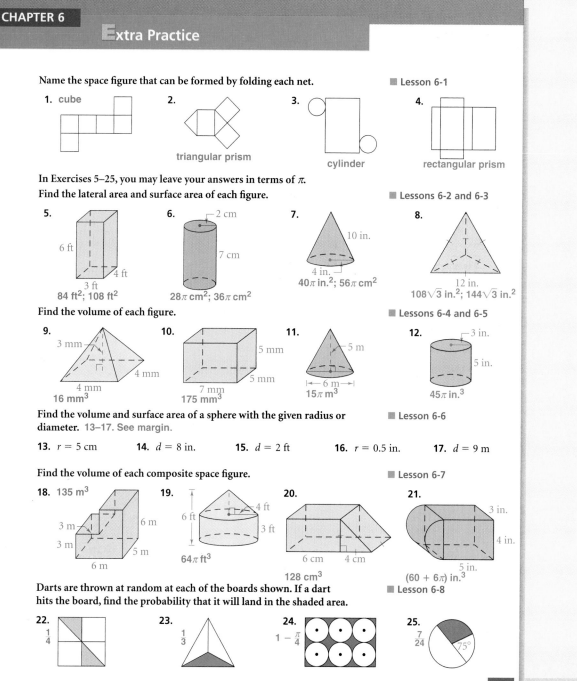

Name the space figure that can be formed by folding each net. ■ Lesson 6-1

1. cube
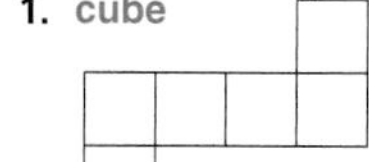

2.
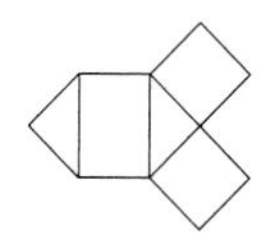
triangular prism

3.
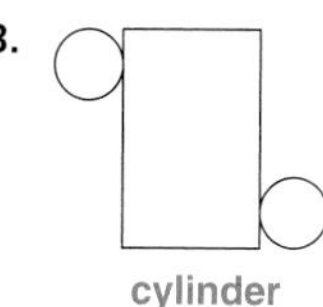
cylinder

4.
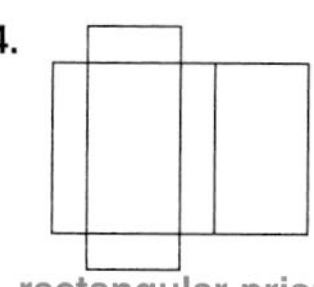
rectangular prism

In Exercises 5–25, you may leave your answers in terms of π.

Find the lateral area and surface area of each figure. ■ Lessons 6-2 and 6-3

5.
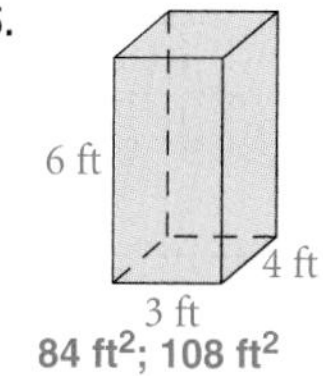

84 ft^2; 108 ft^2

6.
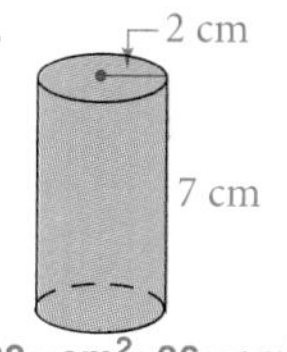

28π cm^2; 36π cm^2

7.
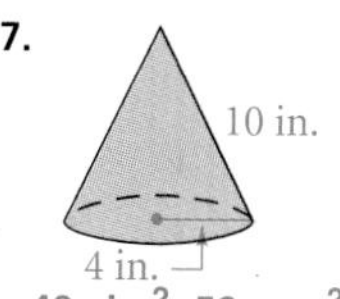

40π in.^{2}; 56π cm^2

8.
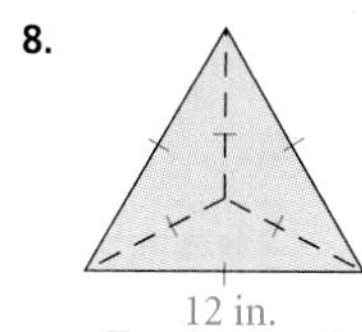

$108\sqrt{3}$ in.^{2}; $144\sqrt{3}$ in.^{2}

Find the volume of each figure. ■ Lessons 6-4 and 6-5

9.

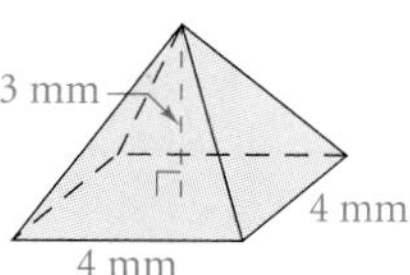

16 mm^3

10.

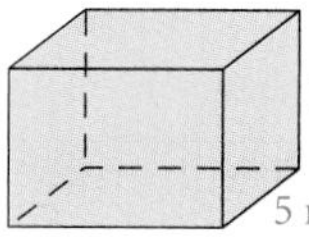

175 mm^3

11.
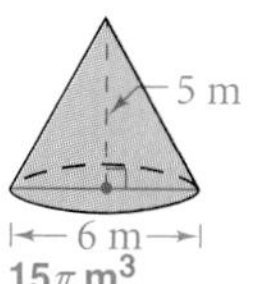

15π m^3

12.
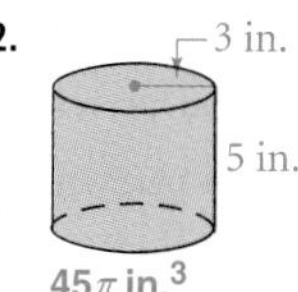

45π in.^{3}

Find the volume and surface area of a sphere with the given radius or diameter. 13–17. See margin. ■ Lesson 6-6

13. $r = 5$ cm 14. $d = 8$ in. 15. $d = 2$ ft 16. $r = 0.5$ in. 17. $d = 9$ m

Find the volume of each composite space figure. ■ Lesson 6-7

18. 135 m^3
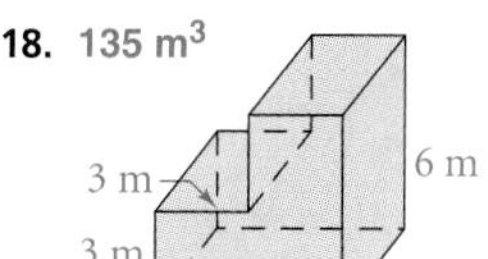

19.
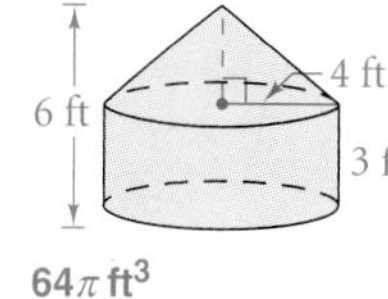

64π ft^3

20.
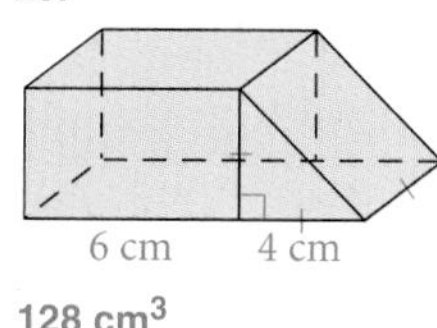

128 cm^3

21.
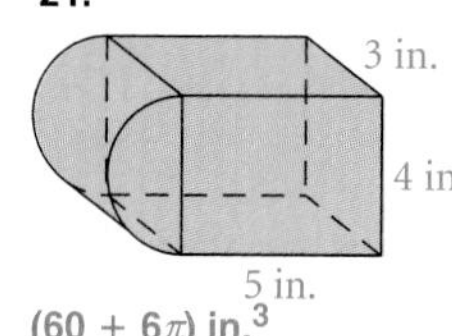

$(60 + 6\pi)$ in.^{3}

Darts are thrown at random at each of the boards shown. If a dart hits the board, find the probability that it will land in the shaded area. ■ Lesson 6-8

22. $\frac{1}{4}$
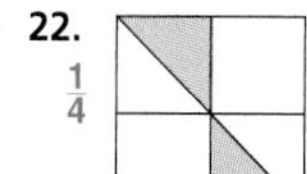

23. $\frac{1}{3}$

24. $1 - \frac{\pi}{4}$
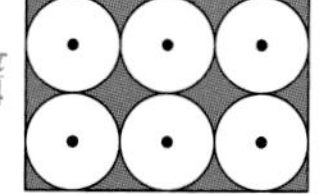

25. $\frac{7}{24}$

Chapter 7 Extra Practice

1. $m\angle 1 = 134$, if $\parallel$ lines, then same-side int. $\angle$s are supplementary; $m\angle 2 = 46$, Angle Addition Post. (or, if $\parallel$ lines, then alt. int. $\angle$s are $\cong$).
2. $m\angle 1 = 125$, if $\parallel$ lines, then corres. $\angle$s are $\cong$; $m\angle 2 = 55$, if $\parallel$ lines, then same-side int. $\angle$s are supplementary (or Angle Addition Post.).
3. $m\angle 1 = 58$, if $\parallel$ lines, then alt. int. $\angle$s are $\cong$; $m\angle 2 = 122$, Angle Addition Post. (or, if $\parallel$ lines, then same-side int. $\angle$s are supplementary).
4. $m\angle 1 = 64$, if $\parallel$ lines, then alt. int. $\angle$s are $\cong$; $m\angle 2 = 116$, if $\parallel$ lines, then same-side int. $\angle$s are supplementary.
6. $r \parallel s$; if $\cong$ corres. $\angle$s, then lines are $\parallel$.
7. $c \parallel d$; if supplementary same-side int. $\angle$s , then lines are $\parallel$.
9. $r \parallel s$; if $\cong$ corres. $\angle$s , then lines are $\parallel$.

13.

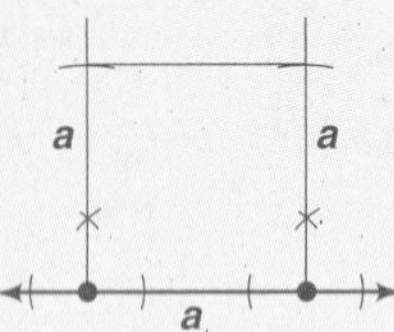

14.

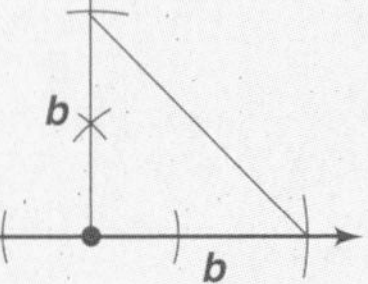

15.

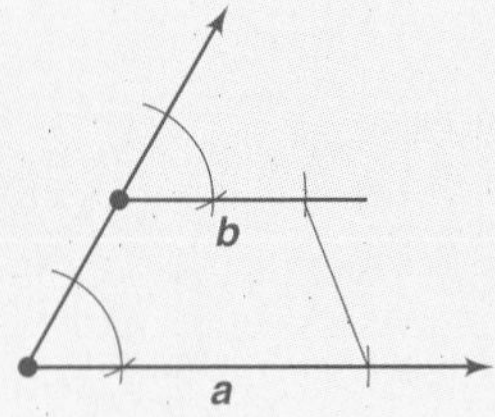

16.

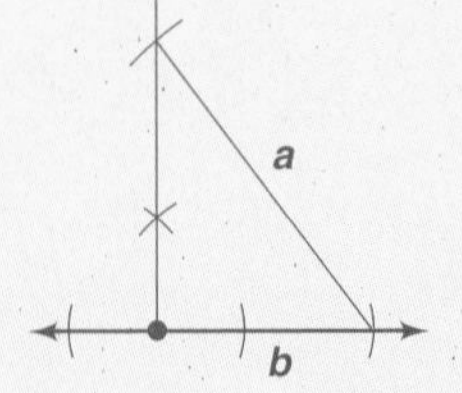

21.

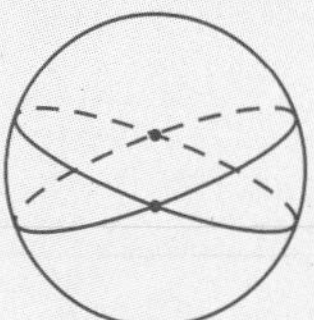

22.

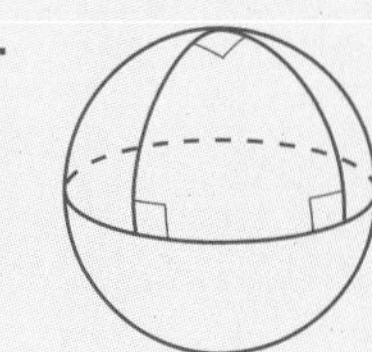

23. The measure of an exterior angle with vertex C is clearly less than $m\angle A + m\angle B$.

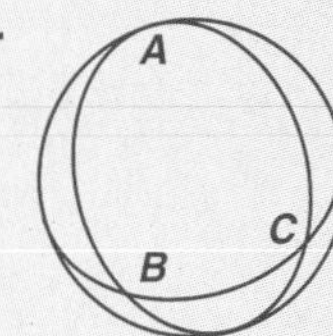

CHAPTER 7

Extra Practice

■ Lesson 7-1

Find $m\angle 1$ and then $m\angle 2$. State the theorems or postulates that justify your answers. 1–4. See margin.

1. 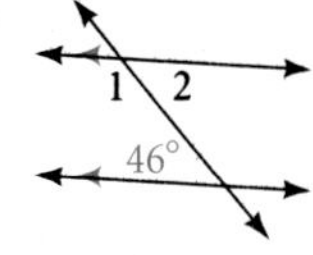

2. 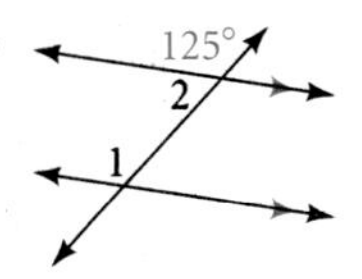

3. 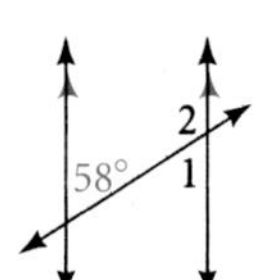

4. 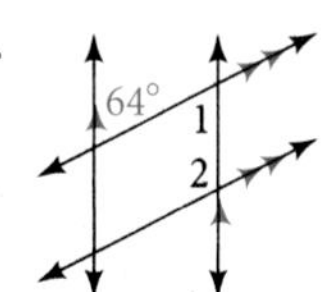

■ Lesson 7-2

Refer to the diagram. Use the given information to determine which lines, if any, must be parallel. If any lines are parallel, use a theorem or postulate to tell why. 6–7, 9. See margin.

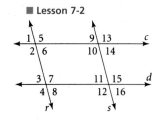

5. $\angle 9 \cong \angle 14$ none
6. $\angle 1 \cong \angle 9$
7. $\angle 2$ is supplementary to $\angle 3$.
8. $\angle 7 \cong \angle 14$ none
9. $m\angle 6 = 60$, $m\angle 13 = 120$
10. $\angle 4 \cong \angle 13$ none
11. $\angle 3$ is supplementary to $\angle 10$. none
12. $\angle 10 \cong \angle 15$ $c \parallel d$; if $\cong$ alt. int. $\angle$s, then lines are $\parallel$.

■ Lesson 7-3

Use the segments at the right for each construction.

13. Construct a square with side length a. 13–16. See margin.
14. Construct an isosceles right triangle with legs of length b.
15. Construct a trapezoid with bases of lengths a and b.
16. Construct a right triangle in which the length of a leg is b and the length of the hypotenuse is a.

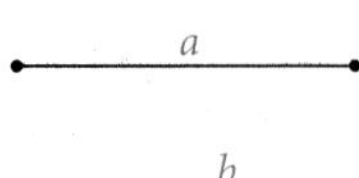

■ Lesson 7-4

Is each object drawn in one- or two-point perspective?

17. 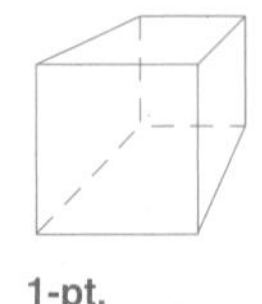
1-pt.

18. 2-pt. 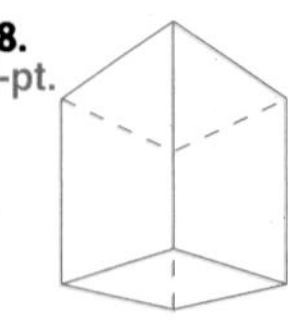

19. 2-pt. 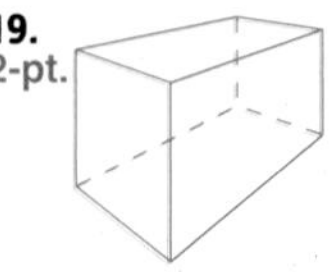

20. 1-pt. 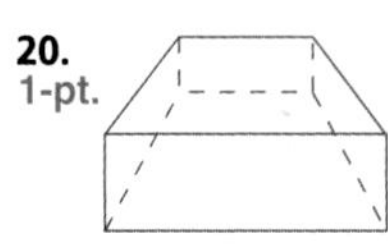

■ Lesson 7-5

Draw a sketch to illustrate each property of spherical geometry.

21. Two distinct lines intersect in two points. 21–23. See margin for samples.
22. A triangle can have three right angles.
23. The measure of an exterior angle of a triangle is less than the sum of the measures of the remote interior angles.

Chapter 8 Extra Practice

10. $\overleftrightarrow{OL} \parallel \overleftrightarrow{MN}$, so $\angle OLN \cong \angle MNL$. $\overline{LN} \cong \overline{LN}$ by Reflexive Prop. of $\cong$. Since $\overline{LO} \cong \overline{MN}$, $\triangle MLN \cong \triangle ONL$ by SAS, and $\angle MLN \cong \angle ONL$ by CPCTC.

11. $\overline{OS} \cong \overline{OS}$ by Reflexive Prop. of $\cong$. Since $\angle T \cong \angle E$ and $\angle TSO \cong \angle EOS$, $\triangle TSO \cong \triangle EOS$ by AAS, and $\overline{TO} \cong \overline{ES}$ by CPCTC.

12. $\overline{BI} \cong \overline{BI}$ by Reflexive Prop. of $\cong$. Since $\angle MBI \cong \angle RIB$ and $\angle MIB \cong \angle RBI$, $\triangle MBI \cong \triangle RIB$ by ASA, and $\overline{MB} \cong \overline{RI}$ by CPCTC.

CHAPTER 8

Extra Practice

■ Lessons 8-1 and 8-2

Can you prove that the triangles are congruent? If so, write the congruence and tell whether you would use SSS, SAS, ASA, or AAS. If not, write *not possible*.

1. 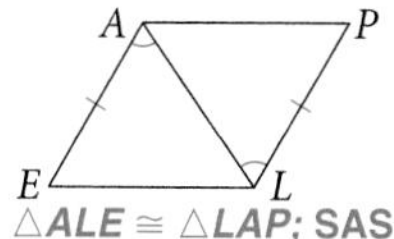

$\triangle ALE \cong \triangle LAP$; SAS

2. $\triangle CAN \cong \triangle GLO$; SSS
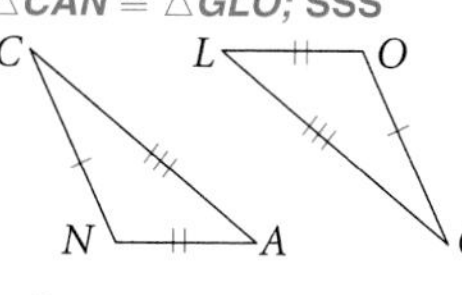

3. not possible
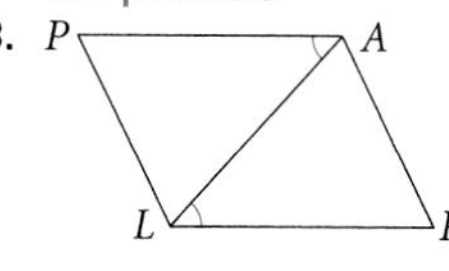

4. 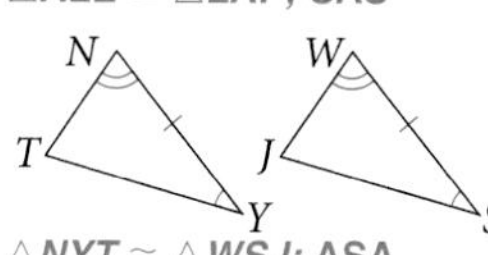

$\triangle NYT \cong \triangle WSJ$; ASA

5. 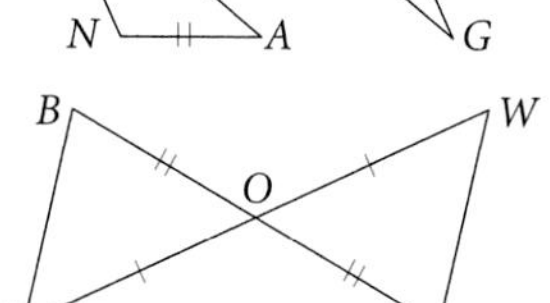

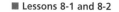

$\triangle BOI \cong \triangle TOW$; SAS

6. 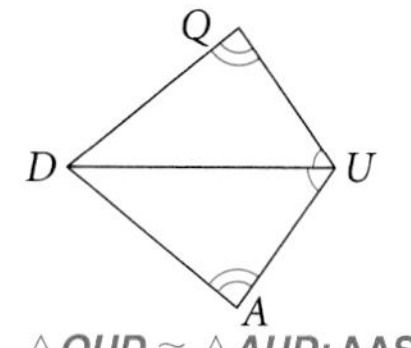

$\triangle QUD \cong \triangle AUD$; AAS

■ Lesson 8-3

What additional information would you need to prove the triangles congruent by the HL Theorem?

7. 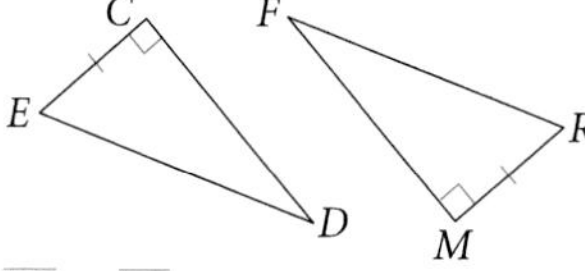

$\overline{ED} \cong \overline{RF}$

8. 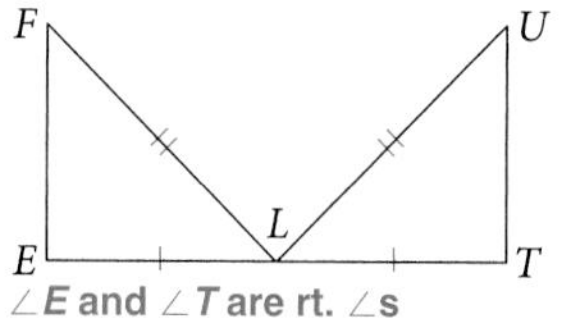

$\angle E$ and $\angle T$ are rt. $\angle$s

9. 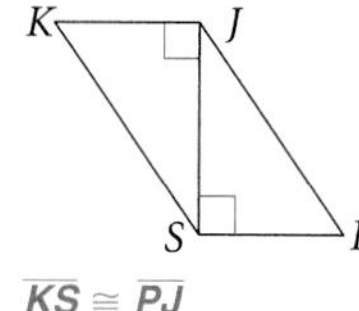

$\overline{KS} \cong \overline{PJ}$

■ Lesson 8-4

Explain how you would use SSS, SAS, ASA, AAS, or HL with CPCTC to prove each statement. 10–12. See margin.

10. $\angle MLN \cong \angle ONL$
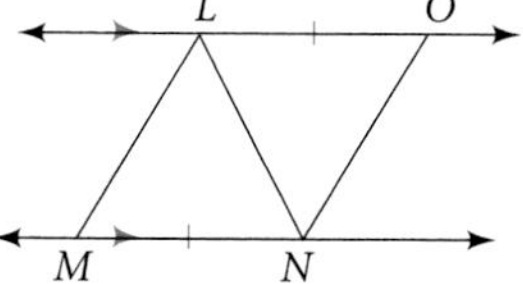

11. $\overline{TO} \cong \overline{ES}$
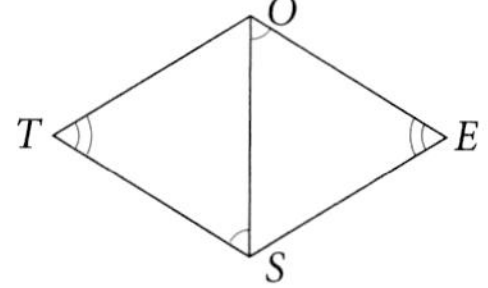

12. $\overline{MB} \cong \overline{RI}$
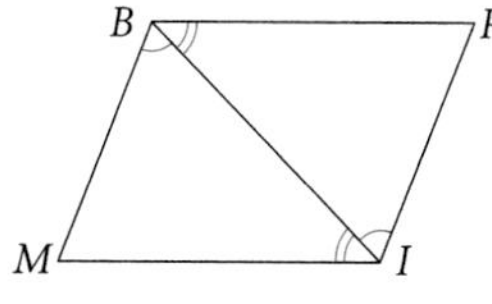

■ Lesson 8-5

Name a pair of overlapping congruent triangles in each diagram. State whether the triangles are congruent by SSS, SAS, ASA, AAS, or HL.

13. 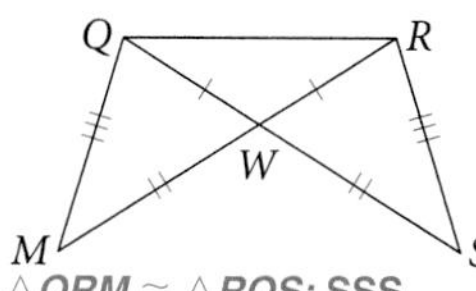

$\triangle QRM \cong \triangle RQS$; SSS

14. 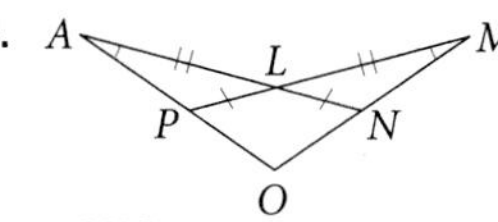

$\triangle ANO \cong \triangle MPO$; AAS

15. $\overline{AF} \cong \overline{BE}$
$\triangle FAD \cong \triangle EBC$; AAS
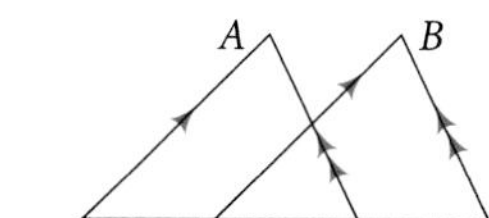

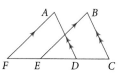

Chapter 9 Extra Practice

6. Yes; if diags. of a quad. bisect each other, then the quad. is a ▱.
7. Yes; Triangle Angle-Sum Thm., if both pairs of opp. ∠s of a quad. are ≅, then the quad. is a ▱.
12. parallelogram; $m\angle 1 = 45$; $m\angle 2 = 45$; $m\angle 3 = 80$; $m\angle 4 = 55$
21. Given: Square *DRSQ* with *K, L, M, N* midpts. of $\overline{DR}, \overline{RS}, \overline{SQ}$, and $\overline{QD}$, respectively. Prove: *KLMN* is a square.

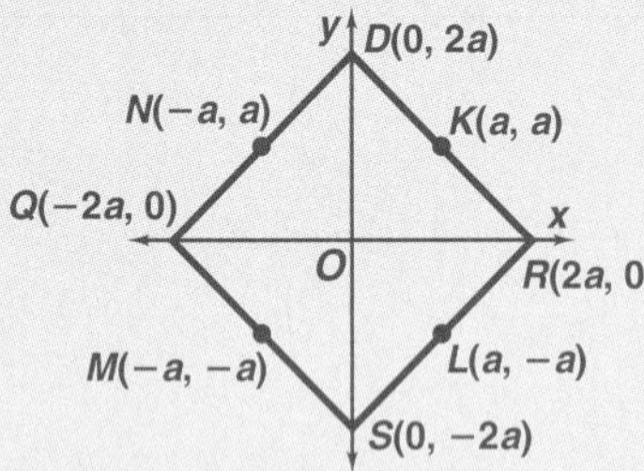

K(*a*, *a*), *L*(*a*, −*a*), *M*(−*a*, −*a*), and *N*(−*a*, *a*) are midpts. of the sides of the square. *KL* = *LM* = *MN* = *NK* = 2*a*. The slopes of $\overline{KL}$ and $\overline{MN}$ are undefined. The slopes of $\overline{LM}$ and $\overline{NK}$ are 0, so adjacent sides are ⊥ to each other. Since all angles are rt. angles, the quad. is a rectangle. A rectangle with all ≅ sides is a square.

CHAPTER 9

Extra Practice

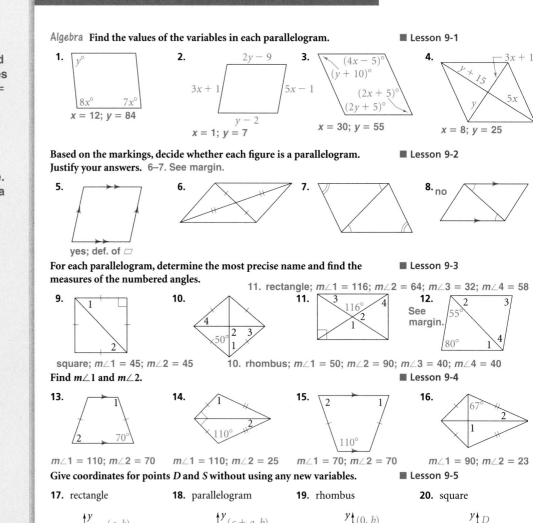

Algebra **Find the values of the variables in each parallelogram.** ■ Lesson 9-1

1. $x = 12$; $y = 84$

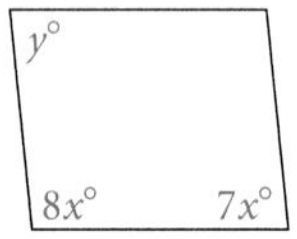

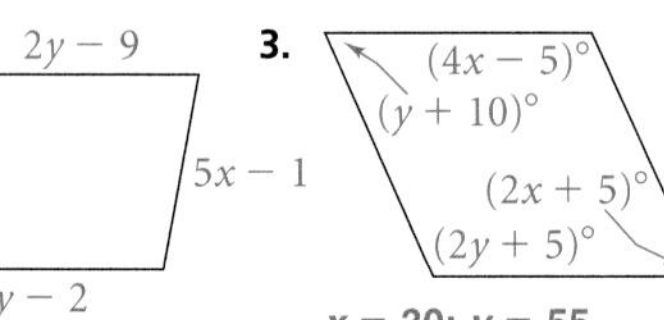

2. $x = 1$; $y = 7$

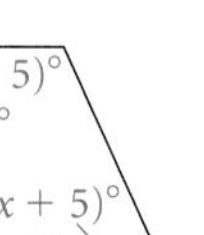

3. $x = 30$; $y = 55$

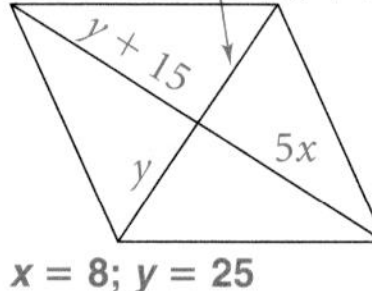

4. $x = 8$; $y = 25$

Based on the markings, decide whether each figure is a parallelogram. Justify your answers. 6–7. See margin. ■ Lesson 9-2

5.

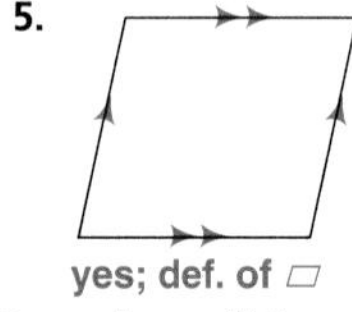

yes; def. of ▱

6.

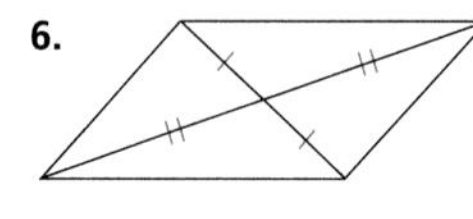

7.

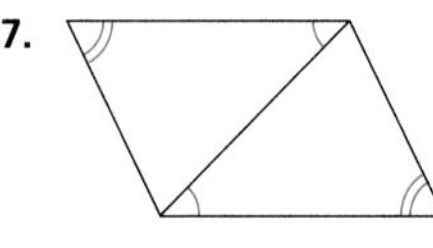

8. no

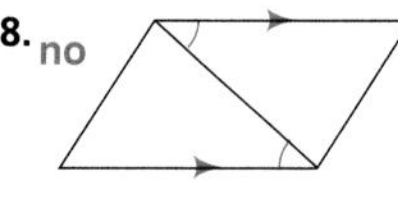

For each parallelogram, determine the most precise name and find the measures of the numbered angles. ■ Lesson 9-3

11. rectangle; $m\angle 1 = 116$; $m\angle 2 = 64$; $m\angle 3 = 32$; $m\angle 4 = 58$

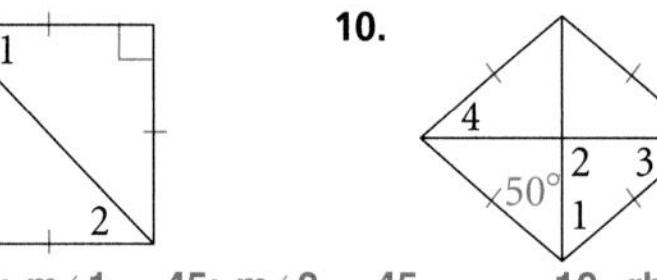

9. square; $m\angle 1 = 45$; $m\angle 2 = 45$

10. rhombus; $m\angle 1 = 50$; $m\angle 2 = 90$; $m\angle 3 = 40$; $m\angle 4 = 40$

11.

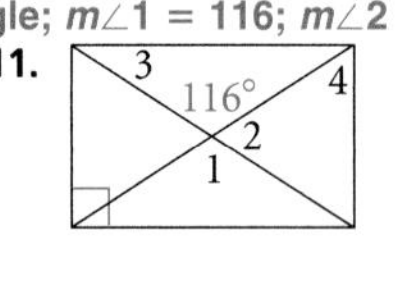

12. See margin.

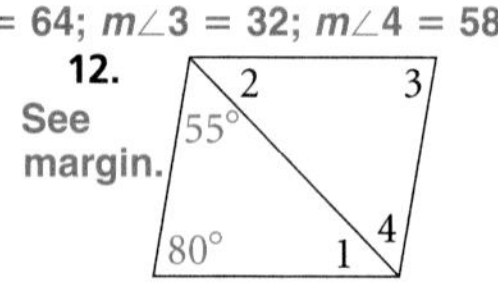

Find $m\angle 1$ and $m\angle 2$. ■ Lesson 9-4

13. $m\angle 1 = 110$; $m\angle 2 = 70$

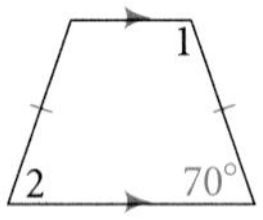

14.

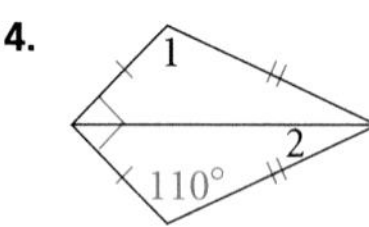

$m\angle 1 = 110$; $m\angle 2 = 25$

15.

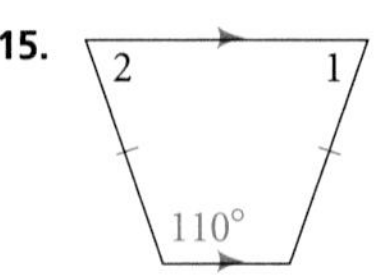

$m\angle 1 = 70$; $m\angle 2 = 70$

16.

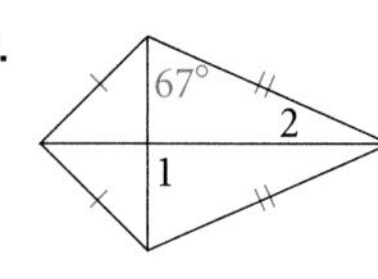

$m\angle 1 = 90$; $m\angle 2 = 23$

Give coordinates for points *D* and *S* without using any new variables. ■ Lesson 9-5

17. rectangle — *D*(0, *b*), *S*(*a*, 0)

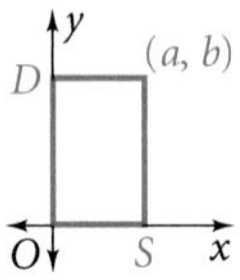

18. parallelogram — *D*(0, *b*), *S*(−*a*, 0)

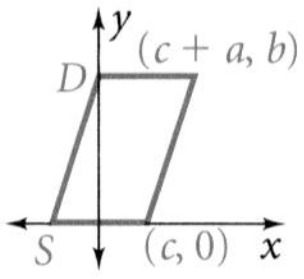

19. rhombus — *D*(−*c*, 0), *S*(0, −*b*)

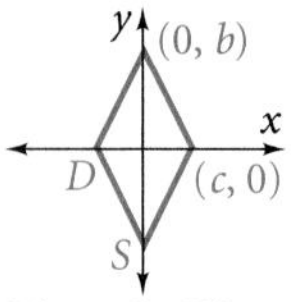

20. square

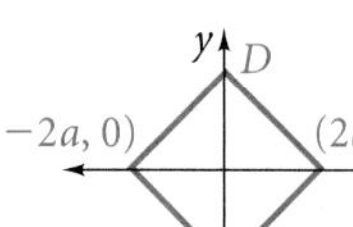

D(0, 2*a*), *S*(0, −2*a*)

21. For the figure in Exercise 20, use coordinate geometry to prove that the midpoints of the sides of a square determine a square. See margin. ■ Lesson 9-6

CHAPTER 10

Extra Practice

Algebra Solve for x. ■ Lesson 10-1

1. $\frac{2}{3} = \frac{x}{15}$ 10
2. $\frac{4}{9} = \frac{16}{x}$ 36
3. $\frac{x}{4} = \frac{6}{12}$ 2
4. $\frac{2}{x} = \frac{3}{9}$ 6
5. $\frac{3}{4} = \frac{x}{6}$ 4.5
6. $\frac{3}{7} = \frac{9}{x}$ 21

Can you prove that the triangles are similar? If so, write the similarity statement and tell whether you would use AA~, SAS~, or SSS~.

7. 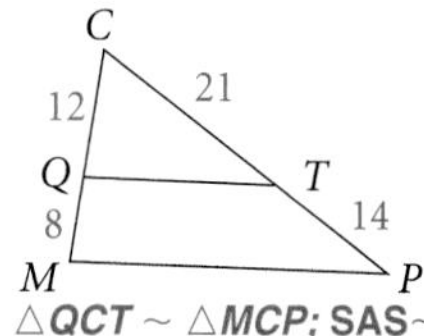

$\triangle QCT \sim \triangle MCP$; SAS~

8. 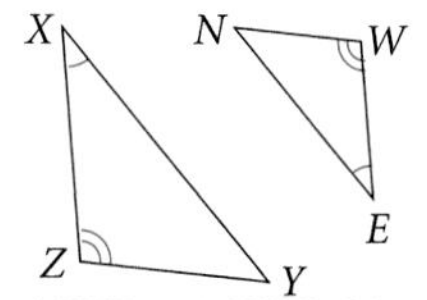

$\triangle XYZ \sim \triangle ENW$; AA~

9. 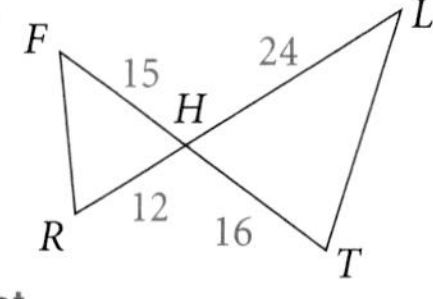

not ~

Algebra Find the value of each variable. If an answer is not a whole number, leave it in simplest radical form. ■ Lessons 10-3 and 10-4

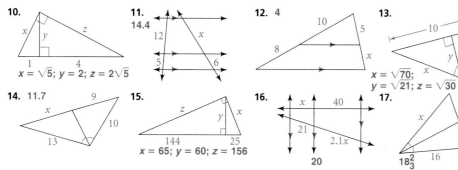

10. 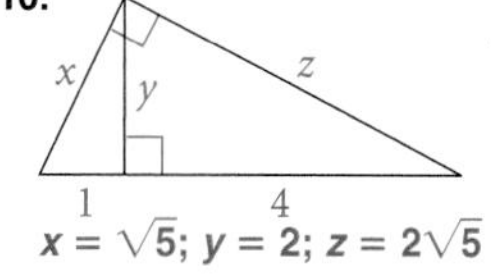

$x = \sqrt{5}$; $y = 2$; $z = 2\sqrt{5}$

11. 14.4
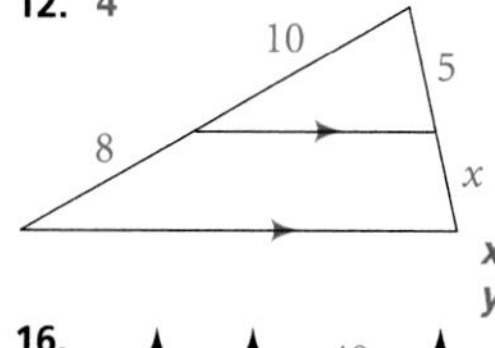

12. 4

13.

$x = \sqrt{70}$; $y = \sqrt{21}$; $z = \sqrt{30}$

14. 11.7

15. 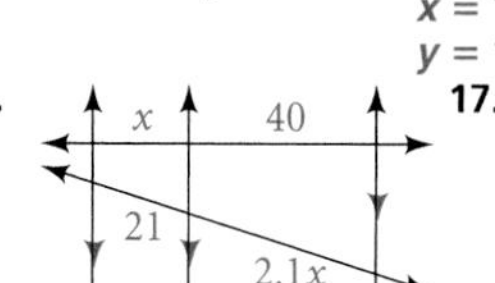

$x = 65$; $y = 60$; $z = 156$

16. 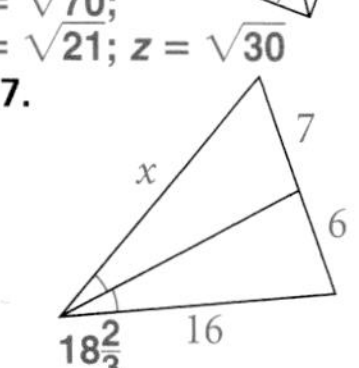

20

17.

$18\frac{2}{3}$

Find the ratio of the perimeters and the ratio of the areas of the blue figure to the red one. ■ Lesson 10-5

18. 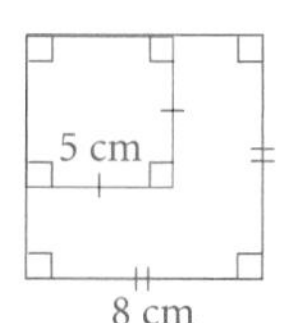

5 : 8; 25 : 64

19. 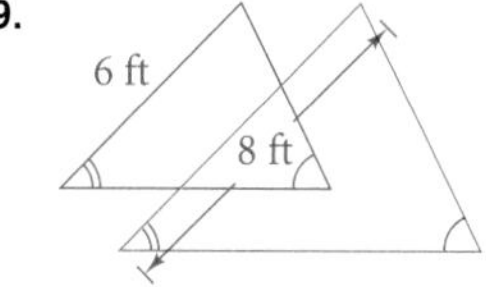

4 : 3; 16 : 9

20. 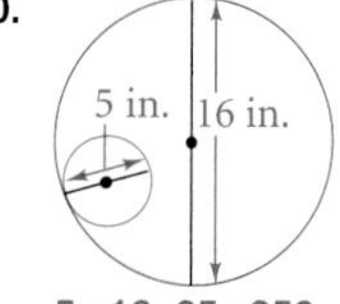

5 : 16; 25 : 256

Copy and complete for two similar solids. ■ Lesson 10-6

	Similarity Ratio	Ratio of Surface Areas	Ratio of Volumes
21.	2 : 3	4 ■ : ■ 9	8 ■ : ■ 27
22.	5 ■ : ■ 8	25 : 64	125 ■ : ■ 512
23.	3 ■ : ■ 4	9 ■ : ■ 16	27 : 64

657

Chapter 11 Extra Practice

11a. ⟨−49, 142⟩, ⟨38, 47⟩
b. ⟨−11, 189⟩
12a. ⟨−118, −55⟩, ⟨86, 110⟩
b. ⟨−32, 55⟩
13a. ⟨−54, 72⟩, ⟨−95, −33⟩
b. ⟨−149, 39⟩
14a. ⟨−21, −56⟩, ⟨27, −64⟩
b. ⟨6, −120⟩

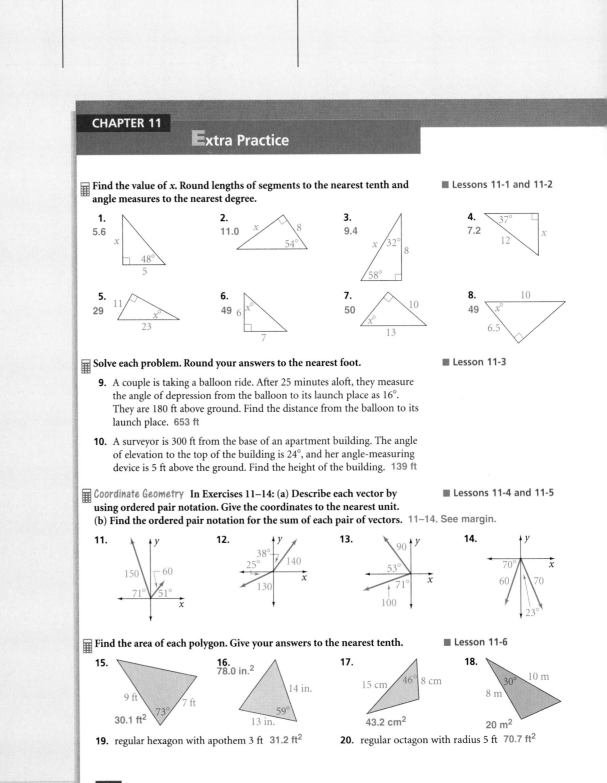

CHAPTER 11

Extra Practice

Find the value of x. Round lengths of segments to the nearest tenth and angle measures to the nearest degree. ■ Lessons 11-1 and 11-2

1. 5.6
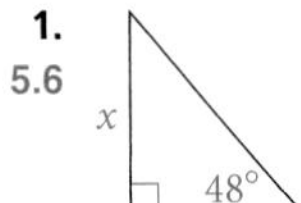

2. 11.0
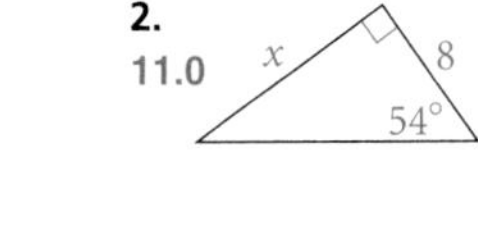

3. 9.4
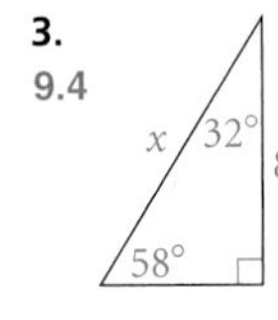

4. 7.2
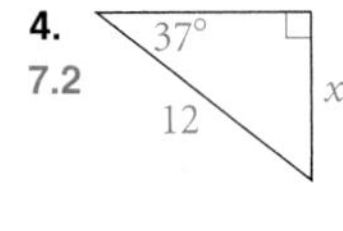

5. 29
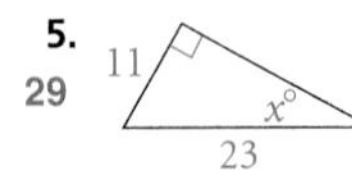

6. 49
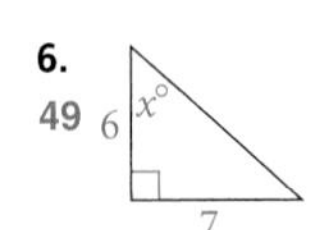

7. 50
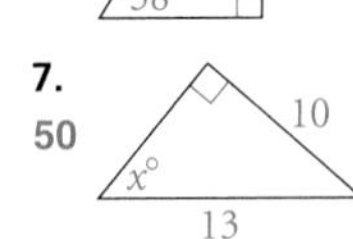

8. 49
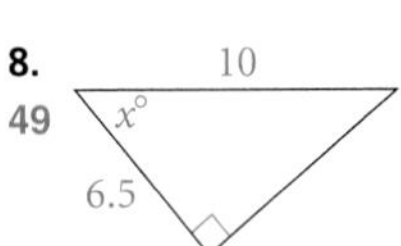

Solve each problem. Round your answers to the nearest foot. ■ Lesson 11-3

9. A couple is taking a balloon ride. After 25 minutes aloft, they measure the angle of depression from the balloon to its launch place as 16°. They are 180 ft above ground. Find the distance from the balloon to its launch place. 653 ft

10. A surveyor is 300 ft from the base of an apartment building. The angle of elevation to the top of the building is 24°, and her angle-measuring device is 5 ft above the ground. Find the height of the building. 139 ft

Coordinate Geometry **In Exercises 11–14: (a) Describe each vector by using ordered pair notation. Give the coordinates to the nearest unit. (b) Find the ordered pair notation for the sum of each pair of vectors.** 11–14. See margin. ■ Lessons 11-4 and 11-5

11.
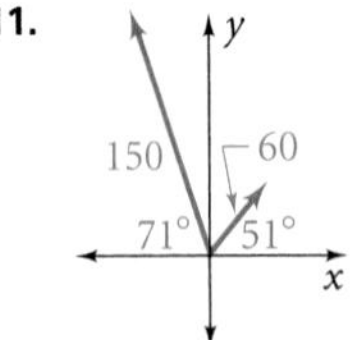

12.
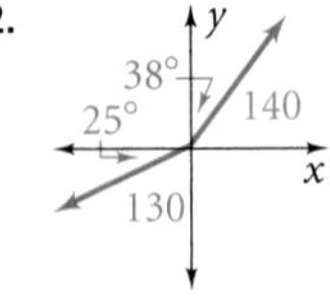

13.
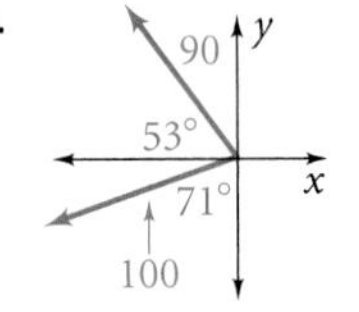

14.
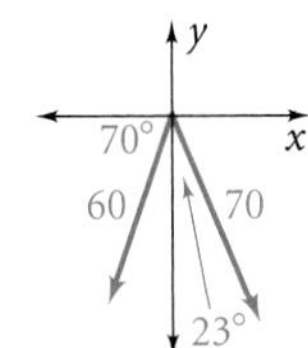

Find the area of each polygon. Give your answers to the nearest tenth. ■ Lesson 11-6

15. 9 ft, 7 ft, 73° — 30.1 ft^2

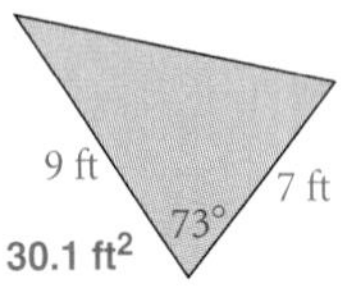

16. 78.0 in.^{2} — 14 in., 13 in., 59°

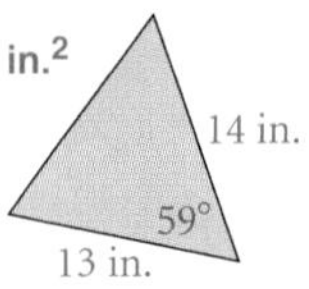

17.
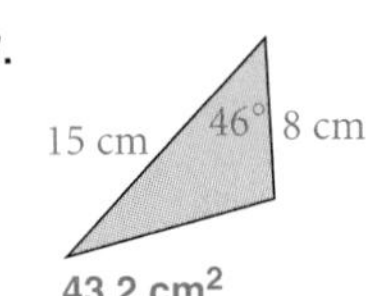

43.2 cm^2

18.
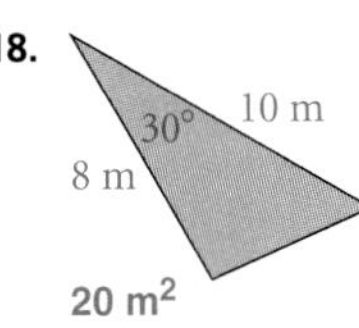

20 m^2

19. regular hexagon with apothem 3 ft 31.2 ft^2

20. regular octagon with radius 5 ft 70.7 ft^2

Chapter 12 Extra Practice

1. $x^2 + y^2 = 16$
2. $(x + 1)^2 + (y - 4)^2 = 25$
3. $(x - 9)^2 + (y + 3)^2 = 49$

CHAPTER 12

Extra Practice

Write an equation of each circle. 1–3. See margin. ■ Lesson 12-1

1. center (0, 0); $r = 4$
2. center (−1, 4); through (−1, 9)
3. center (9, −3); $r = 7$
4. center (−4, 0); through (2, 1) $(x + 4)^2 + y^2 = 37$
5. center (−6, −2); through (−8, 1) $(x + 6)^2 + (y + 2)^2 = 13$
6. center (0, 5); $r = 3$ $x^2 + (y - 5)^2 = 9$

Assume that lines that appear to be tangent are tangent. *P* is the center of each circle. Find the value of *x*. ■ Lesson 12-2

7. 65

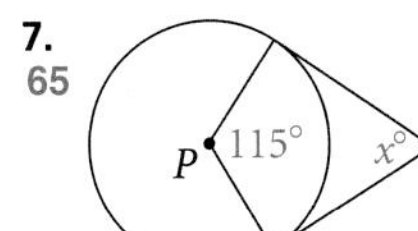

8. 10

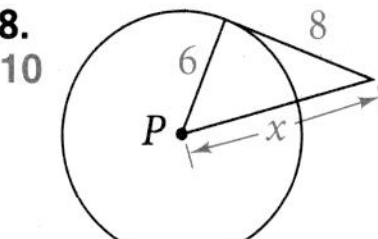

9. 6

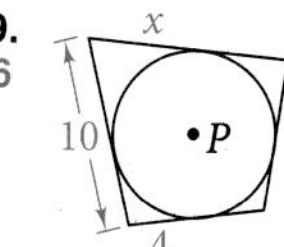

10. $2\sqrt{3}$

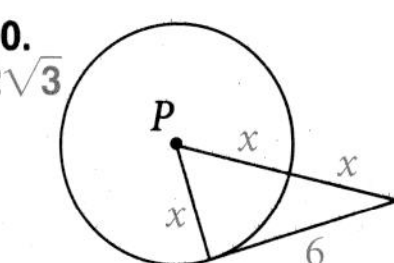

Find the value of each variable. If your answer is not an integer, round it to the nearest tenth. ■ Lessons 12-3 and 12-4

14. $a = 55$; $b = 72$; $c = 178$; $d = 89$

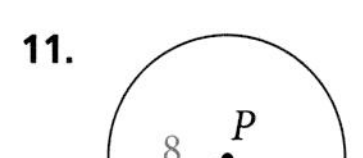

11. 14.8

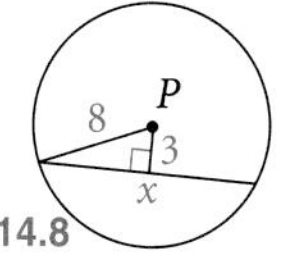

12. 5.2

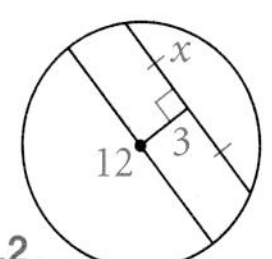

13. 5.3

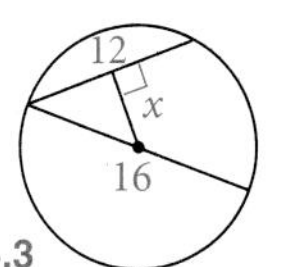

14.

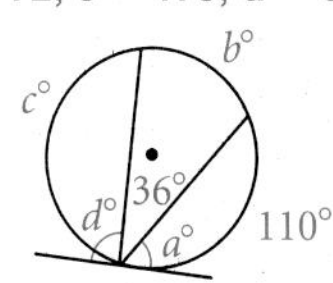

15.

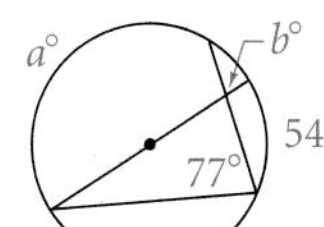

16.

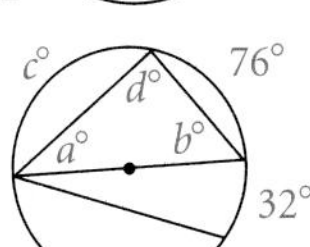

17.

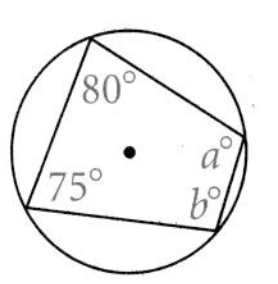

18. 20

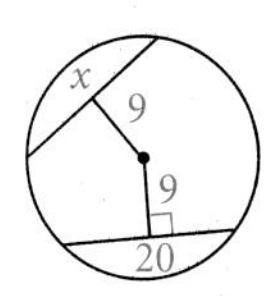

$a = 154$; $b = 76$ 16. $a = 38$; $b = 52$; $c = 104$; $d = 90$ $a = 105$; $b = 100$

Assume that lines that appear to be tangent are tangent. Find the value of each variable. If your answer is not an integer, round it to the nearest tenth. 19. $x = 193$; $y = 60.5$ ■ Lessons 12-5 and 12-6

19.

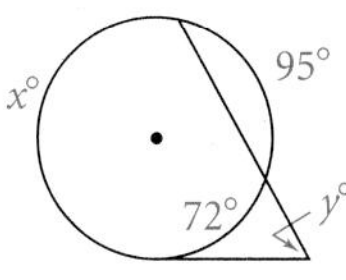

20. 5.6

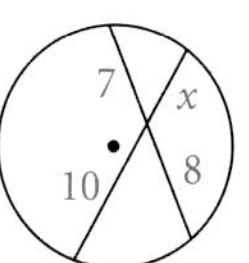

21. 10.4

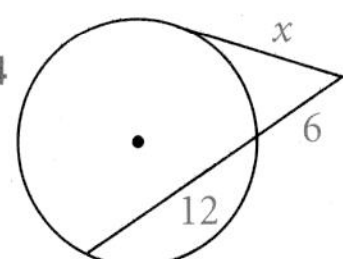

22. 70

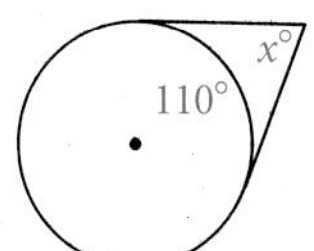

23.

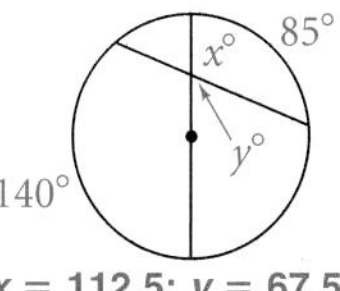

24. 11.5

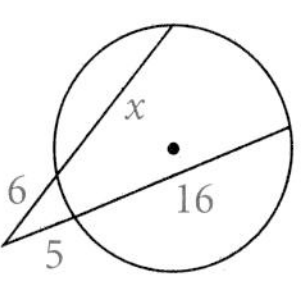

25. 42.5

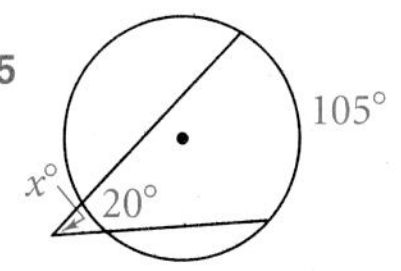

26.

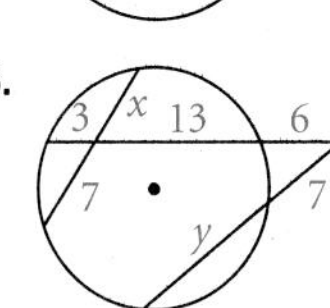

$x = 112.5$; $y = 67.5$ $x = 5.6$; $y = 11.9$

Problem Solving Strategies

You may find one or more of these strategies helpful in solving a word problem.

STRATEGY	WHEN TO USE IT
Draw a Diagram	You need help in visualizing the problem.
Guess and Test	Solving the problem directly is too complicated.
Look for a Pattern	The problem describes a relationship.
Make a Table	The problem has data that need organizing.
Solve a Simpler Problem	The problem is complex or has numbers that are too unmanageable to use at first.
Use Logical Reasoning	You need to reach a conclusion from some given information.
Work Backward	The answer can be arrived at by undoing various operations.

Problem Solving: Draw a Diagram

Example **Antoine is 1.91 m tall. He measures his shadow and finds that it is 2.34 m long. He then measures the length of the shadow of a flagpole and finds that it is 13.2 m long. How tall is the flagpole?**

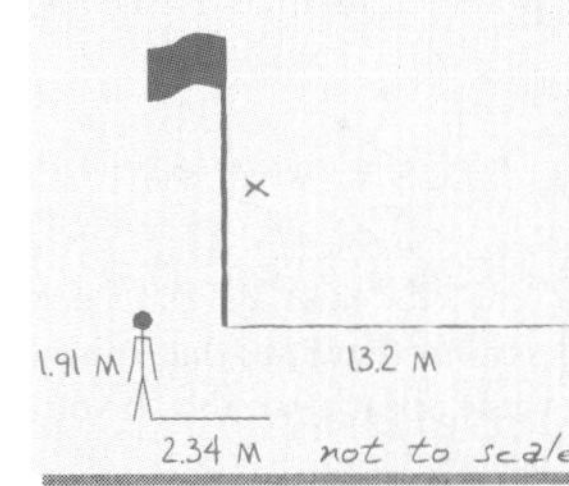

Start by drawing a diagram showing the given information. The diagram shows that the problem can be solved by using a proportion.

$\frac{1.91}{2.34} = \frac{x}{13.2}$ ← Write a proportion.

$x \approx 10.77$ ← Solve for x.

The flagpole is about 10.8 m tall.

EXERCISES

1. Five people meet and shake hands with one another. How many handshakes are there in all? 10 handshakes
2. Three tennis balls fit snugly in a standard cylindrical container. Which is greater, the circumference of a ball or the height of the container? circumference
3. Three lines that each intersect a circle can determine at most 7 regions within the circle, as shown in the diagram. What is the greatest number of regions that can be determined by 5 lines? 16 regions
4. A triangle has vertices (1, 3), (2, 3), and (7, 5). Find its area. 1 unit^2

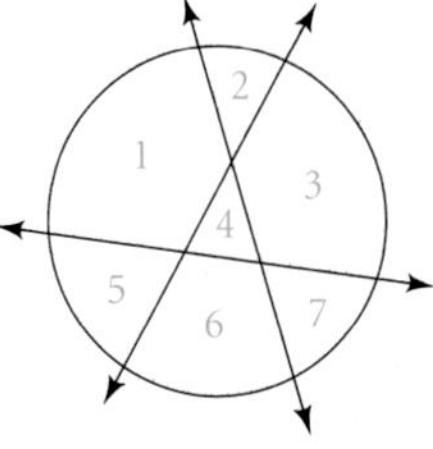

660

Problem Solving: Guess and Test

Have you ever weighed yourself on a balance scale at a doctor's office? You start by guessing your weight, then you see if the scale balances. If it doesn't, you slide the weights back and forth until the scale does balance. This is an example of the *Guess and Test* strategy, a strategy that is helpful for solving many types of problems.

Example **You are offered two payment plans for a CD club. Plan 1 involves paying a $20 membership fee and $7 per CD. Plan 2 involves paying no membership fee and $10 per CD. What is the least number of CDs you would have to buy to make Plan 1 the less expensive plan?**

	Plan 1	**Plan 2**	
Guess 4 CDs.	20 + 7(4)	10(4)	
	48 >	40	← Too low. Guess higher.
Guess 7 CDs.	20 + 7(7)	10(7)	
	69 <	70	← Plan 1 is less expensive!

You need to check 6 CDs, however, to be sure that 7 CDs is the *least* number you would have to buy to make Plan 1 less expensive.

20 + 7(6)	10(6)	
62 >	60	← Plan 1 is more expensive.

You need to buy at least 7 CDs to make Plan 1 the less expensive plan.

EXERCISES

1. Find three consecutive even integers whose product is 480. 6, 8, 10
2. The combined age of a father and his twin daughters is 54 years. The father was 24 years old when the twins were born. How old is each of the three people? Each daughter is 10 years old; the father is 34 years old.
3. What numbers can x represent in the rectangle? See below.

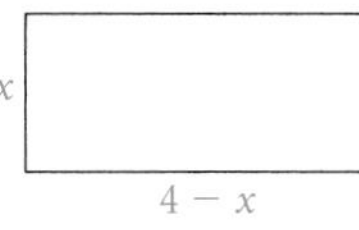

4. You are offered two payment plans for a video rental store. Plan 1 involves paying a $30 membership fee and $2 per rental. Plan 2 involves paying $3.50 per rental. What is the least number of videos you would have to rent to make Plan 1 the less expensive plan? 21 videos
5. Ruisa bought 7 rolls of film to take 192 pictures on a field trip. Some rolls had 36 exposures and the rest had 24 exposures. How many rolls of each type did Ruisa buy? 2 rolls with 36 exposures and 5 rolls with 24 exposures
6. The sum of five consecutive integers is 5. Find the integers. −1, 0, 1, 2, 3
7. Paul buys a coupon for $20 that allows him to see movies for half price at a local theater over the course of one year. The cost of seeing a movie is normally $7.50. What is the least number of movies Paul would have to see to pay less than the normal price? at least 6

3. any real number between 0 and 4

Problem Solving: Make a Table and Look for a Pattern

There are two important ways that making a table can help you solve a problem. First, a table is a handy method of organizing information. Second, once the information is in a table, it is easier to find patterns.

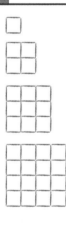

Example **The squares at the right are made of toothpicks. How many toothpicks are in the square with 7 toothpicks on a side?**

Make a table to organize the information.

No. of toothpicks on a side	1	2	3	4
Total no. of toothpicks in square	4	12	24	40

+8 +12 +16

Notice the pattern in the increases in the total number of toothpicks in each figure. The total number in the 5th square is 40 + 20, or 60. The number in the 6th is 60 + 24, or 84, and the number in the 7th is 84 + 28, or 112.

EXERCISES

1. The triangles are made up of toothpicks. How many toothpicks are in Figure 10? 165 toothpicks

Figure 1 Figure 2 Figure 3

2. In each figure, the vertices of the smallest square are midpoints of the sides of the next larger square. Find the area of the ninth shaded square. $\frac{1}{256}$ in.^{2}

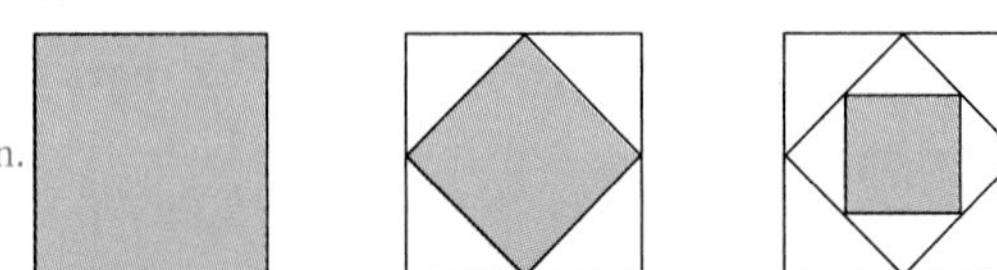

3. This pattern is known as the Sierpinski triangle. Find the total number of shaded triangles in Figure 8. 3280 triangles

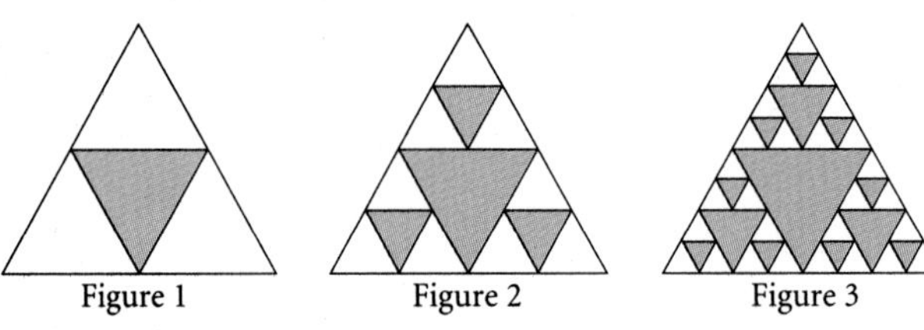

Figure 1 Figure 2 Figure 3

Problem Solving: Solve a Simpler Problem

Looking at a simpler version of a problem can be helpful in suggesting a problem-solving approach.

Example **A fence along the highway is 570 meters long. There is a fence post every 10 meters. How many fence posts are there?**

You may be tempted to divide 570 by 10, getting 57 as an answer, but looking at a simpler problem suggests that this answer isn't right. Suppose there are just 10 or 20 meters of fencing.

10 m — two fence posts; 20 m — three fence posts

These easier problems suggest that there is always *one more* fence post than one tenth the length. So for a 570 meter fence, there are $\frac{570}{10} + 1$, or 58 fence posts.

EXERCISES

1. A farmer wishes to fence in a square lot with dimensions 70 yards by 70 yards. He will install a fence post every 10 yards. How many fence posts will he need? 28 posts
2. Janette is planning to walk from her house to her friend Barbara's house. How many different paths can she take to get there? Assume that she walks only east and south. 84 paths

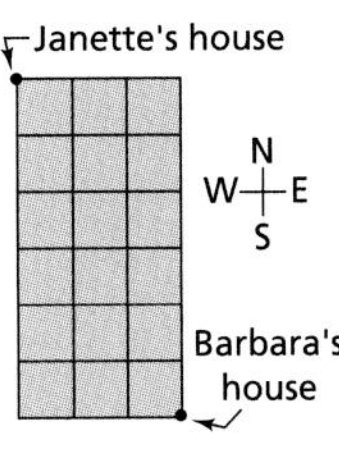

3. A square table can seat four people. For a banquet, a long rectangular table is formed by placing 14 such tables edge-to-edge in a straight line. How many people can sit at the long table? 30 people
4. Find the sum of the whole numbers from 1 to 999. 499,500
5. How many trapezoids are in the figure below? (*Hint:* Solve several simpler problems, then look for a pattern.) 25 trapezoids

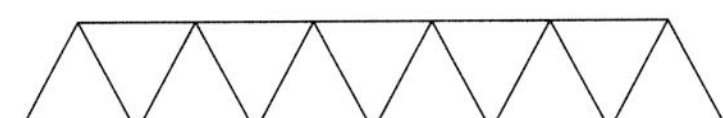

6. At a business luncheon, 424 handshakes took place. No two people shook hands with each other more than once. What is the least number of people in attendance at the luncheon? 30 people
7. On his fiftieth birthday, the President was honored with a 21-gun salute. The sound of each gunshot lasted 1 second, and 4 seconds elapsed between shots. How long did the salute last? 101 s

663

Problem Solving: Use Logical Reasoning

Some problems can be solved without the use of numbers. They can be solved by the use of logical reasoning, given some information.

Example **Anna, Bill, Carla, and Doug are siblings. Each lives in a different state beginning with W. Use these clues to determine where each sibling lives:**
(1) Neither sister lives in a state containing two words.
(2) Bill lives west of his sisters.
(3) Anna doesn't cross the Mississippi River when she visits Doug.

Make a table to organize what you know. Use an initial for each name.

State	A	B	C	D
West Virginia	✗	✗	✗	
Wisconsin		✗		
Wyoming		✗		
Washington	✗	✓	✗	✗

← From Clue 1, you know that neither Anna nor Carla lives in West Virginia.

← Using Clues 1 and 2, you know that Bill must live in Washington if he lives west of his sisters.

Use logical reasoning to complete the table.

State	A	B	C	D
West Virginia	✗	✗	✗	✓
Wisconsin	✓	✗	✗	✗
Wyoming	✗	✗	✓	✗
Washington	✗	✓	✗	✗

← Doug lives in West Virginia because none of his siblings do.

← From Clue 3, you know that Anna must live in Wisconsin.

← Carla, therefore, lives in Wyoming.

EXERCISES

1. Harold has a dog, a canary, a goldfish, and a hamster. Their names are J.T., Izzy, Arf, and Blinky. Izzy has neither feathers nor fins. Arf can't bark. J.T. weighs less than the four-legged pets. Neither the goldfish nor the dog has the longest name. Arf and Blinky don't get along well with the canary. What is each pet's name? **Izzy is the dog; J.T. is the canary; Arf is the goldfish; Blinky is the hamster**

2. At the state basketball championship tournament, 42 basketball games are played to determine the winner of the tournament. After each game, the loser is eliminated from the tournament. How many teams are in the tournament? **43 teams**

3. The sophomore class has 124 students. Of these students, 47 are involved in muscial activities: 25 in band and 36 in choir. How many students are involved in both band and choir? **14 students**

4. Tina's height is between Kimiko's and Ignacio's. Ignacio's height is between Jerome's and Kimiko's. Tina is taller than Jerome. List the people in order from shortest to tallest. **Jerome, Ignacio, Tina, Kimiko**

Problem Solving: Work Backward

In some situations it is easier to start with the end result and work backward to find the solution. You work backward in order to solve linear equations. The equation $2x + 3 = 11$ means "double x and add 3 to get 11." To find x, you "undo" those steps in reverse order.

$2x + 3 = 11$
$2x = 8$ ← Subtract 3 from each side.
$x = 4$ ← Divide each side by 2.

Another time it is convenient to work backward is when you want to "reverse" a set of directions.

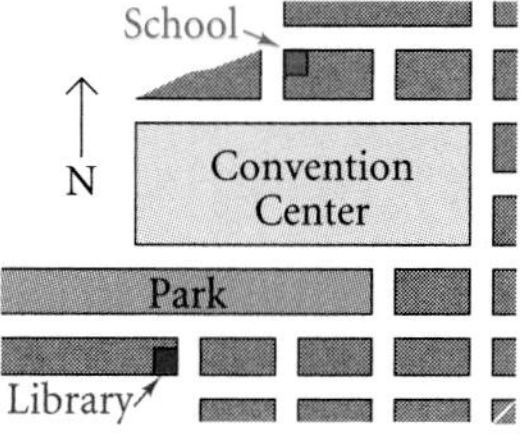

Example **To get from the library to the school, go 3 blocks east, then 5 blocks north, then 2 blocks west. How do you go from the school to the library?**

To reverse the directions, start at the school and work backward. Go 2 blocks east, 5 blocks south, and 3 blocks west.

EXERCISES

1. To go from Bedford to Worcester, take Route 4 south, then Route 128 south, then Route 90 west. How do you get from Worcester to Bedford? Route 90 east, Route 128 north, Route 4 north
2. Sandy spent $\frac{1}{10}$ of the money in her purse for lunch. She then spent \$23.50 for a gift for her brother, then half of what she had left on a new CD. If Sandy has \$13 left in her purse, how much money did she have in it before lunch? \$55
3. Algae are growing on a pond's surface. The area covered doubles each day. It takes 24 days to cover the pond completely. After how many days will the pond be half covered with algae? 23 d
4. Don sold $\frac{1}{5}$ as many raffle tickets as Carlita. Carlita sold 3 times as many as Ranesha. Ranesha sold 7 fewer than Russell. If Russell sold 12 tickets, how many did Don sell? 3 tickets
5. At 6% interest compounded annually, the balance in a bank account will double about every 12 years. If such an account has a balance of \$16,000 now, how much was deposited when the account was opened 36 years ago? \$2000
6. Solve the puzzle that Yuan gave to Inez: I am thinking of a number. If I triple the number and then halve the result, I get 12. What number am I thinking of? 8
7. Carlos paid \$14.60 for a taxi fare from a hotel to the airport, including a \$2.00 tip. Green Cab Co. charges \$1.20 per passenger plus \$0.20 for each additional $\frac{1}{5}$ mile. How many miles is the hotel from the airport? 11.4 mi

665

Using a Ruler and Protractor page 666

1–2. Answers may vary slightly.

1. 39 mm; 51 mm
2. $m\angle A = 48$; $m\angle B = 97$; $m\angle C = 35$
3. 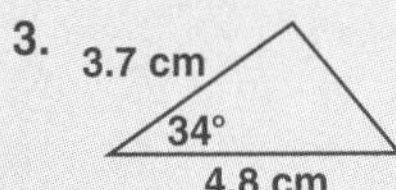

4. 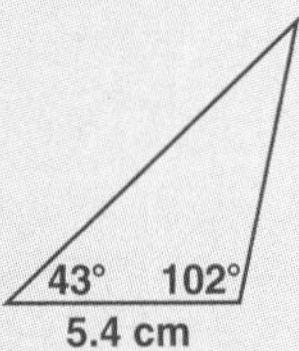
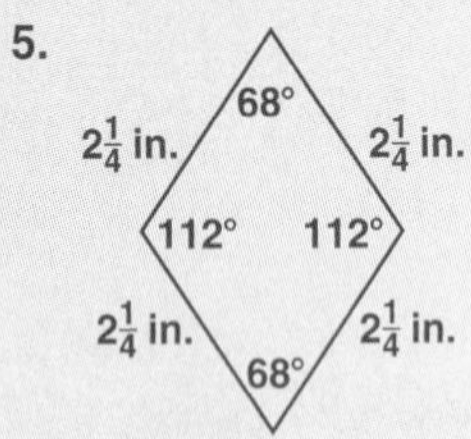

5.
6. Sample: 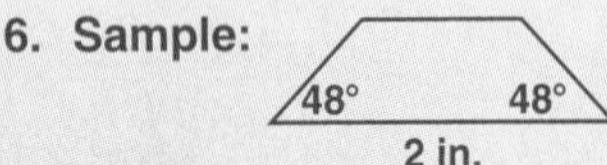

7. 

Using a Ruler and Protractor

Knowing how to use a ruler and protractor is crucial for success in Geometry.

Example **Draw a triangle that has sides of length 5.2 cm and 3.0 cm and a 68° angle between these two sides.**

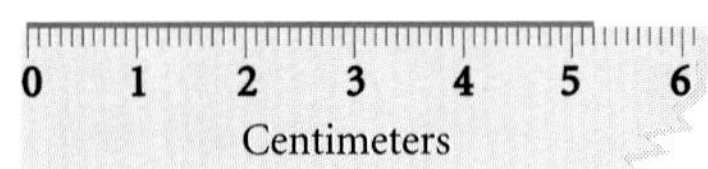

Step 1: Use a ruler to draw a segment 5.2 cm long.

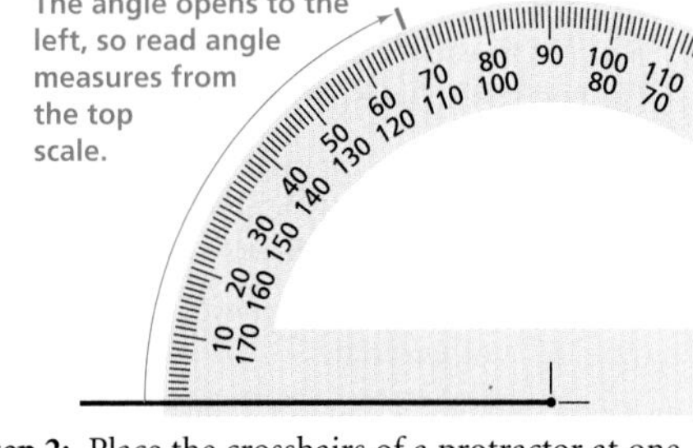

The angle opens to the left, so read angle measures from the top scale.

Step 2: Place the crosshairs of a protractor at one endpoint of the segment. Make a small mark at the 68° position along the protractor.

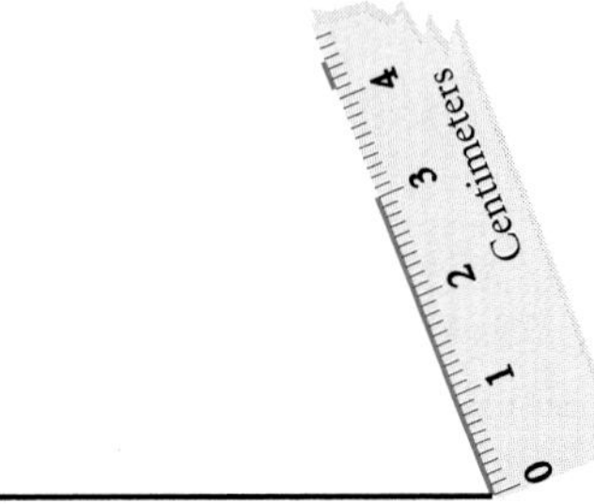

Step 3: Align the ruler along the small mark and the endpoint you used in Step 2. Place the zero point of the ruler at the endpoint. Draw a segment 3.0 cm long.

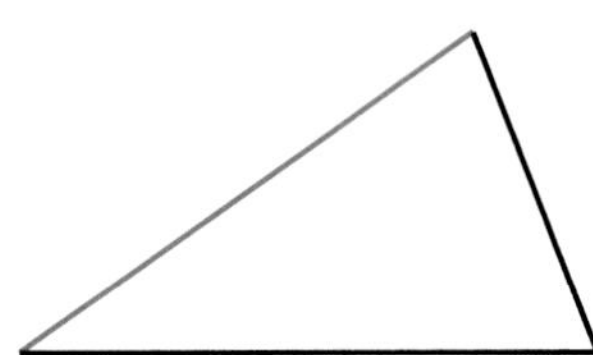

Step 4: Complete the triangle by connecting the endpoints of the first segment and the second.

EXERCISES

1. Measure sides $\overline{AB}$ and $\overline{BC}$ to the nearest millimeter. 1–7. See margin.
2. Measure each angle of $\triangle ABC$ to the nearest degree.
3. Draw a triangle that has sides of length 4.8 cm and 3.7 cm and a 34° angle between these two sides.
4. Draw a triangle that has 43° and 102° angles and a side of length 5.4 cm between these two angles.
5. Draw a rhombus that has sides of length $2\frac{1}{4}$ in. and 68° and 112° angles.
6. Draw an isosceles trapezoid that has a pair of 48° base angles and a base of length 2 in. between these two base angles.
7. Draw an isosceles triangle that has two congruent sides $3\frac{1}{2}$ in. long and a 134° vertex angle.

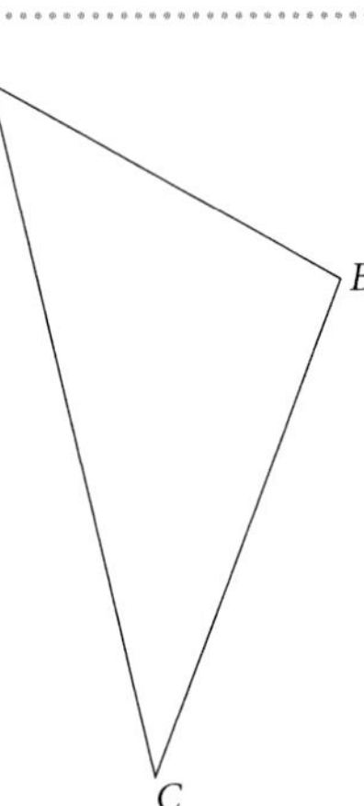

Measurement Conversions

To convert from one unit of measure to another, you multiply by a conversion factor. A *conversion factor* is a fraction equal to 1 that has different units in the numerator and the denominator. An example of a conversion factor is $\frac{1 \text{ ft}}{12 \text{ in.}}$. Other conversion factors are given in the table on page 668.

Example 1 **Complete.**

a. **88 in. = ■ ft** **b.** **5.3 m = ■ cm**

c. **3700 mm = ■ cm** **d.** **90 in. = ■ yd**

a. $88 \text{ in.} \cdot \frac{1 \text{ ft}}{12 \text{ in.}} = \frac{88}{12} \text{ ft} = 7\frac{1}{3} \text{ ft}$

b. $5.3 \text{ m} \cdot \frac{100 \text{ cm}}{1 \text{ m}} = 5.3(100) \text{ cm} = 530 \text{ cm}$

c. $3700 \text{ mm} \cdot \frac{1 \text{ cm}}{10 \text{ mm}} = 370 \text{ cm}$

d. $90 \text{ in.} \cdot \frac{1 \text{ ft}}{12 \text{ in.}} \cdot \frac{1 \text{ yd}}{3 \text{ ft}} = \frac{90}{36} \text{ yd} = 2\frac{1}{2} \text{ yd}$

Area is always in square units, and volume is always in cubic units.

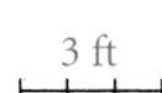

1 yd = 3 ft

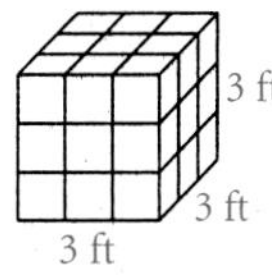

$1 \text{ yd}^2 = 9 \text{ ft}^2$

3 ft
3 ft
3 ft

$1 \text{ yd}^3 = 27 \text{ ft}^3$

Example 2 **Complete.**

a. **$300 \text{ in.}^2 = ■ \text{ ft}^2$** **b.** **$200{,}000 \text{ cm}^3 = ■ \text{ m}^3$**

a. $1 \text{ ft} = 12 \text{ in.}$, so $1 \text{ ft}^2 = (12 \text{ in.})^2$ or 144 in.^2

$300 \text{ in.}^2 \cdot \frac{1 \text{ ft}^2}{144 \text{ in.}^2} = 2\frac{1}{12} \text{ ft}^2$

b. $1 \text{ m} = 100 \text{ cm}$, so $1 \text{ m}^3 = (100 \text{ cm})^3$ or $1{,}000{,}000 \text{ cm}^3$

$200{,}000 \text{ cm}^3 \cdot \frac{1 \text{ m}^3}{1{,}000{,}000 \text{ cm}^3} = 0.2 \text{ m}^3$

EXERCISES

Complete.

1. 40 cm = ■ m 0.4
2. 1.5 kg = ■ g 1500
3. 60 cm = ■ mm 600
4. 200 in. = ■ ft $16\frac{2}{3}$
5. 28 yd = ■ in. 1008
6. 1.5 mi = ■ ft 7920
7. 42 fl oz = ■ qt $1\frac{5}{16}$
8. 430 mg = ■ g 0.43
9. 34 L = ■ mL 34,000
10. 1.2 m = ■ cm 120
11. 43 mm = ■ cm 4.3
12. 3600 s = ■ min 60
13. 15 g = ■ mg 15,000
14. 12 qt = ■ c 48
15. 0.03 kg = ■ mg 30,000
16. 14 gal = ■ qt 56
17. 4500 lb = ■ t $2\frac{1}{4}$
18. 234 min = ■ h 3.9
19. 12 mL = ■ L 0.012
20. 2 pt = ■ fl oz 32
21. 20 m/s = ■ km/h 72
22. $3 \text{ ft}^2 = ■ \text{ in.}^2$ 432
23. $108 \text{ m}^2 = ■ \text{ cm}^2$ 1,080,000
24. $2100 \text{ mm}^2 = ■ \text{ cm}^2$ 21
25. $1.4 \text{ yd}^2 = ■ \text{ ft}^2$ 12.6
26. $0.45 \text{ km}^2 = ■ \text{ m}^2$ 450,000
27. $1300 \text{ ft}^2 = ■ \text{ yd}^2$ $144\frac{4}{9}$
28. $1030 \text{ in.}^2 = ■ \text{ ft}^2$ $7\frac{11}{72}$
29. $20{,}000{,}000 \text{ ft}^2 = ■ \text{ mi}^2$ about 0.72
30. $1000 \text{ cm}^3 = ■ \text{ m}^3$ 0.001
31. $1.4 \text{ ft}^3 = ■ \text{ in.}^3$ 2419.2
32. $3.56 \text{ cm}^3 = ■ \text{ mm}^3$ 3560
33. $0.013 \text{ km}^3 = ■ \text{ m}^3$ 13,000,000

Measurement, Rounding Error and Reasonableness page 668

1. $23\frac{1}{2}$ ft to $24\frac{1}{2}$ ft
2. $123\frac{1}{2}$ cm to $124\frac{1}{2}$ cm
3. $339\frac{1}{2}$ mL to $340\frac{1}{2}$ mL
4. $5\frac{1}{4}$ mi to $5\frac{3}{4}$ mi
5. 73.15 cm to 73.25 cm
6. $33\frac{1}{2}$ yd^2 to $34\frac{1}{2}$ yd^2
7. 5.35 mi to 5.45 mi
8. 6 ft $4\frac{3}{4}$ in. to 6 ft $5\frac{1}{4}$ in.
9. 8.7 cm to 9.1 cm

Measurement, Rounding Error, and Reasonableness

There is no such thing as an *exact* measurement. Measurements are always approximate. No matter how precise it is, a measurement actually represents a range of values.

The possible difference between a measurement and the actual value is called the error. The *error* is equal to half the unit of greatest precision.

Example 1 **Chris's height, to the nearest inch, is 5 ft 8 in. Find the range of values this measurement represents.**

The height is given to the nearest inch, so the error is $\frac{1}{2}$ in. Chris's height, then, is between 5 ft $7\frac{1}{2}$ in. and 5 ft $8\frac{1}{2}$ in., or it is 5 ft 8 in. $\pm\ \frac{1}{2}$ in. Within this range are all measures that, when rounded to the nearest inch, equal 5 ft 8 in.

As you calculate with measurements, error can accumulate.

Example 2 **Jean drives 18 km to work each day. The distance is given to the nearest kilometer.**
a. Find the range of values this measurement represents.
b. Find the error in the round-trip distance.

a. The driving distance is between 17.5 and 18.5 km, or 18 $\pm$ 0.5 km.

b. Double the lower limit, 17.5, and the upper limit, 18.5. Thus, the round trip can be anywhere between 35 and 37 km, or 36 $\pm$ 1 km. The error for the round trip is twice the error of a single leg of the trip.

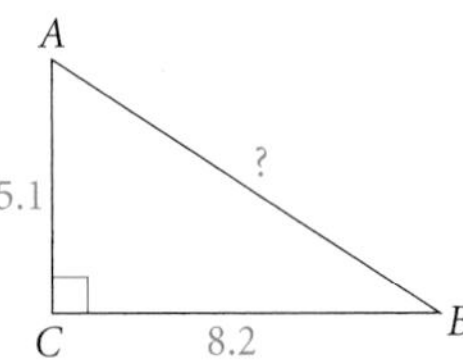

So that your answers will be reasonable, keep precision and error in mind as you calculate. For example, in finding AB, the length of the hypotenuse of $\triangle ABC$, it would be inappropriate to give the answer as 9.6566 if the sides are given to the nearest tenth. Round your answer to 9.7.

EXERCISES

Each measurement is followed by its unit of greatest precision. Find the range of values that each measurement represents. 1–9. See margin.

1. 24 ft (ft)	**2.** 124 cm (cm)	**3.** 340 mL (mL)	**4.** $5\frac{1}{2}$ mi ($\frac{1}{2}$ mi)
5. 73.2 cm (mm)	**6.** 34 yd^2 (yd^2)	**7.** 5.4 mi (0.1 mi)	**8.** 6 ft 5 in. (0.5 in.)

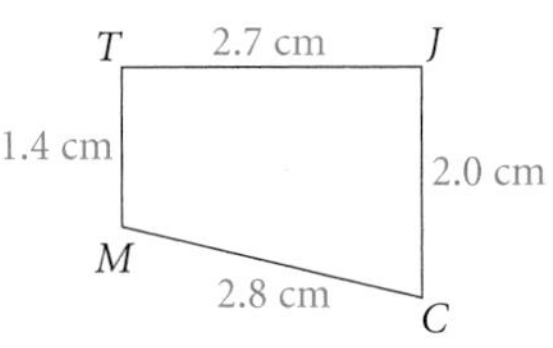

9. The lengths of the sides of $TJCM$ are given to the nearest millimeter. Find the range of values for the figure's perimeter.

10. To the nearest degree, two angles of a triangle are 49° and 73°. What is the range of values for the measure of the third angle? 57 to 59

11. The lengths of the legs of a right triangle are given as 131 m and 162 m. You use a calculator to find the length of the hypotenuse. The calculator display reads 208.33867. What should your answer be? 208 m

Mean, Median, and Mode
page 669

5. Median; the mode does not represent most of the data; the mean is significantly affected by the single highest salary.

Mean, Median, and Mode

Measures of central tendency, such as mean, median, and mode, are numbers that describe a set of data.

Example **Eighteen students were asked to measure the angle formed by the three objects in the diagram. Their answers, in order from least to greatest, are as follows:**

65, 66, 66, 66, 66, 66, 66, 67, 67, 67, 67, 67, 68, 68, 69, 70, 74, 113

Find the mean, median, and mode of the data.

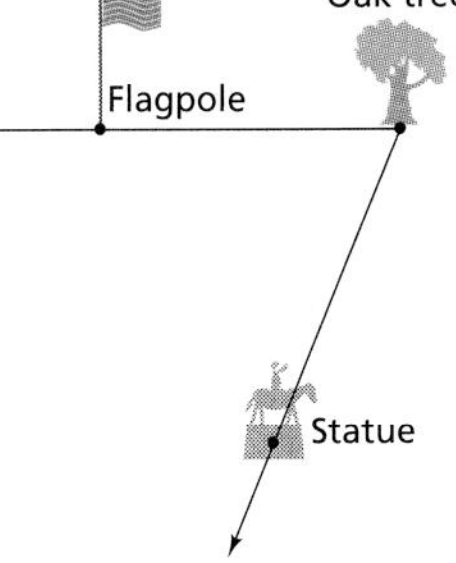

To find the *mean* (sometimes called the average), add the numbers and divide by the number of items.

Mean $= \frac{\text{sum of the 18 measures}}{18} = \frac{1258}{18} = 69\frac{8}{9}$

The *median* is the middle number when the items are placed in order. (When there is an even number of items, take the mean of the two middle numbers.) Here, the two middle numbers—the ninth and the tenth numbers on the list—are both 67. So the median is 67.

The *mode* is the number that appears most frequently. A set of data may have more than one mode or no modes. There are more 66's than any other number, so the mode is 66.

EXERCISES

Find the mean, median, and mode of each set of data.

1. 353.6; 301; no mode
2. \$3.53; \$3.56; no mode

1. Numbers of students per school in Newtown: 234, 341, 253, 313, 273, 301, 760
2. Amounts spent for lunch: \$4.50, \$3.26, \$5.02, \$3.58, \$1.25, \$3.05, \$4.24, \$3.56, \$3.31
3. Salaries at D. B. Widget & Co.: \$15,000; \$18,000; \$18,000; \$21,700; \$26,500; \$27,000; \$29,300; \$31,100; \$43,000; \$47,800; \$69,000; \$140,000
   \$40,533; \$28,150; \$18,000
4. Population of towns in Brower County: 567, 632, 781, 902, 1034, 1100, 1598, 2164, 2193, 3062, 3074, 3108, 3800, 3721, 4104
   2123; 2164; no mode
5. In Exercise 3, which measure or measures of central tendency do you think best represent the data? Explain. See margin.
6. Find the mean, median, and mode of the exam scores at the right.
7. In the example, the student who reported the angle measure as 113 most likely made an error. If this measure is dropped from the list, what are the mean, median, and mode of the remaining 17 scores?
8. In the example, if the smallest measurement were 51 instead of 65, would the mean decrease? Would the median? Would the mode? yes; no; no
9. In the example, if the two students who measured the angle at 68 both reduced their measurements to 67, would the mode be affected? How?
   Yes; the mode would be 67.

6. 75.3; 78; 85

Final Exam Scores

34, 47, 53, 56, 57, 62, 62, 64, 67, 70, 74, 74, 74, 78, 82, 85, 85, 85, 85, 86, 88, 92, 93, 93, 94, 95, 97

7. $67\frac{6}{17}$; 67; 66

Bar Graphs and Line Graphs page 670

1.

Sales of Rock Music

Sales (in millions of dollars)

4000
2000
0

1989 1990 1991 1992 1993 1994

Year

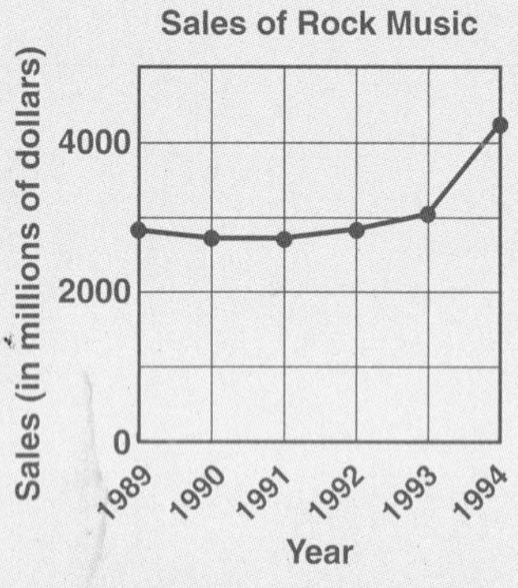

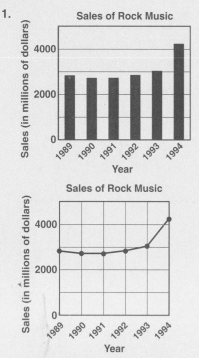

5. No; you cannot tell how the temperature changed between the measurements.
6. Answers may vary. Sample: A line graph; the line graph shows change over time more clearly.

Bar Graphs and Line Graphs

Data displayed in a table can be very useful, but a table is not as easy to interpret as a graph. A bar graph and a line graph can show the same data, but sometimes one type of graph will have advantages over the other.

Example **Make a bar graph and a line graph showing the data in the table at the left.**

Revenue of HJL Co.

Year	Revenue
1993	$39,780
1994	$40,019
1995	$51,772
1996	$63,444
1997	$79,855

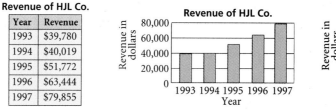

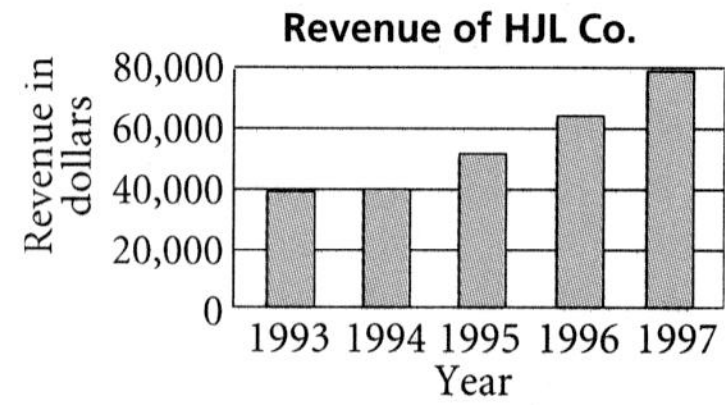

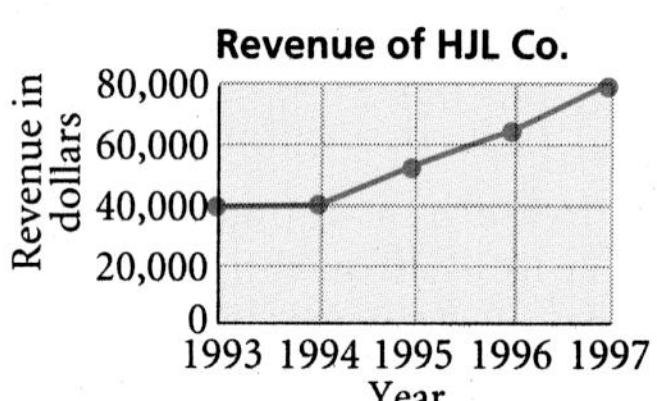

Bar graphs are useful when you wish to compare amounts. In the example, the tallest bar is clearly twice the height of the shortest bar. At a glance, it is evident that in four years the revenue approximately doubled.

Line graphs allow you to see how a set of data changes over time. In the example, the slope of the line shows that revenue has increased at a steady rate since 1994.

Did revenue increase from 1993 to 1994? You can't tell by looking at either graph; for that information, you would have to look back at the table.

EXERCISES

1. Create a bar graph and a line graph to display the data in the table. Show years along the horizontal axis and sales along the vertical axis. See margin for sample.

Sales of Rock Music (in millions of dollars)

Year	1989	1990	1991	1992	1993	1994
Sales	$2833	$2722	$2726	$2852	$3034	$4236

Source: *Recording Industry Association of America*

For Exercises 2–6, refer to the line graph at the right. 3. 8 A.M.–2 P.M.

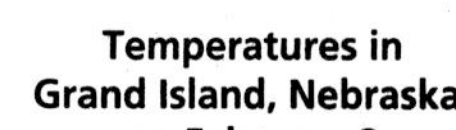

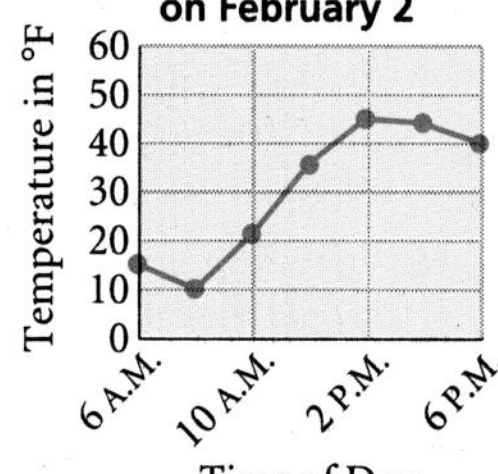

2. What was the lowest temperature recorded between 6 A.M. and 6 P.M.? 10°F
3. During which time periods did the temperature appear to increase?
4. Estimate the temperature at 11 A.M. and at 5 P.M. 28°F; 42°F
5. Can you tell from the graph what the actual maximum and minimum temperatures were between 6 A.M. and 6 P.M.? Explain. 5–6. See margin.
6. The same data could be presented in a bar graph. Which presentation is better for these data, a line graph or a bar graph? Why?

Circle Graphs page 671

4. Age of Cars on the Road

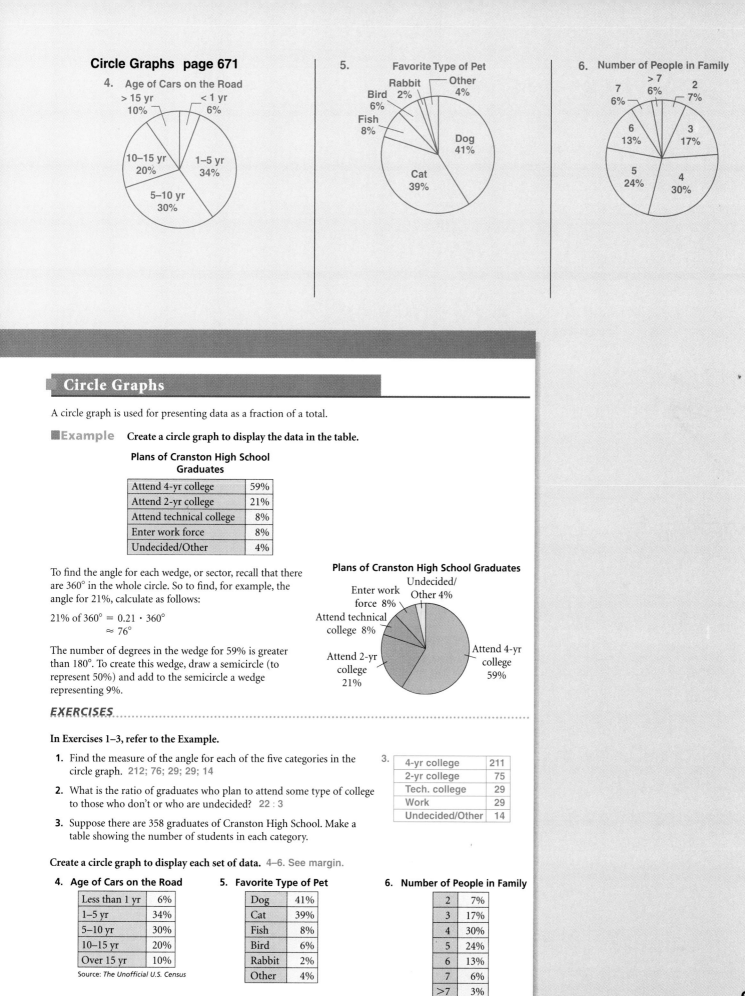

> 15 yr 10%
< 1 yr 6%
1–5 yr 34%
5–10 yr 30%
10–15 yr 20%

5. 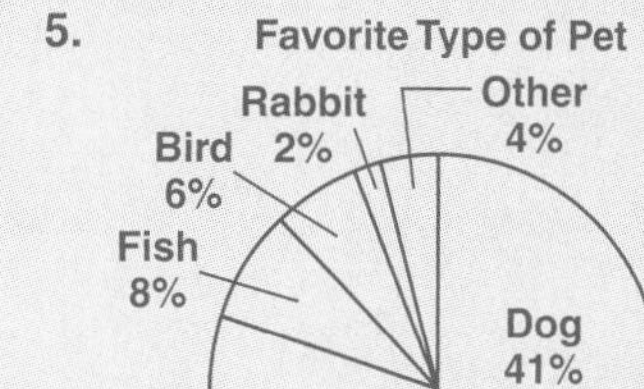

6. 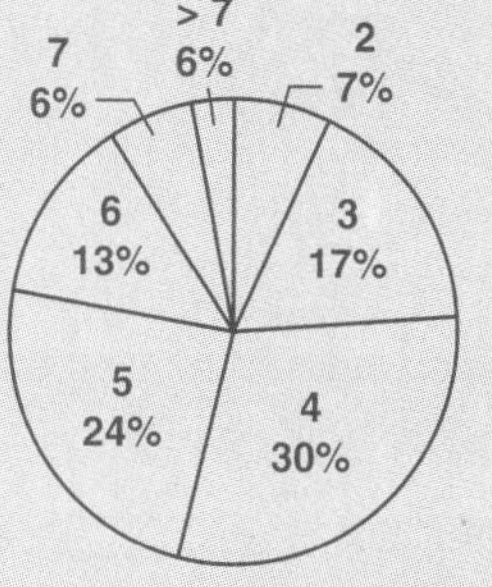

Circle Graphs

A circle graph is used for presenting data as a fraction of a total.

Example **Create a circle graph to display the data in the table.**

Plans of Cranston High School Graduates

Attend 4-yr college	59%
Attend 2-yr college	21%
Attend technical college	8%
Enter work force	8%
Undecided/Other	4%

To find the angle for each wedge, or sector, recall that there are 360° in the whole circle. So to find, for example, the angle for 21%, calculate as follows:

$$21\% \text{ of } 360° = 0.21 \cdot 360°$$
$$\approx 76°$$

The number of degrees in the wedge for 59% is greater than 180°. To create this wedge, draw a semicircle (to represent 50%) and add to the semicircle a wedge representing 9%.

Plans of Cranston High School Graduates

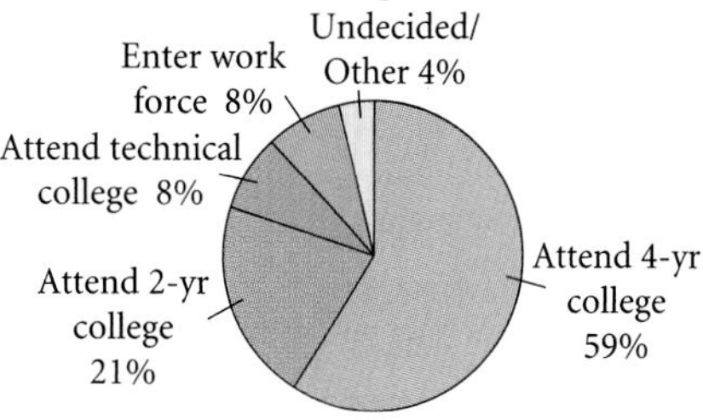

EXERCISES

In Exercises 1–3, refer to the Example.

1. Find the measure of the angle for each of the five categories in the circle graph. 212; 76; 29; 29; 14
2. What is the ratio of graduates who plan to attend some type of college to those who don't or who are undecided? 22 : 3
3. Suppose there are 358 graduates of Cranston High School. Make a table showing the number of students in each category.

3.

4-yr college	211
2-yr college	75
Tech. college	29
Work	29
Undecided/Other	14

Create a circle graph to display each set of data. 4–6. See margin.

4. **Age of Cars on the Road**

Less than 1 yr	6%
1–5 yr	34%
5–10 yr	30%
10–15 yr	20%
Over 15 yr	10%

Source: *The Unofficial U.S. Census*

5. **Favorite Type of Pet**

Dog	41%
Cat	39%
Fish	8%
Bird	6%
Rabbit	2%
Other	4%

6. **Number of People in Family**

2	7%
3	17%
4	30%
5	24%
6	13%
7	6%
>7	3%

Box-and-Whisker Plots

A *box-and-whisker plot* is a way to display data on a number line. It provides a picture of how tightly the data cluster around the median and how wide a range the data have. The diagram below shows the various points associated with a box-and-whisker plot.

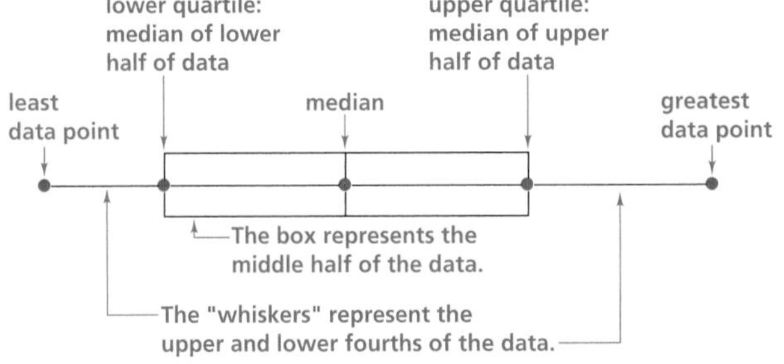

Example **The heights, in inches, of 23 students are as follows:**

58, 61, 63, 63, 63, 64, 64, 65, 65, 65, 67, 68, 68, 68, 69, 70, 70, 70, 72, 72, 72, 74, 75

Draw a box-and-whisker plot.

The heights vary from 58 in. to 75 in. The median is 68. The lower quartile (the median of the lower eleven heights) is 64. The upper quartile (the median of the upper eleven heights) is 70.

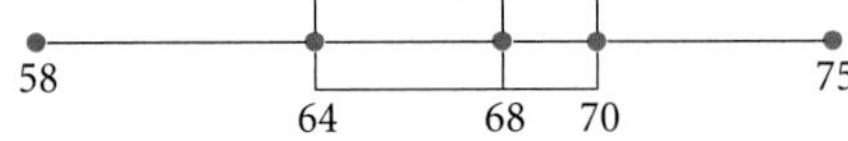

EXERCISES

1. All of the physical education students at Martin Luther King, Jr., High School were timed sprinting the 100-meter dash. The box-and-whisker plot below summarizes the data. Use it to find the following:
   a. Median 16.6 b. Lower quartile 15.1 c. Upper quartile 19.4

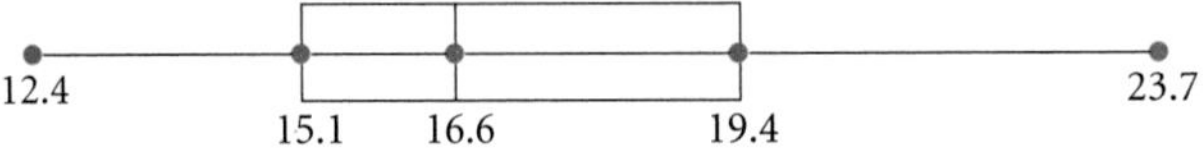

2. Make a box-and-whisker plot for the following set of data, which lists the weights, in pounds, of the students trying out for the wrestling team at South Side High School.

   104, 121, 122, 130, 130, 131, 140, 144, 147, 147, 148, 155, 160, 163, 171

   104 130 144 155 171

672

Evaluating and Simplifying Expressions

Order of Operations

1. Perform any operation(s) inside grouping symbols.
2. Simplify any term with exponents.
3. Multiply and divide in order from left to right.
4. Add and subtract in order from left to right.

You *evaluate* an expression with variables by substituting a number for each variable. Then simplify the expression using the order of operations.

Be especially careful with exponents and negative signs. For example, the expression $-x^2$ always yields a negative or zero value, and $(-x)^2$ is always positive or zero.

Example 1 **Evaluate each expression for $r = 4$.**
a. $-r^2$ **b.** $-3r^2$ **c.** $(-3r)^2$

a. $-r^2 = -(4)^2 = -16$
b. $-3r^2 = -3(4)^2 = -3(16) = -48$
c. $(-3r)^2 = (-3 \cdot 4)^2 = (-12)^2 = 144$

To simplify an expression, you combine like terms and eliminate any parentheses.

Example 2 **Simplify each expression.**
a. $5r - 2r + 1$ **b.** $\pi(3r - 1)$ **c.** $(r + \pi)(r - \pi)$

a. Combine like terms: $5r - 2r + 1 = 3r + 1$
b. Use the distributive property: $\pi(3r - 1) = 3\pi r - \pi$
c. Multiply polynomials: $(r + \pi)(r - \pi) = r^2 - \pi^2$

EXERCISES

Evaluate each expression for $x = 5$ and $y = -3$.

1. $-2x^2$ −50
2. $-y + x$ 8
3. $-xy$ 15
4. $(x + 5y) \div x$ −2
5. $x + 5y \div x$ 2
6. $(-2y)^2$ 36
7. $(2y)^2$ 36
8. $(x - y)^2$ 64
9. $\frac{x + 1}{y}$ −2
10. $y - (x - y)$ −11
11. $-y^x$ 243
12. $\frac{2(1 - x)}{y - x}$ 1
13. $x \cdot y - x$ −20
14. $x - y \cdot x$ 20
15. $\frac{y^3 - x}{x - y}$ −4
16. $-y(x - 3)^2$ 12

17. Which expression gives the area of the shaded region of the figure at the right? B
A. $\pi(R - S)^2$ **B.** $\pi(R^2 - S^2)$
C. $\pi(S^2 - R^2)$ **D.** $\pi R^2 - 2\pi S$

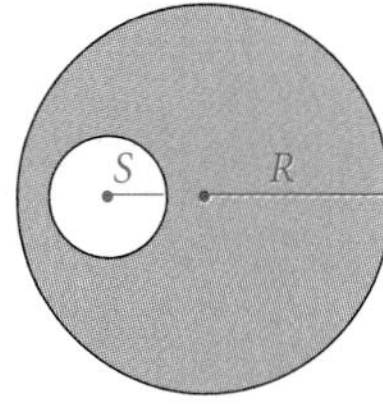

Simplify.

18. $6x - 4x + 8 - 5$ $2x + 3$
19. $2(\ell + w)$ $2\ell + 2w$
20. $3x - 5 + 2x$ $5x - 5$
21. $-(4x + 7)$ $-4x - 7$
22. $-4x(x - 2)$ $-4x^2 + 8x$
23. $3x - (5 + 2x)$ $x - 5$
24. $2t^2 + 4t - 5t^2$ $-3t^2 + 4t$
25. $(r - 1)^2$ $r^2 - 2r + 1$
26. $(1 - r)^2$ $r^2 - 2r + 1$
27. $(y + 1)(y - 3)$ $y^2 - 2y - 3$
28. $4h + 3h - 4 + 3$ $7h - 1$
29. $\pi r - (1 + \pi r)$ −1
30. $(x + 4)(2x - 1)$ $2x^2 + 7x - 4$
31. $2\pi h(1 - r)^2$ $2\pi hr^2 - 4\pi hr + 2\pi h$
32. $3y^2 - (y^2 + 3y)$ $2y^2 - 3y$
33. $-(x + 4)^2$ $-x^2 - 8x - 16$

Simplifying Radicals

A radical expression is in its *simplest form* when all three of the following statements are true.

1. The expression under the radical sign contains no perfect square factors (other than 1).
2. The expression under the radical sign does not contain a fraction.
3. The denominator does not contain a radical expression.

Example 1 **Simplify.**

a. $\sqrt{\frac{4}{9}}$ b. $\sqrt{12}$

a. $\sqrt{\frac{4}{9}} = \frac{\sqrt{4}}{\sqrt{9}} = \frac{2}{3}$ b. $\sqrt{12} = \sqrt{4} \cdot \sqrt{3} = 2\sqrt{3}$

Example 2 **Find the length of the diagonal of rectangle *HJKL*.**

$c^2 = 7^2 + 1^2$ ← Use the Pythagorean Theorem.
$c^2 = 50$ ← Simplify the right side.
$c = \sqrt{50}$ ← Find the square root of each side.
$= \sqrt{25 \cdot 2}$
$= 5\sqrt{2}$ ← Simplify the radical.

Example 3 **Simplify $\frac{1}{\sqrt{3}}$.**

$\frac{1}{\sqrt{3}} \cdot \frac{\sqrt{3}}{\sqrt{3}} = \frac{\sqrt{3}}{3}$ ← Multiply by $\frac{\sqrt{3}}{\sqrt{3}}$, or 1, to eliminate the radical in the denominator.

EXERCISES

Simplify each radical expression.

1. $\sqrt{27}$ $3\sqrt{3}$
2. $\sqrt{24}$ $2\sqrt{6}$
3. $\sqrt{150}$ $5\sqrt{6}$
4. $\sqrt{\frac{1}{9}}$ $\frac{1}{3}$
5. $\sqrt{\frac{72}{9}}$ $2\sqrt{2}$
6. $\frac{\sqrt{228}}{\sqrt{16}}$ $\frac{\sqrt{57}}{2}$
7. $\sqrt{\frac{2}{5}}$ $\frac{\sqrt{10}}{5}$
8. $\sqrt{\frac{27}{75}}$ $\frac{3}{5}$
9. $\frac{3}{\sqrt{8}}$ $\frac{3\sqrt{2}}{4}$
10. $\frac{6\sqrt{18}}{\sqrt{48}}$ $\frac{3\sqrt{6}}{2}$

Find the value of x. Leave your answer in simplest radical form.

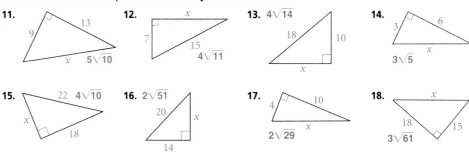

11. 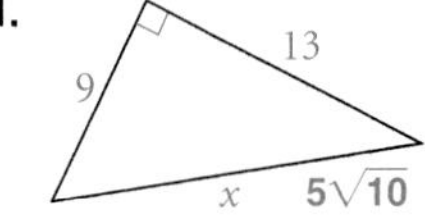

$5\sqrt{10}$

12. 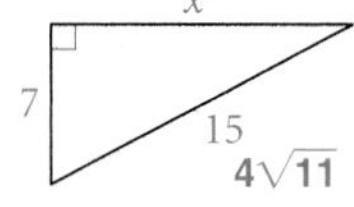

$4\sqrt{11}$

13. $4\sqrt{14}$ 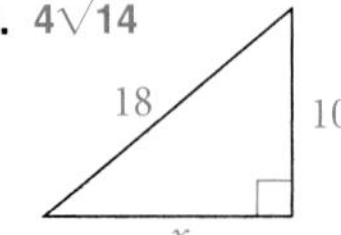

14. 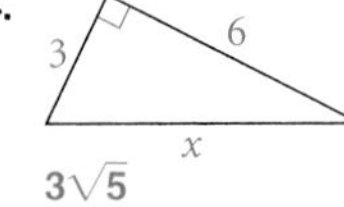

$3\sqrt{5}$

15. 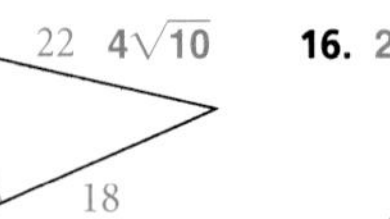

$4\sqrt{10}$

16. $2\sqrt{51}$
20
x
14

17. 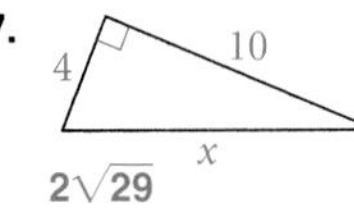

$2\sqrt{29}$

18. 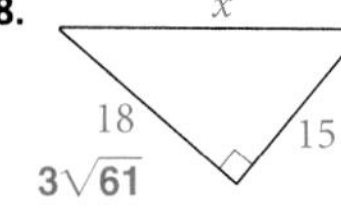

$3\sqrt{61}$

Simplifying Ratios

The ratio of the shorter leg to the longer leg of this right triangle is 4 to 6. This ratio can be written in several ways:

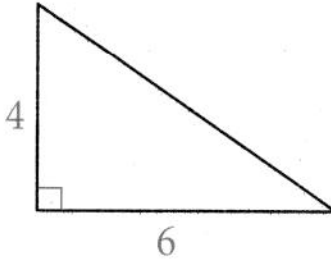

4 to 6 $\quad \frac{4}{6} \quad$ 4 : 6

You simplify ratios the same way you simplify fractions, by dividing out common factors from the numerator and denominator.

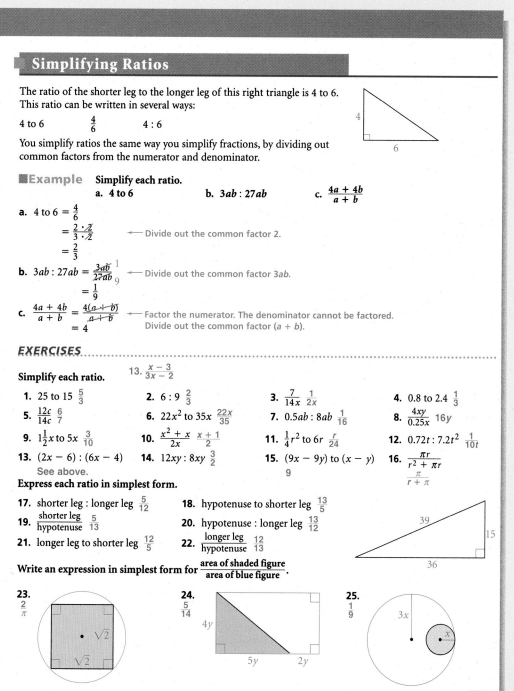

Example **Simplify each ratio.**

a. **4 to 6** **b.** **$3ab : 27ab$** **c.** $\frac{4a + 4b}{a + b}$

a. $4 \text{ to } 6 = \frac{4}{6}$

$= \frac{2 \cdot \cancel{2}}{3 \cdot \cancel{2}}$ ← Divide out the common factor 2.

$= \frac{2}{3}$

b. $3ab : 27ab = \frac{\cancel{3ab}^{1}}{\cancel{27ab}_{9}}$ ← Divide out the common factor $3ab$.

$= \frac{1}{9}$

c. $\frac{4a + 4b}{a + b} = \frac{4\cancel{(a + b)}}{\cancel{a + b}}$ ← Factor the numerator. The denominator cannot be factored. Divide out the common factor $(a + b)$.

$= 4$

EXERCISES

Simplify each ratio. 13. $\frac{x - 3}{3x - 2}$

1. 25 to 15 $\frac{5}{3}$
2. $6 : 9$ $\frac{2}{3}$
3. $\frac{7}{14x}$ $\frac{1}{2x}$
4. 0.8 to 2.4 $\frac{1}{3}$
5. $\frac{12c}{14c}$ $\frac{6}{7}$
6. $22x^2$ to $35x$ $\frac{22x}{35}$
7. $0.5ab : 8ab$ $\frac{1}{16}$
8. $\frac{4xy}{0.25x}$ $16y$
9. $1\frac{1}{2}x$ to $5x$ $\frac{3}{10}$
10. $\frac{x^2 + x}{2x}$ $\frac{x + 1}{2}$
11. $\frac{1}{4}r^2$ to $6r$ $\frac{r}{24}$
12. $0.72t : 7.2t^2$ $\frac{1}{10t}$
13. $(2x - 6) : (6x - 4)$ See above.
14. $12xy : 8xy$ $\frac{3}{2}$
15. $(9x - 9y)$ to $(x - y)$ 9
16. $\frac{\pi r}{r^2 + \pi r}$ $\frac{\pi}{r + \pi}$

Express each ratio in simplest form.

17. shorter leg : longer leg $\frac{5}{12}$
18. hypotenuse to shorter leg $\frac{13}{5}$
19. $\frac{\text{shorter leg}}{\text{hypotenuse}}$ $\frac{5}{13}$
20. hypotenuse : longer leg $\frac{13}{12}$
21. longer leg to shorter leg $\frac{12}{5}$
22. $\frac{\text{longer leg}}{\text{hypotenuse}}$ $\frac{12}{13}$

39 15 36

Write an expression in simplest form for  $\frac{\textbf{area of shaded figure}}{\textbf{area of blue figure}}$.

23. 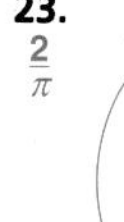 $\frac{2}{\pi}$

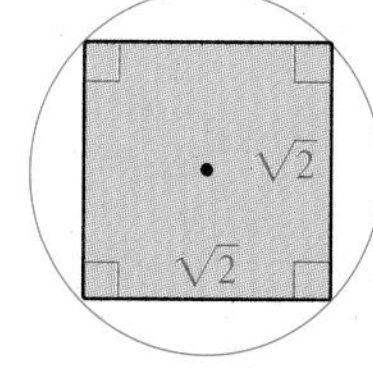

24.  $\frac{5}{14}$

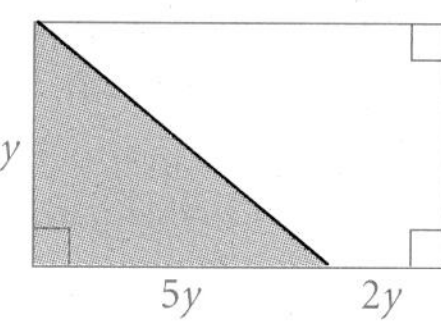

25. $\frac{1}{9}$

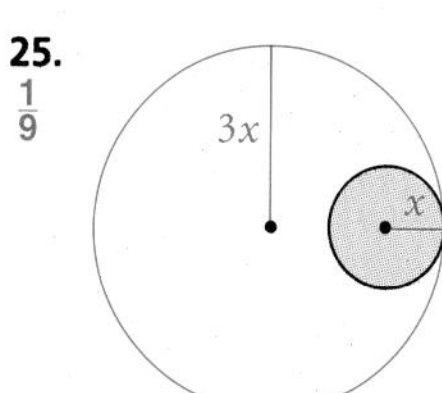

Solving Proportions

An equation in which both sides are ratios is called a *proportion.* A proportion can be written in three equivalent ways:

$\frac{a}{b} = \frac{c}{d}$ $\quad$ a is to b as c is to d

Because the product of the *means* (in this case, b and c) is equal to the product of the *extremes* (a and d), you can solve proportions by cross-multiplying.

Example 1 **Solve for n.**

a. $\frac{n}{8} = \frac{5}{2}$ $\quad$ **b.** $\frac{(n+1)}{4} = \frac{5}{9}$

a.
$$\frac{n}{8} = \frac{5}{2}$$
$$2n = 8 \cdot 5 \quad \text{Cross-multiply.}$$
$$2n = 40 \quad \text{Simplify and solve for } n.$$
$$n = 20$$

b.
$$\frac{(n+1)}{4} = \frac{5}{9}$$
$$9(n+1) = 4 \cdot 5$$
$$9n + 9 = 20$$
$$9n = 11$$
$$n = \frac{11}{9}$$

Example 2 **A map has the scale 1 in. = 4 mi. What actual distance does $3\frac{1}{4}$ in. represent on the map?**

$$\frac{1 \text{ in.}}{4 \text{ mi}} = \frac{3.25 \text{ in.}}{x \text{ mi}} \quad \text{Write a proportion.}$$
$$x \cdot 1 = 4(3.25) \quad \text{Cross-multiply.}$$
$$x = 13 \quad \text{Solve for } x.$$

$3\frac{1}{4}$ inches represents 13 miles.

EXERCISES

Solve each proportion.

1. $\frac{5}{2} = \frac{x}{7}$ 17.5
2. $\frac{x+2}{3} = \frac{8}{15}$ −0.4
3. $\frac{8}{x} = \frac{x}{2}$ −4 or 4
4. $\frac{9}{w} = \frac{16}{144}$ 81
5. $\frac{18}{x} = 6$ 3
6. $\frac{13t}{26} = \frac{40}{16}$ 5
7. $\frac{8}{11} = \frac{12}{x}$ 16.5
8. $\frac{3}{4} = \frac{x}{48}$ 36
9. $\frac{52}{p} = \frac{2}{3}$ 78
10. $12 = \frac{36}{p}$ 3
11. $\frac{7}{3} = \frac{28}{t+9}$ 3
12. $\frac{5}{7} = \frac{10}{y+2}$ 12
13. $\frac{a+5}{9} = \frac{14}{4}$ 26.5
14. $\frac{x+10}{6} = \frac{3}{2}$ −1
15. $\frac{2}{c+1} = \frac{9}{8c+1}$ 1
16. $\frac{m+4}{7} = \frac{15-m}{12}$ 3
17. A map has the scale 1 cm = 1200 km. What actual distance does 10.4 cm represent on the map? 12,480 km
18. A model airplane has the scale 1 : 72. The wingspan of the model is 11.5 in. What is the wingspan, in feet, of the actual plane? 69 ft
19. An architect builds a model of an apartment complex with the scale 1 in. = 5 ft. Find the area of a rectangular patio that measures 5 in.-by-7.25 in. on the model. 906.25 ft^2

676

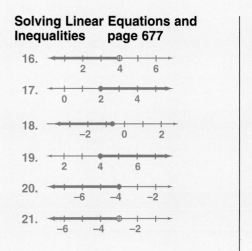

Solving Linear Equations and Inequalities page 677

16. 

17. 

18. 

19. 

20. 

21. 

22. 

23. 

24. 

Skills Handbook

Solving Linear Equations and Inequalities

An equation or inequality is *linear* if its variables are raised only to the power of 1. So $5x - 3 = 2$ is linear, but $x^2 - x + 1 = 0$ is not. To solve an equation, use the properties of equality and properties of real numbers (see page 672) to find all the values of the variable that satisfy the equation.

Example 1 **Solve each equation.**
a. $5x - 3 = 2$ **b.** $1 - 2(x + 1) = x$

a. $5x - 3 = 2$
$5x = 5$ ← Add 3 to each side.
$x = 1$ ← Divide each side by 5.

b. $1 - 2(x + 1) = x$
$1 - 2x - 2 = x$ ← Use the Distributive Property.
$-1 - 2x = x$ ← Simplify the left side.
$-1 = 3x$ ← Add $2x$ to each side.
$-\frac{1}{3} = x$ ← Divide each side by 3.

To solve a linear inequality, use properties of inequality (see page 672). Remember that when you multiply or divide both sides by a negative number, you reverse the order of the inequality.

Example 2 **Solve. Graph the solution on a number line.**
a. $2x - 1 \geq 5$ **b.** $1 - x > -1$

a. $2x - 1 \geq 5$
$2x \geq 6$ ← Add 1 to each side.
$x \geq 3$ ← Divide each side by 2.

Solid bullet at 3 means that 3 is a solution.

b. $1 - x > -1$
$-x > -2$ ← Subtract 1 from each side.
$x < 2$ ← Divide each side by −1. Reverse the order of the inequality.

Open bullet at 2 means that 2 is *not* a solution.

EXERCISES

Solve each equation.

1. $3n + 2 = 17$ 5
2. $3n - 4 = -6$ $-\frac{2}{3}$
3. $2x + 4 = 10$ 3
4. $3(n - 4) = 15$ 9
5. $5a - 2 = -12$ −2
6. $4 - 2y = 8$ −2
7. $-6z + 1 = 13$ −2
8. $\frac{m}{-2} - 3 = 1$ −8
9. $\frac{2}{3}(n + 1) = -\frac{1}{4}$ $-1\frac{3}{8}$
10. $7 = -2(4n - 4.5)$ 0.25
11. $2(1 - 3n) = 2n + 4$ $-\frac{1}{4}$
12. $5k + 2(k + 1) = 23$ 3
13. $\frac{5}{7}p - 10 = 30$ 56
14. $6 - (3t + 4) = -17$ $6\frac{1}{3}$
15. $(w + 5) - (2w + 5) = 5$ −5

Solve each inequality. Graph the solution on a number line. 16–24. See margins for graphs.

16. $2n < 8$ $n < 4$
17. $6 - x \leq 4$ $x \geq 2$
18. $\frac{1}{2}n \leq -\frac{3}{8}$ $n \leq -\frac{3}{4}$
19. $5t + 3 \geq 23$ $t \geq 4$
20. $3 - z \geq 7$ $z \leq -4$
21. $y - 4 > 2 + 3y$ $y < -3$
22. $-6m - 4 < 32$ $m > -6$
23. $2(k - 4) \leq -12$ $k \leq -2$
24. $5 - (n - 3) \geq -4n$ $n \geq -2\frac{2}{3}$

22. 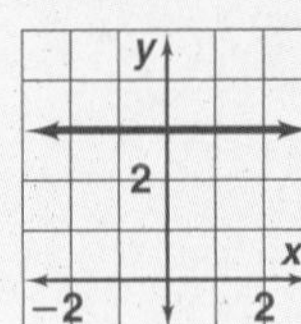

Slope and Intercepts

The slope of a line is a number that describes how steep it is. A line with a positive slope goes upward from left to right, and a line with a negative slope goes downward from left to right. The *slope* of a line is defined as $\frac{\text{vertical change (rise)}}{\text{horizontal change (run)}}$ or, more formally, as follows:

The slope m of a line through the points (x_1, y_1) and (x_2, y_2) is $m = \frac{y_2 - y_1}{x_2 - x_1}$.

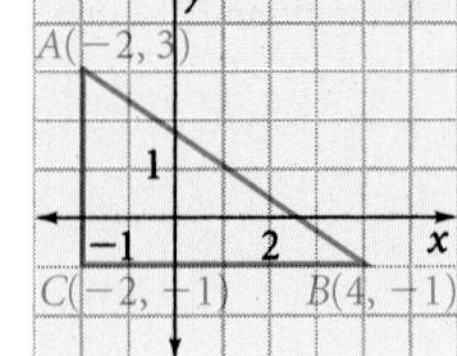

Example 1 **Find the slope of the hypotenuse of △ABC.**

Let $(x_1, y_1) = (-2, 3)$ and let $(x_2, y_2) = (4, -1)$.

Then $m = \frac{y_2 - y_1}{x_2 - x_1} = \frac{-1 - 3}{4 - (-2)} = \frac{-4}{6} = -\frac{2}{3}$

An intercept is the x- or y-value where the line crosses an axis.

Example 2 **For the line $2y - x = 4$, find the following:**
a. the x-intercept **b. the y-intercept**

a. To find the x-intercept, let $y = 0$.

$$2y - x = 4$$
$$2(0) - x = 4$$
$$x = -4$$

The x-intercept is -4.

b. To find the y-intercept, let $x = 0$.

$$2y - x = 4$$
$$2y - 0 = 4$$
$$y = 2$$

The y-intercept is 2.

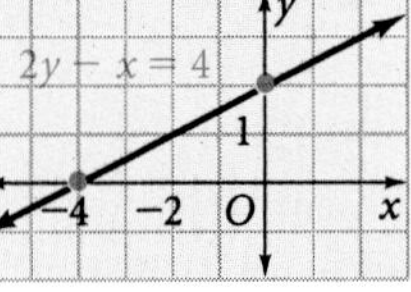

Thus, the graph of $2y - x = 4$ passes through $(-4, 0)$ and $(0, 2)$.

Lines with positive or negative slopes have both x- and y- intercepts. However, horizontal and vertical lines have only one intercept. The slope of a horizontal line is zero, and the slope of a vertical line is undefined.

EXERCISES

Find the slope of the line through each pair of points.

1. $(5, 1), (2, 7)$ -2
2. $(-2, 3), (4, -7)$ $-\frac{5}{3}$
3. $(0, 5), (5, 0)$ -1
4. $(-4, -2), (-5, 8)$ -10
5. $(5, 7), (-2, 7)$ 0
6. $(0, 0), (4, -3)$ $-\frac{3}{4}$
7. $(3, -2), (3, 9)$ undef.
8. $(\frac{1}{2}, -2), (-\frac{3}{2}, 1)$ $-\frac{3}{2}$

Find the x- and y-intercepts for each linear equation.

9. $3x - y = 1$ $\frac{1}{3}; -1$
10. $2y + x = 2$ 2; 1
11. $y = -1$ no intercept; -1
12. $-4x - y = 8$ $-2; -8$
13. $5x + 5y = 5$ 1; 1
14. $y = x$ 0; 0
15. $x = -4$ 15. -4; no intercept
16. $\frac{1}{2}x - \frac{1}{4}y = \frac{3}{4}$ $1\frac{1}{2}; -3$
17. $1 = x - 2y$ $1; -\frac{1}{2}$
18. $y = 4x - 5$ $1\frac{1}{4}; -5$
19. $0.9y - 0.5x = 2$ $-4; 2\frac{2}{9}$
20. $y = -2x - 31$ $-15\frac{1}{2}; -31$
21. The vertices of a triangle are $(-3, -1), (-3, 5)$, and $(6, -1)$. Find the slope of each side of the triangle. undef.; $-\frac{2}{3}$; 0
22. Graph the line with y-intercept 3 and no x-intercept. Find its slope. See margin for graph; 0.

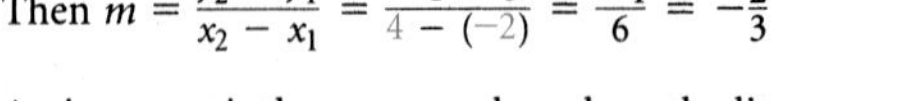
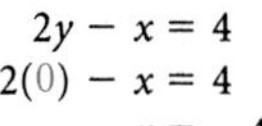
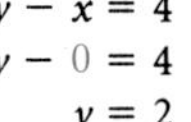

Graphing Linear Equations and Inequalities page 679

1. 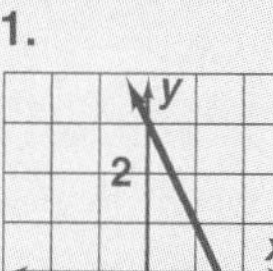

2. 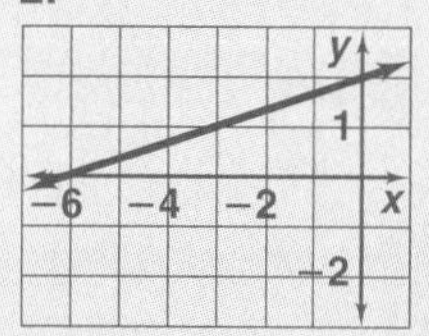

3. 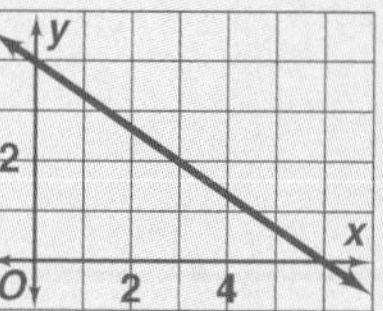

4. 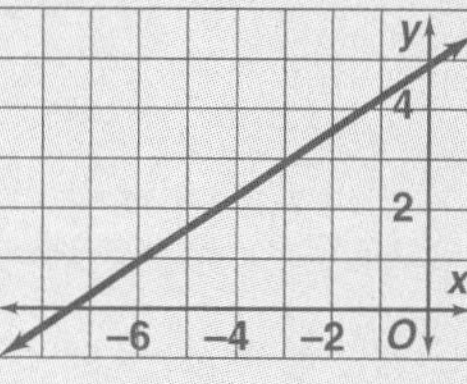

5. 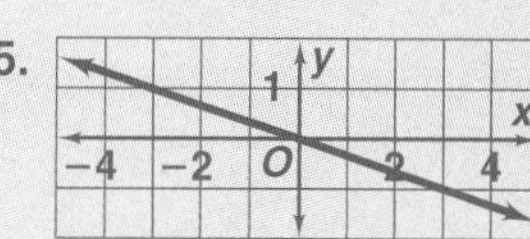

6. 7. 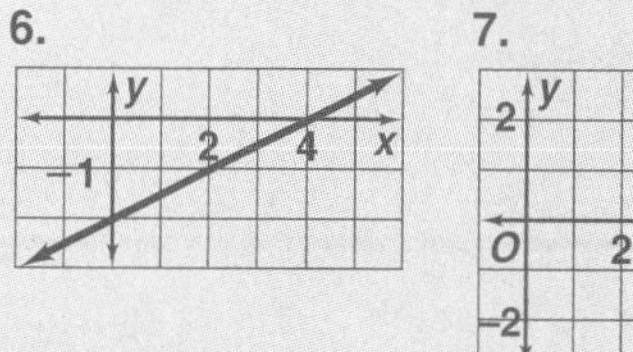

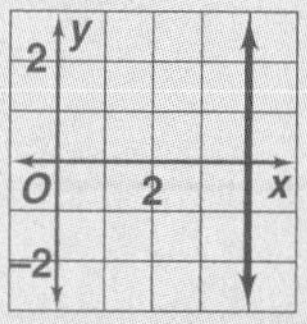

8. 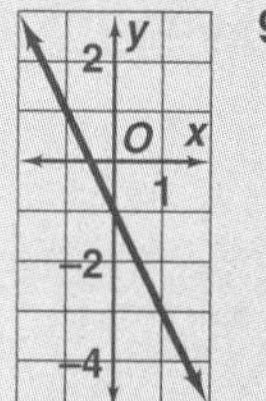

9. 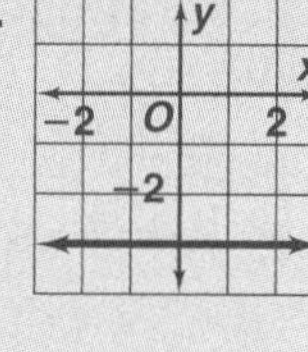

10. 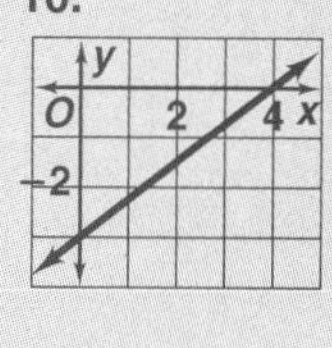

11. 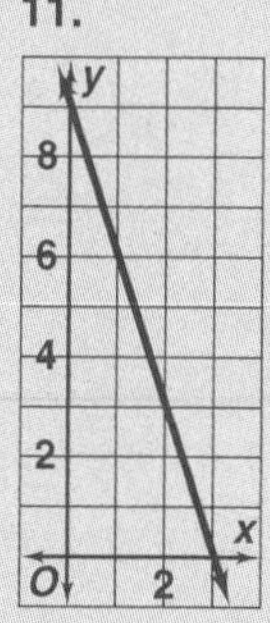

12. 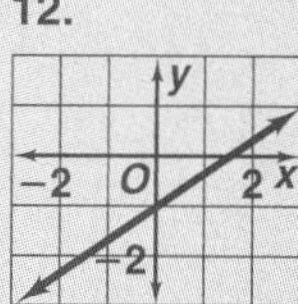

13. 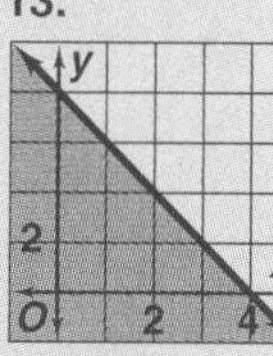

14. 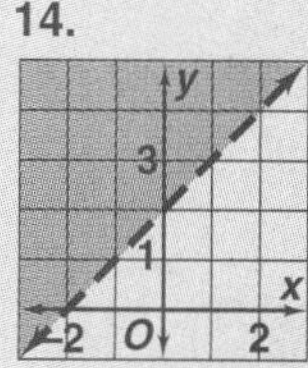

15. 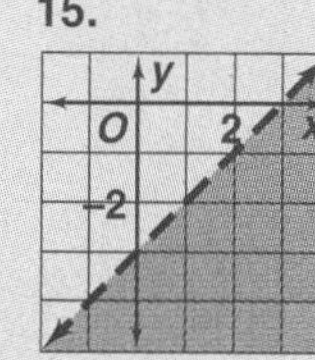

16. 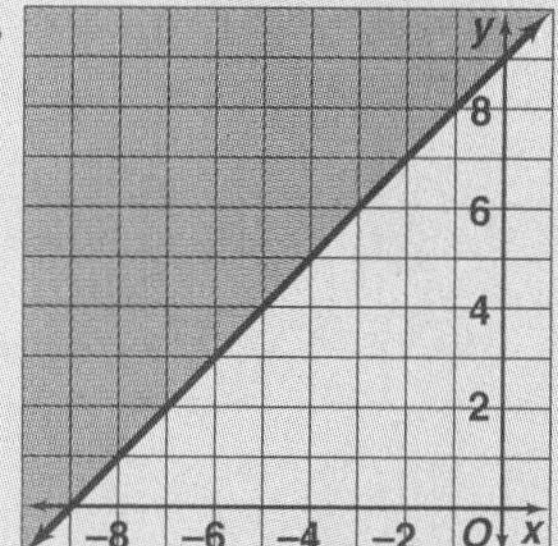

17. 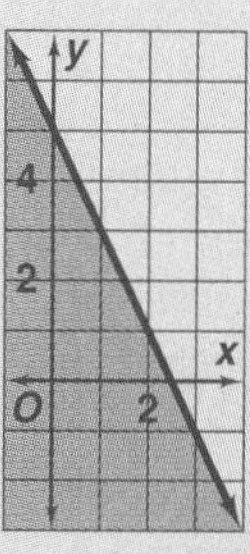

18. 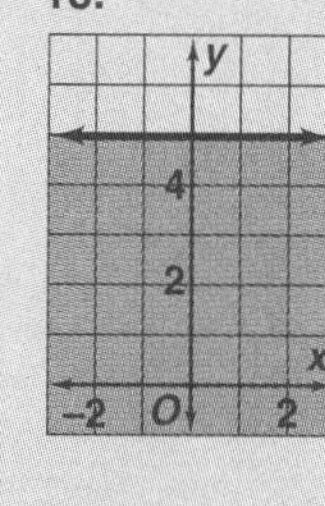

19. 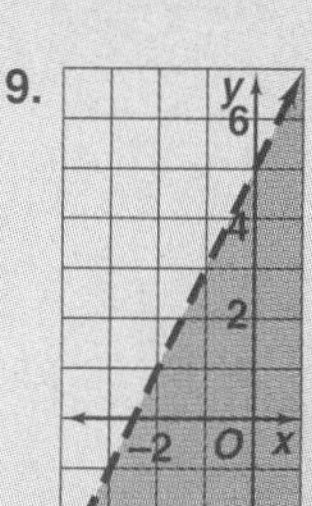

20. 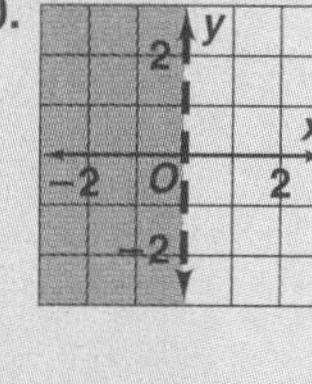

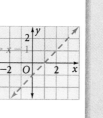

Graphing Linear Equations and Inequalities

Examples 1 and 2 give two methods for graphing a linear equation.

Example 1 **Graph the equation $3x - y = 4$.**

Make a table by selecting several x-values and substituting each in the equation to find the corresponding y-value. Only two points are needed to graph a line, but finding a third is a good check for accuracy. Plot the points and draw the line.

x	0	1	2
y	−4	−1	2

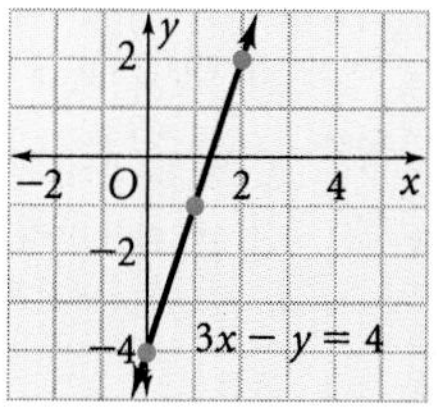

Example 2 **Graph the equation $2y - 3x = 2$.**

You can use a table as in Example 1, or you can use the slope-intercept form $y = mx + b$. In this form, m is the slope and b is the y-intercept. To write the equation in slope-intercept form, solve for y.

$2y - 3x = 2$

$2y = 3x + 2$ ← Subtract $3x$ from each side.

$y = \frac{3}{2}x + 1$ ← Multiply each side by $\frac{1}{2}$.

So the slope m is $\frac{3}{2}$, and the y-intercept b is 1. Plot (0, 1). From there, use the fact that $\frac{\text{rise}}{\text{run}} = \frac{3}{2}$ to move up 3 units and right 2 units. Plot a second point there. Draw a line connecting the two points.

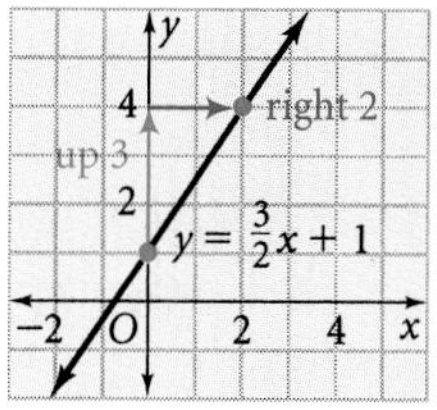

Example 3 **Graph the inequality $y > x - 1$.**

Start by graphing the equation $y = x - 1$. Points on this line are *not* solutions of the inequality. You show this by using a dashed line. (In general, use a dashed line for $<$ or $>$ and a solid line for $\le$ or $\ge$.) To find which side of the line contains solutions of the inequality, test a point not on the line.

$(0) > (0) - 1$ ← Test (0, 0) in the inequality $y > x - 1$.

$0 > -1$ ← The point makes the inequality true, so shade the region containing (0, 0).

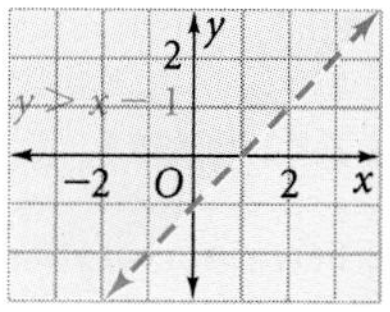

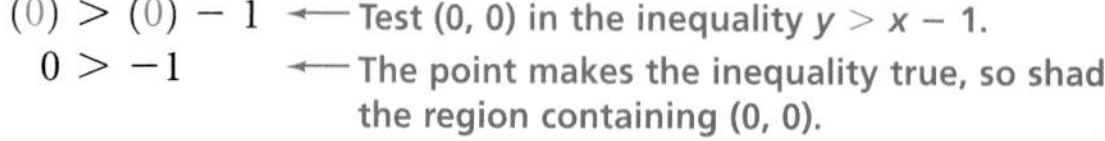

EXERCISES

Graph each equation. 1–12. See margin.

1. $2x + y = 3$
2. $3y - x = 6$
3. $2x + 3y = 12$
4. $y = \frac{2}{3}x + 5$
5. $y = -\frac{1}{3}x$
6. $x - 2y = 4$
7. $x = 4$
8. $y = -2x - 1$
9. $y = -3$
10. $y = \frac{3}{4}x - 3$
11. $3x + y = 9$
12. $4x - 6y = 6$

Graph each inequality. 13–20. See margin.

13. $x + y \le 4$
14. $y > x + 2$
15. $y < x - 3$
16. $y \ge x + 9$
17. $2x + y \le 5$
18. $y \le 5$
19. $y - 3 < 2x + 2$
20. $x < 0$

Solving Literal Equations page 680

11. $h = \frac{3V}{\ell w}$

15. $\ell = \frac{S - \pi r^2}{\pi r} = \frac{S}{\pi r} - r$

16. $b_1 = \frac{2A - hb_2}{h} = \frac{2A}{h} - b_2$

19. $\ell = \frac{2S - 2B}{p}$

20. $h = \frac{S - 2\pi r^2}{2\pi r} = \frac{S}{2\pi r} - r$

680

Solving Literal Equations

An equation with two or more variables is called a *literal equation.* These equations appear frequently in geometry, often as formulas. You can solve a literal equation for any of its variables.

Example 1 **The formula $p = 2(\ell + w)$ gives the perimeter p of a rectangle with length ℓ and width w. Solve the equation for ℓ.**

$p = 2(\ell + w)$

$p = 2\ell + 2w$ ← Use the Distributive Property.

$p - 2w = 2\ell$ ← Subtract $2w$ from each side.

$\frac{p - 2w}{2} = \ell$ ← Divide each side by 2.

Example 2 **The formula $A = \frac{1}{2}(b_1 + b_2)h$ gives the area A of a trapezoid with bases b_1 and b_2 and height h. Solve for h.**

$A = \frac{1}{2}(b_1 + b_2)h$

$2A = h(b_1 + b_2)$ ← Multiply each side by 2.

$\frac{2A}{b_1 + b_2} = h$ ← Divide each side by $(b_1 + b_2)$.

Example 3 **The formula for converting from degrees Celsius C to degrees Fahrenheit F is $F = \frac{9}{5}C + 32$. Solve for C.**

$F = \frac{9}{5}C + 32$

$F - 32 = \frac{9}{5}C$ ← Subtract 32 from each side.

$\frac{5}{9}(F - 32) = C$ ← Multiply each side by $\frac{5}{9}$.

EXERCISES

Solve each equation for the variable in red. 11, 15–16, 19–20. See margin.

1. Perimeter of rectangle: $p = 2w + 2\ell$ $w = \frac{p - 2\ell}{2}$
2. Volume of prism: $V = \ell wh$ $w = \frac{V}{\ell h}$
3. Surface area of sphere: $S = 4\pi r^2$ $r = \frac{1}{2}\sqrt{\frac{S}{\pi}} = \frac{\sqrt{\pi S}}{2\pi}$
4. Lateral area of cylinder: $A = 2\pi rh$ $r = \frac{A}{2\pi h}$
5. Area of kite or rhombus: $A = \frac{1}{2}d_1 d_2$ $d_2 = \frac{2A}{d_1}$
6. Area of circle: $A = \pi r^2$ $r = \sqrt{\frac{A}{\pi}} = \frac{\sqrt{\pi A}}{\pi}$
7. Area of regular polygon: $A = \frac{1}{2}ap$ $a = \frac{2A}{p}$
8. Volume of cylinder: $V = \pi r^2 h$ $h = \frac{V}{\pi r^2}$
9. Area of triangle: $A = \frac{1}{2}bh$ $h = \frac{2A}{b}$
10. Tangent of $\angle A$: $\tan A = \frac{y}{x}$ $x = \frac{y}{\tan A}$
11. Volume of rectangular pyramid: $V = \frac{1}{3}\ell wh$
12. Circumference of circle: $C = 2\pi r$ $r = \frac{C}{2\pi}$
13. Cosine of $\angle A$: $\cos A = \frac{b}{c}$ $b = c \cos A$
14. Volume of cone: $V = \frac{1}{3}\pi r^2 h$ $r = \sqrt{\frac{3V}{\pi h}} = \frac{\sqrt{3\pi hV}}{\pi h}$
15. Surface area of right cone: $S = \pi r^2 + \pi r\ell$
16. Area of trapezoid: $A = \frac{1}{2}(b_1 + b_2)h$
17. Volume of pyramid: $V = \frac{1}{3}Bh$ $B = \frac{3V}{h}$
18. Pythagorean Theorem: $a^2 + b^2 = c^2$ $b = \sqrt{c^2 - a^2}$
19. Surface area of regular pyramid: $S = B + \frac{1}{2}p\ell$
20. Surface area of right cylinder: $S = 2\pi r^2 + 2\pi rh$

Systems of Linear Equations

Normally, there are many ordered pairs that satisfy a given equation. For example, (3, 4), (4, 5), (5, 6), and infinitely many other pairs all satisfy the equation $y = x + 1$. To solve a system of two linear equations, however, you need to find ordered pairs that satisfy both equations at once. Ordinarily, there is just one such ordered pair; it is the point where the equations of the two lines intersect.

One method you can always use to solve a system of linear equations is the substitution method.

Example **Solve the system.** $\mathbf{2x - y = -10}$
$\mathbf{-3x - 2y = 1}$

Solve one of the equations for a variable. Looking at the two equations, it seems easiest to solve the first equation for y.

$2x - y = -10$
$-y = -2x - 10$ ← Subtract $2x$ from each side.
$y = 2x + 10$ ← Multiply each side by -1.

Now substitute $2x + 10$ for y in the other equation.

$-3x - 2y = 1$ ← Write the other equation.
$-3x - 2(2x + 10) = 1$ ← Substitute $(2x + 10)$ for y.
$-3x - 4x - 20 = 1$ ← Use the distributive property.
$-7x = 21$ ← Simplify the left side and add 20 to each side.
$x = -3$ ← Divide each side by -7.

So $x = -3$. To find y, substitute -3 for x in either equation.

$2x - y = -10$ ← Write one of the equations.
$2(-3) - y = -10$ ← Substitute -3 for x.
$-6 - y = -10$ ← Simplify.
$-y = -4$ ← Add 6 to each side.
$y = 4$ ← Multiply each side by -1.

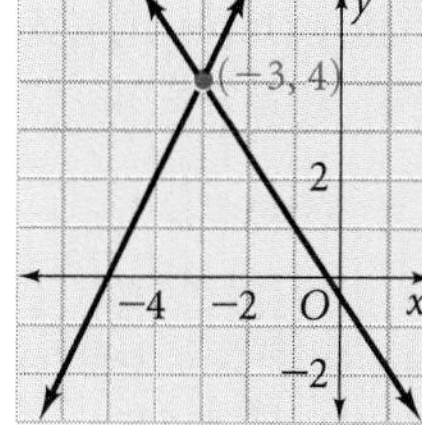

So the solution is $x = -3$ and $y = 4$, or $(-3, 4)$. If you graph $2x - y = -10$ and $-3x - 2y = 1$, you will find that the lines intersect at $(-3, 4)$.

EXERCISES

Solve each system.

1. $x + y = 3$, $x - y = 5$ **(4, −1)**
2. $y - x = 4$, $x + 3 = y$ **no solution**
3. $y = 1$, $5x - 2y = 18$ **(4, 1)**
4. $4y - x = -3$, $2x - 6 = 8y$ **infinitely many solutions**
5. $8x - 1 = 4y$, $3x = y + 1$ $\left(\frac{3}{4}, 1\frac{1}{4}\right)$
6. $2x + 2y = -4$, $-x + 3y = 6$ **(−3, 1)**
7. $12y - 3x = 11$, $x - 2y = -2$ $\left(-\frac{1}{3}, \frac{5}{6}\right)$
8. $5x + 7y = 1$, $4x - 2y = 16$ **(3, −2)**
9. Give an example of a system of linear equations with no solution. What do you know about the slopes of the lines of such a system?
Check students' work; they are = or both undef.

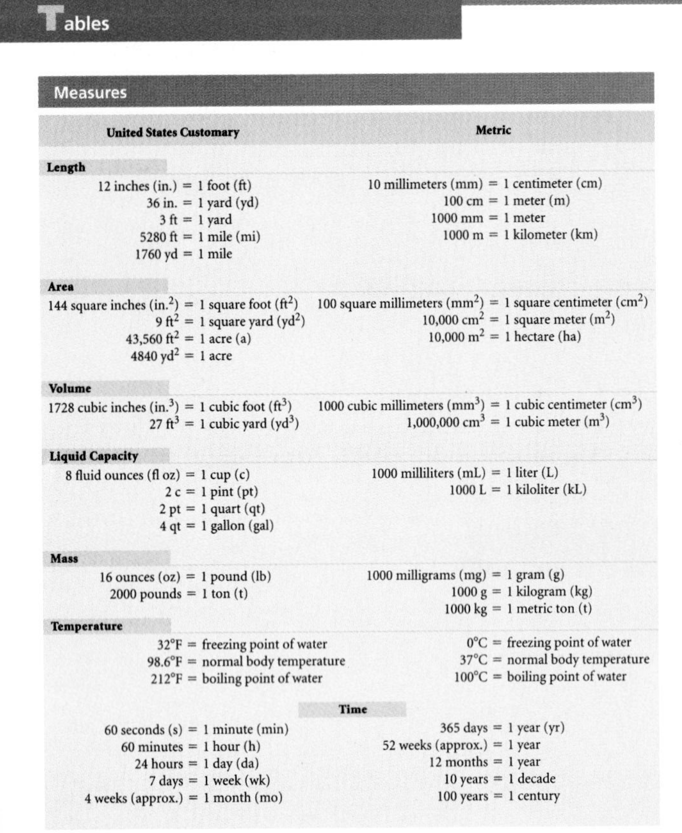

Tables

Measures

United States Customary	Metric
Length	
12 inches (in.) = 1 foot (ft)	10 millimeters (mm) = 1 centimeter (cm)
36 in. = 1 yard (yd)	100 cm = 1 meter (m)
3 ft = 1 yard	1000 mm = 1 meter
5280 ft = 1 mile (mi)	1000 m = 1 kilometer (km)
1760 yd = 1 mile	
Area	
144 square inches (in.^{2}) = 1 square foot (ft^2)	100 square millimeters (mm^2) = 1 square centimeter (cm^2)
9 ft^2 = 1 square yard (yd^2)	10,000 cm^2 = 1 square meter (m^2)
43,560 ft^2 = 1 acre (a)	10,000 m^2 = 1 hectare (ha)
4840 yd^2 = 1 acre	
Volume	
1728 cubic inches (in.^{3}) = 1 cubic foot (ft^3)	1000 cubic millimeters (mm^3) = 1 cubic centimeter (cm^3)
27 ft^3 = 1 cubic yard (yd^3)	1,000,000 cm^3 = 1 cubic meter (m^3)
Liquid Capacity	
8 fluid ounces (fl oz) = 1 cup (c)	1000 milliliters (mL) = 1 liter (L)
2 c = 1 pint (pt)	1000 L = 1 kiloliter (kL)
2 pt = 1 quart (qt)	
4 qt = 1 gallon (gal)	
Mass	
16 ounces (oz) = 1 pound (lb)	1000 milligrams (mg) = 1 gram (g)
2000 pounds = 1 ton (t)	1000 g = 1 kilogram (kg)
	1000 kg = 1 metric ton (t)
Temperature	
32°F = freezing point of water	0°C = freezing point of water
98.6°F = normal body temperature	37°C = normal body temperature
212°F = boiling point of water	100°C = boiling point of water

Time

60 seconds (s) = 1 minute (min)	365 days = 1 year (yr)
60 minutes = 1 hour (h)	52 weeks (approx.) = 1 year
24 hours = 1 day (da)	12 months = 1 year
7 days = 1 week (wk)	10 years = 1 decade
4 weeks (approx.) = 1 month (mo)	100 years = 1 century

682 Tables

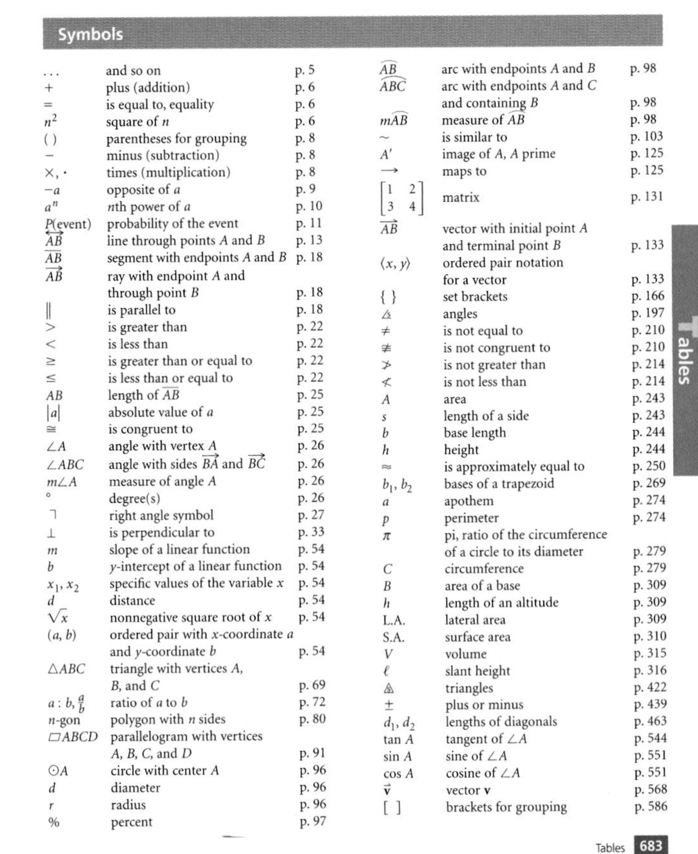

Symbols

...	and so on	p. 5
+	plus (addition)	p. 6
=	is equal to, equality	p. 6
n^2	square of n	p. 6
( )	parentheses for grouping	p. 8
−	minus (subtraction)	p. 8
×, ·	times (multiplication)	p. 8
$-a$	opposite of a	p. 9
a^n	nth power of a	p. 10
P(event)	probability of the event	p. 11
$\overleftrightarrow{AB}$	line through points A and B	p. 13
$\overline{AB}$	segment with endpoints A and B	p. 18
$\overrightarrow{AB}$	ray with endpoint A and through point B	p. 18
$\parallel$	is parallel to	p. 18
$>$	is greater than	p. 22
$<$	is less than	p. 22
$\geq$	is greater than or equal to	p. 22
$\leq$	is less than or equal to	p. 22
AB	length of $\overline{AB}$	p. 25
$\lvert a \rvert$	absolute value of a	p. 25
$\cong$	is congruent to	p. 25
$\angle A$	angle with vertex A	p. 26
$\angle ABC$	angle with sides $\overrightarrow{BA}$ and $\overrightarrow{BC}$	p. 26
$m\angle A$	measure of angle A	p. 26
°	degree(s)	p. 26
⌐	right angle symbol	p. 27
$\perp$	is perpendicular to	p. 33
m	slope of a linear function	p. 54
b	y-intercept of a linear function	p. 54
x_1, x_2	specific values of the variable x	p. 54
d	distance	p. 54
$\sqrt{x}$	nonnegative square root of x	p. 54
(a, b)	ordered pair with x-coordinate a and y-coordinate b	p. 54
$\triangle ABC$	triangle with vertices A, B, and C	p. 69
$a : b, \frac{a}{b}$	ratio of a to b	p. 72
n-gon	polygon with n sides	p. 80
▱$ABCD$	parallelogram with vertices A, B, C, and D	p. 91
$\odot A$	circle with center A	p. 96
d	diameter	p. 96
r	radius	p. 96
%	percent	p. 97
$\overparen{AB}$	arc with endpoints A and B	p. 98
$\overparen{ABC}$	arc with endpoints A and C and containing B	p. 98
$m\overparen{AB}$	measure of $\overparen{AB}$	p. 98
~	is similar to	p. 103
A'	image of A, A prime	p. 125
$\rightarrow$	maps to	p. 125
$\begin{bmatrix} 1 & 2 \\ 3 & 4 \end{bmatrix}$	matrix	p. 131
$\overrightarrow{AB}$	vector with initial point A and terminal point B	p. 133
$\langle x, y \rangle$	ordered pair notation for a vector	p. 133
{ }	set brackets	p. 166
∡	angles	p. 197
$\neq$	is not equal to	p. 210
$\ncong$	is not congruent to	p. 210
$\ngtr$	is not greater than	p. 214
$\nless$	is not less than	p. 214
A	area	p. 243
s	length of a side	p. 243
b	base length	p. 244
h	height	p. 244
$\approx$	is approximately equal to	p. 250
b_1, b_2	bases of a trapezoid	p. 269
a	apothem	p. 274
p	perimeter	p. 274
π	pi, ratio of the circumference of a circle to its diameter	p. 279
C	circumference	p. 279
B	area of a base	p. 309
h	length of an altitude	p. 309
L.A.	lateral area	p. 309
S.A.	surface area	p. 310
V	volume	p. 315
ℓ	slant height	p. 316
▵	triangles	p. 422
$\pm$	plus or minus	p. 439
d_1, d_2	lengths of diagonals	p. 463
tan A	tangent of $\angle A$	p. 544
sin A	sine of $\angle A$	p. 551
cos A	cosine of $\angle A$	p. 551
$\vec{v}$	vector **v**	p. 568
[ ]	brackets for grouping	p. 586

Tables 683

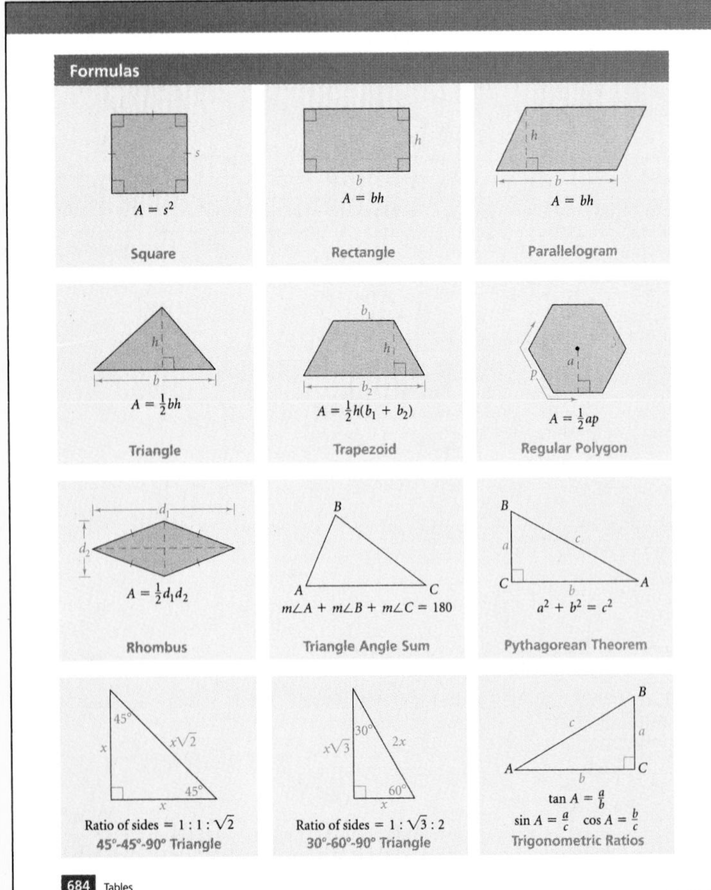

Formulas

684 Tables

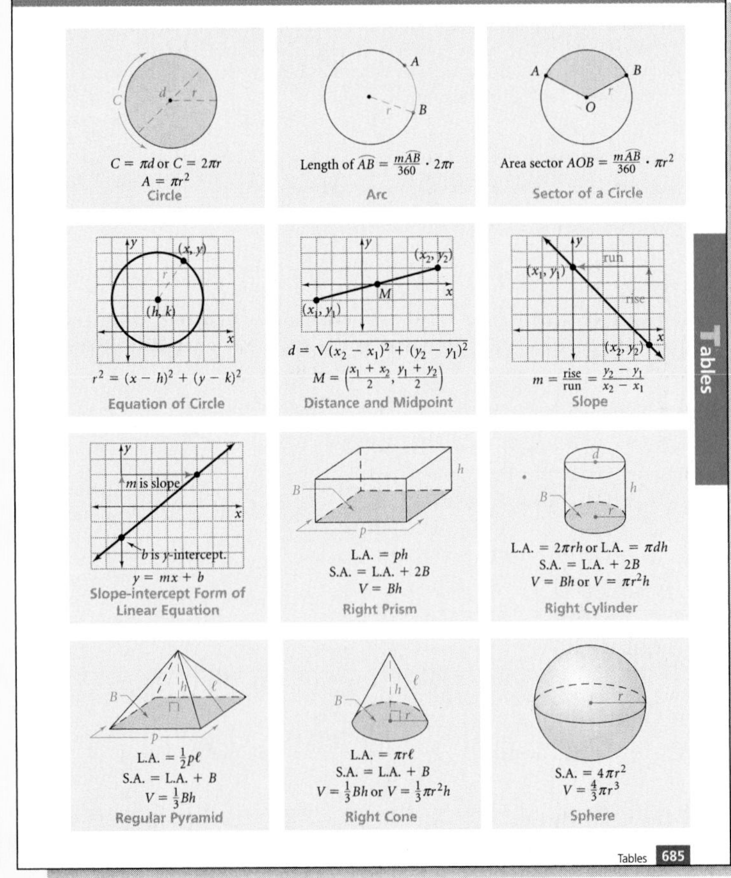

Tables 685

Properties of Real Numbers

Unless otherwise stated, *a*, *b*, *c*, and *d* are real numbers.

Identity Properties

Addition $a + 0 = a$ and $0 + a = a$

Multiplication $a \cdot 1 = a$ and $1 \cdot a = a$

Commutative Properties

Addition $a + b = b + a$

Multiplication $a \cdot b = b \cdot a$

Associative Properties

Addition $(a + b) + c = a + (b + c)$

Multiplication $(a \cdot b) \cdot c = a \cdot (b \cdot c)$

Inverse Properties

Addition
The sum of a number and its *opposite*, or *additive inverse*, is zero.

$a + (-a) = 0$ and $-a + a = 0$

Multiplication
The *reciprocal*, or *multiplicative inverse*, of a rational number $\frac{a}{b}$ is $\frac{b}{a}$ $(a, b \neq 0)$.

$a \cdot \frac{1}{a} = 1$ and $\frac{1}{a} \cdot a = 1$ $(a \neq 0)$

Distributive Properties

$a(b + c) = ab + ac$ $(b + c)a = ba + ca$
$a(b - c) = ab - ac$ $(b - c)a = ba - ca$

Properties of Equality

Addition If $a = b$, then $a + c = b + c$.

Subtraction If $a = b$, then $a - c = b - c$.

Multiplication If $a = b$, then $a \cdot c = b \cdot c$.

Division If $a = b$ and $c \neq 0$, then $\frac{a}{c} = \frac{b}{c}$.

Substitution If $a = b$, then b can replace a in any expression.

Reflexive $a = a$

Symmetric If $a = b$, then $b = a$.

Transitive If $a = b$ and $b = c$, then $a = c$.

Properties of Proportions

$\frac{a}{b} = \frac{c}{d}$ is equivalent to

(1) $ad = bc$ (2) $\frac{b}{a} = \frac{d}{c}$

(3) $\frac{a}{c} = \frac{b}{d}$ (4) $\frac{a + b}{b} = \frac{c + d}{d}$

Zero-Product Property

If $ab = 0$, then $a = 0$ or $b = 0$.

Properties of Inequality

Addition If $a > b$ and $c \geq d$, then $a + c > b + d$.

Multiplication If $a > b$ and $c > 0$, then $ac > bc$.
If $a > b$ and $c < 0$, then $ac < bc$.

Transitive If $a > b$ and $b > c$, then $a > c$.

Comparison If $a = b + c$ and $c > 0$, then $a > b$.

Properties of Exponents

For any nonzero numbers *a* and *b*, any positive number *c*, and any integers *m* and *n*,

Zero Exponent $a^0 = 1$

Negative Exponent $a^{-n} = \frac{1}{a^n}$

Product of Powers $a^m \cdot a^n = a^{m+n}$

Quotient of Powers $\frac{a^m}{a^n} = a^{m-n}$

Power to a Power $(c^m)^n = c^{mn}$

Product to a Power $(ab)^n = a^n b^n$

Quotient to a Power $\left(\frac{a}{b}\right)^n = \frac{a^n}{b^n}$

Properties of Square Roots

For any nonnegative numbers *a* and *b*, and any positive number *c*,

Product of Square Roots $\sqrt{a} \cdot \sqrt{b} = \sqrt{ab}$

Quotient of Square Roots $\frac{\sqrt{a}}{\sqrt{c}} = \sqrt{\frac{a}{c}}$

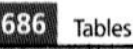

Squares and Square Roots

Number n	Square n^2	Positive Square Root $\sqrt{n}$	Number n	Square n^2	Positive Square Root $\sqrt{n}$	Number n	Square n^2	Positive Square Root $\sqrt{n}$
1	1	1.000	51	2601	7.141	101	10,201	10.050
2	4	1.414	52	2704	7.211	102	10,404	10.100
3	9	1.732	53	2809	7.280	103	10,609	10.149
4	16	2.000	54	2916	7.348	104	10,816	10.198
5	25	2.236	55	3025	7.416	105	11,025	10.247
6	36	2.449	56	3136	7.483	106	11,236	10.296
7	49	2.646	57	3249	7.550	107	11,449	10.344
8	64	2.828	58	3364	7.616	108	11,664	10.392
9	81	3.000	59	3481	7.681	109	11,881	10.440
10	100	3.162	60	3600	7.746	110	12,100	10.488
11	121	3.317	61	3721	7.810	111	12,321	10.536
12	144	3.464	62	3844	7.874	112	12,544	10.583
13	169	3.606	63	3969	7.937	113	12,769	10.630
14	196	3.742	64	4096	8.000	114	12,996	10.677
15	225	3.873	65	4225	8.062	115	13,225	10.724
16	256	4.000	66	4356	8.124	116	13,456	10.770
17	289	4.123	67	4489	8.185	117	13,689	10.817
18	324	4.243	68	4624	8.246	118	13,924	10.863
19	361	4.359	69	4761	8.307	119	14,161	10.909
20	400	4.472	70	4900	8.367	120	14,400	10.954
21	441	4.583	71	5041	8.426	121	14,641	11.000
22	484	4.690	72	5184	8.485	122	14,884	11.045
23	529	4.796	73	5329	8.544	123	15,129	11.091
24	576	4.899	74	5476	8.602	124	15,376	11.136
25	625	5.000	75	5625	8.660	125	15,625	11.180
26	676	5.099	76	5776	8.718	126	15,876	11.225
27	729	5.196	77	5929	8.775	127	16,129	11.269
28	784	5.292	78	6084	8.832	128	16,384	11.314
29	841	5.385	79	6241	8.888	129	16,641	11.358
30	900	5.477	80	6400	8.944	130	16,900	11.402
31	961	5.568	81	6561	9.000	131	17,161	11.446
32	1024	5.657	82	6724	9.055	132	17,424	11.489
33	1089	5.745	83	6889	9.110	133	17,689	11.533
34	1156	5.831	84	7056	9.165	134	17,956	11.576
35	1225	5.916	85	7225	9.220	135	18,225	11.619
36	1296	6.000	86	7396	9.274	136	18,496	11.662
37	1369	6.083	87	7569	9.327	137	18,769	11.705
38	1444	6.164	88	7744	9.381	138	19,044	11.747
39	1521	6.245	89	7921	9.434	139	19,321	11.790
40	1600	6.325	90	8100	9.487	140	19,600	11.832
41	1681	6.403	91	8281	9.539	141	19,881	11.874
42	1764	6.481	92	8464	9.592	142	20,164	11.916
43	1849	6.557	93	8649	9.644	143	20,449	11.958
44	1936	6.633	94	8836	9.695	144	20,736	12.000
45	2025	6.708	95	9025	9.747	145	21,025	12.042
46	2116	6.782	96	9216	9.798	146	21,316	12.083
47	2209	6.856	97	9409	9.849	147	21,609	12.124
48	2304	6.928	98	9604	9.899	148	21,904	12.166
49	2401	7.000	99	9801	9.950	149	22,201	12.207
50	2500	7.071	100	10,000	10.000	150	22,500	12.247

Tables

Trigonometric Ratios

Angle	Sine	Cosine	Tangent	Angle	Sine	Cosine	Tangent
1°	0.0175	0.9998	0.0175	46°	0.7193	0.6947	1.0355
2°	0.0349	0.9994	0.0349	47°	0.7314	0.6820	1.0724
3°	0.0523	0.9986	0.0524	48°	0.7431	0.6691	1.1106
4°	0.0698	0.9976	0.0699	49°	0.7547	0.6561	1.1504
5°	0.0872	0.9962	0.0875	50°	0.7660	0.6428	1.1918
6°	0.1045	0.9945	0.1051	51°	0.7771	0.6293	1.2349
7°	0.1219	0.9925	0.1228	52°	0.7880	0.6157	1.2799
8°	0.1392	0.9903	0.1405	53°	0.7986	0.6018	1.3270
9°	0.1564	0.9877	0.1584	54°	0.8090	0.5878	1.3764
10°	0.1736	0.9848	0.1763	55°	0.8192	0.5736	1.4281
11°	0.1908	0.9816	0.1944	56°	0.8290	0.5592	1.4826
12°	0.2079	0.9781	0.2126	57°	0.8387	0.5446	1.5399
13°	0.2250	0.9744	0.2309	58°	0.8480	0.5299	1.6003
14°	0.2419	0.9703	0.2493	59°	0.8572	0.5150	1.6643
15°	0.2588	0.9659	0.2679	60°	0.8660	0.5000	1.7321
16°	0.2756	0.9613	0.2867	61°	0.8746	0.4848	1.8040
17°	0.2924	0.9563	0.3057	62°	0.8829	0.4695	1.8807
18°	0.3090	0.9511	0.3249	63°	0.8910	0.4540	1.9626
19°	0.3256	0.9455	0.3443	64°	0.8988	0.4384	2.0503
20°	0.3420	0.9397	0.3640	65°	0.9063	0.4226	2.1445
21°	0.3584	0.9336	0.3839	66°	0.9135	0.4067	2.2460
22°	0.3746	0.9272	0.4040	67°	0.9205	0.3907	2.3559
23°	0.3907	0.9205	0.4245	68°	0.9272	0.3746	2.4751
24°	0.4067	0.9135	0.4452	69°	0.9336	0.3584	2.6051
25°	0.4226	0.9063	0.4663	70°	0.9397	0.3420	2.7475
26°	0.4384	0.8988	0.4877	71°	0.9455	0.3256	2.9042
27°	0.4540	0.8910	0.5095	72°	0.9511	0.3090	3.0777
28°	0.4695	0.8829	0.5317	73°	0.9563	0.2924	3.2709
29°	0.4848	0.8746	0.5543	74°	0.9613	0.2756	3.4874
30°	0.5000	0.8660	0.5774	75°	0.9659	0.2588	3.7321
31°	0.5150	0.8572	0.6009	76°	0.9703	0.2419	4.0108
32°	0.5299	0.8480	0.6249	77°	0.9744	0.2250	4.3315
33°	0.5446	0.8387	0.6494	78°	0.9781	0.2079	4.7046
34°	0.5592	0.8290	0.6745	79°	0.9816	0.1908	5.1446
35°	0.5736	0.8192	0.7002	80°	0.9848	0.1736	5.6713
36°	0.5878	0.8090	0.7265	81°	0.9877	0.1564	6.3138
37°	0.6018	0.7986	0.7536	82°	0.9903	0.1392	7.1154
38°	0.6157	0.7880	0.7813	83°	0.9925	0.1219	8.1443
39°	0.6293	0.7771	0.8098	84°	0.9945	0.1045	9.5144
40°	0.6428	0.7660	0.8391	85°	0.9962	0.0872	11.4301
41°	0.6561	0.7547	0.8693	86°	0.9976	0.0698	14.3007
42°	0.6691	0.7431	0.9004	87°	0.9986	0.0523	19.0811
43°	0.6820	0.7314	0.9325	88°	0.9994	0.0349	28.6363
44°	0.6947	0.7193	0.9657	89°	0.9998	0.0175	57.2900
45°	0.7071	0.7071	1.0000	90°	1.0000	0.0000	

Postulates & Theorems

Chapter 1: Tools of Geometry

Postulate 1-1
Through any two points there is exactly one line. (p. 14)

Postulate 1-2
If two lines intersect, then they intersect in exactly one point. (p. 14)

Postulate 1-3
If two planes intersect, then they intersect in a line. (p. 14)

Postulate 1-4
Through any three noncollinear points there is exactly one plane. (p. 14)

Postulate 1-5
Ruler Postulate
The points of a line can be put into a one-to-one correspondence with the real numbers so that the distance between any two points is the absolute value of the difference of the corresponding numbers. (p. 25)

Postulate 1-6
Segment Addition Postulate
If three points *A*, *B*, and *C* are collinear and *B* is between *A* and *C*, then $AB + BC = AC$. (p. 26)

Postulate 1-7
Protractor Postulate
Let $\overrightarrow{OA}$ and $\overrightarrow{OB}$ be opposite rays in a plane. $\overrightarrow{OA}$, $\overrightarrow{OB}$, and all the rays with endpoint *O* that can be drawn on one side of $\overleftrightarrow{AB}$ can be paired with the real numbers from 0 to 180 in such a way that:

a. $\overrightarrow{OA}$ is paired with 0 and $\overrightarrow{OB}$ is paired with 180.
b. If $\overrightarrow{OC}$ is paired with *x* and $\overrightarrow{OD}$ is paired with *y*, then $m\angle COD = |x - y|$. (p. 27)

Postulate 1-8
Angle Addition Postulate
If point *B* is in the interior of $\angle AOC$, then $m\angle AOB + m\angle BOC = m\angle AOC$.
If $\angle AOC$ is a straight angle, then $m\angle AOB + m\angle BOC = 180$. (p. 28)

Properties of Congruence
Reflexive Property
$\overline{AB} \cong \overline{AB}$ and $\angle A \cong \angle A$
Symmetric Property
If $\overline{AB} \cong \overline{CD}$, then $\overline{CD} \cong \overline{AB}$.
If $\angle A \cong \angle B$, then $\angle B \cong \angle A$.
Transitive Property
If $\overline{AB} \cong \overline{CD}$ and $\overline{CD} \cong \overline{EF}$, then $\overline{AB} \cong \overline{EF}$.
If $\angle A \cong \angle B$ and $\angle B \cong \angle C$, then $\angle A \cong \angle C$. (p. 47)

Theorem 1-1
Vertical Angles Theorem
Vertical angles are congruent. (p. 48)
Proof on p. 48, Example 2

Theorem 1-2
Congruent Supplements Theorem
If two angles are supplements of congruent angles (or of the same angle), then the two angles are congruent. (p. 49)
Proof on p. 51, Exercise 33

Theorem 1-3
Congruent Complements Theorem
If two angles are complements of congruent angles (or of the same angle), then the two angles are congruent. (p. 49)
Proof on p. 51, Exercise 32

The Distance Formula
The distance *d* between two points $A(x_1, y_1)$ and $B(x_2, y_2)$ is $d = \sqrt{(x_2 - x_1)^2 + (y_2 - y_1)^2}$. (p. 54)
Proof on p. 261, Exercise 37

The Midpoint Formula
The coordinates of the midpoint *M* of $\overline{AB}$ with endpoints $A(x_1, y_1)$ and $B(x_2, y_2)$ are the following:
$M = \left(\frac{x_1 + x_2}{2}, \frac{y_1 + y_2}{2}\right)$ (p. 55)

Chapter 2: Investigating Geometric Figures

Theorem 2-1
Triangle Angle-Sum Theorem
The sum of the measures of the angles of a triangle is 180. (p. 68)
Proof on p. 396, Exercise 14

Postulates & Theorems

Theorem 2-2
Exterior Angle Theorem
The measure of each exterior angle of a triangle equals the sum of the measures of its two remote interior angles. (p. 70)
Proof on p. 73, Exercise 32
Corollary
The measure of an exterior angle of a triangle is greater than the measure of either of its remote interior angles. (p. 70)
Proof on p. 70, Question 8

Theorem 2-3
Polygon Interior Angle-Sum Theorem
The sum of the measures of the interior angles of an n-gon is $(n - 2)180$. (p. 77)
Proof on p. 81, Question 30

Theorem 2-4
Polygon Exterior Angle-Sum Theorem
The sum of the measures of the exterior angles of a polygon, one at each vertex, is 360. (p. 78)
Proof using computer on p. 75

Slopes of Parallel Lines
The slopes of two nonvertical parallel lines are equal. Two lines with the same slope are parallel. Vertical lines are parallel. (p. 85)

Slopes of Perpendicular Lines
The product of the slopes of two perpendicular lines, neither of which is vertical, is -1. If the product of the slopes of two lines is -1, then the lines are perpendicular. A horizontal and a vertical line are perpendicular. (p. 85)

Theorem 2-5
Two lines parallel to a third are parallel to each other. (p. 85)
Proof on p. 642, Exercise 7-5(2)

Theorem 2-6
In a plane, two lines perpendicular to a third line are parallel to each other. (p. 85)
Proof on p. 375, Exercise 20

Postulate 2-1
Arc Addition Postulate
The measure of the arc formed by two adjacent arcs is the sum of the measure of two arcs. (p. 98)

Chapter 3: Transformations: Shapes in Motion

Properties of a Reflection
A reflection reverses orientation. A reflection is an isometry. (p. 126)

Properties of a Translation
A translation is an isometry. A translation does not change orientation. (p. 132)

Properties of a Rotation
A rotation is an isometry. A rotation does not change orientation. (p. 139)

Theorem 3-1
A composition of reflections in two parallel lines is a translation. (p. 144)

Theorem 3-2
A composition of reflections in two intersecting lines is a rotation. (p. 144)

Theorem 3-3
In a plane, two congruent figures can be mapped onto one another by a composition of at most three reflections. (p. 146)

Theorem 3-4
Isometry Classification Theorem
There are only four isometries. They are reflection, translation, rotation, and glide reflection. (p. 147)

Chapter 4: Triangle Relationships

Theorem 4-1
Isosceles Triangle Theorem
If two sides of a triangle are congruent, then the angles opposite those sides are also congruent. (p. 189)
Proofs on p. 428, Example 3 and p. 428, Question 4
Corollary
If a triangle is equilateral, then it is equiangular. (p. 190)
Proof on p. 198, Exercise 17

Theorem 4-2
The bisector of the vertex angle of an isosceles triangle is the perpendicular bisector of the base. (p. 189)
Proof on p. 431, Exercise 13

Theorem 4-3
Converse of the Isosceles Triangle Theorem
If two angles of a triangle are congruent, then the sides opposite the angles are congruent. (p. 189)
Proof on p. 430, Exercise 9
Corollary
If a triangle is equiangular, then it is equilateral. (p. 190)
Proof on p. 190, Question 7

Theorem 4-4
If a triangle is a right triangle, then the acute angles are complementary. (p. 195)
Proof on p. 195

Theorem 4-5
If two angles of one triangle are congruent to two angles of another triangle, then the third angles are congruent. (p. 195)
Proof on p. 195, in the Example

Theorem 4-6
All right angles are congruent. (p. 195)
Proof on p. 196, Question 2

Theorem 4-7
If two angles are congruent and supplementary, then each is a right angle. (p. 195)
Proof on p. 196, Question 3

Theorem 4-8
Triangle Midsegment Theorem
If a segment joins the midpoints of two sides of a triangle, then the segment is parallel to the third side and half its length. (p. 201)
Proof on p. 202

Theorem 4-9
Triangle Inequality Theorem
The sum of the lengths of any two sides of a triangle is greater than the length of the third side. (p. 214)
Proof on p. 639, Exercise 4-6(2)

Theorem 4-10
If two sides of a triangle are not congruent, then the larger angle lies opposite the larger side. (p. 215)
Proof on p. 218, Exercise 35

Theorem 4-11
If two angles of a triangle are not congruent, then the longer side lies opposite the larger angle. (p. 215)
Proof on p. 215

Theorem 4-12
Perpendicular Bisector Theorem
If a point is on the perpendicular bisector of a segment, then it is equidistant from the endpoints of the segment. (p. 219)
Proof on p. 430, Exercise 11

Theorem 4-13
Converse of Perpendicular Bisector Theorem
If a point is equidistant from the endpoints of a segment, then it is on the perpendicular bisector of the segment. (p. 219)
Proof on p. 643, Exercise 8-4(1)

Theorem 4-14
Angle Bisector Theorem
If a point is on the bisector of an angle, then it is equidistant from the sides of the angle. (p. 222)
Proof on p. 428, Example 4

Theorem 4-15
Converse of Angle Bisector Theorem
If a point in the interior of an angle is equidistant from the sides of the angle, then it is on the angle bisector. (p. 222)
Proof on p. 643, Exercise 8-4(2)

Theorem 4-16
The perpendicular bisectors of the sides of a triangle are concurrent at a point equidistant from the vertices. (p. 227)
Proof on p. 228

Theorem 4-17
The bisectors of the angles of a triangle are concurrent at a point equidistant from the sides. (p. 227)
Proof on p. 232, Exercise 18

Theorem 4-18
The lines that contain the altitudes of a triangle are concurrent. (p. 230)
Proof on p. 487, Exercise 11

Theorem 4-19
The medians of a triangle are concurrent. (p. 230)

Chapter 5: Measuring in the Plane

Postulate 5-1
The area of a square is the square of the length of a side.
$A = s^2$ (p. 243)

Postulate 5-2
If two figures are congruent, their areas are equal. (p. 243)

Postulate 5-3
The area of a region is the sum of the areas of its nonoverlapping parts. (p. 243)

Theorem 5-1
Area of a Rectangle
The area of a rectangle is the product of its base and height.
$A = bh$ (p. 244)

Theorem 5-2
Area of a Parallelogram
The area of a parallelogram is the product of any base and the corresponding height.
$A = bh$ (p. 249)

Theorem 5-3
Area of a Triangle
The area of a triangle is half the product of any base and the corresponding height.
$A = \frac{1}{2}bh$ (p. 251)

Theorem 5-4
Pythagorean Theorem
In a right triangle, the sum of the squares of the lengths of the legs is equal to the square of the length of the hypotenuse.
$a^2 + b^2 = c^2$ (p. 257)
Proofs on p. 256, Questions 1–4; p. 259; p. 261, Exercise 46; p. 273; p. 515, Exercise 32; p. 625, Exercise 23

Theorem 5-5
Converse of the Pythagorean Theorem
If the square of the length of one side of a triangle is equal to the sum of the squares of the lengths of the other two sides, then the triangle is a right triangle. (p. 258)

Theorem 5-6
45°-45°-90° Triangle Theorem
In a 45°-45°-90° triangle, both legs are congruent and the length of the hypotenuse is $\sqrt{2}$ times the length of a leg.
hypotenuse $= \sqrt{2} \cdot$ leg (p. 264)
Proof on p. 263, Question 3

Theorem 5-7
30°-60°-90° Triangle Theorem
In a 30°-60°-90° triangle, the length of the hypotenuse is twice the length of the shorter leg. The length of the longer leg is $\sqrt{3}$ times the length of the shorter leg.
hypotenuse $= 2 \cdot$ shorter leg
longer leg $= \sqrt{3} \cdot$ shorter leg (p. 265)
Proof on p. 265

Theorem 5-8
Area of a Trapezoid
The area of a trapezoid is half the product of the height and the sum of the lengths of the bases.
$A = \frac{1}{2}h(b_1 + b_2)$ (p. 269)
Proof in Work Together, p. 269

Theorem 5-9
Area of a Regular Polygon
The area of a regular polygon is half the product of the apothem and the perimeter.
$A = \frac{1}{2}ap$ (p. 274)
Proof on p. 274, Question 1

Theorem 5-10
Circumference of a Circle
The circumference of a circle is π times the diameter.
$C = \pi d$ or $C = 2\pi r$ (p. 279)

Theorem 5-11
Arc Length
The length of an arc of a circle is the product of the ratio $\frac{\text{measure of the arc}}{360}$ and the circumference of the circle.
Length of $\widehat{AB} = \frac{m\widehat{AB}}{360} \cdot 2\pi r$ (p. 281)

Theorem 5-12
Area of a Circle
The area of a circle is the product of π and the square of the radius.
$A = \pi r^2$ (p. 285)

Theorem 5-13
Area of a Sector of a Circle
The area of a sector of a circle is the product of the ratio $\frac{\text{measure of the arc}}{360}$ and the area of the circle.
Area of sector $AOB = \frac{m\widehat{AB}}{360} \cdot \pi r^2$ (p. 286)

Chapter 6: Measuring in Space

Theorem 6-1
Lateral and Surface Areas of a Right Prism
The lateral area of a right prism is the product of the perimeter of the base and the height.
L.A. $= ph$
The surface area of a right prism is the sum of the lateral area and the areas of the two bases.
S.A. $=$ L.A. $+ 2B$ (p. 310)

Theorem 6-2
Lateral and Surface Areas of a Right Cylinder
The lateral area of a right cylinder is the product of the circumference of the base and the height of the cylinder.
L.A. $= 2\pi rh$ or L.A. $= \pi dh$
The surface area of a right cylinder is the sum of the lateral area and the areas of the two bases.
S.A. $=$ L.A. $+ 2B$ (p. 311)

Theorem 6-3
Lateral and Surface Areas of a Regular Pyramid
The lateral area of a regular pyramid is half the product of the perimeter of the base and the slant height.
L.A. $= \frac{1}{2}p\ell$
The surface area of a regular pyramid is the sum of the lateral area and the area of the base.
S.A. $=$ L.A. $+ B$ (p. 317)

Theorem 6-4
Lateral and Surface Areas of a Right Cone
The lateral area of a right cone is half the product of the circumference of the base and the slant height.
L.A. $= \frac{1}{2} \cdot 2\pi r\ell$ or L.A. $= \pi r\ell$
The surface area of a right cone is the sum of the lateral area and the area of the base.
S.A. $=$ L.A. $+ B$ (p. 318)

Theorem 6-5
Cavalieri's Principle
If two space figures have the same height and the same cross-sectional area at every level, then they have the same volume. (p. 324)

Theorem 6-6
Volume of a Prism
The volume of a prism is the product of the area of a base and the height of the prism.
$V = Bh$ (p. 324)

Theorem 6-7
Volume of a Cylinder
The volume of a cylinder is the product of the area of a base and the height of the cylinder.
$V = Bh$ or $V = \pi r^2 h$ (p. 325)

Theorem 6-8
Volume of a Pyramid
The volume of a pyramid is one third the product of the area of the base and the height of the pyramid.
$V = \frac{1}{3}Bh$ (p. 331)

Theorem 6-9
Volume of a Cone
The volume of a cone is one third the product of the area of the base and the height of the cone.
$V = \frac{1}{3}Bh$ or $V = \frac{1}{3}\pi r^2 h$ (p. 332)

Theorem 6-10
Surface Area of a Sphere
The surface area of a sphere is four times the product of π and the square of the radius of the sphere.
$S.A. = 4\pi r^2$ (p. 338)

Theorem 6-11
Volume of a Sphere
The volume of a sphere is $\frac{4}{3}$ the product of π and the cube of the radius of the sphere.
$V = \frac{4}{3}\pi r^3$ (p. 339)

Chapter 7: Reasoning and Parallel Lines

Postulate 7-1
Corresponding Angles Postulate
If two parallel lines are cut by a transversal, then corresponding angles are congruent. (p. 364)

Theorem 7-1
Alternate Interior Angles Theorem
If two parallel lines are cut by a transversal, then alternate interior angles are congruent. (p. 364)
Proof on p. 364

Theorem 7-2
Same-Side Interior Angles Theorem
If two parallel lines are cut by a transversal, then the pairs of same-side interior angles are supplementary. (p. 364)
Proof on p. 365, Question 5

Postulate 7-2
Converse of Corresponding Angles Postulate
If two lines are cut by a transversal so that a pair of corresponding angles are congruent, then the lines are parallel. (p. 371)

Theorem 7-3
Converse of Alternate Interior Angles Theorem
If two lines are cut by a transversal so that a pair of alternate interior angles are congruent, then the lines are parallel. (p. 372)
Proof on p. 372

Theorem 7-4
Converse of Same-Side Interior Angles Theorem
If two lines are cut by a transversal so that a pair of same-side interior angles are supplementary, then the lines are parallel. (p. 372)
Proof on p. 375, Exercise 28

Postulate 7-3
Euclid's Parallel Postulate
Through a point not on a line, there is one and only one line parallel to the given line. (p. 394)

Postulate 7-4
Spherical Geometry Parallel Postulate
Through a point not on a line, there is no line parallel to the given line. (p. 394)

Chapter 8: Proving Triangles Congruent

Postulate 8-1
Side-Side-Side Postulate (SSS Postulate)
If three sides of one triangle are congruent to three sides of another triangle, then the two triangles are congruent. (p. 406)

Postulate 8-2
Side-Angle-Side Postulate (SAS Postulate)
If two sides and the included angle of one triangle are congruent to two sides and the included angle of another triangle, then the two triangles are congruent. (p. 408)

Postulate 8-3
Angle-Side-Angle Postulate (ASA Postulate)
If two angles and the included side of one triangle are congruent to two angles and the included side of another triangle, then the two triangles are congruent. (p. 414)

Theorem 8-1
Angle-Angle-Side Theorem (AAS Theorem)
If two angles and a nonincluded side of one triangle are congruent to two angles and the corresponding nonincluded side of another triangle, then the triangles are congruent. (p. 416)
Proof on p. 416, Question 5

Theorem 8-2
Hypotenuse-Leg Theorem (HL Theorem)
If the hypotenuse and a leg of one right triangle are congruent to the hypotenuse and a leg of another right triangle, then the triangles are congruent. (p. 420)
Proof on p. 420

Chapter 9: Quadrilaterals

Theorem 9-1
Opposite sides of a parallelogram are congruent. (p. 448)
Proof on p. 449, Example 1

Theorem 9-2
Opposite angles of a parallelogram are congruent. (p. 449)
Proof on p. 452, Exercise 27

Theorem 9-3
The diagonals of a parallelogram bisect each other. (p. 450)
Proof on p. 485, Exercise 2

Theorem 9-4
If three (or more) parallel lines cut off congruent segments on one transversal, then they cut off congruent segments on every transversal. (p. 450)
Proof on p. 452, Exercise 28

Theorem 9-5
If the diagonals of a quadrilateral bisect each other, then the quadrilateral is a parallelogram. (p. 455)
Proof on p. 455, Example 1

Theorem 9-6
If one pair of opposite sides of a quadrilateral are both congruent and parallel, then the quadrilateral is a parallelogram. (p. 456)
Proof on p. 456, Question 6

Theorem 9-7
If both pairs of opposite sides of a quadrilateral are congruent, then the quadrilateral is a parallelogram. (p. 456)
Proof on p. 456, Question 7

Theorem 9-8
If both pairs of opposite angles of a quadrilateral are congruent, then the quadrilateral is a parallelogram. (p. 456)
Proof on p. 456, Question 8

Theorem 9-9
Each diagonal of a rhombus bisects two angles of the rhombus. (p. 463)
Proof on p. 463, Question 1

Theorem 9-10
The diagonals of a rhombus are perpendicular. (p. 463)
Proof on p. 463, Example 1

Theorem 9-11
The area of a rhombus is equal to half the product of the lengths of its diagonals (p. 463)
Proof on p. 466, Exercise 17

Theorem 9-12
The diagonals of a rectangle are congruent. (p. 464)
Proof on p. 464, Question 4

Theorem 9-13
If one diagonal of a parallelogram bisects two angles of the parallelogram, then the parallelogram is a rhombus. (p. 464)
Proof on p. 467, Exercise 29

Theorem 9-14
If the diagonals of a parallelogram are perpendicular, then the parallelogram is a rhombus. (p. 464)
Proof on p. 467, Exercise 30

Theorem 9-15
If the diagonals of a parallelogram are congruent, then the parallelogram is a rectangle. (p. 464)
Proof on p. 467, Exercise 31

Theorem 9-16
Base angles of an isosceles trapezoid are congruent. (p. 470)
Proof on p. 475, Exercise 24

Theorem 9-17
The diagonals of an isosceles trapezoid are congruent. (p. 471)
Proofs on p. 471, Example 2; p. 485, Exercise 3

Theorem 9-18
The diagonals of a kite are perpendicular. (p. 472)
Proof on p. 472, Question 7

Theorem 9-19
Trapezoid Midsegment Theorem
The midsegment of a trapezoid is (1) parallel to the bases and (2) half as long as the sum of the lengths of the bases. (p. 483)
Proof on p. 483, Questions 1–3

Chapter 10: Similarity

Postulate 10-1
Angle-Angle Similarity Postulate (AA ~ Postulate)
If two angles of one triangle are congruent to two angles of another triangle, then the triangles are similar. (p. 504)

Theorem 10-1
Side-Angle-Side Similarity Theorem (SAS ~ Theorem)
If an angle of one triangle is congruent to an angle of a second triangle, and the sides including the two angles are proportional, then the triangles are similar. (p. 506)
Proof on p. 506

Theorem 10-2
Side-Side-Side Similarity Theorem (SSS ~ Theorem)
If the corresponding sides of two triangles are proportional, then the triangles are similar. (p. 506)
Proof on p. 506

Theorem 10-3
The altitude to the hypotenuse of a right triangle divides the triangle into two triangles that are similar to the original triangle and to each other. (p. 511)
Proof on p. 511

Corollary 1
The length of the altitude to the hypotenuse of a right triangle is the geometric mean of the lengths of the segments of the hypotenuse. (p. 512)
Proof on p. 512

Corollary 2
The altitude to the hypotenuse of a right triangle intersects it so that the length of each leg is the geometric mean of the length of its adjacent segment of the hypotenuse and the length of the entire hypotenuse. (p. 512)
Proof on p. 512

Theorem 10-4
Side-Splitter Theorem
If a line is parallel to one side of a triangle and intersects the other two sides, then it divides those sides proportionally. (p. 517)
Proof on p. 517

Corollary
If three parallel lines intersect two transversals, then the segments intercepted on the transversals are proportional. (p. 518)
Proof on p. 521, Exercise 24

Theorem 10-5
Triangle-Angle-Bisector Theorem
If a ray bisects an angle of a triangle, then it divides the opposite side into two segments that are proportional to the other two sides of the triangle. (p. 519)
Proof on p. 519

Theorem 10-6
Perimeters and Areas of Similar Figures
If the similarity ratio of two similar figures is $a : b$, then (1) the ratio of their perimeters is $a : b$, and (2) the ratio of their areas is $a^2 : b^2$. (p. 525)

Theorem 10-7
Areas and Volumes of Similar Solids
If the similarity ratio of two similar solids is $a : b$, then (1) the ratio of their areas is $a^2 : b^2$, and (2) the ratio of their volumes is $a^3 : b^3$. (p. 532)

Chapter 11: Right Triangle Trigonometry

Theorem 11-1
Area of a Triangle Given SAS
The area of a triangle is one half the product of the lengths of two sides and the sine of the included angle.
Area of triangle =
$\frac{1}{2}$ · side length · side length · sine of included angle (p. 575)
Proof on p. 575 for the case in which the given angle is acute

Chapter 12: Chords, Secants, and Tangents

Theorem 12-1
Equation of a Circle
The standard form of an equation of a circle with center (h, k) and radius r is
$(x - h)^2 + (y - k)^2 = r^2$. (p. 586)
Proof on p. 586

Theorem 12-2
If a line is tangent to a circle, then it is perpendicular to the radius drawn to the point of tangency. (p. 593)
Proof on p. 594

Theorem 12-3
Converse of Theorem 12-2
If a line in the same plane as a circle is perpendicular to a radius at its endpoint on the circle, then the line is tangent to the circle. (p. 595)
Proof on p. 646, Exercise 12-2(2)

Theorem 12-4
Two segments tangent to a circle from a point outside the circle are congruent. (p. 596)
Proof on p. 597, Exercise 10

Theorem 12-5
In the same circle or in congruent circles, (1) congruent central angles have congruent arcs, and (2) congruent arcs have congruent central angles. (p. 601)

Theorem 12-6
In the same circle or in congruent circles, (1) congruent chords have congruent arcs, and (2) congruent arcs have congruent chords. (p. 601)
Proof on p. 601, Question 7

Theorem 12-7
A diameter that is perpendicular to a chord bisects the chord and its arc. (p. 601)
Proof on p. 604, Exercise 18

Theorem 12-8
The perpendicular bisector of a chord contains the center of the circle. (p. 602)
Proof on p. 602, Question 9

Theorem 12-9
In the same circle or in congruent circles, (1) chords equidistant from the center are congruent, and (2) congruent chords are equidistant from the center. (p. 602)
Proof of part (1) on p. 603, Example 3

Theorem 12-10
Inscribed Angle Theorem
The measure of an inscribed angle is half the measure of its intercepted arc. (p. 608)
Proof of Case 1 on p. 608
Proof of Case II on p. 611, Exercise 13

Corollary 1
Two inscribed angles that intercept the same arc are congruent. (p. 609)
Proof on p. 611, Exercise 14

Corollary 2
An angle inscribed in a semicircle is a right angle. (p. 609)
Proof on p. 612, Exercise 20

Corollary 3
The opposite angles of a quadrilateral inscribed in a circle are supplementary. (p. 609)
Proof on p. 612, Exercise 21

Theorem 12-11
The measure of an angle formed by a chord and a tangent that intersect on a circle is half the measure of the intercepted arc. (p. 610)
Proof on p. 646, Exercise 12-4(2)

Theorem 12-12
The measure of an angle formed by two chords that intersect inside a circle is half the sum of the measures of the intercepted arcs. (p. 615)
Proof on p. 615

Theorem 12-13
The measure of an angle formed by two secants, two tangents, or a secant and a tangent drawn from a point outside the circle is half the difference of the measures of the intercepted arcs. (p. 615)
Proof of part (1) on p. 618, Exercise 14

Theorem 12-14
If two chords intersect inside a circle, then the product of the lengths of the segments of one chord equals the product of the lengths of the segments of the other chord. (p. 621)
Proof on p. 622

Theorem 12-15
If two secant segments are drawn from a point outside a circle, the product of the lengths of one secant segment and its external segment equals the product of the lengths of the other secant segment and its external segment. (p. 622)
Proof on p. 624, Exercise 9

Theorem 12-16
If a tangent and a secant are drawn from a point outside a circle, then the product of the lengths of the secant segment and its external segment equals the square of the length of the tangent segment. (p. 622)
Proof on p. 624, Exercise 10

Constructions

Construction 1
Congruent Segments
Construct a segment congruent to a given segment. (p. 40)

Construction 2
Congruent Angles
Construct an angle congruent to a given angle. (p. 40)

Construction 3
Perpendicular Bisector
Construct the perpendicular bisector of a segment. (p. 42)

Construction 4
Angle Bisector
Construct the bisector of an angle. (p. 42)

Construction 5
Parallel through a Point Not on a Line
Construct a line parallel to a given line and through a given point not on the line. (p. 377)

Construction 6
Perpendicular through a Point on a Line
Construct the perpendicular to a given line through a given point on the line. (p. 378)

Construction 7
Perpendicular through a Point Not on a Line
Construct the perpendicular to a given line from a given point not on the line. (p. 379)

Glossary/Study Guide

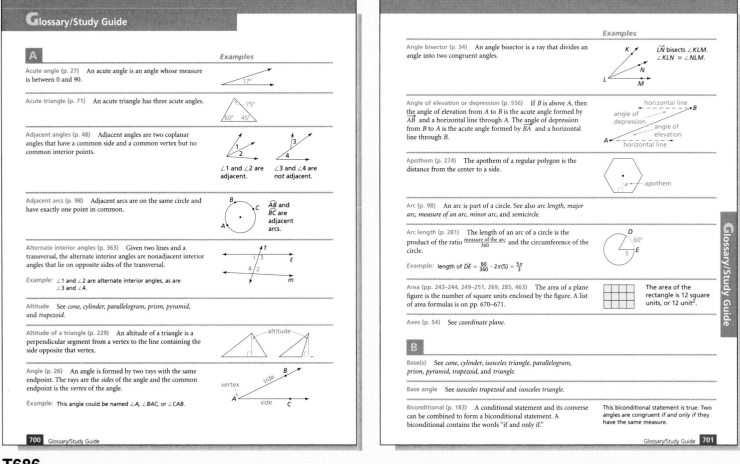

A

Examples

Acute angle (p. 27) An acute angle is an angle whose measure is between 0 and 90.

17°

Acute triangle (p. 71) An acute triangle has three acute angles.

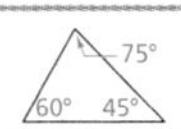

Adjacent angles (p. 48) Adjacent angles are two coplanar angles that have a common side and a common vertex but no common interior points.

$\angle 1$ and $\angle 2$ are adjacent. $\angle 3$ and $\angle 4$ are *not* adjacent.

Adjacent arcs (p. 98) Adjacent arcs are on the same circle and have exactly one point in common.

$\overset{\frown}{AB}$ and $\overset{\frown}{BC}$ are adjacent arcs.

Alternate interior angles (p. 363) Given two lines and a transversal, the alternate interior angles are nonadjacent interior angles that lie on opposite sides of the transversal.

Example: $\angle 1$ and $\angle 2$ are alternate interior angles, as are $\angle 3$ and $\angle 4$.

Altitude See *cone, cylinder, parallelogram, prism, pyramid,* and *trapezoid.*

Altitude of a triangle (p. 229) An altitude of a triangle is a perpendicular segment from a vertex to the line containing the side opposite that vertex.

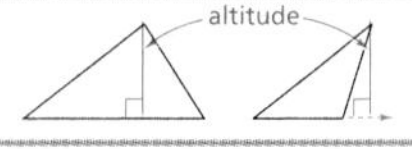

Angle (p. 26) An angle is formed by two rays with the same endpoint. The rays are the *sides* of the angle and the common endpoint is the *vertex* of the angle.

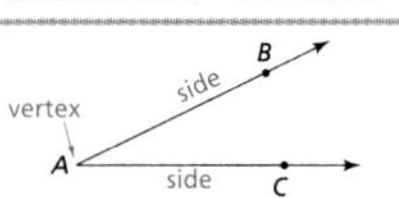

Example: This angle could be named $\angle A$, $\angle BAC$, or $\angle CAB$.

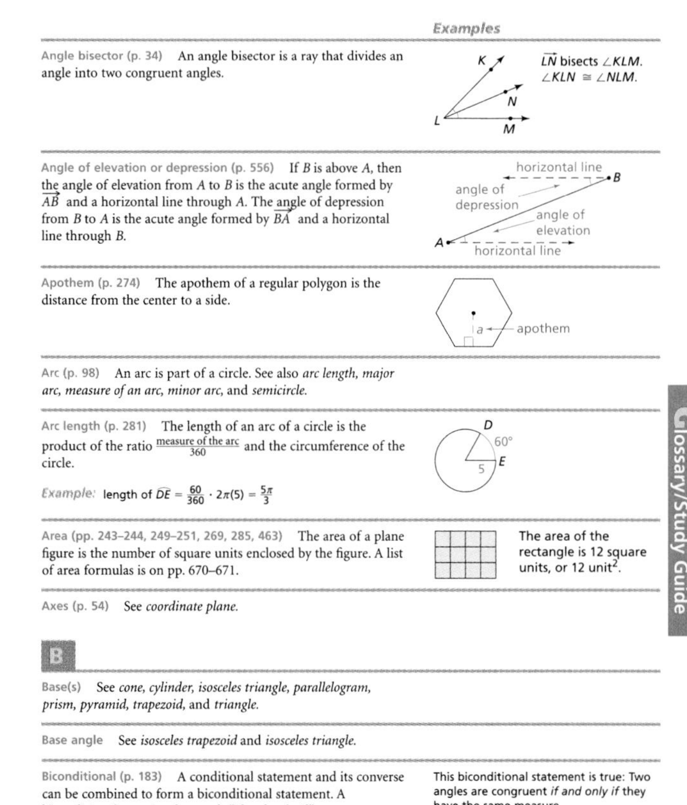

Examples

Angle bisector (p. 34) An angle bisector is a ray that divides an angle into two congruent angles.

$\overrightarrow{LN}$ bisects $\angle KLM$. $\angle KLN \cong \angle NLM$.

Angle of elevation or depression (p. 556) If B is above A, then the angle of elevation from A to B is the acute angle formed by $\overrightarrow{AB}$ and a horizontal line through A. The angle of depression from B to A is the acute angle formed by $\overrightarrow{BA}$ and a horizontal line through B.

Apothem (p. 274) The apothem of a regular polygon is the distance from the center to a side.

Arc (p. 98) An arc is part of a circle. See also *arc length, major arc, measure of an arc, minor arc,* and *semicircle.*

Arc length (p. 281) The length of an arc of a circle is the product of the ratio $\frac{\text{measure of the arc}}{360}$ and the circumference of the circle.

Example: length of $\overset{\frown}{DE} = \frac{60}{360} \cdot 2\pi(5) = \frac{5\pi}{3}$

Area (pp. 243–244, 249–251, 269, 285, 463) The area of a plane figure is the number of square units enclosed by the figure. A list of area formulas is on pp. 670–671.

The area of the rectangle is 12 square units, or 12 unit^2.

Axes (p. 54) See *coordinate plane.*

B

Base(s) See *cone, cylinder, isosceles triangle, parallelogram, prism, pyramid, trapezoid,* and *triangle.*

Base angle See *isosceles trapezoid* and *isosceles triangle.*

Biconditional (p. 183) A conditional statement and its converse can be combined to form a biconditional statement. A biconditional contains the words "if and only if."

This biconditional statement is true: Two angles are congruent *if and only if* they have the same measure.

Examples

Bisector See *segment bisector* and *angle bisector.*

C

Center See *circle, dilation, regular polygon,* and *sphere.*

Central angle of a circle (p. 97) A central angle of a circle is an angle whose vertex is the center of the circle.

∠ROK is a central angle of ⊙O.

Central angle of a regular polygon (p. 573) A central angle of a regular polygon is an angle formed by two consecutive radii.

∠EFG is a central angle of the regular pentagon.

Chord (p. 600) A chord of a circle is a segment whose endpoints are on the circle.

$\overline{HD}$ and $\overline{HR}$ are chords of ⊙C.

Circle (p. 96) A circle is the set of all points in a plane that are a given distance, the *radius,* from a given point, the *center.* The standard form for an equation of a circle with center (h, k) and radius r is $(x - h)^2 + (y - k)^2 = r^2$.

Example: The equation of the circle whose center is (1, 3) and whose radius is 3 is $(x - 1)^2 + (y - 3)^2 = 9$.

Circumference of a circle (p. 279) The circumference of a circle is the distance around the circle. Given the radius r of a circle, you can find its circumference C by using the formula $C = 2\pi r$.

$C = 2\pi r = 2\pi(4) = 8\pi$

Circumference is distance around the circle.

Circumference of a sphere (p. 340) See *sphere.*

Circumscribe (pp. 228, 596, 607) A circle is circumscribed about a polygon if the vertices of the polygon are on the circle. A polygon is circumscribed about a circle if all the sides of the polygon are tangent to the circle.

⊙G is circumscribed about ABCD.

△XYZ is circumscribed about ⊙P.

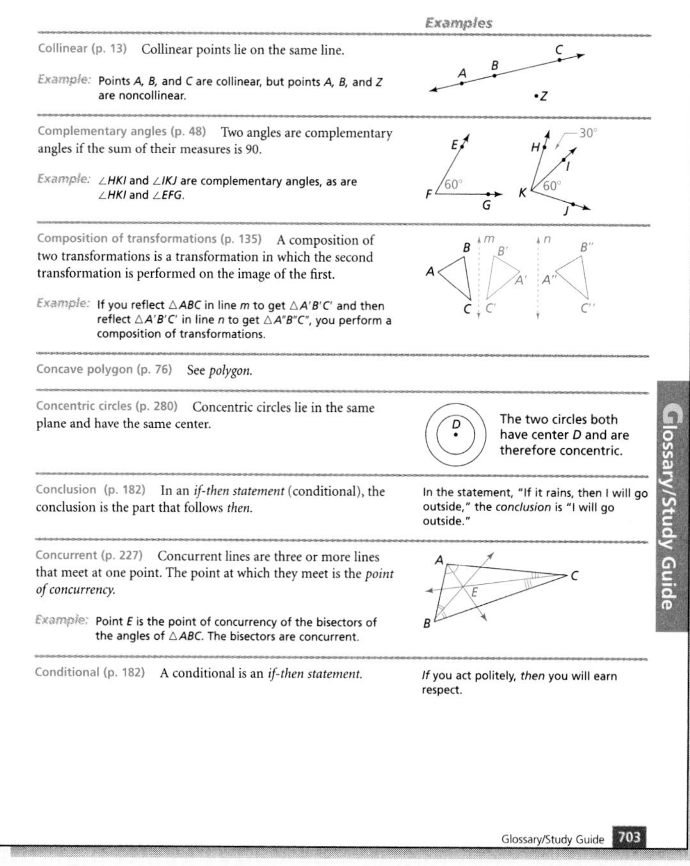

Examples

Collinear (p. 13) Collinear points lie on the same line.

Example: Points A, B, and C are collinear, but points A, B, and Z are noncollinear.

Complementary angles (p. 48) Two angles are complementary angles if the sum of their measures is 90.

Example: ∠HKI and ∠IKJ are complementary angles, as are ∠HKI and ∠EFG.

Composition of transformations (p. 135) A composition of two transformations is a transformation in which the second transformation is performed on the image of the first.

Example: If you reflect △ABC in line m to get △A′B′C′ and then reflect △A′B′C′ in line n to get △A″B″C″, you perform a composition of transformations.

Concave polygon (p. 76) See *polygon.*

Concentric circles (p. 280) Concentric circles lie in the same plane and have the same center.

The two circles both have center D and are therefore concentric.

Conclusion (p. 182) In an *if-then statement* (conditional), the conclusion is the part that follows *then.*

In the statement, "If it rains, then I will go outside," the *conclusion* is "I will go outside."

Concurrent (p. 227) Concurrent lines are three or more lines that meet at one point. The point at which they meet is the *point of concurrency.*

Example: Point E is the point of concurrency of the bisectors of the angles of △ABC. The bisectors are concurrent.

Conditional (p. 182) A conditional is an *if-then statement.*

If you act politely, *then* you will earn respect.

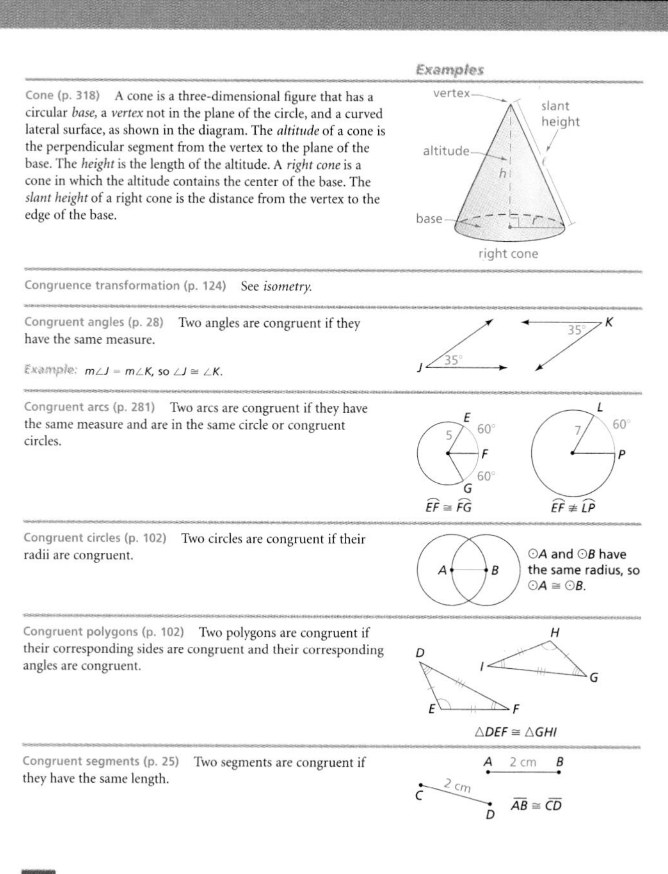

Examples

Cone (p. 318) A cone is a three-dimensional figure that has a circular *base,* a *vertex* not in the plane of the circle, and a curved lateral surface, as shown in the diagram. The *altitude* of a cone is the perpendicular segment from the vertex to the plane of the base. The *height* is the length of the altitude. A *right cone* is a cone in which the altitude contains the center of the base. The *slant height* of a right cone is the distance from the vertex to the edge of the base.

right cone

Congruence transformation (p. 124) See *isometry.*

Congruent angles (p. 28) Two angles are congruent if they have the same measure.

Example: m∠J = m∠K, so ∠J ≅ ∠K.

Congruent arcs (p. 281) Two arcs are congruent if they have the same measure and are in the same circle or congruent circles.

$\overset{\frown}{EF} \cong \overset{\frown}{FG}$ $\quad \overset{\frown}{EF} \ncong \overset{\frown}{LP}$

Congruent circles (p. 102) Two circles are congruent if their radii are congruent.

⊙A and ⊙B have the same radius, so ⊙A ≅ ⊙B.

Congruent polygons (p. 102) Two polygons are congruent if their corresponding sides are congruent and their corresponding angles are congruent.

△DEF ≅ △GHI

Congruent segments (p. 25) Two segments are congruent if they have the same length.

$\overline{AB} \cong \overline{CD}$

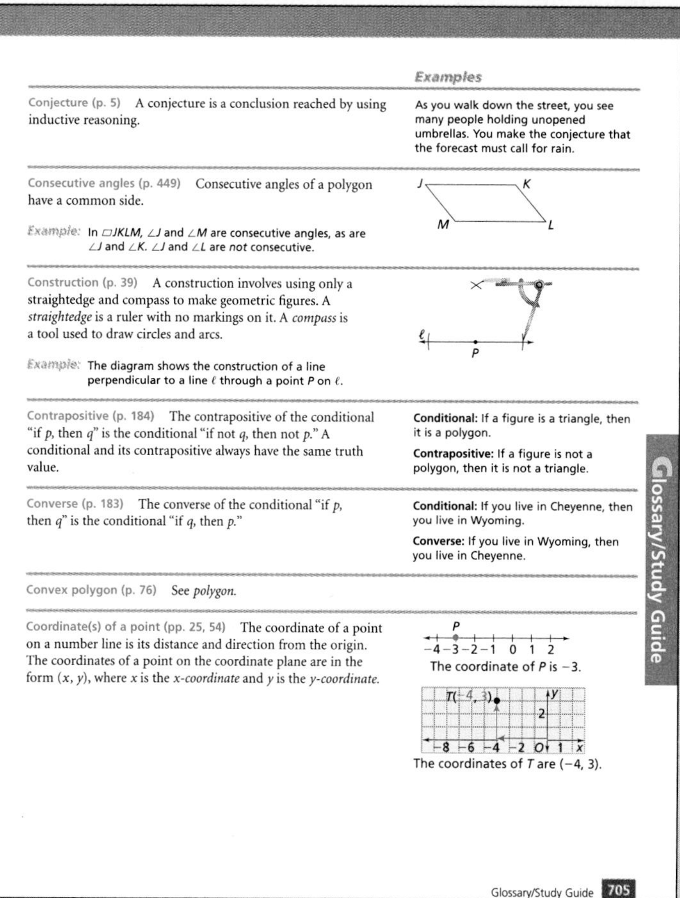

Examples

Conjecture (p. 5) A conjecture is a conclusion reached by using inductive reasoning.

As you walk down the street, you see many people holding unopened umbrellas. You make the conjecture that the forecast must call for rain.

Consecutive angles (p. 449) Consecutive angles of a polygon have a common side.

Example: In ▱JKLM, ∠J and ∠M are consecutive angles, as are ∠J and ∠K. ∠J and ∠L are *not* consecutive.

Construction (p. 39) A construction involves using only a straightedge and compass to make geometric figures. A *straightedge* is a ruler with no markings on it. A *compass* is a tool used to draw circles and arcs.

Example: The diagram shows the construction of a line perpendicular to a line ℓ through a point P on ℓ.

Contrapositive (p. 184) The contrapositive of the conditional "if p, then q" is the conditional "if not q, then not p." A conditional and its contrapositive always have the same truth value.

Conditional: If a figure is a triangle, then it is a polygon.

Contrapositive: If a figure is not a polygon, then it is not a triangle.

Converse (p. 183) The converse of the conditional "if p, then q" is the conditional "if q, then p."

Conditional: If you live in Cheyenne, then you live in Wyoming.

Converse: If you live in Wyoming, then you live in Cheyenne.

Convex polygon (p. 76) See *polygon.*

Coordinate(s) of a point (pp. 25, 54) The coordinate of a point on a number line is its distance and direction from the origin. The coordinates of a point on the coordinate plane are in the form (x, y), where x is the *x-coordinate* and y is the *y-coordinate.*

The coordinate of P is −3.

The coordinates of T are (−4, 3).

Examples

Coordinate plane (p. 54) The coordinate plane is formed by two number lines, called the *axes,* intersecting at right angles. The *x-axis* is the horizontal axis, and the *y-axis* is the vertical axis. The two axes meet at the *origin,* $O(0, 0)$. The axes divide the plane into four *quadrants.*

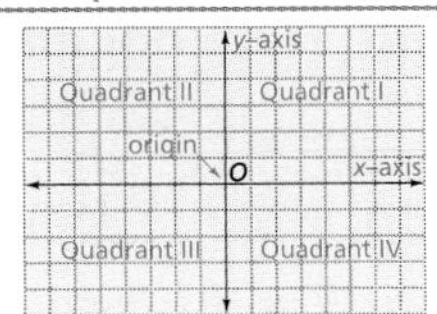

Coordinate proof (p. 201) See *proof.*

Coplanar (p. 13) Points and lines in the same plane are coplanar.

Example: Point C and $\overleftrightarrow{AB}$ are coplanar but points A, B, C, and Q are noncoplanar.

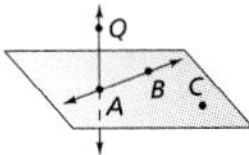

Corollary (p. 70) A corollary is a statement that follows directly from a theorem.

Theorem: If two sides of a triangle are congruent, then the angles opposite those sides are congruent.

Corollary: If a triangle is equilateral, then it is equiangular.

Corresponding angles (p. 363) Corresponding angles lie on the same side of the transversal t and in corresponding positions relative to ℓ and m.

Example: $\angle 1$ and $\angle 2$ are corresponding angles, as are $\angle 3$ and $\angle 4$, $\angle 5$ and $\angle 6$, and $\angle 7$ and $\angle 8$.

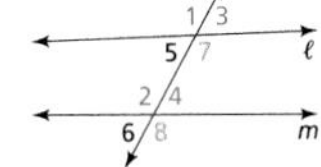

Cosine ratio (p. 551) See *trigonometric ratios.*

Counterexample (p. 182) A counterexample to a statement is a particular example or instance of the statement that is not true.

Statement: If you live in a state that begins with W, then you live in a state that does not border an ocean.

Counterexample: Washington

CPCTC (p. 426) CPCTC is an abbreviation for "corresponding parts of congruent triangles are congruent."

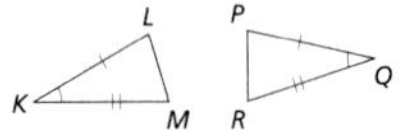

Example: By the SAS Congruence Postulate, $\triangle KLM \cong \triangle QPR$. By CPCTC, you also know that $\angle L \cong \angle P$, $\angle M \cong \angle R$, and $\overline{LM} \cong \overline{PR}$.

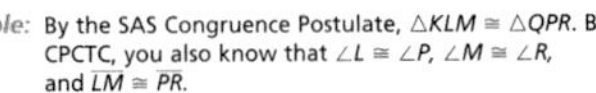

Examples

Cube (p. 310) A cube is a prism with all square faces.

Cylinder (p. 310) A cylinder is a three-dimensional figure with two congruent circular *bases* that lie in parallel planes. An *altitude* of a cylinder is a perpendicular segment that joins the planes of the bases. Its length is the *height* of the cylinder. In a *right cylinder,* the segment joining the centers of the bases is an altitude. In an *oblique cylinder,* the segment joining the centers of the bases is not perpendicular to the planes containing the bases.

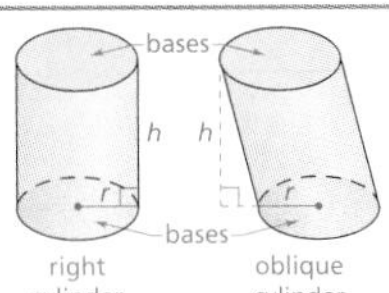

D

Decagon (p. 76) A decagon is a polygon with ten sides.

Deductive reasoning (p. 46) Deductive reasoning is a process of reasoning logically from given facts to a conclusion.

Based on the fact that the sum of any two even numbers is even, you can deduce that the product of an even number and any whole number is even.

Diagonal (p. 76) See *polygon.*

Diameter (p. 96) A diameter of a circle is a segment that contains the center of the circle and whose endpoints are on the circle. The term *diameter* can also mean the length of this segment.

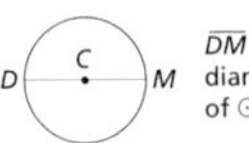

$\overline{DM}$ is a diameter of $\odot C$.

Dilation (p. 166) A dilation, or *similarity transformation,* with *center* C and *scale factor* n, where $n > 0$, maps a point R to R' in such a way that R' is on $\overrightarrow{CR}$ and $CR' = n \cdot CR$. The center of a dilation is its own image. If $n > 1$, the dilation is an *enlargement,* and if $0 < n < 1$, the dilation is a *reduction.*

Example: $\overline{R'Q'}$ is the image of $\overline{RQ}$ under a dilation with center C and scale factor 3.

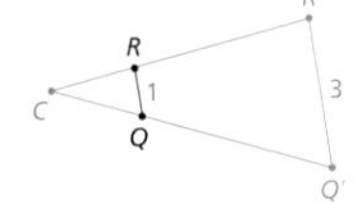

Distance from a point to a line (p. 221) The distance from a point to a line is the length of the perpendicular segment from the point to the line.

Example: The distance from point P to line ℓ is PT.

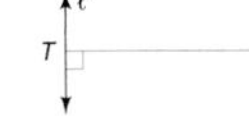

Glossary/Study Guide

Examples

Dodecagon (p. 76) A dodecagon is a polygon with twelve sides.

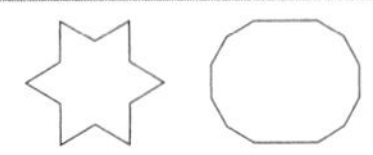

E

Edge (p. 302) See *polyhedron.*

Endpoint (p. 18) See *ray* and *segment.*

Enlargement (p. 167) See *dilation.*

Equiangular triangle (polygon) (pp. 71, 78) An equiangular triangle (polygon) is a triangle (polygon) whose angles are all congruent.

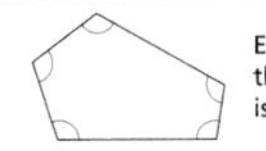

Each angle of the pentagon is a 108° angle.

Equilateral triangle (polygon) (pp. 71, 78) An equilateral triangle (polygon) is a triangle (polygon) whose sides are all congruent.

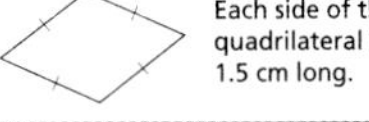

Each side of the quadrilateral is 1.5 cm long.

Euclidean geometry (p. 393) Euclidean geometry is a geometry of the plane in which Euclid's Parallel Postulate is true.

Example: In Euclidean geometry, there is exactly one line parallel to line ℓ through point P.

Exterior angle of a polygon (p. 69) An exterior angle of a polygon is an angle formed by a side and an extension of an adjacent side.

Example: $\angle KLM$ is an exterior angle of $\triangle JKL$.

F

Face (p. 302) See *polyhedron.*

Flow proof (p. 372) See *proof.*

Examples

Foundation drawing (p. 110) A foundation drawing shows the base of a structure and the height of each part.

Example: The first drawing is a foundation drawing; the second is an isometric drawing based on the foundation drawing.

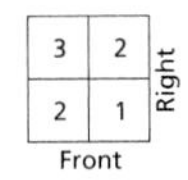

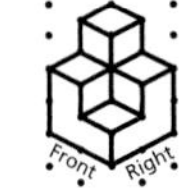

Frieze pattern (p. 137) A frieze pattern, also known as a *strip pattern,* repeats itself along a straight line. A frieze pattern can be mapped onto itself by a *translation.*

G

Geometric mean (p. 512) The geometric mean of two positive numbers a and b is the positive number x such that $\frac{a}{x} = \frac{x}{b}$.

The geometric mean of 6 and 24 is 12. $\frac{6}{x} = \frac{x}{24} \longrightarrow x^2 = 144 \longrightarrow x = 12$

Glide reflection (p. 146) A glide reflection is a composition of three reflections in lines that intersect in more than one point. Equivalently, a glide reflection is a composition of a translation followed by a reflection in a line parallel to the translation vector.

Example: The blue G in the diagram is the glide reflection image of the black G.

Glide reflectional symmetry (p. 161) A repeating pattern has glide reflectional symmetry if it can be mapped onto itself by a glide reflection.

Example: The tessellation shown can be mapped onto itself by a glide reflection in the given line and the given vector.

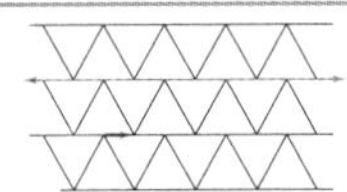

Golden rectangle, Golden ratio (p. 498) A *golden rectangle* is a rectangle that can be divided into a square and a rectangle that is similar to the original rectangle. The *golden ratio* is the ratio of the length of a golden rectangle to its width. The value of the golden ratio is $\frac{1 + \sqrt{5}}{2}$, or about 1.62.

$ABCD$ is a rectangle. $ADFE$ is a square. $ABCD \sim FEBC$

Great circle (p. 340) A great circle is the intersection of a sphere and a plane containing the center of the sphere. A great circle divides a sphere into two *hemispheres.*

Glossary/Study Guide

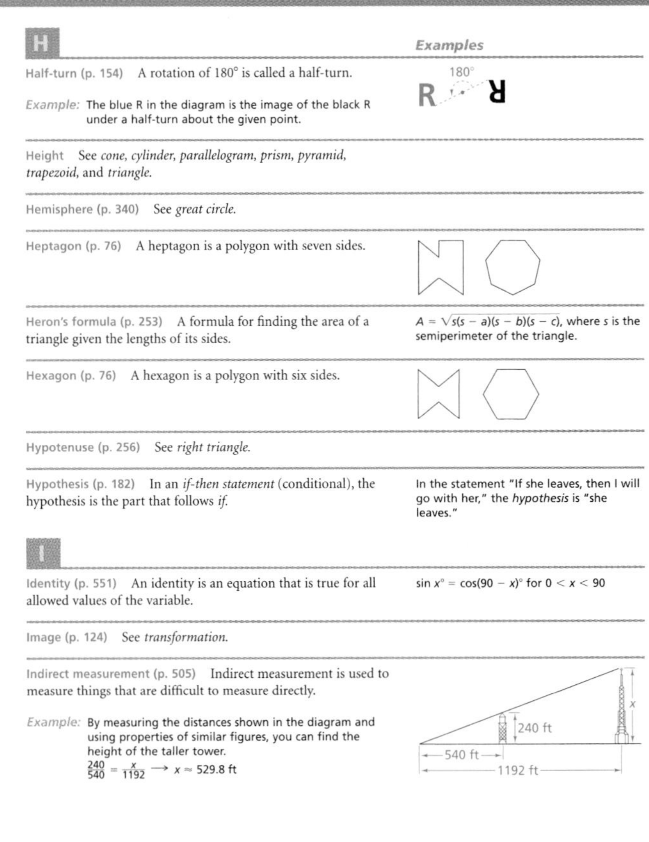

H

Examples

Half-turn (p. 154) A rotation of 180° is called a half-turn.

Example: The blue R in the diagram is the image of the black R under a half-turn about the given point.

Height See *cone, cylinder, parallelogram, prism, pyramid, trapezoid,* and *triangle.*

Hemisphere (p. 340) See *great circle.*

Heptagon (p. 76) A heptagon is a polygon with seven sides.

Heron's formula (p. 253) A formula for finding the area of a triangle given the lengths of its sides.

$A = \sqrt{s(s-a)(s-b)(s-c)}$, where s is the semiperimeter of the triangle.

Hexagon (p. 76) A hexagon is a polygon with six sides.

Hypotenuse (p. 256) See *right triangle.*

Hypothesis (p. 182) In an *if-then statement* (conditional), the hypothesis is the part that follows *if.*

In the statement "If she leaves, then I will go with her," the *hypothesis* is "she leaves."

I

Identity (p. 551) An identity is an equation that is true for all allowed values of the variable.

$\sin x° = \cos(90 - x)°$ for $0 < x < 90$

Image (p. 124) See *transformation.*

Indirect measurement (p. 505) Indirect measurement is used to measure things that are difficult to measure directly.

Example: By measuring the distances shown in the diagram and using properties of similar figures, you can find the height of the taller tower.
$\frac{240}{540} = \frac{x}{1192} \longrightarrow x \approx 529.8$ ft

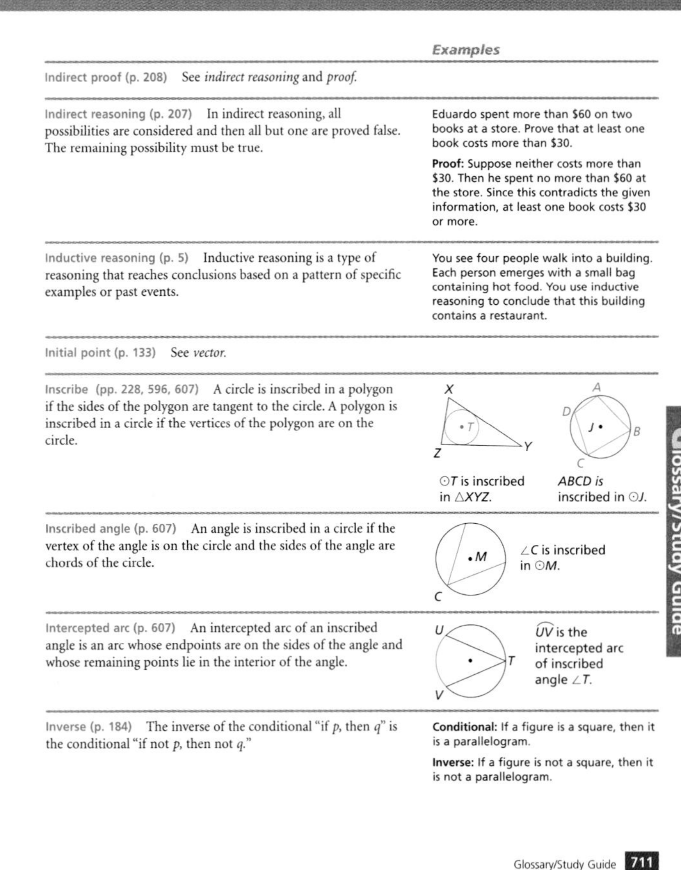

Examples

Indirect proof (p. 208) See *indirect reasoning* and *proof.*

Indirect reasoning (p. 207) In indirect reasoning, all possibilities are considered and then all but one are proved false. The remaining possibility must be true.

Eduardo spent more than \$60 on two books at a store. Prove that at least one book costs more than \$30.

Proof: Suppose neither costs more than \$30. Then he spent no more than \$60 at the store. Since this contradicts the given information, at least one book costs \$30 or more.

Inductive reasoning (p. 5) Inductive reasoning is a type of reasoning that reaches conclusions based on a pattern of specific examples or past events.

You see four people walk into a building. Each person emerges with a small bag containing hot food. You use inductive reasoning to conclude that this building contains a restaurant.

Initial point (p. 133) See *vector.*

Inscribe (pp. 228, 596, 607) A circle is inscribed in a polygon if the sides of the polygon are tangent to the circle. A polygon is inscribed in a circle if the vertices of the polygon are on the circle.

$\odot T$ is inscribed in $\triangle XYZ$.

ABCD is inscribed in $\odot J$.

Inscribed angle (p. 607) An angle is inscribed in a circle if the vertex of the angle is on the circle and the sides of the angle are chords of the circle.

$\angle C$ is inscribed in $\odot M$.

Intercepted arc (p. 607) An intercepted arc of an inscribed angle is an arc whose endpoints are on the sides of the angle and whose remaining points lie in the interior of the angle.

$\overset{\frown}{UV}$ is the intercepted arc of inscribed angle $\angle T$.

Inverse (p. 184) The inverse of the conditional "if p, then q" is the conditional "if not p, then not q."

Conditional: If a figure is a square, then it is a parallelogram.

Inverse: If a figure is not a square, then it is not a parallelogram.

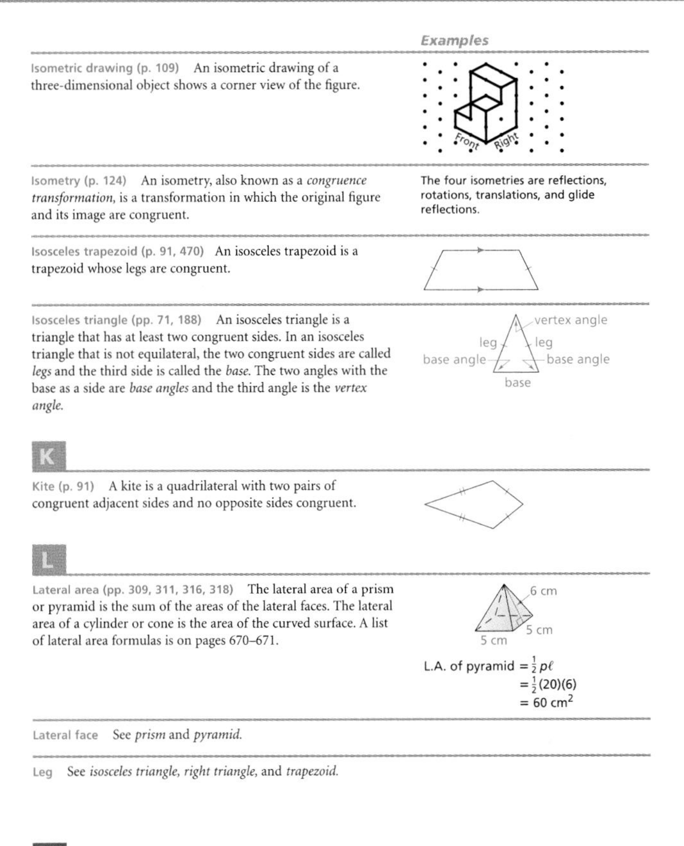

Examples

Isometric drawing (p. 109) An isometric drawing of a three-dimensional object shows a corner view of the figure.

Isometry (p. 124) An isometry, also known as a *congruence transformation,* is a transformation in which the original figure and its image are congruent.

The four isometries are reflections, rotations, translations, and glide reflections.

Isosceles trapezoid (p. 91, 470) An isosceles trapezoid is a trapezoid whose legs are congruent.

Isosceles triangle (pp. 71, 188) An isosceles triangle is a triangle that has at least two congruent sides. In an isosceles triangle that is not equilateral, the two congruent sides are called *legs* and the third side is called the *base.* The two angles with the base as a side are *base angles* and the third angle is the *vertex angle.*

K

Kite (p. 91) A kite is a quadrilateral with two pairs of congruent adjacent sides and no opposite sides congruent.

L

Lateral area (pp. 309, 311, 316, 318) The lateral area of a prism or pyramid is the sum of the areas of the lateral faces. The lateral area of a cylinder or cone is the area of the curved surface. A list of lateral area formulas is on pages 670–671.

$$\text{L.A. of pyramid} = \tfrac{1}{2}p\ell = \tfrac{1}{2}(20)(6) = 60 \text{ cm}^2$$

Lateral face See *prism* and *pyramid.*

Leg See *isosceles triangle, right triangle,* and *trapezoid.*

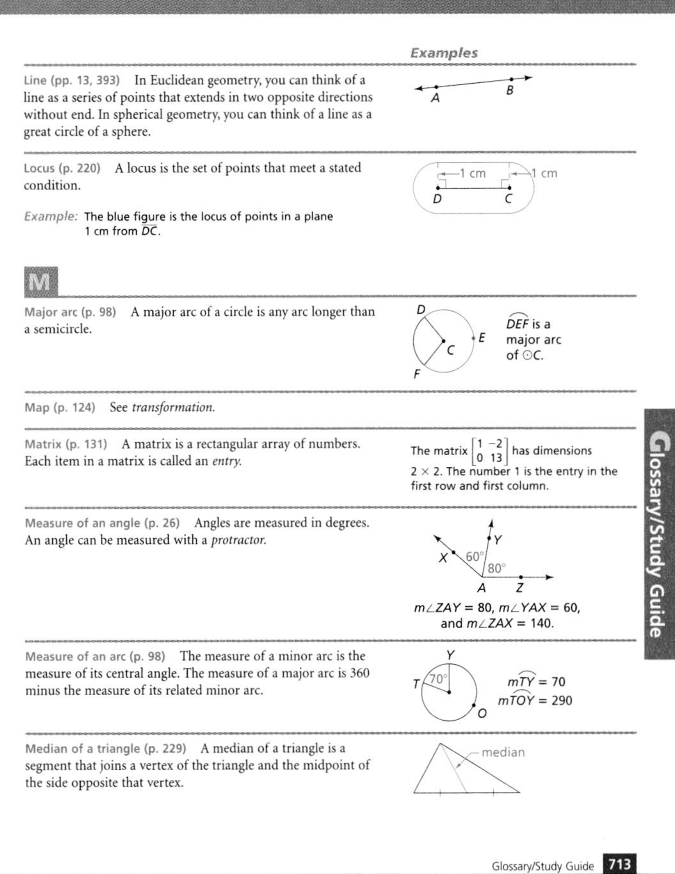

Examples

Line (pp. 13, 393) In Euclidean geometry, you can think of a line as a series of points that extends in two opposite directions without end. In spherical geometry, you can think of a line as a great circle of a sphere.

Locus (p. 220) A locus is the set of points that meet a stated condition.

Example: The blue figure is the locus of points in a plane 1 cm from $\overline{DC}$.

M

Major arc (p. 98) A major arc of a circle is any arc longer than a semicircle.

$\overset{\frown}{DEF}$ is a major arc of $\odot C$.

Map (p. 124) See *transformation.*

Matrix (p. 131) A matrix is a rectangular array of numbers. Each item in a matrix is called an *entry.*

The matrix $\begin{bmatrix} 1 & -2 \\ 0 & 13 \end{bmatrix}$ has dimensions 2×2. The number 1 is the entry in the first row and first column.

Measure of an angle (p. 26) Angles are measured in degrees. An angle can be measured with a *protractor.*

$m\angle ZAY = 80$, $m\angle YAX = 60$, and $m\angle ZAX = 140$.

Measure of an arc (p. 98) The measure of a minor arc is the measure of its central angle. The measure of a major arc is 360 minus the measure of its related minor arc.

$m\overset{\frown}{TY} = 70$
$m\overset{\frown}{TOY} = 290$

Median of a triangle (p. 229) A median of a triangle is a segment that joins a vertex of the triangle and the midpoint of the side opposite that vertex.

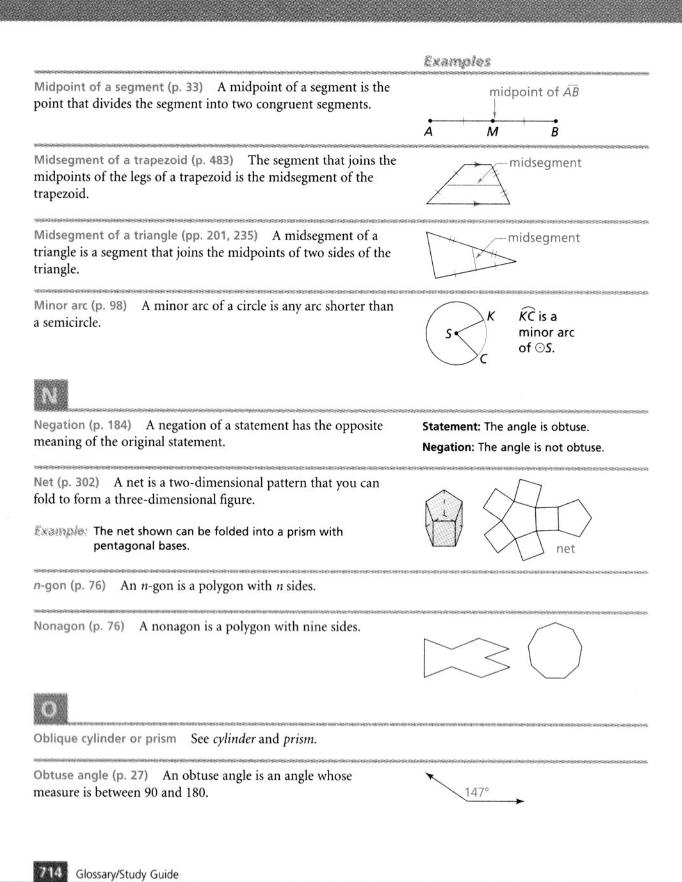

Examples

Midpoint of a segment (p. 33) A midpoint of a segment is the point that divides the segment into two congruent segments.

midpoint of $\overline{AB}$ — A M B

Midsegment of a trapezoid (p. 483) The segment that joins the midpoints of the legs of a trapezoid is the midsegment of the trapezoid.

midsegment

Midsegment of a triangle (pp. 201, 235) A midsegment of a triangle is a segment that joins the midpoints of two sides of the triangle.

midsegment

Minor arc (p. 98) A minor arc of a circle is any arc shorter than a semicircle.

$\overset{\frown}{KC}$ is a minor arc of ⊙S.

N

Negation (p. 184) A negation of a statement has the opposite meaning of the original statement.

Statement: The angle is obtuse.
Negation: The angle is not obtuse.

Net (p. 302) A net is a two-dimensional pattern that you can fold to form a three-dimensional figure.

Example: The net shown can be folded into a prism with pentagonal bases.

net

n-gon (p. 76) An *n*-gon is a polygon with *n* sides.

Nonagon (p. 76) A nonagon is a polygon with nine sides.

O

Oblique cylinder or prism See *cylinder* and *prism.*

Obtuse angle (p. 27) An obtuse angle is an angle whose measure is between 90 and 180.

147°

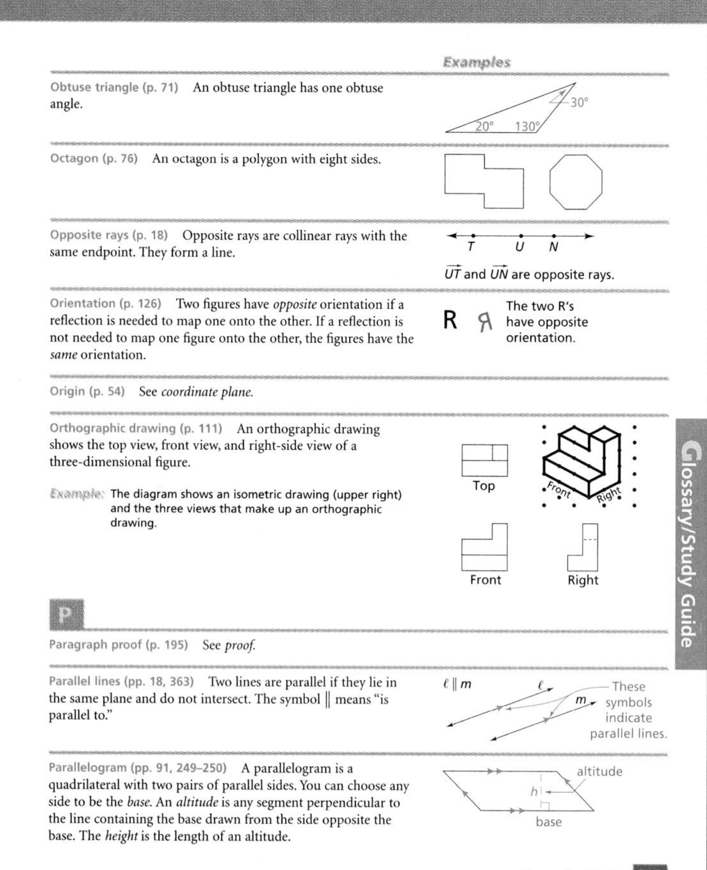

Examples

Obtuse triangle (p. 71) An obtuse triangle has one obtuse angle.

20° 130° 30°

Octagon (p. 76) An octagon is a polygon with eight sides.

Opposite rays (p. 18) Opposite rays are collinear rays with the same endpoint. They form a line.

T U N

$\overrightarrow{UT}$ and $\overrightarrow{UN}$ are opposite rays.

Orientation (p. 126) Two figures have *opposite* orientation if a reflection is needed to map one onto the other. If a reflection is not needed to map one figure onto the other, the figures have the *same* orientation.

R Я The two R's have opposite orientation.

Origin (p. 54) See *coordinate plane.*

Orthographic drawing (p. 111) An orthographic drawing shows the top view, front view, and right-side view of a three-dimensional figure.

Example: The diagram shows an isometric drawing (upper right) and the three views that make up an orthographic drawing.

Top Front Right

P

Paragraph proof (p. 195) See *proof.*

Parallel lines (pp. 18, 363) Two lines are parallel if they lie in the same plane and do not intersect. The symbol ∥ means "is parallel to."

$\ell \parallel m$ — These symbols indicate parallel lines.

Parallelogram (pp. 91, 249–250) A parallelogram is a quadrilateral with two pairs of parallel sides. You can choose any side to be the *base.* An *altitude* is any segment perpendicular to the line containing the base drawn from the side opposite the base. The *height* is the length of an altitude.

altitude h base

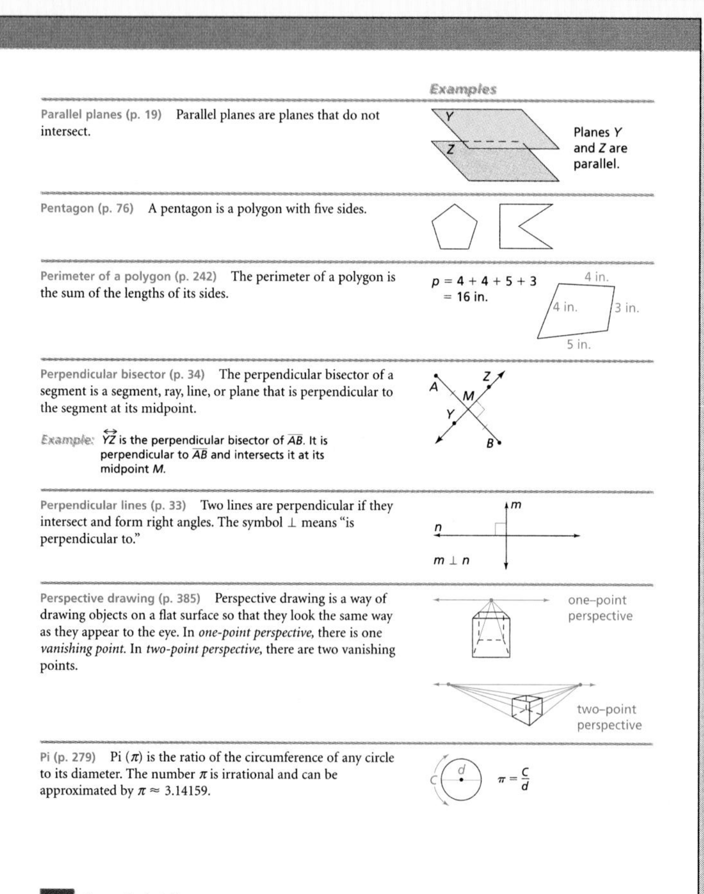

Examples

Parallel planes (p. 19) Parallel planes are planes that do not intersect.

Planes Y and Z are parallel.

Pentagon (p. 76) A pentagon is a polygon with five sides.

Perimeter of a polygon (p. 242) The perimeter of a polygon is the sum of the lengths of its sides.

$p = 4 + 4 + 5 + 3$
$= 16$ in.

4 in. 4 in. 3 in. 5 in.

Perpendicular bisector (p. 34) The perpendicular bisector of a segment is a segment, ray, line, or plane that is perpendicular to the segment at its midpoint.

Example: $\overleftrightarrow{YZ}$ is the perpendicular bisector of $\overline{AB}$. It is perpendicular to $\overline{AB}$ and intersects it at its midpoint *M.*

Perpendicular lines (p. 33) Two lines are perpendicular if they intersect and form right angles. The symbol ⊥ means "is perpendicular to."

$m \perp n$

Perspective drawing (p. 385) Perspective drawing is a way of drawing objects on a flat surface so that they look the same way as they appear to the eye. In *one-point perspective,* there is one *vanishing point.* In *two-point perspective,* there are two vanishing points.

one-point perspective

two-point perspective

Pi (p. 279) Pi (π) is the ratio of the circumference of any circle to its diameter. The number π is irrational and can be approximated by $\pi \approx 3.14159$.

$\pi = \frac{C}{d}$

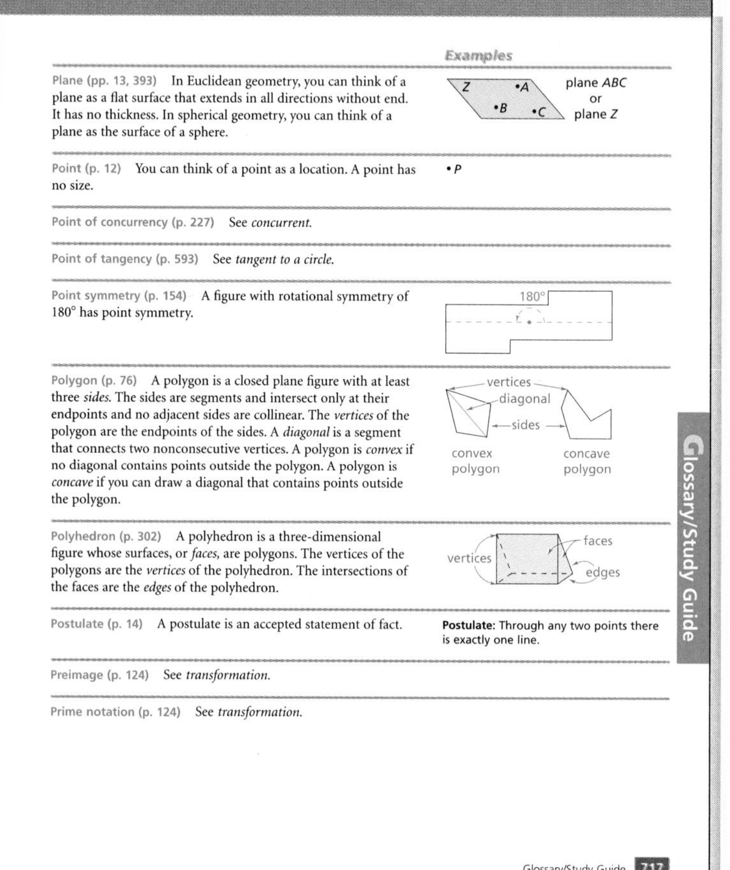

Examples

Plane (pp. 13, 393) In Euclidean geometry, you can think of a plane as a flat surface that extends in all directions without end. It has no thickness. In spherical geometry, you can think of a plane as the surface of a sphere.

plane *ABC* or plane *Z*

Point (p. 12) You can think of a point as a location. A point has no size.

• P

Point of concurrency (p. 227) See *concurrent.*

Point of tangency (p. 593) See *tangent to a circle.*

Point symmetry (p. 154) A figure with rotational symmetry of 180° has point symmetry.

180°

Polygon (p. 76) A polygon is a closed plane figure with at least three *sides.* The sides are segments and intersect only at their endpoints and no adjacent sides are collinear. The *vertices* of the polygon are the endpoints of the sides. A *diagonal* is a segment that connects two nonconsecutive vertices. A polygon is *convex* if no diagonal contains points outside the polygon. A polygon is *concave* if you can draw a diagonal that contains points outside the polygon.

vertices, diagonal, sides; convex polygon, concave polygon

Polyhedron (p. 302) A polyhedron is a three-dimensional figure whose surfaces, or *faces,* are polygons. The vertices of the polygons are the *vertices* of the polyhedron. The intersections of the faces are the *edges* of the polyhedron.

vertices, faces, edges

Postulate (p. 14) A postulate is an accepted statement of fact.

Postulate: Through any two points there is exactly one line.

Preimage (p. 124) See *transformation.*

Prime notation (p. 124) See *transformation.*

Examples

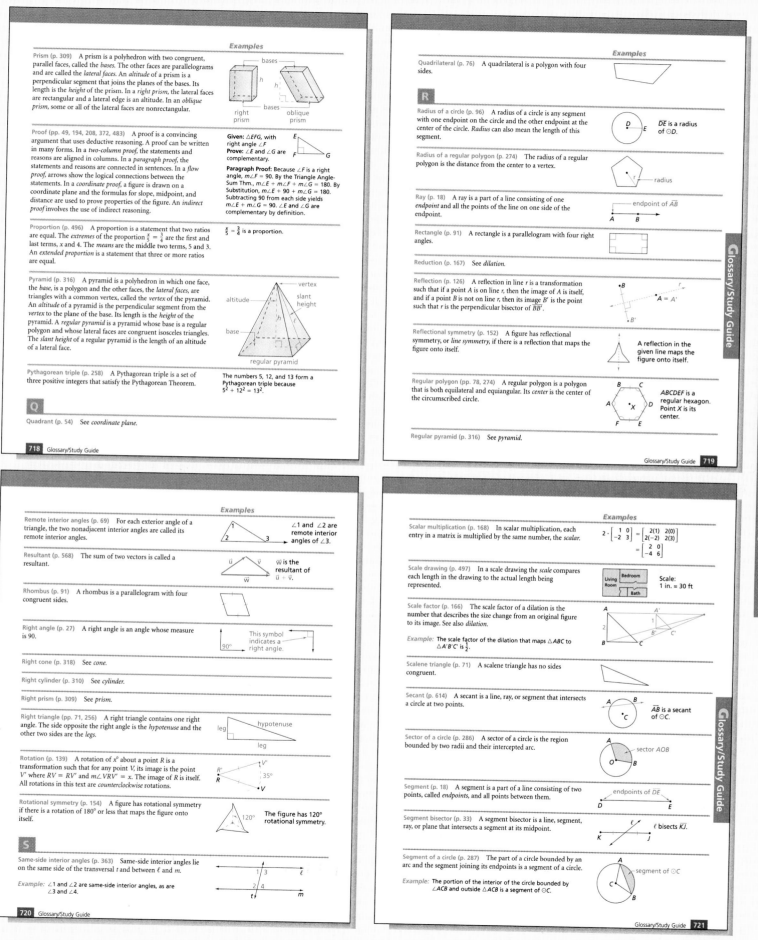

Prism (p. 309) A prism is a polyhedron with two congruent, parallel faces, called the *bases*. The other faces are parallelograms and are called the *lateral faces*. An *altitude* of a prism is a perpendicular segment that joins the planes of the bases. Its length is the *height* of the prism. In a *right prism*, the lateral faces are rectangular and a lateral edge is an altitude. In an *oblique prism*, some or all of the lateral faces are nonrectangular.

bases; h; right prism; oblique prism

Proof (pp. 49, 194, 208, 372, 483) A proof is a convincing argument that uses deductive reasoning. A proof can be written in many forms. In a *two-column proof*, the statements and reasons are aligned in columns. In a *paragraph proof*, the statements and reasons are connected in sentences. In a *flow proof*, arrows show the logical connections between the statements. In a *coordinate proof*, a figure is drawn on a coordinate plane and the formulas for slope, midpoint, and distance are used to prove properties of the figure. An *indirect proof* involves the use of indirect reasoning.

Given: $\triangle EFG$, with right angle $\angle F$
Prove: $\angle E$ and $\angle G$ are complementary.

Paragraph Proof: Because $\angle F$ is a right angle, $m\angle F = 90$. By the Triangle Angle-Sum Thm., $m\angle E + m\angle F + m\angle G = 180$. By Substitution, $m\angle E + 90 + m\angle G = 180$. Subtracting 90 from each side yields $m\angle E + m\angle G = 90$. $\angle E$ and $\angle G$ are complementary by definition.

Proportion (p. 496) A proportion is a statement that two ratios are equal. The *extremes* of the proportion $\frac{x}{5} = \frac{3}{4}$ are the first and last terms, x and 4. The *means* are the middle two terms, 5 and 3. An *extended proportion* is a statement that three or more ratios are equal.

$\frac{x}{5} = \frac{3}{4}$ is a proportion.

Pyramid (p. 316) A pyramid is a polyhedron in which one face, the *base*, is a polygon and the other faces, the *lateral faces*, are triangles with a common vertex, called the *vertex* of the pyramid. An *altitude* of a pyramid is the perpendicular segment from the *vertex* to the plane of the base. Its length is the *height* of the pyramid. A *regular pyramid* is a pyramid whose base is a regular polygon and whose lateral faces are congruent isosceles triangles. The *slant height* of a regular pyramid is the length of an altitude of a lateral face.

vertex; altitude; slant height; base; regular pyramid

Pythagorean triple (p. 258) A Pythagorean triple is a set of three positive integers that satisfy the Pythagorean Theorem.

The numbers 5, 12, and 13 form a Pythagorean triple because $5^2 + 12^2 = 13^2$.

Q

Quadrant (p. 54) See *coordinate plane*.

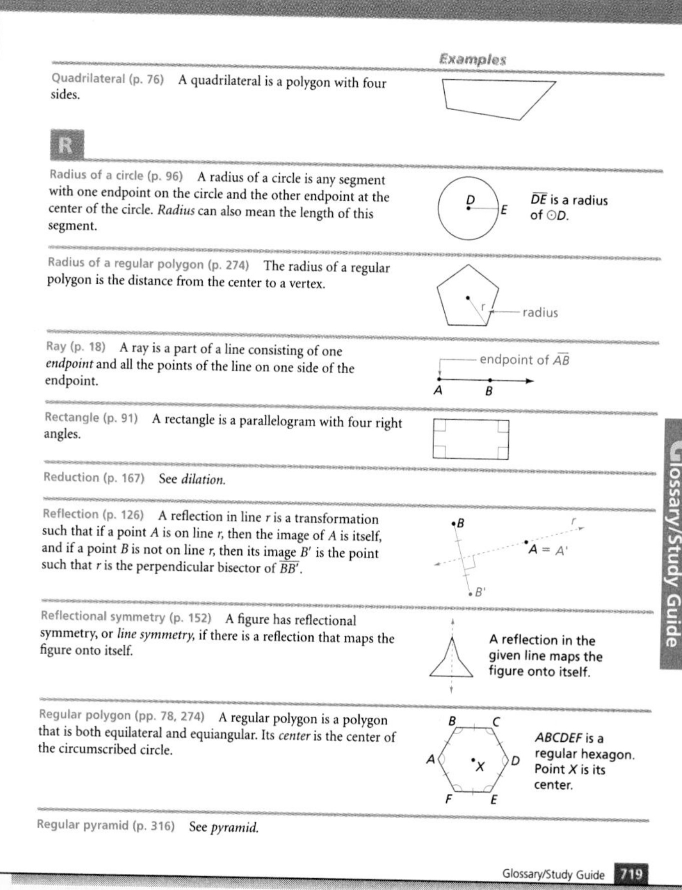
Examples

Quadrilateral (p. 76) A quadrilateral is a polygon with four sides.

R

Radius of a circle (p. 96) A radius of a circle is any segment with one endpoint on the circle and the other endpoint at the center of the circle. *Radius* can also mean the length of this segment.

$\overline{DE}$ is a radius of $\odot D$.

Radius of a regular polygon (p. 274) The radius of a regular polygon is the distance from the center to a vertex.

radius

Ray (p. 18) A ray is a part of a line consisting of one *endpoint* and all the points of the line on one side of the endpoint.

endpoint of $\overrightarrow{AB}$

Rectangle (p. 91) A rectangle is a parallelogram with four right angles.

Reduction (p. 167) See *dilation*.

Reflection (p. 126) A reflection in line r is a transformation such that if a point A is on line r, then the image of A is itself, and if a point B is not on line r, then its image B' is the point such that r is the perpendicular bisector of $\overline{BB'}$.

$A = A'$

Reflectional symmetry (p. 152) A figure has reflectional symmetry, or *line symmetry*, if there is a reflection that maps the figure onto itself.

A reflection in the given line maps the figure onto itself.

Regular polygon (pp. 78, 274) A regular polygon is a polygon that is both equilateral and equiangular. Its *center* is the center of the circumscribed circle.

ABCDEF is a regular hexagon. Point *X* is its center.

Regular pyramid (p. 316) See *pyramid*.

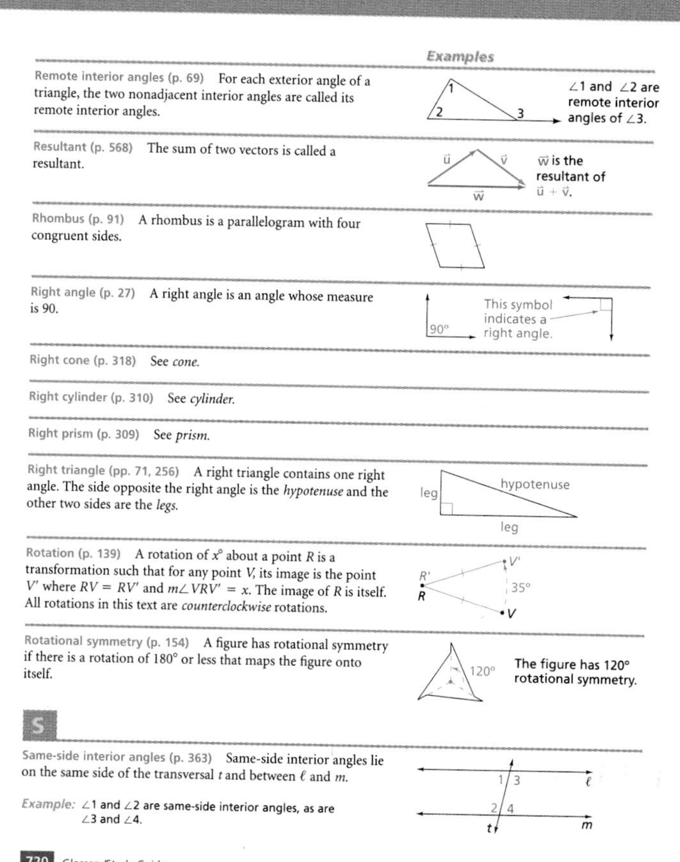
Examples

Remote interior angles (p. 69) For each exterior angle of a triangle, the two nonadjacent interior angles are called its remote interior angles.

$\angle 1$ and $\angle 2$ are remote interior angles of $\angle 3$.

Resultant (p. 568) The sum of two vectors is called a resultant.

$\vec{w}$ is the resultant of $\vec{u} + \vec{v}$.

Rhombus (p. 91) A rhombus is a parallelogram with four congruent sides.

Right angle (p. 27) A right angle is an angle whose measure is 90.

This symbol indicates a right angle.

Right cone (p. 318) See *cone*.

Right cylinder (p. 310) See *cylinder*.

Right prism (p. 309) See *prism*.

Right triangle (pp. 71, 256) A right triangle contains one right angle. The side opposite the right angle is the *hypotenuse* and the other two sides are the *legs*.

hypotenuse; leg; leg

Rotation (p. 139) A rotation of $x°$ about a point R is a transformation such that for any point V, its image is the point V' where $RV = RV'$ and $m\angle VRV' = x$. The image of R is itself. All rotations in this text are *counterclockwise* rotations.

Rotational symmetry (p. 154) A figure has rotational symmetry if there is a rotation of 180° or less that maps the figure onto itself.

The figure has 120° rotational symmetry.

S

Same-side interior angles (p. 363) Same-side interior angles lie on the same side of the transversal t and between ℓ and m.

Example: $\angle 1$ and $\angle 2$ are same-side interior angles, as are $\angle 3$ and $\angle 4$.

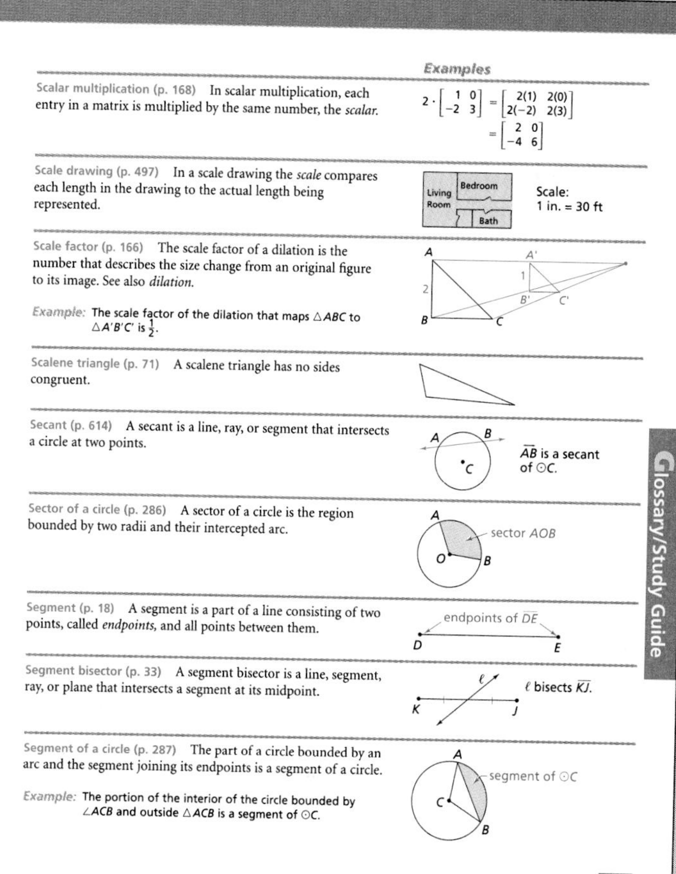
Examples

Scalar multiplication (p. 168) In scalar multiplication, each entry in a matrix is multiplied by the same number, the *scalar*.

$$2 \cdot \begin{bmatrix} 1 & 0 \\ -2 & 3 \end{bmatrix} = \begin{bmatrix} 2(1) & 2(0) \\ 2(-2) & 2(3) \end{bmatrix} = \begin{bmatrix} 2 & 0 \\ -4 & 6 \end{bmatrix}$$

Scale drawing (p. 497) In a scale drawing the *scale* compares each length in the drawing to the actual length being represented.

Scale: 1 in. = 30 ft

Scale factor (p. 166) The scale factor of a dilation is the number that describes the size change from an original figure to its image. See also *dilation*.

Example: The scale factor of the dilation that maps $\triangle ABC$ to $\triangle A'B'C'$ is $\frac{1}{2}$.

Scalene triangle (p. 71) A scalene triangle has no sides congruent.

Secant (p. 614) A secant is a line, ray, or segment that intersects a circle at two points.

$\overleftrightarrow{AB}$ is a secant of $\odot C$.

Sector of a circle (p. 286) A sector of a circle is the region bounded by two radii and their intercepted arc.

sector *AOB*

Segment (p. 18) A segment is a part of a line consisting of two points, called *endpoints*, and all points between them.

endpoints of $\overline{DE}$

Segment bisector (p. 33) A segment bisector is a line, segment, ray, or plane that intersects a segment at its midpoint.

ℓ bisects $\overline{KJ}$.

Segment of a circle (p. 287) The part of a circle bounded by an arc and the segment joining its endpoints is a segment of a circle.

segment of $\odot C$

Example: The portion of the interior of the circle bounded by $\angle ACB$ and outside $\triangle ACB$ is a segment of $\odot C$.

Examples

Semicircle (p. 98) A semicircle is half a circle.

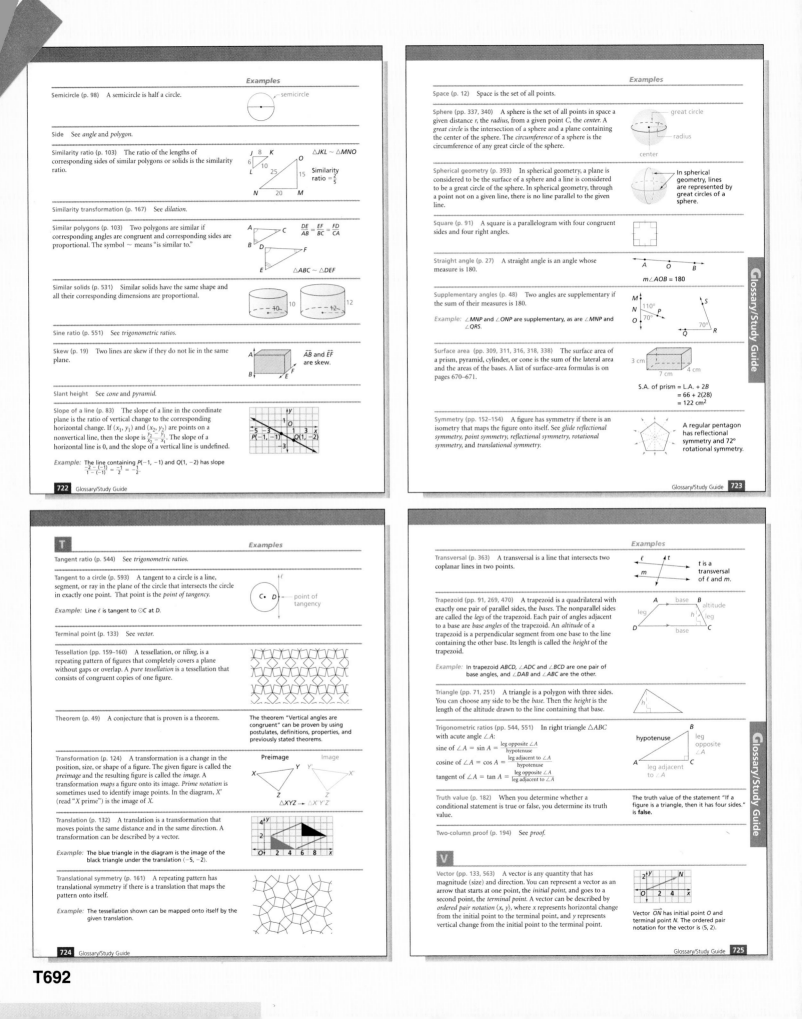

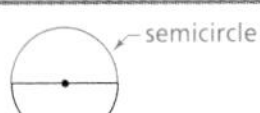

Side See *angle* and *polygon*.

Similarity ratio (p. 103) The ratio of the lengths of corresponding sides of similar polygons or solids is the similarity ratio.

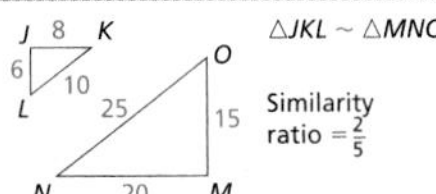

Similarity transformation (p. 167) See *dilation*.

Similar polygons (p. 103) Two polygons are similar if corresponding angles are congruent and corresponding sides are proportional. The symbol ~ means "is similar to."

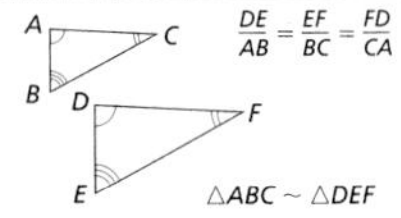

DE/AB = EF/BC = FD/CA
△ABC ~ △DEF

Similar solids (p. 531) Similar solids have the same shape and all their corresponding dimensions are proportional.

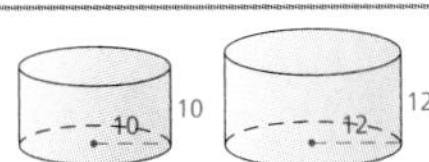

Sine ratio (p. 551) See *trigonometric ratios*.

Skew (p. 19) Two lines are skew if they do not lie in the same plane.

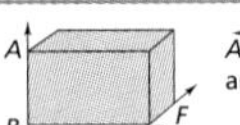

AB and EF are skew.

Slant height See *cone* and *pyramid*.

Slope of a line (p. 83) The slope of a line in the coordinate plane is the ratio of vertical change to the corresponding horizontal change. If (x_1, y_1) and (x_2, y_2) are points on a nonvertical line, then the slope is $\frac{y_2 - y_1}{x_2 - x_1}$. The slope of a horizontal line is 0, and the slope of a vertical line is undefined.

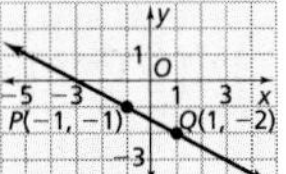

Example: The line containing $P(-1, -1)$ and $Q(1, -2)$ has slope $\frac{-2-(-1)}{1-(-1)} = \frac{-1}{2} = -\frac{1}{2}$.

Examples

Space (p. 12) Space is the set of all points.

Sphere (pp. 337, 340) A sphere is the set of all points in space a given distance *r*, the *radius*, from a given point *C*, the *center*. A *great circle* is the intersection of a sphere and a plane containing the center of the sphere. The *circumference* of a sphere is the circumference of any great circle of the sphere.

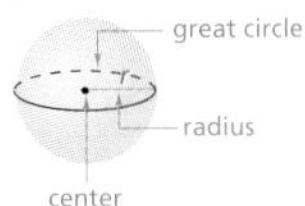

Spherical geometry (p. 393) In spherical geometry, a plane is considered to be the surface of a sphere and a line is considered to be a great circle of the sphere. In spherical geometry, through a point not on a given line, there is no line parallel to the given line.

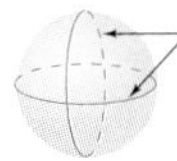

In spherical geometry, lines are represented by great circles of a sphere.

Square (p. 91) A square is a parallelogram with four congruent sides and four right angles.

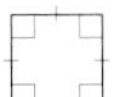

Straight angle (p. 27) A straight angle is an angle whose measure is 180.

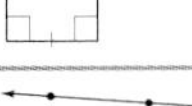

Supplementary angles (p. 48) Two angles are supplementary if the sum of their measures is 180.

Example: ∠MNP and ∠ONP are supplementary, as are ∠MNP and ∠QRS.

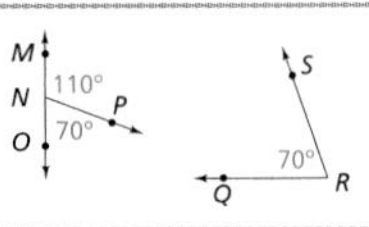

Surface area (pp. 309, 311, 316, 318, 338) The surface area of a prism, pyramid, cylinder, or cone is the sum of the lateral area and the areas of the bases. A list of surface-area formulas is on pages 670–671.

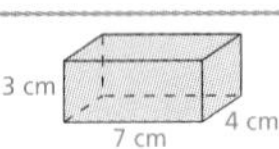

S.A. of prism = L.A. + 2B
= 66 + 2(28)
= 122 cm²

Symmetry (pp. 152–154) A figure has symmetry if there is an isometry that maps the figure onto itself. See *glide reflectional symmetry*, *point symmetry*, *reflectional symmetry*, *rotational symmetry*, and *translational symmetry*.

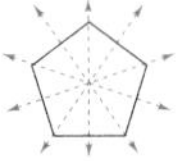

A regular pentagon has reflectional symmetry and 72° rotational symmetry.

T

Examples

Tangent ratio (p. 544) See *trigonometric ratios*.

Tangent to a circle (p. 593) A tangent to a circle is a line, segment, or ray in the plane of the circle that intersects the circle in exactly one point. That point is the *point of tangency*.

Example: Line ℓ is tangent to ⊙C at D.

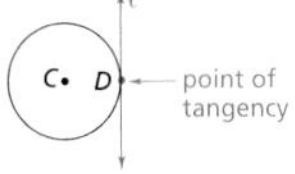

Terminal point (p. 133) See *vector*.

Tessellation (pp. 159–160) A tessellation, or *tiling*, is a repeating pattern of figures that completely covers a plane without gaps or overlap. A *pure tessellation* is a tessellation that consists of congruent copies of one figure.

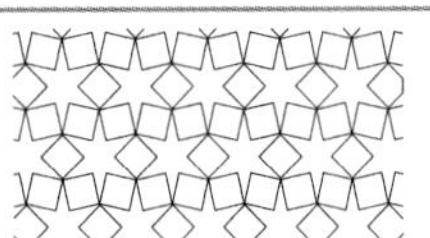

Theorem (p. 49) A conjecture that is proven is a theorem.

The theorem "Vertical angles are congruent" can be proven by using postulates, definitions, properties, and previously stated theorems.

Transformation (p. 124) A transformation is a change in the position, size, or shape of a figure. The given figure is called the *preimage* and the resulting figure is called the *image*. A transformation *maps* a figure onto its image. *Prime notation* is sometimes used to identify image points. In the diagram, X' (read "X prime") is the image of X.

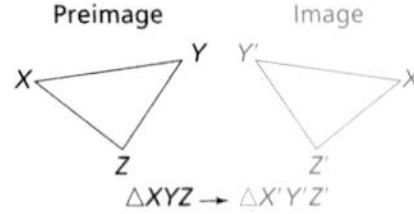

Translation (p. 132) A translation is a transformation that moves points the same distance and in the same direction. A transformation can be described by a vector.

Example: The blue triangle in the diagram is the image of the black triangle under the translation ⟨−5, −2⟩.

Translational symmetry (p. 161) A repeating pattern has translational symmetry if there is a translation that maps the pattern onto itself.

Example: The tessellation shown can be mapped onto itself by the given translation.

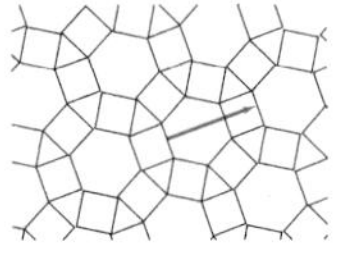

Examples

Transversal (p. 363) A transversal is a line that intersects two coplanar lines in two points.

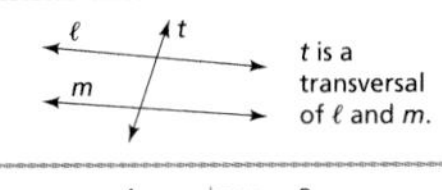

Trapezoid (pp. 91, 269, 470) A trapezoid is a quadrilateral with exactly one pair of parallel sides, the *bases*. The nonparallel sides are called the *legs* of the trapezoid. Each pair of angles adjacent to a base are *base angles* of the trapezoid. An *altitude* of a trapezoid is a perpendicular segment from one base to the line containing the other base. Its length is called the *height* of the trapezoid.

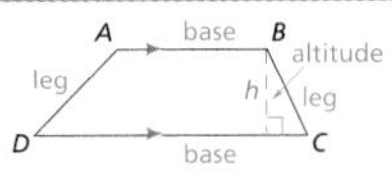

Example: In trapezoid ABCD, ∠ADC and ∠BCD are one pair of base angles, and ∠DAB and ∠ABC are the other.

Triangle (pp. 71, 251) A triangle is a polygon with three sides. You can choose any side to be the *base*. Then the *height* is the length of the altitude drawn to the line containing that base.

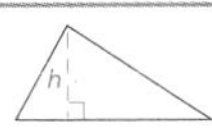

Trigonometric ratios (pp. 544, 551) In right triangle △ABC with acute angle ∠A:

sine of ∠A = sin A = $\frac{\text{leg opposite } \angle A}{\text{hypotenuse}}$

cosine of ∠A = cos A = $\frac{\text{leg adjacent to } \angle A}{\text{hypotenuse}}$

tangent of ∠A = tan A = $\frac{\text{leg opposite } \angle A}{\text{leg adjacent to } \angle A}$

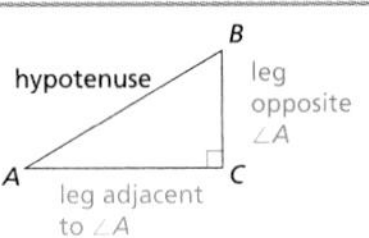

Truth value (p. 182) When you determine whether a conditional statement is true or false, you determine its truth value.

The truth value of the statement "If a figure is a triangle, then it has four sides." is **false**.

Two-column proof (p. 194) See *proof*.

V

Vector (pp. 133, 563) A vector is any quantity that has magnitude (size) and direction. You can represent a vector as an arrow that starts at one point, the *initial point*, and goes to a second point, the *terminal point*. A vector can be described by *ordered pair notation* ⟨*x*, *y*⟩, where *x* represents horizontal change from the initial point to the terminal point, and *y* represents vertical change from the initial point to the terminal point.

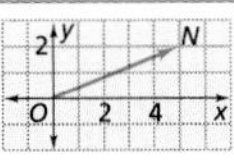

Vector $\overrightarrow{ON}$ has initial point O and terminal point N. The ordered pair notation for the vector is ⟨5, 2⟩.

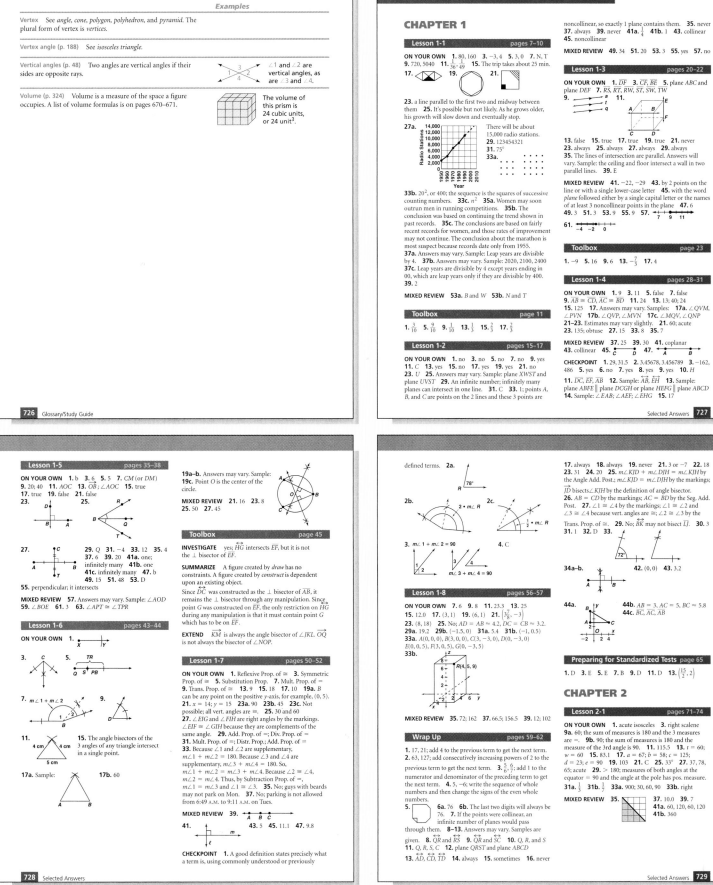

Examples

Vertex See *angle, cone, polygon, polyhedron,* and *pyramid.* The plural form of vertex is *vertices.*

Vertex angle (p. 188) See *isosceles triangle.*

Vertical angles (p. 48) Two angles are vertical angles if their sides are opposite rays.

∠1 and ∠2 are vertical angles, as are ∠3 and ∠4.

Volume (p. 324) Volume is a measure of the space a figure occupies. A list of volume formulas is on pages 670–671.

The volume of this prism is 24 cubic units, or 24 unit^3.

Selected Answers

CHAPTER 1

Lesson 1-1 pages 7–10

ON YOUR OWN **1.** 80, 160 **3.** −3, 4 **5.** 3, 0 **7.** N, T **9.** 720, 5040 **11.** $\frac{1}{36}, \frac{1}{49}$ **15.** The trip takes about 25 min. **17.** **19.** **21.**

23. a line parallel to the first two and midway between them **25.** It's possible but not likely. As he grows older, his growth will slow down and eventually stop.

27a.

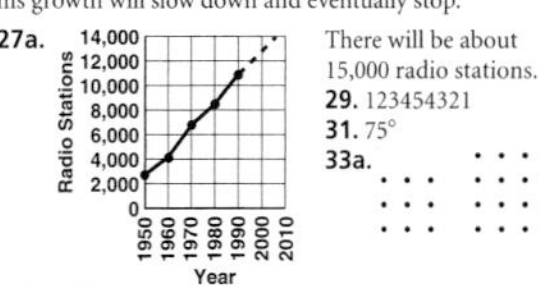

There will be about 15,000 radio stations. **29.** 123454321 **31.** 75° **33a.**

33b. 20^2, or 400; the sequence is the squares of successive counting numbers. **33c.** n^2 **35a.** Women may soon outrun men in running competitions. **35b.** The conclusion was based on continuing the trend shown in past records. **35c.** The conclusions are based on fairly recent records for women, and those rates of improvement may not continue. The conclusion about the marathon is most suspect because records date only from 1955. **37a.** Answers may vary. Sample: Leap years are divisible by 4. **37b.** Answers may vary. Sample: 2020, 2100, 2400 **37c.** Leap years are divisible by 4 except years ending in 00, which are leap years only if they are divisible by 400. **39.** 2

MIXED REVIEW **53a.** *B* and *W* **53b.** *N* and *T*

Toolbox page 11

1. $\frac{3}{10}$ **5.** $\frac{9}{10}$ **9.** $\frac{1}{10}$ **13.** $\frac{1}{3}$ **15.** $\frac{2}{3}$ **17.** $\frac{2}{3}$

Lesson 1-2 pages 15–17

ON YOUR OWN **1.** no **3.** no **5.** no **7.** no **9.** yes **11.** *C* **13.** yes **15.** no **17.** yes **19.** yes **21.** no **23.** *U* **25.** Answers may vary. Sample: plane *XWST* and plane *UVST* **29.** An infinite number; infinitely many planes can intersect in one line. **31.** C **33.** 1; points *A*, *B*, and *C* are points on the 2 lines and these 3 points are noncollinear, so exactly 1 plane contains them. **35.** never **37.** always **39.** never **41a.** $\frac{1}{4}$ **41b.** 1 **43.** collinear **45.** noncollinear

MIXED REVIEW **49.** 34 **51.** 20 **53.** 3 **55.** yes **57.** no

Lesson 1-3 pages 20–22

ON YOUR OWN **1.** $\overline{DF}$ **3.** $\overline{CF}, \overline{BE}$ **5.** plane *ABC* and plane *DEF* **7.** $\overline{RS}, \overline{RT}, \overline{RW}, \overline{ST}, \overline{SW}, \overline{TW}$ **9.** **11.**

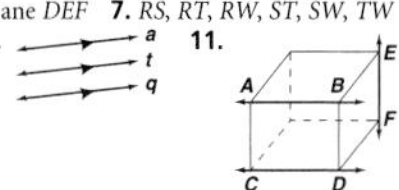

13. false **15.** true **17.** true **19.** true **21.** never **23.** always **25.** always **27.** always **29.** always **35.** The lines of intersection are parallel. Answers will vary. Sample: the ceiling and floor intersect a wall in two parallel lines. **39.** E

MIXED REVIEW **41.** −22, −29 **43.** by 2 points on the line or with a single lower-case letter **45.** with the word *plane* followed either by a single capital letter or the names of at least 3 noncollinear points in the plane **47.** 6 **49.** 3 **51.** 3 **53.** 9 **55.** 9 **57.** **61.**

Toolbox page 23

1. −9 **5.** 16 **9.** 6 **13.** $-\frac{7}{3}$ **17.** 4

Lesson 1-4 pages 28–31

ON YOUR OWN **1.** 9 **3.** 11 **5.** false **7.** false **9.** $\overline{AB} \cong \overline{CD}, \overline{AC} \cong \overline{BD}$ **11.** 24 **13.** 13; 40; 24 **15.** 125 **17.** Answers may vary. Samples: **17a.** ∠*QVM*, ∠*PVN* **17b.** ∠*QVP*, ∠*MVN* **17c.** ∠*MQV*, ∠*QNP* **21–23.** Estimates may vary slightly. **21.** 60; acute **23.** 135; obtuse **27.** 15 **33.** 8 **35.** 7

MIXED REVIEW **37.** 25 **39.** 30 **41.** coplanar **43.** collinear **45.** **47.**

CHECKPOINT **1.** 29, 31.5 **2.** 3.45678, 3.456789 **3.** −162, 486 **5.** yes **6.** no **7.** yes **8.** yes **9.** yes **10.** *H* **11.** $\overline{DC}, \overline{EF}, \overline{AB}$ **12.** Sample: $\overleftrightarrow{AB}, \overleftrightarrow{EH}$ **13.** Sample: plane *ABFE* ∥ plane *DCGH* or plane *HEFG* ∥ plane *ABCD* **14.** Sample: ∠*EAB*; ∠*AEF*; ∠*EHG* **15.** 17

Lesson 1-5 pages 35–38

ON YOUR OWN **1.** b **3.** 6 **5.** 5 **7.** *CM* (or *DM*) **9.** 20; 40 **11.** *AOC* **13.** $\overrightarrow{OB}$; ∠*AOC* **15.** true **17.** true **19.** false **21.** false **23.** **25.**

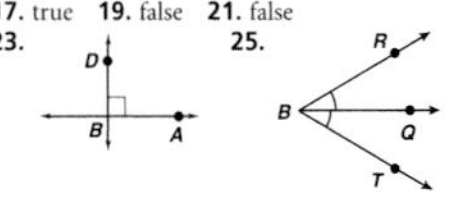

27. **29.** *Q* **31.** −4 **33.** 12 **35.** 4 **37.** 6 **39.** 20 **41a.** one; infinitely many **41b.** one **41c.** infinitely many **47.** b **49.** 15 **51.** 48 **53.** D **55.** perpendicular; it intersects

MIXED REVIEW **57.** Answers may vary. Sample: ∠*AOD* **59.** ∠*BOE* **61.** 3 **63.** ∠*APT* ≅ ∠*TPR*

Lesson 1-6 pages 43–44

ON YOUR OWN **1.** **3.** **5.** **7.** **9.** **11.** **15.** The angle bisectors of the 3 angles of any triangle intersect in a single point. **17a.** Sample: **17b.** 60

19a–b. Answers may vary. Sample: **19c.** Point *O* is the center of the circle.

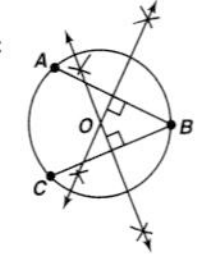

MIXED REVIEW **21.** 16 **23.** 8 **25.** 50 **27.** 45

Toolbox page 45

INVESTIGATE yes; $\overleftrightarrow{HG}$ intersects $\overline{EF}$, but it is not the ⊥ bisector of $\overline{EF}$.

SUMMARIZE A figure created by *draw* has no constraints. A figure created by *construct* is dependent upon an existing object.

Since $\overleftrightarrow{DC}$ was constructed as the ⊥ bisector of $\overline{AB}$, it remains the ⊥ bisector through any manipulation. Since point *G* was constructed on $\overline{EF}$, the only restriction on $\overleftrightarrow{HG}$ during any manipulation is that it must contain point *G* which has to be on $\overline{EF}$.

EXTEND $\overrightarrow{KM}$ is always the angle bisector of ∠*JKL*. $\overrightarrow{OQ}$ is not always the bisector of ∠*NOP*.

Lesson 1-7 pages 50–52

ON YOUR OWN **1.** Reflexive Prop. of ≅ **3.** Symmetric Prop. of ≅ **5.** Substitution Prop. **7.** Mult. Prop. of = **9.** Trans. Prop. of ≅ **13.** 9 **15.** 18 **17.** 10 **19a.** *B* can be any point on the positive *y*-axis, for example, (0, 5). **21.** $x = 14$; $y = 15$ **23a.** 90 **23b.** 45 **23c.** Not possible; all vert. angles are ≅. **25.** 30 and 60 **27.** ∠*EIG* and ∠*FIH* are right angles by the markings. ∠*EIF* ≅ ∠*GIH* because they are complements of the same angle. **29.** Add. Prop. of =; Div. Prop. of = **31.** Mult. Prop. of =; Distr. Prop.; Add. Prop. of = **33.** Because ∠1 and ∠2 are supplementary, $m\angle 1 + m\angle 2 = 180$. Because ∠3 and ∠4 are supplementary, $m\angle 3 + m\angle 4 = 180$. So, $m\angle 1 + m\angle 2 = m\angle 3 + m\angle 4$. Because ∠2 ≅ ∠4, $m\angle 2 = m\angle 4$. Thus, by Subtraction Prop. of =, $m\angle 1 = m\angle 3$ and ∠1 ≅ ∠3. **35.** No; guys with beards may not park on Mon. **37.** No; parking is not allowed from 6:49 A.M. to 9:11 A.M. on Tues.

MIXED REVIEW **39.** **41.** **43.** 5 **45.** 11.1 **47.** 9.8

CHECKPOINT **1.** A good definition states precisely what a term is, using commonly understood or previously defined terms. **2a.** **2b.** **2c.** **3.** $m\angle 1 + m\angle 2 = 90$; $m\angle 3 + m\angle 4 = 90$ **4.** C

Lesson 1-8 pages 56–57

ON YOUR OWN **7.** 6 **9.** 8 **11.** 23.3 **13.** 25 **15.** 12.0 **17.** (3, 1) **19.** (6, 1) **21.** $\left(3\frac{7}{8}, -3\right)$ **23.** (8, 18) **25.** No; $AD = AB \approx 4.2$, $DC = CB \approx 3.2$. **29a.** 19.2 **29b.** (−1.5, 0) **31a.** 5.4 **31b.** (−1, 0.5) **33a.** *A*(0, 0, 0), *B*(3, 0, 0), *C*(3, −3, 0), *D*(0, −3, 0) *E*(0, 0, 5), *F*(3, 0, 5), *G*(0, −3, 5) **33b.**

MIXED REVIEW **35.** 72; 162 **37.** 66.5; 156.5 **39.** 12; 102

Wrap Up pages 59–62

1. 17, 21; add 4 to the previous term to get the next term. **2.** 63, 127; add consecutively increasing powers of 2 to the previous term to get the next term. **3.** $\frac{5}{6}, \frac{6}{7}$; add 1 to the numerator and denominator of the preceding term to get the next term. **4.** 5, −6; write the sequence of whole numbers and then change the signs of the even whole numbers. **5.** **6a.** 76 **6b.** The last two digits will always be 76. **7.** If the points were collinear, an infinite number of planes would pass through them. **8–13.** Answers may vary. Samples are given. **8.** $\overleftrightarrow{QR}$ and $\overleftrightarrow{RS}$ **9.** $\overleftrightarrow{QR}$ and $\overleftrightarrow{SC}$ **10.** *Q*, *R*, and *S* **11.** *Q*, *R*, *S*, *C* **12.** plane *QRST* and plane *ABCD* **13.** $\overleftrightarrow{AD}, \overleftrightarrow{CD}, \overleftrightarrow{TD}$ **14.** always **15.** sometimes **16.** never **17.** always **18.** always **19.** never **21.** 3 or −7 **22.** 18 **23.** 31 **24.** 20 **25.** $m\angle KJD + m\angle DJH = m\angle KJH$ by the Angle Add. Post.; $m\angle KJD = m\angle DJH$ by the markings; $\overrightarrow{JD}$ bisects ∠*KJH* by the definition of angle bisector. **26.** $AB = CD$ by the markings; $AC = BD$ by the Seg. Add. Post. **27.** ∠1 ≅ ∠4 by the markings; ∠1 ≅ ∠2 and ∠3 ≅ ∠4 because vert. angles are ≅; ∠2 ≅ ∠3 by the Trans. Prop. of ≅. **29.** No; $\overleftrightarrow{BK}$ may not bisect $\overline{LJ}$. **30.** 3 **31.** 1 **32.** D **33.**

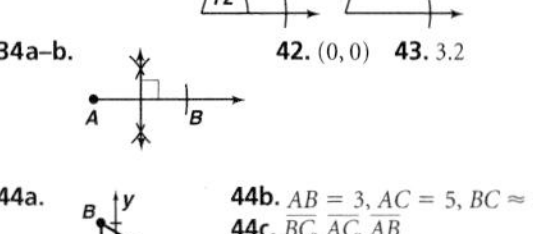

34a–b. **42.** (0, 0) **43.** 3.2 **44a.** **44b.** $AB = 3$, $AC = 5$, $BC \approx 5.8$ **44c.** $\overline{BC}, \overline{AC}, \overline{AB}$

Preparing for Standardized Tests page 65

1. D **3.** E **5.** E **7.** B **9.** D **11.** D **13.** $\left(\frac{15}{2}, 2\right)$

CHAPTER 2

Lesson 2-1 pages 71–74

ON YOUR OWN **1.** acute isosceles **3.** right scalene **9a.** 60; the sum of measures is 180 and the 3 measures are =. **9b.** 90; the sum of measures is 180 and the measure of the 3rd angle is 90. **11.** 115.5 **13.** $t = 60$; $w = 60$ **15.** 83.1 **17.** $a = 67$; $b = 58$; $c = 125$; $d = 23$; $e = 90$ **19.** 103 **21.** C **25.** 33° **27.** 37, 78, 65; acute **29.** > 180; measures of both angles at the equator = 90 and the angle at the pole has pos. measure. **31a.** $\frac{1}{3}$ **31b.** $\frac{1}{7}$ **33a.** 900; 30, 60, 90 **33b.** right

MIXED REVIEW **35.**

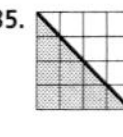

37. 10.0 **39.** 7 **41a.** 60, 120, 60, 120 **41b.** 360

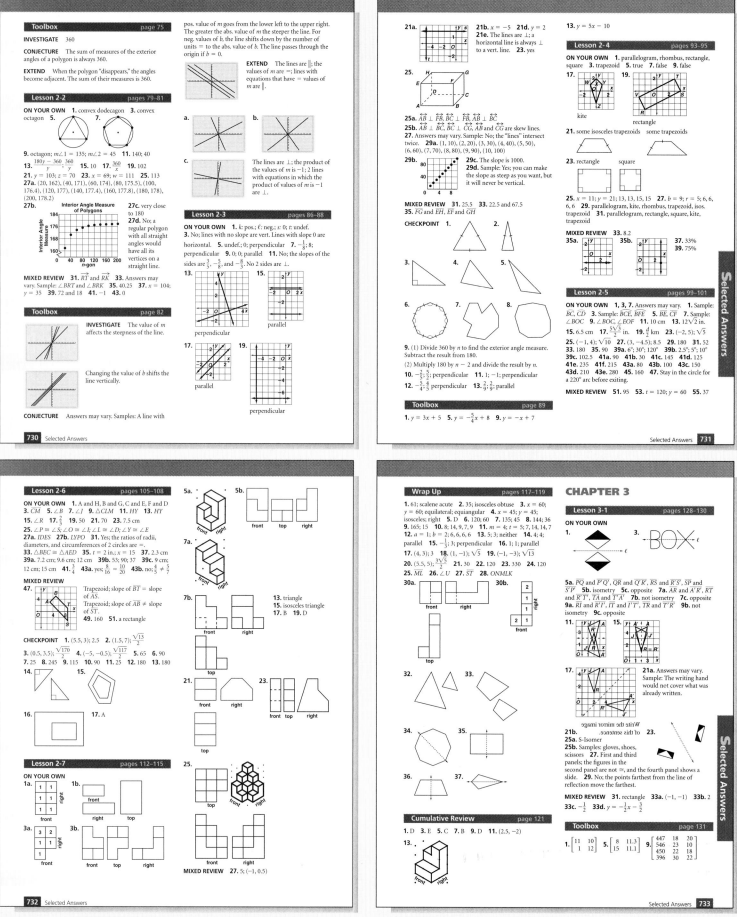

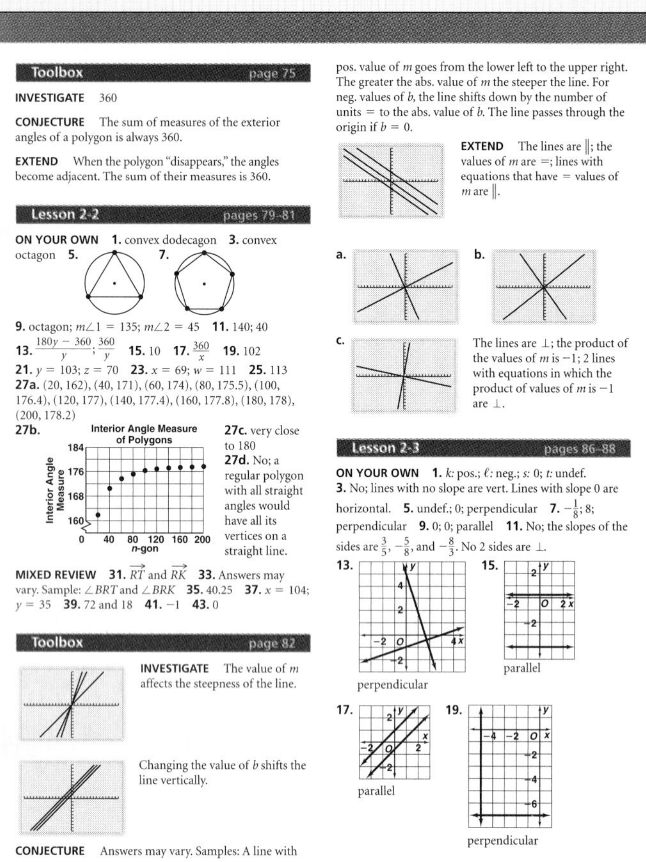

Toolbox page 75

INVESTIGATE 360

CONJECTURE The sum of measures of the exterior angles of a polygon is always 360.

EXTEND When the polygon "disappears," the angles become adjacent. The sum of their measures is 360.

Lesson 2-2 pages 79–81

ON YOUR OWN **1.** convex dodecagon **3.** convex octagon **5.** **7.**

9. octagon; $m\angle 1 = 135$; $m\angle 2 = 45$ **11.** 140; 40 **13.** $\frac{180y - 360}{y}$; $\frac{360}{y}$ **15.** 10 **17.** $\frac{360}{x}$ **19.** 102 **21.** $y = 103$; $z = 70$ **23.** $x = 69$; $w = 111$ **25.** 113 **27a.** (20, 162), (40, 171), (60, 174), (80, 175.5), (100, 176.4), (120, 177), (140, 177.4), (160, 177.8), (180, 178), (200, 178.2)

27b.

27c. very close to 180 **27d.** No; a regular polygon with all straight angles would have all its vertices on a straight line.

MIXED REVIEW **31.** $\overrightarrow{RT}$ and $\overrightarrow{RK}$ **33.** Answers may vary. Sample: $\angle BRT$ and $\angle BRK$ **35.** 40.25 **37.** $x = 104$; $y = 35$ **39.** 72 and 18 **41.** −1 **43.** 0

Toolbox page 82

INVESTIGATE The value of m affects the steepness of the line.

Changing the value of b shifts the line vertically.

CONJECTURE Answers may vary. Samples: A line with pos. value of m goes from the lower left to the upper right. The greater the abs. value of m the steeper the line. For neg. values of b, the line shifts down by the number of units = to the abs. value of b. The line passes through the origin if $b = 0$.

EXTEND The lines are ∥; the values of m are =; lines with equations that have = values of m are ∥.

a. **b.**

c. The lines are ⊥; the product of the values of m is −1; 2 lines with equations in which the product of values of m is −1 are ⊥.

Lesson 2-3 pages 86–88

ON YOUR OWN **1.** k: pos.; ℓ: neg.; s: 0; t: undef. **3.** No; lines with no slope are vert. Lines with slope 0 are horizontal. **5.** undef.; 0; perpendicular **7.** $-\frac{1}{8}$; 8; perpendicular **9.** 0; 0; parallel **11.** No; the slopes of the sides are $\frac{3}{5}$, $-\frac{5}{8}$, and $-\frac{8}{3}$. No 2 sides are ⊥.

13. perpendicular **15.** parallel

17. parallel **19.** perpendicular

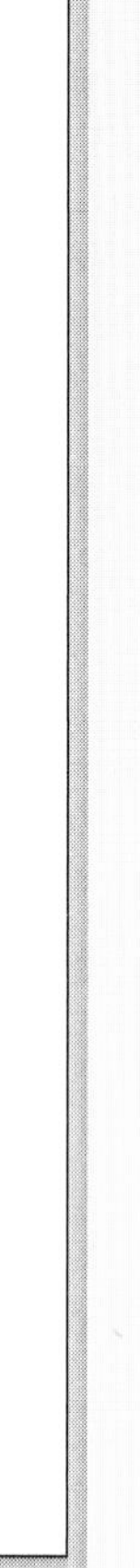

21a. **21b.** $x = -5$ **21d.** $y = 2$ **21e.** The lines are ⊥; a horizontal line is always ⊥ to a vert. line. **23.** yes

25.

25a. $\overleftrightarrow{AB} \perp \overleftrightarrow{FB}$, $\overleftrightarrow{BC} \perp \overleftrightarrow{FB}$, $\overleftrightarrow{AB} \perp \overleftrightarrow{BC}$ **25b.** $\overleftrightarrow{AB} \perp \overleftrightarrow{BC}$, $\overleftrightarrow{BC} \perp \overleftrightarrow{CG}$, $\overleftrightarrow{AB}$ and $\overleftrightarrow{CG}$ are skew lines. **27.** Answers may vary. Sample: No; the "lines" intersect twice. **29a.** (1, 10), (2, 20), (3, 30), (4, 40), (5, 50), (6, 60), (7, 70), (8, 80), (9, 90), (10, 100)

29b. **29c.** The slope is 1000. **29d.** Sample: Yes; you can make the slope as steep as you want, but it will never be vertical.

MIXED REVIEW **31.** 25.5 **33.** 22.5 and 67.5 **35.** $\overline{FG}$ and $\overline{EH}$, $\overline{EF}$ and $\overline{GH}$

CHECKPOINT **1.** **2.**

3. **4.** **5.**

6. **7.** **8.**

9. (1) Divide 360 by n to find the exterior angle measure. Subtract the result from 180.
(2) Multiply 180 by $n - 2$ and divide the result by n.
10. $-\frac{2}{5}$; $\frac{5}{2}$; perpendicular **11.** 1; −1; perpendicular **12.** $-\frac{5}{4}$; $\frac{4}{5}$ perpendicular **13.** $\frac{2}{9}$; $\frac{2}{9}$; parallel

Toolbox page 89

1. $y = 3x + 5$ **5.** $y = -\frac{5}{4}x + 8$ **9.** $y = -x + 7$

13. $y = 5x - 10$

Lesson 2-4 pages 93–95

ON YOUR OWN **1.** parallelogram, rhombus, rectangle, square **3.** trapezoid **5.** true **7.** false **9.** false

17. kite **19.** rectangle

21. some isosceles trapezoids some trapezoids

23. rectangle square

25. $x = 11$; $y = 21$; 13, 13, 15, 15 **27.** $b = 9$; $r = 5$; 6, 6, 6, 6 **29.** parallelogram, kite, rhombus, trapezoid, isos. trapezoid **31.** parallelogram, rectangle, square, kite, trapezoid

MIXED REVIEW **33.** 8.2 **35a.** **35b.** **37.** 33% **39.** 75%

Lesson 2-5 pages 99–101

ON YOUR OWN **1, 3, 7.** Answers may vary. **1.** Sample: $\overline{BC}$, $\overline{CD}$ **3.** Sample: $\widehat{BCE}$, $\widehat{BFE}$ **5.** $\widehat{BE}$, $\widehat{CF}$ **7.** Sample: $\angle BOC$ **9.** $\angle BOC$, $\angle EOF$ **11.** 10 cm **13.** $12\sqrt{2}$ in. **15.** 6.5 cm **17.** $\frac{5\sqrt{3}}{2}$ in. **19.** $\frac{d}{2}$ km **23.** (−2, 5); $\sqrt{5}$ **25.** (−1, 4); $\sqrt{10}$ **27.** (3, −4.5); 8.5 **29.** 180 **31.** 52 **33.** 180 **35.** 90 **39a.** 6°; 30°; 120° **39b.** 2.5°; 5°; 10° **39c.** 102.5 **41a.** 90 **41b.** 30 **41c.** 145 **41d.** 125 **41e.** 235 **41f.** 215 **43a.** 80 **43b.** 100 **43c.** 150 **43d.** 210 **43e.** 280 **45.** 160 **47.** Stay in the circle for a 220° arc before exiting.

MIXED REVIEW **51.** 95 **53.** $t = 120$; $y = 60$ **55.** 37

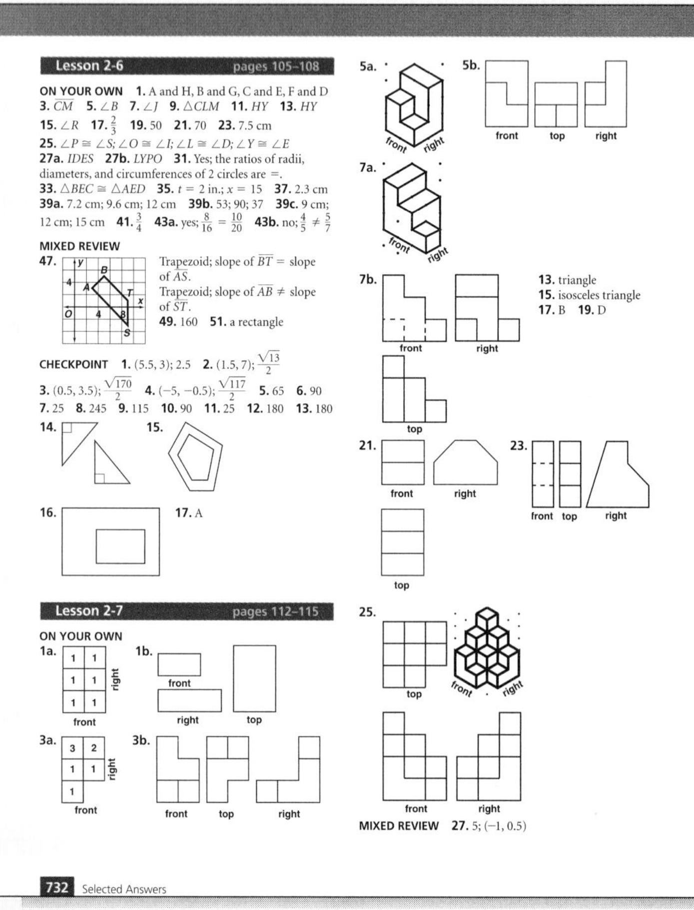

Lesson 2-6 pages 105–108

ON YOUR OWN **1.** A and H, B and G, C and E, F and D **3.** $\overline{CM}$ **5.** $\angle B$ **7.** $\angle J$ **9.** $\triangle CLM$ **11.** HY **13.** HY **15.** $\angle R$ **17.** $\frac{2}{3}$ **19.** 50 **21.** 70 **23.** 7.5 cm **25.** $\angle P \cong \angle S$; $\angle O \cong \angle I$; $\angle L \cong \angle D$; $\angle Y \cong \angle E$ **27a.** *IDES* **27b.** *LYPO* **31.** Yes; the ratios of radii, diameters, and circumferences of 2 circles are =. **33.** $\triangle BEC \cong \triangle AED$ **35.** $t = 2$ in.; $x = 15$ **37.** 2.3 cm **39a.** 7.2 cm; 9.6 cm; 12 cm **39b.** 53; 90; 37 **39c.** 9 cm; 12 cm; 15 cm **41.** $\frac{3}{4}$ **43a.** yes; $\frac{8}{16} = \frac{10}{20}$ **43b.** no; $\frac{4}{5} \neq \frac{5}{7}$

MIXED REVIEW

47. Trapezoid; slope of $\overline{BT}$ = slope of $\overline{AS}$. Trapezoid; slope of $\overline{AB} \neq$ slope of $\overline{ST}$. **49.** 160 **51.** a rectangle

CHECKPOINT **1.** (5.5, 3); 2.5 **2.** (1.5, 7); $\frac{\sqrt{13}}{2}$ **3.** (0.5, 3.5); $\frac{\sqrt{170}}{2}$ **4.** (−5, −0.5); $\frac{\sqrt{117}}{2}$ **5.** 65 **6.** 90 **7.** 25 **8.** 245 **9.** 115 **10.** 90 **11.** 25 **12.** 180 **13.** 180

14. **15.**

16. **17.** A

Lesson 2-7 pages 112–115

ON YOUR OWN

1a. **1b.**

3a. **3b.**

5a. **5b.**

7a.

7b. **13.** triangle **15.** isosceles triangle **17.** B **19.** D

21. **23.**

25.

MIXED REVIEW **27.** 5; (−1, 0.5)

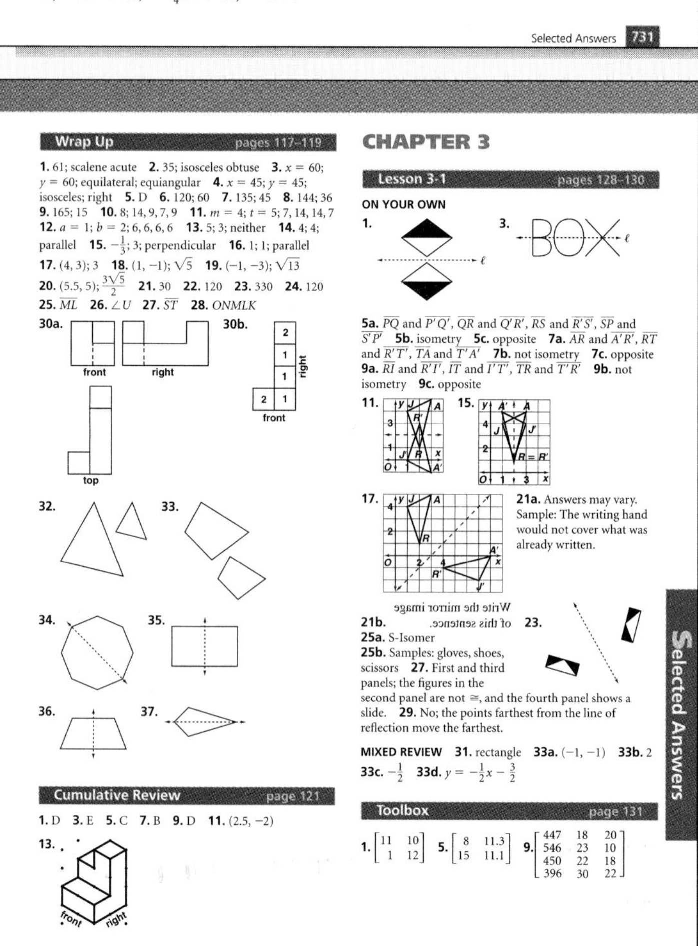

Wrap Up pages 117–119

1. 61; scalene acute **2.** 35; isosceles obtuse **3.** $x = 60$; $y = 60$; equilateral; equiangular **4.** $x = 45$; $y = 45$; isosceles; right **5.** D **6.** 120; 60 **7.** 135; 45 **8.** 144; 36 **9.** 165; 15 **10.** 8; 14, 9, 7, 9 **11.** $m = 4$; $t = 5$; 7, 14, 14, 7 **12.** $a = 1$; $b = 2$; 6, 6, 6, 6 **13.** 5; 3; neither **14.** 4; 4; parallel **15.** $-\frac{1}{3}$; 3; perpendicular **16.** 1; 1; parallel **17.** (4, 3); 3 **18.** (1, −1); $\sqrt{5}$ **19.** (−1, −3); $\sqrt{13}$ **20.** (5.5, 5); $\frac{3\sqrt{5}}{2}$ **21.** 30 **22.** 120 **23.** 330 **24.** 120 **25.** $\overline{ML}$ **26.** $\angle U$ **27.** $\overline{ST}$ **28.** *ONMLK*

30a. **30b.**

32. **33.**

34. **35.**

36. **37.**

Cumulative Review page 121

1. D **3.** E **5.** C **7.** B **9.** D **11.** (2.5, −2)

13.

CHAPTER 3

Lesson 3-1 pages 128–130

ON YOUR OWN

1. **3.**

5a. $\overline{PQ}$ and $\overline{P'Q'}$, $\overline{QR}$ and $\overline{Q'R'}$, $\overline{RS}$ and $\overline{R'S'}$, $\overline{SP}$ and $\overline{S'P'}$ **5b.** isometry **5c.** opposite **7a.** $\overline{AR}$ and $\overline{A'R'}$, $\overline{RT}$ and $\overline{R'T'}$, $\overline{TA}$ and $\overline{T'A'}$ **7b.** not isometry **7c.** opposite **9a.** $\overline{RI}$ and $\overline{R'I'}$, $\overline{IT}$ and $\overline{I'T'}$, $\overline{TR}$ and $\overline{T'R'}$ **9b.** not isometry **9c.** opposite

11. **15.**

17. **21a.** Answers may vary. Sample: The writing hand would not cover what was already written.

21b. **23.**

25a. S-Isomer **25b.** Samples: gloves, shoes, scissors **27.** First and third panels; the figures in the second panel are not ≅, and the fourth panel shows a slide. **29.** No; the points farthest from the line of reflection move the farthest.

MIXED REVIEW **31.** rectangle **33a.** (−1, −1) **33b.** 2 **33c.** $-\frac{1}{2}$ **33d.** $y = -\frac{1}{2}x - \frac{3}{2}$

Toolbox page 131

1. $\begin{bmatrix} 11 & 10 \\ 1 & 12 \end{bmatrix}$ **5.** $\begin{bmatrix} 8 & 11.3 \\ 15 & 11.1 \end{bmatrix}$ **9.** $\begin{bmatrix} 447 & 18 & 20 \\ 546 & 23 & 10 \\ 450 & 22 & 18 \\ 396 & 30 & 22 \end{bmatrix}$

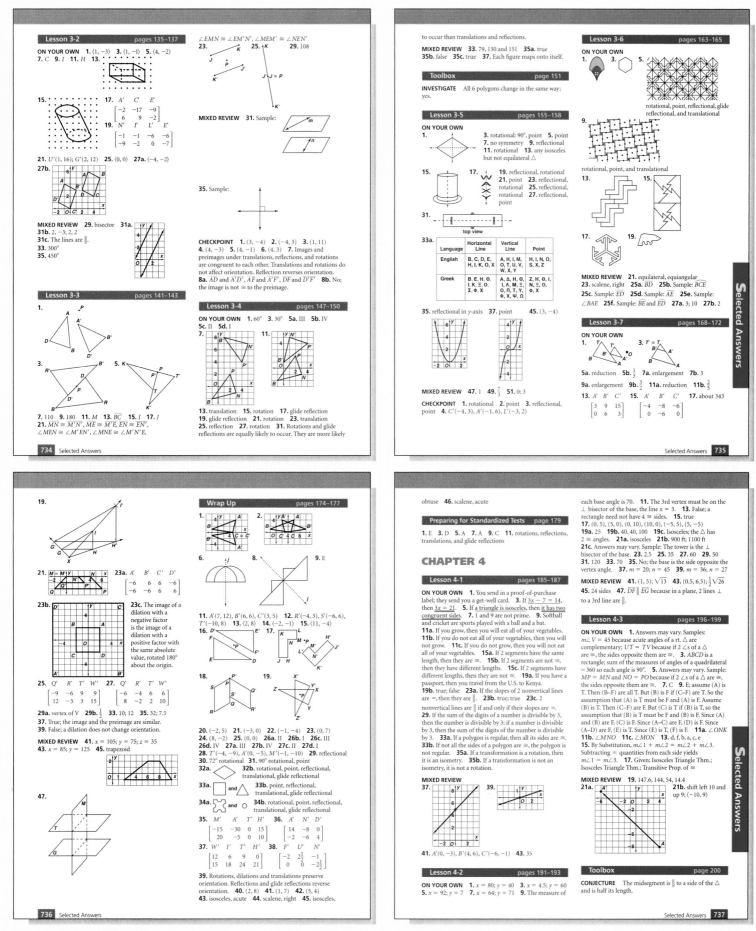

Lesson 3-2 pages 135–137

ON YOUR OWN **1.** ⟨1, −3⟩ **3.** ⟨1, −1⟩ **5.** ⟨4, −2⟩ **7.** *C* **9.** *I* **11.** *H* **13.**

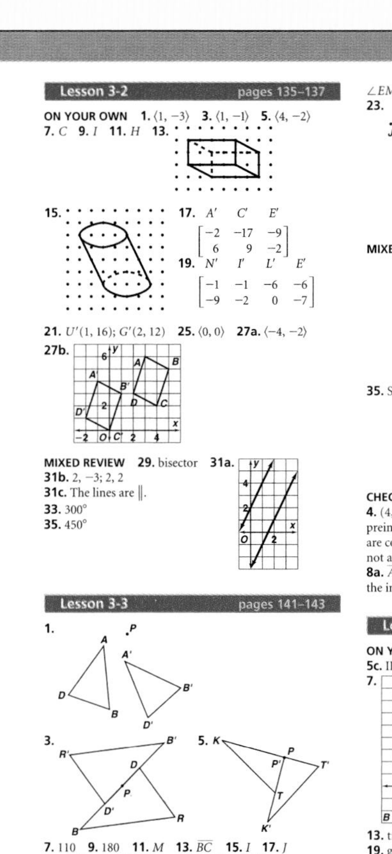

15. **17.** $\begin{matrix} A' & C' & E' \end{matrix}$ $\begin{bmatrix} -2 & -17 & -9 \\ 6 & 9 & -2 \end{bmatrix}$ **19.** $\begin{matrix} N' & I' & L' & E' \end{matrix}$ $\begin{bmatrix} -1 & -1 & -6 & -6 \\ -9 & -2 & 0 & -7 \end{bmatrix}$

21. $U'(1, 16)$; $G'(2, 12)$ **25.** ⟨0, 0⟩ **27a.** ⟨−4, −2⟩
27b.

MIXED REVIEW **29.** bisector **31a.**
31b. 2, −3; 2, 2
31c. The lines are ∥.
33. 300°
35. 450°

$\angle EMN \cong \angle EM'N'$, $\angle MEM' \cong \angle NEN'$
23. **25.** **29.** 108

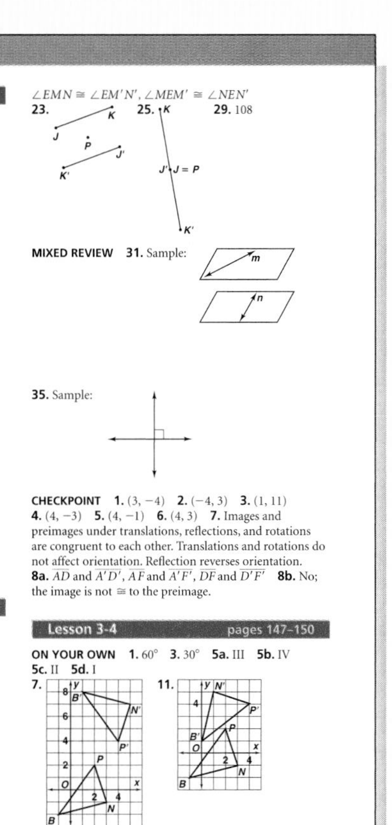

MIXED REVIEW **31.** Sample:

35. Sample:

CHECKPOINT **1.** (3, −4) **2.** (−4, 3) **3.** (1, 11) **4.** (4, −3) **5.** (4, −1) **6.** (4, 3) **7.** Images and preimages under translations, reflections, and rotations are congruent to each other. Translations and rotations do not affect orientation. Reflection reverses orientation. **8a.** $\overline{AD}$ and $\overline{A'D'}$, $\overline{AF}$ and $\overline{A'F'}$, $\overline{DF}$ and $\overline{D'F'}$ **8b.** No; the image is not ≅ to the preimage.

Lesson 3-3 pages 141–143

1.

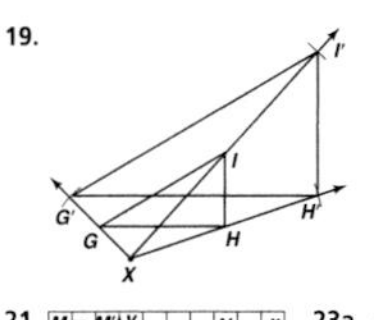

3. **5.**

7. 110 **9.** 180 **11.** *M* **13.** $\overline{BC}$ **15.** *I* **17.** *J*
21. $\overline{MN} \cong \overline{M'N'}$, $\overline{ME} \cong \overline{M'E}$, $\overline{EN} \cong \overline{EN'}$, $\angle MEN \cong \angle M'EN'$, $\angle MNE \cong \angle M'N'E$,

Lesson 3-4 pages 147–150

ON YOUR OWN **1.** 60° **3.** 30° **5a.** III **5b.** IV **5c.** II **5d.** I
7. **11.**

13. translation **15.** rotation **17.** glide reflection **19.** glide reflection **21.** rotation **23.** translation **25.** reflection **27.** rotation **31.** Rotations and glide reflections are equally likely to occur. They are more likely

to occur than translations and reflections.

MIXED REVIEW **33.** 79, 130 and 151 **35a.** true **35b.** false **35c.** true **37.** Each figure maps onto itself.

Toolbox page 151

INVESTIGATE All 6 polygons change in the same way; yes.

Lesson 3-5 pages 155–158

ON YOUR OWN
1. **3.** rotational: 90°, point **5.** point **7.** no symmetry **9.** reflectional **11.** rotational **13.** any isosceles but not equilateral △

15. **17.** **19.** reflectional, rotational **21.** point **23.** reflectional, rotational **25.** reflectional, rotational **27.** reflectional, point

31. top view

33a.

Language	Horizontal Line	Vertical Line	Point
English	B, C, D, E, H, I, K, O, X	A, H, I, M, O, T, U, V, W, X, Y	H, I, N, O, S, X, Z
Greek	B, E, H, Θ, I, K, Ξ, O, Σ, Φ, X	A, Δ, H, Θ, I, Λ, M, Ξ, O, Π, T, Y, Φ, X, Ψ, Ω	Z, H, Θ, I, N, Ξ, O, Φ, X

35. reflectional in *y*-axis **37.** point **45.** (3, −4)

MIXED REVIEW **47.** 1 **49.** $\frac{7}{3}$ **51.** 0; 3

CHECKPOINT **1.** rotational **2.** point **3.** reflectional, point **4.** $C'(-4, 3)$, $A'(-1, 6)$, $L'(-3, 2)$

Lesson 3-6 pages 163–165

ON YOUR OWN
1. **3.** **5.**
rotational, point, reflectional, glide reflectional, and translational
9.
rotational, point, and translational
13. **15.**

17. **19.**

MIXED REVIEW **21.** equilateral, equiangular **23.** scalene, right **25a.** $\overline{BD}$ **25b.** Sample: $\widehat{BCE}$ **25c.** Sample: $\widehat{ED}$ **25d.** Sample: $\widehat{AE}$ **25e.** Sample: $\angle BAE$ **25f.** Sample: $\widehat{BE}$ and $\widehat{ED}$ **27a.** 3; 10 **27b.** 2

Lesson 3-7 pages 168–172

ON YOUR OWN
1. **3.**

5a. reduction **5b.** $\frac{1}{3}$ **7a.** enlargement **7b.** 3
9a. enlargement **9b.** $\frac{3}{2}$ **11a.** reduction **11b.** $\frac{2}{5}$
13. $\begin{matrix} A' & B' & C' \end{matrix}$ $\begin{bmatrix} 3 & 9 & 15 \\ 0 & 6 & 3 \end{bmatrix}$ **15.** $\begin{matrix} A' & B' & C' \end{matrix}$ $\begin{bmatrix} -4 & -8 & -6 \\ 0 & -6 & 0 \end{bmatrix}$ **17.** about 343

19.

21. **23a.** $\begin{matrix} A' & B' & C' & D' \end{matrix}$ $\begin{bmatrix} -6 & 6 & 6 & -6 \\ -6 & -6 & 6 & 6 \end{bmatrix}$

23b. **23c.** The image of a dilation with a negative factor is the image of a dilation with a positive factor with the same absolute value, rotated 180° about the origin.

25. $\begin{matrix} Q' & R' & T' & W' \end{matrix}$ $\begin{bmatrix} -9 & -6 & 9 & 9 \\ 12 & -3 & 3 & 15 \end{bmatrix}$ **27.** $\begin{matrix} Q' & R' & T' & W' \end{matrix}$ $\begin{bmatrix} -6 & -4 & 6 & 6 \\ 8 & -2 & 2 & 10 \end{bmatrix}$

29a. vertex of V **29b.** $\frac{1}{2}$ **33.** 10; 12 **35.** 32; 7.5
37. True; the image and the preimage are similar.
39. False; a dilation does not change orientation.

MIXED REVIEW **41.** $x = 105$; $y = 75$; $z = 35$ **43.** $x = 85$; $y = 125$ **45.** trapezoid

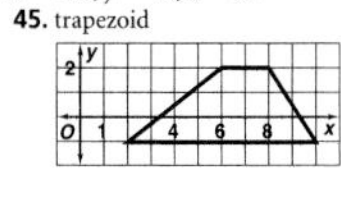

47.

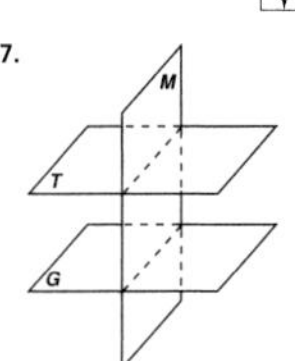

Wrap Up pages 174–177

1. **2.**

6. **8.** **9.** E

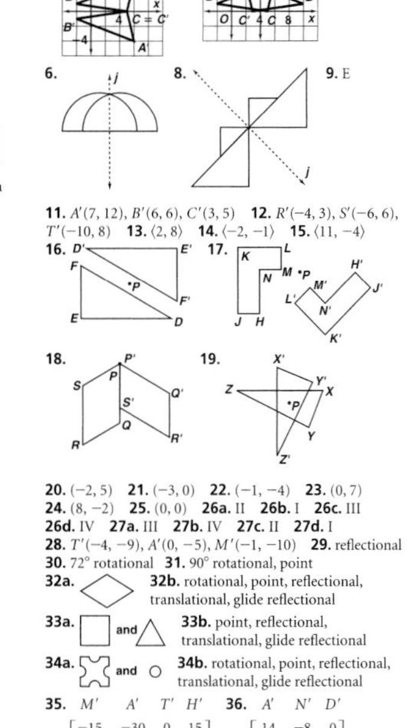

11. $A'(7, 12)$, $B'(6, 6)$, $C'(3, 5)$ **12.** $R'(-4, 3)$, $S'(-6, 6)$, $T'(-10, 8)$ **13.** (2, 8) **14.** ⟨−2, −1⟩ **15.** ⟨11, −4⟩
16. **17.**

18. **19.**

20. (−2, 5) **21.** (−3, 0) **22.** (−1, −4) **23.** (0, 7) **24.** (8, −2) **25.** (0, 0) **26a.** II **26b.** I **26c.** III **26d.** IV **27a.** III **27b.** IV **27c.** II **27d.** I **28.** $T'(-4, -9)$, $A'(0, -5)$, $M'(-1, -10)$ **29.** reflectional **30.** 72° rotational **31.** 90° rotational, point
32a. **32b.** rotational, point, reflectional, translational, glide reflectional
33a. and **33b.** point, reflectional, translational, glide reflectional
34a. and **34b.** rotational, point, reflectional, translational, glide reflectional
35. $\begin{matrix} M' & A' & T' & H' \end{matrix}$ $\begin{bmatrix} -15 & -30 & 0 & 15 \\ 20 & -5 & 0 & 10 \end{bmatrix}$ **36.** $\begin{matrix} A' & N' & D' \end{matrix}$ $\begin{bmatrix} 14 & -8 & 0 \\ -2 & -6 & 4 \end{bmatrix}$
37. $\begin{matrix} W' & I' & T' & H' \end{matrix}$ $\begin{bmatrix} 12 & 6 & 9 & 0 \\ 15 & 18 & 24 & 21 \end{bmatrix}$ **38.** $\begin{matrix} F' & U' & N' \end{matrix}$ $\begin{bmatrix} -2 & 2\frac{1}{2} & -1 \\ 0 & 0 & -2\frac{1}{2} \end{bmatrix}$

39. Rotations, dilations and translations preserve orientation. Reflections and glide reflections reverse orientation. **40.** (2, 8) **41.** (1, 7) **42.** (5, 4) **43.** isosceles, acute **44.** scalene, right **45.** isosceles,

obtuse **46.** scalene, acute

Preparing for Standardized Tests page 179

1. E **3.** D **5.** A **7.** A **9.** C **11.** rotations, reflections, translations, and glide reflections

CHAPTER 4

Lesson 4-1 pages 185–187

ON YOUR OWN **1.** You send in a proof-of-purchase label; they send you a get-well card. **3.** If $\underline{3x - 7 = 14}$, then $\underline{3x = 21}$. **5.** If a triangle is isosceles, then it has two congruent sides. **7.** 1 and 9 are not prime. **9.** Softball and cricket are sports played with a ball and a bat. **11a.** If you grow, then you will eat all of your vegetables. **11b.** If you do not eat all of your vegetables, then you will not grow. **11c.** If you do not grow, then you will not eat all of your vegetables. **15a.** If 2 segments have the same length, then they are ≅. **15b.** If 2 segments are not ≅, then they have different lengths. **15c.** If 2 segments have different lengths, then they are not ≅. **19a.** If you have a passport, then you travel from the U.S. to Kenya. **19b.** true; false **23a.** If the slopes of 2 nonvertical lines are =, then they are ∥. **23b.** true; true **23c.** 2 nonvertical lines are ∥ if and only if their slopes are =. **29.** If the sum of the digits of a number is divisible by 3, then the number is divisible by 3; if a number is divisible by 3, then the sum of the digits of the number is divisible by 3. **33a.** If a polygon is regular, then all its sides are ≅. **33b.** If not all the sides of a polygon are ≅, the polygon is not regular. **35a.** If a transformation is a rotation, then it is an isometry. **35b.** If a transformation is not an isometry, it is not a rotation.

MIXED REVIEW
37. **39.**

41. $A'(0, -3)$, $B'(4, 6)$, $C'(-6, -1)$ **43.** 35

Lesson 4-2 pages 191–193

ON YOUR OWN **1.** $x = 80$; $y = 40$ **3.** $x = 4.5$; $y = 60$ **5.** $x = 92$; $y = 7$ **7.** $x = 64$; $y = 71$ **9.** The measure of each base angle is 70. **11.** The 3rd vertex must be on the ⊥ bisector of the base, the line $x = 3$. **13.** False; a rectangle need not have 4 ≅ sides. **15.** true **17.** (0, 5), (5, 0), (0, 10), (10, 0), (−5, 5), (5, −5) **19a.** 25 **19b.** 40, 40, 100 **19c.** Isosceles; the △ has 2 ≅ angles. **21a.** isosceles **21b.** 900 ft; 1100 ft **21c.** Answers may vary. Sample: The tower is the ⊥ bisector of the base. **23.** 2.5 **25.** 35 **27.** 60 **29.** 50 **31.** 120 **33.** 70 **35.** No; the base is the side opposite the vertex angle. **37.** $m = 20$; $n = 45$ **39.** $m = 36$; $n = 27$

MIXED REVIEW **41.** (1, 5); $\sqrt{13}$ **43.** (0.5, 6.5); $\frac{1}{2}\sqrt{26}$ **45.** 24 sides **47.** $\overline{DF} \parallel \overline{EG}$ because in a plane, 2 lines ⊥ to a 3rd line are ∥.

Lesson 4-3 pages 196–199

ON YOUR OWN **1.** Answers may vary. Samples: $m\angle V = 45$ because acute angles of a rt. △ are complementary; $UT = TV$ because if 2 ∠s of a △ are ≅, the sides opposite them are ≅. **3.** *ABCD* is a rectangle; sum of the measures of angles of a quadrilateral = 360 so each angle is 90°. **5.** Answers may vary. Sample: $MP = MN$ and $NO = PO$ because if 2 ∠s of a △ are ≅, the sides opposite them are ≅. **7.** C **9.** E; assume (A) is T. Then (B–F) are all T. But (B) is F if (C–F) are T. So the assumption that (A) is T must be F and (A) is F. Assume (B) is T. Then (C–F) are F. But (C) is T if (B) is T, so the assumption that (B) is T must be F and (B) is F. Since (A) and (B) are F, (C) is F. Since (A–C) are F, (D) is F. Since (A–D) are F, (E) is T. Since (E) is T, (F) is F. **11a.** ∠*ONK* **11b.** ∠*MNO* **11c.** ∠*MON* **13.** d, f, b, a, c, e **15.** By Substitution, $m\angle 1 + m\angle 2 = m\angle 2 + m\angle 3$. Subtracting = quantities from each side yields $m\angle 1 = m\angle 3$. **17.** Given; Isosceles Triangle Thm.; Isosceles Triangle Thm.; Transitive Prop. of ≅

MIXED REVIEW **19.** 147.6, 144, 54, 14.4
21a. **21b.** shift left 10 and up 9; (−10, 9)

Toolbox page 200

CONJECTURE The midsegment is ∥ to a side of the △ and is half its length.

EXTEND Opp. angles of the orig. △ and the midsegment △ have = measures; corr. angles in the 4 smaller △s have = measures.
The sides of the midsegment △ are each $\frac{1}{2}$ of the corr. side of the original △; the 4 △s are ≅; the 4 △s are ~ to the original △. The area of each smaller △ is $\frac{1}{4}$ the area of the original △; the perimeter of each smaller △ is $\frac{1}{2}$ the perimeter of the orig. △.

Lesson 4-4 — pages 203–206

ON YOUR OWN **1.** 9 **3.** 31 **5a.** $H(2, 0); J(4, 2)$ **5b.** slope of $\overline{HJ} = 1$, slope of $\overline{EF} = 1$ ✔ **5c.** $HJ = 2\sqrt{2}, EF = 4\sqrt{2}, HJ = \frac{1}{2}EF$ **7a.** Answers may vary. Sample:

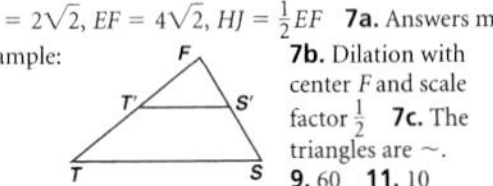

7b. Dilation with center F and scale factor $\frac{1}{2}$ **7c.** The triangles are ~. **9.** 60 **11.** 10 **13.** 45 **15.** 154 cm **17.** 2 cm; the length of a side of the largest square = the length of the diagonal of the middle square. The length of the diagonal of that square is twice the length of the sides of the smallest square.

MIXED REVIEW **19.** 5 **21.** (−2, 6) **23.** Lines m and n do not intersect. **25.** △ABC is isosceles. **27.** 180; it must be a straight angle.

CHECKPOINT **1a.** If the measure of at least one of the angles of a triangle is 60, then the triangle is equilateral. **1b.** true; false **2a.** If all the angles of a polygon are ≅, then the polygon is regular. **2b.** true; false **3.** A converse reverses the hypothesis and the conclusion. The truth value of a converse does not depend on the truth value of the original statement. A contrapositive reverses and negates the hypothesis and the conclusion of the original statement. The truth values of a statement and its contrapositive are the same. **4.** C **5a.** 9 **5b.** 54, 54, 72 **5c.** Isosceles; the △ has 2 ≅ angles. **6.** False; a △ with angles 30°, 30°, 120° is an obtuse isosceles △. **7.** 36

Lesson 4-5 — pages 209–211

ON YOUR OWN **1.** Assume it is not raining outside. **3.** Assume △PEN is scalene. **5.** Assume $\overline{XY} \not\cong \overline{AB}$. **7.** I and II **9.** I and III **11.** This bridge is a bascule. **13.** Sumiko is not an air traffic controller. **15.** Assume ∠A ≅ ∠B. Then △ABC is isosceles with $BC = AC$. This contradicts the assumption. Therefore, ∠A ≇ ∠B. **17.** E **19.** Assume that the driver had not applied the brakes. Then the wheels would not have locked and there would be no skid marks. There are skid marks. Therefore, the assumption is false. The driver had applied the brakes. **21.** Assume the polygon is a hexagon. Then the sum of measures of its interior angles is 720. But the sum of measures of the polygon's interior angles is 900, not 720. Therefore, the assumption is false. The polygon is not a hexagon. **23.** Assume $m\angle P = 90$. By def., $m\angle Q > 90$. The sum of the angle measures of △PQR is > 180. By the Triangle Angle-Sum Thm., the sum of the angle measures of a △ is 180. Therefore, the assumption is false, and an obtuse △ cannot contain a rt. angle. **25.** Mr. Pitt was in Maine on April 8 and stayed there at least until 12:05 A.M. Assume Mr. Pitt is the robber. Then he took < 55 min to travel from Maine to Charlotte. It is not possible to travel from Maine to Charlotte in 55 min or less. Therefore, Mr. Pitt is not the robber. **27.** The hole in the roof; of 5 possibilities, 4 have been eliminated.

MIXED REVIEW **29.** Answers may vary. Sample: $ABCD$ and $BCFG$ **31.** Answers may vary. Sample: A, B, C, and D **33.** B **35.**

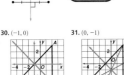

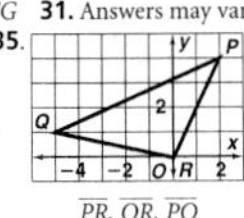

$\overline{PR}, \overline{QR}, \overline{PQ}$

Toolbox — page 212

1. $x \le -1$ **5.** $a \le 18$ **9.** $n \le -3\frac{1}{2}$ **13.** $n \ge -119$ **17.** $b \ge 8$ **21.** $x < -5$ **25.** $a \ge -1$

Lesson 4-6 — pages 216–218

ON YOUR OWN **1.** no; 2 + 3 ≯ 6 **3.** Yes; the length of each segment is < the sum of the lengths of the other 2. **5.** Yes; the length of each segment is < the sum of the lengths of the other 2. **7.** Yes; the length of each segment is < the sum of the lengths of the other 2. **9.** $\overline{MN}, \overline{ON}, \overline{OM}$ **11.** $\overline{TU}, \overline{UV}, \overline{TV}$ **13.** $\overline{AK}, \overline{AR}, \overline{KR}$ **15.** ∠Q, ∠R, ∠S **17.** ∠G, ∠H, ∠I **19.** ∠A, ∠B, ∠C **21.** ∠Z, ∠Y, ∠X **23.** $\frac{1}{2}$ **25b.** The directions of each pair of inequalities match. **25c.** The 3rd side of the 1st triangle is longer than the 3rd side of the 2nd triangle. **27.** The 2 cities may not be both straight ahead. For instance, Topeka might be 110 mi east, and Wichita might be 90 mi south. **29.** $\overline{CD}$ **31.** $4 < z < 20$ **33.** $0 < z < 12$ **35a.** Given **35b.** Isosceles Triangle Thm. **35c.** Angle Addition Post. **35d.** Substitution **35e.** Exterior Angle Thm. **35f.** Transitive Prop. of Inequality

MIXED REVIEW **37.** $S'(-2, -7), Y'(4, -3)$ **39.** 156; 24 **41.** The set of red pts. is 3 units from the set of blue pts.

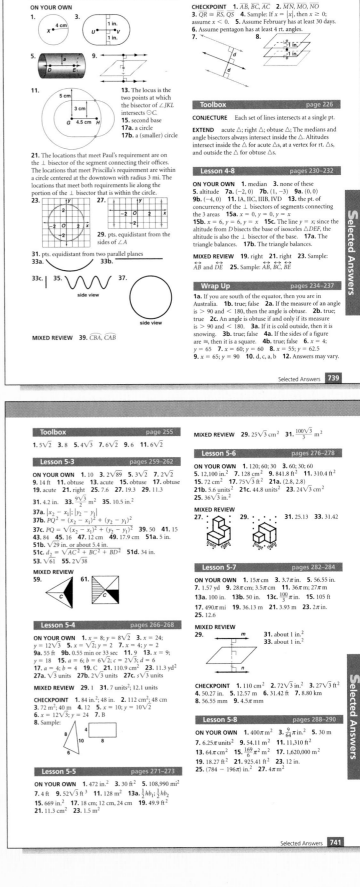

Lesson 4-7 — pages 223–225

ON YOUR OWN

1. **3.** **5.** **9.** **11.**

13. The locus is the two points at which the bisector of ∠JKL intersects ⊙C. **15.** second base **17a.** a circle **17b.** a (smaller) circle

21. The locations that meet Paul's requirement are on the ⊥ bisector of the segment connecting their offices. The locations that meet Priscilla's requirement are within a circle centered at the downtown with radius 3 mi. The locations that meet both requirements lie along the portion of the ⊥ bisector that is within the circle.

23. **27.**

29. pts. equidistant from the sides of ∠A

31. pts. equidistant from two parallel planes

33a. **33b.**

33c. **35.** side view **37.** side view

MIXED REVIEW **39.** $\widehat{CBA}, \widehat{CAB}$ **41.**

CHECKPOINT **1.** $\overline{AB}, \overline{BC}, \overline{AC}$ **2.** $\overline{MN}, \overline{MO}, \overline{NO}$ **3.** $\overline{QR} \cong \overline{RS}, \overline{QS}$ **4.** Sample: If $x = |x|$, then $x \ge 0$; assume $x < 0$. **5.** Assume February has at least 30 days. **6.** Assume pentagon has at least 4 rt. angles. **7.** **8.**

Toolbox — page 226

CONJECTURE Each set of lines intersects at a single pt.

EXTEND acute △; right △; obtuse △; The medians and angle bisectors always intersect inside the △. Altitudes intersect inside the △ for acute △s, at a vertex for rt. △s, and outside the △ for obtuse △s.

Lesson 4-8 — pages 230–232

ON YOUR OWN **1.** median **3.** none of these **5.** altitude **7a.** (−2, 0) **7b.** (1, −3) **9a.** (0, 0) **9b.** (−4, 0) **11.** IA, IIC, IIIB, IVD **13.** the pt. of concurrency of the ⊥ bisectors of segments connecting the 3 areas **15a.** $x = 0, y = 0, y = x$ **15b.** $x = 6, y = 6, y = x$ **15c.** The line $y = x$; since the altitude from D bisects the base of isosceles △DEF, the altitude is also the ⊥ bisector of the base. **17a.** The triangle balances. **17b.** The triangle balances.

MIXED REVIEW **19.** right **21.** right **23.** Sample: $\overleftrightarrow{AB}$ and $\overleftrightarrow{DE}$ **25.** Sample: $\overleftrightarrow{AB}, \overleftrightarrow{BC}, \overleftrightarrow{BE}$

Wrap Up — pages 234–237

1a. If you are south of the equator, then you are in Australia. **1b.** true; false **2a.** If the measure of an angle is > 90 and < 180, then the angle is obtuse. **2b.** true; true **2c.** An angle is obtuse if and only if its measure is > 90 and < 180. **3a.** If it is cold outside, then it is snowing. **3b.** true; false **4a.** If the sides of a figure are ≅, then it is a square. **4b.** true; false **6.** $x = 4$; $y = 65$ **7.** $x = 60; y = 60$ **8.** $x = 55; y = 62.5$ **9.** $x = 65; y = 90$ **10.** d, c, a, b **12.** Answers may vary.

Sample: ∠ABC is a rt. angle by def. of complementary angles and the Angle Addition Post. ∠A and ∠C are complementary because acute angles of a rt. △ are complementary. **13.** ∠E ≅ ∠F because base ∠s of an isosceles △ are ≅. **14.** Answers may vary. Samples: ∠HIG ≅ ∠JIK because they are vert. angles. ∠HIG ≅ ∠G and ∠JIK ≅ ∠J because base ∠s of an isosceles △ are ≅. **15.** 15 **16.** 12 **17.** 11 **18.** Assume that the room had been painted with oil-based paint. Then the brushes would be soaking in paint thinner, but they are not. So the assumption is false. The room must not have been painted with oil-based paint. **19.** Assume that both numbers are odd. The product of 2 odd numbers is always odd, which contradicts the fact that their product is even. So the assumption that both numbers are odd is false, and at least 1 must be even. **20.** Assume that a triangle has 2 or more obtuse angles. By def., the measure of each of these angles is > 90. Then the sum of angle measures of the △ is > 180. By the Triangle Angle-Sum Thm., the sum of angle measures of a △ is 180. Therefore the assumption was false, and a △ has no more than 1 obtuse angle. **21.** Assume 1 angle of an equilateral △ is obtuse. Then its measure is > 90 and < 180. By the Isosceles Triangle Thm., the remaining angles are each ≅ to the 1st angle. By def. of ≅ angles and the Transitive Prop. of =, the measures of the 3 angles are =, and all the angles are obtuse. Then the sum of the measures of the angles is > 270. But the sum of the measures of angles of a △ is 180. Therefore, the assumption is false. An equilateral △ cannot have an obtuse angle. **22.** ∠T, ∠R, ∠S; $\overline{SR}, \overline{TS}, \overline{TR}$ **23.** ∠C, ∠A, ∠B; $\overline{AB}, \overline{BC}, \overline{AC}$ **24.** ∠G, ∠O, ∠F; $\overline{OF}, \overline{FG}, \overline{OG}$ **25.** B

27. **28.**

30. (−1, 0)

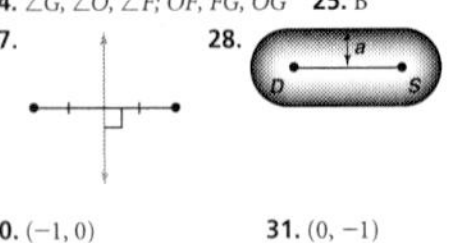

31. (0, −1)

32. (2, −3)

33. 16 cm; 15 cm^2 **34.** 30.4 ft; 55.8 ft^2 **35.** 4 m; 0.75 m^2 **36.** 5 **37.** 13 **38.** 15

Cumulative Review — page 239

1. E **3.** A **5.** B **7.** A **9.** C **11.** D **13.** Sample:

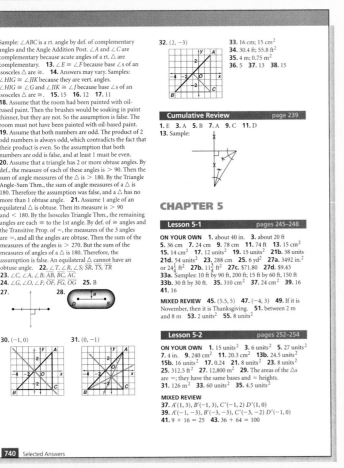

CHAPTER 5

Lesson 5-1 — pages 245–248

ON YOUR OWN **1.** about 40 in. **3.** about 20 ft **5.** 36 cm **7.** 24 cm **9.** 78 cm **11.** 74 ft **13.** 15 cm^2 **15.** 14 cm^2 **17.** 12 $units^2$ **19.** 15 $units^2$ **21b.** 38 units **21d.** 54 $units^2$ **23.** 288 cm **25.** 6 yd^2 **27a.** 3492 $in.^2$ or $24\frac{1}{4}$ ft^2 **27b.** $11\frac{3}{4}$ ft^2 **27c.** \$71.80 **27d.** \$9.43 **33a.** Samples: 10 ft by 90 ft, 200 ft; 15 ft by 60 ft, 150 ft **33b.** 30 ft by 30 ft. **35.** 310 cm^2 **37.** 24 cm^2 **39.** 16 **41.** 16

MIXED REVIEW **45.** (5.5, 5) **47.** (−4, 3) **49.** If it is November, then it is Thanksgiving. **51.** between 2 m and 8 m **53.** 2 $units^2$ **55.** 8 $units^2$

Lesson 5-2 — pages 252–254

ON YOUR OWN **1.** 15 $units^2$ **3.** 6 $units^2$ **5.** 27 $units^2$ **7.** 4 in. **9.** 240 cm^2 **11.** 20.3 cm^2 **13b.** 24.5 $units^2$ **15b.** 16 $units^2$ **17.** 0.24 **21.** 8 $units^2$ **23.** 8 $units^2$ **25.** 312.5 ft^2 **27.** 12,800 m^2 **29.** The areas of the △s are =; they have the same bases and = heights. **31.** 126 m^2 **33.** 60 $units^2$ **35.** 4.5 $units^2$

MIXED REVIEW
37. $A'(1, 3), B'(-1, 3), C'(-1, 2)\ D'(1, 0)$
39. $A'(-1, -3), B'(-3, -3), C'(-3, -2)\ D'(-1, 0)$
41. 9 + 16 = 25 **43.** 36 + 64 = 100

Toolbox — page 255

1. $5\sqrt{2}$ **3.** 8 **5.** $4\sqrt{3}$ **7.** $6\sqrt{2}$ **9.** 6 **11.** $6\sqrt{2}$

Lesson 5-3 — pages 259–262

ON YOUR OWN **1.** 10 **3.** $2\sqrt{89}$ **5.** $3\sqrt{2}$ **7.** $2\sqrt{2}$ **9.** 14 ft **11.** obtuse **13.** acute **15.** obtuse **17.** obtuse **19.** acute **21.** right **25.** 7.6 **27.** 19.3 **29.** 11.3 **31.** 4.2 in. **33.** $\frac{9\sqrt{3}}{2}$ m^2 **35.** 10.5 $in.^2$
37a. $|x_2 - x_1|; |y_2 - y_1|$
37b. $PQ^2 = (x_2 - x_1)^2 + (y_2 - y_1)^2$
37c. $PQ = \sqrt{(x_2 - x_1)^2 + (y_2 - y_1)^2}$ **39.** 50 **41.** 15 **43.** 84 **45.** 16 **47.** 12 cm **49.** 17.9 cm **51a.** 5 in. **51b.** $\sqrt{29}$ in. or about 5.4 in. **51c.** $d_2 = \sqrt{AC^2 + BC^2 + BD^2}$ **51d.** 34 in. **53.** $\sqrt{61}$ **55.** $2\sqrt{38}$

MIXED REVIEW
59. **61.**

Lesson 5-4 — pages 266–268

ON YOUR OWN **1.** $x = 8; y = 8\sqrt{2}$ **3.** $x = 24$; $y = 12\sqrt{3}$ **5.** $x = \sqrt{2}; y = 2$ **7.** $x = 4; y = 2$ **9a.** 55 ft **9b.** 0.55 min or 33 sec **11.** 9 **13.** $x = 9$; $y = 18$ **15.** $a = 6; b = 6\sqrt{2}; c = 2\sqrt{3}; d = 6$ **17.** $a = 4; b = 4$ **19.** C **21.** 110.9 cm^2 **23.** 11.3 yd^2 **27a.** $\sqrt{3}$ units **27b.** $2\sqrt{3}$ units **27c.** $s\sqrt{3}$ units

MIXED REVIEW **29.** 1 **31.** 7 $units^2$; 12.1 units

CHECKPOINT **1.** 84 $in.^2$; 48 in. **2.** 112 cm^2; 48 cm **3.** 72 m^2; 40 m **4.** 12 **5.** $x = 10; y = 10\sqrt{2}$ **6.** $x = 12\sqrt{3}; y = 24$ **7.** B **8.** Sample:

Lesson 5-5 — pages 271–273

ON YOUR OWN **1.** 472 $in.^2$ **3.** 30 ft^2 **5.** 108,990 mi^2 **7.** 4 ft **9.** $52\sqrt{3}$ ft^3 **11.** 128 m^2 **13a.** $\frac{1}{2}hb_1; \frac{1}{2}hb_2$ **15.** 669 $in.^2$ **17.** 18 cm; 12 cm, 24 cm **19.** 49.9 ft^2 **21.** 11.3 cm^2 **23.** 1.5 m^2

MIXED REVIEW **29.** $25\sqrt{3}$ cm^2 **31.** $\frac{100\sqrt{3}}{3}$ m^2

Lesson 5-6 — pages 276–278

ON YOUR OWN **1.** 120; 60; 30 **3.** 60; 30; 60 **5.** 12,100 $in.^2$ **7.** 128 cm^2 **9.** 841.8 ft^2 **11.** 310.4 ft^2 **15.** 72 cm^2 **17.** $75\sqrt{3}$ ft^2 **21a.** (2.8, 2.8) **21b.** 5.6 $units^2$ **21c.** 44.8 $units^2$ **23.** $24\sqrt{3}$ cm^2 **25.** $36\sqrt{3}$ $in.^2$

MIXED REVIEW
27. **29.** **31.** 25.13 **33.** 31.42

Lesson 5-7 — pages 282–284

ON YOUR OWN **1.** 15π cm **3.** 3.7π in. **5.** 56.55 in. **7.** 1.57 yd **9.** 28π cm; 3.5π cm **11.** 36π m; 27π m **13a.** 100 in. **13b.** 50 in. **13c.** $\frac{100}{3}\pi$ in. **15.** 105 ft **17.** 490π mi **19.** 36.13 m **21.** 3.93 m **23.** 2π in. **25.** 12.6

MIXED REVIEW
29. **31.** about 1 $in.^2$ **33.** about 1 $in.^2$

CHECKPOINT **1.** 110 cm^2 **2.** $72\sqrt{3}$ $in.^2$ **3.** $27\sqrt{3}$ ft^2 **4.** 50.27 in. **5.** 12.57 m **6.** 31.42 ft **7.** 8.80 km **8.** 56.55 mm **9.** 4.5π mm

Lesson 5-8 — pages 288–290

ON YOUR OWN **1.** 400π m^2 **3.** $\frac{9}{64}\pi$ $in.^2$ **5.** 30 m **7.** 6.25π $units^2$ **9.** 54.11 m^2 **11.** 11,310 ft^2 **13.** 64π cm^2 **15.** $\frac{169}{6}\pi^2$ m^2 **17.** 1,620,000 m^2 **19.** 18.27 ft^2 **21.** 925.41 ft^2 **23.** 12 in. **25.** (784 − 196π) $in.^2$ **27.** 4π m^2

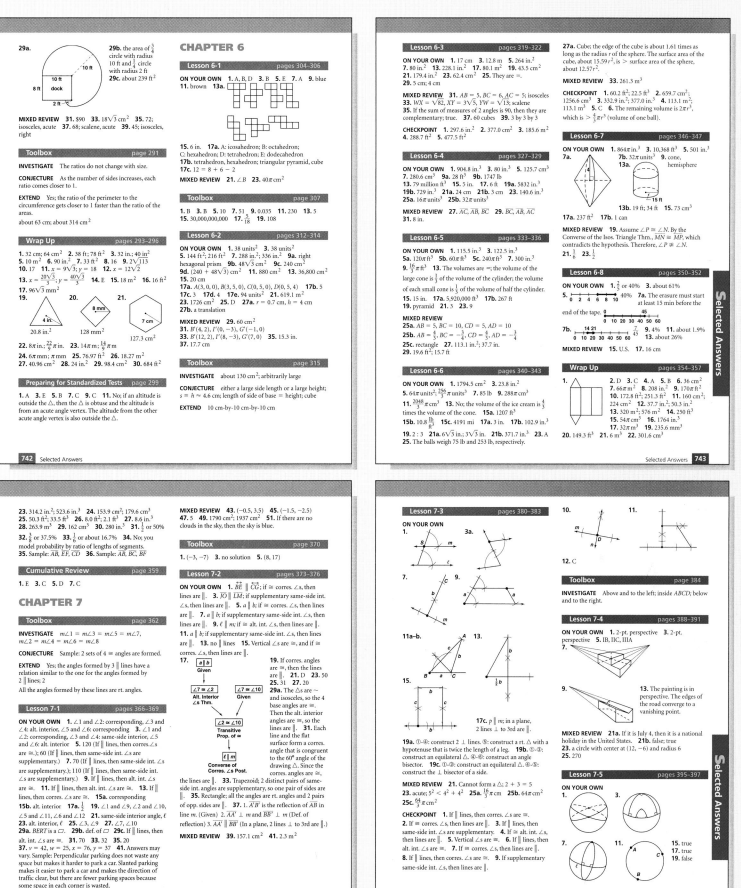

29a.

10 ft	
8 ft	dock
2 ft	10 ft

29b. the area of $\frac{3}{4}$ circle with radius 10 ft and $\frac{1}{4}$ circle with radius 2 ft **29c.** about 239 ft^2

MIXED REVIEW 31. \$90 **33.** $18\sqrt{3}$ cm^2 **35.** 72; isosceles, acute **37.** 68; scalene, acute **39.** 45; isosceles, right

Toolbox — page 291

INVESTIGATE The ratios do not change with size.

CONJECTURE As the number of sides increases, each ratio comes closer to 1.

EXTEND Yes; the ratio of the perimeter to the circumference gets closer to 1 faster than the ratio of the areas.

about 63 cm; about 314 cm^2

Wrap Up — pages 293–296

1. 32 cm; 64 cm^2 **2.** 38 ft; 78 ft^2 **3.** 32 in.; 40 in^2 **5.** 10 m^2 **6.** 90 in.^{2} **7.** 33 ft^2 **8.** 16 **9.** $2\sqrt{113}$ **10.** 17 **11.** $x = 9\sqrt{3}$; $y = 18$ **12.** $x = 12\sqrt{2}$ **13.** $x = \frac{20\sqrt{3}}{3}$; $y = \frac{40\sqrt{3}}{3}$ **14.** E **15.** 18 m^2 **16.** 16 ft^2 **17.** $96\sqrt{3}$ mm^2

19. 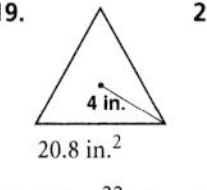

20.8 in.^{2}

20. 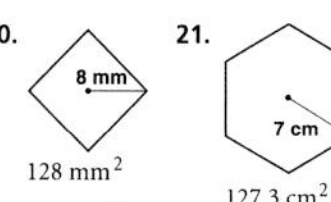

128 mm^2

21. 127.3 cm^2

22. 8π in.; $\frac{22}{9}\pi$ in. **23.** 14π m; $\frac{14}{9}\pi$ m **24.** 6π mm; π mm **25.** 76.97 ft^2 **26.** 18.27 m^2 **27.** 40.96 cm^2 **28.** 24 in.^{2} **29.** 98.4 cm^2 **30.** 684 ft^2

Preparing for Standardized Tests — page 299

1. A **3.** E **5.** B **7.** C **9.** C **11.** No; if an altitude is outside the △, then the △ is obtuse and the altitude is from an acute angle vertex. The altitude from the other acute angle vertex is also outside the △.

CHAPTER 6

Lesson 6-1 — pages 304–306

ON YOUR OWN 1. A, B, D **3.** B **5.** E **7.** A **9.** blue **11.** brown **13a.**

15. 6 in. **17a.** A: icosahedron; B: octahedron; C: hexahedron; D: tetrahedron; E: dodecahedron **17b.** tetrahedron, hexahedron; triangular pyramid, cube **17c.** $12 = 8 + 6 - 2$

MIXED REVIEW 21. $\angle B$ **23.** 40π cm^2

Toolbox — page 307

1. B **3.** B **5.** 10 **7.** 51 **9.** 0.035 **11.** 230 **13.** 5 **15.** 30,000,000,000 **17.** $\frac{5}{18}$ **19.** 108

Lesson 6-2 — pages 312–314

ON YOUR OWN 1. 38 units^2 **3.** 38 units^2 **5.** 144 ft^2; 216 ft^2 **7.** 288 in.^{2}; 336 in.^{2} **9a.** right hexagonal prism **9b.** $48\sqrt{3}$ cm^2 **9c.** 240 cm^2 **9d.** $(240 + 48\sqrt{3})$ cm^2 **11.** 880 cm^2 **13.** 36,800 cm^2 **15.** 20 cm **17a.** $A(3, 0, 0)$, $B(3, 5, 0)$, $C(0, 5, 0)$, $D(0, 5, 4)$ **17b.** 5 **17c.** 3 **17d.** 4 **17e.** 94 units^2 **21.** 619.1 m^2 **23.** 1726 cm^2 **25.** D **27a.** $r = 0.7$ cm, $h = 4$ cm **27b.** a translation

MIXED REVIEW 29. 60 cm^2 **31.** $B'(4, 2)$, $I'(0, -3)$, $G'(-1, 0)$ **33.** $B'(12, 2)$, $I'(8, -3)$, $G'(7, 0)$ **35.** 15.3 in. **37.** 17.7 cm

Toolbox — page 315

INVESTIGATE about 130 cm^2; arbitrarily large

CONJECTURE either a large side length or a large height; $s = h \approx 4.6$ cm; length of side of base = height; cube

EXTEND 10 cm-by-10 cm-by-10 cm

Lesson 6-3 — pages 319–322

ON YOUR OWN 1. 17 cm **3.** 12.8 m **5.** 264 in.^{2} **7.** 80 in.^{2} **13.** 228.1 in.^{2} **17.** 80.1 m^2 **19.** 43.5 cm^2 **21.** 179.4 in.^{2} **23.** 62.4 cm^2 **25.** They are =. **29.** 5 cm; 4 cm

MIXED REVIEW 31. $AB = 5$, $BC = 6$, $AC = 5$; isosceles **33.** $WX = \sqrt{82}$, $XY = 3\sqrt{5}$, $YW = \sqrt{13}$; scalene **35.** If the sum of measures of 2 angles is 90, then they are complementary; true. **37.** 60 cubes **39.** 3 by 3 by 3

CHECKPOINT 1. 297.6 in.^{2} **2.** 377.0 cm^2 **3.** 185.6 m^2 **4.** 288.7 ft^2 **5.** 477.5 ft^2

Lesson 6-4 — pages 327–329

ON YOUR OWN 1. 904.8 in.^{3} **3.** 80 in.^{3} **5.** 125.7 cm^3 **7.** 280.6 cm^3 **9a.** 28 ft^3 **9b.** 1747 lb **13.** 79 million ft^3 **15.** 5 in. **17.** 6 ft **19a.** 5832 in.^{3} **19b.** 729 in.^{3} **21a.** 24 cm **21b.** 3 cm **23.** 140.6 in.^{3} **25a.** 16π units^3 **25b.** 32π units^3

MIXED REVIEW 27. $\overline{AC}, \overline{AB}, \overline{BC}$ **29.** $\overline{BC}, \overline{AB}, \overline{AC}$ **31.** 8 in.

Lesson 6-5 — pages 333–336

ON YOUR OWN 1. 115.5 in.^{3} **3.** 122.5 in.^{3} **5a.** 120π ft^3 **5b.** 60π ft^3 **5c.** 240π ft^3 **7.** 300 in.^{3} **9.** $\frac{16}{3}\pi$ ft^3 **13.** The volumes are =; the volume of the large cone is $\frac{1}{3}$ of the volume of the cylinder; the volume of each small cone is $\frac{1}{3}$ of the volume of half the cylinder. **15.** 15 in. **17a.** 5,920,000 ft^3 **17b.** 267 ft **19.** pyramid **21.** 3 **23.** 9

MIXED REVIEW
25a. $AB = 5$, $BC = 10$, $CD = 5$, $AD = 10$ **25b.** $AB = \frac{4}{3}$, $BC = -\frac{3}{4}$, $CD = \frac{4}{3}$, $AD = -\frac{3}{4}$ **25c.** rectangle **27.** 113.1 in.^{2}; 37.7 in. **29.** 19.6 ft^2; 15.7 ft

Lesson 6-6 — pages 340–343

ON YOUR OWN 1. 1794.5 cm^2 **3.** 23.8 in.^{2} **5.** 64π units^2; $\frac{256}{3}\pi$ units^3 **7.** 85 lb **9.** 288π cm^3 **11.** $\frac{2048}{3}\pi$ cm^3 **13.** No; the volume of the ice cream is $\frac{4}{3}$ times the volume of the cone. **15a.** 1207 ft^3 **15b.** $10.8\ \frac{\text{lb}}{\text{ft}^3}$ **15c.** 4191 mi **17a.** 3 in. **17b.** 102.9 in.^{3} **19.** 2 : 3 **21a.** $6\sqrt{3}$ in.; $3\sqrt{3}$ in. **21b.** 371.7 in.^{3} **23.** A **25.** The balls weigh 75 lb and 253 lb, respectively.

27a. Cube; the edge of the cube is about 1.61 times as long as the radius r of the sphere. The surface area of the cube, about $15.59r^2$, is > surface area of the sphere, about $12.57r^2$.

MIXED REVIEW 33. 261.3 m^3

CHECKPOINT 1. 60.2 ft^2; 22.5 ft^3 **2.** 659.7 cm^2; 1256.6 cm^3 **3.** 332.9 in.^{2}; 377.0 in.^{3} **4.** 113.1 m^2; 113.1 m^3 **5.** C **6.** The remaining volume is $2\pi r^3$, which is $> \frac{4}{3}\pi r^3$ (volume of one ball).

Lesson 6-7 — pages 346–347

ON YOUR OWN 1. 864π in.^{3} **3.** 10,368 ft^3 **5.** 501 in.^{3} **7a.** **7b.** 32π units^3 **9.** cone, hemisphere **13a.**

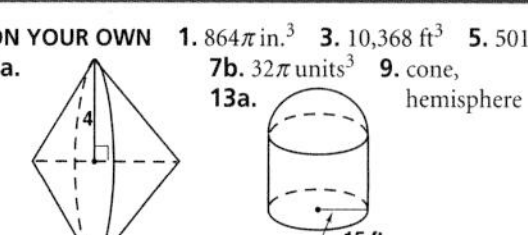

13b. 19 ft; 34 ft **15.** 73 cm^3 **17a.** 237 ft^2 **17b.** 1 can

MIXED REVIEW 19. Assume $\angle P \cong \angle N$. By the Converse of the Isos. Triangle Thm., $\overline{MN} \cong \overline{MP}$, which contradicts the hypothesis. Therefore, $\angle P \ncong \angle N$. **21.** $\frac{1}{6}$ **23.** $\frac{1}{2}$

Lesson 6-8 — pages 350–352

ON YOUR OWN 1. $\frac{2}{5}$ or 40% **3.** about 61% **5.** (number line 0 2 4 6 8 10) 40% **7a.** The erasure must start at least 15 min before the end of the tape. (number line 0 10 20 30 40 50 60; 0, 45) **7b.** (number line 0 10 20 30 40 50 60; 14 21) $\frac{7}{45}$ **9.** 4% **11.** about 1.9% **13.** about 26%

MIXED REVIEW 15. U.S. **17.** 16 cm

Wrap Up — pages 354–357

1. 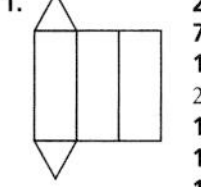

2. D **3.** C **4.** A **5.** B **6.** 36 cm^2 **7.** 66π m^2 **8.** 208 in.^{2} **9.** 170π ft^2 **10.** 172.8 ft^2; 251.3 ft^2 **11.** 160 cm^2; 224 cm^2 **12.** 37.7 in.^{2}; 50.3 in.^{2} **13.** 320 m^2; 576 m^2 **14.** 250 ft^3 **15.** 54π cm^3 **16.** 1764 in.^{3} **17.** 32π m^3 **19.** 235.6 mm^3 **20.** 149.3 ft^3 **21.** 6 m^3 **22.** 301.6 cm^3

23. 314.2 in.^{2}; 523.6 in.^{3} **24.** 153.9 cm^2; 179.6 cm^3 **25.** 50.3 ft^2; 33.5 ft^3 **26.** 8.0 ft^2; 2.1 ft^3 **27.** 8.6 in.^{3} **28.** 263.9 m^3 **29.** 162 cm^3 **30.** 280 in.^{3} **31.** $\frac{1}{2}$ or 50% **32.** $\frac{3}{8}$ or 37.5% **33.** $\frac{1}{6}$ or about 16.7% **34.** No; you model probability by ratio of lengths of segments. **35.** Sample: $\overline{AB}, \overline{EF}, \overline{CD}$ **36.** Sample: $\overline{AB}, \overline{BC}, \overline{BF}$

Cumulative Review — page 359

1. E **3.** C **5.** D **7.** C

CHAPTER 7

Toolbox — page 362

INVESTIGATE $m\angle 1 = m\angle 3 = m\angle 5 = m\angle 7$, $m\angle 2 = m\angle 4 = m\angle 6 = m\angle 8$

CONJECTURE Sample: 2 sets of 4 ≅ angles are formed.

EXTEND Yes; the angles formed by 3 ∥ lines have a relation similar to the one for the angles formed by 2 ∥ lines; 2

All the angles formed by these lines are rt. angles.

Lesson 7-1 — pages 366–369

ON YOUR OWN 1. ∠1 and ∠2: corresponding, ∠3 and ∠4: alt. interior, ∠5 and ∠6: corresponding **3.** ∠1 and ∠2: corresponding, ∠3 and ∠4: same-side interior, ∠5 and ∠6: alt. interior **5.** 120 (If ∥ lines, then corres. ∠s are ≅.); 60 (If ∥ lines, then same-side int. ∠s are supplementary.) **7.** 70 (If ∥ lines, then same-side int. ∠s are supplementary.); 110 (If ∥ lines, then same-side int. ∠s are supplementary.) **9.** If ∥ lines, then alt. int. ∠s are ≅. **11.** If ∥ lines, then alt. int. ∠s are ≅. **13.** If ∥ lines, then corres. ∠s are ≅. **15a.** corresponding **15b.** alt. interior **17a.** $\frac{1}{2}$ **19.** ∠1 and ∠9, ∠2 and ∠10, ∠5 and ∠11, ∠6 and ∠12 **21.** same-side interior angle, ℓ **23.** alt. interior, ℓ **25.** ∠3, ∠9 **27.** ∠7, ∠10 **29a.** *BERT* is a ▱. **29b.** def. of ▱ **29c.** If ∥ lines, then alt. int. ∠s are ≅. **31.** 70 **33.** 32 **35.** 20 **37.** $v = 42$, $w = 25$, $x = 76$, $y = 37$ **41.** Answers may vary. Sample: Perpendicular parking does not waste any space but makes it harder to park a car. Slanted parking makes it easier to park a car and makes the direction of traffic clear, but there are fewer parking spaces because some space in each corner is wasted.

MIXED REVIEW 43. (−0.5, 3.5) **45.** (−1.5, −2.5) **47.** 5 **49.** 1790 cm^2; 1937 cm^2 **51.** If there are no clouds in the sky, then the sky is blue.

Toolbox — page 370

1. (−3, −7) **3.** no solution **5.** (8, 17)

Lesson 7-2 — pages 373–376

ON YOUR OWN 1. $\overleftrightarrow{BE} \parallel \overleftrightarrow{CG}$; if ≅ corres. ∠s, then lines are ∥. **3.** $\overline{JO} \parallel \overline{LM}$; if supplementary same-side int. ∠s, then lines are ∥. **5.** $a \parallel b$; if ≅ corres. ∠s, then lines are ∥. **7.** $a \parallel b$; if supplementary same-side int. ∠s, then lines are ∥. **9.** $\ell \parallel m$; if ≅ alt. int. ∠s, then lines are ∥. **11.** $a \parallel b$; if supplementary same-side int. ∠s, then lines are ∥. **13.** no ∥ lines **15.** Vertical ∠s are ≅, and if ≅ corres. ∠s, then lines are ∥.

17. 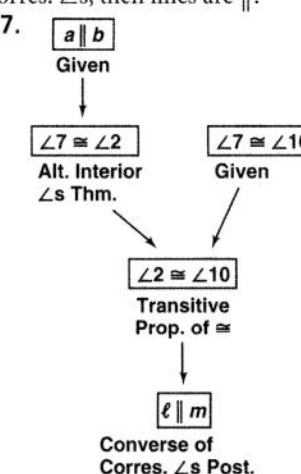

19. If corres. angles are ≅, then the lines are ∥. **21.** D **23.** 50 **25.** 31 **27.** 20 **29a.** The △s are ~ and isosceles, so the 4 base angles are ≅. Then the alt. interior angles are ≅, so the lines are ∥. **31.** Each line and the flat surface form a corres. angle that is congruent to the 60° angle of the drawing △. Since the corres. angles are ≅, the lines are ∥. **33.** Trapezoid; 2 distinct pairs of same-side int. angles are supplementary, so one pair of sides are ∥. **35.** Rectangle; all the angles are rt. angles and 2 pairs of opp. sides are ∥. **37.** 1. $\overline{A'B'}$ is the reflection of $\overline{AB}$ in line m. (Given) 2. $\overline{AA'} \perp m$ and $\overline{BB'} \perp m$ (Def. of reflection) 3. $\overline{AA'} \parallel \overline{BB'}$ (In a plane, 2 lines ⊥ to 3rd are ∥.)

MIXED REVIEW 39. 157.1 cm^2 **41.** 2.3 m^2

Lesson 7-3 — pages 380–383

ON YOUR OWN

1. **3a.** **7.** **9.**

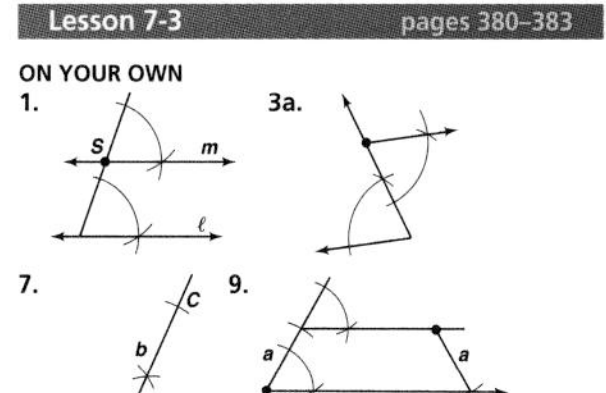

11a–b. **13.** **15.**

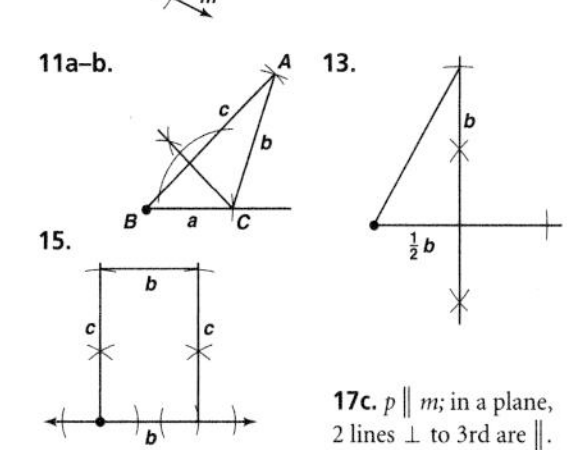

17c. $p \parallel m$; in a plane, 2 lines ⊥ to 3rd are ∥.

19a. ①-④: construct 2 ⊥ lines. ⑤: construct a rt. △ with a hypotenuse that is twice the length of a leg. **19b.** ①-③: construct an equilateral △. ④-⑥: construct an angle bisector. **19c.** ①-③: construct an equilateral △. ④-⑤: construct the ⊥ bisector of a side.

MIXED REVIEW 21. Cannot form a △; 2 + 3 = 5 **23.** acute; $5^2 < 4^2 + 4^2$ **25a.** $\frac{16}{3}\pi$ cm **25b.** 64π cm^2 **25c.** $\frac{64}{3}\pi$ cm^2

CHECKPOINT 1. If ∥ lines, then corres. ∠s are ≅. **2.** If ≅ corres. ∠s, then lines are ∥. **3.** If ∥ lines, then same-side int. ∠s are supplementary. **4.** If ≅ alt. int. ∠s, then lines are ∥. **5.** Vertical ∠s are ≅. **6.** If ∥ lines, then alt. int. ∠s are ≅. **7.** If ≅ corres. ∠s, then lines are ∥. **8.** If ∥ lines, then corres. ∠s are ≅. **9.** If supplementary same-side int. ∠s, then lines are ∥.

10. **11.**

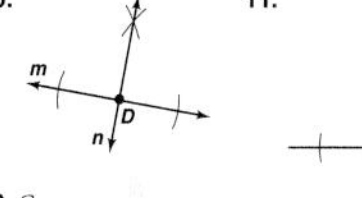

12. C

Toolbox — page 384

INVESTIGATE Above and to the left; inside *ABCD;* below and to the right.

Lesson 7-4 — pages 388–391

ON YOUR OWN 1. 2-pt. perspective **3.** 2-pt. perspective **5.** IB, IIC, IIIA

7.

9. 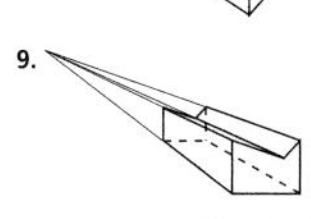

13. The painting is in perspective. The edges of the road converge to a vanishing point.

MIXED REVIEW 21a. If it is July 4, then it is a national holiday in the United States. **21b.** false; true **23.** a circle with center at (12, −6) and radius 6 **25.** 270

Lesson 7-5 — pages 395–397

ON YOUR OWN

1. **3.** **7.** **11.**

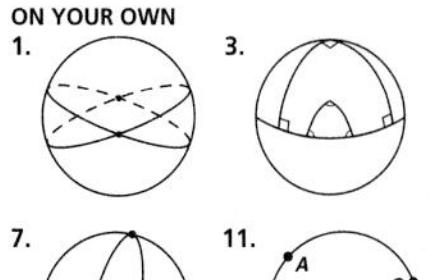

15. true **17.** true **19.** false

MIXED REVIEW
21. yes **23.** yes

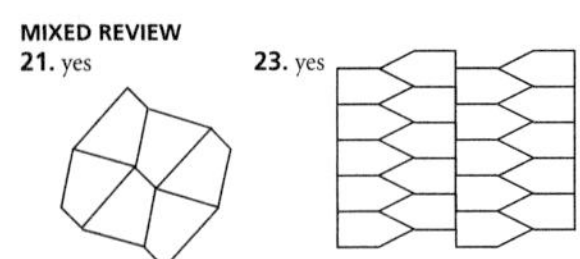

25. $-\frac{2}{3}$ **27.** $\frac{1}{3}$ **29.** 36, 54

Wrap Up pages 399–401

1. 120, If ∥ lines, then corres. ∠s are ≅; 120, Vertical ∠s are ≅. **2.** 75, If ∥ lines, then same-side int. ∠s are supplementary; 105, If ∥ lines, then alt. int. ∠s are ≅. **3.** 55, If ∥ lines, then same-side int. ∠s are supplementary; 90, If ∥ lines, then alt. int. ∠s are ≅. **6.** C **7.** 20 **8.** 20 **9.** 24 **10.**

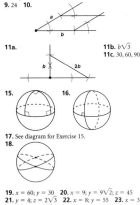

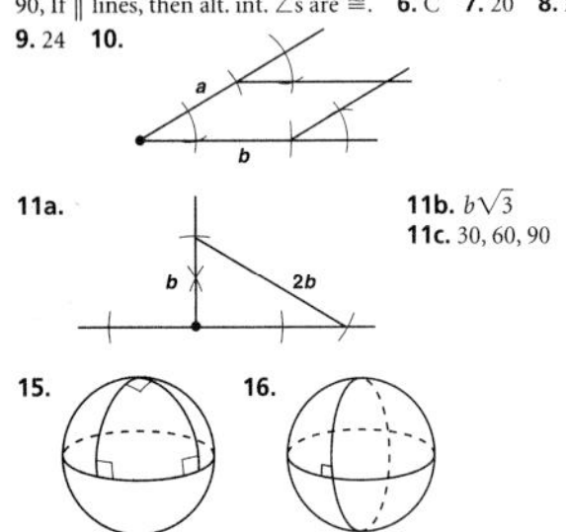

11a. **11b.** $b\sqrt{3}$ **11c.** 30, 60, 90

15. **16.**

17. See diagram for Exercise 15.
18.

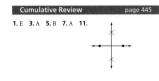

19. $x = 60; y = 30$ **20.** $x = 9; y = 9\sqrt{2}; z = 45$ **21.** $y = 4; z = 2\sqrt{3}$ **22.** $x = 8; y = 55$ **23.** $x = 35; y = 10; z = 10$ **24.** $w = 88; x = 7; y = 52; z = 40$

Preparing for Standardized Tests page 403

1. C **3.** D **5.** C **7.** B **9.** B

CHAPTER 8

Lesson 8-1 pages 409–412

ON YOUR OWN **1.** $\overline{XZ}$ **3.** SAS **7.** △JKL ≅ △NMO; SSS **9.** not possible **11.** △PQR ≅ △NMO; SAS **13.** △XYP ≅ △QYP; SAS **17.** yes; SAS Post. **19.** 1. $\overline{AE}$ and $\overline{BD}$ bisect each other. (Given) 2. $\overline{AC} \cong \overline{CE}$; $\overline{BC} \cong \overline{CD}$ (Def. of segment bisector) 3. ∠ACB ≅ ∠ECD (Vertical ∠s are ≅.) 4. △ACB ≅ △ECD (SAS) **21a.** = (equality) and ~ (similarity) **23.** 1. $\overline{FG} \parallel \overline{KL}$ (Given) 2. ∠GFK ≅ ∠LKF (If ∥ lines, then alt. int. ∠s are ≅.) 3. $\overline{FG} \cong \overline{KL}$ (Given) 4. $\overline{FK} \cong \overline{FK}$ (Reflexive Prop. of ≅) 5. △FGK ≅ △KLF (SAS)

MIXED REVIEW **27.** 314.2 mm³; 282.7 mm² **29.** 34, 34

Toolbox page 413

INVESTIGATE yes; no; yes

INVESTIGATE yes; yes; no; only when the segments coincide

CONJECTURE No; no; the above constructions demonstrate SSA △s that are not ≅ and AAA △s that are not ≅.

EXTEND no; no; yes

Lesson 8-2 pages 416–419

ON YOUR OWN **1.** AAS **3.** AAS **5.** ASA **7.** not possible **9.** ∠D ≅ ∠B **11.** ∠M ≅ ∠P **15.** yes; SSS **19.** 1. $\overline{FG} \parallel \overline{JH}$ (Given) 2. ∠FGJ ≅ ∠HJG (If ∥ lines, then alt. int. ∠s are ≅.) 3. ∠F ≅ ∠H (Given) 4. $\overline{JG} \cong \overline{JG}$ (Reflexive Prop. of ≅) 5. △FGJ ≅ △HJG (AAS) **21.** 1. ∠MON ≅ ∠QOP (Vertical ∠s are ≅.) 2. ∠N ≅ ∠P (Given) 3. $\overline{MO} \cong \overline{QO}$ (Given) 4. △MON ≅ △QOP (AAS) **23.** The hypotenuse of a rt. △ is longer than each leg. So FE > 5 cm and FE ≇ AC.

MIXED REVIEW **25.** (2, 0) **27.** $x = \frac{7\sqrt{3}}{3}; y = \frac{14\sqrt{3}}{3}$ **29.** $x = 4; y = 4\sqrt{2}$

Lesson 8-3 pages 422–425

ON YOUR OWN **1.** E **3.** $\overline{XV} \cong \overline{TV}$ or $\overline{RX} \cong \overline{RT}$ **5.** ∠AQC and ∠GJC are rt. angles. **7.** $\overline{RT} \cong \overline{NQ}$ **9.** You need to know which side is the hypotenuse. **11b.** −1; −1; 1 **11c.** They are rt. ∠s. **11d.** $\sqrt{26}$; $\sqrt{26}$ **11e.** △EGD and △EGF share a common leg $\overline{EG}$. Since the hypotenuses are ≅, the right △s are ≅ by HL Thm. **13.** 1. $\overline{OM}$ and $\overline{ON}$ are radii of ⊙O. (Given)

2. $\overline{OM} \cong \overline{ON}$ (All radii of a ⊙ are ≅.) 3. ∠M and ∠N are rt. angles. (Given) 4. △LMO and △LNO are rt. △s. (Def. of rt. △s) 5. $\overline{OL} \cong \overline{OL}$ (Reflexive Prop. of ≅) 6. △LMO ≅ △LNO (HL Thm.) **17.** All sides of a regular polygon are ≅. Since the △s are rt. △s, and the shorter legs are all ≅, by HL Thm., all the △s are ≅.
19.

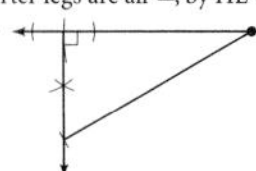

MIXED REVIEW **21.** Angle Addition Post. **23.** If ∥ lines, then same-side int. ∠s are supplementary. **25.** If ∥ lines, then corres. ∠s are ≅. **27.** 7.64 m²

CHECKPOINT **1.** ASA **2.** SSS **3.** SAS **4.** not possible **5.** AAS **6.** HL **7b.** No; if 2 pairs of angles are ≅, the 3rd pair of angles is also ≅. Then the △s are ≅ by AAS or ASA. **8.** E **9.** If the hypotenuse and an acute angle of one right triangle are congruent to the hypotenuse and an acute angle of another right triangle, then the triangles are congruent. The HA Theorem is true. Since the right angles are congruent, the triangles are congruent by AAS.

Lesson 8-4 pages 429–432

ON YOUR OWN **1.** Use ASA to prove △ABD ≅ △CBD. **3.** Use SAS to prove △STP ≅ △OTP. **5.** Use HL to prove △OER ≅ △OEP. **7.** Yes; the △s are ≅ by SSS, and the angles are ≅ by CPCTC. **9a.** Given **9b.** Given **9c.** Def. of angle bisector **9d.** Reflexive Prop. of ≅ **9e.** AAS **9f.** CPCTC **11a.** Given **11b.** Def. of ⊥ lines **11c.** All rt. ∠s are ≅. **11d.** Given **11e.** Def. of segment bisector **11f.** Reflexive Prop. of ≅ **11g.** SAS **11h.** CPCTC **13.** It is given that $\overline{BA} \cong \overline{BC}$ and $\overline{BD}$ bisects ∠ABC. ∠ABD ≅ ∠CBD by def. of ∠ bisector, and ∠A ≅ ∠C because base ∠s of an isosceles △ are ≅. Then △ABD ≅ △CBD by AAS. $\overline{AD} \cong \overline{CD}$ by CPCTC. Therefore, $\overline{BD}$ bisects $\overline{AC}$ by def. of segment bisector. By the Angle Addition Post., m∠ADB + m∠CDB = 180. ∠ADB ≅ ∠CDB by CPCTC. So, the measure of each angle is $\frac{1}{2}(180) = 90$. Therefore, $\overline{BD} \perp \overline{AC}$ by def. of ⊥ lines. **15a.** Use SAS on 2 legs and rt. angle. **15b.** $\overline{BF}$; CPCTC **15c.** The △s are rt. △s with ≅ hypotenuses and ≅ legs. By HL, △FAB ≅ △BCD. **17a.** $\overline{PA} \cong \overline{PB}$; $\overline{AC} \cong \overline{BC}$ **17b.** $\overline{CP} \cong \overline{CP}$ by Reflexive Prop. of ≅. Then, △APC ≅ △BPC by SSS and ∠APC ≅ ∠BPC by CPCTC. Therefore, m∠APC = m∠BPC = 90 by Angle Addition Post., and $\overline{CP} \perp \overline{AB}$ by def. of ⊥ lines.

MIXED REVIEW **21.** 89% **23.** about 79°

25.

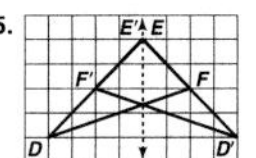

∠E

Lesson 8-5 pages 436–438

ON YOUR OWN **1.** ∠M **3.** $\overline{XY}$ **5.** △STU, △TSR; SSS **7.** △PQT, △URS; AAS **9.** △WYX, △ZXY; HL **11.** Prove △QTB ≅ △QUB by ASA. So $\overline{QT} \cong \overline{QU}$. Then use SAS to prove △QET ≅ △QEU. **13a.** Given **13b.** Reflexive Prop. of ≅ **13c.** ITE **13d.** SSS **13e.** TID **13f.** Given **13g.** All rt. ∠s are ≅. **13h.** AAS **13i.** $\overline{TD}$; $\overline{RO}$ **13j.** CPCTC **15.** B **17.** Since $\overline{TQ}$ bisects $\overline{PR}$, $\overline{PQ} \cong \overline{RQ}$. Since $\overline{TQ} \perp \overline{PR}$, ∠PQT and ∠RQT are ≅ rt. ∠s. Also, $\overline{QT} \cong \overline{QT}$, so △PQT ≅ △RQT by SAS. ∠PTQ ≅ ∠RTQ by CPCTC. Since $\overline{TQ}$ bisects ∠VQS, ∠VQT ≅ ∠SQT. So, △VQT ≅ △SQT by ASA, and $\overline{VQ} \cong \overline{SQ}$ by CPCTC.

MIXED REVIEW **19.** isosceles rt. △ **21.** 8 units²; $(8 + 4\sqrt{2})$ units

Toolbox page 439

1. 2, −7 **3.** −0.5, −3 **5.** −0.27, −3.06 **7.** −3, 9 **9.** −0.5, 0.75

Wrap Up pages 441–443

1. SSS; △DMR ≅ △TMR **2.** not possible **3.** SAS; △MNQ ≅ △PNO **4.** The order of the vertices indicates the corresponding parts. **5.** D **6.** not possible **7.** AAS **8.** ASA **9.** 1. $\overline{PS} \perp \overline{SQ}$ and $\overline{RQ} \perp \overline{QS}$ (Given) 2. ∠PSQ and ∠RQS are rt. ∠s. (Def. of ⊥ lines) 3. △PSQ and △RQS are rt. △s. (Def. of rt. △s) 4. $\overline{PQ} \cong \overline{RS}$ (Given) 5. $\overline{QS} \cong \overline{QS}$ (Reflexive Prop. of ≅) 6. △PSQ ≅ △RQS (HL Thm.) **10.** 1. U is the midpt. of $\overline{TV}$. (Given) 2. $\overline{TU} \cong \overline{UV}$ (Def. of midpt.) 3. $\overline{XU} \perp \overline{TV}$ and $\overline{WV} \perp \overline{TV}$ (Given) 4. ∠XUT and ∠WVU are rt. ∠s. (Def. of ⊥ lines) 5. △TXU and △UWV are rt. △s. (Def. of rt. △s) 6. △TXU ≅ △UWV (HL Thm.) **11.** 1. $\overline{LN} \perp \overline{KM}$ (Given) 2. ∠LNK and ∠LNM are rt. ∠s. (Def. of ⊥ lines.) 3. △KLN and △MLN are rt. △s. (Def. of rt. △s.) 4. $\overline{KL} \cong \overline{ML}$ (Given) 5. $\overline{LN} \cong \overline{LN}$ (Reflexive Prop. of ≅) 6. △KLN ≅ △MLN (HL Thm.) **13.** Use AAS to show △TVY ≅ △YWX. $\overline{TV} \cong \overline{YW}$ by CPCTC. **14.** Use ASA to show △BCE ≅ △DCE. ∠B ≅ ∠D by CPCTC. **15.** Use HL to show △KLM ≅ △MNK. $\overline{KN} \cong \overline{ML}$ by CPCTC. **16.** △ADB, △ACE; SAS **17.** △FIH, △GHI; SAS **18.** △PST, △RAT; ASA **19.** rectangle **20.** square **21.** parallelogram **22.** kite

23. The diagonals are ⊥ bisectors of each other. Each diagonal is an angle bisector of 2 of the angles of the rhombus. The area of the rhombus is half the product of the lengths of the diagonals.

Cumulative Review page 445

1. E **3.** A **5.** B **7.** A **11.**

CHAPTER 9

Lesson 9-1 pages 451–453

ON YOUR OWN **1.** m∠1 = 118; m∠2 = 62; m∠3 = 118 **3.** m∠1 = 81; m∠2 = 28; m∠3 = 71 **5.** 32 **7.** 16 **9.** ST = 7 cm; TW = 17 cm; WR = 7 cm **11.** Pick 6 equally spaced lines on the paper. Place the paper so that the 1st button is on the 1st line and the last button is on the 6th line. Draw a line between the first and last buttons. The remaining buttons should be placed where the drawn line crosses the 4 ∥ lines. **15.** 1. ▱LENS (Given) 2. $\overline{LS} \parallel \overline{EH}$ (Def. of ▱) 3. ▱NGTH (Given) 4. $\overline{GT} \parallel \overline{EH}$ (Def. of ▱) 5. $\overline{LS} \parallel \overline{GT}$ (2 lines ∥ to a 3rd line are ∥.) **17.** 60 **19.** x = 109; y = 88; z = 76 **21.** x = y = 6 **23.** x = 0; y = 5 **27a.** If a quad. is a ▱, then opp. angles are ≅. **27b.** Given: ▱ABCD. Prove: ∠A ≅ ∠C; ∠B ≅ ∠D. Draw diagonal $\overline{BD}$. 1. ▱ABCD (Given) 2. $\overline{AB} \parallel \overline{CD}$ (Def. of ▱) 3. ∠ABD ≅ ∠BDC (If ∥ lines, then alt. int. ∠s are ≅.) 4. $\overline{BC} \parallel \overline{DA}$ (Def. of ▱) 5. ∠ADB ≅ ∠CBD (If ∥ lines, then alt. int. ∠s are ≅.) 6. $\overline{BD} \cong \overline{BD}$ (Reflexive Prop. of ≅) 7. △ABD ≅ △CDB (ASA) 8. ∠A ≅ ∠C (CPCTC) Similarly, use diagonal $\overline{AC}$ to prove ∠B ≅ ∠D. **29.** 1. ▱RSTW and ▱XYTZ (Given) 2. ∠R ≅ ∠T (Opp. angles of a ▱ are ≅.) 3. ∠X ≅ ∠T (Opp. angles of a ▱ are ≅.) 4. ∠R ≅ ∠X (Transitive Prop. of ≅) **31.** kite **33.** trapezoid

MIXED REVIEW **41a.** (2.5, 1.5), (2.5, 1.5); $\overline{AC}$ and $\overline{BD}$ bisect each other. **41b.** $\frac{1}{3}$; $\frac{1}{3}$; the slopes are =. **41c.** $\overline{AB} \parallel \overline{DC}$ because they are vertical. **41d.** parallelogram

Lesson 9-2 pages 457–460

ON YOUR OWN **1.** Yes; if both pairs of opp. sides of a quad. are ≅, the quad. is a ▱. **3.** Yes; if both pairs of opp. angles of a quad. are ≅, the quad. is a ▱. **5.** Yes; both pairs of opp. sides are ∥ because alt. int. ∠s are ≅. The quad. is a ▱ by def. **7.** Yes; the quad. is a ▱ by def. **9.** yes **11.** yes **13.** yes **15.** 60; yes; both pairs of opp. angles are ≅. **17.** 6; yes; both pairs of opp. sides are ≅. **19.** x = 3; y = 11 **21.** B **25a.** (4, 0) **25b.** (6, 6) **25c.** (−2, 4) **27.** 1. △TRS ≅ △RTW (Given) 2. $\overline{RS} \cong \overline{TW}$; $\overline{ST} \cong \overline{WR}$ (CPCTC) 3. RSTW is a ▱. (If both pairs of opp. sides of a quad. are ≅, then the quad. is a ▱.) **29a.** 1. E is midpt. of $\overline{BC}$, and F is midpt. of $\overline{AD}$. (Given) 2. $BE = \frac{1}{2}BC$; $AF = \frac{1}{2}AD$ (Def. of midpt.) 3. ▱ABCD (Given) 4. AD = BC (Opp. sides of a ▱ are ≅.) 5. $\frac{1}{2}AD = \frac{1}{2}BC$ (Mult. Prop. of =) 6. AF = BE (Substitution) 7. $\overline{AD} \parallel \overline{BC}$ (Opp. sides of a ▱ are ∥.) 8. ABEF is a ▱. (If 1 pair of opp. sides of a quad. is ≅ and ∥, then the quad. is a ▱.) **29b.** Opp. angles of a ▱ are ≅. **29c.** Opp. sides of a ▱ are ≅. **31a.** ∥ threads remain ∥; the small rectangles are replaced with small nonrectangular ▱s. **31b.** The fabric stretches along one direction of threads and shrinks along the other.

MIXED REVIEW **33.** 50.3 cm² **35.** 166.3 ft² **37.** A ▱ is a quad. with 2 pairs of ∥ sides. **39.** A rectangle is a ▱ with 4 rt. angles.

CHECKPOINT **1.** m∠1 = 59; m∠2 = 121; m∠3 = 59 **2.** m∠1 = 43; m∠2 = 62; m∠3 = 62 **3.** m∠1 = 106; m∠2 = 74; m∠3 = 26 **4.** x = 45; y = 60 **5.** x = 7; y = 16 **6.** x = 1; y = 2 **7.** D

Toolbox page 461

INVESTIGATE Sample: The diagonals are ≅. Sample: The diagonals are ⊥.

CONJECTURE Sample: Diags. of a rectangle are ≅; diags. of a rhombus are ⊥ bisectors of each other; diags. of a rhombus bisect the angles of the rhombus.

Sample: All the properties of the diags. of rectangles and rhombuses are true for the diags. of squares.

EXTEND In a ▱, perpendicular diags. determine a rhombus; ≅ diags. determine a rectangle; diags. that bisect the angles of the ▱ determine a rhombus.

Lesson 9-3 pages 465–468

ON YOUR OWN **1a.** rhombus **1b.** m∠1 = 38; m∠2 = 38; m∠3 = 38; m∠4 = 38 **3a.** rectangle **3b.** m∠1 = 56; m∠2 = 68; m∠3 = 112; m∠4 = 56 **5.** 26.8 in. **7.** LB = 10; BP = 5; LM = 8 **9.** LB = 12; BP = 12; LM = $2\sqrt{11}$ **11.** C **13.** x = 45; y = 45; z = 30 **15.** x = 7.5; y = 3 **17a.** $\overline{BD}$ **17b.** AE **17c.** EC **17d.** AE; EC **17e.** AE; EC **17f.** AC **19.** 15.9 **21.** Yes; $2.5^2 + 6^2 = 6.5^2$, so the diagonals divide the ▱ into 4 rt. △s. Since the diagonals are ⊥, ▱JKLM is a rhombus. **23.** 24 m² **25.** 18 cm² **27.** Yes; 4 sides are ≅, so the opp. sides are ≅, and the quad. is a ▱. A ▱ with all sides ≅ is a rhombus. **29.** 1. $\overline{AC} \cong \overline{AC}$ (Reflexive Prop. of ≅) 2. $\overline{AC}$ bisects ∠BAD and ∠BCD. (Given) 3. ∠1 ≅ ∠2; ∠3 ≅ ∠4 (Def. of angle bisector) 4. △ABC ≅ △ADC (ASA) 5. $\overline{AB} \cong \overline{DA}$; $\overline{BC} \cong \overline{CD}$ (CPCTC) 6. ▱ABCD (Given) 7. $\overline{AB} \cong \overline{CD}$; $\overline{BC} \cong \overline{DA}$ (Opp. sides of a ▱ are ≅.) 8. $\overline{AB} \cong \overline{BC} \cong \overline{CD} \cong \overline{DA}$ (Transitive Prop. of ≅) 9. ABCD is a rhombus. (Def. of rhombus) **31.** In ▱ABCD, $\overline{AB} \cong \overline{DC}$ because opp. sides of a ▱ are ≅. $\overline{AD} \cong \overline{AD}$ by the Reflexive Prop. of ≅. Since $\overline{AC} \cong \overline{BD}$, △BAD ≅ △CDA by SSS and ∠BAD ≅ ∠CDA by CPCTC. ∠BAD and ∠CDA are consecutive angles of a ▱, so they are supp. Therefore, both angles are rt. ∠s and the angles opp. them are rt. ∠s. So ▱ABCD is a rectangle by def. **33a.** Since ABCD is a ▱, opp. ∠s are ≅. So ∠B ≅ ∠D, therefore ∠D is a rt. angle. In a ▱, consecutive ∠s are supp. Therefore, ∠A and ∠C are each supp. to ∠B. The supp. of a rt. angle is a rt. angle, so ∠A and ∠C are rt. ∠s. Therefore, ABCD is a rectangle by def. **33b.** If one ∠ of a ▱ is a rt. angle, then the ▱ is a rectangle.

Toolbox page 469

INVESTIGATE parallelogram

CONJECTURE The quad. whose vertices are midpts. of another quad. is a ▱; yes; no.

EXTEND
- rectangle; rhombus
- The ratio of lengths of sides and perimeters is $\frac{1}{2}$; the ratio of areas is $\frac{1}{4}$; MNOP ~ FGHE.

Lesson 9-4 pages 473–476

ON YOUR OWN **1.** m∠1 = 77; m∠2 = 103 **3.** m∠1 = 90; m∠2 = 68 **5.** UI = 6; IT = 15; UT = 21 **7.** 12 cm, 12 cm, 21 cm, 21 cm **9a.** Isosceles trapezoid; all the large rt. △s appear to be ≅. **9b.** 112; 68; 68 **11a.** No; if one pair of consecutive ∠s is supplementary, then another pair must be also because a pair of opp. ∠s of a kite is ≅. Therefore, the opp. sides are ∥, which means the figure is a ▱ and cannot be a kite. **11b.** Yes; if 2 ≅ angles are rt. angles, they are supplementary. The other 2 angles are also supplementary. **13.** 1.5 **15.** x = 35; y = 30 **19.** $\overline{AA'} \cong \overline{AA''}$ and $\overline{BA'} \cong \overline{BA''}$, so it is a kite (unless x = 60, in which case the 4 sides are ≅ and it is a rhombus). **25a.** isosceles trapezoids **25b.** 45, 135, 135, 45 **27.** 1. Isosceles trapezoid TRAP (Given) 2. $\overline{TA} \cong \overline{PR}$ (Diagonals of an isos. trap. are ≅.) 3. $\overline{TR} \cong \overline{PA}$ (Given) 4. $\overline{RA} \cong \overline{RA}$ (Reflexive Prop. of ≅) 5. △TRA ≅ △PAR (SSS) 6. ∠1 ≅ ∠2 (CPCTC)

MIXED REVIEW **29.** $\frac{3}{8}$ **31a.** $x(x + 7)$ or $x^2 + 7x$ **31b.** 78 cm² **33.** parallelogram **35.** square

Toolbox page 477

1. 4, $x \neq -3$ **3.** $\frac{x-3}{x+3}$, $x \neq -3$ **5.** $7w + 3$ **7.** $\frac{1}{5t}$, $t \neq 0$ **9.** $4x^2$, $x \neq 3$ **11.** $v + 1$, $v \neq -1$ **13.** $\frac{3}{r}$, $r \neq 0$ **15.** $15c$, $c \neq -2$ **17.** $15x$, $x \neq 0$ **19.** $\frac{3a}{2}$, $a \neq 0$ **21.** $\frac{t+2}{5}$, $t \neq -3$ or 2 **23.** $\frac{1}{2a+10}$, $a \neq -5$ or 5 **25.** $3y^4 + 3y^3$, $y \neq -1$ or 0 **27.** $\frac{3c^2 - 2c - 1}{c^2 + 1}$, $c \neq 1$

Lesson 9-5 pages 480–482

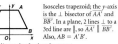

ON YOUR OWN **1.** W(0, h); Z(b, 0) **3.** W(−b, b); Z(−b, −b) **5.** W(−r, 0); Z(0, −t) **7.** $\left(\frac{b}{2}, \frac{h}{2}\right)$, $\sqrt{b^2 + h^2}$ **9.** (−b, 0), 2b **11.** $\left(-\frac{r}{2}, -\frac{t}{2}\right)$, $\sqrt{r^2 + t^2}$ **15a.** **15b.** (−b, 0), (0, b), (b, 0), (0, −b) **15c.** $b\sqrt{2}$ **15d.** 1 and −1 **15e.** Yes, because the product of the slopes is −1. **17.** (c − a, b) **19.** (−b, 0) **21a.** (0, 0, 0), (0, 0, 2a), (0, 2a, 0), (2a, 0, 0), (0, 2a, 2a), (2a, 0, 2a), (2a, 2a, 0), (2a, 2a, 2a) **21b.** (−a, −a, −a), (−a, −a, a), (−a, a, −a), (a, −a, −a), (−a, a, a), (a, −a, a), (a, a, −a), (a, a, a) **23.** Isosceles trapezoid; the y-axis is the ⊥ bisector of $\overline{AA'}$ and $\overline{BB'}$. In a plane, 2 lines ⊥ to a 3rd line are ∥, so $\overline{AA'} \parallel \overline{BB'}$. Also, AB = A′B′. **25a.** The diagonals of a rhombus are ⊥.

MIXED REVIEW **27.** $36\sqrt{3}$ in.² **29.** 76 ft²

CHECKPOINT **1.** $x = 51; y = 51$ **2.** 3 **3.** $x = 58;$ $y = 32$ **4.** $x = 2; y = 4$ **5.** The diagonals of a rhombus are ⊥; each diagonal bisects 2 opp. angles of the rhombus.

Lesson 9-6 pages 485–487

ON YOUR OWN **3.** $E(-a, 0), F(-b, c)$; use the Distance Formula to find the lengths of $\overline{EG}$, $\sqrt{(b+a)^2 + c^2}$, and of $\overline{HF}$, $\sqrt{(a+b)^2 + (-c)^2}$. The lengths are =, so the diagonals are ≅. **5.** $T(-2a, 0), R(-2b, 2c),$ $D(-a-b, c), E(0, 2c), F(a+b, c), G(0, 0);$ $DE = EF = FG = GD = \sqrt{(a+b)^2 + c^2}$
7. $K(-b, a+c), L(b, a+c), M(b, c), N(-b, c)$; slope of $\overline{KL}$ and slope of $\overline{MN}$ are 0. Slope of $\overline{LM}$ and slope of $\overline{NK}$ are undef. Lines with 0 slope and with undef. slope are ⊥ to each other. Therefore, $KLMN$ is a rectangle. **11a.** $\frac{b}{c}$ **11b.** Let a pt. on line p be (x, y). Then the equation of p is $\frac{y-0}{x-a} = \frac{b}{c}$ or $y = \frac{b}{c}(x-a)$. **11c.** $x = 0$ **11d.** When $x = 0$, $y = \frac{b}{c}(x-a) = \frac{b}{c}(-a) = \frac{-ab}{c}$. So p and q intersect at $\left(0, \frac{-ab}{c}\right)$. **11e.** $\frac{a}{c}$ **11f.** Let a pt. on line r be (x, y). Then the equation of r is $\frac{y-0}{x-b} = \frac{a}{c}$ or $y = \frac{a}{c}(x-b)$. **11g.** $-\frac{ab}{c} = \frac{a}{c}(b-0)$ ✔ $-\frac{ab}{c} = \frac{b}{c}(a-0)$ ✔ **11h.** $\left(0, -\frac{ab}{c}\right)$

MIXED REVIEW **13.** 36% **15.** The percent figure in each category is rounded to the nearest integer.

Wrap Up pages 489–491

1. $m\angle 1 = 101; m\angle 2 = 79; m\angle 3 = 101$ **2.** $m\angle 1 = 71;$ $m\angle 2 = 54; m\angle 3 = 55$ **3.** $m\angle 1 = 38; m\angle 2 = 43;$ $m\angle 3 = 99$ **4.** $m\angle 1 = 52; m\angle 2 = 25; m\angle 3 = 25$ **5.** E **6.** $x = 2; y = 1$ **7.** $x = 29; y = 28$ **8.** $x = 4;$ $y = 5$ **9.** $m\angle 1 = 124; m\angle 2 = 28; m\angle 3 = 62$ **10.** $m\angle 1 = 60; m\angle 2 = 90; m\angle 3 = 30$ **11.** $m\angle 1 = 50;$ $m\angle 2 = 130$ **12.** $m\angle 1 = 90; m\angle 2 = 25$ **13.** 26 in. **14.** 19 ft **15.** 20 cm **16.** 96 ft^2 **18.** (a, b) **19.** $(-a, 0)$ **20.** $(0, c)$ **21.** $(a-b, c)$ **22.** Sample: $A(0, a), B(b, a), C(b, 0), D(0, 0);$ $AC = \sqrt{a^2 + b^2}$, $BD = \sqrt{a^2 + b^2}$, so $AC = BD$, and $\overline{AC} \cong \overline{BD}$.
23. Sample: $F(0, a), G(a, a), H(a, 0), I(0, 0)$. The slope of $\overline{FH}$ is −1. The slope of $\overline{GI}$ is 1. Since the product of the slopes is −1, $\overline{FH} \perp \overline{GI}$. **31.** 6 **32.** 6 **33.** 3 **34.** 5

Preparing for Standardized Tests page 493

1. E **3.** C **5.** B **7.** C **9.** 140 cm^2

CHAPTER 10

Lesson 10-1 pages 499–502

ON YOUR OWN **1.** true **3.** true **5.** true **7.** true **9.** true **11.** 1 : 360 **13.** no; $\frac{36}{52} \neq \frac{20}{30}$
15. $JKLM \sim OPQN; \frac{3}{5}$ **17.** No; the corres. angles are not ≅. **19.** 6 **21.** 16.5 **23.** 7.5 **25.** −6 or 6 **27.** 3 ft by 2 ft **29.** (−4, 24), (16, 24) **31.** $x = 6; y = 8; z = 10$ **33.** $x = 20; y = 17.5; z = 7.5$ **35.** No; the ratios of the corres. sides are not =; $\frac{17}{14} \neq \frac{25}{21}$.

39a. 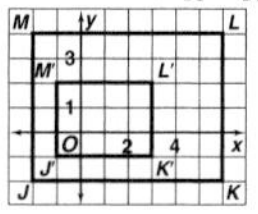

39b. $JKLM \sim J'K'L'M'$ with similarity ratio 2 : 1 **39c.** reduction

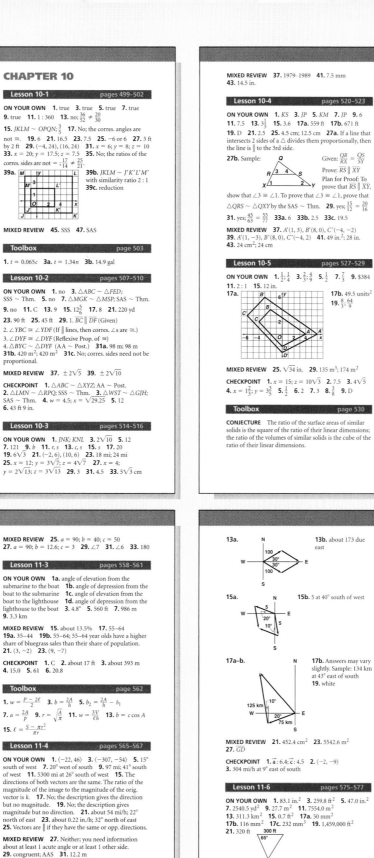

MIXED REVIEW **45.** SSS **47.** SAS

Toolbox page 503

1. $t = 0.065c$ **3a.** $t = 1.34n$ **3b.** 14.9 gal

Lesson 10-2 pages 507–510

ON YOUR OWN **1.** no **3.** $\triangle ABC \sim \triangle FED$; SSS ~ Thm. **5.** no **7.** $\triangle MGK \sim \triangle MSP$; SAS ~ Thm. **9.** no **11.** C **13.** 9 **15.** $12\frac{5}{6}$ **17.** 8 **21.** 220 yd **23.** 90 ft **25.** 45 ft **29.** 1. $\overline{BC} \parallel \overline{DF}$ (Given)
2. $\angle YBC \cong \angle YDF$ (If ∥ lines, then corres. ∠s are ≅.)
3. $\angle DYF \cong \angle DYF$ (Reflexive Prop. of ≅)
4. $\triangle BYC \sim \triangle DYF$ (AA ~ Post.) **31a.** 98 m; 98 m **31b.** 420 m^2; 420 m^2 **31c.** No; corres. sides need not be proportional.

MIXED REVIEW **37.** $\pm 2\sqrt{5}$ **39.** $\pm 2\sqrt{10}$

CHECKPOINT **1.** $\triangle ABC \sim \triangle XYZ$; AA ~ Post. **2.** $\triangle LMN \sim \triangle RPQ$; SSS ~ Thm. **3.** $\triangle WST \sim \triangle GJH$; SAS ~ Thm. **4.** $w = 4.5; x = \sqrt{29.25}$ **5.** 12 **6.** 43 ft 9 in.

Lesson 10-3 pages 514–516

ON YOUR OWN **1.** $JNK; KNL$ **3.** $2\sqrt{10}$ **5.** 12 **7.** 121 **9.** b **11.** r, s **13.** c, s **15.** s **17.** 20 **19.** $6\sqrt{3}$ **21.** (−2, 6), (10, 6) **23.** 18 mi; 24 mi **25.** $x = 12; y = 3\sqrt{7}; z = 4\sqrt{7}$ **27.** $x = 4;$ $y = 2\sqrt{13}; z = 3\sqrt{13}$ **29.** 3 **31.** 4.5 **33.** $5\sqrt{3}$ cm

MIXED REVIEW **37.** 1979–1989 **41.** 7.5 mm **43.** 14.5 in.

Lesson 10-4 pages 520–523

ON YOUR OWN **1.** KS **3.** JP **5.** KM **7.** JP **9.** 6 **11.** 7.5 **13.** $3\frac{1}{3}$ **15.** 3.6 **17a.** 559 ft **17b.** 671 ft **19.** D **21.** 2.5 **25.** 4.5 cm; 12.5 cm **27a.** If a line that intersects 2 sides of a △ divides them proportionally, then the line is ∥ to the 3rd side.

27b. Sample: 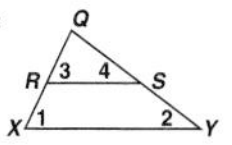

Given: $\frac{QR}{RX} = \frac{QS}{SY}$
Prove: $\overline{RS} \parallel \overline{XY}$
Plan for Proof: To prove that $\overline{RS} \parallel \overline{XY}$, show that $\angle 3 \cong \angle 1$. To prove that $\angle 3 \cong \angle 1$, prove that $\triangle QRS \sim \triangle QXY$ by the SAS ~ Thm. **29.** yes; $\frac{15}{12} = \frac{20}{16}$ **31.** yes; $\frac{45}{63} = \frac{55}{77}$ **33a.** 6 **33b.** 2.5 **33c.** 19.5

MIXED REVIEW **37.** $A'(1, 3), B'(8, 0), C'(-4, -2)$ **39.** $A'(1, -3), B'(8, 0), C'(-4, 2)$ **41.** 49 in.^{2}; 28 in. **43.** 24 cm^2; 24 cm

Lesson 10-5 pages 527–529

ON YOUR OWN **1.** $\frac{1}{2}; \frac{1}{4}$ **3.** $\frac{2}{3}; \frac{4}{9}$ **5.** $\frac{1}{2}$ **7.** $\frac{7}{3}$ **9.** $384 **11.** 2 : 1 **15.** 12 in.

17a. 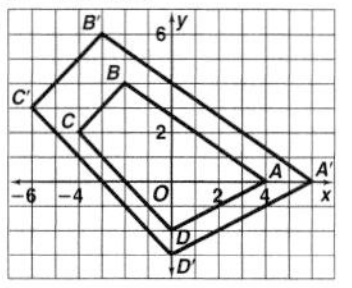

17b. 49.5 units^2 **19.** $\frac{8}{3}; \frac{64}{9}$

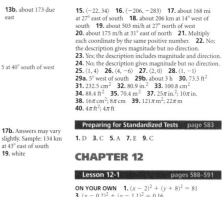

MIXED REVIEW **25.** $\sqrt{34}$ in. **29.** 135 m^3; 174 m^2

CHECKPOINT **1.** $x = 15; z = 10\sqrt{3}$ **2.** 7.5 **3.** $4\sqrt{5}$ **4.** $x = 1\frac{2}{3}; y = 3\frac{3}{5}$ **5.** $\frac{1}{2}$ **6.** 2 **7.** 3 **8.** $\frac{3}{8}$ **9.** D

Toolbox page 530

CONJECTURE The ratio of the surface areas of similar solids is the square of the ratio of their linear dimensions; the ratio of the volumes of similar solids is the cube of the ratio of their linear dimensions.

Lesson 10-6 pages 533–535

ON YOUR OWN **1.** no; $\frac{18}{27} \neq \frac{9}{12}$ **3.** yes; $\frac{4}{6} = \frac{6}{9} = \frac{8}{12}$ **5.** E **7.** $\sqrt[3]{9} : 1$ or $3 : \sqrt[3]{3}$ **9.** about 1000 cm^2 **11.** 9 : 25; 27 : 125 **13.** 5 : 8; 25 : 64 **17.** about 27,000 qt **19a.** 100 times **19b.** 1000 times **19c.** 600 times **19d.** Paul Bunyan's weight is 1000 times the weight of an average person, but his bones can only support 600 times the weight of an average person.

MIXED REVIEW **21.** 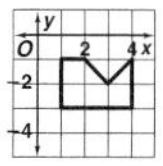

Wrap Up pages 537–539

1. 4 **2.** 9 **3.** $x = 12; y = 15$ **4.** $\triangle ABC \sim \triangle FDE$; AA ~ Post. **5.** no **6.** $\triangle XYZ \sim \triangle JKL$; SAS ~ Thm. **7.** C **8.** $x = 15; y = 12; z = 20$ **9.** $x = 2\sqrt{21};$ $y = 4\sqrt{3}; z = 4\sqrt{7}$ **10.** $x = 2\sqrt{3}; y = 6; z = 4\sqrt{3}$ **12.** 7.5 **13.** 5.5 **14.** 37.5 **15.** 4 : 9 **16.** 9 : 4 **17.** 1 : 4 **18.** 27 : 64 **19.** 64 : 27 **20.** 125 : 343 **22.** $\frac{3}{5}; \frac{4}{5}; \frac{3}{4}$ **23.** $\frac{\sqrt{2}}{2}; \frac{\sqrt{2}}{2}; 1$ **24.** $\frac{\sqrt{3}}{2}; \frac{1}{2}; \sqrt{3}$

Cumulative Review page 541

1. D **3.** B **5.** C **7.** C

CHAPTER 11

Lesson 11-1 pages 547–549

ON YOUR OWN **1.** $\frac{1}{2}$; 2 **3.** 1; 1 **5.** 74.1 **7.** 114.5 **9.** 11.2 **11.** 14.4 **13.** 32 **15.** 48 **17.** 1.6 **19.** 21.4 **21.** about 51° **23.** 52 m

25a.

x	$\tan x°$
5	0.1
10	0.2
15	0.3
20	0.4
25	0.5
30	0.6
35	0.7
40	0.8
45	1

x	$\tan x°$
50	1.2
55	1.4
60	1.7
65	2.1
70	2.7
75	3.7
80	5.7
85	11.4

25b. 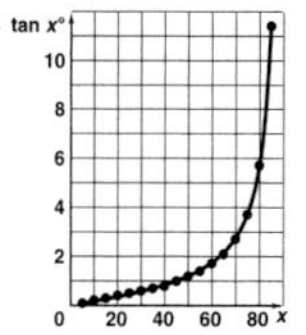

25c. The ratio approaches 0; the ratio increases rapidly. **25d.** Estimates may vary slightly. Sample: 82; 2.5; 74 **27.** $w = 6.7; x = 8.1$ **29.** $w = 59; x = 36$ **31.** 53.1 **33.** 33.7

MIXED REVIEW **37a.** If a flag is a United States flag, then it contains the colors red, white, and blue. **37b.** false; true **39a.** If you live on an island, then you live in Hawaii. **39b.** true; false **43.** $\frac{10}{19}; \frac{3\sqrt{29}}{19}$ **45.** $\frac{9}{15}$ or $\frac{3}{5}$; $\frac{12}{15}$ or $\frac{4}{5}$

Toolbox page 550

INVESTIGATE No; as $m\angle A$ increases, so does the ratio; 0; 1

$m\angle A$	$\frac{DE}{AE}$
10	0.17
20	0.34
30	0.5
40	0.64
50	0.77
60	0.87
70	0.94
80	0.98

CONJECTURE The values match those in the sine column; sine

EXTEND The smaller the measure of the angle, the closer DA is to AE; the values are between 0 and 1.

The greater the measure of the angle, the greater is the ratio; the values are positive and can be arbitrarily large.

$m\angle A$	$\frac{DA}{AE}$
10	0.98
20	0.94
30	0.87
40	0.77
50	0.64
60	0.5
70	0.34
80	0.17

$m\angle A$	$\frac{DE}{DA}$
10	0.18
20	0.36
30	0.58
40	0.84
50	1.19
60	1.73
70	2.75
80	5.67

Lesson 11-2 pages 554–555

ON YOUR OWN **1.** $\frac{7}{25}; \frac{24}{25}$ **3.** $\frac{1}{2}; \frac{\sqrt{3}}{2}$ **7.** 8.3 **9.** 21 **11.** 46 **13.** 106.5 **15.** D **19a.** about 1.51 AU **19b.** about 5.19 AU **21.** $w = 37; x = 7.5$ **23.** $w = 59; x = 20.0$

MIXED REVIEW **25.** $a = 90; b = 40; c = 50$ **27.** $a = 90; b = 12.6; c = 3$ **29.** ∠7 **31.** ∠6 **33.** 180

Lesson 11-3 pages 558–561

ON YOUR OWN **1a.** angle of elevation from the submarine to the boat **1b.** angle of depression from the boat to the submarine **1c.** angle of elevation from the boat to the lighthouse **1d.** angle of depression from the lighthouse to the boat **3.** 4.8° **5.** 560 ft **7.** 986 m **9.** 3.3 km

MIXED REVIEW **15.** about 13.5% **17.** 55–64 **19a.** 35–44 **19b.** 55–64; 55–64 year olds have a higher share of bluegrass sales than their share of population. **21.** (3, −2) **23.** (9, −7)

CHECKPOINT **1.** C **2.** about 17 ft **3.** about 393 m **4.** 15.0 **5.** 61 **6.** 20.8

Toolbox page 562

1. $w = \frac{P - 2\ell}{2}$ **3.** $b = \frac{2A}{h}$ **5.** $b_2 = \frac{2A}{h} - b_1$ **7.** $a = \frac{2A}{p}$ **9.** $r = \sqrt{\frac{A}{\pi}}$ **11.** $w = \frac{3V}{\ell h}$ **13.** $b = c\cos A$ **15.** $\ell = \frac{S - \pi r^2}{\pi r}$

Lesson 11-4 pages 565–567

ON YOUR OWN **1.** ⟨−22, 46⟩ **3.** ⟨−307, −54⟩ **5.** 15° south of west **7.** 20° west of south **9.** 97 mi; 41° south of west **11.** 5300 mi at 26° south of west **15.** The directions of both vectors are the same. The ratio of the magnitude of the image to the magnitude of the orig. vector is k. **17.** No; the description gives the direction but no magnitude. **19.** No; the description gives magnitude but no direction. **21.** about 54 mi/h; 22° north of east **23.** about 0.22 in./h; 32° north of east **25.** Vectors are ∥ if they have the same or opp. directions.

MIXED REVIEW **27.** Neither; you need information about at least 1 acute angle or at least 1 other side. **29.** congruent; AAS **31.** 12.2 m

Lesson 11-5 pages 570–572

ON YOUR OWN **1.** ⟨−2, 1⟩ **3.** ⟨−6, 2⟩ **5.** ⟨−2, −9⟩ **7.** ⟨1, −1⟩ **9a.** $\frac{2}{3}$ **11a.** 15° south of west **11b.** about 6.7 h or 6 h 40 min

13a. 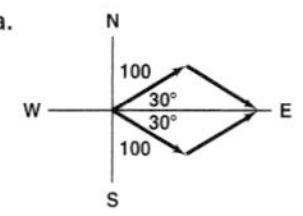

13b. about 173 due east

15a. 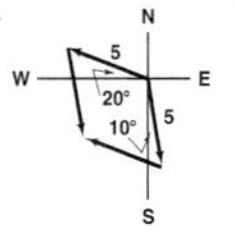

15b. 5 at 40° south of west

17a–b. 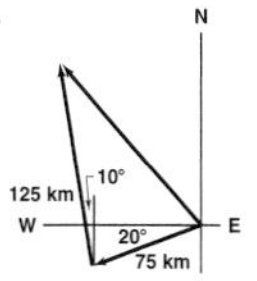

17b. Answers may vary slightly. Sample: 134 km at 43° east of south **19.** white

MIXED REVIEW **21.** 452.4 cm^2 **23.** 5542.6 m^2 **27.** $\overline{GD}$

CHECKPOINT **1.** $\vec{a}$: 6.4; $\vec{c}$: 4.5 **2.** ⟨−2, −9⟩ **3.** 304 mi/h at 9° east of south

Lesson 11-6 pages 575–577

ON YOUR OWN **1.** 83.1 in.^{2} **3.** 259.8 ft^2 **5.** 47.0 in.^{2} **7.** 2540.5 yd^2 **9.** 27.7 m^2 **11.** 7554.0 m^2 **13.** 311.3 km^2 **15.** 0.7 ft^2 **17a.** 50 mm^2 **17b.** 116 mm^2 **17c.** 232 mm^3 **19.** 1,459,000 ft^2 **21.** 320 ft 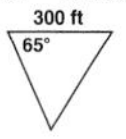

MIXED REVIEW **23.** 5 in. **25.** 8.5 m **27.** 281.5 cm^3; 140.7 cm^2

Wrap Up pages 579–581

1. $\frac{4}{5}; \frac{3}{5}; \frac{4}{3}$ **2.** $\frac{\sqrt{19}}{10}; \frac{9}{10}; \frac{\sqrt{19}}{9}$ **3.** $\frac{\sqrt{3}}{2}; \frac{1}{2}; \frac{\sqrt{3}}{1}$ **4.** $\frac{8}{17}; \frac{15}{17}; \frac{8}{15}$ **5.** 51 **6.** 16.5 **7.** 33 **8.** 13.8 **9.** D **10.** 1410 ft **11.** 280 ft **13.** ⟨126, 82⟩ **14.** ⟨37, −93⟩ **15.** ⟨−22, 34⟩ **16.** ⟨−206, −283⟩ **17.** about 168 mi at 27° east of south **18.** about 206 km at 14° west of south **19.** about 503 mi/h at 27° north of west **20.** about 175 m/h at 31° east of north **21.** Multiply each coordinate by the same positive number. **22.** No; the description gives magnitude but no direction. **23.** Yes; the description includes magnitude and direction. **24.** No; the description gives magnitude but no direction. **25.** ⟨1, 4⟩ **26.** ⟨4, −6⟩ **27.** ⟨2, 0⟩ **28.** ⟨1, −1⟩ **29a.** 5° west of south **29b.** about 3 h **30.** 73.5 ft^2 **31.** 232.5 cm^2 **32.** 80.9 in.^{2} **33.** 100.8 cm^2 **34.** 88.4 ft^2 **35.** 70.4 m^2 **37.** 25π in.^{2}; 10π in. **38.** 16π cm^2; 8π cm **39.** 121π m^2; 22π m **40.** 4π ft^2; 4π ft

Preparing for Standardized Tests page 583

1. D **3.** C **5.** A **7.** E **9.** C

CHAPTER 12

Lesson 12-1 pages 588–591

ON YOUR OWN **1.** $(x-2)^2 + (y+8)^2 = 81$ **3.** $(x-0.2)^2 + (y-1.1)^2 = 0.16$ **5.** $(x+6)^2 + (y-3)^2 = 64$ **7.** B **9.** C **11.** (−7, 5); 4 **13.** (0.3, 0); 0.2

15. 6 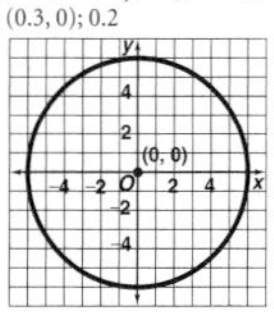

17. 3 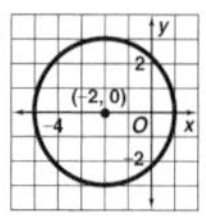

19a. ⟨−5, 3⟩ **19b.** (0, 0); 8 **21.** $x^2 + y^2 = 9$ **23.** $(x-2)^2 + (y-2)^2 = 16$ **25.** $(x+2)^2 + (y-3)^2 = 9$ **27.** $(x+2)^2 + (y-6)^2 = 16$ **29.** $(x-7)^2 + (y+2)^2 = 52$ **31.** $(x-3)^2 + (y+5)^2 = 100$ **33a.** $x^2 + y^2 = 15{,}681{,}600$ **33b.** 69.1 mi **33c.** 1.2 mi **33d.** about 32 days **35.** $(x-5)^2 + (y-3)^2 = 13$ **37.** $(x+3)^2 + (y+1.5)^2 = 6.25$ **39.** $(x-2)^2 + (y+2)^2 = 41$ **43a.** $\sqrt{6}$ **43b.** $(x+1)^2 + (y-3)^2 + (z-2)^2 = 6$

MIXED REVIEW **45.** $\angle AEB \cong \angle DEC$ because vertical $\angle$s are $\cong$. Then $\triangle ABE \cong \triangle DCE$ by AAS, and $\overline{BE} \cong \overline{CE}$, $\overline{AE} \cong \overline{DE}$ by CPCTC. $\overline{AC} \cong \overline{DB}$ by the Segment Addition Post. $\overline{BC} \cong \overline{BC}$ by Reflexive Prop. of $\cong$. Then $\triangle ABC \cong \triangle DCB$ by SSS. **47.** 512 in.^{3} **49.** 17°; 107° **51.** 3°; 93°

Toolbox page 592

1. (3, 120°) **3.** (5, 315°) **5.** (2, 240°) **13.** Read the measures of the central $\angle$s for points X and Y from the graph, and subtract the measures.

Lesson 12-2 pages 596–599

ON YOUR OWN **1.** 63 **3.** 72 **5.** 13 **7.** 9 **9b.** the lines bisecting the angles formed by the axes **9c.** $y = x, y = -x$ **11.** D **13a.** 14.5 in. **13b.** 16.5 in. **15.** 14.2 in. **17.** 1. $\overline{BC}$ is tangent to $\odot A$ at D. (Given) 2. $\overline{BC} \perp \overline{AD}$ (A tangent to a $\odot$ is $\perp$ to the radius drawn to the pt. of tangency.) 3. $\overline{DB} \cong \overline{DC}$ (Given) 4. $\overline{AD}$ is the $\perp$ bisector of $\overline{BC}$. (Def. of $\perp$ bisector) 5. $\overline{AB} \cong \overline{AC}$ (A pt. on the $\perp$ bisector of a segment is equidistant from the endpts. of the segment.) **19.** They are $\cong$; $\overline{CE} \cong \overline{FE}$ and $\overline{FE} \cong \overline{DE}$ because 2 segments tangent to a $\odot$ from a pt. outside the $\odot$ are $\cong$; $\overline{CE} \cong \overline{DE}$ by Transitive Prop. of $\cong$. **21.** Blue segments are common external tangents to the sun and the moon; green segments are common internal tangents to the sun and the moon; red segments are common external tangents to the sun and Earth. **23.** 4 **25.** about 34.6 in.

MIXED REVIEW **27.** $\frac{13}{17}; \frac{2\sqrt{30}}{17}$ **29a.** rectangle **31.** 8.1

Lesson 12-3 pages 603–606

ON YOUR OWN **1.** 6 **3.** 5 **5.** 7 **7.** 18.8 **9a.** 5.9 cm **11.** 90 **13.** about 123.9 **15.** 6 in. **17.** $8\sqrt{3}$ cm **21.** 1. $\overline{CE} \perp \overline{BD}$ (Given) 2. $\overline{BF} \cong \overline{FD}$ (A diameter $\perp$ to a chord bisects the chord.) 3. $\overline{CE}$ is the $\perp$ bisector of $\overline{BD}$. (Def. of $\perp$ bisector) 4. $\overline{BC} \cong \overline{DC}$ (A point on the $\perp$ bisector of a segment is equidistant from the endpts. of the segment.) 5. $\widehat{BC} \cong \widehat{DC}$ ($\cong$ chords have $\cong$ arcs.) **23a.** $\overline{EC}$; $\overline{ED}$; $\overline{BC}$; $\overline{BD}$ **23b.** center of the $\odot$ **23c.** A diameter $\perp$ to a chord bisects the chord and its arc; the $\perp$ bisector of a chord contains the center of the $\odot$. **25.** The thms. are not true for angles, chords, or arcs that are in noncongruent $\odot$s. **27a.** 2 **27b.** 3.5 cm and 15.5 cm

MIXED REVIEW **29.** obtuse **31.** obtuse **33.** acute **35.** 80 **37.** 125

CHECKPOINT **1.** $(x - 1.5)^2 + (y - 0.5)^2 = 2.5$ **2.** $(x - 3.5)^2 + (y - 1)^2 = 46.25$ **3.** $(x + 1.5)^2 + (y + 4)^2 = 22.25$ **4.** 76 cm **5.** 48 in. **6.** 51 m **7.** 24 **8.** 5 **9.** 8 **10b.** 3 **10c.** Kites; the sides inside the $\odot$ are $\cong$ because they are radii of the same $\odot$; the sides outside the $\odot$ are $\cong$ because they are tangent segments to a $\odot$ drawn from a pt. outside the $\odot$.

Lesson 12-4 pages 610–613

ON YOUR OWN **1.** inscribed in **3.** circumscribed about **5.** 58 **7.** $a = 218; b = 109$ **9.** $a = 85; b = 47.5; c = 90$ **11.** $a = 112; b = 124; c = 42$ **13.** 1. $\angle ABC$ is inscribed in $\odot O$. (Given) 2. $m\angle ABP = \frac{1}{2}m\widehat{AP}$ and $m\angle PBC = \frac{1}{2}m\widehat{PC}$ (Inscribed Angle Thm., Case I) 3. $m\angle ABP + m\angle PBC = \frac{1}{2}m\widehat{AP} + \frac{1}{2}m\widehat{PC}$ (Addition Prop. of =) 4. $m\angle ABP + m\angle PBC = \frac{1}{2}(m\widehat{AP} + m\widehat{PC})$ (Distributive Prop.) 5. $m\angle ABP + m\angle PBC = m\angle ABC$ (Angle Addition Post.) 6. $m\widehat{AC} = m\widehat{AP} + m\widehat{PC}$ (Arc Addition Post.) 7. $m\angle ABC = \frac{1}{2}m\widehat{AC}$ (Substitution) **15.** 1. $m\widehat{AD} = m\widehat{BC}$ (Given) 2. $m\angle ABD = \frac{1}{2}m\widehat{AD}$ and $m\angle BAC = \frac{1}{2}m\widehat{BC}$ (Measure of an inscribed $\angle$ is half the measure of its intercepted arc.) 3. $m\angle BAC = m\angle ABD$ (Substitution) 4. $\overline{AD} \cong \overline{BC}$ ($\cong$ arcs have $\cong$ chords.) 5. $\angle ACB \cong \angle BDA$ (2 inscribed angles that intercept the same arc are $\cong$.) 6. $\triangle ABD \cong \triangle BAC$ (AAS) **17a.** rectangle **17b.** Opp. angles are $\cong$ and supplementary. So they are rt. angles. **19.** Draw the diameter through the given pt. Construct the line $\perp$ to the diameter through this pt. **21a.** 360 **21b.** $m\widehat{DAB} + m\widehat{BCD} = 360$. $m\angle A = \frac{1}{2}m\widehat{BCD}$ and $m\angle C = \frac{1}{2}m\widehat{DAB}$, so $m\angle A + m\angle C = \frac{1}{2} \cdot 360 = 180$. $\angle A$ and $\angle C$ are supplementary. **23.** $\angle ACB$ is inscribed in a semicircle so it is a rt. angle. Then $\overleftrightarrow{BC}$ is $\perp$ to radius $\overline{AC}$ and passes through its endpt. on the $\odot$. Therefore, $\overleftrightarrow{BC}$ is tangent to $\odot A$. **25a.** 30 **25b.** 78 **25c.** 95 **25d.** 105 **25e.** 85 **25f.** 75 **27a.** 64 **27b.** 116 **27c.** 58 **27d.** 58 **27e.** 58 **27f.** 64 **27g.** 32 **31.** 180

MIXED REVIEW **33.** 5 cm **35.** 108 **37.** 130

Lesson 12-5 pages 617–619

ON YOUR OWN **1.** 46 **3.** $x = 60; y = 70$ **5.** $x = 100; y = 30$ **7.** $x = 50; y = 97.5$ **9a.** 160° **9b.** about 18,800 mi **11.** A **13a.** $360 - x$ **13b.** $180 - x$ **13c.** $180 - y$ **15a.** $m\angle X = 30; 30 < m\angle Y < 180; 0 < m\angle Z < 30$ **15b.** The ship is in safe waters if the measure of the angle is ≤ 30. **17.** $x = 80; y = 50; z = 90$

MIXED REVIEW **19.** 35% **21.** 25–44 **23.** *HF*; *UT*

CHECKPOINT **1.** 58 **2.** $a = 30; b = 42; c = 80; d = 116$ **3.** 30 **4.** $a = 140; b = 70; c = 47.5$

5. A secant extends outside the $\odot$, a chord does not.

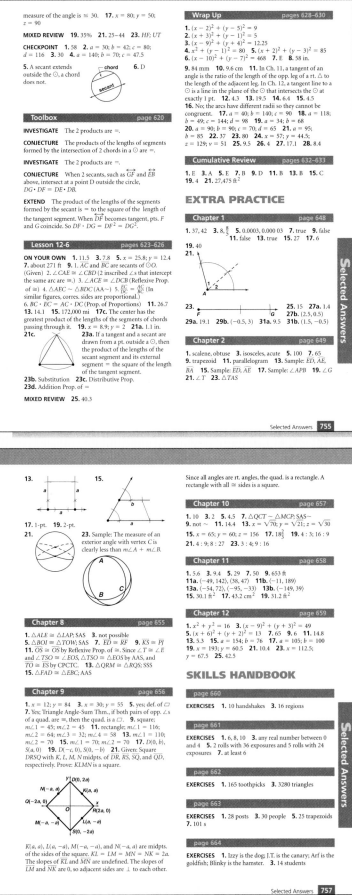

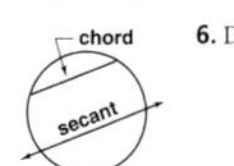

6. D

Toolbox page 620

INVESTIGATE The 2 products are =.

CONJECTURE The products of the lengths of segments formed by the intersection of 2 chords in a $\odot$ are =.

INVESTIGATE The 2 products are =.

CONJECTURE When 2 secants, such as $\overleftrightarrow{GF}$ and $\overleftrightarrow{EB}$ above, intersect at a point D outside the circle, $DG \cdot DF = DE \cdot DB$.

EXTEND The product of the lengths of the segments formed by the secant is = to the square of the length of the tangent segment. When $\overleftrightarrow{DF}$ becomes tangent, pts. F and G coincide. So $DF \cdot DG = DF^2 = DG^2$.

Lesson 12-6 pages 623–626

ON YOUR OWN **1.** 11.5 **3.** 7.8 **5.** $x = 25.8; y = 12.4$ **7.** about 271 ft **9.** 1. $\overline{AC}$ and $\overline{BC}$ are secants of $\odot O$. (Given) 2. $\angle CAE \cong \angle CBD$ (2 inscribed $\angle$s that intercept the same arc are $\cong$.) 3. $\angle ACE \cong \angle DCB$ (Reflexive Prop. of $\cong$) 4. $\triangle AEC \sim \triangle BDC$ (AA~) 5. $\frac{EC}{DC} = \frac{AC}{BC}$ (In similar figures, corres. sides are proportional.) 6. $BC \cdot EC = AC \cdot DC$ (Prop. of Proportions) **11.** 26.7 **13.** 14.1 **15.** 172,000 mi **17c.** The center has the greatest product of the lengths of the segments of chords passing through it. **19.** $x = 8.9; y = 2$ **21a.** 1.1 in. **21c.**

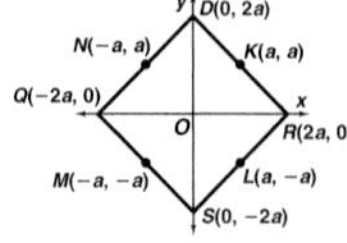

23a. If a tangent and a secant are drawn from a pt. outside a $\odot$, then the product of the lengths of the secant segment and its external segment = the square of the length of the tangent segment. **23b.** Substitution **23c.** Distributive Prop. **23d.** Addition Prop. of =

MIXED REVIEW **25.** 40.3

Wrap Up pages 628–630

1. $(x - 2)^2 + (y - 5)^2 = 9$ **2.** $(x + 3)^2 + (y - 1)^2 = 5$ **3.** $(x - 9)^2 + (y + 4)^2 = 12.25$ **4.** $x^2 + (y - 1)^2 = 80$ **5.** $(x + 2)^2 + (y - 3)^2 = 85$ **6.** $(x - 10)^2 + (y - 7)^2 = 468$ **7.** E **8.** 58 in. **9.** 84 mm **10.** 9.6 cm **11.** In Ch. 11, a tangent of an angle is the ratio of the length of the opp. leg of a rt. $\triangle$ to the length of the adjacent leg. In Ch. 12, a tangent line to a $\odot$ is a line in the plane of the $\odot$ that intersects the $\odot$ at exactly 1 pt. **12.** 4.3 **13.** 19.5 **14.** 6.4 **15.** 4.5 **16.** No; the arcs have different radii so they cannot be congruent. **17.** $a = 40; b = 140; c = 90$ **18.** $a = 118; b = 49; c = 144; d = 98$ **19.** $a = 34; b = 68$ **20.** $a = 90; b = 90; c = 70; d = 65$ **21.** $a = 95; b = 85$ **22.** 37 **23.** 80 **24.** $x = 57; y = 44.5; z = 129; v = 51$ **25.** 9.5 **26.** 4 **27.** 17.1 **28.** 8.4

Cumulative Review pages 632–633

1. E **3.** A **5.** E **7.** B **9.** D **11.** B **13.** B **15.** C **19.** 4 **21.** 27,475 ft^2

EXTRA PRACTICE

Chapter 1 page 648

1. 37, 42 **3.** 8, $\frac{8}{5}$ **5.** 0.0003, 0.000 03 **7.** true **9.** false **11.** false **13.** true **15.** 27 **17.** 6 **19.** 40 **21.**

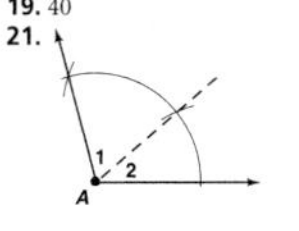

23.

25. 15 **27a.** 1.4 **27b.** (2.5, 0.5) **29a.** 19.1 **29b.** (−0.5, 3) **31a.** 9.5 **31b.** (1.5, −0.5)

Chapter 2 page 649

1. scalene, obtuse **3.** isosceles, acute **5.** 100 **7.** 65 **9.** trapezoid **11.** parallelogram **13.** Sample: $\overrightarrow{ED}$, $\overrightarrow{AE}$, $\overrightarrow{BA}$ **15.** Sample: $\overline{ED}$, $\overline{AE}$ **17.** Sample: $\angle APB$ **19.** $\angle G$ **21.** $\angle T$ **23.** $\triangle TAS$

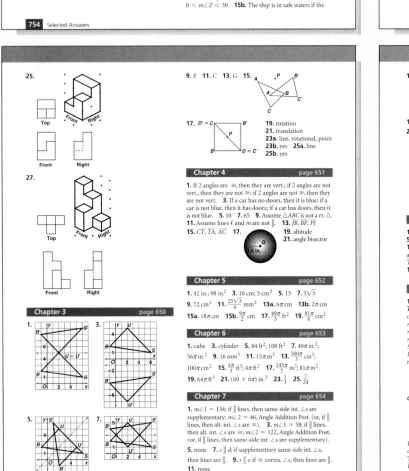

Selected Answers

25.

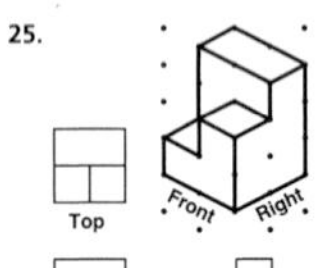

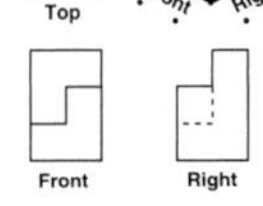

27.

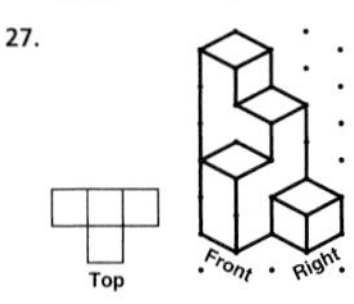

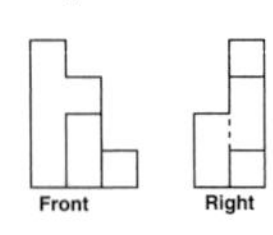

Chapter 3 page 650

1. **3.** **5.** **7.**

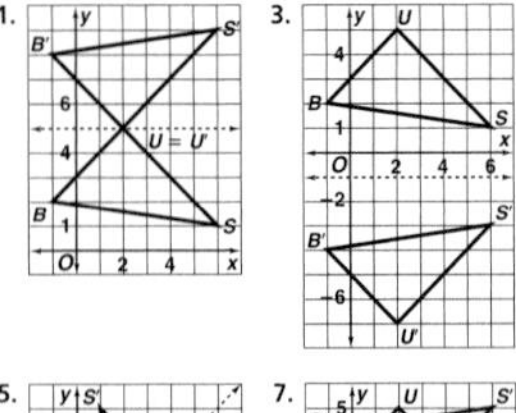

9. E **11.** C **13.** G **15.**

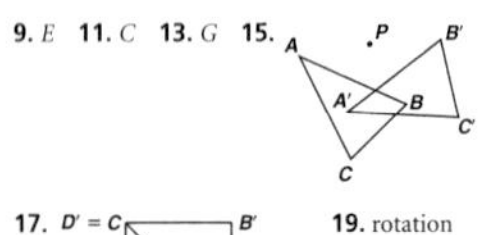

17.

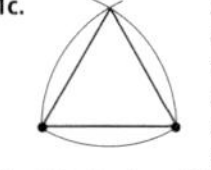

19. rotation **21.** translation **23a.** line, rotational, point **23b.** yes **25a.** line **25b.** yes

Chapter 4 page 651

1. If 2 angles are $\cong$, then they are vert.; if 2 angles are not vert., then they are not $\cong$; if 2 angles are not $\cong$, then they are not vert. **3.** If a car has no doors, then it is blue; if a car is not blue, then it has doors; if a car has doors, then it is not blue. **5.** 10 **7.** 65 **9.** Assume $\triangle ABC$ is not a rt. $\triangle$. **11.** Assume lines ℓ and m are not $\parallel$. **13.** $\overline{JB}$, $\overline{BP}$, $\overline{PJ}$ **15.** $\overline{CT}$, $\overline{TA}$, $\overline{AC}$ **17.**

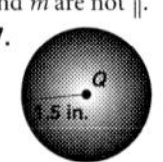

19. altitude **21.** angle bisector

Chapter 5 page 652

1. 42 in.; 98 in.^{2} **3.** 10 cm; 5 cm^2 **5.** 15 **7.** $3\sqrt{5}$ **9.** 72 cm^2 **11.** $\frac{25\sqrt{3}}{4}$ mm^2 **13a.** 6π cm **13b.** 2π cm **15a.** 18π cm **15b.** $\frac{9\pi}{2}$ cm **17.** $\frac{49\pi}{3}$ ft^2 **19.** $\frac{81\pi}{8}$ cm^2

Chapter 6 page 653

1. cube **3.** cylinder **5.** 84 ft^2; 108 ft^2 **7.** 40π in.^{2}; 56π in.^{2} **9.** 16 mm^3 **11.** 15π m^3 **13.** $\frac{500\pi}{3}$ cm^3; 100π cm^2 **15.** $\frac{4\pi}{3}$ ft^3; 4π ft^2 **17.** $\frac{243\pi}{2}$ m^3; 81π m^2 **19.** 64π ft^3 **21.** $(60 + 6\pi)$ in.^{3} **23.** $\frac{1}{3}$ **25.** $\frac{7}{24}$

Chapter 7 page 654

1. $m\angle 1 = 134$; if $\parallel$ lines, then same-side int. $\angle$s are supplementary; $m\angle 2 = 46$, Angle Addition Post. (or, if $\parallel$ lines, then alt. int. $\angle$s are $\cong$). **3.** $m\angle 1 = 58$; if $\parallel$ lines, then alt. int. $\angle$s are $\cong$; $m\angle 2 = 122$, Angle Addition Post. (or, if $\parallel$ lines, then same-side int. $\angle$s are supplementary). **5.** none **7.** $c \parallel d$; if supplementary same-side int. $\angle$s, then lines are $\parallel$. **9.** $r \parallel s$; if $\cong$ corres. $\angle$s, then lines are $\parallel$. **11.** none

13. **15.** **17.** 1-pt. **19.** 2-pt. **21.**

23. Sample: The measure of an exterior angle with vertex C is clearly less than $m\angle A + m\angle B$.

Chapter 8 page 655

1. $\triangle ALE \cong \triangle LAP$; SAS **3.** not possible **5.** $\triangle BOI \cong \triangle TOW$; SAS **7.** $\overline{ED} \cong \overline{RF}$ **9.** $\overline{KS} \cong \overline{PJ}$ **11.** $\overline{OS} \cong \overline{OS}$ by Reflexive Prop. of $\cong$. Since $\angle T \cong \angle E$ and $\angle TSO \cong \angle EOS$, $\triangle TSO \cong \triangle EOS$ by AAS, and $\overline{TO} \cong \overline{ES}$ by CPCTC. **13.** $\triangle QRM \cong \triangle RQS$; SSS **15.** $\triangle FAD \cong \triangle EBC$; AAS

Chapter 9 page 656

1. $x = 12; y = 84$ **3.** $x = 30; y = 55$ **5.** yes; def. of ▱ **7.** Yes; Triangle Angle-Sum Thm., if both pairs of opp. $\angle$s of a quad. are $\cong$, then the quad. is a ▱. **9.** square; $m\angle 1 = 45; m\angle 2 = 45$ **11.** rectangle; $m\angle 1 = 116; m\angle 2 = 64; m\angle 3 = 32; m\angle 4 = 58$ **13.** $m\angle 1 = 110; m\angle 2 = 70$ **15.** $m\angle 1 = 70; m\angle 2 = 70$ **17.** $D(0, b)$, $S(a, 0)$ **19.** $D(-c, 0)$, $S(0, -b)$ **21.** Given: Square $DRSQ$ with K, L, M, N midpts. of $\overline{DR}$, $\overline{RS}$, $\overline{SQ}$, and $\overline{QD}$, respectively. Prove: $KLMN$ is a square.

$K(a, a)$, $L(a, -a)$, $M(-a, -a)$, and $N(-a, a)$ are midpts. of the sides of the square. $KL = LM = MN = NK = 2a$. The slopes of $\overline{KL}$ and $\overline{MN}$ are undefined. The slopes of $\overline{LM}$ and $\overline{NK}$ are 0, so adjacent sides are $\perp$ to each other. Since all angles are rt. angles, the quad. is a rectangle. A rectangle with all $\cong$ sides is a square.

Chapter 10 page 657

1. 10 **3.** 2 **5.** 4.5 **7.** $\triangle QCT \sim \triangle MCP$; SAS~ **9.** not ~ **11.** 14.4 **13.** $x = \sqrt{70}; y = \sqrt{21}; z = \sqrt{30}$ **15.** $x = 65; y = 60; z = 156$ **17.** $18\frac{2}{3}$ **19.** 4 : 3; 16 : 9 **21.** 4 : 9; 8 : 27 **23.** 3 : 4; 9 : 16

Chapter 11 page 658

1. 5.6 **3.** 9.4 **5.** 29 **7.** 50 **9.** 653 ft **11a.** (−49, 142), (38, 47) **11b.** (−11, 189) **13a.** (−54, 72), (−95, −33) **13b.** (−149, 39) **15.** 30.1 ft^2 **17.** 43.2 cm^2 **19.** 31.2 ft^2

Chapter 12 page 659

1. $x^2 + y^2 = 16$ **3.** $(x - 9)^2 + (y + 3)^2 = 49$ **5.** $(x + 6)^2 + (y + 2)^2 = 13$ **7.** 65 **9.** 6 **11.** 14.8 **13.** 5.3 **15.** $a = 154; b = 76$ **17.** $a = 105; b = 100$ **19.** $x = 193; y = 60.5$ **21.** 10.4 **23.** $x = 112.5; y = 67.5$ **25.** 42.5

SKILLS HANDBOOK

page 660

EXERCISES **1.** 10 handshakes **3.** 16 regions

page 661

EXERCISES **1.** 6, 8, 10 **3.** any real number between 0 and 4 **5.** 2 rolls with 36 exposures and 5 rolls with 24 exposures **7.** at least 6

page 662

EXERCISES **1.** 165 toothpicks **3.** 3280 triangles

page 663

EXERCISES **1.** 28 posts **3.** 30 people **5.** 25 trapezoids **7.** 101 s

page 664

EXERCISES **1.** Izzy is the dog; J.T. is the canary; Arf is the goldfish; Blinky is the hamster. **3.** 14 students

Selected Answers

page 665

EXERCISES **1.** Route 90 east, Route 128 north, Route 4 north **3.** 23 d **5.** $2000 **7.** 11.4 mi

page 666

EXERCISES **1.** 39 mm; 51 mm **3.**

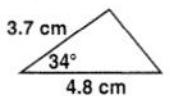

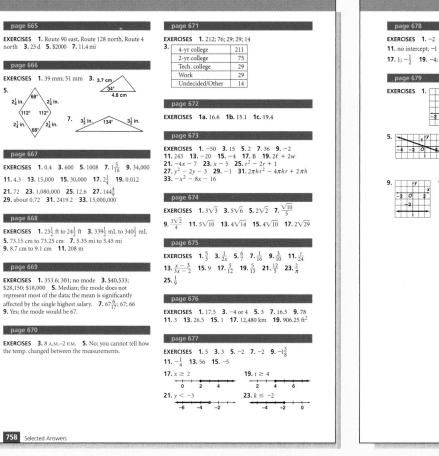

5.

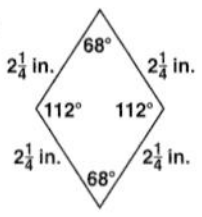

7.

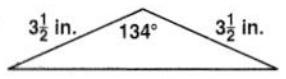

page 667

EXERCISES **1.** 0.4 **3.** 600 **5.** 1008 **7.** $1\frac{5}{16}$ **9.** 34,000 **11.** 4.3 **13.** 15,000 **15.** 30,000 **17.** $2\frac{1}{4}$ **19.** 0.012 **21.** 72 **23.** 1,080,000 **25.** 12.6 **27.** $144\frac{4}{9}$ **29.** about 0.72 **31.** 2419.2 **33.** 13,000,000

page 668

EXERCISES **1.** $23\frac{1}{2}$ ft to $24\frac{1}{2}$ ft **3.** $339\frac{1}{2}$ mL to $340\frac{1}{2}$ mL **5.** 73.15 cm to 73.25 cm **7.** 5.35 mi to 5.45 mi **9.** 8.7 cm to 9.1 cm **11.** 208 m

page 669

EXERCISES **1.** 353.6; 301; no mode **3.** $40,533; $28,150; $18,000 **5.** Median; the mode does not represent most of the data; the mean is significantly affected by the single highest salary. **7.** $67\frac{6}{17}$; 67; 66 **9.** Yes; the mode would be 67.

page 670

EXERCISES **3.** 8 A.M.–2 P.M. **5.** No; you cannot tell how the temp. changed between the measurements.

page 671

EXERCISES **1.** 212; 76; 29; 29; 14

3.

4-yr college	211
2-yr college	75
Tech. college	29
Work	29
Undecided/Other	14

page 672

EXERCISES **1a.** 16.6 **1b.** 15.1 **1c.** 19.4

page 673

EXERCISES **1.** −50 **3.** 15 **5.** 2 **7.** 36 **9.** −2 **11.** 243 **13.** −20 **15.** −4 **17.** B **19.** $2\ell + 2w$ **21.** $-4x - 7$ **23.** $x - 5$ **25.** $r^2 - 2r + 1$ **27.** $y^2 - 2y - 3$ **29.** −1 **31.** $2\pi hr^2 - 4\pi hr + 2\pi h$ **33.** $-x^2 - 8x - 16$

page 674

EXERCISES **1.** $3\sqrt{3}$ **3.** $5\sqrt{6}$ **5.** $2\sqrt{2}$ **7.** $\frac{\sqrt{10}}{5}$ **9.** $\frac{3\sqrt{2}}{4}$ **11.** $5\sqrt{10}$ **13.** $4\sqrt{14}$ **15.** $4\sqrt{10}$ **17.** $2\sqrt{29}$

page 675

EXERCISES **1.** $\frac{5}{3}$ **3.** $\frac{1}{2x}$ **5.** $\frac{6}{7}$ **7.** $\frac{1}{16}$ **9.** $\frac{3}{10}$ **11.** $\frac{r}{24}$ **13.** $\frac{x-3}{3x-2}$ **15.** 9 **17.** $\frac{5}{12}$ **19.** $\frac{5}{13}$ **21.** $\frac{12}{5}$ **23.** $\frac{2}{\pi}$ **25.** $\frac{1}{9}$

page 676

EXERCISES **1.** 17.5 **3.** −4 or 4 **5.** 3 **7.** 16.5 **9.** 78 **11.** 3 **13.** 26.5 **15.** 1 **17.** 12,480 km **19.** 906.25 ft^2

page 677

EXERCISES **1.** 5 **3.** 3 **5.** −2 **7.** −2 **9.** $-1\frac{3}{8}$ **11.** $-\frac{1}{4}$ **13.** 56 **15.** −5

17. $x \geq 2$

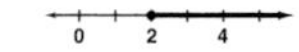

19. $t \geq 4$

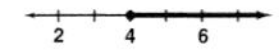

21. $y < -3$

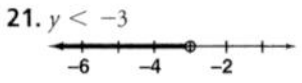

23. $k \leq -2$

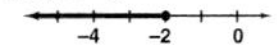

page 678

EXERCISES **1.** −2 **3.** −1 **5.** 0 **7.** undef. **9.** $\frac{1}{3}$; −1 **11.** no intercept; −1 **13.** 1; 1 **15.** −4; no intercept **17.** 1; $-\frac{1}{2}$ **19.** −4; $2\frac{2}{9}$ **21.** undef.; $-\frac{2}{3}$; 0

page 679

EXERCISES **1.**

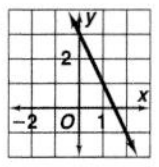

3.

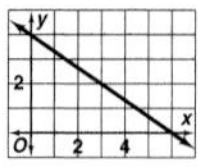

5.

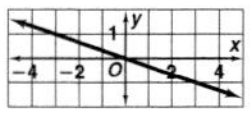

7.

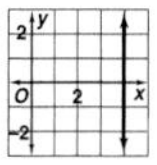

9.

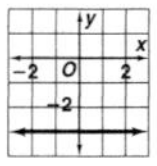

11.

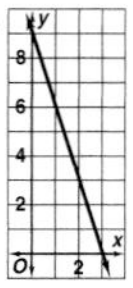

13.

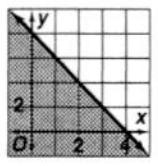

15.

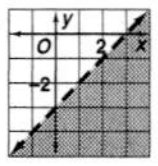

17.

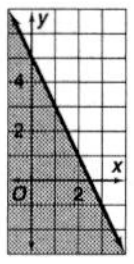

19.

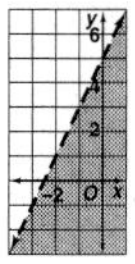

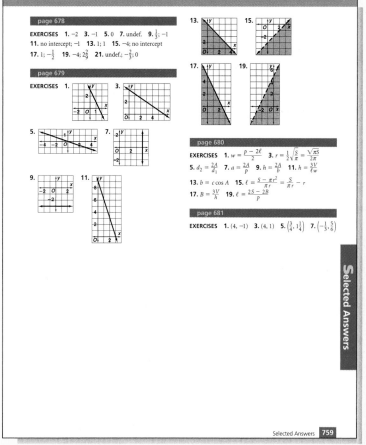

page 680

EXERCISES **1.** $w = \frac{p - 2\ell}{2}$ **3.** $r = \frac{1}{2}\sqrt{\frac{S}{\pi}} = \frac{\sqrt{\pi S}}{2\pi}$ **5.** $d_2 = \frac{2A}{d_1}$ **7.** $a = \frac{2A}{p}$ **9.** $h = \frac{2A}{b}$ **11.** $h = \frac{3V}{\ell w}$ **13.** $b = c\cos A$ **15.** $\ell = \frac{S - \pi r^2}{\pi r} = \frac{S}{\pi r} - r$ **17.** $B = \frac{3V}{h}$ **19.** $\ell = \frac{2S - 2B}{p}$

page 681

EXERCISES **1.** (4, −1) **3.** (4, 1) **5.** $\left(\frac{3}{4}, 1\frac{1}{4}\right)$ **7.** $\left(-\frac{1}{3}, \frac{5}{6}\right)$

CHAPTER 1

LESSON 1-1

page 10 Mixed Review

41–52.

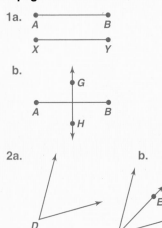

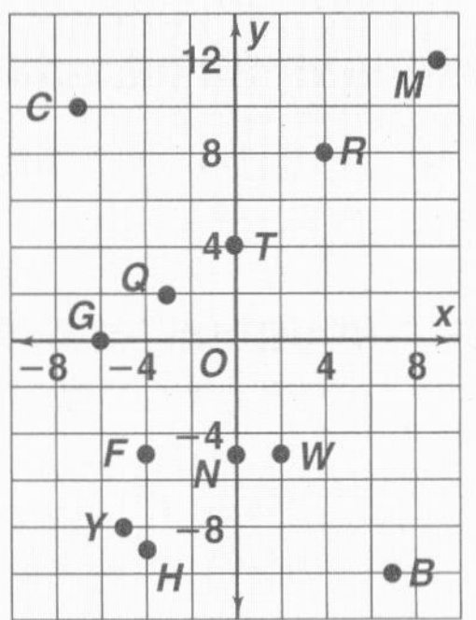

TE page 44 Lesson Quiz

1a.

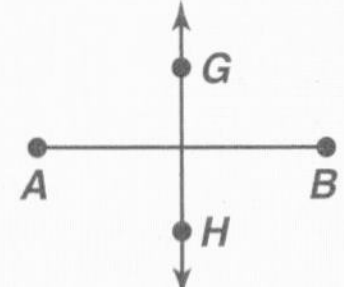

b.

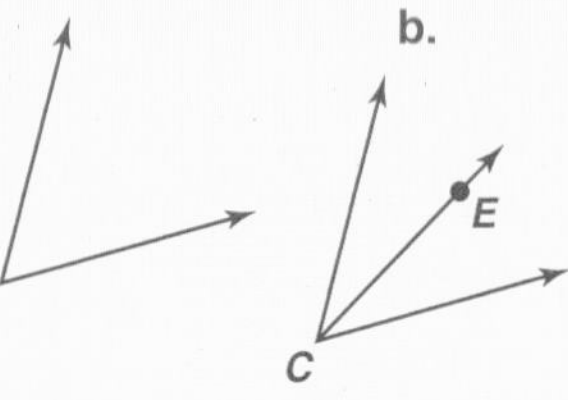

2a. b.

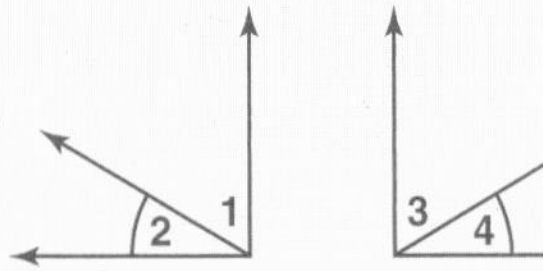

LESSON 1-7

TE page 47 Lesson Quiz

4.

Since ∠1 and ∠2 are complements and ∠3 and ∠4 are complements, $m\angle 1 + m\angle 2 = 90$ and $m\angle 3 + m\angle 4 = 90$. By the Transitive Prop. of =, $m\angle 1 + m\angle 2 = m\angle 3 + m\angle 4$. Since $\angle 2 \cong \angle 4$, $m\angle 1 + m\angle 2 = m\angle 3 + m\angle 2$. By the Subtraction Prop. of =, $m\angle 1 = m\angle 3$ and $\angle 1 \cong \angle 3$.

CHAPTER 2

LESSON 2-2

pages 76–77 Think and Discuss

1. Sample:

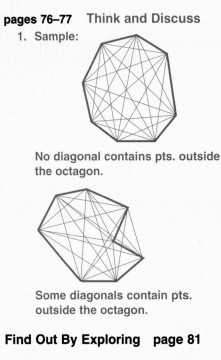

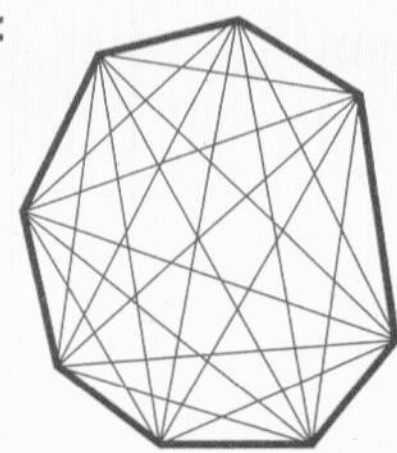

No diagonal contains pts. outside the octagon.

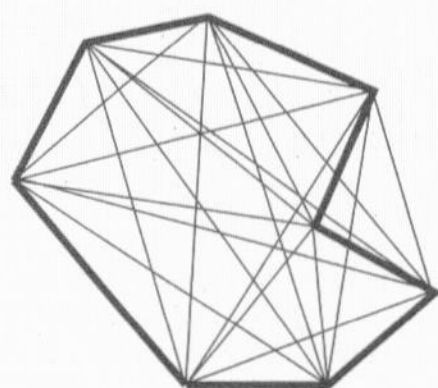

Some diagonals contain pts. outside the octagon.

Find Out By Exploring page 81

triangle

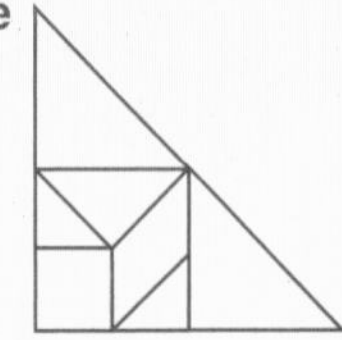

quadrilaterals

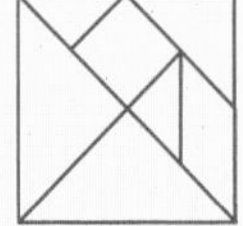

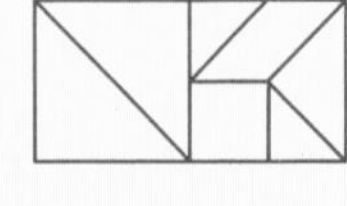

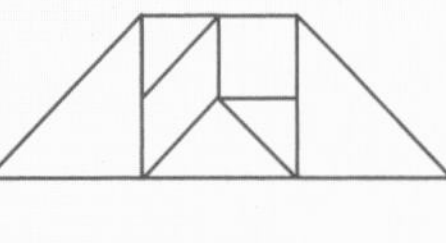

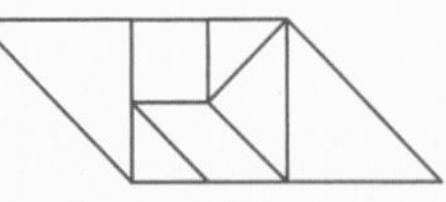

pentagons

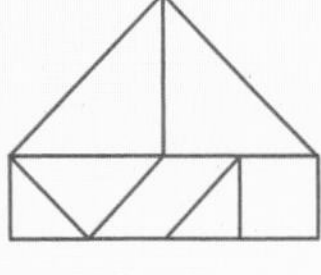

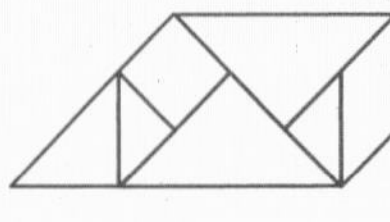

hexagons

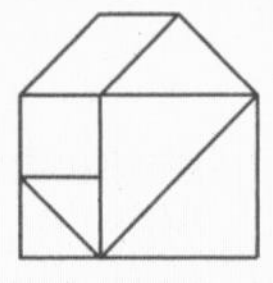

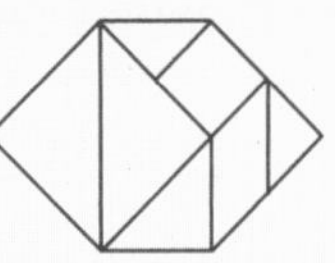

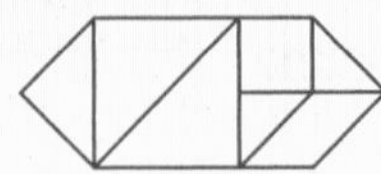

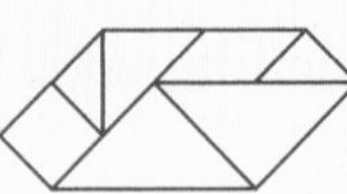

Math Toolbox page 82

Extend

a.

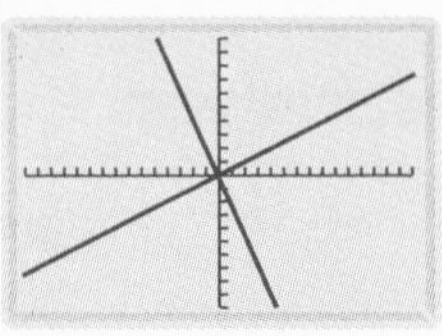

b.

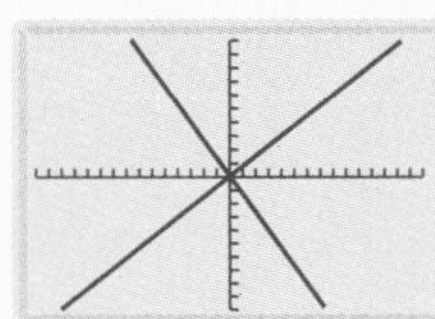

c.

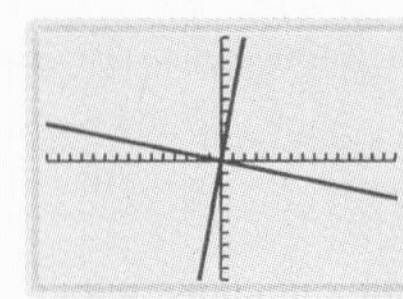

The lines are ⊥; the product of the values of m is -1; 2 lines with equations in which the product of values of m is -1 are ⊥.

LESSON 2-3

pages 83–84 Think and Discuss

2a.

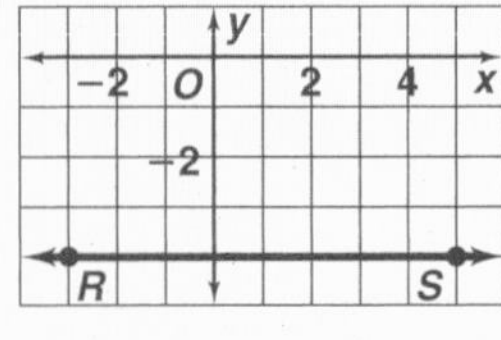

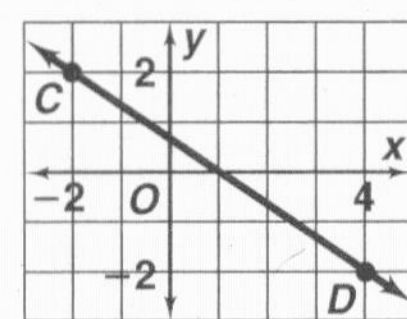

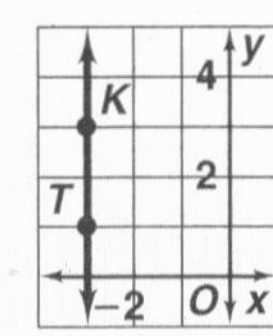

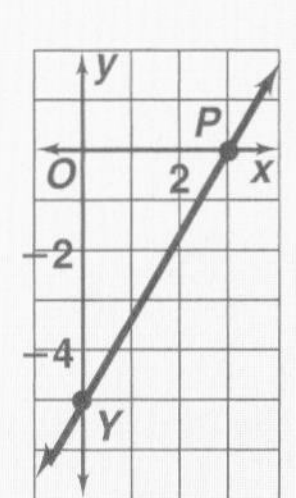

3a.

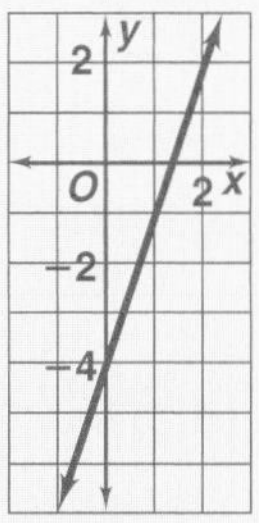

b.

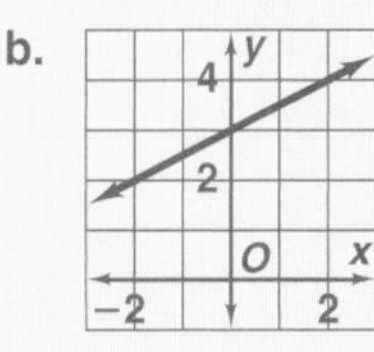

c.

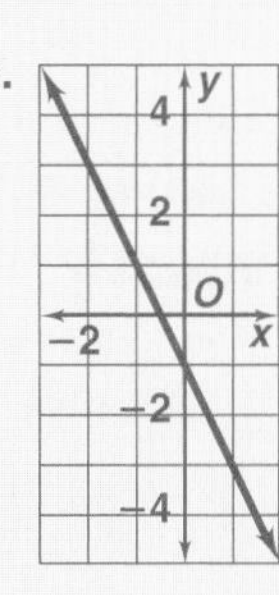

LESSON 2-7

pages 109–111 Think and Discuss

4a.

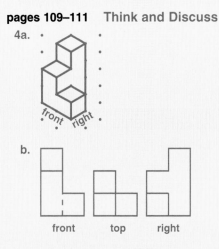

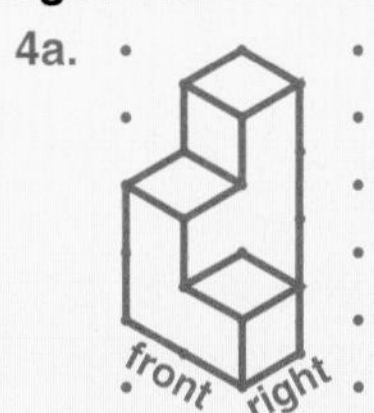

b.

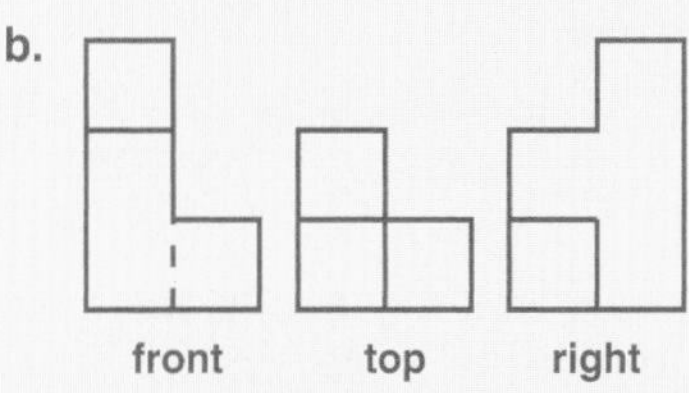

pages 112–115 On Your Own

7a.

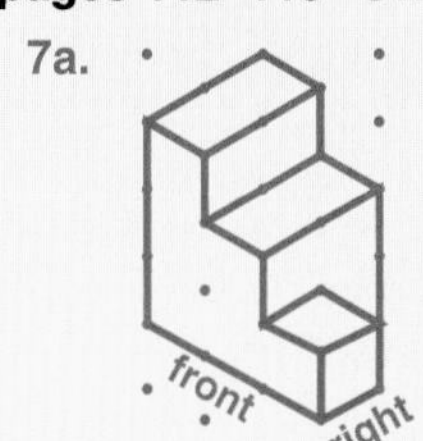

b.

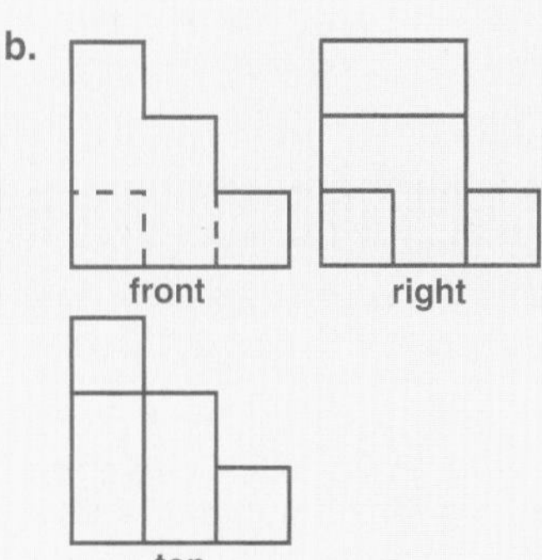

8a.

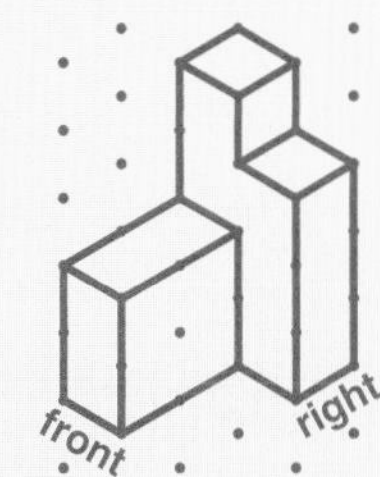

b.

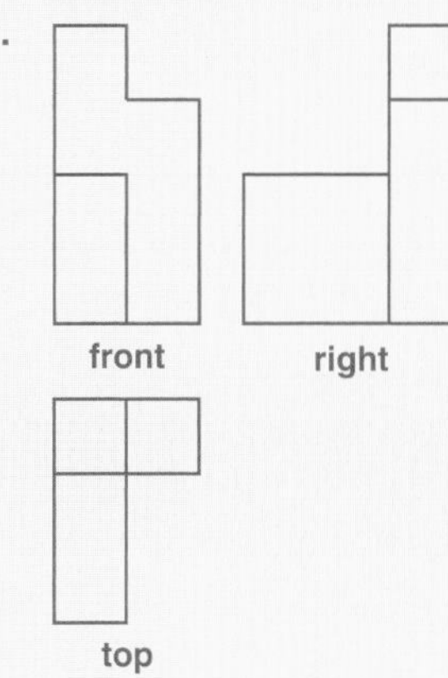

9a. Sample:

b. For sample in part (a):

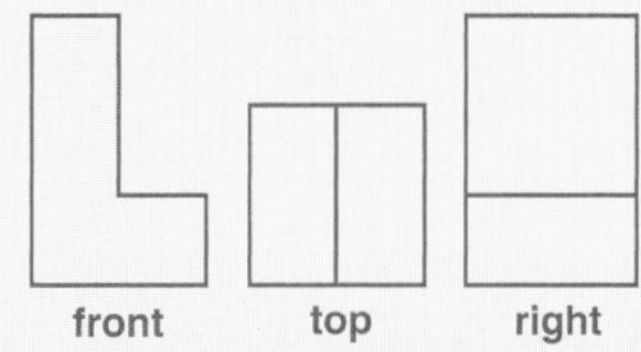

c. For sample in part (a):

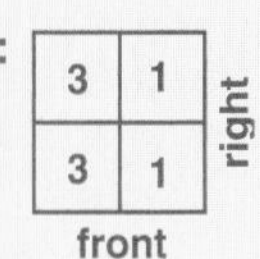

25.

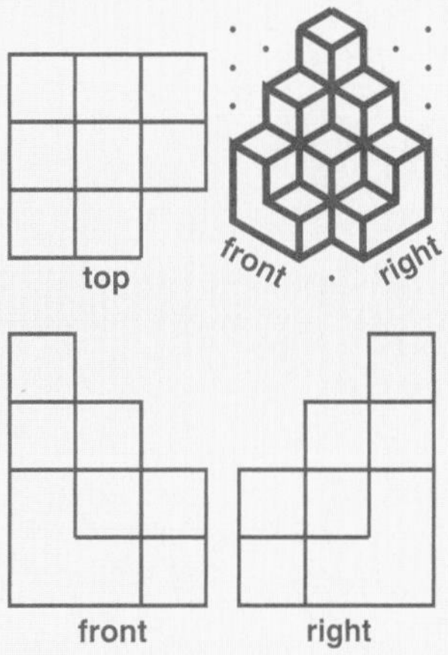

top

front

right

front

right

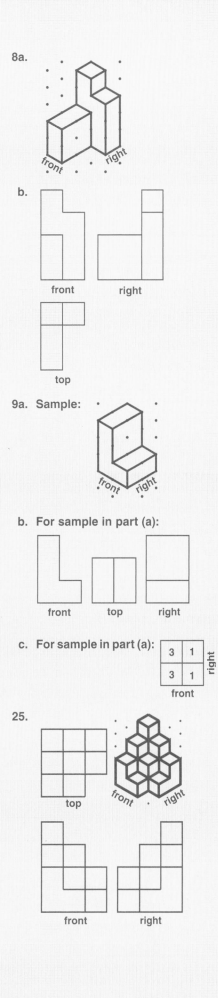

Find Out By Modeling page 115

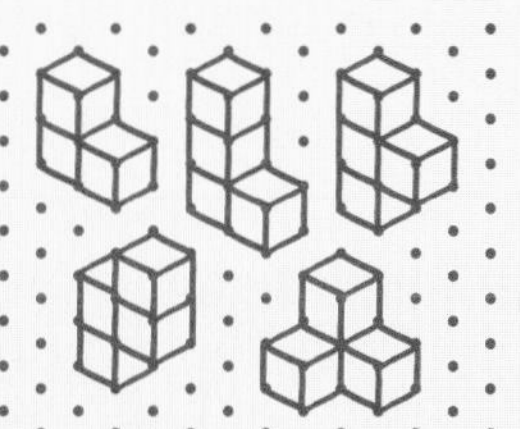

page 115 Mixed Review

29. Sample:

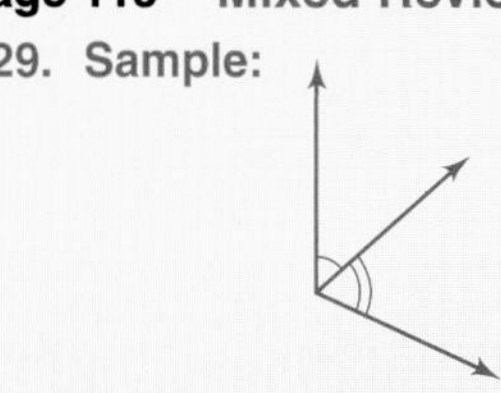

30. Sample:

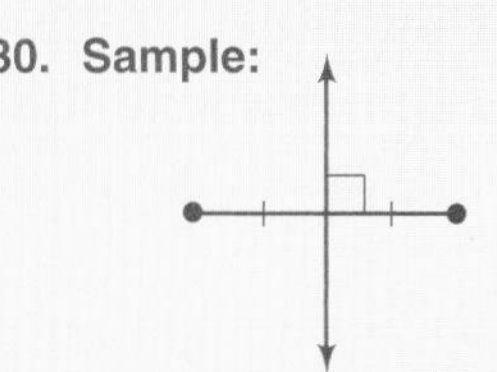

TE page 115 Lesson Quiz

1.

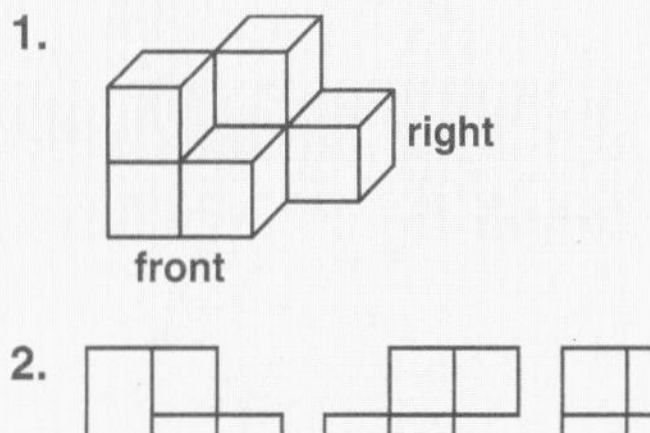

2.

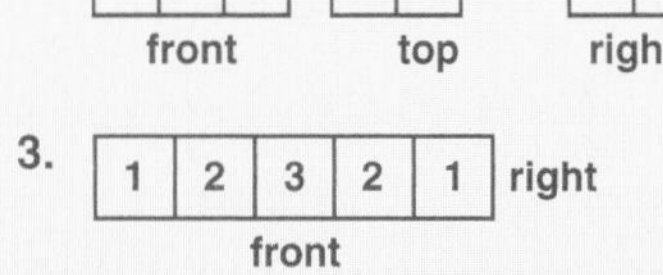

3.

1	2	3	2	1

right

front

Chapter Assessment page 120

26.

27.

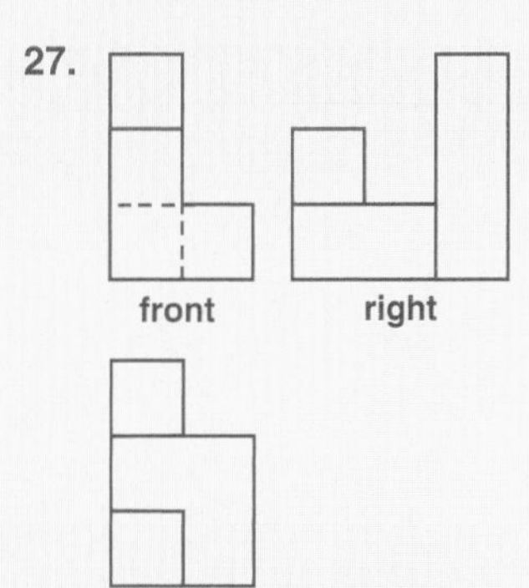

Cumulative Review **page 121**

13.

CHAPTER 3

LESSON 3-3

pages 138–140 Think and Discuss

3.

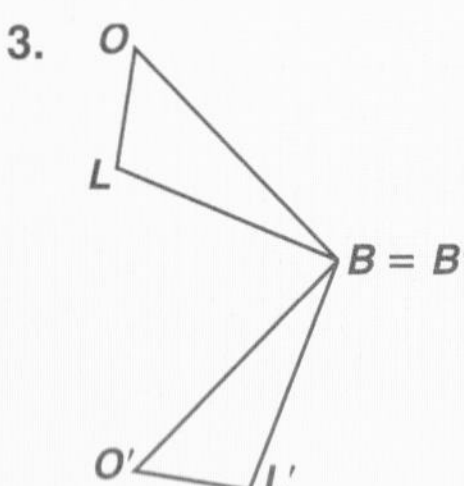

page 143 Mixed Review

31.

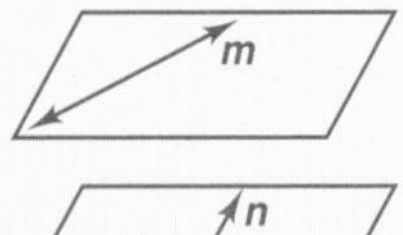

32.

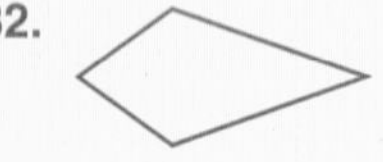

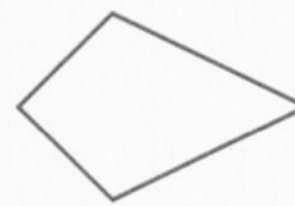

33.

34.

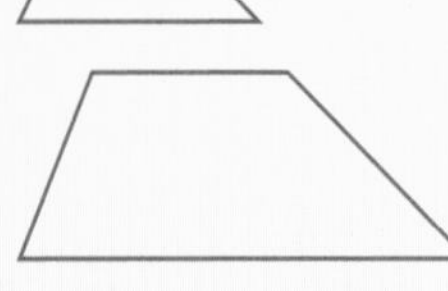

35.

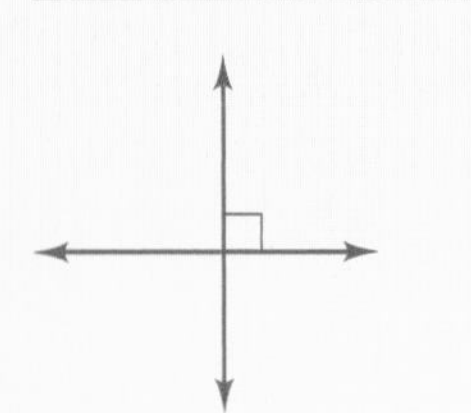

36.

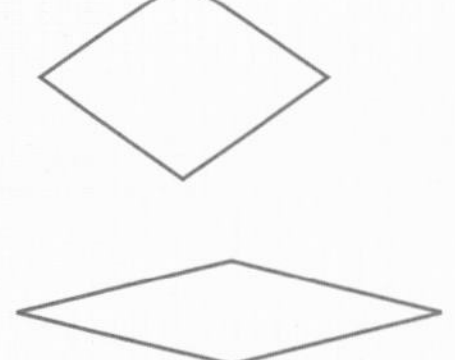

TE page 143 Lesson Quiz

1.

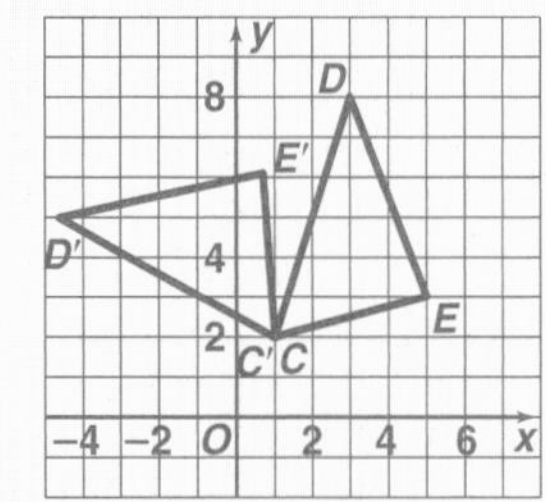

2.

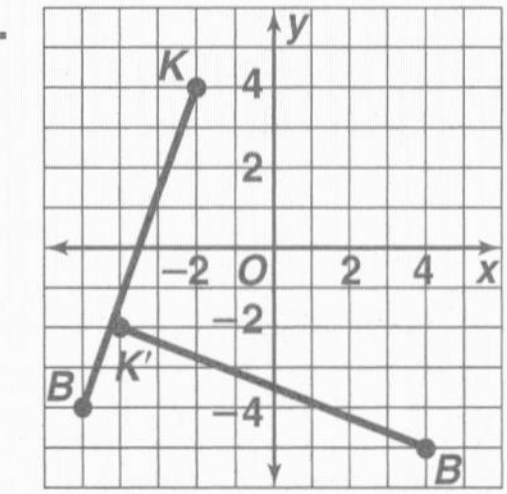

Checkpoint **page 158**

5.

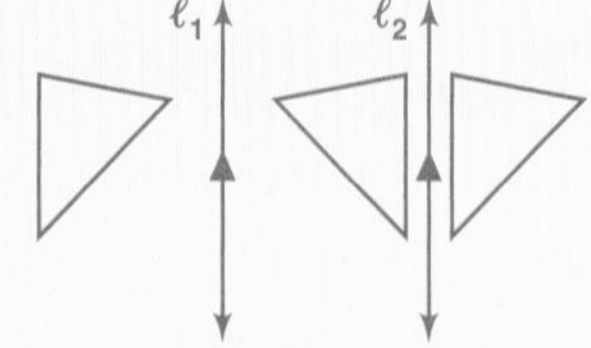

Assessment **page 178**

14. Answers may vary. Sample: No; line *m* is a bisector of $\overline{UH}$ but not necessarily a ⊥ bisector.

15.  16.  17. 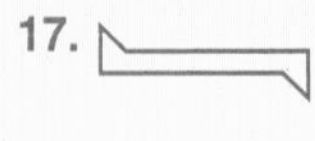

22. A' B' C'
$$\begin{bmatrix} 8 & 12 & 20 \\ 16 & 28 & 4 \end{bmatrix}$$

23. A' B' C'
$$\begin{bmatrix} 0 & -1\frac{1}{2} & \frac{1}{2} \\ 0 & 1 & 3\frac{1}{2} \end{bmatrix}$$

24. A' B' C'
$$\begin{bmatrix} -6 & 6 & 9 \\ 6 & -6 & 12 \end{bmatrix}$$

CHAPTER 4

LESSON 4-1

pages 186–187 On Your Own

20a. If coord. of a point are positive, then the point is in quadrant I.

b. true; true

c. The point is in quadrant I if and only if its coord. are pos.

21a. If the chemical formula of a substance is H_2O, then the substance is water.

b. true; true

c. A substance is water if and only if its chemical formula is H_2O.

22a. If a figure has rotational symmetry, then it has 2 lines of symmetry.

b. true; false

23a. If the slopes of 2 nonvertical lines are =, then they are ∥.

b. true; true

c. 2 nonvertical lines are ∥ if and only if their slopes are =.

24a. If the sums of the measures of 2 angles is 90, then the angles are complementary.

b. true; true

c. 2 angles are complementary if and only if the sum of their measures is 90.

25a. If you are in Indianapolis, then you are in Indiana.

b. false; true

26a. If an event is certain to occur, then the probability that the event will occur is 1.

b. true; true

c. The probability that an event will occur is 1 if and only if the event is certain to occur.

27a. Answers may vary. Sample: If you buy Tread Master Tires, then you do not get a flat tire.

b. Check students' work.

28. If a swimmer swims the fastest, then she wins the race; if a swimmer wins the race, then she swims the fastest.

29. If the sum of the digits of a number is divisible by 3, then the number is divisible by 3; if a number is divisible by 3, then the sum of the digits of the number is divisible by 3.

32a. If a △ is a rt. △, then it has exactly 2 acute angles.

b. If a △ does not have exactly 2 acute angles, then it is not a rt. △.

33a. If a polygon is regular, then all its sides are ≅.

b. If not all the sides of a polygon are ≅, the polygon is not regular.

34a. If lines have = slope, then they are ∥.

b. If lines are not ∥, they do not have = slope.

35a. If a transformation is a rotation, then it is an isometry.

b. If a transformation is not an isometry, it is not a rotation.

Find Out by Listing page 187

There are only 2 ways all 3 boxes can be labeled incorrectly. By selecting a hat from the box labeled "1 red, 1 blue" you know which possibility is correct.

page 187 Mixed Review

36.

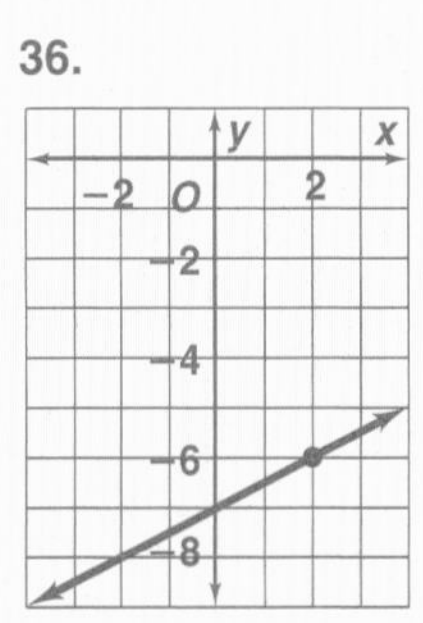

37.

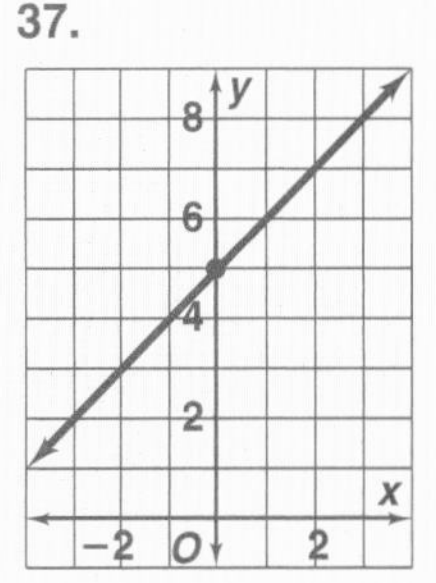

38.

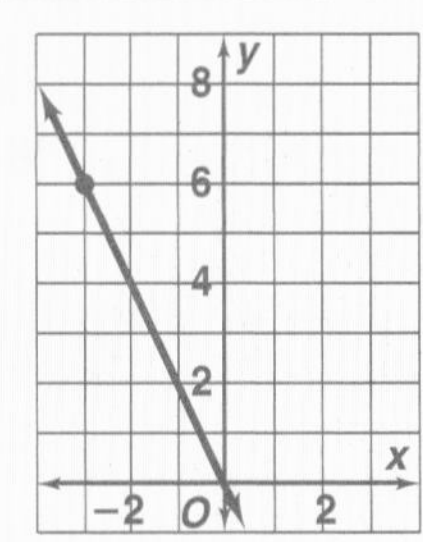

LESSON 4-3

pages 196–198 On Your Own

1. Answers may vary. Samples: $m\angle V = 45$ because acute angles of a rt. △ are complementary; $UT = TV$ because if 2 ∠s of a △ are ≅, the sides opposite them are ≅.
2. Answers may vary. Sample: △*FED* is equilateral; $\angle E \cong \angle D$ because base ∠s of an isosceles △ are ≅; $m\angle F = 60$ by Triangle Angle-Sum Thm.
3. *ABCD* is a rectangle; sum of the measures of angles of a quadrilateral = 360 so each angle is 90°.
4. Answers may vary. Sample: $m\angle DCA = m\angle A + m\angle B$; Exterior Angle Thm.
5. Answers may vary. Sample: $MP = MN$ and $NO = PO$ because if 2 ∠s of a △ are ≅, the sides opposite them are ≅.
6. Answers may vary. Samples: $\angle LRO \cong \angle QRN$ by Angle Addition Post.
8. Answers may vary. Sample: Both proofs list the hypothesis, the conclusion, and the reasoning. The reasoning does not depend on the form of the proof. A paragraph proof gives statements and the reasons for them in full sentences within a paragraph. In a 2-column proof, statements and reasons appear in different columns.

TE page 199 Lesson Quiz

3. Given: △*EFG,* with right angle ∠*F.* Prove: ∠*E* and ∠*G* are complementary. $m\angle F = 90$ because ∠*F* is a right angle. By the Triangle Angle-Sum Theorem, $m\angle E + m\angle F + m\angle G = 180$. Then, $m\angle E + 90 + m\angle G = 180$ and $m\angle E + m\angle G = 90$. So ∠*E* and ∠*G* are complementary by def.

LESSON 4-5

TE page 208 Additonal Example 2

Given: pentagon *ABCDE*

Prove: pentagon *ABCDE* has at most four acute angles.

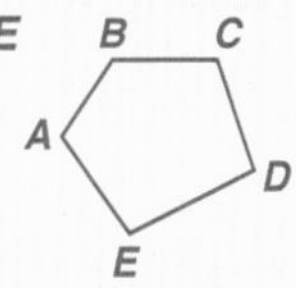

Assume *ABCDE* has 5 acute angles. By definition, an acute angle's measure is < 90. Therefore the sum of measures of int. angles is < 450. The sum of the measures of the angles of *ABCDE* is 3(180) = 540, which contradicts the hypothesis. So the assumption that pentagon *ABCDE* has 5 acute angles is false. Therefore, a pentagon has at most 4 acute angles.

pages 209–211 On Your Own

23. Assume $m\angle P = 90$. By def., $m\angle Q > 90$. The sum of the angle measures of △*PQR* is > 180. By the Triangle Angle-Sum Thm., the sum of the angle measures of a △ is 180. Therefore, the assumption is false, and an obtuse △ cannot contain a rt. angle.
24. Assume ∠*B* is a rt. angle. Then $m\angle B = 90$. By Isosceles Triangle Thm., $m\angle A = 90$. Then the sum of the angle measures of △*ABC* is > 180. By the Triangle Angle-Sum Thm., the sum of angle measures of a △ is 180. Therefore, the assumption is false, and a base angle of an isosceles △ cannot be a rt. angle.

page 211 Mixed Review

32a. If a figure is a square, then it is a rhombus.

If a figure is a rhombus, then it is a square.

If a figure is a rhombus, then it is a ▱.

If a figure is a ▱, then it is a rhombus.

If a figure is a square, then it is a ▱.

If a figure is a ▱, then it is a square.

LESSON 4-7

pages 223–225 On Your Own

33a.

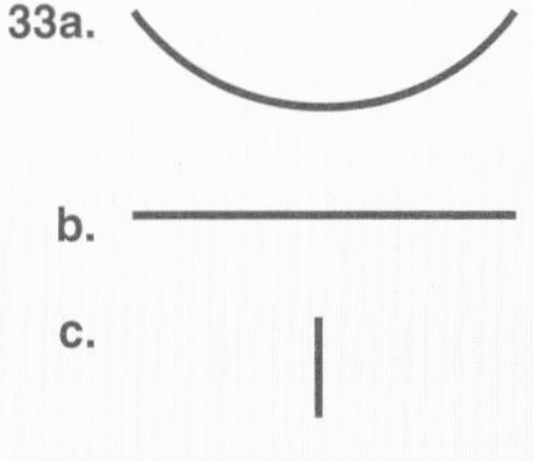

b.

c.

34a.

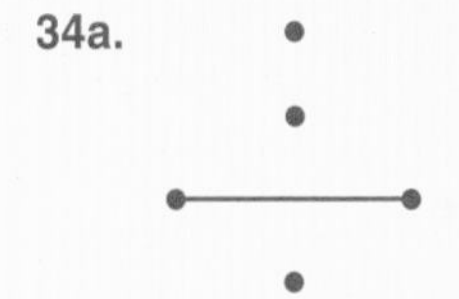

35.

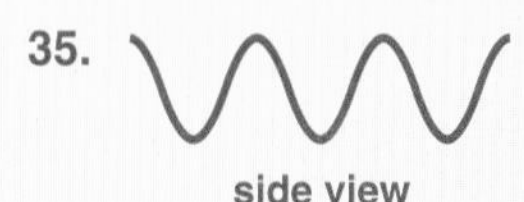
side view

36.

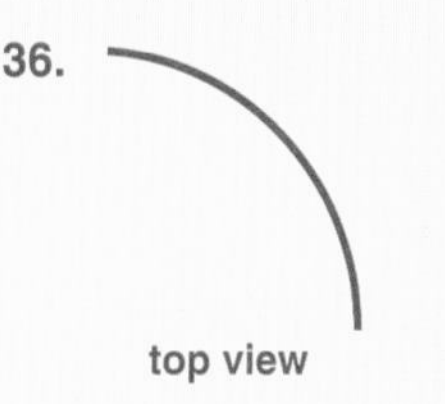
top view

37.

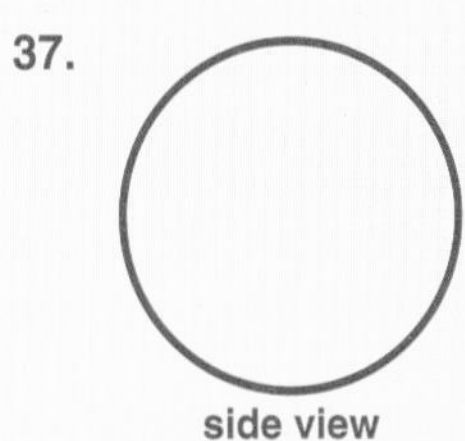
side view

page 225 Mixed Review

41.

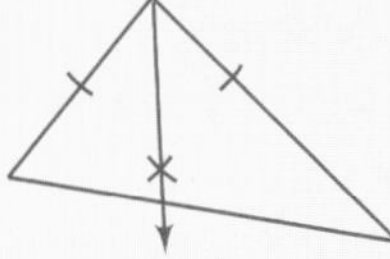

42.

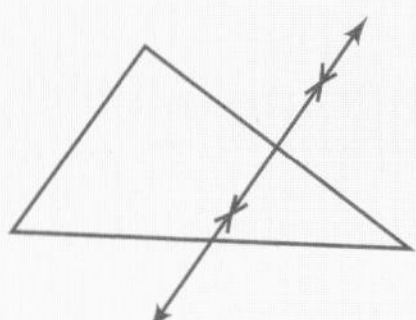

Checkpoint page 225

7.

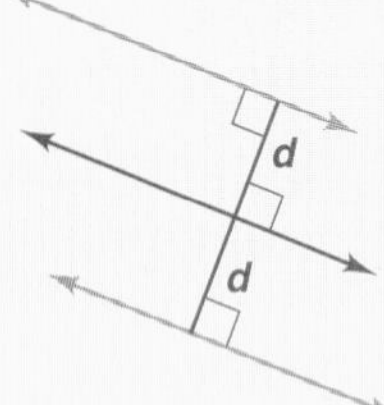

8.

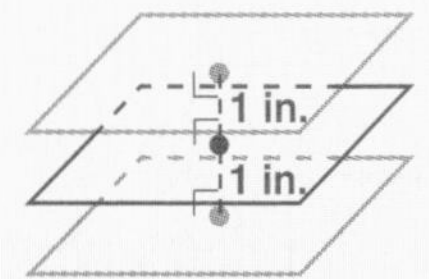

LESSON 4-8

TE page 232 Lesson Quiz

1a–b.

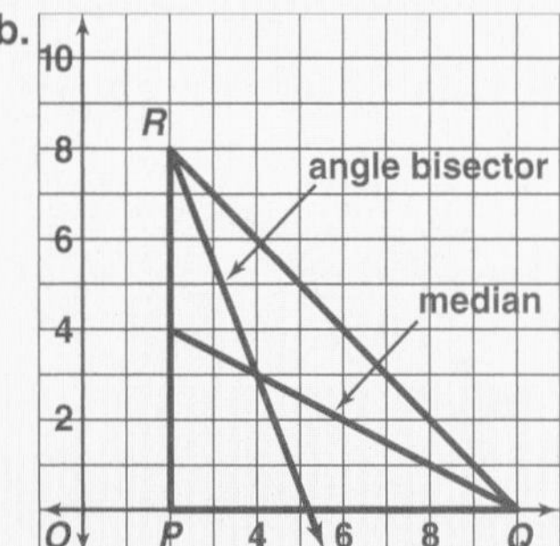

Assessment page 238

17. Assume that the obtuse angle is not the vertex angle. Then it must be a base angle of an isosceles △. Then the 2nd base angle is ≅ to the 1st and also obtuse, because base ∠s of an isosceles △ are ≅. By def., obtuse angles measure > 90, so the sum of the angle measures of the △ is > 180. This contradicts the Triangle Angle-Sum Thm. Therefore, the obtuse angle must be at the vertex.

18.

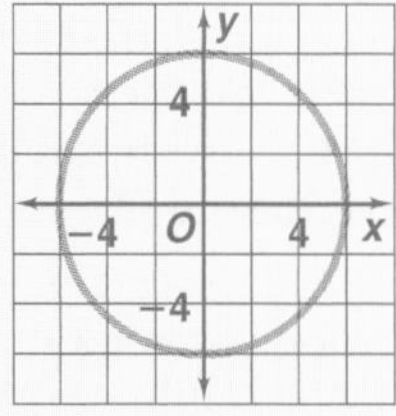

19.

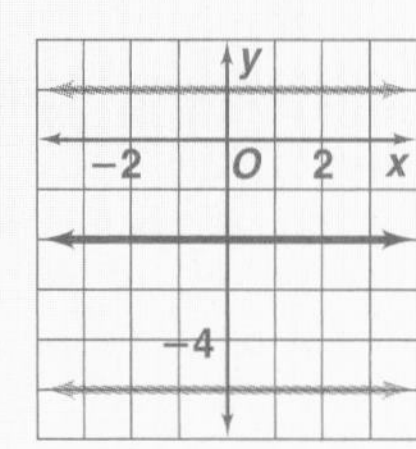

20.

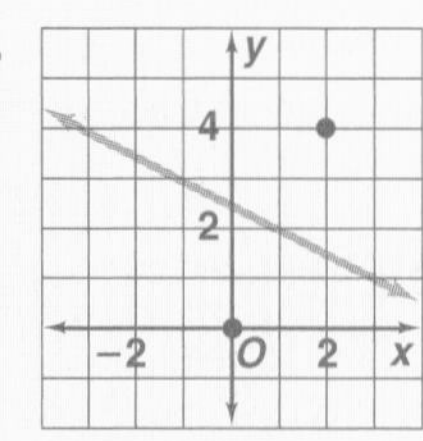

21.

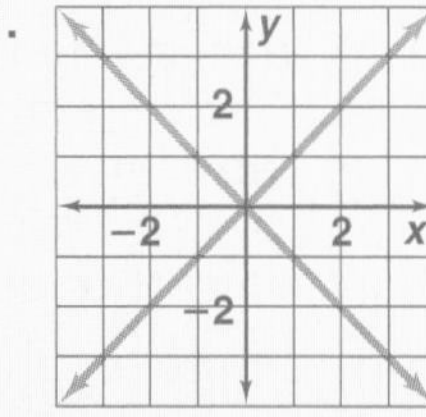

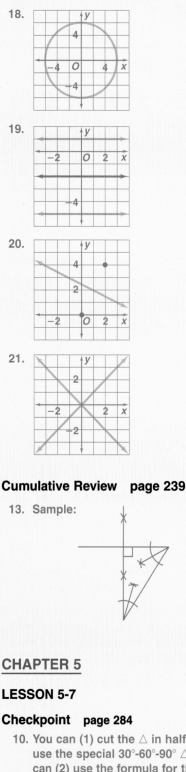

Cumulative Review page 239

13. Sample:

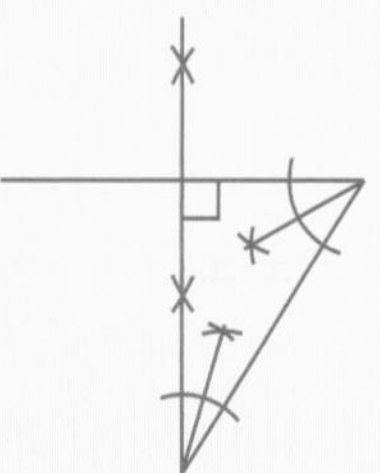

CHAPTER 5

LESSON 5-7

Checkpoint page 284

10. You can (1) cut the △ in half and use the special 30°-60°-90° △ or you can (2) use the formula for the area of regular polygons. Suppose the length of each side, *b*, is 4.

(1) $h = \frac{\sqrt{3}}{2}b = 2\sqrt{3}$;

$A = \frac{1}{2}bh =$

$\frac{1}{2} \cdot 4 \cdot 2\sqrt{3} = 4\sqrt{3}$

(2) $a = \frac{1}{\sqrt{3}} \cdot \frac{b}{2} = \frac{\sqrt{3}}{3} \cdot \frac{4}{2} = \frac{2\sqrt{3}}{3}$;

$A = \frac{1}{2}ap = \frac{1}{2}a(3b) = 4\sqrt{3}$

CHAPTER 6

LESSON 6-1

page 302 Work Together

2b. Answers may vary. Sample: A cube is a 3-dimensional figure whose faces are 6 ≅ squares.

page 303 Think and Discuss

4. Sample:

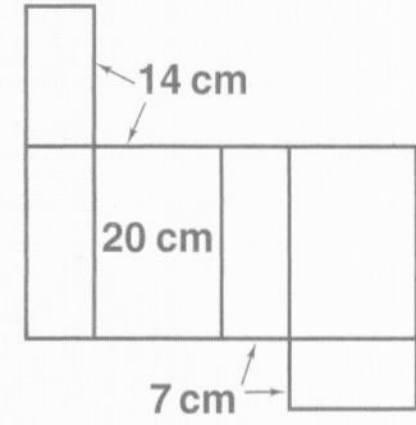

TE page 306 Lesson Quiz

1.

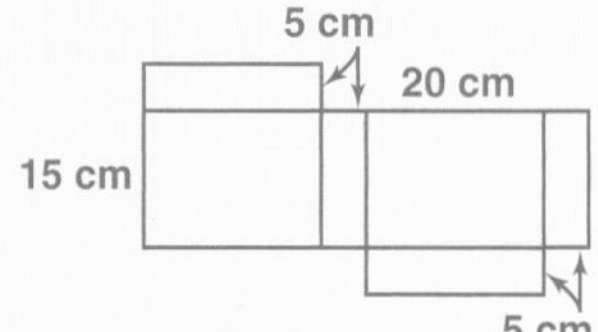

2.

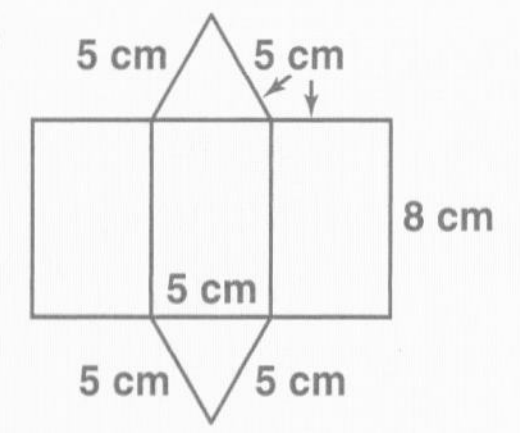

LESSON 6-7

pages 346–347 On Your Own

4.

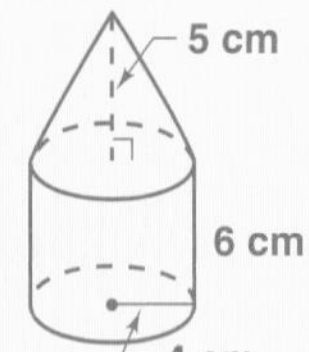

$V = \frac{368}{3}\pi \text{ cm}^3$

7a.

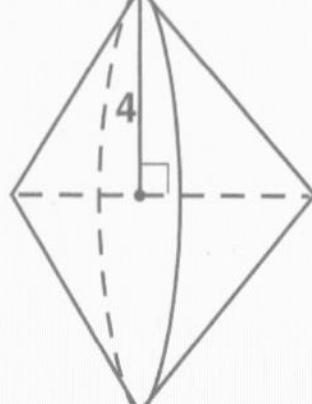

11. An octahedron is a figure combining 2 pyramids with square bases. Find the volume of 1 pyramid; multiply the result by 2.

page 347 Mixed Review

18. Assume a base angle of an isos. △ is a rt. angle. Then the 2nd base angle is also a rt. angle by the Isos. Triangle Thm. So the sum of the measures of 3 angles of the △ is > 180. By the Triangle Angle-Sum Thm., the sum of the measures of the angles is 180. Therefore, a base angle of an isos. △ is not a rt. angle.

LESSON 6-8

Assessment page 358

10.

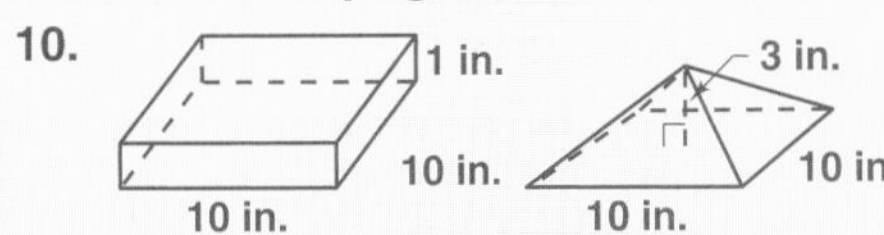

14. Sample: You need to know the volume of a planter to fill it with soil; you need to know the lateral area of a planter to paint its exterior sides.

Cumulative Review page 359

9.

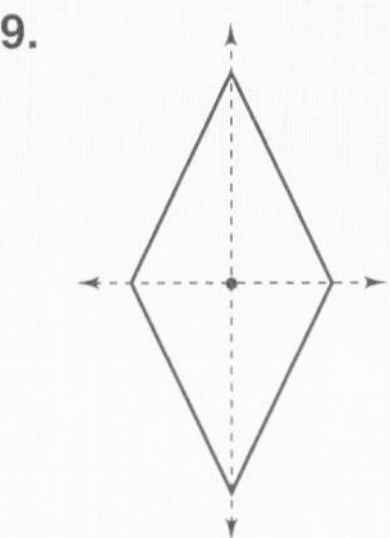

CHAPTER 7

LESSON 7-1

TE page 369 Lesson Quiz

2a. If ∥ lines, then corres. ∠s are ≅.

b. If ∥ lines, then same-side int. ∠s are supplementary.

LESSON 7-2

TE page 372 Additional Example 1

H′ and *I′* are the images of *H* and *I* under dilation with center *G*, so △*GH′I′* is the image of △*GHI*. Then, △*GH′I′* ~ △*GHI* because dilation is a similarity transformation. By def. of ~ polygons, ∠*GH′I′* ≅ ∠*GHI*. If corres. ∠s are ≅, then lines are ∥, and $\overline{H'I'} \parallel \overline{HI}$.

TE page 372 Additional Example 2

∠1 and ∠2 are supplementary same-side int. ∠s, so ℓ ∥ *m*. ∠3 and ∠4 are ≅ alt. int. ∠s, so *m* ∥ *q*. Since ℓ and *q* are 2 lines ∥ to a 3rd line, ℓ ∥ *q*.

pages 373–376 On Your Own

16.

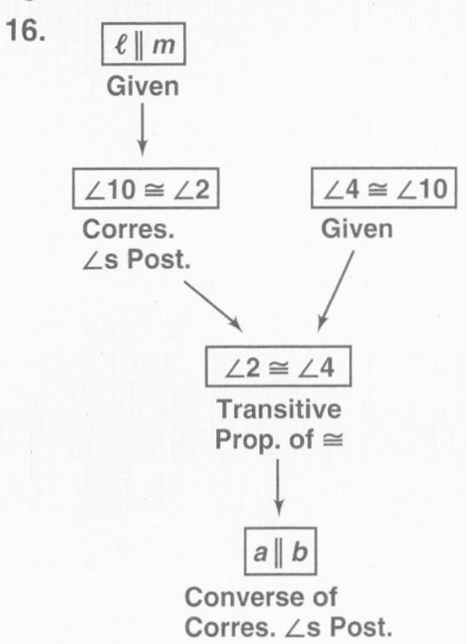

17.

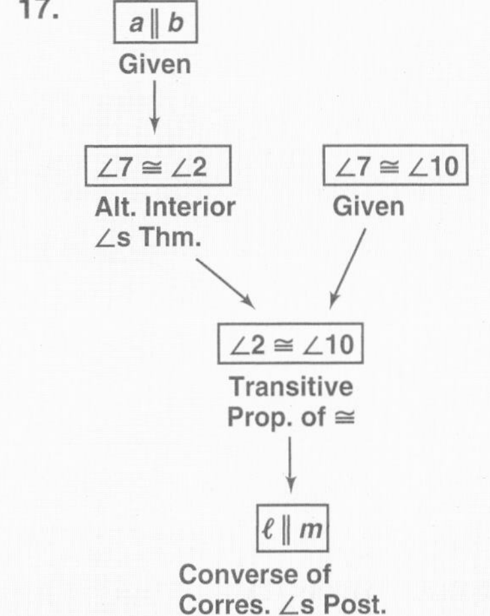

18.

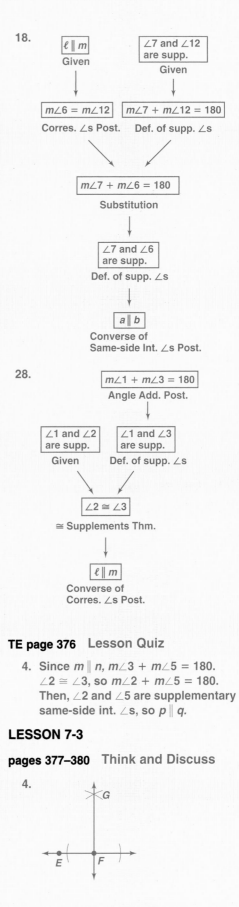

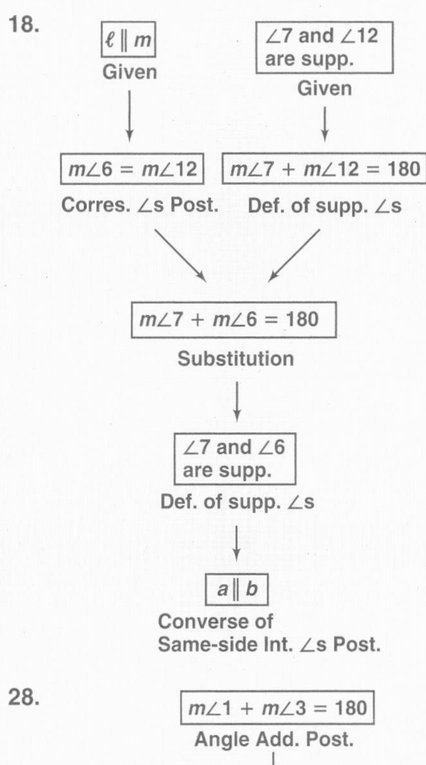

28.

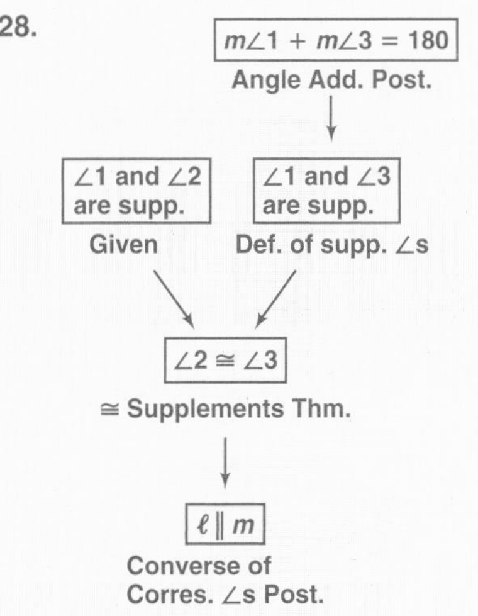

TE page 376 Lesson Quiz

4. Since *m* ∥ *n*, *m*∠3 + *m*∠5 = 180. ∠2 ≅ ∠3, so *m*∠2 + *m*∠5 = 180. Then, ∠2 and ∠5 are supplementary same-side int. ∠s, so *p* ∥ *q*.

LESSON 7-3

pages 377–380 Think and Discuss

4.

G
E F

pages 380–383 On Your Own

11a–b.

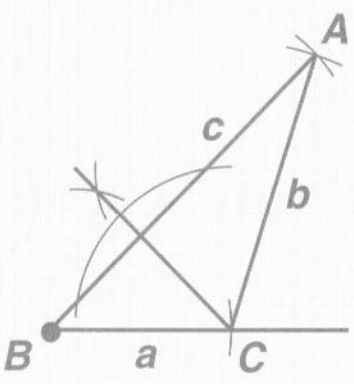

12.

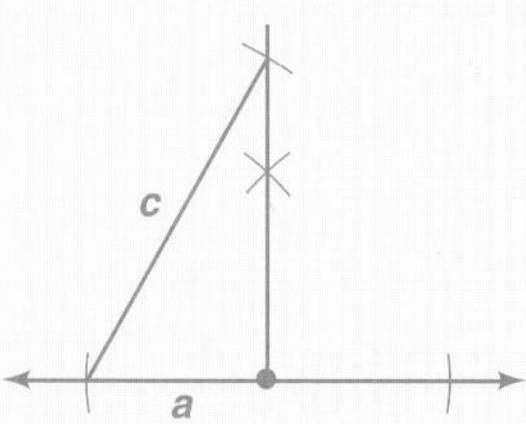

13.

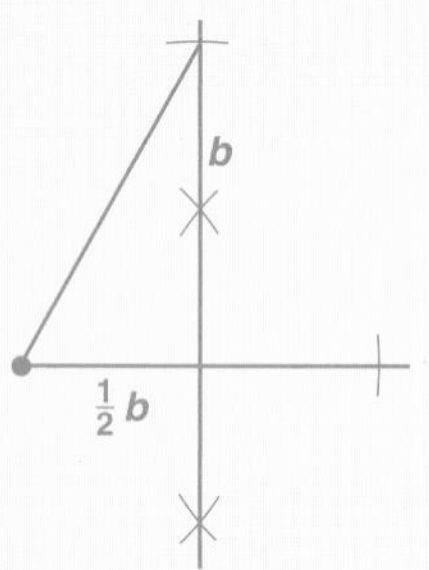

14a.

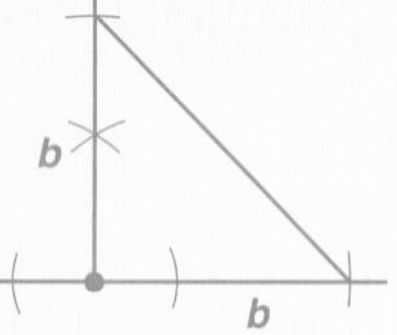

15.

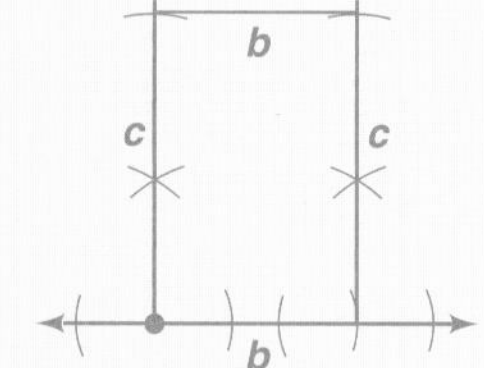

16.

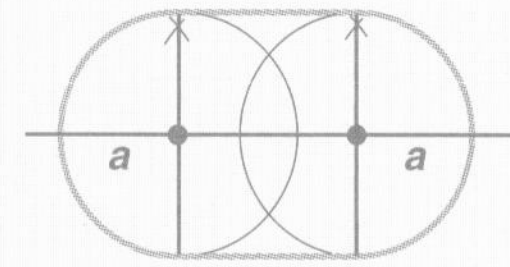

page 383 Mixed Review

26.

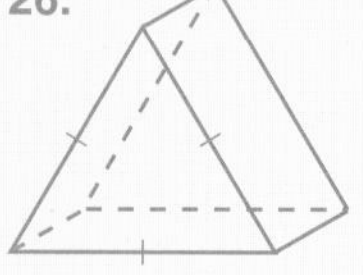

27.

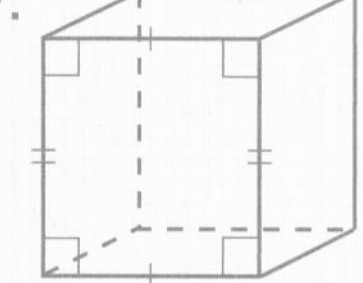

28.

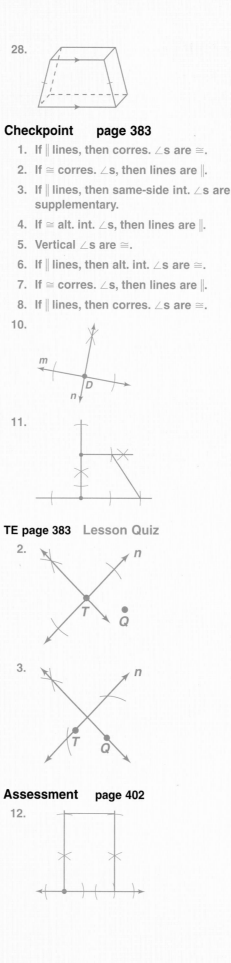

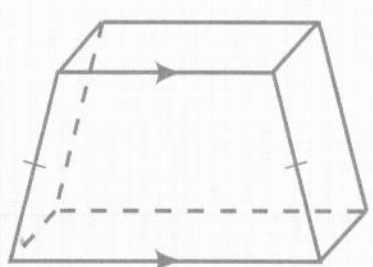

Checkpoint **page 383**

1. If ∥ lines, then corres. ∠s are ≅.
2. If ≅ corres. ∠s, then lines are ∥.
3. If ∥ lines, then same-side int. ∠s are supplementary.
4. If ≅ alt. int. ∠s, then lines are ∥.
5. Vertical ∠s are ≅.
6. If ∥ lines, then alt. int. ∠s are ≅.
7. If ≅ corres. ∠s, then lines are ∥.
8. If ∥ lines, then corres. ∠s are ≅.

10.

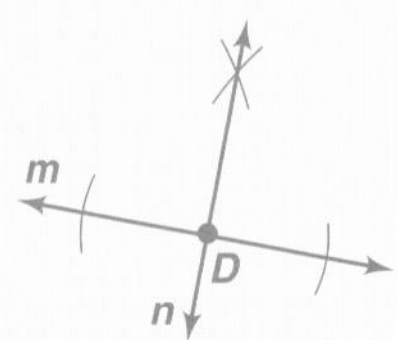

11.

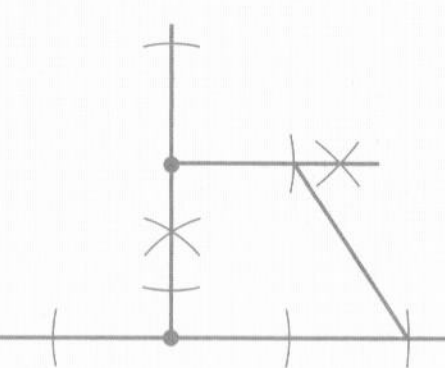

TE page 383 Lesson Quiz

2.

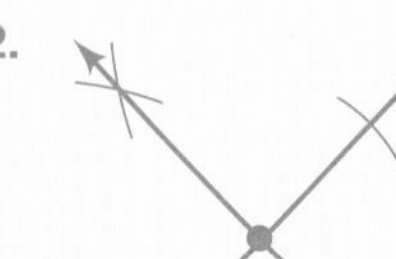

3.

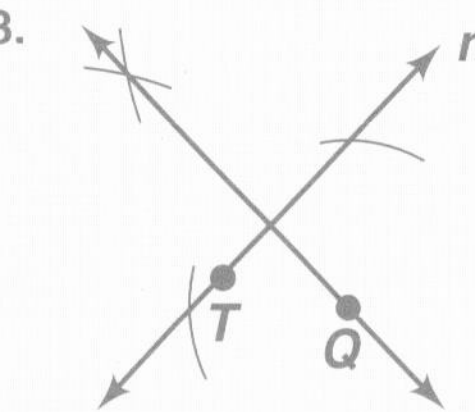

Assessment **page 402**

12.

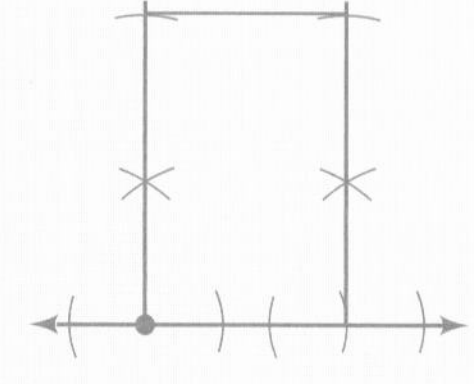

16.

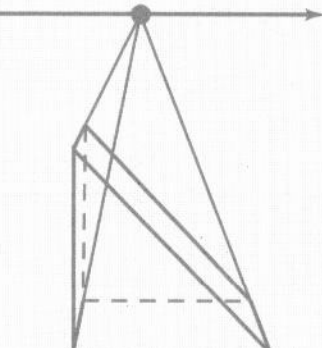

17.

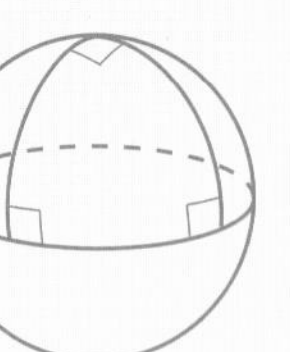

18.

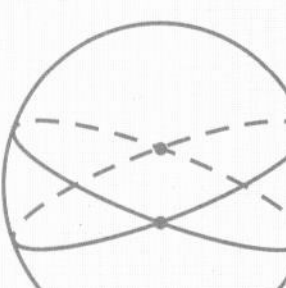

19. A "plane" in spherical geometry is a sphere, "lines" are great circles, and "points" are pts. on the sphere.

    Check students' work for sketches.

Preparing for Standardized Tests page 403

10. The volume of the cone is $\frac{1}{3}$ the volume of the cylinder.
11. Answers may vary. Sample: The sum of the angle measures of a △ on a sphere > 180, while the sum of the angle measures of a △ in a plane = 180. An equiangular △ on a sphere can have angle measures between 60 and 180. An equiangular △ in a plane has angle measures of 60.

CHAPTER 8

LESSON 8-1

TE page 412 Lesson Quiz

3. 1. $\overline{YG}$ bisects $\overline{XZ}$ (Given) 2. $\overline{XG} \cong \overline{GZ}$ (Def. of segment bisector) 3. $\overline{YX} \cong \overline{YZ}$ (Given) 4. $\overline{YG} \cong \overline{YG}$ (Reflexive Prop. of ≅) 5. $\triangle XYG \cong \triangle ZYG$ (SSS Post.)

LESSON 8-2

TE page 415 Additional Example 2

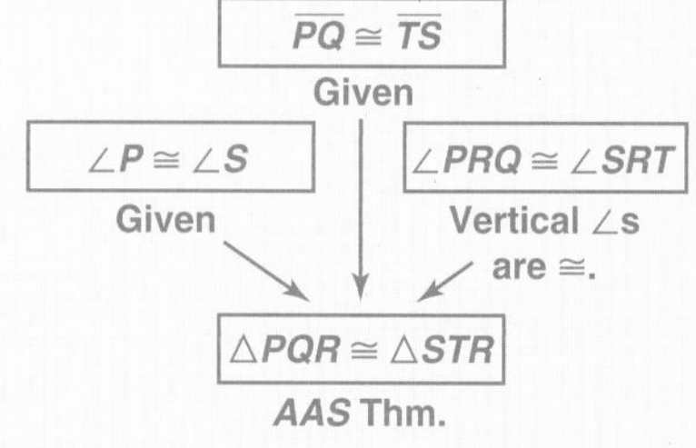

TE page 419 Lesson Quiz

3.

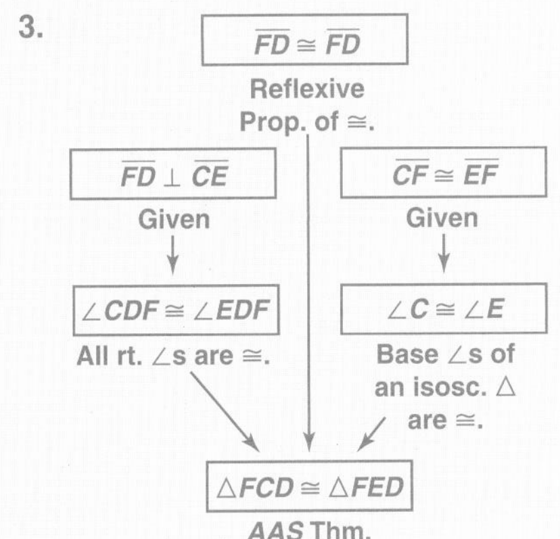

LESSON 8-3

TE page 421 Additional Example 2

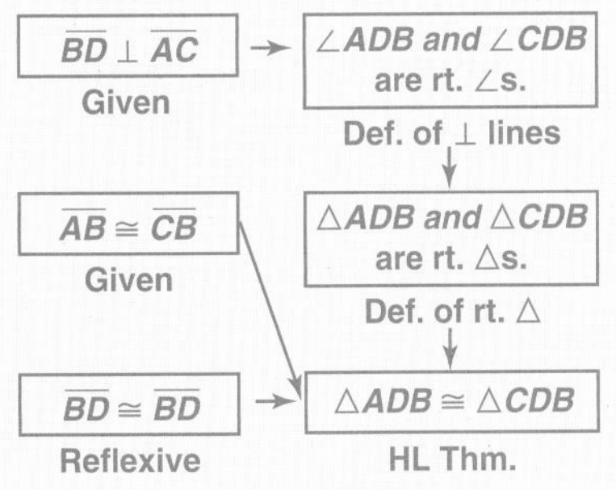

page 425 Mixed Review

21. Angle Addition Post.
22. If ∥ lines, then alt. int. ∠s are ≅.
23. If ∥ lines, then same-side int. ∠s are supplementary.
24. If ∥ lines, then alt. int. ∠s are ≅.
25. If ∥ lines, then corres. ∠s are ≅.
26. If ∥ lines, then corres. ∠s are ≅

Checkpoint page 425

7a.

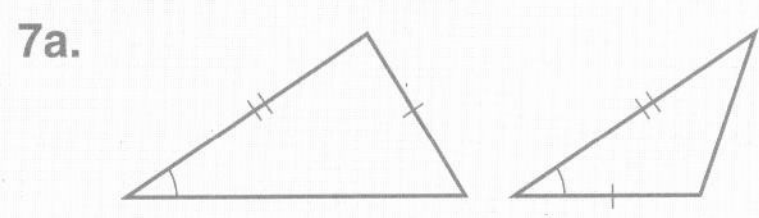

b. No; if 2 pairs of angles are ≅, the 3rd pair of angles is also ≅. Then the △s are ≅ by AAS or ASA.

9. If the hypotenuse and an acute angle of one right triangle are congruent to the hypotenuse and an acute angle of another right triangle, then the triangles are congruent. The HA Theorem is true. Since the right angles are congruent, the triangles are congruent by AAS.

LESSON 8-4

TE page 427 Additional Example 1

You can show $\overline{MN} \cong \overline{PO}$ if these sides are corres. parts of ≅ △s. Prove △MXN ≅ △PXO by ASA. Then use CPCTC.

TE page 427 Additional Example 2

Given: *C* bisects $\overline{AE}$ and $\overline{BD}$ Prove: $\overline{AB} \parallel \overline{DE}$ 1. *C* bisects $\overline{AE}$ and $\overline{BD}$ (Given) 2. $\overline{AC} \cong \overline{EC}$, $\overline{BC} \cong \overline{DC}$ (Def. of segment bisector) 3. ∠ACB ≅ ∠ECD (Vert ∠s are ≅) 4. △ACB ≅ △ECD (SAS Post.) 5. ∠A ≅ ∠E (CPCTC) 6. $\overline{AB} \parallel \overline{DE}$. (If ≅ alt. int. ∠s, then lines are ∥.

TE page 427 Additional Example 3

$\overline{AC} \cong \overline{AC}$ by the Reflexive Prop. of ≅. Since ∠D ≅ ∠B and ∠DAC ≅ ∠BCA, △DAC ≅ △BCA by the AAS Thm. $\overline{AB} \cong \overline{CD}$ by CPCTC.

TE page 432 Lesson Quiz

1. △PQR ≅ △TQR by SSS; ∠PQR ≅ ∠TQR by CPCTC
2. △FGH ≅ △FIH by ASA; $\overline{FG} \cong \overline{FI}$ by CPCTC.
3. Answers may vary. Sample: 1. $\overline{DC} \cong \overline{CE}$ (Given) 2. $\overline{DO} \cong \overline{EO}$ (All radii of a circle are ≅)
   3. $\overline{CO} \cong \overline{CO}$ (Reflexive Prop. of ≅)
   4. △DOC ≅ △EOC (SSS Post.)
   5. ∠DOC ≅ ∠COE (CPCTC)
   6. ∠DOC and ∠COE are suppl. (Def. of supplementary ∠s) 7. ∠DOC and ∠COE are right ∠s (≅ supplementary ∠s are rt. ∠s.)

LESSON 8-5

page 433 Work Together

1. △AGF ≅ △BGC by SAS, ASA, AAS or HL; △DGF ≅ △DGC by AAS or HL; △ABC ≅ △BAF by SAS, ASA, or AAS; △BFC ≅ △ACF by SAS, ASA, AAS, or HL

TE page 434 Additional Example 2

1. $\overline{BA} \cong \overline{DE}$, $\overline{BE} \cong \overline{DA}$ (Given)
2. $\overline{AE} \cong \overline{AE}$ (Reflexive Prop. of ≅)
3. △BEA ≅ △DAE (SSS Post.)
4. ∠BEA ≅ ∠DAE (CPCTC)

TE page 434 Additional Example 3

It is given that ∠1 ≅ ∠2 and $\overline{BD} \cong \overline{BE}$. $\overline{BF} \cong \overline{BF}$ by the Reflexive Prop. of ≅. △BDF ≅ △BEF by the SAS Post. and $\overline{DF} \cong \overline{EF}$ by CPCTC. Then ∠DFA and ∠EFC are ≅ vert. ∠s and ∠3 ≅ ∠4. Therefore, △DAF ≅ △ECF by the AAS Thm.

TE page 438 Lesson Quiz

1.

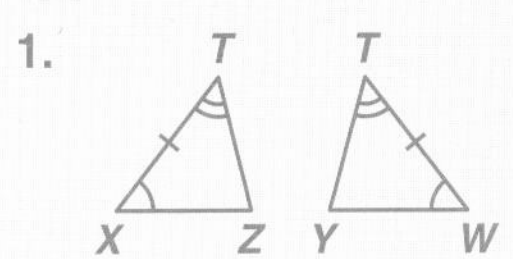

1. ∠XTZ ≅ ∠WTY, $\overline{XT} \cong \overline{WT}$, ∠X ≅ ∠W (Given) 2. △XTZ ≅ △WTY (ASA Post.) 3. $\overline{XZ} \cong \overline{WY}$ (CPCTC)

2.

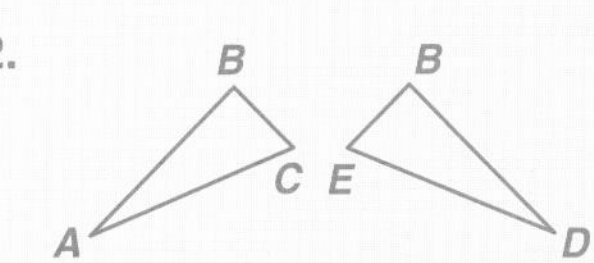

1. $\overline{BA} \cong \overline{BD}$, ∠A ≅ ∠D (Given)
2. ∠B ≅ ∠B (Reflexive Prop of ≅) 3. △BAC ≅ △BDE (ASA Post.)
4. $\overline{AC} \cong \overline{DE}$ (CPCTC)

Cumulative Review page 445

9.

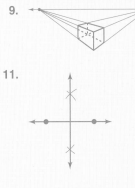

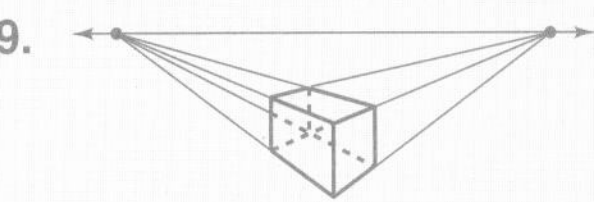

11.

CHAPTER 9

LESSON 9-1

pages 448–450 Think and Discuss

4.

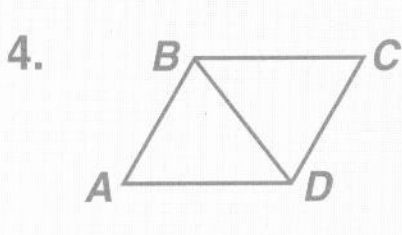

Draw diagonal $\overline{BD}$. Prove △ABD ≅ △CDB by ASA and use CPCTC to prove ∠A ≅ ∠C. Use diagonal $\overline{AC}$ to prove ∠B ≅ ∠D.

6a. $(x + y) + (x + y) = 360$ (The sum of the measures of the ∠s of a quad. is 360.); $2(x + y) = 360$ (Distributive Property); $x + y = 180$ (Division Prop. of =)

TE page 449 Additional Example 1

1. ▱ABCD (Given) 2. $\overline{AB} \parallel \overline{DC}$, $\overline{BC} \parallel \overline{AD}$ (Def. of ▱) 3. ∠1 ≅ ∠4, ∠3 ≅ ∠2 (If ∥ lines, then alt. int. ∠s are ≅). 4. $\overline{AC} \cong \overline{AC}$ (Refl. Prop. of ≅) 5. △ABC ≅ △CDA (ASA Postulate) 6. $\overline{AB} \cong \overline{CD}$, $\overline{BC} \cong \overline{DA}$ (CPCTC)

TE page 449 Additional Example 2

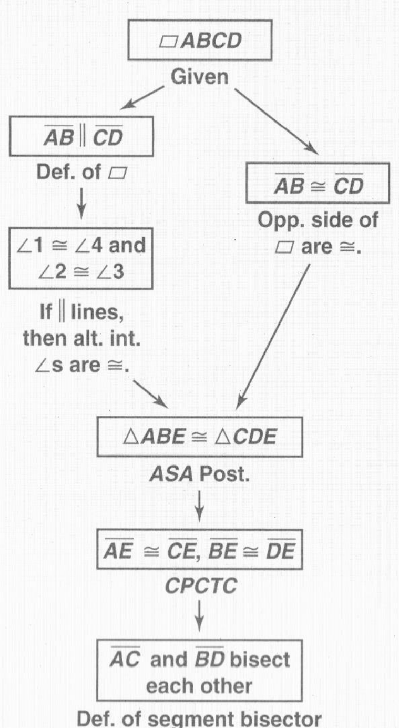

page 451–453 On Your Own

16. 1. ▱*NGTH* (Given) 2. ∠*T* ≅ ∠*GNH* (Opp. ∠s of a ▱ are ≅.) 3. ∠*GNH* ≅ ∠*SNE* (Vert. angles are ≅.) 4. ∠*T* ≅ ∠*SNE* (Transitive Prop. of ≅) 5. *m*∠*T* = *m*∠*SNE* (Def. of ≅ angles) 6. ∠*E* and ∠*SNE* are supplementary. (Consecutive ∠s of a ▱ are supplementary. See p. 449, Question 6.) 7. *m*∠*E* + *m*∠*SNE* = 180 (Def. of supplementary angles) 8. *m*∠*E* + *m*∠*T* = 180 (Substitution) 9. ∠*E* and ∠*T* are supplementary. (Def. of supplementary angles)

page 453 Mixed Review

34. 35. 36. 37.

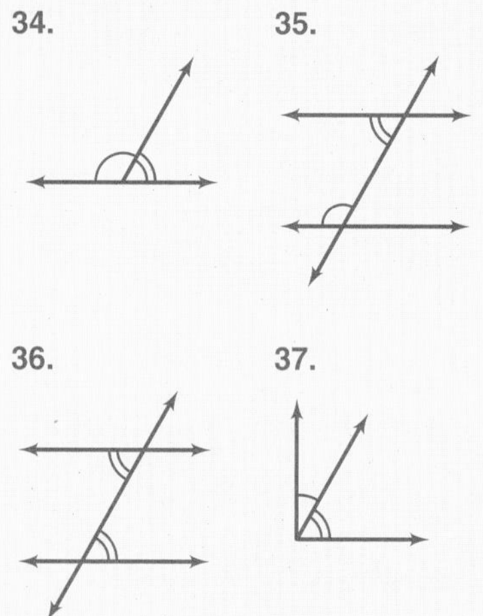

38. 39.

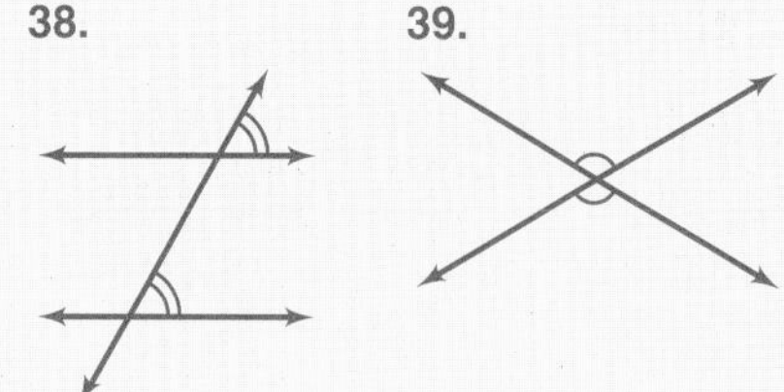

TE page 453 Lesson Quiz

3. Answers may vary. Sample:
   1. ▱*ACDF* and ▱*ABEF* (Given)
   2. $\overline{AF} \parallel \overline{CD}$, $\overline{AF} \parallel \overline{BE}$, (Def. of ▱) 3. $\overline{CD} \parallel \overline{BE}$ (2 lines ∥ to a 3rd line are ∥)
   4. *BCDE* is ▱ (Def. of ▱)

LESSON 9-3

TE page 463 Additional Example 1

1. $\overline{AB} \cong \overline{AD}$ (Def. of rhombus) 2. ∠1 ≅ ∠2 (Each diag. of a rhombus bisect 2 ∠s of the rhombus.) 3. $\overline{AE} \cong \overline{AE}$ (Reflexive Prop. of ≅) 4. △*ABE* ≅ △*ADE* (SAS Post.) 5. ∠*AEB* ≅ ∠*AED* (CPCTC) 6. ∠*AEB* and ∠*AED* are rt. ∠s . (≅ supplementary ∠s are rt. ∠s.)
7. $\overline{AC} \perp \overline{BD}$ (Def. of ⊥ lines)

LESSON 9-4

TE page 471 Additional Example 2

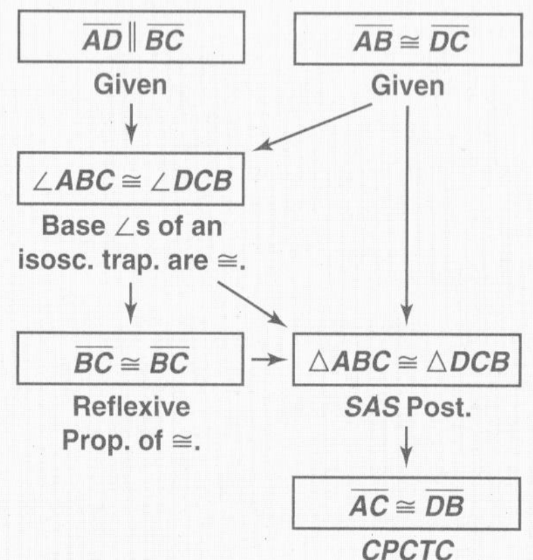

LESSON 9-5

page 479 Problem Solving

$\overline{TW}$ and $\overline{UV}$ are ∥ to $\overline{OX}$ because they are midsegments of △*OIX* and △*ORX*, respectively. They are ∥ to each other, because 2 lines ∥ to a 3rd line are ∥. Similarly, $\overline{TU} \parallel \overline{VW}$. Then *TUVW* is a ▱ by def.

TE page 479 Additional Example 2

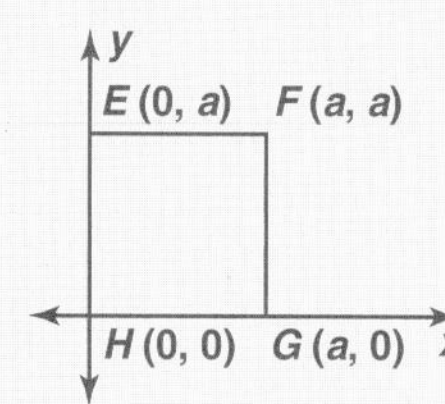

The slope of $\overline{EG}$ = −1. The slope of $\overline{FH}$ = 1. The product of the slopes is −1, so the lines are perpendicular.

pages 480–482 On Your Own

15a.

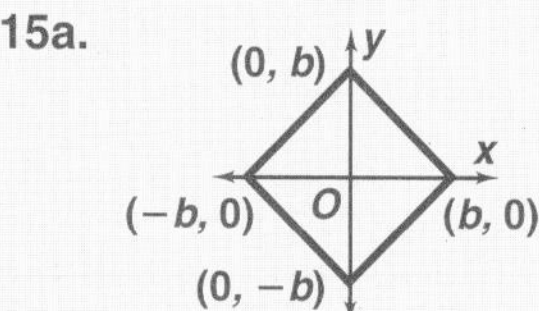

16a.

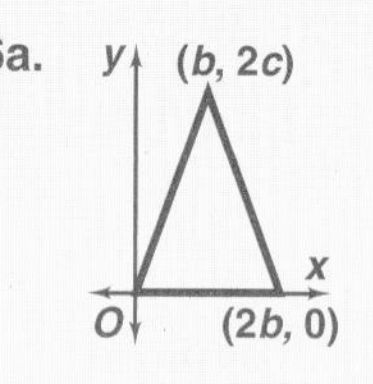

b.

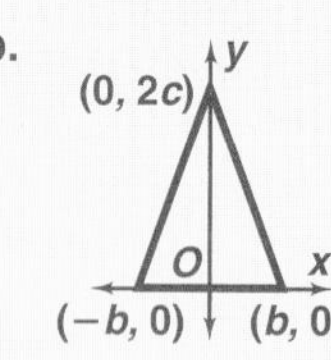

26.

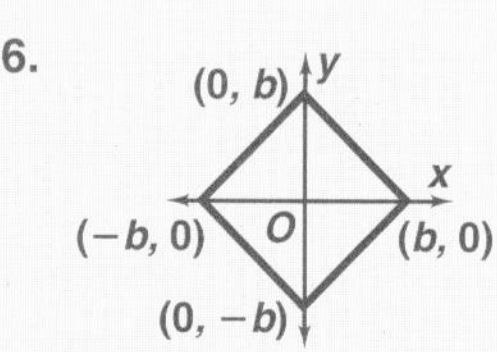

TE page 482 Lesson Quiz

3.

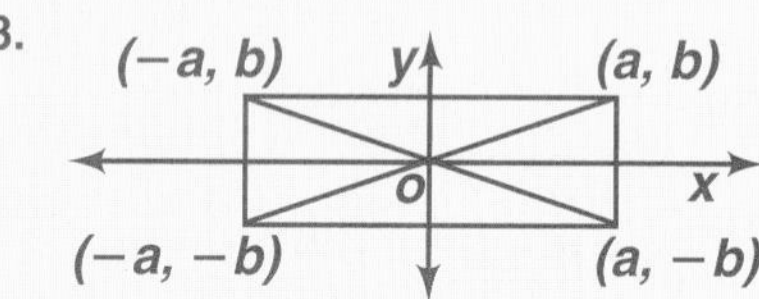

LESSON 9-6

pages 483–484 Think and Discuss

5. Answers may vary. Sample: The slope of $\overline{TV}$ is 0. The slope of $\overline{UW}$ is undefined. A line with an undefined slope is ⊥ to a line with slope 0. The diagonals of ▱*TUVW* are ⊥. Therefore, *TUVW* is a rhombus.

pages 485–487 On Your Own

11b. Let a pt. on line *p* be (x, y). Then the equation of *p* is $\frac{y - 0}{x - a} = \frac{b}{c}$ or $y = \frac{b}{c}(x - a)$.

d. When $x = 0$, $y = \frac{b}{c}(x - a) = \frac{b}{c}(-a) = \frac{-ab}{c}$. So *p* and *q* intersect at $\left(0, \frac{-ab}{c}\right)$.

f. Let a pt. on line r be (x, y). Then the equation of r is $\frac{y-0}{x-b} = \frac{a}{c}$ or $y = \frac{a}{c}(x - b)$.

g. $-\frac{ab}{c} = \frac{a}{c}(b - 0)$ ✔

$-\frac{ab}{c} = \frac{b}{c}(a - 0)$ ✔

page 487 Mixed Review

14. Method 1: Add the percents for the 6 age groups younger than 65. Answer: 95% Method 2: Subtract the percent for the 65-and-over group from 100%. Answer: 94% The answers don't agree because the sum for all groups is 101% instead of 100%.

TE page 487 Lesson Quiz

1. $C(0, t)$, $E(s, 0)$;
   $CE = \sqrt{s^2 + t^2}$
   $DF = \sqrt{s^2 + t^2}$
   $CE = DF$, so $\overline{CE} \cong \overline{DF}$

2. $M(0, 0)$, $O(s + a, t)$;
   $NO = \sqrt{a^2}$
   $MP = \sqrt{a^2}$
   $NM = \sqrt{s^2 + t^2}$
   $OP = \sqrt{s^2 + t^2}$
   Since $NO = MP$ and $NM = OP$, opp. sides are $\cong$.

CHAPTER 11

LESSON 11-3

pages 558–560 On Your Own

13a.

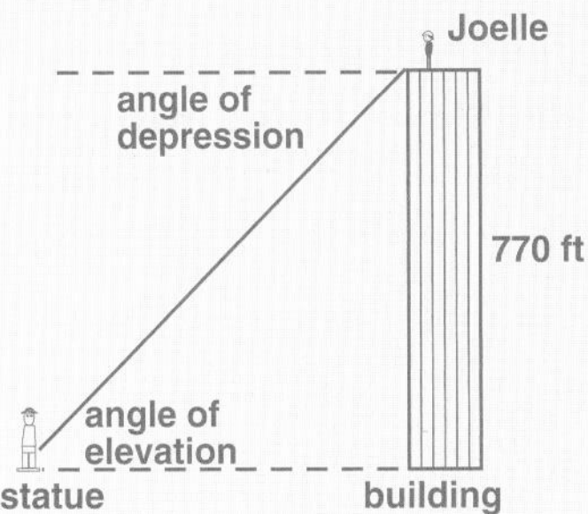

b. For sample in part (a): Joelle is standing at the top of 770 ft building. She sees a famous statue at street level several blocks away. The angle of depression between the top of the building and the statue is 4°. How far is the statue from the base of the building? Answer: about 11,000 ft, or 2 mi

LESSON 11-5

page 570 Work Together

3. Answers may vary. Sample:

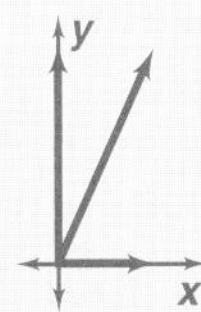

The magnitude of the force along the y-axis was greater.

4. Answers may vary. Sample: Have each member of the group "compete" against each other member. The person blowing along the x-axis wins if the marble stops below the line $y = x$, and the other person wins if the marble stops above $y = x$. Whoever wins the most times is the one who can exert the force with the greatest magnitude.

pages 570–572 On Your Own

9b. $\frac{2}{3}$

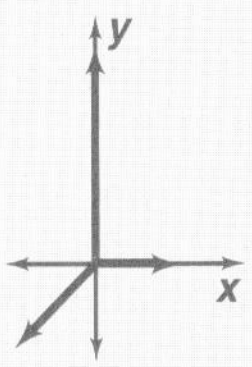

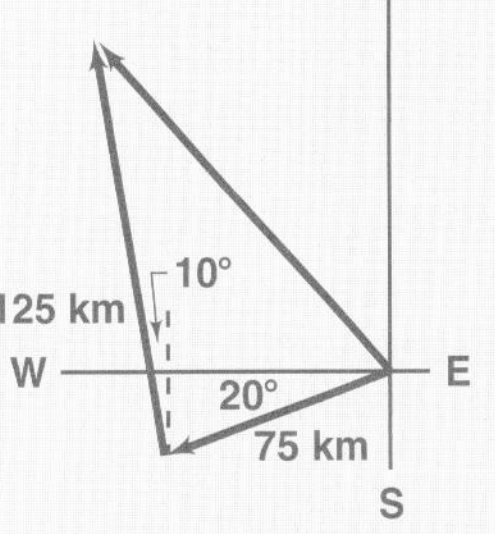

17a–b.

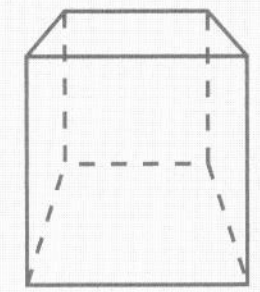

Answers may vary slightly. Sample: 134 km at 43° east of south

page 572 Mixed Review

25.

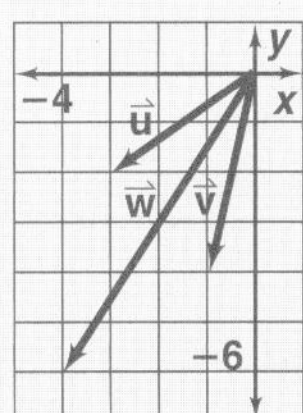

Checkpoint page 572

4. $\vec{u} : \langle -3, -2 \rangle$, $\vec{v} : \langle -1, -4 \rangle$, $\vec{w} : \langle -4, -6 \rangle$

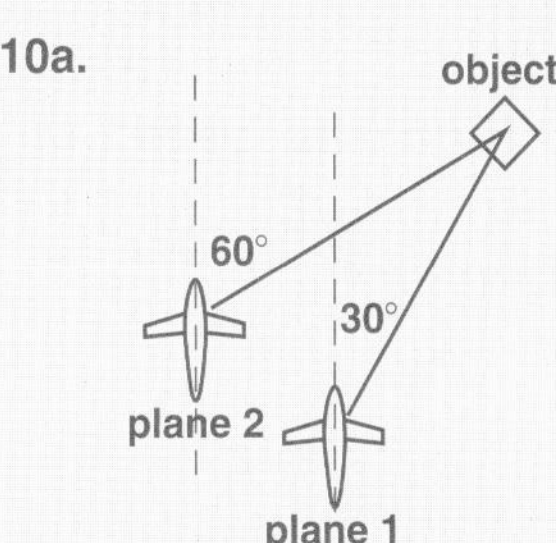

Preparing for Standardized Tests page 583

10a.

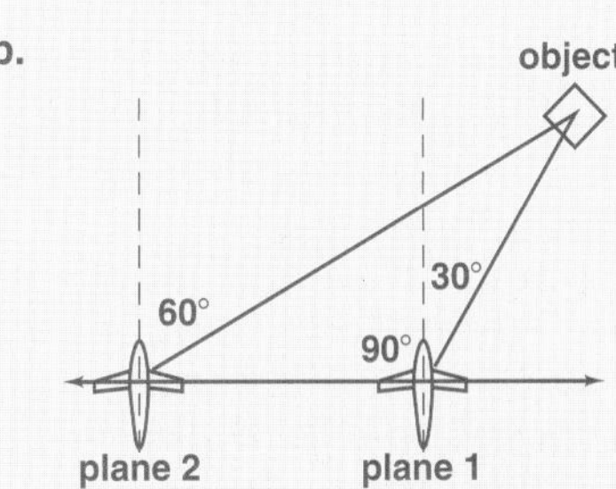

b.

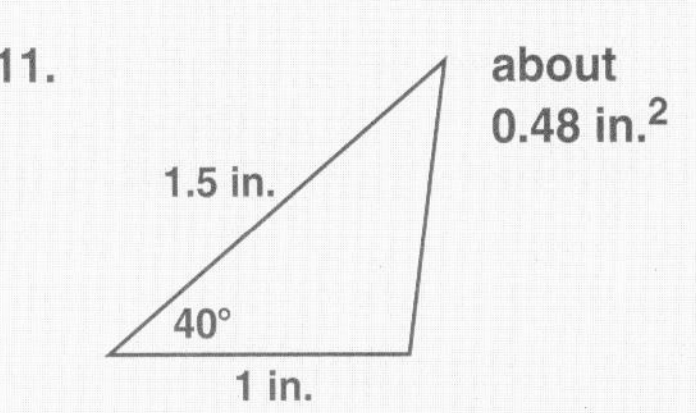

11. about 0.48 in.^2

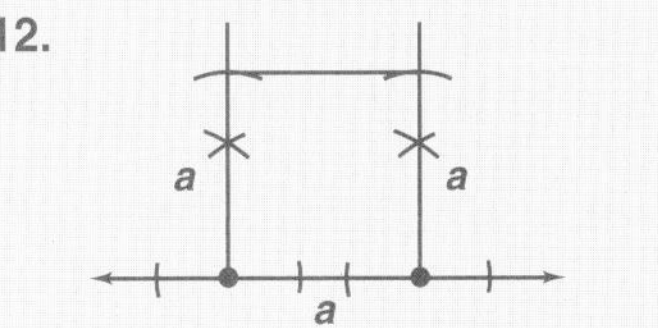

12.

Additional Answers

Challenge Problems

Ch. 5 Challenge Problems page 639

5-5 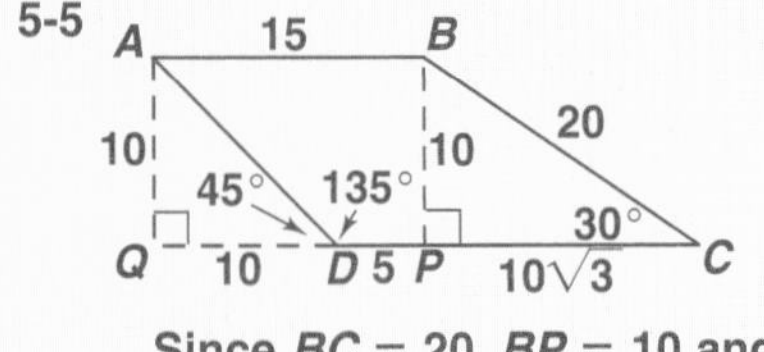

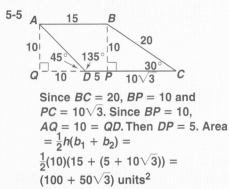

Since $BC = 20$, $BP = 10$ and $PC = 10\sqrt{3}$. Since $BP = 10$, $AQ = 10 = QD$. Then $DP = 5$. Area $= \frac{1}{2}h(b_1 + b_2) =$ $\frac{1}{2}(10)(15 + (5 + 10\sqrt{3})) =$ $(100 + 50\sqrt{3})$ units^2

Ch. 9 Challenge Problems page 643

9-1(1)a. 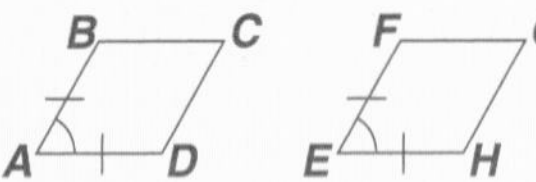

Given $\square ABCD$, $\square EFGH$, $\overline{AB} \cong \overline{EF}$, $\overline{AD} \cong \overline{EH}$, $\angle A \cong \angle E$

Prove: $\square ABCD \cong \square EFGH$

Plan: Use Thm. 9-1 and transitivity to show that $\overline{BC} \cong \overline{FG}$ and $\overline{CD} \cong \overline{GH}$. Use Thm. 9-2 and transitivity to show that $\angle C \cong \angle G$. Use Thm. 7-2 and Thm. 1-2 to show that $\angle B \cong \angle F$ and $\angle D \cong \angle H$. Then $\square ABCD \cong \square EFGH$ because all the corresponding angles and sides are congruent.

b. There is no similar theorem for trapezoids. Since a trapezoid has only one pair of parallel sides, SAS is not sufficient to guarantee that all corresponding parts are congruent.

9-1(2) Sample answer: Since $ABCD$ is a parallelogram, $\overline{AB} \parallel \overline{DC}$. $\angle 1 \cong \angle 2$ because they are alternate interior angles formed by parallel lines. Similarly, $\overline{BC} \parallel \overline{AD}$, so $\angle 3 \cong \angle 4$. It is given that $\overline{AC}$ bisects $\angle BAD$, so $\angle 1 \cong \angle 3$. Then $\angle 2 \cong \angle 4$ by the transitive property of $\cong$. So $\overline{AC}$ bisects $\angle BCD$ by the definition of angle bisector.

Ch. 10 Challenge Problems page 645

10-3(1)c. 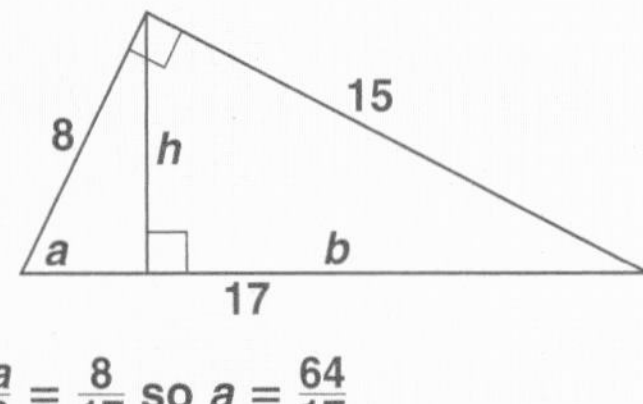

$\frac{a}{8} = \frac{8}{17}$ so $a = \frac{64}{17}$

$b = 17 - a = \frac{225}{17}$

$\frac{\frac{64}{17}}{h} = \frac{h}{\frac{225}{17}}$ so $h = \frac{120}{17}$

10-3(2) Britt is correct.

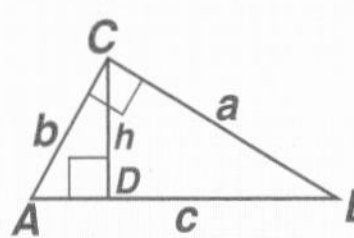

$\triangle ABC \sim \triangle CDB$ by AA, so $\frac{a}{h} = \frac{c}{b}$ and $ab = hc$.

10-4 Sample answers:

a. A midsegment of a parallelogram is a segment that joins the midpoints of opposite sides of the parallelogram.

b. 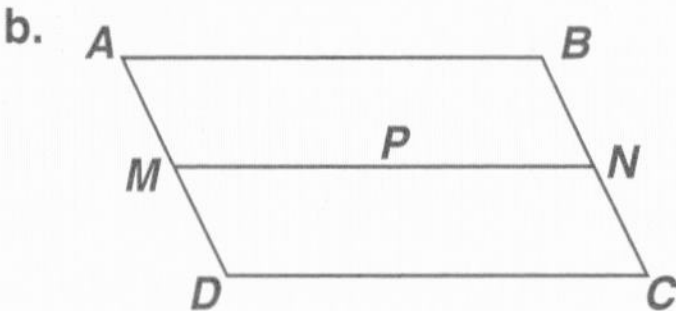

Given: $ABCD$ is a parallelogram and $\overline{MN}$ is a midsegment.
Prove: $\overline{MN} \parallel \overline{AB} \parallel \overline{DC}$
Proof: Since $ABCD$ is a parallelogram, $\overline{AD} \parallel \overline{BC}$ and $AD = BC$. Since $\overline{MN}$ is a midsegment, M is the midpoint of $\overline{AD}$ and $AM = \frac{1}{2}(AD)$. Similarly, $BN = \frac{1}{2}(BC)$. Then $AM = BN$ by substitution. $ABNM$ is a parallelogram because a pair of sides is parallel and congruent, and $\overline{MN} \parallel \overline{AB}$ because opposite sides of a parallelogram are parallel. $\overline{MN} \parallel \overline{DC}$ because if two lines are parallel to a third line, they are parallel to each other.

c. 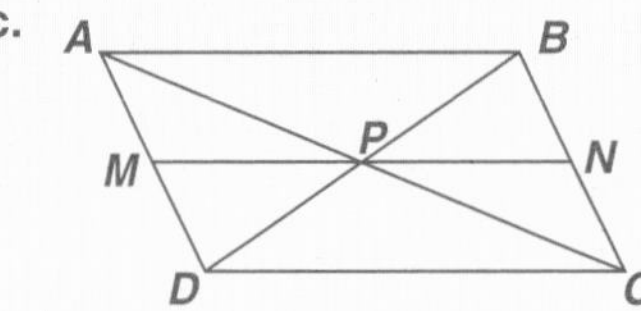

Given: $ABCD$ is a parallelogram and $\overline{MN}$ is a midsegment.
Prove: $\overline{MN}$ bisects $\overline{AC}$ and $\overline{BD}$.
Proof: From part (a) $\overline{MN} \parallel \overline{AB} \parallel \overline{DC}$ and $AM = MD$. $AP = PC$ and $BP = PD$ because if three parallel lines intersect two transversals, then the segments intercepted on the transversals are proportional. So $\overline{MN}$ bisects $\overline{AC}$ and $\overline{BD}$.

10-5a. always; If p is the perimeter of a rectangle, the perimeter of a similar rectangle with a similarity ratio k is kp. If $p = kp$, then $k = 1$. If the similarity ratio is 1, the rectangles are congruent.

b. sometimes; Congruent rectangles have the same area and are similar. A 1-by-4 rectangle and a 2-by-2 rectangle have the same area but are not similar.

c. always; The measure of each interior angle of a regular hexagon is 120. Since the sides of a regular hexagon are congruent, the corresponding sides of any two regular hexagons are proportional. Therefore the regular hexagons are similar.

d. never; A pentagon has 5 sides and a hexagon has 6 sides. Therefore they do not have corresponding sides or corresponding angles.

e. sometimes; If the similar triangles are congruent, they have the same area, but otherwise they do not.

f. never; A trapezoid can have only one pair of parallel sides. Therefore the opposite angles of a trapezoid cannot be congruent. The opposite angles of a parallelogram are congruent. Therefore the angles of a trapezoid cannot be congruent to the angles of a parallelogram.

10-6a. The similarity ratio of the two similar pyramids is 12 : 3 or 4 : 1. So the ratio of their volumes is $4^3 : 1^3$ or 64 : 1.

$\frac{\text{volume of pyramid } A}{\text{volume of pyramid } B} = \frac{64}{1}$

$\frac{\text{volume of pyramid } A}{6} = \frac{64}{1}$

volume of pyramid $A = 384$ cm^3

b. The ratio of their surface areas is $4^2 : 1^2$ or 16 : 1.

c. For pyramid B, $V = \frac{1}{3}Bh$, so $6 = \frac{1}{3}(9)(h)$ and $h = 2$. The slant height $\ell = \sqrt{2^2 + 1.5^2} = 2.5$. S.A. $= B + \frac{1}{2}p\ell = 3(3) + \frac{1}{2}(4)(3)(2.5) = 24$ cm^2.

$\frac{\text{S.A. of pyramid } A}{\text{S.A. of pyramid } B} = \frac{16}{1}$

$\frac{\text{S.A. of pyramid } A}{24} = \frac{16}{1}$

S.A. of pyramid $A = 384$ cm^2

Ch. 11 Challenge Problems page 645

11-1a. $\tan 2A = 9.5144$, so $2A = \tan^{-1}(9.5144) \approx 84°$. Then $A \approx 42°$.

b. $\tan \frac{A}{3} = 0.4663$, so $\frac{A}{3} = \tan^{-1}(0.4663) \approx 24.9996°$. Then $A \approx 75°$.

c. $(\tan 5A)^2 = 0.3610$, so $\tan 5A = \sqrt{0.3610} \approx 0.6008$ and $5A \approx \tan^{-1}(0.6008) \approx 30.9988°$, and $A \approx 6°$.

d. $\frac{\tan A}{1 + \tan A} = 0.5437$
$(0.5437)(1 + \tan A) = \tan A$
$\tan A = \frac{0.5437}{0.4563} \approx 1.1915$
$A = \tan^{-1}(1.1915) \approx 50°$

11-2a. $(\sin A)^2 + (\cos A)^2 = \left(\frac{a}{c}\right)^2 + \left(\frac{b}{c}\right)^2 = \frac{a^2 + b^2}{c^2} = \frac{c^2}{c^2} = 1$

b. $(\sin B)^2 + (\cos B)^2 = \left(\frac{b}{c}\right)^2 + \left(\frac{a}{c}\right)^2 = \frac{b^2 + a^2}{c^2} = \frac{c^2}{c^2} = 1$

c. $\frac{1}{(\cos A)^2} - (\tan A)^2 =$
$\frac{1}{\left(\frac{b}{c}\right)^2} - \left(\frac{a}{b}\right)^2 = \frac{c^2}{b^2} - \frac{a^2}{b^2}$
$\frac{c^2 - a^2}{b^2} = \frac{b^2}{b^2} = 1$

11-3

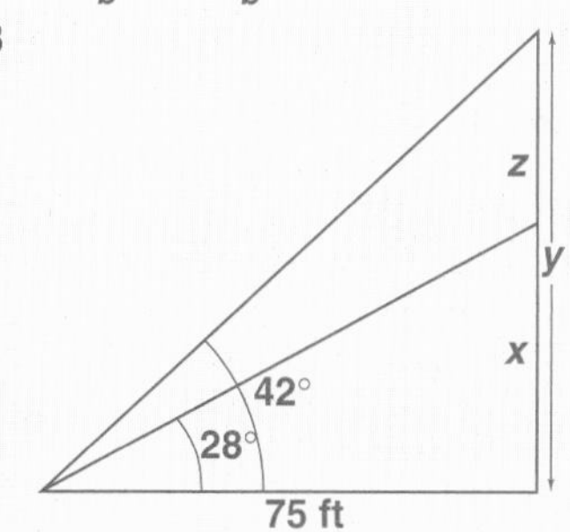

$\tan 28° = \frac{x}{75}$, so $x = 75(\tan 28°) \approx 39.878$. $\tan 42° = \frac{y}{75}$, so $y = 75(\tan 42°) \approx 67.530$.

$z = 67.530 - 39.878 \approx 27.7$ ft. The 30-ft ladder will reach the window.

Ch. 12 Challenge Problems pages 646–647

12-3. Given: The two circles are concentric. $\overline{AB}$ is tangent to the smaller circle at C. Prove: C is the midpoint of $\overline{AB}$.

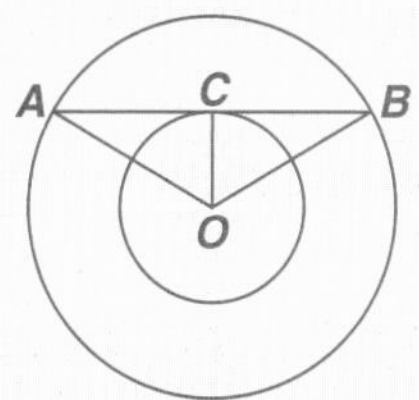

$\overline{AB}$ is tangent to the smaller circle at C. $\overline{CO} \perp \overline{AB}$ because a radius drawn to the point of tangency is perpendicular to the tangent. $AO = OB$ because they are radii of the same circle. $CO = CO$ by reflexivity. $\triangle ACO \cong \triangle BCO$ by the HL theorem and $AC = BC$ by CPCTC. Therefore C is the midpoint of $\overline{AB}$.

12-4(1) Given: Trapezoid $ABCD$ inscribed in $\odot O$ with $\overline{AB} \parallel \overline{DC}$ Prove: $ABCD$ is isosceles.

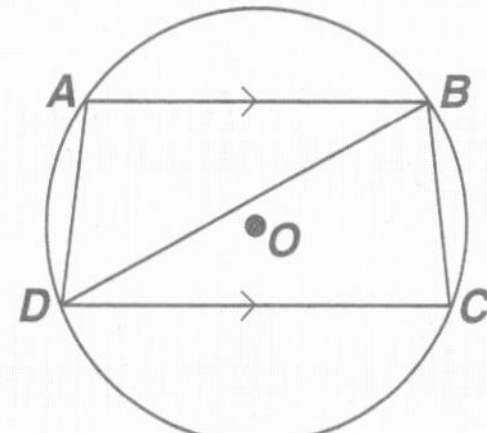

$\overline{AB} \parallel \overline{DC}$, so $\angle ABD \cong \angle BDC$ because they are alternate interior angles. $\overset{\frown}{AD} \cong \overset{\frown}{BC}$ since these arcs are intercepted by congruent inscribed angles. $\overline{AD} \cong \overline{BC}$ since congruent chords intercept congruent arcs. Therefore, $ABCD$ is isosceles.

12-4(2) It is a rectangle. (It can be shown that its angles intercept semicircles.)

12-4(3)a. O is on $\overline{BD}$, so $\overline{BD}$ is a diameter and $m\overset{\frown}{BDC} = 180$. Radius $\overline{OB}$ is perpendicular to tangent $\overleftrightarrow{AB}$, so $m\angle ABC = 90$. Therefore $m\angle ABC = \frac{1}{2}m\overset{\frown}{BDC}$.

b. $m\angle ABD = \frac{1}{2}m\overset{\frown}{BED}$ by Case 1. $m\angle DBC = \frac{1}{2}m\overset{\frown}{DC}$ since the measure of an inscribed angle is half the measure of its intercepted arc. $m\angle ABC = m\angle ABD + m\angle DBC$ by the Angle Addition Theorem. By substitution, $m\angle ABC = \frac{1}{2}m\overset{\frown}{BED} + \frac{1}{2}m\overset{\frown}{DC}$ and this equals $\frac{1}{2}(m\overset{\frown}{BED} + m\overset{\frown}{DC})$ by the distributive property. $m\overset{\frown}{BED} + m\overset{\frown}{DC} = m\overset{\frown}{BDC}$ by the Arc Addition Postulate. By substitution, $m\angle ABC = \frac{1}{2}m\overset{\frown}{BDC}$.

c. $m\angle ABD = \frac{1}{2}m\overset{\frown}{BCD}$ by Case 1. $m\angle CBD = \frac{1}{2}\overset{\frown}{CD}$ since the measure of an inscribed angle is half the measure of its intercepted arc. $m\angle ABD = m\angle ABC + m\angle CBD$ by the Angle Addition Theorem. So $m\angle ABC = m\angle ABD - m\angle CBD$. By substitution, $m\angle ABC = \frac{1}{2}m\overset{\frown}{BCD} - \frac{1}{2}m\overset{\frown}{CD}$ and this equals $\frac{1}{2}(m\overset{\frown}{BCD} - m\overset{\frown}{CD})$ by the distributive property. $m\overset{\frown}{BC} + m\overset{\frown}{CD} = m\overset{\frown}{BCD}$ by the Arc Addition Postulate, so $m\overset{\frown}{BC} = m\overset{\frown}{BCD} - m\overset{\frown}{CD}$. By substitution, $m\angle ABC = m\angle ABC = \frac{1}{2}m\overset{\frown}{BC}$

12-5

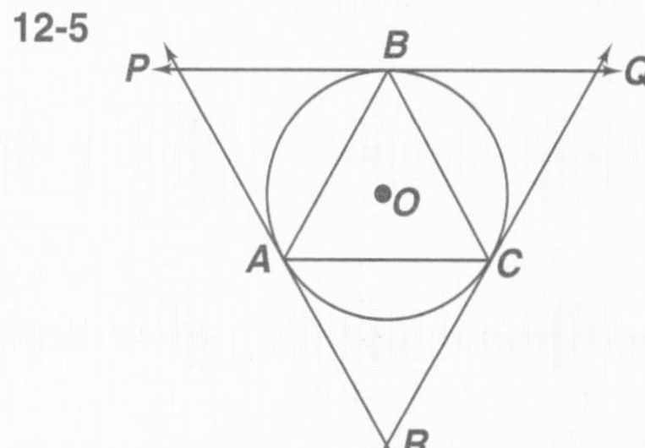

Given: $\triangle ABC$ is an equilateral triangle. $\overleftrightarrow{PR}$ is tangent to $\odot O$ at A. $\overleftrightarrow{RQ}$ is tangent to $\odot O$ at C. $\overleftrightarrow{PQ}$ is tangent to $\odot O$ at B.
Prove: $\triangle PQR$ is equilateral.
Proof: $\triangle ABC$ is equilateral so $m\angle BAC = 60$. $\angle A$ intercepts $\overset{\frown}{BC}$ so $m\overset{\frown}{BC} = 2(60) = 120$. $m\overset{\frown}{BAC} = 360 - 120 = 240$. $m\angle PQR = \frac{1}{2}(m\overset{\frown}{BAC} - m\overset{\frown}{BC}) = 60$. Similarly, $m\angle PRQ = 60$ and $m\angle RPQ = 60$. $\triangle PQR$ is equiangular and therefore equilateral.

12-6

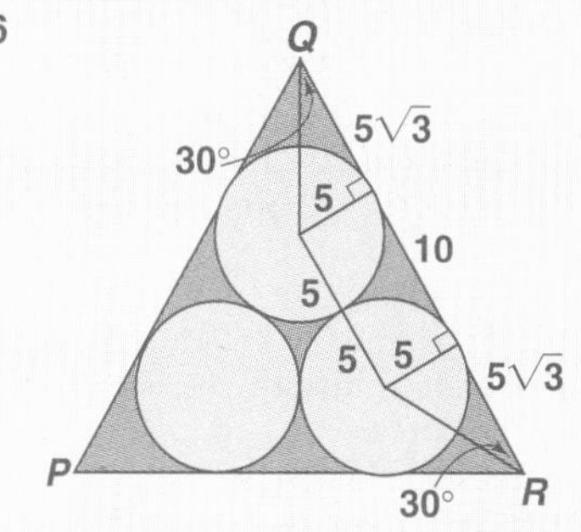

a. Based on the 30°-60°-90° triangles and the rectangle drawn in the diagram, each side of $\triangle PQR$ is $10 + 10\sqrt{3}$, so its perimeter is $30 + 30\sqrt{3} \approx 81.96$.

b. The total area of the three circles is $3(\pi 5^2) = 75\pi$. Using the formula $A = \frac{s^2\sqrt{3}}{4}$ for the area of an equilateral triangle (see page 277, Exercise 19) $A = \frac{(10 + 10\sqrt{3})^2\sqrt{3}}{4} = 150 + 100\sqrt{3}$. The area of the triangle not covered by the circles is $(150 + 100\sqrt{3}) - (75\pi) \approx 87.59$ cm^2.

Index

Teacher's Edition entries appear in blue type.

Acknowledgments

Cover Design: Suzanne Schineller; Sweetlight Creative Partners

Technical Illustration Fran Jarvis, Technical Illustration Manager; ANCO/Outlook

Illustration

Leo Abbett: 97 ml, 205 t, 388 b
Susan Avishai: 427
Kim Barnes: 24, 199
Tom Barrett: 186, 341 b(inset)
Judith Pinkham-Cataldo: 302 inset, 613
Jim DeLapine: 228, 289 b, 339, 340, 390 m
Kathleen Dempsey: 486
Peggy Dressel: 167 b
Howard S. Friedman: 365
Function Thru Form Inc.: 53, 134, 220 t, 303 all, 312 b, 313 t, 336, 341 t, 345 all, 346 all
Dave Garbot: 247 t, 253 t
GeoSystems Global Corporation: 127 b
Dale Glasgow & Associates: 369, 432
Kelley Hersey: 97, 509
Linda Johnson: 156 m, 157 b
Ellen Korey-Lie: 429, 572
Seymour Levy: 129 m, 150 m, 186 inset, 246, 341 b
Andrea G. Maginnis: 17 t, 30 b, 90, 137 t
Ortelius Design Inc.: 13 t, 24 inset, 270 b, 271, 395
Gary Phillips: 30 m
Lois Leonard Stock: 162 b, 164 b, 508 all, 556 all
Peter Siu: 590
Gary Torrisi: 205 t, 270 t, 352 t, 516, 558 all, 560 m, 563 all, 598 b
Gregg Valley: 224 t
Joe Veno: 4, 32

Feature Design Alan Lee Associates

Photography

Photo Research Sue McDermott

Abbreviations: JC = Jon Chomitz; FPG = Freelance Photographer's Guild; KO = Ken O'Donoghue; PR = Photo Researchers, Inc.; PH = Prentice Hall File Photo; SB = Stock Boston; SM = The Stock Market; MT = Mark Thayer; TSI = Tony Stone Images

Cover Photos: Globe, Bill Westheimer; concept car, Ron Kimball

Front matter: Page vii, David Young-Wolff/PhotoEdit; **viii,** Jerry Jacka; **ix,** Photofest; **x,** Superstock; **xi,** Tony Freeman/PhotoEdit; **xii,** Tom & Pat Leeson/DRK Photo; **xiii,** JC; **xiv,** Stephen Frisch/SB; **xv,** Geoffrey Clifford/Woodfin Camp; **xvi,** Alan and Linda Detrick/PR; **xvii,** Bob Daemmrich/SB; **xviii,** Steve Niedorf/The Image Bank.

Chapter 1: Pages 2-3, Anselm Spring/The Image Bank; **2 & 3 insets,** Used with permission of Sterling Publishing Co., Inc., 387 Park Ave. Sl, NY, NY 10016 from BEST EVER PAPER AIRPLANES by Norman Schmidt. ©1994 by Norman Schmidt. A Sterling/Tamos Book; **2 & 3 insets,** JC; **5,** David Young-Wolff/PhotoEdit; **8,** Tom Pantages; **9,** JC; **12,** Jack Newton/Masterfile; **16,** Johnny Johnson/DRK Photo; **18,** Superstock; **19,** John Gerlach/DRK Photo; **20,** JC; **21,** Will Ryan/SM; **22,** KO; **26,** Mark Bolster/International Stock Photo; **27,** JC; **29 t,** Glyn Kirk/TSI; **29 b,** Ralph Cowan/FPG; **33,** Michael Hart/FPG; **34,** JC; **36,** KO; **38,** Dan McCoy/SM; **39,** JC; **41,** JC; **44,** KO; **46,** Larry Grant/FPG; **48,** Telegraph Colour Library/FPG; **55,** Mike Agliolo/International Stock Photo; **56,** Paul Chesley/TSI; **57,** Tom Pantages.

Chapter 2: Pages 66-67, Jason Hawkes/TSI; **67 inset,** Russ Lappa; **68,** KO; **70,** Sunstar/The Picture Cube; **72,** John Coletti/The Picture Cube; **73 t,** Tom Van Sant/Geosphere Project, Santa Monica/PR; **73 bl & br,** Jerry Jacka; **76,** John Elk/SB; **78,** Richard Pasley/SB; **79 t,** KO; **79 bl,** Superstock; **79 bml,** Nawrocki Stock Photo/Picture Perfect; **79 bmr,** Jerry Jacka; **80,** Barbara Adams/FPG; **83,** Gary Brettnacher/TSI; **85,** Photo courtesy of Jacob Albert; **87 t,** B. Busco/The Image Bank; **87 b,** Frank Rossotto/SM; **90,** KO; **93,** Michael Nelson; **94,** Photograph copyright ©1996: WHITNEY MUSEUM OF AMERICAN ART, NEW YORK. Photography by Sheldan C. Collins; **96,** Courtesy of Paramount's Carowinds; **98,** Dale O'Dell/SM; **100,** David Weintraub/SB; **101,** David Weintraub/SB;**102,** NASA; **104,** Rosanne Olson/TSI; **105,** Cathlyn Melloan/TSI; **106,** Rod Planck/Tom Stack & Associates; **108,** MT; **109,** ©1996, Microsoft Corporation. Image created with SOFTIMAGE (R/3D); **110,** Barry Durand/Odyssey/Chicago; **112,** MT; **113,** Reprinted by Permission: Tribune Media Services; **115 t,** MT; **115 b,** Rick Altman/SM.

Chapter 3: Pages 122-123, MT; **123,** Bob Daemmrich/SB; **124,** KO; **126,** Frances M. Roberts; **129,** Biblioteca Ambrosiana, Milan/The Bridgeman Art Library; **130,** MAURICE HORN, THE WORLD ENCYCLOPEDIA OF COMICS (PAGE 41), reprinted with permission of Chelsea House Publishers; **132,** Photri, Inc.; **136,** Chris Michaels/FPG; **140,** NASA; **142,** Jerry Jacka; **145 l,** JC; **145 r,** Alfred Pasieka/SPL/PR; **147 bl,** Viviane Moos/SM; **147 bm,** Paul Jablonka/International Stock Photo; **147 br,** Adam Peirport/SM; **149,** KO; **152 t,** Keystone/Sygma; **152 b,** JC; **153,** PH; **154,** Frank Fornier/Contact Press Images; **155 tl,** John Kaprielian/PR; **155 tr,** Floyd Dean/FPG; **155 bl,** Michael Simpson/FPG; **155 br,** Dave Gleiter/FPG; **156,** PH; **159 t,** Tom Pantages; **160,** KO; **161,** KO; **163 l,** Russ Lappa; **163 tr,** M.A. Chappell/Animals Animals; **164 tm,** Guido Alberto Rossi/The Image Bank; **164 tr,** Courtesy of Francois Brisse; **165,** Robert Frerck/Odyssey/Chicago; **167,** Charles Gupton/TSI; **169,** Photofest; **172,** Stephen Frisch/SB; **176 l,** Patti Murray/Animals Animals; **176 m,** Russ Lappa; **178 l,** Don & Pat Valenti/DRK Photo; **178 r,** Jeff Foott/DRK Photo.

Chapter 4: Pages 180-181, Richard T. Nowitz/PR; **181,** Peter Menzel/SB; **182,** Framed. ©William Wegman 1995. 20 x 24 inches. Unique Polacolor ER photograph. Courtesy PaceWildenstein MacGill Gallery. New York; **183,** JC; **185,** ©1977 NEA, Inc.; **188,** Visuals Unlimited; **191,** Fernando Serna/Department of the Air Force; **193,** Russ Lappa, **194,** JC; **198,** John M. Roberts/SM; **199,** Corbis-Bettmann; **204,** Superstock; **207,** MT; **209 t,** Mike Penney/David Frazier Photolibrary; **209 m,** Peter Menzel/SB; **209 b,** Lynn McLaren/The Picture Cube; **211 t,** Photofest; **211 b,** PH; **213,** JC; **216,** George Holton/PR; **217,** PH; **218,** Larry Lefever/Grant Heilman Photography; **219,** JC; **220,** The Granger Collection; **223,** Mike

Shirley/Picture Perfect; **224,** Martin Rogers/TSI; **225,** Globus Brothers/SM; **230,** KO; **232,** KO.

Chapter 5: Pages 240-241, John Madere/SB; **241,** Wolfgang Kaehler/Liason International; **242,** Superstock; **244,** Tony Freeman/PhotoEdit; **246,** Bill Gallery/SB; **249,** MT; **251,** Bill Horsman/SB; **254,** MT; **257,** Tom Dietrich/TSI; **260,** Robert Caputo/SB; **263,** Superstock; **264,** Nathan Bilow/Allsport; **267,** Joe Towers/SM; **270,** Terry Donnelly/TSI; **272,** William R. Sallaz/Duomo; **273 t,** Doll by Mary Tiger. Photo courtesy of the U.S. Department of the Interior, Indian Arts and Crafts Board; **273 b,** The Granger Collection; **275,** Photo courtesy of Nida-Core; **277,** G. Ross/FPG; **279,** Russ Lappa; **280,** Tony Freeman/PhotoEdit; **283 t,** CALVIN AND HOBBES ©Watterson. Dist. by UNIVERSAL PRESS SYNDICATE. Reprinted with permission. All rights reserved; **283 b,** Superstock; **286,** Gerald French/FPG; **287,** Jerry Tobias/Sharpshooters; **288,** Joe McDonald/DRK Photo; **290,** America Hurrah Archive, NYC.

Chapter 6: Pages 300-301, MT; **301,** Russ Lappa; **302,** Leigh/Stock Imagery; **304,** Sleeveless Tunic (?) with Stepped Triangles, Middle Horizon, 500-800 AD., Textile Income Purchase Fund and General Funds, Courtesy of Museum of Fine Arts, Boston; **306,** Tom & Pat Leeson/DRK Photo; **308,** KO; **311,** Greig Cranna/SB; **312,** David Young-Wolff/PhotoEdit; **313,** Scala/Art Resource; **314,** KO; **316-317,** David Sutherland/TSI; **320,** Richard Clintsman/TSI; **321 t,** KO; **321 b,** Uniphoto; **323,** KO; **326 t,** David Harp/Folio, Inc.; **326 b,** L. Kolvoord/The Image Works; **328,** Mark C. Burnett/PR; **330,** KO; **331,** Uniphoto; **334,** Uniphoto; **337,** KO; **338 l,** Mark C. Burnett/PR; **340 tl,** Mark C. Burnett/PR; **340 tml,** Richard Hutchings/PR; **340 tmr,** Tony Freeman/PhotoEdit; **340 tr,** David Young-Wolff/PhotoEdit; **340 b,** Breck Kent/Earth Scenes; **343,** KO; **344,** Don Spiro/TSI; **345,** Tom Stewart/SM; **347,** Robert Brenner/PhotoEdit; **349,** Jim Corwin/SB; **351,** Frank Fournier/SM.

Chapter 7: Pages 360-361, T. Tracy/FPG; **360 tl inset,** John Henley/SM; **360 ml inset,** Bob Daemmrich/SB; **360 bl inset,** Bill Bachman/PR; **361,** John Feingersh/SM; **363,** Charles Feil/SB; **367,** Richard Bryant/ARCAID; **368,** David Frazier/TSI; **373,** JC; **374,** JC; **375,** Paul Yandoli/SB; **376,** AP/Wide World Photos; **379 t,** Photo by Richard Cheek; **379 b,** Jock Reynolds, Installation view from Sol Lewitt: Twenty-five Years of Wall Drawings, 1968-1993, ©1993, Addison Gallery of American Art, Phillips Academy, Andover, MA; **381,** JC; **382 t,** JC; **382 b,** Andrew Brookes/TSI; **385 l,** The Granger Collection; **385 r,** Giraudon/Art Resource; **386,** Artothek; **387 l,** D & J Heaton/SB; **387 r,** Jeff Greenberg/SB; **389,** CALVIN AND HOBBES ©Watterson. Dist. by UNIVERSAL PRESS SYNDICATE. Reprinted with permission. All rights reserved; **390 tl,** Melville McLean/Portland Museum of Art; **390 tr,** Courtesy Allan Stone Gallery, New York; **390 br,** Superstock; **392,** ©AAA used by permission; **392 inset,** JC; **393,** AP/Wide World Photos; **395 tr,** Bob Krist/TSI; **395 bl,** Louis Rosendo/FPG; **395 br,** Glen Allison/TSI; **397,** JC.

Chapter 8: Pages 404-405, David Lissy/The Picture Cube; **405,** KO; **407,** Tom Alexander/TSI; **408,** MT; **409,** PH; **411,** PEANUTS reprinted by permission of United Feature Syndicate, Inc.; **415 l,** Amwell/TSI; **415 r,** Superstock; **417,** Charles Winters/PR; **419,** Charlie Westerman/Liason International; **421 l,** Lori Adamski Peek/TSI; **421 r,** Superstock; **423,** Stephen Frisch/SB; **424,** John Bechtold/International Stock Photo; **429,** Leif Skoogfors/Woodfin Camp; **434,** Jim Rudnick/SM; **435,** Miriam Nathan-Roberts; **436,** Charlie Westerman/Liason International; **438,** MT.

Chapter 9: Pages 446-447, Scott Barrow/International Stock Photo; **447,** Joy Syverson/SB; **451,** Gale Zucker/SB; **454,** KO; **457 l,** Dave Bartruff/SB; **457 r,** MT; **459,** Sepp Seitz/Woodfin Camp; **462,** Judith Larzelere; **465,** Jose Carillo/Photophile; **467,** Gabe Palmer/SM; **471,** Jan Halaska/Index Stock; **473,** Bernard Van Berg/The Image Bank; **474,** Wallace Garrison/Index Stock; **475,** PEANUTS reprinted by permission of United Feature Syndicate, Inc.; **476,** Don Smetzer/TSI; **479,** Bachman/Photo Network; **481,** Lawrence Naylor/PR; **482,** Geoffrey Clifford/Woodfin Camp; **484,** John Eastcott/Woodfin Camp; **486,** Kunio Owaki/SM.

Chapter 10: Pages 494-495, Chuck Place/The Image Bank; **495,** Russ Lappa; **497 l,** Jon Riley/TSI; **497 r,** Boden/Ledingham/Masterfile; **498 l,** Russ Lappa; **498 m,** Kathleen Campbell/TSI; **498 r,** Telegraph Colour Library/FPG; **500,** ©AAA reprinted with permission; **501,** KO; **502,** NASA; **505,** Francis Lepine/Earth Scenes; **510,** Photofest; **513,** Baron Wolman/TSI; **514 t,** Randy Wells/TSI; **514 l,** Philip & Karen Smith/TSI; **514 m,** John Chard/TSI; **514 tr,** Mulvehill/The Image Works; **518,** Chuck Kuhn/The Image Bank; **520,** William Helsel/TSI; **522,** Joe Sohm/SM; **523,** Michael Dwyer/SB; **524,** JC; **526,** Alan and Linda Detrick/PR; **528,** Bob Daemmrich/The Image Works; **531,** B. Swersey/Gamma Liason; **534,** Kevin Schafer/TSI; **535,** The Granger Collection.

Chapter 11: Pages 542-543, Jim Olive/Uniphoto; **543,** KO; **545,** Richard Steedman/SM; **547,** Courtesy of Katoomba Scenic Railway; **548,** Kaluzny/Thatcher/TSI; **552,** AGE Fotostock/First Light; **554,** Toyohiro Yamada/FPG; **557 tl,** Paul Berger/TSI; **557 tr,** Tom Carroll; **557 bl,** Bob Daemmrich/SB; **561,** Hideo Kurihara/TSI; **565,** Gary Buss/FPG; **566,** THE FAR SIDE ©1993 FARWORKS, INC/Dist. by UNIVERSAL PRESS SYNDICATE. Reprinted with permission. All rights reserved; **569,** Superstock; **570,** JC; **572,** NOAA; **574,** Guido Alberto Rossi/The Image Bank; **576,** Philip Jon Bailey/SB; **577,** Ralph Cowan/FPG.

Chapter 12: Pages 584-585, Superstock; **585,** A Joyful Scene of Spring, 1969 by Alma Thomas. From the collection of Ruth and Jacob Kainen. Photo by Gene Young; **587,** Jose Luis Pelaez/SM; **589,** Stephen J. Krasemann/PR; **590,** PEANUTS reprinted by permission of United Feature Syndicate, Inc.; **594,** Michael Rosenfeld/TSI; **597,** MT **598,** David Parker/SPL/PR; **599,** Steve Niedorf/The Image Bank; **602 l,** Robert Frerck/TSI; **602 r,** Richard Quataert/Folio, Inc.; **603,** Chad Slattery/TSI; **604,** Chad Ehlers/TSI; **611,** Chris Sorensen/SM; 613, Nicola Goode/The Kobal Collection; **616 l,** Timothy Eagan/Woodfin Camp; **616 r,** David W. Hamilton/The Image Bank; **623,** Less Reiss/Index Stock; **626,** Telegraph Colour Library/FPG.

Flowchart information on page 158 from *Geometry and Its Applications: Symmetry & Patterns* by Nancy Crisler, ©1995, COMAP, Inc. Used with permission.

Teacher's Edition

Editorial Services Ruttle Graphics, Inc.
Design Coordination Susan Gerould/Perspectives